Price Guide and Bibliographic Checklist
for
Children's & Illustrated Books
for the years 1880 - 1970

2004 Edition

Price Guide and Bibliographic Checklist
for
Children's & Illustrated Books
for the years 1880 - 1970

2004 Edition

Compiled by:

E. Lee Baumgarten

Martinsburg, WV

E. Lee Baumgarten Books

DISCLAIMER: PLEASE READ!

New, expanded edition first published: October 2003.

First Printing

ISBN: 0-9647285-6-7   (Hardback Edition)

             0-9647285-7-5   (Softbound Edition)

Library of Congress Control Number: 2003106429

Dedicated to:

my wife, Nancy,

for her encouragement and patience,

and

my parents,

Alice-Lee and Edward T. Baumgarten,

for their support and encouragement.

INTRODUCTION

Welcome to the 2004 edition of the **Price Guide & Bibliographic Checklist for Children's & Illustrated Books.** Once again (it doesn't seem like 8-plus years have passed by!), I can state with absolute confidence that this guide is the most comprehensive single-source reference work of its kind on the market, and one that I believe you'll frequently utilize in the years to come for timeless bibliographic information and quick determination of market values. This new 2004 edition has an expanded scope that now reaches to the year 1970, and contains 18,150 entries. That's a *74% increase* above and beyond the 10,405 entries in the 1996 edition.

The research for this book became somewhat of an obsession, much the same as for the 1996 edition, and had to be conducted around a full-time job in the computer field; otherwise, I could have completed the project long before now. On a personal note, I had to fight the big "C" soon after publishing the 1996 edition. Fortunately the cancer was still localized when discovered, and it looks like a complete recovery has taken place. At any rate, I hope my latest effort pays off by providing you with the information you need for this increasingly popular genre of the book market.

What's New for 2004:

Original Dust Jacket Prices: I've included the original dust jacket prices for most American-published books after 1934. I obtained those prices from the Cumulative Book Index and, when possible, compared those with the prices printed on Library of Congress catalog cards or actual copies in the Rare Book division at LC.

Expanded Date Range - Now thru 1970: Books published up to and including 1970 are featured in this year's guide. There are a total of 3,446 titles between 1961 and 1970.

Updated Market Values: Book value ranges have been updated to reflect the market changes of the last 8 years. As you might expect, many books have increased considerably in value, while others remained somewhat flat, and some books (admittedly few!), for which I estimated the price last time, had to be modified downward. Finally, there were a handful (Ann Petry's <u>Drugstore Cat</u> comes to mind) for which my estimated price was woefully low to begin with, and these have been appropriately adjusted upward in price range.

Four New Book Award Designations: Books that won the **Jane Addams Book Award**, the **New York Times Best Illustrated** award, the **Kate Greenaway Medal** award for best illustrated British children's book, and the **Carnegie Medal** award for best written British children's book are included in this edition.

Ongoing Update of Bibliographic Details: Wherever necessary, I updated and expanded the bibliographic information for titles originally featured in the 1996 edition.

Full Names of Authors and Illustrators. I thought this would be preferable to using only last name and first initial of the individual.

I used 4 primary reference works as an initial springboard for adding new titles to this year's edition. They are: (1) **Newbery and Caldecott Medalists and Honor Book Winners**, compiled by Jim Roginski, published by Librairies Unlimited in 1982; (2) **Twentieth Century Children's Writers** (2nd edition), edited by D.L. Kirkpatrick, published by Macmillan in 1983; (3) **Anthology of Children's Literature** (5th edition), published by Houghton in 1976; and (4) **A to Zoo** (3rd edition), by Carolyn and John Lima, published by Bowker in 1989.

From that point, and utilizing additional resources, I culled specific bibliographic data from 4 main sources: **(1) Library of Congress (LC) catalog cards** and, more importantly, **physical examination of the actual deposit copies; (2) the National Union Catalog (NUC)**, which contains not only reference to the entire collection at LC, but books at other libraries as well. NUC is especially helpful for referencing scarce books that are not in the LC collection; **(3) British Museum Catalog**, primarily the electronic version on the internet; **(4) Cumulative Book Index (CBI)**, the resource I used to provide the original dust jacket prices for the books in this guide. I then established either a real price range based on recent dealer catalog (or online) for-sale entries located for that book, or my own best-guess range based on a number of factors explained later in the introduction.

I also continued with my original goal of physically examining each LC deposit copy for all American-published books documented in the guide (with few exceptions, the LC deposit copy is the first edition). Unfortunately, not all LC deposit copies were available for examination. Over time, many books have been stolen from the collection. Additionally, a significant number were not on the shelf for reasons other than pilfering, and still more have long-since been rebound in standard "library binding", thereby eliminating the opportunity to see the original binding type and endpapers. I did, however, place special emphasis on examining books that could possibly be "stated" first editions. Please refer to the "First Editions" section for a more in-depth discussion of this topic.

For some unexplained reason, most LC catalog card information for books published in the 1950's and 1960's contained only minimal information. Unlike entries for the previous 40 or 50 years, features such as pictorial endpapers, type of illustration (color or b/w) and specific page count for unpaginated books were rarely documented, therefore requiring a physical examination of the actual book to determine these and other features. For reasons outlined above, it was not always possible to see a particular deposit copy, resulting in a number of entries for which only the catalog card data is currently listed. Also, there were a number of books simply not included in the Library's collection. In such cases, NUC provided the bibliographic data most of the time, but there were still others for which there is no reference available that I'm aware of other than an occasional offer for sale in dealer or auction catalogs. Interestingly, many titles in the latter category were published by the P.F. Volland company.

Inclusions/Exclusions: As with previous printings, I focus primarily on trade editions and have excluded, with very few exceptions, private-press and limited-edition books. Such books are typically worth considerably more than their counterpart trade editions, and deserve a more thorough description than space permits here. I've also excluded many series books, notably **Nancy Drew**, **Tom Swift**, **Bobbsey Twins** and **Dick and Jane** titles, as well as most moveables and pop-up books. Furthermore, books that typically market for less than $20 are not included. As a general rule, books that commonly sell below $20 fall into one or both of the following categories: 1) books not widely collected; 2) reprints published by companies such as Grosset/Dunlap, A.L. Burt, Hurst, Sun Dial, Triangle and others, or by a children's book club. The principal purpose of this guide is to provide both bibliographic detail and the average retail price range for collectible children's and illustrated books of the time period, rather than attempting to distinguish between, let's say, a resale value of $7 or $10 for reprints and less desirable titles. All that said, I urge you not to assume that a book has little or no value simply because it is not listed in this guide, especially if it's by an author or illustrator featured in this book. While my research has been extensive, it is by no means exhaustive.

The format for this edition is identical to the 1996 edition. There are three sections to the book: (1) Sorted by Author; (2) Sorted by Artist; and (3) Sorted by Title. See page 9 (**Section Outline**) for a detailed breakdown. Throughout the next few pages, I write briefly on some important points to consider when using this guide. I urge you to read the entire introduction before proceeding on to the list itself, especially page 8 - **Key to Descriptive Terms** - for abbreviation translations.

Condition:

Condition is of the utmost importance in determining the value of any book. Having said that, I believe the standards are not quite as strict for children's books as they are for modern first editions since, after all, it is commonly understood that children's books typically have been subjected to rough handling over the years by their intended users. Therefore, pay close attention to any and all defects, and keep in mind also that the prices listed within this guide are for books in Very Good (VG) condition; that is, books that are free from major defects such as excessive cover soiling, water damage, loose or broken hinges, dog-eared, loose or missing pages, crayoned plates and/or text, and any other defect which would significantly detract from the aesthetic value of the book. Generally, a VG book is one with a minimum of wear, the text and covers reasonably clean and tight, with no major internal or external faults. Only the rarest books will sell for more than a few dollars in poor condition. For this reason, *downward pricing adjustments should be made for copies that are below the "VG" standard!* Conversely, books which are in exceptionally fine condition may be worth considerably more than the price listed in this guide.

Book Values:

Price ranges represent **retail values** and are given in U.S. dollars. The actual dollar sign has been omitted to avoid redundancy. Most values are based on examining and cross-referencing dealer catalogs, major book auction "prices-realized" slips and various internet sites that I have studied and compared over the last six years. As you are no doubt aware, numerous factors must be considered in pricing a book, one of the most important being condition. You should also keep in mind that many of the prices in this guide are based on books that receive a broad exposure primarily through the internet, nationwide catalog distribution, major antiquarian book fairs and various national trade publications. A book that may sell rather quickly when nationally advertised or offered for sale by an established dealer with a large customer base may not sell for a long time or for nearly the same price to a walk-in customer at the local used bookshop. Additional factors such as geographic location and the seller's business philosophy can play a large part in determining the sale price of any given book. For the above reasons, I've provided a value range for the titles in this guide. In establishing this range, I have attempted to eliminate anomalies (i.e., a one-time auction price that is far outside the value range -- on either end of the scale -- determined by comparing prices online and in dealer and auction catalogs). Furthermore, pay close attention to entries that have an asterisk {*} in the **LC** column. The value range for these titles is strictly "best-guess" on my part. I didn't want to lose the bibliographic entry simply because I couldn't determine a reliable market price for that book. One final point on values: as was the case 7 years ago, the trend seems to continue in the upward direction, especially for titles by highly collected authors and illustrators. However, there is always the possibility that a given author or illustrator may diminish in popularity, resulting in a decrease in market value for that individual's works.

First Editions:

Within the context of this price guide, the designation "**1st**" (first edition) should be interpreted to mean: *"the first illustrated edition by the respective artist"*. In many cases the listed book may also be a true first edition, but that is not always the case. To illustrate the point (no pun intended!), the true 1st edition of Kipling's **Brushwood Boy** was published in 1899 and illustrated by Orson Lowell. Less than 10 years later, another edition was published which featured color plates by an artist named Townsend. In this case, the edition by Townsend would accurately be termed a **first thus**; that is, the first edition with Townsend's plates, although not a true 1st. Each, however, is listed as a **1st** in this guide. Another good example is Charles Dickens, whose book titles have been illustrated by numerous artists over the years. Many editions of his **Christmas Carol** appear in this guide, most of which are listed as a 1st for the corresponding illustrator, according to the above criteria. One final - and more recent - example is Jack Schaefer's **Shane**. The true 1st edition was published in 1949 and is not illustrated. The first illustrated edition was published in 1954, but is listed as "**1st**" in this guide.

As a general rule, if the date on the title page corresponds to that on the copyright page, it is a first, or first thus, edition. Unfortunately though, the determination is rarely quite that simple. A number of publishing companies, such as David McKay, Reilly-Britton, Bobbs-Merrill, Doran, Farrar and Harcourt Brace rarely placed a date on the title page for *any* edition. Some publishers, including Doran and Farrar, used a design on the copyright page to signify a first edition, and then removed the logo for subsequent printings. And still others stated concisely: "First Edition", or "First Printing", or used letters of the alphabet to signify a first edition. Scribner and Rand/McNally are two examples of companies that used the letter "A" on the copyright page to signify first edition. Macmillan concisely stated "First Printing" on most titles published after 1944. Harper, Crowell, Random and Knopf are inconsistent; sometimes stating "First Printing" (in Knopf's and Harper's case, "First Edition"), sometimes not. Crowell, in particular, was one of the first companies to signify their first editions with the now-popular numbering scheme (i.e., 1 2 3 4 5 etc., removing the "1" to indicate a second printing, and so forth). At any rate, the designation {std} appears in the "Title" column of the guide, and signifies a "stated" first edition or first printing.

As if determining the first edition isn't sometimes difficult enough, in a number of instances you must also determine what features comprise a first "state" of a 1st edition. With children's books, the number of color plates can help make the determination. Whether or not any edges are gilt or uncut can also play a part in this process. Many of the Scribner Illustrated Classics (identified as SC in the guide) may appear to be first printings, but if the top edge is not gilt, it is in fact a later printing of the first edition, in most cases. Typographical errors, binding type and the presence or absence of pictorial endpapers are additional features that can assist in identifying a first state of a first edition. Hopefully I've made it easier for you by including many of these designations in the guide.

First edition points of some books, such as the Oz titles by L. Frank Baum, and later by Ruth P. Thompson, have already been exhaustively researched by others in the field. The finer points of first edition/first state identification (i.e., "period instead of comma on line [x], page [y]", or "misspelling of [such-and-such word] on page [z]") are outside the scope of this guide, and I therefore defer to the expertise and research of others for these details. Here, I simply use the designation: [1] to denote the first state of a first edition, as defined in reference works such as Jacob Blanck's **Bibliography of American Literature**, or Hanff/Greene's **Bibliographia Oziana**. I would also highly recommend obtaining a copy of **First Editions: A Guide to Identification**, available from the Spoon River Press, for a more in-depth discussion of each publisher's methods for designating their first editions.

Change for 2004 edition: I decided to remove the {A} designation in the title and description field for books published by Scribner. Every first edition book that I examined by this company after about 1931 had the letter "A" somewhere either on the copyright page or title page. It is the rule, rather than the exception. Other companies, such as Rand/McNally and Abingdon Press, are not as consistent with this designation, and so I include it when appropriate and known.

Original Publishers | Later Printings | Reprint Publishers:

Original Publishers: The vast majority of books documented in this guide are the *original* first or "first thus" editions, as verified by the corresponding deposit copies on file at the Library of Congress. I list the specific publisher, rather than simply stating New York, London, Boston, etc. This is important because most collectors look for the first edition of a title, and want to know which company published it.

Later Printings: I have not included *later printings by the original publisher*, unless the title is in a different format or features a different illustrator. I believe no useful purpose is served by listing numerous later printings of a title with the same publisher/illustrator combination in exactly the same format, since the value for these can be roughly determined by subtracting a percentage of the 1st edition value. For example, a 1919 reprint of "**Treasure Island**", in the Scribner Illustrated Classic format and illustrated by N.C. Wyeth, would be worth less than the first edition (published in 1911), and a 1940 printing of the same title would be worth still less.

Reprint Publishers: Grosset & Dunlap, A.L. Burt, Hurst, Donohue, Barse, Sun Dial are examples of reprint publishers. Generally, books that bear these imprints are worth considerably less than the original publication. Exceptions include the turn-of-the-century "gift books" illustrated by artists such as Harrison Fisher, Howard Chandler Christy and Coles Phillips. This type of book is sought for the color plates, without regard for the publisher. Early reprints of children's *picture* books appear to hold value much better than reprints of novels. For example, books illustrated by Johnny Gruelle, most of which were originally published by Volland, were reprinted by Donohue, and from what I've been able to determine, have a value of 60% - 80% of the Volland originals, all else being equal. Likewise, reprints of L. Frank Baum and W. W. Denslow published by Donohue, while not quite as valuable as the originals, are nevertheless collectible, and should not be considered worthless by any means. The "Teddy Bear" titles, originally published by Stern and reprinted by Barse/Hopkins also fall into this category.

> **A Word about Grosset & Dunlap**: Although the vast majority of early 20th century books published by this company are reprints, there are numerous instances, primarily after 1930, in which Grosset & Dunlap published the first edition, and I've tried to list only those titles for which National Union Catalog lists no other books by the same author/title/illustrator combination published the same year or earlier by another company.

Book Club Editions:

Prices in this guide are for trade editions *by the original publishing company*. There are a number of book clubs for children's books, including: **Weekly Reader Children's Book Club, Scholastic Book Services, Young America Book Club** and **Children's Choice Book Club**. Fortunately, most book club copies are clearly marked as such, but not always in the same place. Look on the half-title page, title page, copyright page, and outside covers of the book for any marks indicating a book club edition, especially if it was published after about 1945. The dust jacket, if present, should also be clearly marked as being a book club edition, most often on the inside flap. Another big giveaway indicator on the dust jacket is the lack of a price. Additionally, a book club edition is often produced using cheaper paper, and/or a smaller format than the original. If the book in question "tests positive" for book club, you must make a significant pricing adjustment (*downward!*). I've seen thousands of books at the Library of Congress, and not a single one was a book club edition!

Dust Jackets:

One of the major upgrades planned for this edition was the inclusion of original dust jacket prices for nearly all post-1934 American-published books, and is probably the most important enhancement for the 2004 edition. I was already aware of the considerable difficulty in determining the first editions of books published by Harper - a publishing company notorious for its inconsistency in denoting first editions - and so I used CBI to glean the original dust jacket prices, thereby providing an additional clue to help determine the first editions by this and other publishing companies. CBI also, in many cases after 1950, lists prices for library editions as well. Often, the library edition price is a seemingly off-the-wall number (i.e., $2.49, $3.48, $4.37, etc.), whereas the trade edition prices usually end with a "5" or a "0". The dust jacket prices listed in this guide are for the trade editions only. *Please note*: in very rare instances, I've noticed a discrepancy between the DJ price listed in CBI, and the price on either an LC catalog card, Rare Book Room deposit copy, or a book from my own collection. In the 4 or 5 cases that I've seen, the CBI price was slightly higher, and the publication date was often pre-1956, back when CBI was published in large, 5-year volumes. This could account for the anomalies, which, fortunately, are rare.

You'll note that most pre-1935 titles in the guide are listed without dust jackets. I would estimate that a children's book from this time period that includes the original DJ should be worth at least 150% of a copy lacking the DJ, and in some cases the price discrepancy can be far greater, depending on factors such as author, title, artist and/or scarcity. Again, any collectible children's book published prior to 1935 that still has its original DJ in acceptable condition is considered exceptionally desirable, and can command a much higher price than a copy lacking it.

Convention for Publication Dates:

The presence, absence, and/or location of a publication date in a given book is, in many instances, an important determining factor for distinguishing between first or later editions. Not all sources make note of the publication date in the same manner, and because of this there may be discrepancies in date format, especially for books published in Great Britain that I was unable to physically examine. In this guide, publication date information should be interpreted according to the following example:

1900 = Date appears on the title page. This includes books that have all publishing information, including copyright notice, on title page only. Many picture books were so designed.

(1900) = (Enclosed in parenthesis): Date appears on copyright page only.

[1900] = [Enclosed in brackets]: Date does not appear on either the title or copyright page, and "1900" represents an actual or approximate date of publication. The designations "n.d." (no-date) and "circa 1900" (sometimes abbreviated "ca 1900"), used by some dealers, are equivalent terms for this notation.

The "LC" Column:

The far-right column (LC) contains, when applicable, either of two designations (in some cases both): 1) the letter "R", signifying a book that the Library of Congress has placed in its Rare Book Division; 2) the asterisk symbol: (*), highlighting a book I discovered by searching through the LC card catalog file, NUC or other sources, and for which I have not determined a *reliable* price range. This feature should be especially helpful in identifying additional scarce titles by collectible authors, illustrators and publishing companies.

PLEASE NOTE: The price range given for any book with the "*" symbol is admittedly an educated guess on my part, based on factors such as author, illustrator, subject matter, physical appearance, whether the book in question has received one of the many awards in the field, is a **Peter Parley to Penrod** title, is included in LC Rare Book Division, etc. I tried to limit this group to titles that I believe are collectible for one or more of these reasons.

Regarding the "**R**" designation: I was told by Library staff that the inclusion of a given title in Rare Books doesn't necessarily indicate a bona fide rarity, even though this is true in many cases. A book may have been placed in this division because of an author's or illustrator's signature, or as a result of a donation by a collector who wanted his/her collection to remain separate and intact, or because the Library staff wanted to preserve the dust jacket (copies placed in the general collection are stripped of their dust jackets). I mention this because I'm sure you'll find examples of books that are both rare and valuable, but nevertheless are not included in the LC Rare Book Division. You may also occasionally notice the opposite: a book designated as rare, and yet one for which numerous offers for sale appear on the internet. I'll leave you to draw your own conclusions in this matter.

Exceptions & Clarifications:

The vast majority of books within this price guide contain either color or black and white plates and/or in-text illustrations by the designated artist/illustrator. The few exceptions are as follows:

Margaret Armstrong	:	Cover Art, textual designs (books are usually illustrated by another artist or not at all)
Frank Hazenplug	:	Cover Art, title-page design
Bruce Rogers	:	Title-page design, devices & designs on cover & spine, typeface design
Unknown	:	Unable to determine specific artist
Various	:	Illustrated by 2 or more artists
Chromos	:	Chromolithographs (undetermined artist). When known, books illustrated with chromos are listed under the specific artist name.

Special Acknowledgements:

Once again, I'd like to thank the staff at both the Main Reading Room and the Rare Book Department at the Library of Congress. Special thanks also to Mr. Joseph Puccio in the Collections Access, Loan & Management Division who made me aware of the Library's "Special Retrieval Service" that allows a researcher to examine a large number of books in a single day, rather than submitting 10 call slips per hour. This greatly expedited the completion of this year's guide.

I also thank the following dealers, listed here either by individual name or business name who, in 1998, graciously sent me their surplus children's books dealer catalogs that I had requested in writing. They are (I hope I included all of you!): Cattermole Books, Steve Cieluch, Ann Dumler, First Folio Books, Joshua Heller, Hobbyhorse Books, Marvelous Books, Jeryl Metz, Monroe Street Books, Page Books, Thorn Books, Joy Wheeler and Elaine Woodford.

Finally, I'd like to once again mention Mr. Bill Mobley, formerly in the Catalog Development section at the Library of Congress. Although I didn't have contact with him in preparation for this latest edition, he was a major influence in the development and refinement of this project in previous years. Way back in 1991, he took the time to walk me through the children's section of the Library's collection and helped me obtain a stack pass. He also went out of his way to regularly set aside dealer catalogs for me as I conducted my research.

Enjoy the Guide!

I hope this year's edition proves useful to you, and assists you in both saving and making money, building a collection by a specific author/publisher/illustrator, or identifying a previously unknown (or long-forgotten) title. Please feel free to either write or e-mail me for any reason. As always I welcome your opinions (both critical and complimentary!), as well as any reference to other illustrated books not currently included in the guide. One final comment here - the prices in this guide, or any other for that matter, are not "set in stone". Rather, they are meant to function as an eye-opener to those not familiar with this field, and as a convenient reminder to those who are. Enjoy the guide, and again, don't hesitate to write me for any reason.

Check Out my Website!

If you are currently making use of this guide in a library or other institution and would like your own personal copy, simply get on the internet and go to: **www.baumgartenguide.com** to check out more information about this guide, as well as helpful links to sites that concentrate on vintage children's books. As always, feel free to e-mail me or drop me a note at the address listed below and I'll send free ordering details as soon as I hear from you.

E. Lee Baumgarten
P.O. Box 2876
Martinsburg, WV 25401

E-Mail: **elbaum@adelphia.net**

Web Site: **www.baumgartenguide.com**

KEY TO DESCRIPTIVE TERMS *(including book sizes):*

1-color	=	Single color combined with black/white/grey in the illustrations.
2-color	=	Two different colors combined with black/white/grey in the illustrations.
1st	=	First edition. Could be the true 1st, or 1st illustrated by respective artist (i.e., 1st thus).
[1]	=	a number in brackets indicates the "state" of the first edition (i.e., 1st [1], or, 1st [2]), as defined in narrowly-focused references such as **Bibliography of American Literature** or **Bibliographia Oziana**.
1st AM	=	1st American edition. Used when the true 1st was originally published in Britain or elsewhere.
1st UK	=	1st British edition. Used when the true 1st was originally published in America or elsewhere.
12mo	=	Twelvemo: Book is 7 - 8" (17.9 - 20 cm) tall.
16mo	=	Sixteenmo: Book is 6 - 7" (15.2 - 17.8 cm) tall.
24mo	=	Twentyfourmo: Book is 5 - 6" (12.7 - 15 cm) tall.
4to	=	Quarto: Book is 10.5" - 13" (26 - 33 cm) tall.
8vo	=	Octavo: Book is 8" - 10" (20 - 25.4 cm) tall.
{A}	=	Letter "A" notation used by some publishing companies to signify first editions. Often found on copyright page.
AEG	=	All Edges Gilt (gold coating on all page edges)
b/w	=	Black & White illustrations.
box	=	Original publisher's box.
buckram	=	Coarse cloth binding, with almost a "burlap" feel.
cep	=	Colored endpapers (solid color other than white; no design)
CgM	=	**Carnegie Medal** winner. (British book award for best-written children's book)
cl (or) cloth	=	Cloth-covered hardback book.
CM [or] CH	=	**Caldecott Medal** [or] **Caldecott Honor** award winner for best illustrated American children's book.
color (or) col	=	Color illustrations on pages that are integral parts of the book (as opposed to color <u>plates</u>).
cp	=	Color plates.
cvr by...	=	The front cover of the book was designed/decorated by <ARTIST NAME>.
dep	=	Designed endpapers (includes lines, marbling and other patterns).
DJ	=	Dust Jacket present (also abbreviated DW by some dealers).
DJ/x.xx	=	Dust Jacket with original publication price noted (i.e., DJ/2.95, DJ/3.50, etc.)
dp	=	Double-page. Used with plate designation (i.e., dp cp, or 5 dp pl)
folio (or) fol	=	Size reference: Book is 13" (33.1 cm) or taller.
fp	=	Full-page (example: fp b/w = full-page black & white illustrations)
frn by...	=	Frontispiece by <ARTIST NAME>. Frequently used when this is the <u>only</u> illustration in the book.
gilt (or) glt	=	Cover and/or spine is decorated to some extent in gilt
ibds (or) ipcb	=	Illustrated boards (or) illustrated paper-covered boards; in both cases, a hardback book.
JABA	=	**Jane Addams Book Award** winner (American).
KGM	=	**Kate Greenaway Medal** (British book award for best-illustrated children's book)
lg	=	Large (used with size designations).
LGB	=	Little Golden Book. (When possible, the specific number of the book is included.)
ltr [or] later	=	An edition subsequent to the first (a reprint).
NM [or] NH	=	**Newbery Medal** [or] **Newbery Honor** award winner for best-written American children's book.
NYTBI or NYT	=	**New York Times Best Illustrated** Award. (**NYT** is used when space is an issue.)
ob	=	Oblong -- used with size designations. Book is wider than it is tall.
p-o	=	Paste-on. A pictorial paper label glued (pasted down) to the front cover of the book.
pep	=	Pictorial endpapers (more elaborate than dep)
pl	=	Plates (in the majority of instances, "pl" refers to black & white plates)
PPP [or] PPPa	=	A selection from Jacob Blanck's **Peter Parley to Penrod** reference work. (**PPPa** = Borderline selection)
p (or) pp	=	Number of pages in the text of the book, not including the ads or index, if any.
SC	=	Scribner Illustrated Classic title.
sm	=	Small (used with book size designations)
sq	=	Square (used with size designations)
{std}	=	Stated first edition. The term "first edition", or "first printing" is stated - almost always on copyright page.
teg	=	Top edge gilt (top edge of book coated with gold)
{this fmt}	=	this format -- Book was previously published in larger or smaller size by the same publisher.
{this pub}	=	this publisher -- Most often refers to the first printing of a title featuring the work of the same illustrator which was previously released by a different publishing company.
ticp	=	Tipped-in color plates. In most cases, a color sheet is pasted down on one edge onto heavier stock paper in the book.
uncut	=	Foredge and bottom edge of the pages have not been trimmed, creating a rough & uneven look.
unpag	=	No page numbering in book - exact page count unknown (variation: see "[xx]p" term below).
WS	=	Windermere Series published by Rand, McNally.
wraps	=	Soft-covered paper or cardboard binding, much the same as a paperback book.
[xx]p	=	Unpaginated book, where "xx" = specific number as counted by hand (i.e., [57]p, [104]p)
"/"	=	The slash is used to truncate the title when space is an issue.
<color>/gilt	=	Color of cloth and gilt design [or lettering] on cover or spine (i.e., red/gilt, aqua/gilt, etc.)

INTRODUCTION: 8

Section Outline

The data file for the 2004 edition contains exactly 18,150 records, indexed 3 ways to provide you with an easy method for locating any given book. Each section has its own page-numbering scheme, as opposed to an overall page count from beginning to end, and is located at the bottom of each page.

Section 1: **Author-Sorted Index (full information).** The principal sort column is farthest to the left. Within each author designation, the list is "sub-sorted" first according to title, then date, finally artist. This is especially helpful for titles such as "Alice in Wonderland", allowing you to scan chronologically for this or any other multi-edition title in the guide.

Section 2: **Illustrator-Sorted Index (full information).** The principal sort column is third from the right -- <ARTIST>. Each artist designation is "sub-sorted" first according to title, and then date.

Section 3: **Title Cross-Reference (partial information).** This section allows quick lookup of any title in the file for which the author/editor/illustrator is unknown to you. The information is presented in a 3-column format, with the title first, separated by a comma, and then the author's name in parenthesis. Once you locate the author's name next to a given title, you can then utilize the full information in Sections 1 or 2.

NOTE: *Section 3 is an abbreviated listing!* Titles that contain obvious reference to author, editor, compiler and/or illustrator have been excluded from this section (i.e., "Fairy Tales by Andersen", "Willy Pogany's Mother Goose", "Canterbury Tales of Chaucer", "Poems by....", and so forth). Such titles can be easily found in either the author- or illustrator-sorted section.

Title Count by Decade

For those of you who are interested, I've included (entirely as an afterthought!) the breakdown of title count by decade -- and the lonely 1970 -- for this year's edition:

1880 - 1889 :	252
1890 - 1899 :	1201
1900 - 1909 :	2326
1910 - 1919 :	2011
1920 - 1929 :	1894
1930 - 1939 :	2281
1940 - 1949 :	2170
1950 - 1959 :	2302
1960 - 1969 :	3310
1970....... :	395

Section 1

Author-Sorted

Index

AUTHOR	TITLE	PUBLISHER	DATE	ARTIST	PRICE	LC
A.E.	Earth Breath (1st, 12mo, 94p, ipcb, uncut, cover & title page by...)	J. Lane	(1897)	Bradley, Will	180-260	R
Aanrud, Hans.	Sidsel Longskirt & Solve Suntrap (1st, 8vo, 257p, gilt, 4cp, pep, DJ/2.00)	Winston	(1935)	D'Aulaire, I.& E.	70-100	
Aardema, Verna	Tales from the Story Hat (1st, 4to, 72p, b/w, DJ/3.50)	Coward	(1960)	Fax, Elton C.	40-65	*
Abbey, Edward	Desert Solitaire (1st {std}, 8vo, 269p, b/w, DJ/5.95)	McGraw-Hill	(1968)	Parnall, Peter	300-500	
Abbot, Alice B.	Frigate's Namesake (1st, sm8vo, 204p, blue cl, 17pl)	Century	1901	Varian, George	30-50	*
Abbott, Charles C.	Freedom of the Fields (1st, 12mo, 233p, gilt, teg, frn by...)	Lippincott	1898	Stephens, Alice B.	40-60	
Abbott, Charles C.	Travels in a Treetop (1st, 12mo, 215p, frn by...)	Lippincott	1898	Stephens, Alice B.	40-60	
Abbott, Charles D.	Howard Pyle: A Chronicle (1st, lg8vo, 249p, grey bds, 6cp)	Harper	1925	Pyle, Howard	125-200	
Abbott, Eleanor H.	Molly Make-Believe (1st, 12mo, 211p, 14pl)	Century	1910	Tittle, Walter	25-45	
Abbott, Eleanor H.	Sick-a-Bed-Lady (1st, 8vo, 371p, 9pl)	Century	1911	Greer, Blanche	30-50	
Abbott, Jacob	Franconia Stories (1st, 8vo, 321p, p-o, blue/gilt, col frn, 12pl, pep)	Putnam	1923	Armstrong, Helen	40-70	
Abbott, Lyman	Christ's Secret of Happiness (1st, 8vo, bds, gilt, cvr by...)	Crowell	(1907)	Armstrong, Margaret	55-80	*
Abdullah, Achmed	Cat Had Nine Lives (1st, lg8vo, 312p, gilt, b/w)	Farrar/Rinehart	(1933)	Berry, Erick	30-50	*
Abdullah, Achmed	Year of the Wood Dragon (1st, 12mo, 249p, fp b/w woodcuts)	Brentano's	(1926)	Dobias, Frank	30-50	
Aberconway, Christabel	Story of Mr. Korah (1st, sm4to, [42]p, gilt, 3 ticp, b/w, DJ)	L: M. Joseph	(1954)	Whistler, Rex	60-100	
Abingdon, Alex	Boners (1st, sq16mo, 102p, b/w)	Viking	1931	Seuss, Dr.	250-400	
Abingdon, Alex	More Boners (1st, 16mo, green cl, 89p, b/w)	Viking	1931	Seuss, Dr.	250-400	
Abingdon, Alex	Omnibus Boners (1st, 16mo, b/w)	Viking	1931	Seuss, Dr.	250-400	
About, Edmond	King of the Mountains (1st, sm8vo, 246p, cvr by...)	Rand/McNally	1897	Denslow, W.W.	30-50	*
Acker, Helen	School Train (1st, 8vo, 122p, b/w, DJ/2.00)	Abelard Press	(1953)	Smalley, Janet	20-35	
Ackerman, A.W.	Price of Peace (1st, sm8vo, 390p, rust/gilt, cvr by...)	McClurg	1894	Armstrong, Margaret	35-60	*
Ackerman, Francis	Tonk and Tonka (1st {std}, 8vo, 47p, b/w, DJ/2.95)	Dutton	(1962)	Burger, Carl	20-30	
Adam, Helen D.	Charms and Dreams from Pedlar's Pack (1st, 8vo, 118p, red cl, col frn)	L: Hodder	1924	Adam, Helen D.	35-50	
Adams, Andy	Log of a Cowboy (1st, 8vo, 387p, gilt, 6pl, map, PPPa)	Houghton	1903	Smith, E. Boyd	150-225	
Adams, Andy	Texas Matchmaker (1st, 12mo, 355p, 6pl)	Houghton	1904	Smith, E. Boyd	100-150	
Adams, Andy	The Outlet (1st, 8vo, 371p, brown/gilt, 6pl)	Houghton	1905	Smith, E. Boyd	100-150	
Adams, Andy	Trail Drive (1st, 8vo, 250p, b/w, DJ/3.95)	Holiday House	(1965)	Rounds, Glen	25-40	
Adams, Darwin	Adventures of Monte & Molly (1st, 4to, blue cl, 152p, fp color, DJ/2.00)	Macaulay	(1938)	Van Zelm, Franklin	90-120	
Adams, Francis	Child of the Age (1st, 8vo, 244p, green/gilt, cvr by...)	L: John Lane	1894	Beardsley, Aubrey	45-70	
Adams, Frederick	John Henry Smith (1st, 8vo, 346p, gilt, p-o, b/w)	Doubleday/Page	1905	Frost, A.B.	80-140	
Adams, Julia D.	Mountains are Free (1st {std}, 8vo, gilt, 250p, 10pl, NH)	Dutton	(1930)	Nadejen, Theodore	60-90	*
Adams, Julia D.	Vaino: Boy of New Finland (1st, 8vo, 273p, pep, NH)	Dutton	1929	Ostman, Lempi	50-80	*
Adams, Katharine	Blackthorn (1st, sm8vo, 218p, col frn)	Macmillan	1931	Dobias, Frank	20-35	
Adams, Katharine	Red Caps and Lilies (1st, sm8vo, 351p, b/w pl)	Macmillan	1924	Van Everen, Jay	25-40	
Adams, Kathleen	Book of Enchantment (1st, lg8vo, 23p, pep, gilt, 4cp, pep)	Dodd	1928	Lenski, Lois	60-100	
Adams, Kathleen	Book of Giant Stories (1st, lg8vo, 205p, 8pl, pep)	Dodd	(1926)	Lahr, Robert W.	20-30	
Adams, Kathleen	Book of Princess Stories (1st, lg8vo, blue/gilt, 223p, 4cp, b/w, pep)	Dodd	1927	Lenski, Lois	100-160	
Adams, Kathleen	There Were Giants (1st, 8vo, 234p, green cl, 4pl, pep)	Dodd	1929	Lenski, Lois	50-80	
Adams, Mary J.	Choir Visible (1st, 12mo, 185p, gilt, teg, cvr by...)	Way & Williams	1897	Hazenplug, Frank	100-170	
Adams, Ruth	Fidelia (1st, lg8vo, [32]p, 1-color, pep, DJ/3.95)	Lothrop, Lee	1970	Froberg, Ati	25-40	
Adams, Samuel H.	Flying Death (1st, 12mo, brown cl, 239p, 4pl)	McClure	1908	Macauley, Charles R.	60-100	
Adams, Samuel H.	Secret of Lonesome Cove (1st, 12mo, 340p, olive cl, 6pl)	Bobbs-Merrill	(1912)	Schoonover, Frank	20-35	
Adams, Sherred W.	Five Little Friends (1st, 12mo, 139p, color)	Macmillan	1922	Petershams	55-80	
Adams, Veotta M.	Captain Joe & the Eskimo (1st, lg8vo, ipcb, [40]p, 1-color, DJ/1.35)	W.R. Scott	1943	Tobey, Barney	75-100	
Adams, W.I.L.	In Nature's Image (1st, sm4to, gilt, 114p, AEG)	Baker/Taylor	1898	(Photos)	80-125	
Adams, W.I.L.	Sunlight and Shadow (1st, 8vo, 141p, AEG)	Baker/Taylor	1897	(Photos)	90-160	
Adamson, Joy	Elsa: Story of a Lioness (1st, 4to, [50]p, b/w, DJ/3.50)	Pantheon	1961	(Photos)	30-45	
Adcock, Marion	Littlest One (1st, 4to, 41p, ibds, 4 ticp)	L: Harrap	1914	Tarrant, Margaret	70-100	
Adcock, Marion	Littlest One (1st AM, 8vo, ibds, p-o, 4 ticp)	Stokes	[1915]	Tarrant, Margaret	60-90	
Addams, Charles	Black Maria (1st {std}, 4to, ibds, 96p, b/w, pep, DJ/3.95)	Simon/Schuster	1960	Addams, Charles	50-80	
Addams, Charles	Groaning Board (1st, 4to, green bds, 88p, fp color, DJ/3.95)	Simon/Schuster	1964	Addams, Charles	60-85	
Addams, Charles	Homebodies (1st {std}, 4to, 90p, fp b/w, DJ/2.95)	Simon/Schuster	1954	Addams, Charles	40-65	
Addams, Charles	Nightcrawlers (1st, 4to, 96p, ipcb, color, DJ/3.95)	Simon/Schuster	1957	Addams, Charles	50-80	
Addington, Sarah	Boy Who Lived in Pudding Lane (1st, 8vo, 93p, 6cp, pep, p-o)	Atl. Monthly Pr.	(1922)	Kay, Gertrude A.	50-80	
Addington, Sarah	Grammar Town (1st, 8vo, p-o, 79p, 4cp, pep)	McKay	(1927)	Kay, Gertrude A.	30-60	
Addington, Sarah	Great Adventure of Mrs. Santa Claus (1st, 8vo, p-o, 107p, 5cp)	Little/Brown	1923	Kay, Gertrude A.	55-80	
Addington, Sarah	Jerry Juddikins (1st, 8vo, 65p, p-o, 4cp, pep)	McKay	(1926)	Kay, Gertrude A.	35-60	
Addington, Sarah	Pied Piper of Pudding Lane (1st, 8vo, p-o, 97p, 4cp, pep)	Atl. Monthly Pr.	(1923)	Kay, Gertrude A.	35-60	
Addington, Sarah	Pudding Lane People (1st, 8vo, p-o, 183p, 4cp, pep)	Little/Brown	1926	Scott, Janet L.	30-60	
Addington, Sarah	Round the Year on Pudding Lane (1st, lg8vo, 231p, p-o, 9pl, pep)	Little/Brown	1924	Kay, Gertrude A.	55-80	
Addington, Sarah	Tommy Tingle-Tangle (1st, sq8vo, ibds, 39p, color, pep)	Volland	(1927)	Kay, Gertrude A.	70-100	
Addison, Julia	Mrs. John Vernon (1st, 12mo, p-o, 205p, frn by...)	Badger	1909	Gibson, Charles D.	25-40	*
Ade, George	Artie (1st {1st bk.}, 16mo, 192p, teg, blue cl, b/w)	Herbert Stone	1896	McCutcheon, J.T.	60-90	
Ade, George	In Pastures New (1st, 12mo, 309p, red cl, b/w)	McClure	1906	Levering, Albert	30-50	
Ade, George	Knocking the Neighbors (1st, 12mo, 229p, brown cl, 15pl)	Doubleday/Page	1912	Levering, Albert	55-80	R
Ade, George	More Fables (1st, 16mo, 218p, teg, title page by..)	Herbert Stone	1900	Hazenplug, Frank	35-60	
Ade, George	People You Know (1st, 12mo, blue cl, 224p, b/w)	R.H. Russell	1903	McCutcheon, J.T.	40-60	
Ade, George	Pink Marsh (1st, 12mo, green cl, 197p, teg, uncut, b/w)	Herbert Stone	1897	McCutcheon, J.T.	70-100	
Ade, George	Sultan of Sulu (1st, 12mo, 127p, b/w)	R.H. Russell	1903	Unknown	55-80	*
Ade, George	True Bills (1st, 16mo, 154p, b/w)	Harper	1904	Smith, Harry L.	35-60	
Adelson, Leone	House with Red Sails (1st, 8vo, 185p, fp b/w, DJ/2.50)	McKay	(1951)	Wiese, Kurt	20-30	
Adelson, Leone	Please Pass the Grass! (1st, sm4to, [32]p, fp 3-color, pep, DJ/3.00)	McKay	1960	Duvoisin, Roger	30-50	
Adelson, Leone	Who Blew that Whistle? (1st, lg8vo, ipcb, 45p, 1-color, pep, DJ/1.50)	W.R. Scott	(1946)	Fabres, Oscar	45-70	
Adoff, Arnold	City in All Directions (1st {std}, 8vo, 128p, fp b/w, DJ/5.95)	Macmillan	(1969)	Carrick, Donald	25-40	
Adoff, Arnold (ed)	Black Out Loud (1st {std}, lg8vo, 86p, b/w, DJ/4.95)	Macmillan	(1970)	Hollingsworth, Alvin	25-40	
Adoff, Arnold (ed)	I am the Darker Brother (1st {std} [1st bk.], 8vo, 128p, b/w, DJ/4.95)	Macmillan	(1968)	Andrews, Benny	40-65	
Adrian, Mary	Fiddler Crab (1st, 8vo, 40p, aqua cl, 2-color, DJ/2.00)	Holiday House	(1953)	Martinez, Jean	25-45	
Adrian, Mary	Garden Spider (1st, sm8vo, 38p, blue cl, 2-color, pep, DJ/2.00)	Holiday House	(1951)	Ray, Ralph	25-45	

AUTHOR	TITLE	PUBLISHER	DATE	ARTIST	PRICE	LC
Adrian, Mary	Gray Squirrel (1st, 8vo, 46p, rust cl, 2-color, cep, DJ/2.00)	Holiday House	(1955)	Ferguson, Walter	25-40	
Adrian, Mary	Honeybee (1st, 8vo, 40p, fp 2-color, cep, DJ/2.00)	Holiday House	(1952)	Latham, Barbara	50-80	R
Adshead, Gladys	Brownies - Hush! (1st, ob12mo, [64]p, orange cl, 1-color, cep, DJ/1.00)	NY: Oxford U.Pr.	(1938)	Jones, Eliz. O.	50-80	
Adshead, Gladys	Seventeen to Sing (1st, 4to, 39p, 1-color, DJ/2.50)	NY: Oxford U.Pr.	1946	Merwin, Decie	25-45	
Adshead, Gladys	What Miranda Knew (1st, 16mo, [48]p, beige cl, color, DJ/1.50)	NY: Oxford U.Pr.	(1944)	Jones, Eliz. O.	40-65	
Aesopus	Aesop for Children (1st, 4to, p-o, 112p, color, pep)	Rand/McNally	(1919)	Winter, Milo	100-160	
Aesopus	Aesop's Fables (4to, ibds, 390p, b/w)	NY: Cassell	1884	Griset, Ernest H.	200-300	*
Aesopus	Aesop's Fables (1st {1st bk}, 16mo, [60]p, red/gilt, teg, b/w, pep)	L: J.M. Dent	1895	Robinson, Charles	170-240	
Aesopus	Aesop's Fables (1st, 8vo, 275p, 16cp)	Moffat	1905	Conde, J.M.	120-180	
Aesopus	Aesop's Fables (1st, sm4to, p-o, 111p, 12cp)	Stokes	(1908)	Perkins, Lucy F.	90-150	
Aesopus	Aesop's Fables (1st AM, 16mo, gilt, p-o, 47p, 24cp)	Jack/Dutton	[1910]	Praeger, Sophia R.	70-100	*
Aesopus	Aesop's Fables (1st, 8vo, 172p, teg, brown/gilt, 6pl)	Century	1911	Smith, E. Boyd	120-185	
Aesopus	Aesop's Fables (1st, 8vo, 209p, gilt, 12cp)	L: A&C Black	(1912)	Folkard, Charles	100-165	
Aesopus	Aesop's Fables (1st, sm4to, green/gilt, 223p, 13cp, pep)	L: Heinemann	1912	Rackham, Arthur	300-500	
Aesopus	Aesop's Fables (1st AM, sq8vo, 224p, p-o, 13cp)	Doubleday/Page	1912	Rackham, Arthur	225-350	
Aesopus	Aesop's Fables (1st, 8vo, 259p, gilt, p-o, cp)	Platt/Peck	(1913)	Conde, J.M.	40-60	*
Aesopus	Aesop's Fables (1st, 8vo, 318p, color)	Lippincott	1916	Opper, Frederick B.	55-80	*
Aesopus	Aesop's Fables (1st, 8vo, 340p, green cl, p-o, 48cp, pep)	L: Ward Lock	[1920]	Rountree, Harry	140-220	
Aesopus	Aesop's Fables (1st, 8vo, black/gilt, p-o, 194p, fp color)	Harper	(1927)	Rhead, Louis	50-80	
Aesopus	Aesop's Fables (1st, lg8vo, gilt, p-o, 136p, 8cp)	McKay	(1929)	Fry, Nora	60-100	
Aesopus	Aesop's Fables (1st AM, lg8vo, p-o, 86p, b/w wood engravings, pep)	Viking	1933	Artzybasheff, Boris	60-90	
Aesopus	Aesop's Fables (8vo, gilt, p-o, t.e. red, 13cp)	Garden City	(1939)	Rackham, Arthur	75-100	
Aesopus	Aesop's Fables (1st, lg4to, brown/gilt, 134p, 1-color, pep, case)	Heritage Press	(1941)	Lawson, Robert	70-100	
Aesopus	Aesop's Fables (1st, 4to, 71p, ipcb, color, pep)	Duell, Sloan	(1944)	Kelen, Emery	35-50	
Aesopus	Aesop's Fables (1st, 8vo, 162p, color, DJ/2.50)	Lippincott	(1949)	Rounds, Glen	35-50	
Aesopus	Aesop's Fables (1st, 4to, ipcb, 92p, color, pep)	Doubleday	1954	Palazzo, Tony	30-45	
Aesopus	Animals of Aesop (1st, lg8vo, 210p, color)	Dana Estes	1900	Mora, Joseph J.	75-100	*
Aesopus	Baby's Own Aesop (1st, sq12mo, ipcb, 56p, color, pep)	L: Routledge	1887	Crane, Walter	250-350	
Aesopus	Book of Fables (12mo, 249p, 32cp)	Am. Book Exch.	1880	Griset, Ernest H.	100-150	
Aesopus	Fables of Aesop (1st, 12mo, 222p, gilt, AEG, b/w)	L: Macmillan	1894	Heighway, Richard	100-165	
Aesopus	Fables of Aesop (1st, lg4to, 152p, brown/gilt, pep, 23 ticp)	L: Hodder	[1909]	Detmold, Edward J.	500-750	
Aesopus	Fables of Aesop (1st, 8vo, 254p, p-o, gilt, color, pep)	Whitman	(1925)	Dash, Joseph E.	30-50	
Aesopus	Famous Fables (4to, ibds, 40p, fp b/w)	Harter	(1933)	Sampson, Florence	70-100	
Aesopus	Hare and the Tortoise (1st, ob4to, [31]p, fp 2-color, pep, DJ/2.50)	Whittlesey	(1962)	Galdone, Paul	25-45	
Aesopus	Hundred Fables of Aesop (1st, 4to, 201p, yellow cl, fp b/w)	L: John Lane	1899	Billinghurst, Percy	125-180	
Aesopus	Miller, His Son & their Donkey (1st, sm4to, 30p, fp 2-color, pep, DJ/2.50)	Whittlesey	(1962)	Duvoisin, Roger	30-50	
Aesopus	Never-Grow-Old Stories (1st, 8vo, 144p, color)	Lyons/Carnahan	(1925)	Billinghurst, Percy	35-60	*
Aflalo, F.G.	Fisherman's Weather (1st, 8vo, teg, gilt, 256p, 8cp)	L: A&C Black	1906	Whymper, Charles	60-100	
Agle, Nan H.	Joe Bean (1st, 8vo, 126p, b/w, DJ/3.25)	Seabury Press	(1967)	Ilsley, Velma	35-50	*
Agle, Nan H.	Makon and the Dauphin (1st, 8vo, 126p, b/w, DJ/2.95)	Scribner	(1961)	Frankenberg, Rbt.	20-35	
Agle, Nan H.	Maple Street (1st, 8vo, 126p, b/w, DJ/4.50)	Seabury Press	(1970)	Prince, Leonora	25-40	*
Agle, Nan H.	Princess Mary of Maryland (1st, 8vo, 108p, tan cl, b/w, DJ/2.50)	Scribner	(1956)	Sopher, Aaron	45-70	
Agle, Nan H.	Three Boys & the Remarkable Cow (1st, sm8vo, 127p, b/w, pep, DJ/2.00)	Scribner	(1952)	Honigman, Marion	30-50	
Agle, Nan H.	Three Boys and a Lighthouse (1st, sm8vo, 100p, b/w, pep, DJ/2.00)	Scribner	(1951)	Honigman, Marion	30-50	
Agle, Nan H.	Three Boys and a Tugboat (1st, sm8vo, 121p, b/w, DJ/2.25)	Scribner	(1953)	Honigman, Marion	25-40	
Agnew, Edith	Larry (1st, 8vo, 125p, gilt, b/w, cep, DJ/2.95)	Friendship Pr.	(1960)	Turkle, Brinton	25-40	*
Agnew, Edith	Leo of Alaska (1st, 8vo, 114p, b/w, DJ/2.95)	Friendship Pr.	(1958)	Turkle, Brinton	30-45	*
Agnew, Georgette	Let's Pretend (1st, 12mo, 63p, blue/gilt, teg, b/w, pep)	L: J. Saville	1927	Shepard, Ernest H.	70-100	
Aguilar, Grace	Vale of Cedars (1st, 8vo, 428p, uncut, teg, col frn, 11pl, pep)	L: Dent	1902	Robinson, Thomas H.	60-90	
Aichinger, Helga	Elephant, Mouse & the Flea (1st AM {std}, 12mo, [32]p, col, pep, DJ/3.25)	Atheneum	1967	Aichinger, Helga	30-45	
Aichinger, Helga	Rain Mouse (1st AM, lg sq8vo, [25]p, dp color, DJ/4.95)	F. Watts	(1970)	Aichinger, Helga	20-30	
Aichinger, Helga	The Shepherd (1st AM, ob4to, ibds, [20]p, fp color, pep, DJ/3.75)	Crowell	1967	Aichinger, Helga	40-65	*
Aiken, Conrad	Cats & Bats & Things with Wings (1st {std}, 4to, [38]p, color, pep, DJ/4.50)	Atheneum	1965	Glaser, Milton	50-80	R
Aiken, Conrad	Tom, Sue and the Clock (1st {std}, 8vo, 24p, fp b/w, DJ/2.95)	Collier Books	(1966)	Maas, Julie	30-50	R
Aiken, Joan	All You've Ever Wanted (1st [1st bk.], 12mo, 191p, gilt, fp b/w, DJ)	L: J. Cape	(1953)	Marriott, Pat	180-250	
Aiken, Joan	Armitage, Armitage, Fly Away Home (1st {std}, 8vo, 214p, b/w, DJ/3.95)	Doubleday	(1968)	Fraser, Betty	80-125	
Aiken, Joan	Black Hearts in Battersea (1st {std}, 8vo, 240p, b/w, DJ/3.50)	Doubleday	(1964)	Jacques, Robin	50-80	
Aiken, Joan	Kingdom and the Cave (1st, ob12mo, 162p, fp b/w, DJ)	L: Abelard-Sch.	(1960)	Hart, Dick	400-650	
Aiken, Joan	More than You Bargained For (1st AM, 8vo, 192p, b/w, DJ/2.50)	Abelard-Schuman	(1957)	Marriott, Pat	50-85	
Aiken, Joan	Necklace of Raindrops (1st AM, lg8vo, 109p, fp color, cep, DJ/3.95)	Doubleday	1968	Pienkowski, Jan	150-225	
Aiken, Joan	Nightbirds on Nantucket (1st AM {std}, 8vo, 216p, b/w, pep, DJ/3.25)	Doubleday	1966	Jacques, Robin	80-125	R
Aiken, Joan	Whispering Mountain (1st AM, 8vo, 237p, b/w, pep, DJ/3.95)	Doubleday	(1969)	Bozzo, Frank	70-90	R*
Aiken, Joan	Wolves of Willoughby Chase (1st AM {std}, 8vo, 168p, b/w, DJ/2.95)	Doubleday	(1963)	Marriott, Pat	50-80	R
Aikins, Ruth	Smiling Princess (1st, sq8vo, [31]p, p-o, color, pep)	Norcross	(1922)	Boyle, Mildred	100-165	
Ainslie, Kathleen	At Great Aunt Martha's (ob8vo, ibds, [32]p, 16 color, p-o)	L: Castell	[1905]	Ainslie, Kathleen	100-160	
Ainslie, Kathleen	Catharine Susan and Me Goes Abroad (16mo, wraps, [24]p, color)	L: Castell	[1900]	Ainslie, Kathleen	120-170	
Ainslie, Kathleen	Catharine Susan and Me's Coming Out (16mo, wraps, [32]p, color)	L: Castell	[1910]	Ainslie, Kathleen	100-160	
Ainslie, Kathleen	Catharine Susan in Hot Water (sq16mo, wraps, color)	L: Castell	[1905]	Ainslie, Kathleen	100-160	
Ainslie, Kathleen	Catharine Susan's Little Holiday (12mo, wraps, color)	L: Castell	[1905]	Ainslie, Kathleen	90-120	*
Ainslie, Kathleen	Lady Tabitha and Us (ob12mo, wraps, [24]p, 14 color, pep)	L: Castell	[1900]	Ainslie, Kathleen	100-150	
Ainslie, Kathleen	Me and Catharine Susan (16mo, wraps, [40]p, 20 fp color)	L: Castell	[1903]	Ainslie, Kathleen	120-180	
Ainslie, Kathleen	Me and Catharine Susan Earns an Honest Penny (sq16mo, wraps, color)	L: Castell	[1905]	Ainslie, Kathleen	120-180	
Ainslie, Kathleen	Mops Versus Tails (ob8vo, [24]p, ibds, color, pep)	L: Castell	[1905]	Ainslie, Kathleen	120-200	
Ainslie, Kathleen	Oh! Poor Amelia Jane! (12mo, [28]p, wraps, color)	L: Castell	[1900]	Ainslie, Kathleen	120-170	
Ainslie, Kathleen	Sammy Goes a Hunting (8vo, ibds, [24]p, 12 fp color, pep)	L: Castell	[1900]	Ainslie, Kathleen	100-165	
Ainslie, Kathleen	Why Was He Late? (ob12mo, [22]p, 12cp, wraps)	L: Castell	[1905]	Ainslie, Kathleen	100-165	
Aitken, James R.	In a City Garden (1st, 8vo, 106p, tan bds, gilt, 7 ticp)	L: Foulis	1913	Cameron, Katharine	80-125	
Akers, Dwight	King's Mule (1st, 8vo, 173p, black/gilt, b/w, pep)	Minton Balch	(1933)	Illingworth, L.G.	30-50	

AUTHOR	TITLE	PUBLISHER	DATE	ARTIST	PRICE	LC
Akers, Floyd	Boy Fortune Hunters in Alaska (1st [1], sm8vo, 291p, brown cl, 3pl)	Reilly/Britton	(1908)	Heath, Howard	200-300	
Akers, Floyd	Boy Fortune Hunters in China (1st [1], 12mo, brown cl, frn by)	Reilly/Britton	(1909)	Nelson, Emile A.	165-250	*
Akers, Floyd	Boy Fortune Hunters in Egypt (1st [1], 12mo, 291p, 3pl)	Reilly/Britton	(1908)	Nelson, Emile A.	200-300	
Akers, Floyd	Boy Fortune Hunters in the South Seas (1st, 8vo, 263p, tan cl, frn by)	Reilly/Britton	(1911)	Nelson, Emile A.	200-300	
Akers, Floyd	Boy Fortune Hunters in Yucatan (1st, sm8vo, 343p, tan cl, frn by)	Reilly/Britton	(1910)	Rieman, G.A.	200-300	
Alan, Sandy	Plaid Peacock (1st, ob4to, [40]p, color, cep, DJ/3.95)	Pantheon	(1965)	Oechsli, Kelly	25-40	
Albee, George	Three Young Kings (1st {std}, 4to, 47p, yellow cl, 1-color, pep, DJ/2.75)	F. Watts	1956	Keats, Ezra J.	45-60	
Alcott, Louisa M.	Candy Country (1st, 12mo, 52p, 3pl)	Little/Brown	(1900)	Unknown	70-100	R
Alcott, Louisa M.	Christmas Dream (1st, 12mo, green cl, 55p, 3pl)	Little/Brown	(1901)	Unknown	60-90	*
Alcott, Louisa M.	Eight Cousins (1st, sm8vo, 292p, gilt, teg, 8pl)	Little/Brown	1904	Richards, Harriet R.	50-80	
Alcott, Louisa M.	Eight Cousins (1st, 8vo, 278p, 6cp)	Little/Brown	1927	Price, Hattie L.	25-45	
Alcott, Louisa M.	Eight Cousins (1st, 8vo, 253p, p-o, 4cp, pep)	Winston	(1931)	Burd, Clara M.	30-50	
Alcott, Louisa M.	Frost King (4to, ipcb, unpag, color, pep)	Whitman	(1929)	Frobisher, Marie S.	140-200	
Alcott, Louisa M.	Garland for Girls (1st, 8vo, 286p, 8pl)	Little/Brown	1908	Atwood, Clara E.	30-50	
Alcott, Louisa M.	Good Wives (1st UK, 12mo, teg, 316p, 8cp, pep)	L: G. Bell	1911	Wheelhouse, Mary V.	30-50	
Alcott, Louisa M.	Hole in the Wall (1st, sm8vo, 62p, orange/gilt, cvr by...)	Little/Brown	(1899)	Sacker, Amy	60-90	
Alcott, Louisa M.	Jack and Jill (1st, 8vo, green cl, 334p, 8pl)	Little/Brown	1905	Richards, Harriet R.	35-50	
Alcott, Louisa M.	Jo's Boys... (sm8vo, teg, 358p, 10pl)	Little/Brown	1903	Ahrens, E.W.	50-80	*
Alcott, Louisa M.	Little Men (sm8vo, 381p, teg, green/gilt, 15pl)	Little/Brown	1901	Birch, Reginald	35-60	
Alcott, Louisa M.	Little Men (1st, 8vo, 349p, p-o, 4cp, pep)	Winston	(1928)	Burd, Clara M.	30-50	
Alcott, Louisa M.	Little Women (8vo, 617p, teg, 15pl)	Little/Brown	1914	Stephens, Alice B.	40-70	
Alcott, Louisa M.	Little Women (1st, 8vo, p-o, 617p, green/gilt, 8cp, pep)	Little/Brown	1915	Smith, Jessie W.	180-250	
Alcott, Louisa M.	Little Women (1st, lg8vo, green cl, p-o, 475p, 8cp)	Garden City	1932	Stein, Harve	30-50	
Alcott, Louisa M.	Little Women (1st {std}, lg8vo, 554p, b/w, DJ/3.50)	Crowell	(1955)	Cooney, Barbara	70-100	
Alcott, Louisa M.	Little Women (1st, 8vo, 544p, red/gilt, 8 fp color, DJ/5.95)	World	(1969)	Tudor, Tasha	200-300	
Alcott, Louisa M.	May Flowers (1st, 12mo, grey/gilt, 56p, b/w)	Little/Brown	(1899)	Unknown	60-90	
Alcott, Louisa M.	Old-Fashioned Girl (1st, sm8vo, green/gilt, teg, 371p, 12pl)	Little/Brown	1902	Smith, Jessie W.	100-165	
Alcott, Louisa M.	Old-Fashioned Girl (1st, 8vo, 342p, p-o, 4cp)	Winston	(1928)	Burd, Clara M.	25-40	
Alcott, Louisa M.	Old-Fashioned Girl (1st, 8vo, 319p, color, pep, RC, DJ/1.25)	World	(1947)	Weber, Nettie	20-30	
Alcott, Louisa M.	Rose in Bloom (1st, 8vo, gilt, teg, 344p, 8pl)	Little/Brown	1904	Richards, Harriet R.	50-80	
Alcott, Louisa M.	Rose in Bloom (1st, 8vo, p-o, 320p, 4cp)	Winston	(1933)	Burd, Clara M.	25-40	
Alcott, Louisa M.	Round Dozen Stories by Louisa M. Alcott (1st, 8vo, 256p, b/w, DJ/4.00)	Viking	(1963)	Tudor, Tasha	150-220	
Alcott, Louisa M.	Silver Pitchers (1st, 8vo, 365p, 8pl)	Little/Brown	1908	Kennedy, J.W.	35-60	
Alcott, Louisa M.	Under the Lilacs (1st, 8vo, 302p, green/gilt, teg, 8pl)	Little/Brown	1905	Stephens, Alice B.	60-90	*
Alcott, Louisa M.	Under the Lilacs (1st, 8vo, 284p, p-o, 6cp, pep)	Little/Brown	1928	Davis, Marguerite	30-50	
Alcott, Louisa M.	Under the Lilacs (1st, 8vo, 282p, p-o, 12cp, pep)	Winston	1934	Stephenson, Eunice	50-80	
Alden, Raymond M.	Christmas Tree Forest (1st, sm4to, [32]p, fp color, pep, DJ/2.25)	Bobbs-Merrill	1958	Busoni, Rafaello	30-45	
Alden, Raymond M.	Knights of the Silver Shield (1st, lg8vo, tan cl, 149p, 10cp)	Bobbs-Merrill	(1906)	Greenland, Katharine	100-150	*
Alden, Raymond M.	Once there Was a King (1st, lg8vo, 176p, 9cp, DJ/2.00)	Bobbs-Merrill	1946	Copelman, Evelyn	30-50	*
Alden, Raymond M.	Why the Chimes Rang (1st, lg8vo, 148p, 10pl)	Bobbs-Merrill	(1908)	Greenland, Katharine	60-90	
Alden, Raymond M.	Why the Chimes Rang (sm8vo, olive cl, p-o, [40]p)	Bobbs-Merrill	(1909)	Bunker, Mayo	30-50	
Alden, Raymond M.	Why the Chimes Rang (1st, 8vo, 148p, orange cl, p-o, 8cp)	Bobbs-Merrill	(1924)	Sturges, Katharine	55-80	*
Alden, Raymond M.	Why the Chimes Rang (1st, 4to, red cl, [28]p, color, pep, DJ/1.75)	Bobbs-Merrill	1954	Busoni, Rafaello	30-45	
Alden, William L.	Among the Freaks (1st, 195p, 45 illus)	Longmans	1896	Upton, Florence	200-350	
Aldin, Cecil	Artist's Models (1st AM, 4to, blue cl, 80p, 20 fp b/w)	Scribner	1930	Aldin, Cecil	180-240	
Aldin, Cecil	Artist's Models (1st, 4to, 80p, grey cl, 20 1-color)	L: Witherby	(1930)	Aldin, Cecil	200-300	
Aldin, Cecil	Bobtail Puppy Book (1st AM, lg8vo, 37p, ibds, 12 fp color)	NY: Hodder	[1915]	Aldin, Cecil	200-300	
Aldin, Cecil	Bunnyborough (1st, 4to, ibds, unpag, 16 fp color, pep)	L: H. Milford	(1919)	Aldin, Cecil	600-900	
Aldin, Cecil	Bunnyborough (1st [new ed.], lg8vo, [48]p, color, DJ)	L: Eyre/Spotts.	(1946)	Aldin, Cecil	150-220	
Aldin, Cecil	Cathedrals & Abbey Churches of England (1st, 4to, 111p, teg, 16cp, pep)	L: Eyre/Spotts.	(1924)	Aldin, Cecil	200-300	
Aldin, Cecil	Cecil Aldin Book (1st, lg8vo, cloth, p-o, 192p, 15cp)	L: Eyre/Spotts.	1932	Aldin, Cecil	130-200	
Aldin, Cecil	Dogs of Character (1st, sm4to, p-o, gilt, 118p, teg, 2cp)	L: Eyre/Spotts.	1927	Aldin, Cecil	160-225	
Aldin, Cecil	Farm Babies (4to, ipcb, 24cp, pep)	L/NY: Hodder	[1910]	Aldin, Cecil	350-500	
Aldin, Cecil	Farmyard Puppies (1st, lg sq8vo, ibds, 12cp)	L: H. Frowde	[1911]	Aldin, Cecil	250-350	
Aldin, Cecil	Field Babies (4to, ipcb, 24cp, pep)	L: H. Frowde	[1910]	Aldin, Cecil	250-400	
Aldin, Cecil	Gay Dog (1st, 4to, ibds, [50]p, 24cp)	L: Heinemann	1905	Aldin, Cecil	200-300	
Aldin, Cecil	Great Adventure (1st, folio, ibds, 16cp, pep)	L: H. Milford	(1920)	Aldin, Cecil	300-500	
Aldin, Cecil	Gyp's Hour of Bliss (1st, lg4to, ibds, 48p, 15cp, pep)	L: Collins	(1919)	Aldin, Cecil	300-450	
Aldin, Cecil	Happy Annual (1st AM, sm folio, ibds, 48p, color)	Dutton	(1907)	Aldin/Hassall	250-350	
Aldin, Cecil	Jack and Jill (1st, 4to, 24p, ibds, fp color, pep)	L: Frowde/Hodder	[1921]	Aldin, Cecil	400-650	
Aldin, Cecil	Just Among Friends (1st AM, lg4to, 28p, color)	Scribner	1934	Aldin, Cecil	160-220	
Aldin, Cecil	Mac (1st AM, 4to, ibds, 24 fp color)	NY: Hodder	(1912)	Aldin, Cecil	350-500	
Aldin, Cecil	Merry and Bright (1st, lg4to, bds, p-o, 24cp, pep)	L: H. Frowde	(1911)	Aldin, Cecil	300-500	
Aldin, Cecil	Merry Puppy Book (1st, 4to, ibds, 36cp)	L: Frowde/Hodder	[1913]	Aldin, Cecil	350-500	
Aldin, Cecil	Mongrel Puppy Book (1st, sq4to, ibds, 12cp)	L: H. Milford	[1909]	Aldin, Cecil	250-400	
Aldin, Cecil	Mrs. Tickler's Caravan (1st AM, lg8vo, p-o, 91p, color, pep)	Scribner	1931	Aldin, Cecil	120-200	
Aldin, Cecil	Mrs. Tickler's Caravan (1st, sm4to, ibds, 91p, color, pep)	L: Eyre/Spotts.	1931	Aldin, Cecil	160-220	
Aldin, Cecil	Old Inns (1st AM, sm4to, teg, 149p, 16cp, fp b/w)	Doubleday/Page	1921	Aldin, Cecil	100-165	
Aldin, Cecil	Old Manor Houses (1st, sm4to, 108p, grey/gilt, 12cp, pep)	L: Heinemann	(1923)	Aldin, Cecil	140-200	
Aldin, Cecil	Pickles (1st, lg4to, ibds, [50]p, 24cp)	L: Frowde/Hodder	[1909]	Aldin, Cecil	250-400	
Aldin, Cecil	Ratcatcher to Scarlet (1st, sq8vo, 123p, black cl, 15 fp b/w)	L: Eyre/Spotts.	[1926]	Aldin, Cecil	140-200	
Aldin, Cecil	Red Puppy Book (1st, lg sq8vo, blue cl, 48p, 12cp)	L: H. Frowde	[1910]	Aldin, Cecil	250-400	
Aldin, Cecil	Romance of the Road (1st, folio, 123p, teg, buckram, 11 ticp)	L: Eyre/Spotts.	1928	Aldin, Cecil	200-300	
Aldin, Cecil	Rough and Tumble (4to, ibds, p-o, 24cp, pep)	L: H. Frowde	[1912]	Aldin, Cecil	350-500	
Aldin, Cecil	Scarlet to M.F.H. (1st AM, 4to, 151p, red/gilt, color)	Scribner	(1933)	Aldin, Cecil	180-250	
Aldin, Cecil	Sleeping Partners (1st, 4to, blue bds, unpag, 20 ticp)	L: Eyre/Spotts.	1929	Aldin, Cecil	250-400	
Aldin, Cecil	The Twins (1st, lg4to, ibds, p-o, 24cp, pep)	L: Hodder	[1910]	Aldin, Cecil	200-300	
Aldin, Cecil	The Widow (1st AM, 12mo, 31p, ibds, p-o, 3 ticp)	Dutton	1909	Aldin, Cecil	80-125	*

AUTHOR	TITLE	PUBLISHER	DATE	ARTIST	PRICE	LC
Aldin, Cecil	Time I Was Dead (1st, lg8vo, 389p, gilt, 9cp)	L: Eyre/Spotts.	1934	Aldin, Cecil	140-200	
Aldin, Cecil	Us (1st AM, 4to, [36]p, color, wraps)	A.& W. Guild	(1935)	Aldin, Cecil	80-120	
Aldin, Cecil	White Kitten Book (1st, lg sq8vo, ibds, [48]p, 12cp)	L: Frowde/Hodder	[1909]	Aldin, Cecil	200-300	
Aldin, Cecil	White Puppy Book (1st, lg sq8vo, ibds, [48]p, 12cp)	L: Frowde/Hodder	[1909]	Aldin, Cecil	200-300	
Aldington (tr.)	The Decameron... (1st, lg8vo, black cl, p-o, 576p, 16cp)	Garden City	(1930)	DeBosschere, Jean	55-80	
Aldington, Richard	All Men are Enemies (1st {std}, 8vo, 574p, gilt, b/w, DJ/2.50)	Doubleday/Doran	1933	Kent, Rockwell	70-120	
Aldredge, Edna	The Timbertoes (1st, 8vo, pep, p-o, red cl, 117p, color)	Harter	(1932)	Gee, John	75-100	*
Aldrich, Anne R.	Songs about Life, Love and Death (1st, 12mo, 133p, gilt, teg)	Scribner	1892	Armstrong, Margaret	55-80	
Aldrich, Mary M.	Too Many Pets (1st {std}, 8vo, 66p, fp b/w, DJ/2.00)	Macmillan	1952	Cooney, Barbara	70-100	*
Aldrich, Thomas B.	Judith of Bethulia (1st, 8vo, gilt, 98p, teg, p-o)	Houghton	1904	Rogers, Bruce	30-50	
Aldrich, Thomas B.	Marjorie Daw (1st, lg8vo, teg, 123p, gilt, col frn)	Houghton	1908	Clay, John Cecil	35-60	
Aldrich, Thomas B.	Sea Turn (1st, 12mo, grey cl, 300p)	Houghton	1902	Rogers, Bruce	30-50	
Aldridge, Josephine	Penny and a Periwinkle (1st {std}, 4to, [30]p, color, pep, DJ/2.95)	Parnassus Press	(1961)	Robbins, Ruth	30-50	
Alessios, Alison B.	Spear of Ulysses (1st {std}, 8vo, 213p, b/w, pep, DJ/1.75)	Longmans	1941	Busoni, Rafaello	30-50	
Alexander, Anne	ABC of Cars and Trucks (1st {std}, ob4to, [30]p, ibds, color, pep, DJ/2.50)	Doubleday	1956	Ninon	40-65	
Alexander, Anne	Noise in the Night (1st {A}, 4to, [41]p, fp color, pep, DJ/2.75)	Rand/McNally	1960	Graboff, Abner	20-30	
Alexander, Cecil	All Things Bright and Beautiful (1st, sm4to, [32]p, color, DJ/3.25)	Scribner	1962	Politi, Leo	60-90	
Alexander, Charles	Fang in the Forest (1st, sm8vo, 244p, 4pl)	Dodd	1923	Bransom, Paul	20-30	
Alexander, Lillie M.	Candy (1st, 8vo, 310p, 5pl, pep, DJ/2.50)	Dodd	1934	Kent, Rockwell	80-140	
Alexander, Lloyd C.	Black Cauldron (1st {std}, 8vo, 224p, DJ/3.95, NH)	Holt, Rinehart	(1965)	No Illustrations	60-90	R
Alexander, Lloyd C.	Border Hawk: August Bondi (1st {std}, 8vo, 182p, b/w, pep, DJ/2.95)	Farrar, Straus	(1958)	Krigstein, Bernard	30-50	
Alexander, Lloyd C.	Coll and His White Pig (1st {std}, sq8vo, [32]p, color, cep, DJ/3.50)	Holt, Rinehart	(1965)	Ness, Evaline	50-80	R
Alexander, Lloyd C.	Flagship Hope and Aaron Lopez (1st, 8vo, 179p, pep, DJ/2.95)	Farrar, Straus	(1960)	Krigstein, Bernard	30-45	
Alexander, Lloyd C.	High King (1st {std}, 8vo, 285p, ibds, b/w map, DJ/4.50, NM)	Holt, Rinehart	(1968)	No Illustrations	140-200	
Alexander, Lloyd C.	My Five Tigers (1st, 8vo, 118p, green cl, fp b/w, DJ/3.00)	Crowell	(1956)	Bacon, Peggy	30-50	
Alexander, Lloyd C.	My Love Affair with Music (1st, 8vo, 274p, DJ/3.95, decor by...)	Crowell	(1960)	Vasiliu, Mircea	20-35	
Alexander, Lloyd C.	Taran Wanderer (1st {std}, 8vo, 256p, cep, DJ/4.50, b/w map by...)	Holt, Rinehart	(1967)	Ness, Evaline	40-65	
Alexander, Lloyd C.	Time Cat... (1st {std}, 8vo, 191p, b/w, DJ/3.50)	Holt, Rinehart	(1963)	Sokol, Bill	30-50	
Alexander, Lloyd C.	Truthful Harp (1st {std}, sq8vo, [32]p, ibds, color, cep, DJ/3.50)	Holt, Rinehart	(1967)	Ness, Evaline	40-65	
Alexander, Martha G.	Blackboard Bear (1st {std}, ob12mo, [32]p, ipcb, 2-color, cep, DJ/2.95)	Dial Press	(1969)	Alexander, Martha	20-35	
Alexander, Martha G.	Bobo's Dream (1st {std}, sm8vo, [32]p, color, DJ/2.95)	Dial Press	(1970)	Alexander, Martha	25-40	
Alexander, Martha G.	Story Grandmother Told (1st {std}, 8vo, [31]p, ipcb, 1-color, cep, DJ/2.95)	Dial Press	(1969)	Alexander, Martha	20-35	*
Alexenberg, Melvin	Light and Sight (1st, 4to, [46]p, 2-color, cep, DJ/4.50)	Prentice-Hall	(1969)	DePaola, Tomie	25-40	*
Alexenberg, Melvin	Sound Science (1st, 4to, [48]p, 2-color, cep, DJ/4.75)	Prentice-Hall	(1968)	DePaola, Tomie	25-40	*
Alger, Horatio	Finding a Fortune (1st, 12mo, 364p, 7pl)	Penn	1904	Lukens, W.S.	60-90	R
Alger, Horatio	Young Musician (1st, 8vo, 341p, 7pl)	Penn	1906	DeLand, Clyde O.	50-80	
Alger, Leclaire	Dougal's Wish (1st {std}, 4to, 244p, rust cl, fp b/w, DJ/2.00)	Harper	1942	Simont, Marc	60-90	
Alger, Leclaire	Jan & Wonderful Mouth-Organ (1st {std}, 8vo, 177p, col frn, pep, DJ/2.00)	Harper	1939	Becker, Charlotte	40-65	
Aliki	Diogenes: Story of Greek Philosopher (1st, sq8vo, [32]p, color, DJ/4.25)	Prentice-Hall	(1968)	Aliki	25-45	
Aliki	George and the Cherry Tree (1st, 8vo, 32p, fp color, DJ/3.75)	Dial Press	1964	Aliki	20-30	*
Aliki	Hush Little Baby (1st, lg8vo, [32]p, color, cep, DJ/4.25)	Prentice-Hall	(1968)	Aliki	30-50	
Aliki	Keep Your Mouth Closed, Dear (1st, 8vo, [48]p, fp 1-color, cep, DJ/3.50)	Dial Press	(1966)	Aliki	20-30	*
Aliki	My Five Senses (1st, sq8vo, [40]p, 2-color, DJ/2.50)	Crowell	(1962)	Aliki	20-30	*
Aliki	My Visit to the Dinosaurs (1st, ob8vo, 33p, color, DJ/3.50)	Crowell	(1969)	Aliki	25-40	
Aliki	Story of Johnny Appleseed (1st, 8vo, [32]p, color, DJ/3.50)	Prentice-Hall	(1963)	Aliki	20-30	*
Aliki	Story of William Tell (1st, lg8vo, [32]p, fp color, DJ/3.25)	A.S. Barnes	(1961)	Aliki	20-30	*
Aliki	The Eggs (1st, 4to, [32]p, fp color, DJ/3.95)	Pantheon	(1969)	Aliki	20-30	*
Aliki	Three Gold Pieces (1st, 4to, [31]p, fp color, DJ/3.50)	Pantheon	1967	Aliki	20-30	*
Aliki	Wish Workers (1st, ob4to, unpag, color, DJ/3.50)	Dial Press	(1962)	Aliki	30-45	*
Allan, Marguerite B.	Rhyme Garden (1st, lg8vo, 64p, ipcb, 8cp)	L: Bodley Head	1917	Allan, Marguerite B.	40-65	
Allee, Marjorie H.	Ann's Surprising Summer (1st, sm8vo, 198p, b/w, pep)	Houghton	1933	DeGogorza, Maitland	30-50	*
Allee, Marjorie H.	Camp at Westlands (1st, 8vo, 241p, b/w, pep, DJ/2.00)	Houghton	1941	Berry, Erick	20-30	
Allee, Marjorie H.	Great Tradition (1st, 8vo, 205p, uncut, 5cp, DJ/2.00)	Houghton	1937	Baldridge, Cyrus L.	25-40	
Allee, Marjorie H.	House of Her Own (1st, 8vo, 220p, b/w, pep, DJ/2.00)	Houghton	1934	Lee, Manning De V.	25-40	
Allee, Marjorie H.	Jane's Island (1st, 8vo, 235p, green cl, fp b/w, pep, NH)	Houghton	1931	DeGogorza, Maitland	50-80	*
Allee, Marjorie H.	Judith Lankester (1st, sm8vo, 241p, b/w, pep)	Houghton	1930	Price, Hattie L.	25-40	
Allee, Marjorie H.	Little American Girl (1st, 8vo, 237p, b/w, pep, DJ/2.00)	Houghton	1938	Quinn, Paul	25-45	*
Allee, Marjorie H.	Off to Philadelphia (1st, 8vo, 214p, col frn, b/w, DJ/2.00)	Houghton	1936	Hendrickson, David	20-30	
Allee, Marjorie H.	Road to Carolina (1st sm8vo, 240p, b/w, DJ/2.00)	Houghton	1932	Lee, Manning De V.	20-30	
Allee, Marjorie H.	Runaway Linda (1st, 8vo, 220p, b/w, DJ/2.25)	Houghton	1939	Hendrickson, David	20-35	*
Allee, Marjorie H.	Smoke Jumper (1st, sm8vo, 160p, b/w, pep, DJ/2.00)	Houghton	1945	Lee, Manning De V.	20-30	
Allee, Marjorie H.	Susanna and Tristram (1st, sm8vo, 220p, b/w, pep)	Houghton	1929	Price, Hattie L.	30-50	
Allee, Marjorie H.	The House (1st, 8vo, 181p, b/w pl, DJ/2.00)	Houghton	1944	Blair, Helen	30-50	
Allee, Marjorie H.	Winter's Mischief (1st, 8vo, 216p, b/w, pep, DJ/2.00)	Houghton	1942	Whitney, George	20-35	*
Allen, Daphne	Birth of the Opal (1st, 4to, p-o, bds, 95p, 12 ticp)	L: Allen	1913	Allen, Daphne	80-130	
Allen, F.M.	Brayhard (1st, 8vo, teg, 308p, green/gilt, b/w, pep)	L: Ward/Down.	1890	Furniss, Harry	60-90	
Allen, Frank W.	Golden Road (1st, 8vo, 228p, gilt, teg, col frn, 2pl, pep)	Wessels/Bissell	1910	Hood, George	40-60	
Allen, Grant	British Barbarians (1st, 8vo, olive/gilt, 202p, cvr by...)	L: John Lane	1895	Beardsley, Aubrey	100-175	
Allen, Grant	Miss Cayley's Adventures (1st AM, 8vo, 344p, tan cl, b/w)	Putnam	1899	Browne, Gordon	50-80	*
Allen, Grant	Woman Who Did (1st, 8vo, 241p, green cl, uncut, cvr by...)	L: John Lane	1895	Beardsley, Aubrey	100-175	
Allen, Hazel	Little Church on the Big Rock (1st, 8vo, [48]p, fp 3-color, DJ/2.50)	Scribner	(1958)	Duvoisin, Roger	40-65	*
Allen, James L.	Kentucky Cardinal Aftermath (1st AM [new ed], 12mo, gilt, 276p, AEG, b/w)	Macmillan	1900	Thomson, Hugh	70-100	
Allen, Marian	Wind in the Chimney (1st, 8vo, 89p, grey cl, 6 ticp)	L: Blackwell	[1931]	Allen, Marian	30-50	*
Allen, Marie L.	Pocketful of Rhymes (1st {std}, 8vo, 47p, ibds, 16 fp color, DJ/1.25)	Harper	1939	(Photos)	45-70	
Allen, Merritt	Blow, Bugles, Blow (1st {std}, 8vo, 217p, uncut, DJ/3.00, b/w decor by...)	Longmans	1956	Moyler, Alan	20-35	
Allen, Phil S.	Begging Bear (1st, lg ob4to, 60p, p-o, 20cp)	Reilly/Lee	(1932)	Moe, Louis M.	100-165	
Allen, Phil S.	King Arthur and his Knights (1st, lg8vo, 455p, black cl, p-o, 8cp)	Rand/McNally	(1924)	Neill/Schaeffer	60-90	*
Allen, Ralph B.	Saga of Gisli (1st {std}, lg8vo, 148p, uncut, b/w, DJ/2.50)	Harcourt	(1936)	Kent, Rockwell	100-165	

AUTHOR	TITLE	PUBLISHER	DATE	ARTIST	PRICE	LC
Allen, Willis B.	Play Away (1st, 12mo, 171p, tan cl, 6pl)	D. Estes	(1902)	Bridgman, L.J.	25-45	
Allingham, William	Rhymes for the Young Folks (1st, 8vo, 75p, 2 illus by...)	L: Cassell	(1887)	Greenaway, Kate	170-240	
Allison, James M.	Five Black Cousins... (1st, sm8vo, 63p, white/gilt, uncut, designs)	L: J. Cape	(1924)	Austen, John	45-75	
Allred, Gordon	Old Crackfoot (1st {std}, 8vo, 116p, fp b/w, dep, DJ/2.95)	NY: I. Obolensky	(1965)	Brown, Margery	25-45	
Allstrom, Elizabeth	Songs Along the Way (1st, lg8vo, 64p, 2-color, pep, DJ/2.50)	Abingdon Press	(1961)	Silverman, Mel	25-40	
Almedingen, Edith M.	Young Mark (1st AM {std}, 8vo, 177p, b/w, DJ/3.75)	Farrar, Straus	(1968)	Ambrus, Victor	30-45	
Almond, Linda S.	Little Glad Heart (1st, sm8vo, 317p, 6pl)	L.C. Page	1922	Withington, Eliz.	25-40	*
Almond, Linda S.	Mary Redding Takes Charge (1st, 8vo, 310p, col frn, cp)	Crowell	1926	Whittemore, C.	25-40	*
Almond, Linda S.	Peter Rabbit and the Little Girl (1st, 24mo, 58p, col frn)	Altemus	(1930)	Willis, Bess G.	35-60	*
Almond, Linda S.	Peter Rabbit and the Tinybits (24mo, 62p, cloth, color)	Platt/Munk	(1935)	Hoopes, Margaret	50-80	*
Almond, Linda S.	Peter Rabbit Goes-a-Visiting (1st, 16mo, 60p, ibds, p-o)	Altemus	(1921)	J.L.G.	60-90	*
Almond, Linda S.	When Peter Rabbit Went a-Fishing (24mo, ibds, p-o, 64p, 25 color, pep)	Altemus	(1923)	Hoopes, Margaret	30-50	
Almond, Linda S.	When Peter Rabbit Went to School (1st, 16mo, p-o, 58p, 27 color)	Platt/Munk	(1935)	Almond, Linda	40-60	
Alsop, Reese F.	George and his Horse Bill (1st, 8vo, 164p, red cl, b/w, DJ/2.50)	Dodd	1948	Brown, Paul	60-100	
Altsheler, J.A.	Free Rangers (1st, 8vo, 365p, 4cp)	Appleton	1909	Unknown	120-200	
Altsheler, Joseph A.	Apache Gold (1st, sm8vo, 382p, cp)	Appleton	1913	Unknown	120-200	
Amber	Rosemary and Rue (1st, 12mo, 303p, cvr by...)	Rand/McNally	1896	Denslow, W.W.	40-60	*
Ambrose, Blanche A.	Coppa Hamba (1st, 4to, [82]p, orange cl, 3cp, fp b/w, pep)	Suttonhouse	1936	Pogany, Willy	250-350	
Ambrus, Victor G.	Brave Soldier Janosh (1st AM {std}, 4to, [24]p, gilt, color, DJ/3.50)	Harcourt	(1967)	Ambrus, Victor	30-50	
Ambrus, Victor G.	Little Cockerel (1st AM {std}, 4to, [24]p, ibds, color, DJ/3.50)	Harcourt	1968	Ambrus, Victor	30-50	
Ambrus, Victor G.	Seven Skinny Goats (1st AM {std}, sm4to, ibds, [24]p, color, DJ/3.95)	Harcourt	1970	Ambrus, Victor	30-45	
Ambrus, Victor G.	Three Poor Tailors (1st AM {std}, 4to, [24]p, bds, color, DJ/3.50, KGM)	Harcourt	(1966)	Ambrus, Victor	45-70	
Amend, Ottillie	Jolly Jungle Jingles (1st, ob4to, ibds, 30p, color)	Volland	(1929)	Barte, Eleanor	100-170	
Ames, Esther M.	Patsy for Keeps (1st, sm4to, ibds, 95p, doll bk., color)	NY: S. Gabriel	(1932)	Hicks, A.L.	70-100	*
Ames, Esther M.	Twistum Tales (1st, 8vo, 96p, p-o, col frn, fp b/w)	Rand/McNally	(1929)	Hicks, Lorne	30-50	
Ames, Evelyn	My Brother Bird (1st, 8vo, 125p, red cl, fp b/w, pep, DJ/2.75)	Dodd	1954	DuBois, W.P.	40-65	
Ames, Gerald	First Days of the World (1st, sm4to, 48p, ibds, fp color, DJ/2.95)	Harper	(1958)	Weisgard, Leonard	50-80	
Ames, Gerald	First People in the World (1st, sm4to, ibds, 48p, fp color, DJ/2.95)	Harper	(1958)	Weisgard, Leonard	30-50	*
Ames, Mrs. E.	Really and Truly (1st, ob4to, ibds, [44]p, color)	L: E. Arnold	[1899]	Ames, Mrs. E.	250-400	
Ames, Mrs. E.	Tim and the Dusty Man (ob4to, 51p, ibds, 24cp)	L: Richards	[1903]	Ames, Mrs. E.	250-400	
Ames, Mrs. E.	Tremendous Twins (1st, lg ob8vo, 95p, ibds, color)	L: Richards	1900	Ames, Mrs. E.	250-400	
Amrein, Vera A.	Cabin for the Mary Christmas (1st {std}, 8vo, 183p, b/w, DJ/2.75)	Harcourt	(1955)	Spier, Peter E.	20-35	*
Amsden, Dora	Macaroni Tree (1st, 4to, ipcb, 58p, 1-color)	Hebberd	1927	Paget-Fredericks, J.	30-50	
Andersen, Hans C.	Andersen Fairy Book (1st, lg8vo, 416p, 8cp, pep)	Stokes	(1921)	Choate/Curtis	60-90	*
Andersen, Hans C.	Andersen in German (1st, 8vo, 219p, beige cl, b/w)	L: J.M. Dent	1902	Robinson Brothers	225-325	
Andersen, Hans C.	Andersen's Best Fairy Tales (1st, 12mo, 200p, color, pep)	Rand/McNally	(1911)	Henderson, W.P.	50-80	
Andersen, Hans C.	Danish Fairy Tales (1st {1st bk.}, 8vo, red/gilt, 332p, 16pl)	L: Bliss Sands	1897	Robinson, W. Heath	225-300	
Andersen, Hans C.	Emperor and the Nightingale (1st, lg ob8vo, [32]p, dp color, b/w, DJ/2.95)	Pantheon	1959	Sokol, Bill	40-65	*
Andersen, Hans C.	Emperor's New Clothes (1st, 8vo, 43p, ibds, color, pep, DJ/2.00)	Houghton	1949	Burton, Virginia L.	80-120	
Andersen, Hans C.	Fairy Stories (lg4to, 160p, gilt, ibds, 8cp, pep)	L: Collins	[1915]	Anderson, Anne	170-250	
Andersen, Hans C.	Fairy Stories (1st, sm4to, 340p, blue cl, p-o, 48cp, pep)	L: Ward Lock	1917	Tarrant, Margaret	200-300	
Andersen, Hans C.	Fairy Tales (lg8vo, AEG, 288p, 6 chromos)	L: Nister	[1890]	Hardy, E. Stuart	160-225	
Andersen, Hans C.	Fairy Tales (1st, lg8vo, 219p, b/w)	L: E. Arnold	1893	Lemann, E.A.	90-120	
Andersen, Hans C.	Fairy Tales (1st, 12mo, 539p, teg, uncut, col frn, b/w, pep)	L: Dent	1899	Robinson Brothers	200-300	
Andersen, Hans C.	Fairy Tales (1st AM, 4to, blue/gilt, AEG, 320p, b/w, cep)	NY: Truslove	1899	Stratton, Helen	150-220	*
Andersen, Hans C.	Fairy Tales (1st, 4to, white/gilt, AEG, 320p, col frn, b/w)	L: G. Newnes	1899	Stratton, Helen	180-250	
Andersen, Hans C.	Fairy Tales (1st AM, lg4to, 524p, gilt, 85pl)	Century	1900	Tegner, Hans	250-350	R
Andersen, Hans C.	Fairy Tales (1st, 4to, 2 volumes, bds, gilt, b/w)	L: Heinemann	1900	Tegner, Hans	250-400	
Andersen, Hans C.	Fairy Tales (1st {this fmt}, 16mo, 312p, 12 b/w)	L: Dent	1901	Robinson Brothers	120-180	*
Andersen, Hans C.	Fairy Tales (1st, lg8vo, 188p, 24pl)	Dana Estes	(1902)	Mora, Joseph J.	180-250	
Andersen, Hans C.	Fairy Tales (4to, ibds, [86]p, 24cp)	L: Blackie	[1905]	Stratton, Helen	180-250	
Andersen, Hans C.	Fairy Tales (1st AM, 8vo, 380p, green/gilt, 28cp)	Dodge	[1905]	Stratton, Helen	200-300	
Andersen, Hans C.	Fairy Tales (sm8vo, 441p, col frn, dep)	Lippincott	(1908)	Stratton, Helen	50-90	*
Andersen, Hans C.	Fairy Tales (1st, 8vo, 408p, b/w)	L: Seeley	(1909)	Brock, Henry M.	75-100	*
Andersen, Hans C.	Fairy Tales (1st, sm4to, 392p, gilt, 24cp, pep)	Dent/Dutton	1910	Armfield, Maxwell	140-200	
Andersen, Hans C.	Fairy Tales (1st, sm8vo, 324p, cp)	Nister/Dutton	[1910]	Pape, Frank	70-100	*
Andersen, Hans C.	Fairy Tales (1st, 8vo, 219p, teg, pep, cp)	Lippincott	1911	Kirk, Maria L.	120-180	
Andersen, Hans C.	Fairy Tales (1st AM, sm4to, blue/gilt, teg, 431p, uncut, 24cp)	Stokes	(1911)	Walton, Cecile	180-250	R
Andersen, Hans C.	Fairy Tales (1st, 4to, black/gilt, teg, 431p, 24cp, pep)	L: Jack	1911	Walton, Cecile	225-325	
Andersen, Hans C.	Fairy Tales (1st, 8vo, 373p, 12cp, pep)	L: A&C Black	(1912)	Carse, A. Duncan	70-100	
Andersen, Hans C.	Fairy Tales (1st, 12mo, 170p, b/w)	Chi: Flanagan	(1912)	Hodge, H.	35-60	*
Andersen, Hans C.	Fairy Tales (1st AM, 4to, red/gilt, 16 ticp)	Henry Holt & Co.	1913	Robinson, W. Heath	225-300	
Andersen, Hans C.	Fairy Tales (1st, 4to, red/gilt, 289p, 16 ticp)	L: Constable	1913	Robinson, W. Heath	350-500	
Andersen, Hans C.	Fairy Tales (4to, 320p, red/gilt, 16 ticp)	L: Hodder	[1913]	Robinson, W. Heath	180-240	
Andersen, Hans C.	Fairy Tales (1st, sm4to, 141p, AEG, blue/gilt, 12cp)	L: R. Tuck	(1914)	Attwell, Mabel L.	250-400	
Andersen, Hans C.	Fairy Tales (1st UK, lg8vo, 268p, p-o, 12cp, 20pl)	L: Harrap	(1914)	Walker, Dugald S.	200-270	
Andersen, Hans C.	Fairy Tales (1st, lg8vo, p-o, gilt, 267p, 12cp)	Doubleday/Page	1914	Walker, Dugald S.	150-225	
Andersen, Hans C.	Fairy Tales (1st AM, 4to, 319p, grey cl, p-o, teg, 16 ticp)	Brentano's	(1916)	Clarke, Harry	600-900	
Andersen, Hans C.	Fairy Tales (1st, 4to, 319p, teg, 16 ticp, 24pl)	L: Harrap	1916	Clarke, Harry	800-1100	
Andersen, Hans C.	Fairy Tales (1st, lg8vo, 286p, p-o, gilt, 15cp, pep, WS)	Rand/McNally	(1916)	Winter, Milo	120-170	
Andersen, Hans C.	Fairy Tales (1st, sm8vo, 489p, 7cp)	Jacobs	[1917]	Abbott, Elenore P.	70-120	
Andersen, Hans C.	Fairy Tales (1st, 8vo, p-o, 513p, 12cp)	L: Chambers	[1917]	Robinson, Gordon	140-200	
Andersen, Hans C.	Fairy Tales (8vo, 380p, ibds, 16cp)	L: Blackie	[1920]	Stratton, Helen	150-200	
Andersen, Hans C.	Fairy Tales (4to, ibds, 176p, 24cp)	L: Ward Lock	[1920]	Tarrant, Margaret	100-150	
Andersen, Hans C.	Fairy Tales (1st, lg8vo, 349p, grey/gilt, 17 ticp)	L: H. Milford	(1921)	Cramer, Rie	250-350	
Andersen, Hans C.	Fairy Tales (1st AM, 4to, blue/gilt, 179p, 12cp, pep)	NY: Nelson	[1922]	Appleton, Honor C.	150-250	
Andersen, Hans C.	Fairy Tales (1st, lg8vo, p-o, 180p, blue/gilt, 2cp, b/w)	Cupples/Leon	(1923)	Neill, John R.	150-250	
Andersen, Hans C.	Fairy Tales (1st AM, 4to, p-o, 281p, pep, 12 ticp)	Doran	(1924)	Nielsen, Kay	600-900	

AUTHOR	TITLE	PUBLISHER	DATE	ARTIST	PRICE	LC
Andersen, Hans C.	Fairy Tales (1st, 4to, 197p, green/gilt, 12 ticp, pep)	L: Hodder	(1924)	Nielsen, Kay	900-1300	
Andersen, Hans C.	Fairy Tales (1st, lg8vo, [310]p, ibds, col frn, b/w)	Saalfield	(1925)	Brundage, Frances	30-50	*
Andersen, Hans C.	Fairy Tales (1st, 8vo, 309p, cream cl, 8cp)	L: Harrap	1925	Orr, Monro S.	60-90	*
Andersen, Hans C.	Fairy Tales (4to, 245p, 16cp, pep)	Donohue	(1926)	Lee, Ella D.	75-120	
Andersen, Hans C.	Fairy Tales (1st, 8vo, p-o, 276p, black/gilt, pep, 4cp)	Winston	(1926)	Richardson, F.	50-80	
Andersen, Hans C.	Fairy Tales (2nd AM, 4to, 16cp)	Brentano's	(1930)	Clarke, Harry	160-240	
Andersen, Hans C.	Fairy Tales (2nd, 4to, 320p, green cl, 16cp, 24pl)	L: Harrap	(1930)	Clarke, Harry	225-325	
Andersen, Hans C.	Fairy Tales (1st, lg8vo, 367p, gilt, p-o, 24cp)	Penn	(1930)	Kutcher, Ben	55-80	*
Andersen, Hans C.	Fairy Tales (1st {this pub}, lg8vo, 355p, color)	Houghton	1931	Robinson, W. Heath	75-100	*
Andersen, Hans C.	Fairy Tales (1st {this pub}, lg8vo, p-o, 272p, 8cp)	Garden City	(1932)	Nielsen, Kay	80-130	
Andersen, Hans C.	Fairy Tales (1st, 4to, 287p, gilt, teg, uncut, 12cp, pep)	L: Harrap	(1932)	Rackham, Arthur	400-600	
Andersen, Hans C.	Fairy Tales (1st AM, lg8vo, teg, 288p, 12cp, pep)	McKay	(1932)	Rackham, Arthur	350-500	
Andersen, Hans C.	Fairy Tales (1st {std}, 4to, 253p, p-o, color, pep)	Coward	(1933)	MacKinstry, Eliz.	150-220	
Andersen, Hans C.	Fairy Tales (1st [this fmt.], 12mo, 127p, gilt, 8cp, pep)	L: Ward Lock	[1935]	Tarrant, Margaret	30-50	
Andersen, Hans C.	Fairy Tales (1st, sm8vo, 224p, tan cl, 13 fp b/w, DJ/1.50)	Appleton-Century	(1935)	Tenggren, Gustaf	60-100	
Andersen, Hans C.	Fairy Tales (1st, 8vo, [26]p, ibds, color, pep, DJ/0.60)	Wilcox/Follett	(1945)	Hart, Dick	25-45	
Andersen, Hans C.	Fairy Tales (1st, 8vo, 343p, color, DJ/1.25)	Grosset/Dunlap	(1945)	Szyk, Arthur	70-120	R
Andersen, Hans C.	Fairy Tales (1st, 8vo, blue cl, 273p, 10 fp color, DJ/3.50)	NY: Oxford U.Pr.	(1945)	Tudor, Tasha	180-250	
Andersen, Hans C.	Fairy Tales (1st, 4to, blue/silver, 56p, color, pep, DJ/2.50)	Duell, Sloan	(1946)	Taylor, John A.	35-50	
Andersen, Hans C.	Fairy Tales and Legends (1st, 8vo, gilt, 470p, a.e. red, 10 b/w)	L: Cobden	(1935)	Whistler, Rex	200-300	R
Andersen, Hans C.	Fairy Tales and Legends (1st AM, 8vo, 470p, gilt, fp b/w, pep, DJ/2.50)	NY: Oxford U.Pr.	1936	Whistler, Rex	100-165	
Andersen, Hans C.	Fairy Tales and Stories (1st, 8vo, blue/gilt, 512p, 4cp)	L: Routledge	1903	Bayes, Alfred W.	90-120	
Andersen, Hans C.	Fairy Tales and Stories (1st, 8vo, blue/gilt, 512p, cvr by...)	L: Routledge	1903	King, Jessie	90-120	
Andersen, Hans C.	Fairy Tales and Stories (1st AM, sm8vo, 408p, 8pl)	C.L. Bowman	1909	Brock, Henry M.	75-100	*
Andersen, Hans C.	Fairy Tales and Stories (1st, 8vo, 214p, gilt, col frn, pep)	L: Macmillan	1921	Pape, Eric	75-100	
Andersen, Hans C.	Fairy Tales and Wonder Stories (1st, 8vo, 442p, b/w, dep)	Harper	1914	Rhead, Louis	70-100	*
Andersen, Hans C.	Fairy Tales, Stories and Legends (1st, 8vo, 541p, 4pl)	L: Cassell	(1910)	Attwell, Mabel L.	60-90	*
Andersen, Hans C.	Favorite Fairy Tales (1st, lg8vo, ibds, [33]p, fp color, DJ/1.00)	Wilcox/Follett	(1946)	Stearns, Sharon	50-80	
Andersen, Hans C.	Fir Tree (1st, 4to, ibds, [24]p, color, pep, DJ/1.00)	Grosset/Dunlap	(1947)	Schlesinger, Alice	40-60	*
Andersen, Hans C.	Fir Tree (1st, 8vo, 34p, p-o, color, DJ/3.95)	Harper	(1970)	Burkert, Nancy	40-65	
Andersen, Hans C.	Flower Maiden (1st, sm8vo, 118p, p-o, pep, 3cp by...)	Jacobs	(1922)	Abbott, Elenore P.	30-60	*
Andersen, Hans C.	Great Claus and Little Claus (1st {std}, folio, 31p, 1-color, DJ/3.95)	Grove Press	(1968)	Schreiter, Rick	45-60	
Andersen, Hans C.	It's Perfectly True... (1st, 8vo, 305p, 29pl, pep, DJ/2.50)	Harcourt	(1938)	Bennett, Richard	70-100	R
Andersen, Hans C.	Little Match Girl (1st, 4to, ibds, [24]p, pep, fp color, DJ/1.00)	Grosset/Dunlap	(1944)	Tenggren, Gustaf	60-90	
Andersen, Hans C.	Little Match Girl (1st, 4to, 43p, color, DJ/3.50)	Houghton	(1968)	Lent, Blair	40-70	R
Andersen, Hans C.	Little Mermaid (1st, 8vo, 384p, gilt, teg, uncut, fp b/w)	L: Lawrence/Bul.	1893	Weguelin, John R.	120-185	
Andersen, Hans C.	Little Mermaid (1st, 12mo, 56p, green/gilt, 1-color, pep, DJ/1.25)	Holiday House	1935	Bianco, Pamela	60-90	
Andersen, Hans C.	Little Mermaid (1st, sm4to, blue/gilt, [48]p, 6 fp color, pep, DJ/2.50)	Macmillan	1939	Lathrop, Dorothy	150-220	
Andersen, Hans C.	Mermaid and other Tales (1st, sm8vo, 127p, p-o, gilt, 8cp)	Dent/Dutton	(1914)	Armfield, Maxwell	70-120	
Andersen, Hans C.	Old Man is Always Right (1st {std}, sq8vo, ibds, 28p, color, pep)	Harper	(1940)	Rojankovsky, Feodor	50-80	
Andersen, Hans C.	Real Princess (1st, 4to, green cl, p-o, [18]p, color)	Whitman	1932	Collin, Hedvig	40-60	
Andersen, Hans C.	Seven Tales (1st, 8vo, 128p, blue/gilt, 5cp, fp b/w, DJ/3.95)	Harper	1959	Sendak, Maurice	200-300	R
Andersen, Hans C.	Snow Queen (1st, sm8vo, ibds, 49p, fp color)	L: Wells/Gard.	(1883)	Pym, T.	180-250	
Andersen, Hans C.	Snow Queen (1st, 8vo, 232p, 35 illus, AEG)	L: E. Arnold	1894	Lemann, E.A.	90-120	
Andersen, Hans C.	Snow Queen (sq8vo, 32p, ibds, 15 fp color)	L: Blackie	[1910]	Cramer, Rie	70-100	
Andersen, Hans C.	Snow Queen (4to, ibds, 31p, 8cp)	L: Nelson	[1919]	Appleton, Honor C.	100-165	
Andersen, Hans C.	Snow Queen (1st, lg8vo, red cl, 209p, col frn, 1-color, pep)	Dutton	(1929)	Beverly/Ellender	70-120	
Andersen, Hans C.	Snow Queen (1st, sm4to, 63p, pep, 6 fp color, DJ/2.00)	Macmillan	1942	Hauman, G.& D.	45-60	
Andersen, Hans C.	Steadfast Tin Soldier (1st, sq16mo, ibds, [42]p, color, pep)	Macmillan	1927	Richards, George M.	50-80	
Andersen, Hans C.	Steadfast Tin Soldier (1st, sm4to, ibds, [28]p, color, pep)	NY: Maxton	1946	Harriet	40-60	*
Andersen, Hans C.	Steadfast Tin Soldier (1st, 4to, [30]p, color, DJ/2.25, CH)	Scribner	(1953)	Brown, Marcia	80-130	R*
Andersen, Hans C.	Steadfast Tin Soldier (1st, 8vo, [38]p, 2-color woodcuts)	Holt, Rinehart	1964	Quackenbush, Rbt.	20-35	*
Andersen, Hans C.	Stories and Fairy Tales (1st, 2 vols, 8vo, teg, green/gilt, uncut)	L: G. Allen	1893	Gaskin, Arthur J.	250-350	
Andersen, Hans C.	Stories and Fairy Tales (1st AM, sm8vo, 826p, green cl, b/w)	Dodd	1897	Gaskin, Arthur J.	100-165	
Andersen, Hans C.	Stories from Andersen (4to, 288p, AEG, grey/gilt, 6 chromos)	L: Nister	[1890]	Hardy, E. Stuart	120-180	
Andersen, Hans C.	Stories from Andersen (4to, blue cl, 16cp)	Doubleday/Doran	(1930)	Dulac, Edmund	100-160	
Andersen, Hans C.	Stories... (1st, 4to, 250p, orange/gilt, 28 ticp, pep)	L: Hodder	[1911]	Dulac, Edmund	450-650	R
Andersen, Hans C.	Tales from Andersen (1st, 12mo, 194p, gilt, 1-color title pg, 5pl)	L: Constable	1896	Stratton, Helen	120-180	*
Andersen, Hans C.	Tales from Andersen (1st {std}, lg8vo, 78p, color, DJ/1.50)	Dutton	1946	Paflin, Roberta	75-100	*
Andersen, Hans C.	The Mermaid (1st, sm4to, p-o, green cl, color)	Doubleday/Page	1923	Walker, Dugald S.	60-85	
Andersen, Hans C.	The Nightingale (1st, 4to, blue/gilt, 125p, 12 ticp)	L: Hodder	[1911]	Dulac, Edmund	350-500	
Andersen, Hans C.	The Nightingale (1st {std}, 12mo, 20p, color, pep, DJ/1.00)	Harper	1937	Marine, Edmund	40-60	
Andersen, Hans C.	The Nightingale (1st, lg8vo, 31p, fp 3-color, DJ/2.95)	Lippincott	(1962)	Berson, Harold	30-50	R
Andersen, Hans C.	The Nightingale (1st, 4to, 32p, ibds, color, DJ/3.95)	Harper	(1965)	Burkert, Nancy	40-60	R
Andersen, Hans C.	The Swineherd (folio, ibds, unpag, color, pep)	Knopf	[1924]	Nerman, Einar R.	175-300	
Andersen, Hans C.	The Swineherd (1st {std}, sq8vo, 32p, color, DJ/2.75)	Harcourt	(1958)	Blegvad, Erik	50-85	R
Andersen, Hans C.	Three Tales/Hans Andersen (lg sq8vo, 79p, blue/gilt, 22 b/w)	L: Macmillan	1910	Sambourne, Linley	90-160	
Andersen, Hans C.	Thumbelina (1st, 16mo, 79p, fp color, pep)	Macmillan	1928	Nerman, Einar R.	40-60	*
Andersen, Hans C.	Thumbelina (1st, sq32mo, ipcb, [60]p, color, dep)	Holiday House	(1939)	Scott, Hilda	70-120	R
Andersen, Hans C.	Thumbelina (1st, 4to, ibds, [48]p, fp color, pep, DJ/1.75)	Hyperion Press	(1943)	Fabres, Oscar	60-100	
Andersen, Hans C.	Thumbelina (1st, sm4to, 64p, color, DJ/3.50)	Scribner	(1961)	Adams, Adrienne	45-70	
Andersen, Hans C.	Thumbelina (1st, 4to, 42p, ibds, color, DJ/1.95)	Macmillan	1962	Nardini/Fontana	45-70	
Andersen, Hans C.	Thumbelisa... (1st, lg8vo, [80]p, p-o, 3cp)	Doubleday/Page	1923	Walker, Dugald S.	75-100	*
Andersen, Hans C.	Tumble-Bug (1st, lg8vo, green cl, 166p, pep, fp 1-color, DJ/2.00)	Harcourt	(1940)	List, Hertha	50-80	
Andersen, Hans C.	Ugly Duckling (1st, 4to, unpag, color)	L: D. Nutt	1894	Van Hoytema, T.	80-120	*
Andersen, Hans C.	Ugly Duckling (1st, sm4to, 24p, ibds, 3 fp color)	Moffat	1905	Squire, Maud H.	125-200	R*
Andersen, Hans C.	Ugly Duckling (1st, 16mo, bds, p-o, 57p, color)	Reilly/Britton	(1912)	Neill, John R.	70-100	
Andersen, Hans C.	Ugly Duckling (1st, sm8vo, gilt, 127p, p-o, 8cp)	L: Dent	(1913)	Armfield, Maxwell	70-100	

AUTHOR	TITLE	PUBLISHER	DATE	ARTIST	PRICE	LC
Andersen, Hans C.	Ugly Duckling (1st, 24mo, [42]p, ibds, color, pep)	Macmillan	1927	Hader, B.& E.	35-60	
Andersen, Hans C.	Ugly Duckling (1st, 4to, [40]p, ibds, 5cp, pep)	Saalfield	1931	Peat, Fern B.	60-100	
Andersen, Hans C.	Ugly Duckling (1st, ob4to, [40]p, p-o, color, pep, DJ/1.00)	Lippincott	(1939)	Disney Studios	200-300	
Andersen, Hans C.	Ugly Duckling (1st, lg8vo, ibds, [32]p, color, DJ/0.50)	Grosset/Dunlap	(1945)	Rojankovsky, Feodor	30-60	
Andersen, Hans C.	Ugly Duckling (1st AM, ob4to, ibds, 54p, 24 fp color, DJ/2.50)	Macmillan	1955	Larsen, Johannes	60-90	*
Andersen, Hans C.	Ugly Duckling (1st, 4to, [48]p, color, DJ/3.50)	Scribner	1965	Adams, Adrienne	30-45	
Andersen, Hans C.	What Good Man Does is Always Right (1st, 4to, [32]p, ibds, color, DJ/3.95)	Dial Press	1968	Schreiter, Rick	25-45	
Andersen, Hans C.	Wild Swans (1st AM, ob4to, 48p, ibds, 14 chromos)	Dutton	[1880]	Havers, Alice	200-270	
Andersen, Hans C.	Wild Swans (1st, sm8vo, 117p, color, pep)	Jacobs	(1922)	Abbott, Elenore P.	50-80	*
Andersen, Hans C.	Wild Swans (1st, sm4to, 80p, 1-color, DJ/3.50)	Scribner	(1963)	Brown, Marcia	50-80	R*
Anderson, Anne	Ann Anderson's Fairy Tale Book (1st AM, 4to, 190p, p-o, 12cp, pep)	Nelson	[1923]	Anderson, Anne	180-300	
Anderson, Anne	Betty Book (1st, 4to, ibds, 32p, 13cp, pep)	L: Nelson	[1912]	Anderson, Anne	120-200	
Anderson, Anne	Dickie-Burdie Book (8vo, tan cl, p-o, 12cp)	L: Nelson	[1916]	Anderson, Anne	160-225	
Anderson, Anne	Maisie-Daisie Book (lg8vo, 24p, p-o, 12cp)	Nelson	[1918]	Anderson, Anne	120-165	
Anderson, Anne	Nursery Zoo (4to, p-o, red cl, unpag, color)	L: Nelson	[1925]	Anderson, Anne	80-125	
Anderson, Anne	Old French Nursery Songs (1st, sm4to, 64p, ibds, p-o, 8cp)	L: Harrap	[1915]	Anderson, Anne	120-200	
Anderson, Anne	Patsy Book (1st, lg4to, ibds, unpag, 12cp, pep)	L: Nelson	[1919]	Anderson, Anne	150-225	
Anderson, Anne	Purple Book (1st, 12mo, [16]p, purple cl, p-o, 12 fp color)	L: Frowde/Hodder	[1910]	Anderson, Anne	80-130	
Anderson, Anne	Rosie-Posie Book (4to, p-o, blue cl, 12cp)	T. Nelson	[1917]	Anderson, Anne	140-200	
Anderson, Bernice	Topsy Turvy's Pigtails (1st, lg8vo, 91p, p-o, fp 2-color, b/w, pep)	Rand/McNally	(1930)	Friend, Esther	60-100	
Anderson, C.W.	Big Red (1st, ob4to, tan cl, pep, 64p, b/w, DJ/2.00)	Macmillan	1943	Anderson, C.W.	60-90	
Anderson, C.W.	Billy and Blaze (1st, sm4to, orange cl, [56]p, fp b/w)	Macmillan	1936	Anderson, C.W.	80-120	
Anderson, C.W.	Black Bay and Chestnut (1st, ob folio, [52]p, b/w, pep, DJ/2.50)	Macmillan	1939	Anderson, C.W.	70-100	*
Anderson, C.W.	Blaze and the Forest Fire (1st, sm4to, [55]p, fp b/w, DJ/1.25)	Macmillan	1938	Anderson, C.W.	60-90	*
Anderson, C.W.	Blaze and the Gray Spotted Pony (1st {std}, lg8vo, 46p, b/w, DJ/3.50)	Macmillan	1968	Anderson, C.W.	40-65	
Anderson, C.W.	Blaze and the Gypsies (1st, sm4to, green cl, [56]p, fp b/w, DJ/1.50)	Macmillan	1937	Anderson, C.W.	70-120	
Anderson, C.W.	Blaze and the Indian Cave (1st {std}, lg8vo, [47]p, b/w, DJ/2.95)	Macmillan	(1964)	Anderson, C.W.	40-65	
Anderson, C.W.	Blaze and the Lost Quarry (1st {std}, lg8vo, 46p, b/w, DJ/2.95)	Macmillan	1966	Anderson, C.W.	40-65	*
Anderson, C.W.	Blaze Finds the Trail (1st {std}, sm4to, [48]p, b/w, cep)	Macmillan	1950	Anderson, C.W.	45-60	
Anderson, C.W.	Bobcat (1st {std}, 8vo, 97p, b/w, DJ/2.50)	Macmillan	1949	Anderson, C.W.	50-80	
Anderson, C.W.	Crooked Colt (1st {std}, sq8vo, [48]p, fp b/w, cep, DJ/2.00)	Macmillan	1954	Anderson, C.W.	65-90	
Anderson, C.W.	Deep Through the Heart (1st, lg ob4to, [52]p, pep, b/w, DJ/3.00)	Macmillan	1940	Anderson, C.W.	70-100	
Anderson, C.W.	Filly for Joan (1st {std}, 8vo, 104p, fp b/w, DJ/3.00)	Macmillan	1960	Anderson, C.W.	45-70	
Anderson, C.W.	Heads Up and Heels Down (1st {std}, lg8vo, 144p, fp b/w, DJ/2.50)	Macmillan	1944	Anderson, C.W.	50-80	
Anderson, C.W.	High Courage (1st, 8vo, red cl, 124p, fp b/w, DJ/1.75)	Macmillan	1941	Anderson, C.W.	45-70	
Anderson, C.W.	Horse of Hurricane Hill (1st {std}, 8vo, 107p, fp b/w, DJ/2.75)	Macmillan	1956	Anderson, C.W.	70-100	
Anderson, C.W.	Horse Show (1st, 4to, ibds, [94]p, b/w, DJ/2.50)	Harper	(1951)	Anderson, C.W.	50-80	
Anderson, C.W.	Horses are Folks (1st, ob4to, ibds, 89p, b/w, pep, DJ/3.50)	Harper	(1950)	Anderson, C.W.	60-100	
Anderson, C.W.	Linda and the Indians (1st {std}, 8vo, [50]p, b/w, DJ/2.00)	Macmillan	1952	Anderson, C.W.	45-70	*
Anderson, C.W.	Lonesome Little Colt (1st {std}, 4to, 46p, fp b/w, DJ/2.75)	Macmillan	1961	Anderson, C.W.	40-65	
Anderson, C.W.	Outlaw (1st {std}, 8vo, 99p, fp b/w, DJ/3.50)	Macmillan	(1967)	Anderson, C.W.	40-65	
Anderson, C.W.	Salute (1st, sm4to, tan cl, p-o, 63p, b/w, pep, DJ/2.00)	Macmillan	1940	Anderson, C.W.	70-100	*
Anderson, C.W.	The Smashers (1st, ob folio, 100p, b/w, DJ/5.00)	Harper	(1954)	Anderson, C.W.	70-100	
Anderson, C.W.	Thoroughbreds (1st, ob4to, 72p, b/w, pep, DJ/2.00)	Macmillan	1942	Anderson, C.W.	70-100	
Anderson, C.W.	Tomorrow's Champion (1st, ob4to, [84]p, green/gilt, fp b/w, DJ/3.00)	Macmillan	1946	Anderson, C.W.	70-100	
Anderson, C.W.	Touch of Greatness (1st, ob4to, blue cl, 96p, b/w, DJ/3.00)	Macmillan	1945	Anderson, C.W.	60-90	
Anderson, Florence	Rainbow Twins (4to, ibds, 12cp, pep)	L: J. Johnson	(1919)	Anderson, Florence	250-400	
Anderson, Isabel	Great Sea Horse (1st, 4to, red/gilt, teg, 251p, 24cp, pep)	Little/Brown	1909	Elliott, John	180-250	
Anderson, John (ed)	Fifteenth Century Cook'ry Boke (1st, 8vo, blue/gilt, 92p, color, DJ/4.50)	Scribner	(1962)	Adams, Adrienne	25-40	
Anderson, Joy	Hippolyte: Crab King (1st {std}, 8vo, 39p, b/w, DJ/2.25)	Harcourt	(1956)	Spier, Peter E.	25-40	*
Anderson, Lonzo	Bag of Smoke: Story of First Balloon (1st, 8vo, 179p, fp b/w, pep, DJ/2.00)	Viking	1942	Adams, Adrienne	30-50	*
Anderson, Lonzo	Ponies of Mykillengi (1st, 8vo, [48]p, fp color, DJ)	Scribner	(1966)	Adams, Adrienne	40-65	
Anderson, Lonzo	Two Hundred Rabbits (1st, ob4to, [32]p, ibds, fp color, DJ/3.95)	Viking	(1968)	Adams, Adrienne	30-50	
Anderson, Mildred	Sandra and the Right Prince (1st, 8vo, 70p, b/w, DJ/2.50)	Oxford U. Pr.	1951	Paget-Fredericks, J.	25-40	
Anderson, Neil	Freckle Face (1st, 8vo, 32p, fp 1-color, dep, DJ/2.50)	Crowell	(1957)	Cooney, Barbara	45-70	*
Anderson, Neil	Tina and the Too-Big Doll (1st, sm4to, 44p, color, pep, DJ/2.50)	Crowell	(1956)	Wiggins, Mary C.	30-50	
Anderson, Paul S.	Red Fox and the Hungry Tiger (1st, lg ob8vo, [48]p, 3-color, DJ/3.50)	W.R. Scott	1962	Kraus, Robert	30-50	*
Anderson, Rbt. G.	Half-Past Seven Stories (1st, lg8vo, p-o, 251p, 16cp)	Putnam	(1922)	Smith, Dorothy H.	35-60	*
Anderson, Rbt. G.	Seven O'Clock Stories (1st, lg8vo, 180p, gilt, p-o, 20cp, pep)	Putnam	(1920)	Smith, E. Boyd	120-200	
Anderson, Richard C.	Animals in Social Captivity (1st, 8vo, gilt, p-o, 96p, 10cp dep)	Stewart/Kidd	(1914)	Herschede, Lilian N.	55-80	*
Andre, R.	Little Blossoms (sm4to, [32]p, ibds, 10 chromos)	L: G. Allen	1885	Andre, R.	400-600	
Andreas, Evelyn	Big Treasure Book of Fairy Tales (1st, folio, unpag, color, DJ/1.00)	Grosset/Dunlap	1954	Weisgard, Leonard	40-65	
Andrews, Mary S.	Better Treasure (1st, 8vo, red/gilt, 72p, cvr by...)	Bobbs-Merrill	(1908)	Armstrong, Margaret	30-50	
Andrews, Mary S.	Bob and the Guides (1st, 8vo, green/gilt, 351p, teg)	Scribner	1906	Armstrong, Margaret	25-40	
Andrews, Mary S.	Eternal Masculine (1st, 8vo, 430p, green/gilt)	Scribner	1913	Armstrong, Margaret	40-60	
Andrews, Mary S.	Good Samaritan (1st, 12mo, 51p, green cl, 6pl)	McClure	1906	Harding, Charlotte	30-50	*
Andrews, Mary S.	The Militants (1st, 12mo, teg, 378p, green/gilt, cvr by...)	Scribner	1907	Armstrong, Margaret	55-80	
Andrews, Mary S.	The Militants (1st, 12mo, 379p, teg, 2pl by...)	Scribner	1907	Wyeth, N.C.	55-80	
Andrews, Roy	Quest in the Desert (1st, 8vo, 192p, b/w, DJ/2.50)	Viking	1950	Wiese, Kurt	60-90	*
Andrews, Roy	Quest of the Snow Leopard (1st, 8vo, 190p, b/w, DJ/2.50)	Viking	1955	Wiese, Kurt	50-80	*
Angelo, Valenti	Acorn Tree (1st, sm4to, 39p, 1-color, DJ/2.50)	Viking	(1958)	Angelo, Valenti	30-50	
Angelo, Valenti	Angelino and Barefoot Saint (1st, sm4to, 62p, 1-color, DJ/2.75)	Viking	(1961)	Angelo, Valenti	30-45	*
Angelo, Valenti	Bells of Bleecker Street (1st, 8vo, 185p, pep, b/w, DJ/2.50)	Viking	1949	Angelo, Valenti	70-100	R
Angelo, Valenti	Big Little Island (1st, 8vo, 190p, pep, b/w, DJ/2.75)	Viking	1955	Angelo, Valenti	25-40	
Angelo, Valenti	Candy Basket (1st, sm4to, 38p, color, cep, DJ/2.50)	Viking	(1960)	Angelo, Valenti	30-45	*
Angelo, Valenti	Golden Gate (1st, 8vo, aqua/gilt, 273p, 1-color, dep, DJ/2.00)	Viking	1939	Angelo, Valenti	40-60	
Angelo, Valenti	Hill of Little Miracles (1st, 8vo, 200p, b/w, DJ/2.00)	Viking	1942	Angelo, Valenti	40-60	
Angelo, Valenti	Honey Boat (1st, 8vo, 160p, b/w, DJ/3.00)	Viking	(1959)	Angelo, Valenti	25-45	*

AUTHOR	TITLE	PUBLISHER	DATE	ARTIST	PRICE	LC
Angelo, Valenti	Look Out Yonder (1st, 8vo, 197p, b/w, DJ/2.00)	Viking	1943	Angelo, Valenti	30-45	
Angelo, Valenti	Marble Fountain (1st, 8vo, 223p, tan cl, b/w, pep, DJ/2.50)	Viking	1951	Angelo, Valenti	30-50	
Angelo, Valenti	Merry Marcos (1st, 8vo, 141p, red cl, b/w, DJ/3.25)	Viking	(1963)	Angelo, Valenti	30-50	
Angelo, Valenti	Nino (1st, lg8vo, beige cl, 244p, 1-color, pep, DJ/2.00, NH)	Viking	1938	Angelo, Valenti	50-80	
Angelo, Valenti	Paradise Valley (1st, 8vo, 230p, 1-color, DJ/2.00)	Viking	1940	Angelo, Valenti	40-65	*
Angelo, Valenti	Rooster Club (1st, 8vo, 150p, rust/gilt, b/w, dep, DJ/2.00)	Viking	1944	Angelo, Valenti	40-65	
Angelo, Valenti	Tale of a Donkey (1st, 8vo, 110p, b/w, DJ/3.00)	Viking	(1966)	Angelo, Valenti	25-45	
Anglund, Joan W.	A is for Always (1st {std}, 32mo, [32]p, color, DJ/1.95)	Harcourt	(1968)	Anglund, Joan W.	25-40	
Anglund, Joan W.	Book of Good Tidings (1st {std}, 32mo, [30]p, color, DJ/1.95)	Harcourt	(1965)	Anglund, Joan W.	25-40	
Anglund, Joan W.	Brave Cowboy (1st {std}, 12mo, unpag, 2-color, pep, DJ/1.95)	Harcourt	(1959)	Anglund, Joan W.	50-80	
Anglund, Joan W.	Childhood is a Time of Innocence (1st {std}, 12mo, [32]p, 2-color, DJ/1.95)	Harcourt	(1964)	Anglund, Joan W.	20-35	
Anglund, Joan W.	Christmas is a Time of Giving (1st {std}, 12mo, [32]p, 2-color, DJ/1.75)	Harcourt	(1961)	Anglund, Joan W.	30-45	
Anglund, Joan W.	Cowboy and his Friend (1st {std}, 12mo, [32]p, fp 1-color, pep, DJ/1.95)	Harcourt	(1961)	Anglund, Joan W.	25-40	
Anglund, Joan W.	Cup of Sun (1st {std}, 12mo, 63p, b/w, DJ/2.75)	Harcourt	(1967)	Anglund, Joan W.	25-40	
Anglund, Joan W.	Friend is Someone who Likes You (1st {std}, 12mo, [27]p, col, DJ/1.75, NYT)	Harcourt	(1958)	Anglund, Joan W.	35-50	
Anglund, Joan W.	In a Pumpkin Shell (1st {std}, lg8vo, yellow cl, [30]p, color, DJ/2.95)	Harcourt	(1960)	Anglund, Joan W.	40-65	
Anglund, Joan W.	Look Out the Window (1st {std}, 8vo, yellow cl, [36]p, 2-color, DJ/1.95)	Harcourt	(1959)	Anglund, Joan W.	45-70	
Anglund, Joan W.	Love is a Special Way of Feeling (1st {std}, 12mo, [30]p, 2-color, DJ/1.75)	Harcourt	(1960)	Anglund, Joan W.	35-50	
Anglund, Joan W.	Morning is a Little Child (1st {std}, lg8vo, [32]p, color, DJ/3.50)	Harcourt	(1969)	Anglund, Joan W.	40-65	
Anglund, Joan W.	Nibble Nibble Mousekin (1st {std}, lg8vo, [30]p, color, DJ/3.25)	Harcourt	(1962)	Anglund, Joan W.	50-80	
Anglund, Joan W.	Pocketful of Proverbs (1st, 24mo, [32]p, ibds, color, DJ/1.95)	Harcourt	(1964)	Anglund, Joan W.	30-45	
Anglund, Joan W.	Slice of Snow (1st {std}, 12mo, 63p, b/w, DJ/2.95)	Harcourt	(1970)	Anglund, Joan W.	25-45	
Anglund, Joan W.	Spring is a New Beginning (1st {std}, 12mo, [32]p, ipcb, color, DJ/1.95)	Harcourt	(1963)	Anglund, Joan W.	25-45	
Anglund, Joan W.	What Color is Love? (1st {std}, 12mo, unpag, color, DJ/1.95)	Harcourt	(1966)	Anglund, Joan W.	25-45	
Anglund, Joan W.	Year is Round (1st {std}, 16mo, unpag, color, DJ/1.95)	Harcourt	(1966)	Anglund, Joan W.	20-35	
Angus, Douglas	Lions Fed the Tigers (1st {std}, 8vo, 176p, b/w, DJ/3.00)	Houghton	1958	Spier, Peter E.	25-40	
Annett, Cora	Dog Who Thought He was a Boy (1st {std}, sm4to, 48p, 2-color, cep, DJ/3.25)	Houghton	1965	Lorraine, Walter	30-45	
Annixter, Jane	Ahmeek (1st, 8vo, 63p, b/w, DJ/3.75)	Holiday House	(1970)	Frankenberg, Rbt.	20-35	
Annixter, Jane	Buffalo Chief (1st, 8vo, 219p, red cl, DJ/2.95, pep by...)	Holiday House	(1958)	Wilson, Charles B.	30-50	*
Annixter, Jane	The Runner (1st, 8vo, 220p, red cl, pep, DJ/2.75)	Holiday House	(1956)	Laune, Paul	20-35	
Annixter, Paul	Cat that Clumped (1st, lg8vo, [36]p, fp b/w, pep, DJ/2.95)	Holiday House	(1966)	Turkle, Brinton	25-40	
Annixter, Paul	Wilderness Ways (1st, lg8vo, p-o, 313p, col frn, 13pl)	Penn	(1930)	Bull, Charles L.	60-80	*
Anno, Mitsumasa	Topsy Turvies (1st {std}, 4to, 27p, color, DJ/3.50, NYTBI)	Walker/Weatherh.	(1970)	Anno, Mitsumasa	50-80	
Anthony, E. & J.	Fairies Up-to-Date (1st, 8vo, red cl, p-o, [207]p, color)	Little/Brown	1923	DeBosschere, Jean	180-250	
Anthony, Edward	Every Dog has his Say (1st, sm4to, 63p, fp b/w, DJ/3.00)	Watson-Guptill	(1947)	Dennis, Morgan	50-80	
Anthony, Edward	Oddity Land (1st AM {std}, 8vo, 64p, b/w, DJ/2.50)	Doubleday	(1957)	Blegvad, Erik	25-40	
Anthony, Edward	Pussycat Princess (1st, sm4to, red cl, 157p, b/w)	Century	1922	(Photos)	120-185	
Anthony, Joseph	Casanova Jones (1st, sm8vo, gilt, 206p, b/w, pep)	Century	1930	Pogany, Willy	35-50	
Appel, Benjamin	Shepherd of the Sun (1st {std}, 8vo, 87p, fp b/w, DJ/2.95)	Obolensky	(1961)	Bryson, Bernarda	25-40	
Appel, David	Comanche... (1st {std}, 8vo, 224p, dp b/w, DJ/2.50)	World	(1951)	Daugherty, James	30-50	*
Appiah, Peggy	Ananse the Spider (1st, lg8vo, 152p, b/w, DJ/3.75, NYTBI)	Pantheon	(1966)	Wilson, Peggy	30-50	*
Appleton, Honor	Bad Mrs. Ginger (1st, 32mo, 96p, stripe cl, color)	L: G. Richards	1902	Appleton, Honor C.	85-130	
Arason, Steingrimus	Smoky Bay (1st, 8vo, 189p, b/w, pep, DJ/2.00)	Macmillan	1942	Howe, Gertrude	40-65	
Arcambeau, Edme	Book of Bridges (1st, 4to, 149p, teg, green/gilt, p-o, 18cp)	L: Gowans/Gray	1911	King, Jessie	600-800	
Archer, Jean C.	Rosalina (1st, 16mo, 95p, 24cp)	L: Richards	1904	Archer, Jean C.	60-90	
Ardizzone, Edward	Baggage to the Enemy (1st, 12mo, blue cl, 121p, b/w, DJ)	L: J. Murray	1941	Ardizzone, Edward	100-150	
Ardizzone, Edward	Diana and her Rhinoceros (1st AM, ob4to, 32p, color, DJ/3.50)	H.Z. Walck	1964	Ardizzone, Edward	50-80	
Ardizzone, Edward	Johnny the Clockmaker (1st AM, 4to, [48]p, color, DJ/3.00)	H.Z. Walck	1960	Ardizzone, Edward	50-85	
Ardizzone, Edward	Little Girl & the Tiny Doll (1st, 8vo, 48p, color, DJ)	L: Constable	(1966)	Ardizzone, Edward	45-70	*
Ardizzone, Edward	Little Girl & the Tiny Doll (1st AM {std}, lg8vo, [48]p, color, DJ/2.75)	Delacorte Pr.	(1967)	Ardizzone, Edward	60-100	
Ardizzone, Edward	Little Tim & the Brave Sea Captain (1st AM, folio, [64]p, ibds, color)	Oxford U. Pr.	1936	Ardizzone, Edward	300-500	
Ardizzone, Edward	Lucy Brown and Mr. Grimes (1st AM, sm folio, ibds, 32p, color)	Oxford U. Pr.	[1937]	Ardizzone, Edward	300-450	R
Ardizzone, Edward	Nicholas and Fast Moving Diesel (1st, lg4to, yellow bds, 35p, color)	L: Eyre/Spotts.	[1947]	Ardizzone, Edward	250-400	R
Ardizzone, Edward	Paul, Hero of the Fire (1st AM, 8vo, ibds, [40]p, color, pep, DJ/1.00)	Houghton	(1948)	Ardizzone, Edward	120-200	
Ardizzone, Edward	Paul, Hero of the Fire (1st AM {revised, std}, sm4to, unpag, color, DJ/3.00)	H.Z. Walck	(1963)	Ardizzone, Edward	40-65	
Ardizzone, Edward	Peter the Wanderer (1st AM {std}, sm4to, [48]p, color, DJ/3.50)	H.Z. Walck	(1964)	Ardizzone, Edward	50-80	
Ardizzone, Edward	Sarah & Simon & No Red Paint (1st AM {std}, lg8vo, 48p, 2-color, DJ/2.75)	Delacorte Pr.	(1966)	Ardizzone, Edward	50-80	
Ardizzone, Edward	Tim All Alone (1st, 4to, red cl, unpag, color, DJ, KGM)	L: Oxford U.Pr.	(1957)	Ardizzone, Edward	200-300	
Ardizzone, Edward	Tim and Charlotte (1st, sm4to, ibds, [48]p, color, DJ/2.00)	Oxford U. Pr.	(1951)	Ardizzone, Edward	150-220	
Ardizzone, Edward	Tim and Ginger (1st AM, 4to, [48]p, color, DJ/3.50)	H.Z. Walck	(1965)	Ardizzone, Edward	50-80	*
Ardizzone, Edward	Tim and Lucy Go to Sea (1st AM, folio, ibds, [64]p, color, DJ/2.00)	Oxford U. Pr.	(1938)	Ardizzone, Edward	300-500	
Ardizzone, Edward	Tim in Danger (1st, 4to, ipcb, [48]p, color, DJ/2.50)	Oxford U. Pr.	(1953)	Ardizzone, Edward	140-220	
Ardizzone, Edward	Tim to the Lighthouse (1st, sm4to, ibds, [48]p, color, DJ)	L: Oxford U.Pr.	1968	Ardizzone, Edward	80-125	
Ardizzone, Edward	Tim to the Rescue (1st, sm4to, [48]p, ibds, color, DJ/2.50)	Oxford U. Pr.	(1949)	Ardizzone, Edward	150-250	
Ardizzone, Edward	Tim's Friend Towser (1st AM, sm4to, [48]p, color, DJ/3.50)	H.Z. Walck	(1962)	Ardizzone, Edward	50-85	
Ardizzone, Edward	Wrong Side of the Bed (1st AM {std}, 8vo, [32]p, color DJ/3.50)	Doubleday	(1970)	Ardizzone, Edward	50-80	R*
Ardley, Patricia B.	Adventures of Mr. Horace Hedgehog (1st, ob4to, ibds, 56p, 6 fp color)	L: Collins	(1935)	Ardley, E.C.	90-120	*
Aris, Ernest A.	Famous Animal Tales (1st, lg8vo, 158p, 8cp, pep)	L: Harrap	(1935)	Aris, Ernest A.	80-120	
Aris, Ernest A.	Three Bad Ducklings (1st, 24mo, ibds, [32]p, p-o, 8cp)	L: Partridge	[1917]	Aris, Ernest A.	70-120	
Aristophanes	Eleven Comedies (1st, 8vo, 2 vols, black/gilt, 16cp)	H. Liveright	1928	DeBosschere, Jean	100-160	
Arkhurst, Joyce C.	Adventures of Spider (1st {std}, lg8vo, 58p, color, DJ/2.95)	Little/Brown	(1964)	Pinkney, Jerry	30-50	
Arkle, Phyllis	Magic at Midnight (1st AM, ob8vo, 80p, b/w, cep, DJ/3.50)	Funk/Wagnalls	(1968)	Williams, Eccles	20-35	*
Arkwright, Ruth	Brownikins and Other Fancies (1st, 4to, p-o, [82]p, 5 ticp, pep)	L: Wells/Gard.	[1910]	Robinson, Charles	300-425	
Armer, Laura A.	Cactus (1st, 8vo, 102p, col frn, b/w)	Stokes	1934	Armer, Sidney	30-50	*
Armer, Laura A.	Dark Circle of Branches (1st {std}, lg8vo, 212p, 8pl, pep, DJ/2.50)	Longmans	1933	Armer, Sidney	30-45	
Armer, Laura A.	Farthest West (1st {std}, lg8vo, 190p, 8pl, pep, DJ/2.50)	Longmans	1939	Armer, Sidney	35-50	
Armer, Laura A.	Forest Pool (1st {std}, 4to, 40p, pep, 8cp, DJ/2.50, CH)	Longmans	(1938)	Armer, Laura A.	125-200	R
Armer, Laura A.	In Navajo Land (1st, 8vo, 107p, gilt, fp b/w, DJ/3.95)	McKay	1962	(Photos)	30-50	*

AUTHOR	TITLE	PUBLISHER	DATE	ARTIST	PRICE	LC
Armer, Laura A.	Trader's Children (1st {std}, 8vo, 241p, b/w, DJ/2.50)	Longmans	1937	Armer, Sidney	50-85	*
Armer, Laura A.	Waterless Mountain (1st {std}, lg8vo, 212p, cloth, 16pl, DJ/2.50, NM)	Longmans	1931	Armer, Laura A.	120-200	R
Armfield, Constance	Armfield's Animal Book (1st, 8vo, 96p, orange cl, 8 ticp)	L: Duckworth	(1922)	Armfield, Maxwell	75-100	
Armfield, Constance	Flower Book (1st, lg8vo, 153p, teg, bds, uncut, 18cp)	L: Chatto	1910	Armfield, Maxwell	100-175	
Armfield, Constance	Sylvia's Travels (1st, sm4to, 256p, gilt, 16cp, pep)	L: Dent	1911	Armfield, Maxwell	120-180	
Armfield, Constance	Tales from Timbuktu (1st, lg8vo, 179p, gilt, col frn, 11 fp b/w)	L: Chatto	(1923)	Armfield, Maxwell	50-80	
Armfield, Constance	Tales from Timbuktu (1st AM, 8vo, 179p, col frn, 11 fp b/w)	Harcourt	[1924]	Armfield, Maxwell	45-70	
Armfield, Constance	Wonder Tales of the World (1st AM, 4to, 271p, color)	Harcourt	1920	Armfield, Maxwell	70-100	*
Armfield, Maxwell	Hanging Garden... (1st, 4to, 75p, 8cp)	L: Simpkin	1914	Armfield, Maxwell	60-100	*
Armour, Margaret	Shadow of Love (1st, 8vo, 124p, 2 fp b/w)	L: Duckworth	1898	MacDougall, W.B.	75-100	*
Armour, Margaret (ed)	Eerie Book (1st, lg8vo, teg, 211p, uncut, 15pl)	L: Shiells & Co.	1898	MacDougall, W.B.	180-280	
Armour, Margaret (tr)	Fall of the Nibelungs (1st, 8vo, 260p, 16pl)	L: Dent	1897	MacDougall, W.B.	200-300	
Armour, Richard	Adventures of Egbert the Easter Egg (1st, sm4to, 43p, color, cep, DJ/2.75)	McGraw-Hill	(1965)	Galdone, Paul	30-45	
Armour, Richard	All Sizes and Shapes of Monkeys and Apes (1st, 4to, 37p, color, DJ/4.50)	McGraw-Hill	(1970)	Galdone, Paul	30-45	*
Armour, Richard	Animals on the Ceiling (1st, 4to, 32p, fp 2-color, dep, DJ/2.95)	McGraw-Hill	(1966)	Galdone, Paul	30-50	
Armour, Richard	Dozen Dinosaurs (1st, 4to, 32p, 2-color, DJ/3.95)	McGraw-Hill	(1967)	Galdone, Paul	30-45	
Armour, Richard	Odd Old Mammals (1st, 4to, 36p, 2-color, DJ/3.95)	McGraw-Hill	(1968)	Galdone, Paul	30-45	
Armour, Richard	Our Presidents (1st, sm4to, 80p, fp 3-color, cep, DJ/3.50)	Norton	(1964)	Fisher, Leonard	30-50	*
Armour, Richard	Year Santa Went Modern (1st, 4to, [32]p, 3-color, DJ/2.75)	McGraw-Hill	(1964)	Galdone, Paul	30-50	
Armstrong, Annie	Marian (1st, 8vo, 224p, 4pl)	L: Blackie	1892	Brooke, L. Leslie	60-90	*
Armstrong, Anthony	Livestock in Barracks (1st, 12mo, 153p, gilt, 20 fp b/w)	L: Methuen	(1929)	Shepard, Ernest H.	30-50	
Armstrong, Leroy	Byrd Flam in Town (1st, 8vo, 139p, cvr & illus by...)	Chi: Bearhope	(1894)	Denslow, W.W.	35-60	*
Armstrong, Margaret	Fieldbook of Western Wilderness (1st, 12mo, 596p, color)	Putnam	1915	Armstrong, Margaret	120-200	
Armstrong, Richard	Cold Hazard (1st, 8vo, 181p, b/w, DJ/2.50)	Houghton	1956	Hodges, C. Walter	20-35	
Armstrong, Richard	Mystery of Obadiah (1st, 8vo, 160p, col frn, b/w, DJ)	L: J.M. Dent	1943	Sankey, Marjorie	30-50	
Armstrong, Richard	Sea Change (1st, 8vo, 211p, b/w, DJ, CgM)	L: J.M. Dent	1948	Leszczynski, M.	70-100	*
Armstrong, William	Animal Tales (1st {std}, 4to, 30p, ibds, color, DJ)	Doubleday	(1970)	Hanak, Mirko	50-80	
Armstrong, William	Sounder (1st, 8vo, 116p, grey cl, fp b/w, cep, DJ/3.95, NM)	Harper, Row	(1969)	Barkley, James	120-200	R
Arnold, Edwin	Adzuma (1st, 12mo, 170p, green/gilt)	Scribner	1893	Armstrong, Margaret	35-60	*
Arnold, Edwin	Japonica (1st, sm4to, teg, uncut, gilt, 128p, b/w pl)	Scribner	1891	Blum, Robert	100-160	
Arnold, Edwin	Light of Asia (1st, sm4to, black/silver, p-o, 182p, 12pl)	McKay	(1932)	Pogany, Willy	120-175	
Arnold, Edwin	Potiphar's Wife (1st, 12mo, 127p, green/gilt)	Scribner	1892	Armstrong, Margaret	30-50	*
Arnold, Edwin	Song Celestial (1st, sm4to, 135p, black/silver, p-o, 18pl)	McKay	(1934)	Pogany, Willy	100-165	
Arnold, Edwin	Voyage of Ithobal (1st, 8vo, 226p, teg, blue cl, 8pl)	Dillingham	1901	Lumley, Arthur	25-40	
Arnold, Matthew	Poems (1st, 12mo, brown/gilt, 374p, teg, uncut, 18pl)	J. Lane	1900	Ospovat, Henry	50-80	
Arnold, Matthew	Scholar-Gypsy (1st, 4to, gilt, unpag, 10 ticp, 10 tipl)	L: Nicholson	1933	Adams, Frank	70-100	
Arnold, Matthew	Scholar-Gypsy and Thyrsis (1st, 4to, 67p, 10cp)	L: P.L. Warner	(1910)	Flint, William R.	100-170	
Arnott, Kathleen	Tales of Temba (1st, 8vo, 144p, fp b/w, cep, DJ/4.50)	H.Z. Walck	(1969)	Feelings, Tom	25-45	
Arora, Shirley L.	What Then, Raman? (1st, 8vo, 176p, fp, b/w, DJ/3.50, JABA)	Follett	(1960)	Guggenheim, Hans	40-65	
Arthur, Lady Kate	Dream of Little Hazy Cream (1st, folio, 40p, ibds, p-o, 12cp)	L: Bickers	[1909]	Frere, Catherine	125-200	*
Arthur, Ruth	Requiem for a Princess (1st {std}, 8vo, 182p, b/w, DJ)	Atheneum	1967	Gill, Margery	40-65	
Artzybasheff, Boris	As I See (1st, 4to, unpag, col frn, fp b/w, DJ/7.50)	Dodd	1954	Artzybasheff, Boris	250-400	
Artzybasheff, Boris	Busiest Man in Town (1st, sm8vo, 45p, gilt)	Time Inc.	1933	Artzybasheff, Boris	75-100	
Artzybasheff, Boris	Fairy Shoemaker (1st, sq8vo, bds, 114p, b/w)	Macmillan	1928	Artzybasheff, Boris	90-120	
Artzybasheff, Boris	Poor Shaydullah (1st, sq8vo, [59]p, grey cl, 10 fp b/w)	Macmillan	1931	Artzybasheff, Boris	60-90	
Artzybasheff, Boris	Seven Simeons (1st, 4to, [32]p, green cl, color, dep, DJ/2.00, CH)	Viking	1937	Artzybasheff, Boris	125-200	
Aruego, Jose	Juan and the Asuangs (1st, 4to, ibds, [32]p, fp color, cep, DJ)	Scribner	1970	Aruego, Jose	30-50	
Aruego, Jose	King and his Friends (1st [1st bk.], ob4to, [40]p, 2-color, DJ/3.50)	Scribner	(1969)	Aruego, Jose	30-50	
Arundel, Jocelyn	Dugan and the Hobo (1st {std}, 8vo, 121p, b/w, DJ/2.95)	Whittlesey	(1960)	Dennis, Wesley	25-40	
Arundel, Jocelyn	Mighty Mo (1st {std}, 8vo, 124p, green cl, col frn, b/w, pep, DJ/2.95)	Whittlesey	(1961)	Dennis, Wesley	30-50	
Arundel, Jocelyn	Simba of the White Mane (1st {std}, 8vo, 127p, b/w, DJ/2.95)	Whittlesey	(1958)	Dennis, Wesley	30-45	
Asbjornsen, P.C.	East of the Sun, West o/t Moon (1st, 12mo, 218p, 9cp)	Row, Peterson	(1912)	Richardson, F.	70-100	
Asbjornsen, P.C.	East of the Sun, West o/t Moon (1st, 4to, gilt, 206p, pep, 25 ticp)	L: Hodder	(1914)	Nielsen, Kay	1400-2000	
Asbjornsen, P.C.	East of the Sun, West o/t Moon (1st AM, 4to, 205p, p-o, 25 ticp pep)	Doran	[1914]	Nielsen, Kay	600-800	
Asbjornsen, P.C.	East of the Sun, West o/t Moon (1st, 8vo, p-o, 289p, green cl, 8cp, pep)	McKay	(1921)	Cooke, Edna	75-100	
Asbjornsen, P.C.	East of the Sun, West o/t Moon (1st, lg8vo, 248p, col frn)	Saalfield	(1924)	Brundage, Frances	35-60	*
Asbjornsen, P.C.	East of the Sun, West o/t Moon (1st, 8vo, 192p, color, p-o, gilt, pep)	Whitman	(1924)	Higgins, Violet M.	50-80	
Asbjornsen, P.C.	East of the Sun, West o/t Moon (1st, 12mo, 198p, cp, pep)	Macmillan	1928	Collin, Hedvig	50-80	
Asbjornsen, P.C.	East of the Sun, West o/t Moon (8vo, 204p, p-o, cp, pep, later)	Garden City	[1930]	Nielsen, Kay	80-130	
Asbjornsen, P.C.	East of the Sun, West o/t Moon (1st, 4to, 188p, 22 fp b/w, pep, DJ/3.50)	Viking	1938	D'Aulaire, I.& E.	50-80	
Asbjornsen, P.C.	Fairy Tales from the Far North (1st AM, 8vo, 303p, b/w)	A.C. Armstrong	1897	Werenskiold, E.	100-160	*
Asbjornsen, P.C.	Fairy Tales from the Far North (1st, 8vo, 303p, b/w pl)	L: D. Nutt	1897	Werenskiold, E.	120-200	
Asbjornsen, P.C.	Fifteen Norse Tales (1st, 8vo, 180p)	L: Nelson	1931	Pailthorpe, Doris	60-80	*
Asbjornsen, P.C.	Norse Fairy Tales (1st, sm8vo, 463p, 8cp, 20pl, pep)	L: Freemantle	1910	Knowles, H.& R.	225-325	
Asbjornsen, P.C.	Norse Fairy Tales (16mo, ibds, 8cp)	L: Routledge	(1920)	Knowles, R.L.	180-240	
Asbjornsen, P.C.	Round the Yule Log (1st, sm8vo, 316p, b/w)	L: Sampson Low	1881	Unknown	80-120	*
Asbjornsen, P.C.	Tales from the Field (1st AM, 8vo, 403p, gilt, 11pl)	Putnam	1896	Smith, J. Moyr	60-100	
Asbjornsen, P.C.	Three Billy Goats Gruff (1st {std}, sm4to, green cl, unpag, color, DJ/3.00)	Harcourt	(1957)	Brown, Marcia	60-90	
Asch, Frank	Elvira Everything (1st, ob8vo, [48]p, ibds, b/w, DJ/2.95)	Harper	(1970)	Asch, Frank	50-80	
Asch, Frank	George's Store (1st, ob4to, [46]p, b/w, DJ/2.95)	McGraw-Hill	(1969)	Asch, Frank	30-45	
Asch, Frank	Linda (1st, ob4to, [46]p, b/w, DJ/3.95)	McGraw-Hill	(1969)	Asch, Frank	30-45	
Ash, Fenton	Black Opal (1st, 8vo, 320p, blue cl, 3 color)	L: J.F. Shaw	(1915)	E.S.H.	180-250	
Ash, Fenton	By Airship to Ophir (1st, 8vo, 320p, AEG, red/gilt, 3 color)	L: J.F. Shaw	(1911)	Pearse, Alfred	200-300	
Ash, Fenton	Trip to Mars (1st AM, 8vo, red/gilt, 318p, 6cp)	Chambers/Lipp.	1909	Groome, W.H.C.	250-350	
Ashford, Daisy	Young Visitors (1st, 8vo, 91p, ibds, b/w, DJ/1.75)	Doubleday	1951	DuBois, W.P.	45-70	
Ashley, Doris	Children's Stories from French Fairy Tales (1st, lg8vo, 136p, ibds, 12cp)	L: R. Tuck	[1917]	Attwell, Mabel L.	200-300	
Ashley, Doris	Fairy Stories from France (lg8vo, ibds, 108p, 6cp)	L: R. Tuck	[1915]	Attwell, Mabel L.	160-250	
Ashley, Fred	Temple of Fire (1st, 8vo, green/gilt, 332p, 8pl)	L: I. Pitman	1905	Daniel, Vincent S.	80-130	

AUTHOR	TITLE	PUBLISHER	DATE	ARTIST	PRICE	LC
Ashmore, Marion	Lost, Stolen and Strayed (1st AM, 8vo, 96p, col frn, b/w)	Scribner	1931	Aldin, Cecil	80-130	
Asimov, Isaac	The Moon (1st {std}, 8vo, 29p, color, DJ/1.00)	Follett	1966	Ebel, Alex	25-45	
Aspden, Don	Barney's Barges (1st, 8vo, 192p, green cl, fp b/w, pep, DJ/2.00)	Holiday House	(1944)	Pitz, Henry C.	30-50	
Aspden, Don	Mike of Company D. (1st, 8vo, 261p, green cl, b/w, DJ/2.00)	Scribner	1939	Brown, Paul	60-95	*
Aspinwall, Alicia	Short Poems for Short People (1st {std}, 8vo, pink/gilt, 129p, b/w, cep)	Dutton	(1929)	Cory, Fanny	30-45	*
Asquith, C. (ed.)	Flying Carpet (1st, 4to, 200p, cloth, 4 ticp)	Scribner	(1925)	Various	35-60	
Asquith, C. (ed.)	Sails of Gold (1st AM, 4to, 166p, ticp)	Scribner	(1927)	Various	35-60	*
Asquith, C. (ed.)	Treasure Cave (1st, 4to, 144p, 5 ticp)	Scribner	(1928)	Various	35-60	
Asquith, C. (ed.)	Treasure Ship (1st, 4to, 198p, 4 ticp)	Scribner	(1926)	Various	35-60	
Astor, John J.	Journey in Other Worlds (1st, sm8vo, blue/silver, 476p, 10pl)	Appleton	1894	Beard, Dan	200-300	
Atherton, Gertrude	Gorgeous Isle (1st, sm8vo, 223p, orange cl, 4cp, pep)	Doubleday/Page	1908	Phillips, Coles	40-60	
Atherton, Gertrude	Splendid Idle Forties (1st, 8vo, 389p, gilt, 8pl)	Macmillan	1902	Fisher, Harrison	100-160	
Atherton, Gertrude	Valiant Runaways (1st, sm8vo, 276p, 8pl)	Dodd	1898	Greenough, Walter C.	45-70	
Atkey, Bertram	Easy Money (1st, 8vo, p-o, 311p, b/w)	Dana Estes	(1908)	Stampa, George L.	25-40	
Atkins, Elizabeth H.	Pot of Gold (1st, 8vo, p-o, 164p, 4cp, 6pl, pep)	Stokes	1930	LaDow, St. C.	55-80	*
Atkins, Elizabeth H.	Toby's Goblin (1st, lg ob8vo, 96p, brown cl, b/w)	Rand/McNally	(1930)	Trippe, Uldene	30-40	
Atkinson, Brooks	Once Around the Sun (1st {std}, 8vo, 376p, blue cl, fp b/w, DJ/4.00)	Harcourt	(1951)	Freeman, Don	40-65	
Atkinson, Eleanor	Greyfriars Bobby (1st, 12mo, 291p, gilt, frontis, PPPa)	Harper	1912	Unknown	80-125	
Atkinson, Eleanor	Greyfriars Bobby (1st, lg8vo, red cl, 269p, uncut, 4pl)	Harper	1929	Kirmse, Marguerite	30-50	
Atkinson, Eleanor	Johnny Apple-Seed (1st, sm8vo, gilt, 340p, b/w)	Harper	1915	Merrill, Frank T.	50-80	
Atkinson, Eleanor	Poilu, Dog of Roubaix (1st, sm8vo, 225p, frn by...)	Harper	1918	Schneider, Sophie	60-100	
Atkinson, John C.	Scenes in Fairyland (1st, 8vo, 246p, green/gilt, 4pl)	L: Macmillan	1892	Brock, Charles E.	80-140	
Atkinson, Mary E.	Smuggler's Gap (1st, sm8vo, 307p, fp b/w, pep, DJ)	L: Bodley Head	1939	Jones, Harold	60-90	
Attwell, Mabel L.	Boo-Boos at the Seaside (8vo, unpag, ipcb, p-o, 13cp, pep)	Valentine	[1915]	Attwell, Mabel L.	100-160	*
Attwell, Mabel L.	Fairy-Land (1st, 4to, 32p, bds, 8cp)	Nelson	(1918)	Attwell, Mabel L.	150-225	
Attwell, Mabel L.	Lucie Attwell's Book of Verses (1st, 4to, ibds, color)	L: Dean	1960	Attwell, Mabel L.	60-100	
Attwell, Mabel L.	Lucie Attwell's Fairy Book (1st, 4to, 255p, red cl, 12cp)	L: Partridge	(1932)	Attwell, Mabel L.	220-300	
Attwell, Mabel L.	Lucie Attwell's Jolly Book (1st, 4to, ibds, 45p, color, pep)	L: Dean	(1950)	Attwell, Mabel L.	60-100	
Attwell, Mabel L.	Lucie Attwell's Painting Book (1st, 4to, ibds, color)	L: Dean	1961	Attwell, Mabel L.	60-100	
Attwood, Frederic	Vavache: Cow who Painted Pictures (1st {std}, sm8vo, 77p, color, DJ/2.25)	Aladdin	(1950)	Duvoisin, Roger	30-50	*
Attwood, William	Man Who Could Grow Hair (1st {std}, sm8vo, 240p, ipcb, b/w, DJ/2.75)	Knopf	1949	Duvoisin, Roger	50-80	
Atwater, Richard	Doris and the Trolls (1st, 8vo, 124p, blue cl, 1-color, pep)	Rand/McNally	(1931)	Gee, John	60-100	
Atwater, Richard	Mr. Popper's Penguins (1st {std}, 8vo, 138p, 1-color, pep, DJ/1.75, NH)	Little/Brown	1938	Lawson, Robert	100-165	R
Aubrey, Frank	Devil-Tree of El Dorado (1st, 8vo, brown/gilt, 392p, 8pl)	L: Hutchinson	1896	Hyland/Ellis	170-240	
Aubrey, Frank	Queen of Atlantis (1st AM, 8vo, red/gilt, 391p, 8pl)	Lippincott	1900	Smith, D. Murray	125-200	
Auerbach, Marjorie	King Lavra & the Barber (1st, ob4to, [40]p, fp 3-color, cep, DJ/3.50)	Knopf	(1964)	Auerbach, Marjorie	30-50	*
Ault, L.& N.	Podgy Book of Tales (1st, 12mo, 223p, pict cl, 16cp)	L: Richards	(1907)	Ault, Norman	150-220	*
Ault, L.& N.	Sammy and the Snarlywink (1st, 16mo, 95p, green cl, 24cp)	L: Richards	1904	Ault, Norman	120-180	
Ault, Norman	Dreamland Shores (1st AM, sm4to, 83p, 6 ticp, pep)	Dodd	(1920)	Ault, Norman	130-200	
Aunt Jo	Jo and Uncle George Kritters (1st, lg8vo, ibds, color)	Little/Brown	1922	Brown, Paul	80-140	
Aunt Jo	Kritters of Kitchen Kingdom (1st, sm4to, 39p, ibds, 16 fp color)	Little/Brown	1922	Brown, Paul	80-125	R
Austen, Jane	Emma (1st, 12mo, green/gilt, 504p, teg, b/w)	L: G. Allen	1898	Hammond, Chris	55-80	
Austen, Jane	Northanger Abbey (1st, 12mo, AEG, 444p, red/gilt, b/w)	L: Macmillan	1897	Thomson, Hugh	100-165	
Austen, Jane	Northanger Abbey (1st, 8vo, 206p, gilt, 24cp)	L: J.M. Dent	1907	Brock, Charles E.	60-90	
Austen, Jane	Pride and Prejudice (1st, 12mo, 476p, AEG, green/gilt, b/w, cep)	L: G. Allen	1894	Thomson, Hugh	200-300	
Austen, Jane	Pride and Prejudice (1st, 8vo, 336p, teg, gilt, uncut, 24 color)	L: J.M. Dent	1907	Brock, Charles E.	55-80	
Austen, Jane	Pride and Prejudice (1st, lg8vo, 374p, b/w, DJ/3.95)	Macmillan	1962	Bryson, Bernarda	25-40	*
Austen, Jane	Rogues in Porcelain (1st, sm4to, 258p, pink bds, p-o, 15cp, pep)	L: Chapman/Hall	1924	Austen, John	60-90	
Austen, Jane	Rogues in Porcelain (1st AM, lg8vo, 258p, bds, 15cp, pep)	Greenberg	1924	Austen, John	70-100	
Austen, Jane	Sense and Sensibility (1st, 8vo, AEG, 389p, gilt, b/w)	L: G. Allen	1899	Hammond, Chris	200-300	
Austin, Cyril F.	Adventures of Benjamin and Christabel (1st, ob4to, unpag, color)	Nister/Dutton	(1911)	Austin, Hilda	60-90	*
Austin, Cyril F.	Edward Buttoneye and his Adventures (sq24mo, ibds, chromos)	L: Nister	[1910]	Austin, Hilda	75-100	*
Austin, Cyril F.	Little Blue Rabbit (sq24mo, ibds, [54]p, fp color)	L: Nister	[1905]	Austin, Hilda	80-125	
Austin, Margot	Archie Angel (1st {std}, sm4to, yellow cl, 45p, b/w, pep, DJ/2.50)	Dutton	1957	Austin, Margot	45-65	
Austin, Margot	Barney's Adventure (1st {std}, sm4to, ibds, [42]p, b/w, pep, DJ/1.00)	Dutton	(1941)	Austin, Margot	30-50	
Austin, Margot	Brave John Henry (1st {std}, sm4to, 43p, b/w, pep, DJ/1.75)	Dutton	(1955)	Austin, Margot	30-45	
Austin, Margot	Churchmouse Stories (1st, 8vo, 171p, 5 fp color, pep, DJ/3.50)	Dutton	(1956)	Austin, Margot	30-45	
Austin, Margot	Effelli (1st {std}, 4to, ibds, [56]p, fp b/w, pep, DJ/1.50)	Dutton	1942	Austin, Margot	45-70	
Austin, Margot	First Prize for Danny (1st {std}, sm4to, ibds, 43p, b/w, pep, DJ/1.50)	Dutton	(1952)	Austin, Margot	40-65	
Austin, Margot	Gabriel Churchkitten (1st {std}, sm4to, ipcb, [36]p, pep, b/w, DJ/1.00)	Dutton	1942	Austin, Margot	70-100	
Austin, Margot	Gabriel Churchkitten & Moths (1st {std}, sm4to, ipcb, [41]p, b/w, pep, DJ/1.25)	Dutton	1948	Austin, Margot	65-90	
Austin, Margot	Growl Bear (1st {std}, sm4to, ipcb, 42p, pep, b/w, DJ/1.50)	Dutton	(1951)	Austin, Margot	45-70	
Austin, Margot	Lutie (1st {std}, sm4to, ibds, [42]p, b/w, DJ/1.25)	Dutton	1944	Austin, Margot	40-65	
Austin, Margot	Manuel's Kite String (1st, sm8vo, 112p, color, DJ/1.50)	Scribner	1943	Austin, Margot	40-65	
Austin, Margot	Moxie and Hanty and Bunty (1st, lg8vo, ipcb, [44]p, 1-color, DJ/1.00)	Scribner	1939	Austin, Margot	45-70	
Austin, Margot	Once Upon a Springtime (1st, lg8vo, [43]p, ipcb, fp 1-color, DJ/1.00)	Scribner	1940	Austin, Margot	30-50	
Austin, Margot	Peter Churchmouse (1st {std}, sm4to, ipcb, [41]p, b/w, pep, DJ/1.00)	Dutton	1941	Austin, Margot	70-100	
Austin, Margot	Poppet (1st {std}, sm4to, ibds, [38]p, b/w, DJ/1.50)	Dutton	(1949)	Austin, Margot	40-65	
Austin, Margot	Three Silly Kittens (1st {std}, 8vo, ibds, 44p, b/w, DJ/1.50)	Dutton	(1950)	Austin, Margot	35-60	
Austin, Margot	Trumpet (1st {std}, sq4to, ipcb, [40]p, b/w, pep, DJ/1.25)	Dutton	1943	Austin, Margot	40-65	
Austin, Margot	Tumble Bear (1st, sm4to, [44]p, olive cl, fp b/w, cep, DJ/1.50)	Scribner	(1940)	Austin, Margot	40-65	
Austin, Margot	Willamette Way (1st, sm4to, [44]p, tan cl, fp color, DJ/1.75)	Scribner	1941	Austin, Margot	45-70	
Austin, Margot	William's Shadow (1st {std}, sm4to, ibds, 43p, b/w, pep, DJ/1.75)	Dutton	(1954)	Austin, Margot	30-50	
Austin, Mary	California: Land of the Sun (1st, lg8vo, 178p, gilt, 32 ticp)	L: A&C Black	1914	Palmer, Sutton	125-200	
Austin, Mary	Can Prayer Be Answered? (1st, 8vo, 55p, black/silver, 3pl)	Farrar/Rinehart	1934	Ward, Lynd	50-80	
Austin, Mary	Children Sing in the Far West (1st, sm8vo, 187p, b/w)	Houghton	1928	Cassidy, Gerald	40-65	
Austin, Mary	Isidro (1st, sm8vo, 425p, green/gilt, dep, 4cp)	Houghton	1905	Pape, Eric	60-100	
Austin, Mary	Land of Little Rain (1st, 8vo, green/gilt, 281p, p-o, teg, 4pl)	Houghton	1903	Smith, E. Boyd	280-400	

AUTHOR	TITLE	PUBLISHER	DATE	ARTIST	PRICE	LC
Austin, Mary	The Flock (1st, 8vo, 266p, brown/gilt, teg, frn by...)	Houghton	1906	Smith, E. Boyd	100-165	
Austin, Mary	The Ford (1st, sm8vo, 440p, 4pl)	Houghton	1917	Smith, E. Boyd	60-90	
Austin, Mary	Trail Book (1st, 8vo, 304p, p-o, 4cp)	Houghton	1918	Winter, Milo	50-80	
Austin, Phyllis	Goldfish Bowl (1st, 8vo, gilt, 254p, 4cp)	L: Hutchinson	[1928]	Robinson, Charles	100-170	
Averill, Esther	Adventures of Jack Ninepins (1st {std}, sm4to, 63p, color, DJ/1.75)	Harper	(1944)	Averill, Esther	80-120	
Averill, Esther	Cartier Sails the St. Lawrence (1st, sm4to, 108p, fp b/w, DJ/3.00)	Harper	(1956)	Rojankovsky, Feodor	40-65	R
Averill, Esther	Cat Club (1st, sm8vo, 32p, 1-color, DJ/1.50)	Harper	1944	Averill, Esther	160-250	
Averill, Esther	Daniel Boone (1st AM {std}, 4to, ipcb, 58p, color, pep, DJ/1.50)	Harper	(1945)	Rojankovsky, Feodor	80-120	R
Averill, Esther	Fire Cat (1st, 8vo, 63p, ibds, fp 3-color, DJ/1.95)	Harper	(1960)	Averill, Esther	100-165	
Averill, Esther	Flash: Story of a Horse (1st AM, narrow 4to, 32p, color, ibds)	Smith/Haas	(1934)	Rojankovsky, Feodor	150-225	
Averill, Esther	How the Brothers Joined Cat Club (1st {std}, sm8vo, 32p, 1-color, DJ/1.50)	Harper	(1953)	Averill, Esther	80-120	
Averill, Esther	Jenny's Adopted Brothers (1st, sm8vo, 32p, color, DJ/1.50)	Harper	(1952)	Averill, Esther	65-90	
Averill, Esther	Jenny's Bedside Book (1st, ob4to, ipcb, [36]p, color, DJ/2.50)	Harper	1959	Averill, Esther	100-140	
Averill, Esther	Jenny's Birthday Book (1st, ob4to, [32]p, ibds, color, DJ/2.00, NYTBI)	Harper	1954	Averill, Esther	100-165	
Averill, Esther	Jenny's First Party (1st, 12mo, 31p, color, DJ/1.50)	Harper	(1948)	Averill, Esther	70-100	
Averill, Esther	King Philip: Indian Chief (1st {std}, 8vo, 147p, b/w, DJ/2.50)	Harper	(1950)	Belsky, Vera	45-60	
Averill, Esther	Powder (1st AM, 4to, ibds, 29p, color)	Smith/Haas	(1933)	Rojankovsky, Feodor	80-125	
Averill, Esther	School for Cats (1st, 12mo, 31p, color, DJ/1.50)	Harper	(1947)	Averill, Esther	70-130	
Averill, Esther	Voyages of Jacques Cartier (1st, 4to, 94p, gilt, fp b/w)	Domino Press	(1937)	Rojankovsky, Feodor	100-160	R*
Averill, Esther	When Jenny Lost her Scarf (1st, sm8vo, 30p, color, DJ/1.50)	Harper	(1951)	Averill, Esther	80-125	
Averill, Naomi	Choochee: Story of an Eskimo Boy (1st, lg sq8vo, [40]p, ibds, pep, color)	Grosset/Dunlap	1937	Averill, Naomi	70-100	
Averill, Naomi	Whistling-Two-Teeth (1st, lg sq8vo, [24]p, color, pep, DJ/0.50)	Grosset/Dunlap	1939	Averill, Naomi	60-100	
Avery, Harold	Play the Game (1st, 8vo, 343p, gilt, 4cp)	L: T. Nelson	[1906]	Shepard, Ernest H.	60-90	
Avery, Kay	Wee Willow Whistle (1st {std}, sm4to, ipcb, [32]p, color, DJ/1.50)	Knopf	(1947)	Bromhall, Winifred	50-80	
Aydelotte, Dora	Green Gravel (1st, 12mo, green cl, uncut, 249p, b/w, DJ/2.00)	Appleton-Century	1937	Daugherty, James	25-40	
Ayer, Jacqueline	Little Silk (1st {std}, sm ob4to, [32]p, color, DJ/4.50)	Harcourt	(1970)	Ayer, Jacqueline	25-45	
Ayer, Jacqueline	Nu Dang and his Kite (1st {std}, ob4to, [32]p, 3-color, pep, DJ/2.75)	Harcourt	(1959)	Ayer, Jacqueline	40-65	R*
Ayer, Jacqueline	Paper-Flower Tree (1st {std}, sm ob4to, [32]p, color, pep, DJ/2.95)	Harcourt	(1962)	Ayer, Jacqueline	25-40	
Ayer, Jacqueline	Wish for Little Sister (1st {std}, ob4to, [32]p, color, pep, DJ/2.95)	Harcourt	(1960)	Ayer, Jacqueline	25-40	
Ayer, Jean	Donald Duck & his Friends (8vo, 102p, pep, color)	D.C. Heath	(1939)	Disney Studios	100-160	
Ayer, Jean	Picnic Book (1st, 12mo, 46p, color, wraps)	Macmillan	1934	Petershams	35-60	
Ayers, Ray F.	King of Kinkiddie... (1st, sm8vo, 262p, 15pl)	Dutton	1904	Bobbett, Walter	100-165	
Ayme, Marcel	Magic Pictures (1st {std}, 8vo, blue cl, 116p, b/w, DJ/2.50)	Harper	(1954)	Sendak, Maurice	180-250	R
Ayme, Marcel	Wonderful Farm (1st {std}, 8vo, 182p, red cl, b/w, DJ/2.50)	Harper	(1951)	Sendak, Maurice	300-450	R
B.B.	Little Grey Men (1st, lg8vo, 203p, b/w, DJ, CgM)	L: Eyre/Spotts.	1942	Watkins-Pitchford, D	200-300	
B.B.	Little Grey Men (1st AM, 8vo, 248p, b/w, DJ/2.50, CgM)	Scribner	(1949)	Watkins-Pitchford, D	150-225	
Babbitt, Natalie	Dick Foote & Shark (1st {std} [1st bk.], 4to, 25p, pep, 1-color, DJ/3.50)	Farrar, Straus	(1967)	Babbitt, Natalie	25-45	
Babbitt, Natalie	Knee-Knock Rise (1st {std}, sm8vo, 117p, b/w, pep, DJ/3.95, NH)	Farrar, Straus	(1970)	Babbitt, Natalie	60-90	
Babbitt, Natalie	Phoebe's Revolt (1st, ob4to, [36]p, 1-color, pep, DJ/3.50)	Farrar, Straus	1968	Babbitt, Natalie	25-40	
Babbitt, Natalie	Search for Delicious (1st {std}, 8vo, 167p, b/w, pep, DJ/3.95)	Farrar, Straus	(1969)	Babbitt, Natalie	30-50	R*
Babbitt, Natalie	The Something (1st {std}, 12mo, [39]p, b/w, pep, DJ/2.95)	Farrar, Straus	(1970)	Babbitt, Natalie	30-55	
Babbitt, Samuel F.	Forty-Ninth Magician (1st, 4to, [48]p, fp b/w, dep, DJ/2.95)	Pantheon	(1966)	Babbitt, Natalie	25-40	
Babcock, William H.	Cian of the Chariots (1st, sm8vo, 406p, b/w pl, gilt)	Lothrop Pub.	1898	Barnes, George F.	70-100	
Bacheller, Irving	Charge It (1st, 12mo, p-o, 192p, b/w)	Harper	1912	Koerner, W.H.D.	20-35	
Bacmeister, Rhoda	Voices in the Night (1st {std}, 8vo, 117p, b/w, DJ/3.25)	Bobbs-Merrill	(1965)	Grifalconi, Ann	30-45	
Bacon, Frances A.	Kitty Come Down (1st, sq12mo, 30p, b/w, DJ/1.25)	NY: Oxford U.Pr.	1944	Wilkin, Eloise B.	70-120	
Bacon, Frances A.	Turkey Tale (1st, sq12mo, 48p, ipcb, fp b/w, pep)	Oxford U. Pr.	(1935)	Paull, Grace	25-40	*
Bacon, Josephine D.	Biography of a Boy (1st, 8vo, 322p, blue cl, 14pl)	Harper	1910	O'Neill, Rose	60-90	
Bacon, Josephine D.	Idyll of All Fool's Day (1st, sm8vo, 120p, p-o, 10pl)	Dodd	1908	Crosby, Raymond M.	25-40	*
Bacon, Josephine D.	In the Border Country (1st, sm8vo, 130p, 5cp)	Doubleday/Page	1909	Peck, Clara E.	30-50	
Bacon, Josephine D.	Luck O'Lady Joan (1st, 12mo, 58p, frn by)	F.G. Browne	1913	Williams, C.E.	25-40	*
Bacon, Josephine D.	Luck of Lowry (1st {std}, sm8vo, 303p, b/w, pep)	Longmans	1931	Esley, Joan	20-35	*
Bacon, Josephine D.	Ten to Seventeen (1st, sm8vo, 261p, green/gilt, p-o, 3pl by...)	Harper	1908	Smith, Jessie W.	60-90	
Bacon, Martha	Sophia Scrooby Preserved (1st {std}, 8vo, 227p, b/w, DJ/4.95)	Little/Brown	(1968)	White, David O.	25-40	
Bacon, Peggy	Animosities (1st {std}, 8vo, 106p, ibds, b/w)	Harcourt	(1931)	Bacon, Peggy	50-80	
Bacon, Peggy	Ballad of Tangle Street (1st, ob4to, ibds, 24p, b/w)	Macmillan	1929	Bacon, Peggy	120-180	
Bacon, Peggy	Cat Calls (1st {std}, lg8vo, 87p, b/w, DJ/2.50)	McBride	(1935)	Bacon, Peggy	55-80	
Bacon, Peggy	Ghost of Opalina (1st {std}, 8vo, 243p, b/w, DJ/4.95)	Little/Brown	(1967)	Bacon, Peggy	250-400	*
Bacon, Peggy	Lion-Hearted Kitten (1st, 8vo, 102p, 10pl)	Macmillan	1927	Bacon, Peggy	40-65	
Bacon, Peggy	Magic Touch (1st {std}, 8vo, 112p, b/w, DJ/3.95)	Little/Brown	(1968)	Bacon, Peggy	45-70	
Bacon, Peggy	Mercy and the Mouse (1st, 8vo, pink cl, 85p, 7pl, cep)	Macmillan	1928	Bacon, Peggy	50-80	*
Bacon, Peggy	Mischief in Mayfield (1st {std}, lg8vo, 177p, 15pl)	Harcourt	(1933)	Bacon, Peggy	60-100	
Bacon, Peggy	Mystery at East Hatchett (1st, 8vo, 170p, b/w, DJ/2.00)	Viking	1939	Bacon, Peggy	60-90	
Bacon, Peggy	Off With Their Heads! (1st {std}, lg4to, ibds, [89]p, b/w)	McBride	(1934)	Bacon, Peggy	60-100	
Bacon, Peggy	Starting from Scratch (1st {spiral}, [48]p, ibds, b/w, DJ/3.00)	J. Messner	1945	Bacon, Peggy	60-90	
Bacon, Peggy	Terrible Nuisance (1st {std}, 8vo, 142p, blue cl, 8pl, DJ/2.50)	Harcourt	(1931)	Bacon, Peggy	70-120	R
Bacon, Peggy	The Oddity (1st, 8vo, 71p, b/w, DJ/3.00)	Pantheon	(1962)	Bacon, Peggy	30-50	
Bacon, Peggy	True Philosopher (1st, 12mo, blue cl, 55p, 13pl)	Bos: Four Seas	1919	Bacon, Peggy	80-130	
Badger, Joseph E.	Lost City (1st, 8vo, 326p, blue/gilt, 8pl)	Dana Estes	(1898)	Bridgman, L.J.	60-90	
Baer, Howard	Now This, Now That (1st ob4to, [30]p, tan cl, b/w, cep, DJ/2.25)	Holiday House	1957	Baer, Howard	30-50	
Bagnold, Enid	Alice and Thomas and Jane (1st AM, 8vo, ibds, 173p, color)	Knopf	1931	Jones, Laurian	30-50	
Bagnold, Enid	National Velvet (1st AM, 8vo, 303p, b/w, pep, DJ/2.50)	Wm. Morrow	(1935)	Jones, Laurian	100-160	
Bagnold, Enid	National Velvet (1st [new. ed.], 8vo, 306p, b/w, DJ/3.00)	Wm. Morrow	1949	Brown, Paul	60-100	*
Bailey, Alice C.	Katrina and Jan (1st, lg8vo, ibds, [93]p, color, pep)	Volland	(1923)	Rosse, Herman	55-80	*
Bailey, Alice C.	Kimo (1st, lg8vo, ibds, 96p, color, pep)	Volland	(1928)	Holling, Lucille W.	50-75	
Bailey, Alice C.	Skating Gander (1st, 8vo, ibds, 93p, color, pep)	Volland	(1927)	Myers, Marie H.	60-90	
Bailey, Alice W.	Roberta and her Brothers (1st, sm8vo, 310p, 4pl)	Little/Brown	1906	Richards, Harriet R.	25-40	*
Bailey, Bernadine	Iceland in Story and Pictures (1st, ob8vo, [28]p, color, pep, DJ/0.50)	Whitman	1942	Wiese, Kurt	45-70	

AUTHOR	TITLE	PUBLISHER	DATE	ARTIST	PRICE	LC
Bailey, Carolyn S.	Children of the Handcrafts (1st, lg8vo, 192p, b/w, dep, DJ/2.00)	Viking	1935	Paull, Grace	30-50	
Bailey, Carolyn S.	Country-Stop (1st, 8vo, 128p, dep, 8 fp color, DJ/2.00)	Viking	1942	Paull, Grace	35-50	
Bailey, Carolyn S.	Finnegan II - His Nine Lives (1st, sm4to, red cl, 95p, b/w, pep, DJ/2.50)	Viking	1953	Seredy, Kate	50-85	R
Bailey, Carolyn S.	Firelight Stories (1st, sm8vo, 192p, 9pl)	Milton Bradley	1907	Horne, Diantha W.	25-40	*
Bailey, Carolyn S.	For the Children's Hour (1st, 8vo, 336p, 8pl)	Milton Bradley	1906	Breck, G. William	25-40	*
Bailey, Carolyn S.	Li'l Hannibal (1st, 8vo, [24]p, p-o, color, pep)	Platt/Munk	(1938)	Carlson, George	60-90	
Bailey, Carolyn S.	Miss Hickory (1st, lg8vo, tan cl, 123p, fp b/w, pep, DJ/2.50, NM)	Viking	1946	Gannett, Ruth C.	80-130	R
Bailey, Carolyn S.	Peter Newell's Mother Goose (1st, 8vo, 265p, 20pl)	Henry Holt & Co.	1905	Newell, Peter	140-200	
Bailey, Carolyn S.	Read Aloud Stories (1st, sm8vo, 215p, red/gilt, 6cp, pep)	Milton Bradley	(1929)	Lupprian, Hildegard	30-50	*
Bailey, Carolyn S.	Stories and Rhymes for a Child (1st, 8vo, 194p, col frn, p-o, 5pl)	Milton Bradley	1909	Wright, Cameron	25-40	*
Bailey, Carolyn S.	Tops and Whistles (1st, lg8vo, 193p, 20 fp b/w, pep, DJ/2.00)	Viking	1937	Paull, Grace	30-50	
Bailey, Carolyn S.	Wonder Stories (1st, 8vo, p-o, 344p, 6cp, pep)	Milton Bradley	1920	Burd, Clara M.	30-50	*
Bailey, Carolyn S.	Wonderful Days (1st, lg8vo, 254p, col frn, pep)	Whitman	(1929)	Falls, Charles B.	40-60	*
Bailey, Margery	Seven Peas in the Pod (1st, 8vo, 201p, gilt, 8cp, pep)	Little/Brown	1919	Preston, Alice B.	50-85	
Bailey, Margery	Seven Peas in the Pod (1st UK, 8vo, 201p, 4cp by...)	L: Harrap	(1921)	Nixon, Kathleen I.	70-100	
Bailey, Temple	Star in the Well (1st, sm8vo, 46p, wraps, color decor by...)	Volland	(1928)	Moschcowitz, P.	55-80	*
Bain, Robert N.	Cossack Fairy Tales & Folk Tales (1st, 8vo, 290p, teg, fp b/w)	L: Lawrence/Bul.	1894	Mitchell, E.W.	80-130	
Bain, Robert N.	Russian Fairy Tales (1st, 8vo, 264p, gilt, b/w)	Way & Williams	1895	Gere, Charles M.	120-170	*
Bain, Robert N.	Russian Fairy Tales (1st, lg8vo, teg, p-o, 283p, 4cp, 12pl)	L: Harrap	1915	Nisbet, Noel L.	170-240	
Bain, Robert N.	Weird Tales from Northern Seas (1st, 8vo, 201p, blue/gilt, 12pl)	L: Kegan Paul	1893	Housman, Laurence	160-240	
Baity, Eliz. C.	America Before Man (1st, lg8vo, 224p, pep, maps, b/w, DJ/4.50)	Viking	1953	Falls, Charles B.	45-60	R
Baity, Eliz. C.	Americans Before Columbus (1st, lg8vo, 256p, gilt, pep, b/w, DJ/4.00, NH)	Viking	1951	Falls, Charles B.	40-65	
Baker, Augusta	Golden Lynx (1st {std}, 8vo, 160p, red cl, fp b/w, DJ/3.00)	Lippincott	(1960)	Troyer, Johannes	40-65	
Baker, Augusta	Talking Tree (1st {std}, 8vo, 255p, maroon cl, b/w, DJ/3.00)	Lippincott	(1955)	Troyer, Johannes	40-65	
Baker, Betty	Killer-of-Death (1st {std}, 8vo, 142p, ipcb, b/w, DJ/2.95)	Harper	(1963)	Kaufman, John	20-35	
Baker, Betty	Little Runner of the Longhouse (1st, 8vo, 63p, ibds, fp 2-color, DJ/1.95)	Harper	(1962)	Lobel, Arnold	40-65	
Baker, Charlotte	Green Poodles (1st, 8vo, 218p, b/w, DJ/3.00)	McKay	(1956)	Baker, Charlotte	45-70	*
Baker, Charlotte	Nellie and the Mayor's Hat (1st, 8vo, 96p, color, pep, DJ/2.50)	Coward	(1947)	Baker, Charlotte	40-65	
Baker, Cornelia	Coquo and the King's Children (1st, 8vo, 250p, brown/gilt, 6 color)	McClurg	1902	Perkins, Lucy F.	40-70	
Baker, Cornelia	Court Jester (1st, 8vo, 259p, gilt, b/w pl)	Bobbs-Merrill	(1906)	Webb, Margaret E.	25-40	*
Baker, Cornelia	Magic Image from India (1st, sm4to, 163p, 6cp)	Stern	1909	Lachman, Harry B.	65-90	
Baker, Cornelia	Queen's Page (1st, sm8vo, 319p, 12pl)	Bobbs-Merrill	(1905)	Cory, Fanny	50-85	
Baker, Cornelia	Young People in Old Places (1st, 8vo, green cl, 322p, fp b/w)	Bobbs-Merrill	(1906)	Booth, Franklin	35-60	*
Baker, Edna D.	Child is Born (1st, folio, ibds, 60p, color, pep)	Reilly/Lee	(1932)	Royt, Mary	50-85	*
Baker, Elizabeth	Stronger than Hate (1st {std}, 8vo, 185p, b/w, DJ/3.50)	Houghton	1969	Gretzer, John	20-30	
Baker, Elizabeth W.	Sonny-Boy Sim (1st {std}, lg8vo, ipcb, 31p, fp 2-color, DJ/1.00)	Rand/McNally	(1948)	Suba, Susanne	40-70	R
Baker, George A.	Point Lace and Diamonds (1st, 4to, 82p, gilt, 12cp)	Stokes	1892	Day, Francis	100-165	
Baker, Karle W.	Garden of the Plynck (1st, lg8vo, ibds, 112p, col frn, b/w)	Yale U. Press	(1920)	Minard, Florence	80-120	*
Baker, Laura N.	Friendly Beasts (1st, 12mo, [24]p, ibds, 3-color, dep, DJ/1.50, NYTBI)	Parnassus Press	(1957)	Sidjakov, Nicolas	40-65	R*
Baker, Margaret	Bears Back in Business (1st, 8vo, 116p, b/w, DJ/3.25)	Farrar, Straus	(1967)	Rowles, Daphne	20-30	
Baker, Margaret	Black Cats and the Tinker's Wife (1st, 8vo, 112p, fp silhouettes)	L: Richards	1923	Baker, Mary	50-80	*
Baker, Margaret	Dunderpate (1st, 8vo, [96]p, fp silhouettes, DJ/2.00)	Dodd	1938	Baker, Mary	40-65	
Baker, Margaret	Family that Grew and Grew (1st, 8vo, 121p, b/w, DJ/2.25)	Whittlesey	(1952)	Unwin, Nora S.	30-45	*
Baker, Margaret	Fifteen Tales for Lively Children (1st AM, 8vo, 144p, b/w, DJ/2.00)	Dodd	1939	Baker, Mary	60-90	*
Baker, Margaret	Four Farthings and a Thimble (1st {std}, 8vo, 150p, b/w, pep, DJ/2.50)	Longmans	1950	Merwin, Decie	25-40	
Baker, Margaret	Hannibal and the Bears (1st AM {std}, sm8vo, 115p, b/w, DJ/2.95)	Farrar, Straus	(1966)	Hodges, C. Walter	30-45	
Baker, Margaret	Lady Arabella's Birthday Party (1st, 8vo, [95]p, silhouettes, pep, DJ/2.00)	Dodd	1940	Baker, Mary	40-65	
Baker, Margaret	Patsy and the Leprechaun (1st, 8vo, [109]p, silhouettes)	Duffield/Green	(1933)	Baker, Mary	40-65	
Baker, Margaret	Porterhouse Major (1st AM, 8vo, 116p, b/w, DJ/3.95)	Prentice-Hall	(1967)	Hughes, Shirley	20-35	
Baker, Margaret	Puppy Called Spinach (1st, 8vo, [96]p, silhouettes, DJ/2.00)	Dodd	1939	Baker, Mary	40-65	
Baker, Margaret	Three for an Acorn (1st AM, 8vo, [96]p, silhouettes, pep)	Dodd	(1935)	Baker, Mary	25-45	
Baker, Michael	Mountain and the Summer Stars (1st AM {std}, 8vo, 124p, b/w, DJ/3.95)	Harcourt	(1969)	Weihs, Erika	25-40	
Baker, Nina B.	Garibaldi (1st, 8vo, 315p, b/w, DJ/2.50)	Vanguard Press	(1944)	Slobodkin, Louis	25-40	*
Baker, Nina B.	Lenin (1st, 8vo, 257p, col frn, b/w, DJ/2.50)	Vanguard Press	(1945)	Slobodkin, Louis	25-40	
Baker, Nina B.	Peter the Great (1st, 8vo, 310p, fp b/w, DJ/2.50)	Vanguard Press	(1943)	Slobodkin, Louis	30-45	
Baker, Olaf	Dusty Star (1st, 8vo, 302p, aqua/gilt, uncut, 4pl, pep)	Dodd	1922	Bransom, Paul	40-65	
Baker, Olaf	Panther Magic (1st, 8vo, gilt, 312p, 8cp, pep)	Dodd	1928	Wiese, Kurt	30-50	
Baker, Olaf	Shasta of the Wolves (1st, 8vo, 276p, 4cp)	Dodd	1919	Bull, Charles L.	30-45	
Baker, Olaf	Thunder Boy (1st, 8vo, red cl, 288p, 4pl, pep)	Dodd	1924	Bransom, Paul	30-50	*
Balch, Frederic H.	Bridge of the Gods (1st, sm8vo, teg, 280p, 8pl)	McClurg	1902	Dixon, Maynard	35-60	
Balch, Glenn	Brave Riders (1st {std}, 8vo, 191p, green cl, b/w, DJ/2.75)	Crowell	(1959)	Keats, Ezra J.	30-50	
Balch, Glenn	Hide-Rack Kidnapped (1st, sm8vo, 302p, dp pl, DJ/2.00)	Crowell	1939	Mason, George F.	25-40	*
Balch, Glenn	Horse in Danger (1st, 8vo, 181p, b/w, DJ/2.75)	Crowell	(1960)	Ames, Lee	30-50	
Balch, Glenn	Indian Paint (1st, 8vo, 244p, b/w, DJ/2.00)	Crowell	(1942)	Hogner, Nils	30-50	*
Balch, Glenn	Indian Saddle-Up (1st, 8vo, 210p, b/w, DJ/2.50)	Crowell	(1953)	Frankenberg, Rbt.	30-50	
Balch, Glenn	Little Hawk and the Free Horses (1st {std}, 8vo, 180p, b/w, DJ/2.75)	Crowell	(1957)	Keats, Ezra J.	30-50	
Balch, Glenn	Midnight Colt (1st, 8vo, 194p, b/w, DJ/2.50)	Crowell	1952	Crowell, Pers	30-50	
Balch, Glenn	Stallion King (1st, 8vo, 118p, bds, b/w, DJ/2.95)	Crowell	1960	Paull, Grace	30-45	
Balderson, Margaret	When Jays Fly to Barbmo (1st AM {std}, 8vo, 239p, b/w, DJ/4.25)	World	(1969)	Ambrus, Victor	20-35	
Baldwin, Anne	Sunflowers for Tina (1st, sm4to, [45]p, fp 3-color, cep, DJ/4.50)	Four Winds Pr.	(1970)	Grifalconi, Ann	40-65	*
Baldwin, Clara	Little Tuck (1st {std}, lg8vo, 95p, yellow cl, b/w, DJ/2.00)	Doubleday	(1959)	Galdone, Paul	30-50	
Baldwin, James	Story of Roland (1st, lg8vo, 347p, p-o, 10cp, pep, SC)	Scribner	(1930)	Hurd, Peter	100-165	
Baldwin, James	Story of Siegfried (1st, 12mo, red/gilt, 306p, teg, PPP)	Scribner	1882	Pyle, Howard	170-240	
Baldwin, James	Story of Siegfried (1st, lg8vo, p-o, 279p, black cl, 6cp, pep, SC)	Scribner	(1931)	Hurd, Peter	100-165	
Baldwin, James	Story of the Golden Age (1st, 12mo, 286p, gilt, uncut, 12pl, PPP)	Scribner	1887	Pyle, Howard	150-250	
Baldwin, James	The Sampo (1st, 8vo, green/gilt, 368p, 4cp)	Scribner	1912	Wyeth, N.C.	150-220	
Baldwin, May	Dora: High School Girl (1st, 12mo, 319p, 6 fp b/w)	L: Chambers	1906	Attwell, Mabel L.	70-100	
Baldwin, May	Holly House and Ridges Row (1st, 8vo, 339p, AEG, red/gilt, 12cp)	L: Chambers	1908	Wheelhouse, Mary V.	40-65	

AUTHOR: 12

AUTHOR	TITLE	PUBLISHER	DATE	ARTIST	PRICE	LC
Baldwin, May	That Little Limb (1st, 8vo, 199p, ibds, 4pl)	L: Chambers	1905	Attwell, Mabel L.	180-240	
Balet, Jan B.	Amos and the Moon (1st, 4to, [26]p, ibds, dp color, pep, DJ/2.50)	NY: Oxford U.Pr.	1948	Balet, Jan B.	50-80	R*
Balet, Jan B.	Five Rollatinis (1st {std}, 4to, [24]p, fp color, pep, DJ/3.50)	Lippincott	(1959)	Balet, Jan B.	60-90	R*
Balet, Jan B.	Joanjo (1st, lg ob4to, [31]p, color, DJ/4.50)	Delacorte Pr.	(1967)	Balet, Jan B.	45-70	
Balet, Jan B.	King and the Broom Maker (1st, 4to, [23]p, fp color, DJ/4.50)	Delacorte Pr.	(1968)	Balet, Jan B.	30-50	
Balet, Jan B.	Ned and Ed and the Lion (1st, 4to, [28]p, ibds, color, pep, DJ/2.50)	Oxford U. Pr.	1949	Balet, Jan B.	40-70	
Balet, Jan B.	The Fence (1st {std}, 4to, [26]p, color, DJ/4.50)	Delacorte Pr.	(1969)	Balet, Jan B.	30-45	*
Ballantyne, Joan	Holiday Trench (1st, 8vo, blue/gilt, 120p, b/w, DJ)	L: T. Nelson	(1959)	Ardizzone, Edward	60-90	
Ballantyne, Joan	Kidnappers at Coombe (1st, 8vo, 203p, green/gilt, b/w, DJ)	L: T. Nelson	1960	Ardizzone, Edward	35-60	
Ballantyne, R.M.	Kitten Pilgrims (1st, lg8vo, ibds, 70p, color)	L: J. Nesbit	1882	Ballantyne, R.M.	80-140	
Ballard, Martin	Benjie's Portion (1st AM {std}, 8vo, 208p, b/w, DJ/3.95)	World	(1969)	Phillips, Douglas	20-35	
Ballard, Martin	Emir's Son (1st AM {std}, sm4to, 32p, color, DJ/3.75)	World	1967	Floyd, Gareth	25-45	
Bancroft, Alberta	Goblins of Haubeck (1st, 12mo, 117p, green/gilt, pep, col frn)	McBride	1925	Sichel, Harold	30-50	
Bancroft, Alberta	Lost Village (1st, 8vo, 130p, green cl, 4 fp color)	Doran	(1927)	Barney, Maginel W.	55-80	
Bancroft, Henreitta	Down Come the Leaves (1st, ob8vo, [37]p, 2-color, DJ)	Crowell	(1961)	Hogrogian, Nonny	30-45	
Bancroft, Hubert H.	New Pacific (1st, 8vo, 738p, map, green/gilt, cvr by...)	Bancroft Co.	1900	Armstrong, Margaret	80-130	
Bancroft, Laura	Babes in Birdland (1st, lg8vo, green ipcb, 116p, 8cp)	Reilly/Britton	(1911)	Enright, Maginel W.	400-650	R
Bancroft, Laura	Bandit Jim Crow (1st, 12mo, 62p, 15cp)	Reilly/Britton	(1906)	Enright, Maginel W.	350-500	R
Bancroft, Laura	Mr. Woodchuck (1st, 8vo, 62p, ibds, color, cep)	Reilly/Britton	(1906)	Enright, Maginel W.	350-550	R
Bancroft, Laura	Policeman Blue Jay (1st, 12mo, ibds, 115p, 8cp)	Reilly/Britton	(1907)	Enright, Maginel W.	400-600	R
Bancroft, Laura	Prairie-Dog Town (1st, 8vo, 61p, 14 fp color)	Reilly/Britton	(1906)	Enright, Maginel W.	350-500	R
Bancroft, Laura	Prince Mud-Turtle (1st, 12mo, 61p, tan cl, cep, 14 fp color)	Reilly/Britton	(1906)	Enright, Maginel W.	300-450	R
Bancroft, Laura	Sugar-Loaf Mountain (1st, 12mo, 64p, 16cp, cep)	Reilly/Britton	(1906)	Enright, Maginel W.	300-450	R
Bancroft, Laura	Twinkle and Chubbins (1st, 12mo, 384p, yellow cl, color)	Reilly/Britton	(1911)	Enright, Maginel W.	400-600	
Bancroft, Laura	Twinkle's Enchantment (1st, 12mo, 64p, 15cp)	Reilly/Britton	(1906)	Enright, Maginel W.	350-500	R
Bangs, John K.	Alice in Blunderland (1st, 12mo, 124p, brown cl, p-o, b/w)	Doubleday/Page	1907	Levering, Albert	60-90	
Bangs, John K.	Andiron Tales (1st, lg8vo, green cl, p-o, 101p, 8cp)	Winston	(1906)	Dwiggins, C.V.	120-200	*
Bangs, John K.	Autobiography of Methuselah (1st, sm8vo, 185p, grey cl, 12cp)	Dodge	1909	Cooper, F.G.	45-70	
Bangs, John K.	Bikey the Skycycle (1st, sm8vo, blue/gilt, 321p, col frn, 7pl)	NY: Riggs	1902	Newell, Peter	80-130	
Bangs, John K.	Booming of Acre Hill (1st, 12mo, teg, uncut, 265p, b/w)	Harper	1900	Gibson, Charles D.	40-65	
Bangs, John K.	Dreamers, A Club (1st, 12mo, brown/gilt, 247p, b/w)	Harper	1899	Penfield, Edward	50-85	
Bangs, John K.	Emblemland (1st, 8vo, 164p, blue/gilt, fp b/w)	R.H. Russell	1902	Macauley, Charles R.	70-100	*
Bangs, John K.	Enchanted Typewriter (1st, 16mo, 171p, uncut, 10pl)	Harper	1899	Newell, Peter	70-125	
Bangs, John K.	From Pillar to Post (1st, sm8vo, 339p, gilt, b/w)	Century	1916	Neill, John R.	50-80	
Bangs, John K.	Ghosts I Have Met (1st, 16mo, 191p, uncut, 23pl)	Harper	1898	Various	50-80	
Bangs, John K.	Half-Hours with Jimmie-Boy (1st, 12mo, green cl, 212p, b/w)	R.H. Russell	1893	Various	60-80	
Bangs, John K.	House Boat on the Styx (1st, 12mo, green/gilt, 171p, 23pl)	Harper	1896	Newell, Peter	60-100	
Bangs, John K.	Idiot at Home (1st, 12mo, 314p, teg, uncut, b/w pl)	Harper	1900	Richards, F.T.	60-90	
Bangs, John K.	In Camp with a Tin Soldier (1st, 12mo, grey cl, 194p, b/w)	R.H. Russell	1892	Ashe, E.M.	60-90	
Bangs, John K.	Jack and the Check Book (1st, 12mo, 236p, green cl, b/w)	Harper	1911	Levering, Albert	60-90	
Bangs, John K.	Little Book of Christmas (1st, 12mo, 173p, 4cp)	Little/Brown	1912	Becher, Arthur E.	50-85	
Bangs, John K.	Mantel-Piece Minstrels (1st, 16mo, 84p, pcb, p-o, b/w)	R.H. Russell	1896	Unknown	60-100	
Bangs, John K.	Molly and The Unwiseman (1st, sm8vo, 198p, 8pl)	Coates	1902	Levering, Albert	70-120	
Bangs, John K.	Molly and Unwiseman Abroad (1st, 8vo, p-o, 262p, teg, 10cp)	Lippincott	1910	Wiederseim, Grace	150-220	
Bangs, John K.	Mr. Bonaparte of Corsica (1st, 16mo, 265p, gilt, b/w)	Harper	1895	McVickar, H.W.	70-120	
Bangs, John K.	Mr. Munchausen (1st, 12mo, 180p, tan cl, 15cp)	Noyes/Platt	1901	Newell, Peter	50-80	
Bangs, John K.	Olympian Nights (1st, 12mo, red/gilt, 224p, 16pl)	Harper	1902	Levering, Albert	50-80	
Bangs, John K.	Peeps at People (1st, 12mo, 184p, gilt, 36pl)	Harper	1899	Penfield, Edward	50-80	
Bangs, John K.	Pursuit of the House Boat (1st, 12mo, 204p, 24pl)	Harper	1897	Newell, Peter	70-100	
Bangs, John K.	R. Holmes and Co. (1st, 12mo, 230p, blue cl, 6pl)	Harper	1906	Adamson, Sydney	100-165	
Bangs, John K.	Real Thing... (1st, sm8vo, 135p, brown/gilt, uncut, 4pl)	Harper	1909	Unknown	50-80	
Bangs, John K.	Rebellious Heroine (1st, 12mo, 225p, yellow/gilt, 8pl)	Harper	1896	Smedley, W.T.	40-65	
Bangs, John K.	The Bicyclers (1st, 12mo, 176p, blue/gilt, 4pl)	Harper	1896	Penfield, Edward	60-100	
Bangs, John K.	The Idiot (1st, 12mo, 115p, gilt, 8pl)	Harper	1895	Richards, F.T.	60-100	
Bangs, John K.	Tiddledywink Tales (1st, 12mo, red/gilt, 236p, b/w)	R.H. Russell	1891	Johnson, Charles H.	90-120	
Bangs, John K.	Tiddledywink's Poetry Book (1st, sm8vo, [64]p, b/w)	R.H. Russell	1892	Johnson, Charles H.	75-100	*
Banks, Charles E.	Child of the Sun (1st, 8vo, tan cl, teg, 166p, 16cp)	Herbert Stone	1900	Betts, Louis	60-90	
Banks, Helen M.	Polly's Garden (1st, sm8vo, 96p, grey cl, 4cp)	Macmillan	1918	Pogany, Willy	60-100	
Banks, Helen W.	Life of Jesus Retold for Children (1st AM, 4to, 93p, p-o, 5cp, 9pl)	Stokes	(1922)	Choate/Curtis	35-60	*
Banks, Richard	Mysterious Leaf (1st {std}, 8vo, 51p, fp b/w, DJ/2.50)	Harcourt	(1954)	Haas, Irene	150-225	R
Bannerman, Helen	All About Little Black Sambo (1st, 16mo, 48p, bds, p-o, 8cp)	Cupples/Leon	(1917)	Gruelle, Johnny	250-400	
Bannerman, Helen	Little Black Bobtail (1st AM, 16mo, bds, 115p, p-o, 27cp)	Stokes	(1909)	Bannerman, Helen	200-300	
Bannerman, Helen	Little Black Mingo (1st, 16mo, 143p, green cl, color)	L: J. Nisbet	(1901)	Bannerman, Helen	300-500	
Bannerman, Helen	Little Black Mingo (1st AM, 16mo, ibds, 144p, color)	Stokes	[1902]	Bannerman, Helen	280-400	
Bannerman, Helen	Little Black Quasha (1st AM, 16mo, 110p, cp)	Stokes	(1908)	Bannerman, Helen	300-500	
Bannerman, Helen	Little Black Quibba (1st, 16mo, 143p, color)	L: J. Nisbet	(1902)	Bannerman, Helen	500-700	
Bannerman, Helen	Little Black Quibba (1st AM, 16mo, 143p, ibds, p-o, color)	Stokes	1903	Bannerman, Helen	350-500	
Bannerman, Helen	Little Black Sambo (1st, 16mo, green cl, 57p, 25 fp color)	L: Richards	1899	Bannerman, Helen	5000-8000	
Bannerman, Helen	Little Black Sambo (1st AM, 16mo, tan bds, 56p, fp color)	Stokes	[1901]	Bannerman, Helen	1500-2500	
Bannerman, Helen	Little Black Sambo (1st {large fmt}, sq8vo, AEG, 109p)	L: Richards	1903	Bannerman, Helen	1200-2000	
Bannerman, Helen	Little Black Sambo (1st, 24mo, ibds, 56p, color)	Reilly/Britton	1905	Bannerman, Helen	300-450	
Bannerman, Helen	Little Black Sambo (sq8vo, ibds, 28p, color)	Reilly/Britton	(1908)	Neill, John R.	200-300	
Bannerman, Helen	Little Black Sambo (folio, wraps, [16]p, color)	Whitman	[1915]	Smith, T.& M.	200-300	
Bannerman, Helen	Little Black Sambo (1st, 16mo, bds, p-o, 64p, color)	Altemus	[1920]	Bannerman, Helen	140-200	
Bannerman, Helen	Little Black Sambo (folio, wraps, color)	NY: S. Gabriel	[1920]	Russell, Mary L.	150-225	
Bannerman, Helen	Little Black Sambo (sq8vo, ibds, [42]p, color)	Saalfield	[1920]	Williams, Florence	250-350	
Bannerman, Helen	Little Black Sambo (1st, lg8vo, p-o, 63p, col frn, color, pep)	Whitman	(1925)	Shinn, Cobb X.	180-300	
Bannerman, Helen	Little Black Sambo (1st, 16mo, ibds, [39]p, color)	Macmillan	1927	Dobias, Frank	160-225	

AUTHOR	TITLE	PUBLISHER	DATE	ARTIST	PRICE	LC
Bannerman, Helen	Little Black Sambo (4to, 40p, green bds, p-o, color)	Platt/Munk	(1927)	Eulalie	200-300	
Bannerman, Helen	Little Black Sambo (ob12mo, 95p, ibds, color)	Winston	(1930)	Stephenson, Eunice	100-175	*
Bannerman, Helen	Little Black Sambo (8vo, 59p, ibds, color)	McKay	(1931)	Bannerman, Helen	90-120	*
Bannerman, Helen	Little Black Sambo (1st {std}, 4to, [20]p, p-o, 6cp)	Harter	(1931)	Peat, Fern B.	300-450	
Bannerman, Helen	Little Black Sambo (1st {this fmt}, 4to, 59p, blue cl, DJ)	L: Chatto	(1932)	Bannerman, Helen	350-500	
Bannerman, Helen	Little Black Sambo (1st, 16mo, [42]p, ibds, color)	Whitman	(1932)	Jordan, Nina	150-250	*
Bannerman, Helen	Little Black Sambo (8vo, [20]p, ibds, color, pep)	Saalfield	(1932)	Peat, Fern B.	200-300	
Bannerman, Helen	Little Black Sambo (1st, folio, [16]p)	Whitman	(1935)	Ward, Keith	250-350	*
Bannerman, Helen	Little Black Sambo (12mo, ibds, color)	McLoughlin	(1938)	Lupprian, Hildegard	100-175	
Bannerman, Helen	Little Black Sambo (12mo, 113p, p-o, bds)	L: Chatto	1941	Bannerman, Helen	130-200	
Bannerman, Helen	Little Black Sambo (lg4to, ipcb, color)	Saalfield	1942	Hays, Ethel	160-225	
Bannerman, Helen	Little Black Sambo (1st, lg8vo, ibds, [22]p, color, pep)	Grosset/Dunlap	(1942)	Moore, Robert	200-300	
Bannerman, Helen	Little Black Sambo (1st, 8vo, ibds, unpag, color)	NY: Harrison Co.	(1945)	Romyns, Marjorie	200-300	
Bannerman, Helen	Little Black Sambo (1st {A}, sm8vo, ibds, [42]p, color, LGB/#57)	Simon/Schuster	(1948)	Tenggren, Gustaf	50-80	
Bannerman, Helen	Little Black Sambo & Baby Elephant (24mo, 62p, ibds, p-o, 30 color, pep)	Platt/Munk	1925	VerBeck, Frank	100-160	
Bannerman, Helen	Little Black Sambo Story Book (1st, sm4to, 63p, col frn)	Altemus	(1930)	VerBeck, Frank	250-350	R
Bannerman, Helen	Little Black Sambo Story Book (4to, 63p, ipcb, color)	Platt/Munk	(1935)	VerBeck, Frank	120-180	
Bannerman, Helen	Little Degchie Head (1st, 16mo, 143p, green cl, p-o, fp color)	L: J. Nisbet	1903	Bannerman, Helen	400-600	
Bannerman, Helen	Little Kettle-Head (1st AM, 16mo, 144p, ibds, col frn, cp)	Stokes	1904	Bannerman, Helen	350-500	
Bannerman, Helen	New Story of Little Black Sambo (folio, wraps, [12]p, color)	Whitman	1932	Bennett, Juanita C.	200-300	
Bannerman, Helen	Pat and the Spider (1st, 16mo, 143p, fp color)	L: J. Nisbet	(1904)	Bannerman, Helen	350-500	
Bannerman, Helen	Pat and the Spider (1st AM, 16mo, ipcb, 143p, color)	Stokes	(1905)	Bannerman, Helen	250-400	
Bannerman, Helen	Sambo and the Twins (1st, 16mo, 92p, red cl, color, DJ/1.00)	Stokes	1936	Bannerman, Helen	200-300	
Bannerman, Helen	Sambo and the Twins (16mo, green bds, 90p, color, pep)	L: Nisbet	[1937]	Bannerman, Helen	120-200	
Bannerman, Helen	Story of the Teasing Monkey (1st AM, 16mo, 142p, cp)	Stokes	(1907)	Bannerman, Helen	300-425	*
Banning, Kendall	Pirates! (1st {this pub}, 12mo, [31]p, wraps, 13 fp woodcuts)	Chi: Woodworth	1918	Baumann, Gustave	125-200	
Bannon, Laura	Baby Roo (1st, 8vo, 28p, b/w, pep, DJ/1.50)	Houghton	1947	Bannon, Laura	30-50	*
Bannon, Laura	Big Brother (1st, 4to, 48p, color, pep, DJ/2.50)	Whitman	1950	Bannon, Laura	35-50	*
Bannon, Laura	Billy and the Bear (1st, 4to, 47p, fp color, pep, DJ/2.50)	Houghton	1949	Bannon, Laura	30-50	
Bannon, Laura	Burro Boy and his Big Trouble (1st {A}, 8vo, 48p, b/w, pep, DJ/1.50)	Abingdon Press	(1955)	Bannon, Laura	20-35	
Bannon, Laura	Famous Baby-Sitter (1st, 8vo, 47p, p-o, color, DJ/2.75)	Whitman	(1960)	Bannon, Laura	30-45	
Bannon, Laura	Gregorio & the White Llama (1st, lg8vo, 44p, pep, p-o, color, DJ/2.00)	Whitman	1944	Bannon, Laura	30-50	
Bannon, Laura	Hawaiian Coffee Picker (1st {std}, lg8vo, 48p, color, DJ/3.00)	Houghton	1962	Bannon, Laura	30-50	
Bannon, Laura	Hop-High, the Goat (1st {std}, 8vo, 64p, color, DJ/3.25)	Bobbs-Merrill	(1960)	Bannon, Laura	20-30	
Bannon, Laura	Horse on a Houseboat (1st, 8vo, 94p, pep, b/w, DJ/2.50)	Whitman	(1951)	Bannon, Laura	25-40	
Bannon, Laura	Katy Comes Next (1st, sq8vo, 47p, color, DJ/2.75)	Whitman	(1959)	Bannon, Laura	30-45	
Bannon, Laura	Little People of the Night (1st, 8vo, 31p, DJ/2.75)	Houghton	1963	Bannon, Laura	25-40	
Bannon, Laura	Little Sister Doll (1st, lg8vo, p-o, 30p, fp color, cep, DJ/2.00)	Whitman	(1955)	Bannon, Laura	30-45	*
Bannon, Laura	Manuela's Birthday in Old Mexico (1st, sq4to, 46p, p-o color, pep, DJ/2.00)	Whitman	1939	Bannon, Laura	40-60	
Bannon, Laura	Nemo Meets the Emperor (1st, lg8vo, p-o, 45p, color, pep, DJ/2.75)	Whitman	(1957)	Evans, Katherine	40-60	
Bannon, Laura	Patty Paints a Picture (1st, lg sq8vo, [48]p, p-o, color, pep, DJ/2.00)	Whitman	1946	Bannon, Laura	40-65	
Bannon, Laura	Scary Thing (1st, sm8vo, 28p, b/w, DJ/2.00)	Houghton	1956	Bannon, Laura	30-50	
Bannon, Laura	Watchdog (1st, 4to, [48]p, p-o, fp color, pep, DJ/2.50)	Whitman	1948	Bannon, Laura	40-65	
Bannon, Laura	When the Moon is New (1st, sq8vo, [48]p, color, pep, DJ/2.75)	Whitman	(1953)	Bannon, Laura	30-50	
Bannon, Laura	Whistle for a Pilot (1st, 8vo, 48p, fp, color, pep, DJ/3.00)	Houghton	1959	Bannon, Laura	20-30	
Bannon, Laura	Wonderful Fashion Doll (1st, 8vo, 86p, color, pep, DJ/2.25)	Houghton	1953	Bannon, Laura	200-300	
Banta, Nathaniel M.	Brownie Primer (1st, sm8vo, 98p, color)	Chi: Flanagan	(1905)	Benson, Alpha B.	70-120	
Banta, Nathaniel M.	Brownies and the Goblins (1st, 8vo, 128p, color, pep)	Chi: Flanagan	1915	Dulin, J.H.	60-90	
Banta, Nathaniel M.	Four-and-Forty Fairies (1st, 12mo, grey cl, 128p, 1-color, pep)	Chi: Flanagan	1923	Dulin, Dorothy	60-90	
Barbour, Ralph H.	Boys' Book of Dogs (1st, sm8vo, 238p, b/w)	Dodd	1928	Dennis, Morgan	30-50	*
Barbour, Ralph H.	Captain Chub (1st, sm8vo, 413p, 22pl)	Century	1909	Relyea, Charles M.	100-160	
Barbour, Ralph H.	Finkler's Field (1st, sm8vo, 226p, 4cp)	Appleton	1911	Heath, Howard	50-80	
Barbour, Ralph H.	Golden Heart (1st, 8vo, gilt, 219p, teg, p-o, 5cp, pep)	Lippincott	1910	Underwood, C.F.	30-45	
Barbour, Ralph H.	Half-Back (1st, 8vo, orange cl, 267p, b/w, PPP)	Appleton	1899	Clinedinst, B. West	120-200	
Barbour, Ralph H.	Hearts Content (1st, 8vo, teg, 204p, p-o, 4cp)	Lippincott	1915	Taylor, H. Weston	40-65	
Barbour, Ralph H.	Hitting the Line (1st, sm8vo, 322p, 5cp)	Appleton	1917	Rockwell, Norman	90-120	*
Barbour, Ralph H.	House in the Hedge (1st, sm8vo, 251p, col frn, 3pl)	Moffat	1911	Kay, Gertrude A.	35-60	*
Barbour, Ralph H.	Lady Laughter (1st, 8vo, 176p, teg, p-o, 4cp)	Lippincott	1913	Hoskins, Gayle	30-50	*
Barbour, Ralph H.	Lucky Seventh (1st, sm8vo, 310p, 4cp)	Appleton	1915	Rockwell, Norman	80-120	*
Barbour, Ralph H.	On Your Mark (1st, 8vo, 267p, p-o, 4cp)	Appleton	1904	Relyea, Charles M.	25-40	
Barbour, Ralph H.	Orchard Princess (1st, 8vo, p-o, 219p, 4cp)	Lippincott	1905	Flagg, James M.	25-40	
Barbour, Ralph H.	Purple Pennant (1st, sm8vo, 322p, 4cp)	Appleton	1916	Rockwell, Norman	250-350	*
Barbour, Ralph H.	Secret Play (1st, 12mo, p-o, gilt, 335p, 4cp)	Appleton	1915	Rockwell, Norman	250-350	*
Barbour, Ralph H.	Story my Doggie Told to Me (1st, sm8vo, p-o, 182p, fp b/w)	Dodd	1914	Rae, John	35-60	*
Barbour, Ralph H.	Weatherby's Inning (1st, 8vo, gilt, 249p, 6cp)	Appleton	1907	Relyea, Charles M.	70-100	
Barclay, Florence	Following of the Star (1st, sm8vo, 426p, teg, cvr by...)	Putnam	1911	Armstrong, Margaret	40-65	*
Barclay, Florence	Following of the Star (1st, sm8vo, 426p, teg, 8cp by...)	Putnam	1911	Townsend, F.H.	40-65	*
Barclay, Florence	Mistress of Shenstone (1st, lg8vo, 340p, teg, uncut, gilt, 8cp)	Putnam	1910	Armstrong, Margaret	50-80	
Barclay, Florence	The Rosary (1st, lg8vo, 389p, teg, blue/gilt)	Putnam	1910	Armstrong, Margaret	35-60	
Bare, Arnold E.	Maui's Summer (1st, 4to, yellow cl, [48]p, color, pep, DJ/2.50)	Houghton	1952	Bare, Arnold E.	45-70	
Barfield, Arthur O.	Silver Trumpet (1st, 8vo, green cl, 142p, 8cp)	L: Faber/Gwyer	1925	James, Gilbert	40-60	*
Baring, Maurice	Glass Mender (1st, 8vo, blue/gilt, 260p, teg, 12cp)	L: J. Nisbet	1910	Baring, Maurice	60-95	
Baring-Gould, Sabine	Amazing Adventures (1st, ob folio, 53p, fp color)	L: Skeffington	[1903]	Neilson, Harry B.	180-260	
Baring-Gould, Sabine	Bladys of the Stewponey (1st, 8vo, 319p)	L: Methuen	1897	Townsend/Munns	55-80	*
Baring-Gould, Sabine	Book of Fairy Tales (1st, 8vo, teg, 244p, gilt, uncut, 5pl)	L: Methuen	1894	Gaskin, Arthur J.	120-170	
Baring-Gould, Sabine	Book of Ghosts (1st, 8vo, 383p, gilt, 8pl)	L: Methuen	1904	Smith, D. Murray	150-250	*
Baring-Gould, Sabine	Book of Nursery Songs and Rhymes (1st, 8vo, 160p, gilt, uncut, teg, 16pl)	L: Methuen	1895	Various	150-250	
Baring-Gould, Sabine	Book of Pictured Carols (1st, 8vo, ibds, uncut, 75p, wood engravings)	L: G. Allen	1893	Various	140-200	

AUTHOR	TITLE	PUBLISHER	DATE	ARTIST	PRICE	LC
Baring-Gould, Sabine	Broom-Squire (1st, 8vo, 384p, uncut, gilt, 12pl)	L: Methuen	1896	Dadd, Frank	100-160	*
Baring-Gould, Sabine	Crock of Gold (1st AM, 8vo, gilt, teg, 8pl)	L.C. Page	1899	Bedford, Francis D.	70-100	
Baring-Gould, Sabine	Grettir and Outlaw (1st, sm8vo, 384p, gilt, 10pl)	L: Blackie	1890	Diemer, M. Zeno	60-90	
Baring-Gould, Sabine	Old English Fairy Tales (1st AM, 8vo, teg, 400p, gilt, b/w)	Way & Williams	1895	Bedford, Francis D.	120-180	
Baring-Gould, Sabine	Siegfried (1st, 8vo, red/gilt, 351p, col frn, 10 fp b/w)	L: Dean	1904	Robinson, Charles	140-225	
Barker, Cecily M.	Groundsel and Necklaces (1st, 16mo, p-o, 48p, 12cp, pep)	L: Blackie	[1946]	Barker, Cicely M.	50-85	
Barker, Cicely M.	Book of Flower Fairies (1st, 8vo, green/gilt, 92p, color)	L: Blackie	(1927)	Barker, Cicely M.	220-300	
Barker, Cicely M.	Children's Book of Hymns (1st, lg8vo, blue/gilt, 84p, 12 ticp)	L: Blackie	[1929]	Barker, Cicely M.	80-120	
Barker, Cicely M.	Fairies of the Trees (16mo, ibds, p-o, unpag, fp color, pep)	L: Blackie	(1940)	Barker, Cicely M.	150-250	
Barker, Cicely M.	Flower Fairies of Autumn (12mo, ibds, p-o, 24cp)	L: Blackie	[1927]	Barker, Cicely M.	120-200	
Barker, Cicely M.	Flower Fairies of Spring (12mo, bds, p-o, 24cp)	L: Blackie	[1925]	Barker, Cicely M.	120-200	
Barker, Cicely M.	Flower Fairies of Summer (1st, 12mo, 25p, 24cp)	L: Blackie	[1923]	Barker, Cicely M.	120-200	
Barker, Cicely M.	Flower Fairy Alphabet (1st, 12mo, 24p, brown bds, p-o, 24cp)	L: Blackie	(1934)	Barker, Cicely M.	120-200	
Barker, Cicely M.	Flower Songs of the Seasons (1st, lg8vo, ibds, p-o, 12 ticp)	L: Blackie	[1928]	Barker, Cicely M.	100-165	
Barker, Cicely M.	Spring Songs with Music (4to, ibds, p-o, 12 ticp)	L: Blackie	[1918]	Barker, Cicely M.	200-300	
Barker, Cicely M.	Summer Songs with Music (4to, bds, p-o, 12 ticp)	L: Blackie	[1920]	Barker, Cicely M.	200-300	
Barker, Dorothy O.	He Leadeth Me (1st AM, 8vo, 256p, gilt, 16cp, DJ/2.00)	NY: M.S. Mill	[1938]	Barker, Cicely M.	60-90	
Barker, Mrs. S.	Birthday Book for Children (1st, 32mo, 128p, green/gilt, p-o, 12cp)	L: Routledge	(1880)	Greenaway, Kate	200-300	
Barker, Mrs. S.	Feathered and Four-Footed Friends (1st, sq8vo, 96p, 24cp)	L: Routledge	1883	Zwecker, John B.	80-120	*
Barksdale, Lena	First Thanksgiving (1st {std}, sm8vo, 57p, 6cp, pep, DJ/1.50)	Knopf	1942	Lenski, Lois	60-90	
Barksdale, Lena	Milly and her Dogs (1st {std}, ob4to, ibds, [31]p, color, DJ/1.25)	Doubleday/Doran	1942	Steiner, Charlotte	40-70	
Barlow, Jane	Battle of the Frogs and Mice (1st, 8vo, green cl, unpag, 4pl)	L: Methuen	1894	Bedford, Francis D.	100-165	
Barlow, Jane	End of Elfintown (1st, 8vo, gilt, uncut, 77p, AEG, 8pl)	L: Macmillan	1894	Housman, Laurence	350-500	
Barlow, Jane	Irish Ways (1st, 8vo, 262p, teg, gilt, uncut, 16cp)	L: G. Allen	(1909)	Goble, Warwick	185-250	
Barlow, Jane (tran)	Book of Nursery Rhymes (1st, 4to, ibds, 91p, 21cp)	L: Methuen	1897	Bedford, Francis D.	180-250	
Barlow, Jane (tran)	Book of Nursery Rhymes (1st AM, lg8vo, 91p, 21cp)	Doub./McClure	1897	Bedford, Francis D.	150-225	
Barman, Christian	The Bridge (1st, sm4to, green/gilt, 249p, uncut, 24cp)	J. Lane	1926	Brangwyn, Frank	120-180	
Barnaby, Horace T.	Tale of the Long-Eared Bat (1st, 4to, [60]p, ibds, 4cp)	Saalfield	(1929)	Peat, Fern B.	70-90	
Barne, Kitty	She Shall Have Music (1st AM, 8vo, 261p, b/w, DJ)	Dodd	1939	Gervis, Ruth	30-50	
Barne, Kitty	Visitors from London (1st, 8vo, 262p, b/w, DJ, CgM)	L: J.M. Dent	1940	Gervis, Ruth	70-120	
Barnes, James	Drake and his Yeomen (1st, 8vo, 415p, teg, gilt, col frn, 7pl)	Macmillan	1899	Chapman, Carlton	30-50	
Barnes, James	Loyal Traitor (1st, 12mo, 306p, gilt, 21pl)	Harper	1897	Keller, Arthur I.	30-50	*
Barnes, James	Ships and Sailors (1st, ob folio, 124p, ibds, 12cp)	Stokes	1898	Zogbaum, Rufus F.	160-240	
Barnes, James	Son of Light Horse (1st, 12mo, 242p, 8pl)	Harper	1904	Mears, W.E.	30-50	*
Barnes, James	Yankee Ships and Yankee Sailors (1st, sm8vo, gilt, 281p, 13pl)	Macmillan	1897	Zogbaum, Rufus F.	30-50	
Barnes, Madeline	Stirabout Stories (1st, 4to, ibds, 80p, 8cp)	L: Blackie	[1929]	Anderson, Anne	120-170	
Barnes, Madeline	Tub-Time Tales (1st, 4to, 79p, ibds, p-o, 8cp)	L: Blackie	1920	Anderson, Anne	180-250	
Barnes, Nancy	Carlota (1st, 8vo, spiral-bound, 214p, uncut, b/w pl, DJ/2.75)	J. Messner	(1943)	Barber, John	25-40	
Barnes, Nancy	Wonderful Year (1st, 8vo, 185p, b/w, DJ/2.50, NH)	J. Messner	(1946)	Seredy, Kate	40-65	
Barnes, Ruth A.	I Hear America Singing (1st, 8vo, 346p, 1-color, pep, DJ/2.00)	Winston	(1937)	Lawson, Robert	80-140	
Barney, Maginel W.	Weather Signs & Rhymes (1st {std}, sq8vo, yellow cl, [103]p, 1-color, pep)	Knopf	1931	Barney, Maginel W.	80-125	
Barnouw, Victor	Dream of the Blue Heron (1st {std}, 8vo, 191p, b/w, cep, DJ/4.50)	Delacorte Pr.	(1966)	Ward, Lynd	30-50	
Barnstone, Aliki	Real Tin Flower (1st {std}, 8vo, 54p, fp b/w, cep, DJ/3.95)	Crowell-Collier	(1968)	Giovanopoulos, P.	30-50	*
Barnum, Jay H.	Little Old Truck (1st, 8vo, 46p, blue cl, color, pep, DJ/2.00)	Wm. Morrow	1953	Barnum, Jay H.	40-65	
Barnum, Jay H.	Motorcycle Dog (1st, 8vo, blue cl, 48p, 2-color, pep, DJ/2.50)	Wm. Morrow	1958	Barnum, Jay H.	40-65	
Barnum, Jay H.	New Fire Engine (1st, 8vo, red cl, 47p, 2-color, pep, DJ/2.00)	Wm. Morrow	1952	Barnum, Jay H.	40-65	
Barr, Amelia E.	Knight of the Nets (1st, 8vo, 314p, cvr by...)	Dodd	1896	'AM'	25-40	*
Barr, Amelia E.	Song of a Single Note (1st, sm8vo, 330p, 4pl)	Dodd	1902	Betts, Anna W.	25-40	
Barr, Amelia E.	Souls of Passage (1st, sm8vo, 327p, 6pl)	Dodd	1901	McConnell, Emlen	25-40	*
Barr, Amelia E.	Thyra Varrick (1st, sm8vo, green cl, 343p, 12pl)	J.F. Taylor	1903	Zeigler, Lee W.	25-40	
Barr, Catherine	Raffie (1st, 8vo, 32p, rust cl, 1-color, DJ/3.00)	H.Z. Walck	1968	Barr, Catherine	25-45	
Barr, Jene	Little Circus Dog (1st, 8vo, [32]p, p-o, color, pep)	Whitman	1949	Wiese, Kurt	30-50	
Barr, Jene	Little Prairie Dog (1st, 8vo, [32]p, p-o, color, pep)	Whitman	1949	Wiese, Kurt	30-50	
Barr, Robert	Strong Arm (1st, 8vo, 336p, cvr by...)	Stokes	1899	Edwards, George W.	20-30	
Barr, Stringfellow	Copydog in India (1st, lg8vo, 127p, b/w, DJ/2.75)	Viking	1955	Wiese, Kurt	30-50	
Barrett, Leone	Buffin (1st, 8vo, 30p, green cl, p-o, color, pep, DJ/1.00)	Whitman	1935	Gaug, Margaret	40-65	
Barrie, James M.	Admirable Crichton (1st, 4to, 235p, gilt, 21 ticp)	L: Hodder	[1914]	Thomson, Hugh	130-200	
Barrie, James M.	Blampied Edition of Peter Pan (1st, 4to, 216p, white cl, 12 ticp, pep)	L: Hodder	1939	Blampied, Edmund	300-500	
Barrie, James M.	Little One's Peter Pan and Wendy (1st, 24mo, 44p, cp, pep)	Scribner	(1930)	Atkins, Kathleen	60-90	R*
Barrie, James M.	Little White Bird (1st AM, 8vo, 286p, teg, uncut, 2pl by...)	Scribner	1912	Rackham, Arthur	150-225	
Barrie, James M.	Little White Bird (1st, 8vo, teg, 242p, 2pl by...)	L: Hodder	1912	Rackham, Arthur	250-350	
Barrie, James M.	My Lady Nicotine (1st {this pub}, sm8vo, teg, 276p)	J. Knight	1896	Prendergast, Mabel	100-165	
Barrie, James M.	Nursery Peter Pan (1st, 16mo, 48p, ibds, color)	L: Hodder	[1938]	Atkins, Kathleen	60-100	
Barrie, James M.	Peter and Wendy (1st AM, lg8vo, 267p, gilt, 13pl)	Scribner	(1911)	Bedford, Francis D.	250-350	
Barrie, James M.	Peter and Wendy (1st, 8vo, 267p, green/gilt, 13pl)	L: Hodder	(1911)	Bedford, Francis D.	300-500	
Barrie, James M.	Peter Pan (1st AM, lg8vo, 125p, green/gilt, 50 ticp)	Scribner	1906	Rackham, Arthur	500-700	
Barrie, James M.	Peter Pan (1st, sm4to, 125p, red/gilt, 50 ticp)	L: Hodder	1906	Rackham, Arthur	500-700	
Barrie, James M.	Peter Pan (1st, sm8vo, blue cl, 73p, 16 illus, pep)	Silver Burdette	(1916)	Woodward, Alice B.	70-100	
Barrie, James M.	Peter Pan (1st, 8vo, 27p, color)	Grosset/Dunlap	1942	Miss Elliott	30-50	*
Barrie, James M.	Peter Pan (1st, 8vo, 242p, pink cl, fp b/w, DJ/2.50)	Scribner	1950	Unwin, Nora S.	40-65	R
Barrie, James M.	Peter Pan (1st UK, 8vo, 192p, red/gilt, 23 b/w illus, DJ)	L: Hodder	1951	Unwin, Nora S.	55-80	
Barrie, James M.	Peter Pan (1st, lg4to, 64p, fp color, DJ/2.95)	Random	1957	Torrey, Marjorie	40-65	*
Barrie, James M.	Peter Pan (1st AM, 8vo, 175p, 6 fp color, DJ/5.00)	Scribner	(1962)	Ardizzone, Edward	60-95	
Barrie, James M.	Peter Pan and Wendy (1st, lg8vo, 185p, blue/gilt, 12 ticp)	L: Hodder	(1921)	Attwell, Mabel L.	250-350	
Barrie, James M.	Peter Pan and Wendy (1st AM, lg8vo, gilt, p-o, 185p, 12cp, pep, SC)	Scribner	1921	Attwell, Mabel L.	180-250	
Barrie, James M.	Peter Pan and Wendy (1st, 4to, 272p, blue/gilt, color)	L: Hodder	[1925]	Hudson, Gwynedd	140-200	
Barrie, James M.	Peter Pan and Wendy (1st AM, sm4to, 216p, gilt, 12cp, pep, DJ/3.50)	Scribner	1940	Blampied, Edmund	120-200	
Barrie, James M.	Peter Pan Picture Book (1st, lg8vo, 62p, p-o, 28cp, pep)	L: G. Bell	1907	Woodward, Alice B.	200-300	

AUTHOR	TITLE	PUBLISHER	DATE	ARTIST	PRICE	LC
Barrie, James M.	Peter Pan Picture Book (1st, folio, ibds, [89]p, 24cp, pep)	Whitman	(1931)	Best, Roy	80-120	
Barrie, James M.	Quality Street (1st, 4to, 198p, blue/gilt, 22 ticp, pep)	L: Hodder	[1913]	Thomson, Hugh	150-240	
Barrie, James M.	Sentimental Tommy (1st AM, sm8vo, 478p, brown/gilt, cvr by...)	Scribner	1896	Armstrong, Margaret	30-60	
Barrie, James M.	Story of Peter Pan (4to, ibds, 6 fp color, pep)	C.E. Graham	(1926)	Unknown	60-100	
Barringer, Marie	Four and Lena (1st {std}, 8vo, 216p, black cl, 6cp, pep, DJ/2.00)	Doubleday/Doran	1938	Petershams	45-70	
Barringer, Marie	Martin the Goose Boy (1st {std}, 8vo, 188p, black cl, 8cp, pep)	Doubleday/Doran	1932	Petershams	50-85	
Barrows, Marjorie	Ezra the Elephant (1st, sq8vo, ibds, [44]p, color, pep)	Grosset/Dunlap	1934	Smock, Nell S.	25-40	
Barrows, Marjorie	Fraidy Cat (1st, 4to, [28]p, ibds, color, DJ/0.50)	Rand/McNally	1942	Maynard, Barbara	40-65	*
Barrows, Marjorie	Muggins Mouse (1st, folio, black cl, p-o, 60p, color)	Reilly/Lee	(1932)	Ward, Keith	100-170	*
Barrows, Marjorie	My Rhyme & Picture Book (1st, 4to, ibds, [24]p, fp color)	Whitman	(1930)	Best, Roy	60-90	
Barrows, Marjorie	Pudgy: The Little Bear (1st AM, 4to, [22]p, ibds, color, pep)	Rand/McNally	1964	Tamburine, Jean	25-40	
Barrows, Marjorie	Who's Who in the Zoo (1st, folio, 60p, p-o, pep, 25 fp color)	Reilly/Lee	(1932)	Winter, Milo	60-100	
Barry, Katharina	'A' is for Anything (1st {std}, ob12mo, [55]p, fp 2-color, DJ/2.50)	World	(1961)	Barry, Katharina	40-70	R*
Barry, Mary E.	Wonder Flights of Long Ago (1st, sm8vo, 218p, col frn, b/w, pep)	Appleton	(1930)	Ward, Lynd	30-50	
Barry, Robert E.	Faint George Who Wanted to be a Knight (1st, ob4to, 32p, 1-color, DJ/2.50)	Houghton	1957	Barry, Robert E.	40-65	
Barry, Robert E.	Mr. Willowby's Christmas Tree (1st, 4to, 32p, 1-color, pep, DJ/2.50)	Whittlesey	(1963)	Wilde, George	50-80	
Barske, Charlotte	King Cotton (1st, folio, wraps, 23p, color)	A.& W. Guild	1938	Wright, George	100-165	
Bartlett, Ruth	Miracle of the Talking Jungle (1st, 8vo, 96p, fp 1-color, DJ/3.95)	Van Nostrand	(1965)	Lent, Blair	25-40	
Bartlett, Susan	Books (1st {std}, 8vo, unpag, color, DJ/2.95)	Holt, Rinehart	(1968)	Raskin, Ellen	35-50	*
Barto, Emily N.	Chubby Bear (1st {std}, 16mo, [36]p, b/w, pep, DJ/0.85)	Longmans	(1941)	Barto, Emily N.	40-65	*
Barton, Olive R.	Cloud Boat Stories (1st, 8vo, 138p, blue cl, p-o, 4cp)	Houghton	1917	Winter, Milo	60-90	
Barton, William E.	Hero in Homespun (1st, sm8vo, 393p, 10pl)	Lamson/Wolffe	1897	Beard, Dan	50-80	
Barton, William E.	Prairie Schooner (1st, sm8vo, 382p, 5pl)	W.A. Wilde	(1900)	Burgess, H.	25-40	*
Bartos-Hoppner, B.	The Cossacks (1st AM {std}, 8vo, 295p, b/w, DJ/4.00)	H.Z. Walck	1963	Ambrus, Victor	30-45	
Bartrug, Carey M.	Mother Goose Etiquette Rhymes (1st, ob8vo, 32p, blue cl, pep)	Whitman	1941	Peters, Marjorie	55-80	*
Bartruse, Grace	Children in Japan (1st, lg8vo, [32]p, bds, p-o, 16cp)	McBride	1915	Pogany, Willy	200-300	
Bartusek, Libushka	Happy Times in Czechoslovakia (1st {std}, 4to, 61p, color, pep, DJ/2.00)	Knopf	(1940)	Bures, Yarka	50-80	
Baruch, Dorothy W.	Big Fellow at Work (1st {std}, 12mo, 103p, b/w, pep)	Harper	1930	Hader, B.& E.	75-100	
Baruch, Dorothy W.	Blimps and Such (1st, lg4to, 80p, ibds, col frn, b/w, DJ/2.00)	Harper	1932	Wolcott, Elizabeth	60-100	
Baruch, Dorothy W.	Bobby Goes Riding (1st, 8vo, [35]p, red cl, color, pep)	Lothrop, Lee	1934	Brann, Esther	30-50	*
Baruch, Dorothy W.	Funny Little Boy (1st, sq12mo, [36]p, color, pep, DJ/1.00)	Lothrop, Lee	1936	Lietta	30-50	*
Baruch, Dorothy W.	I Like Animals (1st {std}, 16mo, ipcb, 48p, b/w, dep)	Harper	1933	Waterall, Corinne P.	25-45	*
Baruch, Dorothy W.	I Like Automobiles (1st, 8vo, [55]p, color, pep)	NY: J. Day	(1931)	Fujikawa, Gyo	35-60	*
Baruch, Dorothy W.	I Would Like to be a Pony (1st, 8vo, 32p, b/w, DJ/2.00)	Harper	(1959)	Chalmers, Mary	20-30	
Barzini, Luigi	Little Match Man (1st, 8vo, 164p, p-o, 5cp, pep)	Penn	1917	Longstreet, Hattie	35-50	
Bascom, Louise R.	Bugaboo Men (1st, sq4to, green cl, [72]p, pep, color)	Sully/Kleinteich	(1914)	Bascom, Louise R.	100-165	*
Basile, Giovanni B.	Stories from the Pentamerone (1st, 4to, red/gilt, 304p, 32cp)	L: Macmillan	1911	Goble, Warwick	250-400	
Baskin, Esther	Creatures of Darkness (1st {std}, 4to, [48]p, b/w, DJ/4.75)	Little/Brown	(1962)	Baskin, Leonard	40-65	
Baskin, Esther	Poppy and other Deadly Plants (1st {std}, 4to, 74p, fp color, DJ/12.50)	Delacorte Pr.	(1967)	Baskin, Leonard	70-100	
Bason, Lillian	Isabelle and the Library Cat (1st, lg8vo, unpag, color, pep, DJ/3.25)	Lothrop, Lee	(1966)	Werth, Kurt	30-50	
Batchelor, Julie	Cap for Mul Chand (1st {std}, 8vo, 56p, fp 1-color, DJ/2.00)	Harcourt	(1950)	Dillon, Corrine	25-40	*
Bate, Norman	Who Built the Bridge? (1st, 4to, [32]p, fp 1-color, DJ/2.50)	Scribner	1954	Bate, Norman	80-130	R
Bates, Clara D.	Doll Rosy's Days (1st, ob12mo, ipcb, [31]p, 12cp)	D. Lothrop Co.	(1884)	Hassam, F. Childe	170-240	
Bates, Clara D.	On the Tree Top (1st, 4to, [90]p, ibds, 4cp)	D. Lothrop Co.	(1891)	Various	100-160	
Bates, Clara D.	On the Way to Wonderland (1st, 4to, [38]p, ibds, color, pep)	D. Lothrop Co.	(1885)	(Chromos)	120-200	
Bates, Helen D.	Betsy Ross (1st {std}, 8vo, 127p, b/w, pep, DJ/1.00)	Whittlesey	(1936)	Lawson, Robert	40-65	
Bates, Helen D.	Francis Scott Key (1st {std}, 8vo, 118p, b/w, pep, DJ/1.00)	Whittlesey	(1936)	Lawson, Robert	50-80	
Bates, Herbert E.	Achilles the Donkey (1st AM, 4to, [41]p, color, pep, DJ/3.95)	F. Watts	(1963)	Barker, Carol	30-50	
Bates, Herbert E.	Down the River (1st AM, sm4to, 151p, wood engravings, DJ/3.00)	Henry Holt & Co.	1937	Parker, Agnes M.	70-120	
Bates, Herbert E.	My Uncle Silas (1st, 4to, 190p, fp b/w, DJ)	L: J. Cape	(1939)	Ardizzone, Edward	100-180	
Bates, Herbert E.	Sugar for the Horse (1st, 12mo, 120p, b/w, DJ)	L: Joseph	1957	Ardizzone, Edward	50-85	
Bates, Herbert E.	Through the Woods (1st AM, 4to, gilt, 142p, b/w engravings, DJ/3.00)	Macmillan	1936	Parker, Agnes M.	70-120	
Bates, Katharine L.	Once Upon a Time (1st, 4to, p-o, blue cl, 128p, color, pep)	Rand/McNally	(1921)	Price, Margaret E.	60-90	
Bateson, Carlen	Man in the Camlet Cloak (1st, sm8vo, 320p, gilt, teg, 4pl)	Saalfield	1903	Dunton, W. Herbert	35-60	*
Battles, Edith	Terrible Trick or Treat (1st, lg8vo, [48]p, fp color, DJ/3.95)	Young Scott	(1970)	Funk, Tom	25-45	
Bauer, Helen	California Indian Days (1st {std}, 4to, 160p, b/w, DJ/3.50)	Doubleday	1963	Freeman, Don	25-45	
Baum, Betty	Patricia Crosses Town (1st, 8vo, 178p, b/w, DJ/3.50)	Knopf	(1965)	Grossman, Nancy	25-40	
Baum, Frank J.	Laughing Dragon of Oz (1st [Big-Little bk.], sq32mo, 425p, ibds, b/w)	Whitman	(1934)	Youngren, Milt	300-500	
Baum, L. Frank	American Fairy Tales (1st, 8vo, [205]p, teg, cloth, b/w)	George Hill	1901	Various	600-900	*
Baum, L. Frank	Animal ABC (1st, 32mo, ibds, 124p, color)	Reilly/Britton	1905	Unknown	100-165	R
Baum, L. Frank	Army Alphabet (1st, lg4to, [60]p, ibds, 29cp)	George Hill	1900	Kennedy, Harry	900-1200	R
Baum, L. Frank	Baum's American Fairy Tales (1st, 4to, [223]p, p-o, 16cp)	Bobbs-Merrill	(1908)	Kerr, George F.	500-750	
Baum, L. Frank	Daring Twins (1st [1], sm8vo, blue cl, 317p, 4pl)	Reilly/Britton	(1911)	Batchelder, P.M.	250-350	
Baum, L. Frank	Daring Twins (1st [1], sm8vo, 317p, blue cl, cvr by...)	Reilly/Britton	(1911)	Hazenplug, Frank	250-350	
Baum, L. Frank	Dorothy and the Wizard of Oz (1st [1], lg8vo, p-o, 256p, 16cp)	Reilly/Britton	(1908)	Neill, John R.	700-900	
Baum, L. Frank	Dot and Tot of Merryland (1st [1], lg8vo, 225p, gilt, color, pep)	George Hill	1901	Denslow, W.W.	750-1000	R
Baum, L. Frank	Dot and Tot of Merryland (2nd, lg8vo, 225p, color)	Bobbs-Merrill	(1903)	Denslow, W.W.	300-500	
Baum, L. Frank	Emerald City of Oz (1st [1], lg8vo, 296p, p-o, 16cp, pep)	Reilly/Britton	(1910)	Neill, John R.	750-900	R
Baum, L. Frank	Enchanted Island of Yew (1st [1], lg8vo, 242p, tan cl, 8cp, pep)	Bobbs-Merrill	(1903)	Cory, Fanny	600-850	
Baum, L. Frank	Father Goose's Yearbook (1st, 8vo, [128]p, p-o, buckram, color, pep)	Reilly/Britton	(1907)	Enright, Walter J.	300-450	
Baum, L. Frank	Father Goose: His Book (1st [1], 4to, ibds, [106]p, color)	George Hill	(1899)	Denslow, W.W.	3000-4000	R
Baum, L. Frank	Father Goose: His Book (4to, unpag, ibds, color)	Donohue	(1913)	Denslow, W.W.	180-270	
Baum, L. Frank	Gingerbread Man (1st, sm4to, ibds, 62p, col frn)	Reilly/Britton	(1917)	Neill, John R.	200-300	
Baum, L. Frank	Glinda of Oz (1st [1], lg8vo, grey cl, p-o, 279p, 12cp, pep)	Reilly/Lee	(1920)	Neill, John R.	600-800	R
Baum, L. Frank	John Dough and the Cherub (1st [1], lg8vo, tan cl, 314p, color, pep)	Reilly/Britton	(1906)	Neill, John R.	700-900	
Baum, L. Frank	Last Egyptian (1st, 12mo, blue cl, p-o, 287p, 8cp)	Stern	1908	Wightman, Francis P.	250-350	
Baum, L. Frank	Life and Adventures of Santa Claus (1st [1], lg8vo, 206p, 20cp, pep)	Bowen-Merrill	1902	Clark, Mary C.	600-800	
Baum, L. Frank	Little Wizard Stories of Oz (1st [1], sm8vo, p-o, 152p, 42cp)	Reilly/Britton	(1914)	Neill, John R.	400-650	

AUTHOR	TITLE	PUBLISHER	DATE	ARTIST	PRICE	LC
Baum, L. Frank	Lost Princess of Oz (1st [1], 8vo, 312p, p-o, 12cp, pep)	Reilly/Britton	(1917)	Neill, John R.	700-900	
Baum, L. Frank	Magic Cloak... (1st [1], 8vo, 58p, ibds)	Reilly/Britton	(1916)	Neill, John R.	500-700	
Baum, L. Frank	Magic of Oz (1st [1], lg8vo, 265p, p-o, green cl, 12cp, pep)	Reilly/Lee	(1919)	Neill, John R.	500-700	
Baum, L. Frank	Magical Monarch of Mo (1st [1], lg8vo, 237p, p-o, 12cp, pep)	Bobbs-Merrill	(1903)	VerBeck, Frank	600-850	R
Baum, L. Frank	Marvelous Land of Oz (1st [1], lg8vo, 287p, green cl, 16cp, pep)	Reilly/Britton	1904	Neill, John R.	900-1400	
Baum, L. Frank	Master Key (1st [1], 8vo, 245p, olive/gilt, p-o, 12cp)	Bowen-Merrill	(1901)	Cory, Fanny	350-500	
Baum, L. Frank	Mother Goose in Prose (1st [1], 4to, gilt cloth, 265p, 12pl)	Way & Williams	(1897)	Parrish, Maxfield	5000-7000	R
Baum, L. Frank	Mother Goose in Prose (2nd, sm4to, 265p, red cl, 12 fp b/w)	George Hill	1901	Parrish, Maxfield	900-1400	
Baum, L. Frank	Mother Goose in Prose (3rd, sq8vo, 265p, 12pl)	Bobbs-Merrill	(1905)	Parrish, Maxfield	600-800	
Baum, L. Frank	Navy Alphabet (1st, lg4to, [58]p, ibds, color)	George Hill	1900	Kennedy, Harry	900-1200	R
Baum, L. Frank	New Wizard of Oz (2nd, lg8vo, green cl, [261]p, 16cp, pep)	Bobbs-Merrill	(1903)	Denslow, W.W.	1200-1800	
Baum, L. Frank	New Wizard of Oz (1st, lg8vo, 209p, gilt, 8 fp color, DJ/1.75)	Bobbs-Merrill	(1944)	Copelman, Evelyn	80-130	
Baum, L. Frank	New Wizard of Oz (1st, 8vo, 192p, t.e. blue, fp b/w, pep)	Jr. Deluxe Ed.	(1955)	Weisgard, Leonard	50-80	R*
Baum, L. Frank	New Wonderland (1st [1], 4to, [189]p, cloth, 16cp, pep)	R.H. Russell	1900	VerBeck, Frank	2500-4000	
Baum, L. Frank	Ozma of Oz (1st [1], lg8vo, 270p, tan cl, color, pep)	Reilly/Britton	(1907)	Neill, John R.	700-900	
Baum, L. Frank	Ozma of Oz (1st, 4to, [61]p, bds, color, DJ)	Reilly/Lee	(1961)	Martin, Dick	200-300	
Baum, L. Frank	Patchwork Girl of Oz (1st [1], 8vo, 341p, green cl, color, pep)	Reilly/Britton	(1913)	Neill, John R.	700-900	
Baum, L. Frank	Phoebe Daring... (1st, 8vo, 298p, grey cl, 4pl)	Reilly/Britton	(1912)	Nuyttens, Joseph P.	200-300	
Baum, L. Frank	Queen Zixi of Ix (1st [1], lg8vo, 303p, green cl, 16cp)	Century	1905	Richardson, F.	400-600	
Baum, L. Frank	Rinkitink in Oz (1st [1], lg8vo, blue cl, 314p, p-o, 12cp, pep)	Reilly/Britton	(1916)	Neill, John R.	600-800	
Baum, L. Frank	Road to Oz (1st [1], lg8vo, green cl, b/w, p-o, 261p, pep)	Reilly/Britton	(1909)	Neill, John R.	600-800	
Baum, L. Frank	Scarecrow of Oz (1st [1], lg8vo, green cl, p-o, 288p, 12cp, pep)	Reilly/Britton	(1915)	Neill, John R.	500-700	
Baum, L. Frank	Sea Fairies (1st [1], lg8vo, p-o, 240p, green cl, 12pl, pep)	Reilly/Britton	(1911)	Neill, John R.	600-850	
Baum, L. Frank	Sky Island (1st, lg8vo, blue cl, p-o, 287p, 12cp, pep)	Reilly/Britton	(1912)	Neill, John R.	500-700	
Baum, L. Frank	Songs of Father Goose (1st, 4to, ibds, 84p, b/w)	George Hill	1900	Denslow, W.W.	425-600	
Baum, L. Frank	Songs of Father Goose (2nd, 4to, 83p, ibds, b/w)	Bobbs-Merrill	(1909)	Denslow, W.W.	200-300	
Baum, L. Frank	Tik-Tok of Oz (1st [1], lg8vo, 272p, blue cl, p-o, pep, 12cp)	Reilly/Britton	(1914)	Neill, John R.	700-900	
Baum, L. Frank	Tin Woodman of Oz (1st [1], lg8vo, red cl, 288p, p-o, 12cp, pep)	Reilly/Britton	(1918)	Neill, John R.	500-700	
Baum, L. Frank	Wizard of Oz (1st, lg ob8vo, [56]p, ibds, color, pep, DJ/0.50)	Grosset/Dunlap	1939	Lebeck, Oskar	100-175	*
Baum, L. Frank	Woggle-Bug Book (1st, folio, [48]p, wraps, color)	Reilly/Britton	1905	Morgan, Ike	2000-3000	R
Baum, L. Frank	Wonderful Wizard of Oz (1st [1], 8vo, 261p, 24cp, pep, PPP)	George Hill	1900	Denslow, W.W.	6000-9000	R
Baumann, Hans	Fenny the Desert Fox (1st, ob4to, [23]p, color, DJ/3.95)	Random	(1970)	Schmid, Eleonore	30-50	
Baumann, Hans	Son of Columbus (1st {std}, lg8vo, 248p, b/w, DJ)	L: Oxford U.Pr.	1957	Stobbs, William	25-40	
Bawden, Nina	Three on the Run (1st AM {std}, 8vo, 224p, b/w, DJ/3.75)	Lippincott	(1965)	Worth, Wendy	20-30	
Baxter, Betty	Supposin' (1st, 12mo, ibds, 40p, color, pep)	Volland	(1931)	Dudley, Carrie	60-100	
Baylor, Byrd	Before You Came this Way (1st {std}, 4to, [32]p, 1-color, DJ/4.75)	Dutton	(1969)	Bahti, Tom	40-65	
Baylor, Frances C.	Juan and Juanita (1st, 8vo, green/gilt, 276p, b/w, pep, PPP)	Ticknor	1888	Sandham, Henry	125-200	
Baylor, Frances C.	Juan and Juanita (1st, 8vo, 300p, blue cl, p-o, 4cp, pep)	Houghton	1926	Tenggren, Gustaf	70-100	
Bayne, C. (ed.)	My Book of Best Fairy Tales (1st AM, lg8vo, blue/gilt, 368p, 16cp)	Funk/Wagnalls	[1915]	Rountree, Harry	120-200	
Bayne, C. (ed.)	My Book of Best Fairy Tales (1st, lg8vo, blue/gilt, 368p, 16cp)	L: Cassell	(1915)	Rountree, Harry	250-350	
Bayne, Marie	Fairy Tales from Erin's Isle (1st, 8vo, green cl, 132p, teg, b/w)	L: Sands	1908	Dawson/Petts	70-120	
Baynes, Pauline	Victoria and the Golden Bird (1st, 8vo, [32]p, ibds, color)	L: Blackie	(1947)	Baynes, Pauline	40-65	
Bazin, Rene	Juniper Farm (1st, sm8vo, 180p, color)	Macmillan	1928	Peck, Anne M.	30-45	
Beach, Rex	Auction Block (1st, 8vo, 440p, red/gilt, 28pl)	Harper	1914	Gibson, Charles D.	20-40	
Beach, Rex	Iron Trail (1st, sm8vo, red/gilt, 390p, 8pl)	Harper	1913	Bracker, M. Leone	30-50	
Beach, Rex	Ne'er-Do-Well (1st, 12mo, 402p, p-o, 8pl)	Harper	1911	Christy, Howard C.	30-50	
Beach, Rex	Silver Horde (1st, 12mo, red cl, p-o, 389p, 8pl)	Harper	1909	Dunn, Harvey T.	30-50	
Beach, Rex	The Net (1st, 12mo, 333p, gilt, p-o, 4pl)	Harper	1912	Tittle, Walter	30-45	
Beach, Stewart	Good Morning, Sun's Up (1st AM {std}, lg sq8vo, [27]p, color, cep)	NY: Scroll Pr.	(1970)	Sugita, Yutaka	60-90	
Beacom, John	How the Buffalo Lost his Crown (1st, ob folio, 41p, 8 tip-in pl)	Forest/Stream	1894	Russell, Charles M.	2000-3000	
Beale, Will	Binky (1st, lg8vo, 125p, fp b/w, DJ/2.50)	Lothrop, Lee	(1954)	Bobri, Vladimir	20-35	
Bealer, Alex W.	Picture-Skin Story (1st, sq8vo, [27]p, pink cl, color, cep, DJ/2.75)	Holiday House	1957	Bealer, Alex W.	40-65	
Beaman, Emeric H.	Ozmar the Mystic (1st, 8vo, 378p, blue/gilt, 12pl)	L: Bliss Sands	1896	Smith, Thomas	50-85	*
Beaman, S.G.H.	Tales of Toytown (1st, 12mo, 158p, 6cp)	L: H. Milford	(1928)	Beaman, S.G.H.	60-100	
Beard, Dan C.	Animal Book and Campfire Stories (1st, 8vo, 538p, col frn)	Moffat	1907	Beard, Dan	40-60	
Beard, Dan C.	Moonblight ([revised ed.], sm8vo, 238p, green/gilt, uncut, b/w)	A. Brandt	1904	Beard, Dan	60-100	*
Beard, Patten	Billy Cory, Adventurer (1st, 8vo, 196p, p-o, color, pep, DJ/1.50)	Whitman	1936	Young, Eleanor M.	40-65	
Beard, Patten	Marjorie's Literary Dolls (1st, 4to, 114p, b/w)	Stokes	(1916)	(Photos)	100-165	
Beard, Patten	Marjorie's Little Doll School (1st, lg8vo, 208p, p-o, b/w)	Doran	(1917)	(Photos)	100-165	
Beard, Patten	Pantalette Doll (1st, lg8vo, p-o, 160p, color, pep)	Whitman	(1931)	Hubbard, Eleanore	100-165	
Beard, Patten	Pillow-Time Tales (1st, lg8vo, p-o, 96p, color)	Rand/McNally	(1927)	Eger, Ruth C.	60-90	*
Beard, Patten	Twilight Tales (1st, lg8vo, p-o, 96p, 7cp)	Rand/McNally	(1929)	Eger, Ruth C.	55-80	
Beard, Patten	What Happened After Stories (1st, sq4to, 125p, p-o, color, pep)	Whitman	(1929)	Higgins, Violet M.	40-60	
Beardsley, Alice	Turn-Around Book (1st, 8vo, p-o, unpag)	Bobbs-Merrill	(1914)	Beardsley, Alice	120-200	
Beardsley, Aubrey	Book of 50 Drawings (1st, 4to, 212p)	L: Smithers	1897	Beardsley, Aubrey	250-400	
Beardsley, Aubrey	Second Book of 50 Drawings (1st, 4to, red/gilt, 213p, 50pl)	L: Smithers	1899	Beardsley, Aubrey	250-400	
Beardsley, Aubrey	Under The Hill (1st, 4to, teg, blue/gilt, uncut, 16pl)	L: John Lane	1904	Beardsley, Aubrey	400-600	
Beattie, Janet	Good for Scuffles (1st, 4to, ibds, 41p, color, DJ/1.50)	Howell/Soskin	1944	Kirmse, Marguerite	30-50	
Beattie, Janet	In Came Horace (1st, ob8vo, [32]p, b/w, DJ/2.00)	Lippincott	(1954)	Jauss, Anne M.	40-65	
Beatty, Hetty B.	Bronto (1st {std}, 8vo, 136p, b/w, DJ/2.00)	Doubleday	(1952)	Beatty, Hetty	25-40	
Beatty, Hetty B.	Droopy (1st, sm4to, 26p, color, DJ/2.50)	Houghton	1954	Beatty, Hetty	25-40	
Beatty, Hetty B.	Little Owl Indian (1st, sm4to, 32p, color, dep, DJ/2.25)	Houghton	1951	Beatty, Hetty	30-45	*
Beatty, Hetty B.	Little Wild Horse (1st, lg sq8vo, ibds, 31p, color, DJ/2.00)	Houghton	1949	Beatty, Hetty	40-65	*
Beatty, Hetty B.	Moorland Pony (1st, sm4to, 40p, color, cep, DJ/3.00)	Houghton	1961	Beatty, Hetty	50-75	
Beatty, Hetty B.	Thumps (1st, sm4to, 29p, fp color, dep, DJ/2.75)	Houghton	1955	Beatty, Hetty	25-40	
Beatty, Jerome	Bob Fulton's Amazing Soda-Pop Stretcher (1st, 8vo, 239p, b/w, DJ/3.50)	Young Scott	(1963)	Wilson, Gahan	20-30	*
Beatty, Jerome	Clambake Mutiny (1st, lg8vo, 68p, 2-color, DJ/3.50)	Young Scott	(1964)	Ungerer, Tomi	40-65	
Beatty, Jerome	Matthew Looney in the Outback (1st, 8vo, 223p, b/w, DJ/3.95)	W.R. Scott	(1969)	Wilson, Gahan	20-30	*

AUTHOR	TITLE	PUBLISHER	DATE	ARTIST	PRICE	LC
Beatty, Jerome	Matthew Looney's Voyage to the Earth (1st, 8vo, 131p, b/w, DJ/2.75)	Young Scott	(1961)	Wilson, Gahan	20-30	*
Beaty, John Y.	Baby Whale, Sharp Ears (1st, sq8vo, 106p, fp color, pep, DJ/2.00)	Lippincott	(1938)	Carter, Helene	100-175	*
Beauclerk, Helen	Green Lacquer Pavillion (1st, 12mo, tan/gilt, 319p, 10pl)	L: Collins	1926	Dulac, Edmund	100-165	
Beauclerk, Helen	Green Lacquer Pavillion (1st AM, 12mo, 319p, gilt, b/w)	Doran	(1926)	Dulac, Edmund	70-100	
Beauclerk, Helen	Love of the Foolish Angel (1st, 8vo, blue/gilt, 251p, b/w)	L: Collins	1929	Dulac, Edmund	100-180	
Beauclerk, Helen	Love of the Foolish Angel (1st AM, 8vo, blue cl, 271p, b/w, dep)	Cosmopolitan	1929	Dulac, Edmund	100-145	
Beaumont, Cyril W.	Sea Magic... (1st, 8vo, 120p, pcb, gilt, color)	L: Bodley Head	(1928)	Payne, Wyndham	50-85	
Bechstein, Ludwig	Rabbit Catcher (1st, folio, 32p, ibds, fp color)	Macmillan	1962	Fontana, Ugo	100-165	
Bechtle, Raymond	Every Day is a World (1st, 8vo, 63p, b/w, DJ)	Harper	(1957)	Chalmers, Mary	30-50	
Beckenbaugh, G.	Cotton Tails (1st, ob4to, [99]p, ipcb, fp b/w)	R.H. Russell	1900	Beckenbaugh, G.	200-300	
Becker, Charlotte	Surprise for Three Little Steps (1st, 12mo, ibds, [32]p, fp color)	Scribner	1947	Becker, Charlotte	25-45	
Becker, Edna	900 Buckets of Paint (1st, ob8vo, ibds, [22]p, 2-color, DJ/1.50)	Abingdon-Cokes.	1949	Bradfield, Margaret	30-50	*
Becker, John L.	New Feathers for the Old Goose (1st, lg8vo, 60p, color, cep, DJ/3.00)	Pantheon	(1956)	Campbell, Virginia	50-80	R*
Becker, May (ed)	Rainbow Book of Bible Stories (1st, 8vo, 220p, color, RC, DJ/1.25)	World	(1948)	Van Stockum, Hilda	20-35	
Becker, May L.	Golden Tales of Canada (1st, 8vo, 274p, pep, DJ/2.50, decor by...)	Dodd	1938	Lenski, Lois	50-80	*
Becker, May L.	Golden Tales of Far West (1st, sm8vo, 304p, pep, DJ/2.50, decor by...)	Dodd	1935	Lenski, Lois	50-85	
Becker, May L.	Golden Tales of Prairie States (1st, sm8vo, 355p, pep, decor by...)	Dodd	1932	Lenski, Lois	50-85	
Becker, May L.	Golden Tales of the Southwest (1st, sm8vo, 265p, pep, DJ/2.50, decor by...)	Dodd	1939	Lenski, Lois	50-80	*
Becker, May L.	Louisa Alcott's People (1st, lg8vo, 211p, gilt, p-o, 4cp, pep, SC)	Scribner	1936	Fogarty, Thomas	120-165	
Beckman, Ernst	Pax and Carlino (1st, 8vo, 196p, 6pl, pep)	L: T.F. Unwin	1894	Upton, Florence	100-165	
Beckman, Per	Looking for Lucas (1st AM [1st bk.], 4to, [24]p, color)	NY: David White	(1967)	Beckman, Per	25-40	
Bedford, Francis D.	Night of Wonders (1st, ob8vo, ibds, 124p, teg, 24cp, pep)	L: Richards	[1906]	Bedford, Francis D.	200-300	
Bedford, Ruth	Fairies and Fancies (1st, 8vo, ibds, p-o, 8cp, 9pl)	L: A&C Black	1929	Broman, Mela K.	180-240	
Bedier, Joseph	Romance of Tristan and Iseult (1st AM, 12mo, 196p, pcb, gilt, fp b/w)	A.& C. Boni	1927	Harshberger, Mac	60-90	
Beebe, Katharine	Roger and Rose (1st, 12mo, 185p, p-o, 19pl)	Saalfield	1903	Greenland, Katharine	30-50	
Beeching (ed.)	Book of Christmas Verse (1st, sm8vo, 174p, teg, gilt, designs by..)	L: Methuen	1895	Crane, Walter	120-180	
Beecroft, John	Rocco Came In (1st, sm4to, red cl, [30]p, fp color, DJ/3.00)	Dodd	1959	Wiese, Kurt	30-50	
Beecroft, John	What? Another Cat! (1st, 4to, [30]p, color, DJ/3.00)	Dodd	(1960)	Wiese, Kurt	30-50	
Beerbohm, Max	50 Caricatures (1st, 8vo, green/gilt, 50 tipl)	L: Heinemann	1913	Beerbohm, Max	140-220	
Beerbohm, Max	A Survey (1st, 4to, gilt, col frn, 51 tipl)	L: Heinemann	1921	Beerbohm, Max	120-200	
Beerbohm, Max	Caricatures of 25 Gentlemen (1st, 4to, blue/gilt)	L: Smithers	1896	Beerbohm, Max	250-400	
Beerbohm, Max	Cartoons: Second Childhood of John Bull (1st, folio, [34]p, bds, 15cp)	L: Stephen Swift	(1911)	Beerbohm, Max	250-400	
Beerbohm, Max	Dreadful Dragon of Hay Hill (1st, lg8vo, 113p, ibds, gilt, col frn)	L: Heinemann	1928	Beerbohm, Max	60-90	
Beerbohm, Max	Happy Hypocrite (1st, 4to, 70p, white/gilt, uncut, 24cp, dep)	L: John Lane	(1915)	Sheringham, George	120-200	
Beerbohm, Max	Observations (1st, 4to, 52pl, DJ)	L: Heinemann	1925	Beerbohm, Max	300-450	
Beerbohm, Max	Poet's Corner (1st, folio, ibds, 20cp)	L: Heinemann	1904	Beerbohm, Max	250-400	
Beerbohm, Max	Rossetti and his Circle (1st, 4to, blue/gilt, 23 ticp)	L: Heinemann	1922	Beerbohm, Max	140-220	
Beerbohm, Max	Things New and Old (1st, 4to, col frn, 49pl)	L: Heinemann	1923	Beerbohm, Max	120-200	
Beerbohm, Max	Works of... (1st, 8vo, brown/gilt, 165p, uncut)	Scribner	1896	Armstrong, Margaret	180-270	
Beerbohm, Max	Zuleika Dobson (1st, 8vo, brown cl, 350p, gilt)	L: Heinemann	1911	Beerbohm, Max	170-240	
Begbie, Harold	Great Men (1st, sm4to, 51p, ibds, 24cp)	L: Richards	1901	Gould, F. Carruthers	140-240	
Begbie, Harold	Political Struwwelpeter (4to, ipcb, [24]p, color)	L: Richards	1899	Gould, F. Carruthers	160-225	
Begbie, Harold	Struwwelpeter Alphabet (1st, 4to, ipcb, [26]p, color)	L: Richards	1900	Gould, F. Carruthers	180-220	
Behn, Harry	All Kinds of Time (1st {std}, 12mo, ibds, [61]p, color, cep, DJ/2.00)	Harcourt	(1950)	Behn, Harry	65-100	R
Behn, Harry	Faraway Lurs (1st {std}, 8vo, 190p, b/w, DJ/3.00)	World	(1963)	Behn, Harry	40-65	R*
Behn, Harry	Golden Hive (1st {std}, 8vo, 61p, b/w, DJ/3.25)	Harcourt	(1966)	Behn, Harry	25-45	
Behn, Harry	House Beyond the Meadow (1st, 8vo, [46]p, ibds, 2-color, pep, DJ/2.50)	Pantheon	(1955)	Behn, Harry	30-45	
Behn, Harry	Little Hill (1st {std}, 12mo, 58p, ipcb, 1-color, cep, DJ/2.00)	Harcourt	(1949)	Behn, Harry	65-100	R
Behn, Harry	Omen of the Birds (1st {std}, 8vo, 157p, fp b/w, DJ/3.50)	World	(1964)	Behn, Harry	25-45	
Behn, Harry	Painted Cave (1st {std}, 8vo, ipcb, 63p, 1-color, cep, DJ/3.00)	Harcourt	(1957)	Behn, Harry	65-100	R
Behn, Harry	Roderick (1st {std}, 8vo, 63p, DJ/2.75)	Harcourt	(1961)	Silverman, Mel	25-40	
Behn, Harry	Timmy's Search (1st, 8vo, 93p, wraps, fp color)	Seabury Press	(1958)	Cooney, Barbara	50-80	*
Behn, Harry	Two Uncles of Pablo (1st {std}, 8vo, 96p, b/w, DJ/3.00)	Harcourt	(1959)	Silverman, Mel	25-40	*
Behn, Harry	Windy Morning (1st {std}, 12mo, ipcb, 61p, 1-color, cep, DJ/2.00)	Harcourt	(1953)	Behn, Harry	65-100	R
Behn, Harry	Wizard in the Well (1st {std}, 12mo, ipcb, 62p, 1-color, cep, DJ/2.25)	Harcourt	(1956)	Behn, Harry	65-100	R
Behrens, June	Soo Ling Finds a Way (1st lg ob8vo, [31]p, 2-color, DJ/2.95)	Golden Gate	(1965)	Yashima, Taro	30-50	
Beim, Jerrold	Country Garage (1st, 8vo, 48p, color, DJ/2.00)	Wm. Morrow	1952	Darling, Louis	30-50	
Beim, Jerrold	Country School (1st, 8vo, 48p, color, DJ/2.00)	Wm. Morrow	1955	Darling, Louis	30-50	
Beim, Jerrold	Country Train (1st, 8vo, [48]p, color, DJ/2.00)	Wm. Morrow	1950	Shortall, Leonard	30-50	
Beim, Jerrold	Smallest Boy in Class (1st, 8vo, [47]p, 2-color, DJ/2.00)	Wm. Morrow	1949	Wohlberg, Meg	30-50	
Beim, Jerrold	Swimming Hole (1st, 8vo, [45]p, color, DJ/2.00)	Wm. Morrow	1950	Beim, Jerrold	30-50	
Beim, Jerrold	Thin Ice (1st, 8vo, 46p, color, DJ/2.00)	Wm. Morrow	1956	Darling, Louis	30-50	
Beim, Lorraine	Blue Jeans (1st, 8vo, 239p, b/w, pep, DJ/2.00)	Harcourt	(1941)	Hazelton, I.B.	120-200	
Beim, Lorraine	Burro that Had a Name (1st, 8vo, [63]p, fp 1-color, pep, DJ/1.50)	Harcourt	1939	Simon, Howard	30-50	
Beim, Lorraine	Gregori's Lamb (1st, 8vo, 92p, ipcb, color, pep)	Saalfield	1948	Busoni, Rafaello	30-50	
Beim, Lorraine	Just Plain Maggie (1st {std}, 8vo, 185p, green cl, fp b/w, DJ/2.25)	Harcourt	(1950)	Cooney, Barbara	40-65	
Beim, Lorraine	Little Igloo (1st, 8vo, [72]p, fp 1-color, pep, DJ/1.50)	Harcourt	(1941)	Simon, Howard	30-45	*
Beim, Lorraine	Lucky Pierre (1st, 8vo, [61]p, fp 2-color, pep, DJ/1.50)	Harcourt	(1940)	Simon, Howard	30-45	*
Beim, Lorraine	Sasha and the Samovar (1st, 8vo, [68]p, fp b/w, pep, DJ/1.75)	Harcourt	(1944)	Busoni, Rafaello	120-200	
Beim, Lorraine	Two is a Team (1st, 8vo, [61]p, red cl, fp 2-color, pep, DJ/1.75)	Harcourt	(1945)	Crichlow, Ernest	40-65	
Beistle, Aldarilla	I Spy (1st, 8vo, spiral-bound ibds, [17]p, color)	McKay	(1944)	Beistle, Mary A.	35-50	
Beistle, Aldarilla	Just Peggy (1st, sm8vo, ibds, 63p, silhouettes, DJ/0.50)	McKay	(1939)	Beistle, Mary A.	50-80	
Beistle, Aldarilla	Mr. Heinie (1st {std}, ob8vo, [32]p, ipcb, color, pep, DJ/1.00)	McKay	(1938)	Beistle, Mary A.	50-80	
Beistle, Aldarilla	Mr. Heinie & Scroot (1st {std}, ob8vo, [36]p, ibds, color, pep, DJ/1.00)	McKay	(1939)	Beistle, Mary A.	50-80	
Beistle, Aldarilla	Open Daily (1st {std}, lg8vo, ibds, 90p, color, DJ/2.00)	McKay	(1942)	Beistle, Mary A.	30-50	
Belasco, David	Return of Peter Grimm (1st, 12mo, 344p, p-o, 3cp)	Dodd	1912	Rae, John	30-50	
Bell, Corydon	John Rattling-Gourd of Big Cove (1st {std}, lg8vo, 103p, b/w, DJ/2.50)	Macmillan	1955	Bell, Corydon	25-35	
Bell, John J.	Jack of All Trades (1st, 4to, brown cl, 64p, 32cp)	L: John Lane	1900	Robinson, Charles	200-300	

AUTHOR	TITLE	PUBLISHER	DATE	ARTIST	PRICE	LC
Bell, John J.	New Noah's Ark (1st, 4to, brown cl, 64p, color)	L: John Lane	1899	Robinson, Charles	350-500	
Bell, Lilian	Carolina Lee (1st, 12mo, 352p, gilt, p-o, col frn)	L.C. Page	1906	Keith, Dora W.	50-80	*
Bell, Lilian	Land of Don't-Want-To (1st, lg8vo, 212p, blue cl, p-o, 10cp)	Rand/McNally	(1916)	Winter, Milo	70-100	
Bell, Lilian	Little Sister to the Wilderness (1st, 16mo, 267p, gilt, teg, cvr by...)	Stone/Kimball	1895	Rogers, Bruce	60-90	
Bell, Lilian	Runaway Equator (1st, 8vo, 118p, p-o, 16pl)	Stokes	(1911)	Newell, Peter	150-250	
Bell, Louise P.	Kitchen Fun (1st, lg8vo, ibds, 28p, cvr by...)	Harter Pub. Co.	1932	Smith, Jessie W.	45-70	
Bell, Thelma H.	Black Face (1st {std}, lg8vo, ibds, [48]p, color, pep)	Doubleday/Doran	1931	Bell, Corydon	40-65	
Bell, Thelma H.	Dash of Pepper (1st, 8vo, 159p, b/w, DJ/3.50)	Viking	(1965)	Bell, Corydon	25-40	
Bell, Thelma H.	Pawnee (1st, 4to, 63p, ibds, b/w, pep, DJ/2.00)	Viking	1950	Bell, Corydon	40-65	
Bell, Thelma H.	Riddle of Time (1st, 8vo, 160p, b/w, DJ/3.50)	Viking	(1963)	Bell, Corydon	20-35	
Bell, Thelma H.	Snow (1st, sm4to, 55p, 1-color, DJ/2.50)	Viking	1954	Bell, Corydon	30-50	
Bell, Thelma H.	Yaller-Eye (1st, sm4to, 88p, ibds, b/w, pep, DJ/2.00)	Viking	1951	Bell, Corydon	25-45	
Bell-Zano, Gina	Wee Moose (1st, sm4to, unpag, ibds, color, pep, DJ/2.95)	Parents Mag. Pr.	1964	Arno, Enrico	20-35	
Bellairs, John	Face in the Frost (1st {std}, 8vo, 174p, b/w, DJ/4.95)	Macmillan	1969	Fitschen, Marilyn	50-80	
Bellairs, John	Pedant and the Shuffly (1st {std}, 8vo, 75p, b/w, DJ/2.95)	MacMillan	1968	Fitschen, Marilyn	50-85	
Bellamy, William	Century of Charades (1st, 16mo, 100p)	Houghton	1901	Rogers, Bruce	30-50	
Bellew, Frank P.	Chip's Dogs (1st, ob4to, ibds, [64]p, b/w)	R.H. Russell	1895	Bellew, F.P.W.	125-200	*
Belloc, Hilaire	Bad Child's Book of Beasts (1st, sm4to, 47p, grey bds, b/w)	L: Duckworth	(1896)	Blackwood, B.T.	225-350	
Belloc, Hilaire	But Soft - We are Observed (1st, 8vo, 312p, gilt, b/w, DJ)	L: Arrowsmith	(1928)	Chesterton, G.K.	70-100	
Belloc, Hilaire	Cautionary Tales for Children (1st, sq8vo, ibds, 79p, b/w)	L: E. Nash	(1907)	Blackwood, B.T.	130-180	
Belloc, Hilaire	Haunted House (1st, 8vo, 269p, 37 illus, DJ)	L: Arrowsmith	(1927)	Chesterton, G.K.	80-125	
Belloc, Hilaire	Matilda Who Told Lies... (1st, lg8vo, [32]p, b/w, DJ/3.50, NYTBI)	Dial Press	(1970)	Kellogg, Steven	40-65	*
Belloc, Hilaire	Missing Masterpiece (1st, 8vo, 319p, DJ)	L: Arrowsmith	(1929)	Chesterton, G.K.	120-200	
Belloc, Hilaire	Modern Traveller (1st, 8vo, ibds, 80p, b/w)	L: E. Arnold	1898	Blackwood, B.T.	140-200	
Belloc, Hilaire	Moral Alphabet (1st, lg8vo, 63p, ibds, b/w)	L: E. Arnold	1899	Blackwood, B.T.	120-170	
Belloc, Hilaire	More Beasts for Worse Children (1st, ob4to, ibds, 48p)	L: Duckworth	1897	Blackwood, B.T.	160-240	
Belloc, Hilaire	New Cautionary Tales (1st AM, 8vo, ibds, 79p, b/w)	Harper	1931	Bentley, Nicolas	50-80	
Belloc, Hilaire	New Cautionary Tales for Children (1st {std}, sm4to, ibds, 78p)	L: Duckworth	(1930)	Bentley, Nicolas	70-100	
Belloc, Hilaire	Postmaster-General (1st, 8vo, 286p, 30 illus, DJ)	L: Arrowsmith	(1932)	Chesterton, G.K.	120-200	
Belloc, Hilaire	Shadowed! (1st AM {std}, sm8vo, 312p, 37 illus, DJ/2.50)	Harper	1929	Chesterton, G.K.	100-160	
Belloc, Hilaire	Songs from Bad Child's Book of Beasts (1st, 4to, 35p, ibds, b/w)	L: Duckworth	1932	Blackwood, B.T.	60-100	
Belpre, Pura	Ote, a Puerto Rican Folktale (1st, 4to, [32]p, color, DJ/3.95)	Pantheon	(1969)	Galdone, Paul	30-50	
Belpre, Pura	Perez and Martina (1st, lg ob8vo, 79p, 16cp, pep)	Warne	(1932)	Sanchez, Carlos M.	80-140	
Belpre, Pura	Santiago (1st, 4to, 31p, ibds, color, DJ/3.95)	Warne	(1969)	Shimin, Symeon	25-40	*
Belpre, Pura	Tiger and the Rabbit (1st {std}, 8vo, 127p, ipcb, fp b/w, DJ/2.95)	Lippincott	(1965)	DePaola, Tomie	25-40	
Belting, Natalia	Calendar Moon (1st {std}, 8vo, [62]p, ibds, color, DJ/3.50)	Holt, Rinehart	(1964)	Bryson, Bernarda	30-50	
Belting, Natalia	Cat Tales (1st {std}, 8vo, 95p, b/w, DJ/2.50)	Holt	(1959)	Summers, Leo	20-30	*
Belting, Natalia	Christmas Folk (1st {std}, ob4to, [40]p, ipcb, color, DJ/4.95)	Holt, Rinehart	(1969)	Cooney, Barbara	40-65	
Belting, Natalia	Earth is on a Fish's Back (1st {std}, lg8vo, 91p, b/w, DJ/3.50)	Holt, Rinehart	(1965)	Nesbitt, Esta	20-30	*
Belting, Natalia	Elves and Ellefolk (1st {std}, lg8vo, 95p, b/w, DJ/3.00)	Holt, Rinehart	(1961)	Laite, Gordon	20-30	
Belting, Natalia	In Enemy Hands (1st {std}, 8vo, gilt, 168p, b/w, pep, DJ/2.50)	Bobbs-Merrill	(1953)	Lees, Harry	20-30	*
Belting, Natalia	Indy and Mr. Lincoln (1st, ob4to, [32]p, fp 2-color, DJ/2.95)	Holt	(1960)	Fisher, Leonard	30-45	
Belting, Natalia	Long-Tailed Bear (1st, 8vo, 96p, b/w, DJ/2.95)	Bobbs-Merrill	1961	Cary, Louis F.	20-30	
Belting, Natalia	Moon is a Crystal Ball (1st {std}, 8vo, 150p, pep, DJ/2.50)	Bobbs-Merrill	(1952)	Jauss, Anne M.	30-45	*
Belting, Natalia	Pierre of Kaskaskia (1st {std}, 8vo, 162p, b/w, DJ/2.00)	Bobbs-Merrill	(1951)	Busch, Paul	20-30	*
Belting, Natalia	Stars are Silver Reindeer (1st {std}, ob8vo, [46]p, color, DJ/3.50)	Holt, Rinehart	(1966)	Nesbitt, Esta	25-40	*
Belting, Natalia	Summer's Coming In (1st {std}, ob4to, ibds, [48]p, color, DJ/5.50)	Holt, Rinehart	(1970)	Adams, Adrienne	30-45	
Belting, Natalia	Sun is a Golden Earring (1st {std}, ob8vo, [48]p, 3-color, DJ/3.50, CH)	Holt, Rinehart	(1962)	Bryson, Bernarda	45-70	R
Belting, Natalia	Three Apples Fell from Heaven (1st {std}, 8vo, gilt, 158p, pep, DJ/2.50)	Bobbs-Merrill	(1953)	Jauss, Anne M.	30-50	
Belting, Natalia	Verity Mullens and the Indian (1st, 4to, [32]p, fp 3-color, DJ/3.25)	Holt, Rinehart	(1960)	Fisher, Leonard	30-50	*
Belting, Natalia	Winter's Eve (1st {std}, 8vo, [48]p, pcb, color, DJ/4.95, NYTBI)	Holt, Rinehart	(1969)	Cober, Alan E.	30-50	
Bemelmans, Ludwig	Are You Hungry, Are You Cold? (1st {std}, 8vo, 245p, yellow, cl, DJ/3.95)	World	(1960)	Bemelmans, Ludwig	30-50	
Bemelmans, Ludwig	Best of Times (1st, folio, 188p, 50 color, pep, DJ/3.95)	Simon/Schuster	1948	Bemelmans, Ludwig	130-200	
Bemelmans, Ludwig	Blue Danube (1st, 8vo, blue cl, 153p, 14cp, pep, DJ/3.00)	Viking	1945	Bemelmans, Ludwig	70-100	
Bemelmans, Ludwig	Castle Number Nine (1st, 4to, [48]p, green/gilt, color, pep, DJ/2.00)	Viking	1937	Bemelmans, Ludwig	140-200	R
Bemelmans, Ludwig	Dirty Eddie (1st, 8vo, 240p, blue cl, b/w, DJ/2.75)	Viking	1947	Bemelmans, Ludwig	30-45	
Bemelmans, Ludwig	Donkey Inside (1st, 8vo, 224p, 4 dp color, DJ/3.00)	Viking	1941	Bemelmans, Ludwig	80-120	
Bemelmans, Ludwig	Father, Dear Father (1st, 8vo, 247p, b/w, DJ/3.50)	Viking	1953	Bemelmans, Ludwig	30-50	
Bemelmans, Ludwig	Fifi (1st, lg4to, ibds, [46]p, color, DJ/1.00)	Simon/Schuster	1940	Bemelmans, Ludwig	100-165	R
Bemelmans, Ludwig	Golden Basket (1st, sm4to, 96p, pink cl, color, dep, DJ/2.00, NH)	Viking	1936	Bemelmans, Ludwig	200-300	R
Bemelmans, Ludwig	Hansi (1st {1st book}, 4to, ibds, [64]p, color, pep, DJ/2.00)	Viking	1934	Bemelmans, Ludwig	200-320	
Bemelmans, Ludwig	Happy Place (1st {std}, 8vo, 59p, 3 dp color, DJ/2.50, NYTBI)	Little/Brown	(1952)	Bemelmans, Ludwig	70-120	
Bemelmans, Ludwig	High World (1st, 8vo, 113p, fp color, pep, DJ/2.75)	Harper	(1954)	Bemelmans, Ludwig	50-80	
Bemelmans, Ludwig	Holiday in France (1st, 8vo, 335p, ipcb, b/w, DJ/5.00)	Houghton	(1957)	Bemelmans, Ludwig	30-50	
Bemelmans, Ludwig	Hotel Bemelmans (1st, 8vo, 380p, yellow cl, b/w, pep, DJ/3.00)	Viking	1946	Bemelmans, Ludwig	40-65	*
Bemelmans, Ludwig	Italian Holiday (1st {std}, 4to, bds, 102p, b/w, DJ/5.00)	Houghton	1961	Bemelmans, Ludwig	30-50	
Bemelmans, Ludwig	Life Class (1st, 8vo, 260p, red cl, p-o, b/w, DJ/2.50)	Viking	1938	Bemelmans, Ludwig	100-160	
Bemelmans, Ludwig	Madeline (1st, lg4to, [48]p, ibds, color, pep, DJ/2.00, CH)	Simon/Schuster	1939	Bemelmans, Ludwig	400-650	R
Bemelmans, Ludwig	Madeline & the Bad Hat (1st, lg4to, red cl, 54p, pep, color, DJ/3.50)	Viking	(1956)	Bemelmans, Ludwig	200-300	
Bemelmans, Ludwig	Madeline and the Gypsies (1st, 4to, 56p, ibds, pep, color, DJ/3.50)	Viking	(1958)	Bemelmans, Ludwig	200-300	R
Bemelmans, Ludwig	Madeline in London (1st, lg4to, 56p, red cl, color, pep, DJ/3.50)	Viking	(1961)	Bemelmans, Ludwig	200-300	R*
Bemelmans, Ludwig	Madeline's Christmas (1st, 12mo, [24]p, wraps, color)	NY: McCall	1956	Bemelmans, Ludwig	150-250	
Bemelmans, Ludwig	Madeline's Rescue (1st, lg4to, 56p, red cl, color, pep, DJ/3.00, CM, NYTBI)	Viking	1953	Bemelmans, Ludwig	250-350	R
Bemelmans, Ludwig	Marina (1st, ob folio, [32]p, color, pep, DJ/3.95)	Harper	(1962)	Bemelmans, Ludwig	150-225	*
Bemelmans, Ludwig	My Life in Art (1st, folio, ibds, 63p, color, pep, DJ/5.95)	Harper	(1958)	Bemelmans, Ludwig	45-70	
Bemelmans, Ludwig	Now I Lay Me Down to Sleep (1st, 8vo, 299p, DJ/2.50)	Viking	1943	Bemelmans, Ludwig	30-45	
Bemelmans, Ludwig	On Board Noah's Ark (1st, 8vo, pcb, 186p, color, pep, DJ/5.00)	Viking	(1962)	Bemelmans, Ludwig	30-50	*
Bemelmans, Ludwig	Parsley (1st, ob folio, 46p, green cl, fp color, DJ/3.50, NYTBI)	Harper	(1955)	Bemelmans, Ludwig	140-200	R

AUTHOR	TITLE	PUBLISHER	DATE	ARTIST	PRICE	LC
Bemelmans, Ludwig	Quito Express (1st, lg ob8vo, 47p, ibds, 1-color, DJ/1.00)	Viking	1938	Bemelmans, Ludwig	225-325	
Bemelmans, Ludwig	Rosebud (1st, sm4to, ibds, 32p, color, pep, DJ/1.00)	Random	1942	Bemelmans, Ludwig	160-220	
Bemelmans, Ludwig	Small Bear (1st, 8vo, 186p, col frn, b/w, pep, DJ/2.50)	Viking	1939	Bemelmans, Ludwig	80-120	*
Bemelmans, Ludwig	Street Where the Heart Lies (1st {std}, 8vo, 236p, b/w, DJ/3.95)	World	(1963)	Bemelmans, Ludwig	30-50	*
Bemelmans, Ludwig	Sunshine (1st, lg4to, [44]p, ibds, color, pep, DJ/2.50)	Simon/Schuster	(1950)	Bemelmans, Ludwig	180-260	
Bemelmans, Ludwig	Tale of Two Glimps (1st, ob8vo, [48]p, ibds, color)	NY: CBS	(1947)	Bemelmans, Ludwig	140-220	
Bemelmans, Ludwig	To the One I Love Best (1st, 8vo, 255p, b/w, pep, DJ/3.75)	Viking	1955	Bemelmans, Ludwig	70-120	
Bemelmans, Ludwig	Welcome Home! (1st, lg ob4to, [26]p, fp color, DJ/3.95)	Harper	(1960)	Bemelmans, Ludwig	150-220	R
Bemelmans, Ludwig	Woman of My Life (1st, 8vo, 218p, DJ/3.50, title pg & DJ by...)	Viking	1957	Bemelmans, Ludwig	30-50	*
Bemelmans, Ludwig	World of Bemelmans (1st, 8vo, 503p, b/w, pep, DJ/4.95)	Viking	1955	Bemelmans, Ludwig	60-95	
Benary-Isbert, Margot	Blue Mystery (1st {std}, 8vo, 190p, b/w, DJ/2.95, JABA)	Harcourt	(1957)	Arno, Enrico	35-50	
Benary-Isbert, Margot	Wicked Enchantment (1st {std}, 8vo, 181p, b/w, DJ/2.50)	Harcourt	(1955)	Arno, Enrico	25-40	
Benchley, Nathaniel	Flying Lesson of Gerald Pelican (1st, lg8vo, 31p, 2-color, DJ/3.50)	Harper	(1970)	Funai, Mamoru	30-45	*
Benchley, Nathaniel	Oscar Otter (1st, 8vo, 64p, color, DJ/1.95)	Harper	(1966)	Lobel, Arnold	30-50	
Benchley, Nathaniel	Red Fox and His Canoe (1st, 8vo, 62p, ibds, fp 2-color, DJ/1.95)	Harper	(1964)	Lobel, Arnold	30-50	
Benchley, Nathaniel	Sam, the Minuteman (1st, 8vo, ibds, 62p, fp 2-color, DJ/2.50)	Harper	(1969)	Lobel, Arnold	50-80	R
Benchley, Nathaniel	Several Tricks of Edgar Dolphin (1st, 8vo, 60p, color, DJ/2.50)	Harper	(1970)	Funai, Mamoru	20-30	
Benchley, Nathaniel	Strange Disappearance of Arthur Cluck (1st, 8vo, 64p, 2-color, DJ/1.95)	Harper	(1967)	Lobel, Arnold	25-45	
Benchley, Peter	Jonathan Visits the White House (1st, 4to, [32]p, 3-color, DJ/2.50)	McGraw-Hill	(1964)	Bergere, Richard	60-100	
Bender, Eric	I Never Knew that Before (1st, 4to, 123p, ibds, pep, fp color, DJ/1.50)	Saalfield	(1938)	Scott, Janet L.	40-65	*
Bendick, Jeanne	Blonk from Beneath the Sea (1st {std}, ob8vo, 55p, 1-color, pep, DJ/2.50)	F. Watts	1958	Bendick, Jeanne	40-65	
Bendick, Jeanne	First Book of Time (1st, 8vo, 70p, 1-color, DJ/2.50)	F. Watts	1963	Bendick, Jeanne	30-45	
Bendick, Jeanne	Fresh Look at Night (1st, 8vo, [40]p, fp 2-color, DJ/2.50)	F. Watts	1963	Bendick, Jeanne	30-45	
Bendick, Jeanne	Shape of the Earth (1st, 4to, 72p, ibds, 2-color, DJ/2.95)	Rand/McNally	1965	Bendick, Jeanne	25-40	
Benedetti, Mario	Unstill Life (1st {std}, 8vo, 127p, fp b/w, cep, DJ/5.95)	Harcourt	(1969)	Frasconi, Antonio	25-45	*
Benedict, Dorothy	Bandoleer (1st, 8vo, 219p, b/w, DJ/3.50)	Pantheon	(1963)	Papin, Joseph	25-40	
Benet, Laura	Caleb's Luck (1st, lg8vo, [28]p, ibds, pep, color, DJ/0.50)	Grosset/Dunlap	1942	Credle, Ellis	65-80	R
Benet, Laura	Hidden Valley (1st, 8vo, 207p, b/w, pep, DJ/2.00)	Dodd	1938	Wiese, Kurt	25-45	*
Benet, Stephen	John Brown's Body (1st {std}, 8vo, 376p, dp pl)	Doubleday/Doran	1928	Daugherty, James	25-40	
Benet, William R.	Flying King of Kurio (1st, 8vo, 289p, 4cp, pep)	Doran	(1926)	Smalley, Janet	70-120	
Benet, William R.	Timothy's Angels (1st, sm4to, ipcb, [24]p, fp color, pep, DJ/2.00)	Crowell	(1947)	Alajalov, Constantin	55-80	
Bennet, H.	Round the Hearth (4to, ibds)	Dutton	(1880)	13 Chromos	100-165	
Bennet, Robert A.	For the White Christ (1st, 8vo, p-o, 474p, 4cp)	McClurg	1905	Kinneys	25-40	
Bennet, Robert A.	Thyra: Romance of the Polar Pit (1st, 12mo, 258p, gilt, 5pl)	Henry Holt & Co.	1901	Blumenschein, E.L.	30-50	*
Bennett, Anna E.	Little Witch (1st [1st bk.] {std}, 8vo, 127p, green cl, b/w, DJ/2.50)	Lippincott	(1953)	Stone, Helen	350-500	
Bennett, John	Barnaby Lee (1st, 12mo, 454p, blue/gilt, 34pl, PPP)	Century	1902	DeLand, Clyde O.	70-130	
Bennett, John	Master Skylark (1st, 12mo, brown cl, 380p, b/w, PPP)	Century	1897	Birch, Reginald	85-140	
Bennett, John	Master Skylark (1st, lg8vo, blue cl, 322p, p-o, 8cp, pep)	Century	1922	Pitz, Henry C.	45-70	
Bennett, John	Pigtail of Ah Lee Ben Loo (1st, lg8vo, 298p, orange cl, b/w, pep, NH)	Longmans	1928	Bennett, John	120-200	
Bennett, Rainey	Secret Hiding Place (1st {std}, ob4to, [30]p, color, DJ/3.00)	World	(1960)	Bennett, Rainey	30-50	
Bennett, Richard	Hannah Marie (1st {std}, sm4to, 70p, ibds, 1-color, pep, DJ/1.50)	Doubleday/Doran	1939	Bennett, Richard	30-50	
Bennett, Richard	Mister Ole (1st {std}, 4to, 60p, color, DJ/2.00)	Doubleday/Doran	1940	Bennett, Richard	40-65	*
Bennett, Richard	Skookum and Sandy (1st {std}, lg8vo, ipcb, [71]p, b/w, pep)	Doubleday/Doran	1935	Bennett, Richard	40-65	
Bennett, Rowena B.	Around a Toadstool Table (1st, 8vo, ibds, 109p, fp b/w)	Chi: Rockwell	1930	Holling, Lucille W.	65-90	
Bennett, Rowena B.	Songs from Around a Toadstool Table (1st {std}, sm8vo, 61p, b/w, DJ/3.50)	Follett	(1967)	Fraser, Betty	20-30	
Benson, E.F.	David Blaize and the Blue Door (1st, sm8vo, 217p, b/w)	Doran	(1919)	Ford, H.J.	80-120	
Benstead, V. (adap)	Three Little Pigs (1st, lg8vo, ibds, [28]p, color, pep, DJ/0.50)	Random	1942	Cameron, Mary	30-50	*
Berenstain, Stan	Bear Scouts (1st, 8vo, 63p, color, DJ/1.95)	Beginner Books	(1967)	Berenstain, Stan	20-35	
Berenstain, Stan	Bear's Vacation (1st, 8vo, 63p, color, DJ/1.95)	Beginner Books	(1968)	Berenstain, Stan	20-30	
Beresford, Elisabeth	Magic World (1st AM, 8vo, 153p, b/w, DJ/3.50)	Bobbs-Merrill	(1965)	Domanska, Janina	40-65	
Beresford, Elisabeth	The Wombles (1st, 8vo, 189p, green cl, b/w, DJ)	L: Benn	1968	Gordon, Margaret	250-350	
Beresford, Elisabeth	The Wombles (1st AM {std}, 8vo, 183p, b/w, DJ/4.95)	Meredith Press	(1969)	Gordon, Margaret	100-165	
Bergengren, Ralph	David the Dreamer (1st, ob4to, green cl, 67p, p-o, gilt, 10 fp color)	Atl. Monthly Pr.	(1922)	Freud, Tom	500-800	
Bergengren, Ralph	Gentlemen All and Merry Companions (1st {std}, 12mo, 247p, fp b/w)	Bos: Brimmer	1922	Sloan, John	60-80	*
Bergengren, Ralph	Jane, Joseph and John (1st, 4to, ibds, 62p, 6cp)	Atl. Monthly Pr.	(1918)	Day, Maurice	50-85	*
Bergengren, Ralph	Susan and the Butterbees (1st {std}, 8vo, 175p, b/w, pep, DJ/2.00)	Longmans	1947	Vaughan, Anne	30-50	
Berger, Josef	Sleepy Steve (1st, 8vo, 200p, uncut, fp b/w, pep)	Minton Balch	(1931)	Thomas, Dorothy G.	25-45	*
Berger, Terry	Black Fairy Tales (1st {std}, lg8vo, 137p, b/w, DJ/4.75)	Atheneum	1969	White, David O.	30-50	
Berkley, Ethel S.	Big and Little, Up & Down (1st, sm4to, [48]p, b/w, DJ/2.50)	W.R. Scott	(1960)	Elgin, Kathleen	25-45	*
Berlic-Mazuranic	Croatian Tales of Long Ago (1st UK, 8vo, 258p, 10 ticp)	L: Allen/Unwin	(1924)	Kirin, V.	250-350	
Berlyn, Annie	Sunrise-Land (1st, 8vo, 345p, grey cloth, b/w)	L: Jarrold	1894	Rackham, Arthur	225-350	
Berna, Paul	Knights of King Midas (1st AM, 8vo, 187p, orange cl, b/w, DJ/3.00)	Pantheon	(1961)	Wildsmith, Brian	40-65	
Bernard, Florence S.	Through the Cloud Mountain (1st, lg8vo, 215p, gilt, p-o, 8cp, pep)	Lippincott	1922	Kay, Gertrude A.	55-80	
Berry, Erick	Black Folk Tales (1st {std}, 8vo, 80p, 1-color)	Harper	1928	Berry, Erick	50-80	
Berry, Erick	Careers of Cynthia (1st, 8vo, red cl, 320p, 9 fp b/w)	Harcourt	(1932)	King, Ruth	20-35	*
Berry, Erick	Girls in Africa (1st, 8vo, 128p, col frn, fp b/w, DJ/2.00)	Macmillan	1928	Berry, Erick	40-65	
Berry, Erick	Go and Find Wind (1st, 8vo, 251p, 6pl, DJ/2.00)	Oxford U. Pr.	(1939)	Berry, Erick	20-30	
Berry, Erick	Green Door to the Sea (1st, 8vo, 192p, b/w, DJ/2.75)	Viking	1955	Berry, Erick	20-35	
Berry, Erick	Hay-Foot, Straw-Foot (1st, 8vo, 95p, pep, DJ/2.50)	Viking	1954	Berry, Erick	20-30	
Berry, Erick	Honey of the Nile (1st, 8vo, 224p, b/w, DJ/2.00)	Oxford U. Pr.	(1938)	Berry, Erick	20-30	
Berry, Erick	Humbo the Hippo (1st {std}, sm8vo, ipcb, [41]p, color, pep)	Harper	1932	Berry, Erick	60-90	
Berry, Erick	Humbo the Hippo (8vo, ibds, [18]p, 1-color, pep, DJ/0.50)	Grosset/Dunlap	1938	Berry, Erick	50-80	
Berry, Erick	Illustrations of Cynthia (1st {std}, 8vo, 205p, 8 fp b/w)	Harcourt	(1931)	King, Ruth	25-40	*
Berry, Erick	Juma of the Hills (1st, 8vo, 260p, b/w, pep)	Harcourt	(1932)	Berry, Erick	30-50	*
Berry, Erick	King's Jewel (1st, 8vo, 189p, b/w, DJ/2.75)	Viking	1957	Chapman, Fred T.	25-40	
Berry, Erick	Leif the Lucky: Discoverer of America (1st, 8vo, 72p, color, DJ/2.25)	Garrard Pub.	(1961)	Plummer, William	25-35	
Berry, Erick	Little Farm in the Big City (1st, sm4to, ibds, [47]p, 3-color, DJ/1.50)	Viking	1947	Berry, Erick	30-45	
Berry, Erick	Lock her Through (1st, 8vo, 246p, 8pl, DJ/2.00)	Oxford U. Pr.	1940	Berry, Erick	20-30	

AUTHOR	TITLE	PUBLISHER	DATE	ARTIST	PRICE	LC
Berry, Erick	Men, Moss and Reindeer: Challenge of Lapland (1st, 8vo, 96p, b/w, DJ/2.50)	Coward	(1959)	(Photos)	25-40	*
Berry, Erick	Mom Du Jos... (1st {std}, 8vo, 116p, col frn, cep, DJ/1.75)	Doubleday/Doran	1931	Berry, Erick	80-120	
Berry, Erick	Mr. Arctic: Account of Villajalmur Stefansson (1st, 8vo, 185p, DJ/4.50)	McKay	1966	(Photos)	20-35	
Berry, Erick	One-String Fiddle (1st, lg8vo, [64]p, peach cl, pep, color, DJ/1.50)	Winston	(1939)	Berry, Erick	30-50	
Berry, Erick	Penny-Whistle (1st, 8vo, [40]p, yellow cl, color)	Macmillan	1930	Berry, Erick	40-65	
Berry, Erick	Pretty Little Doll (1st, sm sq8vo, ibds, [30]p, color, DJ/1.00)	Oxford U. Pr.	1946	Berry, Erick	30-50	
Berry, Erick	Seven Beaver Skins (1st {std}, 8vo, 275p, b/w, dep, DJ/2.50)	Winston	(1948)	Berry, Erick	20-30	
Berry, Erick	Sojo: Story of Little Lazy Bones (1st, 8vo, ibds, [40]p, b/w, pep)	Harter	(1934)	Berry, Erick	45-70	
Berry, Erick	Springing of the Rice (1st {std}, 8vo, 89p, b/w, DJ/2.95)	Macmillan	1966	Kaufmann, John	20-25	
Berry, Erick	Strings to Adventure (1st, 8vo, 221p, 7pl, pep, DJ/2.00)	Lothrop, Lee	1935	Berry, Erick	30-50	
Berry, Erick	Sunhelmet Sue (1st, 8vo, 239p, yellow cl, fp b/w, DJ/2.00)	Lothrop, Lee	1936	Berry, Erick	25-40	
Berry, Erick	Sybil Lidington's Ride (1st, lg8vo, 128p, blue cl, b/w, pep, DJ/2.50)	Viking	1952	Berry, Erick	25-40	
Berry, Erick	There is the Land (1st, 8vo, 240p, b/w, DJ)	Oxford U. Pr.	(1943)	Berry, Erick	20-35	
Berry, Erick	Underwater Warriors (1st, 8vo, 152p, pep, DJ/3.95)	McKay	1967	(Photos)	25-45	
Berry, Erick	When Wagon Trains Rolled to Sante Fe (1st, lg8vo, 95p, color, pep, DJ)	Garrard Pub.	1966	Waterhouse, Charles	30-50	
Berry, Erick	Whistle Round the Bend (1st, 8vo, 266p, b/w pl, DJ/2.00)	Oxford U. Pr.	(1941)	Berry, Erick	20-35	
Berry, Erick	Winged Girl of Knossos (1st {std}, 8vo, 253p, b/w, pep, DJ/2.00, NH)	Appleton-Century	1933	Berry, Erick	80-140	
Berson, Harold	Raminagrobis and the Mice (1st, sm8vo, [32]p, b/w, DJ/2.50)	Seabury Press	(1965)	Berson, Harold	25-40	
Bertail, Inez	Favorite Nursery Songs (1st, 8vo, ipcb, 42p, color, pep, DJ/0.50)	Random	(1941)	Doane, Pelagie	35-50	
Bertail, Inez	New Illustrated Book of Favorite Hymns (1st, folio, 44p, fp color, pep)	Garden City	1941	Tenggren, Gustaf	60-85	
Bertail, Inez	Time for Bed (1st, ob12mo, ibds, [32]p, color, pep, DJ/0.75)	Doubleday/Doran	1939	Ninon	40-65	*
Bertol, Roland	Sundiata: Epic of the Lion King (1st, 8vo, 81p, fp b/w, DJ/3.95)	Crowell	(1970)	Prestopino, Gregorio	30-50	
Beskow, Elsa	Adventures of Peter and Lotta (1st AM {std}, lg ob8vo, ibds, 15 color)	Harper	(1931)	Beskow, Elsa	120-180	
Beskow, Elsa	Aunt Brown's Birthday (1st AM, ob folio, [23]p, ibds, 16cp)	Harper	1930	Beskow, Elsa	120-180	
Beskow, Elsa	Aunt Green, Aunt Brown & Aunt Lavender (1st AM, ob folio, 30p, bds, 15cp)	Harper	1928	Beskow, Elsa	150-225	
Beskow, Elsa	Buddy's Adventures in Blueberry Patch (1st, lg ob4to, [34]p, ibds, color)	Harper	[1931]	Beskow, Elsa	120-180	
Beskow, Elsa	Elf Children of the Woods (1st, lg ob4to, [32]p, color)	Harper	1932	Beskow, Elsa	120-180	
Beskow, Elsa	Hat House (1st, ob4to, ibds, [34]p, fp color)	Harper	1931	Beskow, Elsa	120-180	
Beskow, Elsa	Olle's Ski Trip (1st AM, lg4to, [29]p, ibds, 14 fp color)	Harper	[1928]	Beskow, Elsa	120-180	
Beskow, Elsa	Peter's Voyage (1st AM, sq4to, ibds, [14]p, color)	Knopf	1931	Beskow, Elsa	80-140	
Beskow, Elsa	Sun-Egg (1st AM, ob4to, [26]p, ibds, 12cp)	Harper	1933	Beskow, Elsa	120-180	R
Beskow, Elsa	Tale of Wee Little Old Woman (1st AM, sq4to, ibds, [22]p, color)	Harper	1930	Beskow, Elsa	120-170	
Besser, Marianne	Cat Book (1st, 8vo, 91p, b/w, DJ/3.75)	Holiday House	(1967)	Stirnweis, Shannon	25-45	
Best, Herbert	Border Iron (1st, 8vo, 219p, b/w, pep, DJ/2.00)	Viking	1945	Berry, Erick	20-35	
Best, Herbert	Bright Hunter of the Skies (1st {std}, 8vo, 164p, b/w, pep, DJ/3.50)	Macmillan	1961	Bryson, Bernarda	20-35	
Best, Herbert	Desmond and Dog Friday (1st, 8vo, 126p, b/w, DJ/3.75)	Viking	(1968)	Mars, Witold T.	20-30	
Best, Herbert	Desmond the Dog Detective (1st, 8vo, 96p, b/w, DJ/2.50)	Viking	(1962)	Obligado, Lilian	20-30	
Best, Herbert	Desmond the Peppermint Ghost (1st, 8vo, 93p, b/w, DJ/3.00)	Viking	1965	Obligado, Lilian	25-40	*
Best, Herbert	Desmond's First Case (1st, 8vo, 96p, b/w, DJ/2.50)	Viking	(1961)	Keats, Ezra J.	25-40	
Best, Herbert	Flag of the Desert (1st, 8vo, 242p, b/w, DJ/2.00)	Viking	1936	Berry, Erick	25-40	*
Best, Herbert	Garram the Chief (1st {std}, 8vo, 261p, b/w, pep)	Doubleday/Doran	1932	Berry, Erick	25-45	
Best, Herbert	Garram the Hunter (1st {std}, 8vo, 332p, 6pl, pep, NH)	Doubleday/Doran	1930	Berry, Erick	30-50	
Best, Herbert	Gunsmith's Boy (1st, 8vo, 220p, col frn, b/w, pep, DJ/2.00)	Winston	1942	Berry, Erick	20-35	
Best, Herbert	Mystery of the Flaming Hut (1st {std}, sm8vo, 307p, b/w)	Harper	1932	Berry, Erick	25-40	
Best, Herbert	Not Without Danger (1st, 8vo, 286p, pep, DJ/2.50)	Viking	1951	Berry, Erick	20-35	
Best, Herbert	Ranger's Ransom (1st {std}, sm8vo, 192p, b/w, DJ/1.75)	Aladdin	1953	Berry, Erick	25-40	
Best, Herbert	Son of the White Man (1st {std}, 8vo, orange cl, 315p, b/w, pep)	Doubleday/Doran	1931	Berry, Erick	30-60	
Best, Herbert	Tal of the Four Tribes (1st {std}, sm8vo, 295p, b/w, pep, DJ/1.00)	Doubleday/Doran	1938	Berry, Erick	20-35	
Beston, Henry	Chimney Farm Bedtime Stories (1st {std}, 8vo, 79p, DJ/3.75)	Holt, Rinehart	(1966)	Day, Maurice	25-45	
Beston, Henry	Firelight Fairy Book (1st, 8vo, 257p, color, pep)	Atl. Monthly Pr.	(1919)	Day, Maurice	65-100	
Beston, Henry	Five Bears & Miranda (1st, lg8vo, [60]p, blue cl, fp color, DJ/2.00)	Macmillan	1939	Dobias, Frank	60-100	*
Beston, Henry	Starlight Wonder Book (1st, 8vo, 262p, gilt, col frn, fp b/w, pep)	Atl. Monthly Pr.	(1923)	Day, Maurice	50-80	*
Beston, Henry	Tree that Ran Away (1st, sm8vo, 69p, green cl, cep, b/w, DJ/1.00)	Macmillan	1941	Eichenberg, Fritz	200-320	
Bettina	Angelo and Rosaline (1st, lg4to, ibds, 48p, color, DJ)	L: Collins	1957	Bettina	50-80	
Bettina	Castle in the Sand (1st, sm4to, 47p, b/w, DJ/1.75)	Harper	(1951)	Bettina	40-65	
Bettina	Cocolo Comes to America (1st, folio, ibds, [32]p, color, DJ/2.50)	Harper	1949	Bettina	60-100	
Bettina	Cocolo's Home (1st, folio, ibds, [32]p, color, DJ/2.50)	Harper	1950	Bettina	60-100	
Bettina	Dolls (1st {std}, 12mo, [24]p, color, DJ/1.95)	Ariel	(1963)	Bettina	30-50	
Bettina	For the Leg of a Chicken (1st AM {std}, folio, color, DJ/4.95)	F. Watts	(1960)	Bettina	35-50	
Bettina	Goat Boy (1st AM {std}, lg8vo, [24]p, color, DJ/3.25)	Norton	(1966)	Bettina	40-60	
Bettina	Horse for the Island (1st {std}, 8vo, 213p, b/w, DJ/2.75)	Harper	(1952)	Bettina	25-40	
Bettina	Of Uncles and Aunts (1st AM {std}, 8vo, [24]p, color, DJ/2.75)	Norton	(1964)	Bettina	30-45	
Bettina	Pantaloni (1st, folio, unpag, ibds, color, DJ/2.50)	Harper	1957	Bettina	50-80	
Bettina	Paolo and Panetto (1st AM, folio, unpag, color, DJ/4.95)	F. Watts	(1960)	Bettina	65-100	
Bettina	Piccolo (1st, 32mo, 64p, fp color, DJ/1.25)	Harper	(1954)	Bettina	40-65	R
Bettina	Poo-Tsee the Water Tortoise (1st, 4to, [32]p, color, DJ)	L: Chatto	(1943)	Bettina	50-80	
Bettina	Sardines and the Angel (1st, sm4to, ibds, [24]p, color, DJ)	L: Oxford U.Pr.	1967	Bettina	30-50	
Bettina	Trovato (1st {std}, 4to, 47p, color, DJ/3.50)	Ariel	1959	Bettina	30-50	
Bevans, Margaret	McCall's Read-Me-a-Story Book (1st, 4to, 256p, DJ/3.95)	Putnam	(1961)	Weisgard, Leonard	30-45	*
Bevans, Tom	Where, O Where? (1st, 8vo, [48]p, ibds, color, dep, DJ/1.00)	Viking	1939	Bevans, Tom	25-45	
Beyer, Audrey W.	Dark Venture (1st {std}, 8vo, 205p, b/w, DJ)	Knopf	1968	Dillon, L.& D.	30-50	*
Beyer, Evelyn	All Babies have Mummies & Daddies Just like You (1st, 8vo, [20]p, color)	W.R. Scott	1946	Ipcar, Dahlov	25-40	
Bialk, Elisa	Colt of Cripple Creek (1st {std}, 8vo, 180p, b/w, DJ/2.50)	World	(1953)	Shenton, Edward	25-40	
Bialk, Elisa	Ride 'Em Peggy! (1st, 8vo, red cl, 196p, dp b/w, DJ/2.25)	Houghton	1950	Brown, Paul	70-120	
Bialk, Elisa	Silver Purse (1st {std}, sm8vo, 169p, orange cl, b/w, DJ/2.50)	World	(1952)	Galdone, Paul	25-45	
Bialk, Elisa	Taffy's Foal (1st, lg8vo, 179p, beige cl, b/w, DJ/2.25)	Houghton	1949	Moyers, William	45-70	
Bialk, Elisa	Wild Horse Island (1st, 8vo, green cl, 201p, fp b/w, pep, DJ/2.00)	Houghton	1951	Brown, Paul	50-80	
Bianco, Margery W.	Adventures of Andy (1st, lg8vo, 227p, 8cp, pep)	Doran	(1927)	Underwood, Leon	40-60	

AUTHOR	TITLE	PUBLISHER	DATE	ARTIST	PRICE	LC
Bianco, Margery W.	All About Pets (1st, sm8vo, 134p, pep, decor by...)	Macmillan	1929	Gilkison, Grace	20-35	
Bianco, Margery W.	Apple Tree (1st, 8vo, bds, p-o, 47p, b/w, dep)	Doran	(1926)	Artzybasheff, Boris	40-65	
Bianco, Margery W.	Bright Morning (1st, 8vo, 143p, b/w, dep, DJ/1.50)	Viking	1942	Platt, Margaret	30-50	
Bianco, Margery W.	Forward, Commandos! (1st, 8vo, 184p, color, DJ/2.00)	Viking	1944	Busoni, Rafaello	20-30	
Bianco, Margery W.	Franzi and Gizi (1st, 4to, p-o, [56]p, fp color, pep, DJ/2.00)	J. Messner	1941	Loeffler, Gisella	40-65	
Bianco, Margery W.	Good Friends (1st, 8vo, 142p, b/w, DJ/1.75)	Viking	1934	Paull, Grace	60-90	
Bianco, Margery W.	Green Grows the Garden (1st, 12mo, 117p, p-o, pep, DJ/1.50)	Macmillan	1936	Paull, Grace	25-45	
Bianco, Margery W.	House that Grew Smaller (1st, 12mo, 40p, p-o, color, cep, DJ/1.50)	Macmillan	1931	Field, Rachel	50-80	
Bianco, Margery W.	Hurdy-Gurdy Man (1st, sq12mo, 56p, ibds, cep, b/w)	Oxford U. Pr.	(1933)	Lawson, Robert	100-165	
Bianco, Margery W.	Little Wooden Doll (1st, 12mo, 65p, blue cl, pep, 6cp)	Macmillan	1925	Bianco, Pamela	70-130	
Bianco, Margery W.	More About Animals (1st, sm8vo, 115p, fp b/w, pep)	Macmillan	1934	Torrey, Helen	25-40	
Bianco, Margery W.	Other People's Houses (1st, 8vo, 201p, pep, DJ/2.00)	Viking	1939	Seredy, Kate	35-50	
Bianco, Margery W.	Penny and the White Horse (1st, lg4to, ibds, [24]p, fp color, DJ/2.00)	J. Messner	(1942)	Collison, Marjory	45-70	
Bianco, Margery W.	Poor Cecco (1st AM, lg8vo, blue/gilt, 175p, tip-in col frn, 6cp, pep)	Doran	(1925)	Rackham, Arthur	180-260	R
Bianco, Margery W.	Rufus the Fox (1st, folio, ibds, [44]p, color, DJ/2.00)	Harper	1937	Unknown	100-165	
Bianco, Margery W.	Skin Horse (1st, 8vo, ibds, 42p, pep, 5cp, DJ)	Doran	(1927)	Bianco, Pamela	160-240	
Bianco, Margery W.	Street of Little Shops (1st {std}, 8vo, 111p, uncut, cep, 8cp)	Doubleday/Doran	1932	Paull, Grace	60-90	R
Bianco, Margery W.	The Candlestick (1st {std}, 8vo, ibds, 46p, color, pep)	Doubleday/Doran	1929	Rodo, Ludovic	30-50	
Bianco, Margery W.	Winterbound (1st, 8vo, blue cl, 234p, pep, DJ/2.00, NH)	Viking	1936	Seredy, Kate	45-60	
Bianco, Pamela	Beginning with A (1st, 4to, [58]p, blue/silver, b/w, DJ/2.50)	NY: Oxford U.Pr.	1947	Bianco, Pamela	75-100	
Bianco, Pamela	Doll in the Window (1st, sq8vo, 32p, blue cl, color, pep, DJ/2.00)	NY: Oxford U.Pr.	1953	Bianco, Pamela	60-90	
Bianco, Pamela	Joy & the Christmas Angel (1st, 8vo, bds, 40p, 3-color, pep, DJ/1.75)	NY: Oxford U.Pr.	1949	Bianco, Pamela	45-70	
Bianco, Pamela	Little Houses far Away (1st, 8vo, green/gilt, 87p, b/w, DJ/2.25)	NY: Oxford U.Pr.	(1951)	Bianco, Pamela	50-85	
Bianco, Pamela	Look-Inside Easter Egg (1st, sq12mo, 38p, bds, dep, 8 fp color, DJ/1.75)	NY: Oxford U.Pr.	1952	Bianco, Pamela	50-80	R
Bianco, Pamela	Paradise Square (1st, sm8vo, 94p, yellow cl, 12 fp 1-color, dep, DJ/2.00)	NY: Oxford U.Pr.	1950	Bianco, Pamela	40-65	
Bianco, Pamela	Playtime in Cherry Street (1st, 8vo, 96p, ibds, fp b/w, pep, DJ/2.00)	NY: Oxford U.Pr.	1948	Bianco, Pamela	50-80	
Bianco, Pamela	Starlit Journey (1st, 12mo, 47p, blue cl, col frn, b/w, pep, DJ/1.25)	Macmillan	1933	Bianco, Pamela	70-100	
Bianki, Vitali	Peek the Piper (1st {std}, 8vo, 63p, b/w, DJ/2.95)	NY: Braziller	(1964)	Galdone, Paul	20-30	
Bibbins, Ruthella	Mammy 'mongst the Wild Nations (1st, sm8vo, 305p, 8pl)	Stokes	(1904)	Wightman, Francis P.	100-150	*
Biber, Yehoash	Treasure of the Turkish Pasha (1st, 8vo, 128p, b/w, DJ/3.50)	Scribner	(1968)	Shulevitz, Uri	35-50	
Bible	And It Was So (1st, sq8vo, 48p, color, pep, DJ)	Westminster Pr.	(1958)	Tudor, Tasha	70-120	
Bible	Book of Job (1st, sm4to, teg, gilt, 103p, uncut, fp b/w)	L: J.M. Dent	1896	Fell, H. Granville	120-200	
Bible	Book of Job (1st, 4to, teg, 102p, gilt, 8 ticp)	L: C. Palmer	1916	Tongue, C. Mary	80-140	
Bible	Book of Psalms (1st, sm folio, teg, gilt, 282p, 24cp)	L: Hutchinson	(1912)	Pape, Frank	120-180	
Bible	Book of Ruth (1st AM, 4to, tan/gilt, 16 designs by...)	Dodd	1896	MacDougall, W.B.	170-240	
Bible	Child's Book of Prayers (1st, lg4to, ibds, 36p, color, pep)	Random	1941	Masha	30-50	
Bible	Christ Story (1st {std}, sm4to, [41]p, color, pep, DJ)	Winston	(1943)	Shinn, Everett	30-50	
Bible	Christmas Book: Gospel of St. Luke (1st, ob4to, [48]p, color, DJ/4.50)	Dodd	(1963)	Ford, Lauren	30-45	*
Bible	Christmas Story from Saint Mark (1st, 24mo, ibds, unpag, color)	Volland	(1921)	Rae, John	55-80	*
Bible	Daniel in the Lion's Den (1st, 16mo, 98p, blue stripe cl, color)	L: G. Richards	1903	Wilson, Patten	100-160	
Bible	Ecclesiasticus... (1st, 4to, black/gilt, 165p, teg, 16cp)	L: John Lane	1927	Brunton, Violet	90-160	
Bible	Favorite Hymns for Children (1st, lg8vo, ibds, [38]p, color, DJ/0.50)	Grosset/Dunlap	(1942)	Miss Elliott	20-30	
Bible	Favorite Psalms for Children (1st, lg8vo, ibds, [38]p, color, DJ/0.50)	Grosset/Dunlap	1942	Stern, Marie	20-35	
Bible	First Bible (1st, 4to, blue/gilt, 109p, 13pl, pep, DJ/2.50)	Oxford U. Pr.	1934	Sewell, Helen	90-160	
Bible	First Graces (1st, 32mo, blue cl, 47p, p-o, color, pep, DJ/1.75)	NY: Oxford U.Pr.	1955	Tudor, Tasha	120-180	
Bible	First Prayers (1st, 32mo, 48p, blue cl, p-o, color, DJ/1.50)	NY: Oxford U.Pr.	(1952)	Tudor, Tasha	250-350	
Bible	In the Beginning... (1st, 4to, cloth, color, DJ/2.00)	NY: Oxford U.Pr.	(1941)	Daugherty, James	55-80	
Bible	In the Morning (1st, ob8vo, ipcb, [26]p, fp 1-color, pep)	Abingdon-Cokes.	1947	Drew, Louise	35-50	*
Bible	Jesus' Story (1st, 12mo, 119p, 6 fp color, cep, DJ/1.50)	Macmillan	1942	Petershams	50-80	
Bible	Kingdom & Power & Glory (1st, 4to, 170p, brown cl, fp b/w, DJ/2.50)	Knopf	1929	Daugherty, James	60-100	
Bible	Little Book about God (1st, 12mo, ibds, [96]p, color, pep)	Doubleday/Doran	1934	Ford, Lauren	40-65	
Bible	Lord is My Shepherd (1st, 4to, 263p, gilt, b/w, DJ/4.50)	Scribner	1949	Barnhart, Nancy	40-65	
Bible	Lord is My Shepherd: 23rd Psalm (1st, sm8vo, [32]p, color, DJ/3.75)	H.Z. Walck	1965	Palazzo, Tony	25-40	
Bible	More Prayers (1st, 32mo, 38p, blue cl, color, DJ/1.95)	H.Z. Walck	1967	Tudor, Tasha	80-135	
Bible	Old Testament (1st {std}, lg4to, 256p, color, pep, DJ)	Doubleday	(1960)	DeAngeli, Marguerite	60-85	
Bible	Psalms of David (1st, sm4to, 284p, red/gilt, 16pl)	Revell	1900	Rhead, Louis	80-120	
Bible	Sermon on the Mount (1st {std}, 4to, [40]p, 18cp, pep, DJ)	Winston	(1946)	Shinn, Everett	45-70	
Bible	Son of God... (1st, 8vo, blue cl, 122p, fp 1-color, pep)	Seabury Press	(1957)	Weisgard, Leonard	45-70	
Bible	Song of Songs... (1st, 4to, 16p, gilt, teg, buckram, 12pl)	L: Chapman	1897	Fell, H. Granville	130-200	
Bible	Song of Songs... (1st AM, narrow 4to, [21]p, 6pl)	R.H. Russell	1902	Burne-Jones, Edward	100-160	*
Bible	Song of Songs... (1st, lg8vo, 66p, teg, brown/gilt, 10 ticp)	L: P.L. Warner	1913	Flint, William R.	75-100	
Bible	This He Believed (1st, lg8vo, 80p, DJ/3.00, 1-color decor by...)	Viking	(1959)	Angelo, Valenti	30-45	
Bible	Three Prayers for Children (1st, lg4to, [32]p, ibds, color, pep, DJ/1.00)	Grosset/Dunlap	(1941)	Doane, Pelagie	45-70	
Bible	Twenty-Third Psalm (1st AM, 8vo, 20p, brown/gilt, color, DJ)	Crowell	1970	Angel, Marie	30-50	
Bice, Clare	Jory's Cove (1st {std}, 8vo, 104p, color, pep, DJ/2.00)	Macmillan	1941	Bice, Clare	25-40	
Bick, Christopher	Bells of Heaven: Story of Joan of Arc (1st, 8vo, 246p, DJ/3.00)	Dodd	1949	Ford, Lauren	30-45	*
Bickley, Francis L.	Adventures of Harlequin (1st, 8vo, 119p, bds, p-o, 20 color, pep)	L: Selwyn	1923	Austen, John	55-80	
Bicknell, Anne G.	Flower Folk (1st, 4to, 71p, gilt, fp color, DJ/2.50)	Putnam	(1936)	Grenwis, Martina	100-150	
Bicknell, Ethel	Dog Book (1st, 24mo, 119p)	L: G. Richards	1902	Park, Carton M.	60-100	*
Biddle, Anthony	Second Froggy Fairy Book (1st, 8vo, 90p, col frn, 11 fp b/w)	Drexel Biddle	1898	Pennock, Anne	100-160	
Bierhorst, John	Ring in the Prairie (1st {std}, ob4to, 36p, fp color, cep, DJ/4.50)	Dial Press	(1970)	Dillon, L.& D.	45-70	*
Bigelow, Poultney	Borderland of Czar and Kaiser (1st, 12mo, 8vo, 343p, gilt, 50pl)	Harper	1895	Remington, Frederic	80-125	
Bigelow, Poultney	White Man's Africa (1st, 8vo, 271p, 3pl by...)	Harper	1900	Remington, Frederic	60-100	
Biggers, Earl D.	Agony Column (1st, 8vo, 193p, brown cl, 9pl)	Bobbs-Merrill	(1916)	Grefe, Will	70-100	
Biggers, Earl D.	Love Insurance (1st, 12mo, 402p, brown cl, 8pl)	Bobbs-Merrill	(1914)	Snapp, Frank	100-150	
Biggers, Earl D.	Seven Keys to Baldpate (1st, sm8vo, blue/gilt, 408p, 5pl)	Bobbs-Merrill	(1913)	Snapp, Frank	120-180	
Bigham, Madge A.	Bad Little Rabbit (1st, sq12mo, 155p, color)	Little/Brown	1927	Young, Florence L.	30-50	*
Bigham, Madge A.	Blackie, His Friends and Enemies (1st, sm8vo, 200p, 5pl)	Little/Brown	1906	Atwood, Clara E.	30-50	*

AUTHOR	TITLE	PUBLISHER	DATE	ARTIST	PRICE	LC
Bigham, Madge A.	Goober Village (1st, sm8vo, 184p, color)	Rand/McNally	(1936)	Winter, Milo	50-80	
Bigham, Madge A.	More Mother Goose Village Stories (1st, 8vo, 274p, color)	Rand/McNally	(1922)	Brock, Emma	50-80	
Bigham, Madge A.	Overheard in Fairyland (1st, sm8vo, 237p, col frn, cp)	Little/Brown	(1909)	Clements, Ruth S.	40-65	
Bigham, Madge A.	Sonny Elephant (1st, sm8vo, 201p, cloth, p-o, col frn, b/w)	Little/Brown	1930	Hader, B.& E.	60-100	
Bigham, Madge A.	Stories of Mother Goose Village (1st, sq8vo, 196p, gilt, color, pep)	Rand/McNally	(1903)	Brison, Ella S.	80-130	
Bigham, Madge A.	Wishing Fairies (1st, 8vo, blue cl, 37p, 8cp)	Dodd	1915	Cory, Fanny	70-125	
Bilibin, Ivan	Russian Wonder Tales (1st AM, 8vo, 323p, tan cl, 12cp)	Century	1912	Bilibin, Ivan	250-400	
Bill, Helen	Shoes Fit for a King (1st {std}, 4to, [42]p, color, DJ/2.75)	F. Watts	(1956)	Slobodkin, Louis	40-65	
Billings, Augusta	Gilbert the Gay Poodle (1st, sm4to, ibds, 32p, 2-color, DJ/1.00)	Viking	1949	Billings, A.& H.	45-70	
Billings, Henry	Diesel-Electric 4030 (1st, 4to, 69p, pep, DJ/2.50)	Viking	1950	Billings, Henry	30-50	R*
Bindloss, Harold	Lorimer of the Northwest (1st, 12mo, 384p, cov by...)	Stokes	(1909)	Hood, George	35-60	
Bindloss, Harold	Masters of the Wheat-Lands (1st, 8vo, 354p, 7pl)	Stokes	(1910)	Cuneo, Cyrus	30-50	*
Bindloss, Harold	Winston of the Prairie (1st, sm8vo, p-o, 340p, 3cp)	Stokes	(1907)	Dunton, W. Herbert	35-60	
Bingham, Clifton	Airship in Animal Land (ob4to, ibds, 8 chromos)	L: Nister	[1910]	Thompson, G.H.	400-600	
Bingham, Clifton	All Sorts of Comical Cats (1st, 4to, [62]p, ibds, chromo frn, 2-col, pep)	L: Nister	[1902]	Wain, Louis	450-650	
Bingham, Clifton	Animal's Rebellion (1st, ob4to, ibds, [36]p, 8 chromos, pep)	Nister/Dutton	(1911)	Thompson, G.H.	200-300	*
Bingham, Clifton	Animals' Trip to Sea (1st ob4to, ibds, [36]p, fp color)	Nister/Dutton	[1900]	Thompson, G.H.	250-350	
Bingham, Clifton	Dandy Lion (4to, ibds, t-i col frn, b/w)	L: Nister	[1900]	Wain, Louis	300-500	
Bingham, Clifton	Dorothy Dimity (4to, ibds, fp 1-color)	L: T.F. Unwin	[1908]	Heatly, E.	100-165	
Bingham, Clifton	Fun and Frolic (1st, sm4to, 143p, ibds, 6cp)	L: Nister	[1900]	Wain, Louis	700-900	
Bingham, Clifton	Funny Doings in Animal Land (ob4to, ibds, 8 chromos, pep)	L: Nister	[1910]	Thompson, G.H.	500-800	
Bingham, Clifton	Funny Favorites (1st, sm4to, [44]p, ibds, tip-in col frn)	L: Nister	(1904)	Wain, Louis	400-650	
Bingham, Clifton	Jingles, Jokes & Funny Folks (sm4to, wraps, b/w)	McLoughlin	[1908]	Wain, Louis	250-400	
Bingham, Clifton	Kittenland (sm folio, ipcb, 8cp)	L: Collins	(1903)	Wain, Louis	700-1000	
Bingham, Clifton	Mixed Pickles (4to, cloth, col frn, 1-color)	L: R. Tuck	[1910]	Wain, Louis	400-600	
Bingham, Clifton	More Jingles, Jokes & Funny Folks (4to, wraps, b/w)	McLoughlin	[1909]	Wain, Louis	250-400	
Bingham, Clifton	Ping Pong (ob narrow 4to, wraps, 6cp)	L: R. Tuck	[1903]	Wain, Louis	400-650	
Bingham, Clifton	Pretty Pets (4to {enlarged ed.}, [20]p, 4 chromos)	L: Nister	[1910]	Foster, W.L.	90-120	
Bingham, Clifton	To Nursery Land (1st, 4to, [56]p, ibds, 16 2-color)	L: R. Tuck	[1900]	Wain, Louis	700-900	
Bingham, D.	The Bastille (1st AM, 8vo, 2 volumes, blue/gilt)	J. Pott	1901	Armstrong, Margaret	100-160	
Binney, Ida	Boppet, Please Stop It (1st, 8vo, ipcb, 48p, 1-color, DJ/1.50)	W.R. Scott	1946	Binney, Ida	40-60	
Birch, Vera B.	Green-Faced Toad (1st AM, lg8vo, 107p, green cl, 8cp, pep)	Stokes	1923	Lenski, Lois	100-150	
Bird, Mary H.	Snow Man's Christmas (1st, 16mo, p-o, green cl, 87p, 24 color, pep)	Stern	1908	Claghorn, Joseph C.	60-100	
Bird, Richard	Ryecroft Rivals (1st, 8vo, beige cl, 256p, 6pl)	L: Blackie	(1923)	Brock, Henry M.	30-50	*
Bird, Zenobia	Muffy: Tale of a Muskrat (1st, 8vo, 46p, p-o, color, pep, DJ/1.25)	Whitman	1941	Wiese, Kurt	45-70	
Birdsall, Katharine N.	Jacks of All Trades (1st, 8vo, 236p, 6cp)	Appleton	1902	Russell, Walter	30-50	*
Birnbaum, Abe	Green Eyes (1st, sq4to, [40]p, pep, color, DJ/3.50, CH, NYTBI)	Capitol Pub. Co.	(1953)	Birnbaum, Abe	70-100	R
Bischoff, Ilse	Wonderful Poodle (1st, lg8vo, 79p, pep, b/w, DJ/2.25)	Crowell	(1949)	Bischoff, Ilse	30-50	
Bischoff, Julia B.	Dog for David (1st, 8vo, 110p, b/w, DJ)	W.R. Scott	(1966)	Moriarty, Jerome	20-30	*
Bishop, Austin	Tom of the Raiders (1st, 8vo, 260p, blue cl, 4pl)	Harcourt	1921	Dennis, Morgan	25-40	*
Bishop, Claire H.	All Alone (1st, lg8vo, 90p, fp b/w, pep, DJ/2.50, NH)	Viking	1953	Rojankovsky, Feodor	60-95	
Bishop, Claire H.	Augustus (1st, sm4to, [32]p, ipcb, color, pep, DJ/1.50)	Viking	1945	Paull, Grace	30-60	
Bishop, Claire H.	Big Loop (1st, 8vo, tan cl, 221p, fp b/w, pep, DJ/3.00)	Viking	1955	Fontsere, Carles	30-50	
Bishop, Claire H.	Christopher the Giant (1st, 8vo, 54p, color, DJ/1.50)	Houghton	1950	Williams, Berkeley	20-35	
Bishop, Claire H.	Ferryman (1st, ob lg8vo, [64]p, ipcb, 1-color, pep, DJ/1.50)	Coward	1941	Wiese, Kurt	40-65	
Bishop, Claire H.	Five Chinese Brothers (1st, lg ob8vo, ipcb, [52]p, 1-color, pep, DJ/1.50)	Coward	(1938)	Wiese, Kurt	70-100	
Bishop, Claire H.	Happy Christmas (1st, lg8vo, 287p, fp b/w, pep, DJ/3.00)	S. Daye Press	(1956)	Raskin, Ellen	50-80	*
Bishop, Claire H.	King's Day (1st, lg8vo, [47]p, ipcb, fp b/w, cep, DJ/1.50)	Coward	1940	Spiegel, Doris	30-60	
Bishop, Claire H.	Lafayette: French-American Hero (1st, 8vo, 80p, fp 2-color, DJ/2.25)	Garrard Pub.	(1960)	Brevannes, Maurice	20-30	
Bishop, Claire H.	Man Who Lost his Head (1st, lg ob8vo, ibds, pep, [53]p, b/w, DJ/1.00)	Viking	1942	McCloskey, Robert	80-140	
Bishop, Claire H.	Martin DePorres, Hero (1st, lg8vo, 120p, beige cl, fp b/w, pep, DJ/2.50)	Houghton	1954	Charlot, Jean	70-120	
Bishop, Claire H.	Mozart: Music Magician (1st, 8vo, 138p, DJ)	Garrard Pub.	(1968)	Frame, Paul	20-35	
Bishop, Claire H.	Pancakes-Paris (1st, sm4to, 63p, grey cl, 1-color, pep, DJ/2.00, NH)	Viking	1947	Schreiber, Georges	50-85	
Bishop, Claire H.	Present from Petros (1st, 8vo, blue cl, 85p, b/w, pep, DJ/2.50)	Viking	(1961)	Davis, Dimitris	20-30	*
Bishop, Claire H.	Toto's Triumph (1st, 8vo, 127p, b/w, DJ/2.50)	Viking	(1957)	Ponsot, Claude	20-30	
Bishop, Claire H.	Twenty & Ten (1st, lg8vo, 76p, pep, b/w, DJ/2.50)	Viking	1952	DuBois, W.P.	40-65	
Bishop, Claire H.	Twenty-Two Bears (1st, ob4to, 31p, 1-color, pep, DJ/2.50)	Viking	(1964)	Wiese, Kurt	30-45	
Bishop, Claire H.	Yeshu, Called Jesus (1st {std}, 8vo, 97p, fp b/w, cep, DJ/3.50)	Farrar, Straus	(1966)	Bolognese, Don	30-50	
Bishop, Elizabeth	Ballad of Burglar of Babylon (1st {std}, ob8vo, [43]p, 3-col, cep, DJ/3.95)	Farrar, Straus	(1968)	Grifalconi, Ann	200-300	R*
Bjornstjerne, Bjorn	Pastor Sang (1st, 8vo, 109p, teg, uncut, frn by...)	L: Longmans	1893	Beardsley, Aubrey	80-130	
Black, Dorothy	Magic Egg (1st, 4to, 111p, col frn, 11pl, pep)	L: A&C Black	1922	Folkard, Charles	100-150	
Black, Irma S.	Barbara's Birthday (1st, 8vo, ibds, 44p, color, DJ/1.25)	W.R. Scott	1946	Takis, Nicholas	45-65	
Black, Irma S.	Big Puppy & Little Puppy (1st, 8vo, yellow cl, [33]p, b/w, pep, DJ/2.50)	Holiday House	1960	Sherman, Theresa	25-40	
Black, Irma S.	Busy Seeds (1st, 4to, [40]p, 2-color, pep, DJ/4.50)	Holiday House	(1970)	Quackenbush, Rbt.	25-40	
Black, Irma S.	Busy Winds (1st, ob8vo, [32]p, 2-color, pep, DJ/3.95)	Holiday House	(1968)	Quackenbush, Rbt.	25-40	*
Black, Irma S.	Dog Doctor (1st, lg ob8vo, ipcb, [40]p, 1-color, DJ/1.25)	W.R. Scott	(1947)	Fischetti, John R.	45-75	
Black, Irma S.	Dusty & his Friends (1st, sm8vo, [56]p, b/w, cep, DJ/1.50)	Holiday House	(1950)	Latham, Barbara	25-40	
Black, Irma S.	Flipper: Sea Lion (1st, 8vo, [50]p, color, pep, DJ/1.75)	Holiday House	1940	Rounds, Glen	30-45	
Black, Irma S.	Hamlet: A Cocker Spaniel (1st, 12mo, [72]p, red cl, fp b/w, DJ/1.50)	Holiday House	(1938)	Wiese, Kurt	30-50	*
Black, Irma S.	Kip: Young Rooster (1st, 12mo, [68]p, purple cl, b/w, DJ/1.50)	Holiday House	(1939)	Wiese, Kurt	25-45	
Black, Irma S.	Maggie, Mischievous Magpie (1st, sm8vo, [61]p, grn cl, b/w, cep, DJ/1.50)	Holiday House	(1949)	Latham, Barbara	60-90	R
Black, Irma S.	Night Cat (1st, lg ob8vo, [32]p, black cl, cep, b/w, DJ/2.25)	Holiday House	1957	Galdone, Paul	40-65	
Black, Irma S.	Spoodles, Puppy Who Learned (1st, ob8vo, [48]p, ipcb, 1-color, DJ/1.25)	W.R. Scott	(1948)	Whistle, Johnny	40-60	*
Black, Irma S.	This is the Bread that Betsy Ate (1st, lg ob8vo, ibds, [26]p, col, DJ/1.50)	W.R. Scott	1945	Ullman, Allen	40-65	*
Black, Irma S.	Toby: A Curious Cat (1st, sm8vo, rust cl, [63]p, b/w, cep, DJ/1.50)	Holiday House	1948	Wiese, Kurt	30-50	
Black, Margaret	Three Brothers and a Lady (1st, 4to, ibds, 62p, color, DJ)	L: Acorn Press	1947	Ardizzone, Edward	100-170	
Black, Mary M.	Summerfield Farm (1st, sm4to, 143p, b/w, DJ/2.50)	Viking	1951	Dennis, Wesley	40-65	
Blackburn, Henry G.	Breton Folk (1st, lg8vo, gilt, 200p, AEG, cep)	L: Sampson Low	1880	Caldecott, Randolph	140-200	

AUTHOR	TITLE	PUBLISHER	DATE	ARTIST	PRICE	LC
Blackmore, R.D.	Fringilla (1st, 8vo, uncut, 128p, 8pl)	L: E. Mathews	1895	Muckley, Louis F.	300-450	
Blackmore, R.D.	Lorna Doone (1st, lg8vo, p-o, 351p, black cl, color, pep)	Milton Bradley	(1921)	Brett, Harold M.	60-90	
Blackmore, R.D.	Lorna Doone (1st, lg8vo, p-o, 646p, black/gilt, 8cp, pep)	Dodd	(1930)	Schaeffer, Mead	45-70	
Blackmore, R.D.	Lorna Doone (1st, lg4to, 520p, teg, gilt, 16 ticp)	L: Boots	[1931]	Brock/Brittan	80-140	
Blackmore, R.D.	Lorna Doone (1st, 4to, 136p, blue cl, col frn)	L: John Lane	1933	Pape, Frank	75-100	
Blair, Matilda	Bunny Cottontail (1st, 4to, ibds, 51p, fp color)	McLoughlin	(1908)	Post, May A.	250-350	*
Blair, Peter	Coming of Pout (1st AM {std}, 8vo, 158p, b/w, DJ/4.50)	Little/Brown	1969	Hyman, Trina S.	25-40	
Blair, Walter	Tall Tale America (1st, 8vo, 262p, b/w, DJ/2.50)	Coward	1944	Rounds, Glen	30-45	
Blaisdell, E. Ward	Animals at the Fair (1st, ob4to, [47]p, color)	R.H. Russell	(1902)	Blaisdell, E. Ward	250-350	
Blaisdell, Elinore	Falcon, Fly Back (1st, 8vo, red/gilt, 177p, fp 3-color, pep, DJ/2.50)	J. Messner	(1939)	Blaisdell, Elinore	50-75	
Blaisdell, Mary F.	Pretty Polly Flinders (1st, 12mo, green cl, 188p, 4cp)	Little/Brown	1914	Wireman, Eugenie	70-100	
Blake, Henry A.	China (1st, sm4to, 138p, blue/gilt, 16cp)	L: A&C Black	1909	Menpes, Mortimer	70-100	
Blake, William	Art of William Blake (1st, 4to, green/gilt, 56p, 51pl)	Moffat	1907	Blake, William	75-100	
Blake, William	Land of Dreams (1st, lg8vo, 42p, gilt, b/w, pep, DJ/2.00)	Macmillan	1928	Bianco, Pamela	55-80	
Blake, William	Songs of Experience (1st, 8vo, 83p, green cl, uncut, 9pl)	L: D. Nutt	(1902)	Levetus, Celia	85-120	
Blake, William	Songs of Innocence (1st, 24mo, pcb, 118p, AEG, designs by...)	L: Wells/Gard.	1899	Levetus, Celia	80-125	*
Blake, William	Songs of Innocence (1st, 8vo, 31p, p-o, 4cp)	L: Jack	[1905]	Allen, Olive	55-90	*
Blake, William	Songs of Innocence (1st, 8vo, green/gilt, p-o, 49p, 12cp, pep)	L: H. Daniel	[1911]	Appleton, Honor C.	100-165	*
Blake, William	Songs of Innocence (1st, 12mo, 56p, teg, gilt, 7cp)	L: Dent	(1911)	Robinson, Charles	140-200	
Blake, William	Songs of Innocence (1st, 4to, 42p, gilt, 12cp)	L: Medici	1927	Parsons, Jacynth	100-165	
Blake, William	Songs of Innocence (1st {std}, ob4to, 48p, color, DJ/3.50)	Doubleday	(1966)	Raskin, Ellen	30-50	*
Blakely, Elizabeth	Fairy Starlight (1st, 12mo, lavender cl, 213p, b/w)	McClurg	1896	Perkins, Lucy F.	70-120	*
Blanchard, Amy	Ida Waugh's Alphabet Book (1st, 4to, [56]p, ibds, 26 illus)	Lippincott	1888	Waugh, Ida	250-350	
Blanchard, Amy E.	Bonny Bairns (1st, 4to, 48p, ibds, 25cp)	Worthington	(1888)	Waugh, Ida	200-270	
Blanchard, Amy E.	Dear Little Girl's Summer Holidays (1st, sm8vo, 283p, 5cp)	Jacobs	(1911)	Otis, E.	30-50	*
Blanchard, Amy E.	Four Corners (1st, sm8vo, 387p, green cl, 5pl)	Jacobs	(1906)	Smith, Wuanita	30-60	*
Blanchard, Amy E.	Janet's College Career (1st, 8vo, 365p, 5pl)	Jacobs	1904	Waugh, Ida	25-40	*
Blanchard, Amy E.	Journey of Joy (1st, 8vo, 305p, 7pl)	Dana Estes	(1908)	Bridgman, L.J.	30-50	
Blanchard, Amy E.	Little Miss Mouse (1st, sm8vo, 230p, p-o, 5cp, pep)	Jacobs	(1906)	Unknown	30-50	
Blanchard, Amy E.	Mammy's Baby (4to, [16]p, ipcb, chromos)	Worthington	(1890)	Waugh, Ida	125-200	
Blanchard, Amy E.	My Own Dolly (1st, 8vo, ipcb, 64p, 15cp)	Dutton	1882	Waugh, Ida	120-200	
Blanchard, Amy E.	Tangles & Curls (1st, 4to, [16]p, ibds, 9pl)	Worthington	1888	Waugh, Ida	120-200	
Blanchard, Amy E.	Tell Me a Story (1st, lg sq8vo, [15]p, ibds, 10 fp color)	Worthington	1888	Waugh, Ida	130-200	
Blanchard, Amy E.	Three Pretty Maids (1st, 12mo, 243p, b/w plates)	Lippincott	1897	Stephens, Alice B.	25-40	
Blanchard, Amy E.	Twenty Little Maidens (1st, lg8vo, 160p, 18pl)	Lippincott	1893	Waugh, Ida	50-80	
Blanchard, Amy E.	Wee Babies (1st, 4to, ibds, [48]p, color)	Dutton	(1882)	Waugh, Ida	160-225	
Blanck, Jacob	Jonathan & the Rainbow (1st, 4to, ibds, 48p, color, DJ/2.00)	Houghton	1948	Slobodkin, Louis	45-65	
Blanck, Jacob	King & Noble Blacksmith (1st, sm4to, yellow cl, 48p, color, DJ/2.25)	Houghton	1950	Slobodkin, Louis	55-80	
Blanton, Catherine	Pedro's Choice (1st, lg8vo, 64p, b/w, DJ/2.00)	Whittlesey	(1948)	Price, Harold	25-45	
Blanton, Catherine	Three Miracles (1st, 8vo, 47p, ipcb, color, DJ/2.00)	John Day	(1946)	Politi, Leo	100-165	
Blatter, Dorothy	Uncle Ali's Secret (1st, lg8vo, 32p, p-o, color, pep, DJ/1.00)	Whitman	1939	Blatter, Dorothy	30-50	
Blegvad, Lenore	Great Hamster Hunt (1st {std}, 8vo, 32p, b/w, DJ/2.95)	Harcourt	(1969)	Blegvad, Erik	30-50	*
Blegvad, Lenore	Mr. Jensen and Cat (1st {std}, 12mo, 32p, color, DJ/2.95)	Harcourt	(1965)	Blegvad, Erik	40-60	
Blegvad, Lenore	One is for the Sun (1st {std}, ob8vo, [32]p, color, DJ/3.50)	Harcourt	(1968)	Blegvad, Erik	30-50	
Blichfeldt, E.H.	Mexican Journey (1st, 8vo, 280p, orange cl, map, cvr by...)	Crowell	(1912)	Armstrong, Margaret	35-60	*
Blishen, Ed (comp)	Oxford Book of Poetry for Children (1st, 4to, 167p, ibds, color, DJ)	L: Oxford U.Pr.	1963	Wildsmith, Brian	50-80	
Blitch, Fleming	Last Dragon (1st, 8vo, [48]p, fp b/w, DJ/3.50)	Lippincott	(1964)	Zemach, Margot	30-50	
Bloch, Bertram	Little Laundress & the Fearful Knights (1st {std}, 8vo, 122p, b/w, DJ/2.50)	Doubleday	1954	Shanks, George	30-45	
Bloch, Marie (tran)	Ivanko and the Dragon (1st {std}, lg sq8vo, [46]p, color, DJ)	Atheneum	1969	Yaroslava	30-50	
Bloch, Marie H.	Big Steve: Doubled Quick Tunnelman (1st, 8vo, 71p, ibds, pep, DJ/2.50)	Coward	1952	Nicolas	30-45	*
Bloch, Marie H.	Two Worlds of Damyan (1st {std}, 8vo, 169p, b/w, DJ/3.95)	Atheneum	1966	Quackenbush, Rbt.	25-40	
Blodgett, Mabel F.	At the Queen's Mercy (1st, 8vo, 261p, teg, uncut, 5pl)	Lamson/Wolffe	1897	Sandham, Henry	70-100	*
Blodgett, Mabel F.	Fairy Tales (1st, sm4to, yellow cl, 204p, teg, 12pl, pep)	Lamson/Wolffe	1896	Reed, Ethel	600-850	
Blodgett, Mabel F.	Giant's Ruby (1st, 8vo, 292p, blue cl, 6pl)	Little/Brown	1903	Pyle, Katharine	80-120	
Blodgett, Mabel F.	Magic Slippers (1st, 12mo, 90p, 4cp)	Little/Brown	1917	Blodgett, Mabel F.	70-100	
Blodgett, Mabel F.	Peasblossom (1st, 8vo, 177p, p-o, 5cp)	Doran	(1917)	Blodgett, Mabel F.	35-60	*
Blodgett, Mabel F.	When Christmas Came Too Early (1st, 12mo, 107p, 6cp)	Little/Brown	1912	McClellan, R.	35-60	*
Blomquist, David	Daddy is Home! (1st, lg8vo, [26]p, fp color, cep, DJ)	Holt, Rinehart	1963	Aliki	25-45	*
Bloomfield, Paul	The Mediterranean (1st, 12mo, 247p, col frn, b/w)	L: Cassell	(1935)	Ardizzone, Edward	60-90	*
Blue, Rose	Black, Black, Beautiful Black (1st, 4to, 43p, fp b/w, DJ/3.95)	F. Watts	(1969)	Wiglesworth, Emmett	30-50	*
Blue, Rose	How Many Blocks is the World? (1st, 4to, [48]p, b/w, DJ/3.50)	F. Watts	(1970)	James, Harold	30-50	*
Blue, Rose	Quiet Place (1st, 8vo, 57p, b/w, DJ/3.50)	F. Watts	(1969)	Feelings, Tom	40-65	*
Blumberg, Fannie B.	Rowena Teena Tot & Blackberries (1st, lg8vo, ibds, p-o, 32p, fp color, pep)	Whitman	(1934)	Grosjean, Mary	100-180	
Blume, Judy	One in the Middle is Green Kangaroo (1st, lg8vo, [32]p, 3-color, DJ/3.95)	Reilly/Lee	(1969)	Axeman, Lois	50-80	*
Blumenthal, Gertrude	Louise's Adventure (1st {std}, ob4to, ibds, [32]p, color, pep, DJ/1.00)	Doubleday/Doran	1941	Becker, Charlotte	30-50	*
Blyton, Enid	Famous Jimmy (1st {std}, 4to, ibds, 58p, 1-color, pep)	Dutton	1937	Rabier, Benjamin	80-140	
Blyton, Enid	Heyo, Brer Rabbit (1st, sm4to, 127p, green cl, 2-color, pep)	L: Newnes	1938	Nixon, Kathleen I.	100-170	*
Blyton, Enid	Silver & Gold (1st AM, sq8vo, uncut, gilt, p-o, 128p, 8cp, pep)	NY: Nelson	(1928)	Everett, Ethel	100-165	
Bock, George E.	What Makes the Wheels Go 'Round (1st, 4to, 76p, pep, dp color)	Macmillan	1931	Artzybasheff, Boris	120-200	*
Boden, Hilda	Marlows Wins a Prize (1st AM {std}, 8vo, 120p, b/w, DJ/2.50)	McKay	(1957)	Buchanan, Lilian	25-40	
Boegehold, Betty	Pawpaw's Run (1st {std}, sm ob4to, [32]p, color, DJ/3.95)	Dutton	(1968)	Price, Christine	30-45	*
Boegehold, Betty	Three to Get Ready (1st, 8vo, 64p, color, DJ/1.95)	Harper	(1965)	Chalmers, Mary	30-45	
Boesel, Ann S.	Sing & Sing Again (1st, 4to, 72p, ibds, color, DJ/2.50)	Oxford U. Pr.	(1938)	Costello, Louise	40-65	
Boesel, Ann S.	Singing with Peter and Patsy (1st, ob4to, 48p, yellow cl, color, DJ/2.00)	Oxford U. Pr.	(1944)	Doane, Pelagie	30-50	
Bogan, Louise	Golden Journey (1st, lg8vo, 275p, 1-color, woodcuts, DJ/5.95)	Reilly/Lee	(1965)	Kredel, Fritz	50-80	R*
Boggs, Ralph S.	Three Golden Oranges (1st {std}, 8vo, 137p, 6pl, pep, DJ/2.00)	Longmans	1936	Brock, Emma	35-50	
Bohanon, Paul	Golden Kate (1st, 8vo, gilt, 62p, fp b/w, pep, DJ/1.50)	Oxford U. Pr.	(1943)	Howe, Gertrude	40-65	*
Bohanon, Paul	Wind and Arabella (1st, 8vo, 70p, 5 fp b/w, DJ/2.00)	Oxford U. Pr.	1947	Holland, Janice	45-70	

AUTHOR	TITLE	PUBLISHER	DATE	ARTIST	PRICE	LC
Bolliger, Max	Golden Apple (1st AM {std}, lg4to, ibds, [27]p, color, DJ/4.95)	Atheneum	(1970)	Piatti, Celestino	30-50	
Bolliger, Max	The Fireflies (1st AM {std}, lg4to, ibds, [43]p, fp color, DJ/4.95)	Atheneum	(1970)	Trnka, Jiri	40-65	
Bolognese, Don	Once Upon a Mountain (1st, 8vo, [34]p, fp 2-color, DJ/2.95)	Lippincott	(1967)	Bolognese, Don	20-35	*
Bolognese, Elaine	Sleepy Watchdog (1st, lg sq8vo, [33]p, fp 1-color, DJ/2.95)	Lothrop, Lee	(1964)	Bolognese, Don	25-45	
Bolton, Charles K.	Love Story of Ursula Wolcott (1st, 16mo, ipcb, 31p, pep, designs by..)	Lamson/Wolffe	1895	Reed, Ethel	100-165	*
Bond, Elizabeth	Crunch: The Squirrel (1st, ob4to, ibds, [48]p, 1-color, pep, DJ/1.50)	Dodd	1939	Wiese, Kurt	70-100	*
Bond, Gladys B.	Blue Chimney (1st, sm8vo, 164p, red cl, b/w, DJ/2.75)	Holiday House	(1959)	Shortall, Leonard	25-40	
Bond, Jean C.	Brown is a Beautiful Color (1st, 4to, 39p, fp 1-color, DJ/3.50)	F. Watts	(1969)	Zuber, Barbara	40-65	*
Bond, Michael	Bear Called Paddington (1st, 8vo, red/silver, 128p, b/w, DJ)	L: Collins	1958	Fortnum, Peggy	130-200	
Bond, Michael	Bear Called Paddington (1st AM, 8vo, 128p, yellow cl, b/w, DJ/2.50)	Houghton	1960	Fortnum, Peggy	100-160	
Bond, Michael	Here Comes Thursday (1st AM {std}, 8vo, 126p, fp b/w, DJ/3.25)	Lothrop, Lee	(1967)	Rowles, Daphne	30-50	
Bond, Michael	More About Paddington (1st AM, 8vo, aqua cl, 128p, b/w, DJ/2.50)	Houghton	(1962)	Fortnum, Peggy	70-100	*
Bond, Michael	Paddington at Work (1st AM, 8vo, 128p, b/w, DJ/3.25)	Houghton	1967	Fortnum, Peggy	50-80	
Bond, Michael	Paddington Goes to Town (1st AM, 8vo, 125p, b/w, DJ/3.25)	Houghton	1968	Fortnum, Peggy	50-80	
Bond, Michael	Thursday Ahoy! (1st AM {std}, 8vo, 130p, b/w, DJ/3.95)	Lothrop, Lee	(1970)	Wood, Leslie	30-50	
Bond, Ruskin	Panther's Moon (1st, 8vo, 68p, fp b/w, DJ/3.50)	Random	(1969)	Feelings, Tom	30-55	*
Bond, Susan	Eric... (1st {std}, lg ob4to, 42p, color, pep, DJ/3.95)	Grove Press	(1968)	Trinkle, Sally	30-50	
Bond, Susan	Ride with Me through ABC (1st AM, 4to, [30]p, ibds, color, pep, DJ/3.75)	NY: Scroll Pr.	1968	Lemke, Horst	30-50	
Bone, Gertrude	This Old Man (1st, lg8vo, 131p, blue bds, gilt, frn by...)	L: Macmillan	1925	Bone, Muirhead	35-60	
Bone, Stephen	Little Boy and his House (1st AM, lg8vo, [90]p, p-o, color, DJ/2.00)	Winston	(1937)	Adshead, Mary	25-40	
Bonham, Frank	Mystery of the Fat Cat (1st {std}, 8vo, 160p, b/w, DJ/3.95)	Dutton	(1968)	Smith, Alvin	20-30	
Bonham, Frank	Mystery of the Red Tide (1st {std}, 8vo, 127p, b/w, DJ/3.50)	Dutton	(1966)	Turkle, Brinton	25-40	*
Bonham, Frank	Nitty Gritty (1st {std}, 8vo, 156p, b/w, DJ/3.95)	Dutton	(1968)	Smith, Alvin	25-45	
Boni, Margaret B.	Favorite Christmas Carols (1st, 4to, 128p, color, DJ/2.95)	Simon/Schuster	(1957)	Spier, Peter E.	50-80	
Bonner, Geraldine	The Pioneer (1st, 12mo, 392p, blue/gilt, cvr by...)	Bobbs-Merrill	(1905)	Armstrong, Margaret	40-60	*
Bonner, Geraldine	The Pioneer (1st, 12mo, 392p, blue/gilt, 6pl)	Bobbs-Merrill	(1905)	Fisher, Harrison	40-60	*
Bonner, Mary G.	365 Bedtime Stories (1st, lg8vo, 302p, p-o, 20cp)	Stokes	1923	Choate/Curtis	40-70	
Bonner, Mary G.	Daddy's Bedtime Fairy Stories (1st, 12mo, p-o, 120p, color)	Stokes	(1916)	Choate/Curtis	40-70	
Bonner, Mary G.	Hundred Trips to Storyland (1st, 8vo, 327p, orange cl, 7cp, pep)	Macaulay	(1930)	Lupprian, Hildegard	55-80	*
Bonner, Mary G.	Madam Red Apple (1st, 8vo, [123]p, fp color, pep)	Milton Bradley	(1929)	Scott, Janet L.	45-65	
Bonner, Mary G.	Magic Clock (1st, 8vo, yellow cl, 187p, 8cp, pep)	Macaulay	(1931)	Price, Luxor	80-120	
Bonner, Mary G.	Magic Journeys (1st, lg8vo, orange cl, 286p, 16cp, pep)	Macaulay	(1928)	Price, Luxor	80-120	
Bonner, Mary G.	Magic Map (1st, lg8vo, 238p, 17cp, pep)	Macaulay	(1927)	Price, Luxor	80-120	
Bonner, Mary G.	Magic Music Shop (1st, lg4to, orange cl, 95p, color, pep)	Macaulay	(1929)	Price, Luxor	90-140	
Bonner, Mary G.	Miss Angelina Adorable (1st, 8vo, [102]p, color, pep)	Milton Bradley	(1928)	Scott, Janet L.	40-65	
Bonner, Mary G.	Mrs. Cucumber Green (1st, 8vo, [108]p, pep, color)	Milton Bradley	(1927)	Scott, Janet L.	40-65	
Bonner, Mary G.	Story Teller's Holiday (1st, lg4to, [64]p, red cl, p-o, color)	McLoughlin	(1938)	Scott, Janet L.	100-165	
Bonner, Mary G.	Surprise Place (1st {std}, 8vo, 119p, green cl, b/w, DJ/2.00)	Knopf	1945	Lenski, Lois	70-120	
Bonney, Thomas G.	The Mediterranean (1st, 8vo, blue/gilt, 367p, gilt)	J. Pott	1902	Armstrong, Margaret	50-80	
Bonsall, Crosby	Case of the Cat's Meow (1st, 8vo, 64p, 2-color, DJ/1.95)	Harper	(1965)	Bonsall, Crosby	25-40	
Bonsall, Crosby	Case of the Dumb Bells (1st, 8vo, 64p, fp 2-color, DJ/1.95)	Harper	(1966)	Bonsall, Crosby	25-40	
Bonsall, Crosby	Case of the Hungry Stranger (1st, 8vo, 64p, 2-color, DJ/1.95)	Harper	(1963)	Bonsall, Crosby	25-40	
Bonsall, Crosby	I'll Show You Cats (1st, lg4to, unpag, DJ/2.95, NYTBI, b/w photos by...)	Harper	(1964)	Ylla	40-65	
Bonsall, Crosby	It's Mine! (1st, 16mo, ipcb, [32]p, 1-color, DJ/1.95)	Harper	(1964)	Bonsall, Crosby	25-40	
Bonsall, Crosby	What Spot? (1st {std}, 8vo, 64p, 2-color, DJ/1.95)	Harper	(1963)	Bonsall, Crosby	20-35	
Bonsels, Waldemar	Adventures of Mario (1st, 8vo, 239p, b/w, DJ/3.00)	A.& C. Boni	1930	Wiese, Kurt	25-40	
Bonsels, Waldemar	Adventures of Maya the Bee (1st, 4to, 224p, p-o, 6 dp 3-color)	Boni	1929	Bock, Vera	25-40	
Bonte, George W.	Christmas Stocking Rhymes (4to, tan cl, p-o, 38p, 17 color)	Caldwell	(1904)	Bridgman, L.J.	180-250	
Bonte, George W.	Fun & Nonsense (1st, 4to, p-o, [40]p, color)	Caldwell	(1904)	Bonte, Willard	80-120	*
Bontemps, Arna	Chariot in the Sky (1st {std}, 8vo, 234p, b/w, DJ/2.50)	Winston	(1951)	Baldridge, Cyrus L.	80-120	
Bontemps, Arna	Drums at Dusk (1st {std}, 8vo, 226p, black cl, b/w, cep, DJ/2.50)	Macmillan	1939	Margenta	200-300	
Bontemps, Arna	Fast Sooner Hound (1st, lg8vo, beige cl, 28p, color, pep, DJ/1.75)	Houghton	(1942)	Burton, Virginia L.	70-130	
Bontemps, Arna	Frederick Douglass... (1st {std}, sm8vo, 177p, b/w, DJ/3.00)	Knopf	1959	Johnson, Harper	35-50	
Bontemps, Arna	Lonesome Boy (1st, 8vo, blue cl, 28p, fp b/w, cep, DJ/2.00)	Houghton	1955	Topolski, Feliks	60-100	
Bontemps, Arna	Mr. Kelso's Lion (1st {std}, 8vo, 48p, DJ/3.95)	Lippincott	(1970)	Ebert, Len	120-180	
Bontemps, Arna	Popo & Fifina (1st, 8vo, 100p, orange cl, 6pl)	Macmillan	1932	Campbell, E. Simms	150-220	R
Bontemps, Arna	Sad-Faced Boy (1st, 8vo, 118p, col frn, 7pl, pep, DJ/2.00)	Houghton	1937	Burton, Virginia L.	80-130	
Bontemps, Arna	Sam Patch... (1st, sq8vo, yellow cl, 39p, color, pep, DJ/2.00)	Houghton	1951	Brown, Paul	100-180	
Bontemps, Arna	Slappy Hooper... (1st, lg ob8vo, 44p, color, pep, DJ/2.00)	Houghton	1946	Koering, Ursula	140-200	
Bontemps, Arna	Story of George Washington Carver (1st, 8vo, 181p, b/w, pep, DJ/1.50)	Grosset/Dunlap	(1954)	Johnson, Harper	50-80	*
Bontemps, Arna	Story of the Negro (1st {std}, 8vo, 239p, b/w, DJ/3.00, NH, JABA)	Knopf	1948	Lufkin, Raymond	80-130	
Bontemps, Arna	We Have Tomorrow (1st, sm8vo, 131p, DJ/2.50, photos by...)	Houghton	1945	Palfi, Marion	80-140	
Bontemps, Arna	You Can't Pet a Possum (1st, 8vo, 120p, red cl, 4cp)	Wm. Morrow	1934	Bischoff, Ilse	60-100	*
Bontemps, Arna (comp)	Golden Slippers (1st {std}, 8vo, 220p, b/w pl, DJ/2.50)	Harper	(1941)	Sharon, Henrietta	45-65	
Booth, Esma	Bright Pathways (1st, sm8vo, 125p, b/w, DJ/2.00)	Friendship Pr.	(1955)	Wiese, Kurt	25-40	
Booth, Maud B.	Sleepy-Time Stories (1st, sm8vo, 177p, teg, gilt, 17pl)	Putnam	1899	Humphrey, Maud	200-300	
Booth, Maud B.	Twilight Fairy Tales (1st, 8vo, 273p, gilt, teg, 16cp)	Putnam	1906	Rand, Amy	80-125	
Borack, Barbara	Gooney (1st, sm4to, [32]p, fp color, cep, DJ/2.95)	Harper	(1968)	McCully, Emily	40-65	*
Borack, Barbara	Grandpa (1st, lg8vo, 32p, color, cep, DJ/2.95)	Harper	(1967)	Shecter, Ben	30-50	
Borack, Barbara	Someone Small (1st, 8vo, 32p, ibds, color, DJ/3.50)	Harper	(1969)	Lobel, Anita	20-35	
Borie, Lysbeth	David Has his Day (1st, lg8vo, ibds, 63p, 2-color, pep, DJ/1.75)	Lippincott	(1934)	Dobias, Frank	40-65	
Borland, Hal	Beyond Your Doorstep (1st {std}, 8vo, 400p, b/w, DJ/5.95)	Knopf	1962	Parnall, Peter	30-45	*
Borland, Hal	Rocky Mountain Tipi Tales (1st [1st bk.] {std}, 8vo, 247p, col frn by...)	Doubleday/Page	1924	Mattsson, Esther M.	90-130	
Borrow, George H.	Lavengro (1st, teg, green/gilt, 655p, 12 ticp, cep)	L: Foulis	(1914)	Sullivan, Edmund J.	55-80	
Borski, Lucia M.	Gypsy and the Bear (1st {std}, 8vo, 129p, b/w, pep)	Longmans	1933	Reid, James	25-45	*
Borski, Lucia M.	Jolly Tailor (1st {std}, 8vo, 156p, col frn, fp b/w, pep)	Longmans	1928	Klepacki, Kazimir	30-50	*
Borten, Helen	Halloween (1st, 8vo, [34]p, fp 2-color, DJ/2.95)	Crowell	(1965)	Borten, Helen	25-40	
Borten, Helen	The Jungle (1st {std}, 4to, [32]p, ipcb, 13 dp color, pep, DJ/3.75)	Harcourt	1968	Borten, Helen	25-40	

AUTHOR	TITLE	PUBLISHER	DATE	ARTIST	PRICE	LC
Borton, Elizabeth	Our Little Aztec Cousin of Long Ago (1st, sm8vo, blue cl, 83p, 6pl)	L.C. Page	(1934)	Cue, Harold	25-40	*
Borton, Elizabeth	Our Little Ethiopian Cousin (1st, sm8vo, 134p, DJ/1.00)	L.C. Page	1935	(Photos)	25-40	*
Borton, Elizabeth	Pollyanna & the Secret Mission (1st, sm8vo, 263p, gilt, DJ/2.50, frn by...)	L.C. Page	(1951)	Cue, Harold	30-45	
Borton, Elizabeth	Pollyanna in Hollywood (1st, sm8vo, gilt, 341p, col frn)	L.C. Page	(1931)	Taylor, H. Weston	30-45	
Borton, Elizabeth	Pollyanna's Castle in Mexico (1st, sm8vo, 322p, gilt, col frn)	L.C. Page	(1934)	Cue, Harold	25-40	*
Borton, Elizabeth	Pollyanna's Door to Happiness (1st, sm8vo, gilt, 359p, col frn, DJ/2.00)	L.C. Page	(1936)	Cue, Harold	30-45	
Borton, Elizabeth	Pollyanna's Golden Horseshoe (1st, sm8vo, 339p, gilt, col frn, DJ/2.00)	L.C. Page	(1939)	Tyng, Griswold	25-40	*
Boston, Lucy M.	Castle of Yew (1st AM {std}, 8vo, 58p, b/w, DJ/2.95)	Harcourt	(1965)	Gill, Margery	30-50	
Boston, Lucy M.	Children of the Green Knowe (1st, sm8vo, 157p, cloth, 6pl, DJ)	L: Faber	(1954)	Boston, Peter	100-170	
Boston, Lucy M.	Children of the Green Knowe (1st AM {std}, 8vo, 157p, pcb, b/w, DJ/2.75)	Harcourt	(1955)	Boston, Peter	80-140	R
Boston, Lucy M.	Enemy at Green Knowe (1st AM {std}, 8vo, 156p, b/w, DJ/3.25)	Harcourt	(1964)	Boston, Peter	70-100	
Boston, Lucy M.	House that Grew (1st, 4to, 28p, DJ)	L: Faber	1969	Hemming, Caroline	70-120	
Boston, Lucy M.	River at Green Knowe (1st AM {std}, 8vo, 153p, green cl, b/w, DJ/3.00)	Harcourt	(1959)	Boston, Peter	80-130	
Boston, Lucy M.	Sea Egg (1st {std}, 8vo, green cl, 94p, fp b/w, DJ/2.50)	Harcourt	(1967)	Boston, Peter	30-50	
Boston, Lucy M.	Stranger at Green Knowe (1st, 8vo, 158p, b/w, DJ, CgM)	L: Faber	(1961)	Boston, Peter	70-125	
Boston, Lucy M.	Stranger at Green Knowe (1st AM {std}, 8vo, 158p, b/w, DJ/3.00)	Harcourt	(1961)	Boston, Peter	70-125	
Boston, Lucy M.	Treasure of Green Knowe (1st AM {std}, 8vo, 185p, b/w, DJ/3.00)	Harcourt	(1958)	Boston, Peter	80-130	
Boswell, Hazel	French Canada (1st, ob8vo, 82p, 25cp, DJ/2.00)	Viking	1938	Boswell, Hazel	40-60	
Bothwell, Jean	Little Flute Player (1st, 8vo, 159p, b/w, DJ/2.00)	Wm. Morrow	1949	Ayer, Margaret	20-35	
Bothwell, Jean	Paddy and Sam (1st, 4to, [38]p, fp 3-color, pep, DJ/2.00)	Abelard Press	(1952)	Ayer, Margaret	25-40	*
Bothwell, Jean	River Boy of Kashmir (1st, 8vo, 246p, pep, DJ/2.00)	Wm. Morrow	1946	Ayer, Margaret	25-40	
Bouchard, Lois K.	Boy Who Wouldn't Talk (1st {std}, lg8vo, 74p, DJ/3.50)	Doubleday	(1969)	Grifalconi, Ann	25-45	
Boult, Ella M.	Romance of Cinderella (1st, sm4to, 146p, color)	R.H. Russell	1902	Stevens, Beatrice	200-300	*
Boult, Katharine F.	Heroes of the Norselands (1st, 8vo, 211p, 9pl)	L: Dent	1903	Robinson, Thomas H.	55-80	*
Bourgeois, Florence	Beachcomber Bobbie (1st {std}, ob12mo, ipcb, [32]p, color, pep)	Doubleday/Doran	1935	Bourgeois, Florence	30-50	
Bourgeois, Florence	Trailer Dog Trix & Nancy (1st {std}, lg ob8vo, [32]p, ibds, DJ/0.75)	Doubleday/Doran	1938	Bourgeois, Florence	40-65	
Bourget, Paul	Antigone (1st, 8vo, red/gilt, uncut, 297p)	Scribner	1898	Armstrong, Margaret	35-60	*
Bourget, Paul	Monica (1st, 12mo, 289p, red cl, cvr by...)	Scribner	1902	Armstrong, Margaret	30-50	*
Bourget, Paul	Tragic Idyl (1st, sm8vo, red/gilt, 452p, uncut)	Scribner	1896	Armstrong, Margaret	35-60	*
Bourke, S.T.E.	Fables in Feathers (1st, sq8vo, 114p, 9pl)	Crowell	(1907)	Conde, J.M.	40-60	
Bourne, Gwen	Wonder World Fairy Tale Book (1st, 4to, blue cl, 90p, 4pl)	L: Cecil Palmer	(1931)	Gaze, Harold	200-300	
Bourne, Miriam	Raccoons are for Loving (1st, ob4to, 44p, fp 3-color, cep, DJ/3.95)	Random	(1968)	Morton, Marian	30-50	
Bouton, Elizabeth	Grandmother's Doll (1st, lg8vo, 106p, gilt, 7cp, pep)	Duffield/Green	(1931)	Carter, Helene	55-80	*
Boutwell, Edna	Red Rooster (1st {std}, 8vo, [48]p, color, DJ/1.75)	Aladdin	(1950)	Garbutt, Bernard	25-45	*
Bouve, Edward T.	Centuries Apart (1st, 8vo, 347p, grey/gilt, 6pl, maps)	Little/Brown	1894	Harper, W. St. J.	40-60	
Bouvet, Marguerite	Bernardo and Laurette (1st, sm8vo, 217p, green cl, b/w, pl)	McClurg	1901	Armstrong, Helen	30-50	
Bouvet, Marguerite	Child of Tuscany (1st, 8vo, 207p, blue cl, 15pl, cep)	McClurg	1895	Hooper, Will P.	25-45	
Bouvet, Marguerite	Little House in Pimlico (1st, 8vo, blue cl, 245p, b/w, cep)	McClurg	1897	Armstrong, Margaret	25-40	
Bouvet, Marguerite	Little Marjorie's Love Story (1st, 12mo, 124p, 16pl)	McClurg	1891	Armstrong, Helen	30-60	
Bouvet, Marguerite	My Lady (1st, 12mo, beige/silver, 284p, 12pl)	McClurg	1894	Armstrong, Helen	40-60	
Bouvet, Marguerite	Prince Tip-Top (1st, 12mo, 134p, olive/white, b/w)	McClurg	1892	Armstrong, Helen	55-80	*
Bouvet, Marguerite	Sweet William (1st, 8vo, 209p, blue cl, 16 b/w, cep)	McClurg	1890	Armstrong, Margaret	35-60	
Bouvet, Marguerite	Tales of an Old Chateau (1st, 12mo, 235p, gilt)	McClurg	1899	Armstrong, Margaret	50-80	
Bowen, Vernon	Lazy Beaver (1st, 4to, [36]p, ibds, color, DJ/2.00)	McKay	1948	Davis, Jim	30-50	*
Bowen, Vernon	Snow for Christmas (1st, 8vo, [32]p, 2-color, DJ/2.50)	McKay	1953	Wiese, Kurt	30-50	*
Bowen, Vernon	Wonderful Adventures of Ting Ling (1st, 8vo, [40]p, b/w, pep, DJ/2.00)	McKay	1952	Wiese, Kurt	25-40	*
Bowen, William	Enchanted Forest (1st, 12mo, 197p, col frn, fp b/w, pep)	Macmillan	1920	Petershams	80-130	
Bowen, William	Merrimeg (1st, 12mo, 166p, green/gilt, 7cp, pep)	Macmillan	1923	Brock, Emma	30-50	*
Bowen, William	Old Tobacco Shop (1st, sm8vo, 236p, green/gilt, p-o, fp b/w, NH)	Macmillan	1921	Unknown	60-90	
Bowen, William	Solario the Tailor (1st, sm8vo, 232p, gilt, 4cp, pep)	Macmillan	1922	Ormsbee, J.	25-40	
Bower, B.M.	Chip of the Flying-U (1st, 12mo, 264p, red cl, 3cp)	Street & Smith	(1906)	Russell, Charles M.	120-200	
Bower, B.M.	Lure of the Dim Trails (1st, sm8vo, red cl, 210p, 3cp)	Dillingham	(1907)	Russell, Charles M.	100-180	
Bower, B.M.	Range Dwellers (1st, 12mo, 356p, 3cp)	Street & Smith	(1907)	Russell, Charles M.	150-200	
Bower, B.M.	Uphill Climb (1st, sm8vo, 283p, 4pl)	Little/Brown	1913	Russell, Charles M.	80-125	
Bowie, Walter R.	Story of Jesus for Young People (1st, 8vo, 125p, blue/gilt, 6cp, DJ/2.00)	Scribner	1937	Lawson, Robert	80-135	
Bowie, Walter R.	When Jesus was Born (1st {std}, sq16mo, [20]p, ibds, color)	Harper	1928	Falls, Charles B.	55-80	
Bowman, James C.	John Henry, Rambling Black Ulysses (1st, 8vo, 288p, 2cp, 12pl, DJ/2.50)	Whitman	1942	LaGrone, Roy	30-50	
Bowman, James C.	Mystery Mountain (1st, 8vo, 293p, blue cl, 4cp, 10pl, pep, DJ/1.75)	Whitman	1940	Wallower, Lucille	30-45	
Bowman, James C.	Pecos Bill (1st, lg8vo, 296p, 6cp, 15pl, pep, DJ/2.50, NH)	Whitman	1937	Bannon, Laura	100-165	
Bowman, James C.	Seven Silly Wise Men (1st, 8vo, p-o, [30]p, fp color, DJ/2.50)	Whitman	(1965)	Faulkner, John	25-40	*
Bowman, James C.	Tales from a Finnish Tupa (1st, 8vo, grey cl, 273p, pep, 6cp, DJ)	Whitman	1936	Bannon, Laura	100-165	
Bowman, James C.	Who Was Tricked? (1st, 8vo, [32]p, fp color, DJ/2.50)	Whitman	(1966)	Faulkner, John	25-40	*
Bowman, James C.	Winabojo (1st, 8vo, 296p, orange cl, col frn, 12pl, pep, DJ/2.50)	Whitman	1941	Sperry, Armstrong	30-50	
Bowman, John G.	Happy all Day Through (1st, lg ob4to, [32]p, ibds, color)	Volland	(1917)	Scott, Janet L.	90-140	
Bowman, Rowland	Freckles & Tan (1st, 16mo, 68p, gilt, b/w)	Rand/McNally	1904	Cory, Fanny	35-50	
Boxer, Devorah	26 Ways to be Somebody Else (1st, ob8vo, [56]p, color, pep, DJ/3.25, NYTBI)	Pantheon	(1960)	Boxer, Devorah	40-65	*
Boyajian, Zabelle C.	Armenian Legends & Poems (folio, cloth, 196p, ticp)	Dent/Dutton	[1915]	Boyajian, Zabelle C.	200-300	
Boyajian, Zabelle C.	Gilgamesh: Dream of Eternal Quest (1st, lg4to, teg, 110p, gilt 15ticp)	L: G.W. Jones	1924	Boyajian, Zabelle C.	250-400	
Boyd, Elizabeth M.	All About David (1st, lg8vo, 117p, pep, b/w, DJ/1.50)	Winston	(1940)	Sarg, Tony	30-50	
Boyd, Harriet	Cabbages & Peanuts (1st, 8vo, [40]p, ibds, color, pep)	Saalfield	(1929)	Peat, Fern B.	60-90	
Boyd, James	Drums (1st, lg8vo, gilt, p-o, 409p, 17cp, pep, SC)	Scribner	1928	Wyeth, N.C.	200-300	
Boyde, Richard	Last Dodo (1st {std}, 8vo, 131p, fp b/w, dep, DJ/3.75)	Farrar, Straus	(1967)	Boyde, Richard	40-65	
Boylan, Eleanor	How to Be a Puppeteer (1st {std}, 8vo, 132p, b/w, DJ/4.95)	McCall Pub.	(1970)	DePaola, Tomie	20-35	
Boylan, Grace D.	Kids of Many Colors (1st, 8vo, tan cl, 156p, color)	Chi: Jamieson	(1901)	Morgan, Ike	120-200	
Boylan, Grace D.	Kiss of Glory (1st, sm8vo, 298p, col frn & cvr by...)	Dillingham	(1902)	Leyendecker, J.C.	35-50	
Boylan, Grace D.	Old House (1st, 12mo, 112p, cvr by...)	E.R. Herrick	(1897)	Denslow, W.W.	40-65	
Boylan, Grace D.	Pipes of Clovis (1st, sm8vo, 258p, green cl, 4cp)	Little/Brown	1913	Chamberlin, E.H.	25-40	*
Boylan, Grace D.	Steps to Nowhere (1st, lg8vo, 230p, p-o, blue cl, 8cp)	Baker/Taylor	1910	Morgan, Ike	120-180	

AUTHOR	TITLE	PUBLISHER	DATE	ARTIST	PRICE	LC
Boylan, Grace D.	Yama Yama Land (1st, sq8vo, 200p, p-o, 14 fp color)	Reilly/Britton	(1909)	Keller, Edgar	90-150	
Boylan, Grace D.	Young Folks Uncle Tom's Cabin (1st, 8vo, ipcb, 166p, 16 fp b/w)	Jamieson-Higgins	1901	Morgan, Ike	200-300	*
Boyle, E.	Scrap Basket Sam (1st, 12mo, 82p, p-o, gilt, 4cp)	Rand/McNally	(1923)	Gregory, Dorothy L.	30-50	
Boyle, Kay	Youngest Camel (1st {std}, 8vo, 96p, beige cl, 6cp, DJ/2.00)	Little/Brown	1939	Kredel, Fritz	50-90	R
Boyle, Virginia F.	Devil Tales (1st, sm8vo, 211p, 28pl)	Harper	1900	Frost, A.B.	200-300	*
Boyles, Kate	Langford of the Three Bars (1st, 8vo, 278p, 4cp)	McClurg	1907	Wyeth, N.C.	70-100	
Boyles, Kate	Spirit Trail (1st, 8vo, 416p, ibds, 4cp)	McClurg	1910	Dixon, Maynard	40-60	
Boylston, Helen D.	Carol on Tour (1st {std}, sm8vo, 205p, red cl, 4pl, DJ/2.50)	Little/Brown	1946	Felten, Major	200-300	
Boylston, Helen D.	Sue Barton: Rural Nurse (1st {std}, 8vo, 244p, b/w, DJ/2.00)	Little/Brown	1939	Orr, Forrest W.	250-400	
Boynton, Henry W.	Golfer's Rubaiyat (1st, 12mo, [83]p, bds, cvr by...)	Herbert Stone	1901	Hazenplug, Frank	250-400	
Bracken, Peg	I Hate to Cook Book (1st {std}, 8vo, 176p, b/w, DJ/3.75)	Harcourt	1960	Knight, Hilary	30-50	*
Bracker, Charles	Chester (1st, sm4to, [48]p, p-o, color, DJ/2.00)	J. Messner	1939	Bracker, Charles	50-75	
Bradbury, Bianca	Antique Cat (1st {std}, sq8vo, [64]p, fp 1-color, pep, DJ/2.00)	Winston	(1945)	Thorne, Diana	40-65	
Bradbury, Bianca	One Kitten too Many (1st, 8vo, 32p, 2-color, DJ/1.50)	Houghton	1952	Nichols, Marie C.	30-50	
Bradbury, Bianca	The Undergrounders (1st, 8vo, 120p, b/w, DJ/2.95)	NY: Washburn	(1966)	Nielsen, Jon	40-65	*
Bradbury, Bianca	Two on an Island (1st, 8vo, 139p, b/w, DJ/3.00)	Houghton	1965	MacLean, Robert	25-40	*
Bradbury, Ray	Switch on the Night (1st, sq8vo, ibds, [48]p, color, cep, DJ/2.50, NYTBI)	Pantheon	1955	Gekiere, Madeleine	400-650	
Bradford, Margaret	Keep Singing, Keep Humming (1st, lg ob8vo, ibds, 66p, color, DJ/2.00)	Young Scott	(1946)	Bloch, Lucienne	35-50	
Bradford, Roark	How Come Christmas (1st, 8vo, ibds, 22p, b/w, DJ/1.00)	Harper	(1948)	Burchard, Peter	20-35	
Bradford, Roark	John Henry (1st {std}, 8vo, 225p, col frn, pep)	Harper	1931	Lankes, Julius J.	30-50	
Bradley, Arthur G.	Highways & Byways of North Wales (1st, 8vo, gilt, 474p, b/w)	L: Macmillan	1898	Thomson/Pennell	75-100	*
Bradley, Duane	Meeting with a Stranger (1st {std}, 8vo, 128p, b/w, DJ/3.75, JABA)	Lippincott	(1964)	Johnson, Harper	25-40	
Bradley, Mary H.	Alice in Elephantland (1st, sm8vo, 187p, b/w, pep)	Appleton	1929	Bradley, Mary H.	55-80	*
Bradley, Mary H.	Alice in Jungleland (1st, 8vo, 170p, green cl, b/w, pep)	Appleton	1927	(Photos)	90-120	*
Bradley, Mary H.	Wine of Astonishment (1st, 12mo, pcb, 313p, cvr by...)	Appleton	1919	Armstrong, Margaret	30-50	
Bradley, Will	Peter Poodle... (1st, sq4to, 166p, ibds, 26 fp color, pep)	Dodd	1906	Bradley, Will	700-1000	
Bradley, Will	Wonderbox Stories (1st, 8vo, 154p, gold cl, fp b/w)	Century	1916	Bradley, Will	400-600	
Bradley-Birt, F.	Bengal Fairy Tales (1st, lg8vo, 209p, gilt, 6 fp color)	L: John Lane	1920	Tagore, A.N.	90-120	
Brady, Cyrus T.	And Thus He Came (1st, sm8vo, 103p, teg, 6 ticp)	Putnam	1916	Everett, Walter	45-70	
Brady, Cyrus T.	Little Angel of Canyon Creek (1st, 8vo, 292p, 6pl)	Revell	1914	Hoskins, Gayle	30-50	
Brady, Cyrus T.	My Lady's Slipper (1st, sm8vo, gilt, teg, 245p, 4pl)	Dodd	1905	Ditzler, C. Weber	25-40	
Brady, Cyrus T.	Reuben James (1st, sm8vo, 158p, pict cl, b/w)	Appleton	1900	Various	25-40	
Brady, Cyrus T.	West Wind (1st, 8vo, gilt, 389p, 4cp)	McClurg	1910	Dixon, Maynard	30-60	
Brady, Loretta E.	Green Forest Fairy Book (1st, 8vo, 271p, 8cp)	Little/Brown	1920	Preston, Alice B.	80-120	
Bragdon, Elspeth	That Jud! (1st, 8vo, ivory cl, 126p, fp b/w, DJ/2.50)	Viking	(1957)	Schreiber, Georges	30-50	
Bragdon, Ollie	Moon Party (1st, 12mo, 122p, p-o, 6pl)	Caldwell	(1904)	Ruyl, Beatrice B.	50-75	
Brailsford, Mabel	Making of William Penn (1st, 8vo, 367p, gilt, t-i frn by...)	Longmans	1930	Leighton, Clare	35-60	
Braine, Sheila E.	Animals' Touring Club (ob4to, ibds, unpag, 8 chromos)	Nister/Dutton	[1900]	Thompson, G.H.	100-170	
Braine, Sheila E.	Princess of Hearts (1st, 8vo, AEG, 172p, green/gilt, col frn)	L: Blackie	1899	Woodward, Alice B.	70-100	
Braine, Sheila E.	To Tell the King the Sky is Falling (1st, 8vo, AEG, 171p, 8pl, cep)	L: Blackie	(1896)	Woodward, Alice B.	60-100	
Braine/Floyd	In Nurseryland (1st, 4to, ibds, [48]p, color)	L: R. Tuck	[1900]	Wain, Louis	800-1200	
Brainerd, Edna S.	Millicent in Dreamland (1st, 12mo, 94p, p-o, b/w)	L.C. Page	1902	Barry, Etheldred B.	25-40	
Brainerd, Eleanor H.	For Love of Mary Ellen (1st, 12mo, 43p, tan cl, 4pl)	Harper	1912	O'Neill, Rose	40-65	
Brainerd, Eleanor H.	How Could You, Jean? (1st, sm8vo, 337p, 4pl)	Doubleday/Page	1917	Flagg, James M.	25-40	*
Braley, Berton	Enchanted Flivver (1st, 8vo, blue/gilt, 255p, b/w)	Century	(1926)	Birch, Reginald	70-100	*
Brand, Christianna	Naughty Children (1st AM {std}, 8vo, 314p, b/w, DJ/4.50)	Dutton	(1963)	Ardizzone, Edward	50-85	
Brand, Christianna	Nurse Matilda (1st AM {std}, 12mo, 128p, b/w, DJ/2.95)	Dutton	(1964)	Ardizzone, Edward	50-80	
Brand, Christianna	Nurse Matilda Goes to Town (1st AM {std}, 12mo, 128p, b/w, cep, DJ/3.25)	Dutton	(1968)	Ardizzone, Edward	40-65	
Brande, Marlie	Sleepy Nicholas (1st {std}, ob8vo, [29]p, 2-color, DJ/3.50)	Follett	(1970)	Brande, Marlie	20-30	
Brandenberg, Franz	I Once Knew a Man (1st {std}, 8vo, [40]p, 1-color, DJ/3.95)	Macmillan	(1970)	Aliki	25-40	
Branley, Franklyn	Big Dipper (1st, ob8vo, [40]p, color, DJ/2.50)	Crowell	(1962)	Emberley, Ed	30-45	
Branley, Franklyn	Book of Mars for You (1st, ob8vo, 56p, 2-color, DJ/3.95)	Crowell	(1968)	Kessler, Leonard	30-45	*
Branley, Franklyn	Christmas Sky (1st, lg8vo, [46]p, gilt, fp 2-color, DJ/3.75)	Crowell	(1966)	Lent, Blair	45-70	R
Branley, Franklyn	Flash, Crash, Rumble and Roll (1st, ob8vo, [40]p, color, DJ/2.75)	Crowell	(1964)	Emberley, Ed	30-50	
Branley, Franklyn	High Sounds, Low Sounds (1st, ob8vo, ibds, [40]p, fp 2-color, DJ/3.25)	Crowell	(1967)	Galdone, Paul	30-45	
Branley, Franklyn	Mickey's Magnet (1st, 8vo, [48]p, yellow cl, color, dep, DJ/2.50)	Crowell	1956	Johnson, Crockett	30-50	
Branley, Franklyn	Moon Seems to Change (1st, sq8vo, [40]p, color, DJ/1.95)	Crowell	(1960)	Borten, Helen	30-50	
Branley, Franklyn	Rain and Hail (1st, sq8vo, [40]p, color, DJ/2.50)	Crowell	(1963)	Borten, Helen	30-50	*
Branley, Franklyn	Rusty Rings a Bell (1st, 8vo, [30]p, 2-color, DJ/2.50)	Crowell	(1957)	Galdone, Paul	25-45	
Branley, Franklyn	Snow is Falling (1st, ob8vo, ibds, [40]p, fp 2-color, DJ/2.50)	Crowell	(1963)	Stone, Helen	30-50	
Branley, Franklyn	Timmy and the Tin-Can Telephone (1st, 8vo, [42]p, 2-color, dep, DJ/2.50)	Crowell	(1959)	Galdone, Paul	30-45	
Branley, Franklyn	What the Moon is Like (1st, ob8vo, ipcb, [40]p, fp 2-color, DJ/2.50)	Crowell	(1963)	Bobri, Vladimir	25-40	
Braucher, Bettye	Belinda and Me (1st, ob24mo, [24]p, fp b/w, dep, DJ/1.95)	Viking	(1966)	Turkle, Brinton	30-45	*
Braun, Kathy	Kangaroo and Kangaroo (1st {std}, ob4to, 36p, color, DJ/3.25, NYTBI)	Doubleday	(1965)	McMullan, Jim	40-65	*
Braune, Anna	Honey Chile (1st {std}, 4to, 153p, color, pep, DJ/2.00)	Doubleday/Doran	1937	Braune, Anna	100-165	
Breakenridge, Wm.	Helldorado (1st, lg8vo, brown cl, 256p, b/w)	Houghton	1928	(Photos)	65-80	
Brebner, Percy	Princess Maritza (1st, 8vo, 357p, frn by...)	McBride	1906	Fisher, Harrison	20-25	
Breckenfeld, Vivian	High Trail (1st {std}, 8vo, uncut, 214p, b/w, DJ/2.50)	Doubleday	1948	Weisgard, Leonard	25-40	
Brennan, George H.	Bill Truetell (1st, 8vo, 282p, col frn & cvr by...)	McClurg	1909	Flagg, James M.	25-40	
Brenner, Anita	Boy Who Could Do Anything (1st, lg8vo, 136p, fp color, cep, DJ/2.75)	W.R. Scott	(1942)	Charlot, Jean	70-120	
Brenner, Anita	Dumb Juan & the Bandits (1st, 8vo, green cl, [47]p, 1-color, DJ/2.50)	W.R. Scott	(1957)	Charlot, Jean	50-80	
Brenner, Anita	Hero by Mistake (1st, 8vo, 43p, ipcb, pep, 1-color, DJ/2.00, NYTBI)	W.R. Scott	(1953)	Charlot, Jean	100-175	
Brenner, Anita	I Want to Fly (1st, lg8vo, [34]p, ipcb, color, pep, DJ/1.50)	W.R. Scott	1943	Bloch, Lucienne	40-60	*
Brenner, Anita	Timid Ghost (1st, 4to, [48]p, cloth, 1-color, DJ/3.95)	W.R. Scott	(1966)	Charlot, Jean	50-80	
Brenner, Barbara	Five Pennies (1st, 8vo, [30]p, color, dep, DJ/3.25)	Knopf	(1964)	Blegvad, Erik	30-50	*
Brenner, Barbara	Mr. Tall & Mr. Small (1st, 8vo, [32]p, 3-color, pep, DJ/3.75)	Young Scott	(1966)	Ungerer, Tomi	30-50	
Brent, Stuart	Strange Disappearance of Mr. Toast (1st, lg8vo, 62p, b/w, DJ/2.50)	Viking	(1964)	Goldstein, Leslie	20-30	
Brentano, Clemens	Fairy Tales from Brentano (1st, 8vo, 252p, gilt, b/w)	L: T.F. Unwin	1885	Gould, F. Carruthers	170-240	*

AUTHOR	TITLE	PUBLISHER	DATE	ARTIST	PRICE	LC
Brentano, Clemens	Fairy Tales from Brentano (sm8vo, 326p, col frn, 8pl)	Stokes	(1925)	Gould, F. Carruthers	35-60	*
Brentano, Clemens	Schoolmaster Whackwell's Wonderful Sons (1st lg8vo ibds 86p, 1-col, DJ/3.50)	Random	(1962)	Sendak, Maurice	200-300	R
Brentano, Clemens	Tale of Gockel, Hinkel & Gackeliah (1st, lg8vo, 143p, fp b/w, pep, DJ/3.95)	Random	(1961)	Sendak, Maurice	200-300	R
Brereton, Frederick	Boy of the Dominion (1st, 8vo, 367p, gilt, 6cp)	L: Blackie	1913	Rainey, William	40-60	
Brereton, Frederick	Indian & Scout (1st, 8vo, 368p, gilt, 6pl)	L: Blackie	1911	Cuneo, Cyrus	35-60	
Brereton, Frederick	On the Field of Waterloo (1st, sm8vo, 400p, gilt, 8pl)	L: Blackie	1915	DeWalton, John	70-100	
Brereton, Frederick	Tom Stapleton the Boy Scout (1st, 12mo, 287p, gilt, col frn, 6pl)	L: Blackie	1911	Browne, Gordon	50-85	
Brett, Edna P.	Circus Day (1st, 12mo, p-o, ibds, 64p, 8 fp color)	Rand/McNally	1922	Riley, Garada C.	30-50	
Brett, Molly	Story of a Toy Car (1st, 4to, 63p)	L: Warne	(1938)	Brett, Molly	60-90	*
Brewton, John	Gaily We Parade (1st, lg8vo, 218p, pep, b/w, DJ/2.00)	Macmillan	1940	Lawson, Robert	50-80	
Brewton, John (ed)	Under the Tent of the Sky (1st, 8vo, 205p, blue cl, pep, fp b/w, DJ/2.00)	Macmillan	1937	Lawson, Robert	100-165	
Brewton, Sara W.	Bridled with Rainbows (1st {std}, lg8vo, 191p, DJ/2.75, b/w decor by...)	Macmillan	1949	Bock, Vera	25-45	
Brewton, Sara W.	Shrieks at Midnight (1st, sm8vo, 177p, b/w, DJ/3.95)	Crowell	(1969)	Raskin, Ellen	30-50	
Brewton, Sara W.	Sing a Song of Seasons (1st {std}, lg8vo, 200p, DJ/3.50, b/w decor by...)	Macmillan	(1955)	Bock, Vera	25-45	
Brickdale, E.F.	Golden Book of Famous Women (1st, 4to, blue/gilt, 200p, 16 ticp)	L: Hodder	[1916]	Brickdale, E.F.	140-200	
Brickdale, E.F.	Golden Book of Songs & Ballads (4to, 198p, green/gilt, 24 ticp)	L: Hodder	[1915]	Brickdale, E.F.	150-225	
Bridges, William	Toco Toucan (1st {std}, 8vo, [32]p, color, DJ/1.00)	Harper	(1940)	Wiese, Kurt	30-50	
Bridgman, Betty	Lullaby for Eggs (1st {std}, 8vo, ibds, [34]p, fp color, DJ/2.25)	Macmillan	1955	Jones, Eliz. O.	50-80	
Bridgman, Clare	Bairn's Coronation Book (1st, 16mo, 120p, 44 fp color, pep)	L: Dent	[1902]	Robinson, Charles	200-300	
Bridgman, Clare	Book of Days for Little Ones (1st, 16mo, 120p, 2-color, pep)	L: Dent	1901	Robinson, Charles	200-300	
Bridgman, Clare	Book of Shops (1st, 16mo, 120p, 2-color, pep)	L: Dent	1902	Robinson, Charles	200-300	
Bridgman, Clare	Shopping Day (1st, 16mo, 120p, color, pep)	Dent/Dutton	1902	Robinson, Charles	150-225	
Bridgman, L.J.	Bridgman's Kewts (1st, sm4to, [94]p, color, pep)	Caldwell	(1902)	Bridgman, L.J.	100-165	
Bridgman, L.J.	Bunny's House (1st, 4to, [40]p, color)	Caldwell	(1904)	Bridgman, L.J.	60-100	
Bridgman, L.J.	Farmer Fox (1st, 4to, [36]p, ibds, p-o, color)	Caldwell	(1900)	Bridgman, L.J.	80-125	
Bridgman, L.J.	Guess (1st, 4to, ibds, [104]p, color, pep)	Caldwell	(1901)	Bridgman, L.J.	100-150	
Bridgman, L.J.	Guess Again (1st, 4to, ibds, [104]p, color)	Caldwell	(1902)	Bridgman, L.J.	100-150	
Bridgman, L.J.	Mother Wild Goose & her Wild Beast Show (1st, lg4to, ibds, [104]p, color)	Caldwell	(1900)	Bridgman, L.J.	225-350	
Bridgman, L.J.	Santa Claus Club (1st, sm8vo, [80]p, color, pep)	Caldwell	(1907)	Bridgman, L.J.	80-130	
Bridgman, L.J.	Seem-So's (1st, 8vo, p-o, [80]p, silhouettes, col frn)	Caldwell	(1906)	Bridgman, L.J.	75-140	*
Brier, Howard M.	Backboard Magic (1st {std}, 8vo, 275p, fp b/w, DJ/2.50)	Random	(1949)	Barnum, Jay H.	40-65	
Briggs, Barbara	Licorice (1st, 4to, [24]p, ibds, 2-color, pep, DJ/2.00)	Aladdin	(1949)	Briggs, Barbara	50-80	
Briggs, Raymond	Fee-Fi-Fo-Fum (1st AM, lg ob8vo, 40p, 2-color, DJ/3.00)	Coward	1964	Briggs, Raymond	60-85	
Briggs, Raymond	Jim & the Beanstalk (1st, 4to, [40]p, color, DJ)	L: Hamilton	1970	Briggs, Raymond	50-80	*
Briggs, Raymond	Mother Goose Treasury (1st AM, 4to, gilt, 217p, color, DJ/8.95, KGM)	Coward	(1966)	Briggs, Raymond	60-90	
Briggs, Raymond	Ring-a-Ring O'Roses (1st AM, sm4to, 48p, fp color, DJ/3.00)	Coward	(1962)	Briggs, Raymond	60-90	
Briggs, Raymond	White Land (1st AM {std}, sm ob4to, 48p, 2-color, DJ/3.00)	Coward	1963	Briggs, Raymond	30-50	*
Brigham, S.J.	Under Blue Skies (4to, bds, unpag)	Worthington	1886	(Chromos)	100-170	
Bright, A.D.	Fortunate Princeling (1st, 8vo, 68p, color)	L: Duckworth	1909	Rountree, Harry	50-80	
Bright, Robert	Georgie and the Magician (1st {std}, ob4to, ibds, 46p, 1-color, DJ/3.25)	Doubleday	(1966)	Bright, Robert	45-70	
Bright, Robert	Georgie to the Rescue (1st {std}, ob4to, [32]p, 2-color, DJ/1.75)	Doubleday	1956	Bright, Robert	45-70	
Bright, Robert	Georgie's Halloween (1st {std}, ob4to, ibds, [32]p, color, DJ/2.00)	Doubleday	1958	Bright, Robert	45-70	
Bright, Robert	Hurrah for Freddie! (1st {std}, ob8vo, [39]p, 1-color, cep, DJ/2.00)	Doubleday	1953	Bright, Robert	30-50	
Bright, Robert	I Like Red (1st {std}, sq8vo, ipcb, [30]p, 2-color, pep, DJ/1.50)	Doubleday	1955	Bright, Robert	30-50	
Bright, Robert	Me & the Bears (1st {std}, ob8vo, ibds, [34]p, fp 1-color, cep, DJ/1.25)	Doubleday	1951	Bright, Robert	30-50	
Bright, Robert	Miss Pattie (1st {std}, sm4to, ipcb, unpag, 2-color, pep, DJ/2.00)	Doubleday	1954	Bright, Robert	30-50	
Bright, Robert	My Red Umbrella (1st, 12mo, [32]p, 1-color, DJ/2.00)	Wm. Morrow	1959	Bright, Robert	25-40	
Bright, Robert	Richard Brown & Dragon (1st {std}, 8vo, 81p, ipcb, 1-color, cep, DJ/2.00)	Doubleday	(1952)	Bright, Robert	25-40	
Bright, Robert	Travels of Ching (1st, ob8vo, ipcb, [65]p, 1-color, pep, DJ/1.25)	W.R. Scott	1943	Bright, Robert	40-65	
Brill, George R.	Rhymes of the Golden Age (1st, lg8vo, 121p, gilt, p-o, pep, 12 color)	Stern	1908	Brill, George R.	70-125	*
Brine, Mary D.	Funnyland Boys (1st, sm8vo, 54p, ipcb, col frn, b/w)	Drexel Biddle	1903	Unknown	70-120	*
Brine, Mary D.	Mother & Baby (1st, 4to, uncut, 48p, 14pl)	R.H. Russell	1901	Various	180-240	*
Brine, Mary D.	Poor Sally/her Christmas (1st, 8vo, 182p, b/w pl)	Dutton	1898	Upton, Florence	150-225	
Brinig, Myron	Flutter of an Eyelid (1st, 12mo, 310p)	Farrar/Rinehart	1933	Ward, Lynd	40-65	R
Brininstool, E.A.	Trail Dust of a Maverick (1st, sm8vo, p-o, 249p)	Dodd	1914	(Photos)	35-60	
Brink, Carol R.	All Over Town (1st, 8vo, 291p, b/w, pep, DJ/2.00)	Macmillan	1939	Bayley, Dorothy	30-45	
Brink, Carol R.	Andy Buckram's Tin Men (1st, 8vo, 192p, yellow cl, b/w, DJ/3.50)	Viking	(1966)	Mars, Witold T.	30-45	
Brink, Carol R.	Anything Can Happen on a River (1st, sm8vo, 224p, blue cl, b/w, DJ/1.75)	Macmillan	1934	Berger, William M.	25-40	
Brink, Carol R.	Baby Island (1st, sm8vo, 172p, pep, 6cp, DJ/2.00)	Macmillan	1937	Sewell, Helen	80-125	
Brink, Carol R.	Caddie Woodlawn (1st, 8vo, 270p, b/w, cep, DJ/2.00, NM)	Macmillan	1935	Seredy, Kate	80-120	R
Brink, Carol R.	Family Grandstand (1st, 8vo, 208p, b/w, pep, DJ/2.50)	Viking	1952	Porter, Jean M.	25-45	*
Brink, Carol R.	Family Sabbatical (1st, 8vo, 256p, b/w, DJ/2.75)	Viking	1956	Foster, Susan	25-40	*
Brink, Carol R.	Highly Trained Dogs/Professor Pettit (1st {std}, 8vo, 139p, b/w, DJ/2.50)	Macmillan	(1953)	Henneberger, Rbt.	20-35	
Brink, Carol R.	Lad with a Whistle (1st, 8vo, 235p, fp b/w, pep, DJ/2.00)	Macmillan	1941	Ball, Robert	30-50	
Brink, Carol R.	Mademoiselle Misfortune (1st, 8vo, 267p, 12 fp b/w, cep, DJ/2.00)	Macmillan	1936	Seredy, Kate	80-120	
Brink, Carol R.	Magical Melons (1st, 8vo, 193p, fp b/w, cep, DJ/2.00)	Macmillan	1944	Davis, Marguerite	70-100	
Brink, Carol R.	Pink Motel (1st {std}, 8vo, 182p, pink cl, b/w, DJ/2.75)	Macmillan	1959	Greenwald, Sheila	20-35	*
Brink, Carol R.	Two are Better than One (1st {std}, 8vo, 180p, b/w, DJ/4.50)	Macmillan	(1968)	Rocker, Fermin	25-45	
Brink, Carol R.	Winter Cottage (1st {std}, 8vo, 178p, b/w, DJ/4.50)	Macmillan	(1968)	Rocker, Fermin	20-35	
Brisley, Joyce L.	Further Doings of Milly-Molly-Mandy (1st AM, 12mo, 95p, color)	L: Harrap	1932	Brisley, Joyce L.	30-50	
Brisley, Joyce L.	Milly-Molly-Mandy Stories (1st, 12mo, 95p, col frn)	L: Harrap	1928	Brisley, Joyce L.	50-85	*
Britton, Fay A.	Shakespearian Fairy Tales (1st, 8vo, ibds, 143p, 8cp)	Reilly/Britton	(1907)	Wilson, Clara P.	60-90	
Bro, Marguerite	How the Mouse Deer Became King (1st {std}, lg8vo, 127p, bds, b/w, DJ/2.95)	Doubleday	(1966)	Low, Joseph	25-40	
Bro, Marguerite	Su-Mei's Golden Year (1st {std}, 8vo, 246p, beige cl, b/w, DJ/2.50)	Doubleday	1950	Wiese, Kurt	30-50	
Bro, Marguerite	Three & Domingo (1st {std}, sm8vo, 127p, b/w, DJ/2.00)	Doubleday	1953	Weisgard, Leonard	30-50	
Broadbent, Helen	Sing-A-Song (1st, ob folio, ibds, unpag, 8cp)	L: M. Goshen	1912	Dowdall, N.	150-220	*
Broadwood, Lucy	English Nursery Rhymes (lg4to, 63p, gilt, p-o, color, pep)	L: A&C Black	(1916)	Wheeler, Dorothy M.	125-180	
Broadwood, Lucy	Songs from Alice in Wonderland (4to, blue/gilt, 48p, p-o, 12 ticp)	L: A&C Black	1921	Folkard, Charles	140-200	

AUTHOR	TITLE	PUBLISHER	DATE	ARTIST	PRICE	LC
Brock, Betty	No Flying in the House (1st, 8vo, 139p, b/w, DJ/3.95)	Harper	(1970)	Tripp, Wallace	40-65	
Brock, Emma	At Midsummer Time (1st {std}, 8vo, 80p, color, pep, DJ/1.50)	Knopf	1940	Brock, Emma	25-40	*
Brock, Emma	Ballet for Mary (1st {std}, sm8vo, 79p, color, pep, DJ/2.50)	Knopf	1954	Brock, Emma	25-40	
Brock, Emma	Beppo (1st, sm4to, 79p, p-o, color, DJ/2.00)	Whitman	1936	Brock, Emma	50-80	*
Brock, Emma	Bird's Christmas Tree (1st {std}, ob12mo, [64]p, color, DJ/1.50)	Knopf	1946	Brock, Emma	45-70	*
Brock, Emma	Greedy Goat (1st, sq8vo, [45]p, 1-color, pep)	Knopf	1931	Brock, Emma	50-80	
Brock, Emma	Heedless Susan (1st {std}, lg8vo, blue cl, 169p, b/w, DJ/1.75)	Knopf	1939	Brock, Emma	40-65	
Brock, Emma	Hen that Kept House (1st {std}, ob4to, [40]p, color, dep)	Knopf	1933	Brock, Emma	60-90	
Brock, Emma	Here Comes Kristie (1st {std}, 8vo, 81p, color, pep, DJ/1.75)	Knopf	1942	Brock, Emma	30-50	
Brock, Emma	High in the Mountains (1st, 4to, 78p, p-o, color, pep, DJ/2.00)	Whitman	1938	Brock, Emma	50-80	
Brock, Emma	Kristie and the Colt (1st {std}, 8vo, [88]p, color, DJ/2.00)	Knopf	1949	Brock, Emma	30-50	
Brock, Emma	Little Duchess Anne of Britany (1st {std}, 8vo, 197p, b/w, DJ/2.50)	Knopf	1948	Brock, Emma	40-65	
Brock, Emma	Little Fat Gretchen (1st {std}, ob8vo, [41]p, 1-color)	Knopf	1934	Brock, Emma	30-50	
Brock, Emma	Nobody's Mouse (1st {std}, sq8vo, [40]p, color, pep, DJ/1.75)	Knopf	1938	Brock, Emma	45-70	
Brock, Emma	One Little Indian Boy (1st, sq8vo, [44]p, fp color, pep)	Knopf	1932	Brock, Emma	40-65	
Brock, Emma	Pancakes and the Merry-Go-Round (1st {std}, 8vo, 77p, b/w, DJ/2.50)	Knopf	1960	Brock, Emma	25-40	
Brock, Emma	Patty on Horseback (1st {std}, 8vo, 79p, b/w, DJ/2.50)	Knopf	1959	Brock, Emma	30-50	
Brock, Emma	Pet for Barbi (1st {std}, sm8vo, 50p, b/w, uncut, DJ/1.50)	Knopf	1947	Brock, Emma	25-40	*
Brock, Emma	Pig with a Front Porch... (1st {std}, sq8vo, [43]p, color, pep, DJ/1.75)	Knopf	1937	Brock, Emma	45-70	*
Brock, Emma	Plaid Cow (1st {std}, 8vo, 80p, b/w, DJ/2.50)	Knopf	1961	Brock, Emma	30-50	
Brock, Emma	Present for Auntie (1st {std}, sm8vo, [96]p, b/w, DJ/1.00)	Knopf	1939	Brock, Emma	30-45	
Brock, Emma	Runaway Sardine (1st, 8vo, ibds, [42]p, color, pep)	Knopf	1929	Brock, Emma	30-45	
Brock, Emma	Skipping Island (1st, sm4to, [33]p, color, pep, DJ/2.95)	Knopf	1958	Brock, Emma	30-50	
Brock, Emma	Three Ring Circus (1st {std}, 8vo, 110p, color, pep, DJ/2.50)	Knopf	1950	Brock, Emma	25-40	*
Brock, Emma	To Market! To Market! (1st, ob8vo, ibds, [41]p, color, pep)	Knopf	1930	Brock, Emma	50-80	
Brock, Emma	Topsy-Turvy Family (1st {std}, 8vo, 86p, 8 fp color, pep, DJ/2.00)	Knopf	1943	Brock, Emma	40-65	
Brock, Emma	Uncle Bennie Goes Visiting (1st {std}, 8vo, ibds, 57p, 8cp, pep, DJ/2.00)	Knopf	1944	Brock, Emma	25-40	
Brodsky, Mimi	House at 12 Rose Street (1st, 8vo, 157p, fp b/w, DJ/3.50)	Abelard-Schuman	(1966)	Hodges, David	25-40	*
Bromhall, Winifred	Chipmunk that Went to Church (1st {std}, sm4to, [40]p, color, DJ/2.00)	Knopf	(1952)	Bromhall, Winifred	40-65	*
Bromhall, Winifred	Mary Ann's First Picture (1st {std}, 4to, ibds, [32]p, color, DJ/1.50)	Knopf	(1948)	Bromhall, Winifred	40-65	
Bromhall, Winifred	Middle Matilda (1st, ob4to, [34]p, fp 2-color, pep, DJ/2.95)	Knopf	(1962)	Bromhall, Winifred	30-45	
Bromhall, Winifred	Mrs. Polly's Party (1st, 4to, ibds, [32]p, 3-color, DJ/1.50)	Knopf	(1949)	Bromhall, Winifred	30-40	
Bromhall, Winifred	Princess & Woodcutter's Daughter (1st, ob4to, [33]p, 3-color, pep, DJ/2.00)	Knopf	(1955)	Bromhall, Winifred	30-50	
Bronson, E.B.	Red Blooded (1st, 8vo, 342p, 10pl)	McClurg	1910	Dixon, Maynard	80-120	
Bronson, E.B.	Reminiscences of a Ranchman (1st [revised ed], 8vo, p-o, 369p, 8cp)	McClurg	(1910)	Dixon, Maynard	100-165	
Bronson, Wilfrid S.	Cats (1st {std}, 8vo, [78]p, color, pep, DJ/2.00)	Harcourt	(1950)	Bronson, Wilfrid	40-65	
Bronson, Wilfrid S.	Children of the Sea (1st, lg8vo, 264p, col frn, pep, b/w, DJ/2.00)	Harcourt	(1940)	Bronson, Wilfrid	60-100	
Bronson, Wilfrid S.	Chisel-Tooth Tribe (1st, 8vo, 200p, 4cp, b/w, pep, DJ/2.50)	Harcourt	(1939)	Bronson, Wilfrid	30-45	
Bronson, Wilfrid S.	Coyotes (1st, 8vo, [63]p, yellow cl, b/w, DJ/1.75)	Harcourt	(1946)	Bronson, Wilfrid	25-45	
Bronson, Wilfrid S.	Fingerfins (1st, 8vo, blue cl, 54p, 2-color)	Macmillan	1930	Bronson, Wilfrid	25-45	
Bronson, Wilfrid S.	Freedom and Plenty (1st {std}, 8vo, 123p, b/w, DJ/2.95)	Harcourt	1953	Bronson, Wilfrid	25-40	
Bronson, Wilfrid S.	Paddlewings (1st, 8vo, 106p, 4 fp color, b/w, cep)	Macmillan	1931	Bronson, Wilfrid	30-50	
Bronson, Wilfrid S.	Pinto's Journey (1st, 8vo, 55p, 4 fp 2-color, pep, DJ/2.50)	J. Messner	1948	Bronson, Wilfrid	30-50	
Bronson, Wilfrid S.	Pollwiggle's Progress (1st, sq8vo, 122p, frn by...)	Macmillan	1932	Bronson, Wilfrid	30-50	
Bronson, Wilfrid S.	Starlings (1st, sq8vo, [78]p, b/w, pep, DJ/2.00)	Harcourt	(1948)	Bronson, Wilfrid	25-40	
Bronson, Wilfrid S.	Water People (1st, lg8vo, 119p, color, pep, DJ/1.00)	Wise-Parlow	(1935)	Bronson, Wilfrid	30-50	
Bronson, Wilfrid S.	Wonder World of Ants (1st, 8vo, 87p, color, pep, DJ/1.50)	Harcourt	(1937)	Bronson, Wilfrid	30-50	
Bronte, Anne	Tenant of Wildfell Hall... (1st AM, 12mo, 548p, green/gilt, 12 color)	Dutton	1922	Dulac, Edmund	60-90	
Bronte, Charlotte	Jane Eyre (1st, 8vo, 576p, pep, fp 1-color, DJ/3.00)	Oxford U. Pr.	(1938)	Sewell, Helen	45-70	
Bronte, Charlotte	Shirley (1st, 8vo, 2 volumes, teg)	L: Dent	1905	Dulac, Edmund	130-200	
Bronte, Emily J.	Wuthering Heights (1st {std}, 4to, 325p, 12pl, DJ)	Random	1931	Leighton, Clare	70-100	
Bronte, Emily J.	Wuthering Heights (1st, sm4to, 213p, ibds, b/w, DJ/5.00)	Random	1943	Eichenberg, Fritz	30-50	
Brook, Arthur W.	Witch's Hollow (1st, 8vo, 211p, 8cp)	L: A&C Black	1920	Folkard, Charles	140-180	*
Brook, Arthur W.	Witch's Hollow (1st AM, 8vo, 211p, 8cp)	Stokes	1921	Folkard, Charles	90-140	
Brooke, L. Leslie	Johnny Crow's Garden (1st, 8vo, ibds, 48p, p-o, 8cp)	L: Warne	1903	Brooke, L. Leslie	125-200	R
Brooke, L. Leslie	Johnny Crow's New Garden (1st, 8vo, [48]p, blue bds, p-o, 8cp, pep)	L: Warne	1935	Brooke, L. Leslie	80-130	
Brooke, L. Leslie	Johnny Crow's Party (1st, sq8vo, green bds, p-o, [48]p, 8cp)	L: Warne	1907	Brooke, L. Leslie	130-200	
Brooke, L. Leslie	Ring O' Roses (lg8vo, [59]p, blue/gilt, pep, 32cp)	L: Warne	[1901]	Brooke, L. Leslie	60-100	
Brooke, L. Leslie	Tailor & the Crow (1st, sq8vo, gilt, p-o, 40p, 6cp, pep)	L: Warne	(1911)	Brooke, L. Leslie	100-175	
Brookfield, Mrs. A.	Aesop's Fables for Little Readers (1st, 4to, red/gilt, 71p, b/w)	L: T.F. Unwin	[1888]	Ford, H.J.	200-300	
Brooks, Charles S.	Journeys to Baghdad (1st, 8vo, bds, p-o, 100p, teg, 27 woodcuts)	Yale U. Press	1915	Lewis, Allen	40-60	*
Brooks, Edward	Story of King Arthur (1st AM, 12mo, 383p, 13pl)	Penn	1900	Beardsley, Aubrey	90-160	*
Brooks, Elbridge S.	Master of Strong Hearts (1st, 8vo, 314p, 10pl)	Dutton	1898	Cary, William M.	35-60	
Brooks, Elbridge S.	Storied Holidays (1st, 8vo, 271p, gilt)	D. Lothrop Co.	[1887]	Pyle, Howard	170-220	
Brooks, Eva C.	Francisco... (1st, sm8vo, 152p, 6pl)	L.C. Page	1910	Goss, John	30-50	*
Brooks, Gwendolyn	Bronzeville Boys & Girls (1st, 8vo, grey cl, 40p, b/w, cep, DJ/2.00)	Harper	(1956)	Solbert, Ronni	100-160	R
Brooks, Noah	Boy Emigrants (1st, lg8vo, brown cl, 381p, teg, 10cp, pep, SC)	Scribner	1914	Dunn, Harvey T.	80-130	
Brooks, Walter	Clockwork Twin (1st {std}, 8vo, 241p, 7 fp b/w, pep, DJ/2.00)	Knopf	1937	Wiese, Kurt	250-400	
Brooks, Walter	Collected Poems of Freddy the Pig (1st {std}, 8vo, 81p, b/w, DJ/2.50)	Knopf	(1953)	Wiese, Kurt	180-250	*
Brooks, Walter	Ernestine Takes Over (1st, sm8vo, 265p, b/w, DJ/2.00)	Wm. Morrow	1935	Roese, Herbert	80-135	
Brooks, Walter	Freddy and Mr. Camphor (1st {std}, 8vo, 244p, b/w, pep, DJ/2.50)	Knopf	1944	Wiese, Kurt	200-300	
Brooks, Walter	Freddy and Simon the Dictator (1st {std}, 8vo, 244p, b/w, DJ/3.00)	Knopf	1956	Wiese, Kurt	160-225	
Brooks, Walter	Freddy and the Baseball Team from Mars (1st {std}, 8vo 241p, b/w, DJ/3.00)	Knopf	1955	Wiese, Kurt	150-200	
Brooks, Walter	Freddy and the Bean Home News (1st {std}, sm8vo, 230p, fp b/w, DJ/2.50)	Knopf	1943	Wiese, Kurt	200-300	
Brooks, Walter	Freddy and the Flying Saucer Plans (1st {std}, 8vo, 243p, b/w, DJ/3.00)	Knopf	1957	Wiese, Kurt	200-300	
Brooks, Walter	Freddy and the Ignoramus (1st {std}, sm8vo, 286p, b/w, DJ/3.00)	Knopf	1941	Wiese, Kurt	250-350	
Brooks, Walter	Freddy and the Men from Mars (1st {std}, 8vo, 246p, pep, b/w, DJ/3.00)	Knopf	1954	Wiese, Kurt	200-300	
Brooks, Walter	Freddy and the Perilous Adventure (1st {std}, 8vo, 245p, b/w, DJ/2.00)	Knopf	1942	Wiese, Kurt	200-300	

AUTHOR	TITLE	PUBLISHER	DATE	ARTIST	PRICE	LC
Brooks, Walter	Freddy and the Popinjay (1st {std}, sm8vo, 244p, red cl, b/w, DJ/2.50)	Knopf	1945	Wiese, Kurt	200-300	
Brooks, Walter	Freddy and the Spaceship (1st {std}, sm8vo, 262p, b/w, pep, DJ/3.00)	Knopf	1953	Wiese, Kurt	200-300	
Brooks, Walter	Freddy Goes Camping (1st {std}, 8vo, 258p, b/w, DJ/2.50)	Knopf	1948	Wiese, Kurt	200-300	
Brooks, Walter	Freddy Goes to Florida (1st, 8vo, 196p, b/w, DJ/2.50)	Knopf	1949	Wiese, Kurt	200-300	
Brooks, Walter	Freddy Goes to the North Pole (1st {std}, 8vo, 306p, b/w, DJ/2.50)	Knopf	1951	Wiese, Kurt	200-300	
Brooks, Walter	Freddy Plays Football (1st {std}, 8vo, 265p, grey cl, b/w, DJ/2.50)	Knopf	1949	Wiese, Kurt	200-300	
Brooks, Walter	Freddy Rides Again (1st {std}, 8vo, 240p, b/w, DJ/2.50)	Knopf	1951	Wiese, Kurt	200-300	
Brooks, Walter	Freddy the Cowboy (1st {std}, sm8vo, 233p, red cl, b/w, DJ/2.50)	Knopf	1950	Wiese, Kurt	200-300	
Brooks, Walter	Freddy the Detective (1st {std}, 8vo, 264p, b/w, pep)	Knopf	1932	Wiese, Kurt	150-220	
Brooks, Walter	Freddy the Magician (1st {std}, 8vo, red cl, 258p, b/w, DJ/2.50)	Knopf	1947	Wiese, Kurt	200-300	
Brooks, Walter	Freddy the Pied Piper (1st {std}, 8vo, 253p, b/w, DJ/2.50)	Knopf	1946	Wiese, Kurt	200-300	
Brooks, Walter	Freddy the Pilot (1st {std}, sm8vo, 247p, b/w, pep, DJ/3.00)	Knopf	1952	Wiese, Kurt	200-300	
Brooks, Walter	Freddy the Politician (1st, 8vo, 252p, red cl, fp b/w, pep, DJ/2.50)	Knopf	1948	Wiese, Kurt	200-300	
Brooks, Walter	Freddy's Cousin Weedly (1st {std}, sm8vo, 283p, b/w, pep, DJ/2.00)	Knopf	1940	Wiese, Kurt	200-300	
Brooks, Walter	Henry's Dog Henry (1st, 8vo, [30]p, fp 1-color, cep, DJ/2.95)	Knopf	(1965)	Watson, Aldren A.	50-85	
Brooks, Walter	Jimmy Takes Vanishing Lessons (1st, lg8vo, [28]p, 1-color, cep, DJ/2.95)	Knopf	(1965)	Bolognese, Don	50-80	
Brooks, Walter	More To and Again (1st, 8vo, 306p, col frn, 8 fp b/w, DJ/2.00)	Knopf	1930	Wiese, Kurt	250-350	
Brooks, Walter	Story of Freginald (1st {std}, lg8vo, 249p, pep, 10 fp b/w, DJ/2.00)	Knopf	1936	Wiese, Kurt	400-600	
Brooks, Walter	To and Again (1st, sm8vo, 196p, 10 fp b/w, pep)	Knopf	1927	Best-Maugard, A.	160-240	
Brooks, Walter	Wiggins for President (1st {std}, 8vo, 252p, yellow cl, fp b/w, DJ/2.00)	Knopf	1939	Wiese, Kurt	200-300	
Brough, James	Dog Who Lives at the Waldorf (1st {std}, 8vo, gold bds, 68p, b/w, DJ)	Little/Brown	(1964)	Vasiliu, Mircea	30-45	
Broughton, Philip	Pandy (1st, 12mo, ibds, 40p, 5 fp color, pep)	Volland	(1930)	Barney, Maginel W.	60-90	
Broun, Heywood	A Shepherd (1st, 8vo, [32]p, color, DJ/4.95)	Prentice-Hall	(1967)	Riswold, Gilbert	25-40	*
Broun, Heywood	Fifty-First Dragon (1st, 12mo, [48]p, fp 1-color, cep, DJ/3.95)	Prentice-Hall	(1968)	Emberley, Ed	30-45	
Brown, Abbie F.	Book of Saints & Friendly Beasts (1st, 12mo, tan cl, 225p, 8pl)	Houghton	1900	Cory, Fanny	75-100	
Brown, Abbie F.	Christmas Angel (1st, sm8vo, ibds, 82p, 6pl)	Houghton	1910	Birch, Reginald	25-45	
Brown, Abbie F.	Curious Book of Birds (1st, 8vo, gilt, 191p, 8pl)	Houghton	1903	Smith, E. Boyd	60-100	
Brown, Abbie F.	Fresh Posies (1st, sq8vo, 199p, p-o, 4cp)	Houghton	1908	Upjohn, Anna M.	40-60	*
Brown, Abbie F.	In the Days of Giants (1st, 12mo, gilt, 259p, 6pl)	Houghton	1902	Smith, E. Boyd	100-160	R
Brown, Abbie F.	John of the Woods (1st, sm8vo, 189p, 15pl)	Houghton	1909	Smith, E. Boyd	50-80	
Brown, Abbie F.	Kisington Town (1st, 8vo, p-o, 213p, col frn, 5pl)	Houghton	1915	Winckler, Ruby	30-50	*
Brown, Abbie F.	Lonesomest Doll (1st, sm8vo, ibds, 76p, 4pl)	Houghton	1901	Pollak, E.	35-60	*
Brown, Abbie F.	Lonesomest Doll (1st, 8vo, 81p, tan cl, 4pl)	Houghton	(1928)	Rackham, Arthur	250-400	
Brown, Abbie F.	Pocket Full of Posies (1st, 8vo, 169p, tan cl, 5pl)	Houghton	1902	Cory, Fanny	35-60	
Brown, Abbie F.	Star Jewels... (1st, 8vo, green/gilt, 133p, 5pl)	Houghton	1905	Brown, Ethel C.	25-40	*
Brown, Abbie F.	Tales of the Red Children (1st, sm8vo, 125p, tan cl, fp b/w)	Appleton	1909	Unknown	40-65	
Brown, Abbie F.	Under the Rowan Tree (1st, 8vo, p-o, 189p, col frn, pep)	Houghton	1926	Day, Maurice	25-45	*
Brown, Alice	Day of His Youth (1st, 12mo, green/gilt, 143p)	Houghton	1897	Rogers, Bruce	50-80	R
Brown, Alice	Meadow Grass (1st, 12mo, olive cl, 315p, cvr by...)	Copeland & Day	1895	Rhead, Louis	70-125	
Brown, Alice	Merrylinks (1st, ob4to, ipcb, p-o, [91]p, fp b/w)	McClure	1903	Clarke, Louise	80-120	R
Brown, Alice	One-Footed Fairy (1st, 8vo, p-o, yellow cl, 182p, 12pl)	Houghton	1911	Various	60-100	*
Brown, Alice	Secret of the Clan (1st, sm8vo, blue/gilt, 314p, 12pl)	Macmillan	1912	Smith, Sarah K.	30-50	
Brown, Alice	Story of Thyrza (1st, 8vo, gilt, 326p, col frn)	Houghton	1909	Stephens, Alice B.	30-50	
Brown, Alice	Tiverton Tales (1st, 12mo, green/gilt, 339p, designs by..)	Houghton	1899	Rogers, Bruce	40-65	
Brown, Anna R.	Wine-Press (1st, 8vo, 390p, rust cl, cvr by...)	Appleton	1905	Armstrong, Margaret	35-60	*
Brown, Annie G.	Fireside Battles (1st, 8vo, teg, 327p, 8pl)	Laird & Lee	1900	Leyendecker, J.C.	75-100	*
Brown, Beatrice B.	Paris Pair (1st, ob8vo, 59p, color)	Dutton	(1923)	Brown, Beatrice B.	40-65	
Brown, Beatrice C.	Jonathan Bing (1st, sq12mo, ipcb, [48]p, fp b/w, dep, DJ/0.75)	Oxford U. Pr.	(1936)	Doane, Pelagie	60-90	*
Brown, Caroline V.	Bold Robin (1st, sm8vo, gilt, 200p, uncut, teg, p-o, 7cp)	Dutton	(1905)	Bennett, F.I.	35-60	*
Brown, Dr. John	Jeems the Door Keeper (1st, 16mo, teg, uncut, 105p, 8 ticp)	L: Foulis	1912	MacGoun, H.C.P.	60-80	
Brown, Dr. John	Little Book of Children (12mo, 57p, ibds, teg, gilt, 8cp)	L: Foulis	1923	MacGoun, H.C.P.	35-60	*
Brown, Edna	Silver Bear (1st, 12mo, 166p, cp, pep)	Lothrop, Lee	(1921)	Inglis, Antoinette	25-45	*
Brown, Elijah P.	Ciderville Folks (1st, lg8vo, tan/gilt, 496p, b/w)	Date Pub. Co.	(1898)	Beard, Frank	50-80	*
Brown, Elinor	Little Story Book (1st, 8vo, 30p, color, pep)	Oxford U. Pr.	1940	Norcross, Grace	30-50	
Brown, Frieda	Last Hurdle (1st {std}, 8vo, 202p, b/w, DJ/2.50)	Crowell	(1953)	Spier, Peter E.	30-45	
Brown, Gladys	Two-Bow Bill (1st, 8vo, 46p, blue cl, color, pep, DJ/2.00)	Wm. Morrow	1955	Barnum, Jay H.	40-65	
Brown, Jeanette	Manuel, Little Boy of Mexico (1st, 24mo, ibds, 61p, fp 2-color)	Friendship Pr.	(1951)	Martinez, Jean	60-90	R*
Brown, Jeanette	Ronnie's Wish (1st, sq8vo, 32p, color, DJ/1.25)	Friendship Pr.	1954	Martinez, Jean	30-45	
Brown, Jeanette	Wishes Come True (1st, 8vo, 128p, color, DJ/1.50)	Friendship Pr.	(1948)	Wireman, Katharine	40-65	*
Brown, Jeff	Flat Stanley (1st, 8vo, [44]p, color, DJ/2.50)	Harper	1964	Ungerer, Tomi	35-50	
Brown, John	Little Book of Dogs (1st, 8vo, 91p, gilt, teg, 8 ticp)	L: Foulis	(1911)	Park, Carton M.	60-90	
Brown, Judith	Max & the Truffle Pig (1st, 8vo, 46p, 2-color, pep, DJ/2.50)	Abingdon Press	(1963)	Brown, Judith	20-35	
Brown, Julia	Enchanted Peacock (1st, 4to, p-o, 4cp, 4pl)	Rand/McNally	(1911)	Perkins, Lucy F.	75-100	
Brown, Julia	Mermaid's Gift (1st, 8vo, blue/gilt, p-o, 168p, 8cp)	Rand/McNally	(1912)	Enright, Maginel W.	120-170	
Brown, Katharine H.	Hallowell Partnership (1st, sm8vo, 241p, 4pl)	Scribner	1912	Peck, Clara E.	25-40	*
Brown, Katharine H.	White Roses (1st, sm8vo, 333p, b/w)	Duffield	1910	Flagg, James M.	30-50	
Brown, Kenneth	Putter Perkins (1st, 12mo, green cl, teg, 121p, 10pl)	Houghton	1923	Kemble, Edward W.	50-80	
Brown, Maggie	Surprising Adventures of Tuppy & Tue (1st, sm8vo, gilt, 190p, 4cp)	L: Cassell	1904	Rackham, Arthur	400-600	
Brown, Marcia	Backbone of the King (1st, 8vo, yellow cl, 180p, 1-color, DJ/4.50)	Scribner	(1966)	Brown, Marcia	40-65	
Brown, Marcia	Felice (1st, sm4to, [32]p, color, pep, DJ/2.95)	Scribner	(1958)	Brown, Marcia	80-125	R
Brown, Marcia	Henry Fisherman (1st, sm ob4to, [32]p, color, pep, DJ/2.00, CH)	Scribner	1949	Brown, Marcia	100-165	
Brown, Marcia	How, Hippo (1st, sq8vo, [32]p, fp color, pep, DJ/3.50)	Scribner	(1969)	Brown, Marcia	60-100	R
Brown, Marcia	Little Carousel (1st {1st Bk}, sm4to, [32]p, ipcb, color, DJ/2.00)	Scribner	1946	Brown, Marcia	100-185	
Brown, Marcia	Once a Mouse (1st, lg8vo, [32]p, 3-color, DJ/2.95, CM, NYTBI)	Scribner	(1961)	Brown, Marcia	220-300	R
Brown, Marcia	Peter Piper's Alphabet (1st, ob4to, ibds, [32]p, color, pep, DJ/2.95)	Scribner	(1959)	Brown, Marcia	100-165	
Brown, Marcia	Skipper John's Cook (1st, sm4to, unpag, color, pep, DJ/2.00, CH)	Scribner	1951	Brown, Marcia	100-165	
Brown, Marcia	Stone Soup (1st, sm4to, [48]p, 2-color, pep, DJ/2.00, CH)	Scribner	1947	Brown, Marcia	100-165	
Brown, Marcia	Tamarindo! (1st, sm4to, tan cl, [32]p, color, DJ/2.95)	Scribner	(1960)	Brown, Marcia	60-90	

AUTHOR	TITLE	PUBLISHER	DATE	ARTIST	PRICE	LC
Brown, Marcia	The Neighbors (1st, 4to, [32]p, fp 3-color, pep, DJ)	Scribner	(1967)	Brown, Marcia	50-85	
Brown, Margaret W.	Baby Animals (1st, lg8vo, ipcb, [48]p, color, pep, DJ/0.50)	Random	(1941)	Cameron, Mary	50-80	
Brown, Margaret W.	Bad Little Duckhunter (1st, sm ob4to, ipcb, [30]p, color, pep, DJ/1.50)	W.R. Scott	(1947)	Hurd, Clement	80-130	
Brown, Margaret W.	Big Red Barn (1st, ob8vo, unpag, 2-color, pep, DJ/2.25)	W.R. Scott	1956	Hartman, Rosella	60-100	
Brown, Margaret W.	Black and White (1st, 4to, ibds, [32]p, fp b/w, DJ/1.25)	Harper	1944	Shaw, Charles G.	100-165	
Brown, Margaret W.	Bumble Bugs & Elephants (1st, lg sq8vo, spiral ibds, [17]p, color)	W.R. Scott	1938	Hurd, Clement	100-160	
Brown, Margaret W.	Child's Good Morning (1st, sq4to, ibds, [32]p, fp color, DJ/2.00)	W.R. Scott	1952	Charlot, Jean	170-250	
Brown, Margaret W.	Child's Good Night Book (1st, 12mo, ibds, [24]p, color, DJ/1.00, CH)	W.R. Scott	1943	Charlot, Jean	120-200	
Brown, Margaret W.	Children's Year (1st {std}, ob12mo, [26]p, ipcb, pep, color)	Harper	1937	Rojankovsky, Feodor	70-100	
Brown, Margaret W.	Christmas in the Barn (1st, ob8vo, red cl, [32]p, color, pep, DJ/1.75)	Crowell	(1952)	Cooney, Barbara	120-180	
Brown, Margaret W.	Country Noisy Book (1st, 8vo, [44]p, bds, color, pep, DJ/1.25)	W.R. Scott	(1940)	Weisgard, Leonard	140-220	
Brown, Margaret W.	Dark Wood o/t Golden Birds (1st, 8vo, ibds, [58]p, 2-color, pep, DJ/1.75)	Harper	(1950)	Weisgard, Leonard	100-165	R
Brown, Margaret W.	David's Little Indian (1st, 16mo, blue cl, [48]p, fp color, DJ/2.50)	W.R. Scott	(1956)	Charlip, Remy	100-170	R
Brown, Margaret W.	Dead Bird (1st, ob8vo, blue cl, [48]p, color, DJ/2.75)	W.R. Scott	(1958)	Charlip, Remy	120-200	R
Brown, Margaret W.	Diggers (1st, ob8vo, unpag, ibds, color, DJ/1.95)	Harper	(1960)	Hurd, Clement	60-100	
Brown, Margaret W.	Don't Frighten the Lion (1st {std}, sq4to, [31]p, p-o, 1-color, DJ/1.75)	Harper	(1942)	Rey, Hans A.	90-150	
Brown, Margaret W.	Dream Book (1st, sm4to, ibds, [24]p, 2-color, pep, DJ/1.50)	Random	(1950)	Floethe, Richard	70-120	
Brown, Margaret W.	Fables of La Fontaine (1st {std}, 4to, ibds, 39p, color, pep, DJ/1.50)	Harper	(1940)	Helle, Andre	80-125	
Brown, Margaret W.	First Story (1st, lg8vo, [31]p, ibds, 1-color, pep, DJ/1.75)	Harper	(1947)	Simont, Marc	70-100	
Brown, Margaret W.	Fish with a Deep Sea Smile (1st {std}, 8vo, 128p, color, cep, DJ/2.00)	Dutton	(1938)	Rauch, Roberta	70-100	
Brown, Margaret W.	Four Fur Feet (1st, 4to, [48]p, ibds, DJ/3.00)	W.R. Scott	1961	Charlip, Remy	50-70	
Brown, Margaret W.	Fox Eyes (1st, 8vo, [32]p, ibds, color, DJ/1.50)	Pantheon	1951	Charlot, Jean	80-130	
Brown, Margaret W.	Golden Bunny (1st, folio, ibds, [25]p, color, pep, GGB)	Simon/Schuster	(1953)	Weisgard, Leonard	60-90	R
Brown, Margaret W.	Golden Egg Book (1st, folio, ibds, [28]p, color, GGB)	Simon/Schuster	(1947)	Weisgard, Leonard	60-90	
Brown, Margaret W.	Goodnight Moon (1st, ob8vo, ibds, [31]p, color, DJ/1.75)	Harper	1947	Hurd, Clement	90-150	
Brown, Margaret W.	Hidden House (1st {std}, sq8vo, ibds, unpag, color, DJ/2.50)	Henry Holt & Co.	(1953)	Fine, Aaron	60-100	
Brown, Margaret W.	Home for a Bunny (1st {A}, folio, ibds, [28]p, color, GGB)	Simon/Schuster	1956	Williams, Garth	80-130	
Brown, Margaret W.	House of a Hundred Windows (1st, 4to, 32p, ibds, color, DJ/1.75)	Harper	1945	DeVeyrac, Robert	80-130	
Brown, Margaret W.	Important Book (1st, 4to, ibds, [21]p, color, DJ/1.50)	Harper	1949	Weisgard, Leonard	80-140	
Brown, Margaret W.	Indoor Noisy Book (1st, 8vo, ipcb, [44]p, color, DJ/1.25)	W.R. Scott	(1942)	Weisgard, Leonard	120-180	
Brown, Margaret W.	Little Brass Band (1st, ob8vo, [25]p, ipcb, dep, color, DJ/2.00)	Harper	(1955)	Hurd, Clement	60-100	
Brown, Margaret W.	Little Chicken (1st {std}, ob8vo, [39]p, color, DJ/1.50)	Harper	(1943)	Weisgard, Leonard	80-130	
Brown, Margaret W.	Little Cowboy (1st, lg8vo, ipcb, [33]p, color, pep, DJ/1.50)	W.R. Scott	(1948)	Slobodkina, Esphyr	70-125	
Brown, Margaret W.	Little Farmer (1st, sm4to, [38]p, ipcb, color, DJ/1.50)	W.R. Scott	1948	Slobodkina, Esphyr	70-130	
Brown, Margaret W.	Little Fir Tree (1st, ob8vo, [32]p, orange cl, color, dep, DJ/2.00)	Crowell	1954	Cooney, Barbara	70-120	
Brown, Margaret W.	Little Fireman (1st, 8vo, ibds, [34]p, color, cep, p-o, DJ/1.50)	W.R. Scott	(1938)	Slobodkina, Esphyr	90-140	
Brown, Margaret W.	Little Fisherman (1st, lg8vo, ibds, [34]p, color, DJ/1.50)	W.R. Scott	1945	Ipcar, Dahlov	80-120	
Brown, Margaret W.	Little Frightened Tiger (1st {std}, ob4to, ibds, [35]p, color, DJ/2.50)	Doubleday	1953	Weisgard, Leonard	80-140	
Brown, Margaret W.	Little Fur Family (1st {this format}, 8vo, [37]p, b/w, DJ/1.50)	Harper	1946	Williams, Garth	90-150	
Brown, Margaret W.	Little Pig's Picnic... (1st, 8vo, 102p, cloth, color, dep)	D.C. Heath	(1939)	Disney Studios	60-90	
Brown, Margaret W.	Mister Dog (1st, sm8vo, unpag, ibds, color, LGB/#128)	Simon/Schuster	(1952)	Williams, Garth	25-40	
Brown, Margaret W.	My World (1st, ob8vo, [34]p, ibds, color, cep, DJ/1.50)	Harper	1949	Hurd, Clement	60-100	
Brown, Margaret W.	Nibble Nibble (1st, 4to, ibds, [64]p, 1-color, DJ/3.75)	W.R. Scott	(1959)	Weisgard, Leonard	50-85	
Brown, Margaret W.	Night and Day (1st {std}, sm4to, [32]p, color, DJ/1.50)	Harper	(1942)	Weisgard, Leonard	120-180	
Brown, Margaret W.	Noisy Bird Book (1st, 8vo, ibds, [41]p, color, DJ/1.25)	W.R. Scott	1943	Weisgard, Leonard	70-100	
Brown, Margaret W.	Noisy Book (1st, sq8vo, [42]p, ibds, color, pep, DJ/1.25)	W.R. Scott	(1939)	Weisgard, Leonard	80-120	
Brown, Margaret W.	Noon Balloon (1st, lg8vo, ibds, [32]p, fp 3-color, pep, DJ/2.00)	Harper	1952	Weisgard, Leonard	120-200	
Brown, Margaret W.	On Christmas Eve (1st, 4to, [48]p, color, DJ/3.50)	W.R. Scott	(1961)	Montresor, Beni	120-200	
Brown, Margaret W.	Peppermint Family (1st, ob8vo, [32]p, ipcb, fp 2-color, dep, DJ/1.75)	Harper	(1950)	Hurd, Clement	80-125	
Brown, Margaret W.	Polite Penguin (1st {std}, sm4to, green cl, 31p, 2-color, pep, DJ/1.75)	Harper	(1941)	Rey, Hans A.	80-130	
Brown, Margaret W.	Poodle & the Sheep (1st {std}, lg ob8vo, [55]p, ibds, 1-color, pep, DJ/1.50)	Dutton	1941	Weisgard, Leonard	80-130	
Brown, Margaret W.	Punch and Judy (1st, lg8vo, [41]p, color)	W.R. Scott	(1940)	Weisgard, Leonard	60-100	
Brown, Margaret W.	Pussy Willow (1st, lg4to, [25]p, color, pep, GGB)	Simon/Schuster	1951	Weisgard, Leonard	50-90	
Brown, Margaret W.	Pussycat's Christmas (1st, sq12mo, yellow cl, [32]p, color, dep, DJ/1.50)	Crowell	1949	Stone, Helen	120-200	
Brown, Margaret W.	Quiet Noisy Book (1st, 4to, ipcb, [34]p, pep, color, DJ/1.50)	Harper	1950	Weisgard, Leonard	100-165	R
Brown, Margaret W.	Runaway Bunny (1st {std}, ob8vo, [40]p, color, pep, DJ/1.50)	Harper	(1942)	Hurd, Clement	180-240	R
Brown, Margaret W.	Seashore Noisy Book (1st, 8vo, ibds, [42]p, color, pep, DJ/1.25)	W.R. Scott	(1941)	Weisgard, Leonard	70-125	
Brown, Margaret W.	Seven Little Postmen (1st {A}, 8vo, ibds, [28]p, color, LGB/#134)	Simon/Schuster	1952	Gergely, Tibor	30-50	
Brown, Margaret W.	Seven Stories about a Cat Named Sneakers (1st, sm8vo, 144p, b/w, DJ/2.50)	W.R. Scott	(1955)	Charlot, Jean	65-90	
Brown, Margaret W.	SHHhhh... Bang! (1st {std}, sm4to, ipcb, [32]p, fp 2-color, cep, DJ/1.50)	Harper	(1943)	DeVeyrac, Robert	80-130	
Brown, Margaret W.	Sleepy ABC (1st, lg8vo, ibds, unpag, color, dep, DJ/2.00)	Lothrop, Lee	1953	Slobodkina, Esphyr	60-100	
Brown, Margaret W.	Streamlined Pig (1st {std}, ob4to, [32]p, color, pep, DJ/1.75)	Harper	1938	Wiese, Kurt	100-165	
Brown, Margaret W.	Summer Noisy Book (1st, sm4to, [36]p, ibds, color, pep, DJ/1.75)	Harper	1951	Weisgard, Leonard	100-160	
Brown, Margaret W.	The Duck (1st AM {std}, 4to, ibds, [40]p, DJ/2.50, b/w photos by...)	Harper	(1953)	Ylla	80-130	
Brown, Margaret W.	Three Little Animals (1st, lg4to, ibds, [30]p, color, DJ/2.50)	Harper	(1956)	Williams, Garth	120-185	R
Brown, Margaret W.	Train to Timbuctoo (1st, sm8vo, ibds, [28]p, color, LGB/#118)	Simon/Schuster	1951	Seiden, Art	20-30	
Brown, Margaret W.	Two Little Miners (1st, sm8vo, [42]p, ibds, color, LGB/#66)	Simon/Schuster	(1949)	Scarry, Richard	25-40	
Brown, Margaret W.	Two Little Trains (1st, lg sq8vo, ipcb, [32]p, pep, color, DJ/1.75)	W.R. Scott	1949	Charlot, Jean	120-185	R
Brown, Margaret W.	Wait Till the Moon is Full (1st, sm4to, ibds, [32]p, 1-color, DJ/1.75)	Harper	(1948)	Williams, Garth	120-170	
Brown, Margaret W.	Wheel on the Chimney (1st, 4to, [28]p, tan cl, color, DJ/3.00, CH)	Lippincott	(1954)	Gergely, Tibor	120-180	R
Brown, Margaret W.	When the Wind Blew (1st {std}-[1st Bk], lg8vo, [31]p, ibds, color, DJ/1.50)	Harper	1937	Slocum, Rosalie	120-180	
Brown, Margaret W.	Where Have You Been? (1st, ob16mo, [29]p, 1-color, dep, DJ/1.25)	Crowell	1952	Cooney, Barbara	100-165	R
Brown, Margaret W.	Willie's Adventures (1st, sm8vo, grey cl, 68p, b/w, DJ/2.00)	W.R. Scott	(1954)	Johnson, Crockett	70-120	R*
Brown, Margaret W.	Willie's Walk to Grandmama (1st, sm8vo, ipcb, [26]p, color)	W.R. Scott	1944	Bloch, Lucienne	70-100	
Brown, Margaret W.	Winter Noisy Book (1st, 8vo, [42]p, ipcb, pep, color, DJ/1.50)	W.R. Scott	1947	Shaw, Charles G.	70-125	
Brown, Margaret W.	Wonderful House (1st, sm8vo, [42]p, ibds, color, LGB/#76)	Simon/Schuster	1950	Miller, John P.	20-30	
Brown, Margaret W.	Wonderful Story (1st, 4to, ibds, 92p, color, pep, BGB)	Simon/Schuster	(1948)	Miller, John P.	60-90	
Brown, Margaret W.	Young Kangaroo (1st, 8vo, 42p, 2-color, pep, DJ/2.25)	W.R. Scott	(1955)	Shimin, Symeon	100-165	R

AUTHOR	TITLE	PUBLISHER	DATE	ARTIST	PRICE	LC
Brown, Margery	Animals Made by Me (1st, 4to, [32]p, color, DJ)	Putnam	(1970)	Brown, Margery	40-65	*
Brown, Margery	That Ruby (1st, 8vo, 154p, b/w, DJ/3.95)	Reilly/Lee	(1969)	Brown, Margery	30-50	*
Brown, Marion	Alexander: Tale of a Monkey (1st {std}, sm8vo, 193p, pep)	Bobbs-Merrill	(1934)	Wiese, Kurt	30-50	*
Brown, Marion	Silent Storm (1st {A}, 8vo, 250p, fp b/w, DJ/3.25)	Abingdon Press	(1963)	Kredel, Fritz	25-40	*
Brown, Marjorie	Pueblo Playmates (1st, 8vo, 61p, color, pep, DJ/1.50)	Whitman	1938	Nay, Carol	30-50	
Brown, Myra B.	Benjy's Blanket (1st {std}, ob8vo, [57]p, 1-color, pep, DJ/1.95)	F. Watts	(1962)	Marino, Dorothy	50-75	*
Brown, Myra B.	Best Friends (1st, 12mo, [47]p, fp 2-color, DJ/2.95)	Golden Gate	(1967)	Freeman, Don	25-40	*
Brown, Myra B.	Best of Luck (1st, 12mo, [46]p, fp 2-color, DJ/3.25)	Golden Gate	(1969)	Freeman, Don	25-40	*
Brown, Myra B.	First Night Away from Home (1st, ob8vo, [60]p, fp 1-color, pep, DJ/2.50)	F. Watts	(1960)	Marino, Dorothy	30-50	
Brown, Myra B.	Where's Jeremy? (1st, 4to, [48]p, 1-color, cep, DJ/3.75)	Golden Gate	(1968)	Thollander, Earl	30-45	
Brown, Neva K.	Uncle Amos Puppet Show (1st {std}, 8vo, 56p, col frn, b/w, pep)	Doubleday/Doran	1930	Brown, Neva K.	25-45	
Brown, Palmer	Beyond the Pawpaw Trees (1st {1st bk}, 12mo, grey cl, 121p, b/w, DJ/2.50)	Harper	(1954)	Brown, Palmer	150-250	R
Brown, Palmer	Cheerful (1st, 16mo, beige cl, 58p, fp color, DJ/1.50)	Harper	(1957)	Brown, Palmer	150-250	R
Brown, Palmer	Silver Nutmeg (1st, 12mo, green cl, 137p, b/w, DJ/2.50)	Harper	(1956)	Brown, Palmer	150-250	
Brown, Palmer	Something for Christmas (1st, 16mo, white cl, 32p, color, DJ/1.95)	Harper	(1958)	Brown, Palmer	150-250	R
Brown, Pamela	Windmill Family (1st {std}, 8vo, 262p, b/w, DJ/2.75)	Crowell	(1954)	Weil, Lisl	30-45	*
Brown, Paul	Black & White (1st, ob4to, ibds, [62]p, b/w, pep, DJ/1.50)	Scribner	1939	Brown, Paul	150-220	
Brown, Paul	Circus School (1st, 4to, [64]p, color, DJ/2.00)	Scribner	1946	Brown, Paul	125-200	
Brown, Paul	Crazy Quilt (1st, ob4to, ipcb, [120]p, fp b/w, pep)	Scribner	1934	Brown, Paul	200-300	
Brown, Paul	Daffy Taffy (1st, 4to, [32]p, color, cep, DJ/2.50)	Scribner	1955	Brown, Paul	100-145	
Brown, Paul	Draw Horses: It's Fun & Easy (1st, 8vo, ibds, 60p, b/w, DJ/2.00)	Scribner	1949	Brown, Paul	100-165	
Brown, Paul	Fire! The Mascot (1st, 4to, red cl, [96]p, b/w, DJ/2.00)	Scribner	1939	Brown, Paul	100-160	
Brown, Paul	Hi Guy the Cinderella Horse (1st, lg8vo, [62]p, b/w, DJ/2.00)	Scribner	(1944)	Brown, Paul	100-165	
Brown, Paul	Merrylegs (1st, sm8vo, [64]p, grey cl, 1-color, pep, DJ/2.00)	Scribner	1946	Brown, Paul	80-120	
Brown, Paul	Mick & Mac (1st, 4to, ibds, [96]p, b/w, pep)	Scribner	1937	Brown, Paul	120-185	
Brown, Paul	No Trouble at All (1st, 8vo, 126p, b/w, DJ/1.50)	Scribner	1940	Brown, Paul	70-100	
Brown, Paul	Piper's Pony (1st, ob4to, ipcb, [120]p, fp b/w, pep)	Scribner	1935	Brown, Paul	150-250	
Brown, Paul	Polo (1st, lg8vo, ibds, 88p, b/w, DJ/2.00)	Scribner	1949	Brown, Paul	80-130	
Brown, Paul	Pony Farm (1st, 8vo, [92]p, ibds, b/w, pep, DJ/2.00)	Scribner	(1948)	Brown, Paul	100-180	
Brown, Paul	Pony School (1st, 8vo, [93]p, ibds, b/w, pep, DJ/2.00)	Scribner	(1950)	Brown, Paul	80-125	
Brown, Paul	Puff Ball (1st, 12mo, blue cl, [32]p, color, cep, DJ/1.00)	Scribner	1942	Brown, Paul	80-120	
Brown, Paul	Silver Heels (1st, 8vo, [125]p, b/w, DJ/2.50)	Scribner	(1951)	Brown, Paul	60-100	
Brown, Paul	Sparkie & Puff Ball (1st, 4to, [32]p, red cl, color, DJ/2.50)	Scribner	1954	Brown, Paul	70-100	
Brown, Paul	Three Rings: A Circus Book (1st, 4to, ibds, [76]p, color, pep, DJ/2.00)	Scribner	1938	Brown, Paul	160-250	
Brown, Paul	War Paint: An Indian Pony (1st, 4to, [96]p, b/w, DJ/2.00)	Scribner	1936	Brown, Paul	70-120	
Brown, Rose	Two Children of Brazil (1st {std}, 8vo, 229p, b/w, pep, DJ/2.00)	Lippincott	(1940)	Sperry, Armstrong	30-45	
Brown, Slater	Talking Skyscraper (1st, 4to, ibds, 48p, fp color, DJ/2.00)	Hyperion Press	(1945)	Fabres, Oscar	45-70	
Brown, Vincent	My Brother (1st, 12mo, 176p, beige cl, frn by...)	L: John Lane	1896	Beardsley, Aubrey	100-165	
Browne, Edgar G.	Magic Whistle (1st, lg8vo, 221p, ibds, p-o, 8cp)	Dodd	1920	Anderson, Florence	125-200	
Browne, Edgar G.	Nutcracker and Mouse King (1st, lg8vo, pink bds, 92p, p-o, 4cp)	Dodd	1916	Anderson, Florence	70-100	
Browne, Edgar G.	Puck's Broom (1st AM, sm8vo, 237p, red/gilt, 4cp)	Moffat	1923	Nixon, Kathleen I.	50-85	*
Browne, Frances	Granny's Wonderful Chair (4to, 95p, 15cp)	Dutton	1891	Lucas, Marie S.	80-130	*
Browne, Frances	Granny's Wonderful Chair (1st, sm8vo, gilt, 213p, 8cp)	McClure	1904	Truman, Edith	35-60	
Browne, Frances	Granny's Wonderful Chair (24mo, gilt, 166p, AEG, 12cp)	L: H. Frowde	1908	Margetson, W.H.	100-175	
Browne, Frances	Granny's Wonderful Chair (1st, lg8vo, 211p, red/gilt, 6cp, pep)	Dutton	(1916)	Pyle, Katharine	90-120	
Browne, Frances	Granny's Wonderful Chair (1st, sm8vo, 184p, 3cp, fp b/w, pep)	Macmillan	1924	Brock, Emma	30-50	*
Browne, K.R.G.	How to Make a Garden Grow (1st, 12mo, 104p, green cl, dep, DJ)	L: Hutchinson	(1938)	Robinson, W. Heath	80-135	
Browne, Maggie	Book of Betty Barber (1st, 8vo, brown cl, teg, p-o, 129p, 6cp)	L: Duckworth	[1910]	Rackham, Arthur	600-800	
Browne, Maggie	Book of Betty Barber (1st AM, sq8vo, teg, p-o, 130p, 6cp)	Badger	[1910]	Rackham, Arthur	300-500	
Browne, Maggie	Wanted - A King (1st, 12mo, 193p, green/gilt, teg, pep)	L: Cassell	1890	Furniss, Harry	140-220	*
Browne, Porter E.	Peace at any Price (1st, sm8vo, brown pcb, 70p, p-o, 6pl)	Appleton	1916	Newell, Peter	150-220	
Browne, Porter E.	Scars & Stripes (1st, sm8vo, gilt, 208p, frn by..)	Doran	(1917)	Newell, Peter	30-50	*
Brownell, Elizabeth	Dream Children (1st, sm8vo, 217p, b/w)	Bowen-Merrill	(1901)	(Photos)	60-90	
Brownell, Elizabeth	Really Babies (1st, 4to, p-o, gilt, 63p)	Rand/McNally	(1908)	(Photos)	150-220	
Browning, Eliz. B.	Rhyme of the Duchess May (1st, 12mo, p-o, wraps, uncut, 5cp)	L: Foulis	[1907]	Cameron, Katharine	70-100	
Browning, Eliz. B.	Sonnets from the Portuguese (1st, 12mo, AEG, gilt, [98]p, color)	Putnam	(1902)	Armstrong, Margaret	50-80	
Browning, Eliz. B.	Sonnets from the Portuguese (1st, lg8vo, 96p, 8 ticp, DJ/2.50)	Crowell	(1936)	Pogany, Willy	60-100	
Browning, Robert	Dramatis Personae... (1st, sm4to, 246p, teg, green/gilt, 10cp)	L: Chatto	1909	Brickdale, E.F.	60-90	
Browning, Robert	Last Ride Together (1st, 8vo, [48]p, gilt, AEG, pep, cvr by...)	Putnam	1906	Armstrong, Margaret	100-170	
Browning, Robert	Men and Women (1st, sm8vo, green/gilt, teg, 312p, 15pl)	L: Dent	1903	Ospovat, Henry	70-100	
Browning, Robert	Pied Piper of Hamelin (1st, 4to, orange ibds, 64p, a.e. blue, color)	L: Routledge	[1888]	Greenaway, Kate	220-300	
Browning, Robert	Pied Piper of Hamelin (1st, 8vo, 64p, uncut, 12pl)	L: Heinemann	1893	Thomson, Hugh	100-160	
Browning, Robert	Pied Piper of Hamelin (1st, lg4to, [54]p, red/gilt, b/w)	L: Quilter	1898	Quilter, Harry	140-220	
Browning, Robert	Pied Piper of Hamelin (1st AM, sm ob4to, [26]p, ibds, fp color)	Nister/Dutton	(1906)	Butler-Stoney, T.	100-165	*
Browning, Robert	Pied Piper of Hamelin (1st, sm4to, p-o, gilt, 56p, pep, color)	Rand/McNally	(1910)	Dunlap, Hope	100-145	
Browning, Robert	Pied Piper of Hamelin (1st, 8vo, 41p, green/gilt, teg, 8cp)	L: J.M. Dent	1912	Tarrant, Margaret	60-100	
Browning, Robert	Pied Piper of Hamelin (1st, lg8vo, p-o, [64]p, color, pep)	Whitman	1927	McCracken, James	55-90	
Browning, Robert	Pied Piper of Hamelin (1st, 8vo, 44p, wraps, 4cp, pep, DJ)	L: Harrap	(1934)	Rackham, Arthur	200-300	
Browning, Robert	Pied Piper of Hamelin (1st AM, 8vo, 45p, p-o, 4cp, pep, DJ/1.50)	Lippincott	[1934]	Rackham, Arthur	150-225	
Browning, Robert	Pied Piper of Hamelin (1st, folio, ibds, [42]p, color, pep)	Grosset/Dunlap	(1936)	Duvoisin, Roger	80-120	R
Browning, Robert	Pied Piper of Hamelin (1st AM, 4to, [48]p, fp color, cep, DJ/3.00)	F. Watts	(1962)	Jones, Harold	45-70	
Browning, Robert	Pippa Passes (1st, 8vo, green cl, 72p, 7pl)	L: Duckworth	1898	Brooke, L. Leslie	75-125	
Browning, Robert	Pippa Passes (1st, 8vo, teg, uncut, green/gilt, [133]p, pep)	Dodd	1900	Armstrong, Margaret	70-125	
Browning, Robert	Pippa Passes (1st, 8vo, 254p, gilt, teg, uncut, 10cp)	L: Chatto	1908	Brickdale, E.F.	80-125	
Browning, Robert	Pippa Passes (1st AM, 8vo, 254p, grey/gilt, 10cp)	Lippincott	1909	Brickdale, E.F.	70-100	
Browning, Robert	Rabbi Ben Ezra (1st, 16mo, 16p, pcb, p-o)	(Concord)	(1902)	Bradley, Will	75-100	
Browning, Robert	Rabbi Ben Ezra... (1st, 4to, 84p, 12 ticp)	L: Hodder	(1915)	Partridge, J.B.	90-120	
Brownjohn, Alan	Brownjohn's Beasts (1st AM, 8vo, 48p, b/w, DJ/3.95)	Scribner	(1970)	Lawson, Carol	20-35	

AUTHOR	TITLE	PUBLISHER	DATE	ARTIST	PRICE	LC
Bruce, Josephine	School Days (1st, 4to, 165p, ipcb, 11cp, pep)	Brentano's	1907	Bruce, Josephine	70-120	
Bruce, Marie	Kris & Kristina (1st {std}, 8vo, ibds, 60p, color, pep)	Doubleday/Doran	(1927)	Daugherty, James	40-65	
Bruce, Marjory	Book of Tales for Little Folks (1st, 8vo, 284p, ibds, 8cp by…)	L: Harrap	(1932)	Appleton, Honor C.	60-100	
Brumbaugh, Florence	Donald Duck & his Nephews (1st, 8vo, cloth, 66p, pep, color)	D.C. Heath	(1940)	Disney Studios	55-80	
Brummitt, Stella W.	Brother Van (1st sm8vo, 171p, pict cl, 2 illus by…)	NY: M. Ed. Mov.	(1919)	Russell, Charles M.	60-90	
Bruna, Dick	Dick Bruna's Cinderella (1st {std}, sq12mo, ibds, 28p, fp color, DJ/1.00)	Follett	(1966)	Bruna, Dick	30-45	*
Brundage, Frances	Cat's Pajamas (sq4to, ipcb, shape book, [16]p, color)	NY: Stecher	1932	Brundage, Frances	80-120	
Bryan, Dorothy	Bobby Wanted a Pony (1st {std}, 8vo, [32]p, ibds, color, DJ/1.00)	Dodd	1937	Bryan, Marguerite	30-50	
Bryan, Dorothy	Friendly Little Jonathan (1st, lg ob8vo, ibds, [32]p, b/w, cep, DJ/1.25)	Dodd	1939	Bryan, Marguerite	30-50	*
Bryant, Bernice M.	Pedie and the Twins (1st, 8vo, 32p, p-o, color, pep, DJ/1.00)	Whitman	1942	Chisholm, Christine	30-45	
Bryant, Bernice M.	Yammy Buys a Bicycle (1st, 8vo, 168p, pep, 5cp, DJ/1.75)	Whitman	1940	Woodward, Hildegarde	30-45	
Bryant, Sara Cone	Best Stories to Tell Children (1st, 8vo, blue/gilt, 181p, 16cp)	Houghton	1912	Beard, Patten	50-80	
Bryant, Sara Cone	Brother Rabbit (1st, 16mo, p-o, 59p, 4cp, pep)	L: Harrap	1926	Appleton/Wilson	70-120	
Bryant, Sara Cone	Epaminondas & his Auntie (1st, sq8vo, ibds, 16p, 2-color, pep, DJ/0.75)	Houghton	1938	Hogan, Inez	100-170	R
Bryant, Sara Cone	Stories to Tell the Littlest Ones (1st UK, 12mo, 178p, 6cp, pep)	L: Harrap	1918	Pogany, Willy	100-170	
Bryce, Marion	Nancy in the Wood (1st, 8vo, 200p, 8cp, pep)	L: John Lane	1914	Clausen, Katharine	45-60	
Brymer, John	Gammon and Spinach (1st, ob4to, ibds, 103p, fp color)	L: Blackie	[1901]	Orr, Stewart	250-350	
Bryson, Bernarda	Gilgamesh: Man's First Story (1st {std}, 4to, ipcb, 112p, color, DJ/4.95)	Holt, Rinehart	(1967)	Bryson, Bernarda	60-95	R
Bryson, Bernarda	Twenty Miracles of St. Nicolas (1st {std}, 4to, 88p, 1-color, DJ/4.75)	Little/Brown	(1960)	Bryson, Bernarda	30-50	
Bryson, Bernarda	Zoo of Zeus (1st, 4to, [56]p, fp color, DJ/6.00)	NY: Grossman	1964	Bryson, Bernarda	40-60	*
Bryson, Charles L.	Tan & Teckle (1st, 8vo, grey cl, 238p, 8pl)	Revell	(1908)	Bull, Charles L.	35-60	
Buchan, John	Lake of Gold (1st AM, 8vo, 189p, green cl, b/w, pep, DJ/2.00)	Houghton	1941	Levenson, S.	40-60	
Buchan, John	Magic Walking Stick (1st, 8vo, red/gilt, 176p, b/w, pep)	Houghton	1932	Becher, Arthur E.	40-60	
Buchan, John	Thirty-Nine Steps (1st AM, 8vo, 145p, col frn, b/w, DJ/3.25)	Dent/Dutton	(1964)	Ardizzone, Edward	40-70	*
Buchanan, George	Jeptha (1st {1st illus bk.}, 8vo, blue/gilt, 130p, 5pl)	L: A. Gardner	[1903]	King, Jessie	300-450	
Buchanan, Thompson	Castle Comedy (1st, 8vo, lavender cl, teg, 235p, 4cp, pep)	Harper	1904	Green, Eliz. S.	50-80	
Buck, Pearl S.	Beech Tree (1st, 8vo, 60p, b/w, DJ/2.50)	John Day	(1955)	Werth, Kurt	80-125	R
Buck, Pearl S.	Big Flight (1st, 8vo, 47p, fp b/w, DJ/2.95)	John Day	(1965)	Funai, Mamoru	70-100	R*
Buck, Pearl S.	Chinese Children Next Door (1st, lg ob8vo, red cl, 62p, 1-color, DJ/2.00)	John Day	1942	Smith, William A.	80-125	R*
Buck, Pearl S.	Dragon Fish (1st, 8vo, 63p, b/w, DJ/2.00)	John Day	(1944)	Bird, Esther B.	80-120	*
Buck, Pearl S.	Fairy Tales of the Orient (1st {std}, 8vo, 320p, ibds, color, DJ/5.95)	Simon/Schuster	(1965)	Wong, Jeanyee	50-80	
Buck, Pearl S.	Johnny Jack & his Beginnings (1st, 8vo, 47p, green cl, 1-color, DJ/2.50)	NY: John Day	(1954)	Werth, Kurt	80-125	R
Buck, Pearl S.	Little Fox in the Middle (1st {std}, 8vo, 31p, b/w, DJ/2.95)	Collier Books	(1966)	Jones, Robert	40-70	R*
Buck, Pearl S.	Stories for Little Children (1st, ob8vo, [48]p, 10 fp 2-color, DJ/1.50)	NY: John Day	(1940)	Yap, Weda	100-165	R
Buck, Pearl S.	Water-Buffalo Children (1st, 8vo, ipcb, 59p, b/w, DJ/1.50)	NY: John Day	(1943)	Smith, William A.	80-125	R
Buck, Pearl S.	Yu Lan, Flying Boy of China (1st, 8vo, 60p, fp b/w, DJ/1.50)	NY: John Day	(1945)	Hartmann, George	100-165	R
Buckland, James	Two Little Runaways (1st, 8vo, 358p, teg, tan/gilt, fp b/w)	L: Longmans	1898	Aldin, Cecil	150-225	
Buckley, Elsie F.	Children of the Dawn (1st, 8vo, 348p, gilt, 24pl)	L: Wells/Gard.	1908	Pape, Frank	90-160	
Buckley, Elsie F.	Children of the Dawn (1st AM, 8vo, 348p, 24pl)	Stokes	(1909)	Pape, Frank	70-100	
Buckley, Helen E.	Grandfather and I (1st, ob4to, [32]p, fp color, DJ/2.75)	Lothrop, Lee	(1959)	Galdone, Paul	30-45	
Buckley, Helen E.	Grandmother and I (1st, 4to, [30]p, fp color, DJ/2.75)	Lothrop, Lee	(1961)	Galdone, Paul	25-40	
Buckley, Helen E.	Josie and the Snow (1st, lg ob8vo, [32]p, color, DJ/2.95)	Lothrop, Lee	(1964)	Ness, Evaline	30-50	
Buckley, Helen E.	Josie's Buttercup (1st, ob4to, [28]p, 2-color, DJ/3.50)	Lothrop, Lee	1967	Ness, Evaline	30-50	
Buckley, Helen E.	Little Boy & the Birthdays (1st, 8vo, [36]p, color, DJ/3.00)	Lothrop, Lee	(1965)	Galdone, Paul	30-50	
Buckley, Helen E.	Little Pig in the Cupboard (1st, 4to, [32]p, color, DJ/3.50)	Lothrop, Lee	(1968)	Howard, Rob	30-50	*
Buckley, Helen E.	My Sister and I (1st, 4to, [32]p, 3-color, cep, DJ/2.95)	Lothrop, Lee	(1963)	Galdone, Paul	30-50	
Buckley, Helen E.	Some Cheese for Charles (1st, ob4to, [30]p, ibds, color, cep, DJ/2.95)	Lothrop, Lee	(1963)	Ness, Evaline	30-50	
Buckley, Helen E.	Too Many Crackers (1st, 4to, [28]p, color, DJ/3.50)	Lothrop, Lee	(1966)	Ness, Evaline	40-60	*
Buckley, Helen E.	Where Did Josie Go? (1st, smob4to, 33p, 3-color, DJ/2.95)	Lothrop, Lee	(1962)	Ness, Evaline	40-65	
Buckley, Helen E.	Wonderful Little Boy (1st, 4to, [31]p, color, DJ/4.50)	Lothrop, Lee	(1970)	Howard, Rob	40-65	
Buckmaster, Henrietta	Lucy and Loki (1st, sq8vo, [32]p, yellow cl, fp 2-color, DJ/2.50)	Scribner	(1958)	Cooney, Barbara	50-80	*
Budd, Lillian	Bell of Kamela (1st, 8vo, 76p, b/w, pep, DJ/2.95)	Rand/McNally	(1960)	Hutchinson, Paula	20-30	
Budney, Blossom	Cat Can't Count (1st, lg8vo, [32]p, color, dep, DJ/2.95)	Lothrop, Lee	(1962)	Wondriska, William	25-40	
Budney, Blossom	Huff Puff Hickory Hill (1st, 4to, [29]p, color, DJ/2.50)	Lothrop, Lee	1955	Werth, Kurt	30-50	
Budney, Blossom	Kiss is Round: Verses (1st, 4to, [34]p, fp color, dep, DJ/2.50, NYTBI)	Lothrop, Lee	1954	Bobri, Vladimir	100-165	R*
Budney, Blossom	N is for Nursery School (1st, 4to, [27]p, color, pep, DJ/2.50)	Lothrop, Lee	1956	Bobri, Vladimir	40-65	
Bufano, Remo	Magic Strings… (1st, 8vo, 182p, 11 b/w, DJ/1.50)	Macmillan	1939	Artzybasheff, Boris	45-70	*
Buff, M.& C.	Apple and the Arrow (1st, sm4to, 75p, gilt, color, pep, DJ/3.00, NH)	Houghton	1951	Buff, M.& C.	70-100	
Buff, M.& C.	Colorado: River of Mystery (1st, 4to, 86p, fp 1-color, cep, DJ/4.95)	CA: Ritchie Pr.	(1968)	Buff, M.& C.	30-50	
Buff, M.& C.	Elf Owl (1st, 4to, 74p, 1-color, pep, DJ/2.75)	Viking	(1958)	Buff, M.& C.	65-100	R
Buff, M.& C.	Forest Folk (1st, 4to, 64p, 1-color, pep, DJ/3.00)	Viking	(1962)	Buff, M.& C.	30-50	
Buff, M.& C.	Hah-Nee of the Cliff Dwellers (1st, 4to, 68p, color, DJ/3.00)	Houghton	1956	Buff, M.& C.	60-100	R
Buff, M.& C.	Hurry, Skurry & Flurry (1st, sm4to, 73p, pep, 1-color, DJ/2.75)	Viking	1954	Buff, M.& C.	65-100	R
Buff, M.& C.	Kemi: An Indian Boy Before White Man Came (1st, 8vo, 90p, b/w, DJ/3.50)	CA: Ritchie Pr.	(1966)	Buff, M.& C.	40-65	
Buff, M.& C.	Kobi, a Boy of Switzerland (1st, sm4to, 128p, dp color, dep, DJ/2.00)	Viking	1939	Buff, Conrad	35-60	
Buff, M.& C.	Peter's Pinto (1st, 4to, 95p, b/w, DJ/2.00)	Viking	1949	Buff, M.& C.	25-45	
Buff, M.& C.	Trix and Vix (1st, 4to, 24p, b/w, DJ/2.75)	Houghton	1960	Buff, M.& C.	25-40	
Buff, Mary	Big Tree (1st, 4to, 79p, grey cl, b/w, DJ/3.00, NH)	Viking	1946	Buff, M.& C.	60-90	
Buff, Mary	Dancing Cloud (1st, ob4to, ipcb, 80p, fp color, cep, DJ/2.00)	Viking	1937	Buff, Conrad	80-120	R
Buff, Mary	Dash and Dart (1st, sm4to, 73p, 4 dp cp, dep, DJ/2.00, CH)	Viking	1942	Buff, M.& C.	80-125	
Buff, Mary	Magic Maize (1st, 4to, 76p, pep, 9 fp color, DJ/3.00, NH)	Houghton	1953	Buff, M.& C.	70-100	
Bulfinch, Thomas	Book of Myths (1st, sm4to, 126p, color, DJ/2.75)	Macmillan	1942	Sewell, Helen	50-80	
Bulfinch, Thomas	Legends of Charlemagne (1st, lg8vo, gilt, teg, p-o, 273p, 8cp, pep)	Cosmopolitan	1924	Wyeth, N.C.	200-300	
Bull, Angela	Wayland's Keep (1st AM {std}, 8vo, 198p, b/w, DJ/3.95)	Holt, Rinehart	(1967)	McCully, Emily	25-45	
Bull, Charles L.	Under the Roof of the Jungle (1st, 8vo, green/gilt, 271p, 4cp)	L.C. Page	1911	Bull, Charles L.	50-80	
Bulla, Clyde R.	Donkey Cart (1st, 8vo, yellow cl, 89p, b/w, pep, DJ/2.25)	Crowell	(1946)	Lenski, Lois	60-100	
Bulla, Clyde R.	Ghost Town Treasure (1st, 8vo, yellow cl, 86p, b/w, pep, DJ/2.50)	Crowell	(1957)	Freeman, Don	30-60	
Bulla, Clyde R.	I Went for a Walk (1st, ob12mo, 48p, 1-color, DJ/2.00)	H.Z. Walck	1958	Lenski, Lois	60-90	

AUTHOR	TITLE	PUBLISHER	DATE	ARTIST	PRICE	LC
Bulla, Clyde R.	Indian Hill (1st, 8vo, 74p, fp b/w, DJ/3.75)	Crowell	(1963)	Spanfeller, James	20-30	
Bulla, Clyde R.	John Billington, Friend of Squanto (1st, 8vo, 88p, b/w, DJ/2.50)	Crowell	(1956)	Burchard, Peter	20-35	
Bulla, Clyde R.	Johnny Hong of Chinatown (1st, 8vo, 69p, b/w, DJ/2.00)	Crowell	(1952)	Kingman, Dong	25-40	
Bulla, Clyde R.	Moon Singer (1st, sq8vo, [46]p, fp color, DJ/3.95)	Crowell	(1969)	Hyman, Trina S.	70-100	
Bulla, Clyde R.	Old Charlie (1st, sm8vo, 80p, b/w, DJ/2.50)	Crowell	1957	Galdone, Paul	30-50	
Bulla, Clyde R.	Poppy Seeds (1st, lg8vo, [38]p, color, pep, DJ/2.75)	Crowell	(1955)	Charlot, Jean	125-200	
Bulla, Clyde R.	Riding the Pony Express (1st, 8vo, 95p, b/w, pep, DJ/2.25)	Crowell	(1948)	Paull, Grace	30-45	*
Bulla, Clyde R.	Secret Valley (1st, sq8vo, 100p, blue cl, fp b/w, DJ/2.25)	Crowell	(1949)	Paull, Grace	30-45	
Bulla, Clyde R.	Song of Saint Francis (1st {std}, 8vo, 71p, b/w, pep, DJ/2.50)	Crowell	(1952)	Angelo, Valenti	35-50	
Bulla, Clyde R.	Songs of Mr. Small (1st, 4to, 40p, 2-color, pep, DJ/2.75)	Oxford U. Pr.	1954	Lenski, Lois	70-125	
Bulla, Clyde R.	St. Valentine's Day (1st, 8vo, [38]p, fp 1-color, DJ/2.95)	Crowell	(1965)	Angelo, Valenti	25-45	
Bulla, Clyde R.	Sugar Pear Tree (1st, 8vo, 54p, b/w, dep, DJ/2.75)	Crowell	(1961)	Yashima, Taro	30-50	
Bulla, Clyde R.	Sword in the Tree (1st {std}, 8vo, 113p, red cl, b/w, DJ/2.50)	Crowell	1956	Galdone, Paul	30-50	
Bulla, Clyde R.	Valentine Cat (1st, sm4to, [62]p, pink cl, 2-color, DJ/3.00)	Crowell	(1959)	Weisgard, Leonard	50-80	
Bulla, Clyde R.	We Are thy Children (1st {std}, ob4to, 32p, 1-color, pep, DJ/2.75)	Crowell	(1952)	Lenski, Lois	80-145	
Bulla, Clyde R.	What Makes a Shadow (1st, ob8vo, [38]p, fp 3-color, DJ/2.50)	Crowell	(1962)	Adams, Adrienne	40-70	
Bulla, Clyde R.	White Bird (1st, 8vo, 79p, b/w, DJ/3.75)	Crowell	1966	Weisgard, Leonard	25-40	
Bullard, Marion	Somersaulting Rabbit (1st, ob4to, 45p, ibds, 12pl)	Dutton	(1927)	Bullard, Marion	100-170	*
Bullen, Frank T.	Cruise of the Cachalot (1st, lg8vo, 301p, 8cp, pep)	Dodd	1926	Schaeffer, Mead	35-60	
Bunce, William	Son of the Iroquois (1st {std}, 8vo, 127p, 2-color, pep, DJ/1.50)	Macrae Smith	1936	Quinn, Paul	45-70	
Bunn, Harriet	Johann Sebastian Bach (1st, 4to, 56p, ipcb, color, DJ/1.00)	Random	(1942)	Busoni, Rafaello	20-30	
Bunn, Harriet	Trailer Tracks (1st, 8vo, 241p, b/w, pep, DJ/1.75)	Macmillan	1937	Dobias, Frank	30-50	
Bunner, H.C.	Jersey Street and Jersey Lane (1st, 8vo, blue/gilt, teg, 201p)	Scribner	1896	Armstrong, Margaret	70-100	R
Bunner, H.C.	Love in Old Cloathes (1st, sm8vo, 217p, gilt, teg, uncut)	Scribner	1896	Armstrong, Margaret	30-50	
Bunner, H.C.	Three Operettas (1st, ob4to, 163p, gilt, b/w)	Harper	1897	Weldon/Taylor	60-100	
Buntain, Ruth J.	Birthday Story (1st, sm8vo, [47]p, fp 2-color, DJ/2.00)	Holiday House	(1953)	Wilkin, Eloise B.	50-80	
Bunyan, John	Life & Death of Mr. Badman (1st, folio, ibds, teg, 12pl)	R.H. Russell	1900	Rhead Brothers	140-200	
Bunyan, John	Life & Death of Mr. Badman (1st UK, folio, gilt, 143p, teg, 12pl)	L: Heinemann	1900	Rhead Brothers	120-185	
Bunyan, John	Pilgrim's Progress (1st, 4to, 379p, teg, uncut, black/gilt, fp b/w)	L: Nimmo	1895	Strang, William	90-120	
Bunyan, John	Pilgrim's Progress (1st, 8vo, 284p, red cl, 24pl)	L: Bliss Sands	1897	Robinson, W. Heath	150-225	*
Bunyan, John	Pilgrim's Progress (1st, folio, 184p, ibds, b/w)	Century	1898	Rhead Brothers	120-170	
Bunyan, John	Pilgrim's Progress (1st UK, folio, gilt, 201p)	L: A. Pearson	[1898]	Rhead Brothers	140-200	
Bunyan, John	Pilgrim's Progress (1st, lg8vo, 315p, green/gilt, 12cp, pep)	L: J.M. Dent	1910	Pape, Frank	100-170	
Bunyan, John	Pilgrim's Progress (sm4to, gilt, 393p, teg, 29cp, pep)	L: Jack	[1910]	Shaw, Byam	70-125	
Burbank, Addison	Cedar Deer (1st, 8vo, 157p, dp color, DJ/2.00)	Coward	1940	Burbank, Addison	20-30	
Burch, Robert	Joey's Cat (1st, 8vo, [40]p, color, DJ/3.50)	Viking	(1969)	Freeman, Don	30-50	
Burch, Robert	Queenie Peavy (1st, 8vo, 159p, fp b/w, DJ/3.50, JABA)	Viking	(1966)	Lazare, Jerry	30-50	
Burch, Robert	Simon and the Game of Chance (1st {std}, 8vo, 128p, b/w, DJ/4.50)	Viking	(1970)	Rocker, Fermin	25-45	
Burch, Robert	Traveling Bird (1st, 8vo, green cl, 42p, b/w, DJ/3.50)	McDowell/Obl.	(1959)	Suba, Susanne	20-30	
Burchard, Peter	Bimby (1st, 8vo, 91p, b/w, DJ/3.50)	Coward	(1968)	Burchard, Peter	25-45	*
Burchard, Peter	Jed (1st, 8vo, 94p, DJ/3.00)	Coward	(1960)	Burchard, Peter	20-35	
Burchard, Peter	River Queen (1st {std} [1st bk.], sm4to, 40p, ipcb, color, pep, DJ/3.00)	Macmillan	(1957)	Burchard, Peter	40-65	
Burchardt, Nellie	Project Cat (1st, 8vo, 66p, yellow cl, fp 1-color, DJ/2.95)	F. Watts	(1966)	Rocker, Fermin	30-50	
Burchardt, Nellie	Reggie's No-Good Bird (1st {std}, 8vo, uncut, 140p, b/w, DJ/3.50)	F. Watts	(1967)	Berson, Harold	50-80	*
Burdette, Robert J.	Smiles Yoked with Sighs (1st, sm8vo, 180p, green/gilt, b/w)	Bowen-Merrill	(1900)	Vawter, J. Will	25-40	
Burgess, Gelett	Blue Goops & Red (1st, sm4to, green cl, 81p, 2-color, pep)	Stokes	(1909)	Burgess, Gelett	250-400	
Burgess, Gelett	Burgess Nonsense Book (1st, 8vo, teg, 239p, gilt, b/w)	Stokes	(1901)	Burgess, Gelett	170-240	
Burgess, Gelett	Cat's Elegy (1st, 12mo, tan ipcb, [43]p, 1-color)	McClurg	1913	Burgess, Gelett	90-160	R*
Burgess, Gelett	Goop Directory of Juvenile Offenders (1st, 12mo, 78p, ibds)	Stokes	(1913)	Burgess, Gelett	100-160	
Burgess, Gelett	Goop Tales Alphabetically Told (1st, sq4to, blue cl, 106p, b/w)	Stokes	(1904)	Burgess, Gelett	140-200	
Burgess, Gelett	Goops & How to be Them (1st, sq4to, [96]p, ibds, fp b/w, PPP)	Stokes	(1900)	Burgess, Gelett	350-500	
Burgess, Gelett	Heart Line (1st, sm8vo, 584p, p-o, 12pl)	Bobbs-Merrill	(1907)	Ralph, Lester	40-60	
Burgess, Gelett	Lady Mechante (1st, 8vo, 393p, lavender cl, 8pl)	Stokes	(1909)	Burgess, Gelett	50-80	
Burgess, Gelett	Lively City O'Ligg (1st, 8vo, 219p, ibds, 8cp)	Stokes	(1899)	Burgess, Gelett	130-200	
Burgess, Gelett	Maxims of Methuselah (1st, 12mo, ibds, 108p, 4cp)	Stokes	(1907)	Fancher, Louis D.	40-65	
Burgess, Gelett	Maxims of Noah (1st, 12mo, ibds, 119p, color)	Stokes	(1913)	Fancher, Louis D.	40-65	
Burgess, Gelett	Why Be a Goop? (1st, sq8vo, p-o, red cl, 159p)	Stokes	1924	Burgess, Gelett	120-180	
Burgess, Thornton	Adventures of Bob White (1st, 16mo, grey cl, 6pl)	Little/Brown	1919	Cady, Harrison	120-180	
Burgess, Thornton	Adventures of Bobby Coon (1st, 16mo, 117p, 6pl)	Little/Brown	1918	Cady, Harrison	120-180	
Burgess, Thornton	Adventures of Buster Bear (1st, 16mo, 120p, tan cl, 6pl)	Little/Brown	1916	Cady, Harrison	120-180	
Burgess, Thornton	Adventures of Chatterer the Red Squirrel (1st, 16mo, 120p, 6pl)	Little/Brown	1915	Cady, Harrison	120-185	
Burgess, Thornton	Adventures of Grandfather Frog (1st, 12mo, 120p, 6pl)	Little/Brown	1915	Cady, Harrison	120-180	
Burgess, Thornton	Adventures of Jerry Muskrat (1st, 12mo, 120p, 6pl)	Little/Brown	1914	Cady, Harrison	120-180	
Burgess, Thornton	Adventures of Jimmy Skunk (1st, 12mo, 118p, grey cl, 6pl)	Little/Brown	1918	Cady, Harrison	120-185	
Burgess, Thornton	Adventures of Johnny Chuck (1st, 12mo, 120p, 6pl)	Little/Brown	1913	Cady, Harrison	120-185	
Burgess, Thornton	Adventures of Mr. Mocker (1st, 8vo, tan cloth, 120p, 6pl)	Little/Brown	1914	Cady, Harrison	120-185	
Burgess, Thornton	Adventures of Ol' Mistah Buzzard (1st, 12mo, 119p, 6pl)	Little/Brown	1919	Cady, Harrison	120-180	
Burgess, Thornton	Adventures of Old Mr. Toad (1st, 12mo, 120p, 6pl)	Little/Brown	1916	Cady, Harrison	120-185	
Burgess, Thornton	Adventures of Peter Cottontail (1st, 12mo, 120p, 6pl)	Little/Brown	1914	Cady, Harrison	120-180	
Burgess, Thornton	Adventures of Poor Mrs. Quack (1st, 12mo, 119p, cloth, 6pl)	Little/Brown	1917	Cady, Harrison	120-185	
Burgess, Thornton	Adventures of Prickly Porky (1st, 12mo, grey cl, 116p, 6pl)	Little/Brown	1916	Cady, Harrison	120-180	
Burgess, Thornton	Adventures of Reddy Fox (1st, 16mo, grey cl, 120p, 6pl)	Little/Brown	1913	Cady, Harrison	120-170	
Burgess, Thornton	Adventures of Sammy Jay (1st, 12mo, 119p, 6pl)	Little/Brown	1915	Cady, Harrison	120-200	
Burgess, Thornton	Adventures of Uncle Billy Possum (1st, 12mo, 117p, grey cl, 6pl)	Little/Brown	1914	Cady, Harrison	120-180	
Burgess, Thornton	At Paddy the Beaver's Pond (1st {std}, 8vo, 146p, col frn, DJ/2.00)	Little/Brown	1950	Cady, Harrison	65-80	
Burgess, Thornton	At the Smiling Pool (1st {std}, sq8vo, 185p, red cl, color, pep, DJ/2.00)	Little/Brown	1945	Cady, Harrison	80-140	
Burgess, Thornton	Aunt Sally's Friends in Fur (1st {std}, 8vo, 146p, b/w, DJ/2.75)	Little/Brown	(1955)	(Photos)	60-90	
Burgess, Thornton	Billy Mink (1st, 8vo, p-o, 196p, 8cp)	Little/Brown	1924	Cady, Harrison	80-140	

AUTHOR	TITLE	PUBLISHER	DATE	ARTIST	PRICE	LC
Burgess, Thornton	Blacky the Crow (1st, sm8vo, 206p, p-o, 8cp)	Little/Brown	1922	Cady, Harrison	80-140	
Burgess, Thornton	Bowser the Hound (1st, 8vo, p-o, 206p, 8cp)	Little/Brown	1920	Cady, Harrison	100-160	
Burgess, Thornton	Boy Scouts in a Trappers' Camp (1st, sm8vo, 362p, 5pl)	Penn	1915	Anderson, F.A.	120-200	*
Burgess, Thornton	Boy Scouts of Woodcraft Camp (1st, sm8vo, p-o, 345p, 5pl)	Penn	1912	Corson, C.S.	120-170	*
Burgess, Thornton	Bride's Primer (1st, lg4to, ipcb, [62]p, 24 fp color)	NY: Phelps	(1905)	Strothmann, F.	300-500	R*
Burgess, Thornton	Burgess Animal Book for Children (1st, 8vo, 363p, green cl, p-o, cp)	Little/Brown	1920	Fuertes, Louis A.	100-170	
Burgess, Thornton	Burgess Animal Paint Book (ob folio, [24]p, wraps, 7 fp color)	Saalfield	1925	Cady, Harrison	120-200	
Burgess, Thornton	Burgess Animal Stories (1st, sq8vo, [96]p, cloth, color, DJ/0.75)	Platt/Munk	(1942)	Cady, Harrison	80-125	
Burgess, Thornton	Burgess Bird Book for Children (1st, 8vo, p-o, 351p, 32cp)	Little/Brown	1919	Fuertes, Louis A.	120-180	
Burgess, Thornton	Buster Bear's Twins (1st, 8vo, p-o, 207p, 8cp)	Little/Brown	1923	Cady, Harrison	90-150	
Burgess, Thornton	Christmas Reindeer (1st, 12mo, 139p, red/gilt, 7pl, pep)	Macmillan	1926	Chase, Rhoda	120-200	
Burgess, Thornton	Crooked Little Path (1st {std}, 8vo, red cl, 185p, fp 2-color, DJ/2.00)	Little/Brown	1946	Cady, Harrison	45-70	
Burgess, Thornton	Cubby Finds an Open Door (ob24mo, ibds, [24]p, color)	Whitman	1929	Jordan, Nina	80-140	*
Burgess, Thornton	Farmer Brown's Boy Becomes Curious (ob24mo, ibds, 24p, color)	Whitman	1929	Jordan, Nina	80-140	
Burgess, Thornton	Frightened Baby (1st, ob32mo, ipcb, color)	Whitman	(1929)	Jordan, Nina	70-100	
Burgess, Thornton	Grandfather Frog Gets a Ride (1st, 12mo, ibds, 29p, color)	Stoll/Edwards	(1928)	Cady, Harrison	75-100	
Burgess, Thornton	Great Joke on Jimmy Skunk (1st, 12mo, ibds, 29p, color)	Stoll/Edwards	(1928)	Cady, Harrison	75-100	
Burgess, Thornton	Happy Jack (1st, 8vo, 204p, p-o, 8cp)	Little/Brown	1918	Cady, Harrison	100-160	
Burgess, Thornton	Jerry Muskrat at Home (1st, 8vo, 206p, p-o, 8cp)	Little/Brown	1926	Cady, Harrison	80-140	
Burgess, Thornton	Jerry Muskrat Wins Respect (4to, wraps, color)	NY: J. Eggers	(1928)	Cady, Harrison	70-120	*
Burgess, Thornton	Lightfoot the Deer (1st, 8vo, p-o, blue cl, 205p, 8cp)	Little/Brown	1921	Cady, Harrison	70-125	
Burgess, Thornton	Little Joe Otter (1st, 8vo, olive cl, p-o, 198p, 8cp)	Little/Brown	1925	Cady, Harrison	80-140	
Burgess, Thornton	Little Pete's Adventure (1st, 12mo, ibds, [59]p, fp color)	McLoughlin	(1941)	Cady, Harrison	40-65	
Burgess, Thornton	Little Red's Adventure (1st, 12mo, ibds, [59]p, fp color)	McLoughlin	(1942)	Cady, Harrison	45-65	
Burgess, Thornton	Longlegs the Heron (1st, 8vo, olive cl, p-o, 207p, 8cp)	Little/Brown	1927	Cady, Harrison	80-140	
Burgess, Thornton	Mother West Wind How Stories (1st, 12mo, 228p, 8cp)	Little/Brown	1916	Cady, Harrison	100-160	
Burgess, Thornton	Mother West Wind When Stories (1st, 12mo, tan cl, 227p, 8cp)	Little/Brown	1917	Cady, Harrison	130-185	
Burgess, Thornton	Mother West Wind Why Stories (1st, 12mo, 230p, 8cp)	Little/Brown	1915	Cady, Harrison	120-185	
Burgess, Thornton	Mother West Wind's Animal Friends (1st, 12mo, 221p, 6pl)	Little/Brown	1912	Kerr, George F.	120-200	
Burgess, Thornton	Mother West Wind's Children (1st, 12mo, 243p, 7pl)	Little/Brown	1911	Kerr, George F.	120-200	
Burgess, Thornton	Mother West Wind's Neighbors (1st, 12mo, tan cl, 223p, 6pl)	Little/Brown	1913	Kerr, George F.	120-200	
Burgess, Thornton	Mrs. Peter Rabbit (1st, 8vo, 205p, p-o, 8cp)	Little/Brown	1919	Cady, Harrison	90-140	
Burgess, Thornton	Neatness of Bobby Coon (1st, 12mo, ibds, 29p, color)	Stoll/Edwards	(1927)	Cady, Harrison	70-100	
Burgess, Thornton	Old Granny Fox (1st, 8vo, p-o, green cl, 202p, 8cp)	Little/Brown	1920	Cady, Harrison	80-130	
Burgess, Thornton	Old Mother West Wind (1st, 12mo, 169p, 7pl, PPP)	Little/Brown	(1910)	Kerr, George F.	250-400	
Burgess, Thornton	On the Green Meadows (1st {std}, 8vo, 182p, red cl, color, DJ/2.00)	Little/Brown	1944	Cady, Harrison	50-80	
Burgess, Thornton	Tales from Storyteller's House (1st {std}, sq8vo, 195p, 8cp, DJ)	Little/Brown	1937	Palmer, Lemuel	90-150	
Burgess, Thornton	Thornton Burgess Bedtime Stories (1st, lg4to, ibds, 105p, color, pep)	Grosset/Dunlap	(1959)	Hauge, Carl & Mary	30-45	
Burgess, Thornton	Tommy & the Wishing-Stone (1st, 12mo, 290p, gilt, b/w pl)	Century	1915	Cady, Harrison	100-165	*
Burgess, Thornton	While the Story Log Burns (1st {std}, 8vo, 195p, 8cp, DJ/2.00)	Little/Brown	1938	Palmer, Lemuel	80-130	
Burgess, Thornton	Whitefoot the Wood Mouse (1st, 8vo, p-o, blue cl, 181p, 8cp)	Little/Brown	1922	Cady, Harrison	90-120	
Burglon, Nora	Children of the Soil (1st {std}, 8vo, 272p, pep, col frn, NH)	Doubleday/Doran	1932	D'Aulaire, E. Parin	75-100	*
Burglon, Nora	Cuckoo Calls (1st, 8vo, 280p, col frn, pep, DJ/2.00)	Winston	(1940)	D'Aulaire, I.& E.	50-80	
Burglon, Nora	Deep Silver (1st, 8vo, 215p, blue cl, 12pl, DJ/2.00)	Houghton	1938	Hurd, Peter	60-90	
Burglon, Nora	Gate Swings In (1st {std}, 8vo, 208p, pep, b/w, DJ/2.00)	Little/Brown	1937	Floethe, Richard	50-80	
Burglon, Nora	Ghost Ship (1st, sm8vo, 275p, blue cl, 8pl, pep, DJ/2.00)	Little/Brown	1936	Nelson, Arthur R.	30-50	
Burglon, Nora	Lost Island (1st, 8vo, 261p, col frn, b/w, DJ/2.00)	Winston	1939	Ried, James	30-50	
Burglon, Nora	Shark Hole (1st, sm8vo, 244p, fp b/w, DJ/2.25)	Holiday House	(1943)	Baldridge, Cyrus L.	25-45	
Burglon, Nora	Sticks Across the Chimney (1st, sm8vo, 256p, 1-color, DJ/2.00)	Holiday House	(1938)	Eichenberg, Fritz	60-90	
Burgwyn, Mebane	Crackajack Pony (1st {std}, 8vo, uncut, 190p, fp b/w, DJ/3.95)	Lippincott	1969	Payson, Dale	50-80	
Burgwyn, Mebane	Lucky Mischief (1st, 8vo, 246p, fp b/w, DJ/2.50)	NY: Oxford U.Pr.	1949	Howe, Gertrude	150-225	*
Burgwyn, Mebane	River Treasure (1st, 8vo, 150p, blue cl, fp b/w, DJ/2.50)	Oxford U. Pr.	1947	Ray, Ralph	250-350	
Burke, Thos. (ed.)	Children in Verse (1st, 8vo, 135p, blue cl, 8cp)	L: Duckworth	1913	Appleton, Honor C.	60-90	
Burke, Thos. (ed.)	Children in Verse (1st AM, 8vo, 135p, teg, 8 ticp)	(Boston)	1914	Appleton, Honor C.	60-90	
Burke, Trude	Wild Stranger (1st {std}, 8vo, 129p, b/w, DJ/2.50)	Holt	(1953)	Brown, Paul	80-140	
Burland, Brian	St. Nicholas and the Tub (1st, sm4to, [36]p, 2-color, pep, DJ/3.25)	Holiday House	(1964)	Low, Joseph	30-50	*
Burlingame, Eugene W.	Grateful Elephant (1st, sm4to, 172p, yellow cl, col frn, 10pl)	Yale U. Press	1923	Lathrop, Dorothy	100-165	
Burn, John H.	Mother's Book of Song (1st, 8vo, 216p, blue/gilt, teg, b/w)	L: Wells/Gard.	(1902)	Robinson, Charles	150-220	
Burnand, Francis	Fox's Frolic (ob4to, ibds, [50]p, color, pep)	L: Collins	[1920]	Neilson, Harry B.	100-165	
Burnand, Francis (ed)	Incompleat Angler (1st, 8vo, 94p, b/w)	L: Bradbury	1887	Furniss, Harry	100-170	
Burne-Jones, Edward	Beginning of the World (1st, lg4to, 23p, ibds, fp b/w)	L: Longmans	1902	Burne-Jones, Edward	250-350	
Burnett, Frances H.	Cozy Lion (1st, 12mo, 104p, blue cl, 20cp)	Century	1907	Cady, Harrison	70-100	R
Burnett, Frances H.	Dawn of a To-Morrow (1st, 12mo, brown/gilt, 156p, 8cp)	Scribner	1906	Yohn, F.C.	45-70	
Burnett, Frances H.	Editha's Burglar (1st [1], 12mo, blue/gilt, 64p, 13pl)	J. Marsh	1888	Sandham, Henry	200-300	
Burnett, Frances H.	Giovanni & the Other (1st, 8vo, 193p, olive/gilt, 9pl, cep)	Scribner	1892	Birch, Reginald	100-160	
Burnett, Frances H.	Good Wolf (1st, 8vo, gilt, 125p, 5cp)	Moffat	1908	Sichel, Harold	30-50	
Burnett, Frances H.	His Grace of Osmonde (1st, 12mo, 465p, buckram, cvr by...)	Scribner	1897	Armstrong, Margaret	35-50	
Burnett, Frances H.	In the Closed Room (1st, 8vo, green/gilt, teg, 130p, 8cp, dep)	McClurg	1904	Smith, Jessie W.	140-200	
Burnett, Frances H.	Lady of Quality (1st, 12mo, 363p, buckram/gilt, b/w)	Scribner	1896	Armstrong, Margaret	60-90	
Burnett, Frances H.	Land of the Blue Flower (1st, sm8vo, gilt, 67p, teg, col frn)	Moffat	1909	Ivanowski, Sigismond	40-60	
Burnett, Frances H.	Little Hunchback Zia (1st, 12mo, p-o, 55p, 5pl, pep)	Stokes	(1916)	Benda, W.T.	40-65	
Burnett, Frances H.	Little Lord Fauntleroy (1st [1], 8vo, 209p, gilt, 26 b/w, PPP)	Scribner	1886	Birch, Reginald	600-900	
Burnett, Frances H.	Little Lord Fauntleroy (1st [new ed.], 8vo, 246p, teg, p-o, 10cp)	Scribner	1911	Birch, Reginald	100-160	
Burnett, Frances H.	Little Princess (1st, sm4to, 266p, blue/gilt, teg, p-o, 12cp)	Scribner	1905	Betts, Ethel F.	120-180	
Burnett, Frances H.	Little Princess (1st UK, 8vo, 302p, p-o, 8cp)	L: Warne	(1905)	Piffard, Harold	100-170	
Burnett, Frances H.	Little Princess (1st, 8vo, 240p, gilt, fp color, DJ/5.00)	Lippincott	(1963)	Tudor, Tasha	120-185	R
Burnett, Frances H.	Little St. Elizabeth (1st AM, 8vo, 146p, 12 b/w)	Scribner	1890	Birch, Reginald	75-125	
Burnett, Frances H.	Lost Prince (1st, sm8vo, 415p, blue/gilt, 16pl)	Century	1915	Bower, Maurice L.	50-80	

AUTHOR	TITLE	PUBLISHER	DATE	ARTIST	PRICE	LC
Burnett, Frances H.	Lost Prince (1st, 8vo, 342p, t.e. red, fp b/w, cep, DJ/3.95)	Lippincott	(1967)	Weisgard, Leonard	30-45	
Burnett, Frances H.	My Robin (1st, 12mo, green/gilt, 42p, col frn)	Stokes	(1912)	Brennan, Alfred	80-120	
Burnett, Frances H.	One I Knew Best of All (1st, 12mo, 325p, gilt, teg, b/w)	Scribner	1893	Birch, Reginald	70-100	
Burnett, Frances H.	Piccino (1st, sq8vo, olive/gilt, 203p, 15pl)	Scribner	1894	Birch, Reginald	80-130	
Burnett, Frances H.	Pretty Sister of Jose (1st [1], 12mo, 127p, gilt, 12pl)	Scribner	1889	Reinhart, C.S.	100-160	
Burnett, Frances H.	Queen Silver-Bell (1st, 16mo, p-o, 132p, 20cp)	Century	1906	Cady, Harrison	140-200	R
Burnett, Frances H.	Racketty-Packetty House (1st, 12mo, 130p, p-o, 24cp)	Century	1906	Cady, Harrison	150-225	
Burnett, Frances H.	Sara Crew (1st [1], 8vo, 83p, gilt, 6pl)	Scribner	1888	Birch, Reginald	180-250	
Burnett, Frances H.	Secret Garden (1st, 8vo, p-o, teg, 375p, gilt, 4cp)	Stokes	(1911)	Kirk, Maria L.	500-650	
Burnett, Frances H.	Secret Garden (1st, 8vo, green/gilt, 306p, 8cp, pep)	L: Heinemann	1911	Robinson, Charles	450-650	
Burnett, Frances H.	Secret Garden (1st, 8vo, 284p, 4 dp color, b/w, DJ/2.50)	Lippincott	(1949)	Unwin, Nora S.	25-40	
Burnett, Frances H.	Secret Garden (1st, 8vo, 256p, red/gilt, fp color, DJ/5.00)	Lippincott	(1962)	Tudor, Tasha	120-185	
Burnett, Frances H.	Spring Cleaning (1st, 12mo, p-o, 100p, 20cp)	Century	1908	Cady, Harrison	100-150	
Burnett, Frances H.	Two Little Pilgrims' Progress (1st, sq8vo, 191p, gilt, 12pl)	Scribner	1895	Birch, Reginald	120-200	R
Burnett, Frances H.	Way to the House of Santa Claus (1st, lg ob4to, p-o, [25]p, color)	Harper	1916	Unknown	120-175	
Burnett, Frances H.	White People (1st, 12mo, 112p, grey/gilt, 4pl)	Harper	(1917)	Green, Eliz. S.	40-65	
Burnett, Whit	Literary Life & the Hell with It (1st, 8vo, 276p, b/w, dep, DJ/2.50)	Harper	1939	Bemelmans, Ludwig	35-50	
Burney, Fanny	Evelina... (3rd ed., sm8vo, teg, 2 vols, uncut, gilt)	L: J.M. Dent	1893	Beardsley, Aubrey	350-450	
Burney, Fanny	Evelina... (1st, sm8vo, teg, blue/gilt, 16 b/w, 416p)	L: Newnes	1898	Rackham, Arthur	200-300	
Burney, Fanny	Evelina... (1st, 8vo, 477p, gilt, b/w)	L: Macmillan	(1903)	Thomson, Hugh	60-90	
Burnford, Sheila	Incredible Journey (1st {std}, 8vo, 145p, fp b/w, DJ/3.75)	Little/Brown	1961	Burger, Carl	75-120	
Burnham, Clara L.	Clever Betsy (1st, sm8vo, red/gilt, 402p, 3pl)	Houghton	1910	O'Neill, Rose	40-65	
Burnham, Clara L.	Jewel's Story Book (1st, 12mo, 343p, green cl, 6pl, pep)	Houghton	1904	Schmitt, Albert	25-40	
Burnham, Clara L.	Quest Flower (1st, sm8vo, 132p, red/gilt, 4cp)	Houghton	1908	Upjohn, Anna M.	55-80	
Burningham, John	Borka (1st, 4to, ibds, [32]p, fp color, pep, KGM)	L: J. Cape	1963	Burningham, John	50-80	
Burningham, John	Cannonball Simp (1st AM {std}, 4to, [32]p, color, DJ/3.95)	Bobbs-Merrill	(1967)	Burningham, John	50-80	*
Burningham, John	Harquin (1st AM {std}, 4to, [32]p, color, DJ/3.50)	Bobbs-Merrill	(1968)	Burningham, John	50-85	*
Burningham, John	John Burningham's ABC (1st, 4to, ibds, dep)	L: J. Cape	(1964)	Burningham, John	45-70	
Burningham, John	Mr. Gumpy's Outing (1st {std}, 4to, [32]p, ibds, fp color, KGM, NYTBI)	L: J. Cape	1970	Burningham, John	80-125	
Burningham, John	The Seasons (1st, 4to, [32]p, bds, dp color, DJ)	L: J. Cape	1969	Burningham, John	50-85	
Burningham, John	Trubloff (1st AM {std}, 4to, [41]p, ibds, color, DJ/3.95)	Random	(1965)	Burningham, John	45-70	
Burns, Esther	Mrs. Peregrine & the Yak (1st, 12mo, ibds, [53]p, 2-color, pep, DJ/1.00)	Henry Holt & Co.	(1938)	Wilkin, Eloise B.	80-140	
Burns, Esther	Mrs. Peregrine at the Fair (1st, 12mo, [55]p, ibds, color, pep, DJ/1.00)	J. Messner	(1939)	Wilkin, Eloise B.	70-120	
Burns, Robert	Cotter's Saturday Night (1st, 12mo, ibds, 17p, frn by..)	L: Hewetson	(1908)	Rackham, Arthur	130-200	
Burns, Robert	Hand in Hand We'll Go (1st, 8vo, 28p, fp 2-color, pep, DJ/3.75)	Crowell	(1965)	Hogrogian, Nonny	50-80	R
Burns, Robert	Songs & Lyrics of Robert Burns (1st, 8vo, uncut, teg, 12ticp)	L: P.L. Warner	1911	Flint, William R.	250-400	
Burroughs, Edgar R.	Beasts of Tarzan (1st, sm8vo, 336p, b/w)	McClurg	1916	St. John, J. Allen	450-650	
Burroughs, Edgar R.	Princess of Mars (1st, sm8vo, black cl, 326p, 5pl)	McClurg	1917	Schoonover, Frank	450-650	
Burroughs, Edgar R.	Tarzan & the Jewels of Opar (1st, 8vo, green/gilt, 350p, 8pl)	McClurg	1918	St. John, J. Allen	350-500	
Burroughs, Edgar R.	Tarzan Twins (1st, 8vo, 126p, ibds, 14 fp color)	Volland	(1927)	Grant, Doug	180-270	*
Burroughs, Margaret	Jasper the Drummin' Boy (1st, lg8vo, ibds, 63p, fp b/w, DJ/1.75)	Viking	1947	Taylor, Margaret	70-100	
Burroughs, Margaret	Jasper the Drummin' Boy (1st {std}, 8vo, 64p, b/w, DJ/2.95)	Follett	(1970)	Lewin, Ted	30-45	
Burrows, Elizabeth	Irene of Tundra Towers (1st {std}, 8vo, 311p, col frn, pep)	Doubleday/Doran	1928	Daugherty, James	35-60	*
Burrows, Elizabeth	Judy of the Whale Gates (1st {std}, 8vo, 296p, col frn)	Doubleday/Doran	1930	Daugherty, James	25-40	
Burt, Mary E.	Odysseus, Hero of Ithaca (1st, 12mo, 223p, red cl, cvr by...)	Scribner	1898	Armstrong, Margaret	35-60	*
Burt, Nathaniel	War Cry of the West (1st {std}, 8vo, 86p, b/w, cep, DJ/3.00)	Holt, Rinehart	(1964)	Turkle, Brinton	30-55	
Burtis, Thomson	Straight Shooting (1st {std}, 8vo, 279p, col frn)	Doubleday/Doran	1931	Dobias, Frank	25-45	*
Burtis, Thomson	War of the Ghosts (1st {std}, 8vo, 262p, col frn, pep)	Doubleday/Doran	1932	Dobias, Frank	25-45	*
Burton, Earl & L.	Exciting Adventures of Waldo (1st, sm4to, 64p, grey cl, fp col, DJ/2.00)	Whittlesey	(1945)	Stone, Helen	45-60	
Burton, Earl & L.	Taffy & Joe (1st, sm4to, green cl, 60p, dp col frn, b/w, DJ/2.25)	Whittlesey	1947	Stone, Helen	40-65	
Burton, Hester	Beyond the Weir Bridge (1st AM {std}, 8vo, 221p, b/w, DJ/4.50)	Crowell	(1970)	Ambrus, Victor	20-30	
Burton, Hester	Castors Away! (1st AM {std}, 8vo, 254p, b/w, DJ/3.00, CgM)	World	(1963)	Ambrus, Victor	30-50	*
Burton, Hester	Flood at Reedsmere (1st AM {std}, 8vo, 204p, b/w, DJ/3.95)	World	(1968)	Jacques, Robin	25-40	
Burton, Hester	No Beat of Drum (1st {std}, 8vo, red cl, 190p, b/w, DJ)	L: Oxford U.Pr.	(1967)	Ambrus, Victor	30-45	
Burton, Hester	Time of Trial (1st AM {std}, 8vo, 216p, b/w, DJ/3.75, CgM)	World	(1964)	Ambrus, Victor	30-50	*
Burton, John B.	Across the Salt Seas (1st, 12mo, teg, 446p, cvr by...)	Herbert Stone	1897	Hazenplug, Frank	55-90	
Burton, Richard F.	Kasidah of Haji Abdu El-Yezdi (1st, sm4to, gilt, p-o, 129p, 12pl)	McKay	(1931)	Pogany, Willy	80-140	
Burton, Virginia L.	Calico the Wonder Horse (1st, narrow ob8vo, color, [58]p, DJ/1.00)	Houghton	1941	Burton, Virginia L.	170-250	
Burton, Virginia L.	Choo-Choo (1st, lg4to, red cl, [48]p, b/w, pep, DJ/1.50)	Houghton	(1937)	Burton, Virginia L.	100-160	R*
Burton, Virginia L.	Katy & the Big Snow (1st, sm ob4to, 32p, blue cl, color, pep, DJ/2.50)	Houghton	1943	Burton, Virginia L.	100-150	
Burton, Virginia L.	Life Story: Play in Five Acts (1st, sm ob4to, 67p, gilt, fp color, DJ/5.00)	Houghton	1962	Burton, Virginia L.	60-90	R
Burton, Virginia L.	Little House (1st, lg sq8vo, 40p, green cl, color, pep, DJ/2.00, CM)	Houghton	1942	Burton, Virginia L.	180-250	R
Burton, Virginia L.	Maybelle the Cable Car (1st, sq lg8vo, 42p, pep, color, DJ/2.75)	Houghton	1952	Burton, Virginia L.	125-200	R
Burton, Virginia L.	Mike Mulligan & his Steam Shovel (1st, sq8vo, [48]p, color, pep, DJ/1.50)	Houghton	1939	Burton, Virginia L.	140-200	R
Busoni, Rafaello	Somi Builds a Church (1st, lg8vo, 109p, b/w, pep, DJ/2.00)	Viking	1943	Busoni, Rafaello	20-35	
Butler, Charles	Pigs is Pigs (1st [this pub.], 12mo, 37p, 5pl)	McClure	1906	Crawford, Will	30-50	
Butler, Edward C.	Our Little Mexican Cousin (1st, 12mo, 100p, 10pl)	L.C. Page	1905	(Photos)	30-60	*
Butler, Elinor B.	Diamond Spider & other Stories (1st, sm8vo, 201p, b/w pl)	A. Harriman	1910	Dowling, C.M.	30-55	
Butler, Ellis P.	Confessions of a Daddy (1st, 8vo, red cl, 107p, 9pl)	Century	1907	Cory, Fanny	40-65	
Butler, Ellis P.	Incubator Baby (1st, 12mo, 111p, 4cp)	Funk/Wagnalls	1906	Preston, May W.	25-40	
Butler, Francelia	Skip Rope Book (1st, 12mo, [40]p, ipcb, color, pep, DJ/1.95)	Dial Press	1963	Haley, Gail E.	20-30	
Butler, William A.	Animal Book (1st [this pub], 8vo, bds, p-o, 42p, 8cp, pep)	Stokes	(1914)	Pattee, Elsie D.	40-65	
Butt, Geraldine	Esther, a Story for Children (1st, 8vo, 271p, green cl, 4 ticp)	L: Marcus Ward	1878	Greenaway, Kate	220-280	
Butterfield, Marguerite	Adventures of Esteban (1st, 8vo, 121p, 3-color, DJ/2.50)	Scribner	(1956)	Arno, Enrico	20-30	
Butters, Dorothy	Enchanted Caravan (1st, 8vo, 207p, b/w, DJ/2.50)	Macrae Smith	(1949)	Smalley, Janet	40-65	
Butters, Dorothy	Papa Dolphin's Table (1st {std}, 8vo, 88p, fp b/w, DJ/2.00)	Knopf	1955	Werth, Kurt	50-80	
Butterworth, Oliver	Enormous Egg (1st {std}, 8vo, 187p, b/w, DJ/2.95)	Little/Brown	1956	Darling, Louis	45-70	
Butterworth, Oliver	Trouble with Jenny's Ear (1st {std}, 8vo, 275p, fp b/w, DJ)	Little/Brown	(1960)	DeMiskey, Julian	80-125	

AUTHOR	TITLE	PUBLISHER	DATE	ARTIST	PRICE	LC
Buzzati, Dino	Bear's Famous Invasion of Sicily (1st, 4to, 146p, 16 fp color, DJ/2.75)	Pantheon	1947	Buzzati, Dino	80-150	
Byars, Betsy C.	Clementine (1st [1st bk.], 8vo, 70p, fp 1-color, DJ/2.75)	Houghton	1962	Wilton, Charles	40-65	
Byars, Betsy C.	Dancing Camel (1st, 8vo, 30p, b/w, DJ/2.75)	Viking	(1965)	Berson, Harold	30-50	*
Byars, Betsy C.	Midnight Fox (1st, 8vo, 157p, fp b/w, DJ/4.50)	Viking	(1968)	Grifalconi, Ann	30-50	
Byars, Betsy C.	Rama, the Gypsy Cat (1st, 8vo, 109p, fp b/w, DJ/3.50)	Viking	1966	Bacon, Peggy	30-45	
Byars, Betsy C.	Summer of the Swans (1st {std}, 8vo, 142p, fp b/w, DJ/3.95, NM)	Viking	(1970)	Coconis, Ted	100-160	
Byars, Betsy C.	The Groober (1st, ob8vo, ibds, 32p, b/w, DJ/2.50)	Harper	(1967)	Byars, Betsy	30-50	
Byars, Betsy C.	Trouble River (1st, 8vo, 158p, dp fp b/w, DJ/4.50)	Viking	(1969)	Negri, Rocco	40-65	*
Byington, Eloise	Mother Goose Fun (1st, sm8vo, p-o, gilt, 128p, color, pep)	Whitman	(1931)	Frantz, Kathleen	45-60	
Byington, Eloise	Pancake Brownies (1st, 8vo, p-o, 96p, color, pep)	Whitman	(1928)	Jones, Marguerite	50-80	
Byington, Eloise	Wishbone Children (1st, 8vo, blue cl, p-o, 64p, pep, color)	Whitman	(1934)	Frantz, Kathleen	30-50	
Byng, Douglas	Byng Ballads (1st, 8vo, ibds, [48]p, 8 fp color)	L: John Lane	[1932]	Hutton, Clarke	40-65	
Bynner, Edwin L.	Chase of the Meteor (1st, 8vo, 209p, gilt, 10 b/w)	Little/Brown	1891	Merrill, Frank T.	60-90	
Byrde, Elsie	Polish Fairy Book (1st, 8vo, 231p, color)	Stokes	(1925)	Kadar, Livia	30-45	
Byrne, Donn	Messer Marco Polo (1st, 12mo, 147p, 4pl, DJ)	Century	1921	Falls, Charles B.	40-65	
Byrne, Mary Agnes	One Too Many (1st, 8vo, green cl, 191p, 4pl)	Saalfield	(1912)	Smith, Wuanita	35-60	*
Byrne, Miriam	House of the Red Fox (1st, sq12mo, 116p, 8pl)	Stokes	(1907)	Upjohn, Anna M.	25-45	*
Byrne, Miriam	Would-Be Witch (1st, sq12mo, 127p, 8pl)	Stokes	(1906)	Upjohn, Anna M.	20-35	
Byron, May	Adventures of Trooper Peek-A-Boo (1st, 8vo, unpag, color)	L: Hodder	[1916]	Preston, Chloe	150-250	
Byron, May	Animal Frolics (1st, 4to, unpag)	L: Hodder	[1916]	Aldin, Cecil	90-120	*
Byron, May	Barbara Peek-A-Boo's Holiday (1st, 4to, ibds, p-o, unpag, 8cp)	L: Hodder	[1914]	Preston, Chloe	250-400	
Byron, May	Cat's Cradle (1st, sm4to, ibds, [48]p, color)	L: Blackie	[1908]	Wain, Louis	650-900	
Byron, May	Cecil Aldin's Happy Family (1st, 4to, bds, teg, p-o, 36cp)	L: H. Frowde	[1912]	Aldin, Cecil	225-325	
Byron, May	Cecil Aldin's Merry Party (1st, 4to, ibds, p-o, gilt, teg, 36cp)	L: H. Frowde	1913	Aldin, Cecil	500-700	
Byron, May	Friday & Saturday... (1st, ob4to, ibds, unpag, 12 fp color)	L: H. Frowde	[1910]	Hassall, John	170-240	
Byron, May	Hole in the Wall (1st, 8vo, p-o, ipcb, 6 fp color, pep)	L: H. Milford	[1915]	Aris, Ernest A.	70-100	
Byron, May	Humpty & Dumpty Give a Fancy Dress Ball (sq8vo, ibds, 6 fp color)	L: Milford/OUP	(1913)	Aldin, Cecil	200-350	
Byron, May	Hungry Peter (1st AM, lg8vo, tan bds, p-o, 5cp, pep)	NY: Hodder	1914	Aldin, Cecil	100-165	*
Byron, May	Land of Nod (ob4to, ibds, 12cp)	NY: Hodder	[1909]	Petherick, Rosa	170-240	
Byron, May	Little Brown Rooster (1st, sm4to, ipcb, color, pep)	Doran	(1922)	Robinson, Gordon	40-70	
Byron, May	Little Brown Rooster (1st, lg8vo, p-o, 60p, orange cl, 6cp, pep)	NY: Nelson	1928	Robinson, Gordon	60-100	
Byron, May	Little Wee Bear (24mo, ipcb, 24 fp color)	L: H. Milford	[1908]	Petherick, Rosa	120-180	
Byron, May	Little Yellow Duckling (1st, sm4to, gilt, 60p, 6cp, pep)	Doran	(1922)	Robinson/Rudge	40-70	*
Byron, May	Magic Shop (4to, 36p, ibds, 14 fp color, pep)	L: Alf Cooke	[1905]	Hassall, John	180-240	
Byron, May	Peek-a-Boo Farmers (sq4to, bds, p-o, 6cp)	L: H. Milford	[1912]	Preston, Chloe	300-450	
Byron, May	Peek-a-Boo Gipsies (1st, sq4to, ibds, 43p, 6cp)	L: H. Milford	(1923)	Preston, Chloe	300-450	
Byron, May	Peek-a-Boos at the Zoo (1st, sq4to, ibds, unpag, p-o, 12cp)	L: H. Frowde	[1915]	Preston, Chloe	250-400	
Byron, May	Peek-a-Boos in Town (1st, ob4to, ibds, unpag, 16 fp color)	L: H. Frowde	[1915]	Preston, Chloe	300-500	
Byron, May	Peek-a-Boos in War (sq4to, bds, p-o, 6cp)	L: H. Frowde	[1915]	Preston, Chloe	300-450	
Byron, May	Peek-a-Boos in Winter (ob folio, ibds, 18cp)	L: H. Frowde	[1910]	Preston, Chloe	300-500	
Byron, May	Ruff and Reddy (1st AM, 4to, ibds, 63p, 26cp)	Stokes	(1911)	Hassall, John	300-500	
Byron, May	Sambo & Susanna (ob4to, ibds, 24 color, [french fold paper])	L: Blackie	[1905]	Parkinson, Ethel	400-600	
Byron, May	Teddy Bear Book (sq8vo, ibds, 12cp)	L: H. Frowde	[1911]	Petherick, Rosa	250-400	
Byron, May	Teddy Bearoplane (1st AM, sm4to, ibds, 12cp)	NY: Hodder	[1909]	Sinclair, James R.	250-400	
Byron, May	William & Woggs (sq8vo, bds, p-o, 6cp)	L: H. Frowde	[1910]	Preston, Chloe	150-225	
Cabassa, Victoria	Trixie and the Tiger (1st, sm4to, [41]p, fp color, pep, DJ/3.50)	Abelard-Schuman	1968	Obligado, Lilian	40-65	
Cabell, James B.	Chivalry (1st, 8vo, red cl, teg, 224p, 12cp, dep)	Harper	1909	Pyle, Howard	100-160	
Cabell, James B.	Eagle's Shadow (1st, 8vo, red/gilt, 256p, 8pl, pep)	Doubleday/Page	1904	Grefe, Will	100-160	
Cabell, James B.	Gallantry (1st, 8vo, teg, grey/gilt, 334p, 4 ticp, pep)	Harper	1907	Pyle, Howard	100-160	
Cabell, James B.	Line of Love (1st, 8vo, p-o, teg, 291p, uncut, 10cp)	Harper	1905	Pyle, Howard	100-165	
Cabell, James B.	Soul of Melicent (1st, 8vo, 216p, gilt, p-o, 4cp)	Stokes	(1913)	Pyle, Howard	100-170	
Cable, George W.	Bonaventure (1st, 8vo, 314p, olive/gilt, teg)	Scribner	1902	Armstrong, Margaret	40-60	
Cable, George W.	Bylow Hill (1st, 8vo, teg, uncut, red/gilt, 209p, cvr by...)	Scribner	1902	Armstrong, Margaret	50-80	
Cable, George W.	Doctor Sevier (8vo, 473p, teg, olive/gilt)	Scribner	1898	Armstrong, Margaret	30-50	
Cable, George W.	John March, Southerner (1st, 12mo, green/gilt, teg, 513p)	Scribner	1894	Armstrong, Margaret	70-120	R
Cable, George W.	Kincaid's Battery (1st, 8vo, 396p, gilt, col frn, 6pl, cvr by...)	Scribner	1908	Armstrong, Margaret	40-65	
Cable, George W.	Old Creole Days (1st, lg8vo, 234p, grey cl, teg, 8pl)	Scribner	1897	Herter, Albert	80-120	
Cable, George W.	Posson Jane & Pere Raphael (1st, 12mo, teg, blue/gilt, 162p, uncut)	Scribner	1909	Armstrong, Margaret	40-60	
Cable, George W.	Strong Hearts (1st, 12mo, 214p, olive/gilt, teg)	Scribner	1899	Armstrong, Margaret	35-50	
Cable, George W.	The Cavalier (1st [1], 8vo, red/gilt, 311p, 8pl)	Scribner	1901	Christy, Howard C.	60-90	
Cable, George W.	The Grandissimes (8vo, 448p, teg, olive/gilt)	Scribner	1898	Armstrong, Margaret	30-50	
Cabot, Carolyn S.	Football Grandma (1st, 8vo, 79p, tan cl, b/w, pep by...)	Small/Maynard	1905	Reed, Ethel	40-60	*
Cabot, Elise	Balloon Moon (1st, 8vo, 99p, blue/gilt, col frn, fp b/w)	Henry Holt & Co.	(1927)	Lathrop, Dorothy	60-100	
Cadby, Carine	Brownies in Switzerland (1st AM, lg8vo, p-o, 137p, 6cp)	Macaulay	(1924)	Stephensons	55-90	*
Cadman, S. Parkes	Parables of Jesus (1st, lg8vo, p-o, 163p, purple/gilt, pep, 8cp)	McKay	(1931)	Wyeth, N.C.	500-750	
Cady, Harrison	Caleb Cottontail (1st, 8vo, 127p, 2-color, pep)	Houghton	1921	Cady, Harrison	120-180	
Cady, Harrison	Holiday Time on Butternut Hill (1st, 24mo, ibds, unpag, 12 color)	Whitman	(1929)	Cady, Harrison	60-90	
Cady, Harrison	Time to Get Up (4to, ibds)	Stoll/Edwards	1928	Cady, Harrison	80-120	*
Caffrey, Nancy	Horse Haven (1st {std}, 8vo, 96p, b/w, DJ/2.50)	Dutton	1955	Brown, Paul	70-100	
Cain, Neville	Fairies' Circus (1st, lg4to, ibds, [16]p, calligraphy, color)	R.H. Russell	1903	Unknown	120-185	*
Caire, Helen	Senor Castillo (1st, lg8vo, 76p, ibds, b/w, DJ/1.50)	Rinehart	(1948)	Price, Christine	25-45	
Caldecott, R.	Fox Jumps Over the Parson's Gate (ob8vo, wraps, 24p, 6cp)	L: Routledge	1883	Caldecott, Randolph	120-200	*
Caldecott, R.	Gleanings from the Graphic (1st, ob folio, ibds, gilt, 84p, 32 color)	L: Routledge	1889	Caldecott, Randolph	200-300	
Caldecott, R.	Graphic Pictures (1st, ob folio, 93p, color)	L: Routledge	1883	Caldecott, Randolph	180-270	
Caldecott, R.	Last Graphic Pictures (1st, ob folio, ipcb, [71]p, color)	L: Routledge	1888	Caldecott, Randolph	150-225	
Caldecott, R.	More Graphic Pictures (1st, ob folio, ibds, 32cp)	L: Routledge	1887	Caldecott, Randolph	125-200	
Caldecott, R.	Panjandrum Picture Book (ob. sm4to, [98]p, color)	L: Warne	[1890]	Caldecott, Randolph	120-200	
Caldecott, R.	Queen of Hearts (1st, 8vo, wraps, 32p, 9cp)	L: Routledge	(1881)	Caldecott, Randolph	100-165	

AUTHOR	TITLE	PUBLISHER	DATE	ARTIST	PRICE	LC
Caldecott, R.	Sketch Book (1st, ob4to, 48p, color)	L: Routledge	1883	Caldecott, Randolph	165-220	
Caldecott, R.	Three Jovial Huntsmen (1st, ob8vo, p-o, 7 ticp)	L: Warne	[1908]	Caldecott, Randolph	90-120	*
Caldwell, Erskine	Molly Cottontail (1st {std}, 8vo, 31p, fp 2-color, DJ/2.50)	Little/Brown	1958	Sharp, William	80-125	R
Calhoun, Mary	Goblin Under the Stairs (1st, ob8vo, [32]p, color, DJ/3.50)	Wm. Morrow	(1968)	McCaffery, Janet	30-45	*
Calhoun, Mary	High Wind for Kansas (1st, 8vo, 45p, b/w, DJ/2.75)	Wm. Morrow	1965	Mars, Witold T.	30-45	*
Calhoun, Mary	Houn' Dog (1st, 4to, [32]p, fp 3-color, DJ/2.75)	Wm. Morrow	1959	Duvoisin, Roger	60-90	R
Calhoun, Mary	House of Thirty Cats (1st, 8vo, 218p, b/w, DJ/3.50)	Harper	(1965)	Chalmers, Mary	20-30	
Calhoun, Mary	Hungry Leprechaun (1st, lg ob8vo, [30]p, fp 2-color, pep, DJ/2.75)	Wm. Morrow	1962	Duvoisin, Roger	50-80	
Calhoun, Mary	Katie John (1st, 8vo, 134p, fp b/w, DJ/2.50)	Harper	(1960)	Frame, Paul	25-45	
Calhoun, Mary	Last Two Elves in Denmark (1st, ob8vo, [32]p, fp color, dep, DJ/3.25)	Wm. Morrow	1968	McCaffery, Janet	30-45	
Calhoun, Mary	Magic in the Alley (1st {std}, 8vo, 167p, orange cl, cep, DJ/4.50)	Atheneum	1970	Watson, Wendy	25-40	
Calhoun, Mary	Making the Mississippi Shout (1st, 8vo, 96p, b/w, DJ/2.50)	Wm. Morrow	1957	Galdone, Paul	20-35	
Calhoun, Mary	Nine Lives of Homer C. Cat (1st, sm4to, [32]p, fp 3-color, DJ/2.75)	Wm. Morrow	1961	Duvoisin, Roger	50-80	
Calhoun, Mary	Pixy & the Lazy Housewife (1st, lg ob8vo, [32]p, color, DJ/3.50)	Wm. Morrow	1969	McCaffery, Janet	20-35	
Calhoun, Mary	Sweet Patootie Doll (1st, sm4to, yellow cl, [32]p, 3-color, DJ/2.75)	Wm. Morrow	1957	Duvoisin, Roger	80-135	
Calhoun, Mary	Wobble the Witch Cat (1st, 4to, [30]p, color, DJ/2.75)	Wm. Morrow	1958	Duvoisin, Roger	50-85	
Calhoun, Mary Eliz.	Dorothy's Rabbit Stories (1st, sm8vo, 115p, grey cl, 10pl)	Crowell	(1907)	Blaisdell, E. Ward	55-80	*
Callahan, Lorna	Where the Trail Divides (1st, 8vo, 188p, b/w, DJ/3.00)	Whittlesey	(1957)	Galdone, Paul	45-70	
Calmour, Alfred C.	Rumbo Rhymes (1st, lg8vo, green ibds, 99p, 23cp, pep)	L: Harper	1911	Crane, Walter	250-400	
Cameron, Eleanor	Beast with the Magical Horn (1st {std}, 8vo, 73p, color, DJ/3.75)	Little/Brown	1963	Krush, Beth & Joe	140-200	
Cameron, Eleanor	Mr. Bass's Planetoid (1st {std}, sm8vo, 227p, b/w, DJ/3.00)	Little/Brown	(1958)	Darling, Louis	200-300	
Cameron, Eleanor	Mysterious Christmas Shell (1st {std}, 8vo, 184p, b/w, DJ/3.25)	Little/Brown	(1961)	Krush, Beth & Joe	80-130	
Cameron, Eleanor	Mystery for Mr. Bass (1st {std}, sm8vo, 229p, b/w, DJ/3.00)	Little/Brown	(1960)	Shortall, Leonard	200-300	
Cameron, Eleanor	Spell is Cast (1st {std}, 8vo, 271p, b/w, DJ/3.95)	Little/Brown	(1964)	Krush, Beth & Joe	160-225	
Cameron, Eleanor	Stowaway to the Mushroom Planet (1st {std}, sm8vo, 226p, b/w, DJ/2.75)	Little/Brown	(1956)	Henneberger, Rbt.	150-220	
Cameron, Eleanor	Terrible Churnadryne (1st {std}, 8vo, 125p, b/w, DJ/3.00)	Little/Brown	(1959)	Krush, Beth & Joe	80-130	*
Cameron, Eleanor	Time and Mr. Bass (1st {std}, sm8vo, 247p, b/w, DJ/3.95)	Little/Brown	(1967)	Meise, Fred	200-300	
Cameron, Eleanor	Wonderful Flight to Mushroom Planet (1st {std}, sm8vo, 214p, b/w, DJ/2.75)	Little/Brown	(1954)	Henneberger, Rbt.	250-350	
Cameron, Polly	Cat Who Couldn't Purr (1st, 8vo, [32]p, 1-color, cep, DJ/2.25)	Coward	(1957)	Cameron, Polly	70-100	*
Cameron, Polly	Child's Book of Nonsense (1st, sq8vo, ipcb, [30]p, color, DJ/2.50)	Coward	(1960)	Cameron, Polly	80-125	R
Cameron, Polly	I Can't, Said the Ant (1st, lg8vo, [42]p, fp 1-color, DJ/2.50)	Coward	(1961)	Cameron, Polly	80-125	R
Cammack, Key	Spartan Primer (1st, 4to, ipcb, fp color)	Duffield	1913	Drayton, Grace	160-240	
Camp, Ruth O.	Story of the Markets (1st {std}, 12mo, 128p, col frn, b/w)	Harper	1929	Hader, Elmer	55-80	*
Campbell, A.M.	Fairy Flights in Cloudland (4to, ibds, 16cp)	L: A. Cooke	[1915]	Cook/Christie	160-240	
Campbell, A.M.	Mercury the Story Teller (4to, ibds, 16cp)	L: T.F. Unwin	[1903]	Hassall, John	250-400	
Campbell, Elizabeth	Nails to Nickels (1st {std}, 4to, 58p, 1-color, DJ/3.00)	Little/Brown	(1960)	Weisgard, Leonard	30-50	
Campbell, John F.	Celtic Dragon Myth (1st, 8vo, 172p, gilt, p-o, 5cp)	J. Grant	1911	Duff, Rachel	120-170	
Campbell, Lang	Dinky Ducklings (1st, 12mo, ibds, 39p, color, pep)	Volland	(1928)	Campbell, Lang	80-125	
Campbell, Lang	Funnyfeathers (1st, 4to, 86p, tan cl, 6cp, pep)	Dutton	(1917)	Campbell, Lang	65-100	
Campbell, Lang	Merry Murphy (1st, 12mo, [44]p, color, pep)	Algonquin	1929	Campbell, Lang	40-65	
Campbell, M. Rudolph	Talking Crocodile (1st {std}, 4to, [46]p, color, cep, DJ/4.95)	Atheneum	1968	Piussi-Campbell, J.	30-50	*
Campbell, Mary M.	New England Butt'ry Shelf Almanac (1st {std}, sq12mo, 302p, 6cp, DJ/6.95)	World	(1970)	Tudor, Tasha	80-125	
Campbell, Ruth	Cat Whose Whiskers Slipped (1st, 8vo, ibds, color, pep)	Volland	(1925)	Cadie, V. Eliz.	60-100	
Campbell, Ruth	Runaway Smalls (1st, lg8vo, ibds, 73p, b/w)	Penn	1923	Price, Hattie L.	50-80	
Campbell, Ruth	Small Fry and the Winged Horse (1st, 8vo, ibds, 28p, 10cp, pep)	Volland	(1927)	Tenggren, Gustaf	80-130	
Campbell, Ruth	Turtle Whose Snap Unfastened (1st, lg8vo, 93p, ibds, color, pep)	Volland	(1927)	Cadie, V. Eliz.	70-120	
Campbell, Walter D.	Beyond the Border (1st AM, 12mo, gilt, AEG, 456p, 38pl)	R.H. Russell	1898	Stratton, Helen	100-160	
Canfield, Dorothy	Made-to-Order Stories (1st, 8vo, 263p, col frn, b/w)	Harcourt	(1925)	Lathrop, Dorothy	60-90	
Canfield, Dorothy	Understood Betsy (1st, sm8vo, 271p, green cl, 11pl, PPP)	Henry Holt & Co.	1917	Williamson, Ada C.	80-120	
Cannon, Wilma	Peter is Sweeter (1st, sq12mo, [40]p, bds, 2-color, DJ/1.00)	Lothrop, Lee	(1942)	Cannon, Marian	35-50	
Canton, William	Child's Book of Saints (1st, 8vo, 257p, teg, col frn, 19 fp b/w)	L: J.M. Dent	1898	Robinson, Thomas H.	70-100	*
Canton, William	Child's Book of Warriors (1st, sm8vo, green/gilt, teg, uncut, 319p, 3cp)	L: J.M. Dent	(1912)	Cole, Herbert	80-120	
Canton, William	Reign of King Herla (1st, 8vo, AEG, 367p, gilt, col frn, b/w)	L: J.M. Dent	(1900)	Robinson, Charles	150-225	
Capes, Bernard E.	Romance of Lohengrin (1st, 8vo, blue/gilt, 271p, 14pl)	L: Dean	1905	Pogany, Willy	200-300	
Capuana, Luigi	Golden-Feather (1st {std}, 8vo, 205p, col frn, b/w, pep)	Dutton	(1930)	Freeman, Margaret	35-60	*
Carden, Priscilla	Aldo's Tower (1st {std}, lg8vo, 63p, color, DJ/2.75)	Ariel	(1954)	Werth, Kurt	25-45	
Carden, Priscilla	Vanilla Village (1st {std}, lg8vo, 58p, tan cl, pep, color, DJ/2.00)	Ariel	(1952)	Barnum, Jay H.	30-50	
Carigiet, Alois	Anton and Anne (1st AM, ob folio, [44]p, color, DJ/7.00)	H.Z. Walck	(1969)	Carigiet, Alois	40-65	
Carigiet, Alois	Pear Tree, Birch Tree/Barberry Bush (1st AM {std}, obfol, [33]p, DJ/5.00)	H.Z. Walck	1967	Carigiet, Alois	30-50	*
Carle, Eric	Pancakes, Pancakes (1st AM {std}, 4to, [30]p, color, DJ)	Knopf	(1970)	Carle, Eric	30-50	*
Carle, Eric	Tiny Seed (1st, 4to, [34]p, fp color, dep, DJ/4.50)	Crowell	1970	Carle, Eric	30-50	*
Carleton, Henry G.	Thompson Street Poker Club (1st, 8vo, 48p, ibds, 11 fp b/w)	White & Allen	1888	Kemble, Edward W.	90-120	*
Carleton, Katherine	Dorothy, the Motor Girl (1st, sm8vo, 386p, 33pl)	Century	1911	Various	30-50	
Carlsen, Ruth C.	Ride a Wild Horse (1st {std}, 8vo, 164p, b/w, DJ/3.50)	Houghton	1970	Krush, Beth & Joe	50-80	
Carlsen, Ruth C.	Sam Bottleby (1st, 8vo, 152p, b/w, cep, DJ/3.50)	Houghton	1968	Tripp, Wallace	30-40	
Carlson, Bernice	Listen! And Help Tell the Story (1st, lg8vo, 176p, 2-color, cep, DJ/3.95)	Abingdon Press	(1965)	Burris, Burmah	30-50	
Carlson, Natalie S.	Alphonse, that Bearded One (1st {std}, 8vo, blue cl, 78p, b/w, DJ/2.50)	Harcourt	(1954)	Nicolas	60-90	R
Carlson, Natalie S.	Ann Aurelia and Dorothy (1st, 8vo, 130p, b/w, DJ/3.95)	Harper	(1968)	Payson, Dale	20-30	
Carlson, Natalie S.	Befana's Gift (1st, 8vo, 86p, fp b/w, cep, DJ/3.95)	Harper	(1969)	Quackenbush, Rbt.	25-45	
Carlson, Natalie S.	Brother for the Orphelines (1st, sm4to, 100p, fp b/w, DJ/2.95)	Harper	(1959)	Williams, Garth	40-65	
Carlson, Natalie S.	Carnival in Paris (1st, 8vo, 152p, fp b/w, cep, DJ/2.95)	Harper	(1962)	Rocker, Fermin	45-70	R
Carlson, Natalie S.	Chalou (1st, 8vo, 109p, fp b/w, cep, DJ/3.50)	Harper	(1967)	Loh, George	30-45	
Carlson, Natalie S.	Empty Schoolhouse (1st, 8vo, 119p, b/w, DJ/3.50)	Harper	(1965)	Kaufmann, John	20-35	*
Carlson, Natalie S.	Evangeline, Pigeon of Paris (1st {std}, 8vo, red cl, 70p, fp b/w, DJ/2.75)	Harcourt	(1960)	Nicolas	35-50	
Carlson, Natalie S.	Family Under the Bridge (1st, 8vo, 99p, green cl, 11 fp b/w, DJ/2.95, NH)	Harper	(1958)	Williams, Garth	65-100	R
Carlson, Natalie S.	Half-Sisters (1st, 8vo, 163p, fp b/w, DJ/3.50)	Harper	(1970)	DiGrazia, Thomas	20-35	*
Carlson, Natalie S.	Happy Orpheline (1st, sm4to, blue cl, 96p, fp b/w, DJ/2.95)	Harper	(1957)	Williams, Garth	45-70	
Carlson, Natalie S.	Hortense, the Cow for a Queen (1st {std}, 8vo, 94p, b/w, DJ/2.75)	Harcourt	(1957)	Nicolas	30-45	

AUTHOR	TITLE	PUBLISHER	DATE	ARTIST	PRICE	LC
Carlson, Natalie S.	Jean-Claude's Island (1st, 8vo, 147p, fp b/w, DJ/3.50)	Harper	(1963)	Burkert, Nancy	30-50	R
Carlson, Natalie S.	Letter on the Tree (1st, 8vo, 116p, fp b/w, cep, DJ/3.50)	Harper	(1964)	Kaufmann, John	20-30	
Carlson, Natalie S.	Luigi on the Streets (1st, 8vo, 144p, b/w, DJ/3.95)	Harper	(1967)	McCully, Emily	30-45	
Carlson, Natalie S.	Marchers for the Dream (1st, 8vo, 130p, fp b/w, ipcb, DJ/3.50)	Harper	(1969)	Smith, Alvin	30-50	
Carlson, Natalie S.	Orphelines in the Enchanted Castle (1st, 8vo, 95p, fp b/w, cep, DJ/3.50)	Harper	(1964)	Saviozzi, Adriana	50-80	R
Carlson, Natalie S.	Pet for the Orphelines (1st, sm4to, 97p, fp b/w, DJ/2.95)	Harper	(1962)	Rocker, Fermin	50-80	R
Carlson, Natalie S.	Sailor's Choice (1st, 8vo, 140p, b/w, DJ/3.50)	Harper	(1966)	Loh, George	25-40	
Carlson, Natalie S.	Sashes Red & Blue (1st, 8vo, 107p, b/w, DJ/2.50)	Harper	(1956)	Fava, Rita	20-30	
Carlson, Natalie S.	School Bell in the Valley (1st {std}, sm8vo, 124p, b/w, DJ/3.00)	Harcourt	(1963)	Riswold, Gilbert	20-30	
Carlson, Natalie S.	Song of the Lop-Eared Mule (1st, 8vo, 79p, b/w, DJ/2.75)	Harper	(1961)	Domanska, Janina	20-30	
Carlson, Natalie S.	Talking Cat (1st, sq8vo, 87p, red cl, 15 fp b/w, DJ/2.50)	Harper	(1952)	Duvoisin, Roger	60-90	
Carlson, Natalie S.	Tomahawk Family (1st, sm8vo, 170p, fp b/w, DJ/2.75)	Harper	(1960)	Cook, Stephen	20-30	
Carlson, Natalie S.	Wings Against the Wind (1st, 8vo, 51p, fp b/w, DJ/2.50)	Harper	(1955)	Vasiliu, Mircea	20-35	
Carlton, Maud	Tumble Down Pictures (1st, 4to, ibds, unpag, 6 chromos)	Nister/Dutton	[1898]	Hardy, E. Stuart	200-300	
Carlyle, Thomas	Sartor Resartus (1st, sm8vo, AEG, 352p, blue/gilt, b/w, dep)	L: G. Bell	1898	Sullivan, Edmund J.	100-165	
Carman, Bliss	Low Tide on Grand Pre (2nd, 12mo, gilt, 132p, teg, cvr by...)	Stone/Kimball	1894	Hallowell, G.H.	60-100	
Carman, Bliss	Winter Holiday (1st, 12mo, 43p, cvr by...)	Small/Maynard	1899	Meteyard, Thomas B.	55-80	
Carmer, Carl	Too Many Cherries (1st, 4to, 62p, ipcb, 2-color, pep, DJ/2.00)	Viking	1949	Barnum, Jay H.	45-70	
Carmer, Carl	Wildcat Furs to China (1st {std}, 8vo, 76p, fp color, DJ/2.00)	Knopf	(1945)	Carmer, Elizabeth	30-50	
Carmichael, Philip	Man from the Moon (1st, 8vo, 296p, blue/gilt, 8cp)	L: Richards	1909	Watkins, Frank	90-135	
Carpenter, Frances	African Wonder Tales (1st {std}, lg8vo, 215p, b/w, DJ/3.95)	Doubleday	(1963)	Escourido, Joseph	40-65	
Carpenter, Frances	Elephant's Bathtub (1st {std}, lg8vo, 219p, b/w, DJ/3.50)	Doubleday	(1962)	Guggenheim, Hans	30-50	
Carpenter, Frances	Mouse Palace (1st, 8vo, 60p, 3-color, DJ/2.95)	McGraw-Hill	(1964)	Adams, Adrienne	25-40	
Carpenter, Frances	Tales of a Chinese Grandmother (1st, 8vo, 261p, 9cp)	L: Harrap	(1938)	Hasselriis, Malthe	35-60	
Carpenter, Frances	Tales of a Russian Grandmother (1st AM {std}, lg8vo, 292p, 8cp, dep)	Doubleday/Doran	1933	Bilibin, Ivan	90-120	
Carpenter, Frances	Wonder Tales of Dogs & Cats (1st {std}, lg8vo, 255p, fp b/w, DJ/3.50)	Doubleday	(1955)	Keats, Ezra J.	40-60	
Carpenter, Frances	Wonder Tales of Seas and Ships (1st {std}, 8vo, 285p, b/w, DJ/3.50)	Doubleday	(1959)	Spier, Peter E.	30-55	
Carpenter, John	Improving Songs for Anxious Children (lg ob4to, 50p, ibds, 19 color)	Schirmer	(1913)	Carpenter, J.& R.	120-180	*
Carpenter, John	When Little Boys Sing (1st, ob folio, [39]p, ibds, color)	McClurg	(1904)	Carpenter, J.& R.	120-200	
Carr, Albert	Men of Power (1st, 8vo, red cl, 272p, fp b/w, DJ/2.50)	Viking	1940	Simont, Marc	30-50	*
Carr, Alice V.	Fairy of the Rhone (1st, 12mo, 69p, woodcuts)	L.C. Page	1901	Smith, Winifred	30-50	
Carr, Mary J.	Children of the Covered Wagon (1st, 8vo, 318p, b/w, pep, DJ/2.00)	Crowell	(1934)	Brann, Esther	30-50	
Carr, Mary J.	Peggy & Paul & Laddy (1st, 8vo, 207p, brown cl, b/w, pep, DJ/1.75)	Crowell	(1936)	Voute, Kathleen	25-40	*
Carr, Mary J.	Top of the Morning (1st, ob12mo, [96]p, col frn, DJ/1.50)	Crowell	(1941)	Jones, Henrietta	25-40	*
Carr, Mary J.	Young Mac of Fort Vancouver (1st, 8vo, 238p, p-o, color, DJ/2.00, NH)	Crowell	1940	Holberg, Richard	45-70	
Carr, Robert V.	Cowboy Lyrics (1st, sm8vo, 229p, teg)	Small/Maynard	(1912)	Elwell, Robert F.	60-100	
Carrick, Carol	Clearing in the Forest (1st {std}, ob8vo, [30]p, fp 2-color, DJ/4.50)	Dial Press	(1970)	Carrick, Donald	30-50	*
Carrick, Carol	Swamp Spring (1st {std}, sm4to, [32]p, color, cep, DJ/4.50)	Macmillan	(1969)	Carrick, Donald	30-50	
Carrick, Carol	The Brook (1st {std}, sm4to, [30]p, fp 3-color, DJ/3.95)	Macmillan	(1967)	Carrick, Donald	30-45	
Carrick, Carol	The Pond (1st {std}, sm4to, [30]p, fp color, DJ/4.95)	Macmillan	(1970)	Carrick, Donald	30-50	*
Carrick, Valery	Valery Carrick's Picture Folk-Tales (1st, 4to, 94p, p-o, b/w, DJ)	Stokes	1926	Carrick, Valery	70-100	
Carrighar, Sally	One Day at Teton Marsh (1st {std}, 8vo, 239p, b/w woodcuts, DJ/3.50)	Knopf	1947	Mattson, G.& P.	30-45	
Carrighar, Sally	One Day on Beetle Rock (1st {std}{1st bk}, 8vo, 196p, gilt, pep, DJ/3.00)	Knopf	1944	Kane, Henry B.	40-65	
Carrington, Edith	Animals in the Wrong Places (1st, 24mo, 83p, 11 fp b/w)	L: Bell	1896	Robinson, Charles	200-300	*
Carroll, Lewis	Alice in Wonderland (sm4to, tan cl, 160p, 4cp)	Altemus	(1897)	Tenniel, John	100-165	
Carroll, Lewis	Alice in Wonderland (1st, 4to, 255p, yellow/gilt, 16cp)	Wessels	(1899)	McManus, Blanche	130-200	R
Carroll, Lewis	Alice in Wonderland (1st, 12mo, 179p, color)	NY: McKibbin	1899	Tenniel, John	80-120	*
Carroll, Lewis	Alice in Wonderland (16mo, ibds, p-o, 126p, 30cp, pep)	Altemus	[1900]	Tenniel, John	80-120	
Carroll, Lewis	Alice in Wonderland (sm8vo, green/gilt, 8pl)	L: Ward Lock	(1901)	McManus, Blanche	70-100	
Carroll, Lewis	Alice in Wonderland (1st, 8vo, vellum/gilt, 193p, teg, 40pl)	Harper	1901	Newell, Peter	160-225	
Carroll, Lewis	Alice in Wonderland (1st, 12mo, brown cl, 192p, 12pl)	Rand/McNally	(1902)	Cory, Fanny	50-90	
Carroll, Lewis	Alice in Wonderland (32mo, 127p, 32 color)	L: Macmillan	1903	Tenniel, John	90-160	*
Carroll, Lewis	Alice in Wonderland (1st, 8vo, 247p, grey/gilt, 12cp)	Stokes	(1904)	Kirk, Maria L.	160-240	
Carroll, Lewis	Alice in Wonderland (sm8vo, ibds, 202p, pep)	Caldwell	[1904]	Tenniel, John	90-160	*
Carroll, Lewis	Alice in Wonderland (1st, 8vo, 165p, blue cl, 10cp, pep)	Dodge	1907	Gutmann, Bessie P.	200-300	
Carroll, Lewis	Alice in Wonderland (1st, 12mo, 198p, col frn, gilt)	L: Routledge	[1907]	Maybank, Thomas	120-185	
Carroll, Lewis	Alice in Wonderland (1st, 8vo, green/gilt, 161p, 13cp, pep)	L: Heinemann	(1907)	Rackham, Arthur	275-400	
Carroll, Lewis	Alice in Wonderland (1st AM, 8vo, p-o, 162p, 13cp, pep)	Doubleday/Page	[1907]	Rackham, Arthur	225-350	
Carroll, Lewis	Alice in Wonderland (1st, sm4to, teg, gilt, 179p, 8cp, pep)	L: Cassell	(1907)	Robinson, Charles	500-750	
Carroll, Lewis	Alice in Wonderland (1st, 8vo, teg, p-o, gilt, 166p, 12cp, pep)	L: Chatto	1907	Sowerby, Millicent	250-350	
Carroll, Lewis	Alice in Wonderland (1st, 12mo, blue/gilt, AEG, p-o, 152p, 8cp)	L: John Lane	(1907)	Walker, W.H.	200-300	
Carroll, Lewis	Alice in Wonderland (1st, lg8vo, blue/gilt, teg, 246p, 14cp, pep)	L: Nelson	[1908]	Rountree, Harry	600-800	
Carroll, Lewis	Alice in Wonderland (1st AM, 8vo, p-o, 165p, 12cp)	Duffield	1908	Sowerby, Millicent	200-300	
Carroll, Lewis	Alice in Wonderland (1st, lg8vo, ibds, gilt, 148p, AEG, 12cp, pep)	L: R. Tuck	(1910)	Attwell, Mabel L.	350-500	
Carroll, Lewis	Alice in Wonderland (8vo, 190p, red/gilt, 30pl by...)	L: Collins	[1910]	Robinson, Thomas H.	120-180	
Carroll, Lewis	Alice in Wonderland (1st, 8vo, 48p, color)	Barse/Hopkins	[1910]	Von Hofsten, H.	60-100	*
Carroll, Lewis	Alice in Wonderland (1st, sq8vo, 192p, red cl, 6 ticp)	L: Headley	(1911)	Soper, George	250-350	
Carroll, Lewis	Alice in Wonderland (1st AM, sq8vo, 192p, teg, 192p, 6 ticp, pep)	Baker/Taylor	(1911)	Soper, George	100-165	
Carroll, Lewis	Alice in Wonderland (lg8vo, 192p, red cl, 6 ticp)	Small/Maynard	[1911]	Soper, George	100-170	
Carroll, Lewis	Alice in Wonderland (sm8vo, uncut, 152p, 8cp)	L/NY: J. Lane	[1911]	Walker, W.H.	90-120	*
Carroll, Lewis	Alice in Wonderland (1st {this fmt}, sq12mo, 157p, p-o, 8cp)	L: H. Frowde	1913	Sowerby, Millicent	70-120	
Carroll, Lewis	Alice in Wonderland (1st, 8vo, 161p, 8cp)	L: Bell	1914	Woodward, Alice B.	80-120	
Carroll, Lewis	Alice in Wonderland (1st AM, lg8vo, 232p, 16 ticp, pep)	Doran	[1915]	Jackson, A.E.	140-220	*
Carroll, Lewis	Alice in Wonderland (1st, sm4to, green/gilt, teg, 199p, pep, 16 ticp)	L: H. Frowde	[1915]	Jackson, A.E.	250-400	
Carroll, Lewis	Alice in Wonderland (1st {this pub}, 4to, p-o, ibds, 164p, 8cp)	L: Coker	[1915]	Pease, Bessie C.	120-180	
Carroll, Lewis	Alice in Wonderland (1st, 8vo, gilt, teg, 6cp, pep)	McClurg	1915	St. John, J. Allen	170-240	
Carroll, Lewis	Alice in Wonderland (1st, 8vo, 201p, blue/gilt, 6cp)	L: C.H. Kelly	(1916)	Robinson, Gordon	150-225	
Carroll, Lewis	Alice in Wonderland (1st AM, lg8vo, p-o, 48p, 4cp)	NY: S. Gabriel	(1916)	Robinson, Gordon	100-170	*

AUTHOR	TITLE	PUBLISHER	DATE	ARTIST	PRICE	LC
Carroll, Lewis	Alice in Wonderland (1st AM, lg8vo, p-o, 332p, 48cp, pep)	Platt/Peck	1916	Tarrant, Margaret	170-240	
Carroll, Lewis	Alice in Wonderland (1st, sm4to, p-o, 340p, blue/gilt, 48cp, pep)	L: Ward Lock	1916	Tarrant, Margaret	200-300	
Carroll, Lewis	Alice in Wonderland (1st, sm8vo, 224p, blue/red, b/w)	Ginn & Co.	(1917)	Herford, Oliver	90-120	
Carroll, Lewis	Alice in Wonderland (new ed., 12mo, bds, 157p, 8cp)	L: H. Milford	(1919)	Sowerby, Millicent	180-260	
Carroll, Lewis	Alice in Wonderland (sm8vo, tan cl, 126p, 4cp, pep)	L: Blackie	[1920]	Adams, Frank	80-120	
Carroll, Lewis	Alice in Wonderland (1st AM, 8vo, gilt, 181p, 12 ticp, pep)	Dodd	(1922)	Hudson, Gwynedd	250-350	
Carroll, Lewis	Alice in Wonderland (1st, 4to, red/gilt, 180p, 12 ticp, pep)	L: Hodder	[1922]	Hudson, Gwynedd	250-400	
Carroll, Lewis	Alice in Wonderland (1st, sq8vo, 241p, p-o, gilt, 8cp, pep)	Lippincott	1923	Kay, Gertrude A.	130-200	
Carroll, Lewis	Alice in Wonderland (lg8vo, [new ed.], 8cp)	L: Cassell	1928	Robinson, Charles	140-200	
Carroll, Lewis	Alice in Wonderland (8vo, 174p, blue cl, 6cp)	L: A&C Black	(1929)	Folkard, Charles	130-200	
Carroll, Lewis	Alice in Wonderland (1st, 8vo, purple/gilt, 192p, pep, b/w)	Dutton	(1929)	Pogany, Willy	160-240	
Carroll, Lewis	Alice in Wonderland (1st {this pub}, 8vo, 216p, 8cp, pep)	Garden City	(1930)	Jackson, A.E.	60-100	*
Carroll, Lewis	Alice in Wonderland (lg ob8vo, unpag, [movie ed.], b/w)	Whitman	(1934)	(Photos)	100-160	*
Carroll, Lewis	Alice in Wonderland (1st, 12mo, ipcb, [56]p, 8 fp color)	McLoughlin	(1940)	Tenniel, John	80-120	*
Carroll, Lewis	Alice in Wonderland (1st, 8vo, 150p, color)	Random	(1946)	Kredel, Fritz	55-90	*
Carroll, Lewis	Alice in Wonderland (1st, sq8vo, ibds, [32]p, color, pep)	Rand/McNally	1951	Holland, Janice	35-60	*
Carroll, Lewis	Alice in Wonderland (1st, 4to, 64p, p-o, 15 fp color, pep, DJ/2.95)	Random	1955	Torrey, Marjorie	60-90	
Carroll, Lewis	Alice... & Through... (1st [combined], 12mo, 383p, green cl)	L: Macmillan	1887	Tenniel, John	250-350	
Carroll, Lewis	Alice... & Through... (8vo, teg, 351p, b/w)	Altemus	1895	Tenniel, John	100-165	*
Carroll, Lewis	Alice... & Through... (8vo, 255p, beige cl, 16 fp color)	Platt/Peck	(1900)	McManus, Blanche	200-300	
Carroll, Lewis	Alice... & Through... (1st {this pub}, lg8vo, 255p, yellow cl, 12cp)	Wessels	(1900)	McManus, Blanche	150-225	
Carroll, Lewis	Alice... & Through... (1st {this pub}, sm8vo, 317p, col frn)	Collier	1903	Tenniel/Stevens	70-100	*
Carroll, Lewis	Alice... & Through... (4to, blue/gilt, col frn, b/w)	McLoughlin	[1910]	Tenniel, John	120-200	*
Carroll, Lewis	Alice... & Through... (1st [color ed.], 8vo, 292p, gilt, 16cp)	L: Macmillan	1911	Tenniel, John	175-260	
Carroll, Lewis	Alice... & Through... (8vo, brown cl, p-o, 335p, 7cp)	Jacobs	[1912]	Abbott, Elenore P.	140-200	
Carroll, Lewis	Alice... & Through... (1st, lg8vo, 242p, p-o, 14cp, pep)	Rand/McNally	(1916)	Winter, Milo	150-240	
Carroll, Lewis	Alice... & Through... (lg8vo, 297p, grey cl, col frn)	Grosset/Dunlap	[1919]	(Photos)	80-120	*
Carroll, Lewis	Alice... & Through... (1st, 8vo, 319p, gilt, p-o, 4cp, pep)	Winston	(1923)	Prittie, Edwin J.	60-100	
Carroll, Lewis	Alice... & Through... (8vo, blue/gilt, p-o, 335p, 7cp)	Macrae Smith	(1925)	Abbott, Elenore P.	70-100	*
Carroll, Lewis	Alice... & Through... (1st, 4to, 236p, gilt, p-o, col frn)	Sears	(1926)	Welling, G.	120-200	*
Carroll, Lewis	Alice... & Through... (4to, 143p, green/gilt, 8 ticp)	L: Collins	[1928]	Rountree, Harry	200-300	
Carroll, Lewis	Alice... & Through... (4to, ibds, 5 fp color)	L: Hutchinson	(1934)	Clements, M.L.	200-300	
Carroll, Lewis	Alice... & Through... (1st, 8vo, yellow cl, 317p, col frn, 8pl)	L: Clowes	[1935]	Morton-Sale, J.	40-60	*
Carroll, Lewis	Alice... & Through... (1st {this pub}, 4to, p-o, 59p, cep, color)	Platt/Munk	(1938)	Tenniel, John	100-165	*
Carroll, Lewis	Alice... & Through... (1st, sm8vo, ibds, 234p, b/w, pep)	Whitman	(1945)	Card, Linda	30-50	*
Carroll, Lewis	Alice... & Through... (1st, 4to, 159p, ibds, 24 fp color, pep, DJ/3.50)	Harper	(1949)	Weisgard, Leonard	75-120	
Carroll, Lewis	Alice... & Through... (1st UK, 8vo, 264p, blue/gilt, b/w, DJ)	L: Allan Wingate	1954	Peake, Mervyn	200-300	
Carroll, Lewis	Alice... & Through... (1st, 8vo, 246p, 8 color, DJ/2.95)	Dutton	(1954)	Stanley, Diana	35-50	
Carroll, Lewis	Alice... & Through... (1st, 8vo, ibds, 284p, 2-color, pep)	Whitman	(1955)	Paflin, Roberta	30-50	
Carroll, Lewis	Alice... Through... & Hunting (1st, 8vo, 351p, teg, uncut, b/w)	Boni/Liveright	1925	Tenniel, John	120-180	*
Carroll, Lewis	Further Nonsense Verse & Prose (1st, sm4to, 127p, yellow bds, b/w)	L: T.F. Unwin	1926	Bateman, Henry M.	70-100	
Carroll, Lewis	Further Nonsense Verse & Prose (1st AM, 4to, 118p, ipcb, p-o, b/w)	Appleton	1926	Bateman, Henry M.	70-100	
Carroll, Lewis	Hunting of the Snark (1st, lg8vo, ibds, teg, 248p, 40pl)	Harper	1903	Newell, Peter	150-200	
Carroll, Lewis	Hunting of the Snark (1st, 8vo, red cl, 46p, b/w)	L: Chatto	1941	Peake, Mervyn	150-240	*
Carroll, Lewis	Mad-Hatter's Tea Party (1st, sm8vo, [28]p, ibds, color, LGB/#D23)	Simon/Schuster	(1951)	Disney Studios	20-30	
Carroll, Lewis	Nursery Alice (1st, 4to, ibds, 56p, 20 color, cep)	L: Macmillan	1890	Tenniel, John	700-900	
Carroll, Lewis	Rhyme? And Reason? (1st, 8vo, 214p, green/gilt, b/w)	L: Macmillan	1883	Frost/Holiday	220-285	
Carroll, Lewis	Songs from Alice... & Through... (1st, 4to, 48p, gilt, p-o, 12 ticp)	L: A&C Black	(1921)	Folkard, Charles	250-400	
Carroll, Lewis	Sylvie & Bruno (1st, 8vo, AEG, 400p, gilt, 46 b/w)	L: Macmillan	1889	Furniss, Harry	140-200	
Carroll, Lewis	Sylvie & Bruno Concluded (1st, 8vo, red/gilt, AEG, 423p, b/w)	L: Macmillan	1893	Furniss, Harry	170-270	
Carroll, Lewis	Tangled Tale (1st, 8vo, 152p, AEG, red/gilt, 6pl)	L: Macmillan	1885	Frost, A.B.	400-600	
Carroll, Lewis	Three Sunsets... (1st, sq8vo, green/gilt, AEG, 68p, 12 fp b/w)	L: Macmillan	1898	Thomson, E. Gertrude	300-500	
Carroll, Lewis	Through the Looking Glass (12mo, 175p, grey/gilt, 4 chromos)	DeWolfe/Fiske	1898	Tenniel, John	150-220	
Carroll, Lewis	Through the Looking Glass (1st, lg8vo, 139p, grey/gilt, 12cp)	Mansfield/Wes.	1899	McManus, Blanche	140-200	
Carroll, Lewis	Through the Looking Glass (1st, lg8vo, bds, teg, 211p, 40pl)	Harper	1902	Newell, Peter	125-180	
Carroll, Lewis	Through the Looking Glass (1st, 8vo, gilt, p-o, 271p, 12cp)	Stokes	(1905)	Kirk, Maria L.	225-325	
Carroll, Lewis	Through the Looking Glass (1st, 8vo, blue cl, 185p, 10cp)	Dodge	(1909)	Gutmann, Bessie P.	150-225	
Carroll, Lewis	Through the Looking Glass (1st, 12mo, 218p, tan cl, b/w)	Rand/McNally	(1917)	Cory, Fanny	40-65	
Carroll, Lewis	Through the Looking Glass (1st, 8vo, 235p, red/gilt, 8cp, pep)	Lippincott	(1929)	Kay, Gertrude A.	40-65	
Carroll, Lewis	Through the Looking Glass (1st {this pub}, 4to, ibds, 98p, 2-color)	Whittlesey	[1946]	Tenniel, John	40-60	*
Carroll, Lewis	Through the Looking Glass (1st, sm4to, [30]p, ipcb, color, pep)	NY: Maxton	1947	Collison, Marjory	50-80	*
Carroll, Lewis	Verses from Alice (1st, 4to, blue/gilt, [34]p, color, DJ)	L: Collins	(1944)	Sherwood, G.S.	100-165	
Carroll, Lewis	Walt Disney's Alice in Wonderland (1st UK, 4to, ibds, color, pep)	L: Dean	(1951)	Disney Studios	200-300	
Carroll, Ruth	Beanie (1st, 4to, [48]p, blue cl, fp 1-color, DJ/2.50)	NY: Oxford U.Pr.	1953	Carroll, Ruth	30-45	
Carroll, Ruth	Bounce and the Bunnies (1st, 4to, [48]p, p-o, color, pep. DJ/1.25)	Reynal/Hitchcock	(1934)	Carroll, Ruth	30-50	
Carroll, Ruth	Bumble Pup (1st, 4to, 31p, b/w, DJ/3.50)	H.Z. Walck	1968	Carroll, Ruth	30-50	
Carroll, Ruth	Chessie (1st, 4to, ibds, [48]p, color, pep, DJ/2.00)	J. Messner	(1936)	Carroll, Ruth	40-65	
Carroll, Ruth	Chessie and her Kittens (1st, 4to, [48]p, color, pep, DJ/2.00)	J. Messner	(1937)	Carroll, Ruth	40-65	
Carroll, Ruth	Chimp and the Clown (1st, ob8vo, [31]p, color, DJ/3.50)	H.Z. Walck	1968	Carroll, Ruth	25-40	
Carroll, Ruth	Christmas Kitten (1st, 8vo, [30]p, fp 2-color, DJ/3.50)	H.Z. Walck	1970	Carroll, Ruth	25-40	
Carroll, Ruth	Danny and the Poi Pup (1st, 4to, 47p, fp color, DJ/3.75)	H.Z. Walck	1965	Carroll, Ruth	25-40	
Carroll, Ruth	Digby, the Only Dog (1st, 4to, 47p, 1-color, pep, DJ/2.75)	NY: Oxford U.Pr.	1955	Carroll, Ruth	30-50	
Carroll, Ruth	Flying House (1st {std}, ob8vo, 127p, color, pep, DJ/2.00)	Macmillan	1946	Carroll, Ruth	50-80	
Carroll, Ruth	Luck of the Roll and Go (1st, 12mo, 132p, b/w, pep, DJ/1.50)	Macmillan	1935	Carroll, Ruth	25-40	
Carroll, Ruth	Old Mrs. Billups and the Black Cats (1st, 8vo, 48p, color, DJ/3.50)	H.Z. Walck	1961	Carroll, Ruth	30-45	
Carroll, Ruth	Peanut (1st, 8vo, 45p, fp 1-color, DJ/1.75)	H.Z. Walck	1951	Carroll, Ruth	25-45	
Carroll, Ruth	Pet Tale (1st, sq8vo, [47]p, ibds, b/w, pep, DJ/1.50)	NY: Oxford U.Pr.	1949	Carroll, Ruth	30-50	
Carroll, Ruth	Runaway Pony, Runaway Dog (1st, lg8vo, 80p, fp color, cep, DJ/3.50)	H.Z. Walck	1963	Carroll, Ruth	30-45	

AUTHOR	TITLE	PUBLISHER	DATE	ARTIST	PRICE	LC
Carroll, Ruth	Salt & Pepper (1st, 8vo, 30p. 2-color, cep, DJ/2.00)	NY: Oxford U.Pr.	1952	Carroll, Ruth	25-40	
Carroll, Ruth	School in the Sky (1st, ob8vo, 136p, b/w, pep, DJ/1.75)	Macmillan	1945	Carroll, Ruth	25-35	
Carroll, Ruth	Tough Enough (1st, 4to, [64]p, 1-color, DJ/2.75)	NY: Oxford U.Pr.	1954	Carroll, Ruth	50-85	R
Carroll, Ruth	Tough Enough & Sassy (1st, 4to, 63p, fp 1-color, cep, DJ/2.75)	H.Z. Walck	1958	Carroll, Ruth	50-85	
Carroll, Ruth	Tough Enough's Indians (1st, 4to, 64p, fp 1-color, cep, DJ/2.75)	H.Z. Walck	1960	Carroll, Ruth	50-85	
Carroll, Ruth	Tough Enough's Pony (1st, 4to, 64p, b/w, DJ/2.75)	NY: Oxford U.Pr.	1957	Carroll, Ruth	50-85	
Carroll, Ruth	Tough Enough's Trip (1st, 4to, 64p, 1-color, DJ/2.75)	NY: Oxford U.Pr.	1956	Carroll, Ruth	50-85	
Carroll, Ruth	What Whiskers Did (1st, lg8vo, [39]p, fp b/w, pep)	Macmillan	1932	Carroll, Ruth	40-70	*
Carroll, Ruth	Where's the Bunny? (1st, ob8vo, [30]p, color, DJ/2.00)	Oxford U. Pr.	1950	Carroll, Ruth	40-65	
Carroll, Ruth	Where's the Kitty? (1st, ob8vo, [32]p, color, DJ/2.75)	H.Z. Walck	(1962)	Carroll, Ruth	40-65	
Carruth, Frances W.	Those Dale Girls (1st, 12mo, 318p, cvr by...)	McClurg	1899	Hazenplug, Frank	50-80	*
Carruth, Hayden	Mr. Milo Bush (1st, 12mo, green/gilt, 217p, 4pl)	Harper	1899	Frost, A.B.	70-120	
Carruth, Hayden	Track's End (1st, 12mo, blue cl, 230p, 9pl, pep)	Harper	1911	Carleton, Clifford	40-60	
Carruth, Hayden	Voyage of the Rattletrap (1st, 12mo, gilt, 207p, b/w, PPPa)	Harper	1897	Wilder, H.M.	65-100	
Carryl, Charles E.	Admiral's Caravan (1st, sq8vo, 140p, gilt, b/w, PPP)	Century	1892	Birch, Reginald	100-170	R
Carryl, Charles E.	Capital Ship (1st, ob4to, [32]p, color, dep, DJ/2.75)	Whittlesey	1963	Galdone, Paul	35-50	R
Carryl, Guy W.	Fables for the Frivolous (1st, 8vo, 120p, teg, gilt, 6pl)	Harper	1898	Newell, Peter	70-100	
Carryl, Guy W.	Far from Maddening Girls (1st, 8vo, 185p, 8pl)	McClure	1904	Newell, Peter	60-90	
Carryl, Guy W.	Garden of Years (1st, 12mo, 129p, uncut, teg, dep, frn by...)	Putnam	1904	Parrish, Maxfield	100-170	R
Carryl, Guy W.	Grimm Tales Made Gay (1st, sq8vo, green cl, 142p, b/w)	Houghton	(1902)	Levering, Albert	120-200	R
Carryl, Guy W.	Mother Goose for Grownups (1st, 8vo, gilt, teg, 115p, 3pl by...)	Harper	1900	Newell, Peter	120-200	
Carse, Robert	Great Venture (1st, 8vo, 239p, b/w, DJ/2.50)	Scribner	(1952)	Price, Christine	40-65	
Carse, Roland	Monarchs of Merry England (1st, 4to, 52p, p-o, 10cp)	L: T.F. Unwin	1904	Robinson, W. Heath	280-350	
Carse, Roland	More Monarchs of Merry England (1st, 4to, ibds, 129p, 20cp, pep)	L: T.F. Unwin	[1907]	Robinson, W. Heath	300-450	
Carson, Norma B.	Children's Own Story Book (1st, lg8vo, yellow cl, 160p, color)	Reilly/Britton	(1916)	Sewsmith, Hazeltine	55-80	*
Carson, Thomas	Ranching Sport and Travel (1st AM, 8vo, gilt, 319p, teg, 16pl)	Scribner	(1912)	Various	250-400	
Carter, Angela	Donkey Prince (1st AM {std}, 8vo, 40p, fp color, pep, DJ/4.95)	Simon/Schuster	(1970)	Keith, Eros	40-65	
Carter, Angela	Miss Z: Dark Young Lady (1st {std}, 8vo, 32p, fp color, DJ/3.95)	Simon/Schuster	(1970)	Keith, Eros	50-75	
Carter, Charles F.	Katooticut (1st, lg8vo, ipcb, 153p, fp b/w)	R.H. Russell	1899	Conde, J.M.	160-240	*
Carter, Helene	Smoky and Pinocchio (1st, lg8vo, [36], 2-color, DJ/1.00)	Lippincott	1940	Carter, Helene	30-50	*
Carter, Russell	Brothers of the Frontier (1st, sm8vo, 205p, tan cl, b/w, DJ/2.00)	Appleton-Century	1938	Sperry, Armstrong	30-50	
Carter, Russell	Crimson Cutlass (1st, 8vo, 302p, col frn, pep)	Penn	(1933)	Schoonover, Frank	25-40	*
Carter, Russell	White Plume of Navarre (1st, 8vo, p-o, 192p, fp color, pep)	Volland	(1928)	Stevens, Beatrice	60-90	
Carus, Helena	Metten of Tyre (1st {std}, 8vo, 171p, col frn, fp b/w, pep)	Doubleday/Doran	1930	Bock, Vera	25-40	
Cary, Elisabeth L.	Emerson, Poet and Thinker (1st, lg8vo, blue/gilt, teg, 284p, cvr by...)	Putnam	1904	Armstrong, Margaret	60-90	
Cary, Elisabeth L.	Tennyson (1st, lg8vo, blue/gilt, 312p, teg, cvr by...)	Putnam	1898	Armstrong, Margaret	50-85	
Cary, Elisabeth L.	The Rossettis (1st, lg8vo, 310p, teg, uncut, gilt, cvr by...)	Putnam	1900	Armstrong, Margaret	100-165	
Cary, Elisabeth L.	William Morris (1st, lg8vo, teg, blue/gilt, 296p, uncut)	Putnam	1902	Armstrong, Margaret	70-120	
Cary, Elisabeth L.	Works of James McNeill Whistler (1st, sm4to, bds, 302p, uncut, 31pl)	Moffat	1907	Whistler, James M.	120-200	
Cass, Joan E.	Cat Thief (1st, 8vo, [40]p, fp color, dep, DJ/2.75)	Abelard-Schuman	(1961)	Stobbs, William	40-65	*
Cassedy, Sylvia	Pierino and the Bell (1st {std}, 4to, 47p, color, DJ/3.25)	Doubleday	(1966)	Ness, Evaline	40-65	*
Casserley, Anne	Roseen (1st {std}, sm8vo, green cl, 152p, b/w, pep)	Harper	1929	Casserley, Anne	30-45	
Casserley, Anne	Whins of Knockattan (1st {std}, sm8vo, 178p, silhouettes)	Harper	1928	Casserley, Anne	30-50	*
Castle, A.& E.	Our Sentimental Garden (1st, lg8vo, 304p, gilt, 8 ticp, pep)	L: Heinemann	(1914)	Robinson, Charles	160-250	
Castle, A.& E.	Our Sentimental Garden (1st AM, 8vo, gilt, 304p, 8 ticp, pep)	Lippincott	1914	Robinson, Charles	140-200	
Castle, A.& E.	Rose of the World (1st, 8vo, 414p, tan cl, 4pl by...)	Stokes	(1905)	Fisher, Harrison	20-35	
Castle, Agnes	Heart of Lady Ann (1st, 12mo, 263p, lavender/gilt, 4cp, pep)	Harper	1905	Betts, Ethel F.	35-60	
Castle, Egerton	Marshfield the Observer (1st, sm8vo, 270p, grey ipcb, cvr by...)	Herbert Stone	1900	Hazenplug, Frank	55-80	
Castle, Jane	Peep-Lo (1st, 8vo, [34]p, blue cl, b/w, pep, DJ/2.50)	Holiday House	1959	Castle, Jane	25-40	
Cather, Willa	My Antonia (1st, 12mo, 418p, brown cl, 6pl)	Houghton	1918	Benda, W.T.	250-425	
Catherwood, Mary	Lazarre (1st, sm8vo, 436p, gilt, 5pl)	Bowen-Merrill	1901	Castaigne, Andre	30-50	
Catherwood, Mary	Spanish Peggy (1st, 8vo, uncut, teg, 85p, red cl, p-o, b/w)	Herbert Stone	1899	Leyendecker, J.C.	90-120	
Catherwood, Mary	Story of Tonty (1st, 12mo, 227p, b/w)	McClurg	1890	Ward, Enoch	50-85	
Cathon, Laura	Tot Botot and his Little Flute (1st {std}, 8vo, [32]p, color, DJ/4.50)	Macmillan	(1970)	Lobel, Arnold	30-50	
Catling, Patrick	Chocolate Touch (1st, 8vo, yellow cl, 95p, fp b/w, DJ/2.50)	Wm. Morrow	1952	McNutt, Mildred	70-100	*
Catrevas, Christine	Fairy Tales for Little People (1st, lg8vo, 246p, p-o, col frn, pep)	Sears	(1927)	Becker, Charlotte	35-60	
Caudill, Rebecca	Barrie and Daughter (1st [1st bk], sm8vo, 314p, b/w, pep, DJ/2.00)	Viking	1943	Williams, Berkeley	20-35	
Caudill, Rebecca	Best-Loved Doll (1st {std}, 8vo, [64]p, fp 1-color, DJ/3.50)	Holt, Rinehart	(1962)	Gilbert, Elliott	30-45	
Caudill, Rebecca	Certain Small Shepherd (1st {std}, sq8vo, 48p, ibds, fp color, DJ/3.50)	Holt, Rinehart	(1965)	DuBois, W.P.	45-70	R
Caudill, Rebecca	Come Along! (1st {std}, ob8vo, 30p, ibds, color, DJ/3.95)	Holt, Rinehart	(1969)	Raskin, Ellen	30-45	
Caudill, Rebecca	Contrary Jenkins (1st {std}, ob4to, [40]p, b/w, DJ/3.50)	Holt, Rinehart	(1969)	Rounds, Glen	30-50	R
Caudill, Rebecca	Did You Carry the Flag Today, Charlie? (1st {std}, 8vo, 94p, b/w, DJ/3.50)	Holt, Rinehart	(1966)	Grossman, Nancy	30-50	R*
Caudill, Rebecca	Far-Off Land (1st, sm8vo, 287p, b/w, DJ/3.50)	Viking	(1964)	Turkle, Brinton	25-40	*
Caudill, Rebecca	Happy Little Family (1st {std}, sm8vo, 116p, b/w, pep, DJ/2.00)	Winston	(1947)	Merwin, Decie	20-35	
Caudill, Rebecca	Higgins and the Great Big Scare (1st {std}, 8vo, 87p, b/w, DJ/2.95)	Holt, Rinehart	(1960)	Krush, Beth	20-35	
Caudill, Rebecca	House of the Fifers (1st {std}, 8vo, 184p, b/w, DJ/2.75)	Longmans	1954	Genia	20-30	
Caudill, Rebecca	My Appalachia: A Reminiscence (1st {std}, 4to, black cl, 90p, b/w, DJ/4.95)	Holt, Rinehart	(1966)	(Photos)	25-40	
Caudill, Rebecca	Pocketful of Cricket (1st {std}, 4to, [48]p, color, DJ/3.50, CH)	Holt, Rinehart	(1964)	Ness, Evaline	45-70	
Caudill, Rebecca	Saturday Cousins (1st {std}, 8vo, 120p, b/w, DJ/2.50)	Winston	(1953)	Woltemate, Nancy	20-30	*
Caudill, Rebecca	Schoolhouse in the Woods (1st {std}, sm8vo, 120p, b/w, pep, DJ/2.00)	Winston	(1949)	Merwin, Decie	25-40	
Caudill, Rebecca	Schoolroom in the Parlor (1st {std}, sm8vo, 120p, b/w, pep, DJ/2.95)	Winston	(1959)	Merwin, Decie	25-40	
Caudill, Rebecca	Susan Cornish (1st, 8vo, 286p, ipcb, b/w, DJ/2.75)	Viking	1955	Johnson, Harper	20-35	
Caudill, Rebecca	Time for Lissa (1st, 8vo, 139p, blue cl, b/w, DJ/2.95)	Nelson	(1959)	Ilsley, Velma	20-30	
Caudill, Rebecca	Tree of Freedom (1st, 8vo, 279p, green cl, pep, DJ/2.50, NH)	Viking	1949	Morse, Dorothy B.	50-80	
Caudill, Rebecca	Up and Down the River (1st {std}, sm8vo, 115p, b/w, pep, DJ/2.00)	Winston	(1951)	Merwin, Decie	20-30	
Cautley, Marjorie S.	Building a House in Sweden (1st, sq8vo, 40p, fp brown illus)	Macmillan	1931	Sewell, Helen	35-60	
Cavally, Fred. L.	Mother Goose's Teddy Bears (1st, 4to, red cl, [64]p, p-o, 32cp)	Bobbs-Merrill	1907	Cavally, Frederick	300-500	
Cavanah, Frances	Boyhood Adventures of Our Presidents (1st, 8vo, 256p, fp b/w, DJ/2.00)	Rand/McNally	(1938)	Foster, Genevieve	30-50	

AUTHOR	TITLE	PUBLISHER	DATE	ARTIST	PRICE	LC
Cavanah, Frances	Children of the White House (1st, 8vo, 35p, ipcb, b/w, DJ/0.50)	Rand/McNally	(1936)	Foster, Genevieve	20-35	
Cavanah, Frances	Louis of New Orleans (1st, lg8vo, ipcb, 36p, color, pep, DJ/1.00)	McKay	(1941)	Weisgard, Leonard	60-90	
Cavanah, Frances	Our Country's Story (1st, 8vo, 64p, 2-color, pep, DJ/2.95)	Rand/McNally	(1962)	Keats, Julia	20-35	
Cavanah, Frances	Pedro of Santa Fe (1st, lg8vo, ipcb, [35]p, 3-color, pep, DJ/1.00)	McKay	(1941)	Weisgard, Leonard	50-80	
Cavanna, Betty	Secret Passage (1st {std}, 8vo, 216p, col frn, pep, DJ/2.50)	Winston	(1946)	McLaughlin, Jean	30-50	
Cave, Edward	Boy's Camp Book (1st, 12mo, green cl, 194p, 4 fp b/w)	Doubleday/Page	1914	Rockwell, Norman	80-120	*
Cawein, Madison J.	Message of the Lilies (1st, narrow 8vo, [16]p, pcb, color, pep)	Volland	(1913)	Unknown	60-100	R*
Cawein, Madison J.	So Many Ways (1st, 12mo, pcb, gilt, [12]p, color)	Volland	(1911)	Unknown	60-100	R*
Cecil, Edward	Malachi Mudge (1st, 8vo, 47p, b/w, DJ/3.95)	McGraw-Hill	(1968)	Parnall, Peter	25-40	
Ceder, Georgiana	Ann of Bethany (1st, 8vo, 95p, b/w, DJ/2.00)	Abingdon-Cokes.	(1951)	Torrey, Helen	20-35	
Ceder, Georgiana	Ethan, the Shepherd Boy (1st, 8vo, 94p, b/w, DJ/2.00)	Abingdon-Cokes.	1948	Torrey, Helen	20-35	
Celli, Rose	Wild Animals & their Little Ones (1st AM, folio, [20]p, wraps, 12 color)	A.& W. Guild	(1935)	Rojankovsky, Feodor	50-85	
Cellini, Benvenuto	Autobiography of Benvenuto Cellini (1st, sm4to, 442p, 15cp)	Doubleday	1946	Dali, Salvador	140-200	
Cenac, Claude	Four Paws into Adventure (1st AM {std}, 8vo, 159p, b/w, DJ/3.50)	F. Watts	(1965)	Turkle, Brinton	60-100	*
Cendrars, Blaise	Little Black Stories for Little White Children (1st, 8vo, 138p, cp)	Payson-Clarke	1929	Pinsard, Pierre	50-80	*
Cervantes	Adventures of Don Quixote (1st, 8vo, 532p, teg, uncut, b/w, pep)	Dent/Dutton	1902	Robinson, W. Heath	120-180	
Cervantes	Adventures of Don Quixote (1st, sm4to, 287p, color)	Houghton	1928	Bacharach, Herman I.	35-60	*
Cervantes	Don Quixote (1st AM, lg8vo, 246p, 11cp)	J. Lane	1900	Crane, Walter	120-185	
Cervantes	Don Quixote (1st, lg8vo, 245p, uncut, 11cp)	L: Blackie	1900	Crane, Walter	200-270	
Cervantes	Don Quixote (1st, lg8vo, 340p, 48cp, pep)	L: Ward Lock	[1910]	Theaker, Harry G.	60-90	*
Cervantes	Don Quixote (1st, lg8vo, 341p, p-o, 4cp, pep)	Stokes	1922	Choate/Curtis	30-50	
Cervantes	Don Quixote (1st, 4to, 311p, black/gilt, 25 color)	L: Constable	1922	DeBosschere, Jean	120-200	
Cervantes	Don Quixote (8vo, red/gilt, 614p, 16 b/w)	Dodd	1925	Robinson, W. Heath	70-100	
Cervantes	History of Don Quixote... (1st, 4to, 311p, gilt, 25cp)	L: Constable	1922	DeBosschere, Jean	200-300	
Chabot, Adrien	Dancing-Master (1st, 12mo, teg, green cl, 139p, 4pl)	Lippincott	1901	Smith, Jessie W.	200-300	*
Chaconas, Doris	Way the Tiger Walked (1st {std}, ob8vo, [32]p, ipcb, fp color, DJ/4.95)	Simon/Schuster	(1970)	Bozzo, Frank	35-50	
Chaffee, Allen	Brownie: Engineer of Beaver Brook (1st, lg8vo, 99p, 4cp, pep)	Milton Bradley	(1925)	Bransom, Paul	40-70	
Chaffee, Allen	Tawny Goes Hunting (1st, sm4to, 76p, 2-color, DJ/2.00)	Random	1937	Bransom, Paul	30-50	
Chaffee, Allen	Wild Folk (1st, 8vo, 323p, pep, col frn by...)	Milton Bradley	(1930)	Bull, Charles L.	25-45	
Chalmers, Audrey	Birthday of Obash (1st, 12mo, ibds, 79p, fp b/w, DJ/1.00)	Oxford U. Pr.	(1937)	Chalmers, Audrey	30-50	
Chalmers, Audrey	Fancy Be Good (1st, 8vo, [46]p, ibds, b/w, DJ/1.00)	Viking	1941	Chalmers, Audrey	30-50	*
Chalmers, Audrey	Hundreds and Hundreds of Pancakes (1st, ob4to, ibds, 39p, color, DJ/1.00)	Viking	1942	Chalmers, Audrey	40-70	
Chalmers, Audrey	Kitten's Tale (1st, 8vo, [46]p, ibds, b/w, DJ/1.50)	Viking	1946	Chalmers, Audrey	30-50	
Chalmers, Audrey	Mr. Topple's Wish (1st, ob8vo, [36]p, ibds, fp b/w, pep, DJ/1.50)	Viking	1948	Chalmers, Audrey	30-50	*
Chalmers, Audrey	Poppadilly (1st, 12mo, ibds, 40p, 1-color, pep, DJ/1.00)	Viking	1945	Chalmers, Audrey	30-50	
Chalmers, Mary	Be Good, Harry (1st, 24mo, 32p, 1-color, DJ/1.95)	Harper	(1967)	Chalmers, Mary	40-65	
Chalmers, Mary	Boats Finds a House (1st, 24mo, 32p, ibds, color, DJ/1.50)	Harper	(1958)	Chalmers, Mary	50-80	
Chalmers, Mary	Cat Who Liked to Pretend (1st, 24mo, 32p, ibds, 2-color, DJ/1.95)	Harper	(1959)	Chalmers, Mary	50-80	
Chalmers, Mary	Christmas Story (1st, sq32mo, [24]p, color, DJ/1.00)	Harper	(1956)	Chalmers, Mary	50-80	
Chalmers, Mary	Come for a Walk with Me (1st, 16mo, [30]p, ipcb, 3-color, DJ/1.50)	Harper	(1955)	Chalmers, Mary	50-85	
Chalmers, Mary	George Appleton (1st, 24mo, 32p, color, DJ/1.50)	Harper	(1957)	Chalmers, Mary	40-65	
Chalmers, Mary	Hat for Amy Jean (1st, 24mo, [32]p, 1-color, pep, DJ/1.50)	Harper	(1956)	Chalmers, Mary	50-80	
Chalmers, Mary	Here Comes the Trolley Car (1st, ob4to, [34]p, 2-color, pep, DJ/2.00)	Harper	(1955)	Chalmers, Mary	50-80	
Chalmers, Mary	Kevin (1st, 24mo, [32]p, ibds, 3-color, DJ/1.50)	Harper	(1957)	Chalmers, Mary	40-65	
Chalmers, Mary	Mr. Cat's Wonderful Surprise (1st, 8vo, 32p, ipcb, 3-color, DJ/2.50)	Harper	(1961)	Chalmers, Mary	40-65	
Chalmers, Mary	Take a Nap, Harry (1st, 24mo, 32p, color, DJ/1.95)	Harper	1964	Chalmers, Mary	40-65	
Chalmers, Mary	Throw a Kiss, Harry (1st, 24mo, ibds, 32p, 1-color, DJ/1.25)	Harper	(1958)	Chalmers, Mary	60-90	
Chalmers, Patrick	Cricket in the Cage (1st, 8vo, 77p, gilt, fp b/w, DJ)	L: A&C Black	1933	Shepard, Ernest H.	100-165	
Chalmers, Patrick	Dozen Dogs or So (1st, 4to, 47p, brown cl, 13cp)	L: Eyre/Spotts.	1928	Aldin, Cecil	200-300	
Chalmers, Patrick	Last Muster (1st, 8vo, 127p, 24 b/w illus, DJ)	L: Eyre/Spotts.	1939	Aldin, Cecil	70-120	
Chamberlain, Esther	Coast of Chance (1st, sm8vo, tan/gilt, 464p, 4pl)	Bobbs-Merrill	(1908)	Underwood, C.F.	25-40	*
Chamberlin, Ethel C.	Omar the Discontented Cat (1st, 12mo, [39]p, ipcb, pep, color)	Volland	(1925)	Sturges, Katharine	40-60	*
Chamberlin, Ethel C.	Shoes, Ships & Sealing Wax (1st, 8vo, 123p, ibds, color)	Saalfield	(1928)	Scott, Janet L.	25-45	
Chambers, Maria C.	Boy Heroes of Chapultepec (1st {std}, 8vo, 182p, 1-color, pep, DJ/1.50)	Winston	(1953)	Krush, Joe	30-50	*
Chambers, Maria C.	Three Kings (1st, 8vo, 38p, color, DJ/1.50)	NY: Oxford U.Pr.	1946	Holland, Janice	25-45	
Chambers, Maria C.	Water-Carrier's Secrets (1st, 8vo, 157p, 29 fp 1-color, pep, DJ/2.00)	Oxford U. Pr.	(1942)	Weisgard, Leonard	40-65	
Chambers, Robert	Anne's Bridge (1st, sm8vo, 161p, green/gilt, col frn, 3pl)	Appleton	1914	Hutt, Henry	30-50	
Chambers, Robert	Ashes of Empire (1st, 12mo, 342p, cvr by...)	Stokes	(1898)	Bradley, Will	80-125	
Chambers, Robert	Barbarians (1st, 12mo, 353p, 4pl)	Appleton	1917	Keller, Arthur I.	25-40	
Chambers, Robert	Forest-Land (1st, lg8vo, ipcb, 118p, 8cp, pep)	Appleton	1905	Knipe, Emilie B.	150-220	
Chambers, Robert	Garden-Land (1st, lg8vo, 129p, ipcb, 8cp, pep)	Appleton	1907	Cady, Harrison	160-225	
Chambers, Robert	Gay Rebellion (1st, sm8vo, 299p, red/gilt, p-o, 4pl)	Appleton	1913	Frederick, Edmund	25-40	
Chambers, Robert	Green Mouse (1st, 8vo, 281p, p-o, 6cp, pep)	Appleton	1910	Frederick, Edmund	30-50	
Chambers, Robert	Iole (1st, sm8vo, 142p, p-o, 2pl by...)	Appleton	1905	Leyendeckers	30-50	
Chambers, Robert	Japonette (1st, 8vo, 384p, p-o, 21 b/w)	Appleton	1912	Gibson, Charles D.	30-50	
Chambers, Robert	Maid-at-Arms (1st, 12mo, green/gilt, 343p, 8pl)	Harper	1902	Christy, Howard C.	30-50	
Chambers, Robert	Maker of Moons (1st, 12mo, blue/gilt, teg, 401p, frn by...)	Putnam	1896	Speed, Lancelot	120-200	
Chambers, Robert	Mountain-Land (1st, lg8vo, ibds, 122p, 8cp, pep)	Appleton	1906	Richardson, F.	150-225	R
Chambers, Robert	Orchard-Land (1st, sm4to, 112p, 7cp)	Harper	1903	Birch, Reginald	150-225	
Chambers, Robert	Outdoorland (1st, lg8vo, 105p, 7cp)	Harper	1902	Birch, Reginald	100-165	
Chambers, Robert	Outdoorland (1st, lg8vo, green cl, 311p, 22cp)	Appleton	1931	Green/Birch	100-150	
Chambers, Robert	Police! (1st, sm8vo, 292p, gilt, p-o, cp)	Appleton	1915	Hutt, Henry	25-40	
Chambers, Robert	River-Land (1st, lg8vo, gilt, 92p, 8cp)	Harper	1904	Green, Eliz. S.	120-200	
Chambers, Robert	Streets of Ascalon (1st, sm8vo, 440p, gilt, 14 double pg pl)	Appleton	1912	Gibson, Charles D.	30-50	
Chamisso, A.	Peter Schlemihl (1st, lg8vo, 104p, green/gilt, p-o, 35 woodcuts)	McKay	(1929)	Gincano, John	50-85	
Champney, Elizabeth	Romance of Old Japan (1st, 8vo, 444p, gilt, teg, 96pl)	Putnam	1917	Champney, Frere	70-120	
Chan, Chih-Yi	Good-Luck Horse (1st, ob8vo, [47]p, pep, 10 fp color, DJ/1.50, CH)	Whittlesey	(1943)	Chan, Plato	70-120	
Chandler, Edna W.	Cowboy Andy (1st {std}, lg8vo, 65p, color, pep, DJ/1.95)	Beginner Books	(1959)	Kinstler, Raymond	40-65	

AUTHOR	TITLE	PUBLISHER	DATE	ARTIST	PRICE	LC
Chandler, Edna W.	Five Cent, Five Cent (1st, 4to, unpag, color, DJ/2.95)	Whitman	(1967)	Stull, Betty	30-45	
Chandler, Edna W.	Will You Carry Me? (1st, lg8vo, unpag, color, DJ/2.95)	Whitman	1965	Seltzer, Meyer	25-40	
Chandler, Edna W.	With Books on her Head (1st {std}, 8vo, 154p, ibds, b/w, DJ/3.95)	Meredith Press	(1967)	Keeping, Charles	25-40	
Chandler, Ruth F.	Ladder to the Sky (1st, 8vo, 189p, b/w, DJ/3.00)	Abelard-Schuman	(1959)	Johnson, Harper	30-45	
Channing, Blanche	Zodiac Stories (1st, sm8vo, 311p, gilt, b/w)	Dutton	1899	Channing Blanche	35-60	*
Chanover, Hyman	Happy Hanukah Everybody (1st, 8vo, unpag, ibds, color)	United Synagogue	(1954)	Sendak, Maurice	650-900	
Chapin, Anna A.	Everyday & Nowaday Fairy Book (lg4to, 160p, ibds, 8cp)	L: Coker	[1920]	Smith, Jessie W.	200-300	
Chapin, Anna A.	Everyday Fairy Book (1st, 4to, 160p, p-o, 7cp)	Dodd	1915	Smith, Jessie W.	300-400	
Chapin, Anna A.	Everyday Fairy Book (1st UK, 4to, 160p, p-o, 7cp)	L: Harrap	1917	Smith, Jessie W.	200-300	
Chapin, Anna A.	Nowadays Fairy Book (1st, lg4to, ibds, 159p, 6 ticp)	Dodd	1911	Smith, Jessie W.	350-500	
Chapin, Anna A.	True Story of Humpty Dumpty (1st, lg8vo, 205p, p-o, pep, 6cp)	Dodd	1905	Betts, Ethel F.	200-280	
Chapin, Frederic	Pinkey & the Plumed Knight (1st, 4to, tan cl, 207p, 8cp, cep)	Saalfield	(1909)	Johnson, Merle	70-120	
Chapin, Harry	Adventures of Johnny Appleseed (1st, 8vo, 244p, b/w, DJ/2.50)	Coward	1930	Daugherty, James	40-70	
Chapman, E.R.	Little Child's Wreath (1st, 16mo, 70p, b/w)	L: John Lane	1904	Robertson, W.G.	40-65	
Chapman, Gaynor	Luck Child (1st AM {std}, 4to, [32]p, color, DJ/4.50)	Atheneum	1968	Chapman, Gaynor	25-40	
Chapman, Jean	Do You Remember What Happened? (1st, 8vo, gilt, [42]p, 2-color, DJ)	L: Angus/Rbrtsn.	1969	Ardizzone, Edward	50-85	
Chapman, Katharine H.	Fusing Force (1st, 8vo, 416p, col frn)	McClurg	1911	Dunton, W. Herbert	30-45	
Chapman, Maristan	Clue of the Faded Dress (1st, sm8vo, 237p, b/w, uncut, DJ/2.00)	Appleton-Century	1938	Daugherty, James	30-45	*
Chapman, Maristan	Girls of Glen Hazard (1st, sm8vo, 264p, b/w, DJ/2.00)	Appleton-Century	1937	Daugherty, James	30-45	*
Chapman, William G.	Green Timber Trails (1st, 8vo, green cl, 283p, 8pl)	Century	1919	Bransom/Bull	30-50	
Chappell, George S.	Basket of Poses (1st, sm4to, pcb, p-o, 109p, b/w)	A. & C. Boni	1924	Kent, Rockwell	90-120	
Chappell, George S.	Rollo in Society (1st, 16mo, p-o, 178p, woodcuts)	Putnam	1922	Kent, Rockwell	70-100	R
Chappell, Warren	They Say Stories (1st, 8vo, 79p, color, cep, DJ/3.00)	Knopf	(1960)	Chappell, Warren	40-65	R
Charles, Robert H.	Roundabout Turn (1st, sq8vo, [54]p, orange/gilt, pep, 4cp)	L: Warne	1930	Brooke, L. Leslie	100-160	
Charlip, Remy	Arm in Arm (1st, 4to, [39]p, white cl, color, pep, DJ/3.50, NYTBI)	Parents Mag. Pr.	(1969)	Charlip, Remy	50-85	
Charlip, Remy	Dress Up & Let's Have a Party (1st, ob8vo, ipcb [25]p, 3-col, pep, DJ/1.50)	W.R. Scott	1956	Charlip, Remy	60-90	R
Charlip, Remy	Fortunately (1st, 4to, [41]p, dp color, DJ/2.95)	Parents Mag. Pr.	(1964)	Charlip, Remy	40-65	
Charlip, Remy	Mother, Mother, I Feel Sick... (1st, ob4to, unpag, color, pep, DJ/2.95)	Parents Mag. Pr.	(1966)	Charlip, Remy	45-70	
Charlip, Remy	Where is Everybody? (1st, lg ob8vo, yellow cl, [50]p, 1-color, DJ/2.25)	W.R. Scott	1957	Charlip, Remy	60-100	R
Charlot, Jean	Dance of Death (1st, lg ob8vo, black/silver, [102]p, fp b/w, DJ/2.50)	Sheed/Ward	(1951)	Charlot, Jean	80-130	
Charskaya, L.A.	Little Princess Nina (1st, sm8vo, 288p, col frn by...)	Henry Holt & Co.	1924	Artzybasheff, Boris	40-60	*
Charters, Janet	The General (1st AM {std}, 4to, unpag, ibds, color, pep, DJ/3.50)	Dutton	1961	Foreman, Michael	30-50	
Chase, Mary	Loretta Mason Potts (1st {std}, 8vo, 221p, b/w, DJ/3.50)	Lippincott	(1958)	Berson, Harold	30-50	
Chase, Mary	Mrs. McThing: A Play (1st, lg8vo, 141p, blue cl, b/w, DJ/3.00)	Oxford U. Pr.	1952	Sewell/Gekiere	40-65	
Chase, Mary	Virginia of Elk Creek Valley (1st, sm8vo, 297p, gilt, frn by...)	L.C. Page	1917	Elwell, Robert F.	30-50	
Chase, Mary	Wicked Pigeon Ladies in the Garden (1st, lg8vo, 115p, b/w, cep, DJ/3.95)	Knopf	(1968)	Bolognese, Don	80-140	
Chase, Mary Ellen	Dolly Moses: Cat & the Clam Chowder (1st {std}, sm8vo, 58p, b/w, DJ/2.95)	Norton	(1964)	Kennedy, Paul	25-40	
Chase, Mary Ellen	Mary Christmas (1st, sm8vo, ibds, 142p, b/w frn by...)	Little/Brown	1926	Day, Maurice	50-80	
Chase, Mary Ellen	White Gate (1st {std}, 8vo, 185p, b/w, pep, DJ/3.00)	Norton	(1954)	Unwin, Nora S.	30-50	
Chase, Richard	Jack and the Three Sillies (1st, sq8vo, 39p, color, pep, DJ/2.00)	Houghton	1950	Tolford, Joshua	30-45	*
Chase, Stuart	Primer of Economics (1st, lg8vo, 60p, 1-color, DJ/1.00)	Row, Peterson	(1941)	Ward, Lynd	30-55	
Chater, Melville	Bubble Ballads (1st, lg8vo, p-o, 148p, 16pl)	Century	1914	Kay, Gertrude A.	100-150	
Chaucer, Geoffrey	Canterbury Pilgrims (1st, lg8vo, p-o, gilt, 310p, 12cp, pep)	Stokes	(1914)	Kirk, Maria L.	75-100	
Chaucer, Geoffrey	Canterbury Tales (1st, lg8vo, 235p, teg, gilt, 6cp)	Fox Duffield	1904	Clark, Walter A.	55-80	
Chaucer, Geoffrey	Canterbury Tales (1st, 4to, gilt, 637p, teg, 24cp)	L: Medici	1928	Flint, William R.	140-220	
Chaucer, Geoffrey	Canterbury Tales (1st AM, 8vo, 245p, 12cp)	Cape/Smith	1930	Flint, William R.	70-100	*
Chaucer, Geoffrey	Canterbury Tales (1st, lg8vo, 627p, b/w, pep, DJ)	Garden City	1934	Kent, Rockwell	70-100	
Chaucer, Geoffrey	Chanticleer & the Fox (1st, 4to, [36]p, red cl, color, dep, DJ/3.00, CM)	Crowell	(1958)	Cooney, Barbara	100-165	R
Chaucer, Geoffrey	Complete Poetical Works of... (1st, 4to, 607p, blue/gilt, teg, 32cp)	L: Macmillan	1912	Goble, Warwick	200-300	
Chaucer, Geoffrey	Gateway to Chaucer (1st, sm8vo, blue/gilt, 269p, teg, 16cp)	L: Nelson	(1912)	Anderson, Anne	130-200	
Chaucer, Geoffrey	Romaunt of the Rose (4to, grey/gilt, 107p, teg, uncut, 20 ticp)	L: Chatto	1911	Henderson/Wilkinson	150-200	
Chauncy, Nan	Lighthouse Keeper's Son (1st, 8vo, 133p, b/w, DJ)	L: Oxford U.Pr.	1969	Ambrus, Victor	30-45	
Chauncy, Nan	Tangara (1st {std}, 8vo, 180p, bds, b/w, DJ)	L: Oxford U.Pr.	1960	Wildsmith, Brian	20-30	*
Chaundler, Christine	Arthur & His Knights (1st AM, lg8vo, 311p, 8 ticp, pep)	Stokes	[1923]	Mackenzie, Thomas B.	160-240	
Chaundler, Christine	Ronald's Burglar (1st, 16mo, 62p, col frn, b/w)	L: Nelson	(1919)	Stratton, Helen	30-50	*
Chaundler, Christine	Thirteenth Orphan (1st, 8vo, 255p, col frn, 6pl)	L: J. Nisbet	[1920]	Appleton, Honor C.	40-60	*
Cheatham, Kitty	Nursery Garland (1st, lg4to, ibds, 171p, 14cp)	Schirmer	(1917)	Robertson, W.G.	180-250	
Cheever, Harriet A.	Little Mr. Van Vere of China (1st, sm8vo, 243p, col frn, b/w)	Estes & Lauriat	(1898)	Barry, Etheldred B.	40-60	*
Chekhov, Anton	Kashtanka (1st AM {std}, sm4to, 48p, fp color, DJ/2.75, KGM)	H.Z. Walck	1961	Stobbs, William	30-50	
Chenault, Nell	Parsifal the Poddley (1st {std}, 8vo, 83p, b/w, DJ/2.75)	Little/Brown	(1960)	Guthrie, Vee	45-70	
Chenery, Janet	Wolfie (1st, 8vo, 63p, fp 2-color, DJ/2.50)	Harper	(1969)	Simont, Marc	40-65	R
Cheney, Cora	Key of Gold (1st {std}, 8vo, 127p, DJ/2.25)	Holt	(1955)	Galdone, Paul	25-40	*
Cheney, Cora	Peg-Legged Pirate of Sulu (1st {std}, 8vo, 109p, b/w, cep, DJ/2.75)	Knopf	1960	Keats, Ezra J.	40-65	
Cheney, Cora	Plantation Doll (1st {std}, 8vo, 136p, b/w, pep, DJ/2.50)	Holt	(1955)	Polseno, Jo	30-45	
Cheney, Cora	Rocking Chair Buck (1st {std}, 8vo, 128p, b/w, DJ/2.25)	Holt	(1956)	Galdone, Paul	25-40	
Cheney, Warren	The Challenge (1st, 12mo, 386p, red cl, 4pl)	Bobbs-Merrill	(1906)	Wyeth, N.C.	30-50	
Chermayeff, Ivan	Blind Mice & other Numbers (1st, 4to, 40p, ibds, 2-color, dep)	NY: Colorcraft	(1961)	Chermayeff, Ivan	30-50	
Cherr, Pat	Bear in Fact and Fiction (1st {std}, 8vo, 157p, b/w, DJ/3.25)	Harlin Quist	(1967)	Pinto, Ralph	25-45	
Cherr, Pat	Lion in Fact and Fiction (1st {std}, 8vo, 157p, b/w, DJ/3.25)	Harlin Quist	(1966)	Pinto, Ralph	25-45	
Chesnutt, Charles	Conjure Woman (1st, 8vo, 229p, green cl, designs by...)	Houghton	1899	Rogers, Bruce	350-500	
Chesnutt, Charles	Wife of His Youth (1st, sm8vo, 323p, pink/gilt, b/w)	Houghton	1899	DeLand, Clyde O.	350-500	
Chess, Victoria	Fletcher & Zenobia (1st {std}, 12mo, [68]p, ibds, color, DJ/3.95)	Meredith Press	(1967)	Chess, Victoria	30-50	
Chesson, Nora	Tales from Tennyson (4to, 96p, ibds, 6 chromos)	L: R. Tuck	[1890]	Brundage/Bowley	140-200	
Chesson, Nora	With Louis Wain to Storyland (lg4to, cloth, 12 fp color)	L: R. Tuck	[1910]	Wain, Louis	900-1300	
Chester, Geo. R.	Little Prince Toofat (1st, sq4to, 71p, col frn, cp)	McCann	(1922)	Lawson, Robert	200-300	R
Chester, Geo. R.	The Jingo (1st, sm8vo, grey/gilt, 394p, 10pl)	Bobbs-Merrill	(1912)	Wilson, F. Vaux	50-85	
Chesterton, G.K.	Club of Queer Trades (1st, sm8vo, red/gilt, 270p, 6pl)	Harper	1905	Various	200-300	
Chesterton, G.K.	Coloured Lands (1st, lg8vo, 238p, yellow cl, color, DJ)	L: Sheed/Ward	1938	Chesterton, G.K.	80-120	

AUTHOR	TITLE	PUBLISHER	DATE	ARTIST	PRICE	LC
Chesterton, G.K.	Innocence of Father Brown (1st AM, sm8vo, red/gilt, 334p, 7pl)	NY: J. Lane	1911	Foster, Will F.	175-275	
Chesterton, G.K.	Innocence of Father Brown (1st, 8vo, 334p, red/gilt, 8pl)	L: Cassell	1911	Lucas, Sydney S.	300-500	
Chesterton, G.K.	Napoleon of Notting Hill (1st, 8vo, uncut, 301p, 8pl)	L: John Lane	1904	Robertson, W.G.	160-225	
Chesterton, G.K.	St. Francis of Assissi (1st, sm8vo, 185p, brown/gilt, p-o, 7 ticp)	L: Hodder	[1926]	Robinson, F. Cayley	80-120	
Chiang, May-Ling	Little Sister Su (1st, lg4to, ibds, [20]p, accordian fold, b/w)	John Day	(1942)	Sewall, Janet	50-80	
Chidsey, Alan	Odysseus, Sage of Greece (1st, sm8vo, 320p, fp b/w, pep)	Minton Balch	1931	Lenski, Lois	50-80	
Chidsey, Alan	Rustam Lion of Persia (1st, 8vo, 271p, blue cl, b/w, pep)	Minton Balch	1930	Lenski, Lois	50-80	*
Childs, Mary F.	De Namin ob De Twins (1st, 8vo, teg, 139p, 7pl)	Dodge	1908	Potthast, Edward	100-165	
Chilvers, Hedley A.	Out of the Crucible (1st, 8vo, 273p, gilt, 16 illus)	L: Cassell	1929	Timlin, William M.	120-170	*
Chipman, Charles P.	Aerial Runaway (1st, sm8vo, 387p, 3pl)	Lothrop Pub.	(1901)	McCullough, Wm. A.	70-100	
Chipman, Charles P.	Last Cruise of the Electra (1st, sm8vo, 268p, 4pl)	Saalfield	1902	Provost, Charles	70-100	*
Chipman, Charles P.	Two Boys and a Dog (1st, 12mo, 272p, 4pl)	Saalfield	1903	Dunton, W. Herbert	35-50	R
Chisholm, Arthur M.	Boss of Wind River (1st, sm8vo, blue cl, 341p, 4cp)	Doubleday/Page	1911	Johnson, F. Tenny	30-50	
Chisholm, Louey	Enchanted Land (1st, lg8vo, 211p, p-o, white/gilt, teg, 30cp, cep)	L: Jack	(1906)	Cameron, Katharine	160-250	
Chisholm, Louey	Enchanted Land (1st AM, lg8vo, 211p, AEG, green/gilt, 30cp)	Putnam	[1906]	Cameron, Katharine	150-225	
Chisholm, Louey	Golden Staircase (1st, lg8vo, 361p, uncut, gilt, teg, 16cp)	L: Jack	(1906)	Spooner, M.D.	150-225	
Chisholm, Louey	In Fairyland (1st, lg8vo, 211p, p-o, AEG, 30cp, pep)	Putnam/Jack	(1904)	Cameron, Katharine	130-200	
Chisholm, Louey	Staircase of Stories (1st, sm4to, 527p, p-o, 31cp)	L: Jack	(1919)	Various	100-160	*
Chittenden, Wm. L.	Bermuda Verses (1st, 8vo, 68p, green cl, 29pl)	Putnam	1909	(Photos)	50-80	
Chittenden, Wm. L.	Ranch Verses (1st, sm8vo, 189p, gilt, 14pl)	Putnam	1893	(Photos)	125-200	
Choate, Florence	Abby in the Gobi (1st, ob4to, ibds, 63p, color, pep)	McBride	(1929)	Choate/Curtis	60-90	*
Choate, Florence	Dance of the Hours (1st, 8vo, 242p, pep, fp b/w)	Harcourt	(1934)	Choate/Curtis	25-40	*
Choate, Florence	Little People of the Hills (1st, 8vo, 234p, fp b/w)	Harcourt	(1928)	Choate/Curtis	30-50	*
Choate, Florence	Pinafores & Pantalets (1st, 8vo, 207p, uncut, pep, 8 fp 2-color)	Harcourt	(1931)	Choate/Curtis	30-50	*
Chodsko, A.	Fairy Tales of Slav Peasants & Herdsmen (1st, 8vo, 353p, gilt, teg, fp b/w)	L: G. Allen	1896	Harding, Emily J.	70-100	
Cholmondeley, M.	Red Pottage (1st, 8vo, 202p, tan wraps, 8pl)	L: Newnes	1904	Rackham, Arthur	450-650	
Chonz, Selina	Bell for Ursli (1st AM, ob4to, bds, [44]p, fp color, DJ/2.50)	NY: Oxford U.Pr.	(1950)	Carigiet, Alois	70-100	
Chonz, Selina	Florina & the Wild Bird (1st AM, ob fol, ibds, [28]p, color, DJ/3.00, NYTBI)	NY: Oxford U.Pr.	(1953)	Carigiet, Alois	70-100	
Chonz, Selina	The Snowstorm (1st AM {std}, ob folio, [28]p, 12 fp color)	H.Z. Walck	1958	Carigiet, Alois	70-100	
Chopin, Kate R.	Night in Acadie (1st, 12mo, 416p, blue/gilt, teg, cvr by...)	Way & Williams	1897	Hazenplug, Frank	400-600	
Chrestien, F.H.	Evelyn and the Fish (1st, 4to, 48p, ibds, color, DJ/2.00)	Hyperion Press	(1945)	Chrestien, F.H.	40-65	
Chrisman, Arthur B.	Shen of the Sea (1st, sm8vo, 252p, red/gilt, silhouettes, pep, NM)	Dutton	(1925)	Hasselriis, Else	60-90	R
Chrisman, Arthur B.	Treasures Long Hidden (1st {std}, 8vo, blue cl, 302p, b/w, pep, DJ/2.50)	Dutton	1941	Yap, Weda	30-60	*
Chrisman, Arthur B.	Wind that Wouldn't Blow (1st, sm8vo, 355p, uncut, b/w, pep)	Dutton	(1927)	Hasselriis, Else	35-60	*
Christensen, Haaken	Little Bruin and Per (1st {A}, ob8vo, [24]p, 1-color, DJ/1.25)	Abingdon-Cokes.	1951	Christensen, Haaken	30-45	
Christie, Ella R.	Fairy Tales from England (1st, 8vo, teg, uncut, 232p, 6pl)	L: T.F. Unwin	1896	Holland, Ada	60-100	
Christie, Ella R.	Fairy Tales from Finland (1st, 12mo, 232p, teg, uncut, b/w)	L: T.F. Unwin	1896	Holland, Ada	60-100	
Christie, G.F.	Round De Ole Plantation (1st, 4to, ibds, unpag, 24 fp color)	L: Blackie	[1906]	Christie, G.F.	425-600	*
Christopher, Anne	Monkey Twins (1st, ob8vo, [31]p, pep, ipcb, 2-color)	Whitman	(1935)	Hogan, Inez	60-90	*
Christopher, Anne	Petunia Be Keerful (1st, 8vo, ibds, [41]p, 2-color, pep)	Whitman	(1934)	Hogan, Inez	80-140	
Christy, Howard C.	American Girl (1st, lg8vo, 157p, p-o, 16cp)	Moffat	1906	Christy, Howard C.	80-120	
Christy, Howard C.	Christy Girl (1st, lg8vo, [48]p, p-o, 16cp)	Bobbs-Merrill	(1906)	Christy, Howard C.	140-200	
Christy, Howard C.	Drawings (1st, lg ob folio, [58]p, ibds, gilt, 28pl)	Moffat	1905	Christy, Howard C.	250-350	
Christy, Howard C.	Our Girls (1st, lg8vo, 159p, p-o, 16cp)	Moffat	1907	Christy, Howard C.	140-200	
Christy, Howard C.	Songs of Sentiment (1st, 8vo, 128p, grey/gilt, p-o, 12cp, dep)	Moffat	1910	Christy, Howard C.	90-160	
Chubb, Ida M.	Little Pickaninnies (1st, lg4to, [20]p, wraps, fp color)	Whitman	1929	Chubb, Ida M.	150-225	
Church, Alfred J.	Heroes of Chivalry and Romance (1st, sm8vo, 342p, 8cp)	L: Seeley	1898	Morrow, George	50-80	*
Church, Peggy P.	Burro of Angelitos (1st, 4to, ibds, [42]p, color, pep, DJ/2.00)	Suttonhouse	1936	Johnson, Gigi S.	50-80	
Churchill, Winston	The Crossing... (1st, 8vo, green/gilt, 296p, 10pl)	Macmillan	1930	Rae, John	35-60	
Chute, Marchette	Around and About (1st {std}, 8vo, red cl, 124p, 1-color, pep, DJ/2.95)	Dutton	1957	Chute, Marchette	30-50	
Chute, Marchette	Rhymes About the City (1st, 8vo, 57p, silhouettes, DJ/1.25)	Macmillan	1946	Chute, Marchette	45-60	
Chute, Marchette	Rhymes About the Country (1st, sm4to, tan cl, 74p, b/w, pep, DJ/1.50)	Macmillan	1941	Chute, Marchette	50-70	
Chute, Marchette	Wonderful Winter (1st {std}, 8vo, 216p, pep, DJ/3.00)	Dutton	1954	Golden, Grace	40-65	*
Ciardi, John	I Met a Man (1st, lg8vo, 74p, 1-color, DJ/2.75)	Houghton	1961	Osborn, Robert	40-65	
Ciardi, John	John J. Plenty & Fiddler Dan (1st, 4to, [37]p, fp b/w, DJ/2.95, NYTBI)	Lippincott	(1963)	Gekiere, Madeleine	50-85	R
Ciardi, John	King Who Saved Himself from being Saved (1st {std}, sq12mo, b/w, DJ/2.95)	Lippincott	1965	Gorey, Edward	80-120	
Ciardi, John	Man Who Sang the Sillies (1st {std}, lg8vo, 63p, b/w, DJ/3.00)	Lippincott	(1961)	Gorey, Edward	60-90	
Ciardi, John	Monster Den (1st, lg8vo, 62p, ibds, fp b/w, DJ/2.95, NYTBI)	Lippincott	(1966)	Gorey, Edward	60-100	
Ciardi, John	Reason for the Pelican (1st, lg8vo, 64p, blue cl, b/w, DJ/3.00, NYTBI)	Lippincott	(1959)	Gekiere, Madeleine	50-85	
Ciardi, John	Scrappy the Pup (1st {std}, 4to, unpag, 1-color, cep, DJ/3.00, NYTBI)	Lippincott	(1960)	Miller, Jane	50-80	
Ciardi, John	Someone Could Win a Polar Bear (1st {std}, 8vo, 62p, b/w, DJ/3.95)	Lippincott	(1970)	Gorey, Edward	50-80	R
Ciardi, John	Wish-Tree (1st {std}, 4to, [96]p, b/w)	Crowell-Collier	(1962)	Glanzman, Louis	50-80	
Ciardi, John	You Know Who (1st, lg8vo, 63p, fp b/w, DJ/3.50)	Lippincott	(1964)	Gorey, Edward	50-85	
Ciardi, John	You Read to Me, I'll Read to You (1st AM, lg8vo, 64p, fp 1-color, DJ/3.50)	Lippincott	(1962)	Gorey, Edward	60-90	R
Clapp, Estelle	Laurie (1st {std}, 8vo, 255p, b/w, DJ/2.50)	Doubleday	1953	Wiese, Kurt	30-45	*
Clare, Helen	Five Dolls and the Duke (1st {std}, 8vo, 99p, b/w, DJ/3.95)	Prentice-Hall	(1968)	Aliki	25-40	
Clark, Alfred	As It is in Heaven (1st, 8vo, 261p, AEG, 8 ticp, pep)	L: Sampson Low	1912	Pape, Frank	60-90	
Clark, Ann N.	Along Sandy Trails (1st {std}, lg8vo, 31p, color, DJ/4.95)	Viking	(1969)	Cohn, Alfred	30-45	*
Clark, Ann N.	Bear Cub (1st, sm4to, 62p, 3 dp color, fp b/w, DJ/3.50)	Viking	(1965)	Frace, Charles	20-35	
Clark, Ann N.	Blue Canyon Horse (1st, sm4to, 54p, fp color, pep, DJ/2.75)	Viking	1954	Hauser, Allan	65-90	R
Clark, Ann N.	Brother Andre of Montreal (1st, 8vo, 173p, b/w, DJ/2.25)	Farrar, Straus	(1967)	Lang, Harold	40-65	*
Clark, Ann N.	Circle of Seasons (1st, 8vo, 113p, b/w, DJ/3.95)	Farrar, Straus	(1970)	Mars, Witold T.	25-40	*
Clark, Ann N.	Desert People (1st, sm4to, 59p, 3-color, DJ/3.00)	Viking	(1962)	Houser, Allan	30-50	
Clark, Ann N.	Father Kino: Priest to the Primas (1st, 8vo, 176p, b/w, DJ/2.25)	Farrar, Straus	(1963)	Hoffman, H. Lawrence	20-30	
Clark, Ann N.	In My Mother's House (1st, 4to, 56p, brown cl, pep, color, DJ/2.00, CH)	Viking	1941	Herrera, Velino	80-125	R
Clark, Ann N.	Little Indian Basket Maker (1st, sm ob8vo, 31p, fp color)	Melmont Pub.	(1957)	Begay, Harrison	30-50	*
Clark, Ann N.	Little Indian Pottery Maker (1st, sm ob8vo, 31p, fp color, pep)	Melmont Pub.	(1955)	Perceval, Don	30-50	*
Clark, Ann N.	Little Navajo Bluebird (1st, 8vo, 143p, b/w, pep, DJ/2.50)	Viking	1943	Lantz, Paul	30-50	

AUTHOR	TITLE	PUBLISHER	DATE	ARTIST	PRICE	LC
Clark, Ann N.	Looking for Something (1st, 8vo, 53p, dp color, pep, DJ/2.50)	Viking	1952	Politi, Leo	50-85	
Clark, Ann N.	Magic Money (1st, sm4to, 121p, red cl, pep, fp 1-color, DJ/2.50)	Viking	1950	Politi, Leo	50-80	
Clark, Ann N.	Santiago (1st, 8vo, 189p, color, pep, DJ/2.75)	Viking	1955	Ward, Lynd	40-65	
Clark, Ann N.	Secret of the Andes (1st, lg8vo, 131p, grey cl, col frn, pep, DJ/2.50, NM)	Viking	1952	Charlot, Jean	100-160	R
Clark, Ann N.	Summer is for Growing (1st {std}, 8vo, 180p, fp b/w, DJ/3.50)	Farrar, Straus	(1968)	Tait, Agnes	20-30	*
Clark, Ann N.	Third Monkey (1st, sm4to, 44p, color, pep, DJ/2.50)	Viking	1956	Freeman, Don	40-65	
Clark, Ann N.	This for That (1st, 4to, 62p, fp 3-color, cep, DJ/3.50)	Golden Gate	(1965)	Freeman, Don	30-50	
Clark, Ann N.	Tia Maria's Garden (1st, 8vo, 47p, color, DJ/3.00)	Viking	1963	Keats, Ezra J.	45-70	
Clark, Ann N.	World Song (1st, 8vo, 140p, b/w, DJ/2.75)	Viking	(1960)	Wiese, Kurt	20-35	
Clark, Billy C.	Mooneyed Hound (1st, 8vo, 128p, fp b/w, DJ/2.75)	Putnam	(1958)	Walker, Nedda	40-60	
Clark, Billy C.	Song of the River (1st, 8vo, 120p, black cl, b/w, DJ/2.95)	Crowell	(1957)	Keats, Ezra J.	30-50	
Clark, Denis	Boomer (1st AM, 8vo, 144p, b/w, DJ/2.50)	Viking	1955	Ambler, C. Gifford	20-30	*
Clark, Dorothy	Little Joe (1st, lg ob8vo, [31]p, 3-color, DJ/1.00)	Lothrop, Lee	1940	Weisgard, Leonard	70-100	
Clark, Dorothy	Peter on the Min (1st, 8vo, 170p, 2-color, pep, DJ/2.00)	Lothrop, Lee	(1942)	Yap, Weda	40-65	
Clark, Electa	Tony for Keeps (1st {std}, 8vo, 186p, b/w, DJ/2.00)	Winston	(1955)	Weil, Lisl	30-45	*
Clark, G.O	Nightmare Land (1st, lg4to, [105]p, color)	R.H. Russell	1901	Goodwin, C.L.	200-300	
Clark, G.O.	Moon Babies (1st, ob4to, ibds, 48p, color)	R.H. Russell	1900	Hyde, Helen	200-325	
Clark, Janet M.	Legends of King Arthur & his Knights (8vo, 307p, AEG, 6cp, pep)	L: Nister	[1899]	Margetson, W.H.	70-100	
Clark, Leonard	Explorer's Digest (1st, 8vo, 256p, b/w, DJ/3.00)	Houghton	1955	Ward, Lynd	50-80	
Clark, Leonard	Year Round (1st, 12mo, [32]p, color, DJ)	L: Hart-Davis	1966	Ardizzone, Edward	40-65	*
Clark, Margery	Poppy Seed Cakes (1st {std}, sm sq8vo, 154p, 16cp, pep)	Doubleday/Page	1924	Petershams	120-180	R
Clark, Mary S.	Lost Legends of the Nursery Songs (1st, 12mo, 278p, uncut, 8cp, pep)	L: G. Bell	1920	Woodward, Alice B.	60-90	
Clark, Mary S.	Turnaside Cottage (8vo, [new ed.], green/gilt, 191p, col frn)	L: Marcus Ward	[1880]	Greenaway, Kate	170-240	
Clarke, Arthur	Islands in the Sky (1st {std}, 8vo, 209p, DJ/2.00, pep by...)	Winston	(1952)	Schomburg, Alex	75-120	
Clarke, Mollie	Three Brothers (1st {std}, 8vo, 32p, color, DJ/1.95)	Follett	1967	Stobbs, William	30-50	
Clarke, Olive	Freddy Frizzylocks (1st, ob8vo, ibds, unpag, fp color)	L: Blackie	[1914]	Macgregor, Angusine	150-225	
Clarke, Pauline	Return of the Twelves (1st AM {std}, 8vo, 253p, fp b/w, DJ/3.75)	Coward	(1964)	Bryson, Bernarda	40-65	
Clarke, Pauline	Twelve and the Genii (1st {std}, 8vo, gilt, 185p, b/w, DJ, CgM)	L: Faber	(1962)	Leslie, Cecil	60-100	
Clarke, Sara K.	Lord Will Love Thee (1st, sq8vo, 48p, color, pep, DJ/2.50)	Westminster Pr.	(1959)	Tudor, Tasha	70-120	
Clarkson, L.	Buttercup's Visit... (folio, cloth, chromos)	Dutton	1881	Clarkson, L.	90-120	
Clarkson, L.	Fly-Away Fairies (1st, 4to, ibds, unpag, 16cp)	Dutton	1882	Clarkson, L.	120-200	
Clarkson, L.	Heartsease & Happy Days (folio, AEG, gilt, 12 chromos)	Dutton	1883	Clarkson, L.	120-200	
Clarkson, L.	Indian Summer (1st, folio, 52p, AEG, gilt, 12cp, cep)	Dutton	1881	Clarkson, L.	120-200	
Clarkson, L.	Violet Among the Lilies (4to, silver/gilt, AEG, 8cp)	Dutton	1885	Clarkson, L.	150-250	
Claudel, Paul	Book of Christopher Columbus (1st, 4to, 57p, blue/silver, 2-color, dep)	Yale U. Press	1930	Charlot, Jean	80-130	
Claudy, C.H.	Tell Me Why Stories (1st, lg8vo, tan cl, 154p, 8cp)	McBride	1912	Rockwell, Norman	600-900	*
Claudy, C.H.	Tell Me Why Stories (1st {this fmt}, 8vo, blue cl, 209p, 8cp)	McBride	1914	Wrenn, Thomas	25-40	*
Clay, Beatrice	Stories of King Arthur (1st, 8vo, 322p, gilt, p-o, 8cp)	L: Dent	1905	Curtis, Dora	60-90	
Clay, John Cecil	Lovers' Mother Goose (1st, 4to, 92p, p-o, gilt, color, pep)	Bobbs-Merrill	(1905)	Clay, John Cecil	100-165	
Clay/Herford	Cupid's Cyclopedia (1st, 12mo, ibds, [104]p, color, gilt)	Scribner	1910	Clay/Herford	70-100	
Clayton, Jacqueline	Georgie-Porgie Book (8vo, p-o, unpag, 12cp)	L: Nelson	[1913]	Clayton, Margaret	80-130	
Clayton, Jacqueline	Twirly-Whirly Book (8vo, p-o, unpag, 12cp)	L: Nelson	[1913]	Clayton, Margaret	80-130	
Clayton, John	Bunny Brothers (8vo, pcb, 96p)	L: Sully	(1911)	Clayton, Margaret	80-130	
Clayton, John	Dot in Dreamland (1st, 8vo, 88p, green cl, p-o, 10cp)	Whitman	(1916)	Clayton, Margaret	60-90	
Clayton, Margaret	Amabel and Crispin (1st, 8vo, 133p, blue cl, fp b/w, pep)	L: Chatto	1911	Clayton, Margaret	35-60	
Cleary, Beverly	Beezus and Ramona (1st, 8vo, 159p, b/w, DJ/2.50)	Wm. Morrow	(1955)	Darling, Louis	50-80	*
Cleary, Beverly	Ellen Tebbits (1st, 8vo, 160p, b/w, DJ/2.00)	Wm. Morrow	1951	Darling, Louis	50-80	*
Cleary, Beverly	Emily's Runaway Imagination (1st, 8vo, 221p, b/w, DJ/2.95)	Wm. Morrow	1961	Krush, Beth & Joe	25-40	
Cleary, Beverly	Fifteen (1st, 8vo, 254p, b/w, DJ/2.75)	Wm. Morrow	1956	Krush, Beth & Joe	25-40	
Cleary, Beverly	Henry and Beezus (1st, 8vo, 192p, b/w, DJ/2.50)	Wm. Morrow	1952	Darling, Louis	60-100	
Cleary, Beverly	Henry and Ribsy (1st, 8vo, 192p, b/w, DJ/2.50)	Wm. Morrow	1954	Darling, Louis	60-90	
Cleary, Beverly	Henry Huggins (1st [1st bk.], 8vo, 155p, b/w, DJ/2.00)	Wm. Morrow	1950	Darling, Louis	70-100	
Cleary, Beverly	Hullabaloo ABC (1st, 4to, [36]p, color, pep, DJ/2.95)	Parnassus Press	1960	Thollander, Earl	25-40	*
Cleary, Beverly	Jean & Johnny (1st, 8vo, 284p, b/w, DJ/2.95)	Wm. Morrow	1959	Krush, Beth & Joe	20-35	
Cleary, Beverly	Mitch and Amy (1st, 8vo, 222p, b/w, DJ/3.75)	Wm. Morrow	1967	Porter, George	20-35	
Cleary, Beverly	Mouse & the Motorcycle (1st, 8vo, 158p, b/w, DJ/2.95)	Wm. Morrow	1965	Darling, Louis	25-40	
Cleary, Beverly	Otis Spofford (1st, 8vo, 191p, b/w, DJ/2.50)	Wm. Morrow	1953	Darling, Louis	20-35	
Cleary, Beverly	Ramona the Pest (1st, 8vo, 192p, fp b/w, DJ/3.75)	Wm. Morrow	(1968)	Darling, Louis	20-30	
Cleary, Beverly	Real Hole (1st, sm ob4to, [32]p, 2-color, pep, DJ/2.75)	Wm. Morrow	1960	Stevens, Mary	25-40	
Cleary, Beverly	Ribsy (1st, 8vo, 192p, fp b/w, DJ/2.95)	Wm. Morrow	1964	Darling, Louis	20-35	
Cleary, Beverly	Runaway Ralph (1st, 8vo, 175p, b/w, DJ/3.95)	Wm. Morrow	(1970)	Darling, Louis	30-50	R
Cleary, Beverly	Sister of the Bride (1st, 8vo, 288p, b/w, DJ/3.25)	Wm. Morrow	1963	Krush, Beth & Joe	25-35	
Cleary, Beverly	Two Dog Biscuits (1st, sm ob4to, unpag, color, pep, DJ/2.75)	Wm. Morrow	1961	Stevens, Mary	20-35	
Cleaver, Vera	Ellen Grae (1st {std} [1st bk.], 8vo, 89p, fp b/w, cep, DJ/2.95)	Lippincott	(1967)	Raskin, Ellen	30-50	
Cleaver, Vera	Grover (1st {std}, 8vo, 125p, b/w, DJ/3.50)	Lippincott	(1970)	Marvin, Frederic	30-45	
Cleaver, Vera	Where the Lilies Bloom (1st {std}, 8vo, ipcb, 174p, fp b/w, cep, DJ/3.95)	Lippincott	(1970)	Spanfeller, James	30-45	
Clemens, Nancy	Under Glass (1st {std}, 8vo, 274p, b/w, DJ/2.00)	Longmans	1937	Jones, Wilfred	70-120	
Clemens, Will	Ken of Kipling (1st, 12mo, 141p, orange/gilt, cvr by...)	New Amsterdam	1899	McManus, Blanche	60-90	
Clement, Marguerite	All the World is Colour (1st AM, lg4to, [95]p, 2-color, pep)	Farrar/Rinehart	[1930]	L'Hardy, P.& G.	30-50	
Clement, Marguerite	Flowers of Chivalry (1st {std}, 4to, ipcb, 72p, color, pep)	Doubleday/Doran	1934	L'Hardy, P.& G.	60-100	*
Clement, Marguerite	In France (1st, 8vo, blue cl, 151p, dp b/w, pep, DJ/3.00)	Viking	1956	DuBois, W.P.	30-50	
Clement, Marguerite	Where Was Bobby? (1st {std}, 8vo, 151p, 19cp, pep)	Doubleday/Doran	1928	Petershams	60-90	
Clewes, Dorothy	Fire-Brigade Willie (1st, 12mo, 48p, color, DJ)	L: Hamilton	(1970)	Ardizzone, Edward	30-50	
Clewes, Dorothy	Special Branch Willie (1st, sm8vo, 48p, color, DJ)	L: Hamilton	1969	Ardizzone, Edward	40-65	
Clifford, Eth	Red is Never a Mouse (1st, 4to, [29]p, fp color, DJ/2.95)	Bobbs-Merrill	1960	Heckler, Bill	30-50	
Clifton, Lucille	Black B C's (1st {std}, lg8vo, 45p, fp b/w, cep, DJ/3.95)	Dutton	(1970)	Miller, Don	60-90	*
Clifton, Lucille	Some of the Days/Everett Anderson (1st {std}, ob8vo, [32]p, color, DJ/3.95)	Holt, Rinehart	(1970)	Ness, Evaline	40-65	
Clinton, Althea L.	Treasure Book of Best Stories (1st, 4to, 92p, ibds, 10 fp color)	Saalfield	(1933)	Peat, Fern B.	50-85	

AUTHOR	TITLE	PUBLISHER	DATE	ARTIST	PRICE	LC
Cloud, Virginia W.	Down Durley Lane (1st, lg8vo, 99p, teg, green/gilt, 1-color)	Century	1898	Birch, Reginald	60-90	
Clymer, Eleanor	Belinda's New Spring Hat (1st, 8vo, 32p, 2-color, DJ/3.50)	F. Watts	(1969)	Fiammenghi, Gioia	20-35	
Clymer, Eleanor	Big Pile of Dirt (1st {std}, ob4to, [32]p, 1-color, DJ/3.95)	Holt, Rinehart	1968	Shore, Robert	25-45	
Clymer, Eleanor	Chester (1st, 8vo, 141p, red cl, fp b/w, DJ/2.50)	Dodd	1954	Keats, Ezra J.	30-50	
Clymer, Eleanor	Country Kittens (1st, lg8vo, 108p, fp 2-color, pep, DJ/2.25)	McBride	(1947)	Bendick, Jeanne	30-50	*
Clymer, Eleanor	Grocery Mouse (1st, lg8vo, 94p, color, pep, DJ/2.25)	McBride	1945	Bendick, Jeanne	40-65	
Clymer, Eleanor	Here Comes Pete (1st, lg8vo, 96p, color, DJ/2.00)	McBride	1944	Boyle, Mildred	40-65	*
Clymer, Eleanor	Horatio (1st {std}, 12mo, 63p, 3-color, cep, DJ/3.25)	Atheneum	1968	Quackenbush, Rbt.	25-40	
Clymer, Eleanor	Little Bear Island (1st, 8vo, 143p, uncut, gilt, b/w, DJ/2.25)	McBride	1945	Koering, Ursula	30-50	*
Clymer, Eleanor	Mr. Piper's Bus (1st, 8vo, 92p, b/w, DJ/3.00)	Dodd	1961	Wiese, Kurt	20-30	
Clymer, Eleanor	Sociable Toby (1st, 8vo, 81p, fp b/w, pep, DJ/2.50)	F. Watts	(1956)	Fetz, Ingrid	30-50	*
Clymer, Eleanor	Tommy's Wonderful Airplane (1st, 8vo, 212p, b/w, DJ/2.75)	Dodd	(1951)	Wiese, Kurt	25-40	*
Clymer, Eleanor	Yard for John (1st, 8vo, 94p, fp 2-color, pep, DJ/2.00)	McBride	1943	Boyle, Mildred	40-65	*
Coates, Belle	That Colt, Fireplug (1st, 8vo, 55p, 1-color, DJ/2.50)	Scribner	(1958)	Dennis, Wesley	25-40	
Coatsworth, Eliz.	Alice-All-by-Herself (1st, lg8vo, 181p, col frn, 7pl, pep, DJ/2.00)	Macmillan	1937	DeAngeli, Marguerite	60-90	
Coatsworth, Eliz.	Atlas & Beyond (1st {std}, 12mo, 61p, p-o, dep, woodcuts by...)	Harper	1924	Cimino, Harry	40-60	*
Coatsworth, Eliz.	Aunt Flora (1st {std}, 8vo, 64p, 1-color, DJ/2.00)	Macmillan	1953	Lee, Manning De V.	25-40	
Coatsworth, Eliz.	Away Goes Sally (1st, lg8vo, 122p, p-o, b/w, pep, DJ/2.00)	Macmillan	1934	Sewell, Helen	50-80	R
Coatsworth, Eliz.	Bess and the Sphinx (1st {std}, 8vo, ibds, 88p, b/w, cep, DJ/3.75)	Macmillan	(1967)	Lowenstein, Bernice	20-30	
Coatsworth, Eliz.	Big Green Umbrella (1st, sq8vo, ibds, [28]p, color, pep, DJ/0.50)	Grosset/Dunlap	(1944)	Sewell, Helen	45-65	
Coatsworth, Eliz.	Bob Bodden & the Good Shop Rover (1st, 8vo, 48p, color, pep, DJ)	Garrard Pub.	(1968)	Schroeder, Ted	25-40	
Coatsworth, Eliz.	Boston Bells (1st {std}, 8vo, 64p, grey cl, DJ/2.00)	Macmillan	1952	Lee, Manning De V.	25-40	
Coatsworth, Eliz.	Boy with the Parrot (1st, 8vo, green cl, 101p, dp color, cep)	Macmillan	1930	Bronson, Wilfrid	30-60	*
Coatsworth, Eliz.	Captain's Daughter (1st {std}, 8vo, 198p, DJ/2.50, decor by...)	Macmillan	1950	Ray, Ralph	20-30	
Coatsworth, Eliz.	Cat & the Captain (1st, 16mo, 95p, green cl, 3cp, pep)	Macmillan	1927	Kay, Gertrude A.	35-50	
Coatsworth, Eliz.	Cat Who Went to Heaven (1st, lg8vo, red cl, 57p, 12 fp b/w, NM)	Macmillan	1930	Ward, Lynd	75-100	R
Coatsworth, Eliz.	Cherry Ann & the Dragon Horse (1st {std}, 8vo, ipcb, 64p, b/w, DJ/2.00)	Macmillan	(1955)	Lee, Manning De V.	20-30	
Coatsworth, Eliz.	Children Come Running (1st, 8vo, 96p, ipcb, color, cep, DJ/2.95)	Golden Press	(1960)	Various	25-45	
Coatsworth, Eliz.	Country Neighborhood (1st {std}, 8vo, 181p, DJ/2.50, decor by...)	Macmillan	1944	Woodward, Hildegarde	25-45	
Coatsworth, Eliz.	Creaking Stair (1st, 8vo, 110p, black/silver, b/w, DJ/5.00)	Coward	1949	Dwiggins, W.A.	30-50	
Coatsworth, Eliz.	Cricket & the Emperor's Son (1st, sq8vo, dep, 112p, b/w)	Macmillan	1932	Yap, Weda	55-80	*
Coatsworth, Eliz.	Dancing Tom (1st, sq12mo, tan cl, [49]p, 1-color, DJ/1.00)	Macmillan	1938	Paull, Grace	30-50	
Coatsworth, Eliz.	Desert Dan (1st, lg8vo, 61p, fp b/w, DJ/2.50)	Viking	(1960)	Johnson, Harper	30-50	
Coatsworth, Eliz.	Dog from Nowhere (1st, 8vo, 80p, b/w, DJ/2.20)	Row, Peterson	(1958)	Sibley, Don	20-30	
Coatsworth, Eliz.	Dog Stories (1st {A}, folio, ibds, 66p, color, pep, GGB)	Simon/Schuster	1953	Rojankovsky, Feodor	70-120	*
Coatsworth, Eliz.	Dollar for Luck (1st {std}, 8vo, 151p, b/w, pep, DJ/2.25)	Macmillan	(1951)	Hauman, G.& D.	25-40	
Coatsworth, Eliz.	Door to the North (1st {std}, 8vo, 246p, b/w, DJ/2.50)	Winston	(1950)	Chapman, Fred T.	25-40	
Coatsworth, Eliz.	Down Half the World (1st {std}, 8vo, 98p, b/w, DJ/4.50)	Macmillan	(1968)	Bernstein, Zena	30-45	
Coatsworth, Eliz.	Fair American (1st, lg8vo, 132p, p-o, pep, 14pl, DJ/2.00)	Macmillan	1940	Sewell, Helen	40-65	
Coatsworth, Eliz.	First Adventure (1st {std}, 8vo, 60p, color, DJ/1.50)	Macmillan	1950	Ray, Ralph	25-40	
Coatsworth, Eliz.	Five Bushel Farm (1st, lg8vo, 152p, pep, p-o, b/w, DJ/2.00)	Macmillan	1939	Sewell, Helen	30-50	
Coatsworth, Eliz.	Forgotten Island (1st, 8vo, 65p, tan cl, b/w, DJ/0.50)	Grosset/Dunlap	(1942)	Paull, Grace	30-45	
Coatsworth, Eliz.	Fox Friend (1st {std}, ob8vo, ibds, [32]p, fp 1-color, DJ/2.95)	Macmillan	(1966)	Hamberger, John	25-40	*
Coatsworth, Eliz.	George and Red (1st {std}, 8vo, 55p, brown/gilt, dp b/w, DJ/3.95)	Macmillan	(1969)	Giovanopoulos, P.	25-40	
Coatsworth, Eliz.	Golden Horseshoe (1st, 8vo, 151p, gilt, pep, 14pl, DJ/2.00)	Macmillan	1935	Lawson, Robert	70-100	
Coatsworth, Eliz.	Grandmother Cat & the Hermit (1st {std}, 8vo, 87p, fp b/w, DJ/4.50)	Macmillan	(1970)	Boker, Irving	20-35	
Coatsworth, Eliz.	Hand of Apollo (1st, 8vo, 77p, b/w, DJ/3.00)	Viking	(1965)	Jacques, Robin	20-35	
Coatsworth, Eliz.	Here I Stay (1st, 8vo, 246p, gilt, b/w, DJ/2.00)	Coward	1938	Earle, Edwin	25-40	
Coatsworth, Eliz.	Hide and Seek (1st, 12mo, [32]p, ipcb, fp 1-color, pep, DJ/2.00)	Pantheon	(1956)	Vaughan-Jackson, G.	35-50	*
Coatsworth, Eliz.	House of the Swan (1st {std}, 8vo, 165p, b/w, pep, DJ/2.50)	Macmillan	1948	Voute, Kathleen	25-40	
Coatsworth, Eliz.	House-Boat Summer (1st, 8vo, 191p, p-o, 1-color, pep, DJ/2.00)	Macmillan	1942	Davis, Marguerite	70-100	
Coatsworth, Eliz.	Indian Encounters (1st {std}, 8vo, 264p, b/w, DJ/3.50)	Macmillan	1960	Chapman, Fred T.	30-45	
Coatsworth, Eliz.	Indian Mound Farm (1st {std}, 8vo, 62p, fp b/w, DJ/4.50)	Macmillan	(1969)	Rocker, Fermin	25-40	
Coatsworth, Eliz.	Jock's Island (1st, 8vo, 75p, fp b/w, DJ/2.75)	Viking	(1963)	Obligado, Lilian	20-30	
Coatsworth, Eliz.	Jon the Unlucky (1st {std}, 8vo, 94p, 1-color, DJ/3.50)	Holt, Rinehart	(1964)	Nesbitt, Esta	50-80	R
Coatsworth, Eliz.	Kitten Stand (1st, 8vo, ipcb, [28]p, color, pep, DJ/0.50)	Grosset/Dunlap	(1945)	Keeler, Katherine	30-50	
Coatsworth, Eliz.	Knock at the Door (1st, ob8vo, 73p, gilt, col frn, b/w)	Macmillan	1931	Bedford, Francis D.	40-60	
Coatsworth, Eliz.	Last Fort (1st {std}, 8vo, 250p, b/w, DJ/2.75)	Winston	(1952)	Shenton, Edward	30-45	*
Coatsworth, Eliz.	Lighthouse Island (1st {std}, 8vo, 62p, 2-color, DJ/4.25)	Norton	(1968)	Shimin, Symeon	30-45	*
Coatsworth, Eliz.	Little Haymakers (1st {std}, 8vo, tan cl, 79p, fp b/w, DJ/2.00)	Macmillan	1949	Paull, Grace	30-50	
Coatsworth, Eliz.	Littlest House (1st, 8vo, p-o, 150p, 1-color, pep, DJ/1.50)	Macmillan	1940	Davis, Marguerite	30-50	
Coatsworth, Eliz.	Lonely Maria (1st, 8vo, yellow cl, [38]p, 2-color, DJ/3.25)	Pantheon	(1960)	Ness, Evaline	40-65	
Coatsworth, Eliz.	Lucky Ones (1st {std}, 8vo, 84p, fp b/w, DJ/3.95)	Macmillan	(1968)	Doyle, Janet	20-35	
Coatsworth, Eliz.	Maine Ways (1st {std}, 8vo, 213p, b/w, DJ/2.75)	Macmillan	1947	Coughlin, Mildred	20-30	
Coatsworth, Eliz.	Mouse Chorus (1st, sm8vo, ibds, unpag, 1-color, pep, DJ/2.00)	Pantheon	(1955)	Vaughan-Jackson, G.	25-40	
Coatsworth, Eliz.	Night & the Cat (1st {std}, lg8vo, blue cl, 55p, 10pl, DJ/3.00)	Macmillan	1950	Foujita	45-70	
Coatsworth, Eliz.	Noble Doll (1st, lg8vo, 45p, dp color, pep, DJ/3.00)	Viking	(1961)	Politi, Leo	80-140	
Coatsworth, Eliz.	Old Whirlwind (1st {std}, 8vo, 64p, 2-color, DJ/2.00)	Macmillan	1953	Lee, Manning De V.	20-30	
Coatsworth, Eliz.	Peaceable Kingdom (1st, lg ob8vo, [39]p, 2-color, pep, DJ/2.75)	Pantheon	(1958)	Eichenberg, Fritz	30-50	
Coatsworth, Eliz.	Peddler's Cart (1st {std}, 8vo, 151p, b/w, DJ/2.75)	Macmillan	(1956)	Gay, Zhenya	20-35	
Coatsworth, Eliz.	Plum Daffy Adventure (1st {std}, 8vo, 161p, blue cl, b/w, pep, DJ/2.50)	Macmillan	1947	Davis, Marguerite	30-50	
Coatsworth, Eliz.	Princess and the Lion (1st, 8vo, 77p, dp 1-color, cep, DJ/3.50)	Pantheon	(1963)	Ness, Evaline	45-70	R
Coatsworth, Eliz.	Ronnie and the Chief's Son (1st {std}, 8vo, 38p, fp 1-color, DJ/3.00)	Macmillan	1962	Martin, Stefan	30-50	R
Coatsworth, Eliz.	Silky: An Incredible Tale (1st, 8vo, 143p, ibds, fp b/w, DJ/2.75)	Pantheon	(1953)	Carroll, John	20-35	
Coatsworth, Eliz.	Sod House (1st {std}, 8vo, 64p, b/w, DJ/2.00)	Macmillan	(1954)	Lee, Manning De V.	20-35	
Coatsworth, Eliz.	Sparrow Bush (1st {std}, lg8vo, 63p, b/w, DJ/3.25)	Norton	(1966)	Martin, Stefan	20-35	
Coatsworth, Eliz.	Summer Green (1st {std}, 8vo, ibds, 86p, b/w, DJ/2.00)	Macmillan	1948	Unwin, Nora S.	20-35	
Coatsworth, Eliz.	Sun's Diary (1st, sq8vo, ibds, [98]p, b/w, cep)	Macmillan	1929	McIntosh, Frank	90-140	R

AUTHOR	TITLE	PUBLISHER	DATE	ARTIST	PRICE	LC
Coatsworth, Eliz.	Sword of the Wilderness (1st, 8vo, 160p, b/w, pep, DJ/2.00)	Macmillan	1936	Stein, Harve	25-40	
Coatsworth, Eliz.	The Cave (1st, 8vo, 63p, b/w, DJ/2.50)	Viking	1958	Houser, Allan	30-45	
Coatsworth, Eliz.	The Enchanted, an Incredible Tale (1st, 8vo, 157p, b/w, DJ/2.50)	Pantheon	1951	Winthrop, Robert	30-50	*
Coatsworth, Eliz.	The Place (1st {std}, 8vo, 72p, color, DJ/3.50)	Holt, Rinehart	(1966)	Aeurbach, Marjorie	25-45	*
Coatsworth, Eliz.	The Secret (1st {std}, 4to, [31]p, 1-color, DJ/2.75)	Macmillan	(1965)	Bolognese, Don	25-40	
Coatsworth, Eliz.	They Walk in the Night (1st {std}, ob8vo, 60p, b/w, DJ/4.25)	Norton	(1969)	Martin, Stefan	20-30	
Coatsworth, Eliz.	Thief Island (1st {std}, 8vo, 118p, blue cl, b/w, pep, DJ/1.75)	Macmillan	1943	Wonsetler, Jon	30-50	
Coatsworth, Eliz.	Toast to the King (1st, 8vo, 159p, b/w, pep, DJ/1.50)	Coward	(1940)	Orr, Forrest W.	30-50	
Coatsworth, Eliz.	Tonio & the Stranger (1st, 8vo, 69p, b/w, DJ/0.50)	Grosset/Dunlap	(1941)	Bronson, Wilfrid	25-40	
Coatsworth, Eliz.	Toutou in Bondage (1st, 8vo, 56p, dp illus, pep)	Macmillan	1929	Handforth, Thomas	40-60	*
Coatsworth, Eliz.	Troll Weather (1st {std}, 8vo, 41p, fp b/w, DJ/2.95)	Macmillan	(1967)	Arndt, Ursula	20-30	
Coatsworth, Eliz.	Trudy and the Tree House (1st, 8vo, 114p, fp b/w, DJ/1.75)	Macmillan	1944	Davis, Marguerite	30-50	*
Coatsworth, Eliz.	Twelve Months Make a Year (1st, 8vo, 198p, 1-color, pep, DJ/2.00)	Macmillan	1943	Davis, Marguerite	25-40	
Coatsworth, Eliz.	Up Hill and Down (1st {std}, 8vo, 188p, b/w, DJ/2.50)	Knopf	1947	Davis, James	25-40	
Coatsworth, Eliz.	White Horse (1st {std}, 8vo, 164p, p-o, 14 fp b/w, pep, DJ/2.00)	Macmillan	1942	Sewell, Helen	40-65	
Coatsworth, Eliz.	White Room (1st, 8vo, 143p, b/w, DJ/2.75)	Pantheon	(1958)	Thompson, George	25-45	
Coatsworth, Eliz.	Wishing Pear (1st {std}, 8vo, 64p, fp 1-color, DJ/2.00)	Macmillan	1951	Ray, Ralph	20-30	
Coatsworth, Eliz.	Wonderful Day (1st {std}, 8vo, yellow cl, 126p, p-o, pep, DJ/2.25)	Macmillan	1946	Sewell, Helen	40-65	
Coatsworth, Eliz.	You Say You Saw a Camel? (1st, 8vo, 72p, fp b/w, DJ/2.20)	Row, Peterson	(1958)	Turkle, Brinton	20-35	*
Coatsworth, Eliz.	You Shall Have a Carriage (1st {std}, 8vo, 138p, pep, DJ/2.00)	Macmillan	1941	Pitz, Henry C.	30-45	
Cobb, Irving	Back Home (1st, 8vo, gilt, 348p, 10pl)	Doran	(1912)	Various	55-80	
Cobb, Irving	Cobb's Anatomy (1st, 8vo, tan pcb, 141p, 17pl, pep)	Doran	(1912)	Newell, Peter	40-60	
Cobb, Irving	Cobb's Bill of Fare (1st, 8vo, tan, pcb, 148p, 15pl, pep)	Doran	(1913)	Newell, Peter	40-60	
Cobb, Irving	Fibble, D.D. (1st, 8vo, 279p, blue cl, p-o, b/w, pep)	Doran	(1916)	Sarg, Tony	25-45	
Cobb, Lucy M.	Animal Tales from Old North State (1st, 8vo, 200p, b/w, pep, DJ/2.00)	Dutton	1938	Hogan, Inez	30-50	
Coblentz, Catherine	Animal Pioneers (1st, 8vo, green cl, 241p, b/w, DJ/2.00)	Little/Brown	1936	Wiese, Kurt	35-60	*
Coblentz, Catherine	Beggar's Penny (1st {std}, 8vo, 269p, b/w, map, DJ/2.50)	Longmans	1943	Van Stockum, Hilda	30-50	
Coblentz, Catherine	Bells of Leyden Sing (1st {std}, 8vo, 259p, pep, b/w, DJ/2.25)	Longmans	1944	Van Stockum, Hilda	30-50	
Coblentz, Catherine	Blue & Silver Necklace (1st {std}, 8vo, 242p, blue cl, 6pl, DJ/2.00)	Little/Brown	1937	Earle, Edwin	30-45	*
Coblentz, Catherine	Blue Cat of Castle Town (1st {std}, lg8vo, 123p, b/w, pep, DJ/2.75, NH)	Longmans	1949	Holland, Janice	70-120	R
Coblentz, Catherine	Falcon of Eric the Red (1st {std}, 8vo, 211p, 10 dp pl, DJ/2.25)	Longmans	1942	Pitz, Henry C.	30-50	
Coblentz, Catherine	Martin and Abraham Lincoln (1st, lg8vo, ibds, [24]p, color, pep, DJ/1.00)	Children's Press	(1947)	Trientja	50-80	R*
Coblentz, Catherine	Scatter the Chipmunk (1st, lg8vo, ipcb, [25]p, 1-color, pep, DJ/1.00)	Children's Press	(1946)	Schwartz, Berta	30-45	
Coblentz, Catherine	Sequoya (1st {std}, 8vo, 199p, DJ/2.50, decor by...)	Longmans	1946	Ray, Ralph	25-45	
Coburn, Grace	Heroes & Wizards (1st, 8vo, 246p, col frn, 8 fp b/w)	L: Nelson	1939	Parsons, Jacynth	30-50	*
Coburn, John B.	Anne and the Sand Dobbies (1st, 8vo, 121p, DJ/3.50, pep by...)	Seabury Press	1964	Wyeth, Andrew	30-50	
Coburn, Wallace D.	Rhymes from a Roundup Camp (1st, 12mo, 138p, 7 b/w)	Ridgley Press	1899	Russell, Charles M.	250-350	
Coburn, Wallace D.	Rhymes from a Roundup Camp ({new ed.}, sm8vo, teg, 137p, 7pl)	Putnam	1903	Russell, Charles M.	150-250	
Cocagnac, A.M.	Three Trees of the Samurai (1st, sq4to, 24p, color, DJ/4.25)	Harlin Quist	1969	LeFoll, Alain	30-50	
Cochran, Hamilton	Buccaneer Islands (1st, 8vo, 249p, blue cl, b/w, DJ/2.00)	NY: Nelson	1941	Gay, Zhenya	20-35	
Cocke, Sarah J.	Bypaths in Dixie (1st, 8vo, blue/gilt, 317p, 7pl)	Dutton	(1911)	Smith, Duncan	55-80	*
Codrington, Florence	Chapsticks (1st, 8vo, 154p, b/w)	Macmillan	1929	Jacobs, Helen	25-40	*
Coffin, Julia H.	Vendor of Dreams (1st, lg8vo, 108p, blue/gilt, teg, 3cp)	Dodd	1917	Coffin, Haskell	55-80	*
Coffin, Patricia	Gruesome Green Witch (1st, lg8vo, 85p, color, DJ/4.50)	NY: Walker	(1969)	Parnall, Peter	40-65	
Coggins, Herbert	Busby & Co. (1st, 8vo, 96p, rust cl, fp b/w, pep, DJ/2.25)	Whittlesey	(1952)	Duvoisin, Roger	30-50	
Cohen, Miriam	Will I Have a Friend? (1st {std}, ob8vo, unpag, color, DJ/3.50)	Macmillan	(1967)	Hoban, Lillian	25-40	
Cohen, Octavus R.	Black to Nature (1st, 12mo, 308p, orange cl, b/w, DJ/2.00)	Appleton-Century	1935	Freeman, Margaret	200-300	
Coke, Desmond	Youth Youth! (1st, 8vo, 304p, blue/gilt, teg, 8pl)	L: Chapman/Hall	1919	Brock, Henry M.	30-50	*
Colby, Jean P.	Jim the Cat (1st {std}, lg8vo, yellow cl, 46p, fp b/w, DJ/2.50)	Little/Brown	(1957)	Nichols, Marie C.	30-50	
Colby, Jean P.	Peter Paints the U.S.A. (1st, 4to, 47p, red cl, color, pep, DJ/2.50)	Houghton	1948	Bare, Arnold E.	40-65	
Colcock, Annie T.	Margaret Tudor (1st, 12mo, 169p, green cl)	Stokes	(1902)	Gilbert, W.B.	25-40	
Cole, Frank (ed.)	Picture Birthday Book for Boys & Girls (1st, 16mo, gilt, unpag, 12cp)	L: Harrap	(1915)	Tarrant, Margaret	60-90	
Cole, Walter	ABC Book of People (1st, lg4to, [59]p, color, dep)	Minton Balch	(1932)	Cole, Walter	100-165	
Cole, William	Aunt Bella's Umbrella (1st {std}, sm8vo, [45]p, color, DJ/3.50)	Doubleday	(1970)	Chwast, Jacqueline	30-45	
Cole, William	Beastly Boys and Ghastly Girls (1st {std}, lg8vo, 124p, b/w, DJ/3.75)	World	(1964)	Ungerer, Tomi	80-140	
Cole, William	Birds and the Beasts were There (1st {std}, 8vo, 320p, woodcuts, DJ/4.95)	World	(1963)	Siegl, Helen	30-45	
Cole, William	Book of Nature Poems (1st, 8vo, 256p, b/w, DJ/5.95)	Viking	(1969)	Parker, Robert	20-35	
Cole, William	Cat-Haters Handbook (1st, 8vo, [60]p, ibds, b/w, DJ/2.50)	Dial Press	1963	Ungerer, Tomi	25-40	
Cole, William	Folk Songs of England/Ireland/Scotland (1st AM {std}, 4to, 243p, 1-col, DJ)	Doubleday	1961	Ardizzone, Edward	65-90	
Cole, William	Frances Face-Maker (1st {std}, 8vo, [30]p, fp color, DJ/2.95)	World	(1963)	Ungerer, Tomi	30-50	*
Cole, William	I Went to the Animal Fair (1st {std}, ob4to, 46p, b/w, DJ/2.75)	World	(1958)	Rosselli, Colette	40-65	R*
Cole, William	Oh What Nonsense! (1st, 8vo, 80p, b/w, DJ/2.95)	Viking	(1966)	Ungerer, Tomi	50-85	
Cole, William	Oh, How Silly! (1st {std}, lg8vo, 94p, b/w, DJ/3.50)	Viking	(1970)	Ungerer, Tomi	30-50	*
Cole, William	That Pest Jonathan (1st, sm8vo, [32]p, ibds, color, DJ/3.50)	Harper	(1970)	Ungerer, Tomi	30-50	
Coleman, Oliver	Successful Houses (1st, 8vo, 165p, tan cl, cvr by...)	Herbert Stone	1899	Hazenplug, Frank	60-90	
Coleman, Satis	New Singing Time (1st, 4to, 32p, color, DJ/2.50)	John Day	(1950)	Carroll, Ruth	30-45	
Coleridge, Christabel	Minstrel Dick (1st, 8vo, gilt, 288p, 3pl & cvr by...)	L: Wells/Gard.	1896	Robinson, Charles	100-165	
Coleridge, Samuel T.	Kubla Kahn (1st {std}, 4to, [46]p, gilt, 13 fp brown illus)	Dutton	1933	Vassos, John	100-150	
Coleridge, Samuel T.	Rime of the Ancient Mariner (1st AM, lg4to, gilt, 20 ticp, pep)	Crowell	(1910)	Pogany, Willy	300-500	
Coleridge, Samuel T.	Rime of the Ancient Mariner (1st, lg4to, gilt, teg, pep, 20 ticp)	L: Harrap	(1910)	Pogany, Willy	400-600	
Coleridge, Samuel T.	Rime of the Ancient Mariner (1st {this fmt}, sm4to, teg, gilt, 20 ticp)	Doran	[1915]	Pogany, Willy	200-320	
Coles, Robert	Dead End School (1st {std}, 8vo, 100p, b/w, DJ/3.95)	Little/Brown	(1968)	Rockwell, Norman	40-65	
Coles, Robert	Star of Wonder (1st, sm4to, 48p, fp b/w, pep, DJ/2.25)	Whittlesey	(1953)	Galdone, Paul	30-50	
Colfer, Enid	Cucumber: Story of a Siamese Cat (1st, 8vo, 98p, b/w, DJ/2.95)	Nelson	(1961)	Dowling, Victor	20-30	
Collett, Marjorie	Elizabeth in Toyland (1st, 12mo, bds, 46p, 4cp)	L: Harrap	1925	Tarrant, Margaret	70-100	
Collier, Virginia M.	Roland the Warrior (1st, 8vo, 237p, gilt, color, pep, DJ/2.75)	Harcourt	(1934)	Schoonover, Frank	60-90	
Colling, Susan	Frogmorton (1st AM {std}, 8vo, 148p, grey cl, b/w, pep, DJ/2.50)	Knopf	1956	Shepard, Ernest H.	40-70	
Collins, Charles	All Round the Farm (4to, ibds, [66]p, 12 chromos)	L: Nister	[1880]	Collins, Charles	200-300	

AUTHOR	TITLE	PUBLISHER	DATE	ARTIST	PRICE	LC
Collins, Dale	Shipmates Down Under (1st, sm8vo, green cl, 188p, b/w, cep, DJ/2.25)	Holiday House	(1950)	Busoni, Rafaello	25-40	
Collins, Ruth P.	Flying Cow (1st, 8vo, 123p, fp b/w, DJ/3.50)	H.Z. Walck	1963	Keats, Ezra J.	25-40	
Collins, Ruth P.	Krishna & the White Elephants (1st, 8vo, 119p, dp b/w, DJ/3.00)	H.Z. Walck	1961	Keats, Ezra J.	20-30	
Collis, Maurice	Quest for Sita (1st AM, 8vo, 162p, blue/gilt, uncut, 31 fp b/w, DJ/2.75)	NY: J. Day	(1947)	Peake, Mervyn	100-165	
Collodi, Carlo	Adventures Every Child Should Know (1st, 12mo, 241p, 8cp)	Doubleday/Page	1909	Chamberlin, E.H.	50-80	*
Collodi, Carlo	Adventures of Pinocchio (8vo, 259p, p-o, 8cp)	Winston	(1920)	Richardson, F.	50-80	
Collodi, Carlo	Adventures of Pinocchio (1st AM, lg4to, 404p, cp, DJ)	Macmillan	(1925)	Mussino, Attilio	250-400	
Collodi, Carlo	Adventures of Pinocchio (1st {std}, sm8vo, 280p, col frn)	Doubleday/Doran	1930	Liddell, Mary	60-100	*
Collodi, Carlo	Adventures of Pinocchio (1st {this fmt}, lg8vo, 254p, p-o, 5cp, pep, WS)	Rand/McNally	(1939)	Friend, Esther	60-100	
Collodi, Carlo	Adventures of Pinocchio (1st, folio, ibds, 126p, color, DJ)	Grosset/Dunlap	[1957]	Maraja	45-70	
Collodi, Carlo	Adventures of Pinocchio (1st, 8vo, 224p, fp color, pep, DJ/2.95)	F. Watts	(1959)	Mozley, Charles	20-30	
Collodi, Carlo	Pinocchio (1st, 12mo, 212p, gilt, 12cp, pep)	Ginn & Co.	(1904)	Copeland, Charles	80-140	
Collodi, Carlo	Pinocchio (1st, sq8vo, p-o, ibds, 268p, 13cp)	Dent/Dutton	1911	Folkard, Charles	90-120	
Collodi, Carlo	Pinocchio (1st, 8vo, 234p, red/gilt, teg, 8cp)	Lippincott	1916	Kirk, Maria L.	40-65	
Collodi, Carlo	Pinocchio (1st, lg8vo, 205p, p-o, 8cp)	Whitman	(1917)	Carsey, Alice	60-90	
Collodi, Carlo	Pinocchio (1st {Gift ed.}, lg8vo, 234p, p-o, teg, 14 ticp, pep)	Lippincott	(1920)	Kirk, Maria L.	160-250	
Collodi, Carlo	Pinocchio (1st, 8vo, 167p, gilt, p-o, 21cp, pep)	Winston	(1923)	Richardson, F.	100-165	*
Collodi, Carlo	Pinocchio (1st, lg8vo, 247p, p-o, col frn, b/w)	Saalfield	(1924)	Brundage, Frances	60-100	
Collodi, Carlo	Pinocchio (1st {this pub.}, 8vo, p-o, DJ)	McKay	(1925)	Folkard, Charles	75-100	
Collodi, Carlo	Pinocchio (1st, lg8vo, 255p, pep, p-o, fp color)	Whitman	(1926)	Higgins, Violet M.	60-80	*
Collodi, Carlo	Pinocchio (1st, lg8vo, 236p, p-o, orange cl, col frn, pep)	Sears	(1926)	Rule, Christopher	60-90	
Collodi, Carlo	Pinocchio (1st, 8vo, p-o, 213p, 5cp, pep)	Houghton	1927	Bacharach, Herman I.	80-120	
Collodi, Carlo	Pinocchio (1st, lg8vo, green/gilt, 262p, p-o, 21cp, pep)	Winston	(1927)	Richardson, F.	120-200	
Collodi, Carlo	Pinocchio (1st, 8vo, red/gilt, p-o, 239p, 6cp, pep)	T. Nelson	1928	Wiese, Kurt	70-100	
Collodi, Carlo	Pinocchio (1st {Gift ed.}, lg8vo, 234p, 10cp)	Lippincott	(1930)	Tinker, Jack H.	75-100	*
Collodi, Carlo	Pinocchio (1st, 8vo, p-o, blue cl, 323p, 4cp, pep)	Garden City	1932	Petershams	65-100	R
Collodi, Carlo	Pinocchio (1st, sm8vo, rust cl, 282p, 13 fp b/w)	Appleton-Century	(1935)	Sewell, Helen	35-60	*
Collodi, Carlo	Pinocchio (1st [Movie ed.], sm ob4to, color, [50]p)	Grosset/Dunlap	1939	(Photos)	70-100	*
Collodi, Carlo	Pinocchio (1st, 4to, ibds, 96p, cvr & col frn by...)	Saalfield	(1939)	Madsen, Eleanora	90-120	*
Collodi, Carlo	Pinocchio (1st, 4to, red cl, 122p, pep, 6cp)	Platt/Munk	(1940)	Sarg, Tony	100-160	
Collodi, Carlo	Pinocchio (1st {std}, 8vo, 239p, pep, fp color, pep, DJ/1.00, RC)	World	(1946)	Floethe, Richard	30-50	
Collodi, Carlo	Pinocchio (1st, 4to, yellow bds, [65]p, 7 fp color, pep)	Random	(1946)	Lenski, Lois	100-175	
Collodi, Carlo	Pinocchio (1st, folio, 116p, ibds, color, DGB)	Golden Press	(1963)	Rizzato, Sergio	60-90	
Collodi, Carlo	Pinocchio in Africa (1st AM, 12mo, green cl, 152p, b/w)	Ginn & Co.	(1911)	Copeland, Charles	100-170	
Collodi, Carlo	Pinocchio's Adventures in Wonderland (1st AM, 12mo, green/gilt, 212p, 4cp)	Jordan Marsh	(1898)	Quentin, R.	350-500	R*
Collodi, Carlo	Story of a Puppet (1st AM, sm8vo, 232p, 1-color title pg., b/w, dep)	NY: Cassell	1892	Mazzanti, C.	1800-3000	
Collodi, Carlo	Story of a Puppet (1st {Engl. trans.}, 8vo, green/gilt, 232p, teg, b/w)	L: T.F. Unwin	1892	Mazzanti, C.	2000-4000	
Colman, Hila	Peter's Brownstone House (1st, 8vo, [46]p, fp 1-color, pep, DJ/2.95)	Wm. Morrow	1963	Weisgard, Leonard	30-50	
Colman, Margery	Bramble (1st AM {std}, 4to, ibds, 32p, color, DJ/2.00)	Coward	(1945)	Colman, Margery	35-50	
Colmont, Marie	Along the Coast (1st, folio, ibds, [24]p, fp color, pep, DJ/1.50)	Harper	1939	Exeter, Alexandra	200-300	
Colmont, Marie	Down the River (1st {std}, lg4to, ibds, [24]p, pep, 5 dp color, DJ/1.50)	Harper	1940	Exeter, Alexandra	150-250	
Colt, Terry S.	Knights, Goats & Battleships (1st {std}, 8vo, 316p, color, pep)	Doubleday/Doran	1930	Flack, Marjorie	50-85	*
Colum, Padraic	Adventures of Odysseus (1st, 12mo, 254p, 8cp, pep)	Macmillan	1918	Pogany, Willy	60-90	
Colum, Padraic	At the Gateways of the Day (1st, lg8vo, 217p, fp b/w)	Yale U. Press	1924	Fraser, Juliette M.	30-50	
Colum, Padraic	Big Tree of Bunlahy (1st, 8vo, 166p, col frn, DJ/2.25, NH)	Macmillan	1933	Yeats, Jack B.	100-165	
Colum, Padraic	Boy Apprenticed to an Enchanter (1st, sm8vo, 168p, 5 fp b/w, dep)	Macmillan	1920	Walker, Dugald S.	80-130	
Colum, Padraic	Boy in Eirinn (1st AM, sm8vo, 255p, blue/gilt, col frn, 4pl)	Dutton	(1913)	Yeats, Jack B.	120-180	*
Colum, Padraic	Boy in Eirinn (1st UK, 8vo, bds, 255p, 6pl)	L: Dent	(1916)	Yeats, Jack B.	160-225	
Colum, Padraic	Boy Who Knew what the Birds Said (1st, 12mo, 178p, b/w)	Macmillan	1918	Walker, Dugald S.	45-70	
Colum, Padraic	Bright Islands (1st, 8vo, 233p, gilt, pep, b/w)	Yale U. Press	1925	Fraser, Juliette M.	40-60	
Colum, Padraic	Children of Odin (1st, sm8vo, gilt, 282p, 4cp, pep)	Macmillan	1920	Pogany, Willy	50-80	
Colum, Padraic	Children Who Followed the Piper (1st, 12mo, 152p, col frn, fp b/w)	Macmillan	1922	Walker, Dugald S.	55-80	
Colum, Padraic	Creatures (1st, lg8vo, bds, 56p, 10 illus, pep)	Macmillan	1927	Artzybasheff, Boris	60-90	
Colum, Padraic	Forge in the Forest (1st, sm8vo, 149p, black/gilt, pep, 9cp)	Macmillan	1925	Artzybasheff, Boris	60-100	
Colum, Padraic	Fountain of Youth (1st, sm8vo, 206p, b/w, pep)	Macmillan	1927	Van Everen, Jay	45-70	
Colum, Padraic	Frenzied Prince (1st {std}, sm4to, 196p, gilt, 10 fp color, pep, DJ/3.50)	McKay	(1943)	Pogany, Willy	80-140	
Colum, Padraic	Girl Who Sat by the Ashes (1st, sm8vo, 175p, col frn, b/w)	Macmillan	1919	Walker, Dugald S.	45-70	
Colum, Padraic	Golden Fleece (1st, sq8vo, 290p, gilt, 8cp, pep, NH)	Macmillan	1921	Pogany, Willy	60-100	
Colum, Padraic	Island of the Mighty (1st, sm8vo, 265p, gilt, 3cp, 19pl)	Macmillan	1924	Jones, Wilfred	50-80	
Colum, Padraic	King of Ireland's Son (1st, 8vo, green/gilt, 316p, 4cp)	Henry Holt & Co.	1916	Pogany, Willy	80-145	
Colum, Padraic	King of Ireland's Son (1st UK, 8vo, 316p, 4cp, 9 fp b/w)	L: Harrap	1920	Pogany, Willy	80-120	
Colum, Padraic	King of Ireland's Son (1st {this pub.}, sq8vo, 316p, 4cp)	Macmillan	1921	Pogany, Willy	60-100	
Colum, Padraic	Legend of St. Columbia (1st, 8vo, green cl, 156p, b/w, DJ/2.25)	Macmillan	1935	MacKinstry, Eliz.	50-80	
Colum, Padraic	Orpheus: Myths of the World (1st, 4to, 327p, grey cl, 20pl)	Macmillan	1930	Artzybasheff, Boris	40-70	
Colum, Padraic	Peep-Show Man (1st, 12mo, blue cl, 65p, 4cp, pep)	Macmillan	1924	Lenski, Lois	70-120	
Colum, Padraic	Six Who were Left in a Shoe (1st, sq8vo, ibds, unpag, color, pep)	Volland	(1923)	Walker, Dugald S.	50-80	
Colum, Padraic	Stone of Victory (1st, 8vo, 119p, red cl, b/w, DJ/3.75)	McGraw-Hill	(1966)	Brown, Judith	20-35	
Colum, Padraic	The Voyagers (1st, sm8vo, gilt, 188p, 3cp, fp b/w, pep, NH)	Macmillan	1925	Jones, Wilfred	60-90	
Colum, Padraic	Where the Winds Never Blew... (1st, 8vo, 96p, 1-color, DJ/1.50)	Macmillan	1940	Bennett, Richard	30-50	
Colum, Padraic	White Sparrow (1st, sq8vo, 46p, grey cl, 1-color, pep, DJ/2.00)	Macmillan	1933	Ward, Lynd	55-80	
Colum, Padraic (ed)	Arabian Nights (1st, 8vo, 344p, color, pep, DJ/2.50)	Macmillan	(1953)	Ward, Lynd	30-50	*
Colver, Alice M.	Wish Fairy of Sunshine & Shadow Forest (1st, 24mo, ibds, p-o, 63p, color)	Altemus	(1919)	Colver, Alice	60-90	R
Colver, Anne	Bread & Butter Indian (1st {std}, 8vo, 96p, ibds, b/w, cep, DJ/2.95)	Holt, Rinehart	1964	Williams, Garth	30-50	
Colver, Anne	Bread & Butter Journey (1st {std}, 8vo, 101p, fp b/w, DJ/3.95)	Holt, Rinehart	(1970)	Williams, Garth	30-50	
Colver, Anne	Nobody's Birthday (1st, 8vo, [42]p, color, cep, DJ/2.75)	Knopf	(1961)	Bileck, Marvin	40-65	
Colver, Anne	Old Bet (1st, 4to, [52]p, color, pep, DJ/3.00)	Knopf	(1957)	Palazzo, Tony	25-35	
Colvile, Kathleen	Jason & the Princess (1st AM, 8vo, blue cl, 86p, 4cp)	Houghton	(1926)	Rutherston, Albert	35-60	*
Commager, Henry	America's Robert E. Lee (1st, lg8vo, 112p, color, pep, DJ/3.00)	Houghton	1951	Ward, Lynd	30-50	*

AUTHOR: 48

AUTHOR	TITLE	PUBLISHER	DATE	ARTIST	PRICE	LC
Commager, Henry	Chestnut Squirrel (1st, lg8vo, 122p, b/w, DJ/2.00)	Houghton	1952	Weil, Lisl	25-40	
Commins, Dorothy	Lullabies of the World (1st {std}, lg4to, 266p, b/w, pep, DJ/12.95)	Random	1967	(Photos)	40-65	
Compton, Margaret	Snow Bird & Water Tiger... (1st UK, 8vo, 201p, teg, gilt, b/w)	L: Lawrence	1895	Greenough, Walter C.	80-125	
Comstock, Enos B.	Fairy Frolics (1st, 4to, [64]p, p-o, 6cp)	Rand/McNally	(1913)	Comstock, Enos B.	160-220	
Comstock, Enos B.	Tuck-Me-In Stories (1st, lg8vo, 76p, color)	Moffat	1917	Comstock, Enos B.	80-125	
Comstock, Harriet T.	Princess Rags & Tatters (1st, sm8vo, grey cl, 112p, 4cp)	Doubleday/Page	1912	Thayer, Lee	35-60	
Cone, Helen G.	Baby Sweethearts (1st, folio, [26]p, ipcb, 12cp)	Stokes	1890	Humphrey, Maud	600-800	R
Cone, Helen G.	Bonnie Little People (1st, folio, ibds, 12p, 6cp)	Stokes	1890	Humphrey, Maud	500-700	
Cone, Helen G.	One, Two, Three, Four (1st, lg8vo, ibds, [14]p, 4cp)	Stokes	1889	Humphrey, Maud	300-450	
Cone, Molly	House in the Tree (1st, 8vo, 40p, b/w, DJ/3.75)	Crowell	(1968)	Shimin, Symeon	25-40	
Cone, Molly	Jewish Sabbath (1st, 8vo, [38]p, fp 3-color, DJ/2.95)	Crowell	(1966)	Raskin, Ellen	30-50	*
Cone, Molly	Other Side of the Fence (1st, 8vo, 117p, fp b/w, DJ/3.25)	Houghton	1967	Gretzer, John	30-45	*
Conger, Lesley	Tops and Bottoms (1st, ob4to, [40]p, fp color, DJ/3.95)	Four Winds Pr.	(1970)	Gobbato, Imero	50-80	*
Conger, Marion	Circus Time (1st {A}, sm8vo, [42]p, ibds, color, LGB/#31)	Simon/Schuster	(1948)	Gergely, Tibor	30-45	
Conger, Marion	Rosie the Rhino (1st, 8vo, [32]p, ibds, 1-color, DJ/1.00)	Abingdon Press	(1948)	Wiese, Kurt	30-50	
Conklin, Gladys	Chimpanzee Roams the Forest (1st, 8vo, 48p, 3-color, DJ/3.95)	Holiday House	(1970)	Kalmenoff, Matthew	20-30	
Conklin, Gladys	How Insects Grow (1st, 8vo, 127p, color, DJ/3.95)	Holiday House	(1969)	Goodenow, Girard	20-30	
Conklin, Gladys	I Caught a Lizard (1st, ob8vo, [40]p, color, DJ/3.50)	Holiday House	(1967)	Marokvia, Artur	20-30	
Conklin, Gladys	I Like Caterpillars (1st, sm4to, yellow cl, [26]p, color, DJ/2.75)	Holiday House	(1958)	Latham, Barbara	25-45	
Conklin, Gladys	If I were a Bird (1st, ob8vo, [40]p, color, DJ/3.50)	Holiday House	1965	Marokvia, Artur	20-30	
Conklin, Gladys	Little Apes (1st, 8vo, [40]p, 3-color, DJ/4.50)	Holiday House	(1970)	Cellini, Joseph	25-40	
Conklin, Gladys	Lucky Ladybugs (1st, 4to, [32]p, color, DJ/4.50)	Holiday House	(1968)	Rounds, Glen	25-40	
Conklin, Gladys	When Insects are Babies (1st, 8vo, [40]p, color, DJ/4.50)	Holiday House	(1969)	Marokvia, Artur	25-40	
Conkling, Hilda	Silverhorn (1st, 8vo, p-o, 159p, col frn, b/w, pep)	Stokes	1924	Lathrop, Dorothy	70-120	
Conner, Ralph	Black Rock (1st, 8vo, tan cl, 322p, cvr by...)	Revell	1900	Hazenplug, Frank	30-50	
Conner, Ralph	Black Rock (1st, 8vo, tan cl, 322p, 8pl by...)	Revell	1900	Rhead, Louis	30-50	
Connolly, James B.	Crested Seas (1st, sm8vo, 311p, gilt, teg, 2pl by..)	Scribner	1907	Wyeth, N.C.	40-65	
Connolly, James B.	Hiker Joy (1st, sm8vo, red/gilt, uncut, 244p, 4pl)	Scribner	1920	Wyeth, N.C.	50-80	
Connolly, John	Story of an Old Fashioned Doll (1st, 8vo, 107p)	L: D. Nutt	1905	Ault, Norman	60-90	
Connor, J. Hall	Sandy, Tin Soldier of the A.E.F. (1st, 8vo, 114p, color)	Laidlaw	1931	Wiese, Kurt	30-50	
Conrad, Joseph	Romance (1st AM, sm8vo, dark/gilt, 428p, 8pl)	McClure	1904	Macauley, Charles R.	200-300	
Converse, Florence	House of Prayer (1st, 12mo, 276p, gilt, teg, uncut, 8pl)	L: Dent	1908	Webb, Margaret E.	30-50	
Cook, Bernadine	Curious Little Kitten (1st, sm ob4to, [48]p, green cl, 1-color, DJ/2.25)	W.R. Scott	1956	Charlip, Remy	60-100	*
Cook, Bernadine	Little Fish that Got Away (1st, sm8vo, unpag, 2-color, DJ/2.25)	W.R. Scott	1956	Johnson, Crockett	40-60	*
Cook, Bernadine	Looking for Susie (1st, ob8vo, [48]p, fp 1-color, DJ/2.50)	Young Scott	1959	Shahn, Judith	25-45	
Cook, Hartley K.	Over the Hills and Far Away (1st, 8vo, 263p, DJ, b/w pep by...)	L: Allen/Unwin	1947	Ardizzone, Edward	40-65	
Cook, Walter	Peggy's Travels (1st, 4to, 98p, brown bds, 15cp)	L: Blackie	(1908)	Cook, Alice M.	125-200	
Cook, William W.	Wilby's Dan (1st, 12mo, 325p, 8cp)	Dodd	1904	Falls, Charles B.	50-80	
Cooke, Alistair	Christmas Eve (1st AM {std}, 8vo, 56p, bds, 1-color, DJ/2.00)	Knopf	(1952)	Simont, Marc	40-60	
Cooke, Donald E.	Nutcracker of Nuremberg (1st, 8vo, 148p, gilt, fp 2-color, pep, DJ/2.00)	Winston	(1938)	Cooke, Donald E.	50-80	
Cooke, Donald E.	The Firebird (1st AM, 8vo, 144p, 4cp, fp b/w, gilt, pep, DJ/2.00)	Winston	(1939)	Cooke, Donald E.	35-45	
Cooke, Edmund V.	Biography of Our Baby (1st, sm4to, white/gilt, [60]p, color)	Dodge	(1906)	Pease, Bessie C.	170-240	
Cooke, Edmund V.	Chronicles of a Little Tot (1st, 8vo, 119p, 3cp)	Dodge	(1905)	Pease, Bessie C.	175-250	
Cooke, Edmund V.	Impertinent Poems (1st, 8vo, p-o, teg, uncut, 103p, 11cp)	Dodge	(1907)	Ross, Gordon	35-60	
Cooke, Edmund V.	Story Club (1st, 8vo, p-o, 210p, 8cp)	Dodge	(1912)	Curtis, Eliza	30-50	*
Cooke, Edmund V.	Told to the Little Tot (1st, 8vo, 132p, p-o, teg, 10cp)	Dodge	(1906)	Pease, Bessie C.	160-200	
Cooke, Grace M.	Doings of the Dollivers (1st, 12mo, 174p, 7pl)	Sturgis/Walton	1910	Linnell, Harry	40-60	*
Cooke, Grace M.	Gourd Fiddle (1st, 12mo, 118p, red cl, 1-color)	Altemus	1904	Mudge/Miles	40-60	
Cooke, Grace M.	Huldah (1st, sm8vo, 316p, cvr by...)	Bobbs-Merrill	(1904)	Armstrong, Margaret	35-60	
Cooke, Grace M.	Huldah (1st, sm8vo, 316p, 8pl by...)	Bobbs-Merrill	(1904)	Cory, Fanny	35-60	
Cooke, Grace M.	Their First Formal Call (1st, 8vo, 55p, p-o, gilt, 14pl)	Harper	1906	Newell, Peter	70-120	
Cooke, Marjorie B.	Dual Alliance (1st, sm8vo, 165p, blue cl, col frn, 4pl, dep)	Doubleday/Page	1915	Blumenschein, Mary	25-40	
Coolidge, Dane	Hidden Water (1st, 8vo, ibds, 483p, 4cp)	McClurg	1910	Dixon, Maynard	50-80	
Coolidge, Dane	The Texican (1st, 8vo, beige cl, 369p, 5cp)	McClurg	1911	Dixon, Maynard	60-90	
Coolidge, Florence C.	Little Ugly Face (1st, 12mo, 181p, 2-color)	Macmillan	1925	Petershams	45-70	
Coolidge, Olivia	Ceasar's Gallic War (1st, sm8vo, 245p, b/w, DJ/3.50)	Houghton	1961	Stobbs, William	20-30	*
Coolidge, Olivia	Come by Here (1st {std}, 8vo, 239p, b/w, DJ/4.25)	Houghton	1970	Johnson, Milton	25-40	
Coolidge, Olivia	Cromwell's Head (1st, 8vo, 262p, b/w, DJ/3.00)	Houghton	1955	Wilson, Edward A.	20-30	*
Coolidge, Olivia	Egyptian Adventures (1st, 8vo, 209p, b/w, pep, DJ/3.00)	Houghton	1954	Low, Joseph	35-50	R*
Coolidge, Olivia	Golden Days of Greece (1st, 8vo, 211p, b/w, DJ/3.95)	Crowell	(1968)	Arno, Enrico	20-30	*
Coolidge, Olivia	King of Men (1st {std}, 8vo, 230p, b/w, cep, DJ/3.50)	Houghton	1966	Raskin, Ellen	50-80	R*
Coolidge, Olivia	Legends of the North (1st, 8vo, 260p, b/w, DJ/3.00)	Houghton	1951	Sandoz, Edouard	20-30	*
Coolidge, Olivia	Lives of Famous Romans (1st {std}, 8vo, 248p, b/w, DJ/3.50)	Houghton	1965	Johnson, Milton	20-30	*
Coolidge, Olivia	Maid of Artemis (1st {std}, 8vo, 132p, b/w, DJ/3.50)	Houghton	1969	Holmes, Bea	20-30	*
Coolidge, Olivia	Marathon Looks on the Sea (1st {std}, 8vo, 246p, b/w, DJ/3.50)	Houghton	1967	Schachner, Erwin	40-65	R*
Coolidge, Olivia	Men of Athens (1st, 8vo, 244p, b/w, cep, DJ/3.50, NH)	Houghton	1962	Johnson, Milton	35-50	*
Coolidge, Olivia	Roman People (1st, 8vo, 243p, b/w, DJ/3.00)	Houghton	1959	Lipinsky, Lino	25-40	
Coolidge, Olivia	Trojan War (1st, 8vo, 244p, b/w, DJ/3.00)	Houghton	1952	Sandoz, Edouard	20-30	*
Coolidge, Susan	Guernsey Lily (lg sq8vo, brown/gilt, 238p, pep, 9 b/w by...)	Roberts Bros.	1881	Greenaway, Kate	125-200	
Coolidge, Susan	What Katy Did (1st, 8vo, p-o, 271p, 5cp, pep)	Little/Brown	1924	Coleman, Ralph P.	30-50	
Cooney, Barbara	Captain Pottle's House (1st, 12mo, 172p, green cl, b/w, DJ/1.50)	Farrar/Rinehart	(1943)	Cooney, Barbara	50-80	
Cooney, Barbara	King of Wreck Island (1st {1st bk}, lg8vo, blue cl, 91p, fp b/w, DJ/1.50)	Farrar/Rinehart	(1941)	Cooney, Barbara	70-100	
Cooney, Barbara	Little Juggler (1st, 8vo, 46p, color, pep, DJ/3.00)	Hastings House	(1961)	Cooney, Barbara	40-65	
Cooney, Barbara	Little Prayer (1st, ob16mo, [34]p, ibds, color, DJ/1.25)	Hastings House	(1967)	Cooney, Barbara	40-65	
Cooney, Barbara	The Kellyhorns (1st, 8vo, red cl, 259p, b/w, DJ/2.00)	Farrar/Rinehart	(1942)	Cooney, Barbara	70-100	
Coonley, Lydia A.	Singing Verses for Children (1st, ob4to, 80p, p-o, gilt, color)	Macmillan	1897	Tyler, Alice K.	200-300	
Cooper, Elizabeth	Fish from Japan (1st {std}, 4to, [32]p, color, DJ/3.75)	Harcourt	(1969)	Krush, Beth & Joe	25-45	
Cooper, Elizabeth	Who is Paddy? (1st {std}, 16mo, [32]p, color, DJ/2.95)	Harcourt	1967	Pincus, Harriet	25-40	

AUTHOR	TITLE	PUBLISHER	DATE	ARTIST	PRICE	LC
Cooper, Frederic T.	Argosy of Fables (1st, 4to, 485p, blue cl, 24 ticp, pep)	Stokes	(1921)	Bransom, Paul	150-250	
Cooper, James F.	Last of the Mohicans (1st, 8vo, green/gilt, 398p, AEG, 25pl)	L: Macmillan	1900	Brock, Henry M.	40-70	
Cooper, James F.	Last of the Mohicans (1st, 8vo, p-o, 523p, 8cp)	Henry Holt & Co.	(1910)	Smith, E. Boyd	70-120	
Cooper, James F.	Last of the Mohicans (1st, lg8vo, 370p, p-o, 14cp, pep, SC)	Scribner	1919	Wyeth, N.C.	200-300	
Cooper, James F.	Last of the Mohicans (1st, sm8vo, p-o, 437p, 8cp, pep)	McKay	(1928)	Hurd, Peter	40-65	
Cooper, James F.	Last of the Mohicans (1st, 8vo, 440p, color, RC)	World	1957	Daugherty, James	25-40	
Cooper, James F.	The Deerslayer (1st, 12mo, 522p, gilt, b/w, uncut)	L: Macmillan	1900	Brock, Henry M.	30-50	
Cooper, James F.	The Deerslayer (1st, lg8vo, p-o, 462p, 9cp, pep, SC)	Scribner	1925	Wyeth, N.C.	160-240	
Cooper, James F.	The Deerslayer (1st, 8vo, black cl, p-o, 556p, 4cp)	Harper	(1926)	Rhead, Louis	40-60	
Cooper, James F.	The Pathfinder (1st, 12mo, 463p, red/gilt, b/w)	L: Macmillan	1900	Brock, Charles E.	30-50	
Cooper, James F.	The Pathfinder (1st, 12mo, 516p, b/w pl)	Macrae Smith	(1926)	Humphreys, Donald	25-40	*
Cooper, James F.	The Pathfinder (1st, 8vo, 540p, blue/gilt, p-o, 8cp, pep)	NY: Nelson	(1928)	Boog, Carle M.	30-50	*
Cooper, James F.	The Pathfinder (1st, 8vo, blue cl, p-o, 430p, 6cp, pep)	Minton Balch	1928	Ward, E.F.	40-60	
Cooper, James F.	The Pioneers (1st, 8vo, 455p, red/gilt, AEG, 25pl)	L: Macmillan	1901	Brock, Henry M.	40-70	
Cooper, James F.	The Spy (1st, lg8vo, blue cl, 389p, p-o, 8cp, pep)	Minton Balch	1924	Baldridge, Cyrus L.	35-60	
Cooper, James F.	The Spy (1st, 8vo, 415p, p-o, 8cp)	Houghton	1924	Brett, Harold M.	30-50	
Cooper, Lee	Five Fables from France (1st, 8vo, 86p, brown cl, 2-color, pep, DJ/4.50)	Abelard-Schuman	(1970)	Keeping, Charles	25-40	
Cooper, Lettice U.	Bear Who was Too Big (1st AM {std}, 4to, 30p, color, DJ/3.50)	Follett	(1966)	Ives, Ruth	30-50	*
Cooper, Page	Amigo, Circus Horse (1st {std}, 8vo, 238p, yellow cl, uncut, b/w, DJ/2.50)	World	(1955)	Pitz, Henry C.	30-50	
Cooper, Page	Great Horse Stories (1st {std}, 8vo, 366p, maroon cl, fp b/w, DJ/3.50)	Doubleday	1946	Brown, Paul	50-85	
Cooper, Page (ed)	Famous Dog Stories (1st {std}, 8vo, 336p, b/w, DJ/3.50)	Doubleday	1948	Thorne, Diana	30-45	
Cooper, Susan	Dawn of Fear (1st AM {std}, 8vo, 157p, b/w, DJ/4.95)	Harcourt	(1970)	Gill, Margery	50-80	
Cooper, Susan	Over Sea, Under Stone (1st AM {std}, 8vo, 252p, b/w, DJ/3.50)	Harcourt	(1966)	Gill, Margery	800-1200	
Copeland, Walter	Awful Airship (1st, ob16mo, 62p, 30cp)	L: Blackie	[1906]	Robinson, Charles	225-325	
Copeland, Walter	Babes & Blossoms (1st AM, sm8vo, ipcb, 16cp)	Caldwell	(1908)	Robinson, Charles	200-300	
Copeland, Walter	Babes & Blossoms (1st, 8vo, ibds, [66]p, 16cp, pep)	L: Blackie	(1908)	Robinson, Charles	250-400	
Copeland, Walter	Black Cat Book (1st AM, 8vo, unpag, p-o, ibds, 1-color)	Dodge	(1905)	Robinson, Charles	500-700	
Copeland, Walter	Black Cat Book (1st, lg8vo, [48]p, ipcb, p-o, fp 1-color)	L: Blackie	[1905]	Robinson, Charles	450-650	
Copeland, Walter	Book of the Zoo (1st, 16mo, 120p, 3-color, pep)	L: Dent	1902	Robinson, Charles	200-300	
Copeland, Walter	Bouncing Babies (ob12mo, green cl, color, pep)	L: J.M. Dent	(1906)	Robinson, Charles	450-600	
Copeland, Walter	Farm Book (1st, 16mo, 120p, 3-color, pep)	Dent/Dutton	1901	Robinson, Charles	200-300	
Copeland, Walter	Mad Motor (1st, ob24mo, [60]p, ibds, fp color, pep)	L: Blackie	(1906)	Robinson, Charles	200-300	
Copley, Frank B.	Impeachment of President Israels (1st, 12mo, blue/gilt, 124p, 3pl)	NY: Macmillan	1913	Unknown	40-65	
Copp, Jim	Martha Matilda O'Toole (1st {std}, 4to, [28]p, fp 2-color, cep, DJ/3.95)	Bradbury Press	(1969)	Kellogg, Steven	60-90	*
Corbet, K.& S.	Animal Land Where there are No People (1st AM, ob8vo, 48p, b/w)	Dutton	1897	Corbet, Katherine	120-170	
Corbett, Bertha	Baby Days (1st, 4to, grey cloth, color)	Rand/McNally	(1910)	Corbett, Bertha L.	120-200	
Corbett, Bertha	Sun-Bonnet Babies (1st, sq8vo, green bds, b/w)	(Minneapolis)	1900	Corbett, Bertha L.	180-220	
Corbett, Elizabeth T.	3 Wise Old Couples (1st, 4to, ipcb, unpag, 15 chromos)	L: Cassell	(1881)	Hopkins, Everard	90-120	*
Corbett, Scott	Baseball Trick (1st {std}, 8vo, 105p, b/w, DJ/3.25)	Little/Brown	(1965)	Galdone, Paul	20-30	*
Corbett, Scott	Cutlass Island (1st {std}, 8vo, 151p, b/w, DJ/3.25)	Little/Brown	(1962)	Shortall, Leonard	20-35	
Corbett, Scott	Disappearing Dog Trick (1st {std}, 8vo, 108p, b/w, DJ/3.25)	Little/Brown	(1963)	Galdone, Paul	20-35	
Corbett, Scott	Ever Ride a Dinosaur? (1st {std}, 8vo, 113p, b/w, DJ/3.95)	Holt, Rinehart	(1969)	Vasiliu, Mircea	25-40	*
Corbett, Scott	Hairy Horror Trick (1st {std}, 8vo, 101p, b/w, DJ/3.50)	Little/Brown	(1969)	Galdone, Paul	20-35	
Corbett, Scott	Lemonade Trick (1st {std}, 8vo, 103p, b/w, DJ/2.75)	Little/Brown	(1960)	Galdone, Paul	20-35	
Corbett, Scott	Mailbox Trick (1st {std}, 8vo, 103p, fp b/w, DJ/2.95)	Little/Brown	(1961)	Galdone, Paul	25-45	
Corbett, Scott	Sauce for the Gander (1st AM, 8vo, yellow cl, 238p, fp b/w, DJ/3.00)	Crowell	(1951)	Freeman, Don	30-50	
Corbett, Scott	Susie Sneakers (1st {std}, 8vo, 216p, b/w, DJ/2.75)	Crowell	(1956)	Shortall, Leonard	40-65	
Corbett, Scott	Tree House Island (1st {std}, 8vo, 184p, b/w, DJ/3.00)	Little/Brown	(1959)	Hansen, Gordon	25-40	
Corbett, Scott	Turnabout Trick (1st {std}, 8vo, 105p, b/w, DJ/3.50)	Little/Brown	(1967)	Galdone, Paul	20-35	
Corddry, Thomas	Kibby's Big Feet (1st, lg8vo, 112p, b/w, DJ/3.50)	Follett	(1970)	Blake, Quentin	25-45	
Corelli, Marie	Devil's Motor (1st, 4to, [100]p, red/gilt, 6 ticp)	L: Hodder	[1910]	Severn, Arthur	200-300	
Corkey, Ethel	Magic Circle (1st, lg8vo, gilt, 256p, col frn, b/w)	L: Blackie	[1924]	Brock, Charles E.	50-80	
Corkran, Alice	Down the Snow Stairs (1st, 8vo, gilt, 257p, 5 fp b/w)	L: Blackie	1887	Browne, Gordon	50-90	
Cormack, Maribelle	Wind of the Vikings (1st, 8vo, 259p, tan cl, 6 fp b/w, pep, DJ/2.00)	Appleton-Century	1937	Lawson, Robert	58-80	*
Cornish, Sam	Your Hand in Mine (1st {std}, 8vo, 32p, b/w, DJ/3.25)	Harcourt	(1970)	Owens, Carl	50-80	
Cornwall, Ian W.	Making of Man (1st, 4to, 63p, 1-color, b/w, DJ, CgM)	L: Phoenix House	(1961)	Howard, M. Maitland	50-85	*
Corrin, Stephen	Plucky Sailor and Postage Stamp (1st, 8vo, ibds, unpag, color)	L: Faber	1954	Ardizzone, Edward	60-90	*
Cory, David	Jumble Book (4to, unpag, p-o, 6 ticp)	NY: Sully	(1920)	Kirk, Maria L.	80-140	
Cory, Fanny	Little Me (1st {std}, sm8vo, ipcb, [56]p, fp b/w)	Dutton	(1936)	Cory, Fanny	35-60	*
Cory, Fanny	Our Baby Book (4to, pink cl, [89]p, p-o, color)	Bobbs-Merrill	(1907)	Cory, Fanny	90-120	
Cory, Fanny	Sonny Sayings (1st, ob4to, ibds, 112p, b/w)	Dutton	(1929)	Cory, Fanny	60-90	
Coryell, Hubert	Indian Brother (1st, 8vo, 348p, b/w, pep, DJ/2.00)	Harcourt	(1935)	Pitz, Henry C.	40-65	
Coryell, Hubert	Klondike Gold (1st, 8vo, 319p, blue cl, pep, b/w, DJ/2.00)	Macmillan	1938	Sperry, Armstrong	40-60	
Coryell, Hubert	Tan-Ta-Ka (1st, 8vo, 305p, b/w, pep)	Little/Brown	1934	Townsend, Lee	30-45	
Cosgrove, Margaret	Bone for Bone (1st, lg8vo, 128p, color, DJ/3.95)	Dodd	(1968)	Cosgrove, Margaret	30-45	*
Cosgrove, Rachel R.	Hidden Valley of Oz (1st, lg8vo, blue cl, p-o, 313p, b/w, pep, DJ/2.50)	Reilly/Lee	(1951)	Dirk	250-400	
Cost, March	Bitter Green of the Willow (1st {std}, sm4to, 76p, gilt, color, DJ/4.95)	Chilton	(1967)	Anderson, Anne	30-50	
Costain, Thomas B.	Black Rose (1st {illus ed} {std}, lg8vo, 403p, gilt, dp col, pep, DJ/5.00)	Doubleday	1953	Ryman, Herbert	100-170	*
Costantino, Joan	Pepito at Capistrano (1st, lg8vo, p-o, 32p, color, pep, DJ/1.00)	Whitman	1943	Patton, Lucia	20-30	
Costello, Charles J.	Old Mother Hubbard (1st, 4to, [96]p, pict cl, fp color)	Chi: Jamieson	1902	Kennedy, Harry	120-200	
Costello, F.H.	Nelson's Yankee Boy (1st, 12mo, 293p, 6pl)	Henry Holt & Co.	1904	Dunton, W. Herbert	35-60	*
Cothren, Marion	This is the Moon (1st, lg8vo, 87p, fp b/w, DJ/2.00)	Coward	(1946)	Wiese, Kurt	30-45	*
Countess of Jersey	Eric Prince of Lorlonia (1st, 8vo, gilt, AEG, 182p, 8 fp b/w)	L: Macmillan	1895	Woodward, Alice B.	120-200	
Courlander, Harold	Big Old World of Richard Creeks (1st {std}, 8vo, 118p, b/w, DJ/3.50)	Chilton Books	(1962)	Laurie, Bob	60-90	
Courlander, Harold	Cow-Tail Switch (1st, lg8vo, brown cl, 143p, b/w, DJ/2.50, NH)	Henry Holt & Co.	(1947)	Chastain, Madye L.	50-80	*
Courlander, Harold	Fire on the Mountain (1st, lg8vo, 141p, 4cp, b/w, DJ/3.00)	Henry Holt & Co.	(1950)	Kane, Robert W.	30-45	
Courlander, Harold	Hat-Shaking Dance (1st {std}, 8vo, 115p, b/w, DJ/2.95)	Harcourt	(1957)	Arno, Enrico	40-65	*
Courlander, Harold	Kantchil's Lime Pit (1st {std}, 8vo, 150p, fp b/w, DJ/2.75)	Harcourt	(1950)	Kane, Robert W.	40-65	

AUTHOR: 50

AUTHOR	TITLE	PUBLISHER	DATE	ARTIST	PRICE	LC
Courlander, Harold	King's Drum and other African Stories (1st {std}, 8vo, 125p, b/w, DJ/3.00)	Harcourt	(1962)	Arno, Enrico	30-50	
Courlander, Harold	Olode the Hunter (1st {std}, sm8vo, 153p, b/w, DJ/3.75)	Harcourt	(1968)	Arno, Enrico	20-30	
Courlander, Harold	People of the Short Blue Corn (1st {std}, 8vo, 189p, b/w, DJ/4.95)	Harcourt	(1970)	Arno, Enrico	25-40	
Courlander, Harold	Piece of Fire (1st {std}, 8vo, 128p, b/w, DJ/3.25)	Harcourt	(1964)	Krush, Beth & Joe	45-70	*
Courlander, Harold	Ride with the Sun (1st, 8vo, 296p, green cl, b/w, DJ/3.50)	Whittlesey	1955	Duvoisin, Roger	30-50	*
Courlander, Harold	Terrapin's Pot of Sense (1st {std}, lg8vo, 125p, b/w, DJ/3.00)	Holt	(1957)	Fax, Elton C.	30-50	
Courlander, Harold	Tiger's Whisker (1st {std}, sm8vo, blue cl, 152p, fp b/w, DJ/3.25)	Harcourt	(1959)	Arno, Enrico	30-50	
Courlander, Harold	Uncle Bouqui of Haiti (1st, 8vo, 126p, 1-color, pep, DJ/2.00)	Wm. Morrow	1942	Crockett, Lucy	40-65	
Coussens, Penrhyn W.	Child's Book of Stories (1st, lg8vo, gilt, p-o, 463p, 10cp, pep)	Duffield	1911	Smith, Jessie W.	300-400	
Cowan, James	Daybreak (1st, sm8vo, gilt, 399p, teg, 4pl)	NY: Richmond	1896	Greenough, Walter C.	80-120	
Cowen, William J.	Man with Four Lives (1st, sm8vo, 277p, b/w pl, DJ/2.00)	Farrar/Rinehart	(1934)	Ward, Lynd	50-80	
Cowham, Hilda	Blacklegs and Others (1st, 4to, 76p, teg, gilt, color)	L: Kegan Paul	1911	Cowham, Hilda	200-300	
Cowham, Hilda	Curly Heads and Long Legs (8vo, 140p, ipcb, p-o, 12cp)	L: R. Tuck	[1910]	Cowham, Hilda	250-350	
Cowham, Hilda	Daddy Long Legs (4to, [30]p, ibds, 6cp, pep)	L: Gale/Polden	[1915]	Cowham, Hilda	250-400	
Cowham, Hilda	Fiddlesticks (1st AM, 4to, unpag, ipcb, color)	NY: Young & Co.	1901	Cowham, Hilda	250-350	
Cowham, Hilda	Good Old Nursery Rhymes (8vo, ibds, 10 fp color)	L: Gale/Polden	[1916]	Cowham, Hilda	220-300	
Cowham, Hilda	Somebody's Baby (4to, ibds, 16 fp color)	L: R. Tuck	[1915]	Cowham, Hilda	160-250	
Cowham, Hilda	Winnie Wimple & Ragged Robin (ibds, 9cp)	L: T.F. Unwin	[1910]	Cowham, Hilda	250-350	
Cowie, John	Alliterative Anomalies for Infants & Invalids (1st AM, ob4to, ibds, color)	Dodd	[1914]	Hammond, William	200-300	*
Cowley, Joy	Duck in the Gun (1st {std}, sm8vo, [40]p, ibds, color, pep, DJ/2.95)	Doubleday	(1969)	Sorel, Edward	30-45	
Cowper, William	Diverting History of John Gilpin (1st, ob4to [36]p, gilt, bds, 8cp)	L: Routledge	[1888]	Rosa, H.	120-180	
Cowper, William	Diverting History of John Gilpin (1st, 8vo, 50p, teg, blue/gilt, 12pl)	L: Aldine House	1898	Brock, Charles E.	60-90	*
Cox, Florence T.	Chronicles of Rhoda (1st, 12mo, 287p, red/gilt, 2cp)	Small/Maynard	(1909)	Smith, Jessie W.	80-120	
Cox, Florence T.	Epic of Ebenezer (1st, 12mo, ibds, 72p)	Dodd	1912	Rae, John	25-40	
Cox, Palmer	Another Brownie Book (1st, 4to, 144p, ibds, b/w)	Century	(1890)	Cox, Palmer	200-300	
Cox, Palmer	Brownie Clown of Brownie Town (ob8vo, 103p, ibds, color)	Century	(1908)	Cox, Palmer	300-450	
Cox, Palmer	Brownie Year Book (lg4to, [26]p, ibds, 12cp)	McLoughlin	1895	Cox, Palmer	300-450	
Cox, Palmer	Brownies & Prince Florimel (1st, lg8vo, tan cl, 246p, p-o)	Century	1918	Cox, Palmer	160-225	
Cox, Palmer	Brownies Abroad (1st, 4to, 144p, ibds, b/w)	Century	(1899)	Cox, Palmer	250-400	
Cox, Palmer	Brownies Around the World (1st, 4to, ibds, 144p, b/w)	Century	(1894)	Cox, Palmer	250-400	
Cox, Palmer	Brownies at Home (1st, 4to, ibds, 144p)	Century	(1893)	Cox, Palmer	250-400	
Cox, Palmer	Brownies in Fairyland (1st, sm8vo, 118p, cloth, b/w)	Century	(1925)	Cox, Palmer	250-400	
Cox, Palmer	Brownies in the Philippines (1st, 4to, ibds, 144p)	Century	(1904)	Cox, Palmer	250-400	R
Cox, Palmer	Brownies Through the Union (1st, 4to, ibds, 144p)	Century	(1895)	Cox, Palmer	250-400	R
Cox, Palmer	Brownies: Their Book (1st, 4to, green ipcb, 144p, b/w, cep, PPP)	Century	(1887)	Cox, Palmer	300-500	R
Cox, Palmer	Comic Yarns (1st, 8vo, 517p, blue/gilt, b/w, dep)	Hubbard	1889	Cox, Palmer	120-180	
Cox, Palmer	Frontier Humor (1st, 24mo, 343p, b/w)	Hubbard	(1895)	Cox, Palmer	80-130	R
Cox, Palmer	Palmer Cox Brownie Primer (1st, 12mo, 108p, yellow bds)	Century	1906	Cox, Palmer	140-240	
Cox, Palmer	Palmer Cox's Fairy Book (sm4to, green cloth, 6 fp color)	Hurst	(1902)	Cox, Palmer	200-300	
Cox, Palmer	Queer People with Paws & Claws (1st, lg8vo, ibds, [109]p, b/w)	Hubbard	(1888)	Cox, Palmer	160-220	
Cox, Palmer	Queerie Queers with Hands, Wings & Claws (lg8vo, ibds, b/w)	Larkin	(1887)	Cox, Palmer	600-900	
Cox-McCormack, N.	Peeps: Really Truly Sunshine Fairy (1st, 8vo, [37]p, ibds, color)	Volland	(1918)	Dodge, Katharine S.	75-100	
Coybee, Eden	Flower Book (1st, 24mo, 94p, green cl, fp color)	L: Richards	1901	Benson, Nellie	100-170	
Coyle, Kathleen	Josephine (1st {std}, sm8vo, blue cl, 174p, b/w, DJ/2.00)	Harper	(1942)	Bacon, Peggy	35-50	
Craddock, Charles E.	Phantoms of the Foot-Bridge (1st, 12mo, 353p, green/gilt, 14pl)	Harper	1895	Frost, A.B.	100-165	
Craddock, Charles E.	Young Mountaineers (1st, 12mo, 262p, green/gilt, 4pl)	Houghton	1897	Fraser, Malcolm	40-60	
Craddock, Harry (cmp)	Savoy Cocktail Book (1st, 8vo, 287p, pcb, gilt, color)	L: Constable	1930	Rumbold, Gilbert	180-240	
Cradock, H.C.	Best Teddy Bear in the World (1st, 12mo, 96p, b/w)	L: Nelson	(1926)	Appleton, Honor C.	30-50	
Cradock, H.C.	House of Fancy (1st, 4to, 32p)	L: O'Connor	1922	Appleton, Honor C.	60-90	*
Cradock, H.C.	Josephine and Her Dolls (1st, 4to, ibds, 47p, 12cp)	L: Blackie	1916	Appleton, Honor C.	250-350	
Cradock, H.C.	Josephine Dolly Book (lg8vo, ibds, p-o, 8cp)	L: Blackie	[1920]	Appleton, Honor C.	150-250	
Cradock, H.C.	Josephine is Busy (1st, lg8vo, ibds, 63p, p-o, 8cp)	L: Blackie	1918	Appleton, Honor C.	120-180	
Cradock, H.C.	Josephine Keeps House (1st, lg8vo, bds, p-o, 64p, 8cp)	L: Blackie	(1931)	Appleton, Honor C.	120-180	
Cradock, H.C.	Josephine Keeps School (1st, lg8vo, bds, p-o, 64p, 8cp)	L: Blackie	[1925]	Appleton, Honor C.	120-200	
Cradock, H.C.	Josephine's Birthday (1st, lg8vo, 64p, p-o, ibds, 8cp)	L: Blackie	[1920]	Appleton, Honor C.	200-300	
Cradock, H.C.	Josephine's Christmas Party (lg8vo, 64p, ipcb, p-o, 8cp)	L: Blackie	[1927]	Appleton, Honor C.	70-120	
Cradock, H.C.	Josephine's Happy Family (1st, sm4to, 63p, ipcb, p-o, 8cp)	L: Blackie	1917	Appleton, Honor C.	150-250	
Cradock, H.C.	Josephine's Happy Family (1st AM, 4to, bds, 63p, p-o, 8cp)	Stokes	[1920]	Appleton, Honor C.	150-225	
Cradock, H.C.	Josephine's Pantomime (1st, lg8vo, bds, p-o, 64p, 8cp)	L: Blackie	(1939)	Appleton, Honor C.	120-220	
Cradock, H.C.	Josephine, John and the Puppy (4to, bds, p-o, 8cp)	L: Blackie	[1920]	Appleton, Honor C.	65-90	
Cradock, H.C.	Peggy and Joan (1st, 4to, 96p, p-o, 8cp, pep)	L: Blackie	[1922]	Appleton, Honor C.	70-120	
Craig, Alexander	Ionia... (1st, 8vo, grey buckram, 301p, 6pl)	E.A. Weeks	1898	Leyendecker, J.C.	100-165	
Craig, Edward G.	Woodcuts & Some Words (1st, 4to, 122p, blue cl, 59pl)	L: Dent	1924	Craig, Edward G.	100-180	
Craig, M. Jean	Spring is Like the Morning (1st, lg8vo, 61p, 2-color, DJ/3.00)	Putnam	(1965)	Almquist, Don	20-35	*
Craig, M. Jean	What Did You Dream? (1st, 4to, [42]p, color, DJ/2.95)	Abelard-Schuman	1964	Gill, Margery	20-35	
Craik, Dinah	Adventures of a Brownie (1st, 16mo, 57p, p-o, fp color)	Reilly/Britton	(1908)	Neill, John R.	70-100	
Craik, Dinah	Adventures of a Brownie (sm4to, grey cl, p-o, 12cp)	Whitman	[1920]	Carsey, Alice	35-60	*
Craik, Dinah	Adventures of a Brownie (1st {Gift ed}, lg8vo, teg, 281p, p-o, 14 ticp)	Lippincott	1922	Kirk, Maria L.	80-130	
Craik, Dinah	Adventures of a Brownie (1st, 8vo, p-o, 128p, color)	Rand/McNally	(1923)	Winter, Milo	60-100	
Craik, Dinah	Fairy Book (1st, 4to, 379p, teg, green/gilt, 32cp)	L: Macmillan	1913	Goble, Warwick	350-500	
Craik, Dinah	Fairy Book (1st, 8vo, 416p, gilt, teg, 32cp)	L: Nelson	(1913)	Various	165-225	
Craik, Dinah	Fairy Book (1st, lg8vo, 403p, p-o, col frn, fp b/w)	Harper	(1922)	Rhead, Louis	40-60	*
Craik, Dinah	Fairy Book (1st {this format}, 8vo, 232p, red/gilt, 16cp)	L: Macmillan	1923	Goble, Warwick	180-275	
Craik, Dinah	Little Lame Prince (1st, lg8vo, p-o, 121p, gilt, color)	Rand/McNally	(1909)	Dunlap, Hope	75-100	
Craik, Dinah	Little Lame Prince (1st, lg8vo, 128p, green/gilt, p-o, 9cp, pep)	Whitman	(1927)	Higgins, Violet M.	50-80	
Craik, Dinah	Little Lame Prince (1st, 8vo, 135p, color, pep, RC, DJ/1.25)	World	(1948)	Nielsen, Jon	20-30	
Craine, Edith	Conquistador (1st, 8vo, 288p, gilt, b/w, pep)	Duffield/Green	(1931)	Pitz, Henry C.	25-45	
Craine, Edith	Ki-Ki: Circus Trouper (1st, lg8vo, 64p, p-o, color, pep, DJ/1.50)	Whitman	1937	Wiese, Kurt	40-65	

AUTHOR	TITLE	PUBLISHER	DATE	ARTIST	PRICE	LC
Craine, Edith	Littlebits (1st, 8vo, 133p, p-o, gilt, 4cp)	Rand/McNally	(1926)	Gregory, Dorothy L.	60-100	
Cramer, Rie	Diamond Princess (1st, ob8vo, [56]p, 4 fp color)	L: Warne	(1931)	Cramer, Rie	200-300	
Crampton, Gertrude	Noises & Mr. Flibberty-Jib (1st {A}, sm8vo, [42]p, ibds, color, LGB/#29)	Simon/Schuster	(1947)	Wilkin, Eloise B.	60-100	*
Crane, Donn	Flippy and Skippy (1st, sq8vo, [48]p, color, pep, DJ/1.50)	Winston	(1940)	Crane, Donn	30-50	*
Crane, Stephen	Great Battles of the World (1st, 8vo, red/gilt, 278p, 7pl)	Lippincott	1901	Sloan, John	250-350	R
Crane, Stephen	Open Boat (1st, 8vo, 85p, b/w, DJ/2.95)	F. Watts	(1968)	Quackenbush, Rbt.	30-45	*
Crane, Stephen	The Monster... (1st, 12mo, 188p, orange/gilt, 25pl)	Harper	1899	Newell, Peter	300-500	
Crane, Stephen	War is Kind (1st, tall 8vo, ipcb, woodcuts, 96p, uncut)	Stokes	1899	Bradley, Will	800-1200	
Crane, Stephen	Whilomville Stories (1st, sm8vo, green/gilt, 198p, 34pl)	Harper	1900	Newell, Peter	250-350	
Crane, Thomas	Abroad (sq8vo, ipcb, 56p, pep)	L: Marcus Ward	(1882)	(Chromos)	120-180	
Crane, Thomas	At Home (sq8vo, 56p, ipcb)	L: Marcus Ward	(1880)	(Chromos)	120-180	
Crane, Walter	Aladdin's Picture Book (4to, unpag, ipcb, 24 color)	L: Routledge	[1880]	Crane, Walter	400-600	
Crane, Walter	An Artist's Reminiscences (1st, 8vo, 520p, brown cl, teg)	Macmillan	1907	Crane, Walter	70-100	
Crane, Walter	Baby's Bouquet (1st, ob8vo, ipcb, 56p, 11cp)	L: Routledge	[1878]	Crane, Walter	225-350	
Crane, Walter	Bases of Design (1st, lg8vo, teg, blue/gilt, 365p, b/w, pep)	L: G. Bell	1898	Crane, Walter	150-220	
Crane, Walter	Columbia's Courtship (1st, 4to, [12]p, blue/gilt, 12cp)	Prang Co.	[1893]	Crane, Walter	300-500	
Crane, Walter	Flora's Feast (1st, lg8vo, ibds, 40cp, dep)	L: Cassell	1889	Crane, Walter	225-325	
Crane, Walter	Floral Fantasy (1st, 4to, 48p, 44cp, pep)	L: Harper	1899	Crane, Walter	400-600	
Crane, Walter	Flower Wedding (1st, lg8vo, ipcb, 40cp, pep)	L: Cassell	1905	Crane, Walter	250-400	
Crane, Walter	Flowers from Shakespeare's Garden (1st, 4to, ibds, uncut, 40cp, pep)	L: Cassell	1906	Crane, Walter	250-400	
Crane, Walter	Goody Two Shoes... ([new ed.], 4to, red cl, 18cp, pep)	J. Lane	(1901)	Crane, Walter	200-300	
Crane, Walter	Ideals in Art (1st, 8vo, teg, 287p, gilt, b/w, cvr by...)	L: G. Bell	1905	Crane, Walter	125-200	
Crane, Walter	India Impressions (1st, lg8vo, green/gilt, 325p, 16pl)	Macmillan	1907	Crane, Walter	125-200	
Crane, Walter	Legends for Lionel (1st, lg8vo, ibds, 40p, color, pep)	L: Cassell	1887	Crane, Walter	200-300	
Crane, Walter	Line & Form (1st, 8vo, 282p, teg, blue/gilt, pep)	L: G. Bell	1900	Crane, Walter	180-250	
Crane, Walter	Masque of Days (1st, 4to, [40]p, ipcb, color, pep)	L: Cassell	1901	Crane, Walter	250-325	
Crane, Walter	Pothooks & Perseverance (1st, sq8vo, ibds, [24]p, color, pep)	L: Marcus Ward	1886	Crane, Walter	250-350	
Crane, Walter	Queen Summer (1st, folio, ibds, teg, 40p, color, pep)	L: Cassell	1891	Crane, Walter	280-350	
Crane, Walter	Romance of the Three R's (1st, sq4to, ibds, [80]p, color, pep)	L: Marcus Ward	1886	Crane, Walter	300-450	
Crane, Walter	Sirens Three (1st, 4to, 25p, grey bds, pep)	L: Macmillan	1886	Crane, Walter	300-450	
Crane, Walter	Slateandpencilvania (1st, sq8vo, ibds, 24p, color)	L: Marcus Ward	1885	Crane, Walter	200-300	
Crane, Walter	Sleeping Beauty and Blue Beard (1st, 24mo, [24]p, color, pep)	L: John Lane	1914	Crane, Walter	150-200	R
Crane, Walter	Triplets (1st, lg4to, ibds, color, 1/500 signed)	L: Routledge	1899	Crane, Walter	450-600	
Crane, Walter	Walter Crane's Picture Book (4to, ibds, [145]p, color)	Cupples/Leon	(1903)	Crane, Walter	120-200	
Crane, Walter	William Morris to Whistler (1st, 12mo, 277p, blue cl)	L: G. Bell	1911	Crane, Walter	100-175	
Crary, Mary	Daughter of the Stars (1st, 4to, 190p, 2cp by...)	L: Hatchard	1939	Dulac, Edmund	140-220	R
Crawford, F. Marion	Constantinople (1st, 8vo, 79p, teg, cvr by...)	Scribner	1895	Armstrong, Margaret	40-65	
Crawford, F. Marion	Diva's Ruby (1st, 8vo, 430p, gilt, 12pl)	Macmillan	1908	Flagg, James M.	30-50	*
Crawford, F. Marion	Little City of Hope (1st AM, sm8vo, 209p, grey cl, 8pl)	Macmillan	1907	Benda, W.T.	40-65	
Crawford, F. Marion	Salve Venetia (1st, 8vo, 2 volumes, gilt)	Macmillan	1905	Pennell, Joseph	55-80	
Crawford, Phyllis	Blot: Little City Cat (1st, ob4to, ibds, 56p, b/w)	Cape/Smith	1930	Holling, Holling C.	80-120	
Crawford, Phyllis	Blot: Little City Cat (1st {this pub}, sq8vo, 56p, dep, b/w, DJ/1.50)	Henry Holt & Co.	(1946)	Cooney, Barbara	50-80	
Crawford, Phyllis	Hello, the Boat! (1st, 8vo, 227p, tan cl, fp b/w, pep, DJ/2.00, NH)	Henry Holt & Co.	(1938)	Laning, Edward	40-70	
Crawford, Phyllis	Let's Go! (1st, sm8vo, 73p, b/w, DJ/1.50)	Henry Holt & Co.	(1949)	Guerin, Theodore	30-50	*
Crawford, Phyllis	Second Shift (1st, sm8vo, blue cl, 211p, 1-color, DJ/2.00)	Henry Holt & Co.	(1943)	Bernbach, Graham	25-40	
Crawford, Phyllis	Secret Brother (1st, sm8vo, 238p, b/w, DJ/1.50)	Henry Holt & Co.	(1941)	Woodbury, Mabel	25-40	
Crawford, Phyllis	Walking on Gold (1st, 8vo, 284p, dp b/w, pep, DJ/2.00)	J. Messner	(1940)	Sherman, Russell	20-35	
Credle, Ellis	Across the Cotton Patch (1st, ob4to, green cl, [59]p, b/w, DJ/1.50)	Nelson	1935	Credle, Ellis	60-100	
Credle, Ellis	Adventures of Tittletom (1st {std}, 8vo, 79p, red cl, b/w, DJ/1.75)	NY: Oxford U.Pr.	1949	Credle, Ellis	30-50	*
Credle, Ellis	Big Doin's on Razorback Ridge (1st, 8vo, orange cl, 125p, b/w, DJ/2.75)	Nelson	(1956)	Credle, Ellis	30-50	
Credle, Ellis	Big Fraid, Little Fraid (1st, 4to, [48]p, 1-color, DJ/2.50)	Nelson	(1964)	Credle, Ellis	35-50	
Credle, Ellis	Down, Down the Mountain (1st, 4to, [47]p, 2-color, DJ/2.00)	Nelson	1934	Credle, Ellis	70-100	
Credle, Ellis	Flop-Eared Hound (1st, 8vo, [61]p, fp b/w, DJ/2.00)	NY: Oxford U.Pr.	(1938)	(Photos)	50-80	
Credle, Ellis	Goat that Went to School (1st, lg8vo, [28]p, ipcb, color, pep, DJ/0.50)	Grosset/Dunlap	(1940)	Credle, Ellis	35-50	
Credle, Ellis	Here Comes the Showboat (1st, lg8vo, 95p, b/w, DJ/2.50)	Nelson	(1949)	Credle, Ellis	25-40	
Credle, Ellis	Johnny and his Mule (1st, sq12mo, [44]p, b/w, DJ/1.50)	NY: Oxford U.Pr.	1946	(Photos)	45-70	
Credle, Ellis	Little Jeemes Henry (1st, sq8vo, 44p, b/w, DJ/1.50)	Nelson	1936	Credle, Ellis	70-100	
Credle, Ellis	Monkey See, Monkey Do (1st, 4to, [46]p, bds, 2-color, DJ/3.25)	Nelson	(1968)	Credle, Ellis	25-45	
Credle, Ellis	My Pet Peepelo (1st, lg8vo, green cl, 62p, b/w, DJ/2.00)	NY: Oxford U.Pr.	1948	(Photos)	30-50	
Credle, Ellis	Pig-O-Wee (1st, sm4to, ibds, [44]p, color, DJ/1.00)	Rand/McNally	(1936)	Credle, Ellis	30-50	
Creekmore, Raymond	Ali's Elephant (1st {std}, 4to, ibds, [40]p, fp b/w, DJ/2.00)	Macmillan	1949	Creekmore, Raymond	30-50	
Creekmore, Raymond	Fujio (1st {std}, 8vo, unpag, b/w, pep, DJ/2.00)	Macmillan	1951	Creekmore, Raymond	25-45	
Creekmore, Raymond	Little Fu (1st {std}, 4to, ibds, [49]p, b/w, DJ/2.00)	Macmillan	1947	Creekmore, Raymond	25-45	
Creekmore, Raymond	Little Skipper (1st {std}, 4to, [40]p, b/w, DJ/2.00)	Macmillan	1950	Creekmore, Raymond	35-50	
Creekmore, Raymond	Lokoshi Learns to Hunt Seals (1st {std}, 4to, [48]p, b/w, DJ/1.75)	Macmillan	1946	Creekmore, Raymond	30-50	
Cregan, Mairin	Old John (1st, 8vo, 183p, 11pl, pep, DJ/2.00)	Macmillan	1936	Sewell, Helen	50-80	
Crespi, Pachita	170 Cats (1st {std}, ob4to, ibds, [27]p, 1-color, pep, DJ/1.00)	Random	(1939)	Gay, Zhenya	60-100	
Crespi, Pachita	Cabita's Rancho (1st, 8vo, 208p, b/w, DJ/2.00)	Messner	1942	Gay, Zhenya	25-45	*
Crespi, Pachita	Gift of the Earth (1st, sm8vo, ibds, [32]p, color, DJ/1.25)	Scribner	1946	Crespi, Pachita	30-50	
Crespi, Pachita	Happy Birthday (1st, ob8vo, ipcb, [35]p, 1-color, DJ/1.00)	Viking	1939	Gay, Zhenya	30-45	
Crespi, Pachita	Manuelito of Costa Rica (1st, sm4to, [40]p, color, pep, DJ/1.50)	J. Messner	(1940)	Gay, Zhenya	40-65	
Cresswell, Beatrice	Royal Progress of King Pepito (1st, 4to, tan ibds, 48p, 12cp)	L: SPCK	(1889)	Greenaway, Kate	250-350	
Creswick, Paul	Greypaws... (1st, 8vo, 64p, 5pl)	L: Partridge	[1909]	Lucas, K.	60-80	*
Creswick, Paul	Hastings the Pirate (1st, 8vo, 303p, purple cl, 8pl)	Nister/Dutton	(1902)	Robinson, Thomas H.	55-80	*
Creswick, Paul	In Alfred's Days (sm8vo, teg, gilt, uncut, 304p, 18pl)	L: Nister	[1900]	Robinson, Thomas H.	50-80	
Creswick, Paul	Robin Hood & his Adventures (1st, 8vo, gilt, 312p, 4cp, pep)	Nister/Dutton	(1902)	Robinson, Thomas H.	60-90	
Creswick, Paul	Under the Black Raven (1st, 8vo, 303p, teg, b/w pl)	Nister/Dutton	[1901]	Robinson, Thomas H.	55-80	*
Crew, Alice C.	Mary & her Kitchen Garden (1st, lg8vo, 52p, p-o, 9cp, pep)	Doran	(1917)	Stanley, Lee W.	30-50	

AUTHOR	TITLE	PUBLISHER	DATE	ARTIST	PRICE	LC
Crew, Helen	Alanna (1st {std}, 8vo, 233p, col frn, pep, DJ/2.00)	Harper	1929	Esley, Joan	30-50	
Crews, Donald	Ten Black Dots (1st, 12mo, [26]p, color, DJ/3.50)	Scribner	(1968)	Crews, Donald	30-50	*
Crews, Donald	We Read: A and Z (1st, sq8vo, ipcb, [52]p, color, cep, DJ/3.50)	Harper	(1967)	Crews, Donald	35-50	
Crichton, Frances E.	Peep-in-World (1st, 8vo, 258p, green cl, 4pl)	L: E. Arnold	1908	Rountree, Harry	30-50	*
Criss, Mildred	Malou (1st {std}, 8vo, blue cl, 280p, uncut, col frn, 4 fp b/w)	Doubleday/Doran	1929	Lederer, Charlotte	20-35	
Crissey, Forrest	Country Boy (1st, 8vo, 300p, gilt, uncut, cvr by...)	Revell	(1903)	Hazenplug, Frank	50-80	
Crissey, Forrest	Country Boy (1st, 8vo, 300p, gilt, uncut, 14pl by...)	Revell	(1903)	McClure, Griselda M.	50-80	
Crissey, Forrest	Tattlings of a Retired Politician (1st, lg8vo, red/gilt, teg, 487p, b/w)	Chi: Thompson	1904	McCutcheon, J.T.	30-50	
Crockett, Davy	Adventures of Davy Crockett (1st, 8vo, black/gilt, 258p, p-o, 3cp)	Scribner	1934	Thomason, John W.	100-160	
Crockett, Lucy H.	Lucio and his Nuong (1st, 4to, [56]p, p-o, fp 3-color, pep, DJ/2.00)	Henry Holt & Co.	(1939)	Crockett, Lucy	50-80	R
Crockett, Lucy H.	That Mario (1st, 8vo, 181p, green cl, fp b/w, pep, DJ/1.50)	Henry Holt & Co.	(1940)	Crockett, Lucy	30-45	
Crockett, Samuel R.	Loves of Miss Ann (1st AM, 12mo, blue cl, 421p, cvr by...)	Dodd	1904	Armstrong, Margaret	40-60	*
Crockett, Samuel R.	May Margaret (1st AM, sm8vo, 375p, blue cl, cvr by...)	Dodd	1905	Falls, Charles B.	25-45	*
Crockett, Samuel R.	Red Axe (1st, 8vo, 421p, teg, gilt, 8pl)	L: Smith Elder	1898	Richards, Frank	25-40	
Crockett, Samuel R.	Red Cap Tales (1st, 8vo, 413p, yellow cl, teg, 16cp)	L: A&C Black	1904	Vedder, Simon H.	50-80	
Crockett, Samuel R.	Sir Toady Crusoe (1st, 8vo, 406p, blue cl, 19pl)	L: Wells/Gard.	1905	Browne, Gordon	60-90	
Crockett, Samuel R.	Sir Toady Crusoe (1st AM, 8vo, 356p, b/w)	Stokes	(1905)	Browne, Gordon	40-70	
Crockett, Samuel R.	Surprising Adventures of Sir Toady Lion (1st AM, 8vo, 314p, b/w)	Stokes	(1897)	Browne, Gordon	55-80	
Crockett, Samuel R.	Sweetheart Travellers (1st AM, lg8vo, 310p, ibds, teg, b/w)	Stokes	(1895)	Browne/Groome	60-90	*
Crockett, Samuel R.	Tales of Our Coasts (1st AM, 8vo, 203p, red buckram, teg, uncut)	Dodd	1896	Brangwyn, Frank	70-100	*
Croll, Pauline	Just for You (1st, 12mo, ipcb, 37p, color, dep)	Volland	(1918)	Bassett, Mary R.	50-80	
Cromie, Robert	From the Cliffs of Croaghaun (1st AM, sm8vo, blue/gilt, 343p, 2pl)	Saalfield	1904	Praut, Victor	35-60	
Crommelin, May	Little Soldiers (1st, 4to, ipcb, 94p, 39 color)	L: Hutchinson	[1916]	Wain, Louis	600-900	
Crosby, Alexander	Go Find Hanka! (1st, lg8vo, 44p, fp b/w, cep, DJ/3.95)	Golden Gate	(1970)	Rounds, Glen	25-45	
Crosby, Ernest	Captain Jinks, Hero (1st, sm8vo, tan cl, 393p, 9pl)	Funk/Wagnalls	1902	Beard, Dan	40-65	
Crosby, Percy L.	Dear Sooky (1st, 8vo, ipcb, 124p, 7 ticp, dep)	Putnam	1929	Crosby, Percy L.	60-90	
Cross, Genevieve	Pop-Corn Lamb & Peppermint Sticks (1st, ob4to, ipcb, [32]p, 1-color, pep)	Cross Pub.	1949	Cross, Genevieve	40-65	*
Cross, John K.	Man in the Moonlight (1st, 12mo, 316p, fp b/w, DJ)	L: Westhouse	1947	Jacques, Robin	40-65	
Cross, Launcelot	Book of Old Sun Dials (1st, 8vo, ibds, gilt, 102p, 8cp by...)	L: Foulis	(1914)	Rawlings, Alfred	75-120	
Croswell, Volney	How to Hide a Hippopotamus (1st, ob12mo, [30]p, color, DJ/2.00, NYTBI)	Dodd	(1958)	Croswell, Volney	40-65	*
Crothers, Samuel M.	Children of Dickens (1st, lg8vo, p-o, 259p, 10cp, pep, SC)	Scribner	1925	Smith, Jessie W.	100-150	
Crothers, Samuel M.	Gentle Reader (1st, 12mo, 321p, gilt, teg)	Houghton	1903	Rogers, Bruce	25-40	
Crothers, Samuel M.	Miss Muffet's Christmas Party (1st, sm8vo, blue/gilt, 106p, b/w, pep)	Houghton	1902	Long, Olive M.	35-60	
Crothers, Samuel M.	Pardoner's Wallet (1st, 12mo, 287p, teg)	Houghton	1905	Rogers, Bruce	25-40	
Crowley, Mary C.	Daughter of New France (1st, sm8vo, 409p, blue/gilt, 6pl)	Little/Brown	1901	DeLand, Clyde O.	30-50	
Crowley, Maude	Azor (1st, sm8vo, ibds, 54p, b/w, DJ/2.00)	NY: Oxford U.Pr.	1948	Sewell, Helen	40-65	
Crowley, Maude	Azor & the Blue-Eyed Cow (1st, sm8vo, 70p, b/w, DJ/2.25)	NY: Oxford U.Pr.	1951	Sewell, Helen	40-65	
Crowley, Maude	Azor & the Haddock (1st, sm8vo, 63p, grey cl, b/w, DJ/2.00)	NY: Oxford U.Pr.	1949	Sewell, Helen	40-65	
Crownfield, Gertrude	Little Tailor of Windy Way (1st, sm8vo, 132p, 4cp)	Macmillan	1917	Pogany, Willy	40-65	
Crownfield, Gertrude	Princess White Flame (1st, 8vo, 229p, gilt, fp b/w)	Dutton	(1920)	Peck, Anne M.	30-45	
Crowninshield, Mrs.	Lattitude 19 (1st, sm8vo, 418p, red cl, 7pl)	Appleton	1898	Gibbs, George	40-60	*
Crowninshield, Mrs.	Light-House Children Abroad (1st, 8vo, 446p, 38 b/w, gilt)	D. Lothrop Co.	1889	Bridgman, L.J.	40-65	
Crowninshield, Mrs.	San Isidro (1st, sm8vo, 312p, yellow cl, cvr by...)	Herbert Stone	1900	Hazenplug, Frank	55-80	
Cruikshank, George	Cruikshank Fairy Book (1st, 8vo, 216p, gilt, b/w)	Putnam	1897	Cruikshank, George	250-350	
Crump, Irving	Og - Son of Fire (1st, 8vo, 198p, b/w, pep)	Dodd	1922	Bull, Charles L.	25-45	
Cruse, Laurence	Village in Normandy (1st {std}, ob4to, ibds, [32]p, color, DJ/3.75)	Bobbs-Merrill	(1968)	Cruse, Laurence	30-50	
Culbertson, Anne V.	At the Big House (1st, sm8vo, blue cl, p-o, 348p, b/w)	Bobbs-Merrill	(1904)	Blaisdell, E. Ward	55-80	
Culbertson, Anne V.	Banjo Talks (1st, sm8vo, green/gilt, 171p, 23pl)	Bobbs-Merrill	(1905)	(Photos)	70-120	
Culbertson, Polly	Bear Facts (1st {std}, 8vo, [30]p, ibds, color, DJ/1.25)	Winston	(1948)	Fennell, Paul J.	30-45	
Cule, William E.	Child Voices (1st, 8vo, 139p)	L: A. Melrose	1899	Robinson, Charles	60-100	*
Cullen, Countee	Copper Sun (1st {std}, sm8vo, bds, 89p, b/w)	Harper	1927	Cullen, Charles	120-200	
Cullen, Countee	Lost Zoo (1st {std}, lg8vo, 72p, yellow cl, 16cp, pep, DJ/2.50)	Harper	(1940)	Sebree, Charles	200-300	
Cullen, Countee	Lost Zoo (1st {this pub} {std}, lg8vo, 95p, color, DJ/4.95)	Follett	(1969)	Low, Joseph	30-45	
Cullen, Countee	My Lives & How I Lost Them (1st {std}, lg8vo, 160p, b/w, DJ/2.00)	Harper	(1942)	Macguire, Robert	200-300	
Culver, Henry B.	Book of Old Ships (1st {this pub}, 4to, 306p, ibds, 5cp)	Garden City	(1935)	Grant, Gordon	45-70	
Culver, Henry B.	Forty Famous Ships (1st {std}, 4to, 320p, gilt, 5 fp color, pep, DJ/7.50)	Doubleday/Doran	1936	Grant, Gordon	50-80	
Cumberland, Charles	Seven Glass Gooseberries (1st, 8vo, p-o, 192p, 4cp)	L: G. Richards	1921	Daviel, M.	60-90	
Cuming, E.W.D.	Three Jovial Puppies (1st, folio, bds, 36p, p-o, color)	L: Blackie	[1908]	Shepherd, J.A.	250-350	
Cuming, E.W.D.	Wonders in Monsterland (1st, 12mo, AEG, 257p, 4cp, 14pl)	L: G. Allen	1901	Shepherd, J.A.	125-170	*
Cumming, Marian	Valentine for Candy (1st {std}, 8vo, 160p, DJ/3.00)	Harcourt	(1959)	Suba, Susanne	25-40	
Cummings, E.E.	Fairy Tales (1st {std}, sm4to, 36p, ibds, color, DJ/4.50)	Harcourt	(1965)	Eaton, John	70-100	R
Cummings, Edward	Marmaduke of Tennesee (1st, sm8vo, 371p, 5pl)	McClurg	1914	Schoonover, Frank	30-50	
Cummings, Walter	Girl in the White Hat (1st, 4to, 32p, fp 2-color, pep, DJ/2.25, NYTBI)	Whittlesey	1959	Cummings, Walter	50-80	*
Cunningham, Caroline	Talking Stone (1st {std}, 8vo, 116p, 2-color, DJ/1.75)	Knopf	1939	Floethe, Richard	30-45	
Cunningham, Julia	Burnish Me Bright (1st, 8vo, 78p, fp b/w, DJ/3.95)	Pantheon	(1970)	Freeman, Don	50-80	R*
Cunningham, Julia	Candle Tales (1st, 8vo, 57p, fp 1-color, DJ/3.25)	Pantheon	(1963)	Ness, Evaline	25-40	
Cunningham, Julia	Dear Rat (1st, 8vo, 125p, fp 1-color, cep, DJ/2.75, NYTBI)	Houghton	1961	Lorraine, Walter	30-50	
Cunningham, Julia	Dorp Dead (1st, 8vo, 88p, b/w, DJ/3.50)	Pantheon	(1965)	Spanfeller, James	20-35	
Cunningham, Julia	Macaroon (1st, 8vo, 63p, ibds, fp 2-color, DJ/3.00)	Pantheon	(1962)	Ness, Evaline	20-30	
Cunningham, Julia	Onion Journey (1st, 8vo, 36p, color, DJ/3.50)	Pantheon	(1967)	Cooley, Lydia	20-25	
Cunningham, Julia	Viollet (1st, 8vo, 82p, fp b/w, cep, DJ/3.25)	Pantheon	(1966)	Cober, Alan E.	20-30	*
Cunningham, Julia	Vision of Francois the Fox (1st, 8vo, 31p, 3-color, DJ/2.75)	Houghton	1960	Angelo, Nicholas	20-30	
Cunnington, Susan	Stories from Dante (1st, 8vo, p-o, 255p, teg, uncut, gilt, 16cp)	L: Harrap	1910	Paul, Evelyn	80-120	
Cupples, George	Spliced Yarn (1st, sm8vo, 300p, gilt, 5 fp b/w)	L: Gibbings	1899	Brangwyn, Frank	40-70	
Cuppy, Will	Decline & Fall of Practically Everybody (1st {std}, 8vo, 230p, b/w, DJ/3.00)	Holt	(1950)	Steig, William	30-50	
Cuppy, Will	How to Become Extinct (1st, sm8vo, 181p, cream cl, b/w, DJ/2.00)	Farrar/Rinehart	(1941)	Steig, William	40-65	
Curren, Polly	Hear Ye of Boston (1st, sq4to, 39p, color, pep, DJ/3.95)	Lothrop, Lee	(1964)	Werth, Kurt	30-45	
Curry, Jane L.	Beneath the Hill (1st {std}, 8vo, 255p, b/w, DJ/4.25)	Harcourt	(1967)	Gobbato, Imero	30-50	

AUTHOR	TITLE	PUBLISHER	DATE	ARTIST	PRICE	LC
Curry, Jane L.	Change-Child (1st {std}, 8vo, 174p, b/w, DJ)	Harcourt	(1969)	Floyd, Gareth	30-50	
Curry, Jane L.	Down from the Lonely Mountain (1st {std}, 8vo, 128p, b/w, DJ/3.00)	Harcourt	(1965)	Arno, Enrico	20-30	
Curry, Jane L.	The Daybreakers (1st {std}, 8vo, 191p, b/w, DJ/4.95)	Harcourt	(1970)	Robinson, Charles	25-40	
Curry, Jane L.	The Sleepers (1st {std}, 8vo, 255p, b/w, DJ/4.50)	Harcourt	(1968)	Floyd, Gareth	30-50	
Curtin, Jeremiah	Fairy Tales of Eastern Europe (1st, 8vo, 259p, 4cp)	McBride	1914	Hood, George	60-90	
Curtis, Alice B.	Children of the Prairie (1st, 8vo, 198p, color title pg, b/w, DJ/2.00)	Crowell	(1938)	Holberg, Richard	30-45	
Curtis, Alice B.	Winter on the Prairie (1st, 8vo, 164p, b/w, DJ/2.50)	Crowell	(1945)	Paull, Grace	25-45	
Curtis, Alice T.	Grandpa's Little Girls & Friends (1st, 12mo, p-o, 190p, 5pl, pep)	Penn	1910	Smith, Wuanita	30-50	
Curtis, Alice T.	Grandpa's Little Girls at School (1st, 12mo, 195p, p-o, 5pl)	Penn	1908	Smith, Wuanita	30-50	
Curtis, Alice T.	Little Maid of Old New York (1st, sm8vo, 224p, p-o, 5pl)	Penn	1921	Pilsbry, Elizabeth	25-45	
Curtis, George W.	Prue & I (8vo, teg, 234p)	Crowell	1899	Edwards, Harry C.	25-40	
Cushman, Jean	We Help Mommy (1st {A}, sm8vo, [24]p, ibds, color, pep, LGB/#352)	Golden Press	1959	Wilkin, Eloise B.	40-65	*
Custer, Elizabeth B.	Following The Guidon (1st, sm8vo, gilt, 341p, 2pl by...)	Harper	1890	Remington, Frederic	100-180	
Custer, Elizabeth B.	Tenting on the Plains (1st, lg8vo, 702p, 11 b/w, gilt)	Webster	1887	Remington, Frederic	250-400	
Cutler, Carl	Greyhounds of the Sea (1st {std}, 4to, 592p, gilt, 8cp, photos, pep)	Putnam	1930	Various	100-160	
Cutler, U. Waldo	Stories of King Arthur (1st, 8vo, 308p, fp 1-color, pep, DJ/2.00)	Crowell	(1941)	Blaisdell, Elinore	40-65	
Cutting, Mary S.	Suburban Whirl (1st, 12mo, green cl, uncut, 202p, 7pl)	McClure	1907	Stephens, Alice B.	25-40	
Cutting, Mary S.	The Wayfarers (1st, 8vo, 374p, 16pl)	McClure	1908	Stephens, Alice B.	25-45	
Czaja, Helen	Bountiful Cow (1st, sm ob4to, ibds, [55]p, b/w, DJ/1.50)	Henry Holt & Co.	(1944)	Czaja, Michael	25-45	
D'Annunzio, Gabrielle	Episcopo & Co. (1st, 12mo, 122p, green/gilt, teg, cvr by...)	Stone & Kimball	1896	Hazenplug, Frank	65-100	
D'Arcy, Ella	Monochromes (1st, 8vo, 260p, green cl, cvr & ti page by...)	L: John Lane	1895	Beardsley, Aubrey	75-100	*
D'Aulaire, I.& E.	Abraham Lincoln (1st {std}, folio, 55p, ibds, 5 fp color, DJ/2.00, CM)	Doubleday/Doran	1939	D'Aulaire, I.& E.	200-300	R
D'Aulaire, I.& E.	Animals Everywhere (1st {std}, 4to, folding panels, color, pep)	Doubleday/Doran	1940	D'Aulaire, I.& E.	280-400	
D'Aulaire, I.& E.	Animals Everywhere (1st {this fmt}, 4to, ibds, [29]p, color, pep, DJ/2.00)	Doubleday	1954	D'Aulaire, I.& E.	80-130	
D'Aulaire, I.& E.	Benjamin Franklin (1st {std}, 4to, ibds, [48]p, color, DJ/2.50)	Doubleday	(1950)	D'Aulaire, I.& E.	90-140	
D'Aulaire, I.& E.	Buffalo Bill (1st {std}, 4to, ibds, [40]p, color, DJ/2.75)	Doubleday	1952	D'Aulaire, I.& E.	80-125	
D'Aulaire, I.& E.	Children of the North Lights (1st, lg4to, ibds, [40]p, color, pep, DJ/2.00)	Viking	1935	D'Aulaire, I.& E.	170-250	
D'Aulaire, I.& E.	Columbus (1st {std}, lg4to, ibds, 57p, pep, color, DJ/3.00)	Doubleday	1955	D'Aulaire, I.& E.	100-170	R
D'Aulaire, I.& E.	Conquest of the Atlantic (1st, lg4to, ibds, 55p, color)	Viking	1933	D'Aulaire, I.& E.	120-185	
D'Aulaire, I.& E.	D'Aulaire's Book of Greek Myths (1st {std}, lg4to, 192p, color, DJ/4.95)	Doubleday	1962	D'Aulaire, I.& E.	60-100	
D'Aulaire, I.& E.	Don't Count Your Chicks (1st {std}, folio, [40]p, ibds, col, pep, DJ/2.50)	Doubleday/Doran	1943	D'Aulaire, I.& E.	150-250	R
D'Aulaire, I.& E.	Foxie (1st {std}, ob4to, red cl, [40]p, b/w, pep, DJ/2.00)	Doubleday	1949	D'Aulaire, I.& E.	100-165	
D'Aulaire, I.& E.	George Washington (1st {std}, lg4to, ibds, [55]p, 13 fp color)	Doubleday/Doran	(1936)	D'Aulaire, I.& E.	70-100	
D'Aulaire, I.& E.	Leif the Lucky (1st {std}, lg4to, ibds, [56]p, color, pep, DJ/2.50)	Doubleday/Doran	1941	D'Aulaire, I.& E.	100-160	
D'Aulaire, I.& E.	Lord's Prayer (1st {std}, lg4to, [32]p, ibds, color, pep)	Doubleday/Doran	1934	D'Aulaire, I.& E.	70-100	
D'Aulaire, I.& E.	Magic Meadow (1st {std}, lg4to, ibds, 55p, pep, 25 color, DJ/3.00)	Doubleday	1958	D'Aulaire, I.& E.	100-150	
D'Aulaire, I.& E.	Magic Rug (1st {std}, ob4to, [63]p, ibds, pep, color)	Doubleday/Doran	1931	D'Aulaire, I.& E.	250-350	
D'Aulaire, I.& E.	Nils (1st {std}, 4to, ibds, [40]p, color, pep, DJ/2.50)	Doubleday	(1948)	D'Aulaire, I.& E.	120-185	
D'Aulaire, I.& E.	Norse Gods and Giants (1st {std}, lg4to, 154p, fp color, pep, DJ/5.95)	Doubleday	(1967)	D'Aulaire, I.& E.	80-120	R
D'Aulaire, I.& E.	Ola (1st {std}, lg4to, ibds, [55]p, color, pep, DJ/2.00)	Doubleday/Doran	1932	D'Aulaire, I.& E.	130-180	R
D'Aulaire, I.& E.	Ola & Blakken & Line Sine & Trine (1st {std}, folio, [39]p, ibds, color)	Doubleday/Doran	1933	D'Aulaire, I.& E.	120-185	
D'Aulaire, I.& E.	Pocahantas (1st {std}, 4to, ibds, [40]p, color, DJ/2.50)	Doubleday	1946	D'Aulaire, I.& E.	120-200	
D'Aulaire, I.& E.	Star Spangled Banner (1st {std}, lg4to, ibds, [38]p, color, pep)	Doubleday/Doran	1942	D'Aulaire, I.& E.	75-125	
D'Aulaire, I.& E.	Too Big (1st {std}, sm sq8vo, ibds, [32]p, color, pep, DJ/1.00)	Doubleday/Doran	1945	D'Aulaire, I.& E.	60-90	
D'Aulaire, I.& E.	Two Cars (1st {std}, sq8vo, [30]p, color, DJ/1.50)	Doubleday	1955	D'Aulaire, I.& E.	45-70	
D'Aulaire, I.& E.	Wings for Per (1st {std}, lg4to, ibds, [40]p, color, pep, DJ/2.50)	Doubleday/Doran	(1944)	D'Aulaire, I.& E.	80-125	
D'Aulnoy	D'Aulnoy's Fairy Tales (1st, 4to, gilt, teg, p-o, 457p, 9cp, pep)	McKay	1923	Tenggren, Gustaf	160-225	
D'Aulnoy	Fairy Tales (1st, 8vo, 535p, teg, cvr by...)	L: Lawrence	1892	Crane, Walter	150-225	
D'Aulnoy	Fairy Tales (1st, 8vo, 535p, teg, gilt, b/w by...)	L: Lawrence	1892	Peters, Clinton	150-225	
D'Aulnoy	White Cat... (1st, 4to, ibds, 150p, p-o, 8cp, pep)	Macmillan	1928	MacKinstry, Eliz.	80-140	
D'Harnoncourt, R.	Mexicana (1st {std}, 4to, [104]p, ipcb, fp b/w, dep)	Knopf	1931	D'Harnoncourt, R.	65-90	
Daglish, Alice (ed.)	Land of Nursery Rhyme (1st, 8vo, 240p, fp color, pep)	Dutton	(1932)	Folkard, Charles	70-100	*
Dahl, Roald	Charlie & the Chocolate Factory (1st, lg8vo, gilt, 162p, b/w, cep, DJ/3.95)	Knopf	(1964)	Schindelman, Joseph	400-650	
Dahl, Roald	Fantastic Mr. Fox (1st {std}, 8vo, 62p, gilt, fp b/w, cep, DJ/3.95)	Knopf	(1970)	Chaffin, Donald	300-500	R
Dahl, Roald	Gremlins (1st, 4to, ibds, [48]p, fp color, pep, DJ/1.00)	Random	(1943)	Disney Studios	2000-3000	
Dahl, Roald	James & the Giant Peach (1st [1], sm4to, 118p, gilt, color, cep, DJ/3.95)	Knopf	(1961)	Burkert, Nancy	2000-3000	
Dahl, Roald	James & the Giant Peach (1st [2], sm4to, 118p, gilt, color, cep, DJ/3.95)	Knopf	(1961)	Burkert, Nancy	400-600	
Dahl, Roald	Magic Finger (1st, 8vo, 40p, b/w, pep, DJ/2.50)	Harper	(1966)	DuBois, W.P.	200-300	
Daldorne, Evan	Wooing of the Water-Witch (1st, 8vo, gilt, 132p, b/w, AEG)	Henry Holt & Co.	1880	Smith, J. Moyr	70-100	*
Daley, C.F.	Skating Party (1st, 4to, ibds)	Worthington	(1891)	6 Chromos	100-160	
Daley, C.F.	Sundials (1st, 4to, ibds, 12cp)	Worthington	(1891)	Shepley, Annie B.	120-180	
Dalgliesh, Alice	Adam & the Golden Cock (1st, sm8vo, 64p, grey cl, 1-color, DJ/2.50)	Scribner	(1959)	Weisgard, Leonard	30-50	
Dalgliesh, Alice	Along Janet's Road (1st, 8vo, 208p, gilt, pep, DJ/2.50, decor by...)	Scribner	1946	Milhous, Katherine	30-50	
Dalgliesh, Alice	America Begins... (1st, sq8vo, ibds, [78]p, color, DJ/2.00)	Scribner	(1938)	Maloy, Lois	30-50	
Dalgliesh, Alice	America Builds Homes (1st, sq8vo, ibds, [84]p, color, DJ/2.00)	Scribner	(1938)	Maloy, Lois	35-50	
Dalgliesh, Alice	America Travels... (1st, 8vo, 121p, b/w)	Macmillan	1933	Woodward, Hildegarde	25-40	
Dalgliesh, Alice	Bears on Hemlock Mountain (1st, 8vo, [64]p, 1-color, DJ/2.00, NH)	Scribner	(1952)	Sewell, Helen	60-100	
Dalgliesh, Alice	Blue Teapot (1st, 8vo, 73p, col frn, pep)	Macmillan	1931	Woodward, Hildegarde	35-60	
Dalgliesh, Alice	Book for Jennifer (1st, 8vo, 114p, uncut, 10cp, DJ/2.00)	Scribner	1940	Milhous, Katherine	50-80	
Dalgliesh, Alice	Choosing Book (1st, 16mo, [56]p, red cl, color)	Macmillan	1932	Wilkin, Eloise B.	40-65	*
Dalgliesh, Alice	Christmas (1st, 8vo, 232p, col frn, b/w, pep)	Scribner	1934	Woodward, Hildegarde	40-60	
Dalgliesh, Alice	Columbus Story (1st, 4to, [30]p, ibds, dp color, DJ/2.75)	Scribner	(1955)	Politi, Leo	80-130	R
Dalgliesh, Alice	Courage of Sarah Noble (1st, 8vo, 52p, 7 fp illus, DJ/2.00, NH)	Scribner	(1954)	Weisgard, Leonard	60-100	R
Dalgliesh, Alice	Davenports & Cherry Pie (1st, 8vo, 196p, grey cl, fp b/w, DJ/2.50)	Scribner	(1949)	Gag, Flavia	50-85	
Dalgliesh, Alice	Davenports are at Dinner (1st, 8vo, ivory cl, 182p, b/w, DJ/2.50)	Scribner	1948	Gag, Flavia	50-85	
Dalgliesh, Alice	Enchanted Book (1st, lg8vo, 246p, blue/gilt, pep, fp color, DJ/3.00)	Scribner	(1947)	Cacciola, Concetta	55-80	
Dalgliesh, Alice	Fourth of July Story (1st, 4to, [30]p, fp color, DJ/2.75)	Scribner	(1956)	Nonnast, Marie	60-90	R
Dalgliesh, Alice	Gulliver Joins the Army (1st, 8vo, 936p, fp b/w, DJ/1.50)	Scribner	1942	Segner, Ellen	30-50	

AUTHOR	TITLE	PUBLISHER	DATE	ARTIST	PRICE	LC
Dalgliesh, Alice	Happily Ever After (1st, lg8vo, 60p, 7 fp color, DJ/1.50)	Scribner	(1939)	Milhous, Katherine	70-100	R
Dalgliesh, Alice	Happy School Year (1st, sm8vo, 141p, color)	Rand/McNally	(1924)	Brand, Mary S.	25-40	*
Dalgliesh, Alice	Little Angel (1st, 8vo, 70p, 3 dp cp, pep, DJ/2.00)	Scribner	1943	Milhous, Katherine	40-60	
Dalgliesh, Alice	Little Wooden Farmer (1st, ob8vo, green cl, [43]p, color, pep)	Macmillan	1930	Baumeister, Margaret	40-60	*
Dalgliesh, Alice	Little Wooden Farmer (1st {std} [new ed.], ob8vo, [32]p, color, DJ/3.95)	Macmillan	(1968)	Lobel, Anita	20-35	*
Dalgliesh, Alice	Long Live the King! (1st, sq8vo, ipcb, 76p, color, dep, DJ/1.60)	Scribner	1937	Maloy, Lois	30-50	
Dalgliesh, Alice	Once On a Time (1st, sm4to, 70p, 10 fp color, DJ/1.50)	Scribner	(1938)	Milhous, Katherine	50-80	
Dalgliesh, Alice	Relief's Rocker (1st, 8vo, 62p)	Macmillan	1932	Woodward, Hildegarde	30-45	
Dalgliesh, Alice	Reuben & his Red Wheelbarrow (1st, 4to, ibds, [28]p, pep, color, DJ/0.50)	Grosset/Dunlap	1946	Bischoff, Ilse	30-50	
Dalgliesh, Alice	Ride on the Wind (1st, 8vo, [32]p, ibds, color, DJ/2.75)	Scribner	1956	Schreiber, Georges	25-40	
Dalgliesh, Alice	Roundabout (1st, 8vo, 64p, b/w, pep, DJ/1.75)	Macmillan	1934	Woodward, Hildegarde	30-50	
Dalgliesh, Alice	Sailor Sam (1st, sq12mo, ipcb, [38]p, cep, color)	Scribner	1935	Dalgliesh, Alice	35-60	
Dalgliesh, Alice	Silver Pencil (1st, 8vo, 235p, blue/gilt, b/w, pep, DJ/2.50, NH)	Scribner	1944	Milhous, Katherine	60-90	
Dalgliesh, Alice	Smiths & Rusty (1st, 8vo, 118p, b/w, DJ/1.75)	Scribner	1936	Hader, B.& E.	40-65	
Dalgliesh, Alice	Thanksgiving Story (1st, 4to, red cl, [28]p, fp color, DJ/2.50, CH)	Scribner	(1954)	Sewell, Helen	70-100	R
Dalgliesh, Alice	The Hollyberrys (1st, sq12mo, 59p, 12 fp color, cep, DJ/1.50)	Scribner	(1939)	Herric, Pru	30-50	
Dalgliesh, Alice	Three from Greenways (1st, sm8vo, 63p, ibds, b/w, DJ/1.00)	Scribner	1941	Howe, Gertrude	30-50	
Dalgliesh, Alice	West Indian Play Days (1st, 12mo, 174p, col frn, b/w, pep)	Rand/McNally	(1926)	Price, Margaret E.	30-45	*
Dalgliesh, Alice	Wings Around South America (1st, lg8vo, 158p, fp color, cep, DJ/2.50)	Scribner	1941	Milhous, Katherine	40-65	
Dalgliesh, Alice	Wings for the Smiths (1st, 8vo, blue cl, 89p, 3cp, cep, DJ/1.75)	Scribner	1937	Hader, B.& E.	40-65	
Dalgliesh, Alice	Young Aunts (1st, 8vo, 116p, red cl, fp color, DJ/1.75)	Scribner	1939	Becker, Charlotte	30-45	
Dali, Salvador	50 Secrets of Magic Craftmanship (1st, 4to, 192p, color, DJ/7.50)	Dial	1948	Dali, Salvador	200-300	
Dali, Salvador	Hidden Faces (1st, 8vo, black cl, 413p, b/w frn, DJ/3.00)	Dial	1944	Dali, Salvador	200-300	
Dali, Salvador	Secret Life of Salvador Dali (1st AM, sm4to, p-o, 400p, buckram, 3cp)	Dial	1942	Dali, Salvador	150-225	
Dall, Anna R.	Scamper's Christmas (1st, sq8vo, 71p, dp color)	Macmillan	1934	Flack, Marjorie	50-80	R
Dall, Anna R.	Scamper: Bunny Who Went to the White House (1st, sq8vo, 72p, 5cp, fp b/w)	Macmillan	(1934)	Flack, Marjorie	70-100	
Dallam, Helen	Nursery Rhymes and Songs (1st, 4to, ibds, [65]p, fp color, pep)	Whitman	1944	Malvern, Corrine	25-40	
Dalrymple, Leona	Uncle Noah's Christmas Inspiration (1st, 12mo, 124p, pep, 4cp)	McBride	1912	Yohn, F.C.	35-60	*
Dalton, Agnes M.	From Sioux to Susan (1st, 8vo, 342p, 22 b/w illus)	Century	1905	Gutmann, Bessie P.	75-100	*
Daly, Kathleen N.	Wild Animal Babies (1st {A}, sm8vo, [28]p, ibds, color, LGB/#332)	Simon/Schuster	1958	Rojankovsky, Feodor	20-35	
Daly, Maureen	Ginger Horse (1st, 8vo, 89p, color ti-page, fp b/w, DJ/3.50)	Dodd	1964	Dennis, Wesley	20-30	
Daly, Maureen	Sixteen and other Stories (1st, 8vo, 157p, b/w, DJ/3.00)	Dodd	1961	Rossi, Kendall	20-35	*
Daly, Maureen	Small War of Sargeant Donkey (1st, 8vo, 85p, b/w, DJ/3.50)	Dodd	(1966)	Dennis, Wesley	20-30	
Daly, Thomas A.	Madrigali (1st, sm8vo, 169p, gilt, teg, fp b/w)	McKay	(1912)	Sloan, John	60-90	*
Damjan, Mischa	False Flamingoes (1st AM, 4to, ibds, [31]p, fp color, DJ)	NY: Scroll Pr.	(1970)	Steadman, Ralph	60-95	
Damjan, Mischa	Little Prince and the Tiger Cat (1st AM, 4to, [32]p, color, DJ/4.50)	McGraw-Hill	(1968)	Steadman, Ralph	80-145	
Damjan, Mischa	Mau: King of the Cats (1st AM {std}, 4to, [30]p, 2-color, DJ/2.00)	Putnam	(1963)	Buchi, Werner	30-50	
Damjan, Mischa	Wolf and the Kid (1st AM, 4to, green cl, [32]p, color, cep, DJ/4.50)	McGraw-Hill	1967	Velthuijs, Max	30-50	
Dana, Mary P.	Jingle Book (1st, sm4to, [32]p, 3-color)	W.R. Scott	1940	Dana, Mary P.	50-80	
Dana, Richard H.	Two Years Before the Mast (1st, lg8vo, 533p, p-o, 10cp, pep)	Houghton	1911	Smith, E. Boyd	80-125	
Dana, Richard H.	Two Years Before the Mast (1st, 8vo, 415p, 15cp)	L: Macmillan	1915	Pears, Charles	30-50	*
Dane, George E.	Once There Was and was Not (1st {std}, 8vo, 269p, col frn, b/w, pep)	Doubleday/Doran	1931	Wells, Rhea	30-50	*
Daniel, Hawthorne	Seal of the White Buddha (1st, 8vo, 271p, col frn, 6pl, DJ/2.00)	Coward	1928	Holberg, Richard	35-50	
Daniels, Guy	Foma the Terrible (1st {std}, ob4to, [38]p, color, DJ/4.50)	Delacorte Pr.	(1970)	Gobbato, Imero	40-65	*
Daniels, Guy	Tsar's Riddles (1st, 4to, 32p, 2-color, DJ/3.75)	McGraw-Hill	(1967)	Galdone, Paul	25-40	
Daniels, Guy (tran)	Falcon Under the Hat (1st, 4to, 110p, fp color, DJ/5.95)	Funk/Wagnalls	(1969)	Rojankovsky, Feodor	30-50	
Danks, Bertha M.	Janet & the Fairies (1st, sm8vo, 64p, 4cp)	L: A&C Black	(1937)	Outhwaite, Ida R.	250-400	
Danska, Herbert	Street Kids (1st, lg8vo, 160p, fp b/w, color, DJ)	Knopf	(1970)	Danska, Herbert	30-45	
Dante	Ad Astra (1st, lg4to, ipcb, unpag, b/w)	R.H. Russell	1902	Armstrong, Margaret	170-240	
Dante	New Life (1st, lg8vo, 168p, teg, color, pep)	L: Harrap	[1916]	Paul, Evelyn	100-160	
Darby, Ada C.	Jump Lively, Jeff! (1st, 8vo, 278p, b/w, DJ/2.00)	Stokes	1942	Paull, Grace	30-50	
Darby, Ada C.	Skip-Come-a-Lou (1st, sm8vo, 243p, col frn)	Stokes	1928	Kirk, Maria L.	20-30	*
Daringer, Helen F.	Adopted Jane (1st, sm8vo, 225p, fp b/w, DJ/2.00)	Harcourt	(1947)	Seredy, Kate	30-50	
Daringer, Helen F.	Golden Thorn (1st {std}, 8vo, 181p, b/w, DJ/2.75)	Harcourt	(1956)	Werth, Kurt	30-50	
Daringer, Helen F.	Keepsake Ring (1st {std}, 8vo, 174p, b/w, DJ/2.50)	Harcourt	(1953)	Godwin, E.& S.	50-80	
Daringer, Helen F.	Mary Montgomery, Rebel (1st, 8vo, green cl, 222p, fp b/w, DJ/2.50)	Harcourt	(1948)	Seredy, Kate	40-60	
Daringer, Helen F.	Pilgrim Kate (1st, 8vo, 252p, fp b/w, DJ/2.50)	Harcourt	(1949)	Seredy, Kate	30-50	
Daringer, Helen F.	Stepsister Sally (1st {std}, 8vo, 182p, b/w, DJ/2.25)	Harcourt	(1952)	Price, Garrett	40-65	
Daringer, Helen F.	Yesterday's Daughter (1st {std}, sm8vo, 156p, b/w, DJ/3.25)	Harcourt	(1964)	Hampshire, Michael	25-45	
Darling, Esther B.	Baldy of Nome (1st, 8vo, blue cl, 301p, 15pl)	Penn	1916	(Photos)	50-80	
Darling, Esther B.	Luck of the Trail (1st {std}, 8vo, uncut, 309p, col frn, pep)	Doubleday/Doran	1933	Dennis, Morgan	30-50	*
Darling, Esther B.	Navarre of the North (1st {std}, 8vo, 268p, pep, frn by...)	Doubleday/Doran	1930	Bull, Charles L.	55-80	
Darton, F.J.H.	Seven Champions of Christendom (1st, 8vo, blue/gilt, teg, 416p, col frn)	L: Wells/Gard.	[1913]	Ault, Norman	65-100	R
Darton, F.J.H.	Wonder Book of Beasts (1st, 8vo, 403p, gilt, teg, 22pl)	L: Wells/Gard.	(1909)	Clayton, Margaret	100-165	
Darton, F.J.H.	Wonder Book of Old Romance (1st, sm8vo, 424p, teg, gilt, b/w)	L: Wells/Gard.	1907	Walker, Arthur G.	60-100	
Darwall, Blanche	Martin in Fairyland (1st, 4to, 165p, 10 fp b/w)	L: Simpkin	1924	Ord, E.R.	50-80	
Darwin, Bernard	Elves & Princes (1st, 8vo, 199p, 6cp)	L: Duckworth	[1913]	Monsell, J.R.	130-200	*
Darwin, Bernard	Golf Courses of the British Isles (1st, lg8vo, 253p, gilt, teg, 64cp)	L: Duckworth	1910	Rountree, Harry	1200-2000	
Darwin, Bernard	Ishybushy & Topknot (1st, 4to, tan cl, 64p, 7cp)	L: Country Life	(1946)	Darwin, Elinor	100-165	
Darwin, Bernard	Mr. Tootleoo & Co. (1st AM, ob 4to, [45]p, ibds, 22 fp color)	Harper	(1936)	Darwin, Elinor	350-500	*
Darwin, Bernard	Oboli Boboli & Little Joboli (1st, 4to, 79p, tan cl, 5 fp color)	L: Country Life	(1938)	Darwin, Elinor	100-165	
Darwin, Bernard	Tootleoo Two (1st AM, ob4to, ipcb, [42]p, fp color)	Harper	(1928)	Darwin, Elinor	160-220	
Daskam, Josephine	Her Fiance (1st, 12mo, 164p, 5pl)	Altemus	(1904)	Green, Eliz. S.	50-80	
Daskam, Josephine	Imp & The Angel (1st, 8vo, 168p, tan cl, 8pl)	Scribner	1901	Rosenmeyer, B.J.	35-60	*
Daskam, Josephine	Memoirs of a Baby (1st, sm8vo, 272p, blue cl, b/w)	Harper	1904	Cory, Fanny	30-50	
Daskam, Josephine	Whom the Gods Destroyed (1st, sm8vo, 236p, red/gilt, cvr by...)	Scribner	1902	Armstrong, Margaret	40-60	
Daskein, Tarella	Chimney Town (1st, lg8vo, 238p, blue cl, color)	L: A&C Black	(1934)	Outhwaite, Ida R.	250-400	
Daudet, Alphonse	Brave Little Goat of Monsieur Seguin (1st AM, 4to, [32]p, color, DJ/3.95)	World	(1968)	Nakatani, Chiyoko	60-80	R*

AUTHOR	TITLE	PUBLISHER	DATE	ARTIST	PRICE	LC
Daudet, Alphonse	Letters from my Mill (1st, lg8vo, 236p, tan/gilt, 10cp)	Dodd	1893	Lemaire, Madeleine	35-60	
Daugherty, Charles	Robert Goddard: Trail Blazer to Stars (1st {std}, 8vo, [48]p, col, DJ/2.95)	Macmillan	(1964)	Daugherty, James	25-40	
Daugherty, Charles	Wisher (1st, ob4to, 40p, fp 2-color, pep, DJ/2.50)	Viking	(1960)	Daugherty, James	30-50	
Daugherty, James	Abraham Lincoln (1st, 4to, 216p, fp 1-color, DJ/3.50)	Viking	1943	Daugherty, James	55-80	
Daugherty, James	Andy & the Lion (1st, 4to, ipcb, [79]p, color, pep, DJ/2.00, CH)	Viking	1938	Daugherty, James	140-220	R
Daugherty, James	Daniel Boone (1st {this pub}, 4to, 95p, color, pep, DJ/2.50, NM)	Viking	1939	Daugherty, James	120-180	R
Daugherty, James	Henry David Thoreau (1st, sm4to, 111p, gilt, 2-color, DJ)	Viking	(1967)	Daugherty, James	25-40	
Daugherty, James	Landing of the Pilgrims (1st, 8vo, 186p, color, pep, DJ/1.50)	Random	(1950)	Daugherty, James	25-40	
Daugherty, James	Lincoln's Gettysburg Address (1st {std}, lg4to, ibds, [40]p, color, DJ/5.00)	Whitman	(1947)	Daugherty, James	60-90	
Daugherty, James	Magna Charta (1st, 8vo, 181p, 1-color, DJ/1.50)	Random	(1956)	Daugherty, James	25-45	
Daugherty, James	Marcus and Narcissa Whitman (1st, 8vo, 158p, b/w, pep, DJ/2.50)	Viking	1953	Daugherty, James	40-70	R
Daugherty, James	Of Courage Undaunted (1st, sm4to, 168p, b/w, DJ/3.50)	Viking	1951	Daugherty, James	40-65	
Daugherty, James	Picnic: Frolic in 2 Colors & 3 Parts (1st, 4to, 79p, 2-color, DJ/3.50)	Viking	(1958)	Daugherty, James	30-50	
Daugherty, James	Poor Richard (1st, sm4to, brown cl, 158p, 2-color, pep, DJ/2.50)	Viking	1941	Daugherty, James	100-165	
Daugherty, James	Trappers and Traders of the Far West (1st, 8vo, 181p, 1-color, DJ/1.50)	Random	(1952)	Daugherty, James	30-50	
Daugherty, James	Walt Whitman's America (1st {std}, sm4to, 110p, 3-color, DJ/3.95)	World	(1964)	Daugherty, James	35-50	
Daugherty, James	West of Boston (1st, 4to, 94p, yellow cl, 1-color, DJ/3.00)	Viking	1956	Daugherty, James	40-70	
Daugherty, James	Wild Wild West (1st, 4to, ibds, [34]p, color, pep, DJ/2.50)	McKay	(1948)	Daugherty, James	60-90	
Daugherty, Sonia	All Things New (1st, sm8vo, 296p, orange cl, b/w, DJ/1.75)	Nelson	1936	Daugherty, James	30-50	*
Daugherty, Sonia	Broken Song (1st, sm8vo, 270p, b/w, DJ/2.00)	Nelson	1934	Seredy, Kate	25-45	
Daugherty, Sonia	Mashinka's Secret (1st, 12mo, 276p, 28 b/w)	Stokes	1932	Daugherty, James	30-50	
Daugherty, Sonia	Ten Brave Women (1st {std}, 8vo, 147p, b/w, DJ/2.75)	Lippincott	(1953)	Daugherty, James	30-45	
Daugherty, Sonia	Vanka's Donkey (1st, 8vo, ivory cl, 62p, 1-color, pep, DJ/1.50)	Stokes	1940	Daugherty, James	50-80	
Daugherty, Sonia	Way of an Eagle (1st, 8vo, 352p, fp b/w, DJ/2.50)	NY: Oxford U.Pr.	(1941)	Daugherty, James	30-50	
Daugherty, Sonia	Wings of Glory (1st, 8vo, 236p, gilt, color, DJ/2.50)	NY: Oxford U.Pr.	(1940)	Daugherty, James	40-65	
Daulton, George	Helter Skelters (1st, sm8vo, 294p, 4cp)	Stokes	1909	Kirk, Maria L.	30-50	
Dauzet, Marceline	Forest Friends (1st, sq4to, [16]p, ibds, fp color, pep)	Saalfield	1940	Peat, Fern B.	60-100	
Dauzet, Marceline	One Happy Day (lg sq4to, ibds, [16]p, fp color, pep)	Saalfield	1939	Scott, Janet L.	30-50	
David, Julian	Three Hanses (1st {std}, 8vo, 283p, 6cp, 12pl, DJ/2.00)	Little/Brown	1942	Chappell, Warren	30-50	
Davidson (ed.)	Ali Baba & the Forty Thieves (folio, ibds, 9 fp color)	L: Blackie	[1900]	Stratton, Helen	70-100	
Davidson, Gladys	Arabian Nights Retold for Children (8vo, 352p, red cl, 16cp)	L: Blackie	[1925]	Bull, Rene	75-100	*
Davidson, Gladys	Helpers Without Hands (1st, sm4to, p-o, bds, 118p, 32cp)	L: Wells/Gard.	(1914)	Noble, Edwin	170-240	
Davidson, John	Plays by... (1st, 8vo, gilt, 294p, uncut, cvr by...)	L: E. Mathews	1894	Beardsley, Aubrey	100-160	
Davidson, John	Wonderful Mission of Earl Lavender (1st, 8vo, gilt, uncut, cvr by..)	L: Ward/Down.	1895	Beardsley, Aubrey	70-120	*
Davies, Maria T.	Rose of Old Harpeth (1st, sm8vo, 312p, blue cl, cvr by...)	Bobbs-Merrill	(1911)	Armstrong, Margaret	35-50	
Davies, Mary C.	Little Freckled Person (1st, 8vo, 104p, col, frn, 8pl)	Houghton	1919	Cue, Harold	25-40	
Davies, William H.	Hour of Magic (1st, 12mo, pcb, gilt, teg, 34p, pep)	L: J. Cape	(1922)	Nicholson, Wm.	150-225	
Davies, William H.	True Travellers (1st, 8vo, 53p, grey bds, 2-color)	L: J. Cape	1923	Nicholson, Wm.	140-185	
Davis, Alice V.	Timothy Turtle (1st, lg8vo, [32]p, 2-color, DJ/1.50)	Harcourt	(1940)	Wiser, Guy B.	60-95	
Davis, Duke	Flashlights from Mountain & Plain (1st, sm8vo, 266p, 4cp)	(New Jersey)	1911	Russell, Charles M.	125-180	
Davis, Frederick H.	Myths & Legends of Japan (1st, 8vo, 432p, gilt, 32cp)	L: Harrap	1912	Paul, Evelyn	100-165	
Davis, Katherine	Little Drummer Boy (1st {std}, ob8vo, 34p, ibds, color, cep, DJ/3.95)	Macmillan	1968	Keats, Ezra J.	30-50	
Davis, Lavinia R.	Americans Every One (1st {std}, sm8vo, 123p, color, DJ/1.50)	Doubleday/Doran	1942	Weisgard, Leonard	35-60	
Davis, Lavinia R.	Buttonwood Island (1st {std}, sm8vo, 299p, b/w, pep, DJ/2.00)	Doubleday/Doran	1940	Brown, Paul	70-120	
Davis, Lavinia R.	Clown Dog (1st {std}, lg8vo, 61p, 2-color, pep, DJ/2.75)	Doubleday	(1961)	Lantz, Paul	25-40	
Davis, Lavinia R.	Danny's Luck (1st, ob4to, ipcb, [46]p, fp 2-color, pep, DJ/2.50)	Doubleday	1953	Woodward, Hildegarde	45-60	
Davis, Lavinia R.	Grab Bag (1st {std}, 8vo, 312p, b/w, pep, DJ/2.00)	Doubleday/Doran	1941	Weisgard, Leonard	40-65	
Davis, Lavinia R.	Hobby Horse Hill (1st {std}, 8vo, 270p, uncut, b/w, pep, DJ/2.00)	Doubleday/Doran	1939	Brown, Paul	120-200	
Davis, Lavinia R.	Island City (1st {std}, 8vo, 256p, b/w, DJ/2.95)	Doubleday	(1961)	Spier, Peter E.	20-35	
Davis, Lavinia R.	Melody, Mutton, Bone & Sam (1st {std}, 8vo, 245p, b/w, DJ/2.25)	Doubleday	1947	Brown, Paul	80-125	
Davis, Lavinia R.	Plow Penny Mystery (1st {std}, 8vo, 275p, b/w, pep, DJ/2.00)	Doubleday/Doran	1942	Brown, Paul	60-90	
Davis, Lavinia R.	Roger & the Fox (1st {std}, ob4to, [43]p, ipcb, dep, color, DJ/2.00, CH)	Doubleday	1947	Woodward, Hildegarde	60-100	
Davis, Lavinia R.	Round Robin (1st, 8vo, 147p, b/w, DJ/1.50)	Scribner	1943	Woodward, Hildegarde	25-45	
Davis, Lavinia R.	Sandy's Spurs (1st {std}, 8vo, red cl, b/w, 246p, DJ/2.50)	Doubleday	(1951)	Paull, Grace	25-45	
Davis, Lavinia R.	Summer is Fun (1st {std}, sm ob4to, ibds, 48p, color, pep, DJ/2.50)	Doubleday	1951	Woodward, Hildegarde	35-60	
Davis, Lavinia R.	Very Special Pet (1st, 8vo, ibds, [28]p, color, pep, DJ/0.50)	Grosset/Dunlap	1944	Wiese, Kurt	30-50	
Davis, Lavinia R.	Wild Birthday Cake (1st {std}, ob4to, [50]p, ibds, pep, color, DJ/2.50, CH)	Doubleday	1949	Woodward, Hildegarde	70-120	
Davis, M.E.M.	Moons of Balbanca (1st, 8vo, 180p, 6pl)	Houghton	1908	Rand, Amy	50-80	
Davis, Mary G.	Baker's Dozen (1st {std}, 8vo, 207p, orange cl, dep, decor by...)	Harcourt	(1930)	Brock, Emma	25-40	
Davis, Mary G.	Handsome Donkey (1st, lg8vo, yellow cl, 67p, uncut, fp 3-color, pep)	Harcourt	(1933)	Brock, Emma	30-50	
Davis, Mary G.	Sandy's Kingdom (1st, lg8vo, green cl, 79p, b/w, pep, DJ/1.75)	Harcourt	(1935)	Brock, Emma	30-50	*
Davis, Mary G.	Truce of the Wolf (1st, lg8vo, uncut, 125p, fp b/w, dep, NH)	Harcourt	(1931)	Van Everen, Jay	40-60	*
Davis, Mary G.	Wakaima & the Clay Man (1st {std}, 8vo, 145p, uncut, b/w, pep, DJ/2.00)	Longmans	(1946)	Johnson, Avery	60-90	
Davis, Mary G.	With Cap & Bells (1st, sm8vo, 246p, b/w, pep, DJ/2.00)	Harcourt	(1937)	Bennett, Richard	30-50	*
Davis, Norman	Picken's Exciting Summer (1st, lg8vo, 46p, ibds, 1-color, DJ/2.00)	Oxford U. Pr.	(1949)	Winslade	40-70	
Davis, Norman	Picken's Treasure Hunt (1st, 8vo, 64p, 2-color, DJ/2.50)	Oxford U. Pr.	1955	Winslade	40-65	
Davis, Rebecca H.	Kent Hampden (1st, 12mo, gilt, 152p, 4pl)	Scribner	1892	Zogbaum, Rufus F.	70-100	*
Davis, Reda	Martin's Dinosaur (1st, 4to, [40]p, 1-color, DJ/3.50)	Crowell	(1959)	Slobodkin, Louis	30-50	
Davis, Richard H.	About Paris (1st, 12mo, gilt, 219p, 30pl)	Harper	1895	Gibson, Charles D.	40-65	
Davis, Richard H.	Bar Sinister (1st sm8vo, teg, uncut, 108p, 7cp)	Scribner	1903	Ashe, E.M.	45-70	
Davis, Richard H.	Captain Macklin (1st, sm8vo, teg, uncut, 328p, 7pl)	Scribner	1902	Clark, Walter A.	40-65	
Davis, Richard H.	Congo and Coasts of Africa (1st, 8vo, teg, 220p, 32pl)	Scribner	1907	(Photos)	60-100	*
Davis, Richard H.	Cuba in War Time (1st, 12mo, 143p, brown bds, 24pl)	R.H. Russell	1897	Remington, Frederic	200-300	
Davis, Richard H.	In the Fog (1st, 8vo, 155p, gilt, 1-color)	Russell	1901	Steele/Peirce	80-125	
Davis, Richard H.	Lion & the Unicorn (1st [1], 12mo, 204p, green/gilt, 6pl)	Scribner	1899	Christy, Howard C.	35-60	
Davis, Richard H.	Ranson's Folly (1st, sm8vo, red/gilt, teg, 345p, uncut, 16pl)	Scribner	1902	Various	35-60	
Davis, Richard H.	Scarlet Car (1st, 8vo, tan cl, 166p, uncut, 12pl)	Scribner	1907	Steele, Frederic D.	40-70	
Davis, Richard H.	Soldiers of Fortune (1st, 12mo, 364p, 6pl, yellow/gilt)	Scribner	1897	Gibson, Charles D.	40-70	

AUTHOR: 56

AUTHOR	TITLE	PUBLISHER	DATE	ARTIST	PRICE	LC
Davis, Richard H.	Van Bibber & Others (1st, 12mo, 249p, gilt, 4pl)	Harper	1892	Gibson, Charles D.	30-50	
Davis, Richard H.	West From a Car Window (1st, 12mo, blue cl, 242p, gilt, b/w)	Harper	1892	Remington, Frederic	80-140	
Davis, Robert	Gid Granger (1st, sm8vo, 179p, tan cl, fp b/w, DJ/2.25)	Holiday House	(1945)	Wilson, Charles B.	25-45	
Davis, Robert	Hudson Bay Express (1st, 8vo, 258p, blue cl, b/w, DJ/2.00)	Holiday House	(1942)	Pitz, Henry C.	25-40	*
Davis, Robert	Padre Porko (1st, sm8vo, 165p, grey cl, fp b/w, cep, DJ/2.00)	Holiday House	(1939)	Eichenberg, Fritz	50-80	R
Davis, Robert	Partners of Powder Hole (1st, 8vo, wraps, 167p, b/w)	Holiday House	(1947)	Davis, Marshall	25-40	
Davis, Robert	Pepperfoot of Thursday Market (1st, sm8vo, 187p, b/w, pep, DJ/2.00)	Holiday House	(1941)	Baldridge, Cyrus L.	35-60	R
Davis, Robert	That Girl of Pierre's (1st, 8vo, 230p, rust cl, b/w, pep, DJ/2.50)	Holiday House	(1948)	Goff, Lloyd L.	25-40	
Davis, Robert	Tree Toad (1st [new ed.], 8vo, 276p, b/w, DJ/2.00)	Stokes	1942	McCloskey, Robert	40-65	
Davis, Verne	Time of the Wolves (1st, 8vo, 127p, b/w, DJ/2.95)	Wm. Morrow	1962	Keats, Ezra J.	30-45	
Dawe, William C.	Yellow & White (1st, 12mo, 172p, yellow cl, cvr & ti page by...)	L: John Lane	1895	Beardsley, Aubrey	90-120	
Dawson, Alec J.	The Message (1st, 8vo, 386p, black/gilt, 4ticp)	L: Richards	1907	Brock, Henry M.	45-70	
Dawson, Carley	Dragon Run (1st, 8vo, 282p, b/w, DJ/2.75)	Houghton	1955	Ward, Lynd	200-300	
Dawson, Carley	Mr. Wicker's Window (1st, lg8vo, 272p, gilt, 2-color, DJ/3.25)	Houghton	1952	Ward, Lynd	200-300	
Dawson, Carley	Sign of the Seven Seas (1st, 8vo, 287p, b/w, DJ/2.50)	Houghton	1954	Ward, Lynd	200-300	
Dawson, Coningsby	Little House (1st, 8vo, pcb, p-o, 127p, 8pl, pep)	NY: J. Lane	1920	Langdale, Stella	25-40	
Dawson, Forbes	Sensational Trance (1st, 8vo, 178p, red cl, 20pl)	L: Downey	1895	Mackenzie, F.	90-120	
Dawson, L.H. (ed.)	Stories from Faerie Queen (1st, 8vo, 234p)	L: Harrap	1909	Hammond, Gertrude D.	80-130	
Dawson, Lucy	Dogs as I See Them (1st AM, lg4to, [89]p, fp color, pep, DJ/1.00)	Grosset/Dunlap	(1937)	Dawson, Lucy	70-125	
Dawson, Micthell	Magic Firecrackers (1st, 8vo, 192p, b/w, DJ/2.50)	Viking	1949	Wiese, Kurt	50-80	*
Day, Lal Behari	Folk Tales of Bengal (1st, 4to, red/gilt, 274p, 32cp)	L: Macmillan	1912	Goble, Warwick	350-500	
Day, Leigh G.	In Shadow Town (1st, 4to, p-o, [110]p, b/w)	Saalfield	(1907)	(Photos)	120-180	*
Day, Marguerite	Tell 'Em Again Tales (1st, sq4to, ibds, 48p, 3 fp color, pep)	Duffield	1924	Glackens, Louis M.	70-120	
Day-Lewis, Cecil	Christmas Eve (1st, sm8vo, unpag, wraps, col frn)	L: Faber	1954	Ardizzone, Edward	80-125	
Day-Lewis, Cecil	Otterbury Incident (1st, 8vo, 148p, gilt, b/w, DJ)	L: Putnam	1948	Ardizzone, Edward	80-120	
Day-Lewis, Cecil	Otterbury Incident (1st AM, 8vo, cloth, 160p, b/w, DJ/2.00)	Viking	1949	Ardizzone, Edward	80-130	
Day-Lewis, Cecil	Otterbury Incident (1st [this pub], 8vo, 176p, yellow cl, fp b/w, DJ/3.75)	World	(1969)	Ardizzone, Edward	40-70	
Dayrell, Elphinstone	Why Sun and Moon Live in the Sky (1st {std}, 8vo, 26p, color, DJ/3.25, CH)	Houghton	(1968)	Lent, Blair	60-90	
Dayton, Mona	Earth and Sky (1st, 4to, ibds, [25]p, fp color, pep, DJ/3.50)	Harper	(1969)	Duvoisin, Roger	45-70	
De La Iglesia, Maria	Cat and the Mouse (1st, lg8vo, [62]p, color, DJ/3.50)	Pantheon	(1966)	Low, Joseph	25-45	
De La Iglesia, Maria	Oak that Would not Pay (1st, lg8vo, [39]p, fp b/w, cep, DJ/3.50)	Pantheon	(1968)	Snyder, Jerome	30-50	
De La Mare, Walter	Bells & Grass (1st AM, 8vo, p-o, 144p, b/w, pep, DJ/2.50)	Viking	1942	Lathrop, Dorothy	75-125	
De La Mare, Walter	Broomsticks & other Fairy Tales (1st, 8vo, 378p, fp woodcuts)	L: Constable	1925	Bold	70-100	*
De La Mare, Walter	Child's Day (1st, 8vo, 56p, 24 ti-pl)	L: Constable	1912	(Photos)	150-225	
De La Mare, Walter	Collected Stories for Children (1st, 8vo, 437p, b/w, DJ, CgM)	L: Faber	1947	Hawkins, Irene	50-80	*
De La Mare, Walter	Come Hither (1st, lg8vo, 696p, green cl, b/w)	L: Constable	1923	Buckels, Alec	60-80	*
De La Mare, Walter	Come Hither (1st AM, lg8vo, gilt, 696p, b/w)	Knopf	(1923)	Buckels, Alec	50-80	
De La Mare, Walter	Crossings... (1st, lg8vo, 170p, teg, blue/gilt, col frn)	Knopf	1923	Lathrop, Dorothy	90-160	
De La Mare, Walter	Desert Islands & Robinson Crusoe (1st {std}, 4to, 285p, teg, gilt, b/w)	L: Faber	1930	Whistler, Rex	80-120	*
De La Mare, Walter	Desert Islands & Robinson Crusoe (1st AM, lg8vo, 299p, b/w)	Farrar/Rinehart	1930	Whistler, Rex	60-100	*
De La Mare, Walter	Down-Adown-Derry (1st AM, 8vo, 195p, gilt, uncut, col frn)	Henry Holt & Co.	1922	Lathrop, Dorothy	80-120	R
De La Mare, Walter	Down-Adown-Derry (1st {std}, 4to, 190p, blue/gilt, teg, 3cp)	L: Constable	(1922)	Lathrop, Dorothy	120-180	
De La Mare, Walter	Dutch Cheese (1st {std}, lg8vo, 75p, green/gilt, 4cp)	Knopf	1931	Lathrop, Dorothy	80-130	
De La Mare, Walter	Dutch Cheese (1st, lg8vo, 143p, gilt, b/w, DJ)	L: Faber	(1946)	Hawkins, Irene	60-100	
De La Mare, Walter	Flora: A Book of Drawings (1st AM, 4to, ibds, 45p, uncut, 8cp)	Lippincott	(1919)	Bianco, Pamela	80-120	
De La Mare, Walter	Flora: A Book of Drawings (1st, 4to, 45p, ibds, 8cp)	L: Heinemann	(1919)	Bianco, Pamela	90-120	
De La Mare, Walter	Jack & the Beanstalk (1st, narrow 4to, 52p, fp 3-color, dep, DJ/3.00)	Knopf	(1959)	Low, Joseph	70-100	R
De La Mare, Walter	Lord Fish (1st, 8vo, mauve/gilt, 289p, 3cp, pep)	L: Faber	(1933)	Whistler, Rex	60-90	
De La Mare, Walter	Love (1st, 8vo, 592p, grey/gilt, col frn, 24 b/w)	L: Faber	1943	Freedman, Barnett	55-90	
De La Mare, Walter	Lucy (1st, 8vo, 40p, ipcb, p-o, b/w pl)	L: Blackwell	[1927]	Miller, Hilda T.	55-80	R*
De La Mare, Walter	Magic Jacket (1st, sm8vo, 146p, b/w, DJ)	L: Faber	(1943)	Hawkins, Irene	35-60	*
De La Mare, Walter	Miss Jemima (1st, sm8vo, ipcb, p-o, 36p, col frn, 3 fp b/w)	L: Blackwell	[1925]	Buckels, Alec	90-160	R*
De La Mare, Walter	Mr. Bumps & His Monkey (1st, sq8vo, 69p, 7 fp color, DJ/2.00)	Winston	(1942)	Lathrop, Dorothy	100-160	
De La Mare, Walter	Old Joe (1st, lg8vo, 29p, pcb, p-o, b/w)	L: Blackwell	[1927]	Nightingale, C.T.	30-50	
De La Mare, Walter	Old Lion (1st, 8vo, 155p, b/w, DJ)	L: Faber	(1942)	Hawkins, Irene	30-50	
De La Mare, Walter	Peacock Pie (1st, 8vo, 178p, green/gilt, col frn)	L: Constable	(1916)	Robinson, W. Heath	120-170	
De La Mare, Walter	Peacock Pie (1st AM, 8vo, green/gilt, 178p, col frn)	Henry Holt & Co.	[1917]	Robinson, W. Heath	90-160	
De La Mare, Walter	Peacock Pie (1st AM, lg8vo, 128p, blue/gilt, 16cp)	Henry Holt & Co.	(1924)	Fraser, Claud L.	70-100	
De La Mare, Walter	Peacock Pie (1st, lg8vo, teg, 127p, blue/gilt, 16cp)	L: Constable	(1924)	Fraser, Claud L.	100-165	
De La Mare, Walter	Peacock Pie (1st AM [new ed.], 8vo, 111p, blue/gilt, 2-color, DJ/2.00)	Henry Holt & Co.	1936	Crowe, Jocelyn	40-65	*
De La Mare, Walter	Peacock Pie (1st, 8vo, 107p, yellow cl, b/w, DJ)	L: Faber	(1946)	Ardizzone, Edward	80-130	R
De La Mare, Walter	Peacock Pie (1st, lg8vo, 117p, fp b/w, cep, DJ/3.00)	Knopf	(1961)	Cooney, Barbara	30-50	
De La Mare, Walter	Penny a Day (1st, 8vo, 209p, uncut, fp b/w, cep, DJ/3.00)	Knopf	1960	Kennedy, Paul	25-40	
De La Mare, Walter	Readings (1st, lg8vo, 436p, b/w woodcuts by...)	Knopf	1927	Nightingale, C.T.	30-50	
De La Mare, Walter	Rhymes & Verses (1st {std}, lg8vo, 344p, pl, DJ/3.00)	Henry Holt & Co.	(1947)	Blaisdell, Elinore	30-55	
De La Mare, Walter	Scarecrow & other Stories (1st {std}, sm8vo, 128p, fp b/w, DJ)	L: Faber	1945	Hawkins, Irene	30-50	
De La Mare, Walter	Songs of Childhood (1st, sm8vo, 173p, gilt, teg, 8cp)	L: Longmans	1923	Canziani, Estella	70-100	
De La Mare, Walter	Stories from the Bible (1st AM, lg8vo, gilt, 393p, pep, 9cp)	Cosmopolitan	1929	Nadejen, Theodore	55-80	*
De La Mare, Walter	Stories from the Bible (1st AM {std}, 8vo, 420p, b/w, DJ/4.95)	Knopf	1961	Ardizzone, Edward	50-80	
De La Mare, Walter	Story of Miss Jemima (1st {this fmt}, 8vo, ibds, 55p, color, pep, DJ/0.50)	Grosset/Dunlap	(1940)	Farnam, Nellie	60-90	
De La Mare, Walter	Story of Moses (1st, 8vo, 110p, b/w, DJ)	L: Faber	(1959)	Ardizzone, Edward	50-80	
De La Mare, Walter	Stuff & Nonsense (1st, 12mo, green/gilt, 110p, teg, woodcuts)	L: Constable	1927	Bold	70-100	
De La Mare, Walter	This Year: Next Year (1st AM, sm4to, ibds, [64]p, color, pep, DJ/2.50)	Henry Holt & Co.	(1937)	Jones, Harold	90-160	*
De La Mare, Walter	Three Mulla Mulgars (1st, 8vo, teg, green/gilt, 312p, 2cp)	L: Duckworth	1910	Monsell, J.R.	200-300	
De La Mare, Walter	Three Mulla Mulgars (1st, lg8vo, blue/gilt, 275p, 8cp, pep)	Knopf	1919	Lathrop, Dorothy	125-200	
De La Mare, Walter	Three Mulla Mulgars (1st UK, 4to, 275p, gilt, 8cp, 4pl)	L: Duckworth	1921	Lathrop, Dorothy	100-160	
De La Mare, Walter	Three Royal Monkeys (1st, 8vo, 272p, purple cl, 1-color, DJ)	L: Faber	(1946)	Eldridge, Mildred	45-70	
De La Mare, Walter	Told Again (1st AM, 8vo, 248p, red/gilt, 8cp, b/w)	Knopf	1927	Watson, A.H.	45-70	

AUTHOR	TITLE	PUBLISHER	DATE	ARTIST	PRICE	LC
De La Mare, Walter	Told Again (1st, 8vo, 320p, blue/gilt, 8cp)	L: Blackwell	1927	Watson, A.H.	70-100	
De La Mare, Walter	Tom Tiddler's Ground (1st AM {std}, lg8vo, 253p, b/w, DJ/3.50)	Knopf	(1962)	Gill, Margery	30-45	
De La Rame, L.	Bimbi (1st AM, 8vo, 303p, 8pl)	Lippincott	1892	Garrett, Edmund H.	60-100	*
De La Rame, L.	Bimbi (1st, 8vo, 212p, red/gilt, 8cp)	Lippincott	1910	Kirk, Maria L.	40-60	*
De La Rame, M.	Nurnberg Stove (1st, 12mo, 96p, 4cp)	Lippincott	1916	Kirk, Maria L.	25-40	
De Witt, Johanna	Littlest Reindeer (1st, lg8vo, [28]p, ipcb, color, DJ/1.00)	Children's Press	(1946)	Erickson, Phoebe	30-50	
DeAmicis, Edmondo	Heart of Boyhood (1st, 8vo, 198p, 8cp, 24 fp b/w)	Whitman	(1918)	Carsey, Alice	35-50	
DeAngeli, Marguerite	Black Fox of Lorne (1st {std}, 4to, 191p, 11 fp b/w, DJ/2.95, NH)	Doubleday	1956	DeAngeli, Marguerite	45-70	
DeAngeli, Marguerite	Bright April (1st {std}, sq8vo, 86p, color, pep, DJ/2.50)	Doubleday	(1946)	DeAngeli, Marguerite	55-80	
DeAngeli, Marguerite	Copper-Toed Boots (1st {std}, sm4to, ibds, [92]p, color, pep, DJ/2.00)	Doubleday/Doran	1938	DeAngeli, Marguerite	65-90	
DeAngeli, Marguerite	Door in the Wall (1st {std}, 8vo, 112p, color, pep, DJ/2.50, NM)	Doubleday	(1949)	DeAngeli, Marguerite	80-125	R
DeAngeli, Marguerite	Elin's Amerika (1st {std}, sq8vo, tan cl, [96]p, color, pep, DJ/2.00)	Doubleday/Doran	1941	DeAngeli, Marguerite	70-100	
DeAngeli, Marguerite	Empty Barn (1st, 8vo, 60p, color, DJ/3.25)	Westminster Pr.	(1966)	DeAngeli, Marguerite	30-55	
DeAngeli, Marguerite	Henner's Lydia (1st {std}, sq8vo, ibds, [70]p, color, DJ/2.00)	Doubleday/Doran	1936	DeAngeli, Marguerite	70-100	
DeAngeli, Marguerite	Jared's Island (1st {std}, lg8vo, blue/gilt, 95p, col frn, DJ/2.50)	Doubleday	1947	DeAngeli, Marguerite	40-70	
DeAngeli, Marguerite	Just Like David (1st {std}, 8vo, green cl, 122p, color, pep, DJ/2.50)	Doubleday	(1951)	DeAngeli, Marguerite	50-80	
DeAngeli, Marguerite	Nursery & Mother Goose Rhymes (1st {std}, folio, 192p, color, DJ, CH)	Doubleday	1954	DeAngeli, Marguerite	120-180	R
DeAngeli, Marguerite	Petite Suzanne (1st {std}, sq8vo, ibds, [88]p, color, pep, DJ/2.00)	Doubleday/Doran	1937	DeAngeli, Marguerite	120-160	
DeAngeli, Marguerite	Skippack School (1st {std}, sq8vo, ibds, [88]p, color, pep, DJ/2.00)	Doubleday/Doran	1939	DeAngeli, Marguerite	80-120	
DeAngeli, Marguerite	Summer Day with Ted & Nina (1st {std}, 8vo, ibds, [32]p, color, DJ/0.75)	Doubleday/Doran	1940	DeAngeli, Marguerite	80-130	
DeAngeli, Marguerite	Ted & Nina Go to Grocery Store (1st {std}, ob12mo, [32]p, ibds, color, pep)	Doubleday/Doran	1935	DeAngeli, Marguerite	60-90	
DeAngeli, Marguerite	Ted & Nina Have a Happy Rainy Day (1st {std}, ob12mo, ibds, color)	Doubleday/Doran	1936	DeAngeli, Marguerite	60-90	
DeAngeli, Marguerite	Thee, Hannah! (1st {std}, sq8vo, [94]p, color, DJ/2.00)	Doubleday/Doran	1940	DeAngeli, Marguerite	70-100	R
DeAngeli, Marguerite	Turkey for Christmas (1st, 12mo, [49]p, ibds, 1-color, pep, DJ/0.75)	Westminster Pr.	(1944)	DeAngeli, Marguerite	35-50	
DeAngeli, Marguerite	Turkey for Christmas (1st {this fmt}, lg8vo, 48p, 4 fp color, DJ/2.95)	Westminster Pr.	(1965)	DeAngeli, Marguerite	25-45	
DeAngeli, Marguerite	Up the Hill (1st {std}, sq8vo, tan cl, 88p, color, pep, DJ/2.00)	Doubleday/Doran	1942	DeAngeli, Marguerite	70-125	
DeAngeli, Marguerite	Yonie Wondernose (1st {std}, sq4to, [39]p, ibds, fp col, pep, DJ/2.00, CH)	Doubleday/Doran	1944	DeAngeli, Marguerite	80-140	
DeBeaumont, Marie L.	Beauty and the Beast (1st, folio, ibds, 35p, fp color, DJ/1.95)	Macmillan	1963	Knight, Hilary	80-125	
DeBosschere, Jean	Beasts & Men (4to, 179p, green cl, 12cp, pep)	L: Heinemann	(1918)	DeBosschere, Jean	200-300	
DeBosschere, Jean	Christmas Tales of Flanders (1st AM, 4to, 144p, gilt, 12cp, pep)	Dodd	1917	DeBosschere, Jean	180-240	
DeBosschere, Jean	City Curious (1st AM, sq8vo, yellow cl, 178p, 8cp, pep)	Dodd/Heinemann	1920	DeBosschere, Jean	180-240	
DeBosschere, Jean	City Curious (1st, 8vo, 178p, 8cp, pep)	L: Heinemann	(1920)	DeBosschere, Jean	180-240	
DeBosschere, Jean	Closed Door (1st, 8vo, 131p, 16pl)	L: John Lane	1917	DeBosschere, Jean	100-165	
DeBosschere, Jean	Folk Tales of Flanders (1st AM, 4to, 179p, teg, gilt, 12cp, pep)	Dodd	1918	DeBosschere, Jean	160-240	
DeBosschere, Jean	Gulliver's Travels into Lilliput (1st, 4to, 135p, pink cl, 4cp)	L: Heinemann	(1920)	DeBosschere, Jean	160-235	
DeBosschere, Jean	Love Books of Ovid (1st, lg8vo, 216p, blue/gilt, 16cp)	L: John Lane	1925	DeBosschere, Jean	100-175	
DeBosschere, Jean	Weird Islands (1st, lg8vo, 210p, blue cl, col frn, b/w)	L: Chapman/Hall	1921	DeBosschere, Jean	120-180	*
DeBrunhoff, Jean	ABC of Babar (1st AM, sq8vo, ibds, [60]p, color, pep)	Random	(1936)	DeBrunhoff, Jean	200-325	
DeBrunhoff, Jean	Babar & Father Christmas (1st {this pub.}, sq8vo, ibds, [30]p)	Wonder Books	(1940)	DeBrunhoff, Jean	70-100	
DeBrunhoff, Jean	Babar & Father Christmas (1st AM, folio, ibds, [40]p, color, pep, DJ/3.00)	Random	(1940)	DeBrunhoff, Jean	500-700	
DeBrunhoff, Jean	Babar & His Children (1st AM, folio, ibds, [40]p, color, pep, DJ/3.00)	Random	(1938)	DeBrunhoff, Jean	500-700	R
DeBrunhoff, Jean	Babar & Zephir (1st, 4to, ibds, 39p, color, DJ/1.00)	Random	(1942)	DeBrunhoff, Jean	200-300	
DeBrunhoff, Jean	Babar the King (1st {this format}, sq8vo, ibds, 48p, color, pep)	Random	(1935)	DeBrunhoff, Jean	120-200	*
DeBrunhoff, Jean	Babar the King (1st AM, lg folio, 48p, ibds, color, pep)	Smith/Haas	1935	DeBrunhoff, Jean	500-700	R
DeBrunhoff, Jean	Babar the King (1st UK, folio, 48p, ibds, color)	L: Methuen	1936	DeBrunhoff, Jean	400-600	
DeBrunhoff, Jean	Babar's Friend Zephir (1st UK, folio, 42p, ibds, color)	L: Methuen	1937	DeBrunhoff, Jean	400-600	
DeBrunhoff, Jean	Story of Babar (1st AM, folio, 47p, ibds, color, pep)	Smith/Haas	1933	DeBrunhoff, Jean	500-700	
DeBrunhoff, Jean	Story of Babar (1st {this format}, sq8vo, ibds, 48p, color)	Random	(1933)	DeBrunhoff, Jean	150-225	
DeBrunhoff, Jean	Story of Babar (1st UK, folio, ibds, 48p, color)	L: Methuen	1934	DeBrunhoff, Jean	400-650	
DeBrunhoff, Jean	Travels of Babar (1st {this format}, sq8vo, 48p, ibds, color)	Random	(1934)	DeBrunhoff, Jean	150-220	
DeBrunhoff, Jean	Travels of Babar (1st AM, folio, ibds, 47p, color, pep)	Smith/Haas	1934	DeBrunhoff, Jean	450-650	R
DeBrunhoff, Jean	Zephir's Holidays (1st AM, folio, [40]p, color, pep, DJ/3.00)	Random	(1937)	DeBrunhoff, Jean	400-600	R
DeBrunhoff, Laurent	Anatole & his Donkey (1st AM {std}, ob4to, [38]p, 1-color, cep, DJ/2.95)	Macmillan	1963	DeBrunhoff, Laurent	60-90	
DeBrunhoff, Laurent	Babar & the Professor (1st, lg4to, ibds, 40p, color, pep, DJ/3.95)	Random	(1957)	DeBrunhoff, Laurent	80-125	R
DeBrunhoff, Laurent	Babar at the Seashore (1st, sq32mo, [28]p, ibds, color)	Random	(1969)	DeBrunhoff, Laurent	50-85	
DeBrunhoff, Laurent	Babar Comes to America (1st, lg4to, [64]p, color, pep, DJ/3.95)	Random	(1965)	DeBrunhoff, Laurent	70-100	
DeBrunhoff, Laurent	Babar Goes on a Picnic (1st, sq32mo, ibds, [28]p, color, DJ)	Random	(1969)	DeBrunhoff, Laurent	60-100	
DeBrunhoff, Laurent	Babar Goes Skiing (1st, sq32mo, [28]p, ibds, color, DJ)	Random	(1969)	DeBrunhoff, Laurent	60-100	
DeBrunhoff, Laurent	Babar Loses his Crown (1st, 8vo, 63p, ibds, color, pep, DJ/1.95)	Beginner Books	(1967)	DeBrunhoff, Laurent	50-85	
DeBrunhoff, Laurent	Babar the Gardner (1st, sq32mo, ibds, [28]p, color, DJ)	Random	(1969)	DeBrunhoff, Laurent	50-85	
DeBrunhoff, Laurent	Babar's Birthday Surprise (1st AM, lg4to, [28]p, ibds, color, DJ/3.95)	Random	(1970)	DeBrunhoff, Laurent	50-80	
DeBrunhoff, Laurent	Babar's Castle (1st, lg4to, 30p, ibds, color, pep, DJ/3.95)	Random	(1962)	DeBrunhoff, Laurent	60-100	
DeBrunhoff, Laurent	Babar's Cousin that Rascal Arthur (1st AM, folio, 47p, ibds, col, DJ/3.50)	Random	(1948)	DeBrunhoff, Laurent	400-600	
DeBrunhoff, Laurent	Babar's French Lessons (1st AM, lg4to, [28]p, color, DJ/3.95)	Random	(1963)	DeBrunhoff, Laurent	80-120	
DeBrunhoff, Laurent	Babar's Picnic (1st AM, folio, 39p, ibds, color, DJ/3.50)	Random	(1949)	DeBrunhoff, Laurent	450-600	
DeBrunhoff, Laurent	Babar's Visit to Bird Island (1st UK, sm folio, 39p, ibds, color)	L: Methuen	(1952)	DeBrunhoff, Laurent	350-500	
DeBrunhoff, Laurent	Bonhomme (1st AM, 8vo, [48]p, fp 1-color, cep, DJ/2.95)	Pantheon	1965	DeBrunhoff, Laurent	90-140	
DeBrunhoff, Laurent	Captain Serafina (1st {std}, 4to, [30]p, color, DJ/3.00)	World	(1963)	DeBrunhoff, Laurent	70-120	
DeBrunhoff, Laurent	Picnic at Babar's (1st UK, folio, 40p, ibds, color, pep)	L: Methuen	(1950)	DeBrunhoff, Laurent	300-450	
DeBrunhoff, Laurent	Serafina the Giraffe (1st {std}, 4to, [30]p, color, DJ/3.00)	World	(1961)	DeBrunhoff, Laurent	70-120	
DeBrunhoff, Laurent	Serafina's Lucky Find (1st {std}, 4to, [30]p, color, DJ/3.00)	World	(1962)	DeBrunhoff, Laurent	70-120	
DeChazeau, Eunice	Of Houses and Cats (1st {std}, 8vo, 120p, b/w, DJ/4.95)	Random	(1965)	Parnall, Peter	40-60	
DeHartog, Jan	Sailor's Life (1st {std}, 8vo, 210p, b/w, DJ/3.00)	Harper	1956	Low, Joseph	20-35	
DeJong, David C.	Squirrel and the Harp (1st {std}, 8vo, 46p, b/w, DJ/2.95)	Macmillan	(1966)	Spier, Jo	20-35	
DeJong, Dola	Level Land (1st, 8vo, 176p, b/w, DJ/2.95)	Scribner	(1961)	Spier, Peter E.	30-50	
DeJong, Dola	Picture Story of Holland (1st, 4to, [36]p, color, pep, DJ/2.50)	Reynal/Hitchcock	(1946)	Hordyk, Gerard	40-65	
DeJong, Dola	Sand for the Sandmen (1st, sm8vo, 87p, 1-color, DJ/2.00)	Scribner	1946	Norton, Natalie	20-30	
DeJong, Meindert	Along Came a Dog (1st, 8vo, 172p, b/w, DJ/2.75, NH)	Harper	(1958)	Sendak, Maurice	200-300	R

AUTHOR	TITLE	PUBLISHER	DATE	ARTIST	PRICE	LC
DeJong, Meindert	Bells of the Harbor (1st {std}, 8vo, 289p, pep, b/w, DJ/2.00)	Harper	1941	Wiese, Kurt	40-65	
DeJong, Meindert	Bible Days (1st, ob4to, 80p, fp b/w, pep)	Fideler Co.	(1949)	Collins, Kreigh	30-50	
DeJong, Meindert	Big Goose & Little White Duck (1st {std}, 8vo, 160p, 8cp, pep, DJ/2.00)	Harper	1938	Potter, Edna	60-90	
DeJong, Meindert	Big Goose & Little White Duck (1st, 8vo, 169p, b/w, DJ/3.50)	Harper	(1963)	Burkert, Nancy	25-45	
DeJong, Meindert	Billy & the Unhappy Bull (1st {std}, 4to, 206p, brown cl, b/w, DJ/2.00)	Harper	(1946)	Simont, Marc	40-65	
DeJong, Meindert	Cat that Walked a Week (1st {std}, 8vo, grey cl, 148p, 13 fp bw, DJ/2.00)	Harper	1943	Robinson, Jessie	40-65	
DeJong, Meindert	Dirk's Dog Bello (1st {std}, 8vo, 296p, color, pep, DJ/2.00)	Harper	1939	Wiese, Kurt	40-60	
DeJong, Meindert	Far Out the Long Canal (1st, 8vo, 231p, fp b/w, DJ/3.50)	Harper	(1964)	Grossman, Nancy	20-35	
DeJong, Meindert	Good Luck Duck (1st, lg8vo, yellow cl, 57p, color, pep, DJ/2.00)	Harper	(1950)	Simont, Marc	40-65	
DeJong, Meindert	Horse Came Running (1st {std}, 8vo, 147p, b/w, DJ/4.95)	Macmillan	(1970)	Sagsoorian, Paul	30-45	
DeJong, Meindert	House of Sixty Fathers (1st, 8vo, 189p, tan cl, b/w, DJ/2.50, NH)	Harper	(1956)	Sendak, Maurice	250-350	R
DeJong, Meindert	Hurry Home, Candy (1st, 8vo, 244p, green cl, b/w, DJ/2.50, NH)	Harper	(1953)	Sendak, Maurice	250-350	R
DeJong, Meindert	Journey from Peppermint Street (1st, sm8vo, 242p, fp b/w, DJ/4.50)	Harper	(1968)	McCully, Emily	30-45	
DeJong, Meindert	Last Little Cat (1st, 8vo, 66p, b/w, DJ/2.75)	Harper	(1961)	McMullan, Jim	25-40	
DeJong, Meindert	Little Cow & the Turtle (1st, 8vo, 178p, b/w, DJ/2.50)	Harper	(1955)	Sendak, Maurice	250-350	
DeJong, Meindert	Little Stray Dog (1st {std}, 8vo, 51p, b/w, DJ/1.50)	Harper	(1943)	Shenton, Edward	35-60	
DeJong, Meindert	Mighty Ones (1st, lg8vo, 282p, b/w, DJ/3.50)	Harper	(1959)	Schmidt, Harvey	30-45	*
DeJong, Meindert	Nobody Plays with a Cabbage (1st, lg8vo, 52p, fp b/w, DJ/2.75)	Harper	(1962)	Allen, Tom	25-40	
DeJong, Meindert	Puppy Summer (1st, 8vo, 98p, fp b/w, DJ/3.95)	Harper	(1966)	Lobel, Anita	50-80	R*
DeJong, Meindert	Shadrach (1st {std}, 8vo, rust cl, 182p, b/w, DJ/2.50, NH)	Harper	(1953)	Sendak, Maurice	180-250	R
DeJong, Meindert	Singing Hill (1st, 8vo, 180p, b/w, DJ/2.95, NYTBI)	Harper	(1962)	Sendak, Maurice	120-180	R
DeJong, Meindert	Smoke Above the Lane (1st, 8vo, 58p, b/w, cep, DJ/1.75)	Harper	(1951)	Goodenow, Girard	25-40	
DeJong, Meindert	Tower by the Sea (1st {std}, 8vo, 113p, DJ/2.00)	Harper	(1950)	Comfort, Barbara	25-40	
DeJong, Meindert	Wheel on the School (1st, 8vo, 298p, b/w, uncut, DJ/2.75, NM)	Harper	(1954)	Sendak, Maurice	200-300	R
DeJong, Meindert	Wheels Over the Bridge (1st {std}, 8vo, 219p, pep, 10pl, DJ/2.00)	Harper	(1941)	Watson, Aldren A.	40-65	
DeKoven, Mrs. R.	Sawdust Doll (1st, 12mo, 237p, blue/gilt, teg, cvr by...)	Stone/Kimball	1895	Hazenplug, Frank	100-165	
DeLeeuw, Adele	Nobody's Doll (1st, 8vo, 86p, fp color, pep, DJ/2.00)	Little/Brown	1946	Vaughan, Anne	70-120	
DeLeeuw, Cateau	Dutch West Indies & Philippines (1st, 8vo, ibds, 25p, 2-color, DJ/1.25)	Holiday House	(1943)	Busoni, Rafaello	40-65	
DeLeeuw, Hendrik	Java Jungle Tales (1st {std}, 8vo, 311p, col frn, pep)	Doubleday/Doran	1933	Wiese, Kurt	35-60	*
DeLeeuw, Hendrik	Peewee the Mousedeer (1st {std}, lg ob8vo, ibds, 71p, 1-color, DJ/2.00)	McKay	1943	Gergely, Tibor	60-90	
DeMaupassant, Guy	Diamond Necklace (1st, 8vo, 82p, fp b/w, DJ/2.95)	F. Watts	(1967)	Quackenbush, Rbt.	20-25	*
DeMille, W.M.C.	Forest Ring (1st, lg8vo, 180p, gilt, p-o, 10cp)	Doran	(1914)	Sichel, Harold	60-90	*
DeMontaigne, Michel	Essays (1st, 8vo, 472p, bds, gilt, 15 fp color)	Doubleday	1947	Dali, Salvador	200-350	
DeMonvel, M.B.	Good Children & Bad (1st AM, ob4to, 48p, gilt, color)	Cassell	(1890)	DeMonvel, M.B.	170-220	
DeMonvel, M.B.	Jeanne d' Arc (1st, ob4to, white cl, 47p, color)	(Paris)	[1896]	DeMonvel, M.B.	180-240	
DeMonvel, M.B.	Joan of Arc (1st AM, ob4to, 47p, purple cl, color)	Century	1907	DeMonvel, M.B.	120-180	
DeMonvel, M.B.	Joan of Arc (1st {this pub}, ob8vo, tan cl, p-o, [25]p, 10 color)	McKay	1918	DeMonvel, M.B.	60-90	*
DeMorgan, Mary	Necklace of Princess Fiorimonde (1st, 12mo, gilt, 184p, AEG, dep)	L: Macmillan	1880	Crane, Walter	200-280	
DeMorgan, Mary	Windfairies and other Tales (1st, sm8vo, 236p, gilt, AEG, 6 fp color)	L: Seeley	1900	Cockerell, Olive	90-120	
DeMusset, Paul	Mr. Wind & Madam Rain (lg8vo, 150p, red/gilt, AEG, 25pl)	Putnam	1904	Bennett, Charles	80-120	*
DePaola, Tomie	Fight the Night (1st {std}, 4to, [33]p, color, DJ/3.50)	Lippincott	(1968)	DePaola, Tomie	30-45	
DePaola, Tomie	Joe and the Snow (1st {std}, 8vo, [32]p, color, DJ/4.25)	Hawthorn Books	(1968)	DePaola, Tomie	25-45	
DePaola, Tomie	Journey of the Kiss (1st {std}, ob8vo, [39]p, color, DJ/3.95)	Hawthorn Books	(1970)	DePaola, Tomie	25-45	
DePaola, Tomie	Monsters' Ball (1st {std}, 8vo, [31]p, color, DJ/4.25)	Hawthorn Books	(1970)	DePaola, Tomie	30-45	
DePaola, Tomie	Parker Pig, Esquire (1st {std}, 12mo, [32]p, color, DJ/3.95)	Hawthorn Books	(1969)	DePaola, Tomie	30-45	
DePaola, Tomie	Who Needs Holes? (1st {std}, 8vo, [30]p, color, DJ/3.95)	Hawthorn Books	(1970)	DePaola, Tomie	30-45	*
DePaola, Tomie	Wonderful Dragon of Timlin (1st {std}, lg ob8vo, unpag, color, DJ/3.50)	Bobbs-Merrill	(1966)	DePaola, Tomie	35-50	
DeQuattrociocchi, N.	Love and Dishes (1st {std}, 8vo, 416p, b/w, DJ/4.00)	Bobbs-Merrill	(1950)	Duvoisin, Roger	30-50	*
DeRegniers, Beatrice	Catch a Little Fox (1st {std}, ob8vo, [41]p, fp 1-color, DJ/3.95)	Seabury Press	1970	Turkle, Brinton	30-50	*
DeRegniers, Beatrice	Cats Cats Cats Cats Cats (1st {std}, lg4to, [30]p, 2-color, cep, DJ/2.95)	Pantheon	(1958)	Sokol, Bill	50-80	R
DeRegniers, Beatrice	Child's Book of Dreams (1st {std}, 12mo, [46]p, fp 2-color, DJ/2.25)	Harcourt	1957	Sokol, Bill	40-65	R
DeRegniers, Beatrice	David and Goliath (1st, 4to, brown cl, unpag, color, DJ/3.75)	Viking	1965	Powers, Richard	20-35	
DeRegniers, Beatrice	Day Everybody Cried (1st, ob12mo, [32]p, ipcb, 2-color, cep, DJ/2.50)	Viking	(1967)	Hogrogian, Nonny	30-50	
DeRegniers, Beatrice	Giant Book (1st {std}, 8vo, 188p, b/w, DJ/4.75)	Atheneum	1966	Cummings, Wm. L.	30-50	*
DeRegniers, Beatrice	Giant Story (1st, 4to, [29]p, grey cl, fp 2-color, DJ/2.00)	Harper	(1953)	Sendak, Maurice	200-300	
DeRegniers, Beatrice	How Joe the Bear & Sam the Mouse... (1st, 4to, [40]p, color, pep, DJ/2.95)	Parents Mag. Pr.	1965	Turkle, Brinton	60-90	
DeRegniers, Beatrice	Little Book (1st, 32mo, [24]p, color, dep, DJ/2.50)	H.Z. Walck	1961	DeRegniers, Beatrice	25-40	
DeRegniers, Beatrice	Little Girl and her Mother (1st, ob4to, [30]p, 1-color, DJ/3.25)	Vanguard Press	(1963)	Gilman, Esther	25-45	
DeRegniers, Beatrice	Little House of Your Own (1st {std}, 8vo, [38]p, b/w, DJ/1.75, NYTBI)	Harcourt	(1954)	Haas, Irene	45-70	R*
DeRegniers, Beatrice	May I Bring a Friend? (1st {std}, lg8vo, [46]p, color, DJ/3.50, CM)	Atheneum	1964	Montresor, Beni	70-120	
DeRegniers, Beatrice	Penny (1st, 16mo, 62p, ipcb, fp color, pep, DJ/3.95)	Viking	(1966)	Bileck, Marvin	45-70	
DeRegniers, Beatrice	Shadow Book (1st {std}, sm ob4to, [23]p, DJ/2.75, NYTBI, b/w photos by...)	Harcourt	(1960)	Gordon, Isabel	30-50	*
DeRegniers, Beatrice	Snow Party (1st {std}, sm4to, unpag, color, DJ/2.75)	Pantheon	(1959)	Zimnik, Reiner	65-100	R
DeRegniers, Beatrice	Something Special (1st {std}, 8vo, [46]p, fp b/w, DJ/2.25)	Harcourt	(1958)	Haas, Irene	30-50	
DeRegniers, Beatrice	Was It a Good Trade? (1st {std}, ob8vo, [29]p, ibds, color, DJ/1.95, NYTBI)	Harcourt	1956	Haas, Irene	60-100	R*
DeRegniers, Beatrice	What Can You Do with a Shoe? (1st, ob4to, ipcb, [32]p, 1-color, DJ/1.75)	Harper	(1955)	Sendak, Maurice	500-700	
DeRegniers, Beatrice	Who Likes the Sun? (1st {std}, 4to, [30]p, 2-color, DJ/3.00)	Harcourt	(1961)	Pierce, Leona	50-80	
DeRegniers, Beatrice	Willy O'Dwyer Jumped in the Fire (1st {std}, 4to, [39]p, col, cep, DJ/4.50)	Atheneum	1968	Montresor, Beni	30-45	
DeSegur, Sophie	Memoirs of a Donkey (1st, 16mo, blue cl, 238p, fp b/w, pep)	Macmillan	1924	Ford, Lauren	50-85	
DeSegur, Sophie	Old French Fairy Tales (1st, 4to, 279p, gilt, p-o, 8cp, pep)	Penn	(1920)	Sterrett, Virginia	250-400	
DeSegur, Sophie	Sophie, Story of a Bad Little Girl (1st, sm8vo, 157p, b/w, dep)	Knopf	1929	Barney, Maginel W.	25-45	*
DeSegur, Sophie	Wise Little Donkey (1st, 8vo, p-o, 191p, pep, 4cp)	Whitman	(1931)	Brock, Emma	25-40	
DeSelincourt, Hugh	Oxford From Within (1st, 4to, 180p, blue/gilt, 12cp)	L: Chatto	1910	Markino, Y.	90-120	
DeSeyn, Donna E.	Termite Works for his Colony (1st, 8vo, 47p, fp 3-color, cep, DJ/2.95)	Holiday House	(1967)	Barberis, Juan	25-40	*
DeTrevino, Elizabeth	About Bellamy (1st {std}, 8vo, 214p, b/w, uncut, DJ/2.00)	Harper	(1940)	Robinson, Jessie	20-35	*
DeTrevino, Elizabeth	Carpet of Flowers (1st, 8vo, 88p, b/w, pep, DJ/2.50)	Crowell	(1955)	Crane, Alan H.	25-45	
DeTrevino, Elizabeth	I, Juan de Pareja (1st {std}, 8vo, 180p, cep, DJ/3.25, NM)	Farrar, Straus	(1965)	No Illustrations	80-140	R
DeTrevino, Elizabeth	Nacar, the White Deer (1st, 8vo, 149p, b/w, DJ/3.25)	Farrar, Straus	(1963)	Arno, Enrico	20-30	

AUTHOR	TITLE	PUBLISHER	DATE	ARTIST	PRICE	LC
DeTrevino, Elizabeth	Turi's Poppa (1st {std}, 8vo, green cl, 186p, b/w, DJ/3.75)	Farrar, Straus	(1968)	Arno, Enrico	25-40	
DeVries, P.J.C.	Princess Who Grew (1st, 8vo, 112p, p-o, col frn, 5pl)	Stokes	1927	Cramer, Rie	80-130	
DeWolf, Wallace L.	Mardo's Animal Rhymes (1st, sq8vo, 44p, 4cp)	Rand/McNally	(1916)	Winter, Milo	55-80	
Deakin, Irving	Peter and the Wolf (1st, 4to, [48]p, 2-color, DJ/1.75)	Oxford U. Pr.	(1940)	Jones, Richard	20-35	
Dean, Agnes L.	Devonshire Cream (1st, 8vo, wraps, 49p, 3 fp b/w & cvr by...)	Unity Press	1950	Lathrop, Dorothy	70-100	
Dean, Graham M.	Riders of the Gabilans (1st, 8vo, 191p, b/w, pep, DJ/2.00)	Viking	1944	Dennis, Wesley	25-45	
Dean, Leigh	Looking Down Game (1st, 8vo, 34p, b/w, DJ/2.95)	Funk/Wagnalls	(1968)	Giovanopoulos, P.	25-40	
Dearden, Harold	Wonderful Adventure (1st, sm8vo, 115p, p-o, b/w)	Cosmopolitan	1928	Blood, W.C.	25-40	*
Dearden, Harold	Wonderful Adventure (1st UK, sm4to, ibds, 52p, b/w)	L: Heinemann	1929	Rountree, Harry	50-85	*
Dearmer, Mabel	Book of Penny Toys (1st, lg8vo, ibds, 94p, 14 color)	L: Macmillan	1899	Dearmer, Mabel	300-450	*
Dearmer, Mabel	Child's Life of Christ (1st, 8vo, 290p, 8cp)	L: Methuen	1906	Brickdale, E.F.	60-100	*
Dearmer, Mabel	Cockyolly Bird (1st, 4to, 221p, 10 ticp)	L: Hodder	(1914)	Dearmer, Mabel	170-240	*
Dearmer, Mabel	Playmate, A Christmas Mystery (1st, 8vo, 31p, 4 illus)	L: A. Mowbray	1910	Stratton, Helen	80-125	
Dearmer, Percy	Little Lives of the Saints (1st, 12mo, 144p, green/gilt, fp b/w, dep)	L: Wells/Gard.	1900	Robinson, Charles	80-120	*
Debenham, Mary H.	Whispering Winds & Tales they Told (1st, 8vo, 195p, gilt, 25pl)	L: Blackie	1895	Hardy, Paul	50-85	
Decker, Karl	Evangelina Cisneros (1st, sm8vo, teg, uncut, 257p, 4pl by...)	Continental	1898	Remington, Frederic	80-130	
Defoe, Daniel	Moll Flanders (1st, 4to, 333p, black/gilt, 16pl, pep)	L: John Lane	(1929)	Austen, John	70-125	
Defoe, Daniel	Picture Book of Robinson Crusoe (1st, 4to, 51p, fp color, pep)	Macmillan	1931	Verpilleux, E.A.	70-120	
Defoe, Daniel	Robinson Crusoe (lg8vo, A.E. red, 328p, red/gilt, 6 chromos)	L: Nister	[1890]	6 Chromos	100-170	
Defoe, Daniel	Robinson Crusoe (8vo, 472p, teg, bds, 16cp, pep)	L: J.M. Dent	1895	Symington, J.A.	85-130	
Defoe, Daniel	Robinson Crusoe (1st, 8vo, black cl, p-o, 363p, col frn, b/w)	R.H. Russell	1900	Rhead, Louis	60-90	
Defoe, Daniel	Robinson Crusoe (1st, 8vo, blue/gilt, 435p, p-o, 12cp)	Houghton	1909	Smith, E. Boyd	60-100	
Defoe, Daniel	Robinson Crusoe (1st, lg8vo, 352p, tan/gilt, 24 ticp, pep)	L: Hodder	(1910)	Pocock, Noel	80-120	
Defoe, Daniel	Robinson Crusoe (1st, lg8vo, 382p, p-o, 16cp, pep, WS)	Rand/McNally	(1914)	Winter, Milo	60-100	
Defoe, Daniel	Robinson Crusoe (1st, 4to, ibds, 80p, col frn, 6 color)	L: Blackie	[1916]	Hassall, John	100-160	
Defoe, Daniel	Robinson Crusoe (1st, lg8vo, teg, p-o, 368p, 13cp, pep)	Cosmopolitan	1920	Wyeth, N.C.	250-350	
Defoe, Daniel	Robinson Crusoe (1st, 8vo, blue cl, 320p, 6cp)	L: Harrap	1933	Abbott, Elenore P.	75-100	
Defoe, Daniel	Robinson Crusoe (1st, 8vo, 287p, pcb, pep, 4 fp color, DJ/1.25, RC)	World	(1946)	Duvoisin, Roger	45-70	
Defoe, Daniel	Robinson Crusoe (1st, folio, ibds, 97p, color, GGB/#698)	Golden Press	1960	Rojankovsky, Feodor	60-100	*
Defoe, Daniel	Robinson Crusoe (1st AM {std}, lg8vo, 281p, blue/silver, pep, DJ)	F. Watts	1968	Ardizzone, Edward	30-50	
Dehn, Paul	Quake, Quake, Quake (1st AM, 8vo, 109p, b/w, DJ/3.50)	Simon/Schuster	1961	Gorey, Edward	50-75	
Deihl, Edna G.	Little Black Hen (1st, 8vo, 61p, color, pep)	Whitman	1938	Seeley, Sue	35-50	
Deihl, Edna G.	Magic Lake (1st, 12mo, p-o, 125p, 1-color)	Whitman	(1930)	Builta, Marie V.	30-45	
Deihl, Edna G.	Mother Brown Earth's Children (1st, 8vo, 111p, pep, p-o by...)	Whitman	(1927)	Winter, Milo	60-90	
Deihl, Edna G.	My Twin Kitties (1st, 8vo, [24]p, ibds, color, pep)	S. Gabriel	(1924)	Unknown	40-65	
Deihl, Edna G.	Teddy Bear that Prowled the Night (1st, 4to, ibds, 24p, color)	S. Gabriel	(1924)	Russell, Mary L.	80-120	*
Del Rio, A.M.	Sun, Moon & a Rabbit (1st, sm ob4to, gilt, 191p, color, DJ/3.00)	Sheed/Ward	1935	Charlot, Jean	120-200	R
Delafield, Celia	Mrs. Mallard's Ducklings (1st, 4to, [24]p, fp color, pep, DJ/2.00)	Lothrop, Lee	1946	Weisgard, Leonard	70-100	
Deland, Ellen D.	Oakleigh (1st, 12mo, green cl, 233p, 19pl)	Harper	1896	Stephens, Alice B.	35-60	
Deland, Margaret	An Encore (1st {std}, 8vo, teg, 79p, 3pl)	Harper	1907	Stephens, Alice B.	35-60	
Deland, Margaret	Around Old Chester (1st, sm8vo, 378p, p-o, 6pl)	Harper	1915	Stephens, Alice B.	35-60	
Deland, Margaret	Awakening of Helena Richie (1st, sm8vo, 357p, col frn, 7pl)	Harper	1906	Clark, Walter A.	25-40	
Deland, Margaret	Dr. Lavendar's People (1st, 12mo, 370p, 12pl)	Harper	1903	Hitchcock, Lucius	30-50	
Deland, Margaret	Old Chester Tales (1st [1], 12mo, 360p, green cl, 16pl)	Harper	1899	Pyle, Howard	140-220	
Deland, Margaret	Old Garden (1st, 8vo, 114p, color, pep, cvr by...)	L: McIlvaine	1893	Crane, Walter	200-300	
Deland, Margaret	Old Garden (1st AM, 8vo, 114p, uncut, color, dep)	Houghton	1894	Crane, Walter	150-250	
Deland, Margaret	Way to Peace (1st, 8vo, grey/gilt, teg, uncut, 93p, 7pl, dep)	Harper	1910	Stephens, Alice B.	40-65	
Deland, Margaret	Where Laborers are Few (1st, 8vo, 86p, gilt, teg, 3pl)	Harper	1909	Stephens, Alice B.	40-65	
Delessert, Etienne	Endless Party (1st AM {std}, 4to, [32]p, color, DJ/4.50)	Harlin Quist	(1967)	Delessert, Etienne	30-50	
Delessert, Etienne	The Tree (1st AM {std}, 8vo, [28]p, fp color, pep, DJ/3.95)	Harlin Quist	(1966)	Delessert, Etienne	30-50	
Dell, Stanley	Three-Four Kittens (1st, 4to, 95p, 2-color, DJ/2.00)	Henry Holt & Co.	(1941)	Lamont, Jean	30-50	
Deming, Therese O.	American Animal Life (1st, ob4to, [74]p, p-o, 24cp)	Stokes	1916	Deming, Edwin W.	150-220	
Deming, Therese O.	Animal Folk of Wood & Plain (1st, ob4to, [38]p, p-o, 12cp)	Stokes	(1916)	Deming, Edwin W.	120-180	
Deming, Therese O.	Children of the Wild (1st, 4to, [26]p, 6cp)	Stokes	(1902)	Deming, Edwin W.	90-120	
Deming, Therese O.	Cosel: With Geronimo on His Last Raid (1st, lg8vo, 125p, 6cp, DJ/1.25)	Davis Co.	1938	Deming, Edwin W.	60-100	
Deming, Therese O.	Four-Footed Wilderness People (1st, ob4to, ibds, 38p, 12cp)	Stokes	1916	Deming, Edwin W.	120-200	*
Deming, Therese O.	Indian Child Life (1st, ob4to, ibds, [74]p, 18cp)	Stokes	1899	Deming, Edwin W.	160-225	
Deming, Therese O.	Indians of the Wigwams (1st, 12mo, 239p, 31 fp color, DJ/1.50)	Whitman	1938	Deming, Edwin W.	60-90	
Deming, Therese O.	Little Braves (1st, ob4to, [48]p, 9 fp color)	Stokes	1929	Deming, Edwin W.	80-120	*
Deming, Therese O.	Little Brothers of the West (1st, sm4to, p-o, [26]p, 6cp)	Stokes	(1902)	Deming, Edwin W.	100-160	
Deming, Therese O.	Little Indian Folk (1st, ob4to, [38]p, 9cp)	Stokes	1899	Deming, Edwin W.	170-220	*
Deming, Therese O.	Little Red People (1st, ob4to, [38]p, 9cp)	Stokes	1899	Deming, Edwin W.	160-220	*
Deming, Therese O.	Many Snows Ago (1st, ob4to, [96]p, 18 fp color)	Stokes	1929	Deming, Edwin W.	100-170	
Deming, Therese O.	Red Folk & Wild Folk (1st, 4to, [51]p, p-o, 12cp)	Stokes	(1902)	Deming, Edwin W.	120-200	
Deming, Therese O.	Red People of the Wooded Country (1st, 12mo, 191p, fp color)	Whitman	(1932)	Deming, Edwin W.	60-100	
Deming, Therese O.	Wigwam Children (1st, ob4to, [48]p, 9 fp color)	Stokes	1929	Deming, Edwin W.	90-170	
Demuth, Averil	House in the Mountains (1st AM, {std}, 8vo, 240p, col frn, b/w, DJ/2.00)	Harper	(1941)	Ninon	60-90	
Demuth, Averil	Trudi and Hansel (1st, 8vo, silver cl, 174p, fp color, pep, DJ/2.00)	Winston	(1938)	Lavrin, Nora	30-50	
Denison, Carol	What Every Young Rabbit Should Know (1st, ob4to, [64]p, 1-color, DJ/2.25)	Dodd	1948	Wiese, Kurt	50-85	
Denison, Carol	Where Any Young Cat Might Be (1st, ob4to, [54]p, fp b/w, pep, DJ/2.50)	Dodd	1956	Wiese, Kurt	60-85	
Denison, Mary	Yellow Violin (1st, 12mo, 311p, green/gilt, 4pl)	Saalfield	1902	Fry, W.H.	50-80	R*
Dennis, Morgan	Burlap (1st, ob8vo, ibds, [41]p, b/w, DJ/1.00)	Viking	1945	Dennis, Morgan	40-65	
Dennis, Morgan	Himself and Burlap on TV (1st, ob8vo, 41p, red cl, b/w, DJ/2.00)	Viking	1954	Dennis, Morgan	30-50	
Dennis, Morgan	Kitten on the Keys (1st, lg ob8vo, 43p, b/w, DJ/2.25)	Viking	(1961)	Dennis, Morgan	30-50	
Dennis, Morgan	Pup Himself (1st, ob8vo, ipcb, [42]p, fp 1-color, pep, DJ/1.00)	Viking	1943	Dennis, Morgan	30-50	*
Dennis, Morgan	Skit and Skat (1st, ob8vo, 42p, ibds, b/w, DJ/1.50)	Viking	1951	Dennis, Morgan	30-50	*
Dennis, Wesley	Flip (1st, 8vo, [63]p, b/w, pep, b/w, DJ/1.50)	Viking	1941	Dennis, Wesley	30-50	
Dennis, Wesley	Flip and the Cows (1st, 8vo, [63]p, b/w, DJ/1.50)	Viking	1942	Dennis, Wesley	25-40	*

AUTHOR: 60

AUTHOR	TITLE	PUBLISHER	DATE	ARTIST	PRICE	LC
Dennis, Wesley	Holiday (1st, ob4to, [61]p, ibds, b/w, DJ/2.00)	Viking	1946	Dennis, Wesley	30-50	
Dennis, Wesley	Tumble, Story of a Mustang (1st {std}, lg8vo, 48p, b/w, DJ/3.50)	Hastings House	(1966)	Dennis, Wesley	25-40	
Denslow, W.W.	Billy Bounce (1st, 8vo, orange cl, 279p, p-o, 16cp)	Dillingham	(1906)	Denslow, W.W.	350-500	
Denslow, W.W.	Denslow's 5 Little Pigs (1st, 4to, wraps, [12]p, color, pep)	Dillingham	(1903)	Denslow, W.W.	170-250	
Denslow, W.W.	Denslow's Animal Fair (1st, 4to, wraps, unpag, color)	Dillingham	(1904)	Denslow, W.W.	170-250	
Denslow, W.W.	Denslow's Humpty Dumpty (1st, 4to, grey cl, p-o, 74p, fp color)	Dillingham	(1903)	Denslow, W.W.	300-450	R
Denslow, W.W.	Denslow's Night Before Christmas (1st, 4to, ibds, p-o, 64p, color)	Dillingham	(1902)	Denslow, W.W.	500-800	
Denslow, W.W.	Denslow's Night Before Christmas (lg8vo, p-o, [32]p, color, later)	Donohue	[1915]	Denslow, W.W.	250-350	
Denslow, W.W.	Denslow's One Ring Circus (1st, 4to, wraps, [74]p, color, pep)	Dillingham	(1903)	Denslow, W.W.	300-500	
Denslow, W.W.	Denslow's One Ring Circus (lg4to, [74]p, red cl, p-o, color)	Donohue	[1913]	Denslow, W.W.	300-500	
Denslow, W.W.	Denslow's Three Little Kittens (1st, 4to, wraps, [12]p, color)	Dillingham	(1904)	Denslow, W.W.	250-350	
Denslow, W.W.	Denslow's Tom Thumb (1st, 4to, wraps, [12]p, color, pep)	Dillingham	(1903)	Denslow, W.W.	170-250	
Denslow, W.W.	Denslow's Zoo (1st, 4to, [12]p, wraps, color, pep)	Dillingham	(1903)	Denslow, W.W.	180-250	
Denslow, W.W.	House that Jack Built (1st, 4to, [12]p, wraps, color, pep)	Dillingham	(1903)	Denslow, W.W.	200-280	
Denslow, W.W.	Jack & the Bean Stalk (1st, 4to, wraps, [12]p, color)	Dillingham	(1903)	Denslow, W.W.	180-280	
Denslow, W.W.	Little Red Riding Hood (1st, 4to, [12]p, wraps, color)	Dillingham	(1903)	Denslow, W.W.	170-240	
Denslow, W.W.	Mary Had a Little Lamb (1st, 4to, wraps, [12]p, color)	Dillingham	(1903)	Denslow, W.W.	150-250	
Denslow, W.W.	Old Mother Hubbard (1st, 4to, wraps, [12]p, color)	Dillingham	(1903)	Denslow, W.W.	200-265	
Denslow, W.W.	Scarecrow & the Tin Man (1st, 4to, [74]p, p-o, color)	Dillingham	(1904)	Denslow, W.W.	600-800	
Denslow, W.W.	Scarecrow & the Tin Man (4to, red cl, p-o, [74]p, color)	Donohue	[1913]	Denslow, W.W.	220-325	
Denslow, W.W.	Simple Simon (1st, 4to, wraps, unpag, color)	Dillingham	(1904)	Denslow, W.W.	120-180	
Denslow, W.W.	Tom Thumb (1st, 4to, [12]p, wraps, color)	Dillingham	(1903)	Denslow, W.W.	250-350	
Denslow, W.W.	When I Grow Up (1st, 4to, 104p, 24 color, tan cl)	Century	1909	Denslow, W.W.	170-240	
Denton, Clara J.	Daisy Dells (1st, lg8vo, 222p, p-o, color)	Whitman	(1927)	Cheney, Garnett	60-90	
Derleth, August	Country of the Hawk (1st {std}, 8vo, 192p, b/w, pep, DJ/1.75)	Aladdin	1952	Bjorklund, Lorence	50-85	
Derrick, Freda	Ark Book (1st, ob sm4to, ibds, unpag, p-o, color)	L: Blackie	[1920]	Derrick, Freda	130-200	
Desmond, Alice C.	Boys of the Andes (1st, 8vo, 56p, p-o, color, pep)	D.C. Heath	(1941)	Dobias, Frank	25-45	*
Desmond, Alice C.	Lucky Llama (1st {std}, 8vo, 62p, b/w, DJ/1.50)	Macmillan	1939	Bronson, Wilfrid	40-65	
Desmond, G.G.	The Other Side (1st, lg8vo, green cl, 196p, 4cp)	L: G. Richards	1903	Billinghurst, Percy	60-95	
Deutsch, Babette	Heroes of the Kalevala (1st, lg8vo, 238p, blue cl, 12pl, cep, DJ/2.50)	J. Messner	(1940)	Eichenberg, Fritz	50-80	
Deutsch, Babette	I Often Wish (1st, lg8vo, [60]p, fp 1-color, cep, DJ/4.00)	Funk/Wagnalls	(1966)	Cellini, Eva	30-50	R
Deutsch, Babette	It's a Secret! (1st {std}, sq12mo, 47p, 2-color, pep, DJ/1.00)	Harper	(1941)	Bayley, Dorothy	70-120	R
Deutsch, Babette	More Tales of Faraway Folk (1st {std}, 8vo, 93p, b/w, DJ/2.75)	Harper	(1963)	Domanska, Janina	30-50	R*
Deutsch, Babette	Tales of Faraway Folk (1st, 8vo, yellow cl, 68p, b/w, pep, DJ/2.25)	Harper	(1952)	Lorentowicz, Irena	60-100	
Deutsch, Babette	The Welcome (1st {std}, 8vo, 197p, blue cl, 9 fp b/w, DJ/2.00)	Harper	(1942)	Simont, Marc	100-165	R
Deutsch, Babette (tr)	Crocodile (1st AM, ob4to, 31p, b/w)	Lippincott	(1931)	Chukovsky, Korney	130-200	
Devlin, Wende	How Fletcher was Hatched (1st, sm4to, [39]p, ibds, color, pep, DJ/3.50)	Parents Mag. Pr.	(1969)	Devlin, W.& H.	30-50	
Devlin, Wende	Kiss for a Warthog (1st, 4to, 37p, color, DJ/4.95)	Van Nostrand	(1970)	Devlin, W.& H.	30-50	
Dewar, G.A.B.	Wild Life in Hampshire Highlands (1st, 8vo, teg, green/gilt, b/w, pep)	L: J.M. Dent	1899	Rackham, Arthur	125-200	
Dewey, Katharine F.	Star People (1st, 8vo, 232p, blue cl, fp b/w)	L: Longmans	1910	Comstock, Frances B.	50-85	
DiNoto, Andrea	Star Thief (1st {std}, 4to, [30]p, fp 2-color, pep, DJ/3.50)	Macmillan	1967	Lobel, Arnold	40-65	
Dickens, Charles	Barnaby Rudge (1st, 8vo, 637p, col frn, b/w)	Heritage Press	(1941)	Daugherty, James	25-45	*
Dickens, Charles	Battle of Life (1st, 12mo, gilt, 165p, teg, 8cp)	L: J.M. Dent	1907	Brock, Charles E.	50-85	
Dickens, Charles	Boots of the Holly Tree Inn (8vo, red/gilt, pep, 44p, col frn, b/w)	Harper	1928	Lawson, Marie A.	35-60	*
Dickens, Charles	Boys and Girls from Dickens (1st, lg8vo, 277p, 7pl, pep)	Macaulay	1910	Coll, Joseph C.	80-125	
Dickens, Charles	Captain Boldheart & Magic Fishbone (1st {std}, 8vo, [48]p, col, DJ/3.50)	Macmillan	(1964)	Knight, Hilary	60-90	
Dickens, Charles	Christmas Carol (1st, 4to, 121p, t-i frn, 23pl)	S.E. Cassino	1887	Gaugengigl, I.M.	100-160	*
Dickens, Charles	Christmas Carol (1st, sm8vo, 157p, teg, b/w pl)	Putnam	1900	Coburn, Frederick S.	30-50	*
Dickens, Charles	Christmas Carol (1st, 12mo, 158p, teg, 8cp)	Dent/Dutton	(1905)	Brock, Charles E.	40-65	
Dickens, Charles	Christmas Carol (1st, lg8vo, 198p, gilt, col frn, 9pl)	Baker/Taylor	(1905)	Williams, George A.	70-100	*
Dickens, Charles	Christmas Carol (8vo, AEG, blue cl)	Putnam	1907	Merrill, Frank T.	35-60	
Dickens, Charles	Christmas Carol (1st, 8vo, 48p, 6cp, pep)	Brewer/Barse	(1907)	Von Hofsten, H.	30-50	*
Dickens, Charles	Christmas Carol (1st, 4to, red/gilt, 116p, pep, 12 ticp)	L: Hodder	[1911]	Michael, A.C.	120-200	R
Dickens, Charles	Christmas Carol (1st, 12mo, 157p, tan cl, 12pl)	Rand/McNally	(1912)	Winter, Milo	40-60	*
Dickens, Charles	Christmas Carol (1st, 12mo, 113p, b/w)	L.C. Page	1913	Boog, Carle M.	30-50	
Dickens, Charles	Christmas Carol (1st AM, 8vo, 78p, 4cp)	Stokes	[1913]	Nichols, Spencer B.	40-60	*
Dickens, Charles	Christmas Carol (1st, 8vo, p-o, 153p, 8cp)	L: Simpkin	1914	Appleton, Honor C.	60-90	
Dickens, Charles	Christmas Carol (1st, 8vo, 130p, blue/gilt, teg, 12cp)	McKay	(1914)	Keller, Arthur I.	35-60	
Dickens, Charles	Christmas Carol (8vo, bds, p-o, 168p, 13 ticp)	Crowell	[1915]	Everett, Ethel	70-100	
Dickens, Charles	Christmas Carol (12mo, ipcb, p-o, color)	Reilly/Britton	1915	Neill, John R.	60-100	
Dickens, Charles	Christmas Carol (1st AM, 8vo, 146p, purple/gilt, 12cp, pep)	Lippincott	(1915)	Rackham, Arthur	250-400	
Dickens, Charles	Christmas Carol (1st, 8vo, olive/gilt, 147p, 12cp, pep)	L: Heinemann	(1915)	Rackham, Arthur	300-500	
Dickens, Charles	Christmas Carol (1st, sm8vo, 166p, gilt, 4cp, 15pl, pep)	Macmillan	1923	Bedford, Francis D.	60-90	
Dickens, Charles	Christmas Carol (1st, 8vo, 249p, blue/gilt, 7cp)	Saalfield	(1929)	Peat, Fern B.	60-90	
Dickens, Charles	Christmas Carol (1st AM, 8vo, red/gilt, 77p, 4cp)	Dodd	(1935)	Brock, Henry M.	60-90	*
Dickens, Charles	Christmas Carol (1st {std}, lg8vo, 132p, red/gilt, teg, cep, 12 fp color)	Winston	1938	Shinn, Everett	100-165	R*
Dickens, Charles	Christmas Carol (1st, 4to, ibds, 74p, 11 fp color, pep, DJ/1.00)	Grosset/Dunlap	(1939)	Young, William	40-65	
Dickens, Charles	Christmas Carol (1st, 12mo, ibds, [60]p, color)	McLoughlin	(1940)	Graef, Robert A.	30-50	*
Dickens, Charles	Christmas Carol (1st, 12mo, 148p, ipcb, uncut, color, DJ/2.00)	Holiday House	(1940)	Reed, Philip	50-85	
Dickens, Charles	Christmas Carol (1st {std}, 4to, 110p, dep, color, DJ/4.95)	World	(1961)	Searle, Ronald	25-40	
Dickens, Charles	Christmas in Dickens (1st, 8vo, 63p, ibds, color, pep, DJ/1.00)	Garden City	(1941)	Shinn, Everett	35-50	
Dickens, Charles	Christmas Stories from Dickens (4to, AEG, gilt, 12cp)	L: R. Tuck	[1898]	Brundage, Frances	180-240	
Dickens, Charles	Cricket on the Hearth (1st, sm8vo, teg, uncut, 174p, dep, cvr by..)	Putnam	1900	Armstrong, Margaret	30-50	
Dickens, Charles	Cricket on the Hearth (1st AM, 8vo, 182p, red/gilt, 8cp)	Harper	(1927)	Bedford, Francis D.	80-120	
Dickens, Charles	David Copperfield (1st, 4to, gilt, 572p, 20 ticp, pep)	Westminster Pr	(1911)	Reynolds, Frank	170-250	
Dickens, Charles	David Copperfield (1st, 12mo, 506p, b/w pl)	Macmillan	1925	Smith, Harriet S.	30-50	*
Dickens, Charles	David Copperfield (1st {std}, 8vo, 423p, color, DJ/3.50)	Winston	(1948)	Shinn, Everett	40-60	*
Dickens, Charles	Dickens' Children (1st, lg8vo, [48]p, gilt, p-o, teg, 10cp)	Scribner	1912	Smith, Jessie W.	170-240	

AUTHOR	TITLE	PUBLISHER	DATE	ARTIST	PRICE	LC
Dickens, Charles	Great Expectations (1st, lg8vo, 457p, 8cp)	Heritage Press	(1939)	Ardizzone, Edward	90-120	*
Dickens, Charles	Haunted Man (1st, 8vo, 184p, teg, vellum, 8cp)	Dent/Dutton	1907	Brock, Charles E.	70-120	
Dickens, Charles	Holly Tree Inn (1st, lg8vo, 139p, gilt, teg, 10cp)	Baker/Taylor	(1907)	Williams, George A.	60-90	
Dickens, Charles	Holly Tree... (1st AM, sm4to, green cloth, 192p, 30pl)	Scribner	(1925)	Shepard, Ernest H.	55-80	
Dickens, Charles	Life of Nicholas Nickleby (lg8vo, 711p, gilt, 16cp)	Dodd	1931	Brock, Charles E.	60-100	
Dickens, Charles	Life of Our Lord (1st, lg8vo, 125p, gilt, 12 color, pep)	Garden City	(1939)	Shinn, Everett	40-65	
Dickens, Charles	Magic Fishbone (1st, ob8vo, [40]p, ibds, 7cp, pep)	L: Warne	(1922)	Bedford, Francis D.	70-100	
Dickens, Charles	Magic Fishbone (1st, sm4to, ibds, 36p, color, DJ/2.50)	Vanguard Press	(1953)	Slobodkin, Louis	70-120	R
Dickens, Charles	Mr. Pickwick's Christmas (1st, lg8vo, p-o, AEG, 149p, 6cp)	Baker/Taylor	(1906)	Williams, George A.	60-90	
Dickens, Charles	Mr. Pickwick... (4to, red/gilt, 21 ticp)	(NY & Lon)	[1911]	Reynolds, Frank	170-250	
Dickens, Charles	Old Curiosity Shop (1st, 4to, 359p, teg, red/gilt, 21 ticp)	L: Hodder	[1912]	Reynolds, Frank	200-270	
Dickens, Charles	Old Curiosity Shop (1st, 12mo, 618p, col frn, 23 b/w)	Macrae Smith	(1925)	Green, C.	25-45	*
Dickens, Charles	Posthumous Papers of the Pickwick Club (1st, 2 vols, 4to, bds, color)	L: Chapman	1910	Aldin, Cecil	200-300	
Dickens, Charles	Posthumous Papers of the Pickwick Club (1st, 4to, gilt, 534p, 20 ticp)	Westminster Pr	(1912)	Reynolds, Frank	170-240	
Dickens, Charles	Posthumous Papers of the Pickwick Club (1st AM, lg8vo, 687p, 16cp, pep)	Dodd	1930	Brock, Charles E.	55-80	
Dickens, Charles	Tale of Two Cities (1st, lg8vo, teg, p-o, 362p, 10cp, pep)	Cosmopolitan	1921	Dunn, Harvey T.	75-120	
Dickens, Charles	The Chimes (1st, 12mo, teg, gilt, uncut, 167p, 8cp)	L: J.M. Dent	1906	Brock, Charles E.	40-60	*
Dickens, Charles	The Chimes (1st, lg8vo, p-o, 210p, col frn, 9pl)	Baker/Taylor	(1908)	Williams, George A.	40-60	*
Dickens, Charles	The Chimes (1st, 12mo, 189p, AEG, grey/gilt, 4cp, 11pl)	Putnam	1911	Coburn, Frederick S.	55-80	
Dickens, Charles	The Chimes (1st, 8vo, 137p, red/gilt, 7 ticp, pep)	L: Hodder	[1912]	Thomson, Hugh	200-300	
Dickerson, Mary A.	Wonderful Wishes of Jacky & Jean (1st, sm4to, 146p, 6cp)	Wessels	(1905)	Falls, Charles B.	100-165	*
Dickinson, Peter	Heartsease (1st AM {std}, 8vo, 223p, b/w, DJ/4.95)	Little/Brown	(1969)	Hales, Robert	30-50	
Dickson, George S.	Nursery Geography (1st, 8vo, 256p, white cl, 20cp, pep)	L: Jack	[1915]	Morrow, George	60-100	
Dickson, Maidie	Saga of the Sea-Swallow (1st, 8vo, 159p, gilt, teg, 4pl, cep)	A.D. Innes	1896	Batten/Fairbairn	80-140	
Dike, Helen	Stories from Great Metropolitan Operas (1st, lg8vo, 247p, 12cp, DJ/2.00)	Random	(1943)	Tenggren, Gustaf	30-50	
Diller, Angela	Story of Siegfried (1st, 4to, 33p, col frn)	Cape/Smith	(1931)	Ward, Lynd	70-100	
Dillon, Eilis	Cat's Opera (1st AM, 4to, 63p, fp b/w, DJ/2.75)	Bobbs-Merrill	(1963)	Vanecek, Kveta	30-50	
Dillon, Mary	The Leader (1st, 8vo, 362p, 4pl)	Doubleday/Page	1906	Hallock, Ruth M.	25-40	*
Dimmick, Ruth C.	Bogie Man (1st, lg8vo, ibds, [71]p, fp b/w)	Winston	(1906)	Neale, Marguerite	80-130	
Dines, Glen	Mysterious Machine (1st {std}, 8vo, 140p, b/w, pep, DJ/2.75)	Macmillan	(1957)	Dines, Glen	20-30	
Dines, Glen	Tiger in the Cherry Tree (1st {std}, 4to, unpag, color, DJ/2.50)	Macmillan	(1958)	Dines, Glen	40-65	
Dines, Glen	Useful Dragon of Sam Ling Toy (1st {std}, 4to, ibds, unpag, col, DJ/2.75)	Macmillan	(1956)	Dines, Glen	60-100	
Diska, Pat	Andy Says... Bonjour! (1st, 4to, [46]p, fp 1-color, pep, DJ/2.50, NYTBI)	Vanguard Press	(1954)	Jenkyns, Chris	30-50	R
Disney, Walt	40 Big Pages of Mickey Mouse (folio, wraps, color)	Whitman	(1936)	Disney Studios	125-200	*
Disney, Walt	ABC Mickey Mouse Alphabet Book (1st, lg8vo, [32]p, color, pep)	Whitman	(1936)	Disney Studios	170-240	*
Disney, Walt	Adventures of Mickey Mouse (1st UK [this fmt.], 12mo, ibds, [32]p, color)	L: Harrap	(1931)	Disney Studios	400-600	
Disney, Walt	Adventures of Mickey Mouse Book # 2 (1st, 8vo, [32]p, ibds, pep, color)	McKay	(1932)	Disney Studios	300-450	
Disney, Walt	Animals from Snow White & the Seven Dwarfs (4to, stiff wrps, 11 fp color)	Whitman	1938	Disney Studios	140-200	
Disney, Walt	Ave Maria (1st, 4to, blue/gilt, [32]p, color, pep)	Random	(1940)	Disney Studios	140-200	
Disney, Walt	Bambi Picture Book (folio, [12]p, linen wraps, color)	Whitman	1942	Disney Studios	120-200	
Disney, Walt	Big Bad Wolf & Little Red Riding Hood (1st, 4to, ipcb, 60p, color)	Blue Ribbon	(1934)	Disney Studios	250-350	
Disney, Walt	Bongo (1st {std}, folio, [26]p, ibds, color, GGB)	Simon/Schuster	(1947)	Starr, Edgar	60-90	
Disney, Walt	Cold-Blooded Penguin (1st {std}, sm8vo, ibds, [24]p, pep, color, LGB/#D2)	Simon/Schuster	1944	Disney Studios	40-65	
Disney, Walt	Come Play with Donald Duck (1st, 8vo, ibds, [32]p, fp color, pep)	Grosset/Dunlap	(1948)	Disney Studios	80-130	
Disney, Walt	Come Play with Mickey Mouse (1st, 8vo, ibds, [32]p, fp color, pep)	Grosset/Dunlap	(1948)	Disney Studios	80-130	
Disney, Walt	Country Cousin (1st, 4to, ibds, [20]p, color)	McKay	1937	Disney Studios	100-150	*
Disney, Walt	Dance of the Hours (1st {std}, lg8vo, ibds, [36]p, color, pep)	Harper	(1940)	Disney Studios	140-200	
Disney, Walt	Disney's Bambi (1st, 4to, [52]p, ibds, color)	Simon/Schuster	(1941)	Disney Studios	80-140	
Disney, Walt	Disney's Bambi (8vo, [32]p, color, pep)	Grosset/Dunlap	(1942)	Disney Studios	75-100	
Disney, Walt	Disney's Bambi (8vo, 101p, color)	D.C. Heath	(1944)	Disney Studios	50-80	*
Disney, Walt	Disney's Cinderella (1st, folio, ibds, [26]p, color, GGB)	Simon/Schuster	(1950)	Disney Studios	90-160	
Disney, Walt	Disney's Cinderella (8vo, [34]p, color, pep)	Whitman	1950	Disney Studios	80-120	*
Disney, Walt	Disney's Davy Crockett (1st, 4to, ibds, 48p, color, pep, BGB/#435)	Simon/Schuster	(1955)	Disney Studios	60-90	*
Disney, Walt	Disney's Dumbo (1st, lg ob8vo, wraps, [12]p, color)	Disney Prod.	1941	Disney Studios	170-240	*
Disney, Walt	Disney's Dumbo (1st {this pub}, 8vo, ibds, [42]p, color, LGB/#D3)	Simon/Schuster	(1947)	Disney Studios	30-50	
Disney, Walt	Disney's Forest Friends (lg8vo, [28]p, ibds, color, pep)	Grosset/Dunlap	(1938)	Disney Studios	100-170	*
Disney, Walt	Disney's Lady & the Tramp (1st, folio, unpag, ipcb, color, BGB)	Simon/Schuster	(1955)	Disney Studios	100-165	*
Disney, Walt	Disney's Pedro (1st, 8vo, [32]p, ipcb, color, pep)	A.& W. Guild	1943	Disney Studios	70-100	*
Disney, Walt	Disney's Perri (1st, folio, ibds, [24]p, color, pep, GGB)	Simon/Schuster	(1957)	Kelsey, D.	120-180	*
Disney, Walt	Disney's Peter Pan (1st, folio, ipcb, unpag, color, GGB)	Simon/Schuster	1952	Disney Studios	100-160	*
Disney, Walt	Disney's Pinocchio (1st, 4to, ibds, [76]p, color, pep)	Random	1939	Disney Studios	250-400	R
Disney, Walt	Disney's Pinocchio (folio, [12]p, color)	Whitman	(1940)	Disney Studios	80-120	*
Disney, Walt	Disney's Pinocchio (1st {this pub}, folio, ipcb, color, BGB)	Simon/Schuster	(1954)	Disney Studios	120-200	*
Disney, Walt	Disney's Surprise Package (1st, sm4to, ibds, 92p, color, pep, GGB)	Simon/Schuster	1944	Disney Studios	100-165	
Disney, Walt	Disney's Thumper (1st, 8vo, [32]p, ipcb, color, pep)	Grosset/Dunlap	(1942)	Disney Studios	100-170	*
Disney, Walt	Disney's Tonka (1st, 8vo, ipcb, 60p, color, pep)	Golden Press	(1959)	Greene, Hamilton	90-160	*
Disney, Walt	Disney's Version of Pinocchio (ob8vo, [48]p, color, pep)	Grosset/Dunlap	1939	Disney Studios	100-145	*
Disney, Walt	Disney's Version of Pinocchio (sq12mo, [24]p, color)	Whitman	(1940)	Disney Studios	100-160	*
Disney, Walt	Donald Duck (1st, folio, wraps, [14]p, color)	Whitman	1935	Disney Studios	600-900	R
Disney, Walt	Donald Duck (4to, ibds, [33]p, color, pep)	Grosset/Dunlap	(1936)	Disney Studios	300-500	*
Disney, Walt	Donald Duck & his Friends (1st, 4to, ipcb, 45p, b/w, pep)	Whitman	1937	Disney Studios	170-240	*
Disney, Walt	Donald Duck Days (1st, 8vo, ibds, 2-color)	L: Birn Bros.	(1937)	Disney Studios	200-300	
Disney, Walt	Donald Duck has his Ups & Downs (lg8vo, wraps, 24p, color)	Whitman	(1937)	Disney Studios	170-240	*
Disney, Walt	Donald Duck his Story Book (1st, 4to, ipcb, 46p, pep, b/w)	Whitman	1937	Disney Studios	120-180	*
Disney, Walt	Donald Duck in High Andes (1st, 8vo, [32]p, color)	A.& W. Guild	1943	Disney Studios	120-200	*
Disney, Walt	Donald Duck Off the Beam (1st [Big-Little], 32mo, 425p, ibds)	Whitman	(1943)	Disney Studios	120-180	*
Disney, Walt	Donald Duck Sees South America (1st, 8vo, 138p, maps, color, pep)	D.C. Heath	(1945)	Disney Studios	60-100	
Disney, Walt	Donald Duck Treasury (1st, lg8vo, 116p)	Golden Press	1960	Disney Studios	80-120	*

AUTHOR	TITLE	PUBLISHER	DATE	ARTIST	PRICE	LC
Disney, Walt	Donald's Lucky Day (1st, ob4to, wraps, [20]p, fp color)	Whitman	(1939)	Disney Studios	200-300	
Disney, Walt	Donald's Penguin (1st, sm4to, ibds, [24]p, pep, color)	Garden City	1940	Disney Studios	100-170	*
Disney, Walt	Dopey: He Don't Talk None (1st, sm folio, wraps, [12]p, color)	Whitman	1938	Disney Studios	150-225	
Disney, Walt	Dumbo of the Circus (1st, sq4to, ibds, [52]p, color, pep)	Garden City	(1941)	Disney Studios	200-300	
Disney, Walt	Dumbo of the Circus (1st {this pub}, 8vo, 90p, color, pep)	D.C. Heath	(1948)	Disney Studios	75-100	*
Disney, Walt	Elmer Elephant (1st, 8vo, ibds, 46p, color)	McKay	(1936)	Disney Studios	200-300	
Disney, Walt	Elmer Elephant (folio, wraps, [10]p, fp color, linen)	Whitman	1938	Disney Studios	180-250	
Disney, Walt	Figaro and Cleo (1st, 8vo, ibds, [27]p, color, pep)	Random	1940	Disney Studios	120-200	
Disney, Walt	Golden Touch (1st, 8vo, ibds, 212p, 6cp, pep)	Whitman	(1937)	Disney Studios	120-200	
Disney, Walt	Hiawatha (1st, 4to, ibds, [20]p, fp color, pep)	McKay	1937	Disney Studios	125-200	
Disney, Walt	Honest John & Giddy (1st, 8vo, [24]p, ibds, color, pep)	Random	1940	Disney Studios	80-120	
Disney, Walt	Jiminy Cricket (1st, 8vo, ibds, [24]p, color, pep)	Random	1940	Disney Studios	120-200	
Disney, Walt	Life of Donald Duck (1st, 4to, ibds, 72p, color, pep)	Random	(1941)	Disney Studios	200-300	
Disney, Walt	Little Red Riding Hood & Big Bad Wolf (1st, 8vo, 32p, wraps, fp b/w)	McKay	(1934)	Disney Studios	200-300	
Disney, Walt	Little Wise Hen (1st, ob4to, 48p, ibds, 9 fp color)	Whitman	(1934)	Disney Studios	170-240	
Disney, Walt	Magnificent Mr. Toad (1st, 4to, [32]p, color)	Grosset/Dunlap	(1949)	Disney Studios	150-220	
Disney, Walt	Mickey & the Beanstalk (1st, 8vo, ipcb, [32]p, color, pep)	Grosset/Dunlap	(1947)	Disney Studios	100-160	*
Disney, Walt	Mickey Mouse (1st {Big-Little}, 32mo, ibds, 316p, b/w)	Whitman	1933	Disney Studios	120-200	*
Disney, Walt	Mickey Mouse & his Friends (1st, lg4to, [10]p, wraps, 8cp)	Whitman	(1936)	Disney Studios	200-300	
Disney, Walt	Mickey Mouse & his Friends (1st {this pub}, 8vo, 102p, color)	NY: Nelson	1937	Disney Studios	80-120	*
Disney, Walt	Mickey Mouse & his Horse Tanglefoot (1st, 8vo, ibds, 60p, color)	McKay	(1936)	Disney Studios	300-450	
Disney, Walt	Mickey Mouse & Mail Pilot (1st {Big-Little}, 32mo, ibds, 296p, b/w)	Whitman	1933	Disney Studios	120-200	*
Disney, Walt	Mickey Mouse & Pluto (1st, sm4to, ibds [66]p, 1-color, pep)	Whitman	1936	Disney Studios	250-400	
Disney, Walt	Mickey Mouse ABC Story (1st, 8vo, ipcb, [31]p, color, pep)	Whitman	(1937)	Disney Studios	250-400	
Disney, Walt	Mickey Mouse Air Pilot (1st, 8vo, ibds, 2-color)	L: Birn Bros.	(1937)	Disney Studios	220-320	
Disney, Walt	Mickey Mouse Alphabet ABC (folio, [16]p, linen wraps, color)	W. Disney Prod.	1938	Disney Studios	300-400	
Disney, Walt	Mickey Mouse Alphabet from A to Z (4to, ibds, [32]p, color)	Whitman	(1936)	Disney Studios	250-350	
Disney, Walt	Mickey Mouse Alphabet from A to Z (4to, ibds, [32]p, 1-color)	L: Collins	[1936]	Disney Studios	200-300	
Disney, Walt	Mickey Mouse at the Circus (1st UK, 4to, ibds, color)	L: Birn Bros.	(1937)	Disney Studios	200-300	
Disney, Walt	Mickey Mouse Birthday Book (1st, 4to, ibds, 64p, color, BGB/#482)	Simon/Schuster	(1953)	Disney Studios	60-100	*
Disney, Walt	Mickey Mouse Crusoe (1st, 8vo, stiff wraps, 71p, col frn, b/w)	Whitman	(1936)	Disney Studios	150-250	
Disney, Walt	Mickey Mouse Fire Brigade (1st, 4to, ibds, color)	Whitman	1936	Disney Studios	250-350	
Disney, Walt	Mickey Mouse Fire Brigade (1st UK, ibds, 77p, b/w)	L: Collins	1936	Disney Studios	180-270	
Disney, Walt	Mickey Mouse has a Busy Day (1st, sq4to, wraps, 16p, color)	Whitman	(1937)	Disney Studios	140-240	
Disney, Walt	Mickey Mouse has a Party (1st, lg8vo, wraps, 48p, 2-color)	Whitman	1938	Disney Studios	200-300	
Disney, Walt	Mickey Mouse in Giantland (1st UK, 8vo, 93p, ibds, color)	L: Collins	(1934)	Disney Studios	300-500	
Disney, Walt	Mickey Mouse in Giantland (1st, 8vo, 45p, p-o, fp color, pep)	McKay	(1934)	Disney Studios	350-550	
Disney, Walt	Mickey Mouse in King Arthur's Court (1st, lg8vo, 48p, color)	Blue Ribbon	(1933)	Disney Studios	100-150	R*
Disney, Walt	Mickey Mouse in Pigmy Land (1st, 4to, ipcb, 71p, col frn, b/w)	Whitman	1936	Disney Studios	200-300	*
Disney, Walt	Mickey Mouse Movie Stories (1st, 8vo, gilt, 190p, p-o, b/w)	McKay	(1931)	Disney Studios	450-600	R
Disney, Walt	Mickey Mouse on Tour (8vo, ibds, 1-color)	L: Birn Bros.	(1935)	Disney Studios	200-300	
Disney, Walt	Mickey Mouse Presents Father Noah's Ark (1st, lg8vo, ibds, color)	L: Birn Bros.	(1934)	Disney Studios	180-250	
Disney, Walt	Mickey Mouse Story Book (1st, 8vo, 62p, wraps, b/w)	McKay	(1931)	Disney Studios	350-500	
Disney, Walt	Mickey Mouse the Boat-Builder (1st, ob8vo, [28]p, ibds, color, pep)	Grosset/Dunlap	1938	Disney Studios	250-400	
Disney, Walt	Mickey Mouse Waddle Book (1st, sm4to, ibds, [33]p, color, pep)	Blue Ribbon	(1934)	Disney Studios	300-500	
Disney, Walt	Mickey's Clock (1st, 4to, ibds, 76p, 1-color)	L: Collins	1938	Disney Studios	250-400	
Disney, Walt	Nursery Stories from Silly Symphony (1st, 8vo, 212p, ibds, 6cp, pep)	Whitman	(1937)	Disney Studios	160-240	
Disney, Walt	Nutcracker Suite (1st, lg sq4to, ibds, [72]p, color, pep)	Little/Brown	1940	Disney Studios	125-200	
Disney, Walt	Our Friend the Atom (1st, 4to, 166p, color, GGB)	Simon/Schuster	(1956)	Disney Studios	100-165	
Disney, Walt	Pastoral (1st {std}, lg8vo, [36]p, color, pep)	Harper	(1940)	Disney Studios	120-180	
Disney, Walt	Peculiar Penguins (1st, 8vo, 45p, red cl, p-o, color, pep)	McKay	(1934)	Disney Studios	250-400	
Disney, Walt	Pinocchio Picture Book (lg4to, wraps, color, shape bk.)	Whitman	1940	Disney Studios	170-240	*
Disney, Walt	Pinocchio Picture Book (lg4to, [14]p, wraps, color)	Grosset/Dunlap	(1940)	Disney Studios	140-220	R*
Disney, Walt	Pluto & the Puppy (1st, 4to, ibds, [36]p, color, pep)	Grosset/Dunlap	(1937)	Disney Studios	160-240	
Disney, Walt	Practical Pig (1st, lg sq8vo, ibds, [24]p, color, pep)	Garden City	1940	Disney Studios	170-240	
Disney, Walt	Princess Elizabeth Gift Book (1st, lg8vo, white cl, 224p, color)	L: Hodder	[1933]	Disney Studios	80-130	
Disney, Walt	Robber Kitten (1st, ob4to, ipcb, 46p, 9 fp color, pep)	McKay	(1935)	Disney Studios	200-300	
Disney, Walt	Runaway Lamb at County Fair (1st, sm4to, ipcb, [31]p, color)	Grosset/Dunlap	(1949)	Disney Studios	80-120	*
Disney, Walt	Santa's Workshop (1st UK, 8vo, 124p, 8cp)	L: Collins	1934	Disney Studios	180-250	
Disney, Walt	Snow White & Seven Dwarfs (lg4to, ibds, 80p, color)	Grosset/Dunlap	(1937)	Disney Studios	250-400	
Disney, Walt	Snow White & Seven Dwarfs (1st {this pub}, sq4to, ibds, color)	McKay	1937	Disney Studios	300-500	
Disney, Walt	Snow White & Seven Dwarfs (1st, ob8vo, ipcb, [36]p, color)	Grosset/Dunlap	(1938)	Disney Studios	200-300	
Disney, Walt	Snow White & Seven Dwarfs (1st, 12mo, 63p, ibds, 14 color)	Whitman	(1938)	Disney Studios	200-300	
Disney, Walt	Snow White & Seven Dwarfs (folio, 12p, wraps, color)	Whitman	1938	Disney Studios	400-600	R
Disney, Walt	Snow White & the Seven Dwarfs (1st UK, lg4to, 80p, ibds, color)	L: Collins	(1938)	Disney Studios	185-265	
Disney, Walt	Sorcerer's Apprentice (1st, ob8vo, ibds, 34p, color, pep)	Grosset/Dunlap	(1940)	Disney Studios	200-300	
Disney, Walt	Stories from Fantasia (narrow 4to, [movie ed.], [72]p, ibds, color, pep)	Random	(1940)	Disney Studios	90-145	
Disney, Walt	Story of Casey Jr. (1st, lg8vo, ibds, [26]p, 4 fp color, pep)	Garden City	(1941)	Disney Studios	120-180	
Disney, Walt	Story of Timothy's House (1st, sm4to, ibds, [28]p, color, pep)	Garden City	(1941)	Disney Studios	140-200	
Disney, Walt	Three Little Pigs (1st, sm4to, ibds, 62p, 12 color, pep)	Blue Ribbon	(1933)	Disney Studios	200-350	R
Disney, Walt	Three Orphan Kittens (1st, ob4to, ibds, [46]p, 9 color)	McKay	(1935)	Disney Studios	160-240	
Disney, Walt	Through the Picture Frame (1st, sq8vo, [24]p, ibds, color, LGB/#D1)	Simon/Schuster	1944	Disney Studios	40-65	*
Disney, Walt	Thumper (1st, 8vo, [32]p, ibds, color)	Grosset/Dunlap	(1942)	Disney Studios	60-90	
Disney, Walt	Timid Elmer (1st, sq24mo, ipcb, 64p, b/w)	Whitman	1939	Disney Studios	100-165	
Disney, Walt	Tortoise & the Hare (1st, ob4to, ibds, 48p, 9 fp color)	McKay	(1935)	Disney Studios	200-300	*
Disney, Walt	Walt Disney Parade (1st, 4to, 176p, color, pep)	Garden City	(1940)	Disney Studios	120-200	*
Disney, Walt	Walt Disney's Circus (1st, 4to, [28]p, color, pep)	Simon/Schuster	1944	Disney Studios	160-225	
Disney, Walt	Walt Disney's Clock Cleaners (folio, wraps, [5]p, color)	Whitman	1938	Disney Studios	180-250	

AUTHOR	TITLE	PUBLISHER	DATE	ARTIST	PRICE	LC
Disney, Walt	Walt Disney's Pedro (1st, 8vo, ipcb, [32]p, color, pep)	A.& W. Guild	1943	Disney Studios	80-130	
Disney, Walt	Walt Disney's Sleeping Beauty (1st, folio, ibds, 57p, color, GGB/#757)	Simon/Schuster	(1957)	(Photos)	100-165	
Disney, Walt	Water Babies' Circus (8vo, 78p, color pep)	D.C. Heath	(1940)	Disney Studios	80-130	
Disney, Walt	Who's Afraid of the Big Bad Wolf (1st, 12mo, wraps, 31p, b/w)	McKay	(1933)	Disney Studios	125-200	
Disney, Walt	Wise Little Hen (1st, ob4to, 48p, fp color)	McKay	(1934)	Disney Studios	200-300	*
Disney, Walt	Wise Little Hen (1st {this fmt}, folio, [8]p, wraps, color)	Disney Prod.	(1937)	Disney Studios	200-300	*
Disney, Walt	Wonderful Tar Baby (1st, 8vo, ipcb, [32]p, color, pep)	Grosset/Dunlap	(1946)	Disney Studios	90-160	*
Disston, Harry	Riding Rhymes for Young Readers (1st, 4to, ibds, 67p, b/w, DJ/2.75)	B. Wheelright	1951	Brown, Paul	70-125	
Dix, Beulah M.	Betty-Bide-at-Home (1st, sm8vo, 236p, b/w pl)	Henry Holt & Co.	1912	Avery, Faith	30-50	*
Dix, Beulah M.	Hugh Gwyeth: Roundhead Cavalier (1st, 12mo, pep, b/w)	Macmillan	1928	Daugherty, James	35-60	*
Dix, Beulah M.	Little Captive Lad (1st, sm8vo, 286p, b/w pl)	Macmillan	1902	Grefe, Will	25-40	
Dix, Beulah M.	Merrylips (1st, sm8vo, 307p, 8pl, PPPa)	Macmillan	1906	Merrill, Frank T.	125-200	*
Dix, Dorothy	Fables of the Elite (1st, 12mo, teg, 261p, b/w pl)	Fenno	1902	Swinnerton, James	70-125	*
Dix, Dorothy	Mirandy (1st, 12mo, brown cl, 256p, 21pl)	Hearst	1914	Kemble, Edward W.	80-125	
Dixon, Charles	Fifteen Hundred Miles an Hour (1st, 8vo, 313p, blue/gilt, AEG, 6pl)	L: Bliss Sands	1895	Layard, Arthur	250-400	
Dixon, E. (ed)	Fairy Tales from Arabian Nights (1st AM, 8vo, 477p, gilt, p-o, col frn)	Putnam	(1893)	Batten, John D.	100-165	
Dixon, E. (ed)	Fairy Tales from Arabian Nights (1st, sm4to, 267p, gilt, teg, 5pl)	L: J.M. Dent	1893	Batten, John D.	120-180	
Dixon, E. (ed)	Fairy Tales from Arabian Nights (1st, 8vo, 477p, col frn, 16pl)	L: J.M. Dent	1907	Batten, John D.	100-175	
Dixon, Maynard	Injun Babies (1st, 8vo, 72p, p-o, 7cp, pep)	Putnam	(1923)	Dixon, Maynard	70-100	
Dixon, Royal	Human Side of Birds (1st, 8vo, 246p, green cl, p-o, 4 ticp)	Stokes	(1917)	Wainwright, S.H.	40-65	
Dixon, Thomas	Fall of a Nation (1st, 12mo, red/gilt, 362p, 6pl)	Appleton	1916	Wrenn, Charles	40-65	
Dixon, Thomas	Foolish Virgin (1st, sm8vo, 352p, b/w pl)	Appleton	1915	Tittle, Walter	30-45	*
Dixon, Thomas	Leopard's Spots (1st, sm8vo, bds, teg, gilt, 465p, 8pl)	Doubleday/Page	1902	Williams, C.D.	50-80	
Dixon, Thomas	Life Worth Living (1st, 8vo, 140p, b/w, teg)	Doubleday/Page	1905	(Photos)	30-50	
Dixon, Thomas	The Clansman (1st, 8vo, 374p, red cl, b/w)	Doubleday/Page	1905	Keller, Arthur I.	50-80	
Dixon, Thomas	The One Woman (1st, 8vo, 350p, teg, red/gilt, 8pl)	Doubleday/Page	1903	Clinedinst, B. West	50-80	
Dixon, Thomas	The Traitor (1st, 8vo, red cl, 331p, 4cp)	Doubleday/Page	1907	Williams, C.D.	45-70	
Djurklou, Baron G.	Fairy Tales from Sweedish (1st UK, 8vo, gilt, 178p, 20 fp b/w)	L: Heinemann	1901	Various	125-200	
Doane, Pelagie	Animals Here and There (1st {std}, 4to, ipcb, [48]p, color, DJ/0.50)	Doubleday/Doran	1945	Doane, Pelagie	50-80	
Doane, Pelagie	Book of Nature (1st {std}, 4to, 110p, fp color, DJ/4.00)	Oxford U. Pr.	1952	Doane, Pelagie	30-45	
Doane, Pelagie	One Rainy Night (1st, 16mo, [32]p, color, cep, DJ/2.00)	Oxford U. Pr.	1957	Doane, Pelagie	30-50	
Doane, Pelagie	Small Child's Bible (1st, 4to, 142p, fp color, DJ/3.00)	Oxford U. Pr.	1946	Doane, Pelagie	30-50	
Doane, Pelagie	Small Child's Book of Verse (1st, 4to, 142p, fp color, DJ/3.00)	Oxford U. Pr.	1948	Doane, Pelagie	25-45	
Doane, Pelagie	The Boy Jesus (1st, sm4to, 54p, fp color, DJ/3.00)	NY: Oxford U.Pr.	1953	Doane, Pelagie	30-55	
Doane, Pelagie (ed)	Littlest Ones (1st, 12mo, [32]p, color, DJ/1.75)	Oxford U. Pr.	1956	Doane, Pelagie	30-45	*
Dobbs, Rose	No Room (1st, sm8vo, [48]p, ibds, b/w, DJ/1.50)	Coward	(1944)	Eichenberg, Fritz	30-50	
Dobbs, Rose	Once Upon a Time (1st, 8vo, 117p, b/w, DJ/2.00)	Random	(1950)	Gag, Flavia	25-45	
Dobbs, Rose	Once-Upon-a-Time Story Book (1st, 4to, 63p, ibds, color, pep, DJ/1.00)	Random	(1958)	Hodges, C. Walter	30-50	
Dobias, Dorathea F.	Casey Joins the Circus (1st, sq8vo, ibds, [33]p, color, pep)	Grosset/Dunlap	(1936)	Dobias, Dorathea	55-80	*
Dobias, Frank	Picture Book of Flying (1st, 4to, 64p, fp color, pep, DJ/2.00)	Macmillan	1928	Dobias, Frank	80-125	
Dobrin, Arnold	Gerbils (1st, lg8vo, 63p, DJ/3.75)	Lothrop, Lee	(1970)	Dobrin, Arnold	25-40	*
Dobrin, Arnold	Snow Fox (1st, ob4to, [32]p, fp 2-color, DJ/3.50)	Coward	1968	Dobrin, Arnold	30-45	*
Dobson, Austin	Ballad of Beau Brocade (1st, 8vo, 89p, uncut, gilt, teg, b/w)	L: Kegan Paul	1892	Thomson, Hugh	70-100	
Dobson, Austin	Coridon's Song (1st, 12mo, green/gilt, AEG, 163p, b/w, cep)	L: Macmillan	1894	Thomson, Hugh	100-170	
Dobson, Austin	Proverbs in Porcelain (1st, sq8vo, gilt, teg, 112p, uncut, fp b/w)	L: Kegan Paul	1893	Partridge, J.B.	80-125	
Dobson, Austin	Story of Rosina (1st, sm8vo, AEG, 120p, gilt, 28pl, cep)	L: Kegan Paul	1895	Thomson, Hugh	75-100	
Dobson, L.	Poems by Dobson, Locker & Praed (lg4to, p-o, gilt, 6cp)	Stokes	1892	Humphrey, Maud	400-650	
Dodd, Anna B.	On the Broads (1st, 8vo, 331p, gilt, teg, 24 fp b/w)	L: Macmillan	1896	Pennell, Joseph	70-120	
Dodge, Louis	Everychild (1st, 8vo, 284p, pep, uncut, 6cp)	Scribner	1921	Laite, B.F.	30-50	
Dodge, Louis	Sandman's Forest (1st, 8vo, 293p, p-o, green/gilt, pep, 6cp)	Scribner	1918	Bransom, Paul	80-120	
Dodge, Louis	Sandman's Mountain (1st, 8vo, 278p, green/gilt, pep, 6cp)	Scribner	1920	Bransom, Paul	80-120	
Dodge, Mary Mapes	Hans Brinker (1st, 8vo, 393p, blue cl, cvr by...)	Scribner	1896	Armstrong, Margaret	35-60	
Dodge, Mary Mapes	Hans Brinker (1st, 8vo, 380p, gilt, p-o, teg, 8cp, pep)	Scribner	1915	Edwards, George W.	60-90	
Dodge, Mary Mapes	Hans Brinker (1st, 8vo, 239p, p-o, color, pep)	Whitman	(1917)	Carsey, Alice	40-65	
Dodge, Mary Mapes	Hans Brinker (1st, lg8vo, p-o, teg, 345p, 8cp, pep)	McKay	1918	Enright, Maginel W.	70-120	R
Dodge, Mary Mapes	Hans Brinker (1st, 8vo, 320p, p-o, color, pep)	Whitman	1929	Higgins, Violet M.	45-70	
Dodge, Mary Mapes	Hans Brinker (1st, 8vo, 305p, p-o, 4cp, pep)	Garden City	1932	Hurd, Peter	50-80	
Dodge, Mary Mapes	Hans Brinker (1st, 8vo, 289p, 10cp, pep)	Grosset/Dunlap	(1945)	Baldridge, Cyrus L.	30-50	
Dodge, Mary Mapes	Hans Brinker (1st, 8vo, 335p, color, DJ/1.25, RC)	World	(1946)	Van Stockum, Hilda	20-30	*
Dodge, Mary Mapes	Hans Brinker (1st [Jr. Deluxe], 8vo, 319p, col frn, b/w)	Doubleday	(1954)	Galdone, Paul	30-45	
Dodge, Mary Mapes	Hans Brinker (1st, 8vo, 345p, DJ/3.50)	Scribner	(1958)	Spier, Peter E.	30-50	*
Dodge, Mary Mapes	Land of Pluck (1st, sm8vo, 313p, gilt, teg, b/w)	Century	1894	Various	55-80	
Dodge, Mary Mapes	Rhymes & Jingles (1st, sm8vo, gilt, teg, uncut, 222p, b/w)	Scribner	1904	Stilwell, Sarah	90-120	
Dodge, Mary Mapes	When Life is Young (1st, 12mo, green/gilt, teg, 255p, b/w)	Century	1894	Various	35-60	
Dodge, Theodore A.	Riders of Many Lands (1st, lg8vo, 486p, brown/gilt, teg, b/w)	Harper	1894	Remington, Frederic	120-200	
Dodson, Kenneth	Hector the Stowaway Dog (1st {std}, 8vo, 144p, b/w, DJ/3.00)	Little/Brown	(1958)	Spier, Peter E.	30-50	*
Dodworth, Dorothy	Dangerous Day for Mrs. Doodlepunk (1st, ob8vo, unpag, 1-color, DJ/1.50)	W.R. Scott	(1954)	Dodworth, Dorothy	30-45	
Dodworth, Dorothy	Mrs. Doodlepunk Trades Work (1st, ob8vo, red cl, [48]p, 1-color, DJ/2.25)	W.R. Scott	1957	Dodworth, Dorothy	30-50	
Dolbier, Maurice	Jenny: Bus that Nobody Loved (1st, 4to, 43p, ipcb, color, pep, DJ/1.25)	Random	1944	Gergely, Tibor	45-70	
Dolbier, Maurice	Lion in the Woods (1st {std}, 8vo, 114p, b/w, DJ/2.75)	Little/Brown	(1955)	Henneberger, Rbt.	20-30	
Dolbier, Maurice	Magic Bus (1st, lg8vo, 43p, ibds, color)	Wonder Books	1948	Gergely, Tibor	25-45	
Dolbier, Maurice	Magic Shop (1st, 8vo, 74p, ipcb, 1-color, DJ/1.75)	Random	(1946)	Eichenberg, Fritz	45-70	
Dolbier, Maurice	Torten's Christmas Secret (1st {std}, lg8vo, 62p, 2-color, DJ/2.50)	Little/Brown	1951	Henneberger, Rbt.	30-50	
Dole, Nathan H.	Russian Fairy Book (1st UK, 8vo, 126p, pep, 16cp)	L: Richards	1908	Bilibin, Ivan	450-600	
Dolson, Hildegarde	Sorry to Be So Cheerful (1st {std}, 8vo, 207p, b/w, DJ/3.50)	Random	(1955)	Galdone, Paul	30-50	*
Domanska, Janina	Look: There is a Turtle Flying (1st {std}, 4to, [32]p, color, DJ/4.50)	Macmillan	(1968)	Domanska, Janina	25-40	
Domanska, Janina	Marilka (1st {std}, 8vo, [32]p, color, dep, DJ/4.95)	Macmillan	(1970)	Domanska, Janina	25-40	
Domanska, Janina	Palmiero and the Ogre (1st {std}, ob4to, [32]p, 2-color, DJ/3.95)	Macmillan	(1967)	Domanska, Janina	30-45	

AUTHOR	TITLE	PUBLISHER	DATE	ARTIST	PRICE	LC
Domanska, Janina	The Turnip (1st {std}, ob4to, [32]p, color, DJ/4.95)	Macmillan	(1969)	Domanska, Janina	25-40	
Domanska, Janina	Why So Much Noise? (1st, 8vo, ibds, [32]p, 2-color, DJ/2.50)	Harper	(1965)	Domanska, Janina	25-40	
Donahey, Mary D.	Adventure of a Happy Dolly (4to, p-o, 123p, 5cp)	Barse/Hopkins	(1914)	Evans, G.	80-125	
Donahey, Mary D.	Castle of Grumpy Grouch (1st, sm4to, 150p, color)	Stern	1908	Clay, John Cecil	100-165	
Donahey, Mary D.	Down Spider Web Lane (1st, sm4to, p-o, 130p, 6cp)	Stern	1909	Kay, Gertrude A.	100-150	
Donahey, Mary D.	Magical House of Zur (1st, 4to, 124p, p-o, 6cp)	Barse/Hopkins	(1914)	Wireman, Eugenie	100-165	
Donahey, Mary D.	Peter & Prue... (1st, sm8vo, 258p, p-o, 5cp, pep)	Rand/McNally	(1924)	Gaze, Harold	140-200	
Donahey, Mary D.	Prince Without a Country (1st, sm4to, p-o, 125p, 6cp)	Barse/Hopkins	(1916)	Carlson, George	50-80	
Donahey, Mary D.	Talking Bird & Wonderful Wishes (1st, lg8vo, p-o, 146p, 6cp, pep)	Whitman	(1920)	Falls, Charles B.	200-300	
Donahey, Mary D.	Through the Little Green Door (1st, sm8vo, 176p, p-o, 3cp)	Stern	1910	Kay, Gertrude A.	100-150	*
Donahey, William	Adventures of the Teenie Weenies (1st, 4to, 128p, p-o, 9cp)	Reilly/Lee	(1920)	Donahey, William	300-450	
Donahey, William	Alice & the Teenie Weenies (1st, lg8vo, 105p, p-o, color, pep)	Reilly/Lee	(1927)	Donahey, William	300-450	
Donahey, William	Down the River with the Teenie Weenies (1st, 4to, p-o, 128p, 8cp)	Reilly/Lee	(1921)	Donahey, William	300-450	
Donahey, William	Teenie Weenie Days (1st, lg8vo, 65p, 4 fp color, pep, DJ/1.00)	Whittlesey	(1944)	Donahey, William	200-300	
Donahey, William	Teenie Weenie Neighbors (1st {std}, 8vo, 68p, 5 color, pep, DJ/1.00)	Whittlesey	(1945)	Donahey, William	200-300	
Donahey, William	Teenie Weenie Town (1st, 8vo, 71p, red cl, p-o, color, pep, DJ/1.50)	Whittlesey	(1942)	Donahey, William	200-300	
Donahey, William	Teenie Weenies in Wonderland (1st, 4to, 120p, color)	Reilly/Lee	(1923)	Donahey, William	250-400	
Donahey, William	Teenie Weenies Under the Rose Bush (1st, 4to, p-o, 120p, 8cp)	Reilly/Lee	(1922)	Donahey, William	250-400	
Donaldson, Ellen M.	In Blue Bird Time (1st, 8vo, 160p, ibds, fp 2-color, pep)	Milton Bradley	1926	Lupprian, Hildegard	45-70	*
Donaldson, Lois	Colombia in Story and Pictures (1st, ob8vo, [28]p, color, pep, DJ/0.75)	Whitman	1944	Wiese, Kurt	30-50	*
Donaldson, Lois	Karl's Wooden Horse (1st, ob8vo, [32]p, color)	NY: Laidlaw	1931	Bergman, Annie	30-50	*
Donaldson, Lois	Runzel-Punzel (1st, lg8vo, yellow cl, p-o, 16p, fp color, cep)	Whitman	1933	Ritter, Mathilde	50-80	
Donnell, Annie H.	Rebecca Mary (1st, 12mo, blue/gilt, 194p, p-o, col frn, 8pl)	Harper	1905	Green, Eliz. S.	60-90	
Donnell, Annie H.	Very Small Person (1st, sm8vo, p-o, 193p, 8cp)	Harper	1906	Green, Eliz. S.	60-90	
Doob, Leonard W.	Crocodile has Me by the Leg (1st, 8vo, [54]p, fp 1-color, DJ/2.95)	NY: Walker	(1967)	Wangboje, Solomon I.	40-70	R*
Dooley, Mrs.	Dem Good Ole Times (1st, sm4to, 151p, teg, 16 ticp)	Doubleday/Page	1906	Gutherz, Suzanne	100-170	
Doone, Radko	Nuvat the Brave (1st, 8vo, green cl, 194p, fp b/w)	Macrae-Smith	(1934)	Walleen, Hans A.	25-45	*
Doorly, Eleanor	Radium Woman (1st, 8vo, 184p, b/w woodcuts, CgM)	L: Heinemann	(1939)	Gibbings, Robert	50-80	
Dopp, Katharine E.	Story of the Early Sea People (1st, sm8vo, 219p, col frn, p-o by...)	Rand/McNally	(1913)	Winter, Milo	30-50	*
Dorey, Jacques	Three & the Moon (1st, sm4to, blue/silver, 103p, 8cp)	Knopf	1929	Artzybasheff, Boris	60-90	
Dorian, Edith	Ask Dr. Christmas (1st, 8vo, 144p, b/w, DJ/2.25)	Whittlesey	(1951)	Unwin, Nora S.	20-30	
Dorian, Edith	When the Snow is Blue (1st, 4to, [20]p, 2-color, dep, DJ/2.75)	Lothrop, Lee	(1960)	Dorian, Edith	25-45	
Dorr, Nell	Mother and Child (1st, 8vo, [89]p, grey bds, DJ/4.50)	Harper	(1954)	(Photos)	250-400	
Dorrington, Albert	Our Lady of Darkness (1st, 12mo, 371p, red/gilt, 4pl)	Macaulay	1910	Rae, John	70-100	
Dorrington, Albert	Radium Terrors (1st, sm8vo, red/gilt, 361p, 4pl)	Doubleday/Page	1912	Michael, A.C.	50-80	
Dorritt, Susan	Wait till Sunday (1st, 4to, [42]p, fp color, pep, DJ/2.50)	Abelard-Schuman	1957	Duvoisin, Roger	40-70	
Dostoievsky, Fedor	Poor Folk (1st, 8vo, 192p, title pg & cvr by...)	L: E. Mathews	1894	Beardsley, Aubrey	175-250	
Doubleday, Russell	Cattle-Ranch To College (1st, 8vo, 347p, blue/gilt, 24pl)	Doub./McClure	1899	(Photos)	100-165	
Doucet, Jerome	Tales of the Spinner (1st, lg8vo, [121]p, teg, uncut, gilt, b/w)	R.H. Russell	1902	Jones, Alfred G.	130-200	R
Doughtie, Charles	Gabriel Wrinkles (1st, 4to, [46]p, fp 2-color, DJ/2.75)	Dodd	(1959)	Saxon, Charles	40-65	*
Douglas, Amanda M.	Clover's Princess (1st, 12mo, p-o, 95p, blue/gilt, 6pl)	Altemus	(1904)	Neill, John R.	60-90	R
Douglas, Barbara	Favorite French Fairy Tales (1st AM, 8vo, 255p, 7cp)	Dodd	(1921)	Cramer, Rie	90-120	
Douglas, Emily	Appleseed Farm (1st, 8vo, 127p, b/w, pep, DJ/1.50)	Abingdon-Cokes.	1948	Vaughan, Anne	20-30	*
Douglas, James	Bunch Book (1st AM, 8vo, green/gilt, 173p, col frn, b/w)	Appleton	1932	Aldin, Cecil	40-65	
Douglas, Norman	South Wind (1st, lg8vo, 2 volumes, 15cp)	Argus Books	1929	Austen, John	90-120	
Douglas, Robert B.	Life & Times of Madame Du Barry (1st, lg8vo, 386p, cvr by...)	L: Smithers	1896	Beardsley, Aubrey	140-200	
Dow, Ethel C.	Diary of a Birthday Doll (1st, 8vo, 88p, p-o, 6cp)	Stern	1908	Nosworthy, Florence	160-250	
Dow, Ethel C.	Proud Roxana (1st, 8vo, 130p, p-o, 6cp)	Stern	1909	Wireman, Eugenie	130-200	
Dow, Katherine	My Time of Year (1st, 12mo, [32]p, fp 2-color, DJ/2.25, NYTBI)	H.Z. Walck	1961	Erhard, Walter	25-40	
Dowd, Emma C.	Doodles (1st, 12mo, 347p, grey cl, col frn)	Houghton	1915	Kirk, Maria L.	40-60	
Downer, Mary L.	The Flower (1st, ob8vo, brown cl, [32]p, 3-color, DJ/1.75)	W.R. Scott	1955	Downer, Mary L.	30-50	*
Downey, Fairfax	Army Mule (1st, sm8vo, 192p, b/w, DJ/2.50)	Dodd	1945	Brown, Paul	50-80	
Downey, Fairfax	Cats of Destiny (1st, 8vo, blue cl, 170p, 39 fp b/w, DJ/2.50)	Scribner	1950	Brown, Paul	50-80	
Downey, Fairfax	Cavalry Mount (1st, 8vo, 227p, b/w, DJ/2.50)	Dodd	1946	Brown, Paul	80-120	
Downey, Fairfax	Dogs of Destiny (1st, 8vo, 186p, b/w, DJ/2.50)	Scribner	1949	Brown, Paul	100-165	
Downey, Fairfax	Horses of Destiny (1st, 8vo, 186p, rust cl, fp b/w, DJ/2.50)	Scribner	1949	Brown, Paul	80-140	
Downey, Fairfax	Jezebel the Jeep (1st, 8vo, 150p, grey cl, uncut, b/w, DJ/2.00)	Dodd	1944	Brown, Paul	50-80	
Downey, Fairfax	Portrait of an Era (1st, lg8vo, 391p, b/w, pep, DJ/3.50)	Scribner	(1936)	Gibson, Charles D.	50-80	
Downey, Fairfax	Seventh's Staghound (1st, 8vo, 230p, b/w, DJ/2.50)	Dodd	1948	Brown, Paul	80-135	
Downie, Mary (ed)	Wind Has Wings (1st AM, sm4to, 95p, fp color, cep, DJ/5.95)	H.Z. Walck	(1968)	Cleaver, Elizabeth	25-40	*
Dowson, Ernest	Beauty & the Beast (1st, 4to, 118p, green/gilt, teg, uncut, 4cp)	L: John Lane	1908	Condor, Charles	180-240	
Dowson, Ernest	Poems of E. Dowson (1st, 12mo, 166p, green/gilt, teg, 4pl, cvr by...)	L: John Lane	1905	Beardsley, Aubrey	120-170	
Doyle, Arthur Conan	Adventures of Gerard (1st AM, 8vo, green cl, 297p, uncut, 16pl)	McClure	1903	Wollen, W.B.	70-100	
Doyle, Arthur Conan	Desert Drama (1st AM, sm8vo, 277p, tan cl, 32pl)	Lippincott	1898	Paget, Sidney	120-200	
Doyle, Arthur Conan	Last Galley (1st AM, 12mo, red cl, 321p, col frn by...)	Doubleday/Page	1911	Wyeth, N.C.	250-400	
Doyle, Arthur Conan	Lost World (1st AM, 8vo, 309p, gilt, 11pl by...)	Hodder/Doran	[1912]	Coll, Joseph C.	400-600	
Doyle, Arthur Conan	Memoirs of Sherlock Holmes (1st, 8vo, AEG, blue/gilt, 279p, b/w)	L: G. Newnes	1894	Paget, Sidney	1000-1600	
Doyle, Arthur Conan	Poison Belt (1st, 8vo, 199p, blue/gilt, uncut, 16pl)	L: Hodder	(1913)	Rountree, Harry	450-650	
Doyle, Arthur Conan	Poison Belt (1st {std}, 8vo, 158p, fp b/w, pep, DJ/4.50)	Macmillan	(1964)	DuBois, W.P.	35-50	
Doyle, Arthur Conan	Sir Nigel (1st, sm8vo, green cl, 346p, 6pl)	McClure	1906	Kinneys	100-165	
Doyle, Arthur Conan	The Parasite (1st AM, 12mo, gilt, 143p, 4pl)	Harper	1895	Pyle, Howard	170-250	
Doyle, Arthur Conan	White Company (1st, lg8vo, 363p, teg, p-o, 13cp, pep)	Cosmopolitan	1922	Wyeth, N.C.	180-240	
Doyle, Arthur Conan	White Company (1st, 8vo, 403p, col frn, 2 dp pl, 7pl, pep)	Harper	1928	Daugherty, James	35-50	
Drachmann, Holger	Paul & Virginia of a Northern Zone (1st, 8vo, 208p, gilt, teg, cvr by...)	Way & Williams	1895	Rogers, Bruce	100-165	
Drake, Burgess	Book of Lyonne (1st, 12mo, 260p, blue/gilt, 8cp, DJ)	L: Falcon Press	(1952)	Peake, Mervyn	160-220	
Drayton, Grace	Baby Bears & their Wishing Rings (1st, lg ob8vo, 167p, color)	Century	(1914)	Drayton, Grace	200-300	
Drayton, Grace	Dolly Dimples and Bobby Bounce (1st, 8vo, ibds, 86p, b/w)	Cupples/Leon	(1931)	Drayton, Grace	200-300	
Drayton, Grace	Let's Go to the Zoo (1st, ob4to, 44p, ibds, shape bk., 6cp)	Duffield	(1914)	Drayton, Grace	200-300	

AUTHOR	TITLE	PUBLISHER	DATE	ARTIST	PRICE	LC
Drayton, Michael	Nymphidia (1st, 8vo, blue/gilt, teg, uncut, unpag, 8pl)	L: Routledge	1906	Maybank, Thomas	100-165	*
Drdek, Richard E.	Street Dog (1st, lg ob8vo, 48p, fp 1-color, cep)	L.W. Singer	(1967)	Crichlow, Ernest	45-65	*
Dreiser, Theodore	Hoosier Holiday (1st [1], lg8vo, teg, olive bds, gilt, 513p, 32pl, pep)	NY: J. Lane	1916	Booth, Franklin	80-130	
Drinkwater, John	All About Me (1st, 8vo, 103p, teg, gilt, 9pl, pep)	L: Collins	1928	Brock, Henry M.	50-80	
Drinkwater, John	Christmas Poems (1st, sq8vo, 18p, orange wraps, uncut, 6 b/w)	L: Sidgwick	1931	Shepard, Ernest H.	70-100	
Drinkwater, John	Cotswold Characters (1st, 12mo, bds, p-o, 54p, 5 woodcuts)	Yale U. Press	1921	Nash, Paul	160-240	R
Drinkwater, John	More About Me (1st AM, 8vo, 109p, orange cl, b/w)	Houghton	1930	Brock, Henry M.	30-50	
Drummond, Florence	Fringes of Paradise (1st, 12mo, ipcb, 48p, 4cp)	L: F. Muller	(1935)	King, Jessie	100-165	
Drummond, Henry	Monkey that Would not Kill (1st, 8vo, 115p, AEG, gilt, 16 fp b/w)	L: Hodder	1898	Wain, Louis	250-400	
Drummond, Henry	Monkey that Would not Kill (1st AM, 12mo, 115p, 16 fp b/w)	Dodd	1898	Wain, Louis	200-300	
Drummond, Henry	Monkey that Would not Kill (1st, sm8vo, b/w, pep)	Dodd	1925	Lenski, Lois	60-100	*
Drummond, Violet H.	Flying Postman ([new ed.] {std}, 4to, unpag, color, DJ/3.25)	H.Z. Walck	(1964)	Drummond, Violet	25-45	
Drummond, Violet H.	Mrs. Easter and the Storks (1st, 4to, 31p, color, DJ, KGM)	L: Faber	(1957)	Drummond, Violet	80-125	
Druon, Maurice	Tistou of the Green Thumbs (1st AM, 8vo, 178p, fp b/w, DJ/2.75)	Scribner	(1958)	Duheme, Jacqueline	30-45	
Drury, William P.	Peradventures of Private Pagett (1st, 12mo, orange cl, 242p, 8pl)	L: Chapman	1904	Rackham, Arthur	250-350	
DuBois, Theodora	Banjo the Crow (1st, lg8vo, 142p, pep, b/w, DJ/2.00)	Houghton	1943	Torrey, Helen	30-50	
DuBois, Theodora	Travelling Toys (1st, 8vo, 201p, p-o, 4cp, pep)	Penn	1934	Peat, Fern B.	60-90	
DuBois, W.E.B.	Quest of the Silver Fleece (1st, 8vo, 434p, grey cl, 4pl)	McClurg	1911	DeLay, H.S.	250-400	
DuBois, W.P.	Alligator Case (1st, 8vo, 63p, ibds, fp color, cep, DJ/3.50)	Harper	(1965)	DuBois, W.P.	50-80	R*
DuBois, W.P.	Bear Party (1st, sm8vo, ibds, [48]p, color, DJ/2.00, CH)	Viking	1951	DuBois, W.P.	100-165	
DuBois, W.P.	Call Me Bandicoot (1st, 8vo, 63p, ibds, color, DJ/3.95)	Harper	(1970)	DuBois, W.P.	40-65	
DuBois, W.P.	Elisabeth the Cow Ghost (1st [1st bk.], sq16mo, [47]p, color)	NY: Nelson	1936	DuBois, W.P.	200-300	
DuBois, W.P.	Flying Locomotive (1st, ob8vo, ibds, 47p, color, DJ/1.00)	Viking	1941	DuBois, W.P.	90-130	
DuBois, W.P.	Giant Otto (1st, sq16mo, [40]p, ibds, 17cp, pep)	Viking	1936	DuBois, W.P.	150-225	
DuBois, W.P.	Great Geppy (1st, sm4to, 92p, 22 fp color, dep, DJ/2.00)	Viking	1940	DuBois, W.P.	120-200	R
DuBois, W.P.	Horse in the Camel Suit (1st, sq8vo, 79p, ibds, color, DJ/3.95)	Harper	(1967)	DuBois, W.P.	60-100	
DuBois, W.P.	Lazy Tommy Pumpkinhead (1st, 8vo, ipcb, 28p, fp color, DJ/2.50)	Harper	(1966)	DuBois, W.P.	120-170	
DuBois, W.P.	Lion (1st, sm4to, 36p, color, pep, DJ/3.00, CH)	Viking	1956	DuBois, W.P.	120-200	R
DuBois, W.P.	Otto and the Magic Potatoes (1st, sm4to, 48p, dp color, DJ/4.95)	Viking	(1970)	DuBois, W.P.	60-90	
DuBois, W.P.	Otto at Sea (1st, sq16mo, ibds, [40]p, color, pep)	Viking	1936	DuBois, W.P.	150-225	
DuBois, W.P.	Otto in Africa (1st, 4to, 35p, color, pep, DJ/2.50)	Viking	(1961)	DuBois, W.P.	60-100	R
DuBois, W.P.	Otto in Texas (1st, sm4to, 45p, color, pep, DJ/2.50)	Viking	(1959)	DuBois, W.P.	100-165	R
DuBois, W.P.	Peter Graves (1st, lg8vo, ibds, 168p, dep, b/w, DJ/2.50)	Viking	1950	DuBois, W.P.	80-120	
DuBois, W.P.	Porko Von Popbutton (1st, 8vo, ibds, 80p, fp color, DJ/3.95)	Harper	(1969)	DuBois, W.P.	70-100	R
DuBois, W.P.	Pretty Pretty Peggy Moffitt (1st, 8vo, 32p, ibds, color, DJ/2.95)	Harper	(1968)	DuBois, W.P.	70-120	
DuBois, W.P.	Squirrel Hotel (1st, sm4to, red cl, 48p, pep, b/w, DJ/2.00)	Viking	1952	DuBois, W.P.	70-120	
DuBois, W.P.	The Giant (1st, lg8vo, 124p, grey cl, fp b/w, DJ/2.75)	Viking	1954	DuBois, W.P.	100-165	R
DuBois, W.P.	Three Policemen (1st, sm4to, blue cl, 92p, 16 color, pep, DJ/2.00)	Viking	1938	DuBois, W.P.	120-200	
DuBois, W.P.	Twenty-One Balloons (1st, lg8vo, ibds, 179p, b/w, DJ/2.50, NM)	Viking	1947	DuBois, W.P.	160-225	R
DuChaillu, Paul	Country of the Dwarfs (1st, 12mo, 261p, b/w, pep)	Harper	1928	Berry, Erick	25-45	*
DuChaillu, Paul	Lost in the Jungle (1st, 12mo, 269p, fp b/w, pep)	Harper	1928	Berry, Erick	30-60	*
DuChaillu, Paul	My Apingi Kingdom (1st, 12mo, 263p, b/w, pep)	Harper	1928	Berry, Erick	30-50	*
DuMaurier, George	Legend of Camelot (1st, ob4to, ibds, 95p, b/w)	Harper	1898	DuMaurier, George	120-180	
DuMaurier, George	The Martian (1st, 8vo, orange/gilt, 471p, b/w)	Harper	1897	DuMaurier, George	55-90	
DuMaurier, George	Trilby (1st, sm8vo, 464p, beige/gilt, b/w, cvr by...)	Harper	1894	Armstrong, Margaret	35-60	
DuMond, Frank	Tall Tales of the Catskills (1st {std}, 8vo, 179p, b/w, DJ/4.95)	Atheneum	1968	Parnall, Peter	30-50	
Duarte, Margarida	Legend of the Palm Tree (1st, lg4to, ibds, [47]p, color, DJ/1.00)	Grosset/Dunlap	(1940)	Werneck, Paulo	150-220	
Dubois, Gertrude	Peter & Penny Plant a Garden (1st, sm8vo, 210p, gilt, b/w, pep, DJ/1.25)	Stokes	1936	Lawson, Marie A.	30-50	
Ducorron, C.A.F.	Boy King of the Cannibal Islands (1st {std}, 8vo, p-o, 257p, b/w pl)	Bobbs-Merrill	(1932)	Eskridge, Robert	40-65	
Duddington, Natalie	Russian Folk Tales (1st AM {std}, 8vo, 144p, b/w, DJ)	Funk/Wagnalls	(1967)	Hart, Dick	25-40	
Dudley, Albertus T.	Great Year (1st, sm8vo, 302p, 6pl)	Lothrop, Lee	(1907)	Copeland, Charles	40-65	
Dugdale, Florence E.	Book of Baby Beasts (4to, ibds, p-o, [120]p, 19ticp)	NY: Hodder	[1912]	Detmold, Edward J.	350-500	
Dugdale, Florence E.	Book of Baby Birds (1st, sm4to, 120p, pcb, p-o, 19 ticp)	L: Hodder	[1912]	Detmold, Edward J.	300-500	
Dugdale, Florence E.	Book of Baby Pets (1st, lg4to, ibds, [120]p, p-o, 19 ticp)	L: Hodder	[1913]	Detmold, Edward J.	300-500	
Dugo, Andre	Dogcatcher's Dog (1st {std}, 4to, ibds, [32]p, fp 2-color, DJ/2.00, NYTBI)	Holt	(1952)	Dugo, Andre	30-55	
Dulac, Edmund	Edmund Dulac's Fairy Book (1st, 4to, gilt, 174p, 16 ticp, pep)	L: Hodder	(1916)	Dulac, Edmund	350-500	
Dulac, Edmund	Edmund Dulac's Fairy Book (1st AM, 4to, p-o, gilt 174p, 16 ticp)	Doran	(1916)	Dulac, Edmund	300-450	
Dulac, Edmund	Lyrics Pathetic & Humorous from A to Z (1st, 4to, ibds, [49]p, color, pep)	L: Warne	1908	Dulac, Edmund	400-600	
Dulac, Edmund	Picture Book for the French Red Cross (1st, 4to, gilt, 135p, 19 ticp)	L: Hodder	(1915)	Dulac, Edmund	300-500	R
Dumas, Alexandre	Count of Monte Cristo (lg8vo, 472p, black/gilt, 8cp, pep)	Dodd	[1920]	Schaeffer, Mead	40-65	
Dumas, Alexandre	Dumas Fairy Tale Book (8vo, 290p, grey cl, 4cp, 20pl)	L: Warne	1924	Rountree, Harry	80-140	
Dumas, Alexandre	Fairy Tales by Dumas (1st AM, sm4to, 114p, fp b/w)	Stokes	(1904)	Rountree, Harry	60-95	
Dumas, Alexandre	Nutcracker of Nuremberg (1st, lg8vo, black/gilt, 154p, b/w)	McBride	1930	Hasselriis, Else	35-60	
Dumas, Alexandre	Three Musketeers (1st, 8vo, 545p, p-o, 8cp, pep, WS)	Rand/McNally	(1923)	Winter, Milo	60-100	
Dumas, Alexandre	Three Musketeers (1st, lg8vo, black/gilt, 555p, 8cp)	Dodd	[1929]	Schaeffer, Mead	50-80	
Dumas, Alexandre	Three Musketeers (1st, 8vo, p-o, 459p, 5cp, 10pl, pep)	Winston	(1931)	Higgins, Edward R.	30-50	
Dunbar, Aldis	Once There was a Prince (1st, 8vo, 302p, blue cl, pep, col frn)	Little/Brown	1928	Day, Maurice	40-60	*
Dunbar, Jennie	Young Hopeful (1st, 8vo, 78p, blue/gilt, b/w, pep)	L: H. Jenkins	1932	Robinson, Charles	90-120	*
Dunbar, Paul L.	Candle-Lightin' Time (1st, 8vo, teg, 127p, green cl, uncut, cvr b7...)	Dodd	1901	Armstrong, Margaret	250-400	
Dunbar, Paul L.	Folks from Dixie (1st, 12mo, 263p, gilt, p-o, 8pl)	Dodd	1898	Kemble, Edward W.	350-500	
Dunbar, Paul L.	Heart of Happy Hollow (1st, sm8vo, 309p, gilt, 6pl)	Dodd	1904	Kemble, Edward W.	400-650	
Dunbar, Paul L.	Li'L' Gal (1st, 8vo, 124p, teg, green cl, cvr by...)	Dodd	1904	Armstrong, Margaret	300-450	
Dunbar, Paul L.	Poems of Cabin and Field (1st, 8vo, teg, 125p, uncut, green/gilt)	Dodd	1899	(Photos)	300-500	
Dunbar, Paul L.	Strength of Gideon (1st, 12mo, 362p, gilt, 8pl)	Dodd	1900	Kemble, Edward W.	400-600	
Dunbar, Paul L.	When Malindy Sings (1st, 8vo, 144p, teg, cvr by...)	Dodd	1903	Armstrong, Margaret	300-450	
Duncan, Eula G.	Big Road Walker (1st, lg8vo, 121p, cep, 17 fp b/w, DJ/1.75)	Stokes	1940	Eichenberg, Fritz	140-200	
Duncan, Lois	Giving Away Suzanne (1st, 4to, 46p, fp 1-color, DJ/3.00)	Dodd	(1963)	Weisgard, Leonard	45-70	
Duncan, Norman	Suitable Child (1st, 8vo, ipcb, teg, 96p, pep, 5 ticp)	Revell	1909	Green, Eliz. S.	60-90	

AUTHOR	TITLE	PUBLISHER	DATE	ARTIST	PRICE	LC
Duncombe, Frances	Hoo! Hoo! DeWitt! (1st, 8vo, 31p, fp color, DJ/1.25)	Holt	(1939)	Lamont, Jean	35-50	
Dunham, Curtis	Bobbie in Bugaboo Land (1st, lg8vo, grey cl, 215p, 11 pl)	Bobbs-Merrill	(1907)	Kerr, George F.	180-250	
Dunham, Curtis	Golden Goblin (1st, lg8vo, ipcb, 190p, 8cp)	Bobbs-Merrill	(1906)	Kerr, George F.	200-300	
Dunham, Curtis	Wurra-Wurra (1st, 12mo, green/gilt, 93p, color, pep)	D. Fitzgerald	(1911)	Innes, John	70-120	*
Dunham, Edith	Diary of a Mouse (1st, sm8vo, red cl, p-o, unpag, fp color, pep)	Dodge	(1907)	Gutmann, Bessie P.	200-300	
Dunne, Finley P.	Mr. Dooley's Philosophy (1st, sm8vo, red cl, 263p, b/w by...)	R.H. Russell	1900	Kemble, Edward W.	60-90	
Dunne, Finley P.	Mr. Dooley's Philosophy (1st, sm8vo, 263p, red cl, col frn by...)	R.H. Russell	1900	Nicholson, Wm.	60-90	
Dunne, John W.	Jumping Lions of Borneo (1st AM, lg4to, 60p, dp b/w, pep, DJ/2.00)	Henry Holt & Co.	(1938)	Robinson, Irene	30-45	
Duplaix, Georges	Animal Stories (1st {std}, folio, ibds, 91p, color, pep, GGB)	Simon/Schuster	1944	Rojankovsky, Feodor	60-100	
Duplaix, Georges	Big Brown Bear (1st, 4to, ibds, [52]p, color, pep, BGB)	Simon/Schuster	(1947)	Tenggren, Gustaf	80-120	
Duplaix, Georges	Fluff (1st, sq4to, ibds, [40]p, color, pep)	Harper	1937	Rojankovsky, Feodor	100-165	*
Duplaix, Georges	Gaston & Josephine (1st, 4to, 47p, ibds, color)	NY: Oxford U.Pr.	1933	Duplaix, Georges	200-300	
Duplaix, Georges	Gaston & Josephine (1st {this pub.}, lg4to, 48p, color)	Harper	1936	Duplaix, Georges	120-200	
Duplaix, Georges	Gaston & Josephine (1st {A}, sm8vo, [42]p, ibds, color, LGB/#65)	Simon/Schuster	1948	Rojankovsky, Feodor	25-45	
Duplaix, Georges	Merry Shipwreck (1st {std}, 4to, ibds, [34]p, color, dep, DJ/1.50)	Harper	(1942)	Gergely, Tibor	120-165	
Duplaix, Georges	Pee-Gloo (1st, 4to, [40]p, ibds, pep, color, DJ/2.00)	Harper	1935	Duplaix, Georges	250-350	
Duplaix, Georges	Popo the Hippopotamus (1st, ob12mo, ibds, [28]p, fp color)	Whitman	(1935)	Duplaix, Georges	120-200	
Duplaix, Georges	Topsy Turvy Circus (1st {std}, lg8vo, [40]p, ibds, color, pep, DJ/1.50)	Harper	(1940)	Gergely, Tibor	80-125	
Duplaix, Lily	Pedro, Nina & Perrito (1st, lg4to, [48]p, ibds, fp color, pep, DJ/1.50)	Harper	1939	Latham, Barbara	90-150	
Duplaix, Lily	White Bunny & his Magic Nose (1st, 4to, [28]p, ipcb, fp color, DJ/1.00)	Simon/Schuster	1945	Masha	30-50	
Duppa, C.M.	Stories from Lowly Life (1st, lg8vo, 95p, uncut, red/gilt, b/w)	L: Macmillan	1898	Wain, Louis	120-200	
Durant, Nancy M.	Oliver & the Crying Chip (1st, 8vo, 79p, blue cl, 10 b/w)	Sherman French	1915	Betacourt, A.B.	30-50	*
Durham, Mae	Tit for Tat (1st {std}, 8vo, 126p, b/w, DJ/3.25)	Harcourt	(1967)	Pincus, Harriet	25-40	*
Durrell, Gerald M.	Donkey Rustlers (1st AM {std}, 8vo, 158p, b/w, DJ/4.50)	Viking	(1968)	Jacques, Robin	25-40	*
Durston, Georgia R.	Candle Light (1st, 4to, ibds, 116p, 12 fp 1-color, pep)	Saalfield	(1906)	Greenland, Katharine	80-120	*
Duryea, Elizabeth	Long Christmas Eve (1st, 8vo, 44p, color, DJ/2.00)	Houghton	1954	Weil, Lisl	20-30	
Dussauze, Alice	Little Jack Rabbit (1st, 12mo, 125p, col frn)	Macmillan	1927	Peck, Anne M.	30-50	*
Dutton, Maude B. (tr)	Tortoise and the Geese (1st, sm8vo, 124p, 12pl)	Houghton	1908	Smith, E. Boyd	60-90	*
Duval, Elizabeth	This Earth We Live On (1st, lg8vo, 157p, color, pep)	Stokes	1927	Wharton, Percival	20-35	
Duvoisin, Roger	A for the Ark (1st, 4to, [46]p, ibds, color, DJ/2.00)	Lothrop, Lee	1952	Duvoisin, Roger	70-100	
Duvoisin, Roger	All Aboard! (1st, folio, 44p, ibds, color, DJ/1.00)	Grosset/Dunlap	(1935)	Duvoisin, Roger	130-180	
Duvoisin, Roger	And There was America (1st {std}, 8vo, 75p, color, pep, DJ/2.00)	Knopf	1938	Duvoisin, Roger	30-50	
Duvoisin, Roger	Christmas Cake (1st, ob12mo, [29]p, b/w, ibds, pep, DJ/0.50)	A.A. Group	(1941)	Duvoisin, Roger	60-100	
Duvoisin, Roger	Christmas Whale (1st {std}, ob8vo, [45]p, ibds, color, DJ/1.25)	Knopf	(1945)	Duvoisin, Roger	70-100	
Duvoisin, Roger	Day and Night (1st, 4to, [36]p, fp color, pep, DJ/2.95)	Knopf	(1960)	Duvoisin, Roger	45-70	
Duvoisin, Roger	Donkey-Donkey (1st, 8vo, ibds, [46]p, color, pep)	Whitman	(1933)	Duvoisin, Roger	150-220	
Duvoisin, Roger	Donkey-Donkey (1st {this pub}, sm4to, ipcb, pep, 39p, color, DJ/0.50)	Grosset/Dunlap	(1940)	Duvoisin, Roger	70-120	
Duvoisin, Roger	Easter Treat (1st {std}, sm4to, [16]p, 1-color, DJ/2.00)	Knopf	(1954)	Duvoisin, Roger	70-100	
Duvoisin, Roger	Four Corners of the World (1st {std}, lg8vo, 128p, color, DJ/3.00)	Knopf	1948	Duvoisin, Roger	45-70	
Duvoisin, Roger	Happy Hunter (1st, ob4to, [32]p, fp 3-color, dep, DJ/2.75, NYTBI)	Lothrop, Lee	1961	Duvoisin, Roger	60-90	*
Duvoisin, Roger	House of Four Seasons (1st, 4to, [34]p, color, pep, DJ/2.50)	Lothrop, Lee	1956	Duvoisin, Roger	40-65	
Duvoisin, Roger	Little Boy Who was Drawing (1st, lg8vo, [56]p, color)	Scribner	1932	Duvoisin, Roger	160-225	
Duvoisin, Roger	Lonely Veronica (1st, 4to, [39]p, color, pep, DJ/3.00)	Knopf	(1963)	Duvoisin, Roger	40-60	
Duvoisin, Roger	Missing Milkman (1st, 4to, [32]p, color, pep, DJ/3.25)	Knopf	(1967)	Duvoisin, Roger	30-50	
Duvoisin, Roger	One Thousand Christmas Beards (1st, sm4to, [32]p, ibds, 2-col, pep, DJ/1.95)	Knopf	(1955)	Duvoisin, Roger	80-120	
Duvoisin, Roger	Our Veronica Goes to Petunia's Farm (1st, 4to, [32]p, color, pep, DJ/2.95)	Knopf	(1962)	Duvoisin, Roger	30-45	
Duvoisin, Roger	Petunia (1st {std}, sm4to, ibds, [32]p, color, DJ/1.50)	Knopf	(1950)	Duvoisin, Roger	70-120	
Duvoisin, Roger	Petunia & the Song (1st {std}, sm4to, ibds, [32]p, color, DJ/1.75)	Knopf	(1951)	Duvoisin, Roger	70-100	
Duvoisin, Roger	Petunia Takes a Trip (1st {std}, sm4to, [32]p, color, pep, DJ/2.00)	Knopf	(1953)	Duvoisin, Roger	70-100	R
Duvoisin, Roger	Petunia's Christmas (1st {std}, sm4to, [34]p, color, pep, DJ/2.00)	Knopf	(1952)	Duvoisin, Roger	70-100	
Duvoisin, Roger	Petunia, Beware! (1st, 4to, [32]p, color, DJ/2.95)	Knopf	(1958)	Duvoisin, Roger	40-65	
Duvoisin, Roger	Petunia, I Love You (1st, 4to, [32]p, color, DJ/3.25)	Knopf	(1965)	Duvoisin, Roger	30-50	*
Duvoisin, Roger	Spring Snow (1st, 8vo, [32]p, color, fp 1-color, pep, DJ/2.95)	Knopf	(1963)	Duvoisin, Roger	50-85	R*
Duvoisin, Roger	They Put Out to Sea (1st {std}, lg8vo, 171p, 8 dp color, pep, DJ/3.00)	Knopf	1943	Duvoisin, Roger	70-100	R
Duvoisin, Roger	Three Sneezes... (1st {std}, 8vo, 244p, color, pep, DJ/2.00)	Knopf	1941	Duvoisin, Roger	40-60	
Duvoisin, Roger	Two Lonely Ducks (1st, ob8vo, [36]p, 2-color, pep, DJ/2.00)	Knopf	1955	Duvoisin, Roger	50-80	
Duvoisin, Roger	Veronica (1st, 4to, [36]p, color, pep, DJ/2.95)	Knopf	(1961)	Duvoisin, Roger	45-70	
Duvoisin, Roger	Veronica's Smile (1st, lg8vo, [32]p, color, pep, DJ/3.00)	Knopf	(1964)	Duvoisin, Roger	45-70	
Duvoisin, Roger	What is Right for Tulip (1st, 4to, [30]p, color, cep, DJ/3.95)	Knopf	(1969)	Duvoisin, Roger	40-65	
Dwiggins, Wm. A.	Marionette in Motion (1st, 8vo, 25p, b/w, DJ/1.50)	(Detroit)	1939	Dwiggins, W.A.	140-200	
Dwight, Grace	Yellow Cat & Friends (1st, lg8vo, ipcb, 88p, 14cp)	Appleton	1905	Dimock, Edith	60-90	
Dyer, Caroline	Three Famous Ugly Sisters (1st, sm4to, ibds, [52]p, color, DJ/2.00)	Whittlesey	(1946)	McKay, Donald	25-45	
Dyer, Kate G.	Turkey Trott & the Black Santa (1st, 8vo, orange cl, [39]p, 2-color)	Platt/Munk	(1942)	Robson, Janet	140-200	
Dyer, Ruth O.	Adventures of the Ink Spots (1st, 8vo, orange cl, 158p, col frn, pep)	Lothrop, Lee	(1923)	Bridgman, L.J.	80-120	
Dyer, Ruth O.	Daytime Story Book (1st, sm8vo, 152p, col frn, pep)	Lothrop, Lee	(1917)	Inglis, Antoinette	30-50	
Dyer, Ruth O.	Sleepy-Time Story Book (1st, sm8vo, 147p, gilt, pep, col frn)	Lothrop, Lee	(1915)	Stephens, Alice B.	35-60	*
Dyer, Walter A.	All Around Robin Hood's Barn (1st {std}, lg8vo, 204p, p-o, 24cp)	Doubleday/Page	1926	Bull, Charles L.	70-120	
Dyer, Walter A.	Country Cousins (1st {std}, lg8vo, 164p, col frn, 11pl, pep)	Doubleday/Doran	1927	Bull, Charles L.	60-90	
Eager, Edward	Half Magic (1st {std}, 8vo, 217p, b/w, DJ/2.75)	Harcourt	(1954)	Bodecker, N.M.	120-200	
Eager, Edward	Magic by the Lake (1st {std}, 8vo, 183p, b/w, DJ/2.95)	Harcourt	(1957)	Bodecker, N.M.	70-120	
Eager, Edward	Mouse Manor (1st {std} 8vo, [57]p, 10 fp color, pep, DJ/2.00)	Ariel	(1952)	Bailey-Jones, Beryl	120-200	
Eager, Edward	Playing Possum (1st, lg8vo, [32]p, green cl, 1-color, pep, DJ/2.50)	Putnam	1955	Galdone, Paul	80-125	
Eager, Edward	Red Head (1st [1st bk.], 8vo, 24p, fp color, pep, DJ/1.25)	Houghton	1951	Slobodkin, Louis	60-100	*
Eager, Edward	Time Garden (1st {std}, 8vo, 188p, b/w, DJ/3.00)	Harcourt	(1958)	Bodecker, N.M.	120-200	
Eager, Edward	Well-Wishers (1st {std}, 8vo, 191p, b/w, DJ/3.25)	Harcourt	(1960)	Bodecker, N.M.	80-140	
Eames, Genevieve T.	Ghost Town Cowboy (1st, 8vo, 176p, beige cl, uncut, b/w, pep, DJ/2.50)	J. Messner	(1951)	Brown, Paul	50-80	
Eames, Genevieve T.	Good Luck Colt (1st, 8vo, 191p, red cl, fp b/w, pep, DJ/2.50)	J. Messner	(1953)	Brown, Paul	60-100	
Eames, Genevieve T.	Horse to Remember (1st, 8vo, 146p, b/w, pep, DJ/2.50)	J. Messner	(1947)	Brown, Paul	50-80	

AUTHOR	TITLE	PUBLISHER	DATE	ARTIST	PRICE	LC
Earl of Birkenhead	World in 2030 (1st, lg8vo, 215p, black cl, 9pl)	L: Hodder	(1930)	Kauffer, Edward M.	140-200	
Earl, John P.	Captain of the School Team (1st, 12mo, 324p, 7pl, pep)	Penn	1910	Boyer, Ralph L.	80-125	
Earle, Alice M.	Child Life in Colonial Days (1st, sm8vo, 418p, gilt, teg)	Macmillan	1899	(Photos)	50-80	
Earle, Alice M.	Colonial Days in Old New York (1st, sm8vo, 312p, gilt)	Scribner	1896	Armstrong, Margaret	60-100	
Earle, Alice M.	Costumes of Colonial Times (1st, 8vo, blue/gilt, 264p)	Scribner	1894	Armstrong, Margaret	70-100	
Earle, Alice M.	Curious Punishments of Bygone Days (1st, sm8vo, 149p, gilt, teg, uncut)	Herbert Stone	1896	Hazenplug, Frank	70-100	
Earle, Alice M.	Home Life in Colonial Days (1st, sm8vo, teg, 470p)	Macmillan	1898	(Photos)	50-80	
Earle, Alice M.	Stage Coach and Tavern Days (1st, sm8vo, uncut, 449p, teg, b/w)	Macmillan	1900	(Photos)	60-100	
Eastman, Charles A.	Indian Boyhood (1st, 8vo, gilt, teg, 289p, 4pl)	McClure	1902	Blumenschein, E.L.	100-180	
Eastman, Charles A.	Old Indian Days (1st, sm8vo, p-o, 279p, 4cp)	McClure	1907	Groesbeck, Dan S.	70-100	
Eastman, Charles A.	Wigwam Evenings (1st, 12mo, 253p, 18pl)	Little/Brown	1909	Deming, Edwin W.	80-125	
Eastman, Charlotte	Evolution of Dodd's Sister (1st, 12mo, gilt, 230p, cvr by…)	Rand/McNally	1897	Denslow, W.W.	30-50	*
Eastman, Elaine G.	Little Brother O'Dream (1st, sm8vo, 191p, cvr by…)	Houghton	1910	Peabody, Marion L.	25-45	
Eastwick, Ivy O.	Deck the Stable (1st {std}, 4to, [26]p, 1-color, pep, DJ/2.75)	McKay	(1960)	Unwin, Nora S.	30-45	
Eastwick, Ivy O.	Fairies & Suchlike (1st {std}, sq8vo, 63p, ipcb, 1-color, pep, DJ/1.50)	Dutton	1946	Merwin, Decie	60-100	
Eaton, Anne T.	Animal's Christmas (1st, sm8vo, grey cl, 124p, 1-color, dep, DJ/2.00)	Viking	1944	Angelo, Valenti	45-75	R
Eaton, Anne T.	Welcome Christmas (1st, 8vo, 128p, b/w, pep, DJ/2.50)	Viking	1955	Angelo, Valenti	30-45	
Eaton, Jeanette	America's Own Mark Twain (1st, 8vo, 251p, b/w, DJ/3.00)	Wm. Morrow	1958	Fisher, Leonard	20-35	
Eaton, Jeanette	Betsy's Napoleon (1st, 8vo, 274p, bds, color, pep, DJ/2.50)	Wm. Morrow	1936	Brissaud, Pierre	30-50	
Eaton, Jeanette	Daughter of the Seine (1st {std}, lg8vo, blue cl, 324p, pep, NH)	Harper	1929	(Photos)	60-100	
Eaton, Jeanette	David Livingstone: Foe of Darkness (1st, 8vo, 256p, b/w, DJ/3.00)	Wm. Morrow	1947	Ray, Ralph	20-35	
Eaton, Jeanette	Gandhi: Fighter Without a Sword (1st, 8vo, 253p, b/w, pep, DJ/3.00)	Wm. Morrow	1950	Ray, Ralph	25-40	
Eaton, Jeanette	Jeanne d'Arc: Warrior Saint (1st {std}, 12mo, 102p, b/w)	Harper	1931	Finta, Alexander	20-35	
Eaton, Jeanette	Leader by Destiny (1st, 8vo, 402p, blue/gilt, 19pl, DJ/3.00, NH)	Harcourt	(1938)	Rose, Jack M.	40-70	
Eaton, Jeanette	Leaders in Other Lands (1st, 8vo, 322p, color, DJ)	D.C. Heath	(1950)	Kredel, Fritz	25-40	
Eaton, Jeanette	Lee: Gallant General (1st, 8vo, 72p, b/w, DJ/2.00)	Wm. Morrow	1953	Daugherty, Harry	25-40	
Eaton, Jeanette	Lone Journey (1st, sm8vo, 266p, map, b/w, DJ/2.50, NH)	Harcourt	(1944)	Ishmael, Woodi	40-65	
Eaton, Jeanette	Narcissa Whitman (1st {std}, 8vo, 318p, b/w, pep, DJ/2.50)	Harcourt	(1941)	Ishmael, Woodi	30-50	R*
Eaton, Jeanette	Story of Light (1st {std}, sm8vo, 79p, col frn)	Harper	1928	Schwartz, Max	25-40	
Eaton, Jeanette	Story of Transportation (1st {std}, sm8vo, 52p, cp, pep)	Harper	1927	Day, Maurice	25-40	
Eaton, Jeanette	That Lively Man: Ben Franklin (1st, 8vo, 253p, b/w, DJ/2.50)	Wm. Morrow	1948	Day, Maurice	20-25	
Eaton, Jeanette	Trumpeter's Tale…. (1st, 8vo, 191p, b/w, DJ/3.50)	Wm. Morrow	1955	Fax, Elton C.	40-65	
Eaton, Jeanette	Washington: Nation's First Hero (1st, 8vo, 70p, fp b/w, DJ/2.00)	Wm. Morrow	1951	Ray, Ralph	20-30	
Eaton, Jeanette	Young Lafayette (1st, 8vo, 253p, col frn, pep)	Houghton	1932	Hendrickson, David	20-30	
Eaton, Seymour	Adventures of the Traveling Bears (4to, ibds, 63p, col frn, b/w)	Barse/Hopkins	(1915)	Campbell, V. Floyd	250-400	
Eaton, Seymour	More about Teddy B. & Teddy G. (1st, 4to, 186p, ibds, p-o, 15cp)	Stern	1907	Culver, R.K.	400-600	
Eaton, Seymour	Prince Domino & Muffles (1st, sq8vo, p-o, 146p, 7cp)	Stern	1910	Twelvetrees, C.	200-300	
Eaton, Seymour	Roosevelt Bears (1st, 4to, 180p, bds, p-o, 16cp)	Stern	1906	Campbell, V. Floyd	400-600	R
Eaton, Seymour	Roosevelt Bears Abroad (1st, 4to, ibds, p-o, 178p, 12cp)	Stern	1908	Culver, R.K.	400-600	
Eaton, Seymour	Teddy-B & Teddy-G/Bear Detectives (4to, ipcb, 152p, p-o, 15cp)	Barse/Hopkins	(1909)	Wightman, Francis P.	250-400	
Eaton, Seymour	Teddy-B & Teddy-G/Bear Detectives (1st, 4to, bds, p-o, 15cp)	Stern	1909	Wightman, Francis P.	400-650	
Eaton, Seymour	Travelling Bears Across the Sea (lg8vo, ibds, col frn, b/w)	Barse/Hopkins	(1916)	Campbell, V. Floyd	250-400	
Eaton, Seymour	Travelling Bears at Play (1st, 4to, 62p, color)	Barse/Hopkins	(1916)	Campbell, V. Floyd	250-400	
Eaton, Seymour	Travelling Bears in New York (1st, 4to, 60p, color)	Barse/Hopkins	(1915)	Campbell, V. Floyd	250-400	
Eaton, Seymour	Travelling Bears in Outdoor Sports (1st, 4to, 60p, col frn)	Barse/Hopkins	(1915)	Campbell, V. Floyd	250-400	
Eaton, Seymour	Travelling Bears in the East & West (1st, 4to, bds, 63p, p-o, cp)	Barse/Hopkins	(1915)	Campbell, V. Floyd	250-400	
Eberle, Irmengarde	Apple Orchard (1st, 8vo, 39p, b/w, DJ/3.00)	H.Z. Walck	1962	Keats, Ezra J.	25-40	
Eberle, Irmengarde	Evie & Cookie (1st, 8vo, 122p, 1-color, pep, DJ/2.75)	Knopf	(1957)	Slobodkin, Louis	25-40	
Eberle, Irmengarde	Evie & the Wonderful Kangaroo (1st, 8vo, 128p, 1-color, pep, DJ/2.50)	Knopf	(1955)	Slobodkin, Louis	25-40	
Eberle, Irmengarde	Family to Raise (1st, 8vo, 92p, color, DJ/2.00)	Holiday House	1939	Bostelmann, Else	25-40	
Eberle, Irmengarde	Grasses (1st, lg8vo, green cl, 56p, brown illus, DJ/2.75)	H.Z. Walck	1960	Keats, Ezra J.	45-70	
Eberle, Irmengarde	Hop, Skip & Fly (1st, 8vo, 70p, grey cl, 2-color, DJ/2.00)	Holiday House	(1937)	Bostelmann, Else	30-50	*
Eberle, Irmengarde	Our Oldest Friends (1st, sm8vo, 146p, 1-color, DJ/2.00)	Holiday House	(1942)	Kirmse, Marguerite	40-65	
Eberle, Irmengarde	Phoebe-Belle (1st, 8vo, 63p, 1-color, pep, DJ/1.25)	Greystone Press	(1941)	Eichenberg, Fritz	35-50	
Eberle, Irmengarde	Sea-Horse Adventure (1st, 8vo, [55]p, blue cl, 2-color, DJ/2.00)	Holiday House	(1937)	Bostelmann, Else	30-50	*
Eberle, Irmengarde	Spice on the Wind (1st, 8vo, 56p, brown cl, 2-color, pep, DJ/2.00)	Holiday House	(1940)	Jones, Richard	50-80	R
Eberle, Irmengarde	Through the Harbor from Everywhere (1st {std}, 8vo, 158p, pep, DJ/1.50)	Bobbs-Merrill	(1938)	Weisgard, Leonard	50-80	
Eberle, Irmengarde	Visiting Jimpsons (1st, 8vo, 188p, pep, DJ/2.00)	Harcourt	(1946)	Kreps, Ruth	20-35	*
Eberle, Irmengarde	Wide Fields (1st, lg8vo, 193p, green cl, 8pl, DJ/2.50)	Crowell	1943	Eichenberg, Fritz	30-50	
Eberstadt, Isabel	Where Did Tuffy Hide? (1st {std}, 8vo, [32]p, fp 2-color, DJ/2.50)	Little/Brown	1957	Weisgard, Leonard	30-50	
Eberstadt, Isabel	Who Is at the Door? (1st {std}, 8vo, [32]p, fp 2-color, DJ/2.50)	Little/Brown	(1960)	Weisgard, Leonard	30-50	
Eckenstein, Lina	Little Princess and the Great Plot (1st, 16mo, 160p, pep)	L: T.F. Unwin	1892	Heath, Dudley	70-100	*
Eckert, Allan W.	In Search of a Whale (1st {std}, 4to, 158p, color, DJ/5.95)	Doubleday	(1970)	Cellini, Joseph	25-40	
Eckert, Allan W.	King Snake (1st {std}, 8vo, 143p, b/w, DJ/4.75)	Little/Brown	(1968)	Altschuler, Franz	50-80	
Eckert, Allan W.	Wild Season (1st {std}, 8vo, 244p, green/gilt, cep, b/w, DJ/4.95)	Little/Brown	(1967)	Karalus, Karl	20-30	
Economakis, Olga	Oasis of the Stars (1st, 8vo, [32]p, dp color, DJ/3.50)	Coward	(1965)	Lent, Blair	30-45	
Eddison, Eric R.	Worm Ouroboros (1st AM, 8vo, gilt, 445p, b/w, pep)	A. & C. Boni	1926	Henderson, Keith	60-100	
Edelstat, Vera	Steam Shovel for Me! (1st, sm4to, orange cl, [56]p, color, pep)	Stokes	1933	Romano	70-120	*
Edey, Birdsall O.	Six Giants & a Griffin (1st, 4to, 46p, 6pl)	R.H. Russell	1903	Ruyl, Beatrice B.	160-240	*
Edgar, M.G.	Treasury of Verse for School and Home (1st, 8vo, 523p, color, pep)	Crowell	(1926)	Appleton, Honor C.	40-60	*
Edgar, M.G.	Treasury of Verse… (1st AM, lg8vo, 261p, gilt, pep, 8cp)	Crowell	(1908)	Pogany, Willy	180-250	
Edgeworth, Maria	Helen (1st, 12mo, blue/gilt, 490p, AEG, b/w, dep)	L: Macmillan	1896	Hammond, Chris	70-100	
Edgeworth, Maria	Simple Susan and other Tales (1st, sm8vo, 216p, 4cp, fp b/w)	Macmillan	1929	Burd, Clara M.	25-40	
Edgeworth, Maria	Tales from…. (1st AM, 8vo, brown/gilt, teg, 412p, uncut, b/w)	Stokes	(1903)	Thomson, Hugh	85-130	
Edmonds, Walter D.	Cadmus Henry (1st, 8vo, 137p, b/w, DJ/2.75)	Dodd	1949	Lee, Manning De V.	60-100	R
Edmonds, Walter D.	Corporal Bess: Story of a Boy & a Dog (1st, 8vo, 182p, b/w, DJ/2.75)	Dodd	(1952)	Lee, Manning De V.	40-65	*
Edmonds, Walter D.	Hound Dog Moses & the Promised Land (1st, 8vo, [84]p, b/w, pep, DJ/2.50)	Dodd	(1954)	Gropper, William	40-65	*
Edmonds, Walter D.	Matchlock Gun (1st {std}, sm4to, 50p, dp color, pep, DJ/2.00, NM)	Dodd	1941	Lantz, Paul	90-140	R

AUTHOR	TITLE	PUBLISHER	DATE	ARTIST	PRICE	LC
Edmonds, Walter D.	Mr. Benedict's Lion (1st, 8vo, 154p, fp b/w, gilt, uncut, DJ/2.75)	Dodd	1950	Lee, Doris	60-90	R*
Edmonds, Walter D.	Musket and the Cross (1st {std}, 8vo, 514p, b/w, pep, DJ/10.00)	Little/Brown	(1968)	Bryant, Samuel	30-50	
Edmonds, Walter D.	They Had a Horse (1st, 8vo, 60p, fp b/w, DJ/3.50)	Dodd	(1962)	Gorsline, Douglas	50-80	R
Edmonds, Walter D.	Time to Go House (1st {std}, 8vo, 137p, tan cl, b/w, DJ/4.25)	Little/Brown	(1969)	Victor, Joan B.	30-50	
Edmonds, Walter D.	Tom Whipple (1st, lg8vo, 70p, dp color, pep, DJ/2.00)	Dodd	1942	Lantz, Paul	60-100	
Edmonds, Walter D.	Two Logs Crossing (1st, 8vo, 82p, green/gilt, fp b/w, pep, DJ/2.50)	Dodd	1943	Gergely, Tibor	50-85	
Edmonds, Walter D.	Uncle Ben's Whale (1st, 8vo, [82]p, fp b/w, DJ/2.75, NYTBI)	Dodd	(1955)	Gropper, William	40-65	
Edmonds, Walter D.	Wedding Journey (1st {std}, 8vo, 118p, color, DJ/2.50)	Little/Brown	1947	Tompkins, Alan	30-45	*
Edmonds, Walter D.	Wilderness Clearing (1st, 8vo, 156p, b/w, DJ/2.50)	Dodd	1944	DeMartelly, John	40-65	*
Edmonds, Walter D.	Wolf Hunt (1st {std}, 8vo, 112p, b/w, cep, DJ/4.50)	Little/Brown	(1970)	Bock, William	50-80	R*
Edmondson, Norah M.	Lavender Garden (1st, 8vo, 158p, teg, lavender/gilt, 4cp, pep)	L: Warne	1929	Howard, Charles T.	40-65	
Edwards, George W.	Alsace-Lorraine (1st AM, 4to, 344p, teg, blue/gilt, 18cp, 17pl)	Penn	(1918)	Edwards, George W.	90-120	
Edwards, George W.	Book of Old English Love Songs (1st, 8vo, 159p, gilt, b/w)	NY: Macmillan	1897	Edwards, George W.	100-180	
Edwards, George W.	Forest of Arden (1st, sm4to, red/gilt, 213p, teg, 6cp)	Stokes	(1914)	Edwards, George W.	35-60	
Edwards, George W.	Thus Think and Smoke Tobacco (1st, sm4to, red/gilt, AEG, b/w)	Stokes	1891	Edwards, George W.	250-400	
Edwards, Harry S.	Marbeau Cousins (1st {this pub}, sm8vo, 294p, cvr by....)	Rand/McNally	(1898)	Denslow, W.W.	40-65	
Edwards, Harry S.	Two Runaways (1st, sm8vo, 246p, gilt, 16pl)	Century	(1889)	Kemble, Edward W.	80-125	
Edwards, Lionel	Beasts of the Chase (1st, 4to, 49p, red/gilt, 8 fp color, DJ)	L: Putnam	1950	Edwards, Lionel	80-130	
Edwards, Lionel	Sketches in Stable and Kennel (1st, 4to, brown cl, 59p, 12 ticp)	L: Putnam	1933	Edwards, Lionel	120-200	
Edwards, May	Hobo Hound (1st {std}, sm4to, ibds, [32]p, color, DJ/1.25)	Rand/McNally	1947	Suba, Susanne	40-65	
Eells, Elsie S.	Brazilian Fairy Book (1st, 8vo, 193p, gilt, 6cp, pep)	Stokes	1926	Hood, George	70-100	
Eells, Elsie S.	Magic Tooth (1st, 8vo, orange cl, 243p, col frn, 10 fp b/w)	Little/Brown	1927	Choate/Curtis	40-60	*
Eells, Elsie S.	Tales of Enchantment from Spain (1st, 8vo, 173p, 4cp)	Harcourt	(1920)	Petershams	50-80	
Egan, Constance	Epaminondas & the Lettuces (1st, 16mo, 62p, brown bds, fp color, pep)	L: Collins	[1938]	Kennedy, A.E.	80-125	
Egan, Constance	Epaminondas & the Puppy (1st, 12mo, unpag, fp color, pep, DJ)	L: Collins	1959	Kennedy, A.E.	90-130	
Egan, Constance	Epaminondas Helps in the Garden (1st, 16mo, 62p, blue bds)	L: Collins	[1937]	Kennedy, A.E.	80-125	*
Egan, Constance	Epaminondas Helps in the House (12mo, ibds, unpag, color)	L: Collins	[1937]	Kennedy, A.E.	80-120	
Egan, Maurice F.	Everybody's Saint Francis (1st, 8vo, green/gilt, teg, 191p, 8cp)	Century	1912	DeMonvel, M.B.	60-90	
Eggleston, Edward	Hoosier Schoolboy (1st [1], 12mo, 181p, 5pl, PPP)	Scribner	1883	Bush, G.D.	150-220	
Eggleston, George C.	Last of the Flatboats (1st, sm8vo, green/gilt, 382p, 4pl)	Lothrop Pub.	(1900)	Harding, Charlotte	30-50	
Ehrhardt, Reinhold	Kikeri (1st AM {std}, ob4to, [32]p, color, DJ/4.95)	World	(1969)	Bernadette	40-65	*
Eichenberg, Fritz	Ape in a Cape (1st {std}, 4to, [32]p, color, pep, DJ/2.00, CH)	Harcourt	(1952)	Eichenberg, Fritz	100-160	R
Eichenberg, Fritz	Dancing in the Moon (1st {std}, 4to, red cl, [21]p, color, pep, DJ/2.25)	Harcourt	(1955)	Eichenberg, Fritz	70-120	R
Eickemeyer, Rudolf	Down South (1st, folio, ibds, [47]p, p-o, b/w)	R.H. Russell	1900	(Photos)	400-600	
Eidinoff, Maxwell L.	Atomics for the Millions (1st, lg8vo, 281p, blue cl, b/w, DJ/3.50)	Whittlesey	(1947)	Sendak, Maurice	450-600	
Eisgruber, Elsa	Spin Top Spin (1st AM, 4to, ibds, [32]p, color)	Macmillan	1929	Eisgruber, Elsa	90-120	
Elam, Elizabeth	Chuffer (1st {std}, 8vo, [48]p, ibds, DJ/1.25)	Winston	(1949)	Langford, Dan	25-45	*
Elder, Art	Blue Streak and Doctor Medusa (1st, sm8vo, 248p, b/w, pep, DJ)	Whitman	(1946)	Kirn, Frances	30-50	
Eldridge, Ethel	Ling, Grandson of Yen-Foh (1st, lg8vo, 29p, color, pep, DJ/1.00)	Whitman	1936	Wiese, Kurt	40-70	
Eldridge, Ethel	Yen-Foh, a Chinese Boy (1st, lg8vo, gilt, 29p, p-o, color, pep, DJ/1.00)	Whitman	1935	Wiese, Kurt	45-70	
Elias, E. (ed.)	Cinderella (1st AM, sm4to, red bds, p-o, 8 dp color)	McBride	1915	Pogany, Willy	200-300	
Eliot, Ethel C.	House Above the Trees (1st, 4to, 143p, blue cl, p-o, 5cp)	L: Butterworth	(1921)	Anderson, Anne	140-220	
Eliot, Ethel C.	Wind Boy (1st {std}, 8vo, 238p, col frn, b/w)	Doubleday/Page	1923	Bromhall, Winifred	40-70	
Eliot, George	Adam Bede (1st, 4to, 523p, p-o, teg, gilt, 16cp)	L: Chambers	[1900]	Browne, Gordon	80-120	
Eliot, George	Scenes from Clerical Life (1st, 12mo, 429p, green/gilt, AEG, 16cp)	L: Macmillan	1906	Thomson, Hugh	60-100	
Eliot, George	Silas Marner (1st, sm8vo, green/gilt, 262p, teg, 24cp, dep)	L: Dent	1905	Brock, Charles E.	50-85	
Eliot, T.S.	Old Possum's Book of Practical Cats (1st, 8vo, 51p, 14 fp color, DJ)	L: Faber	(1940)	Bentley, Nicolas	600-900	
Elkin, Benjamin	Big Jump (1st {std}, lg8vo, ibds, [65]p, color, DJ/1.95)	Beginner Books	(1958)	Evans, Katherine	60-90	
Elkin, Benjamin	Gillespie & the Guards (1st, 4to, 62p, fp 1-color, DJ/2.50, CH)	Viking	1956	Daugherty, James	80-125	
Elkin, Benjamin	King's Wish (1st {std}, lg8vo, 59p, color, DJ/1.95)	Beginner Books	1960	Shortall, Leonard	50-85	
Elkin, Benjamin	Loudest Noise in the World (1st, 4to, 64p, fp 1-color, DJ/2.50)	Viking	1954	Daugherty, James	40-70	R
Elkin, Benjamin	Such is the Way of the World (1st, sm4to, [40]p, color, dep, DJ/3.50)	Parents Mag. Pr.	(1968)	Mitsuhashi, Yoko	30-45	
Elkin, Benjamin	Why the Sun was Late (1st, 4to, [48]p, fp color, cep, DJ/2.95)	Parents Mag. Pr.	1966	Snyder, Jerome	25-40	
Elkin, Benjamin	Wisest Man in the World (1st, sm4to, [46]p, fp color, pep, DJ/3.50)	Parents Mag. Pr.	(1968)	Lobel, Anita	25-40	
Elkin, R.H.	Children's Corner (1st AM, lg ob8vo, [30]p, p-o, gilt, 16 ticp)	McKay/Augner	[1915]	LeMair, H.W.	200-300	
Elkin, R.H.	Little People (1st AM, lg8vo, [32]p, red/gilt, p-o, 16 fp color)	McKay/Augener	[1915]	LeMair, H.W.	200-300	
Elkin, R.H.	Old Dutch Nursery Rhymes (1st, ob4to, gilt, p-o, 31p, 16 fp color)	L: Augener	(1917)	LeMair, H.W.	200-300	
Elliot, Geraldine	Long Grass Whispers (1st, 4to, 132p, fp b/w, pep, DJ/2.00)	Putnam	(1939)	Hawkins, Sheila	35-50	
Elliot, Huger	Alliterative Alphabet... (1st, 4to, [55]p, blue bds, color, pep, DJ/2.50)	McKay	(1947)	Green, Eliz. S.	85-120	
Elliot, Kathleen	Jo-Yo's Idea (1st {std}, lg8vo, 114p, fp color, cep, DJ/2.00)	Knopf	1939	Duvoisin, Roger	60-90	
Elliot, Kathleen	Riema... (1st {std}, 8vo, 54p, ibds, color, pep, DJ/2.00)	Knopf	1937	Duvoisin, Roger	70-100	R
Elliot, Kathleen	Soomoon, Boy of Bali (1st {std}, 8vo, 88p, ibds, pep, color, DJ/2.00)	Knopf	1938	Duvoisin, Roger	80-120	R
Ellis, Edward S.	Klondike Nuggets (1st, sm8vo, 255p, 22pl)	Doub./McClure	1898	Lowell, Orson	50-85	
Ellis, Frederick S.	History of Reynard the Fox (1st, sm8vo, 289p, uncut, designs by...)	L: D. Nutt	1897	Crane, Walter	170-250	
Ellison, Virginia	Pooh Cook Book (1st {std}, 8vo, yellow cl, 120p, DJ/4.50)	Dutton	(1969)	Shepard, Ernest H.	25-40	
Elmer, Irene	Lodestone and Toadstone (1st, 4to, [40]p, fp color, cep, DJ/4.50)	Knopf	(1969)	Sidjakov, Nicolas	20-35	
Elmslie, Theodora C.	His Lordship's Puppy (1st, 8vo, 205p, gilt, 4pl)	Penn	1900	Waugh, Ida	30-50	
Elting, Mary	Hopi Way (1st {std}, lg8vo, 63p, fp 1-color, DJ/3.95)	Lippincott	(1969)	Mofsie, Louis	25-45	*
Elting, Mary	Mongo Homecoming (1st {std}, lg8vo, 54p, fp 1-color, DJ/3.95)	M. Evans	(1969)	Barnett, Moneta	30-45	*
Elting, Mary	Patch (1st {std}, sm8vo, 146p, b/w, pep, DJ/2.00)	Doubleday	1948	Koering, Ursula	30-50	*
Elton, Emily D.	Mince Pie Dream (1st, 8vo, 75p, cloth, 8cp)	NY: E.R. Herrick	1897	McManus, Blanche	50-80	*
Ely, Helena R.	Another Hardy Garden Book (1st, 8vo, teg, uncut, 243p, cvr by)	Macmillan	1905	Armstrong, Margaret	35-60	
Emanuel, Walter	Conceited Puppy... (1st AM, 12mo, ibds, p-o, color)	Dutton	(1905)	Aldin, Cecil	100-160	
Emanuel, Walter	Dog Day (1st AM, lg4to, [59]p, ibds, 28cp)	R.H. Russell	1902	Aldin, Cecil	250-400	
Emanuel, Walter	Dog Day (1st, lg4to, ibds, [59]p, 28cp)	L: Heinemann	1902	Aldin, Cecil	250-400	
Emanuel, Walter	Dog Day (24mo, 55p, ibds, 28cp)	Dutton	[1907]	Aldin, Cecil	100-160	
Emanuel, Walter	Dogs of War (1st, 8vo, tan/gilt, 243p, 12cp)	L: Bradbury/Ag	(1906)	Aldin, Cecil	200-300	
Emanuel, Walter	The Snob (1st, 4to, 35p, ibds, 19pl)	L: Lawrence/Bul.	1904	Aldin, Cecil	250-350	

AUTHOR	TITLE	PUBLISHER	DATE	ARTIST	PRICE	LC
Emanuel, Walter	Zoo: A Scamper (4to, 50p, ibds, fp color)	L: Alston Rivers	(1904)	Hassall, John	200-300	
Emberley, Barbara	Drummer Hoff (1st, ob4to, [32]p, color, DJ/4.25, CM)	Prentice-Hall	(1967)	Emberley, Ed	80-135	
Emberley, Barbara	Night's Nice (1st, 12mo, [26]p, color, pep, DJ/1.95)	Doubleday	1963	Emberley, Ed	40-65	
Emberley, Barbara	One Wide River to Cross (1st, ob4to, [32]p, color, DJ/3.95, CH)	Prentice-Hall	(1966)	Emberley, Ed	50-85	
Emberley, Barbara	Simon's Song (1st, 12mo, [32]p, 3-color, DJ/3.95)	Prentice-Hall	(1969)	Emberley, Ed	30-45	
Emberley, Barbara	Story of Paul Bunyan (1st, 4to, [32]p, color, DJ/3.25)	Prentice-Hall	(1963)	Emberley, Ed	30-50	
Emberley, Edward	Cock-a-Doodle-Doo (1st {std}, 12mo, [32]p, ibds, color, DJ/2.50)	Little/Brown	(1964)	Emberley, Ed	30-50	
Emberley, Edward	Green Says Go (1st {std}, 4to, 32p, color, DJ/3.95)	Little/Brown	(1968)	Emberley, Ed	30-50	*
Emberley, Edward	London Bridge is Falling Down (1st {std}, ob4to, 32p, color, DJ/3.50)	Little/Brown	(1967)	Emberley, Ed	30-50	
Emberley, Edward	Parade Book (1st {std}, ob4to, 28p, color, DJ/2.95)	Little/Brown	(1962)	Emberley, Ed	30-50	
Emberley, Edward	Punch and Judy (1st {std}, 4to, 27p, color, DJ/2.95, NYTBI)	Little/Brown	(1965)	Emberley, Ed	40-65	
Emberley, Edward	Rosebud (1st {std}, ob4to, 32p, color, DJ/3.00)	Little/Brown	(1966)	Emberley, Ed	30-50	
Emberley, Edward	Wing on a Flea (1st {std} [1st bk.], 4to, 48p, color, DJ/2.95, NYTBI)	Little/Brown	(1961)	Emberley, Ed	50-80	
Emblen, Don L.	Palomino Boy (1st, 8vo, blue cl, 189p, pep, DJ/2.00, decor by...)	Viking	1948	Ward, Lynd	40-65	
Embry, Margaret	Blue-Nosed Witch (1st, 8vo, 45p, yellow cl, b/w, pep, DJ/2.00)	Holiday House	(1955)	Rose, Carl	25-40	
Embry, Margaret	Kid Sister (1st, sm8vo, 165p, yellow cl, fp b/w, pep, DJ/2.50)	Holiday House	(1958)	Freeman, Don	30-45	
Embry, Margaret	Mr. Blue (1st, 8vo, 71p, b/w, DJ/2.75)	Holiday House	(1963)	Turkle, Brinton	30-50	
Embry, Margaret	My Name is Lion (1st, 8vo, 46p, fp b/w, DJ/3.75)	Holiday House	(1970)	Glattauer, Ned	20-30	
Embry, Margaret	Peg-Leg Willy (1st, 8vo, [45]p, ibds, 1-color, DJ/2.95)	Holiday House	(1966)	Grifalconi, Ann	25-40	
Emerson, Caroline	Hat Tub Tale... (1st {std}, 8vo, 185p, blue cl, uncut, b/w, pep)	Dutton	1928	Lenski, Lois	70-120	
Emerson, Caroline	Indian Hunting Grounds (1st, 8vo, 191p, b/w, DJ/1.75)	Stokes	1938	Schuyler, Remington	40-65	*
Emerson, Caroline	Little Green Car (1st, 8vo, ipcb, [28]p, color, pep, DJ/0.50)	Grosset/Dunlap	(1946)	Galdone, Paul	60-100	*
Emerson, Caroline	Magic Tunnel (1st, 8vo, 120p, b/w, DJ/1.75)	Stokes	1940	Lufkin, Raymond	70-100	*
Emerson, Caroline	Magic Tunnel (1st [this pub.], 8vo, 122p, b/w, DJ)	Four Winds Pr.	(1964)	Robinson, Jerry	40-65	
Emerson, Caroline	Merry-Go-Round of Modern Tales (1st, 8vo, gilt, 173p, b/w, pep)	Dutton	1927	Lenski, Lois	70-120	*
Emerson, Caroline	Mickey Sees the U.S.A. (1st, 8vo, 138p, color, pep)	D.C. Heath	(1944)	Disney Studios	50-80	
Emerson, Caroline	Mr. Nip & Mr. Tuck (1st {std}, 8vo, 173p, aqua/gilt, b/w, dep)	Dutton	1930	Lenski, Lois	70-125	
Emerson, Caroline	School Days in Disneyville (1st, 8vo, 102p, color, pep)	D.C. Heath	(1939)	Disney Studios	60-90	
Emerson, Edwin	Adventures of Theodore Roosevelt (1st {std}, 8vo, 336p, gilt, b/w)	Dutton	(1928)	Hader, Elmer	30-50	*
Emerson, Willis G.	Smoky God (1st, 12mo, 186p, blue cl, 11cp)	Chi: Forbes	1908	Williams, John A.	70-100	*
Emett, Rowland	New World for Nellie (1st AM {std}, 4to, [40]p, ipcb, color, pep, DJ/2.00)	Harcourt	(1952)	Emett, Rowland	60-90	R
Emmet, Rosina	Pretty Peggy... (lg sq8vo, ibds, 64p, chromos)	Dodd	1880	Emmet, Rosina	90-120	
Enckling, Louise	Toy Maker (1st, 8vo, 16p, p-o, color, pep, DJ/1.00)	Whitman	1935	Kukenthal, Fritz	40-70	
Endres, Ernest	Day with The Gnomes (1st, 24mo, [54]p, ibds, pep, 19 color)	L: Nister	[1910]	Endres, Ernest	120-200	
Engdahl, Sylvia	Enchantress from the Stars (1st {std}, lg8vo, 275p, b/w, cep, DJ/5.95, NH)	Atheneum	1970	Shackell, Rodney	65-100	
Engdahl, Sylvia	Journey Between Worlds (1st {std}, 8vo, 235p, DJ/5.25, decor by...)	Atheneum	1970	McCrea, J.& R.	25-40	
Engelhard, Georgia	Peterli and the Mountain (1st, lg8vo, 39p, fp 1-color, pep, DJ/2.25)	Lippincott	(1954)	Gekiere, Madeleine	30-50	*
England, George A.	Air Trust (1st, sm8vo, 333p, red/gilt, 6pl)	Phila: P. Wagner	(1915)	Sloan, John	130-200	
England, George A.	Darkness and Dawn (1st, sm8vo, 672p, col frn, 4pl, pep)	Small/Maynard	(1914)	Monahan, P.J.	150-220	*
England, George A.	Flying Legion (1st, 8vo, 394p, frn by...)	McClurg	1920	Monahan, P.J.	60-90	*
England, George A.	Golden Blight (1st, sm8vo, 350p, brown/gilt, 5pl)	H.K. Fly	(1916)	Sloan, John	75-100	*
Engle, Paul	Golden Child (1st {std}, 8vo, 127p, 1-color, DJ/3.50)	Dutton	(1962)	Fisher, Leonard	30-45	
Engle, Paul	Who's Afraid? (1st {std}, 4to, 64p, 1-color)	Crowell-Collier	1963	Prohaska, Ray	30-50	
Englefield, Cicely	Tail of a Guinea-Pig (1st AM, 24mo, ipcb, 43p, fp b/w, pep)	NY: Oxford U.Pr.	[1937]	Englefield, Cicely	30-45	
English, Doug	Book of Nimble Beasts (1st, sm8vo, green/gilt, 318p)	L: E. Nash	1910	(Photos)	40-60	*
English, James W.	Tailbone Patrol (1st, 8vo, 186p, grey cl, fp b/w, pep, DJ/2.75)	Holiday House	(1955)	Wells, Peter	30-50	*
English, Thomas D.	Little Giant, Big Dwarf (1st, sm4to, 150p, t.e. yellow, 4 fp b/w)	McClurg	1904	Perkins, Lucy F.	70-100	
Engvick, Wm. (ed)	Lullabies and Night Songs (1st, folio, 77p, blue/gilt, color, cep, DJ/6.95)	Harper	(1965)	Sendak, Maurice	150-200	
Enright, Elizabeth	Borrowed Summer (1st, sm8vo, 275p, b/w, DJ/2.50)	Rinehart	(1946)	Enright, Elizabeth	50-80	
Enright, Elizabeth	Christmas Tree for Lydia (1st, 24mo, ipcb, 38p, 1-color, dep, DJ/1.00)	Rinehart	(1951)	Enright, Elizabeth	40-65	
Enright, Elizabeth	Four-Story Mistake (1st, 8vo, 177p, 9 fp 1-color, pep, DJ/1.75)	Farrar/Rinehart	(1942)	Enright, Elizabeth	60-100	
Enright, Elizabeth	Gone-Away Lake (1st {std}, 8vo, 192p, green cl, b/w, DJ/3.00, NH)	Harcourt	(1957)	Krush, Beth & Joe	70-100	
Enright, Elizabeth	Kintu (1st, sm8vo, p-o, 54p, color, DJ/1.00)	Farrar/Rinehart	1935	Enright, Elizabeth	50-85	
Enright, Elizabeth	Return to Gone-Away (1st {std}, 8vo, 191p, fp b/w, DJ/3.25)	Harcourt	(1961)	Krush, Beth & Joe	60-90	R
Enright, Elizabeth	Sea is All Around (1st, 8vo, 124p, green cl, 6cp, pep, DJ/2.00)	Farrar/Rinehart	(1940)	Enright, Elizabeth	40-65	
Enright, Elizabeth	Spiderweb for Two: Melendy Maze (1st, 8vo, 209p, uncut, b/w, DJ/2.50)	Rinehart	(1951)	Enright, Elizabeth	50-80	*
Enright, Elizabeth	Tatsinda (1st {std}, 8vo, 80p, fp color, DJ/3.50)	Harcourt	(1963)	Haas, Irene	70-120	R
Enright, Elizabeth	The Saturdays (1st, sm8vo, red cl, 175p, fp 1-color, pep, DJ/2.00)	Farrar/Rinehart	(1941)	Enright, Elizabeth	30-50	
Enright, Elizabeth	Then There were Five (1st, 8vo, blue cl, 241p, uncut, b/w, DJ/2.00)	Farrar/Rinehart	(1944)	Enright, Elizabeth	30-50	
Enright, Elizabeth	Thimble Summer (1st, 8vo, 124p, color, pep, DJ/2.00, NM)	Farrar/Rinehart	1938	Enright, Elizabeth	150-220	R
Enright, Elizabeth	Zeee (1st {std}, sm8vo, 46p, fp color, DJ/3.50)	Harcourt	(1965)	Haas, Irene	45-70	
Ensor, Dorothy	Adventures of Hatim Tai (1st AM {std}, 8vo, 89p, 6cp, DJ/2.75)	H.Z. Walck	1962	Baynes, Pauline	30-45	
Epstein, Samuel	Take this Hammer (1st {std}, 8vo, [32]p, color, DJ/3.95)	Hawthorn Books	(1969)	DePaola, Tomie	25-40	
Erickson, Phoebe	Double or Nothing (1st, lg8vo, 127p, b/w, DJ/2.75)	Harper	(1958)	Erickson, Phoebe	25-40	
Ershov, Peter P.	Little Magic Horse (1st, sm4to, [128]p, fp 2-color, pep, DJ/2.50)	Macmillan	1942	Bock, Vera	60-90	R
Erskine, Payne	Iona (1st, 8vo, blue cl)	Dibble	1891	Armstrong, Margaret	55-90	
Ervin, Mabel C.	As Told by the Typewriter Girl (1st, 8vo, 245p)	Herrick	(1898)	McManus, Blanche	60-90	
Erwin, John	Mrs. Fox (1st, 8vo, 127p, b/w, DJ/3.95)	Simon/Schuster	(1969)	Tripp, Wallace	20-35	
Escott-Inman, H.	Wulnoth the Wanderer ([new ed.] {std}, sm8vo, 316p, 8pl, pep)	Longmans	1928	Daugherty, James	30-50	
Estes, Eleanor	Echoing Green (1st, 8vo, 263p, b/w, DJ/3.00)	Macmillan	1947	Estes, Eleanor	40-65	
Estes, Eleanor	Ginger Pye (1st {std}, 8vo, 250p, yellow cl, b/w, DJ/2.50, NM)	Harcourt	(1951)	Estes, Eleanor	120-200	R
Estes, Eleanor	Hundred Dresses (1st, 8vo, 80p, red cl, color, DJ/2.50, NH)	Harcourt	(1944)	Slobodkin, Louis	90-140	
Estes, Eleanor	Little Oven (1st {std}, ob8vo, [32]p, color, DJ/2.25)	Harcourt	1955	Estes, Eleanor	70-100	
Estes, Eleanor	Lollipop Princess (1st {std}, ob8vo, [32]p, 1-color, DJ/2.50)	Harcourt	(1967)	Estes, Eleanor	60-90	
Estes, Eleanor	Middle Moffat (1st, 8vo, 317p, p-o, b/w, pep, DJ/2.00, NH)	Harcourt	(1942)	Slobodkin, Louis	90-140	
Estes, Eleanor	Miranda the Great (1st {std}, 8vo, 79p, b/w, DJ/3.25)	Harcourt	(1967)	Ardizzone, Edward	60-80	
Estes, Eleanor	Pinky Pye (1st {std}, sm8vo, 192p, pink cl, b/w, DJ/3.00)	Harcourt	(1958)	Ardizzone, Edward	60-90	R
Estes, Eleanor	Rufus M. (1st, 8vo, 320p, red cl, b/w, pep, DJ/2.00, NH)	Harcourt	(1943)	Slobodkin, Louis	80-130	

AUTHOR	TITLE	PUBLISHER	DATE	ARTIST	PRICE	LC
Estes, Eleanor	Sleeping Giant (1st, 8vo, 101p, green cl, fp color, DJ/3.00)	Harcourt	(1948)	Estes, Eleanor	80-125	
Estes, Eleanor	Sun, Wind & Mr. Todd (1st, 4to, [92]p, brown cl, 1-color, pep, DJ/2.00)	Harcourt	(1943)	Slobodkin, Louis	70-100	
Estes, Eleanor	The Alley (1st {std}, 8vo, 283p, b/w, DJ/3.50)	Harcourt	(1964)	Ardizzone, Edward	50-80	R
Estes, Eleanor	The Moffats (1st [1st bk.], 8vo, pink cl, 290p, b/w, pep, DJ/2.00)	Harcourt	(1941)	Slobodkin, Louis	80-125	R
Estes, Eleanor	Witch Family (1st {std}, 8vo, green cl, 186p, b/w, DJ/3.25)	Harcourt	(1960)	Ardizzone, Edward	40-65	
Ets, Marie H.	Another Day (1st, lg ob8vo, 40p, pep, b/w, DJ/1.75)	Viking	1953	Ets, Marie H.	50-80	R
Ets, Marie H.	Automobiles for Mice (1st, ob4to, 31p, color, DJ/3.00)	Viking	(1964)	Ets, Marie H.	40-65	
Ets, Marie H.	Bad Boy, Good Boy (1st, sm4to, 49p, 1-color, pep, DJ/3.95)	Crowell	(1967)	Ets, Marie H.	30-50	
Ets, Marie H.	Beasts & Nonsense (1st, 8vo, 64p, b/w, pep, DJ/2.00, NYTBI)	Viking	1952	Ets, Marie H.	50-80	
Ets, Marie H.	Cow's Party (1st, 4to, 32p, color, pep, DJ/2.50)	Viking	(1958)	Ets, Marie H.	50-85	
Ets, Marie H.	Gilberto and the Wind (1st, 4to, 32p, 1-color, cep, DJ/3.00)	Viking	(1963)	Ets, Marie H.	60-90	R*
Ets, Marie H.	In the Forest (1st, lg ob8vo, ipcb, [45]p, b/w, DJ/1.00, CH)	Viking	1944	Ets, Marie H.	80-145	
Ets, Marie H.	Just Me (1st, ob8vo, [32]p, b/w, DJ/2.50, CH)	Viking	(1965)	Ets, Marie H.	70-100	*
Ets, Marie H.	Little Old Automobile (1st, 4to, ipcb, [32]p, b/w, pep, DJ/1.50)	Viking	1948	Ets, Marie H.	60-90	
Ets, Marie H.	Mr. Penny (1st {1st book}, ob4to, ibds, 48p, b/w, pep, DJ/1.00)	Viking	1935	Ets, Marie H.	120-200	
Ets, Marie H.	Mr. Penny's Circus (1st, 4to, 64p, b/w, DJ/2.50)	Viking	(1961)	Ets, Marie H.	60-100	
Ets, Marie H.	Mr. Penny's Race Horse (1st, sm4to, 63p, b/w, pep, DJ/2.00, CH)	Viking	1956	Ets, Marie H.	100-165	R
Ets, Marie H.	Mr. T.W. Anthony Woo (1st, ob4to, ibds, 54p, pep, b/w, DJ/2.00, CH)	Viking	1951	Ets, Marie H.	100-160	
Ets, Marie H.	Nine Days to Christmas (1st, 4to, 48p, color, DJ/3.25, CM)	Viking	(1959)	Ets, Marie H.	150-225	
Ets, Marie H.	Oley, the Sea Monster (1st, 4to, ipcb, [32]p, b/w, pep, DJ/1.50)	Viking	1947	Ets, Marie H.	90-140	
Ets, Marie H.	Play with Me (1st, sm4to, 31p, color, DJ/2.50, CH)	Viking	(1955)	Ets, Marie H.	100-170	R
Ets, Marie H.	Story of a Baby (1st, lg4to, 63p, blue cl, pep, b/w, DJ/2.50)	Viking	1939	Ets, Marie H.	70-100	
Ets, Marie H.	Talking Without Words (1st, ob8vo, [32]p, b/w, cep, DJ/2.75, NYTBI)	Viking	(1968)	Ets, Marie H.	40-65	
Ettinger, Harold	Fair, Fantastic Paris (1st {std}, 8vo, 250p, b/w, gilt, DJ/3.00)	Bobbs-Merrill	(1944)	Duvoisin, Roger	45-70	
Eunson, Dale	Day they Gave Babies Away (1st, 8vo, 38p, ibds, b/w, DJ/2.00)	Farrar, Straus	1947	Kredel, Fritz	25-40	
Eustis, Celestine	Cooking in Old Creole Days (1st, 8vo, ipcb, 129p, 8pl)	R.H. Russell	1903	Pennington, Harper	200-300	R
Evans, C.S.	Cinderella (1st, 4to, 110p, cream bds, ti-col frn, dp b/w, pep)	L: Heinemann	(1919)	Rackham, Arthur	250-320	
Evans, C.S.	Reynard the Fox (1st, 4to, 127p, p-o, 6cp)	Dodd	(1923)	Brightwell, L.R.	40-65	
Evans, C.S.	Sleeping Beauty (1st, 4to, ibds, 110p, 1 ticp, 4 dp color)	L: Heinemann	(1920)	Rackham, Arthur	200-300	
Evans, Eva K.	Araminta (1st, 8vo, 84p, b/w, pep, DJ/2.00)	Minton Balch	(1935)	Berry, Erick	50-80	
Evans, Eva K.	Araminta's Goat (1st, 8vo, 92p, b/w, DJ/2.00)	Putnam	(1938)	Berry, Erick	50-80	
Evans, Eva K.	Dirt Book (1st {std}, 8vo, 86p, b/w, DJ/3.75)	Little/Brown	(1969)	Quackenbush, Rbt.	20-30	*
Evans, Eva K.	Jerome Anthony (1st, 8vo, blue cl, 88p, b/w, DJ/2.00)	Putnam	(1936)	Berry, Erick	40-60	*
Evans, Eva K.	Key Corner (1st, 8vo, 206p, tan cl, pep, fp b/w, DJ/2.00)	Putnam	(1938)	Berry, Erick	30-60	
Evans, Eva K.	Mr. Jones & Mr. Finnigan (1st, 8vo, [32]p, tan cl, 2-color, dep, DJ/1.00)	NY: Oxford U.Pr.	(1941)	Berry, Erick	30-50	
Evans, Eva K.	People are Important (1st, 8vo, 86p, b/w, DJ/2.50, JABA)	Capitol Pub. Co.	(1951)	Earle, Vana	30-45	
Evans, Eva K.	Surprise for Araminta (1st, sq8vo, [28]p, col frn, pep, DJ/0.50)	Grosset/Dunlap	1942	Eshner, Ann	65-90	
Evans, F. Gwynne	Puffin, Puma & Co. (1st, sm4to, ipcb, 96p, b/w)	L: Macmillan	1929	Morrow, George	70-100	
Evans, Florence A.	Alice's Adventures in Pictureland (1st, sm4to, 192p, b/w pl)	Dodge	(1900)	Wheelan, A.R.	100-180	
Evans, Florence A.	Jewel Story Book (1st, 12mo, 102p, green cl, 4pl)	Saalfield	1903	Fry, W.H.	25-45	
Evans, Katherine	Michael Angelo Mouse (1st, 8vo, [28]p, ibds, color, DJ/1.00)	Wilcox/Follett	(1945)	Evans, Katherine	25-40	
Evans, Lawton	America First (1st, 8vo, 447p, p-o, pep, col frn, 9pl)	Milton Bradley	1920	Winter, Milo	40-60	*
Evans, Lawton	Once to Every Man (1st, sm8vo, 317p, 4pl)	H.K. Fly	(1914)	Fischer, Anton O.	35-60	
Evans, Melvin	Tiniest Sound (1st {std}, 8vo, [48]p, color, DJ/3.50)	Doubleday	(1969)	Young, Ed	30-50	
Evans, Myfanwy	No Rubbish Here (1st, 4to, green ibds, 34p, color)	L: Collins	(1936)	Tempest, Margaret	70-100	
Evans, Sebastian (tr)	High History of the Holy Grail (1st, 8vo, uncut, gilt, teg, 379p, 22pl)	L: Dent	1903	King, Jessie	700-1000	
Evarts, Hal G.	Bald Face & other Animal Stories (1st, 8vo, 317p, 8pl, pep)	Knopf	1921	Bull, Charles L.	50-80	
Evarts, Hal G.	Passing of the Old West (1st, 8vo, 234p, 8pl)	Little/Brown	1921	Bull, Charles L.	50-80	
Evatt, Harriet	Big Indian and Little Bear (1st, 8vo, [32]p, fp 2-color, pep, DJ/1.75)	Bobbs-Merrill	1954	Evatt, Harriet	30-45	
Everett-Green, Evelyn	King's Butterfly (1st, sm8vo, 72p, p-o, gilt, b/w)	Nister/Dutton	(1900)	Dixon, Arthur A.	30-50	
Everett-Green, Evelyn	Princess's Token (1st, sm8vo, 48p, gilt, b/w)	Nister/Dutton	(1902)	Dixon, Arthur A.	30-50	
Evernden, Margery	Secret of the Porcelain Fish (1st, 8vo, 147p, b/w, dep, DJ/2.25)	Random	(1947)	Handforth, Thomas	25-45	*
Evers, Alf	Abner's Cabin (1st {std}, 4to, [42]p, fp b/w, pep, DJ/2.95)	F. Watts	1957	Weisgard, Leonard	40-70	
Evers, Alf	Colonel's Squad (1st {std}, 8vo, blue/gilt, 200p, b/w, DJ/2.75)	Macmillan	1952	Sewell, Helen	30-50	
Evers, Alf	In the Beginning (1st, lg8vo, aqua cl, [30]p, 2-color, dep, DJ/2.00)	Macmillan	1954	Sewell, Helen	60-90	R
Evers, Alf	Three Kings of Saba (1st, 4to, [30]p, color, DJ/2.50, NYTBI)	Lippincott	1955	Sewell, Helen	50-80	R
Evers, Helen	This Little Pig (1st, 8vo, [32]p, ibds, fp 1-color, pep)	Farrar/Rinehart	(1932)	Unknown	50-80	*
Everson, Dale	Different Dog (1st, 4to, blue cl, 31p, 2-color, pep, DJ/2.75)	Wm. Morrow	1960	Galdone, Paul	30-50	
Everson, Howard	Coming of the Dragon Ships (1st {std}, 8vo, gilt, 128p, 4cp, 6pl, pep)	Dutton	1931	D'Aulaire, E. Parin	60-90	*
Ewald, Carl	Old Willow-Tree & other Stories (1st, 8vo, 157p, p-o, 4cp by...)	Stokes	(1923)	Jacobs, Helen	50-85	
Ewald, Carl	Twelve Sisters (1st, 8vo, 143p, b/w)	L: Butterworth	1923	Noble, Edwin	30-50	*
Ewing, Frank	I-A-Goo & his Forest Friends (1st, 4to, ibds, 110p, b/w, pep, DJ/1.50)	Foster & Stewart	(1947)	Clare, Ernie	30-50	
Ewing, Juliana H.	Blue and Red.... (4to, ibds, 32p, chromos)	L: SPCK	[1881]	Andre, R.	170-240	
Ewing, Juliana H.	Blue Bells on the Lea (1st, ob8vo, ibds, 32p, chromos)	L: SPCK	[1884]	Andre, R.	100-180	
Ewing, Juliana H.	Daddy Darwin's Dovecot (1st, sm8vo, 52p, ibds, gilt, teg, col frn)	L: SPCK	[1884]	Caldecott, Randolph	80-120	
Ewing, Juliana H.	Daddy Darwin's Dovecot (1st AM, 12mo, 62p, ibds)	Roberts Bros.	1886	Caldecott, Randolph	70-100	
Ewing, Juliana H.	Daddy Darwin's Dovecot (1st, 12mo, 78p, grey cl, 6pl)	Dana Estes	1898	Barry, Etheldred B.	35-60	*
Ewing, Juliana H.	Flat Iron for a Farthing (1st, 12mo, 235p, teg, uncut, 8cp, pep)	L: G. Bell	1908	Wheelhouse, Mary V.	35-60	*
Ewing, Juliana H.	Great Emergency (1st, 12mo, 166p, b/w pl)	L.C. Page	1897	Barry, Etheldred B.	30-50	*
Ewing, Juliana H.	Jacanapes (1st, lg8vo, ibds, 184p, teg, col frn)	L: SPCK	1884	Caldecott, Randolph	140-200	
Ewing, Juliana H.	Jacanapes (1st, 8vo, 80p, gilt, AEG, 7pl)	Dutton	1893	Gordon, Frederic C.	40-60	*
Ewing, Juliana H.	Jacanapes (1st, 12mo, 60p, blue cl, b/w)	J. Knight	1895	Sacker, Amy	35-60	*
Ewing, Juliana H.	Jacanapes (1st {this pub}, 12mo, 71p, rust cl, 6pl)	Dana Estes	(1902)	Bruce, Josephine	25-40	*
Ewing, Juliana H.	Jacanapes (1st, 12mo, 72p, col frn, 4 fp b/w, dep)	McLoughlin	(1906)	Noble-Ives, Sarah	35-60	*
Ewing, Juliana H.	Jacanapes (1st, 8vo, 196p, 8cp)	L: Bell	1913	Brock, Henry M.	50-80	
Ewing, Juliana H.	Jacanapes (1st, sm8vo, green/gilt, 62p, color, pep, DJ/2.00)	Oxford U. Pr.	1948	Tudor, Tasha	250-350	
Ewing, Juliana H.	Jan of the Windmill (1st, 12mo, 307p, teg, uncut, 8cp, pep)	L: G. Bell	1909	Wheelhouse, Mary V.	40-60	*
Ewing, Juliana H.	Lob Lie-by-the-Fire (1st, 8vo, 72p, ibds)	L: SPCK	(1885)	Caldecott, Randolph	80-130	

AUTHOR	TITLE	PUBLISHER	DATE	ARTIST	PRICE	LC
Ewing, Juliana H.	Lob Lie-by-the-Fire (1st, sq8vo, teg, 189p, 8cp)	L: Bell	1909	Woodward, Alice B.	50-80	
Ewing, Juliana H.	Lob Lie-by-the-Fire ([new ed.], 8vo, 144p, b/w, DJ/1.50)	NY: Oxford U.Pr.	(1937)	Ivins, Florence	25-40	*
Ewing, Juliana H.	Master Fritz (1st, ob8vo, 32p, ibds, color)	L: SPCK	[1883]	Andre, R.	140-200	*
Ewing, Juliana H.	Mrs. Overtheway's Remembrances (1st, 8vo, 195p, teg, 8cp, pep)	L: G. Bell	1909	Wheelhouse, Mary V.	45-70	
Ewing, Juliana H.	Mrs. Overtheway's Remembrances (12mo, red/gilt, p-o, 209p, color)	L: H. Frowde	(1911)	Brock, Charles E.	30-50	
Ewing, Juliana H.	Old Fashioned Fairy Tales (1st, 12mo, 125p, 8cp, pep)	L: G. Bell	(1919)	Robertson, W.G.	200-300	
Ewing, Juliana H.	Our Garden (1st, ob8vo, ibds, 32p, color)	L: SPCK	[1883]	Andre, R.	120-180	*
Ewing, Juliana H.	Six to Sixteen (1st, 12mo, green cl, 237p, teg, 8cp)	L: G. Bell	1908	Wheelhouse, Mary V.	30-50	
Ewing, Juliana H.	Soldier's Children (ob12mo, 32p, 172p, ibds, chromos)	L: SPCK	[1883]	Andre, R.	200-300	
Ewing, Juliana H.	Stories by J.H. Ewing (1st, lg8vo, blue cl, p-o, 426p, 8cp)	Duffield	1920	Cooke, Edna	60-90	
Ewing, Juliana H.	The Brownies (1st, 12mo, ibds, 50p, 3-color, dep, DJ/1.50)	Scribner	1946	Milhous, Katherine	35-60	
Ewing, Juliana H.	Three Christmas Trees (1st, 12mo, green/gilt, 88p, col frn, dep)	Macmillan	1930	Bianco, Pamela	35-60	
Ewing, Juliana H.	We & the World (1st, 12mo, rust cl, 315p, teg, 8cp, pep)	L: G. Bell	1910	Wheelhouse, Mary V.	30-50	
Ewing, Juliana H.	Week Spent in a Glass Pond (4to, ibds, 32p, chromos)	L: Wells/Gard.	[1883]	Andre, R.	250-450	
F.M.H.	War of the Wooden Soldiers (1st, 12mo, ipcb, [76]p, color)	Rand/McNally	(1915)	Wheeler, M.& W.	50-80	R
Faber, Doris	Wonderful Tumble of Timothy Smith (1st {std}, 8vo, 84p, b/w, DJ/2.50)	Knopf	1958	Shortall, Leonard	20-35	*
Fable, Leonard	Gingerbread Man (1st AM, 4to, [32]p, p-o, 8cp)	McBride	1915	Pogany, Willy	160-220	
Fabre	Fabre's Book of Insects (1st, lg4to, 184p, white/gilt, 12 ticp)	L: Hodder	(1921)	Detmold, Edward J.	250-350	
Fabres, Oscar	Kwik and Kwak (1st, sm4to, [48]p, ibds, fp color, pep, DJ/1.50)	Crown Pub.	1942	Fabres, Oscar	40-70	*
Fadiman, Clifton	Wally the Wordworm (1st {std}, 12mo, [63]p, color, DJ/2.95)	Macmillan	(1964)	Roth, Arnold	20-35	
Fairholme, Elizabeth	Esmeralda Ahoy! (1st AM {std}, 8vo, 212p, DJ/2.95)	Doubleday	1959	Spier, Peter E.	25-40	
Fairless, Michael	Gathering of Brother Hilarius (1st, 8vo, 142p, teg, gilt, 8 ticp)	L: Duckworth	1913	Brickdale, E.F.	45-70	
Fairmont, Ethel	Rhymes for Kindly Children (4to, [127]p, color, pep)	Wise-Parlow	(1937)	Gruelle, Johnny	50-80	
Falkberget, Johan	Broomstick & Snowflake (1st, 8vo, blue cl, 88p, b/w, cep)	Macmillan	1933	Sewell, Helen	30-50	
Fall, Thomas	Canalboat to Freedom (1st, 8vo, 215p, fp b/w, cep, DJ/3.50)	Dial Press	1966	Cellini, Joseph	25-45	
Fall, Thomas	Goat Boy of Brooklyn (1st {std}, 8vo, 192p, b/w, DJ/3.95)	Dial Press	(1968)	Rocker, Fermin	20-30	
Fallon, Sara W.	Animal-Alphabet Book (1st, ob4to, [54]p, color)	L: G. Allen	1899	Fallon, Sara W.	180-250	*
Falls, Charles B.	ABC Book (1st, lg4to, [30]p, ibds, 26cp, pep)	Doubleday/Page	1923	Falls, Charles B.	170-240	
Falls, Charles B.	ABC Book (lg4to, orange ibds, [30]p, fp color)	Doubleday/Doran	1939	Falls, Charles B.	120-185	R*
Falls, Charles B.	First 3000 Years (1st, sm4to, 220p, color, DJ/6.00)	Viking	(1960)	Falls, Charles B.	50-85	
Falls, Charles B.	Modern ABC Book (1st, lg4to, [32]p, 26 col)	NY: J. Day	1930	Falls, Charles B.	160-240	*
Faralla, Dana	Singing Cupboard (1st AM {std}, 8vo, 93p, b/w, DJ/3.25)	Lippincott	(1963)	Ardizzone, Edward	30-50	
Faralla, Dana	Swanhilda-of-the-Swans (1st, 8vo, 92p, blue cl, b/w, DJ)	L: Blackie	(1964)	Ardizzone, Edward	40-65	
Faralla, Dana	Wonderful Flying-Go-Round (1st {std}, 94p, b/w, DJ/3.50)	World	(1965)	Berson, Harold	25-40	
Farjeon, B.L.	Lucy & their Majesties (1st, sm8vo, 332p, tan cl, 20pl)	Century	1904	Cory/Varian	35-60	
Farjeon, Eleanor	Alphabet of Magic (1st, lg8vo, 57p, green cl, b/w)	L: Medici	1928	Tarrant, Margaret	30-50	
Farjeon, Eleanor	Ameliaranne and the Magic Ring (1st AM, 8vo, [63]p, p-o, color, pep)	McKay	[1933]	Pearse, Susan B.	50-80	
Farjeon, Eleanor	Bad Day for Martha (1st, lg8vo, 29p, ipcb, p-o, b/w)	L: Blackwell	[1928]	Richards, Eugenie	30-50	*
Farjeon, Eleanor	Calvacade of Queens (1st AM, sm4to, gilt, 243p, b/w, DJ/5.95)	H.Z. Walck	1965	Ambrus, Victor	25-40	
Farjeon, Eleanor	Cherrystones (1st AM {std}, 12mo, red/gilt, 58p, fp b/w, DJ/1.25)	Lippincott	(1944)	Morton-Sale, J.	30-45	
Farjeon, Eleanor	Children's Bells (1st AM {std}, lg8vo, 212p, b/w, DJ/3.50)	H.Z. Walck	(1960)	Fortnum, Peggy	25-45	
Farjeon, Eleanor	Come Christmas (1st AM, sm8vo, ipcb, 62p, color)	Stokes	1928	Field, Rachel	50-80	
Farjeon, Eleanor	Country Child's Alphabet (1st, 8vo, stiff wraps, [54]p, b/w)	L: Poetry Bkshp.	1924	Rothenstein, Wm. M.	120-200	
Farjeon, Eleanor	Fair of St. James (1st, 8vo, 310p, green/gilt, b/w)	Stokes	1932	Lathrop, Dorothy	60-90	
Farjeon, Eleanor	Glass Slipper (1st, 8vo, 175p, b/w, DJ)	L: Oxford U.Pr.	1955	Shepard, Ernest H.	55-80	
Farjeon, Eleanor	Glass Slipper (1st AM, 8vo, 187p, red cl, b/w, DJ/2.75)	Viking	1956	Shepard, Ernest H.	35-60	
Farjeon, Eleanor	Heroes & Heroines (1st AM, lg8vo, 79p, ibds, fp color, DJ)	Dutton	(1933)	Thornycroft, R.	60-100	
Farjeon, Eleanor	Italian Peepshow (1st, 8vo, gilt, p-o, 146p, 12 fp color, pep)	Stokes	1926	Thornycroft, R.	35-60	*
Farjeon, Eleanor	Jim at the Corner (1st AM, 8vo, 101p, b/w, cep, DJ/2.75)	H.Z. Walck	1958	Ardizzone, Edward	30-50	
Farjeon, Eleanor	Joan's Door (1st, 8vo, 127p, gilt, teg, b/w)	L: Collins	(1926)	Townsend, Will	30-50	
Farjeon, Eleanor	Kaleidoscope (1st AM, 8vo, 157p, b/w, DJ/3.75)	H.Z. Walck	1963	Ardizzone, Edward	30-50	
Farjeon, Eleanor	Kaleidoscope (1st, 8vo, 157p, b/w, DJ)	L: Oxford U.Pr.	1963	Ardizzone, Edward	40-65	
Farjeon, Eleanor	Katy Kruse at the Seaside (1st, 4to, blue cl, 32p, p-o, 12 fp color)	McKay	(1932)	(Photos)	180-240	
Farjeon, Eleanor	Kings & Queens (1st AM, lg8vo, 79p, color, DJ)	Dutton	1932	Thornycroft, R.	50-90	
Farjeon, Eleanor	Kings & Queens (1st, 8vo, 79p, ibds, 38cp, DJ)	L: Gollancz	(1932)	Thornycroft, R.	60-90	
Farjeon, Eleanor	Kings & Queens (sm4to, red cl, 86p, 40 fp color, DJ/2.50)	Dent/Dutton	(1940)	Thornycroft, R.	35-60	*
Farjeon, Eleanor	Kings & Queens (sm4to, ibds, 86p, 40 color, DJ)	Lippincott	[1940]	Thornycroft, R.	35-60	
Farjeon, Eleanor	Little Bookroom (1st, 8vo, 302p, b/w, DJ, CgM)	L: Oxford U.Pr.	1955	Ardizzone, Edward	70-100	*
Farjeon, Eleanor	Little Bookroom (1st AM, 8vo, 302p, red cl, b/w, DJ/3.00)	NY: Oxford U.Pr.	1956	Ardizzone, Edward	70-100	R
Farjeon, Eleanor	Martin Pippin in the Apple Orchard (1st, 8vo, brown cl, 369p, 5 ticp)	L: Collins	(1921)	Brock, Charles E.	60-90	
Farjeon, Eleanor	Martin Pippin in the Daisy-Field (1st AM {std} 8vo, 320p, col frn, DJ/2.50)	Stokes	1938	Morton-Sale, J.	80-125	
Farjeon, Eleanor	More Nursery Rhymes of London Town (1st, 8vo, unpag, red cl, col frn)	L: Duckworth	1917	Gill, MacDonald	60-90	
Farjeon, Eleanor	Mrs. Malone (1st AM, 16mo, [24]p, b/w, DJ/1.75)	H.Z. Walck	1962	Ardizzone, Edward	50-80	
Farjeon, Eleanor	Nursery Rhymes of London Town (1st, 8vo, 63p, blue/gilt, col frn)	L: Duckworth	(1916)	Gill, MacDonald	80-125	
Farjeon, Eleanor	Nuts & May (1st, 4to, p-o, 263p, color)	L: Collins	1926	Thornycroft, R.	90-160	*
Farjeon, Eleanor	Old Nurse's Stocking Basket (1st AM, 8vo, 154p, col frn, b/w)	Stokes	1931	Whydale, E. Herbert	35-60	
Farjeon, Eleanor	Old Nurse's Stocking Basket (1st, 8vo, 115p, col frn, b/w, DJ)	London U. Press	1949	Gough, Philip	40-65	
Farjeon, Eleanor	Old Nurse's Stocking-Basket (1st AM {std}, 8vo, 102p, b/w, DJ/3.50)	H.Z. Walck	1965	Ardizzone, Edward	50-85	
Farjeon, Eleanor	One Foot in Fairyland (1st, 8vo, 261p, gilt, b/w, cep, DJ/2.50)	Stokes	1938	Lawson, Robert	120-200	
Farjeon, Eleanor	Paladins in Spain (1st, 8vo, 168p, col frn, 5pl)	L: T. Nelson	1937	Tozer, Katharine	30-50	*
Farjeon, Eleanor	Perfect Zoo (1st, ob4to, red cl, p-o, 31p, 12cp)	McKay	(1929)	Kruse, Katy	140-200	
Farjeon, Eleanor	Perfect Zoo (1st {this pub.}, 4to, 47p, color)	L: Harrap	1947	Burrell, Kathleen	50-80	*
Farjeon, Eleanor	Perkin the Pedlar (1st, 8vo, blue cl, 205p, 8cp)	L: Faber	(1932)	Leighton, Clare	75-100	
Farjeon, Eleanor	Prayer for Little Things (1st, 8vo, [13]p, color, dep, DJ/1.00)	Houghton	1945	Jones, Eliz. O.	35-60	
Farjeon, Eleanor	Silver Curlew (1st, 8vo, 192p, b/w, DJ)	L: Oxford U.Pr.	1953	Shepard, Ernest H.	60-90	
Farjeon, Eleanor	Singing Games for Children (1st, 8vo, 71p, ipcb, fp color)	Dent/Dutton	[1919]	Littlejohns, J.	60-90	
Farjeon, Eleanor	Songs for Music.... (1st, sm8vo, 61p, frn by...)	L: Selwyn	(1922)	Austen, John	55-80	
Farjeon, Eleanor	Tale of Tom Tiddler (1st, 8vo, 191p, gilt, color)	L: Collins	(1929)	Tealby, Norman	75-100	*

AUTHOR	TITLE	PUBLISHER	DATE	ARTIST	PRICE	LC
Farjeon, Eleanor	Tales from Chaucer (1st, 8vo, red/gilt, 244p, 12cp)	L: Medici	1930	Flint, William R.	60-90	
Farjeon, Eleanor	Ten Saints (1st AM {std}, lg8vo, 124p, 10 fp color, pep, DJ/2.50)	NY: Oxford U.Pr.	1936	Sewell, Helen	60-90	
Farjeon, Eleanor	Westwoods (1st AM, 8vo, ibds, [44]p, b/w, pep)	A.& W. Guild	(1935)	Smith, May	30-50	
Farjeon, Eleanor	Wonders of Herodotus (1st, 8vo, 176p, col frn, 6 b/w)	L: Nelson	1937	Nelson, Edmund	40-60	*
Farley, Walter	Black Stallion (1st {std}, 8vo, 275p, fp b/w, DJ/2.00)	Random	(1941)	Ward, Keith	50-85	*
Farley, Walter	Black Stallion and Satan (1st {std}, 8vo, 208p, b/w, DJ/2.00)	Random	(1949)	Menasco, Milton	50-80	
Farley, Walter	Black Stallion Challenged (1st {std}, 8vo, 246p, b/w, DJ/2.95)	Random	(1964)	Draper, Angie	50-80	
Farley, Walter	Black Stallion Revolts (1st {std}, 8vo, 305p, b/w, DJ/2.00)	Random	(1953)	Eldridge, Harold	50-85	
Farley, Walter	Black Stallion's Filly (1st {std}, 8vo, 309p, b/w, DJ/2.00)	Random	(1952)	Menasco, Milton	45-70	
Farley, Walter	Black Stallion's Sulky Colt (1st {std}, 8vo, 248p, b/w, DJ/2.00)	Random	(1954)	Eldridge, Harold	45-70	*
Farley, Walter	Blood Bay Colt (1st {std}, 8vo, 307p, fp b/w, DJ/2.00)	Random	(1950)	Menasco, Milton	30-50	
Farley, Walter	Horse that Swam Away (1st {std}, 8vo, 75p, b/w, DJ/1.95)	Random	(1965)	Summers, Leo	50-85	*
Farley, Walter	Horse-Tamer (1st {std}, 8vo, 175p, b/w, DJ/2.00)	Random	1958	Schucker, James	45-70	
Farley, Walter	Island Stallion's Fury (1st {std}, 8vo, 243p, b/w, DJ/2.00)	Random	(1951)	Eldridge, Harold	50-80	
Farley, Walter	Larry and the Undersea Raider (1st {std}, 8vo, 225p, b/w, DJ/1.75)	Random	(1942)	Jackson, P.K.	60-90	*
Farley, Walter	Little Black: A Pony (1st, lg8vo, 60p, ibds, p-o, fp 2-color, DJ/1.95)	Beginner Books	(1961)	Schucker, James	70-100	
Farley, Walter	Man O'War (1st, 8vo, 326p, b/w, DJ/3.95)	Random	(1962)	Draper, Alice	50-80	
Farley, Walter	Son of the Black Stallion (1st {std}, 8vo, 330p, b/w, DJ/2.00)	Random	(1947)	Menasco, Milton	60-90	
Farmer, James E.	The Grenadier (1st, sm8vo, 328p, red cl, cvr by...)	Dodd	1898	Edwards, George W.	25-40	
Farmer, Penelope	Charlotte Sometimes (1st AM {std}, 8vo, 192p, b/w, DJ/4.95)	Harcourt	1969	Conner, Chris	80-135	
Farmer, Penelope	Emma in Winter (1st, 8vo, ibds, 160p, DJ)	L: Chatto	1966	Acs, Laszlo	30-45	
Farmer, Penelope	Magic Stone (1st {std}, sm8vo, 224p, b/w, DJ/3.75)	Harcourt	(1964)	Kaufmann, John	30-50	*
Farmer, Penelope	Summer Birds (1st {std}, 8vo, 155p, b/w, DJ/2.95)	Harcourt	(1962)	Spanfeller, James	30-50	
Farmiloe, Edith	Mr. Biddle & the Dragon (1st, 4to, red cl, 47p, 20pl)	L: Skeffington	1904	Farmiloe, Edith	150-225	
Farnol, Jeffery	Amateur Gentleman (1st UK, 8vo, blue/gilt, 599p, teg, 21cp)	L: Sampson Low	(1916)	Brock, Charles E.	75-100	*
Farnol, Jeffery	Broad Highway (1st, lg8vo, 493p, blue/gilt, p-o, 24cp)	L: Sampson Low	1910	Brock, Charles E.	60-90	
Farnol, Jeffery	Broad Highway (1st AM, lg8vo, 518p, p-o, teg, 24cp)	Little/Brown	1912	Brock, Charles E.	55-80	
Farnol, Jeffery	Honorable Mr. Tawnish (1st, 8vo, 118p, gilt, teg, 8cp)	L: Sampson Low	1913	Brock, Charles E.	55-80	
Farnol, Jeffery	Honorable Mr. Tawnish (1st AM, sm8vo, 165p, lavender/gilt, 4cp)	Little/Brown	1913	Brock, Charles E.	45-70	
Farnol, Jeffery	Money Moon (1st, lg8vo, p-o, teg, 385p, 22pl)	Dodd	1911	Keller, Arthur I.	50-80	
Farnol, Jeffery	My Lady Caprice (1st, 8vo, teg, p-o, 289p, color)	Dodd	1907	Ditzler, C. Weber	25-40	
Farquhar, Margaret	Indian Children of America (1st {std}, 8vo, color, DJ/2.50)	Holt, Rinehart	(1964)	Turkle, Brinton	50-80	*
Farr, Florence	Dancing Faun (1st, 8vo, 149p, ti-page & cvr by...)	L: E. Mathews	1894	Beardsley, Aubrey	200-300	
Farrar, Evelyn	Stories from the Bible (1st, 8vo, 243p, gilt, 12pl)	L: Henry Co.	1896	Hallward, Mrs. R.	40-60	*
Farrow, Dorothy P.	Little Brown Hen (1st, sq12mo, [48]p, orange cl, color, cep, DJ/1.00)	Macmillan	1941	Dobias, Frank	40-65	
Farrow, George E.	Absurd Ditties (1st, 8vo, blue/gilt, AEG, 224p, b/w)	L: Routledge	1903	Hassall, John	80-130	
Farrow, George E.	Adventures in Wallypug-Land (1st, 8vo, AEG, gilt, 186p, b/w)	L: Methuen	1898	Wright, Alan	120-200	
Farrow, George E.	Adventures in Wallypug-Land (1st AM, 8vo, blue cl, AEG, b/w)	New Amsterdam	1899	Wright, Alan	100-165	*
Farrow, George E.	Adventures of a Dodo (1st, 8vo, gilt, 245p, 70 b/w, pep)	L: T.F. Unwin	(1907)	Pogany, Willy	200-300	
Farrow, George E.	All About the Wallypug (1st, folio, unpag)	L: R. Tuck	[1904]	Unknown	120-200	*
Farrow, George E.	Baker Minor & Dragon (1st, lg8vo, blue/gilt, AEG, 210p, b/w)	L: A. Pearson	1902	Wright, Alan	120-170	*
Farrow, George E.	Don't Tell (1st, 4to, [56]p, bds, fp color, pep)	L: Alf Cooke	[1905]	Hassall, John	250-400	
Farrow, George E.	Dwindleberry Zoo (1st, lg8vo, gilt, AEG, 208p, b/w)	L: Blackie	1909	Browne, Gordon	125-200	*
Farrow, George E.	Escape of the Mullingong (1st, 12mo, AEG, 148p, gilt)	L: Blackie	1907	Browne, Gordon	120-180	
Farrow, George E.	King's Gardens (1st, 8vo, 43p)	L: Hutchinson	1896	Bowley, Ada L.	75-100	*
Farrow, George E.	Little Panjandrum's Dodo (1st, 8vo, 210p, gilt, b/w)	L: Skeffington	1899	Wright, Alan	70-100	
Farrow, George E.	Mandarin's Kite (1st, 8vo, 154p)	L: Skeffington	1900	Wright, Alan	60-90	*
Farrow, George E.	Missing Prince (1st, lg8vo, 197p, green/gilt, AEG, b/w, cep)	L: Hutchinson	1896	Furniss, H.& D.	100-165	
Farrow, George E.	Missing Prince (1st AM, 8vo, 198p, pict cl, b/w)	Dodd	1897	Furniss, H.& D.	80-120	*
Farrow, George E.	Mysterious Voyage (1st, 12mo, 160p, gilt, 32 illus)	L: Partridge	[1910]	Roberts, K.M.	55-80	*
Farrow, George E.	New Panjandrum (1st, 8vo, 199p, gilt, AEG, b/w)	L: A. Pearson	1902	Wright, Alan	90-120	
Farrow, George E.	Pixie Pickles (1st, lg4to, ibds, 46p, 20 pl)	L: Skeffington	[1904]	Neilson, Harry B.	170-240	
Farrow, George E.	Professor Philanderpan (1st, 8vo, 216p, green/gilt, AEG, b/w)	L: A. Pearson	1904	Wright, Alan	60-100	*
Farrow, George E.	Round the World ABC (1st, 4to, [54]p, ibds, 26 color)	L: Nister	[1904]	Hassall, John	200-300	
Farrow, George E.	Wallypug at Play (folio, ibds, 12 chromos)	L: R. Tuck	[1895]	Wright, Alan	400-650	
Farrow, George E.	Wallypug Birthday Book (1st, sq8vo, gilt, AEG, 143p, 12cp)	L: Routledge	1904	Wright, Alan	180-270	
Farrow, George E.	Wallypug in Fogland (1st, 8vo, 207p, blue/gilt, AEG, b/w)	L: A. Pearson	1904	Wright, Alan	200-300	
Farrow, George E.	Wallypug in London (1st, 8vo, 174p, uncut, b/w)	L: Methuen	1898	Wright, Alan	200-300	
Farrow, George E.	Wallypug in the Moon (1st AM, 8vo, 256p, AEG, blue/gilt, b/w)	Lippincott	1905	Wright, Alan	200-300	
Farrow, George E.	Wallypug in the Moon (1st, 8vo, AEG, 256p, grey/gilt, fp b/w)	L: A. Pearson	1905	Wright, Alan	200-300	
Farrow, George E.	Wallypug of Why (1st, 8vo, green/gilt, AEG, 201p, AEG, 15pl)	L: Hutchinson	(1895)	Furniss, H.& D.	200-300	
Farrow, George E.	Wallypug of Why (1st AM, 8vo, 201p, b/w illus)	Dodd	1896	Furniss, Harry	200-300	
Farrow, George E.	Wallypug Tales (1st, sm folio, [35]p, grey ibds, fp color)	L: R. Tuck	[1904]	Wright, Alan	500-750	
Farrow, George E.	Zoo Babies (4to, green bds, 24 color)	L: H. Frowde	[1905]	Aldin, Cecil	300-425	*
Fast, Howard (ed)	Tony and the Wonderful Door (1st {std}, lg8vo, 64p, b/w, DJ)	Blue Heron Pr.	1952	Vigoda, William	40-65	
Father Tuck	Pa Cats, Ma Cats & their Kittens (1st, lg4to, ibds, [36]p, gilt, 12cp)	L: R. Tuck	[1901]	Wain, Louis	800-1200	
Fatio, Louise	Anna the Horse (1st {std}, 8vo, ipcb, [48]p, 3-color, pep, DJ/1.75)	Aladdin	(1951)	Duvoisin, Roger	50-80	
Fatio, Louise	Christmas Forest (1st, 8vo, ibds, [44]p, pep, fp 3-color, dep, DJ/1.25)	Aladdin	(1950)	Duvoisin, Roger	60-90	
Fatio, Louise	Doll for Marie (1st, sm4to, [24]p, 2-color, DJ/2.50)	Whittlesey	(1957)	Duvoisin, Roger	40-65	
Fatio, Louise	Happy Lion (1st, sm4to, [30]p, yellow cl, 2-color, DJ/1.95, NYTBI)	Whittlesey	(1954)	Duvoisin, Roger	100-165	R
Fatio, Louise	Happy Lion and the Bear (1st, 4to, 32p, gilt, fp 3-color, DJ/2.95)	Whittlesey	(1964)	Duvoisin, Roger	50-85	
Fatio, Louise	Happy Lion in Africa (1st, sm4to, green cl, 30p, 2-color, DJ/2.00, NYTBI)	Whittlesey	(1955)	Duvoisin, Roger	80-130	
Fatio, Louise	Happy Lion Roars (1st, 4to, 32p, 2-color, DJ/2.25)	Whittlesey	(1957)	Duvoisin, Roger	50-85	
Fatio, Louise	Happy Lion's Quest (1st, sm4to, 26p, fp color, DJ/2.75)	Whittlesey	(1961)	Duvoisin, Roger	40-65	
Fatio, Louise	Happy Lion's Vacation (1st, 4to, 32p, fp 3-color, DJ/2.95)	Whittlesey	(1967)	Duvoisin, Roger	40-65	
Fatio, Louise	Red Bantam (1st, sm4to, 32p, fp 2-color, DJ/2.75)	Whittlesey	(1963)	Duvoisin, Roger	50-80	R
Fatio, Louise	Three Happy Lions (1st, sm4to, 32p, fp 2-color, DJ/2.25)	Whittlesey	(1959)	Duvoisin, Roger	45-70	
Faulkner, Georgene	Italian Fairy Tales (1st, 8vo, 95p, gilt, p-o, 5cp, pep)	Chi: Daughaday	(1916)	Richardson, F.	120-165	

AUTHOR	TITLE	PUBLISHER	DATE	ARTIST	PRICE	LC
Faulkner, Georgene	Little Peachling (1st, lg8vo, 91p, ibds, color, pep)	Volland	(1928)	Richardson, F.	70-130	
Faulkner, Georgene	Melindy's Medal (1st, 8vo, 172p, b/w, pep, DJ/2.25)	J. Messner	(1945)	Fax, Elton C.	50-80	*
Faulkner, Georgene	Old English Nursery Tales (1st, 8vo, 91p, black/gilt, p-o, 8cp)	Chi: Daughaday	(1916)	Winter, Milo	100-150	
Faulkner, Georgene	Road to Enchantment (1st, 8vo, 312p, p-o, 8cp)	Sears	(1929)	Richardson, F.	100-160	
Faulkner, Georgene	Squeaky & the Scare Box (1st, 8vo, [32]p, ibds, 4cp, pep)	Grosset/Dunlap	(1931)	Richardson, F.	60-100	
Faulkner, Georgene	Story Lady's Christmas Stories (1st, 8vo, 93p, red cl, 5cp, pep)	Sears	(1927)	Richardson, F.	35-60	*
Faulkner, Georgene	Story Lady's Italian Tales (1st, 8vo, 95p, gilt, uncut, pep, 5cp)	Chi: Daughaday	(1916)	Richardson, F.	75-100	*
Faulkner, Georgene	Story Lady's Nursery Tales (1st, 8vo, 241p, p-o, 8cp)	Sears	(1927)	Winter, Milo	75-100	*
Faulkner, Georgene	White Elephant (1st, lg8vo, ibds, 92p, 10 fp color, pep)	Volland	(1929)	Richardson, F.	60-100	R
Faulkner, John	Chooky (1st {std}, 8vo, 250p, beige cl, b/w, DJ/3.00)	Norton	(1950)	Busoni, Rafaello	30-50	
Faulkner, Nancy	Side Saddle for Dandy (1st {std}, 8vo, 214p, b/w, DJ/2.75)	Doubleday	(1954)	DeAngeli, Marguerite	25-40	
Faulkner, Nancy	Small Clown (1st {std}, 8vo, 62p, fp 1-color, DJ/2.00)	Doubleday	(1960)	Galdone, Paul	25-45	
Faulkner, William	Green Bough (1st, 8vo, green cl, 67p, title page by...)	Smith/Haas	1933	Ward, Lynd	180-300	*
Faulkner, William	Wishing Tree (1st {std}, 8vo, 82p, b/w, pep, DJ/3.95)	Random	(1967)	Bologalese, Don	100-165	
Faure, Gabriel	Gardens of Rome (1st AM, folio, p-o, 100p, cp)	Brentano's	1924	Vignal, Pierre	100-160	
Fay, Erica	Road to Fairyland (1st AM, 8vo, grey cl, 218p, col frn by..)	Putnam	(1926)	Rackham, Arthur	170-240	
Feagles, Anita M.	Genie and Joe Maloney (1st, sm8vo, 62p, b/w, DJ/2.75)	W.R. Scott	(1962)	Sibley, Don	20-35	
Feelings, Muriel	Zamani Goes to Market (1st, 8vo, [44]p, 2-color, DJ/3.95)	Seabury Press	(1970)	Feelings, Tom	45-70	R*
Fehr, Howard F.	This is My Family (1st, lg ob8vo, [27]p, color, cep, DJ)	Holt, Rinehart	1963	Aliki	25-40	
Feld, Freidrich	Mystery of Musical Umbrella (1st AM, lg8vo, 83p, 1-color, pep, DJ/1.95)	Random	(1962)	Jackson, Doris	25-45	
Fellows, Muriel	Land of Little Rain (1st, 8vo, 121p, fp color, pep, DJ/2.00)	Winston	1936	Fellows, Muriel	50-80	
Fellows, Muriel	Little Magic Painter (1st, 8vo, 111p, p-o, 13cp, DJ/2.00)	Winston	(1938)	Fellows, Muriel	40-65	
Felt, Sue	Contrary Woodrow (1st {std}, ob4to, unpag, color, DJ/2.50)	Doubleday	1958	Felt, Sue	50-85	
Felt, Sue	Rosa-Too-Little (1st {std}, ob4to, [30]p, 1-color, DJ/2.00)	Doubleday	(1950)	Felt, Sue	60-90	
Felton, Harold	Bowleg Bill: Seagoing Cowpuncher (1st, 8vo, 174p, 2-color, DJ/2.95)	Prentice-Hall	1957	Moyers, William	30-50	
Felton, Harold	John Henry and his Hammer (1st {std}, lg8vo, 82p, fp b/w, pep, DJ/2.50)	Knopf	(1950)	Watson, Aldren A.	80-120	R
Felton, Harold	New Tall Tales of Pecos Bill (1st, 8vo, 164p, fp 1-color, DJ/2.95)	Prentice-Hall	(1958)	Moyers, William	30-50	
Felton, Harold	Pecos Bill & the Mustang (1st, 4to, [30]p, fp 2-color, cep, DJ/3.50)	Prentice-Hall	(1965)	Shortall, Leonard	30-50	
Felton, Harold	Pecos Bill, Texas Cowpuncher (1st {std}, 8vo, 177p, b/w, DJ/2.50)	Knopf	1949	Watson, Aldren A.	60-90	R
Felton, Harold	Sergeant O'Keefe and his Mule Balaam (1st, 8vo, 94p, b/w, DJ/3.25)	Dodd	1962	Fisher, Leonard	25-40	
Fenn, Geo. Manville	King's Sons (1st, 8vo, blue cl, 48p, 4pl)	L: Nister	1901	Robinson, Thomas H.	40-65	*
Fenn, Geo. Manville	Old Gold (1st, sm8vo, 416p, teg, gilt, 8pl)	L: Nister	(1900)	Wood, Stanley	60-90	
Fenner, Carol E.	Tigers in the Cellar (1st {std}, sm4to, [32]p, color, DJ/3.00)	Harcourt	(1963)	Fenner, Carol	70-125	*
Fenner, Phyllis R.	Adventure Rare & Magical (1st {std}, 8vo, 178p, b/w, DJ/2.50)	Knopf	1945	Pitz, Henry C.	25-40	*
Fenner, Phyllis R.	Circus Parade (1st {std}, lg8vo, beige cl, 174p, uncut, fp b/w, DJ/3.00)	Knopf	1954	Ames, Lee	30-50	
Fenner, Phyllis R.	Demons & Dervishes (1st {std}, 8vo, red cl, 183p, fp b/w, pep, DJ/2.00)	Knopf	(1946)	Pitz, Henry C.	35-60	*
Fenner, Phyllis R.	Fools and Funny Fellows (1st {std}, 8vo, 185p, b/w, DJ/2.50)	Knopf	1947	Pitz, Henry C.	30-50	*
Fenner, Phyllis R.	Giants & Witches (1st {std}, 8vo, red cl, 208p, fp b/w, pep, DJ/2.50)	Knopf	1943	Pitz, Henry C.	40-60	*
Fenner, Phyllis R.	Giggle Box (1st {std}, lg8vo, yellow cl, 144p, uncut, b/w, pep, DJ/2.50)	Knopf	1950	Steig, William	45-80	*
Fenner, Phyllis R.	Horses, Horses, Horses (1st, 8vo, 285p, b/w, pep, DJ/2.50)	F. Watts	(1949)	Crowell, Pers	20-30	
Fenner, Phyllis R.	Princesses & Peasant Boys (1st {std}, 8vo, 188p, b/w, pep, DJ/2.50)	Knopf	1944	Pitz, Henry C.	30-50	*
Fenner, Phyllis R.	Stories of the Sea (1st {std}, lg8vo, beige cl, 178p, b/w, DJ/3.00)	Knopf	1953	Werth, Kurt	30-50	*
Fenner, Phyllis R.	With Might and Main (1st {std}, 8vo, 190p, b/w, DJ/2.50)	Knopf	1948	Pitz, Henry C.	25-40	
Fenner, Phyllis R.	Yankee Doodle (1st {std}, 8vo, red cl, 214p, uncut, fp b/w, DJ/2.50)	Knopf	1951	Maxwell, John	25-45	
Fenton, Edward	Aleko's Island (1st {std}, 8vo, 246p, b/w, pep, DJ/2.50)	Doubleday	1948	Davis, Dimitris	20-35	*
Fenton, Edward	Big Yellow Balloon (1st {std}, ob4to, [48]p, color, DJ/3.95)	Doubleday	(1967)	Ohlsson, Ib	30-50	
Fenton, Edward	Fierce John (1st {std}, 8vo, 59p, fp 1-color, pep, DJ/2.00)	Doubleday	1959	DuBois, W.P.	30-50	
Fenton, Edward	Golden Doors (1st {std}, 8vo, 262p, b/w, DJ/2.95)	Doubleday	1957	Fiammenghi, Gioia	20-35	
Fenton, Edward	Hidden Trapezes (1st {std}, 8vo, 239p, b/w, DJ/2.50)	Doubleday	(1950)	Lonette, Reisie	20-35	
Fenton, Edward	Nine Lives (1st, 4to, ipcb, 62p, pep, b/w, DJ/2.50)	Pantheon	(1951)	Galdone, Paul	40-65	
Fenton, Edward	Nine Questions (1st {std}, 8vo, 235p, b/w, DJ/2.95)	Doubleday	(1959)	Hodges, C. Walter	25-40	
Fenton, Edward	Penny Candy (1st {std}, 8vo, ibds, 46p, DJ/3.95)	Holt, Rinehart	(1970)	Gorey, Edward	65-90	
Fenton, Edward	Phantom of Walkaway Hill (1st {std}, 8vo, 260p, b/w, DJ/2.95)	Doubleday	1961	Stover, Jo Ann	50-85	
Fenton, Edward	Us and the Duchess (1st {std}, 8vo, 208p, b/w, pep, DJ/2.00)	Doubleday	1947	Lonette, Reisie	25-40	
Ferguson, Charles	Abecedarian Book (1st {std}, 8vo, 131p, yellow cl, 2-color, DJ/3.95)	Little/Brown	(1964)	Alcorn, John	25-40	
Fern, Eugene	Pepito's Story (1st, sm4to, [46]p, fp color, DJ/3.25)	Ariel	1960	Fern, Eugene	50-85	*
Ferrer, Melchor	Tito's Hats (1st lg sq8vo, [28]p, ibds, 1-color, dep, DJ/0.50)	Garden City	(1940)	Charlot, Jean	80-120	
Ferris, Helen	Challenge Stories/Courage & Love for Girls (1st {std}, 8vo, 328p, col frn)	Doubleday/Doran	1936	DeAngeli, Marguerite	30-45	*
Ferris, Helen	Favorite Poems Old and New (1st {std}, lg8vo, 598p, fp b/w, DJ/4.75)	Doubleday	(1957)	Weisgard, Leonard	35-50	*
Ferris, Helen	Watch Me, said the Jeep (1st {std}, ob4to, [28]p, ipcb, color, DJ/1.00)	Garden City	(1944)	Gergely, Tibor	40-70	
Fessenden, Laura D.	2002: Childlife One Hundred Years from Now (1st, 8vo, 184p, b/w)	Jamieson-Higgins	(1902)	Campbell, S.P.	400-600	*
Fessenden, Laura D.	Colonial Dame (1st, 12mo, 116p, cvr by...)	Rand/McNally	1897	Denslow, W.W.	40-60	
Feuillet, Octave	Story of Mr. Punch (1st, 8vo, 139p, p-o, col frn, fp b/w, pep)	Dutton	(1929)	Hader, B.& E.	30-50	
Fezandie, Clement	Through the Earth (1st, sm8vo, tan cl, 238p, 15pl by...)	Century	1898	MacKay, William A.	70-100	
Fezandie, Clement	Through the Earth (1st, sm8vo, tan cl, 238p, cvr by...)	Century	1898	McManus, Blanche	70-100	
Fiedler, Jean	Big Brother Danny (1st, sm8vo, unpag, blue cl, fp b/w, DJ/1.75)	Holiday House	1953	Fiedler, Harold	20-35	
Fiedler, Jean	Green Thumb Story (1st, sm8vo, 38p, red cl, 2-color, pep, DJ/1.75)	Holiday House	1952	Latham, Barbara	20-35	
Fiedler, Maggi	Corky's Pet Parade (1st, sm4to, [32]p, ipcb, color)	Pied Piper Bks.	(1946)	Fiedler, Maggi	40-70	*
Field, Eugene	Christmas Tales and Christmas Verse (1st, 4to, 119p, gilt, 8cp)	Scribner	1912	Storer, Florence	80-120	
Field, Eugene	Fiddle Dee-Dee (1st, 8vo, 93p, p-o, color)	Saalfield	(1929)	Nyce, Helen	100-160	
Field, Eugene	Holy Cross (1st, 12mo, blue/gilt, 191p, teg, cep, cvr by...)	Stone & Kimball	1893	Rhead, Louis	50-80	
Field, Eugene	Lullaby Land (1st, 8vo, teg, 229p, green/gilt, b/w)	Scribner	1897	Robinson, Charles	200-300	
Field, Eugene	Lullaby Land (1st UK, sm8vo, 229p, gilt, AEG, b/w)	L: John Lane	1898	Robinson, Charles	200-300	
Field, Eugene	Papillot, Clignot et Dodo (1st, 8vo, [25]p, 1-color, DJ/3.25)	Ariel	(1964)	Cooney, Barbara	30-50	
Field, Eugene	Poems of Childhood (1st UK, 8vo, 199p, red/gilt, teg, pep, 8cp)	L: John Lane	1904	Parrish, Maxfield	150-250	
Field, Eugene	Poems of Childhood (1st, lg8vo, p-o, teg, 199p, 8cp, pep, SC)	Scribner	1904	Parrish, Maxfield	200-300	
Field, Eugene	Songs by Eugene Field (1st, 4to, ipcb, 112p)	Scribner	1914	Armstrong, Margaret	90-120	
Field, Eugene	Sugar-Plum Tree (1st, 4to, ipcb, [58]p, 12cp)	Saalfield	(1930)	Peat, Fern B.	60-90	R

AUTHOR	TITLE	PUBLISHER	DATE	ARTIST	PRICE	LC
Field, Eugene	Tribune Primer (1st, 8vo, ipcb, gilt, 63p, uncut, b/w)	Reilly/Britton	(1916)	Field, Roswell	30-50	
Field, Eugene	With Trumpet and Drum (1st, 8vo, 126p, teg, blue/white, cvr by...)	Scribner	1892	Armstrong, Margaret	45-70	
Field, Eugene	Wynken, Blyken and Nod (1st, lg4to, [34]p, ipcb, color, pep)	C.E. Graham	(1925)	Unknown	80-130	
Field, Eugene	Wynken, Blynken & Nod (1st, folio, wraps, [12]p, color)	Saalfield	1930	Peat, Fern B.	70-120	R
Field, Henry M.	Our Western Archipelago (1st, 8vo, 250p, beige cl, cvr by...)	Scribner	1895	Armstrong, Margaret	100-150	
Field, Louis A.	Peter Rabbit and his Ma (12mo, ibds, fp color)	Saalfield	(1917)	Albert, Virginia	60-90	
Field, Louis A.	Peter Rabbit and his Pa (8vo, [24]p, ibds, color, pep)	Saalfield	(1908)	Albert, Virginia	60-100	R
Field, Louis A.	Peter Rabbit Goes to School (12mo, ibds, fp color)	Saalfield	(1917)	Albert, Virginia	40-65	
Field, Michael	Tragic Mary (1st, 8vo, 261p, ipcb, cvr by...)	L: G. Bell	1890	Image, Selwyn	200-300	
Field, Rachel	All Through the Night (1st, 24mo, ibds, [40]p, 1-color, DJ/0.50)	Macmillan	1940	Field, Rachel	35-60	
Field, Rachel	Alphabet for Boys & Girls (1st {std}, 16mo, red cl, [59]p, color, cep)	Doubleday/Page	1926	Field, Rachel	70-100	
Field, Rachel	American Folk & Fairy Tales (1st, 8vo, 302p, green cl, 8cp, pep)	Scribner	1929	Freeman, Margaret	60-90	
Field, Rachel	Bird Began to Sing (1st, 8vo, 64p, p-o, 4cp, pep)	Wm. Morrow	(1932)	Bischoff, Ilse	30-60	
Field, Rachel	Branches Green (1st, 8vo, green cl, 66p, 12 b/w, DJ/1.50)	Macmillan	1934	Lathrop, Dorothy	80-130	
Field, Rachel	Calico Bush (1st, 8vo, 213p, p-o, 1-color, DJ/2.50, NH)	Macmillan	1931	Lewis, Allen	60-90	R
Field, Rachel	Christmas Time (1st, 24mo, [32]p, white pcb, col frn, cep, DJ/0.50)	Macmillan	1941	Field, Rachel	30-50	
Field, Rachel	Eliza & the Elves (1st, sm8vo, green/gilt, 96p, 2cp, pep)	Macmillan	1926	MacKinstry, Eliz.	60-90	
Field, Rachel	Hepatica Hawks (1st, sm8vo, 239p, blue cl, 5 fp woodcuts, NH)	Macmillan	1932	Lewis, Allen	40-65	
Field, Rachel	Hitty, Her First Hundred Years (1st, sq8vo, 207p, p-o, 3cp, NM, PPPa)	Macmillan	1929	Lathrop, Dorothy	120-200	
Field, Rachel	Just Across the Street (1st, sm8vo, 109p, b/w, DJ/1.50)	Macmillan	1933	Field, Rachel	40-65	
Field, Rachel	Little Book of Days (1st {std}, 16mo, green cl, [59]p, color, cep)	Doubleday/Page	1927	Field, Rachel	35-60	
Field, Rachel	Little Dog Toby (1st, 12mo, blue cl, 118p, 4cp, pep)	Macmillan	1928	Field, Rachel	30-50	
Field, Rachel	Magic Pawnshop (1st, 8vo, ibds, 125p, 3-color, DJ)	Dutton	(1927)	MacKinstry, Eliz.	60-100	
Field, Rachel	Patchwork Plays (1st {std}, sm8vo, 139p, blue cl, b/w, DJ/1.25)	Doubleday/Doran	1930	Field, Rachel	40-60	
Field, Rachel	People from Dickens (1st, lg8vo, p-o, 208p, 8cp, pep, SC)	Scribner	1935	Fogarty, Thomas	70-100	
Field, Rachel	Pocket-Handkerchief Park (1st {std}, 12mo, 61p, color, cep)	Doubleday/Doran	1929	Field, Rachel	35-60	
Field, Rachel	Poems (1st {std}, 8vo, 118p, DJ/2.50, decorations by...)	Macmillan	1957	Field, Rachel	25-40	*
Field, Rachel	Pointed People (1st, sm8vo, 98p, orange cl, b/w, DJ)	Yale U. Press	1924	Field, Rachel	50-80	
Field, Rachel	Polly Patchwork (1st {std}, 16mo, 56p, color)	Doubleday/Doran	1928	Field, Rachel	30-50	
Field, Rachel	Prayer for a Child (1st, 8vo, [31]p, color, cep, DJ/1.00, CM)	Macmillan	1944	Jones, Eliz. O.	120-200	R
Field, Rachel	Rachel Field Story Book (1st {std}, 8vo, 124p, 2-color, dep, DJ/2.50)	Doubleday	(1958)	Adams, Adrienne	40-70	
Field, Rachel	Susanna B. & William C. (1st, 24mo, 62p, yellow cl, cep, color)	Wm. Morrow	1934	Field, Rachel	30-50	
Field, Rachel	Taxis & Toadstools (1st {std}, 8vo, 129p, green cl, color, cep)	Doubleday/Page	1926	Field, Rachel	50-85	R
Field, Rachel	Yellow Shop (1st {std}, 16mo, 62p, tan cl, color, dep, DJ/0.75)	Doubleday/Doran	1931	Field, Rachel	60-90	
Field, Robert	Art of Walt Disney (1st, 4to, tan cl, 290p, color)	Macmillan	1942	Disney Studios	250-400	
Fielding-Hall, H.	Margaret's Book (1st, 4to, AEG, red/gilt, 283p, 12 ticp, pep)	L: Hutchinson	(1913)	Robinson, Charles	250-400	
Fielding-Hall, H.	Margaret's Book (1st AM, 4to, 283p, teg, gilt, 12 ticp, pep)	Stokes	[1913]	Robinson, Charles	250-350	
Fife, Duncan	Scarlet Blue and Green (1st, sm4to, 64p, gilt, 4 fp color)	L: Macmillan	1932	Aldin, Cecil	80-135	
Fillebrown, R.H.	Rhymes of Happy Childhood (1st, lg8vo, 119p, p-o, 3cp, pep)	Winston	(1908)	Prittie, Edwin J.	50-80	
Fillmore, Parker H.	Hickory Limb (1st, 12mo, green cl, 70p, p-o, 4pl)	J. Lane	1910	O'Neill, Rose	55-80	
Fillmore, Parker H.	Laughing Prince (1st, 8vo, 286p, col frn, pep)	Harcourt	1921	Van Everen, Jay	30-50	
Fillmore, Parker H.	Little Question of Ladies' Rights (1st, 12mo, 79p, p-o, b/w)	J. Lane	1916	O'Neill, Rose	40-60	
Fillmore, Parker H.	Shoemaker's Apron (1st, 8vo, 280p, col frn, pep)	Harcourt	1920	Matulka, Jan	30-50	*
Filosa, Dorothea	Parsley the Horse (1st, ob4to, ibds, [32]p, fp color, pep, DJ/1.00)	Garden City	1940	Filosa, Dorothea	60-90	
Filosa, Dorothea	Susi (1st, 4to, 32p, ibds, color, pep, DJ/1.00)	Garden City	1939	Filosa, Dorothea	60-90	
Fine, Warren	Mousechildren & the Famous Collector (1st {std}, 4to, 57p, b/w, DJ/7.50)	Harper	(1970)	Mayer, Mercer	30-50	
Finger, Charles (ed)	Heroes from Hakluyt (1st {std}, 4to, 331p, 3-color woodcuts)	Henry Holt & Co.	(1928)	Honore, Paul	30-50	
Finger, Charles J.	Adventure Under Sapphire Skies (1st, 12mo, 293p, uncut, b/w)	Wm. Morrow	1931	Finger, Helen	30-50	
Finger, Charles J.	Bobbie and Jock and the Mailman (1st, 8vo, 155p, b/w, pep, DJ/2.00)	Henry Holt & Co.	(1938)	Finger, Helen	30-50	
Finger, Charles J.	Bushrangers (1st, 8vo, 216p, color, pep)	McBride	1924	Honore, Paul	50-80	
Finger, Charles J.	Cape Horn Snorter (1st, 8vo, 263p, b/w, pep, DJ/2.00)	Houghton	1939	Pitz, Henry C.	30-50	
Finger, Charles J.	Courageous Companions (1st {std}, lg8vo, 304p, gilt, pep, 10pl)	Longmans	(1929)	Daugherty, James	35-60	
Finger, Charles J.	David Livingstone: Explorer and Prophet (1st, 8vo, 300p, uncut, b/w)	Doubleday/Doran	1930	Zaidenberg, Arthur	20-35	
Finger, Charles J.	Distant Prize... (1st, sm8vo, 330p, red/gilt, col frn, pep, DJ/2.50)	Appleton-Century	1935	Pitz, Henry C.	30-50	
Finger, Charles J.	Dog at His Heel (1st, 8vo, 304p, orange cl, dp color, pep, DJ/2.00)	Winston	(1936)	Pitz, Henry C.	30-50	
Finger, Charles J.	Frontier Ballads (1st {std}, lg8vo, 181p, 3cp, b/w, pep)	Doubleday/Doran	1927	Honore, Paul	60-90	*
Finger, Charles J.	Give a Man a Horse (1st, 8vo, 340p, col frn, dp b/w, pep, DJ/2.00)	Winston	(1938)	Pitz, Henry C.	30-50	
Finger, Charles J.	Golden Tales from Far Away (1st, 8vo, 233p, col frn, pep, DJ/2.00)	Winston	(1940)	Finger, Helen	30-50	
Finger, Charles J.	High Water in Arkansas (1st, 8vo, ibds, [28]p, color, pep, DJ/0.50)	Grosset/Dunlap	1943	Pitz, Henry C.	30-55	
Finger, Charles J.	Highwaymen... (1st, lg8vo, 258p, tan cl, uncut, 8cp, pep)	McBride	1923	Honore, Paul	50-90	*
Finger, Charles J.	Magic Tower (1st, sm8vo, 118p, ipcb, p-o, fp b/w, cep)	Kings Arms Pr.	1933	Finger, Helen	50-80	*
Finger, Charles J.	Romantic Rascals (1st, lg8vo, 251p, uncut, 8cp, pep)	McBride	1927	Honore, Paul	40-65	
Finger, Charles J.	Spreading Stain (1st {std}, 8vo, 245p, cep, col frn by...)	Doubleday/Page	1927	Honore, Paul	30-50	
Finger, Charles J.	Tales from Silver Lands (1st {std}, lg8vo, 225p, 10cp, pep, NM)	Doubleday/Page	1924	Honore, Paul	70-100	R
Finger, Charles J.	Tales Worth Telling (1st, lg8vo, 250p, orange cl, pep, 10cp)	Century	1927	Honore, Paul	45-70	
Finger, Charles J.	When Guns Thundered at Tripoli (1st, sm8vo, 290p, col frn, DJ/2.00)	Henry Holt & Co.	(1937)	Pitz, Henry C.	30-50	
Finger, Charles J.	Yankee Captain in Patagonia (1st, narrow 8vo, 74p, b/w, DJ/0.50)	Grosset/Dunlap	(1941)	Pitz, Henry C.	25-40	
Finnemore, John	Red Men of the Dusk (1st AM, 12mo, 328p, ibds, 8pl)	Lippincott	1900	Wood, Lawson	50-80	*
Finnemore, John	Robin Hood & his Merry Men (1st AM, 4to, 272p, green/gilt, 8cp)	Macmillan	1929	Stewart, Allan	120-165	
Finnemore, John	Robin Hood & his Merry Men (1st, 4to, 272p, gilt, 8cp)	L: A&C Black	1929	Stewart, Allan	130-180	
Finney, Charles G.	Circus of Dr. Lao (1st, lg8vo, red cl, 154p, p-o, 8pl, pep, DJ/2.00)	Viking	1935	Artzybasheff, Boris	250-400	
Finta, Alexander	Herdboy of Hungary (1st {std}, 8vo, 166p, b/w, pep)	Harper	1932	Finta, Alexander	25-40	
Finta, Alexander	My Brothers & I (1st, 8vo, tan cl, 185p, b/w, DJ/2.00)	Holiday House	(1940)	Finta, Alexander	25-45	
Fischer, Hans	Pitschi (1st, ob folio, ibds, [32]p, color, pep, DJ/3.00, NYTBI)	Harcourt	1953	Fischer, Hans	100-160	R
Fischer, Hans	Puss in Boots (1st AM {std}, 4to, [32]p, color, DJ/3.00)	Harcourt	(1959)	Fischer, Hans	60-90	*
Fischer, Hans	The Birthday (1st {std}, ob4to, ipcb, 32p, color, pep, DJ/3.00)	Harcourt	1954	Fischer, Hans	80-130	R
Fischer, Marjorie	All on a Summer's Day (1st {std}, 8vo, 157p, green cl, b/w, pep, DJ/2.00)	Random	(1941)	Eichenberg, Fritz	30-50	
Fischer, Marjorie	Dog Cantbark (1st {std}, lg8vo, [32]p, gilt, color, cep, DJ/1.50)	Random	(1940)	Duvoisin, Roger	60-90	

AUTHOR	TITLE	PUBLISHER	DATE	ARTIST	PRICE	LC
Fischer, Marjorie	Street Fair (1st, 8vo, blue/gilt, 216p, 18cp, pep, DJ/2.00)	Smith/Haas	(1935)	Floethe, Richard	40-65	*
Fish, Anne H.	Noah's Ark Book (1st, lg8vo, ibds, 55p, fp 2-color)	L: Bodley Head	[1918]	Fish, Anne H.	120-200	
Fish, Helen D.	Animals of the Bible (1st, sm4to, 65p, gilt, dp color, DJ/2.00, CM)	Stokes	1937	Lathrop, Dorothy	180-250	R
Fish, Helen D.	Butterfly Land (1st AM, ob4to, [15]p, p-o, 14p, 7cp)	Stokes	1931	Olfers, Sibylle	150-220	
Fish, Helen D.	Four & Twenty Blackbirds (1st, sm4to, 104p, 1-color, pep, DJ/1.50, CH)	Stokes	1937	Lawson, Robert	150-250	
Fish, Helen D.	Little Book of Colors (1st {std}, 8vo, [28]p, color, DJ/1.00)	Lippincott	(1944)	Smith, Catharine	25-40	
Fish, Helen D.	Pegs of History (1st, 4to, 44p, b/w, DJ/2.00)	Stokes	1943	Busoni, Rafaello	30-45	
Fish, Helen D.	When the Root Children Wake Up (1st AM, 4to, [22]p, p-o, 9cp, pep)	Stokes	1930	Olfers, Sibylle	200-300	R
Fisher, Aileen	Arbor Day (1st, 8vo, [40]p, 1-color, DJ/2.95)	Crowell	(1965)	Hogrogian, Nonny	25-45	
Fisher, Aileen	But Ostriches... (1st, 8vo, [48]p, fp b/w, DJ/3.95)	Crowell	(1970)	Parnall, Peter	50-85	R*
Fisher, Aileen	Cherokee Strip: Race for Land (1st {std}, 8vo, 192p, 1-color, DJ/1.75)	Aladdin	1956	Reed, Walt	20-35	*
Fisher, Aileen	Cricket in a Thicket (1st, 8vo, 63p, ibds, b/w, DJ/3.25)	Scribner	(1963)	Rojankovsky, Feodor	20-35	
Fisher, Aileen	Easter (1st, 8vo, [40]p, color, DJ/2.95)	Crowell	(1968)	Forberg, Ati	25-45	
Fisher, Aileen	Fisherman of Galilee (1st, 8vo, 223p, b/w, DJ/2.95)	Nelson	1959	DePol, John	20-35	*
Fisher, Aileen	Going Barefoot (1st, 4to, [34]p, dep, color, DJ/3.00)	Crowell	(1960)	Adams, Adrienne	30-45	*
Fisher, Aileen	I Like Weather (1st, sm4to, [35]p, color, pep, DJ/3.50)	Crowell	(1963)	Domanska, Janina	30-50	
Fisher, Aileen	In One Door and Out the Other (1st {std}, 8vo, 65p, b/w, DJ/3.75)	Crowell	(1969)	Hoban, Lillian	30-50	
Fisher, Aileen	In the Middle of the Night (1st {std}, 4to, [44]p, fp color, DJ/3.75)	Crowell	(1965)	Adams, Adrienne	40-65	R
Fisher, Aileen	In the Woods, In the Meadow, In the Sky (1st, 8vo, 64p, b/w, DJ/3.25)	Scribner	1965	Tomes, Margaret	30-45	
Fisher, Aileen	Jeanne d'Arc (1st, 4to, 52p, fp color, pep, DJ/4.50)	Crowell	(1970)	Forberg, Ati	30-50	R
Fisher, Aileen	Lantern in the Window (1st, 8vo, 126p, b/w, DJ/2.75)	Nelson	(1957)	Johnson, Harper	25-40	
Fisher, Aileen	Like Nothing at All (1st, 4to, [38]p, fp 1-color, DJ/3.50)	Crowell	(1962)	Weisgard, Leonard	30-50	
Fisher, Aileen	Listen Rabbit (1st, 4to, [36]p, 2-color, pep, DJ/3.50)	Crowell	(1964)	Shimin, Symeon	40-65	R
Fisher, Aileen	My Cousin Abe (1st, 8vo, 285p, fp b/w, DJ/3.50)	Nelson	(1962)	Vosburgh, Leonard	25-40	
Fisher, Aileen	My Mother and I (1st, sm4to, [32]p, fp color, DJ/3.95)	Crowell	(1967)	Mizumura, Kazue	25-40	
Fisher, Aileen	Off to the Gold Fields (1st, 8vo, 158p, b/w, DJ/2.75)	Nelson	1955	Powers, Richard	20-30	
Fisher, Aileen	Over the Hills to Nugget (1st {std}, sm8vo, uncut, 121p, fp b/w, DJ/1.75)	Aladdin	1949	James, Sandra	20-35	*
Fisher, Aileen	Runny Days, Sunny Days (1st, 8vo, 126p, ibds, silhouettes, DJ/2.75)	Abelard-Schuman	(1958)	Fisher, Aileen	25-40	
Fisher, Aileen	Sing, Little Mouse (1st, 4to, [36]p, color, pep, DJ/3.95)	Crowell	(1969)	Shimin, Symeon	25-45	
Fisher, Aileen	Timber! Logging in Michigan (1st {std}, 8vo, 191p, color, DJ/1.75)	Aladdin	1955	Crowell, Pers	30-50	
Fisher, Aileen	Trapped by the Mountain Storm (1st {std}, sm8vo, 124p, b/w, DJ/2.00)	Aladdin	1950	Collins, Fred	20-30	*
Fisher, Aileen	Up, Up the Mountain (1st, 4to, [32]p, fp color, DJ/3.95)	Crowell	(1968)	Riswold, Gilbert	30-50	
Fisher, Aileen	We Alcotts (1st {std}, 8vo, 278p, b/w, DJ/4.95)	Atheneum	1968	Raskin, Ellen	35-50	
Fisher, Aileen	We Dickinsons (1st {std}, 8vo, 246p, cep, DJ/4.50, b/w frn & decor by...)	Atheneum	1965	Raskin, Ellen	30-50	R
Fisher, Aileen	We Went Looking (1st, lg ob8vo, blue cl, 25p, color, DJ/3.95)	Crowell	(1968)	Angel, Marie	25-40	
Fisher, Aileen	Where Does Everyone Go? (1st, sm4to, [36]p, color, pep, DJ/3.50)	Crowell	(1961)	Adams, Adrienne	30-45	
Fisher, Anne B.	Stories California Indians Told (1st, lg8vo, 109p, fp 1-color, DJ/2.95)	Parnassus Press	(1957)	Robbins, Ruth	25-45	
Fisher, Cyrus	Avion My Uncle Flew (1st, sm8vo, 244p, fp b/w, DJ/2.50, NH)	Appleton-Century	(1946)	Floethe, Richard	60-90	
Fisher, Dorothea	And Long Remember... (1st, 4to, 118p, b/w, pep, DJ/3.50)	Whittlesey	(1959)	Keats, Ezra J.	30-50	
Fisher, Harrison	American Beauties (1st, 4to, 93p, 21cp)	Bobbs-Merrill	(1909)	Fisher, Harrison	250-400	
Fisher, Harrison	American Belles (1st, folio, ibds, gilt, [64]p, p-o, teg, 16 ticp)	Dodd	1911	Fisher, Harrison	650-800	
Fisher, Harrison	American Girl (1st, folio, brown bds, p-o, 12 ticp)	Scribner	1909	Fisher, Harrison	600-850	
Fisher, Harrison	American Girls in Miniature (1st, 8vo, ibds, p-o, 32cp)	Scribner	1912	Fisher, Harrison	250-350	
Fisher, Harrison	Bachelor Belles (1st, 4to, [134]p, p-o, grey/gilt, 22cp)	Dodd	1908	Fisher, Harrison	250-400	
Fisher, Harrison	Fair Americans (1st, 4to, gilt, [100]p, p-o, 22cp)	Scribner	1911	Fisher, Harrison	300-500	
Fisher, Harrison	Garden of Girls (1st, folio, gilt, [68]p, p-o, ibds, 16 ticp, dep)	Dodd	1910	Fisher, Harrison	600-800	
Fisher, Harrison	Girl's Life (1st, folio, pcb, p-o, 16cp)	Scribner	1913	Fisher, Harrison	700-1000	
Fisher, Harrison	Harrison Fisher Book (1st, 4to, gilt, p-o, 9cp)	Scribner	1907	Fisher, Harrison	300-500	
Fisher, Harrison	Harrison Fisher Girls (1st, lg4to, [48]p, gilt, p-o, teg, 12 ticp, pep)	Dodd	1914	Fisher, Harrison	600-900	
Fisher, Harrison	Little Gift Book (1st, lg8vo, ibds, p-o, 32cp)	Scribner	1913	Fisher, Harrison	200-300	
Fisher, Harrison	Maidens Fair (1st, folio, [63]p, grey bds, gilt, p-o, 16 ticp)	Dodd	1912	Fisher, Harrison	600-800	
Fisher, Harrison	Pictures in Color (1st, folio, gilt, p-o, bds, 16cp)	Scribner	1910	Fisher, Harrison	700-1000	
Fisher, M.F.K.	Alphabet for Gourmets (1st, 8vo, 255p, 2-color, DJ/3.00)	Viking	1949	Bileck, Marvin	80-125	
Fisher, Murray	Golliwogg's Dream... Little Folks (1st, sm4to, unpag, ibds, color)	L: Cassell	[1910]	Hart, Frank	100-170	*
Fiske, John	Life Everlasting (1st, 12mo, 87p, blue cl, teg, designed by...)	Houghton	1901	Rogers, Bruce	25-40	
Fitch, Florence	Book About God (1st, 4to, ibds, [28]p, color, DJ/2.00)	Lothrop, Lee	1953	Weisgard, Leonard	50-85	
Fitch, Florence	Child Jesus (1st, 4to, [32]p, grey cl, fp color, pep, DJ/2.50)	Lothrop, Lee	1955	Weisgard, Leonard	40-65	
Fitch, William C.	Knighting of the Twins (1st {1st bk}, 8vo, tan cl, 275p, b/w)	Roberts Bros.	(1891)	Gerson, Virginia	90-120	*
Fitinghoff, Laura M.	Children of the Moor (1st, 8vo, 282p, col frn, 3pl, pep)	Houghton	1927	Tenggren, Gustaf	30-50	
Fitzgerald, Hugh	Sam Steele's Adventures in Panama (1st, sm8vo, 310p, green cl, 5cp)	Reilly/Britton	(1907)	Heath, Howard	700-900	*
Fitzgerald, Hugh	Sam Steele's Adventures on Land & Sea (1st, sm8vo, 271p, gilt, p-o, 5cp)	Reilly/Britton	(1906)	Heath, Howard	500-700	*
Fitzgerald, John T.	Bixby of Boston (1st, 12mo, uncut, 83p, 20pl)	Broadway	1906	Fitzgerald, John	25-40	*
Fitzgerald, S.	Zankiwank & Bletherwitch (1st AM, 8vo, 188p, gilt, b/w)	Stokes	(1896)	Rackham, Arthur	500-700	
Fitzgerald, S.	Zankiwank & Bletherwitch (1st, 8vo, teg, green/gilt, 188p, fp b/w)	L: J.M. Dent	1896	Rackham, Arthur	700-900	
Fitzhugh, Louise	Bang Bang, You're Dead (1st, ob4to, ibds, 32p, b/w, DJ/3.95, NYTBI)	Harper	(1969)	Fitzhugh, Louise	100-165	
Fitzhugh, Louise	Harriet the Spy (1st, 8vo, 298p, b/w, DJ/3.95)	Harper	(1964)	Fitzhugh, Louise	140-225	
Fitzhugh, Percy K.	Boy's Book of Scouts (1st, 8vo, 317p, 3pl by...)	Crowell	(1917)	Remington, Frederic	70-100	*
Fitzhugh, Percy K.	King Time (1st, 8vo, green/gilt, 233p, 8cp, pep)	Caldwell	(1908)	Bridgman, L.J.	200-300	R
Fitzpatrick, Percy	Jock of the Bushveld (1st, 8vo, 474p, gilt, col frn, 22pl)	L: Longmans	1907	Caldwell, Edmund G.	120-200	
Flack, Edith	Marionettes (1st, sm4to, 115p, b/w)	Stokes	1929	Flack, Marjorie	30-50	
Flack, Marjorie	All Around the Town (1st {std}, 8vo, 283p, col frn, b/w, pep)	Doubleday/Doran	1929	Flack, Marjorie	70-100	
Flack, Marjorie	Angus & the Cat (1st {std}, lg ob8vo, [32]p, ibds, color)	Doubleday/Doran	1931	Flack, Marjorie	100-145	
Flack, Marjorie	Angus & the Ducks (1st {std}, lg ob8vo, [32]p, ibds, color, pep)	Doubleday/Doran	1930	Flack, Marjorie	90-135	
Flack, Marjorie	Angus Lost (1st {std}, sm ob4to, [32]p, ibds, color, pep)	Doubleday/Doran	1932	Flack, Marjorie	80-125	
Flack, Marjorie	Ask Mr. Bear (1st, sq8vo, [32]p, color, pep, DJ/1.00)	Macmillan	1932	Flack, Marjorie	75-100	
Flack, Marjorie	Away Goes Jonathan Wheeler (1st {std}, ob8vo, ibds, [32]p, color, DJ/1.00)	Garden City	1944	Larson, Hilma	40-65	*
Flack, Marjorie	Boats on the River (1st, lg ob4to, 31p, ibds, color, DJ/2.50, CH)	Viking	1946	Barnum, Jay H.	130-200	R
Flack, Marjorie	Humphrey (1st {std}, 4to, ibds, [80]p, color, pep)	Doubleday/Doran	1934	Flack, Marjorie	50-80	

AUTHOR	TITLE	PUBLISHER	DATE	ARTIST	PRICE	LC
Flack, Marjorie	I See a Kitty (1st, sq12mo, ibds, [16]p, color)	Garden City	1943	Larsson, Karl	30-50	
Flack, Marjorie	New Pet (1st {std}, sm4to, ibds, [32]p, color, DJ/1.50)	Doubleday/Doran	(1943)	Flack, Marjorie	55-80	
Flack, Marjorie	Pedro (1st, 8vo, blue cl, 96p, dp color, pep, DJ/2.25)	Macmillan	1940	Larsson, Karl	55-80	
Flack, Marjorie	Restless Robin (1st, sm ob4to, [48]p, green cl, color, pep, DJ/1.50)	Houghton	1937	Flack, Marjorie	80-130	
Flack, Marjorie	Story about Ping (1st, lg8vo, ipcb, [32]p, color)	Viking	1933	Wiese, Kurt	170-225	R
Flack, Marjorie	Taktuk, Arctic Boy (1st {std}, 8vo, 139p, uncut, col frn, pep, DJ)	Doubleday/Doran	1928	Flack, Marjorie	50-80	*
Flack, Marjorie	Tim Tadpole... (1st {std}, sm8vo, [32]p, ibds, p-o, color, pep)	Doubleday/Doran	1934	Flack, Marjorie	60-100	
Flack, Marjorie	Topsy (1st {std}, ob4to, ibds, [32]p, color, pep, DJ/1.00)	Doubleday/Doran	1935	Flack, Marjorie	100-165	
Flack, Marjorie	Up in The Air (1st, lg8vo, blue cl, [40]p, color, DJ/1.75)	Macmillan	1935	Larsson, Karl	30-50	
Flack, Marjorie	Wait for William (1st, ob8vo, ibds, [33]p, color, pep, DJ/1.00)	Houghton	1935	Holberg, Richard	45-70	
Flack, Marjorie	Walter the Lazy Mouse (1st {std}, 4to, [80]p, color, cep, DJ/2.00)	Doubleday/Doran	1937	Flack, Marjorie	200-300	
Flack, Marjorie	Walter the Lazy Mouse (1st {std}, lg8vo, 95p, 2-color, DJ/2.95)	Doubleday	(1963)	Szekeres, Cyndy	50-80	
Flack, Marjorie	William & his Kitten (1st, ob8vo, ibds, [32]p, color, pep, DJ/1.25)	Houghton	1938	Flack, Marjorie	60-100	
Flack, Marjorie	Willy Nilly (1st, 4to, ibds, [32]p, color, pep, DJ/1.00)	Macmillan	1936	Flack, Marjorie	100-165	
Flagg, Elisha	Rookie (1st, 8vo, 63p, beige cl, b/w, DJ/1.00)	Whitman	1940	Flagg, James M.	20-35	
Flagg, James M.	Adventures of Kitty Cobb (1st, lg sq4to, ibds, [67]p, b/w, pep)	Doran	(1912)	Flagg, James M.	100-145	
Flagg, James M.	All in the Same Boat (1st, 12mo, 105p, b/w)	Life Pub. Co.	1908	Flagg, James M.	25-40	
Flagg, James M.	City People (1st, ob folio, ibds, [84]p, b/w)	Scribner	1909	Flagg, James M.	100-160	
Flagg, James M.	I Should Say So (1st, sm8vo, gilt, ipcb, p-o, 202p, b/w, pep)	Doran	(1914)	Flagg, James M.	60-100	
Flagg, James M.	Why they Married (1st, 12mo, 107p, ibds)	Life Pub. Co.	1906	Flagg, James M.	100-150	
Flakkeberg, Ardo	Sea Broke Through (1st AM {std}, 8vo, 179p, b/w, DJ/2.75)	Knopf	1960	Spier, Peter E.	30-45	*
Flanders, Helen H.	Looking Out of Jimmie (1st, sm8vo, 92p, gilt, pep, uncut, fp b/w)	Dutton	(1927)	Pogany, Willy	60-90	
Flanders, Michael	Creatures Great & Small (1st {std}, 8vo, 42p, color, DJ/3.50)	Holt, Rinehart	(1965)	Minale, Marcello	25-40	
Flaubert, Gustave	Madame Bovary (1st, lg8vo, 416p, black/gilt, 13pl, pep)	L: John Lane	(1928)	Austen, John	70-125	
Flaubert, Gustave	Temptation of St. Anthony (1st, sm8vo, 360p, teg, gilt, 8pl)	L: H.S. Nichols	1895	Gorski, S.	100-180	
Fleckenstein, Alfred	Prince of Gravas (1st, sm8vo, 270p, grey/gilt, 3pl)	Jacobs	1898	Waugh, J.	50-80	
Flecker, James E.	Hassan (1st, 4to, 155p, teg, red/gilt, 12 ticp, pep)	L: Heinemann	1924	Mackenzie, Thomas B.	150-225	
Fleischman, Sid	Chancy and the Grand Rascal (1st {std}, 8vo, 179p, b/w, DJ/4.25)	Little/Brown	(1966)	Von Schmidt, Eric	25-40	
Fleischman, Sid	Ghost in the Noonday Sun (1st {std}, 8vo, 173p, b/w, DJ/3.95)	Little/Brown	(1965)	Chappell, Warren	30-50	
Fleischman, Sid	McBroom and the Big Wind (1st {std}, 8vo, [46]p, color, DJ/3.25)	Norton	(1967)	Werth, Kurt	25-40	
Fleischman, Sid	McBroom Tells the Truth (1st {std}, 8vo, 47p, color, DJ/3.25)	Norton	(1966)	Werth, Kurt	25-40	
Fleischman, Sid	McBroom's Ear (1st {std}, 8vo, [48]p, color, DJ/4.25)	Norton	(1969)	Werth, Kurt	25-40	
Fleischman, Sid	Mr. Mysterious and Company (1st {std}, 8vo, 151p, b/w, DJ/3.25)	Little/Brown	(1962)	Von Schmidt, Eric	25-40	
Fleming, Ian	Chitty Chitty Bang Bang! (1st AM, lg8vo, 114p, b/w, pep, DJ/3.50)	Random	(1964)	Burningham, John	80-130	
Fleming, Ian	Chitty Chitty Bang Bang! (1st, 8vo, 63p, ibds, color)	Beginner Books	(1968)	Tobey, Barney	40-65	
Fleming, W.M.M.	Hunted Piccaninnies (1st, 8vo, 185p, grey cl, 7cp)	L: J.M. Dent	1927	Edmunds, Kay	100-170	
Fleming, Waldo	Pygmy's Arrow (1st, 8vo, 310p, pep, DJ/2.00)	Lothrop, Lee	1938	Dobias, Frank	30-50	*
Fleming, Waldo	Talking Drums (1st {std}, 8vo, 307p, col frn, b/w, pep, DJ/2.00)	Doubleday/Doran	1936	Dobias, Frank	30-50	
Flemwell, George	Alpine Flowers & Gardens (1st, 8vo, 167p, gilt, teg, 20cp)	L: A&C Black	1910	Flemwell, George	90-160	
Fletcher, David	Confetti for Cortorelli (1st {std}, 8vo, 147p, b/w, DJ/2.75)	Pantheon	(1957)	Thompson, George	30-45	*
Fletcher, Inglis	White Leopard: Tale of the African Bush (1st {std}, 8vo, 304p, b/w)	Bobbs-Merrill	(1931)	Wiese, Kurt	30-50	
Fletcher, Joseph S.	Life in Arcadia (1st, sm8vo, 265p, green/gilt, cvr by...)	L: John Lane	1896	Wilson, Patten	60-90	
Fletcher, Joseph S.	Making of Matthais (1st, sm8vo, AEG, 141p, blue/gilt, 14pl)	L: John Lane	1898	Kemp-Welch, Lucy	50-85	
Fleuron, Svend	Grim: Story of a Pike (1st, sm8vo, green cl, 186p, 4pl)	Knopf	1921	Lathrop, Dorothy	60-100	
Fleuron, Svend	Wild Horses of Iceland (1st, 8vo, 234p, red cl, 15 fp b/w)	L: Eyre/Spotts.	[1933]	Aldin, Cecil	50-80	
Fleury, Barbara	Runaway Deer (1st, 8vo, [32]p, p-o, b/w, DJ/1.00)	Macmillan	1938	Somppi, Lilly	30-50	*
Flint, William R.	Watercolors of William Russell Flint (1st, ob. folio, 8 ticp)	L: Studio	(1920)	Flint, William R.	120-170	
Floethe, Louise	Fisherman and his Boat (1st, ob4to, [32]p, color, DJ/2.95)	Scribner	(1961)	Floethe, L.& R.	30-45	
Floethe, Louise	Fountain of the Friendly Lion (1st, 4to, [32]p, fp color, DJ)	Scribner	1966	Floethe, Richard	25-40	
Floethe, Richard	If I Were Captain (1st, sm4to, [32]p, fp 2-color, DJ)	Scribner	(1956)	Floethe, Richard	25-40	
Flora, James	Day the Cow Sneezed (1st {std}, 4to, [41]p, 3-color, pep, DJ/2.95)	Harcourt	1957	Flora, James	50-80	R*
Flora, James	Fabulous Firework Family (1st {std}, 4to, [40]p, color, pep, DJ/2.75)	Harcourt	(1955)	Flora, James	50-85	R*
Flora, James	Joking Man (1st {std}, 8vo, [30]p, 2-color, DJ/3.25)	Harcourt	(1968)	Flora, James	30-50	
Flora, James	Kangaroo for Christmas (1st {std}, sm4to, [31]p, fp 3-color, pep, DJ/2.95)	Harcourt	(1962)	Flora, James	30-50	
Flora, James	Leopold, See-through Crumbpicker (1st {std}, 4to, unpag, b/w, pep, DJ/2.75)	Harcourt	(1961)	Flora, James	30-50	
Flora, James	Little Hatchy Hen (1st {std}, 4to, [32]p, color, DJ/3.50)	Harcourt	(1969)	Flora, James	25-40	*
Flora, James	My Friend Charlie (1st {std}, sm4to, [32]p, 2-color, DJ/2.75)	Harcourt	(1964)	Flora, James	30-50	
Flora, James	Sherwood Walks Home (1st {std}, sm ob4to, unpag, color, DJ/3.25)	Harcourt	(1966)	Flora, James	30-50	*
Flower, Esther	Nurse Nora's Up-to-Date Fairy Tales (1st, 12mo, 163p, 9pl)	J. Pott	1903	Cory/Graef	60-90	
Foley, Dorothy C.	When Our Ship Comes In (1st, 4to, ibds, [34]p, color, pep, DJ/1.00)	Saalfield	1938	Orr, Forrest W.	45-70	
Foley, James W.	Christmas Prayer (1st, 16mo, ibds, [24]p, color)	Volland	(1915)	Foley, James W.	55-80	*
Foley, James W.	Some One Like You (1st, 16mo, gilt, ibds, color, pep)	Volland	(1916)	Unknown	50-80	
Foley, James W.	Through All the Years (1st, sq16mo, pep, [22]p, color)	Volland	(1920)	Unknown	30-50	
Folkard, Charles	Teddy Tail of the Daily Mail (1st, 4to, ibds, 32p, 1-color)	L: A&C Black	[1915]	Folkard, Charles	100-165	
Folkard, Charles	Teddy Tail's Fairy Tale (4to, ibds, 32p, b/w)	L: A&C Black	[1920]	Folkard, Charles	80-120	
Follett, Helen T.	House Afire! (1st, 8vo, 102p, b/w, pep, DJ/1.50)	Scribner	1941	Sperry, Armstrong	30-50	
Follett, Helen T.	Magic Portholes (1st, lg8vo, 321p, orange cl, fp b/w, pep)	Macmillan	1932	Sperry, Armstrong	30-45	
Follett, Helen T.	Ocean Outposts (1st, 4to, 133p, DJ/2.00, maps by...)	Scribner	1942	Sperry, Armstrong	30-50	
Follett, Helen T.	Stars to Steer By (1st, sm8vo, blue cl, 257p, fp b/w)	Macmillan	1934	Sperry, Armstrong	35-60	*
Foltz, Mary Jane	Nicolau's Prize (1st, 8vo, 91p, b/w, DJ/3.25)	McGraw-Hill	(1967)	Turkle, Brinton	50-80	*
Fontaine, Robert	Happy Time (1st, 8vo, 269p, p-o, fp b/w, DJ/2.50)	Simon/Schuster	(1945)	Duvoisin, Roger	30-50	
Fontane, Theodore	Sir Ribbeck of Ribbeck... (1st {std}, ob8vo, ibds, [32]p, color, DJ/4.95)	Macmillan	(1969)	Hogrogian, Nonny	30-50	
Foque, De La Motte	Sintram & his Companions (1st, 8vo, gilt, 124p, AEG, b/w)	L: Seeley	1883	Sumner, Heywood	60-90	
Forbes, Elizabeth S.	King Arthur's Wood (1st, ob folio, 120p, buckram, 14cp)	L: Simpkin	1904	Forbes, Eliz. S.	900-1200	
Forbes, Esther	America's Paul Revere (1st, 4to, 46p, color, red cl, DJ/2.50)	Houghton	1946	Ward, Lynd	55-80	
Forbes, Esther	Johnny Tremain (1st, 8vo, 256p, col frn, pep, DJ/3.00, NM)	Houghton	1943	Ward, Lynd	100-175	R
Forbes, Helen	Mario's Castle (1st, 12mo, 198p, col frn, pep, 3pl)	Macmillan	1928	DeAngeli, Marguerite	40-60	*
Forbes, Katherine	Thirsty Lion (1st, lg8vo, 88p, fp b/w, pep, DJ/2.00)	Crowell	(1950)	Weil, Lisl	30-50	

AUTHOR	TITLE	PUBLISHER	DATE	ARTIST	PRICE	LC
Forbus, Ina B.	Magic Pin (1st, 8vo, 138p, b/w, DJ/2.50)	Viking	1956	Bell, Corydon	40-65	
Forbus, Ina B.	Melissa (1st, 8vo, 190p, b/w, DJ/3.00)	Viking	(1962)	Felt, Sue	60-90	
Forbus, Ina B.	Secret Circle (1st, 8vo, 160p, b/w, DJ/2.50)	Viking	1958	Bell, Corydon	60-90	
Forbus, Ina B.	Tawny's Trick (1st, 8vo, 187p, b/w, DJ/3.50)	Viking	1965	Grifalconi, Ann	40-65	
Forbush, Wm. B.	Wonder Book of Myths & Legends (lg8vo, 337p, blue cl, p-o, 3cp, 11 b/w)	Winston	(1928)	Richardson, F.	25-40	*
Ford, Ford Madox	Queen Who Flew (1st, 12mo, 118p, frn by…)	L: Bliss Sands	1894	Burne-Jones, Edward	80-125	*
Ford, Ford Madox	Queen Who Flew (1st, 8vo, 82p, fp b/w, DJ/3.50)	NY: Braziller	(1965)	Miller, Grambs	25-40	
Ford, Henry W.	Fun with the Calendar (1st, 4to, [26]p, color, dep, DJ)	Holt, Rinehart	1964	Aliki	30-45	
Ford, Julia E.	Imagina (1st, lg8vo, 178p, blue/gilt, 2 fp color, pep)	Duffield	1914	Rackham, Arthur	170-240	
Ford, Julia E.	Snickerty Nick (1st, lg8vo, 78p, blue cl, 3cp, 10pl)	Moffat	1919	Rackham, Arthur	400-650	
Ford, Lauren	Ageless Story (1st, sq4to, blue/gilt, [40]p, color, DJ/2.00, CH)	Dodd	1939	Suba, Susanne	65-100	
Ford, Lauren	Lauren Ford's Christmas Book (1st, lg ob8vo, [46]p, fp color, DJ/4.50)	Dodd	(1963)	Ford, Lauren	20-35	
Ford, Lauren	Our Lady's Book (1st, 8vo, 269p, gilt, color, DJ/4.50)	Dodd	(1962)	Ford, Lauren	20-30	
Ford, Margaret	David and the Magic Powder (1st, lg8vo, ibds, [32]p, color, pep, DJ/1.50)	Random	(1946)	Walker, Nedda	25-45	
Ford, Paul L.	Checked Love Affair (1st, 8vo, 112p, teg, gilt, 5pl)	Dodd	1903	Fisher, Harrison	35-60	
Ford, Paul L.	His Version of It (1st, 8vo, gilt, teg, 109p, 5cp)	Dodd	1905	Hutt, Henry	30-50	
Ford, Paul L.	Love Finds the Way (1st, 8vo, teg, 108p, uncut, cvr by…)	Dodd	1904	Armstrong, Margaret	35-60	
Ford, Paul L.	Wanted a Chaperone (1st, 8vo, 109p, teg, uncut, cvr by…)	Dodd	1902	Armstrong, Margaret	40-65	
Ford, Paul L.	Wanted a Chaperone (1st, 8vo, 109p, teg, uncut, 6cp)	Dodd	1902	Christy, Howard C.	40-65	
Ford, Paul L.	Wanted a Matchmaker (1st, 8vo, teg, 112p, cvr by…)	Dodd	1900	Armstrong, Margaret	40-65	
Ford, Paul L.	Wanted a Matchmaker (1st, 8vo, 112p, teg, green/gilt, 5pl by…)	Dodd	1900	Christy, Howard C.	40-65	
Ford, Sewell	Horses Nine (1st, sm8vo, 270p, cvr by…)	Scribner	1903	Falls, Charles B.	40-65	
Foreman, Michael	Great Sleigh Robbery (1st AM {std}, 4to, [32]p, color, DJ/3.95)	Pantheon	(1969)	Foreman, Michael	30-50	*
Foreman, Michael	Perfect Present (1st AM, 4to, 32p, fp color, DJ)	Coward	1967	Foreman, Michael	30-50	
Foreman, Michael	Travels of Horatio (1st AM {std}, 4to, [32]p, color, DJ/3.95)	Pantheon	(1970)	Foreman, Michael	30-50	
Foreman, Michael	Two Giants (1st AM {std}, 4to, [30]p, color, DJ/3.95)	Pantheon	(1967)	Foreman, Michael	30-50	*
Forester, C.S.	Poo Poo & the Dragons (1st {std}, 8vo, 142p, green cl, b/w, pep, DJ/1.75)	Little/Brown	1942	Lawson, Robert	450-650	
Forman, Justus M.	Island of Enchantment (1st, 8vo, blue/gilt, teg, 106p, 4cp, dep)	Harper	1905	Pyle, Howard	80-125	
Forrest, A.S.	Morocco (1st, lg8vo, gilt, 231p, teg, 74cp)	L: A&C Black	1904	Forrest, A.S.	100-165	
Forrester, Izola	Us Fellers (1st, 8vo, blue cl, p-o, 150p, 7cp)	Jacobs	1907	Kilvert, Cory	55-80	*
Forst, S.	Pipkin (1st {std}, lg8vo, 130p, gilt, fp b/w, DJ/4.50)	Delacorte Pr.	(1970)	Jacques, Robin	20-35	
Forster, Frederick J.	On the Road to Make-Believe (1st, lg4to, 128p, p-o, color, pep)	Rand/McNally	(1924)	Trippe, Uldene	60-90	
Forster, Frederick J.	Tippytoes Comes to Town (1st, 4to, p-o, 96p, color)	Rand/McNally	(1926)	Trippe, Uldene	50-80	
Forsyth, George A.	Thrilling Days in Army Life (1st, sm8vo, 196p, 16pl)	Harper	1900	Zogbaum, Rufus F.	125-200	
Forsythe, Clarence	Old Songs for Young Americans (1st, ob4to, 46p, green cl, color)	Doubleday/Page	1901	Ostertag, Blanche	100-160	
Fort, Charles	LO! (1st, 8vo, 411p, 12 illus, DJ/2.50)	NY: Kendall	(1931)	King, Alexander	100-150	
Fortesque, J.W.	Drummer's Coat (1st, 8vo, 184p, uncut, red/gilt, 4pl)	L: Macmillan	1899	Brock, Henry M.	70-100	
Foster, Doris	Tell Me, Little Boy (1st, 4to, [28]p, ibds, color, DJ/2.00)	Lothrop, Lee	1953	Duvoisin, Roger	50-85	*
Foster, Doris	Tell Me, Mister Owl (1st, 4to, [29]p, ibds, color, DJ/2.75)	Lothrop, Lee	1957	Stone, Helen	40-65	R*
Foster, Elizabeth	Gigi (1st, lg8vo, 118p, col frn, b/w, pep, DJ/2.00)	Houghton	1943	Bischoff, Ilse	30-45	
Foster, Elizabeth	Gigi in America (1st, 8vo, 123p, b/w, pep, DJ/2.00)	Houghton	1946	Cote, Phyllis	25-40	
Foster, Genevieve	Abraham Lincoln (1st, sm8vo, 111p, color, DJ/2.00)	Scribner	(1950)	Foster, Genevieve	80-130	
Foster, Genevieve	Abraham Lincoln's World (1st, sm4to, 347p, b/w, cep, DJ/3.50, NH)	Scribner	1944	Foster, Genevieve	80-120	R
Foster, Genevieve	Augustus Ceasar's World (1st, 4to, 330p, col frn, b/w, DJ/3.50)	Scribner	1947	Foster, Genevieve	70-120	
Foster, Genevieve	Birthdays of Freedom (1st, 4to, [59]p, color, DJ/2.75, NH)	Scribner	(1952)	Foster, Genevieve	70-125	
Foster, Genevieve	George Washington (1st, sm4to, 93p, dp color, DJ/2.00, NH)	Scribner	(1949)	Foster, Genevieve	70-125	
Foster, Genevieve	George Washington's World (1st, 4to, 348p, 1-color, cep, DJ/3.00, NH)	Scribner	1941	Foster, Genevieve	70-125	R
Foster, Genevieve	World of Captain John Smith, 1580-1631 (1st, 4to, 406p, bds, b/w, DJ/4.95)	Scribner	(1959)	Foster, Genevieve	70-125	
Foster, Genevieve	Year of Columbus, 1492 (1st, 8vo, 64p, color, DJ)	Scribner	(1969)	Foster, Genevieve	25-45	
Foster, Genevieve	Year of Independence, 1776 (1st, lg8vo, 64p, color, DJ/3.50)	Scribner	(1970)	Foster, Genevieve	25-45	
Foster, Joanna	Pete's Puddle (1st, 8vo, 21p, color, DJ/1.25)	Houghton	1950	Foster, Joanna	25-35	
Foster, Myles B.	Day in a Child's Life (1st, 4to, 29p, ibds, color)	L: Routledge	[1881]	Greenaway, Kate	450-600	
Foulds, Elfrida V.	Lark on the Wing (1st, 8vo, 234p, b/w, DJ, CgM)	L: Oxford U.Pr.	1950	Freeman, Terry	60-90	*
Fouque, La Motte	Sintram and his Companions (1st, 12mo, 12pl)	L: Dent	1900	Robinson, Charles	160-240	
Fouque, La Motte	Sintram and his Companions (1st, 8vo, 193p, uncut, olive/gilt, teg, 20pl)	L: Methuen	(1908)	Sullivan, Edmund J.	80-125	
Fouque, La Motte	Undine (1st, 8vo, blue/gilt, 204p, teg, 19pl)	L: Macmillan	1897	Pitman, R.M.M.	80-120	
Fouque, La Motte	Undine (1st AM, 4to, 136p, grey/gilt, 15 ticp, pep)	Doubleday/Page	1909	Rackham, Arthur	200-300	
Fouque, La Motte	Undine (1st, sm4to, 136p, blue/gilt, 15 ticp, pep)	L: Heinemann	1909	Rackham, Arthur	250-350	
Fournier, Catherine	Coconut Thieves (1st, 4to, [32]p, 3-color, DJ/3.25)	Scribner	(1964)	Domanska, Janina	30-50	*
Fox, Dorothea	Miss Twiggley's Tree (1st, sm4to, unpag, color, DJ/2.95)	Parents Mag. Pr.	(1966)	Fox, Dorothea	25-40	
Fox, Frances M.	Adventures of Sonny Bear (1st, sm8vo, 80p, 15cp)	Rand/McNally	(1916)	Carr, Warner	55-80	
Fox, Frances M.	Angeline Goes Traveling (1st, 12mo, p-o, 256p, 5cp)	Rand/McNally	(1927)	Gregory, Dorothy L.	30-50	*
Fox, Frances M.	Betty of Mackinaw (1st, 12mo, 109p, b/w)	L.C. Page	1901	Barry, Etheldred B.	25-40	*
Fox, Frances M.	County Christmas (1st, 12mo, 111p, 10pl)	L.C. Page	1907	Barry, Etheldred B.	25-45	*
Fox, Frances M.	Ellen Jane (1st, 8vo, 104p, gilt, p-o, 4cp)	Rand/McNally	(1924)	Gregory, Dorothy L.	25-40	
Fox, Frances M.	Janey (1st, 12mo, 151p, blue cl, p-o, 4cp)	Rand/McNally	(1925)	Gregory, Dorothy L.	25-40	
Fox, Frances M.	Little Bear's Adventures (1st, 8vo, 64p, blue cl, p-o, 8 fp color)	Rand/McNally	(1923)	Beem, Frances	45-70	
Fox, Frances M.	Little Cat that Could Not Sleep (1st {std}, 8vo, [31]p, pep, col, DJ/1.50)	Dutton	1941	Suba, Susanne	75-100	*
Fox, Frances M.	Little Giant's Neighbours (1st, 12mo, 132p, b/w)	L.C. Page	1903	Dodge, F.E.	25-40	*
Fox, Frances M.	Mother Nature's Little Ones (1st, 12mo, 92p, fp b/w)	L.C. Page	1904	Barry, Etheldred B.	25-40	*
Fox, Frances M.	Nancy Davenport (1st, 12mo, 261p, p-o, 5cp)	Rand/McNally	(1928)	Eger, Ruth Ç.	25-40	*
Fox, Frances M.	Nannette (1st, 8vo, 80p, red/gilt, color, pep)	Volland	(1929)	Gruelle, Justin	70-100	
Fox, Frances M.	Seven Christmas Candles (1st, sm8vo, 192p, green cl, 6cp, pep)	L.C. Page	1909	Barry, Etheldred B.	45-70	
Fox, Frances M.	Sister Sally (1st, 8vo, 105p, gilt, p-o, 4cp)	Rand/McNally	(1925)	Gregory, Dorothy L.	25-40	
Fox, Frances M.	True Monkey Stories (1st, lg8vo, 55p, green cl, fp color, pep, DJ/1.75)	Lothrop, Lee	(1941)	Gergely, Tibor	35-50	
Fox, Frances M.	What Gladys Saw (1st, 12mo, green cl, 318p, 5pl)	W.A. Wilde	(1902)	Copeland, Charles	30-50	
Fox, Frances M.	Wildling Princess (1st, 8vo, 79p, brown/gilt, 10cp, pep)	Volland	(1929)	Perkins, John E.	80-120	
Fox, John Jr.	Blue Grass and Rhododendron (1st, 8vo, teg, 294p, uncut)	Scribner	1901	Armstrong, Margaret	70-120	

AUTHOR	TITLE	PUBLISHER	DATE	ARTIST	PRICE	LC
Fox, John Jr.	Christmas Eve on Lonesome (1st, sm8vo, 234p, teg, 8cp)	Scribner	1904	Various	25-40	
Fox, John Jr.	Heart of the Hills (1st, 12mo, red/gilt, 396p, 7pl)	Scribner	1913	Yohn, F.C.	25-40	
Fox, John Jr.	In Happy Valley (1st, sm8vo, 229p, red/gilt, 8pl)	Scribner	1917	Yohn, F.C.	30-50	
Fox, John Jr.	Little Shepherd of Kingdom Come (1st, lg8vo, 322p, p-o, 14cp, pep, SC)	Scribner	1931	Wyeth, N.C.	250-350	
Fox, John Jr.	Trail of the Lonesome Pine (1st, 12mo, 422p, teg, uncut, gilt, fp b/w)	Scribner	1908	Yohn, F.C.	40-65	
Fox, Paula	Dear Prosper (1st, 8vo, 67p, b/w, DJ/3.95)	NY: David White	(1968)	McLachlin, Steve	20-35	
Fox, Paula	How Many Miles to Babylon? (1st, 12mo, 117p, b/w, DJ/3.95)	NY: David White	(1967)	Giovanopoulos, P.	50-80	
Fox, Paula	Hungry Fred (1st {std}, 4to, [39]p, color, DJ/3.95)	Bradbury Press	(1969)	Wells, Rosemary	25-40	
Fox, Paula	King's Falcon (1st {std}, 8vo, 56p, fp 1-color, cep, DJ/3.95)	Bradbury Press	(1969)	Keith, Eros	45-70	R*
Fox, Paula	Likely Place (1st {std}, 8vo, 57p, yellow cl, b/w, DJ/2.95)	Macmillan	(1967)	Ardizzone, Edward	30-50	
Fox, Paula	Maurice's Room (1st {std}, 8vo, 63p, b/w, DJ/2.95)	Macmillan	(1966)	Fetz, Ingrid	20-30	
Fox, Paula	Portrait of Ivan (1st {std}, 8vo, 131p, b/w, cep, DJ/4.50)	Bradbury Press	(1969)	Lambert, Saul	60-90	R*
Fox, Paula	Stone-Faced Boy (1st {std}, 8vo, 106p, b/w, DJ/3.95)	Bradbury Press	(1968)	McKay, Donald	30-50	
Foyle, Kathleen	Little Good People (1st AM, 8vo, 163p, 8cp, pep, DJ/2.50)	NY: Warne	(1949)	Fraser, Peter	50-85	
Frame, Janet	Mona Minim & the Smell of the Sun (1st AM, 8vo, 94p, fp color, DJ/4.95)	NY: Brazller	(1969)	Jacques, Robin	30-50	
France, Anatole	At the Sign of the Reine Padauque (1st, 4to, 275p, gilt, 12pl, pep)	L: John Lane	1922	Pape, Frank	50-80	
France, Anatole	Bee, Princess of the Dwarfs (1st, 8vo, gilt, [128]p, teg, 17 ticp)	L: Dent	1912	Robinson, Charles	250-400	
France, Anatole	CLIO (1st, sm8vo, 189p, teg, 12 chromos)	Paris: Calmann	1900	Mucha, Alphonse	500-700	
France, Anatole	Girls & Boys (1st AM, 4to, 25p, ipcb, 12cp)	Duffield	1913	DeMonvel, M.B.	120-180	
France, Anatole	Gods are Athirst (1st, lg8vo, 285p, black/gilt, 12cp)	L: John Lane	(1927)	Austen, John	55-80	
France, Anatole	Golden Tales of Anatole France (1st {this fmt}, lg8vo, 352p, gilt, fp b/w)	Dodd	1927	Patterson, M.	60-100	
France, Anatole	Honey-Bee (1st, lg8vo, red/gilt, 172p, uncut, teg, 12cp, pep)	L: John Lane	1911	Lundborg, Florence	70-125	
France, Anatole	In ALL France (1st, 8vo, gilt, p-o, 110p, color, pep)	Whitman	(1930)	Enders, Lucille	30-50	*
France, Anatole	Little Sea-Dogs (1st, 8vo, 149p, 8cp, pep)	L: Bodley Head	1925	Foster, Marcia L.	40-60	*
France, Anatole	Mother of Pearl (1st, lg8vo, 291p, black/gilt, uncut, pep, 12pl)	L: John Lane	1929	Pape, Frank	50-85	
France, Anatole	Our Children (1st AM, 4to, ibds, 25p, 12cp)	Duffield	1917	DeMonvel, M.B.	100-160	
France, Anatole	Penguin Island (1st, lg8vo, black/gilt, uncut, pep, 12pl)	L: John Lane	1927	Pape, Frank	45-60	
France, Anatole	Revolt of the Angels (1st, 8vo, 357p, black/gilt, 12pl, pep)	L: John Lane	1924	Pape, Frank	90-120	
France, Anatole	Thais (1st, lg8vo, black/gilt, 247p, 12pl, pep)	L: Bodley Head	1926	Pape, Frank	50-85	
France, Anatole	Well of St. Clare (1st, 8vo, black/gilt, 302p, gilt, 12pl, pep)	L: John Lane	(1928)	Pape, Frank	50-85	
Franchere, Ruth	Willa (1st {std}, 8vo, 168p, DJ/3.00, b/w, decor by...)	Crowell	(1958)	Weisgard, Leonard	45-70	R*
Franchi, Anna	Little Lead Soldier (1st, 8vo, p-o, 186p, 5cp)	Penn	1919	Price, Hattie L.	80-130	
Franchot, Annie W.	Bobs, King of Fortunate Isle (1st, 8vo, 210p, blue cl, col frn)	Dutton	(1928)	Smith, Jessie W.	40-60	*
Franchot, Annie W.	Bugs, Wings & other Things (1st, 8vo, 99p, green/gilt, pep, 7cp)	Dutton	(1918)	Cady/Smith	170-220	
Franchot, Annie W.	Bugs, Wings & other Things (1st, 8vo, 99p, green/gilt, pep, 7cp)	Dutton	(1918)	Smith/Cady	170-220	
Franchot, Annie W.	White Giant & Black Giant (1st, lg8vo, ipcb, 72p, fp b/w)	Dutton	(1924)	Gamble, James	50-80	
Francis, Frank	Magic Wallpaper (1st, sm ob4to, [27]p, fp color, DJ/3.95)	Abelard-Schuman	(1970)	Francis, Frank	30-50	*
Francis, Frank	Timimoto's Great Adventure (1st, 4to, [28]p, color, DJ/4.50)	Holiday House	(1969)	Francis, Frank	25-40	
Francis, J.G.	Book of Cheerful Cats (1st, ob8vo, 37p, b/w, PPPa)	Century	1892	Francis, J.G.	120-200	
Francis, J.G.	Joyous Aztecs (1st {std}, ob8vo, 42p, b/w)	Century	(1929)	Francis, J.G.	50-80	
Francis, Philip W.	Remarkable Adventures of Little Boy Pip (1st, 8vo, ibds, 60p, 5cp, pep)	Paul Elder	(1907)	Johnson, Merle	100-185	*
Francis, Sally R.	Scat, Scat (1st, 12mo, [32]p, p-o, color, pep)	Platt/Munk	1940	Collison, Elizabeth	30-50	
Francois, Andre	Crocodile Tears (1st, narrow ob 4to, unpag, fp color, NYTBI)	Universe	(1956)	Francois, Andre	50-80	*
Francois, Andre	You Are Ri-di-cu-lous (1st, ob4to, [32]p, color, DJ/3.95, NYTBI)	Pantheon	(1970)	Francois, Andre	40-65	*
Francoise	Big Rain (1st, 4to, [32]p, pink cl, color, DJ/2.95)	Scribner	1961	Francoise	50-80	
Francoise	Biquette, the White Goat (1st, sm4to, [32]p, fp color, DJ/2.00)	Scribner	1953	Francoise	30-45	*
Francoise	Chouchou (1st, 4to, [32]p, blue cl, fp color, DJ/2.95, NYTBI)	Scribner	1958	Francoise	70-100	
Francoise	Fanchette & Jeannot (1st AM, 4to, ibds, [24]p, color, DJ/0.50)	Grosset/Dunlap	1937	Francoise	80-120	
Francoise	Gay ABC (1st, lg8vo, grey cl, [55]p, fp color, DJ/1.75)	Scribner	(1939)	Francoise	80-120	R
Francoise	Jeanne-Marie Counts her Sheep (1st, sm4to, [32]p, fp color, DJ/2.00)	Scribner	1951	Francoise	70-100	R
Francoise	Jeanne-Marie In Gay Paris (1st, sm4to, unpag, fp color, DJ/2.75)	Scribner	1956	Francoise	100-160	
Francoise	Minou (1st, sm4to, [32]p, fp color, DJ/2.95)	Scribner	1962	Francoise	50-80	
Francoise	Mr. & Mrs. So and So (1st, 4to, [36]p, color, pep, DJ/1.50)	Oxford U. Pr.	(1939)	Francoise	70-100	
Francoise	Noel for Jeanne-Marie (1st {std}, sm4to, unpag, grey cl, color, DJ/2.25)	Scribner	1953	Francoise	60-95	R
Francoise	Small-Trot (1st {std}, sm4to, green cl, [32]p, color, DJ/2.00)	Scribner	1952	Francoise	70-100	
Francoise	Story of Colette (1st, 4to, [32]p, ibds, fp color, pep, DJ/1.50)	Scribner	(1940)	Francoise	70-125	
Francoise	Thank-You Book (1st, sm4to, [32]p, fp 3-color, cep, DJ/2.00)	Scribner	1947	Francoise	40-65	
Francoise	Things I Like (1st, sm4to, [32]p, fp color, DJ/3.25)	Scribner	1960	Francoise	40-65	
Francoise	What Do You Want to Be? (1st, 4to, green cl, [30]p, fp color, DJ/2.75)	Scribner	1957	Francoise	80-130	
Frank, Mabel L.	Child's Day in Song (1st, lg4to, ibds, 31p, 12cp)	Schirmer	(1916)	Whitelaw, Norah	75-100	*
Frankel, Bernice	Half-as-Big and the Tiger (1st {std}, 8vo, [44]p, 2-color, pep, DJ/2.95)	F. Watts	(1961)	Weisgard, Leonard	40-65	
Franklin, Benjamin	Bird in the Hand (1st {std}, 4to, blue cl, [36]p, color, cep, DJ/2.50)	Macmillan	(1951)	Petershams	45-70	
Frasconi, Antonio	Kaleidoscope in Woodcuts (1st {std}, 16mo (accordian)	Harcourt	1968	Frasconi, Antonio	60-80	
Frasconi, Antonio	See & Say (1st {std}, 4to, yellow cl, [32]p, color, pep, DJ/3.00, NYTBI)	Harcourt	(1955)	Frasconi, Antonio	80-125	R
Frasconi, Antonio	See Again, Say Again (1st {std}, 4to, [32]p, ibds, color, DJ/3.25)	Harcourt	(1964)	Frasconi, Antonio	50-80	R
Frasconi, Antonio	Snow & the Sun (1st {std}, 4to, unpag, ibds, color, DJ/3.00)	Harcourt	(1961)	Frasconi, Antonio	30-50	
Frasconi, Antonio	Sunday in Monterey (1st {std}, narrow 24mo, unpag, color, DJ)	Harcourt	(1964)	Frasconi, Antonio	80-130	
Fraser, Beatrice	Arturo and Mr. Bang (1st {std}, 4to, unpag, b/w, DJ/2.50)	Bobbs-Merrill	1963	Storrs, William	30-45	
Fraser, Claud L.	Lute of Love (1st, 16mo, ipcb, 66p, p-o, b/w)	L: Selwyn	(1920)	Fraser, Claud L.	50-80	
Fraser, Claud L.	Nursery Rhymes (1st AM, 8vo, 46p, cp)	Knopf	[1920]	Fraser, Claud L.	100-185	
Fraser, Claud L.	Pirates (1st AM {std}, 4to, ibds, 159p, 8pl)	McBride	1922	Fraser, Claud L.	120-170	
Fraser, William A.	Blood Lilies (1st, 8vo, 262p, 6pl)	Scribner	1903	Schoonover, Frank	30-50	
Fraser, William A.	Sazada Tales (1st, 8vo, 231p, green/gilt, 24 b/w pl)	Scribner	1905	Heming, Arthur	30-50	
Fraser, William A.	The Outcasts (1st, 8vo, green/gilt, 138p, teg, 8pl, pep)	Scribner	1901	Heming, Arthur	50-8?	
Fraser-Simpson, H.	More Very Young Songs (1st, lg4to, p-o, 40p, bds, b/w)	L: Methuen	(1928)	Shepard, Ernest H.	150-2?	
Fraser-Simson, H.	Songs from Now We are Six (1st, sm folio, 33p, bds, p-o, b/w)	L: Methuen	(1927)	Shepard, Ernest H.	170?	
Fraser-Simson, H.	Hums of Pooh (1st AM, lg4to, 67p, ibds, p-o, b/w decor by...)	Dutton	[1930]	Shepard, Ernest H.	8?	
Frazer, Lilly	Leaves from The Golden Bough (1st, 8vo, 248p, gilt, teg, b/w)	L: Macmillan	1924	Brock, Henry M.		

AUTHOR	TITLE	PUBLISHER	DATE	ARTIST	PRICE	LC
Frazer, Mrs. J.G.	Asinette (1st, 8vo, 212p, green cl, 8cp)	L: J.M. Dent	1900	Brock, Henry M.	40-70	
Frazer, Sir James	Pasha the Pom (1st, 12mo, 117p, 4 fp b/w)	L: Blackie	1937	Brock, Henry M.	30-50	
Frazier, Neta L.	One Long Picnic (1st, 8vo, 179p, b/w, DJ/3.50)	McKay	1962	Lambo, Don	20-35	*
Freckles	Pat & Pips (4to, wraps, color, b/w)	L: Gale/Polden	[1905]	Wain, Louis	500-700	
Frederic, Harold	Market Place (1st, 12mo, 401p, 8pl)	Stokes	1899	Fisher, Harrison	40-65	
Freeman, Barbara	Timi: Tale of a Griffin (1st, 8vo, 48p, b/w, DJ/4.50)	Grosset/Dunlap	(1970)	Bileck, Marvin	30-45	
Freeman, Don	Add-a-Line Alphabet (1st, 4to, [32]p, color, DJ/3.95)	Golden Gate	(1968)	Freeman, Don	60-90	
Freeman, Don	Beady Bear (1st, lg8vo, red cl, 48p, fp b/w, DJ/2.00)	Viking	1954	Freeman, Don	50-80	
Freeman, Don	Botts: The Naughty Otter (1st, ob4to, [46]p, b/w, cep, DJ/3.00)	Golden Gate	(1963)	Freeman, Don	50-80	
Freeman, Don	Chuggy & Blue Caboose (1st, ob4to, 48p, red cl, color, DJ/2.50)	Viking	1951	Freeman, Don	50-80	
Freeman, Don	Come Again, Pelican (1st, 8vo, 44p, color, pep, DJ/3.00)	Viking	(1961)	Freeman, Don	80-120	
Freeman, Don	Corduroy (1st, 8vo, 32p, ipcb, color, DJ/3.50)	Viking	(1968)	Freeman, Don	70-120	
Freeman, Don	Cyrano the Crow (1st, 4to, 47p, ibds, color, DJ/2.75)	Viking	(1960)	Freeman, Don	50-80	
Freeman, Don	Dandelion (1st, ob4to, 48p, 2-color, DJ/3.00)	Viking	(1964)	Freeman, Don	40-65	
Freeman, Don	Fly High, Fly Low (1st, 4to, blue cl, 56p, color, pep, DJ/3.00, CH)	Viking	(1957)	Freeman, Don	60-90	
Freeman, Don	Forever Laughter (1st, ob8vo, [64]p, 1-color, cep, DJ/4.50)	Golden Gate	(1970)	Freeman, Don	30-50	
Freeman, Don	Guard Mouse (1st, 4to, 47p, ibds, fp color, DJ/3.50)	Viking	(1967)	Freeman, Don	30-50	
Freeman, Don	Hattie the Backstage Bat (1st {std}, ob4to, [32]p, color, DJ/3.50)	Viking	(1970)	Freeman, Don	30-50	
Freeman, Don	It Shouldn't Happen (1st {std}, 8vo, [212]p, b/w, DJ/2.00)	Harcourt	(1945)	Freeman, Don	30-50	
Freeman, Don	Mop Top (1st, sm4to, beige cl, 48p, 1-color, pep, DJ/2.00)	Viking	1955	Freeman, Don	60-90	
Freeman, Don	Night the Lights Went Out (1st, lg8vo, 48p, blue cl, 1-color, DJ/2.00)	Viking	1958	Freeman, Don	60-90	
Freeman, Don	Norman the Doorman (1st, sm ob4to, yellow cl, 64p, color, pep, DJ/3.00)	Viking	(1959)	Freeman, Don	60-90	
Freeman, Don	Rainbow of My Own (1st, ob8vo, [32]p, fp color, DJ/3.00)	Viking	(1966)	Freeman, Don	30-50	
Freeman, Don	Ski Pup (1st, 4to, 56p, fp color, pep, DJ/3.50)	Viking	(1963)	Freeman, Don	40-65	
Freeman, Don	Space Witch (1st, sm4to, blue cl, 47p, 1-color, DJ/2.00)	Viking	(1959)	Freeman, Don	45-70	
Freeman, Don	Tilly Witch (1st, 4to, [32]p, color, DJ/3.95)	Viking	(1969)	Freeman, Don	30-50	
Freeman, Don	Turtle and the Dove (1st, 8vo, 43p, blue cl, 1-color, DJ/2.50)	Viking	1964	Freeman, Don	25-40	
Freeman, Harry C.	Brief History of Butte Montana (1st, 4to, 123p, pep, 4 illus by..)	H.O. Shepard Co.	1900	Russell, Charles M.	150-250	
Freeman, Jean T.	Cynthia and the Unicorn (1st {std}, 4to, [32]p, color, DJ/3.75)	Norton	1967	Weisgard, Leonard	40-65	
Freeman, Leila C.	Nip & Tuck (1st, 4to, orange cl, p-o, 156p, 8cp, pep)	Sears	(1926)	Freeman, Leila C.	120-200	
Freeman, Leila C.	Nip & Tuck in Toyland (1st, 4to, 160p, p-o, 8cp, pep)	Sears	(1927)	Freeman, Leila C.	120-200	
Freeman, Lydia	Pet of the Met (1st, sm ob4to, 63p, pep, color, DJ/2.50)	Viking	1953	Freeman, Don	90-150	R
Freeman, Mae & Ira	You Will Go to the Moon (1st {std}, 8vo, ibds, 54p, color, DJ/1.95)	Beginner Books	(1959)	Patterson, Robert	50-80	
Freeman, Mary E.W.	Fair Lavinia (1st, 12mo, 308p, lavender/gilt)	Harper	1907	Various	40-65	
Freeman, Mary E.W.	People of Our Neighborhood (1st, 12mo, 161p, gilt, teg, 14pl)	Doub./McClure	1898	Stephens, Alice B.	30-50	
Frees, Harry W.	Little Folks of Animal Land (1st, 8vo, 252p, blue/gilt, p-o, pep)	Lothrop, Lee	(1915)	(Photos)	100-150	*
Frees, Harry W.	Sandman: His Animal Stories (1st, sm8vo, 273p, b/w)	L.C. Page	1916	(Photos)	80-120	
French, Fiona	Jack of Hearts (1st AM {std}, 4to, [24]p, color, DJ/4.50)	Harcourt	(1970)	French, Fiona	45-60	
French, Harry	Lance of Kanana (1st, 8vo, 165p, 4cp, DJ/2.50)	Lothrop, Lee	(1932)	Jones, Wilfred	25-40	
French, Marion	Mr. Bear Goes to Boston (1st, sm4to, 32p, 1-color, DJ/2.00)	Follett	(1955)	Weil, Lisl	100-160	
Freschet, Berniece	Beaver on the Sawtooth (1st, 8vo, [39]p, b/w, DJ/3.50)	Crowell	(1969)	Kalmenoff, Matthew	20-35	
Freschet, Berniece	Flight of the Snow Goose (1st, 8vo, 40p, blue cl, b/w, DJ/3.50)	Crown	(1970)	Polseno, Jo	20-30	*
Freschet, Berniece	Jumping Mouse (1st, 8vo, [48]p, b/w, DJ/3.95)	Crowell	(1970)	Mizumura, Kazue	30-50	*
Freschet, Berniece	Kangaroo Red (1st, 8vo, [47]p, fp 1-color, DJ/3.25)	Scribner	(1966)	Schoenherr, John	25-40	*
Freschet, Berniece	Little Woodcock (1st, lg8vo, unpag, ipcb, 1-color, DJ)	Scribner	(1967)	Weisgard, Leonard	30-45	
Freschet, Berniece	Old Bullfrog (1st, 4to, [25]p, fp color, pep, DJ)	Scribner	(1968)	Duvoisin, Roger	50-80	
Freschet, Berniece	Owl & the Prairie Dog (1st, 8vo, [31]p, color, DJ/3.50)	Scribner	(1969)	Riswold, Gilbert	25-40	
Freschet, Berniece	Young Eagle (1st, lg8vo, unpag, color, DJ/3.25)	Scribner	(1965)	Alexander, James	20-35	
Frey, Nina A.	River Horse (1st, 8vo, 150p, green cl, b/w, DJ/2.50)	W.R. Scott	(1953)	George, Rene	30-50	*
Friedlander, Gerald	Jewish Fairy Book (1st, 8vo, 188p, gilt, 8cp, pep)	Stokes	(1920)	Hood, George	55-90	
Friedrich, Otto	Clean Clarence (1st, 8vo, [40]p, fp color, pep, DJ/2.95)	Lothrop, Lee	(1959)	Slobodkin, Louis	30-50	
Friedrich, Otto	Marshmallow Ghosts (1st, 8vo, 38p, color, DJ/2.95)	Lothrop, Lee	(1960)	Slobodkin, Louis	30-50	*
Friedrich, Otto	Wishing Well in the Woods (1st, sm4to, unpag, ibds, color, DJ/2.75)	Lothrop, Lee	1961	Duvoisin, Roger	40-65	
Friedrich, Priscilla	April Umbrella (1st, 4to, [34]p, fp color, DJ/2.95)	Lothrop, Lee	1963	Duvoisin, Roger	30-50	
Friedrich, Priscilla	Easter Bunny that Overslept (1st, sm4to, yellow cl, [33]p, color, DJ/2.50)	Lothrop, Lee	1957	Adams, Adrienne	45-65	
Frisbie, William A.	ABC Mother Goose (1st, 4to, [52]p, beige cl, color)	Rand/McNally	(1905)	Bartholomew, F.	200-300	
Frisbie, William A.	Pirate Frog (1st, 4to, [94]p, ibds, color)	Rand/McNally	(1901)	Bartholomew, F.	150-220	
Friskey, Margaret	Adventure for Beginners (1st, sm4to, ibds, [28]p, color, DJ/1.00)	Wilcox/Follett	(1944)	Evans, Katherine	35-50	
Friskey, Margaret	Seven Diving Ducks (1st {std}, 4to, ibds, [32]p, 1-color, pep, DJ/1.50)	McKay	(1940)	Patton, Lucia	30-45	
Frith, Henry	King Arthur & his Knights (1st, 8vo, black cl, p-o, 406p, 4cp)	Garden City	1932	Schoonover, Frank	50-80	
Fritz, Jean	121 Pudding Street (1st, 8vo, 219p, b/w, DJ/2.75)	Coward	(1955)	Sofia	45-70	
Fritz, Jean	Animals of Dr. Schweitzer (1st, 8vo, [62]p, b/w, DJ/3.00)	Coward	(1958)	Howland, Douglas	20-35	
Fritz, Jean	Brady (1st, 8vo, 223p, b/w, DJ/3.50)	Coward	(1960)	Ward, Lynd	30-50	*
Fritz, Jean	Cabin Faced West (1st, 8vo, blue cl, 124p, b/w, DJ/3.00)	Coward	(1958)	Rojankovsky, Feodor	30-50	
Fritz, Jean	Early Thunder (1st, 8vo, 255p, b/w, pep, DJ/4.50)	Coward	(1967)	Ward, Lynd	25-40	
Fritz, Jean	Fish Head (1st, sm4to, tan cl, [38]p, fp 3-color, pep, DJ/2.75)	Coward	(1954)	Simont, Marc	50-80	
Fritz, Jean	George Washington's Breakfast (1st, 8vo, [47]p, fp 2-color, DJ/3.75)	Coward	(1969)	Galdone, Paul	30-50	
Fritz, Jean	How to Read a Rabbit (1st, 8vo, [60]p, fp b/w, DJ/2.50)	Coward	(1959)	Shortall, Leonard	30-50	*
Fritz, Jean	I, Adam (1st, 8vo, 255p, b/w, DJ/3.75)	Coward	(1963)	Burchard, Peter	50-80	R
Fritz, Jean	Late Spring (1st, 8vo, [31]p, fp 1-color, cep, DJ/2.50)	Coward	1957	Blegvad, Erik	60-90	
Fritz, Jean	Magic to Burn (1st, 8vo, 255p, b/w, DJ/3.75)	Coward	(1964)	Krush, Beth & Joe	45-70	
Fritz, Jean	Tap, Tap, Lion - 1 2 3 (1st, 8vo, [48]p, fp 1-color, DJ/2.75)	Coward	(1962)	Shortall, Leonard	40-65	*
Frost, A.B.	Book of Drawings (1st, folio, [80]p, p-o, ibds, 39pl)	Collier	1904	Frost, A.B.	150-220	
Frost, A.B.	Bull Calf (1st, ob8vo, 112p, 105pl)	Scribner	1892	Frost, A.B.	160-225	
Frost, A.B.	Carlo (1st, lg ob8vo, 109p, b/w)	Doubleday/Page	1913	Frost, A.B.	120-200	
Frost, A.B.	Stuff & Nonsense (1st, 4to, ipcb, 92p, b/w)	Scribner	(1884)	Frost, A.B.	120-170	
Frost, Frances	Cat that Went to College (1st, lg8vo, 64p, b/w, pep, DJ/2.00)	Whittlesey	(1951)	Dennis, Morgan	60-100	
Frost, Frances	Christmas in the Woods (1st {std}, 16mo, ibds, 28p, fp 1-color, DJ/1.00)	Harper	(1942)	Watson, Aldren A.	30-50	R

AUTHOR: 80

AUTHOR	TITLE	PUBLISHER	DATE	ARTIST	PRICE	LC
Frost, Frances	Little Fox (1st, 8vo, 112p, b/w, pep, DJ/2.25)	Whittlesey	(1952)	Dennis, Morgan	25-40	*
Frost, Frances	Little Naturalist (1st, lg8vo, 47p, 3-color, pep, DJ/2.50)	Whittlesey	(1959)	Werth, Kurt	20-35	*
Frost, Frances	Little Whistler (1st, lg8vo, green cl, 48p, fp color, DJ/2.00)	Whittlesey	(1949)	Duvoisin, Roger	50-80	
Frost, Frances	Maple Sugar for Windy Foot (1st, 8vo, 184p, fp b/w, DJ/2.00)	Whittlesey	(1950)	Townsend, Lee	60-100	
Frost, Frances	Pool in the Meadow (1st, 8vo, 73p, blue cl, b/w)	Houghton	1933	Guglielmi	50-80	*
Frost, Frances	Rocket Away! (1st, 4to, 48p, b/w, DJ/2.00)	Whittlesey	(1953)	Galdone, Paul	30-50	
Frost, Frances	Then Came Timothy (1st, 8vo, 155p, b/w, DJ/2.00)	Whittlesey	(1950)	Bennett, Richard	20-30	*
Frost, Lesley	Really Not Really (1st, 4to, 61p, cloth, 1-color, DJ/2.75)	Channel Press	(1962)	Remington, Barbara	25-40	
Frost, Robert	You Come Too (1st {std}, 8vo, 94p, wood engravings, DJ/3.00)	Holt	(1959)	Nason, Thomas	70-120	R
Frost, William H.	Court of King Arthur (1st, 12mo, red/gilt, 302p, 6pl)	Scribner	1896	Burleigh, Sydney R.	75-100	
Fry, Christopher	Boat that Mooed (1st {std}, ob4to, 30p, fp 1-color, DJ/3.50)	Macmillan	(1965)	Weisgard, Leonard	60-90	R*
Fry, John H.	Revolt Against Beauty (1st, 8vo, 212p, ibds, designs by...)	Putnam	1934	Richardson, F.	30-50	*
Fry, Rosalie K.	Bandy Boy's Treasure Island (1st {std}, 16mo, [29]p, color, pep, DJ/0.75)	Dutton	(1941)	Fry, Rosalie K.	70-100	
Fry, Rosalie K.	Bumblebuzz (1st {std}, lg8vo, ibds, [25]p, color, DJ/1.50)	Dutton	1938	Fry, Rosalie K.	60-100	
Fry, Rosalie K.	Deep in the Forest (1st AM, 12mo, 95p, 5 fp color, DJ/2.50)	Dodd	1956	Fry, Rosalie K.	60-100	*
Fry, Rosalie K.	Ladybug! Ladybug! (1st {std}, 8vo, [33]p, ibds, fp 2-color, dep, DJ/1.00)	Dutton	1940	Fry, Rosalie K.	50-85	*
Fry, Rosalie K.	Matelot, Little Sailor of Brittany (1st {std}, 8vo, 128p, b/w, DJ/2.75)	Dutton	1958	Fry, Rosalie K.	25-35	
Fry, Rosalie K.	Mountain Door (1st AM {std}, 8vo, 128p, b/w, DJ/2.95)	Dutton	1961	Fry, Rosalie K.	50-85	
Fry, Rosalie K.	Pipkin Sees the World (1st {std}, 8vo, 96p, b/w, DJ/2.00)	Dutton	1951	Fry, Rosalie K.	20-30	
Fry, Rosalie K.	Secret of the Ron Mor Skerry (1st AM {std}, 8vo, 95p, b/w, DJ/2.50)	Dutton	1959	Fry, Rosalie K.	100-150	*
Fry, Rosalie K.	Snowed Up (1st, 8vo, 124p, b/w, DJ/3.95)	Farrar, Straus	(1970)	Jacques, Robin	25-40	
Fry, Rosalie K.	Whistler in the Mist (1st, 8vo, 139p, b/w, DJ/3.75)	Farrar, Straus	(1968)	Jacques, Robin	25-45	
Fry, Rosalie K.	Wind Call (1st {std}, sm8vo, gilt, 115p, fp color, DJ/2.50)	Dutton	(1955)	Fry, Rosalie K.	60-90	
Frye, Dean	Days of Sunshine, Days of Rain (1st, 4to, 32p, fp 3-color, pep, DJ/2.95)	McGraw-Hill	1965	Duvoisin, Roger	30-50	
Frye, Dean	Lamb and the Child (1st, 4to, 32p, color, DJ/2.75)	McGraw-Hill	1963	Duvoisin, Roger	30-50	
Fryer, Alfred C.	Fairy Tales from the Harz Mountains (1st, lg8vo, 206p, gilt, b/w)	L: D. Nutt	1908	Ogders, Alice M.	75-100	*
Fryer, Jane E.	Bible Story Book (1st, lg8vo, blue cl, p-o, 352p, 4cp)	Winston	(1924)	Prittie, Edwin J.	60-90	
Fryer, Jane E.	Mary Frances Cook Book (1st, lg8vo, 175p, blue cl, p-o, color)	Winston	(1912)	Hays/Boyer	200-300	
Fryer, Jane E.	Mary Frances First Aid Book (1st, lg8vo, p-o, 144p, gilt, color)	Winston	(1916)	Boyer, Jane A.	200-300	
Fryer, Jane E.	Mary Frances Garden Book (1st, lg8vo, p-o, gilt, 378p, color, pep)	Winston	(1916)	Zwirner, William F.	200-300	
Fryer, Jane E.	Mary Frances Housekeeper (1st, lg8vo, 253p, blue/gilt, p-o, color)	Winston	(1914)	Greene, Julia	250-400	
Fryer, Jane E.	Mary Frances Knitting & Crocheting Book (1st, lg8vo, 270p, gilt, p-o, 7cp)	Winston	(1918)	Boyer, Jane A.	200-300	
Fryer, Jane E.	Mary Frances Sewing Book (1st, lg8vo, p-o, 280p, blue cl, pep)	Winston	(1913)	Boyer, Jane A.	200-300	
Fryer, Jane E.	Mary Frances Story Book (1st, lg8vo, p-o, 328p, fp 3-color, pep)	Winston	(1921)	Prittie, Edwin J.	200-300	
Fujikawa, Gyo	Child's Book of Poems (1st, lg4to, 117p, ipcb, dp color, pep)	Grosset/Dunlap	(1969)	Fujikawa, Gyo	30-50	
Fuller, O. Muriel	Book of Dragons (1st, lg8vo, green cl, 181p, 4cp, DJ/2.50)	McBride	1931	Key, Alexander	60-100	
Fullylove, John	Edinburgh (1st, 8vo, 176p, teg, blue/gilt, 21cp)	L: A&C Black	1904	Fullylove, John	80-125	
Furlong, Charles W.	Let 'er Buck (1st, 8vo, 242p, gilt, p-o, 19pl)	Putnam	1921	(Photos)	80-130	
Furniss, Dorothy	Sky High: Flight of Fancy for Children (1st, ob4to, 169p, 15cp, 31pl)	L: Routledge	[1905]	Furniss, Dorothy	150-220	*
Furth, Dori	Back in Time for Supper (1st {std}, ob4to, [33]p, color, DJ/2.50)	McKay	(1947)	Weil, Lisl	50-80	
Futrelle, Jacques	Chase of the Golden Plate (1st, sm8vo, 220p, green cl, p-o, 11pl)	Dodd	1906	Grefe, Will	50-80	
Fyleman, Rose	40 Good-Night Tales (1st AM, 8vo, 131p, p-o, 4cp, pep)	Doran	(1924)	Grosvenor, Thelma C.	30-50	
Fyleman, Rose	51 New Nursery Rhymes (1st {std}, ob4to, ibds, 98p, color)	Doubleday/Doran	1932	Burroughs, Dorothy	80-130	R
Fyleman, Rose	Adventure Club (1st, 12mo, 80p, blue/gilt, 10 b/w)	L: Methuen	1925	Watson, A.H.	40-65	
Fyleman, Rose	Adventure Club (1st AM, 8vo, p-o, 138p, col frn, b/w)	Doran	(1926)	Watson, A.H.	30-50	*
Fyleman, Rose	Doll's House (1st {std}, 8vo, 99p, color, pep)	Doubleday/Doran	1931	Berry, Erick	50-80	
Fyleman, Rose	Fairies & Chimneys (1st, sm8vo, 62p, col frn, silhouettes)	Doran	(1920)	Grosvenor, Thelma C.	40-65	
Fyleman, Rose	Fairy Queen (1st, 8vo, 64p, cloth, col frn, pep)	Doran	(1923)	Fyleman, Rose	65-90	
Fyleman, Rose	Garland of Roses (1st, 8vo, blue/gilt, 129p, col frn, 16pl)	L: Methuen	1928	Bull, Rene	120-180	
Fyleman, Rose	Katy Kruse Dolly Book (1st AM, ob4to, ibds, 32p, 12cp)	Doran	(1927)	(Photos)	140-200	
Fyleman, Rose	Katy Kruse Play Book (1st, sm4to, ibds, p-o, 32p, 12cp)	L: Harrap	(1930)	Kruse, Katy	125-185	*
Fyleman, Rose	Katy Kruse Play Book (1st AM, sm4to, p-o, 32p, 12cp)	McKay	(1930)	Kruse, Katy	120-180	*
Fyleman, Rose	Letty (1st AM, 8vo, 142p, fp b/w, pep)	Doran	(1927)	Hummel, Lisl	30-50	
Fyleman, Rose	Little Christmas Book (1st, 8vo, orange ibds, pep, 41p, 2-color)	Doran	(1927)	Hummel, Lisl	25-45	
Fyleman, Rose	Old Fashioned Girls (1st, 8vo, 33p, gilt, teg, 12cp)	L: Methuen	1928	Everett, Ethel	30-50	
Fyleman, Rose	Picture Rhymes from Foreign Lands (1st, 8vo, 70p, b/w, DJ/1.00)	Stokes	1935	Carrick, Valery	40-65	
Fyleman, Rose	Princess Comes to Our Town (1st {std}, sm8vo, 158p, col frn, pep)	Doubleday/Doran	1928	Berry, Erick	35-60	*
Fyleman, Rose	Rainbow Cat (1st AM, 8vo, 117p, p-o, 4cp, pep)	Doran	(1923)	Grosvenor, Thelma C.	50-85	
Fyleman, Rose	Rose Fyleman Fairy Book (1st, 4to, 102p, blue/gilt, 16 ticp, pep)	L: Methuen	1923	Miller, Hilda T.	300-500	
Fyleman, Rose	Round the Mulberry Bush (1st, sm4to, 192p, red cl, 6cp)	Dodd	(1928)	Various	50-80	
Fyleman, Rose	Widdy-Widdy-Wurkey (1st, 8vo, 70p, beige cl, b/w)	L: Blackwell	1934	Carrick, Valery	40-60	*
G.R.	Alick's Adventures (1st, sm8vo, brown/gilt, 183p, 8 fp b/w)	L: Longmans	1902	Hassall, John	70-130	
Gaboriau, Emile	Within an Inch of His Life (1st AM, 8vo, teg, 608p, gilt, 4pl)	Scribner	1913	Sloan, John	45-70	
Gaeddert, Lou Ann	Noisy Nancy Norris (1st {std}, sm8vo, 63p, color, DJ/3.25)	Doubleday	(1965)	Fiammenghi, Gioia	25-40	
Gag, Asta	Sue & Sew-and-Sew (1st, 8vo, 63p, ibds, b/w, pep)	Coward	(1931)	Gag, Flavia	40-60	*
Gag, Flavia	A Wish for Mimi (1st {std}, 8vo, 156p, b/w, DJ/2.75)	Holt	(1958)	Fox, Dorothea	50-80	
Gag, Flavia	Chubby's First Year (1st, 24mo, [31]p, fp color, DJ/1.95)	Henry Holt & Co.	1960	Gag, Flavia	30-45	
Gag, Flavia	Four Legs and a Tail (1st {std}, 8vo, 150p, b/w, DJ/2.50)	Holt	(1952)	Gag, Flavia	25-40	
Gag, Flavia	Sing a Song of Seasons (1st, 4to, ibds, 29p, b/w, DJ/1.50)	Coward	(1936)	Gag, Flavia	50-80	*
Gag, Flavia	Tweeter of Prairie Dog Town (1st {std}, 8vo, 61p, b/w, DJ/2.25)	Holt	(1957)	Gag, Flavia	40-65	*
Gag, Wanda	ABC Bunny (1st {std}, lg4to, ibds, [32]p, b/w, pep, NH)	Coward	1933	Gag, Wanda	400-600	R
Gag, Wanda	Funny Thing (1st, lg ob8vo, [32]p, yellow ipcb, b/w, pep)	Coward	1929	Gag, Wanda	200-350	
Gag, Wanda	Gone is Gone (1st, 12mo, yellow cl, [63]p, col frn, b/w, DJ/1.00)	Coward	(1935)	Gag, Wanda	300-450	
Gag, Wanda	Growing Pains (1st, lg8vo, 479p, blue ibds, b/w, DJ/3.75)	Coward	1940	Gag, Wanda	160-240	
Gag, Wanda	Millions of Cats (1st [1st bk.], lg ob8vo, ipcb, [32]p, b/w, pep, NH)	Coward	1928	Gag, Wanda	250-400	R
Gag, Wanda	Nothing at All (1st, lg ob8vo, ibds, [32]p, color, pep, DJ/1.75, CH)	Coward	(1941)	Gag, Wanda	200-300	
Gag, Wanda	Snippy & Snappy (1st, lg ob8vo, yellow ibds, [48]p, b/w, pep)	Coward	1931	Gag, Wanda	160-240	
Gag, Wanda	Three Gay Tales from Grimm (1st, 8vo, ipcb, 63p, b/w, DJ/1.50)	Coward	(1943)	Gag, Wanda	160-225	

AUTHOR	TITLE	PUBLISHER	DATE	ARTIST	PRICE	LC
Gag, Wanda	Wanda Gag's Story Book (1st, ob16mo, [112]p, yellow bds, p-o, pep)	Coward	(1932)	Gag, Wanda	170-240	
Gage, Wilson	Big Blue Island (1st {std}, lg8vo, 120p, b/w, DJ/3.50)	World	(1964)	Rounds, Glen	40-65	R
Gage, Wilson	Dan and the Miranda (1st {std}, 4to, 124p, b/w, DJ/2.95)	World	(1962)	Rounds, Glen	20-30	
Gage, Wilson	Ghost of Five Owl Farm (1st {std}, 8vo, 127p, b/w, DJ/3.50)	World	(1966)	Galdone, Paul	20-30	
Gage, Wilson	Mike's Toads (1st, 4to, 93p, fp b/w, DJ/4.50)	World	(1970)	Rounds, Glen	30-45	
Gage, Wilson	Miss Osborne-the-Mop (1st {std}, 8vo, 156p, b/w, DJ/2.95)	World	(1963)	Galdone, Paul	20-35	
Gage, Wilson	Secret of Fiery Gorge (1st {std}, 8vo, 185p, b/w, DJ/2.95)	World	(1960)	Stevens, Mary	20-35	*
Gage, Wilson	Secret of Indian Mound (1st {std}, 8vo, 186p, b/w, DJ/2.75)	World	(1958)	Stevens, Mary	20-30	
Gage, Wilson	Wild Goose Tale (1st {std}, sm4to, 112p, blue cl, b/w, DJ/2.95)	World	1961	Rounds, Glen	20-30	
Gaggin, Eva R.	All Those Buckles (1st, 8vo, 250p, b/w, DJ/2.00)	Viking	1945	Cloete, Mildred	25-40	
Gaggin, Eva R.	Down Ryton Water (1st, 8vo, green/silver, 369p, b/w, pep, DJ/2.00, NH)	Viking	1941	Hader, Elmer	70-100	
Gaggin, Eva R.	Ear for Uncle Emil (1st, 8vo, 238p, 83 b/w, pep, DJ/2.00)	Viking	1939	Seredy, Kate	40-65	
Gaggin, Eva R.	Jolly Animals (1st, sq4to, p-o, 110p, 7 fp color, pep)	Rand/McNally	(1930)	Ward, Keith	100-160	
Gagliardo, Ruth	Let's Read Aloud (1st {std}, 8vo, 256p, b/w, DJ/4.95)	Lippincott	(1962)	Angelo, Valenti	40-65	
Gaidar, Arkady	Timur and his Gang (1st, 8vo, 125p, b/w, DJ/1.75)	Scribner	1943	Gay, Zhenya	30-50	
Gail, Otto W.	By Rocket to the Moon (1st AM, 8vo, black cl, 303p, te red, 8pl)	Sears	(1931)	Von Grunberg, R.	70-120	
Gaines, Mary L.	I Heah de Voices Callin' (1st, 12mo, p-o, 88p, 11pl)	(Atlanta)	1916	(Photos)	100-165	
Galdone, Paul	Monkey and the Crocodile (1st, 4to, [32]p, color, DJ/4.50)	Seabury Press	(1969)	Galdone, Paul	30-50	*
Galdone, Paul	Paddy the Penguin (1st, sm4to, [30]p, 2-color, pep, DJ/3.00)	Crowell	(1959)	Galdone, Paul	40-65	*
Gale, Agnes C.	Achilles and Hector (1st, 12mo, 176p, red/gilt, fp b/w)	Rand/McNally	(1904)	Armstrong, Helen	30-50	
Gale, Elizabeth	Circus Babies (1st, sq4to, 100p, fp color, pep)	Rand/McNally	(1930)	McKee, John D.	100-150	
Gale, Elizabeth	Katrina Van Ost & Silver Rose (1st, sm8vo, 294p, fp b/w)	Putnam	(1934)	DeAngeli, Marguerite	45-70	
Gale, Elizabeth	Seven Beads of Wampum (1st, 8vo, 298p, 8 fp b/w, pep, DJ/2.00)	Putnam	(1936)	Lawson, Robert	60-90	
Gale, Leah	Hurdy Gurdy Holiday (1st {std}, 4to, ipcb, [48]p, color, pep, DJ/1.50)	Harper	1942	Latham, Barbara	80-130	
Gale, Norman	June Romance (1st, 12mo, teg, blue cl, 193p, b/w)	Stone/Kimball	1899	Oakley, Violet	85-135	
Gale, Norman	Songs for Little People (1st, 8vo, teg, 110p, uncut, gilt, 8pl)	L: Constable	1896	Stratton, Helen	125-185	
Gall, Alice C.	Each in his Way (1st {std}, 8vo, 180p, bds, p-o, 1-color, pep, DJ/2.00)	Oxford U. Pr.	(1937)	Wiese, Kurt	45-70	
Gall, Alice C.	Flat Tail (1st, lg8vo, 126p, color, pep, DJ/1.50)	Oxford U. Pr.	1935	Kihn, W. Langdon	40-65	
Gall, Alice C.	Here and There and Everywhere (1st {std}, 12mo, 56p, 2-color, DJ/1.50)	Oxford U. Pr.	1950	Hogner, Nils	30-50	
Gall, Alice C.	Little Black Ant (1st, 8vo, 128p, b/w, pep, DJ/1.50)	Oxford U. Pr.	(1936)	Torrey, Helen	30-50	
Gall, Alice C.	Ringtail (1st, lg8vo, 119p, pep, 1-color)	Oxford U. Pr.	(1933)	Reid, James	30-50	
Gall, Alice C.	Royal Mimkin (1st, lg8vo, 128p, red cl, 1-color)	Oxford U. Pr.	1934	Masline, Camille	25-45	*
Gall, Alice C.	Splasher (1st, 8vo, 136p, fp 1-color, cep, DJ/2.00)	Oxford U. Pr.	(1945)	Bostelmann, Else	20-30	
Gall, Alice C.	Wagtail (1st, 8vo, 131p, 1-color, pep)	Oxford U. Pr.	1932	Wiese, Kurt	40-65	
Gall, Alice C.	Winter Flight (1st, 8vo, 108p, fp b/w, pep, DJ/2.50)	Oxford U. Pr.	1949	Hogner, Nils	25-40	
Gallant, Kathryn	Flute Player of Beppu (1st, sq8vo, 43p, fp color, DJ/2.75)	Coward	1960	Wiese, Kurt	30-50	
Gallico, Paul	Day Jean-Pierre was Pignapped (1st AM {std}, 4to, 44p, color, pep, DJ/3.25)	Doubleday	(1965)	Dulac, Jean	25-45	
Gallico, Paul	Day the Guinea-Pig Talked (1st AM {std}, sm4to, 44p, color, DJ/3.25)	Doubleday	(1964)	Dulac, Jean	25-40	
Gallico, Paul	Manxmouse (1st AM {std}, 8vo, blue/gilt, 188p, b/w, DJ/4.95)	Coward	1968	Grahame-Johnstone	90-150	
Gallico, Paul	Mrs. 'Arris Goes to New York (1st AM {std}, 12mo, 192p, b/w, DJ/2.50)	Doubleday	1960	Vasiliu, Mircea	25-40	
Gallico, Paul	Mrs. 'Arris Goes to Paris (1st AM {std}, 12mo, 157p, b/w, DJ/2.50)	Doubleday	1958	Fiammenghi, Gioia	25-40	
Gallico, Paul	Mrs. 'Arris Goes to Parliament (1st AM {std}, 12mo, 152p, b/w, DJ/2.95)	Doubleday	1965	Fiammenghi, Gioia	25-40	
Gallico, Paul	Snowflake (1st, sm8vo, 63p, ipcb, 1-color, DJ)	L: M. Joseph	(1952)	Knight, David	30-50	
Gallico, Paul	Thomasina (1st AM {std}, 8vo, 288p, DJ/3.95, frn by...)	Doubleday	1957	Fiammenghi, Gioia	20-30	
Galsworthy, John	Awakening (1st, sm4to, 63p, color, pep)	Scribner	(1920)	Sauter, R.H.	50-90	R*
Galsworthy, John	Memories (1st, 4to, green/gilt, 70p, teg, 4 ticp, 24pl)	Scribner	(1914)	Earl, Maud	90-150	
Galt, John	Annals of the Parish (1st, 12mo, gilt, 334p, AEG, 40pl, pep)	L: Macmillan	1896	Brock, Charles E.	60-80	
Galt, Tom	Seven Days from Sunday (1st {std}, 8vo, rust cl, 215p, b/w, DJ/3.00)	Crowell	(1956)	Freeman, Don	40-65	
Gannett, Lewis	Cream Hill (1st, 8vo, 191p, b/w, pep, DJ/3.50)	Viking	(1949)	Gannett, Ruth C.	25-40	
Gannett, Ruth S.	Dragons of Blueland (1st, 8vo, 87p, blue/gilt, pep, b/w, DJ/2.00)	Random	(1951)	Gannett, Ruth C.	40-65	
Gannett, Ruth S.	Elmer & the Dragon (1st, 8vo, 86p, red/gilt, pep, b/w, DJ/2.00)	Random	(1950)	Gannett, Ruth C.	40-65	
Gannett, Ruth S.	Katie and the Sad Noise (1st, 8vo, [64]p, 2-color, pep, DJ/1.95)	Random	(1961)	Simmons, Ellie	30-50	
Gannett, Ruth S.	My Father's Dragon (1st, 8vo, 86p, gilt, b/w, pep, DJ/2.00, NH)	Random	(1948)	Gannett, Ruth C.	60-90	R
Gannett, Ruth S.	Wonderful House-Boat-Train (1st {std}, 8vo, 63p, pep, b/w, DJ/2.00)	Random	(1949)	Eichenberg, Fritz	45-65	
Gans, Roma	Birds at Night (1st, sq8vo, 33p, color, DJ/3.25)	Crowell	(1968)	Aliki	30-45	
Gans, Roma	Birds Eat and Eat and Eat (1st, ob8vo, ibds, [40]p, fp 2-color, DJ/2.50)	Crowell	(1963)	Emberley, Ed	30-50	
Gans, Roma	It's Nesting Time (1st, ob8vo, [40]p, color, DJ/2.75)	Crowell	(1964)	Mizumura, Kazue	30-50	
Gard, Robert	Horse Named Joe (1st {std}, 8vo, 237p, 6 fp b/w, DJ/2.75)	Duell, Sloan	(1956)	Anderson, C.W.	30-45	
Gardiner, Alice C.	Father's Gone A-Whaling (1st {std}, 8vo, 198p, col frn, DJ)	Doubleday/Page	1926	Berry, Erick	35-60	
Gardiner, Linda	Sylvia in Flowerland (1st, 8vo, grey bds, 198p, gilt, 16 b/w)	L: Seeley	1899	Butler, H.E.	70-125	
Gardner, Fred	Lioness Who Made Deals (1st {std}, sm4to, [22]p, color, DJ/4.25)	Norton	(1969)	Krahn, Fernando	30-45	*
Garelick, May	Look at the Moon (1st, 4to, [32]p, fp 2-color, DJ/3.95)	W.R. Scott	(1969)	Weisgard, Leonard	50-80	
Garelick, May	Sounds of a Summer Night (1st, ob8vo, [32]p, 2-color, DJ/3.25)	Young Scott	(1963)	Montresor, Beni	30-45	
Garelick, May	What Makes a Bird a Bird? (1st {std}, ob4to, ibds, [32]p, color, DJ/.3.95)	Follett	(1969)	Weisgard, Leonard	25-40	
Garelick, May	What's Inside? (1st, ob8vo, unpag, beige cl, b/w, DJ/2.00)	W.R. Scott	(1955)	(Photos)	30-50	
Garelick, May	Wild Ducks and Daffodils (1st, lg ob8vo, [48]p, ibds, color, DJ/3.50)	Young Scott	1965	Ross, Clare	20-35	
Garfield, Leon	Black Jack (1st, 8vo, 243p, b/w, gilt, DJ)	L: Longmans	(1968)	Maitland, Antony	25-40	
Garfield, Leon	Drummer Boy (1st AM, 8vo, 186p, b/w, DJ/4.50)	Pantheon	(1969)	Maitland, Antony	20-30	
Garfield, Leon	God Beneath the Sea (1st, 8vo, 168p, fp b/w, DJ, CgM)	L: Longmans	1970	Keeping, Charles	50-80	
Garfield, Leon	Jack Holburn (1st AM {std}, [1st bk.], 8vo, 250p, red cl, b/w, DJ/3.75)	Pantheon	(1965)	Maitland, Antony	40-65	
Garfield, Leon	Mr. Corbett's Ghost (1st AM, 8vo, 87p, b/w, DJ/3.50, NYTBI)	Pantheon	(1968)	Cober, Alan E.	25-45	
Garfield, Leon	Smith (1st AM {std}, 8vo, 218p, b/w, DJ/3.95)	Pantheon	(1967)	Maitland, Antony	25-40	
Garfield, Nancy	Tuesday Elephant (1st, 4to, [44]p, fp 2-color, DJ/3.95)	Crowell	(1968)	Feelings, Tom	30-50	
Garis, Howard	Joie, Tommie & Kittie Kat (1st, 8vo, 202p, brown cl, col frn, 8pl)	NY: Fenno	1913	Wisa, Louis	80-120	
Garis, Howard	Rick & Ruddy (1st, sm8vo, p-o, 282p, 6pl)	Milton Bradley	1920	Goss, John	30-60	
Garis, Howard	Rick & Ruddy in Camp (1st, sm8vo, 254p, tan cl, 4pl)	Milton Bradley	1921	Winter, Milo	30-50	*
Garis, Howard	Tuftoo the Clown (1st, sm8vo, 283p, 10 b/w, pep)	Appleton	1928	Daugherty, James	40-65	*
Garis, Howard	Uncle Wiggily & Alice in Wonderland (1st, 4to, gilt, 361p, 8cp, pep, p-o)	Fenno	(1918)	Bloomfield, Edward	100-175	

AUTHOR	TITLE	PUBLISHER	DATE	ARTIST	PRICE	LC
Garis, Howard	Uncle Wiggily & his Flying Rug (1st {this pub}, 12mo, 33p, bds, color, pep)	Whitman	(1940)	Campbell, Lang	50-85	
Garis, Howard	Uncle Wiggily & Mother Goose (1st, lg8vo, 175p, p-o, gilt, color)	Fenno	(1916)	Bloomfield, Edward	150-225	
Garis, Howard	Uncle Wiggily & the Beaver Boys (1st, 8vo, olive cl, p-o, color)	C.E. Graham	(1929)	Campbell, Lang	50-80	
Garis, Howard	Uncle Wiggily & the Pirates (1st, 8vo, [31]p, red cl, p-o, color)	C.E. Graham	(1931)	Campbell, Lang	50-80	
Garis, Howard	Uncle Wiggily & the Pirates (sq12mo, 33p, ibds, color)	Whitman	(1940)	Campbell, Lang	35-60	*
Garis, Howard	Uncle Wiggily Goes Camping (sq12mo, ibds, 33p, color)	Whitman	(1940)	Campbell, Lang	35-60	
Garis, Howard	Uncle Wiggily on Roller Skates (1st {this pub}, 12mo, 33p, color)	Whitman	(1940)	Campbell, Lang	35-60	*
Garis, Howard	Uncle Wiggily Plays Indian Hunter (1st, 12mo, bds, 33p, color)	Whitman	(1940)	Campbell, Lang	35-60	*
Garis, Howard	Uncle Wiggily's Apple Roast (1st, 8vo, red cloth, p-o, color)	C.E. Graham	(1924)	Campbell, Lang	35-60	
Garis, Howard	Uncle Wiggily's Arabian Nights (1st, 4to, gilt, 8cp, pep)	Fenno	(1917)	Bloomfield, Edward	200-300	
Garis, Howard	Uncle Wiggily's Automobile (1st, sm8vo, 184p, color)	Platt/Munk	(1939)	Rache, Elmer	30-50	
Garis, Howard	Uncle Wiggily's Happy Days (1st, lg8vo, 211p, col frn, pep, DJ/1.50)	Platt/Munk	(1947)	Rache, Elmer	40-70	
Garis, Howard	Uncle Wiggily's June Bug Friends (1st, 8vo, red cl, p-o, color)	C.E. Graham	(1931)	Campbell, Lang	50-80	
Garis, Howard	Uncle Wiggily's Picture Book (1st, 8vo, 217p, orange cl, 12cp, pep)	Platt/Munk	(1940)	Campbell, Lang	45-70	
Garis, Howard	Uncle Wiggily's Visit to the Farm (1st, sq12mo, 33p, p-o, color)	C.E. Graham	(1927)	Campbell, Lang	35-60	
Garis, Howard	Uncle Wiggily's Woodland Games (1st, sq12mo, [32]p, p-o, color)	C.E. Graham	(1922)	Campbell, Lang	35-60	
Garis, Howard	White Crystals (1st, sm8vo, tan cl, 243p, 6pl)	Little/Brown	1904	Day, Bertha C.	40-60	
Garland, Hamlin	Book of the American Indian (1st {std}, 4to, bds, 274p, p-o, 4cp)	Harper	1923	Remington, Frederic	180-240	
Garland, Hamlin	Boy Life on the Prairie (1st, 12mo, brown/gilt, 423p, teg, 8pl)	Macmillan	1899	Deming, Edwin W.	55-80	
Garland, Hamlin	Money Magic (1st, sm8vo, pcb, 354p, 8pl)	Harper	1907	Marchand, J.N.	35-60	
Garland, Hamlin	Prairie Songs (1st, 8vo, green/gilt, 164p, teg, uncut)	Stone/Kimball	1893	Carpenter, H.T.	70-120	R
Garland, Hamlin	Son of the Middle Border (1st, sm8vo, 467p, 16pl)	Macmillan	1917	Stephens, Alice B.	70-100	
Garland, Hamlin	Tyranny of the Dark (1st, sm8vo, blue/gilt, 438p, 8pl)	Harper	1905	Mears, W.E.	50-80	
Garner, Alan	Owl Service (1st, 8vo, 157p, DJ, CgM)	L: Collins	1967	No Illustrations	120-200	
Garner, Alan	Owl Service (1st AM {std}, 8vo, 202p, DJ/4.00, CgM)	H.Z. Walck	1968	No Illustrations	90-140	
Garner, Elvira	Ezekiel (1st [1st bk.], lg8vo, ibds, [44]p, color, DJ/1.50)	Henry Holt & Co.	(1937)	Garner, Elvira	120-200	
Garner, Elvira	Ezekiel Travels (1st, lg8vo, [46]p, ibds, color, DJ/1.50)	Henry Holt & Co.	(1938)	Garner, Elvira	160-225	
Garner, Elvira	Little Cat Lost (1st, sm sq4to, ibds, [28]p, 2-color, pep, DJ/2.00)	J. Messner	(1943)	Thorne, Diana	80-130	
Garner, Elvira	Sarah Faith Anderson (1st, 8vo, [106]p, color, DJ/2.00)	J. Messner	(1939)	Garner, Elvira	100-175	
Garner, Elvira	Way Down in Tennessee (1st, lg8vo, [96]p, ibds, color, pep, DJ/2.00)	J. Messner	(1941)	Garner, Elvira	200-300	
Garnett (ed.)	Poems by Robert Browning (1st, 8vo, 377p, gilt, b/w)	L: Bell	1900	Shaw, Byam	70-100	
Garnett, Eve	Family from One End Street (1st, 8vo, 212p, b/w, pep, DJ, CgM)	L: Muller	1937	Garnett, Eve	80-125	
Garnett, Louise A.	Creature Songs (1st, folio, 30p, p-o, green/gilt, 10pl)	NY: Ditson	(1912)	Newell, Peter	200-300	
Garnett, Louise A.	Muffin Shop (1st, folio, ibds, p-o, 79p, color)	Rand/McNally	(1908)	Dunlap, Hope	120-200	
Garnett, Louise A.	Ottoman Wonder Tales (1st, sq8vo, 266p, blue/gilt, teg, 12cp)	L: A&C Black	1915	Folkard, Charles	100-175	
Garnett, Louise A.	Rhyming Ring (1st, 4to, ibds, 64p, 7cp, pep)	Rand/McNally	(1910)	Dunlap, Hope	100-165	
Garnett, Louise A.	The Merrymakers (1st, 4to, p-o, 80p, 8 fp color)	Rand/McNally	(1918)	McCracken, James	55-80	
Garrard, Phillis	Banana Tree House (1st, lg8vo, 108p, color, pep, DJ/2.00)	Coward	(1938)	Hader, B.& E.	40-65	
Garrard, Phillis	Running Away with Nebby (1st {std}, lg8vo, 144p, 6cp, 11pl, pep, DJ/2.00)	McKay	(1944)	Pogany, Willy	75-100	
Garrett, Helen	Angelo, the Naughty One (1st, 4to, ipcb, 40p, color, pep, DJ/2.00)	Viking	1944	Politi, Leo	130-200	
Garrett, Helen	Mr. Flip Flop (1st, sm4to, ibds, 41p, 3-color, DJ/2.00)	Viking	1948	Mackenzie, Garry	30-50	
Garrott, Hal	Snythergen (1st, lg8vo, blue/gilt, 157p, 4cp, 16pl, pep)	McBride	1923	Walker, Dugald S.	80-125	
Garrott, Hal	Squiffer (1st {std}, 8vo, 226p, green/gilt, uncut, 4cp, pep)	McBride	1924	Walker, Dugald S.	70-120	
Garson, Eugenia	Laura Ingalls Wilder Songbook (1st, 4to, 160p, ibds, b/w, cep, DJ/5.95)	Harper, Row	(1968)	Williams, Garth	50-85	*
Garst, Shannon	Buffalo Bill (1st, 8vo, 214p, uncut, b/w, pep, DJ/2.75)	J. Messner	(1948)	Fax, Elton C.	30-50	
Garst, Shannon	Cowboy Boots (1st, 8vo, 191p, b/w, DJ/2.00)	Abingdon-Cokes.	1946	Hargens, Charles	25-45	
Garst, Shannon	Rusty at Ram's Horn Ranch (1st {std}{A}, 8vo, 191p, b/w, DJ/2.50)	Abingdon-Cokes.	(1951)	Creekmore, Raymond	30-45	
Garst, Shannon	Story of Buffalo Bill (1st {std}, 8vo, 237p, uncut, fp b/w, pep, DJ/1.75)	Bobbs-Merrill	(1938)	Boog, Carle M.	50-80	*
Garstin, Norman	Suitors of Aprille (1st, 12mo, teg, 212p, uncut, 19pl)	L: John Lane	1900	Robinson, Charles	120-200	
Garten, Jan	Alphabet Tale (1st, ob4to, ipcb, [55]p, fp color, pep, DJ/2.50)	Random	(1964)	Batherman, Muriel	30-50	
Garth, Mary	What Happened to Hannah (1st, 4to, 81p, p-o, color)	L: Goschen	1913	Payne, Irene	50-85	
Garthwaite, Jimmy	Zoo Book (1st {std}, lg4to, ibds, [32]p, color)	Harper	1929	Garthwaite, Jimmy	80-120	
Garthwaite, Marion	Tomas & the Red-Headed Angel (1st, 8vo, 190p, b/w, DJ/2.50)	J. Messner	(1950)	Bjorklund, Lorence	25-40	
Garvey, Robert	Good Shabbos, Everybody (1st, 4to, [26]p, ibds, color, pep)	United Synagogue	(1951)	Sendak, Maurice	600-900	
Gask, Lilian	Babes of the Wild (1st, 4to, 160p, p-o, 5cp)	L: Harrap	1917	Hickson, Wilma	60-100	
Gask, Lilian	Fairies & Christmas Child (1st AM, lg8vo, p-o, 261p, 8cp, pep)	Crowell	(1912)	Pogany, Willy	200-300	
Gask, Lilian	Fairies & Christmas Child (1st, 8vo, 260p, gilt, 8cp, pep)	L: Harrap	(1912)	Pogany, Willy	250-400	
Gask, Lilian	Folk Tales from Many Lands (1st, 8vo, red/gilt, teg, 287p, p-o, 8cp)	L: Harrap	1910	Pogany, Willy	150-225	
Gask, Lilian	Folk Tales from Many Lands (1st AM, 8vo, 286p, p-o, teg, uncut, 8cp, pep)	Crowell	(1910)	Pogany, Willy	125-200	
Gask, Lilian	Legends of our Little Brothers (1st, 8vo, 268p, 15pl)	L: Harrap	1912	Wilson, Patten	55-80	*
Gask, Lilian	Legends of our Little Brothers (1st AM, 8vo, p-o, 268p, 15pl)	Crowell	(1912)	Wilson, Patten	40-60	
Gask, Lilian	Pig Tales (1st, 8vo, 64p, color)	Nister/Dutton	[1906]	Heatly, E.	40-60	*
Gask, Lilian	Quest of the White Merle (1st, 8vo, 282p, p-o, 15pl)	L: Harrap	[1909]	Hardy, Dorothy	100-175	*
Gask, Lilian	True Stories of Big Game & Jungles (1st, 8vo, 235p, 16cp)	L: Harrap	1933	Cameron, W.F.	40-70	
Gaskell, C.M.	Lady Anne's Fairy Tales (1st, 4to, teg, 258p, white/gilt, 12cp)	L: Richards	1914	Atkinson, Maud T.	160-240	
Gaskell, Mrs.	Cranford (1st, sm8vo, 316p, blue/gilt, AEG, b/w)	L: Bliss Sands	1896	Robinson, Thomas H.	40-60	*
Gaskell, Mrs.	Cranford (1st {color ed.}, 12mo, teg, gilt, 298p, 40cp)	L: Macmillan	1898	Thomson, Hugh	70-100	
Gaskell, Mrs.	Cranford (1st, 8vo, 313p, red/gilt, teg, b/w)	L: J. Nisbet	1900	Brock, Henry M.	60-80	
Gaskell, Mrs.	Cranford (1st AM, sm8vo, teg, green/gilt, 255p, 24cp)	Dent/Dutton	1904	Brock, Charles E.	40-60	
Gaskell, Mrs.	Cranford (1st, sm8vo, 247p, gilt, teg, 24cp, pep)	L: Chapman	[1911]	Paul, Evelyn	50-80	
Gaskell, Mrs.	Cranford (1st, sm8vo, 289p, grey/gilt, 8 fp color)	A. & C. Black	1914	Tawse, Sybil	40-70	
Gaskell, Mrs.	Sylvia's Lovers (1st, sm8vo, 542p, gilt, teg, 8cp, pep)	L: G. Bell	1910	Wheelhouse, Mary V.	40-65	
Gaskell, Mrs.	Wives and Daughters (1st, 12mo, 646p, gilt, teg, 8cp, pep)	L:Herbert/Daniel	1912	Wheelhouse, Mary V.	40-70	
Gasquet, Abbot	Greater Abbeys of England (1st, lg8vo, gilt, uncut, 378p, teg, 60cp)	L: Chatto	1908	Goble, Warwick	180-240	
Gasquet, Abbot	Greater Abbeys of England (1st AM, lg8vo, gilt, 378p, teg, 60cp)	Dodd	1908	Goble, Warwick	150-220	
Gaster, Moses	Rumanian Legends & Fairy Tales (1st, 4to, 133p, ibds, 12cp)	L: R. Tuck	(1923)	Brock, Charles E.	100-180	
Gasztold, Carmen	Prayers from the Ark (1st, 8vo, 71p, pep, DJ/2.95, decor by...)	Viking	(1962)	Primrose, Jean	25-40	*
Gate, Ethel M.	Fortunate Days (1st, sm8vo, 127p, silhouettes)	Yale U. Press	1922	Knowlton, Vianna	25-40	

AUTHOR	TITLE	PUBLISHER	DATE	ARTIST	PRICE	LC
Gate, Ethel M.	Punch & Robinetta (1st, sm8vo, 118p, brown cl, 8pl)	Yale U. Press	1923	Field, Rachel	35-60	*
Gate, Ethel M.	Tales from Enchanted Isles (1st, sq8vo, 118p, green cl, col frn, b/w)	Yale U. Press	1926	Lathrop, Dorothy	70-100	
Gate, Ethel M.	Tales from the Secret Kingdom (1st, sm4to, 93p, ibds, silhouettes)	Yale U. Press	1919	Buffam, Katharine G.	45-70	
Gates, Arthur	Friendly Stories (1st, 12mo, 226p, fp color, pep)	Macmillan	1930	Seredy, Kate	30-50	
Gates, Doris	Blue Willow (1st, 8vo, 172p, blue cl, 10pl, pep, DJ/2.00, NH)	Viking	1940	Lantz, Paul	60-100	
Gates, Doris	Cat and Mrs. Cary (1st, 8vo, 216p, b/w, DJ/3.50)	Viking	(1962)	Bacon, Peggy	25-40	
Gates, Doris	Elderberry Bush (1st, 8vo, 160p, fp b/w, DJ/3.50)	Viking	(1967)	Obligado, Lilian	25-40	
Gates, Doris	Little Vic (1st, 8vo, 160p, tan cl, b/w, pep, DJ/2.50)	Viking	1951	Seredy, Kate	30-50	
Gates, Doris	My Brother Mike (1st, 8vo, 191p, b/w, DJ/2.50)	Viking	1948	Dennis, Wesley	30-45	
Gates, Doris	River Ranch (1st, 8vo, 160p, b/w, DJ/2.00)	Viking	1949	Landau, Jacob	20-35	
Gates, Doris	Sarah's Idea (1st, 8vo, orange cl, 146p, fp b/w, pep)	Viking	1938	Torrey, Marjorie	30-50	
Gates, Doris	Sensible Kate (1st, 8vo, yellow cl, 189p, b/w, pep, DJ/2.00)	Viking	1943	Torrey, Marjorie	30-50	
Gates, Doris	Trouble for Jerry (1st, 8vo, 179p, rust cl, fp b/w, pep, DJ/2.00)	Viking	1944	Torrey, Marjorie	30-50	
Gates, Eleanor	Cupid the Cowpunch (1st, sm8vo, 316p, p-o, 8pl)	McClure	1907	Various	45-80	
Gates, Eleanor	Good Night (1st, sm8vo, 53p, bds, 5cp)	Crowell	(1907)	Rackham, Arthur	400-650	
Gates, Josephine S.	April Fool Doll (1st, lg8vo, 152p, red cl, p-o, b/w)	Bobbs-Merrill	(1909)	Keep, Virginia	80-125	
Gates, Josephine S.	Land of Delight (1st, lg8vo, green cl, 115p, 16pl)	Houghton	1915	(Photos)	35-60	*
Gates, Josephine S.	Little Girl Blue Lives in the Woods... (1st, 16mo, 53p, 4cp)	Houghton	1910	Keep, Virginia	55-90	
Gates, Josephine S.	Little Girl Blue Plays I-Spy (1st, 16mo, 61p, color)	Houghton	1913	Keep, Virginia	55-80	*
Gates, Josephine S.	Little Red, White, Blue (1st, lg8vo, 118p, 9pl)	Bobbs-Merrill	(1906)	Keep, Virginia	60-80	
Gates, Josephine S.	Live Doll's Busy Days (1st, lg8vo, 105p, 10pl)	Bobbs-Merrill	(1907)	Keep, Virginia	100-165	
Gates, Josephine S.	Live Doll's House Party (1st, lg8vo, red cl, 102p, p-o, 8pl)	Bobbs-Merrill	(1906)	Keep, Virginia	100-160	
Gates, Josephine S.	Live Doll's Play Days (1st, lg8vo, p-o, red cl, 109p, 9pl)	Bobbs-Merrill	(1908)	Keep, Virginia	100-160	
Gates, Josephine S.	Live Dolls in Fairyland (1st, lg8vo, p-o, 136p, 6cp)	Bobbs-Merrill	(1911)	Keep, Virginia	100-160	
Gates, Josephine S.	Live Dolls in Wonderland (1st, 8vo, 149p, p-o, 5pl)	Bobbs-Merrill	(1912)	Keep, Virginia	100-160	
Gates, Josephine S.	Nanette Goes to Visit Grandmother (1st, 16mo, ibds, 53p, 6cp)	Houghton	1915	(Photos)	60-80	*
Gates, Josephine S.	One Day in Betty's Life (1st, ob4to, gilt, [56]p, 2-color)	Bobbs-Merrill	(1913)	Unknown	100-150	*
Gates, Josephine S.	Story of the Live Dolls (1st, lg8vo, 103p, p-o, b/w)	Bowen-Merrill	1901	Keep, Virginia	80-135	
Gates, Josephine S.	Story of the Lost Doll (1st, lg8vo, red cl, p-o, 10pl)	Bobbs-Merrill	(1905)	Keep, Virginia	80-130	
Gates, Josephine S.	Story of the Mince Pie (1st, 8vo, 164p, p-o, 16cp)	Dodd	1916	Rae, John	80-130	
Gates, Josephine S.	Story of the Three Dolls (1st, sm4to, red cl, 148p, p-o, 9pl)	Bobbs-Merrill	(1905)	Keep, Virginia	80-130	
Gates, Josephine S.	Sunshine Annie (1st, 8vo, 148p, red cl, p-o, 15cp, pep)	Bobbs-Merrill	(1910)	Cory, Fanny	80-125	
Gates, Josephine S.	Tommy Sweet Tooth (1st, sq16mo, ibds, 64p, color, pep)	Houghton	(1911)	Churbuck, Esther V.	60-90	
Gatti, Attilio	Adventure in Black and White (1st, 8vo, 172p, b/w, pep, DJ/1.75)	Scribner	1943	Wiese, Kurt	60-90	
Gatti, Attilio	Saranga the Pygmy (1st, 8vo, 226p, color, pep, DJ/2.00)	Scribner	1939	Wiese, Kurt	40-65	
Gatti, Attilio	Wrath of Moto (1st, lg8vo, 160p, b/w, DJ/2.50)	Scribner	1941	Bransom, Paul	40-65	
Gatty, Mrs. Alfred	Parables from Nature (1st, 8vo, green cl, 350p, 8pl, pep)	L: G. Bell	1910	Woodward, Alice B.	60-80	
Gay, John	Beggar's Opera (1st, 4to, 93p, bds, p-o, 8cp)	L: Heinemann	1921	Fraser, Claud L.	75-125	
Gay, John	Polly: An Opera (1st, lg8vo, blue bds, 107p, 8cp)	L: Heinemann	1923	Nicholson, Wm.	100-165	
Gay, Romney	Bonny's Wish (1st, sq12mo, [36]p, ibds, color, pep, DJ/0.50)	Grosset/Dunlap	1938	Gay, Romney	20-40	
Gay, Romney	Conny and Uncle Dick (1st, ob8vo, ipcb, [32]p, color, pep, DJ/0.50)	Grosset/Dunlap	1941	Gay, Romney	45-70	
Gay, Romney	Five Little Playmates (1st, 12mo, ibds, [61]p, color)	Grosset/Dunlap	(1941)	Gay, Romney	30-50	*
Gay, Romney	Funny Noise (1st, sq12mo, [34]p, ibds, color, pep, DJ/0.50)	Grosset/Dunlap	1935	Gay, Romney	25-40	
Gay, Romney	Peter's Adventure (1st, sq12mo, ibds, [34]p, color)	Whitman	1936	Gay, Romney	30-50	
Gay, Romney	Picture Book of Poems (1st, sq8vo, 36p, ibds, color, pep, DJ/0.50)	Grosset/Dunlap	1940	Gay, Romney	30-50	
Gay, Romney	Romney Gay ABC (1st, 4to, ibds, [30]p, color, DJ/0.50)	Grosset/Dunlap	(1946)	Gay, Romney	60-90	
Gay, Romney	Toby & Sue (1st, sq12mo, ibds, [34]p, color, pep, DJ/0.50)	Grosset/Dunlap	1937	Gay, Romney	35-50	
Gay, Romney	Tommy Grows Wise (1st, sq12mo, ibds, [30]p, color, pep)	Grosset/Dunlap	1939	Gay, Romney	30-50	
Gay, Zhenya	Bits and Pieces (1st, lg8vo, 63p, b/w, DJ/2.50)	Viking	1958	Gay, Zhenya	20-30	
Gay, Zhenya	Dear Friends (1st, 4to, 47p, b/w, DJ/1.95)	Harper	(1959)	Gay, Zhenya	30-50	
Gay, Zhenya	Fish Story (1st, sq8vo, ipcb, [27]p, fp 2-color, pep, DJ/0.50)	Garden City	(1939)	Gay, Zhenya	25-45	
Gay, Zhenya	I'm Tired of Lions (1st, 8vo, 30p, color, DJ/2.50)	Viking	1961	Gay, Zhenya	25-40	
Gay, Zhenya	Look! (1st, sm4to, unpag, 2-color, pep, DJ/2.00)	Viking	1952	Gay, Zhenya	30-45	
Gay, Zhenya	Pancho & His Burro (1st, sm4to, ibds, pep, [29]p, color)	Wm. Morrow	1930	Gay, Zhenya	55-80	
Gay, Zhenya	Sakimura (1st, 8vo, ibds, [42]p, color, DJ/1.50)	Viking	1937	Gay, Zhenya	50-80	
Gay, Zhenya	Shire Colt (1st {std}, lg4to, ibds, [62]p, lithos, pep, DJ/2.00)	Doubleday/Doran	1931	Gay, Zhenya	80-140	R
Gay, Zhenya	Small One (1st, sm4to, 31p, b/w, DJ/2.00)	Viking	(1958)	Gay, Zhenya	25-45	
Gay, Zhenya	Town Cats (1st {std}, sm4to, ipcb, 110p, fp b/w)	Knopf	1932	Gay, Zhenya	60-90	
Gay, Zhenya	What's Your Name? (1st, lg8vo, 47p, 1-color, pep, DJ/2.00)	Viking	1955	Gay, Zhenya	30-45	
Gay, Zhenya	Wonderful Things! (1st, 4to, tan cl, 62p, fp b/w, DJ/2.50)	Viking	1954	Gay, Zhenya	40-65	
Gaze, Harold	Coppertop (1st AM, lg8vo, 338p, blue/gilt, 12cp)	Harper	(1924)	Gaze, Harold	150-200	
Gaze, Harold	Goblin's Glen (1st, 8vo, 242p, red/gilt, 6cp, pep)	Little/Brown	1924	Gaze, Harold	300-500	
Gaze, Harold	Merry Piper (1st UK, lg8vo, 247p, 8cp, 12pl, pep)	L: Longmans	1925	Gaze, Harold	200-300	
Gaze, Harold	Merry Piper (1st AM, 8vo, yellow cl, 247p, 8cp, 12pl, pep)	Little/Brown	1925	Gaze, Harold	200-300	
Gedo, Leopold	Who is Johnny? (1st AM, 8vo, 242p, b/w, pep, DJ/2.00)	Viking	1939	Gedo, Leopold	40-65	
Gee, John	Bunnie Bear (1st, 8vo, ibds, color)	Volland	(1928)	Gee, John	60-100	
Geister, Edna	What Shall We Play? (1st, 8vo, 175p, ibds, p-o, col frn, cep)	Doran	(1924)	MacKinstry, Eliz.	50-80	
Gekiere, Madeleine	Frilly Lily and the Princess (1st, lg8vo, 25p, fp 2-color, DJ/2.75)	Lippincott	(1960)	Gekiere, Madeleine	50-80	*
Gekiere, Madeleine	Who Gave Us Peacocks.... (1st, 4to, unpag, color, cep, DJ/3.00, NYTBI)	Pantheon	(1953)	Gekiere, Madeleine	90-150	
Geller, James J.	Grandfather's Follies (1st, lg sq8vo, 218p, b/w)	Macaulay	(1934)	Held, John	50-80	
Gellibrand, Emma	J. Cole (1st, sm8vo, 86p, beige cl, 4cp)	Lippincott	1917	Kirk, Maria L.	35-60	
Gemmill, Jane B.	Joan Wanted a Kitty (1st, 8vo, blue cl, 150p, color, pep, DJ/2.00)	Winston	(1937)	DeAngeli, Marguerite	60-90	
Gendel, Evelyn	Tortoise & the Turtle (1st {std}, 4to, ibds, [64]p, color, pep, DJ/2.95)	Simon/Schuster	1960	Knight, Hilary	40-70	
Gendel, Evelyn	Tortoise & Turtle Abroad (1st {std}, 4to, ibds, [55]p, b/w, pep, DJ/3.50)	Simon/Schuster	1963	Knight, Hilary	40-70	
Genevoix, Maurice	Last Hunt (1st {std}, 8vo, p-o, 281p, 10 fp 1-color, pep, DJ/2.50)	Random	(1940)	Ward, Lynd	60-90	
Genevoix, Maurice	Rrou (1st, 8vo, 224p, blue cl, b/w, cep)	Minton Balch	1932	Thorne, Diana	25-45	
George, Jean C.	Bubo: Great-Horned Owl (1st {std}, sm8vo, 184p, b/w, DJ/3.00)	Dutton	(1954)	George, Jean C.	25-40	*
George, Jean C.	Coyote in Manhattan (1st, 8vo, 203p, b/w, DJ/3.95)	Crowell	(1968)	Kaufmann, John	25-40	

AUTHOR	TITLE	PUBLISHER	DATE	ARTIST	PRICE	LC
George, Jean C.	Dipper of Copper Creek (1st {std}, sm8vo, 183p, fp b/w, pep, DJ/3.50)	Dutton	(1956)	George, Jean C.	30-50	R*
George, Jean C.	Gull Number 737 (1st, 8vo, 198p, b/w, DJ/3.50)	Crowell	1964	George, Jean C.	20-35	*
George, Jean C.	Hole in the Tree (1st {std}, 8vo, [57]p, grey cl, pep, b/w, DJ/2.50)	Dutton	(1957)	George, Jean C.	25-45	
George, Jean C.	Masked Prowler... (1st {std}, 8vo, 183p, b/w, pep, DJ/2.75)	Dutton	1950	George, Jean C.	25-40	
George, Jean C.	Meph: Pet Skunk (1st {std}, 8vo, 180p, b/w, DJ/2.75)	Dutton	1952	George, Jean C.	25-40	
George, Jean C.	Moon of the Alligators (1st, 8vo, 40p, b/w, DJ/3.75)	Crowell	(1969)	Zanazanian, Adrina	20-35	
George, Jean C.	Moon of the Bears (1st, 8vo, 38p, b/w, DJ/3.25)	Crowell	(1967)	Shepard, Mac	20-30	*
George, Jean C.	Moon of the Chickarees (1st, 8vo, 40p, fp b/w, DJ/3.75)	Crowell	(1968)	Schoenherr, John	20-35	
George, Jean C.	Moon of the Deer (1st, 8vo, 40p, b/w, DJ/3.75)	Crowell	(1969)	Zallinger, Jean	20-30	
George, Jean C.	Moon of the Fox Pups (1st, 8vo, 39p, fp b/w, DJ/3.75)	Crowell	(1968)	Komoda, Kiyoaki	20-35	
George, Jean C.	Moon of the Gray Wolves (1st, 8vo, 37p, b/w, DJ/3.75)	Crowell	(1969)	Bjorklund, Lorence	25-35	
George, Jean C.	Moon of the Moles (1st, 8vo, 37p, color, DJ/3.75)	Crowell	(1969)	Levering, Robert	25-40	
George, Jean C.	Moon of the Monarch Butterflies (1st, 8vo, 40p, b/w, DJ/3.75)	Crowell	(1968)	Tinkelman, Murray	20-35	
George, Jean C.	Moon of the Mountain Lions (1st, 8vo, 39p, fp b/w, DJ/3.75)	Crowell	(1968)	Lubell, Winifred	25-40	
George, Jean C.	Moon of the Owls (1st, 8vo, 40p, b/w, DJ/3.25)	Crowell	(1967)	Zallinger, Jean	20-30	
George, Jean C.	Moon of the Salamanders (1st, 8vo, 39p, fp b/w, DJ/3.25)	Crowell	(1967)	Kaufmann, John	25-40	*
George, Jean C.	Moon of the Wild Pigs (1st, 8vo, 39p, fp b/w, DJ/3.75)	Crowell	(1968)	Parnall, Peter	30-45	
George, Jean C.	Moon of the Winter Bird (1st, 8vo, 38p, b/w, DJ/3.75)	Crowell	(1969)	Mizumura, Kazue	25-35	*
George, Jean C.	My Side of the Mountain (1st {std}, 8vo, 178p, pep, b/w, DJ/3.00, NH)	Dutton	1959	George, Jean C.	40-65	
George, Jean C.	Snow Tracks (1st {std}, 8vo, 61p, b/w, DJ/2.50)	Dutton	1958	George, Jean C.	25-40	
George, Jean C.	Spring Comes to the Ocean (1st, 8vo, 109p, b/w, DJ/3.50)	Crowell	(1965)	Wilson, John	20-25	
George, Jean C.	Summer of the Falcon (1st {std}, 8vo, 153p, b/w, DJ/2.95)	Crowell	(1962)	George, Jean C.	20-35	
George, Jean C.	Vison: The Mink (1st {std}, 8vo, 194p, b/w, pep, DJ/2.50)	Dutton	1949	George, Jean C.	25-45	*
George, Jean C.	Vulpes: The Red Fox (1st {std}, 8vo, 184p, b/w, pep, DJ/2.50)	Dutton	1948	George, Jean C.	30-50	R
Georgiou, Constantine	Proserpina: Duck that Came to School (1st, 4to, 60p, 1-color, pep, DJ/3.50)	Harvey House	(1968)	Lipscomb, Bernard	30-50	
Gerber, Will	Gooseberry Jones (1st, 8vo, 96p, b/w, DJ/2.00)	Putnam	(1947)	Morris, Dudley	45-70	
Gere, Frances K.	Once Upon a Time in Egypt (1st, ob4to, ibds, 71p, color, pep, DJ/2.00)	Longmans	1937	Gere, Frances K.	80-120	R
Gerry, Margarita S.	The Flowers (1st, 8vo, 40p, green cl, p-o, 3cp)	Harper	1910	Green, Eliz. S.	60-90	
Gerson, Virginia	Happy Heart Family (1st, sm4to, 35p, p-o, color)	Fox Duffield	1904	Gerson, Virginia	100-165	
Gerson, Virginia	Little Dignity (1st {1st bk.}, sm4to, 64p, ibds, chromos)	NY: Routledge	1881	Gerson, Virginia	120-200	
Gerson, Virginia	More Adventures of the Happy Heart Family (1st, sm4to, 47p, p-o, 4cp)	Fox Duffield	1905	Gerson, Virginia	100-165	
Gianakoulis, T.P.	Fairy Tales of Modern Greece (1st {std}, 8vo, 126p, pep, b/w)	Dutton	1930	Reiss, Henriette	30-50	*
Gibbings, Robert	Iorana! (1st AM, lg8vo, 157p, uncut, p-o, gilt, b/w, pep)	Houghton	1932	Gibbings, Robert	60-90	R
Gibbings, Robert	Lovely is The Lee (1st AM {std}, 8vo, 199p, green/gilt, b/w, DJ/3.00)	Dutton	1945	Gibbings, Robert	40-60	
Gibbings, Robert	Over the Reefs (1st, 8vo, 240p, gilt, b/w wood engravings, pep, DJ)	L: Dent	1948	Gibbings, Robert	40-70	
Gibbings, Robert	Trumpets from Montparnasse (1st AM {std}, 8vo, 200p, gilt, 8cp, DJ/5.00)	Dutton	(1955)	Gibbings, Robert	30-45	
Gibbon, James M.	Reign of Old King Cole (8vo, pict cl, 338p)	Dutton	(1911)	Robinson, Charles	150-225	
Gibbons, Mary	Story of Ophelia (1st {std}, 4to, ibds, [32]p, color, DJ/2.00)	Doubleday	1954	Ness, Evaline	40-65	
Gibbs, George	American Sea Fights (1st, elephant folio, 12 ticp)	R.H. Russell	1902	Gibbs, George	300-500	
Gibson, Charles D.	Americans (1st, ob folio, ipcb, [88]p, teg, fp b/w)	R.H. Russell	1900	Gibson, Charles D.	170-240	
Gibson, Charles D.	Drawings (1st, ob folio, [88]p, ibds, teg, b/w)	R.H. Russell	1897	Gibson, Charles D.	160-240	
Gibson, Charles D.	Education of Mr. Pipp (1st, ob folio, ibds, [78]p, b/w)	R.H. Russell	1899	Gibson, Charles D.	170-240	
Gibson, Charles D.	Eighty Drawings including Weaker Sex (1st, ob folio, teg, unpag, ibds, b/w)	Scribner/Lane	1903	Gibson, Charles D.	150-240	
Gibson, Charles D.	Everyday People (1st, ob folio, ibds, teg, [80]p, b/w pl)	Scribner	1904	Gibson, Charles D.	160-250	
Gibson, Charles D.	Gibson Book (1st, ob folio, 2 volumes, red cl, teg, b/w)	Scribner	1906	Gibson, Charles D.	250-350	
Gibson, Charles D.	Our Neighbors (1st, ob folio, [68]p, b/w)	Scribner	1905	Gibson, Charles D.	180-250	
Gibson, Charles D.	Pictures of People (1st, ob folio, teg, unpag, ibds, b/w)	R.H. Russell	1896	Gibson, Charles D.	200-300	
Gibson, Charles D.	Sketches in Egypt (1st, sm4to, tan buckram, 115p, b/w)	Doub./McClure	1899	Gibson, Charles D.	200-300	
Gibson, Charles D.	Social Ladder (1st, ob. folio, [79]p, teg, b/w)	R.H. Russell	1902	Gibson, Charles D.	180-240	
Gibson, Charles D.	Widow & Her Friends (1st, ob folio, [79]p, teg, bds, b/w)	R.H. Russell	1901	Gibson, Charles D.	140-200	
Gibson, Eva K.	Zauberlinda: Wise Witch (1st, 8vo, 256p, blue cl, 1-color, pep)	Chi: R. Smith	(1901)	Tibbitts, Mabel	180-250	
Gibson, Josephine	Is There a Mouse in the House? (1st {std}, 12mo, [32]p, pep, b/w, DJ/1.95)	Macmillan	(1965)	Bodecker, N.M.	20-30	
Gibson, Katharine	Bow Bells (1st {std}, 8vo, 124p, fp b/w, pep, DJ/2.00)	Longmans	1943	Bock, Vera	30-50	
Gibson, Katharine	Cinders (1st {std}, sm8vo, 132p, fp b/w, pep, DJ/1.75)	Longmans	1939	Bock, Vera	25-40	
Gibson, Katharine	Jock's Castle (1st {std}, lg8vo, 139p, pep, fp b/w, DJ/2.00)	Longmans	1940	Bock, Vera	25-40	
Gibson, Katharine	Tenggren Tell-It-Again Book (1st, 4to, 199p, fp color, pep, DJ/2.50)	Little/Brown	(1942)	Tenggren, Gustaf	100-165	
Gibson, Lydia	Teacup Whale (1st, ob8vo, ipcb, dep, 23p, b/w)	Farrar/Rinehart	(1934)	Gibson, Lydia	60-100	
Gielow, Martha S.	Old Plantation Days (1st, sm8vo, 183p, tan cl, 13pl)	R.H. Russell	1902	(Photos)	100-150	
Gilbert & Sullivan	Duke of Plaza Toro (1st {std}, 8vo, [32]p, pep, color, DJ/3.95)	Macmillan	(1969)	Wells, Rosemary	25-45	
Gilbert, Helen E.	Go-to-Sleep Book (1st, sm sq4to, wraps, fp color)	Rand/McNally	(1936)	Ward, Keith	40-65	
Gilbert, Henry	King Arthur (1st, lg8vo, 242p, p-o, color, b/w)	Saalfield	1929	Brundage, Frances	50-80	
Gilbert, Henry	King Arthur's Knights (1st AM, lg8vo, 367p, gilt, teg, 16cp, dep)	Stokes	1911	Crane, Walter	200-300	
Gilbert, Henry	King Arthur's Knights (1st, 8vo, gilt, teg, 367p, 16cp)	L: Jack	1911	Crane, Walter	250-350	R
Gilbert, Henry	Robin Hood (1st AM, 8vo, teg, gilt, 16cp, pep)	Stokes	(1912)	Crane, Walter	120-185	
Gilbert, Henry	Robin Hood (1st {std}, 8vo, 398p, fp 2-color, DJ/2.50)	Lippincott	(1948)	Williams, Garth	30-50	
Gilbert, Paul T.	Bertram and his Fabulous Animals (1st, 8vo, 159p, b/w, pep, DJ/1.00)	Rand/McNally	(1937)	Rousseff/Maynard	70-120	
Gilbert, Paul T.	Bertram's Trip to the North Pole (1st, sm8vo, 127p, fp b/w, pep, DJ/1.00)	Rand/McNally	(1940)	Stossel, Anne	60-90	
Gilbert, Paul T.	Egbert & his Marvelous Adventures (1st {std}, sm8vo, 103p, b/w, DJ/1.50)	Harper	(1944)	Rey, Hans A.	50-80	
Gilbert, Paul T.	Elmer Buys a Circus (1st, ibds, 71p, b/w, pep)	Grosset/Dunlap	(1941)	Stossel, Anne	30-50	
Gilbert, Paul T.	With Bertram in Africa (1st {A}, sm8vo, 127p, b/w, pep, DJ/1.00)	Rand/McNally	1939	Stossel, Anne	100-160	
Gilbert, W.S.	Bab Ballads (1st AM, 16mo, 184p, grey bds, uncut, b/w)	R.H. Russell	1901	Gilbert, W.S.	60-90	
Gilbert, W.S.	Iolanthe... (1st, 4to, green/gilt, teg, 224p, uncut, 32cp)	L: G. Bell	1910	Flint, William R.	200-300	
Gilbert, W.S.	Pinafore Picture Book (1st, 4to, 131p, blue cl, 16cp, pep)	L: G. Bell	1908	Woodward, Alice B.	90-160	
Gilbert, W.S.	Princess Ida (1st, lg8vo, 150p, green/gilt, 8cp)	L: G. Bell	1912	Flint, William R.	90-160	
Gilbert, W.S.	Savoy Operas (1st, 4to, 208p, gilt, teg, uncut, 32cp)	L: G. Bell	1909	Flint, William R.	160-240	
Gilbert, W.S.	Story of the Mikado (1st, sm4to, ibds, 114p, 6cp, pep)	L: O'Connor	1921	Woodward, Alice B.	55-80	
Gilbert, W.S.	The Mikado (1st, 8vo, gilt, 96p, 8cp)	L: Macmillan	1928	Flint, William R.	80-130	
Gilbert, W.S.	Yeoman of the Guard (1st, 8vo, 102p, gilt, 8cp)	L: Macmillan	1929	Flint, William R.	80-130	

AUTHOR	TITLE	PUBLISHER	DATE	ARTIST	PRICE	LC
Gilbert, William	Magic Mirror (1st, 8vo, 253p, purple/gilt, p-o, teg, 20cp)	L: MacLaren	1908	Menzies, John	80-125	
Gilbreth, Frank	Held's Angels (1st, lg8vo, 211p, fp b/w, DJ/3.95)	Crowell	(1952)	Held, John	50-85	*
Gilby/Cuming	George Moorland... (1st, 8vo, 290p, teg, 50cp)	L: A&C Black	1907	Moorland, George	80-120	
Gilchrist, Beth B.	Helen and the Fifth Cousins (1st, 12mo, 334p, b/w)	Penn	1915	Williamson, Ada C.	40-65	
Gilchrist, Marie	Story of the Great Lakes (1st {std}, 4to, [32]p, ibds, color, DJ/1.50)	Harper	(1942)	DeWitt, C.H.	50-80	
Gilfillan, Archer B.	Sheep (1st, 8vo, 272p, green cl, b/w)	Little/Brown	1929	Wiese, Kurt	40-70	
Gilkison, Grace	Little Arthur (1st {std}, 8vo, 126p, col frn, fp b/w)	Doubleday/Doran	1931	Gilkison, Grace	20-35	
Gill, Frances	Little Days (1st, 8vo, ibds, 50p, col frn, b/w)	Houghton	1917	Winter, Milo	75-100	
Gill, Joan	Hush, Jon! (1st {std}, lg8vo, 47p, b/w, DJ/3.50)	Doubleday	(1968)	Sugarman, Tracy	30-50	
Gill, Joan	Sara's Granny & the Groodle (1st {std}, 4to, [32]p, color, DJ/3.95, NYTBI)	Doubleday	(1969)	Chwast, Seymour	30-50	
Gill, Richard	Paco Goes to the Fair (1st, 4to, [49]p, color, pep, DJ/2.00)	Henry Holt & Co.	(1940)	Gannett, Ruth C.	30-50	
Gillilan, Strickland	Danny & Fanny (1st, lg8vo, p-o, 96p, color, pep)	Rand/McNally	(1928)	Eger, Ruth C.	40-65	
Gillmore, Inez H.	Angel Island (1st, sm8vo, blue cl, 351p, 2pl)	Henry Holt & Co.	1914	Rae, John	80-130	
Gilly Bear	Adventures of Peterkin (1st, lg8vo, 153p, brown/gilt, 12cp)	NY: S. Gabriel	(1916)	Ohrenschall, Helen	75-100	
Gilly Bear	Tom Tit Tales (1st, 4to, 155p, purple/gilt, 12cp)	NY: S. Gabriel	(1915)	Ohrenschall, Helen	70-100	
Gilman, Eliz. L.	Picnic Adventures (1st, 8vo, green cl, 192p, 12 dp 1-color, DJ/2.00)	Farrar/Rinehart	(1940)	Cosgrave, John O.	80-120	
Gilmour, Margaret	Ameliaranne at the Circus (1st, 12mo, p-o, [63]p, color)	L: Harrap	(1931)	Pearse, Susan B.	80-120	
Gilmour, Margaret	Ameliaranne at the Seaside (1st, 8vo, unpag, color)	L: Harrap	1935	Pearse, Susan B.	80-120	
Gilmour, Margaret	Ameliaranne Gives a Concert (1st, 8vo, unpag, fp color)	L: Harrap	(1944)	Pearse, Susan B.	80-120	
Gilmour, Margaret	Seven Little Spillikins (1st AM, ob8vo, unpag, p-o, color)	McKay	[1930]	Govey, Lilian	70-90	
Gilson, Roy R.	In the Morning Glow (1st, 8vo, gilt, 187p, p-o, 16pl)	Harper	1902	Stephens, Alice B.	35-60	
Gilson, Roy R.	Katrina (1st, 8vo, green cl, 316p, teg, 6cp)	Baker/Taylor	(1906)	Stephens, Alice B.	35-60	
Gilson, Roy R.	Mother & Father (1st, 8vo, teg, 63p, green cl, b/w)	Harper	1903	Stephens, Alice B.	55-80	
Gilstrap, Robert	Sultan's Fool (1st {std}, lg8vo, 95p, fp b/w, DJ/2.75)	Holt	(1958)	Greco, Robert	25-40	
Gimmage, Peter	Picture Book of Ships (1st, 4to, 64p, fp color, pep)	Macmillan	1930	Craig, Helen	45-80	*
Ginsburg, Mirra	Three Rolls & One Doughnut (1st {std}, 4to, 52p, b/w, DJ/4.50)	Dial Press	(1970)	Lobel, Anita	30-45	
Gipson, Fred B.	Old Yeller (1st, 8vo, ibds, 158p, 6 fp b/w, DJ/2.75, NH)	Harper	(1956)	Burger, Carl	45-70	*
Gipson, Fred B.	Recollection Creek (1st, 8vo, 248p, b/w, DJ/2.95)	Harper	(1959)	Burger, Carl	20-25	
Gipson, Fred B.	Savage Sam (1st {std}, 8vo, 214p, bds, b/w, DJ/3.00)	Harper	(1962)	Burger, Carl	20-30	
Gipson, Fred B.	Trail-Driving Rooster (1st, 8vo, grey cl, 79p, b/w, DJ/2.25)	Harper	1955	Simont, Marc	30-50	
Gipson, Morrell	City Country ABC (1st, 4to, [48]p, ibds, color, pep, DJ/0.50)	Garden City	1946	Weisgard, Leonard	80-125	
Gipson, Morrell	Hello Peter (1st {std}, ob8vo, ibds, [31]p, color, pep, DJ/1.25)	Doubleday	(1948)	Hurd, Clement	60-90	
Girvin, Brenda	Alice & the White Rabbit (1st, 8vo, 160p, 33 b/w illus)	L: Partridge	(1909)	Unknown	75-100	*
Girvin, Brenda	Girl Scout (1st, sm8vo, 319p, blue/gilt, 6cp)	L: H. Frowde	1913	Tenison, Nell M.	45-70	
Girvin, Brenda	Good Queen Bees (1st, ob4to, ibds, unpag, 23cp)	L: D. Nutt	[1907]	Hassall, John	100-180	
Girvin, Brenda	Mr. Piccolo (1st, 8vo, 247p)	L: G. Allen	1911	Quick, Horace	30-60	*
Girvin, Brenda	Pam & Billy (1st, 8vo, 209p, col frn, 12pl)	L: G. Allen	1910	Quick, Horace	40-60	*
Girvin, Brenda	Queer Cousin Claude (1st, 8vo, 280p, gilt, col frn, 8pl)	L: G. Allen	1912	Hardy, E. Stuart	40-65	
Girvin, Brenda	Round Fairyland with Alice (1st, 8vo, brown/gilt, 186p, b/w, pep, DJ)	L: Wells/Gard.	(1948)	Cable, W. Lindsay	30-50	*
Girvin, Brenda	Round Fairyland with Alice & the White Rabbit (1st, 8vo, 312p, b/w)	L: Wells/Gard.	1916	Furniss, Dorothy	70-100	
Girvin/Cosens	Wee Men (1st, 12mo, p-o, 160p, 4cp)	L: Hutchinson	[1923]	Robinson, Charles	160-220	
Gissing, George	The Whirlpool (1st AM, 8vo, 424p, green cl, cvr by...)	Stokes	(1897)	Bradley, Will	60-90	
Glasgow, Ellen	The Deliverance (1st, 8vo, 543p, red/gilt, 4cp)	Doubleday/Page	1904	Schoonover, Frank	35-60	
Glave, E.J.	In Savage Africa (1st, lg8vo, 247p, grey cl, b/w)	R.H. Russell	(1892)	Various	120-200	*
Gleason, Jane	Young and Happy Rooster (1st, 8vo, p-o, 64p, gilt, fp color, pep)	Whitman	1934	Gleason, Jane	60-90	*
Gleaves, Suzanne	Tip and Dip (1st, lg8vo, rust cl, [62]p, 1-color, DJ/2.95)	Lippincott	(1960)	Adams, Adrienne	45-65	
Glendinning, Marg.	Gertie the Horse Who Thought & Thought (1st, 8vo, 88p, b/w, pep, DJ/2.25)	Whittlesey	(1951)	Slobodkin, Louis	25-40	*
Glendon, George	Emperor of the Air (1st, 8vo, 311p, red/gilt, 8pl)	L: Methuen	1910	Buckland, Arthur H.	55-80	*
Glenn, Elsie	Dumblebum (1st, ob8vo, [63]p, fp color, pep, DJ/2.00)	Macrae Smith	(1947)	Wiese, Kurt	50-80	*
Glenn, Morris	Amandus, who Was Much Too Big (1st, ob8vo, 63p, fp 1-col, pep, DJ/1.50)	Macrae Smith	(1939)	Wiese, Kurt	45-70	
Glick, Carl	Oswald's Pet Dragon (1st, 4to, [32]p, ibds, color, DJ/1.75)	Coward	(1943)	Wiese, Kurt	45-70	
Glinski, Antoni J.	Polish Fairy Tales (1st, 4to, 96p, gilt, 20cp, pep)	L: John Lane	1920	Walton, Cecile	80-125	
Glover, William J.	British Fairy & Folk Tales (1st, sq8vo, 281p, 8cp)	L: A&C Black	1920	Folkard, Charles	90-140	
Goddard, Julia	Kaspar & Seven Wonderful Pigeons of Wurzburg (12mo, 240p, col frn, 4pl)	L: Marcus Ward	[1880]	Greenaway, Kate	80-120	
Godden, Rumer	Candy Floss (1st, lg8vo, pink cl, 63p, color, dep, DJ/2.50)	Viking	(1960)	Adams, Adrienne	50-80	R
Godden, Rumer	Creature's Choir (1st AM, 4to, ibds, 69p, gilt, dep, DJ/3.50)	Viking	(1965)	Primrose, Jean	30-45	R
Godden, Rumer	Doll's House (1st AM, 8vo, 125p, yellow, cl, 4cp, DJ/2.50)	Viking	1948	Saintsbury, Dana	70-120	R
Godden, Rumer	Doll's House (1st, 8vo, tan cl, 136p, color, pep, DJ/2.75)	Viking	(1962)	Tudor, Tasha	120-185	
Godden, Rumer	Fairy Doll (1st, 8vo, grey cl, 67p, 2-color, pep, DJ/2.50)	Viking	1956	Adams, Adrienne	60-100	R
Godden, Rumer	Home is the Sailor (1st AM, 8vo, 128p, color, pep, DJ/3.00)	Viking	(1964)	Primrose, Jean	40-65	R
Godden, Rumer	Impunity Jane (1st, 8vo, 48p, color, pep, DJ/2.50)	Viking	1954	Adams, Adrienne	65-100	R
Godden, Rumer	Kitchen Madonna (1st AM, 8vo, 89p, ibds, 6 fp color, cep, DJ/3.75)	Viking	(1967)	Barker, Carol	25-45	
Godden, Rumer	Little Plum (1st AM, 8vo, 97p, fp color, pep, DJ/3.25)	Viking	(1963)	Primrose, Jean	40-70	R
Godden, Rumer	Miss Happiness and Miss Flower (1st AM, 8vo, 81p, fp color, pep, DJ/3.00)	Viking	(1961)	Primrose, Jean	45-70	R
Godden, Rumer	Mouse House (1st, lg8vo, tan cl, 63p, color, pep, DJ/2.75)	Viking	1957	Adams, Adrienne	65-100	R
Godden, Rumer	Mousewife (1st, 8vo, 46p, fp b/w, DJ/2.00)	Viking	1951	DuBois, W.P.	60-90	
Godden, Rumer	Operation Sippacik (1st AM, 8vo, 109p, fp b/w, DJ/3.50)	Viking	(1969)	Bryan, James	25-40	
Godden, Rumer	St. Jerome and the Lion (1st, lg8vo, 34p, 1-color, pep, DJ/2.50)	Viking	(1961)	Primrose, Jean	30-45	
Godden, Rumer	Story of Holly and Ivy (1st, lg8vo, 64p, ibds, 2-color, pep, DJ/2.50)	Viking	(1958)	Adams, Adrienne	50-80	
Godfrey, Hollis	Man Who Ended War (1st, 8vo, blue/gilt, 301p, p-o, 4pl)	Little/Brown	1908	Grunwald, Charles	60-100	
Godolphin, Mary	Pilgrims' Progress (1st, sm4to, red cl, 10 fp b/w, 120p, DJ/2.00)	Stokes	1939	Lawson, Robert	60-100	
Goethe	Faust (1st, 4to, red/gilt, teg, 205p, 31 ticp)	L: Hutchinson	1908	Pogany, Willy	250-400	
Goethe	Faust (1st, 8vo, 262p, 6pl, DJ/2.50)	Cape/Smith	(1930)	Ward, Lynd	90-120	
Goetz, Delia	Burro of Burnegat Road (1st, 8vo, 205p, b/w, pep, DJ/2.00)	Harcourt	(1945)	Van Stockum, Hilda	25-45	*
Goetz, Lee G.	Camel in the Sea (1st, 8vo, 58p, 2-color, DJ/2.95)	McGraw-Hill	(1966)	Galdone, Paul	25-45	
Goffstein, M.B.	Across the Sea (1st {std}, 12mo, [38]p, color, DJ/2.50)	Farrar, Straus	(1968)	Goffstein, M.B.	30-50	
Goffstein, M.B.	Brookie and her Lamb (1st {std}, 24mo, [31]p, b/w, DJ/1.95)	Farrar, Straus	(1967)	Goffstein, M.B.	30-50	
Goffstein, M.B.	Goldie the Dollmaker (1st {std}, ob12mo, 55p, b/w, DJ/3.50)	Farrar, Straus	(1969)	Goffstein, M.B.	30-45	

AUTHOR: 86

AUTHOR	TITLE	PUBLISHER	DATE	ARTIST	PRICE	LC
Goffstein, M.B.	Sleepy People (1st {std}, 32mo, blue cl, [28]p, b/w, cep, DJ/1.95)	Farrar, Straus	(1966)	Goffstein, M.B.	25-45	
Goffstein, M.B.	The Gats! (1st, 32mo, [33]p, ipcb, 1-color, cep, DJ/1.95)	Pantheon	1966	Goffstein, M.B.	40-65	
Goffstein, M.B.	Two Piano Tuners (1st {std}, 8vo, 65p, b/w, DJ/3.50)	Farrar, Straus	(1970)	Goffstein, M.B.	30-50	
Goldberg, Martha	Lunch Box Story (1st, sm8vo, red cl, [30]p, b/w, DJ/1.25)	Holiday House	1951	Tobias, Beatrice	20-35	
Goldberg, Martha	Twirly Skirt (1st, 8vo, 45p, green cl, fp b/w, pep, DJ/1.75)	Holiday House	1954	Stone, Helen	40-65	R
Goldberg, Martha	Wait for the Rain (1st, sm8vo, [43]p, blue cl, b/w, cep, DJ/1.50)	Holiday House	(1952)	Price, Christine	25-40	*
Goldin, Augusta	Bottom of the Sea (1st, sq8vo, [28]p, color, DJ/3.25)	Crowell	(1967)	Emberley, Ed	30-45	
Goldin, Augusta	Ducks Don't Get Wet (1st, 8vo, [40]p, color, DJ/2.95)	Crowell	(1965)	Kessler, Leonard	30-45	
Goldin, Augusta	Spider Silk (1st, ob8vo, [40]p, fp 2-color, DJ/2.75)	Crowell	(1964)	Low, Joseph	30-45	
Goldin, Augusta	Straight Hair, Curly Hair (1st, 8vo, ipcb, [38]p, fp 2-color, DJ/3.25)	Crowell	(1966)	Emberley, Ed	20-35	*
Goldin, Augusta	Sunlit Sea (1st, ob8vo, 33p, color, DJ/3.50)	Crowell	(1968)	Galdone, Paul	20-35	*
Golding, Harry	Book of the Clock (1st, 8vo, p-o, 140p, 27cp)	L: Ward Lock	1920	Tarrant, Margaret	90-120	
Golding, Harry	Our Animal Friends (4to, ibds, 176p, p-o, 24cp)	L: Ward Lock	[1920]	Tarrant, Margaret	75-100	
Golding, Harry	Tim Tubby-Toes (16mo, ipcb, p-o, 85p, fp color, pep)	L: Ward Lock	[1912]	Rudge/Braham	70-100	
Golding, Harry	Willie Winkie... (16mo, 96p, ibds, 24 fp color, pep)	L: Ward Lock	[1920]	Tarrant, Margaret	75-100	
Golding, Harry	Zoo Days (1st, lg8vo, 334p, p-o, 48cp, pep)	L: Ward Lock	(1919)	Tarrant, Margaret	70-100	
Golding, Louis	The Pursuer (1st, sm8vo, 275p, uncut, pep, DJ/2.00)	Farrar/Rinehart	(1936)	Ward, Lynd	50-80	*
Goldman, Joan M.	School in Our Village (1st, 8vo, 136p, b/w, cep, DJ)	L: Batsford	1957	Ardizzone, Edward	45-70	
Goldoni, Carlo	The Liar (1st, sm4to, ibds, 93p, p-o, col frn)	L: Selwyn	1922	Fraser, Claud L.	55-80	*
Goldoni, Carlo	The Liar (1st AM, 8vo, 93p, bds, col frn, b/w, DJ)	Knopf	1922	Fraser, Claud L.	75-100	
Goldsmith, Milton	Dorothy's Dolls... (1st, 8vo, 59p, ibds, 14cp)	NY: Ullman	(1908)	Hermony, N.	75-100	*
Goldsmith, Oliver	Comedies of Oliver Goldsmith (1st, 12mo, AEG, gilt, 310p, b/w)	L: G. Allen	1896	Hammond, Chris	75-100	
Goldsmith, Oliver	Deserted Village (1st, lg8vo, 59p, red/gilt, AEG, 119p, 33pl)	Harper	1902	Abbey, Edwin A.	60-90	
Goldsmith, Oliver	Deserted Village (1st, ob4to, 59p, vellum/gilt, 14cp, pep)	L: Gowans/Gray	1907	Reid, Stephen	120-200	
Goldsmith, Oliver	Deserted Village (1st, 4to, 99p, gilt, teg, 40 ticp)	L: Constable	1909	Hankey, William L.	100-165	
Goldsmith, Oliver	Elegy on the Glory of Her Sex... (1st, ob8vo, wraps, [24]p, 6cp)	L: Routledge	(1885)	Caldecott, Randolph	70-100	
Goldsmith, Oliver	Little Goody Two-Shoes (1st, 8vo, [40]p, ibds, pep, color)	Saalfield	(1929)	Peat, Fern B.	55-80	
Goldsmith, Oliver	She Stoops to Conquer (1st, folio, 176p, AEG, fp b/w)	Harper	1887	Abbey, Edwin A.	120-200	
Goldsmith, Oliver	She Stoops to Conquer (1st, 4to, 198p, gilt, 25 ticp)	L: Hodder	(1912)	Thomson, Hugh	140-200	
Goldsmith, Oliver	Vicar of Wakefield (1st, 8vo, 305p, AEG, gilt, b/w)	L: Macmillan	1890	Thomson, Hugh	70-125	
Goldsmith, Oliver	Vicar of Wakefield (1st, 8vo, 222p, green/gilt, uncut, 12cp)	L: Dent	1898	Bedford, Francis D.	80-130	
Goldsmith, Oliver	Vicar of Wakefield (1st, 8vo, AEG, 224p, green/gilt, 5pl)	L: Nister	[1898]	Paget, Henry M.	60-90	
Goldsmith, Oliver	Vicar of Wakefield (1st, 8vo, green/gilt, 260p, teg, 13cp)	L: A&C Black	1903	Wright, John M.	100-160	
Goldsmith, Oliver	Vicar of Wakefield (1st, 8vo, 242p, gilt, teg, uncut, 25cp, dep)	L: Dent	1904	Brock, Charles E.	45-70	
Goldsmith, Oliver	Vicar of Wakefield (1st AM, 8vo, blue/gilt, 7cp)	Lippincott	1912	Brock, Henry M.	60-90	
Goldsmith, Oliver	Vicar of Wakefield (1st AM, sm4to, 345p, blue/gilt, 16cp)	Henry Holt & Co.	1914	Sullivan, Edmund J.	100-160	
Goldsmith, Oliver	Vicar of Wakefield (1st, 4to, 345p, green/gilt, teg, 16cp)	L: Constable	1914	Sullivan, Edmund J.	120-200	
Goldsmith, Oliver	Vicar of Wakefield (1st, 4to, teg, uncut, gilt, 232p, 12cp, pep)	L: Harrap	(1929)	Rackham, Arthur	200-300	
Goldsmith, Oliver	Vicar of Wakefield (1st AM, lg8vo, gilt, 232p, teg, 12cp, pep)	McKay	[1929]	Rackham, Arthur	160-240	
Gomme, Alice B.	Children's Singing Games (1st, ob8vo, 70p, ibds, b/w)	Nutt/Macmillan	1894	Smith, Winifred	125-200	*
Gomme, Alice B.	Old English Singing Games (1st, ob8vo, 56p, ibds, color)	L: G. Allen	1900	Harwood, Edith	140-240	
Gomme, George (ed)	Queen's Story Book (1st, 12mo, 446p, teg, blue/gilt, 20pl)	L: Constable	1898	Robinson, W. Heath	100-175	
Gomme, George L.	Princess's Story Book (1st, 12mo, gilt, teg, 443p, 23pl)	L: Constable	1901	Stratton, Helen	100-170	*
Good, Loren D.	Panchito (1st, 8vo, 159p, b/w, DJ/2.75)	Coward	(1955)	Nicolas	20-30	
Goodall, John S.	Adventures of Paddy Pork (1st AM {std}, ob12mo, [60]p, fp b/w, DJ/2.75)	Harcourt	(1968)	Goodall, John S.	40-65	
Goodenow, Earle	Owl Who Hated the Dark (1st, sm4to, [31]p, 2-color, DJ/3.75)	H.Z. Walck	(1969)	Goodenow, Earle	40-65	
Goodloe, Abbe C.	College Girls (1st, 12mo, gilt, 288p, 11pl)	Scribner	1895	Gibson, Charles D.	30-50	
Goodman, George	Bascombe, Fastest Hound Alive (1st, 4to, 31p, fp 2-color, pep, DJ/2.75)	Wm. Morrow	1958	Galdone, Paul	60-90	
Goodrich, Arthur F.	Gleam O'Dawn (1st, sm8vo, gilt, 307p, 4pl)	Appleton	1908	Hutchison, D.C.	25-40	
Goodsell, Jane	Katie's Magic Glasses (1st, lg8vo, 43p, color, cep, DJ/3.50)	Houghton	1965	Cooney, Barbara	30-50	
Goodwin, John B.	Pleasant Pirate (1st {std}, sm4to, ibds, [32]p, color, DJ/2.00)	Knopf	1940	Chappell, Warren	40-70	
Goodwin, Maud W.	Head of a Hundred (1st, 12mo, green/gilt, 225p, teg, 2pl by...)	Little/Brown	1897	Smith, Jessie W.	200-300	
Goodwin, Maud W.	Head of a Hundred (1st {new ed}, 8vo, 221p, red/gilt, 2pl)	Little/Brown	1900	Smith, Jessie W.	100-160	
Goodwin, Maud W.	Sir Christopher (1st, 12mo, 411p, gilt, frn by...)	Little/Brown	1901	Pyle, Howard	30-50	
Goodwin, Murray	Underground Hideaway (1st, 8vo, 130p, b/w, DJ/3.95)	Harper	(1968)	Parnall, Peter	25-45	
Goodwin, Wilder	Up Grade (1st, sm8vo, 321p, gilt, cvr by...)	Little/Brown	1910	Peabody, Marion L.	20-35	
Gordon, Adam L.	Racing Rhymes (1st, 12mo, 146p, uncut, b/w)	R.H. Russell	1901	Unknown	75-100	*
Gordon, Armistead	Maje: A Love Story (1st, sm8vo, ipcb, uncut, 119p, 4pl)	Scribner	1914	Unknown	40-60	*
Gordon, Charles W.	Man from Glengarry (1st, sm8vo, purple cloth, 473p, cvr by...)	Revell	1901	Hazenplug, Frank	30-50	
Gordon, Elizabeth	Billy Bunny's Fortune (1st, 12mo, [40]p, ibds, color, pep)	Volland	(1919)	Enright, Maginel W.	60-90	
Gordon, Elizabeth	Bird Children (1st, lg8vo, 96p, ibds, color, pep)	Volland	(1912)	Ross, M.T.	120-180	
Gordon, Elizabeth	Book of Bow-Wows (8vo, [40]p, ibds, fp color, pep)	Donohue	(1913)	Tad	90-140	
Gordon, Elizabeth	Buddy Jim (1st, lg8vo, ibds, [93]p, color)	Volland	(1922)	Rae, John	50-80	
Gordon, Elizabeth	Butterfly Babies' Book (1st, 8vo, 78p, ibds, color)	Rand/McNally	(1914)	Ross, M.T.	80-120	
Gordon, Elizabeth	Dolly & Molly at Seashore (1st, 16mo, 32p, color)	Rand/McNally	(1914)	Beem, Frances	40-65	
Gordon, Elizabeth	Dolly & Molly at the Circus (1st, 16mo, 32p, color)	Rand/McNally	(1914)	Beem, Frances	40-65	
Gordon, Elizabeth	Flower Children (1st, 8vo, ibds, [92]p, color, pep)	Volland	(1910)	Ross, M.T.	120-180	
Gordon, Elizabeth	Happy Home Children (1st, 12mo, [34]p, ibds, color, pep)	Volland	(1924)	Foster, Marcia L.	60-90	
Gordon, Elizabeth	I Wonder Why? (1st, sm8vo, 72p, color)	Rand/McNally	(1916)	Ross, M.T.	50-80	
Gordon, Elizabeth	Just You (1st, sq16mo, ipcb, [20]p, pep)	Volland	(1920)	Unknown	30-50	*
Gordon, Elizabeth	King Gumdrop (1st, lg8vo, 112p, p-o, fp color, pep)	Whitman	(1916)	Frazee, Hazel	100-150	
Gordon, Elizabeth	Lorraine & Little People of Spring (1st, sm8vo, 64p, color)	Rand/McNally	(1918)	Lee, Ella D.	40-65	
Gordon, Elizabeth	Lorraine & Little People of Summer (1st, sm8vo, 64p, color)	Rand/McNally	(1920)	McCracken, James	40-65	
Gordon, Elizabeth	Lorraine & the Little People (1st, 12mo, ibds, 73p, color)	Rand/McNally	(1915)	Ross, M.T.	70-100	
Gordon, Elizabeth	More Really So Stories (1st, lg8vo, ibds, 95p, color, pep)	Volland	(1929)	Rae, John	70-100	
Gordon, Elizabeth	Mother Earth's Children (1st, lg8vo, 95p, ibds, color, pep)	Volland	(1914)	Ross, M.T.	150-250	
Gordon, Elizabeth	Really So Stories (1st, lg8vo, ibds, 96p, 11cp, pep)	Volland	(1924)	Rae, John	70-100	
Gordon, Elizabeth	Sheaf of Roses (1st, lg8vo, [72]p, ipcb, color)	Rand/McNally	(1915)	Martin, F.W.	40-60	*

AUTHOR	TITLE	PUBLISHER	DATE	ARTIST	PRICE	LC
Gordon, Elizabeth	Some Smiles (1st, 12mo, ibds, [29]p, color)	W.A. Wilde	(1911)	Ross, M.T.	40-60	
Gordon, Elizabeth	Tale of Johnny Mouse (1st, 12mo, ibds, unpag, color, pep)	Volland	(1920)	Enright, Maginel W.	80-120	
Gordon, Elizabeth	Turned-Intos (1st, 8vo, ipcb, unpag, color, pep)	Volland	(1920)	Scott, Janet L.	80-125	
Gordon, Elizabeth	Wild Flower Children (1st, lg8vo, ibds, [84]p, color, pep)	Volland	(1918)	Scott, Janet L.	160-250	
Gordon, Hampden C.	Flower Name Fancies (1st, 4to, 60p, green cl, 31 fp b/w)	L: John Lane	1918	Fauconnet, Guy P.	55-80	*
Gordon, Hampden C.	Golden Key (1st, 8vo, 223p, col frn, 5 fp b/w)	L: J. Murray	(1932)	Oldfield, M.	35-60	*
Gordon, Hampden C.	Lost Princess (1st, 8vo, 159p, 4cp)	L: J. Murray	(1933)	Dixon, George S.	40-70	*
Gordon, Hampden C.	Paradoc to the Rescue (1st, 8vo, 206p, col frn, fp b/w)	L: J. Murray	(1939)	Tozer, Katharine	40-65	*
Gordon, Hampden C.	Rhymes of the Red Triangle (1st, 8vo, ibds, [60]p, chromos)	J. Lane	[1918]	Dennys, Joyce	120-200	
Gordon, Hampden C.	Through the Enchanted Wood (1st, 8vo, blue cl, 174p, b/w)	L: Murray	1931	Patterson, Cora	30-50	
Gordon, Mary D.	Crystal Ball (1st, 8vo, 235p, 8cp, pep)	Little/Brown	1920	Gordon, Mary D.	25-40	
Gordon, Patricia	Boy Jones (1st, 8vo, red cl, 158p, 10pl, pep, DJ/2.00)	Viking	1943	Adams, Adrienne	45-60	
Gordon, Patricia	Witch of Scrapfaggot Green (1st, sm4to, ibds, 78p, 10 fp b/w, DJ/2.50)	Viking	1948	DuBois, W.P.	65-90	
Gordon, Samuel	Lesser Destinies (1st, sm8vo, 310p, teg, cvr by...)	Herbert Stone	1899	Hazenplug, Frank	30-50	
Gordon, Shirley	Green Hornet Lunchbox (1st {std}, 8vo, [31]p, color, DJ/3.75)	Houghton	(1970)	Graham, Margaret B.	30-45	*
Gorey, Edward	Blue Aspic (1st {std}, ob12mo, [64]p, ipcb, b/w, DJ/2.95)	NY: Meredith Pr.	(1968)	Gorey, Edward	120-200	
Gorey, Edward	Bug Book (1st {std}, 24mo, wraps, [32]p, color)	Looking Glass	(1959)	Gorey, Edward	500-800	R
Gorey, Edward	Doubtful Guest (1st {std}, ob8vo, ibds, [30]p, b/w, DJ/2.00)	Doubleday	1957	Gorey, Edward	200-300	
Gorey, Edward	Epiplectic Bicycle (1st, ob8vo, ibds, [64]p, fp b/w, DJ/3.00)	Dodd	(1969)	Gorey, Edward	90-140	
Gorey, Edward	Gilded Bat (1st {std}, ob12mo, [62]p, ibds, b/w, DJ/3.00)	Simon/Schuster	(1966)	Gorey, Edward	100-165	
Gorey, Edward	Listing Attic (1st {std}, sm8vo, [62]p, ibds, b/w, DJ/2.00)	Duell, Sloan	(1954)	Gorey, Edward	150-225	
Gorey, Edward	Object Lesson (1st {std}, ob8vo, unpag, tan bds, b/w, DJ/2.00)	Doubleday	1958	Gorey, Edward	200-300	
Gorey, Edward	Remembered Visit (1st {std}, 8vo, ibds, [64]p, b/w, DJ/2.50)	Simon/Schuster	(1965)	Gorey, Edward	100-165	
Gorey, Edward	Unstrung Harp (1st {std}-[1st bk.], 8vo, [62]p, ibds, b/w, DJ/2.00)	Duell, Sloan	(1953)	Gorey, Edward	200-300	
Gorey, Edward	Utter Zoo (1st {std}, sq12mo, unpag, ibds, b/w, DJ/3.95)	Meredith Press	(1967)	Gorey, Edward	120-200	
Gorey, Edward	Willowdale Handcar (1st, sq24mo, wraps, unpag, b/w)	Bobbs-Merrill	(1962)	Gorey, Edward	150-220	
Gorham, Maurice	Back to the Local (1st, 8vo, 126p, red/gilt, 21 b/w, DJ)	L: P. Marshall	1949	Ardizzone, Edward	80-120	
Gorham, Maurice	Londoners (1st, 8vo, 158p, brown bds, 24 b/w, DJ)	L: P. Marshall	(1951)	Ardizzone, Edward	70-100	
Gorham, Maurice	Showmen and Suckers (1st, 8vo, 262p, red bds, 35 b/w, DJ)	L: P. Marshall	(1951)	Ardizzone, Edward	80-120	
Gorham, Maurice	The Local (1st, 8vo, 51p, ipcb, 15 fp color)	L: Cassell	1939	Ardizzone, Edward	200-300	
Gorse, Golden	Moorland Mousie (1st AM, sm4to, 106p, 16pl)	Scribner	1929	Edwards, Lionel	45-70	
Goss, Charles F.	Little St. Sunshine (1st, sm8vo, green/gilt, 153p, 6cp)	Bowen-Merrill	(1902)	Keep, Virginia	25-40	
Gosse (intro)	Allies' Fairy Book (1st, 8vo, 121p, blue/gilt, 12cp)	L: Heinemann	(1916)	Rackham, Arthur	280-400	
Gosse, Edmund	In Russet & Silver (1st, 12mo, 159p, tan cl, cvr by...)	Stone/Kimball	1894	Bradley, Will	120-170	*
Gotch, Phyllis M.	Romance of a Boo-Bird Chick (1st, 8vo, ibds, 60p, 15 fp color)	L: R.B. Johnson	1903	Gotch, Phyllis M.	100-150	
Gotch, Phyllis M.	Tuffy and the Merboo (4to, ibds, fp color)	L: R.B. Johnson	[1904]	Unknown	140-200	*
Gottlieb, Suzanne	What is Red? (1st, sm4to, [19]p, fp color, DJ/2.95)	Lothrop, Lee	1961	Bobri, Vladimir	30-50	
Goudey, Alice	Butterfly Time (1st, sm4to, unpag, color, DJ/3.25)	Scribner	(1964)	Adams, Adrienne	40-65	
Goudey, Alice	Day We Saw the Sun Come Up (1st, 4to, [32]p, fp color, DJ/2.95, CH)	Scribner	(1961)	Adams, Adrienne	60-90	
Goudey, Alice	Graywings (1st, 8vo, [63]p, 1-color, DJ/2.95)	Scribner	1964	Nonnast, Marie	30-50	*
Goudey, Alice	Here Come the Bears! (1st, 12mo, 92p, blue cl, fp 1-color, DJ/2.25)	Scribner	(1954)	Mackenzie, Garry	30-50	R
Goudey, Alice	Houses from the Sea (1st, sm4to, [32]p, fp color, DJ/2.95, CH)	Scribner	(1959)	Adams, Adrienne	70-100	
Goudey, Alice	Smokey, the Well-Loved Kitten (1st, 8vo, 114p, b/w, DJ/2.50)	Lothrop, Lee	(1952)	Wohlberg, Meg	20-35	*
Goudey, Alice	Sunnyvale Fair (1st, 8vo, [62]p, fp 1-color, DJ/2.95)	Scribner	(1962)	Galdone, Paul	30-45	
Goudge, Elizabeth	Henrietta's House (1st, 8vo, 252p, green cl, b/w, DJ)	L: Hodder	1942	Steele, Lorna	140-200	
Goudge, Elizabeth	I Saw Three Ships (1st AM {std}, 8vo, 60p, b/w, DJ/3.95)	Coward	(1969)	Tomes, Margot	30-50	R
Goudge, Elizabeth	Linnets and Valderians (1st AM {std}, 8vo, 290p, b/w, DJ/3.95)	Coward	(1964)	Ribbons, Ian	50-80	
Goudge, Elizabeth	Little White Horse (1st, 12mo, gilt, 286p, 4cp, pep, CgM)	London U. Press	(1946)	Hodges, C. Walter	100-165	
Goudge, Elizabeth	Little White Horse (1st AM {std}, 8vo, 280p, blue cl, b/w, pep, DJ/2.50)	Coward	(1947)	Hodges, C. Walter	80-125	
Goudge, Elizabeth	Reward of Faith (1st AM, 8vo, blue cl, 186p, b/w, DJ/2.75)	Coward	(1950)	Unwin, Nora S.	30-50	
Goudge, Elizabeth	Sister of the Angels (1st AM, 8vo, blue/gilt, 154p, fp b/w, DJ/1.50)	Coward	(1939)	Hodges, C. Walter	30-50	
Goudge, Elizabeth	Smoky House (1st AM, 8vo, 286p, 6pl, DJ/2.00)	Coward	(1940)	Floethe, Richard	60-90	
Goudge, Elizabeth	Valley of Song (1st AM, 8vo, 281p, b/w, DJ/3.00)	Coward	(1952)	Floethe, Richard	50-85	
Gould, Elizabeth L.	Little Polly Prentiss (1st, sm8vo, 192p, 5pl)	Penn	1902	Waugh, Ida	30-50	
Gould, F.C.	Tales Told in the Zoo (1st, lg8vo, 136p, col frn, 5pl)	L: T.F. Unwin	1900	Gould, F. Carruthers	55-80	
Gould, Frederick J.	Children's Plutarch (1st, 8vo, 171p, 3pl)	Harper	1910	Crane, Walter	120-200	
Gould, Jean	Miss Emily (1st, 8vo, 220p, b/w, DJ/2.50)	Houghton	1946	Koering, Ursula	30-45	
Gould, Katherine C.	Crystal Rood (1st, sm8vo, 306p, cover by....)	NY: J. Lane	1924	Hazenplug, Frank	35-50	
Goulden, Shirley	Chinese Fairy Tales (1st, 4to, 58p, ibds, color)	Duell, Sloan	(1958)	Maraja	40-60	
Goulden, Shirley	Royal Reflections (1st, 12mo, 136p, ibds, 7 fp b/w, DJ)	L: Methuen	1956	Shepard, Ernest H.	55-80	
Govan, Christine	Carolina Caravan (1st, 8vo, 224p, uncut, 5 fp 1-color, DJ/2.00)	Houghton	1942	Blair, Helen	120-180	
Govan, Christine	Curious Clubhouse (1st {std}, 8vo, 159p, b/w, DJ/3.75)	World	(1967)	Shortall, Leonard	30-50	
Govan, Christine	Delectable Mountain (1st {std}, 8vo, 187p, b/w, DJ/2.95)	World	(1962)	Sherman, Theresa	25-40	
Govan, Christine	Judy and Chris (1st, 8vo, 210p, b/w, pep, DJ/2.00)	Houghton	1936	Caddy, Alice	150-220	
Govan, Christine	Mr. Hermit Miser & Neighborly Pumpkin (1st, 8vo, ibds, [46]p, col, DJ/1.75)	Aladdin	(1949)	Peck, Anne M.	70-100	
Govan, Christine	Mystery at Deserted Mill (1st, 8vo, 152p, b/w, DJ/2.50)	Sterling	1958	Chapman, Fred T.	120-180	
Govan, Christine	Mystery at Moccasin Bend (1st, 8vo, 191p, b/w, DJ/2.50)	Sterling	(1957)	Chapman, Fred T.	60-100	
Govan, Christine	Narcissus an' De Chillun (1st, 8vo, 226p, b/w, DJ/2.00)	Houghton	1938	Caddy, Alice	150-220	
Govan, Christine	Number 5 Hackberry Street (1st {std}, 8vo, 187p, b/w, DJ/3.50)	World	(1964)	Bacon, Peggy	30-50	
Govan, Christine	Phinny's Fine Summer (1st {std}, 8vo, 158p, b/w, DJ/3.75)	World	(1968)	Shortall, Leonard	25-40	
Govan, Christine	Pink Maple House (1st {std}, sm8vo, 283p, b/w, DJ/2.50)	Aladdin	1950	Sari	80-120	
Govan, Christine	Rachel Jackson, Tennessee Girl (1st {std}, 12mo, 192p, b/w, DJ/1.75)	Bobbs-Merrill	(1955)	James, Sandra	70-120	
Govan, Christine	Return to Hackberry Street (1st {std}, 8vo, 159p, b/w, DJ/3.95)	World	(1967)	Bacon, Peggy	25-40	
Govan, Christine	String & the No-Tail Cat (1st, 4to, 40p, 2-color, DJ/1.50)	Houghton	1939	Suba, Susanne	100-165	
Govan, Christine	Super Duper Car (1st, 8vo, green cl, 78p, b/w, pep, DJ/2.00)	Houghton	1952	Weil, Lisl	70-120	
Govan, Christine	Surprising Summer (1st {std}, sm8vo, 171p, b/w, DJ/2.25)	Aladdin	1951	Sari	80-120	
Govan, Christine	Sweet Possom Valley (1st, 8vo, 202p, b/w, pep, DJ/2.00)	Houghton	1940	Lee, Manning De V.	150-220	
Govan, Christine	Those Plummer Children (1st, 8vo, 196p, b/w, pep)	Houghton	1934	Caddy, Alice	140-200	

AUTHOR	TITLE	PUBLISHER	DATE	ARTIST	PRICE	LC
Govan, Christine	Tilly's Strange Secret (1st {std}, sm8vo, 184p, b/w, DJ/2.25)	Aladdin	1952	Sari	80-125	
Govan, Christine	Trash Pile Treasure (1st {std}, 8vo, 126p, b/w, DJ/4.50)	World	(1970)	Shortall, Leonard	25-40	
Govan, Christine	Willow Landing (1st {std}, 8vo, 190p, b/w, DJ/2.95)	World	1961	Stevens, Mary	30-50	
Gowans, Adam I.	Treasury of English Verse (1st, 8vo, 303p, green cl, 50pl, pep)	L: Gowans/Gray	1907	Reid, Stephen	80-120	*
Gower, Margaret L.	Fighting Six (1st, 8vo, 250p, b/w)	Harcourt	(1929)	Millar, H.R.	30-50	*
Grabianski, Janus	Grabianski's Cats (1st AM, ob4to, [32]p, color, cep, DJ/3.95)	F. Watts	1966	Grabianski, Janusz	40-70	
Grabo, Carl H.	Peter & the Princess (1st, sm4to, teg, gilt, p-o, 243p, 8cp, pep)	Reilly/Lee	(1920)	Neill, John R.	250-400	
Graham, Al	Down with Dinosaurs! (1st {std}, 12mo, 61p, b/w, DJ/2.50)	Duell, Sloan	(1963)	Palazzo, Tony	20-30	
Graham, Al	Mouse with a Small Guitar (1st, lg8vo, 35p, grey cl, color, pep, DJ/1.50)	Welch Pub. Co.	(1947)	Palazzo, Tony	50-80	
Graham, Al	Rhymes of Squire O'Squirrel (1st {std}, 4to, 60p, b/w, DJ/2.50)	Duell, Sloan	(1963)	Palazzo, Tony	30-45	
Graham, Al	Songs for a Small Guitar (1st {std}, 4to, ibds, 59p, 1-color, DJ/2.50)	Duell, Sloan	(1962)	Palazzo, Tony	30-45	
Graham, Al	Timothy Turtle (1st, lg4to, [30]p, color, pep, DJ/2.00, CH)	Welch Pub. Co.	(1946)	Palazzo, Tony	80-120	*
Graham, Eleanor	Night Adventures of Alexis (1st, sm4to, 34p, 9cp)	L: Faber/Gwyer	1925	Langlands, Winifred	50-80	*
Graham, Harry	Deportmental Ditties (1st, 4to, 127p, b/w)	L: Mills & Boon	(1909)	Baumer, Lewis	35-60	
Graham, Harry	Deportmental Ditties (1st AM, 16mo, 134p, 3pl)	Duffield	1909	Grant, Gordon	30-60	*
Graham, Harry	Misrepresentative Women (1st, 12mo, ibds, 120p, 12pl)	Duffield	1906	Groesbeck, Dan S.	25-45	
Graham, John	Crowd of Cows (1st {std}, 4to, bds, [32]p, color, DJ/3.50)	Harcourt	(1968)	Rojankovsky, Feodor	30-50	
Graham, Lorenz	How God Fix Jonah (1st, 8vo, 171p, fp b/w, pep, DJ/2.50)	Reynal/Hitchcock	(1946)	Calapai, Letterio	50-80	
Graham, Lorenz	I, Momolu (1st, 8vo, 226p, b/w, DJ/4.00)	Crowell	(1966)	Biggers, John	70-100	
Graham, Lynda	Pinky Marie (1st, 4to, ibds, [16]p, color)	Saalfield	1939	Kirn, Ann	30-50	
Graham, Margaret B.	Be Nice to Spiders (1st, lg8vo, [32]p, 3-color, cep, DJ/2.95)	Harper	(1967)	Graham, Margaret B.	30-45	
Graham, Mary N.	Fifty Songs for Boys & Girls (1st, lg ob8vo, 60p, 2-color)	Whitman	(1935)	Scott, Janet L.	80-120	*
Graham, Ruth M.	Happy Sound (1st {std}, 4to, [32]p, color, DJ/4.95)	Follett	(1970)	Zander, Hans	30-50	*
Graham, Shirley	Story of Phillis Wheatley (1st, 8vo, 176p, b/w, pep, DJ/2.75)	J. Messner	(1949)	Burns, Robert	30-50	*
Graham, Stephen	New York Nights (1st, 8vo, 288p, bds, 14 b/w)	Doran	(1927)	Wiese, Kurt	40-60	*
Graham, Tom	Hike & the Aeroplane (1st, sm8vo, 275p, 4pl)	Stokes	(1912)	Hutchins, Arthur	1200-2000	R
Grahame, Kenneth	Bertie's Escapade (1st, 12mo, pink bds, 42p, b/w, DJ)	L: Methuen	(1949)	Shepard, Ernest H.	80-120	
Grahame, Kenneth	Bertie's Escapade (1st AM, sm8vo, 41p, grey cl, b/w, DJ/1.50)	Lippincott	(1949)	Shepard, Ernest H.	60-90	R
Grahame, Kenneth	Dream Days (1st, sq8vo, teg, 228p, gilt, 9pl, pep)	L: John Lane	(1902)	Parrish, Maxfield	125-200	
Grahame, Kenneth	Dream Days (1st, 8vo, 192p, 4cp, pep)	L: John Lane	1922	Lenski, Lois	100-165	
Grahame, Kenneth	Dream Days (1st AM, 8vo, 172p, gilt, pep)	Dodd	1931	Shepard, Ernest H.	40-60	
Grahame, Kenneth	Golden Age (1st, 8vo, red/gilt, 252p, teg, 19pl, pep)	J. Lane	1900	Parrish, Maxfield	150-220	
Grahame, Kenneth	Golden Age (2nd, 8vo, 252p, 18pl)	J. Lane	1904	Parrish, Maxfield	80-135	
Grahame, Kenneth	Golden Age (1st, sm4to, gilt, 243p, uncut, 19cp)	L: John Lane	1914	Moony, R.J.E.	100-150	
Grahame, Kenneth	Golden Age (1st [1st bk.], 8vo, uncut, 199p, 4 ticp)	L: John Lane	1921	Lenski, Lois	100-160	
Grahame, Kenneth	Golden Age (1st, 12mo, 166p, beige/gilt, t.e. pink, b/w, DJ)	L: John Lane	(1928)	Shepard, Ernest H.	120-185	
Grahame, Kenneth	Golden Age (1st AM, sm8vo, 170p, b/w, pep)	Dodd	1929	Shepard, Ernest H.	75-100	
Grahame, Kenneth	Pagan Papers (1st, 12mo, bds, 165p, teg, title page by...)	Herbert Stone	1894	Beardsley, Aubrey	120-180	R
Grahame, Kenneth	Reluctant Dragon (1st, 8vo, [57]p, cloth, b/w, DJ/1.25)	Holiday House	(1938)	Shepard, Ernest H.	60-100	
Grahame, Kenneth	Reluctant Dragon (1st, 4to, [72]p, ibds, color, pep)	Garden City	(1941)	Disney Studios	250-350	
Grahame, Kenneth	The Headswoman (1st AM, 8vo, 53p, 8cp, DJ)	Dodd	1922	Foster, Marcia L.	70-100	
Grahame, Kenneth	Wind in the Willows (1st AM, 8vo, green/gilt, 302p, teg, frn by...)	Scribner	1908	Robertson, W.G.	600-800	
Grahame, Kenneth	Wind in the Willows (1st, sm8vo, 302p, teg, blue/gilt, frn by)	L: Methuen	(1908)	Robertson, W.G.	1200-2000	R
Grahame, Kenneth	Wind in the Willows (1st, 8vo, blue/gilt, teg, 351p, 10cp, pep)	Scribner	1913	Bransom, Paul	160-240	
Grahame, Kenneth	Wind in the Willows (1st, 8vo, gilt, 302p, p-o, 12cp, pep)	Scribner	1922	Barnhart, Nancy	120-180	
Grahame, Kenneth	Wind in the Willows (1st, 8vo, 247p, blue/gilt, teg, 20 fp 1-color)	L: Methuen	(1927)	Payne, Wyndham	125-200	
Grahame, Kenneth	Wind in the Willows (1st, 12mo, green/gilt, 312p, b/w, pep)	L: Methuen	(1931)	Shepard, Ernest H.	200-300	
Grahame, Kenneth	Wind in the Willows (1st AM, 8vo, 312p, blue/gilt, b/w, pep)	Scribner	1933	Shepard, Ernest H.	150-225	
Grahame, Kenneth	Wind in the Willows (1st {this pub}, lg8vo, 190p, 12cp, box)	Heritage Press	(1940)	Rackham, Arthur	120-170	
Grahame, Kenneth	Wind in the Willows (1st, 8vo, 255p, gilt, 16 fp color, pep, DJ/4.95)	World	(1966)	Tudor, Tasha	140-200	
Gramatky, Hardie	Bolivar (1st, lg8vo, 62p, color, pep, DJ/2.95)	Putnam	(1961)	Gramatky, Hardie	30-50	
Gramatky, Hardie	Creeper's Jeep (1st, lg8vo, [64]p, color, DJ/2.25)	Putnam	(1948)	Gramatky, Hardie	80-140	
Gramatky, Hardie	Happy's Christmas (1st, 8vo, 58p, fp color, DJ/4.50)	Putnam	(1970)	Gramatky, Hardie	30-50	
Gramatky, Hardie	Hercules (1st, sm4to, [72]p, red cl, color, pep, DJ/2.00)	Putnam	(1940)	Gramatky, Hardie	100-160	
Gramatky, Hardie	Homer & the Circus Train (1st, lg8vo, [62]p, pep, color, DJ/2.75)	Putnam	(1957)	Gramatky, Hardie	50-80	
Gramatky, Hardie	Little Toot (1st, sq8vo, [93]p, pep, color, DJ/1.50)	Putnam	1939	Gramatky, Hardie	150-220	R
Gramatky, Hardie	Little Toot on the Grand Canal (1st, 8vo, 86p, fp color, DJ/3.95)	Putnam	(1968)	Gramatky, Hardie	30-50	
Gramatky, Hardie	Little Toot on the Thames (1st, sm8vo, 87p, fp color, DJ/3.50)	Putnam	(1964)	Gramatky, Hardie	60-90	
Gramatky, Hardie	Loopy (1st, 4to, [72]p, color, pep, DJ/2.25)	Putnam	(1941)	Gramatky, Hardie	70-120	
Gramatky, Hardie	Nikos and the Sea God (1st, lg8vo, [64]p, fp color, DJ/3.50)	Putnam	(1963)	Gramatky, Hardie	30-50	
Gramatky, Hardie	Sparky: Story of a Little Trolley Car (1st, 8vo, 66p, color, pep, DJ/2.50)	Putnam	(1952)	Gramatky, Hardie	50-80	
Grant, Bruce	Zachary, the Governor's Pig (1st {std}, lg8vo, 139p, b/w, DJ/2.95)	World	(1960)	Frankenberg, Rbt.	30-45	
Grant, George H.	Boy Overboard! (1st {std}, 8vo, 199p, b/w, DJ/3.00)	Little/Brown	(1961)	Spier, Peter E.	25-40	
Grant, Gordon	Greasy Luck (1st, 4to, white cl, 128p, b/w, pep)	NY: W.F. Payson	(1932)	Grant, Gordon	40-60	
Grant, Gordon	Sail Ho! (1st, 4to, 126p, 1-color, pep)	NY: W.F. Payson	(1931)	Grant, Gordon	50-80	
Grant, Gordon	Secret Voyage (1st, lg8vo, 60p, b/w, DJ/1.50)	Wm. Morrow	1942	Grant, Gordon	30-50	
Grant, Gordon	Ships Under Sail (1st, lg4to, ibds, 25p, color, pep, DJ/1.00)	Garden City	(1939)	Grant, Gordon	35-60	
Grant, Gordon	Story of the Ship (1st, folio, ipcb, [48]p, color, pep)	McLoughlin	1919	Grant, Gordon	55-90	
Grant, Joseph C.	Baby Weems (1st {std}, lg8vo, [64]p, blue cl, 2-color, pep, DJ/1.00)	Doubleday/Doran	1941	Disney Studios	80-140	
Grant, Robert	Art of Living (1st, 8vo, 353p, green/gilt, teg, cvr by...)	Scribner	1895	Armstrong, Margaret	30-50	
Grant, Robert	Bachelor's Christmas (1st, 12mo, olive/gilt, teg, 309p, cvr by...)	Scribner	1895	Armstrong, Margaret	35-60	
Grant, Robert	Jack Hall (1st, sm8vo, blue/gilt, 394p, b/w, PPP)	Jordan Marsh	1888	Attwood, F.G.	100-185	R
Grant, Robert	The Undercurrent (1st, 12mo, blue cl, 480p, cvr by...)	Scribner	1904	Armstrong, Margaret	30-60	
Grant, Robert	Unleavened Bread (1st, 8vo, green/gilt, 431p, cvr by...)	Scribner	1900	Armstrong, Margaret	30-50	
Grant, Vernon	Flibbity Jibbit & the Key Keeper (1st, 12mo, ipcb, [32]p, color)	Junket Folks	1943	Grant, Vernon	50-80	
Grant, Vernon	Tinker Tim the Toy Maker (1st, lg4to, ibds, 29p, color, pep)	Whitman	1934	Grant, Vernon	100-165	R
Granville, Austyn	Fallen Race (1st, 8vo, blue/gilt, 352p, 5pl)	F.T. Neely	(1892)	Mason, Edward	200-300	
Gratacap, L.P.	Mayor of New York (1st, sm8vo, red/gilt, 471p, 4pl)	Dillingham	(1910)	Chase, Joseph C.	70-100	

AUTHOR	TITLE	PUBLISHER	DATE	ARTIST	PRICE	LC
Gratacap, L.P.	New Northland (1st, sm8vo, 391p, blue/gilt, 16pl)	NY: T. Benton	1915	Operti, Albert	120-200	
Grattan, Madeleine	Jexium Island (1st, 8vo, blue cl, 184p, b/w, pep, DJ/2.75)	Viking	(1957)	DuBois, W.P.	50-85	
Graves, Alfred P.	Irish Fairy Book (1st, 8vo, 410p, col frn, 11pl, pep)	L: T.F. Unwin	(1909)	Denham, George	80-140	
Graves, Alfred P.	Irish Fairy Book (1st AM, gilt, 310p, col frn, 13pl, pep)	Stokes	[1910]	Denham, George	80-125	
Graves, Alfred P.	Irish Fairy Book (1st [this pub.], 8vo, 310p, col frn, b/w)	L: A&C Black	(1938)	Denham, George	35-50	
Graves, Elizabeth	Hey, Horses! (1st, lg8vo, 42p, color, pep, DJ)	Garrard Pub.	(1965)	Palazzo, Tony	25-40	
Graves, Robert	Ann at Highwood Hall (1st AM {std}, lg8vo, 48p, color, DJ/2.95)	Doubleday	(1966)	Ardizzone, Edward	45-70	
Graves, Robert	Big Green Book (1st {std}, 4to, [32]p, green cl, fp b/w)	Crowell-Collier	(1962)	Sendak, Maurice	100-170	
Graves, Robert	Big Green Book (1st {this fmt} {std}, 8vo, [63]p, fp b/w, DJ/3.95)	Crowell-Collier	(1968)	Sendak, Maurice	60-100	
Graves, Robert	Greek Gods and their Heroes (1st {std}, lg8vo, 160p, b/w, DJ/2.95)	Doubleday	1960	Davis, Dimitris	30-50	
Graves, Robert	Penny Fiddle (1st AM {std}, lg8vo, 62p, green cl, fp 2-color, DJ/2.50)	Doubleday	(1960)	Ardizzone, Edward	60-90	
Graves, Robert	Penny Fiddle (1st {std}, lg8vo, gilt, 64p, 2-color, DJ)	L: Cassell	(1960)	Ardizzone, Edward	80-125	
Graves, Robert	Poor Boy Who Followed his Star (1st AM {std}, lg8vo, 43p, b/w, DJ/3.50)	Doubleday	1961	Meyer-Wallace, A.	70-120	
Graves, Robert	Two Wise Children (1st {std}, 8vo, [32]p, b/w, DJ/2.75)	Harlin Quist	(1966)	Pinto, Ralph	50-80	
Gray, Eliz. J.	Adam of the Road (1st, lg8vo, 317p, green cl, 23pl, pep, DJ/2.00, NM)	Viking	1942	Lawson, Robert	80-145	R
Gray, Eliz. J.	Beppy Marlowe of Charles Town (1st, 8vo, 281p, color, pep, DJ/2.00)	Viking	1936	Barton, Loren	30-50	*
Gray, Eliz. J.	Cheerful Heart (1st, 8vo, 176p, b/w, pep, DJ/2.75)	Viking	(1959)	Mizumura, Kazue	40-65	
Gray, Eliz. J.	Fair Adventure (1st, 8vo, 298p, b/w, pep, DJ/2.00)	Viking	1940	Reischer, Alice K.	25-45	
Gray, Eliz. J.	I Will Adventure (1st, 8vo, 208p, fp b/w, pep, DJ/4.00)	Viking	(1962)	Bell, Corydon	25-40	
Gray, Eliz. J.	Meggy McIntosh (1st {std}, 8vo, 274p, col frn, pep, NH)	Doubleday/Doran	1930	DeAngeli, Marguerite	60-90	
Gray, Eliz. J.	Meredith's Ann (1st {std}, sm8vo, yellow cl, 267p, col frn, pep)	Doubleday/Page	1927	Cutts, G.B.	30-50	
Gray, Eliz. J.	Penn (1st, 8vo, red cl, 298p, maps, b/w, DJ/2.50, NH)	Viking	1938	Whitney, George	50-85	
Gray, Eliz. J.	Sandy (1st, sm8vo, 233p, DJ/2.00, col frn by...)	Viking	1945	Hallock, Ruth M.	25-40	
Gray, Eliz. J.	Tangle Garden (1st {std}, sm8vo, 327p, pep, col frn by...)	Doubleday/Doran	1928	Cutts, G.B.	25-40	*
Gray, Eliz. J.	Tilly-Tod (1st {std}, sm8vo, 173p, blue cl, col frn, b/w, pep)	Doubleday/Doran	1929	Frye, Mary H.	35-60	*
Gray, Eliz. J.	Young Walter Scott (1st, 8vo, 239p, pep, port. frn, DJ/2.00, NH)	Viking	1935	Seredy, Kate	60-100	*
Gray, Maxwell	Great Refusal (1st, sm8vo, brown/gilt, 438p, cvr by...)	Appleton	1906	Armstrong, Margaret	50-80	
Gray, Nicholas S.	Apple Stone (1st AM {std}, 8vo, 229p, b/w, DJ/4.95)	Meredith Press	(1969)	Keeping, Charles	30-45	
Gray, Nicholas S.	Down in the Cellar (1st, sm8vo, 203p, cloth, b/w, DJ)	L: Dobson	(1961)	Ardizzone, Edward	40-65	
Gray, Nicholas S.	Grimbold's other World (1st AM {std}, 8vo, 184p, b/w, DJ/3.95)	Meredith Press	(1968)	Keeping, Charles	30-50	
Gray, P.L.	In a Car of Gold (1st, 12mo, 156p, brown/gilt, 6pl)	Saalfield	1902	Gutman, Bernard	30-50	
Gray, Thomas	Elegy in a Country Church Yard (4to, gilt, unpag, teg, uncut, 8 ticp)	L: Medici	(1931)	Adams, Frank	70-120	
Gray, Thomas	Elegy in a Country Church Yard (1st, 4to, 75p, ibds, 18pl)	Dutton	(1931)	Vassos, John	80-130	
Gray, William C.	Musings by Campfire & Wayside (1st, 8vo, 337p, black/gilt, cvr by...)	Revell	1902	Hazenplug, Frank	50-80	
Green, Adam	Funny Bunny Factory (1st, folio, [26]p, ibds, color, DJ/1.00)	Grosset/Dunlap	1950	Weisgard, Leonard	50-80	
Green, Allen A.	Good Fairy & the Bunnies (1st, ob4to, ibds, 140p, 11cp)	McClurg	1906	Richardson, F.	200-300	
Green, Anna K.	Dark Hollow (1st, sm8vo, 381p, green cl, 4pl)	Dodd	1914	Fogarty, Thomas	50-80	*
Green, Anna K.	Doctor, his Wife and the Clock (1st, 8vo, 131p, wraps, cvr by...)	L: T.F. Unwin	1895	Beardsley, Aubrey	250-400	
Green, Anna K.	Initials Only (1st, 12mo, 356p, col frn)	Dodd	1911	Keller, Arthur I.	60-90	
Green, Anna K.	Mayor's Wife (1st, sm8vo, gilt, 389p, p-o, b/w)	Bobbs-Merrill	(1907)	Stephens, Alice B.	40-70	
Green, Anna K.	Woman in the Alcove (1st, 12mo, beige/gilt, 372p, 5pl)	Bobbs-Merrill	(1906)	Keller, Arthur I.	45-70	
Green, Louisa M.	Brother of the Birds (1st AM, 4to, 123p, purple/gilt, 21 tipl)	McKay	(1929)	DeMonvel, M.B.	80-125	
Green, Margaret (ed)	Big Book of Animal Fables (1st AM {std}, lg8vo, 240p, color, DJ/4.95)	F. Watts	(1965)	Grabianski, Janusz	30-50	
Green, Mary M.	Everybody Eats (1st, lg8vo, spiral bds, [20]p, color)	W.R. Scott	1946	Glannon, Edward J.	35-50	
Green, Mary M.	Everybody Eats (1st [rev. ed.], 8vo, ibds, [20]p, fp color, DJ/1.00)	Young Scott	1950	Bloch, Lucienne	100-165	
Green, Mary M.	Everybody has a House (1st, lg8vo, spiral-bound, [20]p, color)	W.R. Scott	1944	Bendick, Jeanne	60-90	
Green, Mary M.	Is it Hard? Is it Easy? (1st, sq8vo, ibds, [20]p, 3-color, DJ/1.00)	W.R. Scott	1948	Bloch, Lucienne	60-100	
Green, Roger L.	Modern Fairy Stories (1st AM {std}, 8vo, 270p, 8cp, DJ/2.95)	Dent/Dutton	(1955)	Shepard, Ernest H.	75-100	*
Greenaway, Kate	A Apple Pie (1st, ob4to, green ibds, [44]p, A.E. Red, color, cep)	L: Routledge	[1886]	Greenaway, Kate	300-500	
Greenaway, Kate	Greenaway's Babies (12mo, linen, 12p, color)	Saalfield	1907	Greenaway, Kate	120-180	
Greenaway, Kate	Kate Greenaway's Alphabet (1st, 48mo, ibds, [32]p, color)	L: Routledge	[1885]	Greenaway, Kate	200-300	
Greenaway, Kate	Kate Greenaway's Birthday Book (1st, 24mo, beige cl, color)	L: Routledge	[1880]	Greenaway, Kate	200-300	
Greenaway, Kate	Kate Greenaway's Book of Games (1st, lg sq8vo, ipcb, 64p, 24cp, cep)	L: Routledge	[1889]	Greenaway, Kate	200-300	
Greenaway, Kate	Language of Flowers (1st, 16mo, green ibds, 80p, color)	L: Routledge	[1884]	Greenaway, Kate	250-400	
Greenaway, Kate	Marigold Garden (1st, 4to, green ibds, 60p, color)	L: Routledge	[1885]	Greenaway, Kate	250-350	
Greenaway, Kate	Painting Book (1st, lg8vo, 80p, wraps)	L: Routledge	[1884]	Greenaway, Kate	250-350	
Greenaway, Kate	Queen Victoria's Jubilee Garland (1st, ob8vo, 127p, wraps, AEG, color)	L: Routledge	1887	Greenaway, Kate	300-400	
Greenaway, Kate	Trot's Journey (1st, p-o, 8vo, 79p)	Worthington	(1882)	Greenaway, Kate	100-160	
Greenaway, Kate	Under the Window (1st, lg8vo, green ibds, 64p, color, cep)	L: Routledge	[1878]	Greenaway, Kate	350-500	
Greenaway, Kate	Under the Window (sq8vo, green ibds, 63p, color)	McLoughlin	[1879]	Greenaway, Kate	250-350	
Greenberg, Polly	Oh Lord, I Wish I was a Buzzard (1st, 4to, [31]p, color, DJ/4.50)	Macmillan	(1968)	Aliki	30-50	*
Greene, Constance	Girl Called Al (1st, 8vo, 127p, fp b/w, DJ/3.95)	Viking	(1969)	Barton, Byron	20-35	*
Greene, Ellin	Pumpkin Giant (1st, lg8vo, [40]p, fp 1-color, cep, DJ/3.95)	Lothrop, Lee	(1970)	Hyman, Trina S.	40-65	
Greene, Graham	Little Horse Bus (1st, sq8vo, 35p, gilt, color, DJ)	L: Parrish	1952	Craigie, Dorothy	300-450	
Greene, Graham	Little Steamroller (1st, sq8vo, color, DJ)	L: Parrish	1953	Craigie, Dorothy	300-450	
Greene, Graham	Little Steamroller (1st AM, 8vo, 33p, blue cl, color, DJ/2.00)	Lothrop, Lee	1955	Craigie, Dorothy	200-300	
Greene, Graham	Little Train (1st, ob8vo, 42p, color, DJ)	L: Eyre/Spotts.	1946	Craigie, Dorothy	300-450	
Greene, Grahame	Little Train (1st AM, 8vo, 36p, color, DJ/2.00)	Lothrop, Lee	1958	Craigie, Dorothy	200-300	
Greene, Harry P.	Pilot & Other Stories (1st, 8vo, 229p, 8cp)	Macmillan	1916	Ford, H.J.	120-200	
Greene, Jean	Forgetful Elephant (1st {std}, 4to, ipcb, [32]p, color, pep, DJ/1.00)	McKay	(1945)	Gergely, Tibor	60-90	
Greene, Mrs.	Grey House on the Hill (1st, sm8vo, pink/gilt, 205p, 8cp)	L: Nelson	[1903]	Rackham, Arthur	200-300	
Greene, Roberta	Two and Me Makes Three (1st, 4to, unpag, color, DJ)	Crowell	(1970)	Galdone, Paul	30-50	*
Greene, Sarah P.M.	Deacon Lysander (1st, 12mo, teg, 223p, red/gilt, 4pl)	Baker/Taylor	(1904)	Peck, Henry J.	20-35	
Greene, Sarah P.M.	Power Lot (1st, sm8vo, teg, 396p, 5pl)	Baker/Taylor	1906	Levy, Alex O.	25-40	
Greene, Ward	Lady and the Tramp (1st, 8vo, 139p, b/w, DJ/2.95)	Simon/Schuster	(1953)	Rinaldi, Joe G.	150-220	*
Greener, Leslie	Moon Ahead (1st, 8vo, green cl, 256p, fp b/w, pep, DJ/2.50)	Viking	1951	DuBois, W.P.	30-50	
Greenslet, Ferris	Quest of the Holy Grail (1st, 4to, 78p, gilt, teg, uncut, 26pl)	Curtis/Cameron	1902	Abbey, Edwin A.	160-240	
Greer, Blanche	Thunder's Tail (1st, 4to, ipcb, [24]p, 1-color, DJ/1.00)	Coward	1944	Greer, Blanche	40-70	

AUTHOR: 90

AUTHOR	TITLE	PUBLISHER	DATE	ARTIST	PRICE	LC
Grego, Joseph	Cruikshank's Water Colours (1st, 4to, gilt, teg, 326p, 67cp)	L: A&C Black	1903	Cruikshank, George	200-300	
Gregor, Arthur	Animal Babies (1st, 4to, [37]p, DJ/2.75, b/w, NYTBI, photos by…)	Harper	1959	Ylla	30-50	*
Gregor, Arthur	Does Poppy Live Here? (1st, 4to, [34]p, fp color, pep, DJ/2.50)	Lothrop, Lee	1957	Duvoisin, Roger	30-50	
Gregory, Horace	Alphabet for Joanna (1st {std}, 24mo, [24]p, color, DJ/2.50)	Holt, Rinehart	(1963)	Bryson, Bernarda	30-50	
Gregory, L.F.	Mama Nelly & I (1st, 4to, p-o, 167p, green cl, 5cp)	Stern	1908	Evans, Grace	120-180	
Gregory, Lady Isabella	Golden Apple (1st AM, 8vo, 117p, tan cl, 8cp)	Putnam	1916	Gregory, Margaret	120-180	*
Gretz, Susanna	Teddybears 1 to 10 (1st, sm ob4to, [23]p, color, DJ/2.95)	Follett	1969	Gretz, Susanna	30-50	*
Grey, Eve	Elsa's Secret (1st {std}, 8vo, 174p, b/w, DJ/2.25)	Doubleday	1948	Howe, Gertrude	60-100	*
Grey, Sydney	Story-Land (sq8vo, 111p, ibds, 32 color)	L: R.T.S.	(1884)	Barnes, Robert	100-145	
Grey, Zane	Desert Gold (1st, 12mo, 325p, gilt, p-o, 4pl)	Harper	1913	Duer, Douglas	150-225	
Grey, Zane	Don: Story of Lion Dog (1st {std}, 12mo, 69p, col frn, 4pl, pep)	Harper	1928	Wiese, Kurt	250-400	
Grey, Zane	Last of the Plainsmen (1st, 8vo, 314p, b/w, pl)	McClurg	1908	(Photos)	400-650	
Grey, Zane	Light of Western Stars (1st, sm8vo, 389p, gilt, col frn)	Harper	1914	Unknown	125-180	
Grey, Zane	Riders of the Purple Sage (1st, 12mo, tan/gilt, 335p, p-o, 4pl)	Harper	1912	Duer, Douglas	500-700	
Grey, Zane	Spirit of the Border (1st, 12mo, 266p, blue cl, 4 b/w)	A.L. Burt	(1906)	Davis, J. Watson	250-400	
Grey, Zane	Tappan's Burro (1st {std}, lg8vo, gilt, 253p, p-o, 7cp)	Harper	(1923)	Chapman/Street	250-450	
Grey, Zane	The Shortstop (1st, sm8vo, green cl, 310p, 6pl)	McClurg	1909	DeLay, H.S.	800-1200	
Grey, Zane	Wanderer of the Wasteland (1st, sm8vo, red cl, 419p, 3pl)	Harper	(1923)	Dunton, W. Herbert	120-200	
Grey, Zane	Wolf-Tracker (1st, 12mo, orange cl, 98p, col frn, b/w, pep)	Harper	1930	Wiese, Kurt	150-220	
Gridley, Marion	Indians of Yesterday (1st, lg4to, ibds, 63p, 6 fp color, pep, DJ/1.00)	Donohue	(1940)	Lone Wolf	50-80	
Grierson, Eliz. W.	Children's Tales from Scottish Ballads (1st, 4to, 326p, teg, 12cp)	L: A&C Black	1906	Stewart, Allan	140-200	*
Grierson, Eliz. W.	Scottish Fairy Book (1st, 8vo, 384p, gilt, col frn, b/w, pep)	L: T.F. Unwin	1910	Williams, Morris M.	70-120	
Grierson, Eliz. W.	Vivian's Lesson (1st, 12mo, 292p, gilt, 10pl)	L: Chambers	1907	Cowham, Hilda	40-65	
Grifalconi, Ann	City Rhythms (1st {std}, 4to, ibds, [32]p, color, DJ/4.95)	Bobbs-Merrill	(1965)	Grifalconi, Ann	50-80	
Grifalconi, Ann	Toy Trumpet (1st {std}, 4to, [32]p, color, DJ/4.95)	Bobbs-Merrill	(1968)	Grifalconi, Ann	30-50	
Griffen, Elizabeth	Dog's Book of Bugs (1st {std}, ob8vo, 63p, b/w, DJ, NYTBI)	Atheneum	1967	Parnall, Peter	30-50	*
Griffiths, Helen	The Greyhound (1st AM, {std}, 8vo, 180p, b/w, DJ/3.25)	Doubleday	(1966)	Ambrus, Victor	25-40	
Griggs, Mary	Yellow Cat (1st, 8vo, 110p, yellow cl, 6 doub pg cp)	L: H. Milford	(1936)	Morton-Sale, J.	65-90	
Grimalkin	Cats! (1st, 4to, blue cl, 47p, color)	L: Sands	[1901]	Wain, Louis	450-650	
Grimm Bros.	Bremen Town Musicians (1st, sm ob4to, 32p, 2-color, DJ/3.75)	McGraw-Hill	(1968)	Galdone, Paul	30-50	
Grimm Bros.	Fairy Tales (1st, 4to, ibds)	Worthington	(1888)	Crane, Walter	160-240	
Grimm Bros.	Fairy Tales (1st, sm8vo, 464p, col frn, pep)	L: Freemantle	1900	Rackham, Arthur	120-200	*
Grimm Bros.	Fairy Tales (1st, lg8vo, 305p, 12 illus)	L: Sands	1902	Hassall, John	75-100	*
Grimm Bros.	Fairy Tales (1st, 8vo, 511p, cvr by….)	L: Routledge	(1904)	King, Jessie	120-160	
Grimm Bros.	Fairy Tales (1st, 8vo, 511p, red cl, 4cp)	L: Routledge	(1904)	Wehnert, Edward H.	120-160	
Grimm Bros.	Fairy Tales (1st, 8vo, 336p, 20cp)	L: Blackie	[1905]	Stratton, Helen	200-300	
Grimm Bros.	Fairy Tales (1st, 32mo, gilt, 127p, ibds, fp color, pep)	Reilly/Britton	1905	Unknown	200-300	
Grimm Bros.	Fairy Tales (1st, 8vo, 408p)	L: J. Nisbet	1906	Dudley, Ambrose	80-125	*
Grimm Bros.	Fairy Tales (1st, 8vo, 336p, 16cp)	L: Cassell	1908	Monsell, J.R.	100-160	*
Grimm Bros.	Fairy Tales (1st, 4to, 117p, p-o, brown cl, 6cp)	Stern	1909	Betts, Ethel F.	200-300	
Grimm Bros.	Fairy Tales (1st, sm4to, 325p, gilt, 40 ticp, pep)	L: Constable	1909	Rackham, Arthur	800-1100	
Grimm Bros.	Fairy Tales (1st AM, 4to, ibds, gilt, 325p, 40 ticp)	Doubleday/Page	1909	Rackham, Arthur	700-900	
Grimm Bros.	Fairy Tales (1st, 4to, gilt, p-o, teg, 255p, 12cp)	L: Richards	1909	Sowerby, Millicent	250-400	
Grimm Bros.	Fairy Tales (1st, 8vo, 356p, gilt, p-o, pep, 4cp)	L: Nister	[1910]	Robinson, Charles	220-315	
Grimm Bros.	Fairy Tales (1st AM, 8vo, 255p, 12cp, dep)	Stokes	(1910)	Sowerby, Millicent	200-300	
Grimm Bros.	Fairy Tales (1st, 8vo, 331p, cream cl, 12cp)	L: A&C Black	(1911)	Folkard, Charles	100-170	*
Grimm Bros.	Fairy Tales (1st, sm sq4to, 275p, p-o, 11cp, 7pl, pep, WS)	Rand/McNally	(1913)	Dunlap, Hope	75-100	
Grimm Bros.	Fairy Tales (1st, lg8vo, 346p, 23 ticp)	L: Hodder	(1913)	Pocock, Noel	200-300	
Grimm Bros.	Fairy Tales (1st AM, 4to, blue/gilt, 346p, 23 ticp)	Doran	[1913]	Pocock, Noel	200-300	
Grimm Bros.	Fairy Tales (1st, lg8vo, 275p, p-o, 12cp)	Rand/McNally	(1913)	Winter, Milo	80-140	
Grimm Bros.	Fairy Tales (1st AM, 4to, 136p, blue/gilt, 12cp)	McKay	[1914]	Attwell, Mabel L.	180-250	
Grimm Bros.	Fairy Tales (1st, lg8vo, 419p, p-o, gilt, 11cp)	Cupples/Leon	(1914)	Gruelle, Johnny	350-500	
Grimm Bros.	Fairy Tales (1st, 8vo, 333p, p-o, 20cp)	L: Harrap	(1914)	Orr, Monro S.	80-130	
Grimm Bros.	Fairy Tales (1st, 8vo, 443p, b/w)	Harper	(1917)	Rhead, Louis	40-60	*
Grimm Bros.	Fairy Tales (1st, lg8vo, 308p, p-o, 12cp, pep, SC)	Scribner	1920	Abbott, Elenore P.	120-200	
Grimm Bros.	Fairy Tales (1st, 8vo, ibds, 6cp)	Donohue	(1920)	Burd, Clara M.	35-60	
Grimm Bros.	Fairy Tales (4to, 229p, p-o, 24cp, pep)	Donohue	(1920)	Lee, Ella D.	90-140	*
Grimm Bros.	Fairy Tales (8vo, 336p, green cl, 29cp)	Dodge	[1920]	Stratton, Helen	100-150	
Grimm Bros.	Fairy Tales (1st, lg8vo, 344p, 48cp)	L: Ward Lock	1920	Theaker, Harry G.	80-120	*
Grimm Bros.	Fairy Tales (1st UK, 8vo, 308p, gilt, 12cp, pep)	L: Hodder	1921	Abbott, Elenore P.	160-240	
Grimm Bros.	Fairy Tales (1st, 4to, p-o, 367p, 23cp)	Penn	1922	Cramer, Rie	120-180	
Grimm Bros.	Fairy Tales (1st, 8vo, 310p, cp)	Winston	(1922)	Prittie, Edwin J.	60-90	*
Grimm Bros.	Fairy Tales (1st AM, 8vo, 278p, 6cp, b/w)	Doran	[1924]	Soper, George	55-80	*
Grimm Bros.	Fairy Tales (1st, lg8vo, 244p, p-o, col frn, 1-color, pep)	Sears	(1926)	Combs, Lorraine	80-125	
Grimm Bros.	Fairy Tales (8vo, green cl, 337p, 8cp, pep)	Garden City	[1930]	Pocock, Noel	55-80	
Grimm Bros.	Fairy Tales (lg4to, 128p, gilt, 8cp)	L: Collins	[1931]	Anderson, Anne	90-120	*
Grimm Bros.	Fairy Tales (1st, sm4to, ibds, 282p, col frn, b/w, pep)	Whitman	1934	Young, Goldy	40-65	
Grimm Bros.	Fairy Tales (1st, 8vo, 373p, 10cp, cep)	Grosset/Dunlap	(1945)	Kredel, Fritz	50-80	R
Grimm Bros.	Fairy Tales (1st, 8vo, 382p, color, DJ/1.25, RC)	World	(1947)	Becker, May L.	30-60	*
Grimm Bros.	Fisherman and his Wife (1st, sm4to, [32]p, b/w, DJ/2.50, NYTBI)	Pantheon	1957	Gekiere, Madeleine	80-120	
Grimm Bros.	Fisherman and his Wife (1st {std}, 4to, [48]p, fp 2-color, pep, DJ/3.25)	Norton	1966	Zemach, Margot	30-50	
Grimm Bros.	Four Clever Brothers (1st AM {std}, ob4to, [32]p, color, pep, DJ/4.50)	Harcourt	(1967)	Hoffmann, Felix	40-65	
Grimm Bros.	Four Musicians (1st, 4to, ibds, [24]p, fp color, pep, DJ)	Doubleday	1962	Palazzo, Tony	30-45	*
Grimm Bros.	Golden Bird (1st, sm8vo, 116p, color, pep)	Jacobs	(1922)	Smith, Wuanita	60-90	*
Grimm Bros.	Golden Bird (1st AM {std}, sq4to, [32]p, fp color, DJ/4.50)	Doubleday	1970	Fromm, Lilo	30-50	
Grimm Bros.	Golden Goose (1st, sm8vo, 23p, tan cl, 2-color, pep, DJ/1.00)	Houghton	1947	Bare, Arnold E.	60-100	
Grimm Bros.	Good-for-Nothings (1st AM {std}, ob4to, unpag, color, DJ/2.75)	Harcourt	(1957)	Fischer, Hans	50-80	R*
Grimm Bros.	Goose Girl (1st, 12mo, tan cl, 165p, 3cp, 10 fp b/w, dep)	Macmillan	1929	Nerman, Einar R.	55-80	*

AUTHOR	TITLE	PUBLISHER	DATE	ARTIST	PRICE	LC
Grimm Bros.	Goose Girl (1st {std}, 4to, 31p, fp color, dep, DJ/2.75)	Doubleday	(1964)	DeAngeli, Marguerite	30-50	
Grimm Bros.	Grimm's & Andersen's Fairy Tales (1st, folio, [176]p, color, cep)	L: Blackie	[1906]	Stratton, Helen	200-300	R*
Grimm Bros.	Grimm's Animal Stories (1st, sq8vo, green cl, p-o, 9cp)	Duffield	(1911)	Rae, John	250-350	
Grimm Bros.	Grimm's Tales (1st, 8vo, 142p, 2-color, pep, DJ/3.50)	NY: Oxford U.Pr.	1954	Sewell/Gekiere	50-80	R*
Grimm Bros.	Hansel & Gretel (1st, 12mo, red bds, 58p, p-o, color)	Reilly/Britton	(1908)	Neill, John R.	80-120	
Grimm Bros.	Hansel & Gretel (folio, shape bk, [12]p, wraps, color)	Stecher	1916	Price, Margaret E.	50-80	
Grimm Bros.	Hansel & Gretel (1st AM, lg8vo, teg, gilt, 159p, 20 ticp)	Dutton	(1920)	Rackham, Arthur	350-500	R
Grimm Bros.	Hansel & Gretel (1st, lg8vo, blue/gilt, 159p, 20 ticp)	L: Constable	(1920)	Rackham, Arthur	400-600	
Grimm Bros.	Hansel & Gretel (1st AM, 4to, red cl, p-o, gilt, 310p, 12cp)	Doran	(1925)	Nielsen, Kay	300-425	
Grimm Bros.	Hansel & Gretel (folio, wraps, color)	Harter	1932	Peat, Fern B.	60-90	
Grimm Bros.	Hansel & Gretel (1st, 12mo, ibds, [32]p, fp 1-color)	Rand/McNally	1937	Livings, Bess	25-45	*
Grimm Bros.	Hansel & Gretel (1st, sq12mo, [60]p, color)	McLoughlin	(1943)	Rice, A.	35-60	*
Grimm Bros.	Hansel & Gretel (1st {std}, sm4to, [32]p, color, pep, DJ/2.00)	Knopf	1944	Chappell, Warren	40-60	
Grimm Bros.	Hansel and Gretel (4to, ibds, 12cp, pep)	Dodge	[1920]	Adams, Frank	100-150	
Grimm Bros.	Hansel and Gretel (1st, sq8vo, ibds, color)	Macmillan	1927	Hader, B.& E.	70-100	
Grimm Bros.	Hedgehog and the Hare (1st, lg ob8vo, 30p, fp 1-color, pep, DJ/3.95)	World	(1969)	Watson, Wendy	30-50	*
Grimm Bros.	House in the Wood (1st, lg8vo, 89p, ibds, 7cp, pep)	L: F. Warne	(1909)	Brooke, L. Leslie	140-220	
Grimm Bros.	Household Stories (1st, 12mo, 269p, AEG, 11pl, pep)	L: Macmillan	1882	Crane, Walter	250-350	
Grimm Bros.	Household Tales (1st, sm8vo, 400p, b/w, pep)	L: Dent	1901	Bell, Robert A.	150-250	*
Grimm Bros.	Household Tales (1st, sm4to, 303p, yellow cl, 6 fp color, DJ)	L: Eyre/Spotts.	(1946)	Peake, Mervyn	160-225	
Grimm Bros.	Jorinda and Joringel (1st, 4to, [42]p, color, DJ)	Scribner	(1968)	Adams, Adrienne	30-50	
Grimm Bros.	King Thrushbeard (1st AM {std}, 4to, [32]p, ibds, color, DJ/4.50)	Harcourt	(1970)	Hoffmann, Felix	40-70	
Grimm Bros.	Little Brother and Little Sister (1st, 4to, gilt, 251p, uncut, 12 ticp, pep)	L: Constable	(1917)	Rackham, Arthur	400-600	
Grimm Bros.	Little Brother and Little Sister (1st AM, 4to, 251p, 12 ticp)	Dodd	(1917)	Rackham, Arthur	300-450	
Grimm Bros.	Little Red Riding Hood (1st {std}, 8vo, unpag, color, DJ/3.50)	Harcourt	(1968)	Pincus, Harriet	25-40	
Grimm Bros.	More Tales from Grimm (1st, 8vo, 257p, blue cl, col frn, b/w, DJ/2.75)	Coward	(1947)	Gag, Wanda	180-250	R
Grimm Bros.	Rapunzel (1st AM {std}, 4to, ibds, unpag, color, DJ/3.75)	Harcourt	(1961)	Hoffmann, Felix	40-65	
Grimm Bros.	Robber Bridegroom (1st, lg4to, p-o, 39p, pep, 8 ticp)	L: A&C Black	1922	Owen, H.S.	200-300	
Grimm Bros.	Rumpelstilskin (1st {std}, 4to, [32]p, color, DJ/3.50)	Harcourt	(1967)	Ayer, Jacqueline	30-50	
Grimm Bros.	Seven Ravens (1st AM {std}, ob4to, [32]p, ibds, color, DJ/3.75)	Harcourt	(1963)	Hoffmann, Felix	40-65	
Grimm Bros.	Shoemaker and the Elves (1st, sm4to, [32]p, fp color, DJ/2.95)	Scribner	(1960)	Adams, Adrienne	40-65	
Grimm Bros.	Sleeping Beauty (1st AM {std}, 4to, ibds, unpag, color, DJ/3.50)	Harcourt	(1960)	Hoffmann, Felix	45-60	
Grimm Bros.	Snow White & Rose Red (1st, sm4to, [40]p, fp color, DJ/3.50)	Scribner	(1964)	Adams, Adrienne	30-50	
Grimm Bros.	Snow White & Rose Red (1st AM {std}, lg8vo, 47p, color, DJ/2.75)	Delacorte Pr.	(1966)	Cooney, Barbara	45-70	
Grimm Bros.	Snow White & Seven Dwarfs (sm4to, 236p, green cl, p-o, 12cp, pep)	Dodd	1913	Falls, Charles B.	120-180	
Grimm Bros.	Snow White & Seven Dwarfs (1st, sm8vo, 115p, col frn, cp, pep)	Jacobs	(1922)	Smith, Wuanita	55-80	*
Grimm Bros.	Snow White & Seven Dwarfs (1st, 8vo, green ibds, 43p, b/w, DJ/1.00, CH)	Coward	(1938)	Gag, Wanda	180-260	
Grimm Bros.	Snow White & Seven Dwarfs (1st, 4to, ibds, [38]p, color, DJ/1.00)	Wilcox/Follett	(1946)	Stearns, Sharon	25-45	
Grimm Bros.	Snowdrop... (1st, lg8vo, 165p, blue/gilt, 20 ticp)	L: Constable	(1920)	Rackham, Arthur	200-300	
Grimm Bros.	Snowdrop.... (1st AM, lg8vo, 165p, teg, 20 ticp)	Dutton	(1920)	Rackham, Arthur	170-220	
Grimm Bros.	Tales from Grimm (1st, 8vo, blue cl, 237p, col frn, 6pl, DJ/2.00)	Coward	(1936)	Gag, Wanda	280-400	R
Grimm Bros.	Tales from Grimm (1st {std}, lg8vo, ibds, 78p, color, DJ/1.50)	Dutton	1945	Paflin, Roberta	65-90	
Grimm Bros.	Three Tales from Grimm (1st AM, 8vo, pink cl, [48]p, color, DJ/1.25)	Macmillan	1938	Schlotter, Brunhild	100-150	
Grimm Bros.	Traveling Musicians (1st AM {std}, lg4to, [28]p, color, DJ/3.00)	Harcourt	(1955)	Fischer, Hans	60-95	
Grimm Bros.	Twelve Dancing Princesses (1st, 8vo, [30]p, color, cep, DJ/3.25)	Scribner	(1966)	Shulevitz, Uri	30-50	
Grimm Bros.	Wolf & the Seven Little Kids (1st AM {std}, ob4to, [32]p, 2-color, DJ/3.75)	Harcourt	(1959)	Hoffmann, Felix	40-65	
Grinnell, George B.	Jack Among the Indians (1st, 12mo, 301p, 8pl)	Stokes	(1900)	Deming, Edwin W.	50-80	
Grinnell, George B.	Jack in the Rockies (1st, 12mo, 272p, green cl, 8pl)	Stokes	(1904)	Deming, Edwin W.	40-70	
Grinnell, George B.	Jack, the Young Ranchman (1st, 12mo, 304p, 8pl)	Stokes	1899	Deming, Edwin W.	50-80	
Grinnell, George B.	Trail & Camp Fire (1st, 8vo, 353p, 14pl)	Forest/Stream	1897	Seton, Ernest T.	200-300	
Gripari, Pierre	Tales of the Rue Broca (1st AM {std}, 8vo, 111p, 14 fp b/w, DJ/4.95)	Bobbs-Merrill	(1969)	McCully, Emily	30-50	
Gripe, Maria	Hugo (1st {std}, 8vo, 153p, b/w, DJ/3.95)	Delacorte Pr.	(1970)	Gripe, Harald	40-65	
Gripe, Maria	Josephine (1st AM {std}, 8vo, 133p, pink cl, b/w, DJ/3.95)	Delacorte Pr.	(1970)	Gripe, Harald	40-65	
Grishina-Givago, N.	Gresha and his Clay Pig (1st, 8vo, 138p, p-o, color)	Stokes	1930	Grishina-Givago, N.	80-125	
Grishina-Givago, N.	Magic Squirrel (1st, 8vo, 142p, p-o, 3cp, 7pl)	Stokes	1934	Grishina-Givago, N.	80-125	
Grishina-Givago, N.	Peter-Pea (1st, 8vo, gilt, p-o, 95p, fp color)	Stokes	1926	Grishina-Givago, N.	100-165	
Grishina-Givago, N.	Shorty: Nursery Tale from Far Away (1st, ob12mo, 77p, blue cl, b/w)	Lippincott	1924	Grishina-Givago, N.	60-90	
Grishina-Givago, N.	Sparrow House (1st, 8vo, p-o, 175p, 5cp)	Stokes	1928	Grishina-Givago, N.	100-160	
Griswold, Florence	Hindu Fairy Tales (1st, 8vo, 186p, 4cp)	L: Harrap	1919	Jacobs, Helen	50-80	
Groesbeck, Telford	The Incas (1st, lg8vo, green/gilt, 71p, teg, uncut, 14pl)	Putnam	1896	Pape, Eric	70-125	
Gropper, William	Alay-Oop (1st, 8vo, [194]p, fp b/w)	Coward	1930	Gropper, William	100-165	
Gropper, William	Little Tailor (1st, 8vo, [96]p, fp 1-color, pep, DJ/2.75)	Dodd	1955	Gropper, William	65-100	
Groth, Eleanor	Adventures in a Dishpan (1st, lg8vo, ibds, 31p, color, pep, DJ/0.50)	Grosset/Dunlap	(1936)	Groth, Milt	45-70	
Grove, F.	Story Without an End (1st, 8vo, 165p, teg, gilt, 8 ticp)	L: Duckworth	(1912)	Pape, Frank	80-125	
Grover, Eulalie O.	Kittens and Cats (1st, 8vo, yellow cl, 78p, 39pl, dep)	Houghton	1911	(Photos)	100-180	
Grover, Eulalie O.	Overall Boys (1st, sq8vo, 123p, pict cl, color pep)	Rand/McNally	(1905)	Corbett, Bertha L.	100-165	
Grover, Eulalie O.	Overall Boys in Switzerland (1st, sm8vo, beige cl, 160p, pep, color)	Rand/McNally	(1916)	Melcher, Bertha C.	100-160	
Grover, Eulalie O.	Sonbonnet Babies in Holland (1st, 8vo, map, 150p, color, pep)	Rand/McNally	(1915)	Melcher, Bertha C.	100-165	
Grover, Eulalie O.	Sunbonnet Babies ABC Book... (1st, 4to, p-o, 64p, pep, color)	Rand/McNally	(1929)	Melcher, Bertha C.	100-150	
Grover, Eulalie O.	Sunbonnet Babies in Italy (1st, 8vo, 187p, color, pep)	Rand/McNally	(1922)	Melcher/McCracken	70-120	*
Grover, Eulalie O.	Sunbonnet Babies in Mother Goose Land (1st, lg8vo, 115p, color, pep)	Rand/McNally	(1927)	Melcher, B.C.	120-200	
Grover, Eulalie O.	Sunbonnet Babies' Book (1st [this pub], sq8vo, 106p, color, pep)	Rand/McNally	(1902)	Corbett, Bertha L.	120-200	
Gruelle, Johnny	All About Cinderella (1st, 16mo, brown bds, p-o, color)	Cupples/Leon	(1916)	Gruelle, Johnny	80-120	
Gruelle, Johnny	All About Hansel & Gretel (1st, sq16mo, ibds, p-o, 48p, 8cp)	Cupples/Leon	(1917)	Gruelle, Johnny	120-180	R*
Gruelle, Johnny	All About Little Red Riding Hood (sq16mo, ibds, p-o, 48p, color)	Cupples/Leon	(1916)	Gruelle, Johnny	100-145	
Gruelle, Johnny	All About Mother Goose (sq16mo, 48p, color)	Cupples/Leon	(1916)	Gruelle, Johnny	120-180	*
Gruelle, Johnny	All About the Little Small Red Hen (1st, 16mo, 48p, grey bds, p-o, 8cp)	Cupples/Leon	(1917)	Gruelle, Johnny	100-165	
Gruelle, Johnny	Beloved Belindy (1st, lg8vo, ibds, [95]p, color, pep)	Volland	(1926)	Gruelle, Johnny	100-170	

AUTHOR	TITLE	PUBLISHER	DATE	ARTIST	PRICE	LC
Gruelle, Johnny	Cheery Scarcrow (1st, 12mo, ibds, [39]p, pep, 6cp)	Volland	(1929)	Gruelle, Johnny	100-160	
Gruelle, Johnny	Cruise of the Rickety-Robin (1st, folio, 13p, 3-color, wraps)	Manning Pub.	1931	Gruelle, Johnny	250-350	
Gruelle, Johnny	Eddie Elephant (1st, 12mo, ibds, [39]p, color, pep)	Volland	(1921)	Gruelle, Johnny	100-160	
Gruelle, Johnny	Friendly Fairies (1st, lg8vo, [86]p, ibds, color, pep)	Volland	(1919)	Gruelle, Johnny	140-225	
Gruelle, Johnny	Funny Little Book (1st, 12mo, ibds, [40]p, pep, color)	Volland	(1917)	Gruelle, Johnny	125-200	
Gruelle, Johnny	Johnny Gruelle's Golden Book (lg4to, 79p, ibds, color)	Donohue	(1929)	Gruelle, Johnny	80-140	
Gruelle, Johnny	Johnny Mouse & Wishing Stick (1st, lg8vo, ipcb, 89p, color, pep)	Bobbs-Merrill	(1922)	Gruelle, Johnny	100-160	R
Gruelle, Johnny	Little Brown Bear (1st, 12mo, ibds, [40]p, color, pep)	Volland	(1920)	Gruelle, Johnny	80-120	
Gruelle, Johnny	Little Sunny Stories (1st, 12mo, ibds, [40]p, color, pep)	Volland	(1919)	Gruelle, Johnny	100-170	
Gruelle, Johnny	Magical Land of Noom (1st, lg8vo, ibds, 157p, 12cp, pep)	Volland	(1922)	Gruelle, Johnny	350-500	
Gruelle, Johnny	Marcella Stories (1st, 8vo, ibds, 94p, color, pep)	Volland	(1929)	Gruelle, Johnny	100-165	
Gruelle, Johnny	My Very Own Fairy Stories (1st, lg8vo, ibds, [95]p, color, pep)	Volland	(1917)	Gruelle, Johnny	150-220	
Gruelle, Johnny	Orphant Annie Story Book (1st, lg8vo, 85p, p-o, color, pep)	Bobbs-Merrill	(1921)	Gruelle, Johnny	120-170	
Gruelle, Johnny	Paper Dragon (1st, 8vo, ibds, [96]p, color, pep)	Volland	(1926)	Gruelle, Johnny	100-160	
Gruelle, Johnny	Raggedy Andy Goes Sailing (1st, 12mo, [59]p, ipcb, 10 fp color)	McLoughlin	(1941)	Gruelle, Johnny	55-80	*
Gruelle, Johnny	Raggedy Andy Stories (1st, lg8vo, ibds, unpag, color, pep)	Volland	(1920)	Gruelle, Johnny	140-200	
Gruelle, Johnny	Raggedy Ann & Betsy Bonnet String (1st, lg8vo, 95p, ibds, color)	Gruelle Co.	(1943)	Gruelle, Justin	55-80	
Gruelle, Johnny	Raggedy Ann & Golden Butterfly (1st, lg8vo, 95p, ibds, color, cep)	Gruelle Co.	(1940)	Gruelle, Johnny	50-80	
Gruelle, Johnny	Raggedy Ann & Happy Toad (1st, 12mo, ibds, [50]p, color)	McLoughlin	1940	Gruelle, Johnny	55-80	*
Gruelle, Johnny	Raggedy Ann & Laughing Brook (1st, 12mo, ibds, [59]p, color)	McLoughlin	1940	Gruelle, Johnny	55-80	*
Gruelle, Johnny	Raggedy Ann & Left-Handed Safety Pin (1st, 12mo, 45p, color, pep)	Whitman	(1935)	Gruelle, Johnny	40-60	*
Gruelle, Johnny	Raggedy Ann Helps Grandpa Hoppergrass (1st, 12mo, ibds, [50]p, color)	McLoughlin	1940	Gruelle, Johnny	40-60	*
Gruelle, Johnny	Raggedy Ann in Cookie Land (1st, lg8vo, ibds, 95p, color, pep)	Volland	(1931)	Gruelle, Johnny	120-200	
Gruelle, Johnny	Raggedy Ann in Deep Deep Woods (1st, lg8vo, ibds, [95]p, color, pep)	Volland	(1930)	Gruelle, Johnny	120-200	
Gruelle, Johnny	Raggedy Ann in Snow White Castle (1st, lg8vo, ibds, 95p, color)	Gruelle Co.	(1946)	Gruelle, Justin	70-100	
Gruelle, Johnny	Raggedy Ann in the Garden (1st, 12mo, [61]p, ipcb, 10 fp color)	McLoughlin	1940	Gruelle, Johnny	55-80	*
Gruelle, Johnny	Raggedy Ann in the Golden Meadow (1st, folio, ibds, [58]p, 14 color, pep)	Whitman	1935	Gruelle, Johnny	100-175	R
Gruelle, Johnny	Raggedy Ann in the Magic Book (1st, lg8vo, [91]p, ibds, color)	Gruelle Co.	(1939)	Gruelle, Worth	70-100	
Gruelle, Johnny	Raggedy Ann Stories (1st, lg8vo, ibds, [95]p, color, pep)	Volland	(1918)	Gruelle, Johnny	150-220	
Gruelle, Johnny	Raggedy Ann Stories (1st {this pub}, lg8vo, 95p, color)	Gruelle Co.	(1947)	Gruelle, Johnny	55-80	*
Gruelle, Johnny	Raggedy Ann's Adventure (1st, 8vo, [36]p, spiral bds, color)	Saalfield	(1947)	Hays, Ethel	140-200	
Gruelle, Johnny	Raggedy Ann's Alphabet Book (1st, 12mo, [38]p, ibds, pep, color)	Volland	(1925)	Gruelle, Johnny	140-200	
Gruelle, Johnny	Raggedy Ann's Lucky Pennies (1st, 8vo, ibds, 94p, color, pep)	Volland	(1932)	Gruelle, Johnny	120-180	
Gruelle, Johnny	Raggedy Ann's Magical Wishes (1st, lg8vo, 94p, ibds, color, pep)	Volland	(1928)	Gruelle, Johnny	140-200	
Gruelle, Johnny	Raggedy Ann's Wishing Pebble (1st, lg8vo, ibds, unpag, color, pep)	Volland	(1925)	Gruelle, Johnny	140-200	
Gruelle, Johnny	Raggedy Ann.../Camel/Wrinkled Knees (8vo, ibds, [95]p, pep, color)	Volland	(1924)	Gruelle, Johnny	150-220	
Gruelle, Johnny	Wooden Willie (1st, lg8vo, ibds, 95p, color, pep)	Volland	(1927)	Gruelle, Johnny	150-220	
Gruelle, Justin	Camel with Wrinkled Knees (1st {this pub}, 12mo, ibds, [59]p, color)	McLoughlin	(1941)	Gruelle, Justin	50-85	
Gruelle, Justin	Mother Goose Parade (1st, lg4to, ibds, [31]p, color, pep)	Volland	(1929)	Gruelle, Justin	80-120	
Gugu	Mother Duck's Children (1st, sq4to, 48p, ibds, color)	R.H. Russell	1900	Unknown	170-240	
Guilfoile, Elizabeth	Nobody Listens to Andrew (1st, 8vo, 27p, fp color, DJ)	Follett	(1957)	Stevens, Mary	20-35	*
Guillaume, Jeanette	Amat and the Water-Buffalo (1st, sq8vo, 48p, color, DJ/2.75)	Coward	1962	Wiese, Kurt	25-45	
Guillot, Rene	Elephants of Sargabal (1st AM, 8vo, 170p, b/w, DJ/3.25)	Criterion Bks.	(1957)	Hoffmann, Felix	30-50	
Guillot, Rene	Fofana (1st AM {std}, 8vo, 145p, b/w, DJ/3.00)	Criterion Bks.	(1962)	Ambrus, Victor	30-50	
Guillot, Rene	Little Dog Lost (1st, sq8vo, 64p, b/w, DJ/3.75)	Lothrop, Lee	(1970)	Tripp, Wallace	20-30	
Guirma, Frederic	Princess of the Full Moon (1st {std}, 4to, [32]p, color, DJ/4.95)	Macmillan	(1970)	Guirma, Frederic	30-45	
Guizou, P.	Animals in the Ark (1st, ob8vo, p-o, 31p, 7cp)	Duffield	(1909)	Vimar, Auguste	70-120	R
Gulick, Peggy	Dear Uncle Looy (1st {std}, 4to, ibds, [30]p, 2-color, DJ/1.75)	Knopf	(1951)	Dersser, Elizabeth	70-100	
Gulick, Peggy	Sing Sang Sung & Willie (1st {std}, 4to, ibds, [31]p, color, DJ/1.50)	Knopf	(1947)	Dresser, Elizabeth	70-100	
Gullick, M.E.	Teddy's Year with the Fairies (1st, lg8vo, 176p, ibds, p-o, 3cp, pep)	L: R.T.S.	(1920)	Robinson, Charles	200-300	
Gulliver, Lemeul	Gulliver's Bird Book (1st, lg4to, 103p, color, pep)	L.C. Page	1902	Bridgman, L.J.	120-180	
Gulliver, Lemeul	Over the Nonsense Road (1st, 8vo, 234p, orange cl, 8cp)	Appleton	1910	Strothmann, F.	60-100	
Gurko, Leo	Tom Paine, Freedom's Apostle (1st {std}, 8vo, 213p, b/w, DJ/2.75, NH)	Crowell	(1957)	Kredel, Fritz	50-80	
Gurney, Nancy	King, the Mice and the Cheese (1st, 8vo, 63p, color, DJ/1.95)	Beginner Books	(1965)	Gurney, Nancy	50-80	
Gury, Jeremy	Round and Round Horse (1st, ob4to, [47]p, color, DJ/1.50)	Henry Holt & Co.	(1943)	Marsh, Reginald	80-120	
Gury, Jeremy	Wonderful World of Aunt Tuddy (1st {std}, 4to, ibds unpag, 1-color, DJ/3.50)	Random	(1958)	Knight, Hilary	80-125	
Guy, Anne W.	William (1st, 8vo, 124p, fp b/w, DJ/2.95)	Dial Press	1961	Crichlow, Ernest	25-45	*
Gwynn, Stephen L.	Fair Hills of Ireland (1st, 8vo, 416p, uncut, color)	L: Macmillan	1906	Thomson, Hugh	50-80	
Habberton, John	Tiger & the Insect (1st, sm8vo, ipcb, 235p, uncut, 9pl)	R.H. Russell	1902	Russell, Walter	35-60	
Habberton, John	With the Dream Maker (1st, sm8vo, 112p, 5pl)	Jacobs	1898	Claghorn, Joseph C.	40-65	
Hacker, Lilian P.	Susan (1st, 4to, [52]p, ibds, gilt, 10cp, pep)	L: Hodder	(1912)	Hacker, Lilian	150-250	
Hackett, Walter	Swans of Ballycastle (1st {std}, 8vo, 64p, blue cl, color, DJ/2.75)	Ariel	(1954)	Bettina	30-50	
Hadden, James C.	Operas of Richard Wagner (1st, 8vo, gilt, teg, 246p, 24cp)	L: Jack	1908	Shaw, Byam	80-125	
Hader, B.& E.	Big City (1st, 4to, [60]p, fp color, cep, DJ/2.50)	Macmillan	1947	Hader, B.& E.	120-200	
Hader, B.& E.	Big Snow (1st, sm4to, blue cl, [48]p, color, dep, DJ/2.50, CM)	Macmillan	1948	Hader, B.& E.	180-250	R
Hader, B.& E.	Billy Butter (1st, ob8vo, 92p, color, pep, DJ/2.00)	Macmillan	1936	Hader, B.& E.	50-80	
Hader, B.& E.	Cat & the Kitten (1st, 8vo, 98p, green cl, color, pep, DJ/2.00)	Macmillan	1940	Hader, B.& E.	40-65	
Hader, B.& E.	Chuck-a-Luck & his Reindeer (1st, lg ob8vo, ipcb, 28p, color)	Houghton	1933	Hader, B.& E.	70-120	*
Hader, B.& E.	Cock-a-Doodle-Doo (1st, sm4to, [56]p, fp color, DJ/2.00, CH)	Macmillan	(1939)	Hader, B.& E.	100-175	
Hader, B.& E.	Cricket (1st, 8vo, p-o, red cl, 160p, color, pep, DJ/2.00)	Macmillan	1938	Hader, B.& E.	50-80	
Hader, B.& E.	Ding Dong Bell (1st {std}, 4to, ipcb, 45p, fp color, DJ/2.50)	Macmillan	1957	Hader, B.& E.	40-65	
Hader, B.& E.	Farmer in the Dell (1st, sm4to, green cl, [90]p, color, pep)	Macmillan	1931	Hader, B.& E.	55-80	*
Hader, B.& E.	Friendly Phoebe (1st {std}, 8vo, 45p, color, DJ/2.25)	Macmillan	1953	Hader, B.& E.	40-65	
Hader, B.& E.	Green & Gold (1st, 8vo, 48p, color, pep, DJ/1.00)	Macmillan	1936	Hader, B.& E.	70-125	
Hader, B.& E.	Home on the Range... (1st {std}, 4to, [38]p, picb, fp color, DJ/2.50)	Macmillan	1955	Hader, B.& E.	45-70	*
Hader, B.& E.	Jamaica Johnny (1st, sq8vo, 90p, green cl, 6 fp color, pep, DJ/2.00)	Macmillan	1935	Hader, B.& E.	70-100	
Hader, B.& E.	Lions & Tigers & Elephants Too (1st {std}, lg ob8vo, ibds, [61]p, color)	Longmans	1930	Hader, B.& E.	65-100	
Hader, B.& E.	Little Antelope... (1st {std}, 4to, 41p, ibds, color, DJ/3.00)	Macmillan	1962	Hader, B.& E.	40-65	

AUTHOR	TITLE	PUBLISHER	DATE	ARTIST	PRICE	LC
Hader, B.& E.	Little Appaloosa (1st {std}, sm4to, [43]p, color, DJ/2.50)	Macmillan	(1949)	Hader, B.& E.	60-90	
Hader, B.& E.	Little Chip of Willow Hill (1st {std}, 8vo, 42p, fp color, cep, DJ/2.50)	Macmillan	1958	Hader, B.& E.	50-80	
Hader, B.& E.	Little Red Hen (1st, 24mo, [42]p, color)	Macmillan	1928	Hader, B.& E.	50-85	
Hader, B.& E.	Little Stone House (1st, sm4to, green cl, [63]p, color, DJ/2.00)	Macmillan	(1944)	Hader, B.& E.	50-80	
Hader, B.& E.	Little Town (1st, 4to, [87]p, orange cl, pep, color, DJ/2.00)	Macmillan	1941	Hader, B.& E.	65-90	
Hader, B.& E.	Little White Foot (1st {std}, 8vo, blue cl, unpag, color, cep, DJ/2.25)	Macmillan	1952	Hader, B.& E.	50-85	
Hader, B.& E.	Lost in the Zoo (1st {std}, sm4to, unpag, color, DJ/2.50)	Macmillan	1951	Hader, B.& E.	50-80	*
Hader, B.& E.	Midget & Bridget (1st, lg ob8vo, 90p, orange cl, color, pep, DJ/2.00)	Macmillan	1934	Hader, B.& E.	60-100	
Hader, B.& E.	Mighty Hunter (1st, sm4to, [49]p, color, pep, DJ/2.00, CH)	Macmillan	(1943)	Hader, B.& E.	70-120	
Hader, B.& E.	Mr. Billy's Gun (1st {std}, 4to, unpag, color, DJ/3.50)	Macmillan	1960	Hader, B.& E.	30-50	
Hader, B.& E.	Old Woman & Crooked Sixpence (1st, 16mo, [42]p, color)	Macmillan	1928	Hader, B.& E.	60-90	*
Hader, B.& E.	Picture Book of the States (1st {std}, ob folio, color, [60]p, pep)	Harper	1928	Hader, B.& E.	60-90	
Hader, B.& E.	Picture Book of Travel (1st, 4to, p-o, 63p, color, pep)	Macmillan	1928	Hader, B.& E.	70-100	
Hader, B.& E.	Quack-Quack... (1st {std}, 4to, 47p, ibds, color, DJ/3.00)	Macmillan	1961	Hader, B.& E.	30-50	
Hader, B.& E.	Rainbow's End (1st, sq8vo, 168p, 4 fp color, DJ/2.00)	Macmillan	1945	Hader, B.& E.	45-70	
Hader, B.& E.	Reindeer Trail (1st {std}, sm4to, blue cl, unpag, color, DJ/3.25)	Macmillan	(1959)	Hader, B.& E.	35-50	
Hader, B.& E.	Snow in the City: Winter's Tale (1st {std}, 4to, 41p, color, DJ/3.50)	Macmillan	1963	Hader, B.& E.	30-50	
Hader, B.& E.	Spunky (1st, ob8vo, blue cl, 90p, color, pep)	Macmillan	1933	Hader, B.& E.	55-80	*
Hader, B.& E.	Squirrely of Willow Hill (1st {std}, 8vo, [47]p, color, cep, DJ/2.00)	Macmillan	1950	Hader, B.& E.	50-80	
Hader, B.& E.	Stop, Look & Listen (1st, sq12mo, ipcb, 48p, 2-color, pep, DJ/1.00)	Longmans	(1936)	Hader, B.& E.	60-90	*
Hader, B.& E.	Story of Pancho (1st, sm4to, tan cloth, [56]p, color, DJ/2.00)	Macmillan	1942	Hader, B.& E.	70-125	
Hader, B.& E.	Story of the Three Bears (1st, 16mo, [42]p, ibds, color, pep)	Macmillan	1928	Hader, B.& E.	60-90	
Hader, B.& E.	The Runaways (1st {std}, sm4to, green cl, 38p, color, DJ/3.00)	Macmillan	1956	Hader, B.& E.	40-65	
Hader, B.& E.	The Skyrocket (1st, lg8vo, 148p, grey/red, 4 fp color, cep, DJ/2.50)	Macmillan	1946	Hader, B.& E.	30-55	
Hader, B.& E.	Tommy Thatcher Goes to Sea (1st, sq8vo, 95p, 6 fp color, pep, DJ/2.00)	Macmillan	1937	Hader, B.& E.	35-50	
Hader, B.& E.	Tooky... (1st {std}, lg ob8vo, ibds, [61]p, color, pep)	Longmans	1931	Hader, B.& E.	75-100	*
Hader, B.& E.	Two Funny Clowns (1st, ob8vo, [52]p, color)	Coward	(1929)	Hader, B.& E.	50-85	
Hader, B.& E.	Under the Pig-Nut Tree (1st, sm8vo, 63p, ibds, color, DJ/1.25)	Knopf	1930	Hader, B.& E.	40-65	
Hader, B.& E.	What'll You Do when You Grow Up? (1st {std}, 12mo, ipcb, [63]p, col, pep)	Longmans	1929	Hader, B.& E.	75-100	*
Hader, B.& E.	Wish on the Moon (1st {std}, sm sq4to, 40p, dep, color, DJ/2.75)	Macmillan	1954	Hader, B.& E.	45-70	
Hader, Berta	Whiffy McMann (1st, sq12mo, [56]p, ipcb, 1-color)	NY: Oxford U.Pr.	(1933)	Hader, Berta	80-140	
Hager, Alice R.	Canvas Castle (1st, 8vo, 179p, b/w, pep, DJ/2.50)	J. Messner	(1949)	Stevens, Mary	30-50	
Haggard, H. Rider	Allan Quatermain (1st, 8vo, blue/gilt, 280p, 20pl, pep)	L: Longmans	1887	Kerr, C.H.M.	300-500	
Haggard, H. Rider	Allan the Hunter (1st, 8vo, 111p, red cl, 2pl)	Lothrop Pub.	(1898)	Unknown	120-200	
Haggard, H. Rider	Ancient Allan (1st, sm8vo, 310p, tan/gilt, 8pl)	L: Cassell	1920	Morrow, Albert	150-250	
Haggard, H. Rider	Benita, an African Romance (1st, 8vo, 344p, red/gilt, 16pl)	L: Cassell	1906	Browne, Gordon	120-185	
Haggard, H. Rider	Child of the Storm (1st AM, 8vo, red cl, 335p, 3pl)	NY: Longmans	1913	Michael, A.C.	80-125	*
Haggard, H. Rider	Cleopatra (1st, sm8vo, blue/gilt, 336p, 29pl, pep)	L: Longmans	1889	Greiffenhagen/Wood.	300-500	
Haggard, H. Rider	Heart of the World (1st, 12mo, 347p, green/gilt, 13pl)	NY: Longmans	1895	Sawyer, Amy	200-300	
Haggard, H. Rider	Ivory Child (1st, 8vo, 344p, col frn, 3pl)	L: Cassell	(1916)	Michael, A.C.	70-120	
Haggard, H. Rider	Lysbeth: Tale of the Dutch (1st UK, 8vo, 496p, gilt, 26pl, cep)	L: Longmans	1901	Hood, G.P. Jacomb	100-165	
Haggard, H. Rider	Mahatma & the Hare (1st, 8vo, 165p, red/gilt, 12pl)	L: Longmans	1911	Brock/Horton	250-350	
Haggard, H. Rider	Montezuma's Daughter (1st, 8vo, green/gilt, uncut, 24pl)	L: Longmans	1893	Greiffenhagen, M.	200-300	
Haggard, H. Rider	People of the Mist (1st, 12mo, 343p, blue/gilt, 16pl, cep)	L: Longmans	1894	Layard, Arthur	150-250	
Haggard, H. Rider	She (1st, 8vo, 317p, gilt, b/w pl, pep)	L: Longmans	1887	Unknown	650-900	
Haggard, H. Rider	She ([new ed.], 8vo, 300p, buckram, b/w)	L: Longmans	1894	Greiffenhagen/Kerr	70-120	
Haggard, H. Rider	Spirit of Bambatse (1st AM, 8vo, 329p, green/gilt, 8pl)	NY: Longmans	1906	Browne, Gordon	80-140	
Haggard, H. Rider	Swallow, Tale of the Great Trek (1st, 8vo, tan/gilt, 348p, b/w pl, cep)	NY: Longmans	1899	Hatherall, William	120-200	
Haggard, H. Rider	The Brethren (1st AM, sm8vo, 411p, blue/gilt, 16pl)	McClure	1904	Millar, H.R.	80-130	
Haggard, H. Rider	Wanderer's Necklace (1st, 8vo, 328p, brown/gilt, col frn, 3pl)	L: Cassell	1914	Michael, A.C.	100-150	
Haggard, H. Rider	Winter Pilgrimage (1st, 8vo, blue/gilt, 335p, 31pl)	L: Longmans	1901	(Photos)	250-350	
Hahn, Emily	Picture Story of China (1st, 4to, [52]p, color, pep, DJ/2.50)	Reynal/Hitchcock	(1946)	Wiese, Kurt	50-80	
Hahn, Hannelore	Take a Giant Step (1st, narrow lg4to, 32p, color, DJ/2.75)	Little/Brown	1960	Zemach, Margot	40-70	
Hahn, Julia L.	Everyday Fun (1st [reader ed.], 12mo, 154p, color, pep)	Houghton	(1935)	Hader, B.& E.	50-80	*
Hahn, Julia L.	Who Knows: A Little Primer (1st [reader ed.], 12mo, 46p, color)	Houghton	(1937)	Hader, B.& E.	50-80	*
Hahn, Lotte K.	Unicorn Who Wanted to be Seen (1st, sm4to, [38]p, fp 2-color, cep, DJ)	Warne	(1961)	Price, Christine	40-65	*
Haig-Brown, R.L.	Ki-Yu: Story of Panthers (1st, 8vo, 213p, b/w, cep, DJ/2.50)	Houghton	1934	Wiese, Kurt	80-130	
Haig-Brown, R.L.	Whale People (1st AM {std}, 8vo, 256p, b/w, DJ/3.25)	Wm. Morrow	1963	Weiler, Mary	30-50	
Haile, Ellen	Two Grey Girls & their Opposite Neighbors (1st, 4to, ibds, 258p, b/w)	NY: Cassell	(1880)	Greenaway, Kate	65-100	
Haines, Alice C.	Boys (1st, lg4to, [18]p, ibds, 8cp)	Stokes	(1905)	Knipe, Emilie B.	80-120	
Haines, Alice C.	Girls (1st, lg4to, [18]p, ipcb, 4cp)	Stokes	(1905)	Knipe, Emilie B.	80-120	
Haines, Alice C.	Indian Boys & Girls (1st, sm4to, p-o, 47p, 4cp, 6pl)	Stokes	(1906)	Deming/Mar	100-165	
Haines, Alice C.	Japanese Child Life (1st, lg4to, [34]p, ibds, 8cp)	Stokes	(1905)	Mar, Alice	100-165	
Haines, Alice C.	Little Japs at Home (1st, lg4to, ibds, [26]p, 4cp)	Stokes	(1905)	Mar, Alice	200-300	
Haines, William	Slim (1st, 8vo, 414p, 6 fp b/w, pep, DJ/2.50)	Little/Brown	1934	Lawson, Robert	100-165	
Hains, T. Jenkins	Black Barque (1st, sm8vo, 322p, 5pl)	L.C. Page	1905	Dunton, W. Herbert	40-70	*
Haldane, J.B.S.	My Friend Mr. Leakey (1st AM {std}, 8vo, 179p, b/w, DJ/1.75)	Harper	1938	Rosoman, Leonard	140-200	
Haldane, Winifred A.	Dream Bag (1st, 8vo, 131p, gilt, 6cp)	Laird & Lee	(1904)	Heath, Howard	70-125	
Hale, Kathleen	Orlando Buys a Farm (1st, ob folio, 32p, wraps, color)	L: Country Life	1942	Hale, Kathleen	200-300	
Hale, Kathleen	Orlando, Marmalade Cat-Camping Holiday (1st AM, folio, [32]p, col, DJ/2.50)	Scribner	[1938]	Hale, Kathleen	300-500	
Hale, Lucretia	Peterkin Papers (1st, 8vo, 219p, p-o, 4cp)	Houghton	1924	Brett, Harold M.	30-45	
Hale, Lucretia	Peterkin Papers (1st, 8vo, 192p, col frn, b/w, pep)	Jr. Deluxe Ed.	(1955)	Keats, Ezra J.	30-50	
Haley, Gail E.	My Kingdom for a Dragon (1st, 8vo, [34]p, wraps, fp 2-color)	VA: Crozet	(1962)	Haley, Gail E.	30-50	*
Haley, Gail E.	One Two, Buckle My Shoe (1st {std}, 4to, 63p, color, pep, DJ/3.25)	Doubleday	(1964)	Haley, Gail E.	60-90	*
Haley, Gail E.	Story, a Story (1st {std}, sq4to, [36]p, color, DJ/5.95, CM)	Atheneum	(1970)	Haley, Gail E.	100-150	
Halkett, Sarah P.	Elf King's Flowers (1st, sm4to, 79p, ibds, col frn, pep)	Dutton	(1924)	Pyle, Katharine	40-60	
Hall, A.W. (ed.)	Icelandic Fairy Tales (1st, 12mo, 317p, gilt, 8pl)	L: Warne	1897	Mason, E.A.	70-130	
Hall, Albert N.	Wonder Hill (1st, lg8vo, p-o, 271p, 10cp, pep)	Rand/McNally	(1914)	Hall, Norman	180-260	

AUTHOR	TITLE	PUBLISHER	DATE	ARTIST	PRICE	LC
Hall, Anna G.	Cyrus Holt and the Civil War (1st, 8vo, 128p, b/w, DJ/3.00)	Viking	(1964)	Morse, Dorothy B.	20-30	
Hall, Anna G.	Nansen (1st, lg8vo, 165p, 10pl, pep, DJ/2.50, NH)	Viking	1940	Artzybasheff, Boris	65-100	R
Hall, Arthur V.	Poems of a South African (1st, 8vo, 313p, gilt, 6cp)	L: Longmans	1931	Detmold, Edward J.	120-185	
Hall, Arthur V.	Rainbow Houses for Boys & Girls (1st, 8vo, blue cl, 92p, 6cp)	L: J. Cape	1923	Detmold, Edward J.	140-225	
Hall, Bertha P.	Ducky Daddles and the Three Bears (1st, ob4to, ibds, 57p)	Dutton	(1921)	(Photos)	100-165	
Hall, Bolton	Monkey Shines (1st, sm4to, 78p, ipcb, 10cp)	Wessels	(1904)	Jones, Leon F.	45-70	
Hall, Conrad	Story of a Little Colored Coon (1st, 8vo, 125p, red cl, color)	L: Hodder	(1902)	Myrtle/Rigby	500-800	
Hall, Daniel W.	Arctic Rovings (1st, 8vo, 144p, b/w, DJ/3.95)	Young Scott	1968	Hogarth, William	25-40	
Hall, Donald	Andrew the Lion Farmer (1st, sm4to, [60]p, color, DJ/2.95)	F. Watts	(1959)	Miller, Jane	50-80	
Hall, Eliza C.	Aunt Jane of Kentucky (1st, 12mo, 283p, col frn, decor by...)	Little/Brown	1907	Strong, Beulah	25-40	
Hall, Esther G.	College on Horseback (1st, 12mo, 319p, pep)	Random	1933	Brown, Paul	50-80	*
Hall, Gertrude	Allegretto (1st, 12mo, beige/gilt, 111p, teg, b/w)	Roberts Bros.	1894	Herford, Oliver	60-100	
Hall, Gladys	Cinderella (1st, 4to, [11]p, ibds, color)	Cupples/Leon	1915	Hall, Gladys	80-130	
Hall, Lynn	Ride a Wild Dream (1st {std}, 8vo, 160p, b/w, DJ/3.50)	Follett	(1969)	Roth, George	20-35	*
Hall, Lynn	Secret of Stonehouse (1st {std}, 8vo, 155p, b/w, DJ/3.50)	Follett	(1968)	Cellini, Joseph	40-65	
Hall, Lynn	Shy Ones (1st {std}, 8vo, 188p, b/w, DJ/3.25)	Follett	(1967)	Elgaard, Greta	25-45	
Hall, Rosalys	Animals to Africa (1st, ob8vo, [27]p, fp color, dep, DJ/1.50)	Holiday House	(1939)	Eichenberg, Fritz	45-65	
Hall, Rosalys	Bright and Shining Breadboard (1st, sm4to, [32]p, fp color, cep, DJ/3.75)	Lothrop, Lee	(1969)	Werth, Kurt	30-50	
Hall, Rosalys	Dog's Boy (1st, 8vo, 42p, b/w, DJ/2.75)	Lothrop, Lee	(1962)	Weiss, Emil	30-45	*
Hall, Rosalys	Miranda's Dragon (1st, sm4to, green cl, 39p, color, DJ/3.95)	McGraw-Hill	(1968)	Werth, Kurt	30-45	
Hall, Rosalys	No Ducks for Dinner (1st {std}, 8vo, 40p, color, DJ/2.50)	NY: Oxford U.Pr.	1953	Werth, Kurt	30-45	
Hall, Rosalys	Out of Provincetown (1st sm8vo, 296p, fp b/w, DJ/2.00)	Farrar/Rinehart	(1941)	Malvern, Corrine	20-35	
Hall, Rosalys	Seven for St. Nicholas (1st {std}, 8vo, 156p, b/w, DJ/3.00)	Lippincott	(1958)	Werth, Kurt	25-45	
Hall, Tom	When Cupid Calls (1st, 12mo, 119p, teg, decor by...)	Herrick	1898	McManus, Blanche	25-45	*
Hall, Tom	When Hearts are Trumps (1st, 12mo, gilt, 128p, teg, title page by...)	Stone/Kimball	1894	Bradley, Will	55-80	*
Hall, William N.	Christmas Pony (1st {std}, sm4to, ipcb, [32]p, color, DJ/1.50)	Knopf	(1948)	Duvoisin, Roger	60-90	
Hall, William N.	Seven Little Elephants (1st, 4to, [32]p, ibds, color, DJ/1.50)	Crowell	1947	Fini	25-40	
Hall, William N.	Shoelace Robin (1st, 8vo, ipcb, [20]p, 1-color, color, DJ/1.00)	Crowell	1945	Lawson, Robert	60-100	
Hall, William N.	Walking Hat (1st {std}, 4to, ibds, [32]p, color, DJ/1.50)	Knopf	(1950)	Wiese, Kurt	50-80	
Hall, William N.	Watch the Kitten Grow (1st, sm4to, spiral bds, unpag, color)	Crowell	1946	Carroll, Ruth	30-50	
Hall, William N.	Watch the Pony Grow (1st, ob4to, [30]p, spiral bds, color)	Crowell	1942	Steiner, Charlotte	30-50	
Hall, William N.	Winkie's World (1st {std}, 8vo, [30]p, ibds, color, pep, DJ/2.00)	Doubleday	1958	Duvoisin, Roger	50-80	
Halle, Louis J.	Birds Against Men (1st, 8vo, 228p, b/w, DJ/2.50)	Viking	1938	Ward, Lynd	40-65	
Hallin, Emily	Moya and the Flamingoes (1st, 8vo, 86p, fp b/w, DJ/3.50)	McKay	1969	Anderson, Rus	25-40	
Hallock, Grace T.	Bird in the Bush (1st, ob8vo, 47p, pep, color)	Dutton	1930	Hallock, Grace T.	25-45	*
Hallock, Grace T.	Boy Who Was (1st {std}, lg8vo, 153p, ipcb, 10cp, pep, NH)	Dutton	(1928)	Wood, Harrie	70-125	
Hallock, Grace T.	Petersham's Hill (1st, sm8vo, green cl, 132p, 5 fp b/w, pep)	Dutton	(1927)	Wood, Harrie	35-60	*
Halstead, Murat	Story of the Philippines (1st, lg8vo, 400p, gilt, cvr by...)	(Chicago)	(1898)	Denslow, W.W.	100-165	
Hamberger, John	Day the Sun Disappeared (1st {std}, 4to, [42]p, color, DJ/3.00)	Norton	(1964)	Hamberger, John	25-40	
Hamberger, John	Peacock Who Lost his Tail (1st {std}, ob8vo, [48]p, color, DJ/3.25)	Norton	(1967)	Hamberger, John	25-40	*
Hamblen, Herbert E.	Story of a Yankee Boy (1st, 12mo, 339p, 4pl)	Scribner	1898	Edwards, Harry C.	30-50	
Hamer, Sam H.	Enchanted Wood (1st, 8vo, 100p, 8cp)	L: Duckworth	1909	Rountree, Harry	100-165	
Hamer, Sam H.	Enchanted Wood (1st AM, 12mo, 101p, p-o, 8cp)	Dana Estes	[1910]	Rountree, Harry	80-130	
Hamer, Sam H.	Forest Foundling (1st, lg8vo, 109p, 8cp)	L: Duckworth	1909	Rountree, Harry	120-200	
Hamer, Sam H.	Forest Foundling (1st AM, lg8vo, p-o, 109p, 8cp)	Dana Estes	[1909]	Rountree, Harry	100-175	R
Hamer, Sam H.	Four Glass Balls (1st, 8vo, 109p, color)	L: Duckworth	1911	Rountree, Harry	75-100	*
Hamer, Sam H.	Jungle School (1st, 4to, 64p, color)	L: Cassell	1900	Neilson, Harry B.	80-125	
Hamer, Sam H.	Magic Wand (lg8vo, 88p, cloth, 12cp)	Dana Estes	[1908]	Rountree, Harry	120-200	
Hamer, Sam H.	Micky Magee's Menagerie (1st, lg8vo, ibds, 100p, 8cp)	L: Cassell	1897	Neilson, Harry B.	80-125	
Hamer, Sam H.	Princess & the Dragon (1st, 8vo, p-o, 78p, 12cp)	L: Duckworth	(1908)	Hassall, John	100-150	
Hamer, Sam H.	Princess & the Dragon (1st AM, 8vo, green cl, p-o, 78p, 12cp)	Dana Estes	[1908]	Hassall, John	80-125	
Hamer, Sam H.	Quackles Junior (1st, sm4to, 76p, ibds, 4cp)	L: Cassell	1903	Rountree, Harry	120-200	
Hamer, Sam H.	Story of the Ring (1st AM, 8vo, 53p, 4cp)	Dodd	1907	Rountree, Harry	100-165	
Hamer, Sam H.	Story of the Ring (1st, 8vo, 53p, 4cp)	L: Cassell	1907	Rountree, Harry	120-180	
Hamer, Sam H.	The Dolomites (1st AM, lg8vo, 305p, 16cp, pep)	NY: J. Lane	1910	Rountree, Harry	150-225	
Hamer, Sam H.	The Dolomites (1st, lg8vo, gilt, 305p, 16cp, pep)	L: Methuen	1910	Rountree, Harry	150-225	
Hamer, Sam H.	Transformations of the Truefitts (1st, 4to, ibds, 77p, 4cp)	L: Cassell	1908	Rountree, Harry	150-250	
Hamer, Sam H.	Wonderful Isles (1st AM, sm4to, p-o, 107p, 8cp)	Dana Estes	[1908]	Rountree, Harry	150-250	
Hamer, Sam H.	Wonderful Isles (1st, sm4to, 107p, 8cp)	L: Duckworth	1908	Rountree, Harry	200-300	
Hamil, Thomas A.	Brother Alonzo (1st {std}, 4to, [48]p, ibds, color, DJ/2.50)	Macmillan	1957	Hamil, Tom	50-80	R*
Hamill, Katharine F.	Rhymes for Wee Sweethearts (1st, lg8vo, 181p, p-o, 5cp)	Jacobs	(1906)	Wager-Smith, Curtis	50-90	*
Hamilton, Elizabeth	Go West, Young Bear (1st, lg8vo, 94p, fp b/w, pep, DJ/2.50)	Coward	(1948)	Wiese, Kurt	40-65	*
Hamilton, Elizabeth	P-Zoo (1st, sm ob4to, ipcb, [32]p, 1-color, pep, DJ/1.00)	Coward	(1945)	Hurd, Peter	120-200	*
Hamilton, Myra	Kingdoms Curious (1st, 8vo, 248p, tan/gilt, 8pl)	L: Heinemann	1905	Various	140-200	
Hamilton, Virginia	House of Dies Drear (1st {std}, 8vo, 246p, fp b/w, DJ/4.95)	Macmillan	(1968)	Keith, Eros	30-50	
Hamilton, Virginia	Time-Ago Tales of Jahdu (1st {std}, 8vo, 61p, b/w, cep, DJ/4.50)	Macmillan	(1969)	Hogrogian, Nonny	25-40	
Hamilton, Virginia	Zeely (1st {std}, [1st bk.], 8vo, 122p, fp b/w, DJ/3.95)	Macmillan	(1967)	Shimin, Symeon	45-70	R
Hamilton, William T.	My Sixty Years on the Plains (1st, 8vo, 244p, p-o, 6pl by...)	Forest/Stream	1905	Russell, Charles M.	170-240	
Hamlin, John	Beloved Acres (1st, sm8vo, 228p, 4pl)	Century	1925	Lassell, Charles	25-40	
Hamlin, Myra	Nan in the City (1st, 12mo, 251p, red cl, 3pl)	Roberts Bros.	1897	Bridgman, L.J.	35-60	
Hamlin, Myra	Nan's Chicopee Children (1st, 12mo, 223p, 5pl)	Little/Brown	1900	Bridgman, L.J.	30-50	
Hammond, Harold	Further Fortunes of Pinkey Perkins (1st, sm8vo, 391p, 22pl)	Century	1906	Varian, George	40-70	
Hammond, Harold	Pinkey Perkins, Just a Boy (1st, 8vo, 327p, b/w, PPPa)	Century	1905	Varian, George	60-100	
Hamp, Sidford F.	Coco Bolo (1st, 12mo, 145p, 12pl)	Badger	1911	Hopp, O.	35-60	*
Hampden, John	Gypsy Fiddle (1st, 8vo, 159p, fp b/w, DJ/4.50)	World	(1969)	Jacques, Robin	25-40	*
Hample, Stoo	Silly Book (1st, 8vo, [32]p, ipcb, b/w, DJ/1.50)	Harper	(1961)	Hample, Stoo	30-50	*
Hancock, H. Irving	Chuggins (1st, 12mo, 95p, col frn, 4pl)	Altemus	(1904)	Claghorn, Joseph C.	120-200	
Handasyde, Emily	Four Gardens (1st AM, 8vo, 161p, purple/gilt, 8cp, pep)	Lippincott	1912	Robinson, Charles	90-120	

AUTHOR	TITLE	PUBLISHER	DATE	ARTIST	PRICE	LC
Handforth, Thomas	Faraway Meadow (1st {std}, ob4to, [32]p, color, pep, DJ/2.00)	Doubleday/Doran	1939	Handforth, Thomas	60-100	
Handforth, Thomas	Mei Li (1st {std}, 4to, [58]p, orange/gilt, b/w, pep, DJ/2.00, CM)	Doubleday/Doran	1938	Handforth, Thomas	100-170	R
Hanemann, Henry W.	As Is (1st, 8vo, ipcb, 190p, uncut, b/w)	Harcourt	(1923)	Held, John	60-100	
Hankins, Maude M.	Daddy Gander (1st, 12mo, ibds, [40]p, color, pep)	Volland	(1928)	Cadie, V. Eliz.	80-140	
Hankins, Maude M.	Fermentations of Eliza (1st, 12mo, 203p, 4pl)	Crowell	(1915)	Hankins, C.	55-90	*
Hannon, John	Kings and the Cats (1st, 8vo, 78p, b/w)	L: Burns & Oats	1908	Wain, Louis	120-200	
Hanson, Charles H.	Stories of the Days of King Arthur (1st, 12mo, 271p, gilt, fp b/w)	L: Nelson	1884	Dore, Gustave	80-140	
Hanson, Joseph M.	Frontier Ballads (1st, 8vo, ibds, 92p, 7cp, pep)	McClurg	1910	Dixon, Maynard	60-90	
Harben, William N.	Mam' Linda (1st, 12mo, 387p, green/gilt, 8pl)	Harper	1907	Masters, F.B.	35-60	
Harbour, Henry	Where Flies the Flag (1st, 12mo, 286p, gilt, 6cp, cep)	L: Collins	(1904)	Rackham, Arthur	500-700	
Hardendorff, Jeanne	Little Cock (1st {std}, 4to, [32]p, color, DJ/4.95)	Lippincott	(1969)	Domjan, Joseph	30-50	
Hardendorff, Jeanne	Slip! Slop! Gobble! (1st, 4to, [32]p, color, cep, DJ/4.50)	Lippincott	(1970)	McCully, Emily	30-50	*
Hardendorff, Jeanne	Tricky Peik & other Picture Tales (1st, 8vo, 122p, gilt, fp b/w, DJ/3.25)	Lippincott	(1967)	DePaola, Tomie	30-45	
Hardy, Arthur S.	Aurelie (1st, 8vo, 31p, blue pcb, p-o, 3cp)	Harper	1912	Green, Eliz. S.	70-100	
Hardy, Martha	Tatoosh (1st {std}, 8vo, 239p, b/w, DJ/3.00)	Macmillan	1946	Rounds, Glen	25-40	
Hardy, Mary E.	Girl of the Forest (1st, lg8vo, p-o, 222p, color, pep)	Whitman	1927	Cady, Cora J.	30-50	*
Hardy, Mary E.	Little King and the Princess True (1st, 8vo, p-o, gilt, 182p, 4pl)	Rand/McNally	(1912)	Winter, Milo	80-125	
Hardy, Mary E.	Little Ta-Wish (1st, 8vo, 154p, p-o, gilt, b/w)	Rand/McNally	(1914)	Inukai, Kyohei	30-50	
Hardy, Thomas	Group of Noble Dames (1st, 8vo, 292p, brown/gilt, cvr by....)	Harper	1891	Armstrong, Margaret	50-80	
Hardy, Thomas	Jude the Obscure (1st AM, 8vo, 488p, gilt, 12pl)	Harper	1896	Unknown	150-220	
Hardy, Thomas	Under the Greenwood Tree (1st, 8vo, 271p, green/gilt, teg, 10cp)	L: Chatto	1913	Henderson, Keith	70-120	
Hardy, Thomas	Under the Greenwood Tree (1st, sm4to, gilt, 236p, wood engravings)	L: Macmillan	1940	Leighton, Clare	55-80	*
Hare, Christopher	Story of Bayard (1st, 8vo, 256p, color)	L: Dent	1911	Cole, Herbert	60-90	
Hare, Kenneth	Roads and Vagabonds (1st, lg4to, 189p, red/gilt, 2cp)	L: Eyre/Spotts.	(1930)	Aldin, Cecil	250-350	
Hark, Ann	Story of Pennsylvania Dutch (1st {std}, 4to, [32]p, ibds, col, pep, DJ/1.50)	Harper	1943	DeWitt, C.H.	40-65	
Harker, L. Allen	Romance of the Nursery (1st, 8vo, 333p, teg, red/gilt, uncut, 8pl)	L: John Lane	1903	Roberts, Katharine	30-50	
Harland, Henry	Cardinal's Snuff-Box (1st, sm8vo, red/gilt, uncut, 263p, teg, 20pl)	J. Lane	1903	Wilmshurst, G.C.	50-90	
Harland, Marion	National Cook Book (1st, sm8vo, 550p, yellow cl, cvr by...)	Scribner	1896	Armstrong, Margaret	50-80	
Harland, Marion	When Grandmamma Was 14 (1st, sm8vo, 399p, 4pl)	Lothrop Pub.	1905	Barry, Etheldred B.	25-40	*
Harland, Marion	Where Ghosts Walk (1st, 8vo, green cl, teg, 305p, cvr by...)	Putnam	1898	Armstrong, Margaret	45-70	
Harman, Humphrey	Tales Told Near a Crocodile (1st AM {std}, 8vo, 185p, b/w, DJ/3.95)	Viking	(1967)	Ford, George	25-45	
Harmon, Margaretta	How Santa Found the Cobbler's Shop (1st, 4to, [46]p, color, pep)	Suttonhouse	1936	Pogany, Willy	180-250	
Harnett, Cynthia	Great House (1st AM {std}, 8vo, 191p, col frn, DJ/3.95)	World	1968	Harnett, Cynthia	25-45	
Harnett, Cynthia	Nicholas and the Wool-Pack (1st, 8vo, 184p, b/w, DJ, CgM)	L: Methuen	(1951)	Harnett, Cynthia	60-90	
Harper, Theodore A.	His Excellency & Peter (1st {std}, 8vo, 313p, col frn, pep uncut)	Doubleday/Doran	1930	Wiese, Kurt	40-60	
Harper, Theodore A.	Mushroom Boy (1st, 8vo, 215p, 4cp, pep)	Penn	1924	Clark, Florenz	30-50	
Harper, Theodore A.	Siberian Gold (1st {std}, 8vo, brown cl, 335p, col frn, pep)	Doubleday/Page	1927	Artzybasheff, Boris	30-50	
Harper, Vincent	Mortgage on the Brain (1st, 8vo, brown/gilt, 293p, 4pl)	Doubleday/Page	1905	Macauley, Charles R.	30-50	*
Harper, Wilhelmina	Brownie of the Circus (1st {std}, lg8vo, 107p, fp color, pep, DJ/2.00)	McKay	(1941)	Neville, Vera	40-65	
Harper, Wilhelmina	Dog Show (1st, 8vo, p-o, 182p, fp color, DJ/2.75)	Houghton	1950	Nichols, Marie C.	30-50	
Harper, Wilhelmina	Flying Hoofs (1st, 8vo, 292p, red cl, 3 dp cp, b/w, DJ/2.00)	Houghton	1939	Brown, Paul	200-300	
Harper, Wilhelmina	Harvest Feast (1st {std}, sm8vo, 308p, orange cl, b/w, pep, DJ/2.00)	Dutton	(1938)	Jones, Wilfred	25-45	
Harper, Wilhelmina	Merry Christmas to You (1st {std}, sm8vo, 276p, b/w, DJ/2.00)	Dutton	(1935)	Jones, Wilfred	25-45	*
Harper, Wilhelmina	Selfish Giant... (1st, lg8vo, 86p, 6cp, DJ/2.00)	McKay	(1935)	Seredy, Kate	50-80	
Harper, Wilhelmina	The Gunniwolf (1st {std}, lg8vo, green/gilt, 104p, fp color, pep, DJ/2.00)	McKay	(1936)	Seredy, Kate	70-100	
Harper, Wilhelmina	The Gunniwolf (1st, lg8vo, [32]p, color, DJ/3.95)	Dutton	(1967)	Wiesner, William	70-100	*
Harper, Wilhelmina	Uncle Sam's Story Book (1st {std}, lg8vo, 144p, color, DJ/2.00)	McKay	(1944)	Paull, Grace	30-50	
Harraden, Beatrice	New Book of the Fairies (1st, 8vo, 190p, gilt, 10pl, pep)	L: Griffith	[1891]	Lupton, Dorothy	75-100	*
Harraden, Beatrice	Untold Tales of the Past (1st, 8vo, 273p, uncut, teg, gilt, b/w)	L: Blackwood	1897	Millar, H.R.	70-90	
Harrington, Isis	Told in the Twilight (1st {std}, 8vo, 143p, b/w, DJ/1.75)	Dutton	1938	Ream, Glen	25-40	
Harrington, John W.	Adventures of Admiral Frog (1st, lg8vo, ipcb, 49p, fp 1-color)	R.H. Russell	1902	Price, Willard B.	100-180	
Harrington, John W.	Jumping Kangaroo & Apple-Butter Cat (1st, lg8vo, 130p, b/w)	McClure	1900	Conde, J.M.	80-125	
Harris, Ada V.	Favorites from Fairyland (1st, 12mo, 129p, blue cl, 130p, 6pl)	Harper	1911	Newell, Peter	170-240	
Harris, Christie	Forbidden Frontier (1st {std}, 8vo, 210p, b/w, DJ/4.50)	Atheneum	1968	Kenny, Carey	20-35	
Harris, Christie	Once Upon a Totem (1st {std}, 8vo, 148p, b/w woodcuts, DJ/3.50, NYTBI)	Atheneum	1963	Mills, John F.	25-45	
Harris, Christie	Raven's Cry (1st {std}, 8vo, 192p, b/w, DJ/3.95)	Atheneum	1966	Reid, Bill	20-35	*
Harris, Christie	West with the White Chiefs (1st {std}, 8vo, 214p, b/w, DJ/3.95)	Atheneum	1965	Ferro, Walter	25-40	
Harris, Christie	You Have to Draw the Line Somewhere (1st {std}, 8vo, 249p, b/w, DJ/3.95)	Atheneum	1964	Johnston, Moira	20-35	
Harris, Credo	Where Souls of Men are Calling (1st, 12mo, 298p, col frn by...)	Britton	(1918)	Neill, John R.	30-50	
Harris, Isobel	Frosty Snow (1st {std}, 8vo, [26]p, ibds, DJ/1.50)	Holt	(1951)	Lane/Robertson	20-35	*
Harris, Isobel	Little Boy Brown (1st, sm4to, 44p, tan cl, 1-color, cep, DJ/1.75)	Lippincott	1949	Francois, Andre	80-125	R
Harris, Joel C.	Aaron in the Wildwoods (1st [1], 8vo, yellow cl, 270p, 24pl)	Houghton	1897	Herford, Oliver	150-220	
Harris, Joel C.	Bishop & Boogerman (1st, 12mo, green cl, 184p, 8cp)	Doubleday/Page	1909	Harding, Charlotte	100-160	
Harris, Joel C.	Brer Rabbit Rides the Fox (1st, 8vo, ibds, [32]p, fp color, pep)	Grosset/Dunlap	(1946)	Disney Studios	100-165	
Harris, Joel C.	Chronicles of Aunt Minervy Ann (1st [1], 8vo, teg, uncut, 210p, 31pl)	Scribner	1899	Frost, A.B.	120-180	R
Harris, Joel C.	Daddy Jake the Runaway (1st, 4to, 145p, cream bds, 19 b/w, cep)	Century	1889	Kemble, Edward W.	600-800	
Harris, Joel C.	Free Joe... (1st, 8vo, brown cl, uncut, 236p, 1st cvr by...)	Scribner	1887	Armstrong, Margaret	170-240	
Harris, Joel C.	Little Mr. Thimblefinger (1st, lg8vo, 230p, ae green, 32pl, cep)	Houghton	1894	Herford, Oliver	180-240	R
Harris, Joel C.	Little Union Scout (1st, 8vo, green/gilt, 181p, 8pl)	McClure	1904	Gibbs, George	150-225	
Harris, Joel C.	Mr. Rabbit at Home (1st, 8vo, 304p, tan cl, ae green, 25pl, cep)	Houghton	1895	Herford, Oliver	160-220	R
Harris, Joel C.	Nights with Uncle Remus (1st, 8vo, 416p, blue/gilt, 20pl, cep)	Bos: Osgood	1883	Church/Beard	400-650	
Harris, Joel C.	Nights with Uncle Remus (1st, 8vo, 367p, b/w)	L: A. Moring	[1907]	Shepherd, J.A.	200-300	*
Harris, Joel C.	Nights with Uncle Remus (1st, lg8vo, gilt, p-o, 338p, 12cp, pep)	Houghton	1917	Winter, Milo	150-225	
Harris, Joel C.	On the Plantation (1st, sm8vo, orange/gilt, 233p, b/w)	Appleton	1892	Kemble, Edward W.	170-240	
Harris, Joel C.	Plantation Pageants (1st, sq8vo, green cl, 247p, 20pl, cep)	Houghton	1899	Smith, E. Boyd	160-240	R
Harris, Joel C.	Shadow Between his Shoulder Blades (1st, 12mo, 132p, 4pl)	Small/Maynard	(1909)	Harding, George	120-165	
Harris, Joel C.	Story of Aaron (1st, lg8vo, tan/gilt, 198p, 25pl, cep)	Houghton	1896	Herford, Oliver	200-300	R
Harris, Joel C.	Tales of Home Folks in Peace & War (1st, sm8vo, gilt, 417p, 4pl, cep)	Houghton	1898	Smith, E. Boyd	140-220	

AUTHOR	TITLE	PUBLISHER	DATE	ARTIST	PRICE	LC
Harris, Joel C.	Tar-Baby (1st, 8vo, 90p, gilt, teg, uncut, 9pl)	Appleton	1904	Frost/Kemble	200-300	
Harris, Joel C.	Told by Uncle Remus (1st, 8vo, gilt, p-o, teg, 295p, uncut, 19pl)	McClure	1905	Various	250-350	
Harris, Joel C.	Uncle Remus (1st [1], lg8vo, 231p, gilt, 8pl, dep, PPP)	Appleton	1881	Church/Moser	900-1500	
Harris, Joel C.	Uncle Remus (1st, 8vo, 288p, teg, 9cp, fp b/w)	L: Richards	1901	Shepherd, J.A.	100-165	
Harris, Joel C.	Uncle Remus (1st, folio, [111]p, 12cp)	L: Nelson	[1906]	Rountree, Harry	400-600	
Harris, Joel C.	Uncle Remus (Gift ed., 4to, green/gilt, 265p, 12pl)	Appleton	1920	Frost/Kemble	200-300	
Harris, Joel C.	Uncle Remus (4to, 111p, orange cl, 12 cp by...)	L: Raithby	[1939]	Rountree, Harry	250-400	
Harris, Joel C.	Uncle Remus & Brer Rabbit (1st, ob4to, [63]p, green cl, p-o, color)	Stokes	1907	Conde, J.M.	300-450	
Harris, Joel C.	Uncle Remus & his Friends (1st, 8vo, 357p, green/gilt, 12pl)	Houghton	1892	Frost, A.B.	250-400	
Harris, Joel C.	Uncle Remus & the Little Boy (1st, 8vo, 173p, brown cl, uncut, p-o, 8cp)	Small/Maynard	(1910)	Conde, J.M.	150-220	R
Harris, Joel C.	Uncle Remus Returns (1st, 12mo, 175p, col frn, 7pl)	Houghton	(1918)	Frost/Conde	130-200	R
Harris, Joel C.	Uncle Remus Stories (1st, sm folio, ibds, 92p, color, GGB)	Simon/Schuster	(1947)	Disney Studios	80-120	*
Harris, Joel C.	Wally Wanderoon... (1st, lg8vo, tan cl, 294p, 31pl)	McClure	1903	Moseley, Karl	180-250	
Harris, Joel C.	Witch Wolf... (1st {std}, 12mo, 30p, tan pcb, b/w)	Bacon/Brown	1921	Dwiggins, W.A.	220-300	R
Harris, Laura	Away We Go (1st, 4to, ibds, [47]p, color, pep)	Garden City	1945	Flory, Jane	20-35	
Harris, Leila	Blackfellow Bundi... (1st, lg8vo, 63p, pep, p-o, color, DJ/1.50)	Whitman	1939	Wiese, Kurt	50-80	
Harris, Leon	Great Picture Robbery (1st {std}, ob8vo, [34]p, 2-color, cep, DJ, NYTBI)	Atheneum	1963	Schindelman, Joseph	30-45	*
Harris, Leon	Yvette (1st, 4to, 36p, fp 1-color, DJ/4.95)	McGraw-Hill	(1970)	Turkle, Brinton	50-80	*
Harris, Louise D.	Flash, Life of a Firefly (1st {std}, 8vo, 57p, color, DJ/2.95)	Little/Brown	(1966)	Kane, Henry B.	25-45	
Harris, May V.	Carnival Time at Strobeck (1st, lg8vo, p-o, 64p, fp color, pep, DJ/1.50)	Whitman	1938	Wiese, Kurt	45-75	
Harris, Rosemary	Moon in the Cloud (1st, 8vo, 176p, DJ, CgM)	L: Faber	1968	No Illustrations	45-70	*
Harris-Burland, J.	Gold Worshipers (1st, 12mo, 310p, brown cl, 6pl)	Dillingham	(1906)	Grunwald, Charles	50-80	
Harris-Burland, J.	Princess Thora (1st, 8vo, 360p, blue/gilt, 4pl)	Little/Brown	1904	Cuneo, Cyrus	100-170	
Harrison, Ada	Lucy's Village (1st, 16mo, unpag, 8cp, DJ)	L: Oxford U.Pr.	(1945)	Austin, Robert	45-70	
Harrison, Edith O.	Enchanted House (1st, sm8vo, 126p, 5cp)	McClurg	1913	Richardson, F.	70-120	
Harrison, Edith O.	Flaming Sword (1st, sm4to, blue/silver, 133p, 4cp)	McClurg	1908	Perkins, Lucy F.	60-100	
Harrison, Edith O.	Glittering Festival (1st, 4to, 176p, gilt, p-o, 4cp)	McClurg	1911	Wilson, Clara P.	80-125	
Harrison, Edith O.	Moon Princess (1st, sm4to, 162p, blue cl, 6cp)	McClurg	1905	Perkins, Lucy F.	100-160	
Harrison, Edith O.	Prince Silverwings... (1st, sm4to, blue/silver, 313p, 4cp)	McClurg	1902	Perkins, Lucy F.	80-125	
Harrison, Edith O.	Star Fairies (1st, sm4to, 128p, 6cp)	McClurg	1903	Perkins, Lucy F.	80-125	
Harrison, Elizabeth	In the Story World (1st, 12mo, 204p, gilt, dep, fp b/w)	Milton Bradley	(1931)	Lupprian, Hildegard	30-50	
Harrison, Florence	Elfin Song (1st AM, 8vo, teg, gilt, 142p, pep, 12 ticp)	Caldwell	[1912]	Harrison, Florence	300-450	
Harrison, Florence	Elfin Song (1st, 8vo, gilt, teg, 142p, 12 ticp, pep)	L: Blackie	(1912)	Harrison, Florence	350-500	
Harrison, Florence	In the Fairy Ring (1st, lg4to, 63p, AEG, gilt, pep, 25cp)	L: Blackie	(1908)	Harrison, Florence	280-350	
Harrison, Florence	Pixy Book (1st, lg8vo, [31]p, ibds, p-o, 12cp)	L: Blackie	[1918]	Harrison, Florence	250-400	
Harrison, Florence	Rhyme of a Run... (1st, ob4to, green/gilt, 22 ticp, pep)	L: Blackie	[1907]	Harrison, Florence	400-600	
Harrison, Florence	Rhymes and Reasons (4to, ibds, unpag, fp color)	L: Blackie	[1905]	Harrison, Florence	300-400	
Harrison, Godfrey	Bird Diary (1st, 12mo, 151p, p-o, 20pl, DJ)	L: Dent	1936	Gibbings, Robert	75-100	
Harrison, Mrs. Burton	Bric-a-Brac Stories (1st, 12mo, 299p, 24 illus, pep)	Scribner	1885	Crane, Walter	125-200	
Harrison, Mrs. Burton	The Carlyles (1st, 8vo, 283p, brown cl, cvr by...)	Appleton	1905	Armstrong, Margaret	30-50	*
Harrison, T. Milner	Modern Arms and a Feudal Throne (1st, 12mo, 376p, green cl, 4pl)	Fenno	1904	Starkweather, W.	80-125	
Harry, Robert	Island Boy (1st, 8vo, 209p, b/w, DJ/3.00)	Lothrop, Lee	(1956)	Lonette, Reisie	25-40	
Harshberger, Kay	Zoological Soliloquies (1st, lg4to, ibds, [44]p, color)	A. & C. Boni	1926	Harshberger, Mac	100-160	
Hart, Helen	Little Silver Tail (1st, 8vo, p-o, 96p, fp color)	Whitman	(1916)	Rountree, Harry	120-200	*
Hart, Jeanne M.	Scareboy (1st, sm4to, [48]p, fp 3-color, DJ/2.50)	Parnassus Press	(1957)	Hurt, Gerhardt	30-45	
Hart, Lavinia	When a Maid Marries (1st, sm8vo, 210p, cvr by...)	Dodd	1904	Falls, Charles B.	25-40	
Hart, Ruby	In the Woods (1st, sm sq4to, wraps, color)	Volland	(1931)	Hart, Ruby	55-80	*
Harte, Bret	Her Letter (1st, 8vo, p-o, green/gilt, teg, 98p, color, pep)	Houghton	1905	Keller, Arthur I.	50-80	
Harte, Bret	Queen of the Pirate Isle (1st, 8vo, tan cl, 58p, AEG, color)	L: Chatto	[1886]	Greenaway, Kate	350-500	
Harte, Bret	Queen of the Pirate Isle (1st AM, 8vo, 58p, AEG, color)	Houghton	1887	Greenaway, Kate	250-400	
Harte, Bret	Salomy Jane (1st, 8vo, p-o, blue/gilt, 78p, col frn by...)	Houghton	1910	Fisher, Harrison	80-140	
Hartland, Edwin	English Fairy & Folk Tales (1st, sm8vo, 282p, AEG, 13pl)	L: W. Scott	1893	Brock, Charles E.	75-100	*
Hartley, Dick	Greta and Peter in the Flower Garden (1st, 16mo, ibds, [22]p, color)	Volland	(1914)	Hartley, Dick	60-90	
Hartog, Cecile	Barbara's Song Book (1st, ob4to, 55p, ibds, p-o, 8cp)	L: G. Allen	1900	Hassall, John	200-300	
Hartwell, James (ed)	Jeweled Sea (1st, 12mo, 102p, aqua cl, b/w)	Altemus	(1906)	Neill, John R.	80-135	
Hartwell, James (ed)	Magic Bed (1st, 12mo, 109p, b/w pl)	Altemus	(1906)	Neill, John R.	80-130	
Harvey, Baldwin	Magic Dragon (1st, 8vo, 144p)	L: Duckworth	(1911)	Rountree, Harry	30-50	*
Haskell, Helen E.	Billy's Princess (1st, sm8vo, 248p, 7pl)	L.C. Page	1907	Kennedy, Helen M.	80-125	*
Haskell, Helen E.	Katrinka Grows Up (1st {std}, sm8vo, 310p, gilt, uncut, 6 fp b/w)	Dutton	1932	Bishcoff, Ilse	30-50	
Haskell, Helen E.	Nadya Makes her Bow (1st, sm8vo, green cl, uncut, 349p, b/w, DJ/2.00)	Dutton	1938	Artzybasheff, Boris	60-100	
Haskell, Helen E.	O-Heart-San (1st, 12mo, 128p, 6cp, pep)	L.C. Page	1908	Fairbanks, Frank	30-50	
Haskett, Edytha	Grains of Pepper (1st, lg8vo, 119p, color, DJ)	John Day	(1967)	Miatta, Musu	30-45	
Haslewood, C.	Dear Old Nursery Rhymes (1st, 4to, ibds, 48p, 8 chromos)	NY: Warne	[1896]	Haslewood, C.	100-160	
Hathaway, Cynthia	Two Bridgets (1st {std}, sm4to, [32]p, ibds, color, pep, DJ/1.00)	Doubleday/Doran	1941	Doane, Pelagie	30-50	*
Hauff, Wilhelm	Caravan Tales (1st AM, 8vo, 338p, 15 ticp, pep)	Stokes	(1912)	Ault, Norman	80-125	
Hauff, Wilhelm	Dwarf Long-Nose (1st, lg sq8vo, ipcb, 61p, 1-color, pep, DJ/2.95)	Random	(1960)	Sendak, Maurice	160-220	R
Hauff, Wilhelm	Fairy Tales (1st, 8vo, 344p, gilt, pep, 6cp, 12pl)	Nister/Dutton	[1910]	Dixon, Arthur A.	120-200	
Hauff, Wilhelm	Heart of Stone (1st {std}, sm4to, unpag, 1-color, DJ/3.50)	Macmillan	(1964)	Levine, David	30-50	
Hauff, Wilhelm	The Caravan (1st, 8vo, 220p, b/w, DJ/4.50)	Crowell	(1964)	Silverman, Burt	20-35	
Haugaard, Erik	Hakon of Rogen's Saga (1st, 8vo, 132p, fp b/w, DJ/3.00)	Houghton	1963	Dillon, L.& D.	30-50	
Haugaard, Erik	Little Fishes (1st, 8vo, 214p, b/w, cep, DJ/3.50, JABA)	Houghton	1967	Johnson, Milton	50-85	R*
Haugaard, Erik	Slave's Tale (1st, 8vo, 217p, fp b/w, DJ/3.00)	Houghton	1965	Dillon, L.& D.	30-50	
Hauman, George	Buttons (1st, 8vo, 64p, 2-color, pep, DJ/1.35)	Macmillan	1936	Hauman, G.& D.	30-50	*
Hauman, George	Happy Harbor (1st, 8vo, 60p, 2-color, pep, DJ/1.75)	Macmillan	1939	Hauman, G.& D.	40-65	*
Hauman, George	Surprise for Timmy (1st, 8vo, 78p, fp 1-color, pep, DJ/1.25)	Macmillan	1946	Hauman, G.& D.	30-45	*
Hauser, Heinrich	Folding Father (1st, lg ob8vo, ipcb, [24]p, 2-color, pep, DJ/1.00)	Lothrop, Lee	1942	Gergely, Tibor	40-65	
Hautzig, Esther	At Home, a Visit in Four Languages (1st {std}, 4to, [32]p, color, DJ/4.95)	Macmillan	(1968)	Aliki	30-50	*
Hautzig, Esther	In School (1st {std}, sm4to, [36]p, color, DJ/4.95)	Macmillan	(1969)	Hogrogian, Nonny	30-50	*

AUTHOR	TITLE	PUBLISHER	DATE	ARTIST	PRICE	LC
Hautzig, Esther	In the Park (1st {std}, 4to, [32]p, color, pep, DJ/4.95)	Macmillan	(1968)	Keats, Ezra J.	30-50	
Havighurst, Marion	Climb a Lofty Ladder (1st {std}, 8vo, 242p, b/w, DJ/2.75)	Winston	1952	Elgin, Jill	20-35	*
Havighurst, Marion	First Book of California Gold Rush (1st {std}, 8vo, 61p, 1-color, DJ/1.95)	F. Watts	(1962)	Stein, Harve	25-45	
Havighurst, Marion	First Book of Oregon Trail (1st {std}, 8vo, 60p, fp 1-color, pep, DJ/1.95)	F. Watts	(1960)	Borten, Helen	30-45	
Havighurst, Marion	First Book of Pioneers (1st {std}, 8vo, 69p, fp 1-color, pep, DJ/1.95)	F. Watts	(1959)	Stein, Harve	30-45	
Havighurst, Walter	Long Ships Passing (1st {std}, 8vo, 291p, b/w, DJ/3.00)	Macmillan	1942	Cosgrave, John O.	30-50	
Havighurst, Walter	Song of the Pines (1st {std}, 8vo, 205p, maps, dep, b/w, DJ/2.50, NH)	Winston	(1949)	Floethe, Richard	50-85	
Haviland, Virginia	Fairy Tales from Czechoslovakia (1st {std}, lg8vo, 90p, color, DJ/2.95)	Little/Brown	(1966)	Hyman, Trina S.	50-85	
Haviland, Virginia	Favorite Fairy Tales Told in England (1st {std}, lg8vo, 88p, color, DJ/2.75)	Little/Brown	(1959)	Bettina	50-85	
Haviland, Virginia	Favorite Fairy Tales Told in France (1st {std}, lg8vo, 91p, color, DJ/2.75)	Little/Brown	(1959)	Duvoisin, Roger	50-85	
Haviland, Virginia	Favorite Fairy Tales Told in Germany (1st {std}, lg8vo, 83p, DJ/2.75)	Little/Brown	(1959)	Suba, Susanne	50-85	
Haviland, Virginia	Favorite Fairy Tales Told in Greece (1st {std}, 8vo, 90p, color, DJ/3.25)	Little/Brown	1970	Hogrogian, Nonny	50-85	
Haviland, Virginia	Favorite Fairy Tales Told in Italy (1st {std}, lg8vo, 90p, color, DJ/2.95)	Little/Brown	(1965)	Ness, Evaline	50-85	R
Haviland, Virginia	Favorite Fairy Tales Told in Norway (1st {std}, 8vo, 88p, color, DJ/2.95)	Little/Brown	(1961)	Weisgard, Leonard	50-85	
Haviland, Virginia	Favorite Fairy Tales Told in Poland (1st {std}, lg8vo, 90p, color, DJ/2.95)	Little/Brown	1963	Hoffmann, Felix	50-85	R
Haviland, Virginia	Favorite Fairy Tales Told in Russia (1st {std}, sm8vo, 86p, color, DJ/2.95)	Little/Brown	1961	Danska, Herbert	50-85	
Haviland, Virginia	Favorite Fairy Tales Told in Spain (1st {std}, 8vo, 87p, color, DJ/2.95)	Little/Brown	(1963)	Cooney, Barbara	50-85	R
Haviland, Virginia	Favorite Fairy Tales Told in Sweeden (1st {std}, lg8vo, 95p, color, DJ/2.95)	Little/Brown	(1966)	Solbert, Ronni	50-85	
Haviland, Virginia	Favorite Fairy Tales Told/Scotland (1st {std}, lg8vo, 92p, color, DJ/2.95)	Little/Brown	(1963)	Adams, Adrienne	50-85	R
Haviland-Taylor, K.	Nursery Nights (1st, lg8vo, 95p, 2-color, DJ/1.50)	Lippincott	(1942)	Merwin, Decie	70-100	
Hawes, Charles B.	Dark Frigate (1st, 8vo, yellow cl, 247p, b/w, PPP, NM)	Atl. Monthly Pr.	(1923)	Ripley, A.L.	100-165	
Hawes, Charles B.	Great Quest (1st, 8vo, 359p, 5pl, pep, NH)	Little/Brown	(1921)	Varian, George	50-80	*
Hawes, Elizabeth	Men Can Take It (1st {std}, 8vo, blue cl, 275p, 14pl, DJ/2.00)	Random	(1939)	Thurber, James	75-100	*
Hawes, Judy	Bees and Beelines (1st, ob8vo, [40]p, color, DJ/2.75)	Crowell	(1964)	Aliki	30-45	*
Hawes, Judy	Fireflies in the Night (1st, ob8vo, [38]p, 3-color, DJ/2.50)	Crowell	(1963)	Mizumura, Kazue	25-40	
Hawes, Judy	Goats Who Killed the Leopard (1st, 8vo, [48]p, fp b/w, DJ/3.75)	Crowell	(1970)	Hawes, Judy	30-45	
Hawes, Judy	Ladybug, Ladybug, Fly Away Home (1st, ob8vo, [39]p, 2-color, DJ/3.25)	Crowell	(1967)	Emberley, Ed	30-50	
Hawes, Judy	Shrimps (1st, ob8vo, ipcb, [40]p, 2-color, DJ/3.25)	Crowell	(1967)	Low, Joseph	30-45	
Hawes, Judy	Watch Honeybees with Me (1st, sq8vo, [40]p, fp 2-color, DJ/2.75)	Crowell	(1964)	Stone, Helen	30-45	*
Hawes, Judy	What I Like about Toads (1st, ob8vo, [40]p, color, DJ/3.50)	Crowell	(1969)	McCrea, J.& R.	25-45	
Hawes, Judy	Why Frogs are Wet (1st, ob8vo, 35p, color, DJ/3.50)	Crowell	(1968)	Madden, Don	25-40	
Hawkes, Clarence	Field & Forest Friends (1st, 12mo, 207p, pep, 4pl)	F.G. Browne	1913	Copeland, Charles	30-50	
Hawkes, Clarence	Silversheene: King of Sled Dogs (1st, 12mo, 234p, 4pl)	Milton Bradley	(1924)	Bull, Charles L.	25-40	*
Hawkes, Clarence	White Czar... (1st, 12mo, 202p, b/w pl)	Milton Bradley	1923	Bull, Charles L.	25-40	*
Hawkes, Hester	Ning's Pony (1st, 8vo, [29]p, 1-color, DJ/2.00)	Coward	(1953)	Wiese, Kurt	30-50	
Hawkes, Hester	Three Seeds (1st, 8vo, [41]p, fp 1-color, pep, DJ/2.25)	Coward	(1956)	Wiese, Kurt	30-50	*
Hawkins, Quail	Androcles & the Lion (1st, ob4to, 48p, 3-color, DJ/4.50)	Coward	(1970)	Negri, Rocco	40-65	
Hawkins, Quail	Aunt-Sitter (1st, 8vo, 35p, yellow cl, b/w, pep, DJ/2.50)	Holiday House	(1958)	Turkle, Brinton	25-40	*
Hawkins, Quail	Don't Run, Apple! (1st, 8vo, ipcb, [36]p, b/w, pep)	Holiday House	(1944)	Cote, Phyllis	30-50	
Hawkins, Quail	Little Book of Prayers and Graces (1st, sq12mo, [32]p, ibds, pep, DJ/1.00)	Doubleday	(1952)	DeAngeli, Marguerite	25-45	
Hawkins, Quail	Mark, Mark, Shut the Door! (1st, 8vo, [31]p, ipcb, 2-color, DJ/1.50)	Holiday House	(1947)	Busoni, Rafaello	35-60	*
Hawkins, Quail	Prayers & Graces for Small Children (1st, sq8vo [32]p, ibds, color, DJ/0.50)	Grosset/Dunlap	(1941)	DeAngeli, Marguerite	60-90	
Hawkins, Quail	Puppy for Keeps (1st, 8vo, [28]p, b/w, pep, DJ/1.00)	Holiday House	(1943)	Wiese, Kurt	25-40	
Hawkins, Quail	Too Many Dogs (1st, 8vo, [57]p, olive cl, fp b/w, pep, DJ/1.50)	Holiday House	(1946)	Wiese, Kurt	25-40	
Hawkins, Quail	Who Wants an Apple (1st, 8vo, [39]p, ipcb, b/w, pep, DJ/1.00)	Holiday House	(1942)	Granahan, L.& D.	25-40	
Hawkins, Sheila	Bruzzy Bear & the Cabin Boy (1st {std}, lg4to, [32]p, color, pep, DJ/1.00)	Harper	(1940)	Hawkins, Sheila	30-50	
Hawkins, Sheila	Little Gray Colo (1st, 8vo, [41]p, ibds, color, pep)	Grosset/Dunlap	(1939)	Hawkins, Sheila	40-65	
Hawkinson, Lucy	Dance, Dance, Amy Chan! (1st, lg8vo, unpag, color, pep, DJ/2.75)	Whitman	(1964)	Hawkinson, Lucy	20-35	*
Hawksley, E.D.	Charles Dickens Birthday Book (1st, 8vo, [285]p, 12 fp b/w, DJ)	L: Faber	(1948)	Ardizzone, Edward	60-90	
Hawley, Harriet E.	Story of a Little Tin Soldier (1st, 4to, p-o, 64p, 6cp)	Cupples/Leon	(1914)	Low, Loretta	60-90	
Hawley, Harriet E.	Timothy Toddlekin (1st, 4to, red cl, 64p, p-o, 6cp, 6pl)	Cupples/Leon	(1914)	Low, Loretta	50-80	
Hawley, Harriet E.	Woodland Party (1st, 4to, p-o, 49p, 13cp)	Cupples/Leon	(1913)	Low, Loretta	60-100	
Hawley, Harriet S.	Goose Girl of Nurnberg (1st, 4to, [59]p, col frn, b/w, DJ/1.50)	Suttonhouse	1936	Pogany, Willy	100-140	
Hawthorne, Hildegarde	Lure of the Garden (1st, 4to, uncut, 259p, teg, dep, 6cp by...)	Century	1911	Betts, Anna W.	150-225	
Hawthorne, Hildegarde	Lure of the Garden (1st, 4to, teg, uncut, 259p, dep, 1cp by...)	Century	1911	Parrish, Maxfield	150-225	
Hawthorne, Hildegarde	No Road Too Long (1st {std}, 8vo, 261p, b/w, pep, DJ/2.25)	Longmans	1940	MacDonald, James	30-50	
Hawthorne, Hildegarde	On the Golden Trail (1st {std}, 8vo, 302p, b/w, pep, DJ/2.00)	Longmans	1936	Tousey, Sanford	30-50	
Hawthorne, Hildegarde	Romantic Rebel (1st {std}, 8vo, 231p, fp b/w, NH)	Century	(1932)	Berger, William M.	30-50	
Hawthorne, Hildegarde	Wheels Toward the West (1st {std}, 8vo, 243p, 5 fp b/w, pep)	Longmans	1931	Rodgers, Richard	20-35	
Hawthorne, Julian	Rumpty-Dudget's Tower (1st, 8vo, 72p, col frn)	Stokes	1924	Hood, George	30-50	
Hawthorne, Nathaniel	Golden Touch (1st, 8vo, orange cl, 61p, fp 2-color, dep, DJ/2.50)	Whittlesey	(1959)	Galdone, Paul	40-65	
Hawthorne, Nathaniel	In Colonial Days (1st, 8vo, 104p, teg, beige/gilt, cvr by...)	L.C. Page	1906	McManus, Blanche	40-65	
Hawthorne, Nathaniel	In Colonial Days (1st, 8vo, 104p, teg, beige/gilt, 7cp by...)	L.C. Page	1906	Merrill, Frank T.	40-65	
Hawthorne, Nathaniel	Pandora's Box (1st, 8vo, 58p, fp 1-color, dep, DJ/2.95)	McGraw-Hill	(1967)	Galdone, Paul	30-45	
Hawthorne, Nathaniel	Pegasus, the Winged Horse (1st, folio, ibds, 39p, 11 fp color, DJ/1.95)	Macmillan	1963	Levit, Herschel	30-50	
Hawthorne, Nathaniel	Scarlet Letter (1st, 8vo, AEG, blue bds, 8pl)	L: Bliss Sands	1897	Robinson, Thomas H.	70-120	
Hawthorne, Nathaniel	Scarlet Letter (1st AM, sm4to, 296p, ibds, 31 ticp)	Doran	[1920]	Thomson, Hugh	170-240	
Hawthorne, Nathaniel	Scarlet Letter (1st, 4to, uncut, 296p, gilt, teg, 31 ticp)	L: Methuen	(1920)	Thomson, Hugh	170-250	
Hawthorne, Nathaniel	Scarlet Letter (1st, 8vo, 362p, uncut, color)	Random	1928	Angelo, Valenti	70-120	R*
Hawthorne, Nathaniel	Snow Image (1st, 16mo, blue cl, 69p, dp color, pep)	Macmillan	1930	Lathrop, Dorothy	50-80	
Hawthorne, Nathaniel	Tanglewood Tales (1st, sm4to, AEG, gilt, 190p, b/w pl)	Houghton	1887	Edwards, George W.	100-160	*
Hawthorne, Nathaniel	Tanglewood Tales (1st UK, 4to, 190p, b/w)	L: Chatto	1888	Edwards, George W.	80-130	
Hawthorne, Nathaniel	Tanglewood Tales (1st, sm8vo, 222p, uncut, 12cp)	Dent/Dutton	1903	Fell, H. Granville	100-160	
Hawthorne, Nathaniel	Tanglewood Tales (16mo, 107p, gilt, p-o, uncut, 8cp)	Jack/Dutton	[1908]	Allen, Olive	40-60	*
Hawthorne, Nathaniel	Tanglewood Tales (12mo, red cl, 320p, 4cp, 24pl, pep)	L: T.F. Unwin	[1910]	Pogany, Willy	120-170	
Hawthorne, Nathaniel	Tanglewood Tales (1st, 8vo, 242p, 6cp, pep)	L: Allen/Unwin	1912	Soper, George	70-125	
Hawthorne, Nathaniel	Tanglewood Tales (1st, lg8vo, p-o, gilt, 283p, 10cp, pep, WS)	Rand/McNally	(1913)	Winter, Milo	90-160	
Hawthorne, Nathaniel	Tanglewood Tales (1st UK, lg8vo, 283p, blue/gilt, 10cp)	L: Duckworth	1914	Winter, Milo	80-120	

AUTHOR	TITLE	PUBLISHER	DATE	ARTIST	PRICE	LC
Hawthorne, Nathaniel	Tanglewood Tales (1st, 4to, 245p, gilt, 14 ticp, pep)	L: Hodder	[1919]	Dulac, Edmund	200-270	
Hawthorne, Nathaniel	Tanglewood Tales (1st, 4to, p-o, 261p, gilt, pep, 10cp)	Penn	(1921)	Sterrett, Virginia	250-400	R
Hawthorne, Nathaniel	Wonder Book (1st, lg8vo, 210p, cloth, 19cp)	L: McIlvaine	1892	Crane, Walter	250-350	
Hawthorne, Nathaniel	Wonder Book (1st AM, lg8vo, 210p, 19cp)	Houghton	1893	Crane, Walter	200-300	
Hawthorne, Nathaniel	Wonder Book (1st, lg8vo, p-o, 125p, 12cp)	Stokes	(1908)	Perkins, Lucy F.	70-100	
Hawthorne, Nathaniel	Wonder Book (1st AM, lg8vo, gilt, 320p, 4cp, pep)	Jacobs	(1909)	Pogany, Willy	120-185	
Hawthorne, Nathaniel	Wonder Book (1st, 8vo, teg, ibds, gilt, 24cp)	L: J.M. Dent	1910	Fell, H. Granville	100-160	
Hawthorne, Nathaniel	Wonder Book (1st, lg8vo, p-o, 358p, blue/gilt, pep, 10cp)	Duffield	1910	Parrish, Maxfield	250-350	
Hawthorne, Nathaniel	Wonder Book (1st, lg8vo, p-o, gilt, 254p, 8cp, pep, WS)	Rand/McNally	(1913)	Winter, Milo	70-120	
Hawthorne, Nathaniel	Wonder Book (1st AM, lg8vo, red/gilt, 16 ticp, 8cp)	Doran	[1922]	Rackham, Arthur	250-350	
Hawthorne, Nathaniel	Wonder Book (1st, 4to, 207p, red/gilt, 16 ticp, 8cp, pep)	L: Hodder	[1922]	Rackham, Arthur	270-350	
Hawthorne, Nathaniel	Wonder Book (1st, 8vo, p-o, gilt, 421p, 4cp)	Houghton	1923	Tenggren, Gustaf	35-60	
Hawthorne, Nathaniel	Wonder Book (1st sm8vo, 201p, color, by...)	Macrae Smith	(1925)	Abbott, Elenore P.	30-50	
Hawthorne, Nathaniel	Wonder Book (1st, lg8vo, p-o, 232p, col frn, pep)	Sears	(1928)	Chuse, Anne	30-50	*
Hawthorne, Nathaniel	Wonder Book (1st, 12mo, 234p, color)	Saalfield	(1929)	Peat, Fern B.	35-60	*
Hawthorne, Nathaniel	Wonder Book (8vo, later, yellow cl, p-o, 206p, 7cp)	Garden City	[1930]	Rackham, Arthur	90-130	
Hawthorne, Nathaniel	Wonder Book (1st, 8vo, p-o, 403p, red/gilt, 4cp, pep)	Winston	(1930)	Richardson, F.	40-60	
Hawthorne, Nathaniel	Wonder Book & Tanglewood Tales (1st, 8vo, gilt, teg, 421p)	Houghton	1898	Crane/Edwards	220-300	
Hawthorne, Nathaniel	Wonder Tales (1st, 12mo, 62p, b/w)	Penn	1908	LeFanu, B.	25-40	*
Hawtrey, Valentina	Life of St. Mary Magdalen (1st, 12mo, gilt, 285p, teg, cvr by...)	L: John Lane	1904	King, Jessie	100-160	
Hay, Helen	Beasts & Birds (1st, lg4to, ibds, 15 fp illus)	R.H. Russell	1900	VerBeck, Frank	200-300	
Hay, Helen	Verses for Jock & Joan (1st, lg sq4to, 32p, ibds, 6cp)	Fox Duffield	1905	Harding, Charlotte	200-300	R
Hay, Ian	Lighter Side of School Life (1st, 8vo, 226p, gilt, uncut, teg, 12cp)	L: Foulis	(1914)	Baumer, Lewis	45-70	
Hay, John	Castilian Days (1st, 8vo, 343p, teg, green cl, b/w)	Houghton	1903	Pennell, Joseph	50-80	
Hay, John	Pike County Ballads (1st, 8vo, p-o, 45p, 6cp, pep)	Houghton	(1912)	Wyeth, N.C.	150-225	
Hay, Timothy	Horses (1st {std}, sm ob4to, [32]p, ipcb, fp b/w, DJ/1.50)	Harper	(1944)	Wag	120-200	
Haydon, Arthur L.	Book of Robin Hood (8vo, green cl, 263p, 12cp)	L: Warne	[1931]	Robinson, Thomas H.	60-95	
Haydon, Arthur L.	Stories of King Arthur (1st, 12mo, 94p, p-o, red/gilt, 4cp by...)	L: Cassell	1910	Rackham, Arthur	200-300	R
Hayes, Florence	Eskimo Hunter (1st, sm8vo, 275p, col frn, DJ/2.25)	Random	(1945)	Wiese, Kurt	25-45	
Hayes, Florence	Skid (1st, 8vo, 216p, b/w, DJ/2.50)	Houghton	1948	Fax, Elton C.	40-65	
Hayes, Marjorie A.	Alice-Albert Elephant (1st {std}, 8vo, 134p, pep, fp b/w, DJ/1.75)	Little/Brown	1938	Wiese, Kurt	45-70	
Hayes, Nancy M.	Book of Games (1st, 8vo, ibds, 144p, p-o, dep, 24cp)	L: Ward Lock	1920	Tarrant, Margaret	150-240	
Haynes, Louise M.	Over the Rainbow Bridge (1st, sq8vo, [42]p, ibds, color)	Volland	(1920)	Browne, Carmen L.	80-120	
Hays, Daniel	Charley Sang a Song (1st, ob8vo, 46p, fp color, DJ/2.95)	Harper	(1964)	Shulevitz, Uri	40-65	
Hays, M.G.	Kaptin Kiddo & Puppo (1st, ob4to, ibds, color)	L: Chambers	(1913)	Wiederseim, Grace	600-800	
Hays, M.G.	Kiddie Land (1st, 4to, [52]p, tan bds, p-o, 12cp, pep)	Jacobs	(1910)	Wiederseim, Grace	350-500	
Hays, M.G.	Kiddie Rhymes (1st, 4to, [52]p, ibds, p-o, 6cp, pep)	Jacobs	(1911)	Wiederseim, Grace	300-500	*
Hays, M.G.	Little Pets Book (1st, 4to, ibds, 6cp)	Jacobs	(1911)	Wiederseim, Grace	300-450	
Hays, M.G.	Rag Animals ABC (lg4to, stiff wrps, 30p, color)	Donohue	(1913)	Hays, M.G.	200-350	*
Hays, M.G.	Rosy Childhood (1st, 4to, ibds, 6 fp color, pep)	Jacobs	(1911)	Wiederseim, Grace	200-300	
Hays, M.G.	Vegetable Verselets (1st, 12mo, 60p, ibds, 20 fp 1-color)	Lippincott	1911	Wiederseim, Grace	250-350	R
Hays, Wilma P.	Christmas on the Mayflower (1st, 8vo, unpag, fp 1-color, pep, DJ/2.50)	Coward	(1956)	Duvoisin, Roger	30-45	
Hays, Wilma P.	French Are Coming (1st, 8vo, 102p, fp b/w, gilt, DJ/3.50)	Holt, Rinehart	(1965)	Weisgard, Leonard	25-40	
Hays, Wilma P.	Goose that was a Watchdog (1st {std}, 8vo, 41p, b/w, DJ/2.95)	Little/Brown	(1967)	McClary, Nelson	20-30	
Hays, Wilma P.	Highland Halloween (1st, 8vo, 64p, fp 1-color, DJ/2.50)	Coward	(1962)	Burchard, Peter	20-30	
Hays, Wilma P.	Little Hawaiian Horse (1st {std}, 8vo, 40p, b/w, DJ/2.50)	Little/Brown	(1963)	Dennis, Wesley	25-40	
Hays, Wilma P.	Little Horse that Raced a Train (1st {std}, 8vo, 32p, b/w, DJ/2.75)	Little/Brown	(1959)	Dennis, Wesley	25-40	
Hays, Wilma P.	Little Lone Coyote (1st {std}, 8vo, 34p, blue cl, b/w, DJ/2.75)	Little/Brown	(1961)	Dennis, Wesley	30-45	
Hays, Wilma P.	Pup Who Became a Police Dog (1st {std}, 8vo, 44p, b/w, DJ/2.75)	Little/Brown	(1963)	Dennis, Wesley	20-35	
Hays, Wilma P.	Story of Valentine (1st, 8vo, 55p, 1-color, DJ/2.50)	Coward	(1956)	Weisgard, Leonard	25-40	
Haywood, Carolyn	B is for Betsy (1st, 8vo, 159p, b/w, pep, DJ/2.00)	Harcourt	1939	Haywood, Carolyn	30-50	
Haywood, Carolyn	Back to School with Betsy (1st, 8vo, 176p, b/w, DJ/2.00)	Harcourt	(1943)	Haywood, Carolyn	30-50	*
Haywood, Carolyn	Betsy and Billy (1st, 8vo, 156p, b/w, pep, DJ/2.00)	Harcourt	(1941)	Haywood, Carolyn	40-65	*
Haywood, Carolyn	Betsy and the Boys (1st, 8vo, 175p, b/w, DJ/2.00)	Harcourt	(1945)	Haywood, Carolyn	40-65	*
Haywood, Carolyn	Betsy's Little Star (1st, 8vo, 157p, b/w, DJ/2.00)	Wm. Morrow	1950	Haywood, Carolyn	30-50	*
Haywood, Carolyn	Eddie Makes Music (1st, lg8vo, 191p, b/w, DJ/2.95)	Wm. Morrow	1957	Haywood, Carolyn	40-65	*
Haywood, Carolyn	Here's a Penny (1st, 8vo, 158p, b/w, DJ/2.00)	Harcourt	(1944)	Haywood, Carolyn	30-50	*
Haywood, Carolyn	Penny and Peter (1st, 8vo, 160p, b/w, pep, DJ/2.25)	Harcourt	(1946)	Haywood, Carolyn	30-50	*
Haywood, Carolyn	Primrose Day (1st, 8vo, 200p, b/w, DJ/2.00)	Harcourt	(1942)	Haywood, Carolyn	30-50	*
Haywood, Carolyn	Taffy & Melissa Molasses (1st, 8vo, 191p, b/w, DJ/4.25)	Wm. Morrow	(1969)	Haywood, Carolyn	20-40	
Haywood, Carolyn	Two and Two are Four (1st, 8vo, 171p, b/w, pep, DJ/2.00)	Harcourt	(1940)	Haywood, Carolyn	40-65	*
Haywood, Carolyn	When I Grow Up (1st [1st bk.], folio, [20]p, color)	Whitman	(1931)	Haywood, Carolyn	70-120	*
Hazard, R.H.	House on Stilts (1st, 12mo, red cl, 346p, 4pl)	Dillingham	(1910)	Lemon, J.A.	30-50	
Hazeltine, Alice	Easter Book of Legends and Stories (1st, 8vo, 392p, b/w, DJ/2.75)	Lothrop, Lee	(1947)	Bianco, Pamela	30-50	
Hazeltine, Alice	Just for Fun: Humerous Stories & Poems (1st, 8vo, 332p, b/w, DJ/2.75)	Lothrop, Lee	(1948)	Weisgard, Leonard	30-45	
Hazeltine, Alice	Stories of Love (1st, 8vo, 308p, b/w, DJ/3.00)	Lothrop, Lee	(1951)	Weisgard, Leonard	20-35	*
Hazelton, Elizabeth	Sammy, the Crow Who Remembered (1st, sm ob4to, [40]p, b/w, DJ)	Scribner	(1969)	(Photos)	25-40	
Hazelton, Mary	Our Little African Cousin (1st, 12mo, 98p, b/w)	L.C. Page	1902	Bridgman, L.J.	30-50	
Headland, I.T.	Chinese Boy and Girl (1st, 8vo, ibds, 176p, fp b/w)	Revell	(1901)	(Photos)	100-165	
Headland, I.T.	Chinese Mother Goose Rhymes (1st, 8vo, 157p, ibds)	Revell	(1900)	(Photos)	100-165	
Heady, Eleanor	Brave Johnny O'Hare (1st, sm ob4to, [41]p, fp color, pep, DJ/3.50)	Parents Mag. Pr.	(1969)	Kellogg, Steven	50-80	*
Heady, Eleanor	When the Stones Were Soft (1st, 8vo, 94p, ibds, fp b/w, DJ/3.50)	Funk/Wagnalls	(1968)	Feelings, Tom	40-65	
Heal, Edith	Dogie Boy (1st, lg8vo, 79p, brown cl, pep, 11 fp color, DJ/2.00)	Whitman	1943	Sperry, Armstrong	50-80	
Heal, Edith	Robin Hood (1st, lg8vo, 626p, p-o, 8 fp color, pep, WS)	Rand/McNally	(1928)	Content, Dan	40-65	
Heal, Edith	Siegfried (1st, 8vo, 368p, 5cp, pep)	Chi: Rockwell	1930	Winter, Milo	50-80	
Healy, Daty	Cat Tales from Many Lands (1st, sq8vo, [64]p, fp 2-color, pep)	Scribner	1932	Healy, Daty	140-220	
Hearn, Lafcadio	Boy Who Drew Cats (1st, folio, 40p, ibds, fp color, DJ/1.95)	Macmillan	1963	Saito, Manabu	35-50	
Hearn, Lafcadio	Japanese Fairy Tales (1st, 8vo, 132p, blue cl, 4cp, pep)	Boni/Liveright	(1924)	Kay, Gertrude A.	80-140	

AUTHOR	TITLE	PUBLISHER	DATE	ARTIST	PRICE	LC
Hearn, Lafcadio	Kwaidan (1st, 12mo, 240p, teg, uncut, designs by..)	Houghton	1904	Rogers, Bruce	120-160	
Hearn, Lafcadio	Romance of the Milky Way (1st, 12mo, 209p, t.e. yellow)	Houghton	1905	Rogers, Bruce	80-130	
Heath, Irene	An ABC (1st, 4to, unpag, ibds, color)	L: Warne	[1933]	Heath, Irene	100-175	
Heath, Janet F.	Built-Upon House (1st, lg8vo, 126p, p-o, color, pep)	Whitman	(1929)	Dotterer, Lloyd J.	35-60	*
Heath, Janet F.	Mooky & Tooky (1st, lg8vo, ipcb, [45]p, 1-color, pep, DJ/1.50)	Howell/Soskin	(1946)	Bare, Arnold E.	30-50	
Heathers, Anne	Handful of Surprises (1st {std}, 4to, unpag, 2-color, DJ/2.95)	Harcourt	(1961)	Frances, Esteban	25-45	
Heathers, Anne	Thread Soldier (1st {std}, 12mo, unpag, 1-color, DJ/1.95)	Harcourt	1960	Frances, Esteban	20-35	*
Heaton, John L.	Book of Lies (1st, 12mo, black/silver, 175p, b/w)	NY: Morse	1896	VerBeck, Frank	45-70	
Hecht, Ben	Cat/Jumped Out of the Story (1st {std}, 8vo, bds, p-o, pep, color, DJ/1.25)	Winston	(1947)	Bacon, Peggy	65-100	
Heddle, Enid	Boomerang Book of Legendary Tales (1st, 8vo, 150p, fp b/w, DJ)	Longmans	(1957)	Parker, Nancy	25-45	
Heiberg, Neils	White-Ear and Peter (1st, 8vo, 222p, red/gilt, 16cp)	L: Macmillan	1912	Aldin, Cecil	200-300	
Heide, Florence P.	Alphabet Zoop (1st, ob4to, [61]p, color, DJ/4.75)	McCall Pub.	(1970)	Mathews, Sally	40-65	*
Heide, Florence P.	Benjamin Budge & Barnaby Ball (1st, ob8vo, [32]p, fp 1-color, DJ/2.95)	Four Winds Pr.	(1967)	Mathews, Sally	50-80	
Heide, Florence P.	Day It Snowed in Summer (1st {1}, 4to, [32]p, fp 3-color, dep, DJ/2.95)	Funk/Wagnalls	(1968)	Longtemps, Kenneth	30-50	*
Heide, Florence P.	Giants are Very Brave People (1st, sm4to, [42]p, fp color, dep, DJ/3.50)	Parents Mag. Pr.	(1970)	Robinson, Charles	25-40	
Heide, Florence P.	How Big am I? (1st {std}, 8vo, [32]p, color, DJ/1.95)	Follett	(1968)	Suyeoka, George	20-35	
Heide, Florence P.	It Never is Dark (1st {std}, 8vo, 32p, color, DJ/1.95)	Follett	(1968)	Almquist, Don	20-35	
Heide, Florence P.	Maximilian (1st {1}, 4to, [32]p, fp color, cep, DJ/2.95)	Funk/Wagnalls	(1967)	Renfro, Ed	20-35	
Heide, Florence P.	Sound of Sunshine, Sound of Rain (1st, lg8vo, [40]p, fp color, DJ/3.95)	Parents Mag. Pr.	(1970)	Longtemps, Kenneth	30-50	
Heide, Florence P.	That's What Friends are For (1st, ob8vo, [39]p, color, DJ/3.95)	Four Winds Pr.	(1968)	Turkle, Brinton	30-45	
Heilbroner, Joan	Happy Birthday Present (1st, 8vo, 63p, color, DJ/1.95)	Harper	(1962)	Chalmers, Mary	25-45	
Heilbroner, Joan	This is the House Where Jack Lives (1st, 8vo, 62p, color, DJ/1.95)	Harper	(1962)	Aliki	30-50	*
Heimeran, Ernst	Story of the Coal-Black Horse (1st AM, 4to, [32]p, color, DJ/2.95)	NY: Hart	(1968)	Braun, Beatrice	30-45	
Heine, Heinrich	Atta Troll (1st, 12mo, 185p, grey bds, gilt, pep, b/w)	L: Sidgwick/Jack	1913	Pogany, Willy	150-225	
Heine, Heinrich	Atta Troll (1st AM, 12mo, 185p, bds, gilt, 3pl)	Huebsch	(1914)	Pogany, Willy	140-200	
Heinlein, Robert	Between Planets (1st, 8vo, 222p, b/w, DJ/2.50)	Scribner	1951	Geary, Clifford	200-300	
Heinlein, Robert	Farmer in the Sky (1st, 8vo, 216p, b/w, DJ/2.50)	Scribner	1950	Geary, Clifford	200-300	
Heinlein, Robert	Have Space Suit-Will Travel (1st, 8vo, 276p, b/w, DJ/2.95)	Scribner	1958	Emshwiller, Ed	200-300	
Heinlein, Robert	Red Planet (1st, 8vo, 211p, b/w, DJ/2.50)	Scribner	1949	Geary, Clifford	200-300	
Heinlein, Robert	Rocket Ship Galileo (1st [1st bk.], 8vo, 212p, b/w, DJ/2.00)	Scribner	(1947)	Voter, Thomas	800-1000	
Heinlein, Robert	Space Cadet (1st, 8vo, 242p, b/w, DJ/2.50)	Scribner	1948	Geary, Clifford	350-500	
Heinlein, Robert	Starman Jones (1st, 8vo, 305p, b/w, DJ/2.50)	Scribner	1953	Geary, Clifford	200-300	
Heisenfelt, Kathryn	About Customs (1st, 4to, ibds, 42p, color, pep, DJ/1.00)	Grosset/Dunlap	(1938)	Stone, Charlotte	65-100	
Hekking, Johanna	Pigtails (1st, 8vo, 112p, 10cp, DJ/2.00)	Stokes	1937	Castle, Molly	35-50	
Held, John	Danny Decoy (1st, sq8vo, ibds, [83]p, 2-color, pep, DJ/1.00)	A.S. Barnes	(1942)	Held, John	100-165	
Held, John	Dog Stories (1st, 4to, ibds, 124p, fp b/w)	Vanguard Press	1930	Held, John	100-165	
Held, John	Gods were Promiscuous (1st, sm8vo, 248p, DJ/2.00)	Vanguard Press	1937	Held, John	60-90	
Held, John	Saga of Frankie & Johnny (1st {std}, sm4to, 49p, uncut, red/gilt, fp b/w)	NY: W.V. McKee	(1930)	Held, John	100-160	*
Helle, Andre	Big Beasts & Little Beasts (1st, ob12mo, p-o, 80p, 20cp)	Stokes	1924	Helle, Andre	140-200	
Hellman, Sam	Low Bridge & Punk Pungs (1st, 12mo, 111p, 5pl)	Little/Brown	1924	Sarg, Tony	30-50	
Helm, Clementine	Cecily (1st, lg8vo, p-o, 298p, 8cp, pep)	Lippincott	(1924)	Kay, Gertrude A.	100-160	
Helm, Nellie L.	When Jesus was Here Among Men (1st, 8vo, green cl, 205p, cover by...)	Revell	1902	Hazenplug, Frank	50-80	
Helm, Ruth	Gwendolyn (1st AM, 8vo, 43p, 1-color, dep, DJ/2.00)	NY: Oxford U.Pr.	1952	Gekiere, Madeleine	30-50	
Helm, Ruth	Mr. Putterbee's Jungle (1st AM, 8vo, 47p, fp 1-color, pep, DJ/2.25)	NY: Oxford U.Pr.	(1953)	Gekiere, Madeleine	30-50	
Helps, Racey	Barnaby in Search of a House (1st, 16mo, 47p, ibds, color, pep)	L: Collins	1948	Helps, Racey	20-35	
Helps, Racey	Blow Away Balloon (1st, 8vo, 48p, bds, color, pep, DJ/3.50)	Chilton Books	(1967)	Helps, Racey	25-40	
Helps, Racey	Tail of Hunky Dory (1st, 12mo, 46p, ibds, fp color, cep)	L: Collins	1958	Helps, Racey	20-35	
Helps, Racey	Two from a Teapot (1st {std}, 12mo, 48p, 2-color, pep, DJ/2.95)	Chilton Books	(1966)	Helps, Racey	30-50	
Henderson, Bernard	Wonder Tales of Ancient Wales (1st, 8vo, gilt, 166p, teg, 8cp)	L: P. Allan	(1921)	Williamson, Doris	100-170	
Henderson, Dorothy	Danny the Dream Man (1st, sq8vo, ibds, [48]p, color, pep)	Volland	(1928)	Henderson, Dorothy	80-120	
Henderson, Gertrude	Ring of the Nibelung (1st {std}, lg8vo, 218p, col frn, 12 fp b/w)	Knopf	1932	Tenggren, Gustaf	60-100	
Henderson, John	Jamaica (1st, sm8vo, 86p, blue/gilt, teg, 24cp)	L: A&C Black	1906	Forrest, A.S.	90-160	
Henderson, L.R.S.	Flight Brothers (1st, 4to, 102p, ibds, 6cp)	Reilly/Britton	(1912)	Nelson, Emile A.	200-300	
Henderson, L.R.S.	Magic Aeroplane (1st, 4to, ibds, 96p, 6cp)	Reilly/Britton	(1911)	Nelson, Emile A.	200-300	
Henderson, Lima L.	Resolute (1st, 8vo, 64p, ipcb, fp b/w, DJ/0.50)	McKay	(1940)	Beistle, Mary A.	50-80	
Hendrich, Paula	Trudy's First Day at Camp (1st, sm4to, yellow cl, [29]p, color, DJ/2.75)	Lothrop, Lee	(1959)	Adams, Adrienne	40-65	
Hendry, Hamish	Holidays & Happy Days (1st, 8vo, teg, 120p, 24cp)	L: Richards	1901	Mason, E.F.	90-140	
Hendry, Hamish	Red Apple & Silver Bells (1st, 8vo, 151p, AEG, red/silver, 20cp)	L: Blackie	(1897)	Woodward, Alice B.	90-140	
Henius, Frank	Stories from the Americas (1st, lg8vo, orange cl, 115p, fp b/w, DJ/2.75)	Scribner	1944	Politi, Leo	45-70	
Henley, William E.	London Types (1st, folio, [30]p, ipcb, 12cp)	L: Heinemann	1898	Nicholson, Wm.	500-700	
Henley, William E.	London Types (1st AM, folio, ibds, [29]p, 12cp)	R.H. Russell	1898	Nicholson, Wm.	300-450	
Henry, Alfred H.	By Order of the Prophet (1st, 8vo, orange cl, 402p, 5pl)	Revell	1902	Paxon, E.S.	30-50	
Henry, Jan	Tiger's Chance (1st {std}, 8vo, 138p, b/w, DJ/2.75)	Harcourt	(1957)	Knight, Hilary	50-80	
Henry, Marguerite	Alaska in Story and Pictures (1st, ob8vo, [28]p, color, DJ/0.50)	Whitman	1941	Wiese, Kurt	30-45	
Henry, Marguerite	Album of Horses (1st {A}, 4to, 112p, fp color, pep, DJ/2.95)	Rand/McNally	(1951)	Dennis, Wesley	50-80	R
Henry, Marguerite	All About Horses (1st, lg8vo, 144p, b/w, pep, DJ/1.95)	Random	(1962)	Dennis, Wesley	25-40	
Henry, Marguerite	Always Reddy (1st, 8vo, 79p, tan cloth, 1-color, DJ/1.75)	Whittlesey	(1947)	Dennis, Wesley	30-50	
Henry, Marguerite	Auno and Tauno (1st, 4to, [27]p, ibds, p-o, color, pep, DJ/1.00)	Whitman	1940	Blackwood, Gladys	60-100	
Henry, Marguerite	Benjamin West & his Cat Grimalkin (1st {std}, lg8vo, 147p, pep, DJ/2.50)	Bobbs-Merrill	(1947)	Dennis, Wesley	40-65	
Henry, Marguerite	Black Gold (1st, lg8vo, 172p, b/w, pep, DJ/2.95)	Rand/McNally	(1957)	Dennis, Wesley	30-50	
Henry, Marguerite	Born to Trot (1st {A}, lg8vo, 219p, gilt, pep, color, DJ/2.75)	Rand/McNally	(1950)	Dennis, Wesley	50-85	
Henry, Marguerite	Boy & a Dog (1st, sm4to, [42]p, ibds, 2-color, pep, DJ/1.00)	Wilcox/Follett	1944	Thorne, Diana	60-100	
Henry, Marguerite	Brighty of the Grand Canyon (1st {A}, lg8vo, 224p, pep, 4 fp col, DJ/2.95)	Rand/McNally	(1953)	Dennis, Wesley	45-70	R
Henry, Marguerite	Chile in Story and Pictures (1st, ob8vo, [28]p, color, DJ/0.50)	Whitman	1941	Wiese, Kurt	25-45	
Henry, Marguerite	Cinnabar: One O'Clock Fox (1st {A}, lg8vo, 154p, b/w, pep, DJ/2.95)	Rand/McNally	(1956)	Dennis, Wesley	70-120	
Henry, Marguerite	Dear Readers & Riders (1st, lg8vo, 223p, b/w, DJ/3.95)	Rand/McNally	(1969)	Dennis, Wesley	30-50	
Henry, Marguerite	Dilly-Dally Sally (1st, sq4to, ipcb, [16]p, pep, color)	Saalfield	1940	Blackwood, Gladys	70-100	
Henry, Marguerite	Five O'Clock Charlie (1st {A}, 8vo, [42]p, bds, color, DJ/2.00)	Rand/McNally	1962	Dennis, Wesley	25-40	

AUTHOR	TITLE	PUBLISHER	DATE	ARTIST	PRICE	LC
Henry, Marguerite	Gaudenzia (1st {A}, lg8vo, 237p, red/gilt, 7 fp color, pep, DJ/3.95)	Rand/McNally	(1960)	Ward, Lynd	40-65	
Henry, Marguerite	Geraldine Belinda (1st, sm8vo, [60]p, p-o, color, pep, DJ/0.60)	Platt/Munk	(1942)	Blackwood, Gladys	100-165	
Henry, Marguerite	Justin Morgan had a Horse (1st, 4to, [89]p, 1-color, pep, DJ/2.75, NH)	Wilcox/Follett	1945	Dennis, Wesley	60-100	
Henry, Marguerite	King of the Wind (1st {A}, lg8vo, red cl, 175p, color, pep, DJ/2.75, NM)	Rand/McNally	(1948)	Dennis, Wesley	100-175	R
Henry, Marguerite	Little Fellow (1st, 4to, [64]p, color, pep, DJ/2.00)	Winston	(1945)	Thorne, Diana	50-85	
Henry, Marguerite	Little-or-Nothing from Nottingham (1st, ob8vo, 64p, fp 2-color, DJ/2.00)	Whittlesey	1949	Dennis, Wesley	50-85	*
Henry, Marguerite	Misty of Chincoteague (1st {A}, lg8vo, 173p, color, pep, DJ/2.75, NH)	Rand/McNally	(1947)	Dennis, Wesley	60-100	
Henry, Marguerite	Misty, Wonder Pony: By Misty Herself (1st, 8vo, unpag)	Rand/McNally	1956	McKinley, Clare	50-80	
Henry, Marguerite	Muley-Ears, Nobody's Dog (1st, 4to, [62]p, tan cl, color, cep, DJ/2.75)	Rand/McNally	(1959)	Dennis, Wesley	30-50	
Henry, Marguerite	Mustang: Wild Spirit o/t West (1st {std}, lg8vo, 222p, color, pep, DJ/3.95)	Rand/McNally	(1966)	Lougheed, Robert	40-65	
Henry, Marguerite	Robert Fulton: Boy Craftsman (1st {std}, sm8vo, uncut, 187p, b/w, DJ/1.50)	Bobbs-Merrill	(1945)	Dresser, Lawrence	30-45	
Henry, Marguerite	Sea Star: Orphan of Chincoteague (1st, lg8vo, 172p, color, pep, DJ/2.75)	Rand/McNally	(1949)	Dennis, Wesley	40-65	
Henry, Marguerite	Stormy: Misty's Foal (1st {A}, lg8vo, 224p, fp color, pep, DJ/3.95)	Rand/McNally	(1963)	Dennis, Wesley	50-80	*
Henry, Marguerite	Wagging Tails (1st {A}, 4to, brown cl, 64p, 24 fp color, pep, DJ/2.95)	Rand/McNally	(1955)	Dennis, Wesley	40-65	
Henry, Marguerite	White Stallion of Lipizza (1st {std}, 4to, 116p, color, pep, DJ/3.95)	Rand/McNally	(1964)	Dennis, Wesley	60-90	
Henry, O.	Gift of the Magi (1st, 8vo, 30p, ibds, 8 fp b/w, DJ)	L: Harrap	1939	Gooden, Stephen	80-130	
Henry, O.	Trimmed Lamp (1st, 12mo, 260p, frn by...)	McClure	1907	Stephens, Alice B.	75-100	
Henry, Vera	Ong, the Wild Gander (1st {std}, 8vo, 95p, b/w, DJ/3.50)	Lippincott	(1966)	Rocker, Fermin	20-30	
Henty, G.A.	At Aboukir and Acre (1st AM, 12mo, 320p, gilt, b/w)	Scribner	1898	Rainey, William	100-165	
Henty, G.A.	At Agincourt (1st, 12mo, green cl, 384p, 12pl, cep)	L: Blackie	1897	Paget, Walter	100-175	
Henty, G.A.	Both Sides of the Border (1st sm8vo, 384p, blue/gilt, 12pl)	L: Blackie	1899	Peacock, Ralph	100-170	
Henty, G.A.	By Pike and Dike (1st, 12mo, 384p, 10pl)	L: Blackie	1890	Brown, Maynard	70-100	
Henty, G.A.	Cat of the Bubastes (1st, 12mo, 352p, blue/gilt, 8pl, cep)	L: Blackie	1889	Weguelin, John R.	150-250	
Henty, G.A.	Condemned as a Nihilist (1st, 12mo, 352p, gilt, 10pl, cep)	L: Blackie	1893	Paget, Walter	100-170	
Henty, G.A.	Held Fast for England (1st UK, 12mo, 352p, b/w)	L: Blackie	1892	Browne, Gordon	150-250	
Henty, G.A.	In the Heart of the Rockies (1st, 8vo, grey cl, 352p, 8pl)	L: Blackie	1895	Hindley, Godfrey C.	70-125	
Henty, G.A.	Knight of the White Cross (1st, sm8vo, green/gilt, 392p, 12pl, cep)	L: Blackie	1896	Peacock, Ralph	120-200	
Henty, G.A.	Lion of St. Mark (1st, 12mo, 384p, blue/gilt, 10pl)	L: Blackie	1889	Browne, Gordon	100-185	
Henty, G.A.	Maori and Settler (1st, 12mo, 352p, brown/gilt, b/w, cep)	L: Blackie	1891	Pearse, Alfred	120-200	
Henty, G.A.	No Surrender! (1st AM, 12mo, 345p, red/gilt, b/w)	Scribner	1899	Wood, Stanley	100-165	
Henty, G.A.	On the Irrawaddy (1st, 12mo, 352p, blue/gilt, 8pl)	L: Blackie	1897	Overend, William H.	140-200	
Henty, G.A.	Out on the Pampas (1st, sm8vo, 301p, green cl, cp)	L: H. Frowde	1910	Gough, Arthur J.	120-200	
Henty, G.A.	Out with Garibaldi (1st, 12mo, blue/gilt, 352p, 8pl, cep)	L: Blackie	1901	Rainey, William	120-200	
Henty, G.A.	St. Bartholomew's Eve (1st, 12mo, gilt, 384p, 12pl)	L: Blackie	1894	Draper, Herbert J.	120-185	
Henty, G.A.	Through the Fray (1st, 8vo, 384p, brown cl, fp b/w)	L: Blackie	1886	Paget, Henry M.	80-140	
Henty, G.A.	Tiger of Mysore (1st AM, 12mo, 390p, blue/gilt, 12pl)	Scribner	1895	Margetson, W.H.	120-185	
Henty, G.A.	Treasure of the Incas (1st, 8vo, 340p, green/gilt, 8pl)	L: Blackie	1903	Paget, Walter	80-140	
Henty, G.A.	Under Wellington's Command (1st, 12mo, 386p, blue/gilt, 12pl)	L: Blackie	1899	Paget, Walter	125-200	
Henty, G.A.	When London Burned (1st AM, 12mo, 403p, gilt, b/w)	Scribner	1894	Finnemore, J.	100-165	
Henty, G.A.	With Buller in Natal (1st, 12mo, 384p, blue/gilt, 10pl, cep)	L: Blackie	1901	Rainey, William	100-165	
Henty, G.A.	With Frederick the Great (1st, 12mo, 384p, red/gilt, 12pl)	L: Blackie	1898	Paget, Walter	150-220	
Henty, G.A.	Wulf the Saxon (1st AM, 12mo, gilt, 384p, 12pl)	Scribner	1895	Peacock, Ralph	80-125	
Henty, G.A.	Yuletide Yarns (1st AM, sm8vo, beige cl, 370p, teg)	Longmans	1899	Various	120-200	
Herben, Beatrice S.	Jack O'Health, Peg O'Joy (1st, 12mo, 39p, 10cp)	Scribner	(1921)	Richardson, F.	80-120	
Herbertson, Agnes	Be-Wee the Gnome... (1st AM, 8vo, p-o, ibds, 116p, pep, 20cp)	Cupples/Leon	(1921)	Govey, Lilian	100-170	
Herbertson, Agnes	Book of Happy Gnomes (1st, 8vo, 191p)	L: H. Milford	(1924)	Govey, Lilian	75-100	*
Herbertson, Agnes	Busy Broom (1st, 4to, unpag, color)	L: Cassell	[1910]	Monsell, J.R.	75-100	
Herbertson, Agnes	Dolly Book (1st, 4to, 62p)	L: H. Milford	1920	Govey, Lilian	75-100	*
Herbertson, Agnes	Heroic Legends (1st, 8vo, 253p, AEG, gilt, 16cp, cep)	L: Blackie	1908	Stratton, Helen	120-200	
Herbertson, Agnes	Lucy-Mary (1st, 8vo, 203p, 6cp)	L: Blackie	1910	Tarrant, Margaret	55-80	*
Herbertson, Agnes	Sing Song Stories (4to, ibds, 111p, p-o, 3cp by...)	L: H. Milford	[1922]	Wright, Alan	100-170	
Herbertson, Agnes	Teddy & Trots in Wonderland (1st, 8vo, 254p, 27 illus)	L: Ward Lock	1910	Maybank, Thomas	80-120	*
Herbertson, Agnes	Tinkler Johnny (1st, sm8vo, 239p, green cl, p-o, 4cp)	L: Blackie	[1915]	Harrison, Florence	40-60	
Herford, Beatrice	Monologues (1st, 12mo, 139p, grey cl, 18 b/w)	Scribner	1908	Herford, Oliver	55-80	
Herford, Oliver	Alphabet of Celebrities (1st, lg sq8vo, [58]p, ibds, 26 fp 1-color)	Small/Maynard	1899	Herford, Oliver	120-200	
Herford, Oliver	Artful Antics (1st, sq8vo, tan cl, 100p, b/w)	Century	1894	Herford, Oliver	80-120	*
Herford, Oliver	Astonishing Tale of a Pen & Ink Puppet (1st, ob4to, [62]p, ibds, b/w)	Scribner	1907	Herford, Oliver	100-170	
Herford, Oliver	Bashful Earthquake (1st, 12mo, teg, uncut, ipcb, 126p, b/w)	Scribner	1898	Herford, Oliver	55-90	R
Herford, Oliver	Capers, his Haps and Mishaps (1st, lg4to, unpag, p-o, color, pep)	Devin-Adair	1914	Steinigans, Wm. J.	80-130	
Herford, Oliver	Child's Primer of Natural History (1st UK, 95p, sq4to, b/w)	L: John Lane	1900	Herford, Oliver	80-130	
Herford, Oliver	Confessions of a Caricaturist (1st, 12mo, 65p, 9pl)	Scribner	1917	Herford, Oliver	30-50	
Herford, Oliver	Cupid's Almanac (1st, narrow 8vo, [58]p, ipcb, col frn, pep)	Houghton	1908	Herford/Clay	40-60	*
Herford, Oliver	Deb's Dictionary (1st {std}, sm8vo, [151]p, cloth, b/w)	Lippincott	1931	Herford, Oliver	35-60	
Herford, Oliver	Excuse it Please (1st {std}, sm8vo, 171p, ipcb, b/w, DJ/2.00)	Lippincott	(1929)	Herford, Oliver	35-60	
Herford, Oliver	Fairy Godmother-in-Law (1st, 12mo, 104p, ipcb, teg, b/w)	Scribner	1905	Herford, Oliver	65-100	
Herford, Oliver	Happy Days (1st, 16mo, ipcb, [44]p, color, pep)	Kennerley	1917	Herford/Clay	35-60	
Herford, Oliver	Herford Aesop (1st, 12mo, 90p, col frn, b/w)	Ginn & Co.	(1921)	Herford, Oliver	75-100	
Herford, Oliver	Kitten's Garden of Verses (1st, 12mo, ipcb, gilt, 59p, 25pl)	Scribner	1911	Herford, Oliver	60-90	
Herford, Oliver	Laughing Willow (1st, sm8vo, ipcb, 134p, col frn)	Doran	(1918)	Herford, Oliver	40-60	*
Herford, Oliver	Little Book of Bores (1st, 12mo, 52p, ipcb, b/w)	Scribner	(1906)	Herford, Oliver	60-90	
Herford, Oliver	More Animals (1st, sq8vo, ibds, 99p, 24pl)	Scribner	1901	Herford, Oliver	90-120	R
Herford, Oliver	Mythological Zoo (1st, sq8vo, ibds, 45p, 22pl)	Scribner	1912	Herford, Oliver	60-90	
Herford, Oliver	Overheard in a Garden (1st, sm8vo, ibds, teg, 104p, col frn)	Scribner	1900	Herford, Oliver	70-100	
Herford, Oliver	Pen & Inklings (1st [1st bk.], 12mo, tan cl, b/w)	L: G. Allen	1893	Herford, Oliver	120-170	
Herford, Oliver	Peter Pan Alphabet (1st, sq8vo, ibds, [57]p, fp b/w)	Scribner	1907	Herford, Oliver	160-250	
Herford, Oliver	Rubaiyat of a Persian Kitten (1st, 12mo, [76]p, ibds, 35pl)	Scribner	1904	Herford, Oliver	60-90	
Herford, Oliver	Sea Legs (1st, ob12mo, [55]p, ibds, p-o, 23 fp 2-color)	Lippincott	(1931)	Herford, Oliver	50-80	
Herford, Oliver	Simple Jography (1st, sm8vo, ibds, [100]p, b/w)	Bos: J.W. Luce	(1908)	Herford, Oliver	30-50	

AUTHOR	TITLE	PUBLISHER	DATE	ARTIST	PRICE	LC
Herford, Oliver	Smoker's Yearbook (1st, lg8vo, [28]p, p-o, 12cp)	Moffat	1908	Collins, Sewell	80-125	
Herford, Oliver	This Giddy Globe (1st, 8vo, 138p, tan cl, b/w)	Doran	(1919)	Herford, Oliver	25-40	
Herr, Charlotte	Bear Who Never was Cross (1st, 16mo, ibds, unpag, color)	Volland	(1913)	Beem, Frances	50-80	
Herr, Charlotte	Bee Who Would Not Work (1st, 16mo, ibds, unpag, color)	Volland	(1913)	Beem, Frances	60-90	
Herr, Charlotte	How Punky Dunk Helped Old Prince (1st, 16mo, ibds, unpag, color)	Volland	(1913)	Beem, Frances	50-80	
Herr, Charlotte	Unselfish Pig (1st, 12mo, wraps, [22]p, fp color)	Volland	(1913)	Beem, Frances	50-80	*
Herr, Charlotte	Wise Mamma Goose (1st, 12mo, wrap, [21]p, color)	Volland	(1913)	Beem, Frances	50-80	*
Herr, Charoltte	Brownie Robinson Crusoe (1st, 8vo, 163p, p-o, 8cp)	Dodd	1920	White, Orrin A.	25-45	
Herrick, Christina	Lewis Carroll Birthday Book (16mo, white cl, [255]p, b/w)	Wessels	(1905)	Tenniel, John	120-185	
Herrick, Francis H.	Home Life of Wild Birds (1st, 4to, teg, uncut, 148p, brown/gilt)	Putnam	1901	Armstrong, Margaret	55-90	
Herrick, Robert	Herrick's Poems (lg4to, 188p, green cl)	Harper	1899	Abbey, Edwin A.	120-180	
Herrick, Robert	Love's Dilemmas (1st, sm8vo, 193p, teg, cvr by...)	Herbert Stone	1898	Bradley, Will	100-165	
Herrick, Robert	Poetry of... (1st, 4to, 188p, gilt, uncut, AEG, fp b/w)	Harper	1882	Abbey, Edwin A.	250-350	
Herrmann, Frank	Giant Alexander (1st, 4to, 32p, fp color, pep, DJ/3.50)	McGraw-Hill	(1964)	Him, George	30-50	*
Herrmann, Frank	Giant Alexander & the Circus (1st AM, 4to, [32]p, color, pep, DJ/3.75)	McGraw-Hill	(1966)	Him, George	25-40	
Herzog, Elizabeth	Tinkers of Turntable (1st, 8vo, grey cl, 125p, b/w, DJ/1.75)	W.R. Scott	(1940)	Suba, Susanne	30-50	
Hess, Fjeril	Magic Switch (1st, 8vo, 74p, 4 fp color, pep)	Macmillan	1929	Brown, Neva K.	30-50	
Heward, Constance	Ameliaranne & Green Umbrella (1st AM, 8vo, 109p, p-o, color, pep)	Jacobs	(1920)	Pearse, Susan B.	70-100	
Heward, Constance	Ameliaranne & the Monkey (1st AM, 8vo, p-o, [63]p, color, pep)	McKay	(1929)	Pearse, Susan B.	60-80	
Heward, Constance	Ameliaranne at the Farm (1st AM, 8vo, [58]p, p-o, color, pep)	McKay	(1937)	Pearse, Susan B.	55-90	
Heward, Constance	Ameliaranne at the Farm (1st, 8vo, [58]p, ibds, pep)	L: Harrap	1937	Pearse, Susan B.	55-80	
Heward, Constance	Ameliaranne Camps Out (1st, 8vo, ibds, unpag, color, pep)	L: Harrap	(1939)	Pearse, Susan B.	60-90	
Heward, Constance	Ameliaranne Cinema Star (1st, 8vo, [60]p, tan bds, p-o, color)	L: Harrap	(1929)	Pearse, Susan B.	60-90	
Heward, Constance	Ameliaranne Gives a Party (1st, 8vo, ibds, pep, 28 color)	L: Harrap	(1938)	Pearse, Susan B.	60-90	
Heward, Constance	Ameliaranne Goes Touring (1st, 4to, ibds, unpag, color, pep)	L: Harrap	(1941)	Pearse, Susan B.	60-90	
Heward, Constance	Ameliaranne Keeps Shop (1st AM, 8vo, ibds, [128]p, color, pep)	McKay	(1928)	Pearse, Susan B.	55-80	
Heward, Constance	Grandpa & the Tiger (1st AM, 8vo, 121p, orange cl, p-o, color pep)	Jacobs	(1924)	Govey, Lilian	100-160	
Heward, Constance	Mr. Pickles and the Party (1st, 12mo, 53p, bds, p-o, fp color, pep)	L: Warne	(1926)	Anderson, Anne	100-165	
Heward, Constance	Pillow Stories (1st, sm8vo, 150p, b/w)	L: Richards	1901	Bradley, Gertrude	80-130	
Heward, Constance	Twins & Tabiffa (1st AM, 8vo, 121p, p-o, blue cl, color, pep)	Jacobs	(1923)	Pearse, Susan B.	60-90	
Hewes, Agnes D.	Anabel's Windows (1st, 8vo, orange cl, 240p, b/w, DJ/2.50)	Dodd	1949	Wiese, Kurt	30-45	*
Hewes, Agnes D.	Boy of the Lost Crusade (1st, 8vo, p-o, 279p, gilt, 4cp, pep)	Houghton	1923	Tenggren, Gustaf	40-65	
Hewes, Agnes D.	Codfish Musket (1st {std}, 8vo, 390p, pep, DJ/2.00, NH)	Doubleday/Doran	1936	Sperry, Armstrong	45-70	
Hewes, Agnes D.	Glory of the Seas (1st {std}, sm8vo, 315p, blue cl, col frn, NH)	Knopf	1933	Wyeth, N.C.	45-70	
Hewes, Agnes D.	Spice & Devil's Cave (1st, sm8vo, 331p, gilt, b/w, pep, DJ/2.50, NH)	Knopf	1930	Ward, Lynd	50-80	
Hewes, Agnes D.	Spice Ho! Story of Discovery (1st {std}, 8vo, 198p, grn/gilt, b/w, DJ/1.75)	Knopf	(1941)	Jones, Wilfred	20-35	
Hewes, Agnes D.	Sword of Roland Arnot (1st, 8vo, red cl, 206p, 4cp, DJ/2.50)	Houghton	1939	Strayer, Paul	30-50	
Hewes, Agnes D.	Swords on the Sea (1st, sm8vo, 272p, col frn, 7pl, pep)	Knopf	1928	Bloch, Lucienne	25-40	
Hewes, Agnes D.	Two Oceans to Canton (1st {std}, sm8vo, 184p, color, DJ/2.50)	Knopf	1944	Roth, Harry	20-35	
Hewes, Agnes D.	With the Will to Go (1st {std}, 8vo, 244p, DJ/3.75)	Longmans	1960	Lambo, Don	20-30	
Hewett, Anita	Little White Hen (1st AM, lg ob8vo, 32p, fp 2-color, DJ/2.75)	Whittlesey	1963	Stobbs, William	25-45	
Hewlett, Maurice	Forest Lovers (1st AM, lg8vo, 384p, teg, uncut, 16 ticp)	Scribner	1909	Hartrick, A.S.	50-80	
Hewlett, Maurice	Masque of Dead Florentines (1st, ob8vo, uncut, teg, 51p, 4pl)	L: J.M. Dent	1895	Batten, John D.	90-120	
Hewlett, Pia	Grandmother's Fairy Tales (1st, sm4to, 116p, gilt, p-o, 9cp)	L: Heinemann	1915	Lalau, Maurice	120-180	
Hewson, Isabel	Land of the Lost (1st, 4to, ibds, 60p, color, DJ/2.00)	Whittlesey	(1945)	Bailey, Olive	70-120	*
Heyward, DuBose	Country Bunny & Little Gold Shoes (1st, sm4to, [48]p, color, DJ/2.00)	Houghton	1939	Flack, Marjorie	120-170	
Hiatt, Charles	Picture Posters (1st, 8vo, teg, 367p, 151pl)	L: G. Bell	1895	Various	400-600	
Hichens, Robert	Flames (1st AM, sm8vo, 523p, teg, pcb, cvr by...)	Herbert Stone	1897	Kimbrough, F.R.	55-80	
Hichens, Robert	Holy Land (1st, 4to, 302p, green/gilt, uncut, teg, 18cp)	Century	1910	Guerin, Jules	80-125	
Hichens, Robert	Near East (1st, 4to, teg, blue/gilt, 18cp, fp b/w)	Century	1913	Guerin, Jules	100-165	
Hicks, Granville	One of Us (1st {std}, lg8vo, [64]p, 30 b/w illus, DJ/2.00)	Equinox	(1935)	Ward, Lynd	60-100	
Hieatt, Constance	Knight of the Lion (1st, lg8vo, 68p, fp b/w, DJ/3.95)	Crowell	(1968)	Low, Joseph	30-50	
Hieatt, Constance	Sir Gawain & the Green Knight (1st, lg8vo, 48p, fp 1-color, DJ/3.50)	Crowell	(1967)	Lorraine, Walter	50-80	*
Higgins, Aileen C.	Dream Blocks (1st, lg8vo, p-o, 47p, beige cl, 15cp, pep)	Duffield	1908	Smith, Jessie W.	350-550	
Higgins, Alice	Runaway Rhymes (1st, 8vo, 127p, red bds, gilt, pep, 14 fp color)	Volland	(1931)	Lamb, Tom	75-100	
Higgins, Violet M.	Endless Story (1st, 8vo, ibds, 71p, color, pep)	Whitman	(1916)	Higgins, Violet M.	55-80	
Higgins, Violet M.	Little Juggler (1st, 8vo, 70p, color, pep)	Whitman	(1917)	Higgins, Violet M.	50-80	
Higgins, Violet M.	Magic Circus (8vo, [doll bk.], 64p, ibds, color)	Chi: Stanton	1918	Higgins, Violet M.	80-125	
Higgins, Violet M.	Real Story of a Real Doll (1st, 8vo, 116p, pep, 4cp)	McBride	(1929)	Higgins, Violet M.	35-60	*
Higgins, Violet M.	Silver Ship (1st, lg8vo, ipcb, 63p, color)	Whitman	(1916)	Higgins, Violet M.	50-80	
Higgins, Violet M.	Woodcutter's Son (1st, lg8vo, p-o, 68p, 4cp)	Whitman	1917	Higgins, Violet M.	45-70	
Hightower, Florence	Dark Horse of Woodfield (1st, 8vo, 233p, b/w, DJ/3.25)	Houghton	1962	Tolford, Joshua	25-45	*
Hightower, Florence	Mrs. Wappinger's Secret (1st, 8vo, 280p, b/w, DJ/3.00)	Houghton	1956	Krush, Beth & Joe	30-50	*
Hildick, E.W.	Dragon that Lived Under Manhattan (1st, lg8vo, 62p, fp b/w, DJ/3.95)	Crown	(1970)	Berson, Harold	20-35	
Hildick, E.W.	Manhattan is Missing (1st {std}, 8vo, 239p, b/w, DJ/3.95)	Doubleday	1969	Palmer, Jan	25-40	
Hill, Elizabeth S.	Evan's Corner (1st {std}, sq8vo, [47]p, fp 2-color, DJ/3.95)	Holt, Rinehart	(1967)	Grossman, Nancy	40-65	*
Hill, Frederick T.	Washington: Man of Action (1st, 4to, green/gilt, 329p, 27cp)	Appleton	1914	Job	700-1000	
Hill, Mabel B.	Down Along Apple Market Street (1st, ob8vo, p-o, [32]p, color, pep)	Stokes	1934	Hill, Mabel B.	30-50	*
Hill, William	Jackie Boy in Rainbowland (1st, 8vo, p-o, 84p, color)	Rand/McNally	(1911)	Cory, Fanny	90-145	
Hill, William E.	Among Us Cats (1st {std}, lg8vo, p-o, [128]p, col frn, 61pl, pep)	Harper	1926	Hill, William E.	70-120	
Hillert, Margaret	Three Goats (1st, 8vo, 27p, color, DJ/1.00)	Follett	(1963)	Pekarsky, Mel	20-35	
Hillert, Margaret	Yellow Boat (1st {std}, 8vo, 27p, color, DJ/1.00)	Follett	1966	Young, Ed	20-35	*
Hilles, Helen	Farm Wanted (1st, 8vo, 236p, brown cl, uncut, 1-color, DJ/3.00)	J. Messner	(1951)	Duvoisin, Roger	30-50	
Hilles, Helen	Mile of Freedom (1st, sm8vo, 248p, b/w, DJ/2.00)	Macmillan	1932	Thorne, Diana	25-40	
Hillyer, William	Box of Daylight (1st {std}, 8vo, 179p, b/w, pep)	Knopf	1931	Berry, Erick	25-40	
Hilton, James	Lost Horizon (1st, sm8vo, 277p, b/w, DJ/1.25)	World	(1948)	Wiese, Kurt	25-40	
Himes, Vera C.	Ola and the Runaway Bread (1st, 8vo, ipcb, [64]p, fp color, pep)	Crowell	(1932)	Dewey, Katharine	40-65	*
Hine, Lewis W.	Men at Work (1st, sm4to, [48]p, b/w)	Macmillan	1932	(Photos)	30-50	*

AUTHOR	TITLE	PUBLISHER	DATE	ARTIST	PRICE	LC
Hinkle, Thomas C.	Dr. Rabbit & Ki-Yi Coyote (1st, 12mo, 106p, yellow bds, color)	Rand/McNally	(1918)	Winter, Milo	40-65	
Hinkle, Thomas C.	Snowy Tail: Champion Jack Rabbit (1st, 12mo, ibds, 64p, color)	Rand/McNally	(1921)	Winter, Milo	40-65	
Hinkle, Thomas C.	Split-Ear (1st, sm8vo, 269p, p-o, 1 ticp, fp b/w)	Rand/McNally	1925	Clarke, William W.	40-65	
Hinkson, Henry A.	King's Liege (1st, 8vo, 224p, blue cl, col frn, 3pl)	L: Blackie	1910	Dixon, Arthur A.	55-80	*
Hinkson, Henry A.	Splendid Knight (1st, 8vo, 262p, grey cl, b/w)	L: F.V. White	1905	Wood, Lawson	150-220	
Hinkson, Katharine	Cuckoo Songs (1st, 12mo, brown/gilt, 105p, cvr & title page by....)	L: E. Mathews	1894	Housman, Laurence	120-180	
Hirsh, Marilyn J.	Pink Suit (1st, 4to, [35]p, 2-color, DJ/3.95)	Crown	(1970)	Hirsh, Marilyn	25-40	
Hirsh, Marilyn J.	Where is Yonkela? (1st, 4to, [32]p, fp color, pep, DJ/3.95)	Crown	1969	Hirsh, Marilyn	25-40	*
Hirshberg, Al	Varsity Double Play (1st {std}, sm8vo, 246p, DJ/2.75)	Little/Brown	(1956)	Galdone, Paul	20-35	
Hitte, Kathryn	Mexicali Soup (1st, lg8vo, [38]p, color, DJ/3.95)	Parents Mag. Pr.	(1970)	Rockwell, Anne	30-45	*
Hitte, Kathryn	When Noodlehead Went to the Fair (1st, ob4to, ibds, [42]p, color, DJ/3.50)	Parents Mag. Pr.	(1968)	Watson, Wendy	25-45	*
Hoban, Russell	Baby Sister for Frances (1st, 4to, [31]p, ibds, color, DJ/2.50)	Harper	(1964)	Hoban, Lillian	70-100	
Hoban, Russell	Bargain for Frances (1st, 8vo, 62p, 2-color, DJ/2.50)	Harper	(1970)	Hoban, Lillian	60-100	
Hoban, Russell	Bedtime for Frances (1st, sm4to, [31]p, ibds, 1-color, DJ/2.50)	Harper	(1960)	Williams, Garth	140-200	
Hoban, Russell	Best Friends for Frances (1st, 4to, 31p, color, DJ/2.95)	Harper	(1969)	Hoban, Lillian	30-45	
Hoban, Russell	Birthday for Frances (1st, 4to, 31p, color, DJ/2.95)	Harper	(1968)	Hoban, Lillian	70-120	
Hoban, Russell	Bread & Jam for Frances (1st, 4to, 31p, color, DJ/2.50)	Harper	(1964)	Hoban, Lillian	60-100	
Hoban, Russell	Charlie & the Tramp (1st, 8vo, [48]p, b/w, DJ/2.95)	Four Winds Pr.	(1967)	Hoban, Lillian	60-90	
Hoban, Russell	Goodnight (1st {std}, 8vo, unpag, color, pep, DJ/2.95)	Norton	(1966)	Hoban, Lillian	60-100	
Hoban, Russell	Harvey's Hideout (1st, 4to, [42]p, fp color, DJ/3.50)	Parents Mag. Pr.	(1969)	Hoban, Lillian	70-100	
Hoban, Russell	Henry & the Monstrous Din (1st, sm ob4to, [32]p, fp 3-color, cep, DJ/2.95)	Harper	(1966)	Hoban, Lillian	60-100	
Hoban, Russell	Herman the Loser (1st, 4to, 32p, ibds, b/w, DJ/1.95)	Harper	(1961)	Hoban, Lillian	65-100	
Hoban, Russell	Hester Mouse who Became a Writer (1st {std}, 8vo, 46p, b/w, DJ/2.95)	Norton	(1965)	Hoban, Lillian	70-100	
Hoban, Russell	Little Brute Family (1st {std}, 12mo, [30]p, fp 3-color, DJ/2.95)	Macmillan	(1966)	Hoban, Lillian	60-90	
Hoban, Russell	London Men and English Men (1st, lg ob8vo, ipcb, [32]p, b/w, DJ/1.95)	Harper	(1962)	Hoban, Lillian	30-45	
Hoban, Russell	Mole Family's Christmas (1st, 8vo, [39]p, color, cep, DJ/3.50)	Parents Mag. Pr.	(1969)	Hoban, Lillian	60-100	
Hoban, Russell	Mouse and his Child (1st, 8vo, 181p, ibds, b/w, DJ/4.50)	Harper	(1967)	Hoban, Lillian	100-165	
Hoban, Russell	Nothing to Do (1st, sm4to, unpag, ibds, b/w, DJ/2.50)	Harper	(1964)	Hoban, Lillian	30-45	*
Hoban, Russell	Pedaling Man and other Poems (1st {std}, 8vo, 33p, b/w, DJ/3.50)	Norton	(1968)	Hoban, Lillian	70-120	
Hoban, Russell	Save my Place (1st {std}, 8vo, [32]p, color, DJ/3.95)	Norton	(1967)	Hoban, Lillian	70-100	
Hoban, Russell	Some Snow said Hello (1st, ob8vo, [32]p, b/w, DJ/1.95)	Harper	(1963)	Hoban, Lillian	60-100	
Hoban, Russell	Song in my Drum (1st, ob8vo, [32]p, DJ/1.95)	Harper	(1962)	Hoban, Lillian	70-120	
Hoban, Russell	Sorely Trying Day (1st, 4to, [32]p, b/w, DJ/1.95)	Harper	(1964)	Hoban, Lillian	60-100	
Hoban, Russell	Stone Doll of Sister Brute (1st {std}, 12mo, [32]p, color, DJ/2.95)	Macmillan	1968	Hoban, Lillian	60-90	
Hoban, Russell	Tom and the Two Handles (1st, 8vo, 62p, ibds, fp 3-color, DJ/1.95)	Harper	(1965)	Hoban, Lillian	70-100	
Hoban, Russell	Ugly Bird (1st {std}, 8vo, [32]p, color, DJ/3.95)	Macmillan	(1969)	Hoban, Lillian	75-100	
Hoban, Russell	What Does it Do and How Does it Work? (1st, lg4to, 58p, 2-color, DJ/3.50)	Harper	(1959)	Hoban, Lillian	80-120	
Hobart, George V.	Li'l Verses for Li'l Fellers (1st, 4to, 121p, 7cp, 8pl)	R.H. Russell	1903	Mars/Squire	100-170	*
Hobbes, John O.	Dream & the Business (1st, 8vo, 444p, blue cl, teg, cvr by...)	L: T.F. Unwin	1906	Beardsley, Aubrey	100-150	
Hobbes, John O.	Robert Orange (1st, 12mo, 341p, blue/gilt, teg, title page by...)	Stokes	1900	Bradley, Will	40-65	
Hobbes, John O.	School for Saints (1st, sm8vo, 405p, grey/gilt, cvr by...)	Stokes	(1897)	Bradley, Will	65-90	
Hobbs, Barbara	Alexander's Animals (1st, 4to, 30p, fp 2-color, DJ/2.75)	Houghton	1958	Hobbs, Barbara	40-65	
Hoberman, Mary Ann	All My Shoes Come in Twos (1st {std}, 8vo, 40p, fp color, cep, DJ/2.50)	Little/Brown	(1957)	Hoberman, Norman	50-80	R*
Hobson, Laura Z.	Dog of his Own (1st, ob8vo, ibds, [40]p, fp 2-color, DJ/1.00)	Viking	1941	Miller, Jane	30-50	*
Hodder, William R.	Daughter of the Dawn (1st, 8vo, green cl, 333p, 12pl)	L: Jarrold	1903	Piffard, Harold	55-80	*
Hodeir, Andre	Cleopatra Goes Sledding (1st {std}, 4to, [32]p, color, DJ/3.95)	Grove Press	(1968)	Ungerer, Tomi	50-80	
Hodeir, Andre	Warwick's 3 Bottles (1st {std}, 4to, [32]p, color, DJ/3.95)	Grove Press	(1966)	Ungerer, Tomi	50-80	
Hodges, C. Walter	Flying House (1st, 8vo, 112p, orange/gilt, col frn, b/w, DJ)	L: Benn	1947	Hodges, C. Walter	30-50	
Hodges, C. Walter	Marsh King (1st, 8vo, gilt, 213p, b/w, DJ)	L: G. Bell	(1967)	Hodges, C. Walter	45-70	
Hodges, C. Walter	Marsh King (1st AM, 8vo, 253p, fp b/w, DJ/3.95)	Coward	(1967)	Hodges, C. Walter	30-50	*
Hodges, C. Walter	The Namesake (1st AM {std}, 8vo, 269p, b/w, pep, DJ/3.95)	Coward	1964	Hodges, C. Walter	30-50	
Hodges, Elizabeth	Free as a Frog (1st {std}, 8vo, [32]p, b/w, DJ/3.25, NYTBI)	Addison-Wesley	(1969)	Giovanopoulos, P.	30-50	
Hodges, Elizabeth	Serendipity Tales (1st {std}, lg8vo, 179p, fp b/w, DJ/3.95)	Atheneum	1966	Corwin, June	25-40	*
Hodges, Elizabeth	Three Princes of Serendip (1st {std}, 8vo, 158p, b/w, DJ/3.95)	Atheneum	1964	Berg, Joan	25-40	
Hodges, Margaret	One Little Drum (1st, 8vo, 63p, b/w, DJ/2.25)	Follett	(1958)	Galdone, Paul	25-40	
Hodges, Margaret	The Wave (1st, lg sq8vo, 45p, fp 1-color, DJ/3.25, CH, NYTBI)	Houghton	1964	Lent, Blair	60-100	R
Hodges, Margaret	What's for Lunch, Charlie? (1st, 8vo, 72p, fp b/w, DJ/2.75)	Dial Press	1961	Aliki	25-45	
Hodgins, Eric	Mr. Blanding Builds his Dream House (1st, 8vo, 237p, b/w, DJ/2.75)	Simon/Schuster	(1946)	Steig, William	30-45	
Hodgkin, Lucy V.	Book of Quaker Saints (1st, 8vo, 548p, 7 ticp, pep)	L: Foulis	1917	Robinson, F. Cayley	60-100	
Hoff, Syd	Danny and the Dinosaur (1st, 8vo, 64p, color, DJ/2.50)	Harper	(1958)	Hoff, Syd	30-50	*
Hoff, Syd	Sammy the Seal (1st, 8vo, 64p, color, DJ/2.50)	Harper	(1959)	Hoff, Syd	25-45	
Hoff, Syd	Stanley (1st, 8vo, 64p, ibds, color, DJ/1.95)	Harper	(1962)	Hoff, Syd	30-50	*
Hoffman, Alice S.	Book of the Sagas (1st, 8vo, AEG, 320p, gilt, 6cp)	L: Nister	[1913]	Browne, Gordon	90-135	
Hoffman, Alice S.	Children's Shakespeare (1st, sq8vo, 472p, 21cp)	L: Dent	1911	Folkard, Charles	100-160	
Hoffman, Phyllis	Steffie and Me (1st, sm ob4to, 32p, ipcb, fp 3-color, DJ/3.50)	Harper	(1970)	McCully, Emily	50-85	
Hoffmann, Eleanor	Cat of Paris (1st, 8vo, 145p, blue cl, b/w, pep, DJ/1.75)	Stokes	1940	Gay, Zhenya	30-50	
Hoffmann, Eleanor	Four Friends (1st {std}, 8vo, 105p, fp b/w, DJ/2.00)	Macmillan	1946	Wiese, Kurt	30-45	*
Hoffmann, Eleanor	Lion of Barbary (1st, 8vo, 217p, blue cl, b/w, DJ/2.00)	Holiday House	(1946)	Coggins, Jack	25-45	
Hoffmann, Eleanor	Mischief in Fez (1st, lg8vo, 109p, blue cl, 8 fp 1-color, dep, DJ/2.00)	Holiday House	(1943)	Eichenberg, Fritz	45-70	
Hoffmann, Eleanor	Travels of a Snail (1st, 8vo, 140p, b/w, DJ/1.50)	Stokes	1939	Gay, Zhenya	30-45	
Hoffmann, Ernst T.	Nutcracker & Mouse King (1st, lg8vo, 123p, orange cl, p-o, color)	Whitman	(1930)	Brock, Emma	80-130	
Hoffmann, Ernst T.	Tales of Hoffmann (1st, 4to, 207p, 10cp)	L: Harrap	(1932)	Laboccetta, Mario	140-200	
Hoffmann, Ernst T.	Tales of Hoffmann (sm4to, 207p, 10 fp color)	Dodd	[1933]	Laboccetta, Mario	60-85	
Hoffmann, Heinrich	Slovenly Peter (1st {std}, lg8vo, ibds, [30]p, color)	Harper	1935	Kredel, Fritz	120-180	*
Hofman, Caroline	All Around the Sun-Dial (1st, 4to, 79p, col frn)	Dutton	(1917)	Elmer, Rachel R.	30-50	*
Hofman, Caroline	Little Red Balloon (1st, 12mo, ibds, [39]p, color)	Volland	(1918)	Elmer, Rachel R.	60-90	
Hofman, Caroline	Princess Finds a Playmate (1st, 12mo, ibds, unpag, color)	Volland	(1918)	Elmer, Rachel R.	60-100	*
Hofman, Caroline	Wise Gray Cat (1st, 12mo, ipcb, unpag, color)	Volland	(1918)	Elmer, Rachel R.	80-120	*

AUTHOR	TITLE	PUBLISHER	DATE	ARTIST	PRICE	LC
Hogan, Carol	Eighteen Cousins (1st, ob8vo, [36]p, fp color, DJ/3.50)	Parents Mag. Pr.	(1968)	Komoda, Beverly	25-45	*
Hogan, Erlin	Four Funny Men (1st {std}, 12mo, ibds, [55]p, 1-color, pep, DJ/1.00)	Dutton	(1939)	Hogan, Inez	80-125	
Hogan, Inez	Bear is a Bear (1st, 8vo, 43p, fp b/w, pep, DJ/2.00)	Dutton	(1953)	Hogan, Inez	50-80	*
Hogan, Inez	Bear Twins (1st {std}, 8vo, [45]p, ipcb, 1-color, pep, DJ/1.00)	Dutton	(1935)	Hogan, Inez	60-100	
Hogan, Inez	Big Ones (1st {std}, 4to, yellow cl, [30]p, b/w, pep, DJ/2.95)	Dutton	(1957)	Hogan, Inez	60-90	
Hogan, Inez	Cubby Bear & the Book (1st {std}, 8vo, [42]p, fp b/w, DJ/2.50)	Dutton	(1961)	Hogan, Inez	45-70	
Hogan, Inez	Dinosaur Twins (1st {std}, 8vo, 39p, DJ/2.25)	Dutton	(1963)	Hogan, Inez	45-70	
Hogan, Inez	Eager Beaver (1st {std}, 8vo, 39p, b/w, DJ/2.25)	Dutton	(1963)	Hogan, Inez	50-80	
Hogan, Inez	Elephant Twins (1st {std}, 8vo, ipcb, [45]p, pep, DJ/1.00)	Dutton	(1936)	Hogan, Inez	50-85	
Hogan, Inez	Fox Twins (1st {std}, 8vo, 31p, b/w, DJ/2.25)	Dutton	(1964)	Hogan, Inez	40-65	*
Hogan, Inez	Fraidy Cat (1st {std}, 8vo, 41p, b/w, pep, DJ/2.50)	Dutton	(1962)	Hogan, Inez	40-65	*
Hogan, Inez	Giraffe Twins (1st {std}, 8vo, [48]p, ipcb, 1-color, pep, DJ/1.25)	Dutton	(1948)	Hogan, Inez	70-120	
Hogan, Inez	Kangaroo Twins (1st {std}, 8vo, [49]p, ibds, color, pep, DJ/1.00)	Dutton	(1938)	Hogan, Inez	70-100	
Hogan, Inez	Koala Bear Twins (1st {std}, 8vo, unpag, ibds, DJ/1.50)	Dutton	(1955)	Hogan, Inez	60-90	
Hogan, Inez	Listen Hitler! Gremlins are Coming (1st {std} 8vo ibds, b/w [41]p, DJ/1.00)	Dutton	1943	Hogan, Inez	70-120	
Hogan, Inez	Little Black & White Lamb (1st, sm8vo, black/gilt, [103]p, fp color)	Macrae Smith	(1927)	Hogan, Inez	100-165	
Hogan, Inez	Little Lost Bear (1st {std}, lg8vo, [41]p, fp b/w, pep, DJ/2.50)	Dutton	1960	Hogan, Inez	45-70	
Hogan, Inez	Little Ones (1st {std}, 8vo, 45p, b/w, DJ/2.25)	Dutton	(1956)	Hogan, Inez	40-65	*
Hogan, Inez	Little Toy Airplane (1st, ob8vo, [57]p, color, pep)	Macrae Smith	(1930)	Hogan, Inez	60-90	
Hogan, Inez	Littlest Bear (1st {std}, 8vo, 59p, fp b/w, pep, DJ/2.50)	Dutton	1959	Hogan, Inez	40-65	*
Hogan, Inez	Littlest Satellite (1st {std}, 8vo, unpag, b/w, DJ/2.50)	Dutton	1958	Hogan, Inez	50-80	
Hogan, Inez	Lone Wolf (1st {std}, 8vo, [40]p, fp b/w, pep, DJ/2.50)	Dutton	(1961)	Hogan, Inez	50-80	
Hogan, Inez	Me (1st {std}, 8vo, blue cl, 61p, b/w, pep, DJ/2.00)	Dutton	1954	Hogan, Inez	50-80	
Hogan, Inez	Monkey See, Monkey Do (1st {std}, 8vo, [41]p, b/w, pep, DJ/2.50)	Dutton	1960	Hogan, Inez	40-65	
Hogan, Inez	Monkey Twins, They Saw it All (1st {std}, sm8vo, ipcb, b/w, pep, DJ/1.00)	Dutton	(1943)	Hogan, Inez	50-80	
Hogan, Inez	Mule Twins (1st {std}, 8vo, ibds, [49]p, b/w, pep, DJ/1.00)	Dutton	(1939)	Hogan, Inez	60-100	
Hogan, Inez	Nappy Chooses a Pet (1st {std}, 8vo, [48]p, ipcb, b/w, pep, DJ/1.00)	Dutton	1946	Hogan, Inez	60-100	
Hogan, Inez	Nappy is a Cowboy (1st {std}, 8vo, ibds, [49]p, fp b/w, pep, DJ/1.25)	Dutton	1949	Hogan, Inez	60-100	
Hogan, Inez	Nappy Planted a Garden (1st {std}, 8vo, ibds, [49]p, b/w, pep, DJ/1.00)	Dutton	1944	Hogan, Inez	60-100	
Hogan, Inez	Nappy Wanted a Dog (1st {std}, 8vo, ibds, [49]p, fp b/w, pep, DJ/1.00)	Dutton	1942	Hogan, Inez	50-70	
Hogan, Inez	Nicodemus & his Gran' Pappy (1st {std}, sm8vo, [49]p, color, pep, DJ/1.00)	Dutton	(1936)	Hogan, Inez	150-250	R
Hogan, Inez	Nicodemus & his Little Sister (1st {std}, 12mo, ibds, [47]p, 1-color)	Dutton	1932	Hogan, Inez	100-165	
Hogan, Inez	Nicodemus & his New Shoes (1st {std} 12mo ibds [49]p, 2-color pep, DJ/1.00)	Dutton	(1937)	Hogan, Inez	150-250	R
Hogan, Inez	Nicodemus & Little Black Pig (1st {std}, sm8vo, [61]p, color, pep)	Dutton	(1934)	Hogan, Inez	120-200	R
Hogan, Inez	Nicodemus & New-Born Baby (1st {std} sm8vo ipcb, 1-col, 53p, pep, DJ/1.00)	Dutton	(1940)	Hogan, Inez	150-250	
Hogan, Inez	Nicodemus & Petunia (1st {std}, sm8vo, [51]p, color, pep, DJ/1.00)	Dutton	(1937)	Hogan, Inez	150-250	R
Hogan, Inez	Nicodemus & the Gang (1st {std}, sm8vo, ibds, [53]p, pep, DJ/1.00)	Dutton	(1939)	Hogan, Inez	150-250	
Hogan, Inez	Nicodemus & the Goose (1st {std}, sm8vo, ibds, [47]p, color pep, DJ/1.00)	Dutton	(1945)	Hogan, Inez	80-140	
Hogan, Inez	Nicodemus & the Houn' Dog (1st {std}, sm8vo, [52]p, ibds, color)	Dutton	(1933)	Hogan, Inez	150-250	R
Hogan, Inez	Nicodemus Helps Uncle Sam (1st {std}, sm8vo, ibds, [48]p, color)	Dutton	1943	Hogan, Inez	100-165	
Hogan, Inez	Nicodemus Laughs (1st {std}, sm8vo, ibds, [40]p, color, pep, DJ/1.00)	Dutton	(1941)	Hogan, Inez	150-250	
Hogan, Inez	Party for Poodles (1st {std}, 4to, [54]p, fp b/w, pep, DJ/2.50)	Dutton	(1952)	Hogan, Inez	50-80	*
Hogan, Inez	Raccoon Twins (1st {std}, 8vo, [49]p, ibds, b/w, DJ/1.00)	Dutton	(1946)	Hogan, Inez	50-80	*
Hogan, Inez	Read to Me about Charlie (1st {std}, sm4to, ibds, 43p, b/w, pep, DJ/1.25)	Dutton	(1950)	Hogan, Inez	50-80	
Hogan, Inez	Read to Me about Nono, the Baby Elephant (1st {std}, sm4to, 44p, DJ/1.00)	Dutton	(1947)	Hogan, Inez	50-85	
Hogan, Inez	Read to Me about Peter Platypus (1st {std}, lg8vo, ibds, 45p, b/w, DJ/1.25)	Dutton	(1948)	Hogan, Inez	50-85	
Hogan, Inez	Runaway Toys (1st {std}, lg8vo, [40]p, pep, color, DJ/1.75)	Dutton	(1950)	Hogan, Inez	60-100	
Hogan, Inez	Sandy, Skip & Man in the Moon (1st, sm8vo, gilt, 93p, color)	Macrae Smith	(1928)	Hogan, Inez	50-85	
Hogan, Inez	Twin Colts (1st {std}, 8vo, ibds, [49]p, b/w, pep, DJ/1.25)	Dutton	(1944)	Hogan, Inez	60-90	
Hogan, Inez	Twin Kids (1st, 8vo, [50]p, ipcb, 1-color, pep, DJ/1.00)	Dutton	(1937)	Hogan, Inez	100-160	
Hogan, Inez	Twin Kittens (1st {std}, 8vo, [42]p, fp b/w, pep, DJ/2.25)	Dutton	(1958)	Hogan, Inez	50-85	*
Hogan, Inez	Twin Otters and the Indians (1st {std}, 8vo, 41p, b/w, DJ/2.25)	Dutton	(1962)	Hogan, Inez	50-80	
Hogan, Inez	Twin Puppies (1st {std}, 8vo, [40]p, fp b/w, pep, DJ)	Dutton	1959	Hogan, Inez	45-70	
Hogan, Inez	Twin Seals (1st {std}, 8vo, [48]p, ibds, pep, DJ/1.00)	Dutton	(1940)	Hogan, Inez	50-80	
Hogan, Inez	Upside Down Book (1st {std}, sm4to, [46]p, b/w, pep, DJ/2.50)	Dutton	1955	Hogan, Inez	50-80	
Hogan, Inez	We are a Family (1st {std}, sm sq4to, 93p, b/w, pep, DJ/2.75)	Dutton	(1952)	Hogan, Inez	50-80	
Hogan, Inez	White Kitten and Blue Plate (1st, ob8vo, [44]p, color, pep)	Macmillan	1930	Hogan, Inez	100-165	*
Hogan, Inez	World Round (1st {std}, 4to, [64]p, blue cl, b/w, pep, DJ/2.50)	Dutton	(1949)	Hogan, Inez	60-100	
Hogate, Etta C.	Sunbonnets & Overalls... (1st, 8vo, 83p, color, pep)	Rand/McNally	(1914)	Corbett, Bertha L.	80-125	
Hoge, Dorothy	Black Heart of Indri (1st, 4to, ibds, [44]p, color, DJ/3.50)	Scribner	1966	Domanska, Janina	30-50	
Hogg, James	Kilmeny (1st, 16mo, 31p, 5cp)	L: Foulis	1911	King, Jessie	150-200	
Hogg, James	Songs of Ettrick Shepherd (1st, 12mo, 151p, teg, 7 ticp)	L: Foulis	(1912)	King, Jessie	120-180	
Hogner, Dorothy	Daisy (1st, ob8vo, [48]p, ibds, fp b/w, cep, DJ/1.50)	NY: Oxford U.Pr.	1949	Hogner, Nils	30-50	*
Hogner, Dorothy	Snowflake (1st, 12mo, 31p, color, DJ/1.75)	NY: Oxford U.Pr.	1952	Hogner, Nils	30-50	
Hogrogian, Nonny	Renowned History/Little Red Riding Hood (1st, 24mo, [32]p, color, DJ/2.95)	Crowell	(1967)	Hogrogian, Nonny	30-50	
Hogrogian, Nonny	Thirteen Days of Yule (1st, sq8vo, [31]p, gilt, fp color, cep, DJ/3.95)	Crowell	(1968)	Hogrogian, Nonny	30-50	
Hohler, Mrs. Edwin	Bravest of them All (1st, sm8vo, 214p, blue/gilt, 8pl)	L: Macmillan	1899	Brock, Charles E.	45-70	
Hoke, Helen	Doctor, the Puppy Who Learned (1st, sq8vo, [18]p, ibds, 1-color, DJ/1.00)	J. Messner	1944	Thorne, Diana	35-50	
Hoke, Helen	Furry Bear (1st, 8vo, [16]p, color, DJ/1.25)	J. Messner	1943	Tate, Sally	30-50	
Hoke, Helen	Major and the Kitten (1st, 4to, ibds, 36p, 1-color, DJ/2.00)	Henry Holt & Co.	(1941)	Thorne, Diana	30-50	
Hoke, Helen	Mr. Sweeny (1st, 4to, [76]p, 1-color, pep, DJ/1.50)	Henry Holt & Co.	1940	Wills, William	30-50	
Hoke, Helen	Mrs. Silk (1st, 4to, [24]p, ibds, color, DJ/1.00)	Veritas Press	1945	Thorne, Diana	30-45	
Hoke, Helen	Shep and the Baby (1st, sq8vo, ibds, [17]p, color, DJ/1.00)	J. Messner	1944	Thorne, Diana	30-50	*
Hoke, Helen	Too Many Kittens (1st, 4to, ibds, [34]p, color, DJ/2.00)	McKay	1947	Lees, Harry	30-50	*
Holberg, Ruth	At the Sign of the Golden Anchor (1st {std}, 8vo, 209p, pep, b/w, DJ/2.25)	Doubleday	(1947)	Castle, Jane	20-35	
Holberg, Ruth	Bells of Amsterdam (1st, sm4to, 88p, gilt, fp color, DJ/2.00)	Crowell	1940	Holberg, Richard	45-60	
Holberg, Ruth	Catnip Man (1st {std}, 8vo, 114p, fp b/w, pep, DJ/2.50)	Crowell	(1951)	Weil, Lisl	30-45	*
Holberg, Ruth	Gloucester Boy (1st {std}, 8vo, [48]p, ipcb, 2-color, pep, DJ/1.00)	Doubleday/Doran	1940	Holberg, Richard	40-65	

AUTHOR	TITLE	PUBLISHER	DATE	ARTIST	PRICE	LC
Holberg, Ruth	Hester and Timothy, Pioneers (1st {std}, 8vo, 128p, color, pep, DJ/1.50)	Doubleday/Doran	1937	Holberg, Richard	40-65	
Holberg, Ruth	Jill & the Applebird House (1st {std}, 8vo, 161p, DJ/3.50)	Doubleday	(1968)	Komoda, Kiyoaki	20-35	*
Holberg, Ruth	Mitty and Mr. Syrup (1st {std}, 8vo, ibds, [32]p, color, pep, DJ/1.00)	Doubleday/Doran	1935	Holberg, Richard	40-65	
Holberg, Ruth	Mitty on Mr. Syrup's Farm (1st {std}, 4to, ibds, [32]p, color, pep, DJ/1.00)	Doubleday/Doran	1936	Holberg, Richard	40-65	
Holberg, Ruth	Not So Long Ago (1st, 8vo, 131p, dp color, fp b/w, pep, DJ/1.75)	Crowell	1939	Holberg, Richard	35-50	
Holberg, Ruth	Oh Susannah (1st {std}, 8vo, 108p, color, pep, DJ/1.50)	Doubleday/Doran	1939	Holberg, Richard	40-65	
Holberg, Ruth	Restless Johnny (1st, 8vo, 210p, b/w, pep, DJ/2.50)	Crowell	(1950)	Coe, Lloyd	20-35	
Holberg, Ruth	Rowena Carey (1st {std}, 8vo, 242p, fp b/w, DJ/2.50)	Doubleday	1949	Paull, Grace	20-30	*
Holberg, Ruth	Rowena the Sailor (1st {std}, 8vo, 224p, b/w, DJ/2.75)	Doubleday	(1954)	Paull, Grace	20-30	*
Holberg, Ruth	Smugglers of Sandy Bay (1st {std}, 8vo, uncut, 192p, fp b/w, DJ/2.75)	Doubleday	1957	Werth, Kurt	20-35	*
Holberg, Ruth	Tabitha's Hill (1st {std}, 8vo, 223p, b/w, DJ/2.75)	Doubleday	(1956)	Werth, Kurt	20-35	*
Holberg, Ruth	Tam Morgan (1st {std}, 8vo, 224p, b/w, DJ/2.50)	Doubleday	(1953)	Spier, Peter E.	30-50	*
Holberg, Ruth	Three Birthday Wishes (1st, 8vo, 121p, b/w, pep, DJ/2.50)	Crowell	(1953)	Weil, Lisl	25-40	
Holberg, Ruth	Tibby's Venture (1st {std}, 8vo, 122p, b/w, pep, DJ/1.75)	Doubleday/Doran	(1943)	Cote, Phyllis	25-40	
Holberg, Ruth	Wee Brigit O'Toole (1st {std}, 8vo, ibds, [32]p, color, DJ/1.00)	Doubleday/Doran	1938	Holberg, Richard	40-70	
Holberg, Ruth	Wonderful Voyage (1st {std}, 8vo, 208p, pep, b/w, DJ/2.00)	Doubleday/Doran	(1945)	Cote, Phyllis	30-45	
Holbrook, Florence	Hiawatha Alphabet (1st, 4to, [60]p, p-o, fp color)	Rand/McNally	(1910)	Pohl, H.D.	150-250	
Holbrook, Florence	Hiawatha Primer (1st, sm8vo, 139p, green cl, 148p, 8cp)	Houghton	1898	Smith, E. Boyd	70-120	
Holbrook, Ruth	Katy's Quilt (1st {std}, sm4to, [78]p, color, dep, DJ/2.00)	Doubleday/Doran	1940	Holbrook, Ruth	65-90	
Holbrook, Stewart	America's Ethan Allen (1st, lg8vo, 95p, color, pep, DJ/2.50, CH)	Houghton	1949	Ward, Lynd	60-90	
Holbrook, Stewart	Tall Timber (1st {std}, 8vo, 179p, fp b/w, pep, DJ/1.50)	Macmillan	1941	Sperry, Armstrong	40-65	*
Holder, Charles F.	Treasure Divers (1st, 12mo, 207p, blue/silver, 13pl)	Dodd	1898	Greenough, Walter C.	30-50	
Holding, James	King's Contest (1st, 8vo, 125p, b/w, DJ/3.25)	Abelard-Schuman	(1964)	Keeping, Charles	25-40	
Holding, James	Lazy Little Zulu (1st, 4to, [32]p, fp 3-color, dep, DJ/3.25)	Wm. Morrow	1962	Aliki	30-45	
Holding, James	Mr. Moonlight and Omar (1st, 4to, [32]p, fp 3-color, pep, DJ/3.25)	Wm. Morrow	1963	Aliki	30-45	
Holding, James	Sherlock on the Trail (1st, ob8vo, [32]p, fp color, pep, DJ/2.95)	Wm. Morrow	1964	Aliki	30-45	
Holding, James	Sky-Eater (1st, 8vo, 124p, fp 1-color, pep, DJ/3.25)	Abelard-Schuman	(1965)	Keeping, Charles	25-40	
Holding, James	Three Wishes of Hu (1st, 8vo, 64p, fp color, DJ/2.75)	Putnam	(1965)	Haley, Gail E.	25-40	
Holdridge, Betty	Island Boy (1st, 8vo, 110p, green cl, 1-color, pep, DJ/2.00)	Holiday House	(1942)	Lantz, Paul	25-45	
Hole, Christina	Witchcraft in England (1st, 8vo, 167p, maroon/gilt, fp b/w, DJ)	L: Batsford	1945	Peake, Mervyn	100-150	*
Hole, Christina	Witchcraft in England (1st AM, lg8vo, 168p, fp b/w, DJ/3.00)	Scribner	1947	Peake, Mervyn	100-165	
Holl, Adelaide	Bright, Bright Morning (1st, sm ob4to, [36]p, 2-color, DJ/3.75)	Lothrop, Lee	(1969)	Howard, Rob	25-40	
Holl, Adelaide	Have You Seen my Puppy? (1st, 8vo, 32p, color, DJ/1.50)	Random	(1968)	Veno, Joe	25-40	*
Holl, Adelaide	Jamie Looks (1st {A}, sm8vo, ibds, unpag, color, LGB/#522)	Golden Press	1963	Wilkin, Eloise B.	40-65	
Holl, Adelaide	Journey to the Sea (1st, ob8vo, 32p, fp 1-color, cep, DJ)	L.W. Singer	1968	Sickles, Noel	25-40	
Holl, Adelaide	Lisette (1st, 4to, [32]p, fp 1-color, DJ/2.75)	Lothrop, Lee	1962	Duvoisin, Roger	45-70	
Holl, Adelaide	Moon Mouse (1st, ob4to, 34p, 1-color, cep, DJ/3.50)	Random	(1969)	Szekeres, Cyndy	30-45	
Holl, Adelaide	Mrs. McGarrity's Peppermint Sweater (1st, ob4to, [40]p, 2-color, DJ/3.50)	Lothrop, Lee	1966	Graboff, Abner	30-50	
Holl, Adelaide	One Kitten for Kim (1st {std}, 8vo, [32]p, 3-color, DJ/4.35)	Addison-Wesley	1969	Madden, Don	20-35	
Holl, Adelaide	Rain Puddle (1st, ob4to, [33]p, color, DJ/2.95)	Lothrop, Lee	(1965)	Duvoisin, Roger	30-50	
Holl, Adelaide	Remarkable Egg (1st, ob4to, [26]p, color, DJ/3.50)	Lothrop, Lee	(1968)	Duvoisin, Roger	40-65	*
Holl, Adelaide	Runaway Giant (1st, 4to, [28]p, fp 2-color, pep, DJ/3.50)	Lothrop, Lee	1967	Funai, Mamoru	25-45	*
Holl, Adelaide	Runaway Hat (1st, 4to, 24p, fp color, cep, DJ)	L.W. Singer	(1969)	Hirsh, Marilyn	30-50	*
Holl, Adelaide	Sir Kevin of Devon (1st, lg4to, [29]p, 1-color, pep, DJ/2.95)	Lothrop, Lee	1963	Weisgard, Leonard	30-45	
Holladay, Virginia	Bantu Tales (1st {std}, 8vo, 95p, fp b/w, DJ/3.95)	Viking	(1970)	Negri, Rocco	45-70	*
Holland, Josiah G.	Arthur Bonnicastle (12mo, green/gilt, 422p, cvr by...)	Scribner	1896	Armstrong, Margaret	35-60	*
Holland, Marion	Big Ball of String (1st {std}, lg8vo, 64p, ibds, fp 2-color, DJ)	Beginner Books	(1958)	Holland, Marion	75-120	
Holland, Marion	Billy Had a System (1st {std}, 8vo, uncut, 184p, b/w, pep, DJ/2.50)	Knopf	1952	Holland, Marion	50-80	*
Holland, Marion	Billy's Clubhouse (1st {std}, 8vo, uncut, 180p, b/w, pep, DJ/2.50)	Knopf	1955	Holland, Marion	50-80	*
Holland, Marion	Muggsy (1st, 8vo, [32]p, ibds, 1-color, pep, DJ/2.50)	Knopf	(1959)	Sherman, Theresa	30-50	*
Holland, Marion	No Children, No Pets (1st {std}, 8vo, 182p, fp b/w, DJ/2.50)	Knopf	1956	Holland, Marion	30-50	*
Holland, Marion	No Room for a Dog (1st {std}, 8vo, 79p, 1-color, pep, DJ/1.95)	Random	(1959)	Orbaan, Albert	40-65	*
Holland, Marion	Teddy's Camp Out (1st, 8vo, 60p, b/w, cep, DJ/2.75)	Knopf	(1963)	Holland, Marion	40-65	*
Holland, Marion	Tree for Teddy (1st {std}, 8vo, 60p, b/w, DJ/2.00)	Knopf	1957	Holland, Marion	80-125	*
Holland, R. (ed.)	King Arthur & Knights of Roundtable (1st AM, sm8vo, 360p, p-o, 7cp pep)	Jacobs	(1919)	Speed, Lancelot	50-85	
Holland, Rupert S.	Yankee Ships in Pirate Waters (1st, lg8vo, p-o, 317p, 5cp, pep)	Macrae Smith	(1931)	Schoonover, Frank	50-80	
Hollander, John	Book of Various Owls (1st {std}, lg4to, unpag, ibds, 3-color, DJ/3.00)	Norton	1963	Ungerer, Tomi	50-80	*
Holling, H.C. (ed)	Magic Story Tree (1st, lg4to, 83p, fp color, cep, DJ/2.95)	Platt/Munk	(1964)	Holling, Holling C.	30-45	
Holling, Holling C.	Book of Cowboys (1st, 4to, orange cl, pep, 126p, color, DJ/1.25)	Platt/Munk	(1936)	Holling, Holling C.	60-90	
Holling, Holling C.	Book of Indians (1st, 4to, 125p, pep, 6cp, DJ/1.25)	Platt/Munk	(1935)	Holling, Holling C.	80-130	
Holling, Holling C.	Choo-Me-Shoo (1st {std}, 8vo, ibds, color, pep)	Volland	(1928)	Holling, Holling C.	65-90	
Holling, Holling C.	Claws of the Thunderbird (1st, 8vo, 128p, gilt, fp color, pep)	Volland	(1928)	Holling, Holling C.	60-100	
Holling, Holling C.	Little Big-Bye-and-Bye (1st, 12mo, [40]p, ibds, color, pep)	Volland	(1926)	Holling, Holling C.	60-90	
Holling, Holling C.	Little Buffalo Boy (1st, sq8vo, ibds, [42]p, color, pep, DJ/1.00)	Garden City	(1939)	Holling, Holling C.	70-120	
Holling, Holling C.	Minn of the Mississippi (1st, 4to, 85p, yellow cl, col, pep, DJ/3.00, NH)	Houghton	1951	Holling, Holling C.	80-135	
Holling, Holling C.	Paddle to the Sea (1st, 4to, beige cl, [63]p, color, pep, DJ/2.50, CH)	Houghton	1941	Holling, Holling C.	200-300	R
Holling, Holling C.	Pagoo (1st, 4to, 86p, green cl, pep, color, DJ/3.00)	Houghton	1957	Holling, Holling C.	50-90	
Holling, Holling C.	Rocky Billy (1st, 8vo, blue cl, 148p, color, pep)	Macmillan	1928	Holling, Holling C.	55-80	
Holling, Holling C.	Rum-Tum-Tummy... (sq8vo, ibds, unpag, color)	Saalfield	1936	Holling, Holling C.	60-100	
Holling, Holling C.	Seabird (1st, 4to, 58p, blue cl, color, pep, DJ/3.00, NH)	Houghton	1948	Holling, Holling C.	80-125	
Holling, Holling C.	Tree in the Trail (1st, 4to, [70]p, 35 fp color, pep, DJ/3.00)	Houghton	1942	Holling, Holling C.	60-100	
Holling, Holling C.	Twins Who Flew Around the World (1st, lg4to, gilt, 67p, color, pep)	Platt/Munk	(1931)	Holling, Holling C.	70-125	
Hollister, Mary	Beggars of Dreams (1st, 8vo, 234p, b/w pl, pep, DJ/2.00)	Dodd	1937	Wiese, Kurt	50-85	
Hollister, Mary	Kee-Kee and Company (1st, 8vo, 192p, 5pl, pep, DJ/2.00)	Dodd	1938	Wiese, Kurt	40-60	
Hollister, Mary	Mulberry Village (1st, 8vo, 287p, b/w, pep, DJ/1.75)	Dodd	1936	Wiese, Kurt	30-50	
Holloway, Jane	At Flower Farm (1st, 4to, 71p, ibds, p-o, 4cp)	Stern	1909	Beard/Kay	80-130	
Holman, Felice	At the Top of my Voice (1st {std}, 8vo, 55p, red/gilt, b/w, pep, DJ/3.75)	Norton	(1970)	Gorey, Edward	60-90	
Holman, Felice	Cricket Winter (1st {std}, 8vo, 107p, b/w, gilt, DJ/3.95)	Norton	(1967)	Pinto, Ralph	20-30	

AUTHOR	TITLE	PUBLISHER	DATE	ARTIST	PRICE	LC
Holman, Felice	Holiday Rat & Utmost Mouse (1st {std}, 8vo, ipcb, 80p, b/w, DJ/3.95)	Norton	(1969)	Tripp, Wallace	25-40	
Holman, Felice	Silently, the Cat & Miss Theodosia (1st {std}, 8vo, 58p, b/w, DJ/2.95)	Macmillan	(1965)	Dinnerstein, Harvey	25-35	
Holman, Felice	Solomon's Search (1st, 8vo, [58]p, color, DJ/4.50)	Grosset/Dunlap	(1970)	Richter, Mischa	25-45	*
Holman, Felice	Victoria's Castle (1st {std}, sm4to, 40p, color, pep, DJ/3.25)	Norton	(1966)	Hoban, Lillian	50-85	
Holman, Felice	Witch on the Corner (1st {std}, 8vo, 89p, b/w, DJ/3.50)	Norton	(1966)	Lobel, Arnold	30-45	
Holman, Felice	Year to Grow (1st {std}, 8vo, 100p, color, DJ/3.95)	Norton	(1968)	McCully, Emily	30-50	
Holme, Constance	Trumpet in the Dust (1st, 8vo, 255p, 6 woodcuts)	L: Nicholson	1934	Leighton, Clare	40-65	
Holmes, Mabel D.	Joan of Arc (1st, sm4to, 300p, gilt, p-o, 4cp, pep)	Winston	(1930)	Prittie, Edwin J.	35-60	
Holmes, Oliver W.	Autocrat at the Breakfast Table (1st, 8vo, teg, 2vols, gilt, 15pl)	Houghton	1894	Pyle, Howard	125-200	
Holmes, Oliver W.	Dorothy Q. (1st, sm8vo, grey cl, t.e. silver, 131p, b/w)	Houghton	1893	Pyle, Howard	70-100	
Holmes, Oliver W.	Grandmother's Story of Bunker Hill Battle (1st, lg8vo, 32p, chromos, dep)	Dodd	(1883)	McVickar, H.W.	200-300	
Holmes, Oliver W.	One-Hoss Shay ([new ed.], 8vo, 78p, teg, gilt, 12cp)	Houghton	1905	Pyle, Howard	100-165	
Holt, Ardern	Fancy Dresses Described (2nd, 12mo, 105p, 48pl)	L: Debenham	[1881]	Greenaway, Kate	130-200	
Holt, Isabella	Adventures of Rinaldo (1st {std}, 8vo, 142p, b/w, DJ/3.00)	Little/Brown	(1959)	Blegvad, Erik	25-45	
Holt, Jack	Lance and his First Horse (1st, sm4to, 48p, fp b/w, DJ/2.00)	Whittlesey	(1949)	Dennis, Wesley	25-40	
Holt, Margaret	David McCheever's 29 Dogs (1st, sm4to, 48p, 2-color, DJ/2.95)	Houghton	1963	Lorraine, Walter	25-40	
Holton, Priscilla	Blue Junk (1st {std}, sm8vo, 178p, blue cl, b/w, pep, DJ/1.75)	Longmans	1931	Wiese, Kurt	40-65	
Holton, Priscilla	Chuck Martinez (1st {std}, 8vo, 312p, b/w, pep, DJ/2.25)	Longmans	1940	Watson, Eva A.	30-45	*
Holway, Hope K.	Story of Health (1st {std}, sm8vo, 150p, col frn, fp b/w, dep)	Harper	1931	Hader, Elmer	40-65	*
Homer, A.N.	Hernani the Jew (1st, 8vo, 332p, cvr by...)	Rand/McNally	(1897)	Denslow, W.W.	30-50	
Honness, Elizabeth	Flight of Fancy (1st, 8vo, 44p, 3-color, pep, DJ/1.25)	Oxford U. Pr.	(1941)	Doane, Pelagie	30-50	*
Hood, Flora	Living in Navajoland (1st, 8vo, [64]p, fp 1-color, DJ)	Putnam	(1970)	Funai, Mamoru	30-50	*
Hood, Thomas	Haunted House (1st, 12mo, 56p, AEG, green/gilt, b/w)	L: Lawrence	1896	Railton, Herbert	40-60	
Hood, Thomas	Humerous Poems (1st, sm8vo, AEG, 236p, gilt, b/w, cep)	L: Macmillan	1893	Brock, Charles E.	60-90	
Hood, Thomas	Tom Tucker and Little Bo Peep (4to, ibds, 44p, 13cp)	L: Cassell	1891	Adams, Alice W.	70-120	
Hooker, Forrestine	Garden of the Lost Key (1st {std}, 8vo, 288p, col frn, pep)	Doubleday/Doran	1929	Hader, Elmer	75-100	*
Hooker, Forrestine	Little House on the Desert (1st {std}, 8vo, 220p, col frn)	Doubleday/Page	1924	Grosvenor, Thelma C.	50-80	
Hoover, Bessie R.	Pa Flickinger's Folks (1st, 12mo, grey cl, 274p, 10pl)	Harper	1909	Strothmann, F.	50-80	
Hoover, Helen	Animals Near & Far (1st, 8vo, 64p, color, DJ/4.50)	Parents Mag. Pr.	(1970)	Shimin, Symeon	20-30	
Hoover, Helen	Great Wolf & the Good Woodsman (1st, ob4to, [42]p, color, DJ/3.50)	Parents Mag. Pr.	(1967)	Mikolaycak, Charles	30-50	
Hope, Anthony	Adventure of Lady Ursula (1st, 8vo, grey/gilt, 125p, teg, uncut)	R.H. Russell	1898	(Photos)	50-80	
Hope, Anthony	Adventure of Lady Ursula (1st, 8vo, 125p, grey/silver, teg, cvr by...)	R.H. Russell	1898	Bradley, Will	50-80	
Hope, Anthony	Comedies of Courtship (1st, sm8vo, 377p, buckram/gilt)	Scribner	1896	Armstrong, Margaret	35-60	*
Hope, Anthony	Dolly Dialogues (1st AM, 16mo, 195p, uncut, teg, frn by...)	Henry Holt & Co.	1894	Rackham, Arthur	90-140	
Hope, Anthony	Dolly Dialogues (1st, sm sq8vo, 111p, wraps, 4pl)	(London)	1894	Rackham, Arthur	200-300	
Hope, Anthony	Dolly Dialogues (1st, 8vo, 202p, p-o, teg, 18pl)	R.H. Russell	1901	Christy, Howard C.	55-80	R
Hope, Ascott R.	Tales For Toby (1st, 8vo, 207p, 5pl)	L: Dent	1900	Robinson, W. Heath	120-170	
Hope, Edward	Alice in the Delighted States (1st AM, 8vo, 303p, 12pl, cep)	MacVeagh/Dial	1928	Irvin, Rea	50-90	
Hope, Stanton	Smugglers' Gallows (1st, 8vo, 209p, red cl, col frn, 5pl)	L: Eyre/Spotts.	1936	Aldin, Cecil	45-70	
Hope, Stanton	Smugglers' Gallows (1st AM, 8vo, 209p, col frn, b/w, DJ/2.50)	Scribner	1937	Aldin, Cecil	30-50	
Hopkins, Clark	Cyrus Hunts the Cougar (1st {std}, 8vo, 115p, fp b/w, DJ/2.50)	Little/Brown	(1954)	Rowand, Phyllis	40-65	R
Hopkins, Henry C.	Moon-Boat (1st, 4to, tan/gilt, [27]p, p-o, 11cp)	McKay	(1918)	Clayton, W. Philip	150-200	
Hopkins, Lee B. (comp)	City Spreads its Wings (1st, 4to, 46p, fp 2-color, DJ/4.95)	F. Watts	(1970)	Barnett, Moneta	30-50	
Hopkins, Lee B. (comp)	I Think I Saw a Snail (1st, 4to, [39]p, b/w, DJ/3.50)	Crown	(1969)	James, Harold	30-50	*
Hopkins, Lee B. (comp)	Me! A Book of Poems (1st {std}, lg ob8vo, 30p, fp 1-color, DJ/3.95)	Seabury Press	(1970)	Stubis, Talivaldis	25-40	
Hopkins, Lee B. (comp)	This Street's for Me! (1st, lg8vo, [38]p, color, DJ/3.50)	Crown	(1970)	Grifalconi, Ann	25-45	
Hopkins, Marjorie	And the Jackal Played the Masinko (1st, ob4to, [41]p, 3-color, pep, DJ/3.50)	Parents Mag. Pr.	(1969)	Cole, Olivia, H.	25-40	
Hopkins, Marjorie	Glass Valentine (1st, sm8vo, [40]p, color, cep, DJ/3.50)	Parents Mag. Pr.	(1968)	Rockwell, Anne	20-35	
Hopkins, Marjorie	Three Visitors (1st, ob4to, [40]p, ipcb, color, cep, DJ/2.95)	Parents Mag. Pr.	(1967)	Rockwell, Anne	25-40	
Hopkins, Nevil M.	Raccoon Lake Mystery (1st, sm8vo, blue cl, 319p, 4cp)	Lippincott	1917	Hoskins, Gayle	30-50	
Hopkins, Wm. J.	Airship Dragonfly (1st, 8vo, 346p, 8pl)	Doubleday/Page	1906	Hallock, Ruth M.	50-80	
Hopkinson, Frances	Battle of the Kegs (1st {std}, 4to, [32]p, color, DJ/3.75)	Crowell	(1964)	Galdone, Paul	50-80	*
Horgan, Paul	Habit of Empire (1st {this pub}, 8vo, 114p, 8 dp b/w, DJ/2.00)	Harper	(1939)	Hurd, Peter	30-50	
Horgan, Paul	Return of the Weed (1st {std}, 8vo, 97p, 7 fp b/w, DJ/2.00)	Harper	1936	Hurd, Peter	50-85	
Horn, Gladys	Bounce - Story of a Kitten (1st, 8vo, [32]p, color, pep, DJ/1.25)	Winston	(1941)	Wohlberg, Meg	35-60	
Horn, Madeline D.	Farm on the Hill (1st, lg8vo, 78p, blue cl, 8cp, pep, DJ/2.00)	Scribner	1936	Wood, Grant	175-300	
Horn, Madeline D.	Log Cabin Family (1st, lg8vo, 95p, fp color, cep, DJ/2.00)	Scribner	(1939)	McCray, Francis	45-65	
Horne, Richard H.	Good-Natured Bear (1st {std}, 12mo, 159p, fp b/w, pep)	Macmillan	1927	Hummel, Lisl	30-50	
Horne, Richard H.	King Penguin (1st, 12mo, tan cl, 95p, 4cp, pep)	Macmillan	1925	Daugherty, James	30-50	
Horne, Richard H.	Memoirs of a London Doll (1st UK, 8vo, 175p, blue cl, 2cp)	L: Harrap	1923	Brock, Emma	60-90	*
Hornibrook, Isabel	Scout of Today (1st, 8vo, 290p, 5pl)	Houghton	1913	Reading, J.	25-40	*
Hornung, E.W.	Shadow of the Rope (1st, sm8vo, gilt, teg, 377p, 3pl)	Scribner	1906	Dunn, Harvey T.	40-60	
Horton, George	Edge of Hazard (1st, sm8vo, 429p, aqua cl, cvr by...)	Bobbs-Merrill	(1906)	Armstrong, Margaret	35-60	*
Horvath, Betty	Hooray for Jasper (1st {std}, 4to, [32]p, fp 1-color, DJ/2.95)	F. Watts	(1966)	Rocker, Fermin	30-50	
Horvath, Betty	Jasper Makes Music (1st, 4to, [38]p, fp 1-color, DJ/2.95)	F. Watts	(1967)	Rocker, Fermin	30-50	*
Horwitz, Carolyn N.	Fairy-Lure (1st, 12mo, 345p, 1-color decor by...)	D. Lothrop Co.	(1891)	Bridgman, L.J.	55-80	*
Hosford, Dorothy	By His Own Might (1st {std}, 8vo, 69p, fp b/w, pep, DJ/2.00)	Henry Holt & Co.	(1947)	Matulay, Laszlo	40-60	R
Hosford, Dorothy	Sons of the Volsungs (1st, 8vo, 168p, b/w, pep)	Macmillan	1932	Dobias, Frank	20-35	
Hosie, Margaret	Mother Goose Nursery Rhymes (1st, 8vo, 125p, ibds, 8cp 16pl)	Chi: Stanton	(1919)	Burd/Higgins	80-130	
Hough, Charlotte	Jim Tiger (1st AM, 8vo, 30p, color, DJ/2.00)	Bobbs-Merrill	(1958)	Hough, Charlotte	25-40	
Hough, Emerson	54-40 or Fight (1st, sm8vo, 402p, gilt, 4pl)	Bobbs-Merrill	(1909)	Keller, Arthur I.	40-65	
Hough, Emerson	John Rawn, Prominent Citizen (1st, sm8vo, 385p, 6pl)	Bobbs-Merrill	(1912)	Bracker, M. Leone	30-50	*
Hough, Emerson	King of Gee Whiz (1st, lg8vo, 210p, green cl, 8cp)	Bobbs-Merrill	(1906)	Cesare, Oscar E.	150-240	R
Hough, Emerson	Law of the Land (1st, 8vo, 416p, tan cl, 5pl)	Bobbs-Merrill	(1904)	Keller, Arthur I.	30-50	
Hough, Emerson	Mississippi Bubble (1st, sm8vo, 452p, gilt, col frn, 5pl)	Bowen-Merrill	(1902)	Hutt, Henry	40-65	
Hough, Emerson	Singing Mouse Stories (1st [1st bk], 12mo, gilt, [182]p, teg, cvr by...)	Forest/Stream	1895	Bradley, Will	120-180	
Hough, Emerson	Singing Mouse Stories (1st, 12mo, 235p, green/gilt, decor by...)	Bobbs-Merrill	(1910)	Bunker, Mayo	30-50	
Hough, Emerson	Story of the Cowboy (1st, 8vo, 349p, 6pl by...)	Appleton	1897	Russell, Charles M.	125-200	

AUTHOR: 106

AUTHOR	TITLE	PUBLISHER	DATE	ARTIST	PRICE	LC
Hough, Emerson	Way to the West (1st, sm8vo, grey cl, 446p, 6pl)	Bobbs-Merrill	(1903)	Remington, Frederic	70-100	
Hough, Emerson	Young Alaskans (1st, sm8vo, orange cl, 291p, 4pl, PPP)	Harper	1908	Carpenter, D.	160-220	R*
Housman, Clemence	Were-Wolf (1st, sq8vo, 124p, pink cl, uncut, 6pl)	L: John Lane	1896	Housman, Laurence	250-400	
Housman, Laurence	All-Fellows & Cloak of Friendship (1st, sm8vo, 192p, green cl, 7pl)	L: J. Cape	(1923)	Housman, Laurence	80-125	
Housman, Laurence	All-Fellows... (1st, sm8vo, 138p, green/gilt, uncut, 8pl)	L: Kegan Paul	1896	Housman, Laurence	160-220	
Housman, Laurence	Angels & Ministers (1st, sm8vo, 139p, fp b/w)	L: J. Cape	1922	Rutherston, Albert	35-60	*
Housman, Laurence	Bethlehem (1st, 8vo, green/gilt, 85p, cvr by...)	L: Macmillan	1902	Housman, Laurence	100-170	
Housman, Laurence	Blue Moon (1st, 8vo, 210p, teg, blue/gilt, 9pl)	L: J. Murray	1904	Housman, Laurence	120-170	
Housman, Laurence	Cloak of Friendship (1st, 8vo, 192p, buckram/gilt, uncut, cvr by...)	L: J. Murray	1905	Housman, Laurence	90-120	
Housman, Laurence	Cotton Woolleena (1st, 8vo, 36p, wraps, p-o)	L: Blackwell	[1933]	Allen, Marian	75-100	*
Housman, Laurence	Doorway in Fairyland (1st, 8vo, 220p, 14pl)	L: J. Cape	(1922)	Housman, Laurence	140-225	
Housman, Laurence	Farm in Fairyland (1st [1st bk.], 8vo, gilt, 160p, 12pl)	L: Kegan Paul	1894	Housman, Laurence	300-450	
Housman, Laurence	Farm in Fairyland (1st AM, 8vo, teg, 160p, 12pl)	Dodd	1894	Housman, Laurence	200-300	
Housman, Laurence	Field of Clover (1st, 12mo, green/gilt, uncut, 148p, 11pl)	L: Kegan Paul	1898	Housman, Laurence	250-400	
Housman, Laurence	Field of Clover (1st AM, sm8vo, gilt, 148p, teg, 11pl)	NY: J. Lane	1902	Housman, Laurence	200-300	
Housman, Laurence	Golden Sovereign (1st, 8vo, green/gilt, 349p, b/w, DJ)	L: J. Cape	(1937)	Shepard, Ernest H.	60-100	
Housman, Laurence	Gracious Majesty (1st, 8vo, 222p, gilt, b/w, DJ)	L: J. Cape	1941	Shepard, Ernest H.	60-90	
Housman, Laurence	Green Arras (1st, 8vo, green/gilt, 90p, uncut, 5pl)	L: John Lane	1896	Housman, Laurence	180-240	
Housman, Laurence	House of Joy (1st, 8vo, 181p, gilt, uncut, 9pl)	L: Kegan Paul	1895	Housman, Laurence	180-250	
Housman, Laurence	Little Land (1st, 8vo, 97p, ipcb, uncut, gilt, 4pl)	L: Richards	1899	Housman, Laurence	200-300	
Housman, Laurence	Magic Horse (1st, sm sq8vo, [58]p, gilt, 12cp)	L: Hodder	(1911)	Dulac, Edmund	250-400	
Housman, Laurence	Moonshine & Clover (1st, 8vo, 220p, blue/silver)	L: J. Cape	(1922)	Housman, Laurence	80-120	
Housman, Laurence	Princess Badoura (1st, 4to, teg, 113p, gilt, 10 ticp, pep)	L: Hodder	[1913]	Dulac, Edmund	500-700	
Housman, Laurence	Prunella (1st, sm8vo, 89p, pink/gilt, teg, frn by...)	L: A.H. Bullen	1906	Housman, Laurence	60-85	
Housman, Laurence	Sabrina Warham (1st AM, sm8vo, 439p, teg, brown/gilt)	Macmillan	1904	Housman, Laurence	100-150	
Housman, Laurence	Spikenard (1st AM, sm8vo, 53p, brown pcb, gilt)	Badger	1898	Housman, Laurence	100-165	
Housman, Laurence	Story of the Seven Young Goslings (1st, 4to, ibds, [32]p, 6cp)	L: Blackie	1899	Dearmer, Mabel	300-450	
Housman, Laurence	Turn Again Tales (1st, 4to, 280p, p-o, 6 ticp)	L: B. Blackwell	[1930]	Buckels, Alec	80-125	
Housman, Laurence	What-O'Clock Tales (1st, 8vo, 225p, 14 fp b/w)	L: Blackwell	(1932)	Monsell, J.R.	70-100	
Housman, Laurence (ed)	Stories from Arabian Nights (1st AM, 4to, 133p, gilt, 50 ticp)	Scribner	(1907)	Dulac, Edmund	350-500	
Housman, Laurence (ed)	Stories from Arabian Nights (1st, 4to, 133p, 50 ticp)	L: Hodder	(1907)	Dulac, Edmund	325-450	
Housman, Laurence (ed)	Stories from Arabian Nights (8vo, 24 ticp, later)	L: Hodder	[1911]	Dulac, Edmund	120-180	
Houston, James A.	Akavak, an Eskimo Journey (1st {std}, 8vo, 75p, fp b/w, DJ/3.25)	Harcourt	(1968)	Houston, James	30-50	R*
Houston, James A.	White Archer, an Eskimo Legend (1st {std}, 8vo, 95p, fp b/w, DJ/3.50)	Harcourt	(1967)	Houston, James	30-50	
Houston, Joan	Jump-Shy (1st, 8vo, 261p, b/w, DJ/2.75)	Crowell	(1956)	Brown, Paul	100-170	
Hovey, Richard	Marriage of Guenevere (1st, sm8vo, 179p, teg, cvr by...)	Herbert Stone	1895	Meteyard, Thomas B.	60-100	R
Howard, Alice W.	Ching-Li & the Dragons (1st, sm4to, blue/silver, 55p, 10pl)	Macmillan	1931	Ward, Lynd	70-120	
Howard, Coralie (comp)	First Book of Short Verse (1st, 8vo, 125p, b/w, DJ)	F. Watts	(1964)	Funai, Mamoru	45-75	
Howard, Elizabeth	Dorinda (1st, sm8vo, 303p, beige cl, fp b/w, pep, DJ/2.00)	Lothrop, Lee	(1944)	Weisgard, Leonard	30-50	
Howard, F. Martin	Porpoise of Pirate Bay (1st, lg8vo, 152p, 8 fp b/w, pep, DJ/1.00)	Random	(1938)	Ward, Lynd	40-65	
Howard, Henry	Doings of the Dollymites (1st, 24mo, red cl, 94p, 23cp)	L: Sands	(1905)	Billinghurst, Percy	100-160	
Howard, Janet	Jumpy the Kangaroo (1st, sq12mo, [42]p, ibds, color, pep, DJ/1.00)	Lothrop, Lee	(1944)	Duvoisin, Roger	65-100	
Howard, Joan	13th Is Magic (1st, 8vo, 169p, fp b/w, pep, DJ/2.50)	Lothrop, Lee	(1950)	Adams, Adrienne	40-65	*
Howard, Joan	Light in the Tower (1st, sm4to, unpag, blue/gilt, dp color, DJ/2.50)	Lothrop, Lee	(1957)	Adams, Adrienne	30-50	
Howard, Joan	Summer is Magic (1st, 8vo, 182p, fp b/w, pep, DJ/2.50)	Lothrop, Lee	(1952)	Adams, Adrienne	40-65	
Howard, Keble	Smiths of Surbiton (1st, 8vo, 300p, b/w)	L: Chapman/Hall	1906	Reynolds, Frank	50-80	*
Howe-Nurse, Wilfred	Berkshire Vale (1st, folio, 45p, p-o, 22pl, pep)	L: Blackwell	1927	Aldin, Cecil	140-200	
Howell, Virginia	Who Likes the Dark? (1st, 8vo, [40]p, ibds, color, DJ/1.50)	Howell/Soskin	1945	Thompson, Marjorie	30-50	*
Howells, William D.	Boy's Town (1st, sm8vo, aqua/gilt, 247p, 23pl, PPP)	Harper	1890	Farny, H.F.	170-250	
Howells, William D.	Christmas Every Day... (1st, 12mo, 150p, rust cl, 14 b/w)	Harper	1893	Unknown	70-100	R
Howells, William D.	Coast of Bohemia (1st, 12mo, red/gilt, 340p, 8pl)	Harper	1893	Small, F.O.	55-80	
Howells, William D.	Fennel & Rue (1st, 8vo, 130p, green/gilt, 4pl)	Harper	1908	Harding, Charlotte	30-50	
Howells, William D.	Flight of Pony Baker (1st, 12mo, red/silver, 223p, 8pl, PPP)	Harper	1902	Shinn, Florence S.	120-200	R
Howells, William D.	Stops of Various Quills (1st, 8vo, teg, [110]p, gilt, designs by...)	Harper	1895	Pyle, Howard	80-130	
Howes, Edith	Cradle Ship (1st, 8vo, 219p, blue cl, 4cp)	L: Cassell	1916	Anderson, Florence	80-120	
Howes, Edith	Enchanted Road (1st, 8vo, 246p, blue cl, col frn, b/w)	Wm. Morrow	1927	Smalley, Janet	60-100	*
Howes, Edith	Fairy Rings (1st, 12mo, 248p, p-o, gilt, 4cp)	L: Cassell	1911	Watkins, Frank	80-125	*
Howes, Edith	Long Bright Land (1st, 8vo, 207p, green/gilt, col frn, 12pl, pep)	Little/Brown	1929	Lathrop, Dorothy	65-100	
Howes, Edith	Mrs. Kindbush (1st, 8vo, 160p, 4cp)	L: Cassell	1933	Anderson, Anne	100-150	
Howes, Edith	Rainbow Children (1st, 8vo, blue/gilt, p-o, 250p, 4cp)	L: Cassell	1912	Woodward, Alice B.	70-100	
Howes, Edith	Sandals of Pearl (1st, 8vo, 246p, t-i col frn, 8 pl)	Wm. Morrow	1928	Chalmers, Audrey	50-85	
Howes, Edith	Sun's Babies (1st [1st bk.], sm8vo, gilt, p-o, 236p, 4cp)	L: Cassell	1910	Watkins, Frank	70-100	
Howland, Ethel	Scary-Ann/Cookie Man (1st, 8vo, ibds, 100p, color, pep)	Suttonhouse	1932	Eulalie	60-100	
Howlett, Edwin	Driving Lessons (1st, lg8vo, 159p, 20pl)	R.H. Russell	1894	(Photos)	300-500	
Hoyland, Rosemary	Ethelbert (1st AM, ob folio, [36]p, 2-color, DJ/2.00)	Knopf	1954	Hoyland, Rosemary	40-70	
Hoyle, Zoe	Peek-a-Boo's Desert Island (1st, sq4to, ipcb, b/w, pep)	L: H. Milford	[1915]	Preston, Chloe	220-350	
Hoyt, Eleanor	Nancy's Country Christmas (1st, 8vo, teg, 224p, uncut, col frn)	Doubleday/Page	1904	Betts, Anna W.	35-60	
Hoyt, Vance J.	Silver Boy (1st, 8vo, blue/silver, 265p, pep, 6pl)	Lothrop, Lee	(1929)	Bull, Charles L.	30-50	
Hubbard, Eleanore	Cap that Mother Made (1st, 12mo, ibds, unpag, color)	Volland	(1928)	Hubbard, Eleanore	50-85	
Hubbard, Freeman	Roundhouse Cat and other Railroad Animals (1st, 8vo, 124p, b/w, DJ/2.00)	Whittlesey	(1951)	Wiese, Kurt	30-50	
Hubbard, Freeman	Train that Never Came Back (1st, 8vo, 127p, b/w, DJ/2.25)	Whittlesey	(1952)	Wiese, Kurt	30-45	
Hubbard, Margaret	Boss Chambale (1st, 8vo, 185p, b/w, DJ/2.75)	Crowell	1957	Spier, Peter E.	25-40	
Hubbard, Ralph	Queer Person (1st {std}, 8vo, 336p, doub. plates, pep, NH)	Doubleday/Doran	1930	Von Schmidt, H.	60-100	*
Hubbard, Ralph	Wolf Song (1st {std}, 8vo, 287p, b/w pl, pep, DJ/2.00)	Doubleday/Doran	1935	Kihn, W. Langdon	40-65	
Hubbell, Patricia	Apple Vendor's Fair (1st {std}, 8vo, 53p, DJ/2.75)	Atheneum	1963	Maas, Julie	20-35	*
Hubbell, Rose S.	If I Could Fly (1st, 8vo, teg, 113p, 5cp, pep)	Putnam	1917	Gaze, Harold	120-200	
Hubbell, Rose S.	Quacky Doodles... (1st, 8vo, ibds, [88]p, color)	Volland	(1916)	Gruelle, Johnny	80-130	
Hubbell-Plummer, B.	Little Homespun Songs (1st, lg4to, 104p, ibds, p-o, 12pl, pep)	Stokes	(1920)	Russell, Mary L.	100-170	

AUTHOR	TITLE	PUBLISHER	DATE	ARTIST	PRICE	LC
Huber, Ursula	Nock Family Circus (1st AM {std}, 4to, ibds, [32]p, color, DJ/4.95)	Atheneum	1968	Piatti, Celestino	25-40	
Huckel, Oliver	Wagner's Parsifal (1st, 12mo, 71p, teg, red/gilt, 5cp)	Crowell	1903	Stassen, Franz	35-50	
Hudson, Alma	Peter Rabbit & the Fairies (sq12mo, 48p, red bds, p-o, 8cp, DJ/1.00)	Cupples/Leon	(1921)	Hudson, Richard	80-125	
Hudson, Alma	Peter Rabbit in Mother Goose Land (1st, 16mo, red bds, p-o, 48p, color)	Cupples/Leon	(1921)	Hudson, Richard	80-125	
Hudson, Charles B.	Crimson Conquest (1st, 8vo, 454p, cvr by…)	McClurg	1907	Leyendecker, J.C.	50-80	
Hudson, Wm. Henry	Birds in Town & Village (1st, 8vo, 274p, green/gilt, 8cp)	L: Dent	1919	Detmold, Edward J.	160-225	
Hudson, Wm. Henry	Birds in Town & Village (1st AM, 8vo, blue/gilt, 323p, 8cp)	Dutton	(1920)	Detmold, Edward J.	140-200	
Hudson, Wm. Henry	Disappointed Squirrel (1st, lg8vo, p-o, 144p, 8 ticp, pep)	Doran	(1925)	Kirmse, Marguerite	60-90	
Hudson, Wm. Henry	Green Mansions (1st, lg8vo, 325p, ibds, dp woodcuts)	L: Duckworth	1926	Henderson, Keith	50-80	
Hudson, Wm. Henry	Little Boy Lost (1st, sm8vo, buckram/gilt, teg, 201p, fp b/w pl)	L: Duckworth	1905	McCormick, A.D.	140-200	R
Hudson, Wm. Henry	Little Boy Lost (1st, 4to, teg, 187p, gilt, uncut, pep, 8cp)	Knopf	1920	Lathrop, Dorothy	150-220	
Hudson, Wm. Henry	Purple Land (1st, lg8vo, red/gilt, 368p, b/w)	L: Duckworth	1929	Henderson, Keith	45-70	
Hudson, Wm. Henry	Tales of the Pampas (1st, 8vo, beige cl, 245p, 6pl, DJ/2.00)	Knopf	1939	Duvoisin, Roger	40-65	
Hueffer, F.M.	Cinque Ports… (1st, 4to, 403p, teg, buckram/gilt, 14pl)	L: Blackwood	1900	Hyde, William	425-600	
Huffard, Grace T.	My Poetry Book (1st AM, lg8vo, 504p, blue/gilt, 6cp, pep)	Winston	(1934)	Pogany, Willy	50-90	
Huffard, Grace T.	My Poetry Book (1st, lg8vo, blue cl, 6cp)	(London)	1934	Pogany, Willy	60-100	
Hughes, Langston	Black Misery (1st {std}, ob12mo, black cl, [60]p, b/w, DJ/2.50)	NY: P. Ericksson	(1969)	Arouni	100-165	R
Hughes, Langston	Don't You Turn Back (1st, lg8vo, 78p, color, DJ/3.95)	Knopf	(1969)	Grifalconi, Ann	60-100	
Hughes, Langston	Dream Keeper (1st {std}, 8vo, 77p, blue/silver, b/w)	Knopf	1932	Sewell, Helen	450-600	R
Hughes, Langston	First Book of Negroes (1st {std}, sq8vo, gilt, 69p, color, DJ/1.75)	F. Watts	1952	Koering, Ursula	300-450	
Hughes, Langston	First Book of Rhythms (1st {std}, 8vo, 63p, color, DJ/1.75)	F. Watts	(1954)	King, Robin	200-300	
Hughes, Richard A.	Don't Blame Me! (1st {std}, sm8vo, 159p, b/w, DJ/1.50)	Harper	(1940)	Eichenberg, Fritz	40-65	
Hughes, Richard A.	Gertrude's Child (1st {std}, 8vo, 44p, pcb, fp b/w, pep, DJ/2.95)	Harlin Quist	(1966)	Schreiter, Rick	25-40	
Hughes, Richard A.	Spider's Palace (1st AM {std}, 8vo, 163p, color, DJ/1.50)	Harper	1932	Charlton, George	140-200	
Hughes, Rupert	Colonel Crockett's Cooperative Christmas (1st, sm8vo, 66p, 6cp)	Jacobs	(1906)	Unknown	25-40	
Hughes, Rupert	Fairy Detective (1st, 12mo, 72p, tan cl, p-o, 5pl)	Harper	(1919)	Chase, Rhoda	30-60	*
Hughes, Rupert	Lakerim Athletic Club (1st, sm8vo, gilt, 286p, 20pl, PPPa)	Century	1898	Relyea, Charles M.	200-300	
Hughes, Shirley	Lucy & Tom's Day (1st, ob4to, tan cl, [27]p, fp color, DJ/2.75)	W.R. Scott	(1960)	Hughes, Shirley	40-65	
Hughes, Ted	How the Whale Became (1st AM {std}, lg8vo, 100p, fp b/w, DJ/3.50)	Atheneum	1964	Schreiter, Rick	80-140	
Hughes, Ted	Iron Giant (1st, 8vo, 56p, blue ipcb, fp b/w, DJ/2.95)	Harper	(1968)	Nadler, Robert	250-450	R
Hughes, Thomas	Tom Brown's School Days (1st, 12mo, green/gilt, b/w)	L: Macmillan	1897	Sullivan, Edmund J.	60-90	
Hughes, Thomas	Tom Brown's School Days (1st, lg8vo, 376p, pict cl, b/w)	Harper	(1911)	Rhead, Louis	60-80	
Hugo, Victor	Hunchback of Notre-Dame (1st, 8vo, 424p, b/w)	Dodd	1928	Wheelwright, Rowland	45-70	
Hugo, Victor	Les Miserables (lg8vo, black/gilt, 585p, pep, 12cp)	Dodd	[1925]	Schaeffer, Mead	70-100	
Hugo, Victor	Story of the Bold Pecopin (1st, lg8vo, teg, 92p, gilt, 8pl, cep)	L: Smith Elder	1902	Millar, H.R.	65-90	
Hulbert, Homer B.	Omjee, The Wizard (1st, lg8vo, 156p, black cl, color, pep)	Milton Bradley	(1925)	Lupprian, Hildegard	100-180	
Hull, Eleanor	Trainful of Strangers (1st {std}, 8vo, 114p, b/w, DJ/3.95)	Atheneum	1968	Sandin, Joan	25-45	*
Hume, Fergus	Chronicles of Fairy-Land (1st, 8vo, 191p, teg, gilt, pep, 8cp)	Lippincott	1911	Kirk, Maria L.	300-500	
Hume, Ruth & Paul	Lion of Poland (1st, 8vo, 192p, b/w, pep, DJ/2.95)	Hawthorn Books	1962	Rethi, Lili	20-35	
Humphrey, Henry	What is it For? (1st {std}, lg4to, 48p, b/w, DJ/4.50, NYTBI)	Simon/Schuster	(1969)	(Photos)	30-50	*
Humphrey, Mabel	Book of the Cat (1st, folio, ibds, [40]p, 6cp)	Stokes	1903	Bonsall, Eliz. F.	500-800	R
Humphrey, Mabel	Book of the Child (1st, folio, ibds, 4cp by…)	Stokes	(1903)	Green, Eliz. S.	750-1000	
Humphrey, Mabel	Book of the Child (1st, folio, ibds, 3cp by…)	Stokes	(1903)	Smith, Jessie W.	750-1000	
Humphrey, Mabel	Bright Days… (lg4to, 36p, ibds, 12cp)	Stokes	1901	Spiegle, F.	200-300	
Humphrey, Mabel	Little Continentals (1st, lg4to, ibds, 6cp)	Stokes	1900	Humphrey, Maud	400-600	
Humphrey, Mabel	Little Folk of '76 (1st, 4to, ibds, 6cp)	Stokes	1900	Humphrey, Maud	400-600	
Humphrey, Maud	Babes of the Year (1st, sq8vo, ibds, 25p, 12cp)	Stokes	1888	Humphrey, Maud	500-800	
Humphrey, Maud	Book of Fairy Tales (1st, 4to, ipcb, [30]p, 12cp)	Stokes	1892	Humphrey, Maud	600-850	
Humphrey, Maud	Children of the Revolution (1st, 4to, ibds, [24]p, 12cp)	Stokes	1900	Humphrey, Maud	600-850	
Humphrey, Maud	Gallant Little Patriots (1st, 4to, ipcb, 12cp)	Stokes	1899	Humphrey, Maud	600-850	
Humphrey, Maud	Golf Girl (1st, 4to, ibds, color)	Stokes	(1899)	Humphrey, Maud	500-700	
Humphrey, Maud	Little Heroes & Heroines (1st, 4to, ibds, 6cp)	Stokes	1899	Humphrey, Maud	400-600	
Humphrey, Maud	Little Soldiers & Sailors (1st, 4to, ibds, [19]p, 6cp)	Stokes	(1899)	Humphrey, Maud	400-600	
Humphrey, Maud	Rosebud Stories (1st, 8vo, 24p, ipcb, 6cp)	Holiday Pub.	1906	Humphrey, Maud	350-500	
Humphrey, Maud	Tiny Toddlers (1st, folio, [14]p, color, ibds)	Stokes	1890	Humphrey, Maud	650-900	
Hunt, Blanche S.	Little Brown Koko has Fun (1st, sm4to, 96p, ibds, 1-color)	Amer. Colortype	(1945)	Wagstaff, Dorothy	80-130	
Hunt, Blanche S.	Stories of Little Brown Koko (1st, 4to, bds, 96p, 1-color, pep, DJ/1.00)	Amer. Colortype	1940	Wagstaff, Dorothy	90-140	
Hunt, Clara W.	About Harriet (1st, 8vo, 150p, p-o, fp color)	Houghton	1916	Enright, Maginel W.	35-60	
Hunt, Clara W.	Little House in Green Valley (1st, 12mo, 95p, green cl, fp 1-color)	Houghton	1932	Brock, Emma	30-50	
Hunt, Clara W.	Peggy's Playhouses (1st, sm8vo, 123p, p-o, b/w, pl)	Houghton	1924	Tenggren, Gustaf	30-50	*
Hunt, Enid	Fine Lady Upon a White Horse (1st AM, 4to, gilt, 120p, 8cp)	Dodge	[1929]	Peto, Gladys	100-165	
Hunt, Irene	Across Five Aprils (1st [1st bk.] {std}, 8vo, 223p, pep, DJ/3.95, NH)	Follett	(1964)	Pucci, Albert	80-120	R
Hunt, Irene	Trail of Apple Blossoms (1st {std}, 8vo, 64p, color, DJ/3.95)	Follett	(1968)	Bolognese, Don	30-50	
Hunt, Irene	Up a Road Slowly (1st {std}, 8vo, 192p, cloth, DJ/3.95, NM)	Follett	1966	No Illustrations	150-225	
Hunt, Mabel L.	69th Grandchild (1st {std}, 8vo, 68p, fp b/w, DJ/1.75)	Lippincott	(1951)	Blaisdell, Elinore	25-40	
Hunt, Mabel L.	Benjie's Hat (1st, 8vo, 119p, orange cl, pep, b/w, DJ/1.75)	Stokes	1938	Paull, Grace	30-50	
Hunt, Mabel L.	Better Known as Johnny Appleseed (1st {std}, 8vo, 212p, cep, DJ/2.50, NH)	Lippincott	(1950)	Daugherty, James	60-90	R
Hunt, Mabel L.	Billy Button's Buttered Biscuit (1st, 12mo, 56p, color, cep, DJ/1.00)	Stokes	1941	Milhous, Katherine	40-70	
Hunt, Mabel L.	Boy Who Had no Birthday (1st, 8vo, orange cl, 259p, fp b/w, DJ/1.75)	Stokes	1935	Wright, Cameron	40-65	
Hunt, Mabel L.	Corn-Belt Billy (1st, lg8vo, ibds, [26]p, pep, color, DJ/0.50)	Grosset/Dunlap	(1942)	Wiese, Kurt	45-70	
Hunt, Mabel L.	Cristy at Skippinghills (1st {std}, 8vo, 139p, b/w, DJ/3.00)	Lippincott	(1959)	Ilsley, Velma	20-30	
Hunt, Mabel L.	Cupola House (1st {std}, 8vo, 122p, DJ/3.25)	Lippincott	(1961)	Unwin, Nora S.	20-35	
Hunt, Mabel L.	Double Birthday Present (1st {std}, sm8vo, 52p, red cl, col frn, DJ/1.50)	Lippincott	(1947)	Blaisdell, Elinore	45-70	
Hunt, Mabel L.	Have You Seen Tom Thumb? (1st, sm8vo, 259p, b/w, dep, DJ/2.00, NH)	Stokes	1942	Eichenberg, Fritz	100-175	
Hunt, Mabel L.	John of Pudding Lane (1st, 8vo, 161p, color, pep, DJ/1.75)	Stokes	(1941)	Funk, Clotilde	25-45	
Hunt, Mabel L.	Johnny-Up and Johnny-Down (1st {std}, 8vo, 93p, 1-color, DJ/3.95)	Lippincott	(1962)	Berson, Harold	20-30	
Hunt, Mabel L.	Ladycake Farm (1st, 8vo, 126p, fp b/w, pep, DJ/2.25)	Lippincott	(1952)	Funk, Clotilde	20-30	
Hunt, Mabel L.	Little Girl with Seven Names (1st, 8vo, 63p, b/w, pep, DJ/1.50)	Stokes	1936	Paull, Grace	30-55	

AUTHOR	TITLE	PUBLISHER	DATE	ARTIST	PRICE	LC
Hunt, Mabel L.	Little Grey Gown (1st, 8vo, 168p, b/w, DJ/1.75)	Stokes	1939	Bischoff, Ilse	25-40	
Hunt, Mabel L.	Lucinda: Little Girl of 1860 (1st, sm8vo, 233p, blue cl, b/w)	Stokes	1934	Wright, Cameron	25-40	*
Hunt, Mabel L.	Matilda's Buttons (1st {std}, 8vo, 132p, b/w, DJ/1.75)	Lippincott	(1948)	Blaisdell, Elinore	30-50	
Hunt, Mabel L.	Michel's Island (1st, lg8vo, 265p, gilt, pep, b/w, DJ/2.00)	Stokes	1940	Seredy, Kate	30-50	
Hunt, Mabel L.	Miss Jellytot's Visit (1st {std}, 8vo, 126p, b/w, DJ/2.50)	Lippincott	(1955)	Ilsley, Velma	20-30	*
Hunt, Mabel L.	Peddler's Clock (1st, sq8vo, ipcb, [28]p, pep, color, DJ/0.50)	Grosset/Dunlap	(1943)	Jones, Eliz. O.	30-50	
Hunt, Mabel L.	Peter Piper's Pickled Peppers (1st, 16mo, 62p, cep, 4cp, DJ/1.50)	Stokes	1942	Milhous, Katherine	30-50	
Hunt, Mabel L.	Sibby Botherbox (1st {std}, lg8vo, 174p, blue cl, pep, b/w, DJ/2.00)	Lippincott	(1945)	Collison, Marjory	30-50	
Hunt, Mabel L.	Stars for Cristy (1st {std}, 8vo, 141p, b/w, DJ/2.75)	Lippincott	(1956)	Ilsley, Velma	25-45	
Hunt, Mabel L.	Such a Kind World (1st, sq8vo, [28]p, fp color, pep, DJ/0.50)	Grosset/Dunlap	1947	Potter, Edna	30-50	
Hunt, Mabel L.	Susan Beware! (1st, 8vo, 243p, green cl, b/w, pep, DJ/1.75)	Stokes	1937	Boyle, Mildred	30-50	
Hunt, Mabel L.	Wonderful Baker (1st {std}, 8vo, blue cl, 47p, b/w, dep, DJ/1.50)	Lippincott	(1950)	Paull, Grace	30-50	
Hunt, Mabel L.	Young Man of the House (1st {std}, 8vo, 171p, 10 fp b/w, DJ/2.50)	Lippincott	(1944)	Slobodkin, Louis	30-50	
Hunt, Marigold	Hester & the Gnomes (1st, 8vo, 124p, blue cl, fp b/w, pep, DJ/2.50)	Whittlesey	(1955)	Charlot, Jean	50-80	
Hunt, Wolf R.	Dancing Horses of Acoma (1st {std}, lg8vo, 163p, color, DJ/4.50)	World	(1963)	Hunt, Wolf	80-130	R
Hunter, Mollie	Kelpie's Pearls (1st AM, 8vo, 112p, b/w, DJ/3.25)	Funk/Wagnalls	(1966)	Cellini, Joseph	25-40	
Hunter, Mollie	Walking Stones (1st, 8vo, 143p, ipcb, 7 fp b/w, DJ/3.95)	Harper	(1970)	Hyman, Trina S.	45-70	
Hunter, Norman	Incredible Adventures/Professor Brawnestawm (1st, lg8vo, 203p, col frn)	L: Bodley Head	(1933)	Robinson, W. Heath	180-300	
Hunter, Norman	Larky Legends (1st, 8vo, 220p, col frn, b/w, pep, DJ)	L: John Lane	1938	Arnold, James	80-145	
Hunter, Richard	Dollies (1st, 24mo, olive cl, 95p)	L: Richards	1902	Cobb/Hunter	120-200	*
Hunter, Richard	Little Pickles (sm4to, ibds, 44p, color)	L: Blackie	[1900]	Cobb, Ruth	170-240	
Hunter, Richard	Silver Bubbles... (1st, 4to, [40]p, color)	L: Nelson	[1903]	Cobb, Ruth	170-240	
Huntington, Ida M.	Christmas Party for Santa Claus (1st, lg8vo, 102p, p-o, 6cp)	Rand/McNally	(1912)	Unknown	80-120	*
Huntington, Ida M.	Garden of Hearts' Delight (1st, lg8vo, p-o, gilt, 167p, 15cp)	Rand/McNally	(1911)	Enright, Maginel W.	100-160	
Huntington, Ida M.	Peter Pumpkin in Wonderland (1st, lg sq8vo, 264p, 15pl)	Rand/McNally	(1908)	Hunt, Mary I.	80-120	
Hurd, Clement	Merry Chase (1st {std}, sm4to, [25]p, yellow cl, pep, color, DJ/1.50)	Random	(1941)	Hurd, Clement	50-85	
Hurd, Clement	Race Between the Monkey & the Duck (lg8vo, ibds, [31]p, color, DJ)	Wonder Books	(1946)	Hurd, Clement	30-50	*
Hurd, Clement	The Race (1st {std}, sm4to, [27]p, yellow cl, color, pep, DJ/1.50)	Random	(1940)	Hurd, Clement	50-80	
Hurd, Edith T.	Annie Moran (1st, ob4to, ibds, [32]p, color, pep, DJ/1.25)	Lothrop, Lee	1942	Hurd, Clement	50-80	
Hurd, Edith T.	Benny the Bulldozer (1st, sm ob4to, [33]p, ibds, 1-color, pep, DJ/1.25)	Lothrop, Lee	1947	Hurd, Clement	50-80	
Hurd, Edith T.	Blue Heron Tree (1st {std}, lg8vo, 66p, fp 1-color, DJ/3.95)	Viking	(1968)	Hurd, Clement	25-40	
Hurd, Edith T.	Caboose (1st, sm ob4to, [33]p, ibds, 1-color, DJ/1.25)	Lothrop, Lee	1950	Hurd, Clement	50-80	
Hurd, Edith T.	Cat from Telegraph Hill (1st, lg8vo, [32]p, ipcb, pep, color, DJ/2.00)	Lothrop, Lee	(1955)	Hurd, Clement	45-75	
Hurd, Edith T.	Catfish (1st {std}, lg8vo, [63]p, color, DJ/3.50)	Viking	(1970)	Hurd, Clement	30-50	
Hurd, Edith T.	Christmas Eve (1st, ob4to, [48]p, ibds, 1-color, DJ/2.95)	Harper	(1962)	Hurd, Clement	30-50	
Hurd, Edith T.	Come and Have Fun (1st, 8vo, 32p, 2-color, cep, DJ/1.95)	Harper	(1962)	Hurd, Clement	30-50	*
Hurd, Edith T.	Day the Sun Danced (1st, 4to, ibds, [30]p, color, DJ/3.50)	Harper	(1965)	Hurd, Clement	30-45	
Hurd, Edith T.	Devil's Tail (1st {std}, 8vo, 216p, t.e. red, fp b/w, DJ/2.75)	Doubleday	(1954)	Hurd, Clement	30-50	
Hurd, Edith T.	Engine, Engine No. 9 (1st, sm ob4to, [34]p, ibds, 2-color, pep, DJ/1.25)	Lothrop, Lee	1940	Hurd, Clement	70-100	
Hurd, Edith T.	Faraway Christmas (1st, 8vo, blue cl, [33]p, 1-color, pep, DJ/2.50)	Lothrop, Lee	1958	Hurd, Clement	30-50	
Hurd, Edith T.	Follow Tomas (1st, lg8vo, 61p, fp b/w, dep, DJ/2.95)	Dial Press	(1963)	Hurd, Clement	25-40	
Hurd, Edith T.	Fox in a Box (1st {std}, lg8vo, ibds, [36]p, color, pep, DJ/2.50)	Doubleday	(1957)	Hurd, Clement	45-65	
Hurd, Edith T.	Hurry Hurry (1st, 8vo, ipcb, 45p, 1-color, cep)	W.R. Scott	(1938)	Shipman, M.D.	50-80	
Hurd, Edith T.	It's Snowing (1st, 4to, silver cl, unpag, dep, b/w, DJ/2.50)	NY: Sterling	(1957)	Hurd, Clement	60-100	
Hurd, Edith T.	Jerry the Jeep (1st, ob4to, [32]p, ipcb, 1-color, pep, DJ/1.00)	Lothrop, Lee	(1945)	Friday, Theodore	40-65	
Hurd, Edith T.	Johnny Lion's Bad Day (1st, 8vo, 64p, ibds, color, DJ/2.50)	Harper	(1970)	Hurd, Clement	30-45	
Hurd, Edith T.	Johnny Lion's Book (1st, 8vo, 64p, ibds, 2-color, DJ/1.95)	Harper	(1965)	Hurd, Clement	20-35	
Hurd, Edith T.	Johnny Littlejohn (1st, narrow ob8vo, unpag, yellow cl, 1-color, DJ/1.75)	Lothrop, Lee	(1957)	Hurd, Clement	60-100	
Hurd, Edith T.	Last One Home is a Green Pig (1st, 8vo, ibds, 63p, color, DJ/1.95)	Harper	1959	Hurd, Clement	30-50	
Hurd, Edith T.	Little Dog, Dreaming (1st, ob8vo, [31]p, ibds, 2-color, DJ/2.50)	Harper	(1967)	Hurd, Clement	25-45	
Hurd, Edith T.	Nino & his Fish (1st, lg8vo, [34]p, ipcb, color, pep, DJ/2.00)	Lothrop, Lee	(1954)	Hurd, Clement	30-50	
Hurd, Edith T.	No Funny Business (1st, 8vo, 62p, 3-color, DJ/1.95)	Harper	(1962)	Hurd, Clement	30-45	*
Hurd, Edith T.	Old Silversides (1st, ob4to, [30]p, ibds, 1-color, pep, DJ/1.50)	Lothrop, Lee	1951	Hurd, Clement	50-80	
Hurd, Edith T.	Sandpipers (1st, sq8vo, [40]p, ipcb, 2-color, DJ/1.95, NYTBI)	Crowell	(1961)	Bloch, Lucienne	30-50	*
Hurd, Edith T.	Sky High (1st, sm ob4to, ibds, [34]p, color, pep, DJ/1.25)	Lothrop, Lee	(1941)	Hurd, Clement	60-100	
Hurd, Edith T.	So-So Cat (1st, sm4to, 32p, fp 1-color, cep, DJ/2.95)	Harper	(1964)	Hurd, Clement	30-45	
Hurd, Edith T.	Somebody's House (1st, 4to, 43p, 2-color, DJ/2.00)	Lothrop, Lee	1953	Hurd, Clement	40-65	
Hurd, Edith T.	Speedy, Hook & Ladder Truck (1st, ob4to, ibds, [36]p, 1-color, pep, DJ/1.00)	Lothrop, Lee	1942	Hurd, Clement	50-80	
Hurd, Edith T.	St. George's Day in Williamsburg (1st, ob8vo, wraps, [32]p, fp 1-color)	(Williamsburg)	1952	Hurd, Clement	40-65	
Hurd, Edith T.	Starfish (1st, ob8vo, [40]p, fp 3-color, DJ/2.50)	Crowell	(1962)	Bloch, Lucienne	30-50	*
Hurd, Edith T.	Toughy & his Trailer Truck (1st, ob4to, ibds, [34]p, pep, 1-color, DJ/1.25)	Lothrop, Lee	1948	Hurd, Clement	50-80	
Hurd, Edith T.	What Whale? Where? (1st, ob8vo, [44]p, 1-color, cep, DJ/2.95)	Harper	(1966)	Hurd, Clement	25-40	
Hurd, Edith T.	White Horse (1st {std}, lg8vo, [31]p, color, DJ/3.50)	Harper	(1970)	Chen, Tony	25-40	*
Hurd, Edith T.	Willy's Farm (1st, 4to, 64p, ipcb, color, pep, DJ/2.00)	Lothrop, Lee	(1949)	Hurd, Clement	50-80	
Hurd, Edith T.	Wreck of the Wild Wave (1st, 8vo, 247p, b/w, pep, DJ/2.50)	Oxford U. Pr.	(1942)	Chapman, Fred T.	30-50	*
Hurd, Marian K.	Miss Billy: Neighborhood Story (1st, sm8vo, gilt, 349p, 6pl)	Lothrop Pub.	1905	Copeland, Charles	35-60	*
Hurd, Marian K.	When She Came Home from College (1st, 12mo, 272p, 7pl)	Houghton	1909	Gibbs, George	25-45	*
Hurlimann, Bettina	William Tell and his Son (1st AM {std}, lg ob4to, [36]p, color, DJ/4.25)	Harcourt	(1967)	Nussbaumer, Paul	40-65	
Hurrell, Marian I.	Adventures of Friskers & His Friends (1st, 12mo, 159p, 16cp)	L: R. Culley	[1907]	Wain, Louis	500-750	
Hurst, Edward H.	Mystery Island (1st, sm8vo, 313p, uncut, gilt, col frn by...)	L.C. Page	1907	Tyng, Griswold	25-40	*
Hurter, Albert	He Drew as He Pleased (1st, 4to, [97]p, b/w, DJ/5.00)	Simon/Schuster	1948	Hurter, Albert	600-900	
Huston, Anne	Trust a City Kid (1st, 8vo, 192p, b/w, DJ/3.75)	Lothrop, Lee	(1966)	Kocsis, J.C.	45-70	*
Hutchins, Pat	Clocks and More Clocks (1st {std}, ob4to, [32]p, color, DJ/4.95)	Macmillan	(1970)	Hutchins, Pat	25-40	*
Hutchins, Pat	Rosie's Walk (1st {std}, ob4to, [32]p, color, DJ/3.95)	Macmillan	(1968)	Hutchins, Pat	25-40	
Hutchins, Pat	Surprise Party (1st {std}, ob4to, [32]p, color, DJ/4.50)	Macmillan	(1969)	Hutchins, Pat	25-40	
Hutchins, Pat	Tom and Sam (1st {std}, ob4to, [32]p, color, DJ/4.50)	Macmillan	(1968)	Hutchins, Pat	25-45	
Hutchins, Ross	The Mayfly (1st {std}, 8vo, 48p, color, DJ)	Addison-Wesley	(1970)	Zallinger, Jean	20-35	
Hutchinson, Henry N.	Prehistoric Man & Beast (1st, 8vo, gilt, 298p, 10pl)	L: Smith/Elder	1896	Aldin, Cecil	70-100	

AUTHOR	TITLE	PUBLISHER	DATE	ARTIST	PRICE	LC
Hutchinson, Ruth	Blue Butterfly Goes to South America (1st, 4to, 111p, ibds, color, DJ/2.00)	Whitman	1940	Wiese, Kurt	30-50	
Hutchinson, Veronica	Candle-Light Stories (1st, sm4to, 146p, 6cp, pep)	Minton Balch	1928	Lenski, Lois	80-120	
Hutchinson, Veronica	Chimney Corner Fairy Tales (1st, sm4to, 183p, 6cp, pep)	Minton Balch	1926	Lenski, Lois	80-140	
Hutchinson, Veronica	Chimney Corner Poems (1st, sm4to, 115p, 6cp, pep)	Minton Balch	1929	Lenski, Lois	80-140	
Hutchinson, Veronica	Chimney Corner Stories (1st, sm4to, 149p, 6cp, pep)	Minton Balch	1925	Lenski, Lois	80-140	
Hutchinson, Veronica	Circus Comes to Town (1st, 4to, ipcb, [66]p, color, pep)	Minton Balch	(1932)	Berry, Erick	40-60	
Hutchinson, Veronica	Fireside Poems (1st, sm4to, 147p, 5cp, pep)	Minton Balch	1930	Lenski, Lois	70-120	
Hutchinson, Veronica	Fireside Stories (1st, sm4to, 150p, 6cp, pep)	Minton Balch	1927	Lenski, Lois	80-130	
Hutchinson, W.M.L.	Golden Porch (1st [new ed], sm8vo, 302p, pep, col frn, fp b/w)	NY: Longmans	1925	Walker, Dugald S.	70-100	
Hutchinson, W.M.L.	Orpheus with his Lute (1st, sm8vo, 300p, col frn, b/w, pep)	NY: Longmans	1926	Walker, Dugald S.	60-90	*
Hutchinson, W.M.L.	Sunset of the Heroes (8vo, 281p, green/gilt, pep, teg, 8cp)	L: J.M. Dent	[1910]	Cole, Herbert	70-100	*
Hutchison, Collister	Toward Daybreak (1st {std}, lg8vo, 88p, fp b/w, DJ/3.00)	Harper	(1950)	Chagall, Marc	50-85	
Hutt, Henry	Girls (1st, 4to, [38]p, blue cl, p-o, 16cp)	Scribner	1910	Hutt, Henry	100-165	
Hutt, Henry	Henry Hutt Picture Book (1st, 4to, [84]p, p-o, 10cp)	Century	1908	Hutt, Henry	100-165	
Hutt, Henry	Rosebuds (1st, 4to, 27p, 11 ticp)	Bobbs-Merrill	(1912)	Hutt, Henry	130-200	*
Hutt, Henry	She Loves Me (1st, sm4to, p-o, [40]p, 8cp)	Bobbs-Merrill	(1911)	Hutt, Henry	120-170	
Hutter, Donald	Abraham: Iterant Mouse (1st, lg8vo, 70p, fp 1-color, pep, DJ/2.50)	Dodd	1947	Wiese, Kurt	40-70	
Hutton, William H.	Hampton Court (1st, lg8vo, 244p, blue bds, teg, gilt, fp b/w)	L: Nimmo	1897	Railton, Herbert	60-90	
Huxley, Aldous	Crows of Pearblossom (1st, 8vo, [40]p, 1-color, pep, DJ/3.50)	Random	(1967)	Cooney, Barbara	60-90	
Huxley, Elspeth	Suki: A Little Tiger (1st, 4to, ibds, 46p, b/w, DJ/3.75)	Wm. Morrow	1964	(Photos)	30-50	
Hyde, Elizabeth	Little Brothers to the Scouts (12mo, blu cl, p-o, 72p, 10cp)	Rand/McNally	(1917)	Hyde, Elizabeth	30-50	
Hyde, Fillmore	Ritz Carltons (1st, 8vo, 157p, pcb, b/w)	NY: Macy	1927	Irvin, Rea	40-65	
Hyman, Trina S.	How Six Found Christmas (1st {std}, 8vo, 27p, color, DJ/2.95)	Little/Brown	(1969)	Hyman, Trina S.	50-85	
Hyne, Charles J.	Adventures of Captain Kettle (1st, sm8vo, 318p, red/gilt, 14pl)	L: Pearson	1898	Wood, Stanley	80-140	
Hyne, Charles J.	Captured Cruiser (1st, 8vo, brown/gilt, 288p, 6 fp b/w)	L: Blackie	1893	Brangwyn, Frank	60-95	
Ibbotson, M.C.	Robertson, Ugly & Nohow (1st AM, 8vo, 119p, b/w, DJ)	Pantheon	(1968)	McLachlan, Edward	20-35	
Ibsen, Henrik	Peer Gynt (1st {std}, sm4to, green bds, p-o, 286p, pep, 10cp)	Doubleday/Doran	1929	MacKinstry, Eliz.	70-100	
Ibsen, Henrik	Peer Gynt (1st AM, 4to, 255p, orange cl, 12cp, pep, DJ/4.00)	Lippincott	[1936]	Rackham, Arthur	350-500	
Ibsen, Henrik	Peer Gynt (1st, 4to, 255p, brown/gilt, 12cp, pep)	L: Harrap	(1936)	Rackham, Arthur	250-350	
Iden, Carol	Sidney's Ghost (1st, 8vo, 127p, fp b/w, DJ/2.95)	World	(1969)	Galdone, Paul	20-35	
Ilsley, Velma	Pink Hat (1st, ob8vo, [30]p, fp 1-color, DJ/2.00)	Lippincott	(1956)	Islsey, Velma	30-50	*
Inayat, Noor	Twenty Jataka Tales (1st, 8vo, blue cl, 138p, col frn, 19pl, DJ)	L: Harrap	(1939)	LeMair, H.W.	120-165	
Inayat, Noor	Twenty Jataka Tales (1st AM, lg8vo, 138p, gilt, col frn, 19pl, DJ/2.00)	McKay	(1939)	LeMair, H.W.	120-170	
Inchfawn, Fay	Who Goes to the Wood (1st, 8vo, 229p, col frn, b/w, DJ/2.00)	Winston	(1942)	Thorne, Diana	25-45	
Ingelow, Jean	Mopsa the Fairy (1st, lg8vo, teg, 257p, 10cp, pep)	Lippincott	1910	Kirk, Maria L.	90-120	
Ingelow, Jean	Mopsa the Fairy (1st, 8vo, p-o, 259p, uncut, col frn, 12pl, pep)	Harper	1927	Lathrop, Dorothy	100-160	
Ingelow, Jean	Mopsa the Fairy (1st, 8vo, 259p, blue cl, col frn, pep)	Macmillan	1927	Walker, Dugald S.	100-160	
Ingold, John	Glimpses from Wonderland (1st, 8vo, 287p, blue/gilt, 5pl)	L: J. Long	1900	Bauerle, Amelia	35-60	*
Ingoldsby, Thomas	Ingoldsby Legends (1st, 8vo, teg, 638p, green/gilt, 12cp, pep)	L: Dent	1898	Rackham, Arthur	200-270	
Ingoldsby, Thomas	Ingoldsby Legends (1st, 8vo, 640p, teg, gilt, b/w)	L/NY: J. Lane	1903	Cole, Herbert	50-80	
Ingoldsby, Thomas	Ingoldsby Legends (1st AM, 4to, 549p, teg, green/gilt, 24 ticp, pep)	Dent/Dutton	1907	Rackham, Arthur	350-500	
Ingoldsby, Thomas	Ingoldsby Legends (1st, 8vo, blue/gilt, a.e. blue, 546p, 16cp)	L: Macmillan	1911	Theaker, Harry G.	100-160	
Ingoldsby, Thomas	Jackdaw of Rheims (1st, folio, unpag, white/gilt, teg, 12 ticp)	L: Gay/Hancock	1913	Folkard, Charles	150-225	
Ingoldsby, Thomas	Jackdaw of Rheims (1st AM, lg4to, unpag, teg, purple/gilt, 12 ticp)	Winston	1914	Folkard, Charles	150-220	
Ingoldsby, Thomas	Misadventures at Margate (folio, ibds, 18p, fp color)	L: Eyre/Spotts.	[1885]	Jessop, Ernest M.	70-100	*
Ingpen, Roger	1000 Poems for Children (1st, lg8vo, 563p, 8cp, pep)	Jacobs	(1923)	Betts, Ethel F.	200-300	
Ingraham, Corinne	Cottontail & Wishing-Fairy (1st, lg8vo, pcb, 39p, p-o, 2cp, pep)	Brentano's	(1921)	Walker, Dugald S.	100-165	
Ingraham, Corinne	Elephant & Wishing Fairy (1st, lg8vo, bds, [45]p, p-o, 2cp, pep)	Brentano's	(1921)	Walker, Dugald S.	100-165	
Ingraham, Corinne	Peacock & Wishing-Fairy (1st, lg8vo, p-o, pcb, [42]p, 2cp, pep)	Brentano's	(1921)	Walker, Dugald S.	100-165	
Ingraham, Corinne	Wishing Fairy's Animal Friends (1st, lg8vo, 141p, p-o, 8cp, pep)	Brentano's	(1921)	Walker, Dugald S.	100-165	
Ingraham, Corinne	Zebra & the Wishing Fairy (1st, lg8vo, [45]p, color, pep)	Brentano's	(1921)	Walker, Dugald S.	100-165	
Inman, H.E.	Gobbo Bobo (1st, 8vo, 477p, gilt, AEG, b/w)	L: Warne	1900	Mason, E.A.	100-165	*
Inman, H.E.	One-Eyed Griffin... (1st, 12mo, 353p, teg, gilt, 4pl, dep)	L: Warne	1897	Mason, E.A.	120-170	
Inman, H.E.	Owl King... (1st, 12mo, 378p, teg, 4pl, dep)	L: Warne	1898	Mason, E.A.	120-170	
Inman, Henry	Old Santa Fe Trail (1st, 8vo, 493p, teg, 8pl)	Macmillan	1897	Remington, Frederic	160-225	R
Iogolevitch, Paul	Young Russian Corporal (1st, sm8vo, 327p, frn & b/w by...)	Harper	1919	Neill, John R.	55-80	*
Ionesco, Eugene	Story Number 1 (1st AM, 4to, [32]p, color, DJ/4.50, NYTBI)	Harlin Quist	(1968)	Delessert, Etienne	60-95	
Ionesco, Eugene	Story Number 2 (1st AM, 4to, [30]p, color, DJ/3.95)	Harlin Quist	(1970)	Delessert, Etienne	30-50	
Ipcar, Dahlov	Animal Hide & Seek (1st, lg8vo, [36]p, ipcb, color, pep, DJ/1.50)	W.R. Scott	(1947)	Ipcar, Dahlov	50-80	
Ipcar, Dahlov	Black & White (1st, 4to, [34]p, fp color, pep, DJ/2.95)	Knopf	(1963)	Ipcar, Dahlov	45-70	
Ipcar, Dahlov	Bright Barnyard (1st, 4to, [38]p, color, cep, DJ/3.50)	Knopf	(1966)	Ipcar, Dahlov	45-70	
Ipcar, Dahlov	Brown Cow Farm (1st {std}, ob4to, [44]p, color, pep, DJ/2.50)	Doubleday	1959	Ipcar, Dahlov	40-65	
Ipcar, Dahlov	Calico Jungle (1st, 4to, [40]p, color, pep, DJ/3.50)	Knopf	(1965)	Ipcar, Dahlov	40-65	
Ipcar, Dahlov	Cat at Night (1st {std}, 4to, [48]p, color, DJ/3.95)	Doubleday	(1969)	Ipcar, Dahlov	40-65	
Ipcar, Dahlov	Deep Sea Farm (1st, 4to, [36]p, 2-color, pep, DJ/3.00)	Knopf	(1961)	Ipcar, Dahlov	30-50	
Ipcar, Dahlov	General Felice (1st, 8vo, 159p, b/w, DJ/4.50)	McGraw-Hill	(1967)	Longtemps, Kenneth	50-80	
Ipcar, Dahlov	Horses of Long Ago (1st {std}, 4to, 59p, ibds, color, DJ/3.50)	Doubleday	(1965)	Ipcar, Dahlov	30-45	
Ipcar, Dahlov	I Like Animals (1st, ob4to, [36]p, color, pep, DJ/2.95)	Knopf	(1960)	Ipcar, Dahlov	30-45	*
Ipcar, Dahlov	I Love my Anteater with an A (1st, 4to, [40]p, color, DJ/3.25)	Knopf	(1964)	Ipcar, Dahlov	50-75	R
Ipcar, Dahlov	Lobsterman (1st, ob4to, [36]p, color, pep, DJ/2.95)	Knopf	(1962)	Ipcar, Dahlov	40-65	*
Ipcar, Dahlov	Marvelous Merry-Go-Round (1st {std}, 4to, [48]p, color, DJ/3.95)	Doubleday	(1970)	Ipcar, Dahlov	45-75	
Ipcar, Dahlov	One Horse Farm (1st {std}, ob4to, ibds, [34]p, color, DJ/2.00)	Doubleday	1950	Ipcar, Dahlov	40-65	
Ipcar, Dahlov	Song of the Day Birds & Night Birds (1st {std}, 4to, [60]p, color, DJ/3.75)	Doubleday	(1967)	Ipcar, Dahlov	30-50	
Ipcar, Dahlov	Stripes & Spots (1st {std}, 4to, [44]p, 2-color, pep, DJ/2.50)	Doubleday	(1961)	Ipcar, Dahlov	40-65	
Ipcar, Dahlov	Ten Big Farms (1st, ob4to, [36]p, 3-color, pep, DJ/2.50)	Knopf	(1958)	Ipcar, Dahlov	40-65	
Ipcar, Dahlov	Whisperings & other Things (1st, 4to, [42]p, fp color, pep, DJ/3.50)	Knopf	(1967)	Ipcar, Dahlov	40-65	
Ipcar, Dahlov	Wild and Tame Animals (1st {std}, ob4to, [48]p, fp 2-color, DJ)	Doubleday	(1963)	Ipcar, Dahlov	40-65	
Ipcar, Dahlov	Wild Whirlwind (1st, sm ob4to, [34]p, fp color, pep, DJ/3.95)	Knopf	(1968)	Ipcar, Dahlov	40-65	

AUTHOR	TITLE	PUBLISHER	DATE	ARTIST	PRICE	LC
Ipcar, Dahlov	Wonderful Egg (1st {std}, ob4to, [44]p, color, pep, DJ/2.50)	Doubleday	(1958)	Ipcar, Dahlov	40-65	
Ipcar, Dahlov	World Full of Horses (1st {std}, ob4to, [32]p, color, pep, DJ/2.50)	Doubleday	1955	Ipcar, Dahlov	40-65	
Ironmonger, Ira	Alligator Smiling in the Sawgrass (1st, lg8vo, [44]p, fp color, DJ/3.75)	Young Scott	(1965)	Davidson, Sandra	30-50	
Irving, Washington	Bold Dragoon (1st, lg8vo, 240p, blue cl, b/w, pep, DJ/2.50)	Knopf	1930	Daugherty, James	40-60	
Irving, Washington	Bracebridge Hall (1st, 2 vols, 8vo, teg, 5pl by...)	Putnam	1896	Rackham, Arthur	140-200	
Irving, Washington	Child's Rip Van Winkle (1st, lg8vo, 39p, red cl, p-o, 12cp)	Stokes	(1908)	Kirk, Maria L.	80-120	
Irving, Washington	Christmas at Bracebridge Hall (1st, 8vo, 267p, teg, 24cp, dep)	L: Dent	1906	Brock, Charles E.	50-80	
Irving, Washington	Christmas Dinner (1st, 8vo, ipcb, 22p, b/w)	NY: W. Rudge	1929	Ross, Gordon	60-90	R
Irving, Washington	History of New York (1st, folio, bds, teg, p-o, 299p, 8pl)	R.H. Russell	1900	Parrish, Maxfield	700-1000	
Irving, Washington	History of New York (1st {this format}, 4to, 299p, bds, 8 ticp)	Dodd	1915	Parrish, Maxfield	200-300	
Irving, Washington	History of New York (1st {std}, lg8vo, 427p, uncut, pep, DJ/2.50)	Doubleday/Doran	1928	Daugherty, James	80-130	R
Irving, Washington	Keeping of Christmas... (1st, 12mo, 267p, teg, gilt, 24cp, pep)	Dutton	1906	Brock, Charles E.	55-80	
Irving, Washington	Legend of Sleepy Hollow (1st, 12mo, 61p, ibds, p-o, cvr by...)	R.H. Russell	(1897)	Bradley, Will	120-180	
Irving, Washington	Legend of Sleepy Hollow (1st, sm8vo, teg, 191p, red/gilt, cvr by...)	Putnam	1899	Armstrong, Margaret	90-120	
Irving, Washington	Legend of Sleepy Hollow (1st, 8vo, gilt, 92p, p-o, pep, 14pl)	Bobbs-Merrill	(1906)	Keller, Arthur I.	90-120	
Irving, Washington	Legend of Sleepy Hollow (1st, 4to, gilt, teg, 102p, 8cp, pep)	L: Harrap	(1928)	Rackham, Arthur	270-350	
Irving, Washington	Legend of Sleepy Hollow (1st AM, sm4to, 102p, gilt, teg, p-o, 8cp, pep)	McKay	(1928)	Rackham, Arthur	170-240	
Irving, Washington	Legends of the Alhambra (1st, lg8vo, 229p, teg, p-o, 8cp, pep)	Lippincott	1909	Hood, George	60-90	
Irving, Washington	Old Christmas (8vo, gilt, 165p, b/w, AEG)	L: Macmillan	1894	Caldecott, Randolph	80-120	
Irving, Washington	Old Christmas (1st AM, 8vo, 176p, fp color)	Dodd	(1908)	Aldin, Cecil	100-160	
Irving, Washington	Old Christmas (1st AM, 8vo, [176]p, p-o, red/gilt, 27cp)	NY: Sully	1908	Aldin, Cecil	200-300	
Irving, Washington	Old Christmas (1st, 8vo, 115p, gilt, p-o, teg, 2cp, 16pl, pep)	Putnam	(1916)	Dadd, Frank	40-60	*
Irving, Washington	Old Christmas (1st, 8vo, gilt, 284p, 8cp)	L: Constable	1918	Baumer, Lewis	55-80	*
Irving, Washington	Old Christmas (1st AM, 8vo, gilt, 284p, 8cp)	Houghton	1919	Baumer, Lewis	35-50	
Irving, Washington	Old Christmas & Bracebridge Hall (8vo, red cl, 285p, 8 color)	L: Constable	1918	Baumer, Lewis	35-60	
Irving, Washington	Old Christmas Day (12mo, 34p, p-o, 5cp)	L: Foulis	[1912]	Brock, Henry M.	50-80	
Irving, Washington	Old English Christmas (1st, 12mo, 124p, blue/gilt, 17 ticp)	L: Foulis	[1910]	Brock, Henry M.	70-100	
Irving, Washington	Old English Christmas (1st AM, 12mo, 123p, ibds, p-o, 17 ticp)	Jacobs	(1910)	Brock, Henry M.	55-80	
Irving, Washington	Old Fashioned Christmas Day (1st, 12mo, unpag, ibds, p-o, 6 ticp)	L: Hodder	[1910]	Aldin, Cecil	200-300	
Irving, Washington	Rip Van Winkle (sq4to, [11]p, wraps, 6 chromos)	McLoughlin	[1880]	Nast, Thomas	250-400	
Irving, Washington	Rip Van Winkle (1st, lg4to, AEG, gilt, 49p, b/w pl)	S.E. Cassino	1888	Merrill, Frank T.	120-185	
Irving, Washington	Rip Van Winkle (1st, sm8vo, bds, 35p, frn & cvr by...)	R.H. Russell	(1897)	Bradley, Will	200-300	
Irving, Washington	Rip Van Winkle (1st, sm8vo, teg, uncut, red/gilt, 115p, cvr by)	Putnam	1899	Armstrong, Margaret	60-90	
Irving, Washington	Rip Van Winkle (1st AM, 4to, green/gilt, 51 ticp)	Doubleday/Page	1905	Rackham, Arthur	400-600	
Irving, Washington	Rip Van Winkle (1st, 4to, 57p, green/gilt, 51 ticp, dep)	L: Heinemann	1905	Rackham, Arthur	500-700	
Irving, Washington	Rip Van Winkle (1st, 12mo, 218p, red/gilt, b/w pl)	L: Macmillan	1908	Boughton, George	55-80	*
Irving, Washington	Rip Van Winkle (lg8vo, 68p, col frn, cp)	Stokes	[1915]	Robinson, Charles	100-165	*
Irving, Washington	Rip Van Winkle (1st, lg8vo, 86p, teg, gilt, p-o, 8cp, pep)	McKay	(1921)	Wyeth, N.C.	250-400	
Irving, Washington	Rip Van Winkle (1st, 12mo, 69p, beige cl, 4cp)	Lippincott	(1923)	Cooke, Edna	40-60	*
Irving, Washington	Rip Van Winkle (1st, 12mo, blue cl, 183p, 4cp, fp b/w, pep)	Macmillan	1925	Pape, Eric	40-60	*
Irving, Washington	Rip Van Winkle (1st, sm8vo, 92p, col frn, fp b/w)	Saalfield	(1927)	Brundage, Frances	30-50	*
Irving, Washington	Rip Van Winkle (1st, 8vo, 127p, b/w)	Stokes	1933	Perard, Victor S.	25-45	*
Irving, Washington	Rip Van Winkle (1st, lg4to, ibds, [40]p, fp color, pep, DJ/1.00)	Garden City	(1939)	Shinn, Everett	70-120	
Irving, Washington	Rip Van Winkle (1st, 12mo, ibds, [60]p, fp color)	McLoughlin	(1941)	Graef, Robert A.	30-60	*
Irving, Washington	Rip Van Winkle & Sleepy Hollow (1st, 8vo, 148p, red/gilt, 8cp, pep)	Lippincott	(1924)	Cooke, Edna	30-50	
Irving, Washington	Rip Van Winkle & Sleepy Hollow (1st, 8vo, 105p, 1-color, pep, DJ/2.00)	Macmillan	(1951)	Petershams	60-100	
Irving, Washington	Tales of a Traveller (1st, 2vols, lg8vo, white/gilt, 5pl by...)	Putnam	1895	Rackham, Arthur	150-225	
Irving, Washington	The Alhambra (1st, 12mo, green/gilt, AEG, 436p, b/w, cep)	L: Macmillan	1896	Pennell, Joseph	55-80	
Irving, Washington	The Alhambra (1st, 8vo, blue cl, 3cp)	L: Macmillan	1926	Goble, Warwick	70-125	
Irwin, Violet	Mountain of Jade (1st, sm8vo, 236p, green cl, fp b/w)	Macmillan	1926	Daugherty, James	30-50	
Irwin, Wallace	Nautical Lays of a Landsman (1st, sm8vo, 135p, 5pl, dep)	Dodd	1904	Newell, Peter	70-100	
Isasi, Miriam	White Stars of Freedom (1st, 8vo, 308p, col frn, DJ/2.50)	Whitman	1942	Wiese, Kurt	30-50	
Ish-Kishor, Salamith	Boy of Old Prague (1st, 8vo, 90p, fp b/w, pep, DJ/3.95)	Pantheon	(1963)	Shahn, Ben	45-70	R
Ish-Kishor, Salamith	Carpet of Solomon (1st, lg8vo, 57p, b/w, DJ/3.25)	Pantheon	(1966)	Shulevitz, Uri	45-70	
Ish-Kishor, Salamith	Our Eddie (1st, 8vo, 183p, DJ/4.50, NH)	Pantheon	(1969)	No Illustrations	60-90	
Isham, Frederic S.	Black Friday (1st, 8vo, 409p, 6pl)	Bobbs-Merrill	(1904)	Fisher, Harrison	30-50	
Isham, Frederic S.	The Strollers (1st, sm8vo, 499p, gilt, 8pl)	Bowen-Merrill	(1902)	Fisher, Harrison	25-40	
Isham, Frederic S.	Under the Rose (1st, 8vo, 427p, green cl, cvr by...)	Bobbs-Merrill	(1903)	Armstrong, Margaret	25-40	
Isham, Frederic S.	Under the Rose (1st, 8vo, 427p, green cl, 4cp by...)	Bobbs-Merrill	(1903)	Christy, Howard C.	25-40	
Ishii, Momoko	Issun Boshi, the Inchling (1st AM, ob8vo, gilt, [40]p, col, pep, DJ/3.50)	NY: Walker	(1967)	Akino, Fuku	30-50	
Jacberns, Raymond	Attic Boarders (1st, sm8vo, 298p, 6cp)	L: Chambers	1909	Earnshaw, Harold C.	40-60	*
Jacberns, Raymond	Boy and a Secret (1st, sm8vo, gilt, 304p, 10pl)	L: Chambers	1908	Attwell, Mabel L.	100-165	
Jacberns, Raymond	Crab Cottage (1st, 12mo, 285p, 6pl, cep)	L: Chambers	1905	Menzies, John	60-90	
Jacberns, Raymond	Poor Uncle Harry (1st, 8vo, 275p, red cl, 6cp)	L: Chambers	1910	Cowham, Hilda	55-80	*
Jacberns, Raymond	Tabitha Smallways, Schoolgirl (1st, 8vo, 304p, 6cp)	L: Chambers	(1912)	Attwell, Mabel L.	100-150	
Jacberns, Raymond	Troublesome Dog (1st, 8vo, 297p, 6cp)	L: Chambers	(1911)	Attwell, Mabel L.	100-150	
Jack, Marian	Adventures of Bulgy Billy (1st, 8vo, p-o, 42p, 12cp, pep)	Jacobs	(1920)	Jack, Marian	40-65	
Jackson, C. Paul	Jamesville Jets (1st, 8vo, 143p, b/w, DJ/2.75)	Follett	(1959)	Galdone, Paul	25-40	
Jackson, Charlotte	Little Eskimo (1st, 8vo, [28]p, ibds, color, LGB/#155)	Simon/Schuster	(1952)	Weisgard, Leonard	25-45	
Jackson, Charlotte	Roger and the Fishes (1st, 4to, 76p, ibds, color, DJ/2.00)	Dodd	1943	Wiese, Kurt	40-65	
Jackson, Charlotte	Round the Afternoon (1st, sm4to, blue cl, [63]p, pep, color, DJ/2.25)	Dodd	1946	Weisgard, Leonard	50-85	
Jackson, Charlotte	Sarah Deborah's Day (1st, sm4to, ipcb, 74p, 2-color, pep, DJ/2.00)	Dodd	1941	Simont, Marc	40-65	
Jackson, Charlotte	Tito: Pig of Guatemala (1st, 4to, 73p, ibds, color, pep, DJ/2.00)	Dodd	1940	Wiese, Kurt	45-75	
Jackson, Gabrielle	By Love's Sweet Rule (1st, 12mo, 320p, b/w, pep)	Winston	1906	Smith, Wuanita	30-50	
Jackson, Gabrielle	Maid of Middies' Haven (1st, 12mo, 299p, 4pl)	McBride	1912	Rockwell, Norman	170-240	*
Jackson, Gabrielle	Peterkin (1st, lg8vo, p-o, 75p, col frn by...)	Duffield	1912	Parrish, Maxfield	125-200	*
Jackson, Gabrielle	Wee Winkles & her Friends (1st, 8vo, 155p, 8pl)	Harper	1907	Robinson, Rachael	35-50	
Jackson, Gabrielle	Wee Winkles and Snowball (1st, 8vo, 147p, 8pl)	Harper	1906	Hart, Mary T.	30-50	

AUTHOR	TITLE	PUBLISHER	DATE	ARTIST	PRICE	LC
Jackson, Gabrielle	Wee Winkles and Wideawake (1st, 8vo, p-o, 153p, 8pl)	Harper	1905	Hart, Mary T.	30-50	
Jackson, Helen H.	Father Junipero... (1st, 12mo, 159p, b/w)	Little/Brown	1902	Sandham, Henry	35-60	
Jackson, Helen H.	Ramona (1st [Gift Ed.], lg8vo, 447p, col frn, DJ/2.75)	Little/Brown	1932	Stoops, Herbert M.	30-50	
Jackson, Jacqueline	Chicken Ten Thousand (1st {std}, lg ob8vo, 31p, color, DJ/3.95)	Little/Brown	(1968)	Morrow, Barbara	30-50	*
Jackson, Jacqueline	Taste of Spruce Gum (1st {std}, 8vo, 212p, b/w, DJ/3.95)	Little/Brown	(1966)	Obligado, Lilian	25-40	*
Jackson, Jesse	Anchor Man (1st {std}, 8vo, 142p, red cl, fp b/w, DJ/2.00)	Harper	(1947)	Spiegel, Doris	70-100	
Jackson, Jesse	Call Me Charley (1st {std}, 8vo, 156p, b/w, DJ/2.00)	Harper	(1945)	Spiegel, Doris	55-80	*
Jackson, Jesse	Room for Randy (1st, 8vo, 136p, b/w, DJ/2.50)	Friendship Pr.	1957	Nicholas, Frank	35-50	*
Jackson, Jesse	Tessie (1st, 8vo, 243p, b/w, DJ/4.95)	Harper	1968	James, Harold	30-50	
Jackson, Joseph	Christmas Flower (1st {std}, 8vo, 31p, ibds, 1-color, pep, DJ/1.00)	Harcourt	(1951)	Lea, Tom	40-70	
Jackson, Kathryn	Farm Stories (1st {std}, folio, ibds, 91p, color, pep, GGB)	Simon/Schuster	(1946)	Tenggren, Gustaf	80-120	
Jackson, Kathryn	Tenggren's Cowboys & Indians (1st, folio, ibds, 96p, color, GGB)	Simon/Schuster	(1948)	Tenggren, Gustaf	80-125	
Jackson, Kathryn	Wheels (1st, 8vo, [28]p, ibds, color, pep, LGB/#141)	Simon/Schuster	(1952)	Weisgard, Leonard	30-50	
Jackson, Leroy F.	Jolly Jingle Picture Book (1st, 4to, [96]p, p-o, fp color, pep)	Rand/McNally	(1937)	Eger, Ruth C.	70-90	
Jackson, Leroy F.	Peter Patter Book (1st, lg4to, 110p, color, pep)	Rand/McNally	(1918)	Wright, Blanche F.	70-100	
Jackson, Leroy F.	Rimskittle's Book (1st, lg4to, [110]p, p-o, color, pep)	Rand/McNally	(1926)	Eger, Ruth C.	100-160	
Jackson, Linda	Petey (1st, sq8vo, 56p, fp 1-color, DJ/1.50)	Harcourt	(1942)	Buck, Dorothy	30-50	
Jackson, Richard	Year is a Window (1st {std}, 12mo, [28]p, color, DJ/1.95)	Doubleday	1963	Blegvad, Erik	25-40	
Jackson, Shirley	9 Magic Wishes (1st {std}, lg4to, 45p, fp color, cep)	Crowell-Collier	(1963)	Fox, Lorraine	80-145	
Jackson, Shirley	Famous Sally (1st {std}, 8vo, [40]p, ibds, gilt, color, DJ/3.50)	Harlin Quist	(1966)	Slackman, Charles	70-100	
Jacobs (ed.)	Tales from Boccaccio (1st, sq8vo, gilt, teg, 117p, 20pl)	L: G. Allen	1899	Shaw, Byam	90-120	
Jacobs, Frank	Alvin Steadfast on Vernacular Island (1st, 8vo, 64p, fp b/w, DJ/3.50)	Dial Press	(1965)	Gorey, Edward	60-90	
Jacobs, Joseph	Buried Moon (1st {std}, 4to, [31]p, dp 2-color, DJ/3.95)	Bradbury Press	(1969)	Jeffers, Susan	45-65	
Jacobs, Joseph	Molly Whuppie (1st AM, 8vo, tan cl, [46]p, fp 3-color, DJ/1.50)	Oxford U. Pr.	[1939]	Doane, Pelagie	70-120	
Jacobs, Joseph (ed)	Book of Wonder Voyages (1st, 8vo, 224p, uncut, 7pl)	L: D. Nutt	1896	Batten, John D.	180-240	
Jacobs, Joseph (ed)	Celtic Fairy Tales (1st, lg8vo, AEG, 267p, green cl, 8pl)	L: D. Nutt	1892	Batten, John D.	150-225	
Jacobs, Joseph (ed)	English Fairy Tales (1st, 8vo, 253p, AEG, 8pl)	L: D. Nutt	1890	Batten, John D.	120-170	
Jacobs, Joseph (ed)	English Fairy Tales (1st AM, 8vo, 253p, 8pl)	Putnam	1891	Batten, John D.	75-100	
Jacobs, Joseph (ed)	Fables of Aesop (1st, 8vo, 174p, 2-color, DJ)	Macmillan	(1950)	Wiese, Kurt	50-80	*
Jacobs, Joseph (ed)	Indian Fairy Tales (1st AM, 8vo, 255p, 8pl)	Putnam	1892	Batten, John D.	120-180	
Jacobs, Joseph (ed)	Indian Fairy Tales (1st, 8vo, 255p, uncut, 8pl)	L: D. Nutt	1892	Batten, John D.	120-200	
Jacobs, Joseph (ed)	More Celtic Fairy Tales (1st, 8vo, 234p, 8pl)	L: D. Nutt	1894	Batten, John D.	120-170	
Jacobs, Joseph (ed)	More English Fairy Tales (1st, 8vo, blue cl, 243p, 8pl)	L: D. Nutt	1894	Batten, John D.	80-120	
Jacobs, Joseph (ed)	Three Wishes (1st, ob4to, 32p, fp 2-color, pep, DJ/2.50)	Whittlesey	(1961)	Galdone, Paul	25-45	*
Jacobs, Joseph (ed)	Tom Tit Tot: English Folk Tale (1st, 4to, [32]p, 3-color, DJ/3.25, CH)	Scribner	1965	Ness, Evaline	50-75	
Jacobs, Leland (ed)	Poetry for Chuckles and Grins (1st, lg8vo, 64p, 2-color, DJ)	Garrard Pub.	(1968)	DePaola, Tomie	50-80	
Jacobs, Leland (ed)	Poetry for Young Scientists (1st {std}, 8vo, [42]p, color, DJ)	Holt, Rinehart	1964	Young, Ed	35-50	
Jacobs, Violet	Golden Heart (1st AM, 8vo, 171p, green/gilt, p-o, 16pl)	Doubleday/Page	1905	Sandheim, May	55-80	*
Jacobs-Bond, Carrie	Little Monkey with the Sad Face (1st, 8vo, 48p, 8cp, cep, DJ/1.50)	John Day	(1930)	Wiese, Kurt	30-50	
Jacobs-Bond, Carrie	Tales of Little Cats (1st, sq12mo, ibds, [38]p, color, pep)	Volland	(1918)	Dodge, Katharine S.	80-125	
Jacobs-Bond, Carrie	Tales of Little Dogs (1st, sq8vo, ibds, [35]p, color, pep)	Volland	(1921)	Dodge, Katharine S.	80-125	
Jagendorf, Moritz	In the Days of the Han (1st, lg8vo, gilt, 168p, fp color, pep, DJ/2.50)	Suttonhouse	1936	Neumann, Erwin	45-70	
Jagendorf, Moritz	Priceless Cats (1st, 8vo, 158p, b/w, DJ/3.00)	Vanguard Press	(1956)	Fiammenghi, Gioia	25-40	
Jagendorf, Mortiz	Merry Pranks (1st AM, 8vo, 188p, 2-color, DJ/2.50)	Vanguard Press	1938	Eichenberg, Fritz	40-65	*
Jahn, Mary L.	Deedo and Fawny (1st, ob4to, [32]p, color, pep, DJ/2.00)	Oxford U. Pr.	(1940)	Jahn, Mary L.	30-50	*
Jahn, Mary L.	Yelly (1st, lg ob4to, [32]p, color, pep, DJ/2.00)	Oxford U. Pr.	(1941)	Scott, Hilda	45-65	
James, Ahlee	Tewa Firelight Tales (1st {std}, 8vo, 247p, 11cp, pep)	Longmans	1927	Various	70-120	
James, Grace	Green Willow... (1st, sm4to, blue/gilt, 281p, 40 ticp)	L: Macmillan	1910	Goble, Warwick	400-600	
James, Grace	Green Willow... (1st {this format}, 4to, gilt, 281p, 16cp)	L: Macmillan	1912	Goble, Warwick	150-220	
James, Harry A.	Oddland and other Fairy Tales (1st, 8vo, gilt, 352p, 4pl)	L: G. Newnes	(1901)	Skeaping, K.M.	80-120	
James, Hartwell	Enchanted Castle (1st, 12mo, 123p, b/w)	Altemus	(1906)	Neill, John R.	50-75	*
James, Hartwell	Magic Jaw Bone (1st, 12mo, 107p, 2-color)	Altemus	(1906)	Neill, John R.	60-100	
James, Henry	Daisy Miller (1st, 8vo, stripe cl, 294p, teg, uncut, col frn, b/w)	Harper	1892	McVickar, H.W.	100-170	
James, Henry	English Hours (1st AM, lg8vo, 336p, teg, b/w by...)	Houghton	1905	Pennell, Joseph	200-300	
James, Henry	English Hours (1st AM, lg8vo, teg, 336p, design by...)	Houghton	1905	Rogers, Bruce	200-300	
James, Henry	Italian Hours (1st AM, 4to, 504p, teg, uncut, 32cp)	Houghton	1909	Pennell, Joseph	200-300	
James, Henry	Julia Bride (1st, 8vo, 83p, teg, 4pl)	Harper	1909	Smedley, W.T.	140-200	
James, Henry	Little Tour in France (1st AM, 8vo, teg, 345p, b/w)	Houghton	1900	Pennell, Joseph	150-220	
James, Henry	Question of Our Speech (1st, sm8vo, gilt, teg, 115p, uncut)	Houghton	1905	Rogers, Bruce	180-250	
James, Henry	What Maisie Knew (1st AM, sm8vo, 470p, teg, grey/gilt, cvr by...)	Herbert Stone	1897	Hazenplug, Frank	150-225	
James, Neill	White Reindeer (1st, 8vo, 157p, b/w, pep, DJ/1.75)	Scribner	1940	Baldridge, Cyrus L.	25-45	
James, Will	All in the Day's Riding (1st, lg8vo, gilt, 251p, b/w, DJ/2.50)	Scribner	1933	James, Will	200-300	
James, Will	Big-Enough (1st, 8vo, 314p, cloth, b/w, DJ/2.50)	Scribner	1931	James, Will	165-250	
James, Will	Book of Cowboy Stories (1st, 8vo, 242p, fp b/w, DJ/2.50)	Scribner	1951	James, Will	70-100	
James, Will	Cow Country (1st, lg8vo, 242p, brown cl, 28pl, DJ)	Scribner	1927	James, Will	165-220	
James, Will	Cowboys North & South (1st [1st bk.], lg8vo, 217p, 51 fp b/w)	Scribner	1924	James, Will	200-300	
James, Will	Dark Horse (1st, 8vo, green cl, col frn, 306p, DJ/2.50)	Scribner	1939	James, Will	200-300	
James, Will	Drifting Cowboy (1st, lg8vo, 241p, 36 fp b/w)	Scribner	1925	James, Will	150-240	
James, Will	Flint Spears (1st, 8vo, 269p, cloth, col frn, DJ/2.50)	Scribner	1938	James, Will	200-300	
James, Will	Home Ranch (1st, 8vo, 346p, b/w, DJ/2.75)	Scribner	1935	James, Will	200-300	
James, Will	Horses I've Known (1st, 8vo, 280p, 29pl, col frn, DJ/2.50)	Scribner	1940	James, Will	150-225	
James, Will	In the Saddle with Uncle Bill (1st, 8vo, 289p, 33pl, DJ/2.00)	Scribner	1935	James, Will	160-235	
James, Will	Lone Cowboy, My Life Story (1st, 8vo, gilt, uncut, 431p, fp b/w, DJ/2.75)	Scribner	1930	James, Will	140-200	
James, Will	Look-See with Uncle Bill (1st, 8vo, 253p, col frn, DJ/2.00)	Scribner	1938	James, Will	140-200	
James, Will	My First Horse (1st, lg ob8vo, blue cl, [45]p, fp color, DJ/1.50)	Scribner	1940	James, Will	120-170	
James, Will	Sand (1st, 8vo, 328p, green cl, fp b/w, DJ/2.50)	Scribner	1929	James, Will	180-250	
James, Will	Scorpion: Good Bad Horse (1st, 8vo, 312p, col frn, b/w, DJ/2.50)	Scribner	1936	James, Will	160-240	
James, Will	Smoky the Cow Horse (1st, 8vo, 310p, b/w, PPP, NM)	Scribner	1926	James, Will	160-225	

AUTHOR	TITLE	PUBLISHER	DATE	ARTIST	PRICE	LC
James, Will	Smoky the Cow Horse (1st {this fmt}, lg8vo, p-o, gilt, 263p, 6cp, pep, SC)	Scribner	(1929)	James, Will	80-120	
James, Will	Sun Up, Tales of the Cow Camps (1st, lg8vo, p-o, 342p, b/w)	Scribner	1931	James, Will	100-165	
James, Will	Three Mustangeers (1st, 8vo, 338p, green cl, fp b/w)	Scribner	1933	James, Will	100-160	
James, Will	Uncle Bill (1st, 8vo, 241p, orange cl, DJ/2.00)	Scribner	1932	James, Will	75-120	
James, Will	Will James Cowboy Book (1st, 8vo, 158p, col frn, pep)	Scribner	(1938)	James, Will	500-700	
James, Will	Young Cowboy (1st, lg ob8vo, 72p, p-o, 5cp, DJ/1.50)	Scribner	1935	James, Will	300-500	
Jameson, Anna	Shakespeare's Heroines (lg8vo, 308p, gilt, AEG, 6cp, pep)	L: Nister	[1900]	Paget, Walter	100-150	
Jamieson, M.M.	Little Redskins (sq12mo, [54]p, ibds, chromos)	Nister/Dutton	[1910]	Jamieson, M.M.	100-160	
Jamison, C.V.	Lady Jane (1st, 8vo, gilt, 233p, b/w)	Century	1891	Birch, Reginald	50-80	
Jamison, C.V.	Lady Jane (1st {std}, 8vo, pink cl, 224p, fp b/w, DJ/4.25)	Delacorte Pr.	(1969)	Jacques, Robin	20-25	*
Jane, Mary C.	Rocking-Chair Ghost (1st {std}, 8vo, 58p, b/w, DJ/2.95)	Lippincott	(1969)	DePaola, Tomie	25-45	*
Janeway, Elizabeth	Ivanov Seven (1st, 8vo, 176p, fp b/w, DJ/3.95, pep by...)	Harper	(1967)	Pucci, Albert	45-70	R*
Janice	Angelique (1st, 4to, 32p, color, pep, DJ/2.25)	Whittlesey	1960	Duvoisin, Roger	50-80	
Janice	Little Bear's Sunday Breakfast (1st, lg8vo, [30]p, color, DJ/2.75)	Lothrop, Lee	1958	Mariana	25-45	
Janosch	Dear Snowman (1st AM {std}, sq4to, [32]p, color, DJ/4.95)	World	1970	Janosch	30-45	
Janosch	Thieves & the Raven (1st AM {std}, ob4to, [32]p, 14cp, DJ/4.50)	Macmillan	(1970)	Janosch	60-90	
Jansson, Tove	Book About Moomin, Mymble & Little My (1st UK, 4to, ibds, color, DJ)	L: E. Benn	(1953)	Jansson, Tove	170-250	
Jansson, Tove	Comet in Moominland (1st UK, sm8vo, 190p, b/w, DJ)	L: E. Benn	(1951)	Jansson, Tove	90-140	
Jansson, Tove	Exploits of Moominpappa (1st UK, 8vo, 159p, b/w, DJ)	L: E. Benn	(1952)	Jansson, Tove	90-140	
Jansson, Tove	Finn Family Moomintroll (1st UK, 12mo, 170p, b/w, map, DJ)	L: E. Benn	1950	Jansson, Tove	180-220	
Jansson, Tove	Moominpappa at Sea (1st AM {std}, 8vo, 192p, grey cl, b/w, DJ/4.00)	H.Z. Walck	1967	Jansson, Tove	80-140	
Jansson, Tove	Who Will Comfort Toffle? (1st UK, 4to, unpag, red cl, color, DJ)	L: E. Benn	(1960)	Jansson, Tove	160-220	
Janus, Grete	Teddy (1st, 16mo, unpag, color, DJ/1.50)	Lothrop, Lee	(1964)	Duvoisin, Roger	30-45	
Janvier, Thomas A.	Aztec Treasure House (1st, 12mo, 446p, grey/gilt, 19pl, PPPa)	Harper	1890	Remington, Frederic	80-125	
Janvier, Thomas A.	In Old New York (1st, 12mo, 285p, rust/gilt, cvr by...)	Harper	1894	Armstrong, Margaret	60-100	
Janvier, Thomas A.	In Old New York (1st, 12mo, 285p, rust/gilt, b/w...)	Harper	1894	Pyle, Howard	60-100	
Janvier, Thomas A.	Legends of the City of Mexico (1st, 8vo, gilt, 164p, 6pl by...)	Harper	1910	Clark, Walter A.	60-90	
Janvier, Thomas A.	Santa Fe's Partner (1st, sm8vo, 237p, teg, green/gilt, 8pl)	Harper	1907	Arthurs, S.	30-50	
Jarden, Mary L.	Young Brontes (1st, 8vo, 279p, blue cl, 2-color, pep, DJ/2.50)	Viking	1938	Sewell, Helen	30-45	
Jarrell, Randall	Animal Family (1st, 12mo, 179p, green/gilt, b/w, cep, DJ/3.50, NH, NYTBI)	Pantheon	(1965)	Sendak, Maurice	100-170	R
Jarrell, Randall	Bat-Poet (1st, 8vo, 42p, brown cl, fp b/w, cep, DJ/2.75, NYTBI)	Macmillan	(1964)	Sendak, Maurice	80-145	R
Jarrell, Randall	Gingerbread Rabbit (1st {std}, 8vo, 55p, b/w, DJ/2.95)	Macmillan	(1964)	Williams, Garth	70-120	
Jarrell, Randall	Golden Bird (1st AM, folio, 50p, ibds, color, DJ/1.95)	Macmillan	1962	Nardini, Sandro	35-50	*
Jaszi, Jean	Everybody has Two Eyes (1st, 8vo, [34]p, b/w, DJ/2.50)	Lothrop, Lee	(1956)	Mariana	30-45	
Jaufre	Jaufry the Knight & Fair Brunissende (1st, 12mo, 124p, decor by...)	Holiday House	1935	Atherton, John	30-50	*
Jefferies, Richard	Bevis, Story of a Boy (1st, 8vo, 464p, ibds, 8cp)	L: Duckworth	(1913)	Rountree, Harry	80-125	
Jefferies, Richard	Bevis, Story of a Boy (1st, 8vo, 519p, b/w, pep, DJ)	L: J. Cape	(1932)	Shepard, Ernest H.	80-120	
Jefferson, Charles E.	World's Christmas Tree (1st, sm8vo, 44p, green/gilt, cvr by...)	Crowell	(1906)	Armstrong, Margaret	40-60	*
Jenkins, Alexandra	Pal: Story of an Airedale (1st, sm8vo, 95p, fp b/w, pep)	Appleton	1930	Wiese, Kurt	30-45	
Jenkins, Marie M.	Moon Jelly Swims through the Sea (1st, 8vo, 46p, color, DJ/3.95)	Holiday House	(1969)	Martin, Rene	30-50	*
Jenks, Tudor	Magician for One Day (1st, 24mo, brown ipcb, 107p, color)	Altemus	(1905)	Neill, John R.	80-145	
Jenks, Tudor	Rescue Syndicate (1st, 24mo, ipcb, 110p, b/w, pep)	Altemus	(1905)	Neill, John R.	80-120	
Jenks, Tudor	Timothy's Magical Afternoon (1st, 24mo, ipcb, 98p, b/w, pep)	Altemus	(1905)	Neill, John R.	100-165	
Jenkyn-Thomas, W.	Welsh Fairy Book (1st AM, 8vo, blue/gilt, col frn, 303p)	Stokes	[1907]	Pogany, Willy	200-300	
Jenkyn-Thomas, W.	Welsh Fairy Book (1st, 8vo, 312p, blue/gilt, col frn, 9pl, pep)	L: T.F. Unwin	(1907)	Pogany, Willy	250-400	
Jennings, Alphonso	Beating Back (1st, sm8vo, 355p, gilt, 3pl by...)	Appleton	1914	Russell, Charles M.	70-100	*
Jepson, Edgar	Garden at 19 (1st AM, 12mo, 299p, green/white, 4pl)	Wessels/Bissell	1910	Boehm, H.R.	120-200	
Jepson, Edgar	Happy Pollyooly (1st, sm8vo, 314p, 5pl)	Bobbs-Merrill	(1915)	Birch, Reginald	40-65	
Jerome, Jerome K.	Tea-Table Talk (1st, 12mo, 153p, blue cl, cvr by...)	Dodd	1903	Falls, Charles B.	30-50	
Jerome, Jerome K.	Three Men on Wheels (1st AM, 12mo, 301p, green cl, b/w)	Dodd	1900	Fisher, Harrison	50-80	
Jerome, Jerome K.	Told After Supper (1st, 12mo, 169p, teg, uncut)	Field & Tuer	1891	Skeaping, K.M.	70-100	
Jerrold, A.	Cruise in the Acorn (1st, 8vo, 140p, p-o, gilt, 6 ticp)	L: Marcus Ward	1875	Greenaway, Kate	280-400	
Jerrold, Clare	Road, Rail & Sea (1st, 4to, ibds, [80]p, 10cp)	L: Blackie	[1906]	Robinson, Charles	250-400	
Jerrold, Douglas W.	Fireside Saints (1st, 16mo, teg, 109p, gilt, col frn, 1-color, pep)	L: Blackie	1904	Robinson, Charles	80-120	
Jerrold, Walter	Big Book of Fables (1st, lg8vo, 293p, teg, red cl, 28cp, pep)	L: Blackie	1912	Robinson, Charles	300-500	
Jerrold, Walter	Big Book of Fairy Tales (1st AM, 4to, gilt, teg, 344p, 12cp, pep)	Dodge	[1911]	Robinson, Charles	300-500	
Jerrold, Walter	Big Book of Fairy Tales (1st, 4to, 344p, gilt, AEG, 12cp)	L: Blackie	1911	Robinson, Charles	350-500	
Jerrold, Walter	Big Book of Nursery Rhymes (1st, 4to, red/gilt, 320p, AEG, 18cp)	L: Blackie	[1903]	Robinson, Charles	350-500	
Jerrold, Walter	Bon-Mots of C. Lamb & D. Jerrold (1st, 24mo, 192p, gilt, teg, cvr by...)	L: J.M. Dent	1893	Beardsley, Aubrey	90-120	
Jerrold, Walter	Bon-Mots of the Eighteenth Century (1st, 16mo, 195p, gilt, b/w)	L: Dent	1897	Woodward, Alice B.	60-90	
Jerrold, Walter	Nonsense Nonsense! (1st, 4to, [68]p, ibds, 30cp)	L: Blackie	1902	Robinson, Charles	300-450	
Jerrold, Walter	Reign of King Oberon (1st, sm8vo, 338p, AEG, col frn, pep)	L: Dent	(1902)	Robinson, Charles	200-300	
Jeter, Jacky	Cat and the Fiddler (1st, lg8vo, [41]p, fp color, pep, DJ/3.50)	Parents Mag. Pr.	(1968)	Kalish, Lionel	30-45	
Jewett, Eleanore	Big John's Secret (1st, 8vo, blue cl, 236p, b/w, DJ/3.25)	Viking	(1962)	Chapman, Fred T.	25-40	
Jewett, Eleanore	Cobbler's Knob (1st, 8vo, 192p, b/w, DJ/2.50)	Viking	1956	Price, Christine	50-85	*
Jewett, Eleanore	Egyptian Tales of Magic (1st, 8vo, 257p, 8cp)	Little/Brown	1924	Day, Maurice	50-85	
Jewett, Eleanore	Hidden Treasure of Glaston (1st, 8vo, 307p, b/w, pep, DJ/2.50, NH)	Viking	1946	Chapman, Fred T.	100-175	
Jewett, Eleanore	Judith and Jane (1st, sm8vo, 318p, p-o, color)	Barse/Hopkins	1925	Wrenn, Charles	25-45	
Jewett, Eleanore	Mystery at Boulder Point (1st, 8vo, 281p, grey cl, fp b/w, DJ/2.50)	Viking	1949	Barnum, Jay H.	30-55	
Jewett, Eleanore	Told on the King's Highway (1st, 8vo, 246p, b/w, pep, DJ/2.50)	Viking	1943	Lawson, Marie A.	40-65	
Jewett, Eleanore	Which was Witch? (1st, 8vo, 160p, yellow cl, b/w, pep, DJ/2.50)	Viking	1953	Yashima, Taro	60-90	R
Jewett, Eleanore	Wonder Tales from Tibet (1st, sm8vo, 183p, green cl, 8cp)	Little/Brown	1922	Day, Maurice	50-80	
Jewett, John H.	Bunny Stories (1st, sq8vo, 210p, b/w)	Stokes	1892	Barnes, Culmer	70-100	
Jewett, John H.	Con the Wizard (1st AM, narrow 12mo, 123p, ibds, 8cp)	Stokes	(1905)	Little, Edward R.	55-80	
Jewett, John H.	Little Christmas (1st, sm narrow 8vo, 113p, ibds, 8cp)	Stokes	(1906)	Upjohn, Anna M.	40-60	*
Jewett, John H.	Little Governor in Fableland (1st, narrow 8vo, 104p, ibds, 5cp)	Stokes	(1907)	Farnsworth, Ethel	60-90	
Jewett, John H.	Little Toy Bearkins (16mo, ibds, [78]p, fp color)	L: Nister	[1908]	Petherick, Rosa	120-185	
Jewett, John H.	Snuggy Bedtime Stories (1st, 12mo, 126p, ibds, 8cp)	Stokes	(1906)	Upjohn, Anna M.	55-90	

AUTHOR	TITLE	PUBLISHER	DATE	ARTIST	PRICE	LC
Jewett, Sarah O.	Betty Leicester's Christmas (1st, 12mo, 68p, ibds, 8cp)	Houghton	1899	Betts, Anna W.	55-80	*
Jewett, Sarah O.	Deephaven (1st, 8vo, gilt, 305p, teg, b/w)	Houghton	1894	Woodbury, C.& M.	80-125	
Jewett, Sarah O.	White Heron (1st, 8vo, 34p, fp 3-color, DJ/3.50)	Crowell	(1963)	Cooney, Barbara	70-120	R
Joan, Natalie	Ameliaranne and the Big Treasure (1st AM, 8vo, red cl, unpag, p-o, color)	McKay	[1932]	Pearse, Susan B.	55-80	
Joan, Natalie	Ameliaranne in Town (1st, 12mo, bds, p-o, unpag, color)	L: Harrap	(1930)	Pearse, Susan B.	60-90	
Joan, Natalie	Cosy-Time Tales (1st, 4to, 47p, ibds, 9cp, pep)	L: T. Nelson	[1922]	Anderson, Anne	150-240	
Joan, Natalie	Glad Book (1st, 8vo, [48]p, gilt, ibds, 12 fp color)	L: H. Milford	[1921]	Sowerby, Millicent	100-160	
Joan, Natalie	Lie-Down Stories (1st, lg8vo, p-o, 77p, grey bds, 8cp)	L: Blackie	(1919)	Anderson, Anne	160-240	
Joan, Natalie	Little Mothers (1st, ob8vo, ibds, p-o, 12 fp color)	L: H. Milford	[1923]	Cramer, Rie	120-180	
Joan, Natalie	Tales for Teeny Wee (1st AM, 4to, ibds, 248p, 8cp)	Whitman	(1935)	Anderson/Wright	140-200	
Johns, Rowland	Jock the King's Pony (1st {std}, 8vo, ibds, 60p, b/w, pep, DJ/1.00)	Dutton	(1936)	Brown, Paul	120-200	
Johnson, A.E.	Below Zero (1st, lg4to, 61p, 12 ticp)	L: Hodder	[1911]	Pocock, Noel	160-220	
Johnson, A.E.	John Hassall, R.I. (1st, 8vo, 44p, 7cp, 28pl)	L: A&C Black	1907	Hassall, John	70-130	
Johnson, A.E.	Russian Ballet (1st AM, 4to, gilt, 240p, teg, 12cp)	Houghton	1913	Bull, Rene	250-350	
Johnson, A.E.	Russian Ballet (1st, lg4to, 240p, teg, gilt, uncut, 12cp)	L: Constable	1913	Bull, Rene	300-500	
Johnson, Abner M.	Memories and other Rhymes (1st, sm8vo, 78p, tip-in b/w pl)	H.K. Fly	(1924)	Johnson, F. Tenny	25-40	
Johnson, Annabel	Peculiar Magic (1st {std}, 8vo, 246p, b/w, DJ/3.25)	Houghton	1965	Ward, Lynd	25-40	
Johnson, Annabel	The Grizzly (1st, 8vo, 160p, fp b/w, DJ/3.50)	Harper	(1964)	Riswold, Gilbert	60-90	R*
Johnson, Ben	His Volpone (1st, 4to, 193p, blue/gilt, 7pl)	L: Smithers	1898	Beardsley, Aubrey	250-400	
Johnson, Burges	Bashful Ballads (1st, 8vo, teg, 145p, b/w)	Harper	1911	Walker, A.B.	30-50	
Johnson, Burges	Childhood (1st, 4to, [88]p, teg, uncut, tip-in photos by...)	Crowell	(1912)	Hunter/Ogden	140-200	R
Johnson, Burges	Little Book of Necessary Nonsense (1st {std}, 16mo, 81p, b/w, dep)	Harper	1929	MacKinstry, Eliz.	30-50	*
Johnson, Burges	Pleasant Tragedies of Childhood (1st, lg8vo, gilt, 119p, 30pl, pep)	Harper	1905	Cory, Fanny	100-160	
Johnson, Clifton	Parson's Devil (1st, 8vo, 296p, green cl, 4pl)	Crowell	(1927)	Newell, Peter	70-120	
Johnson, Clifton (ed)	Fir-Tree Fairy Book (1st, 8vo, 333p, color, pep)	Little/Brown	1912	Popini, Alexander	60-90	
Johnson, Clifton (ed)	Oaktree Fairy Book (1st, 8vo, p-o, 365p)	Little/Brown	1905	Bonte, Willard	60-90	
Johnson, Crockett	Barnaby (1st, 12mo, 361p, blue cl, b/w, DJ/2.00)	Henry Holt & Co.	1943	Johnson, Crockett	100-175	
Johnson, Crockett	Barnaby & Mr. O'Malley (1st, 12mo, 328p, b/w, DJ/2.00)	Henry Holt & Co.	(1944)	Johnson, Crockett	100-170	
Johnson, Crockett	Blue Ribbon Puppies (1st, 16mo, ibds, 31p, 2-color, DJ/1.50)	Harper	1958	Johnson, Crockett	140-200	
Johnson, Crockett	Castles in the Sand (1st {std}, 8vo, [48]p, color, DJ/3.50)	Holt, Rinehart	(1965)	Fraser, Betty	25-40	
Johnson, Crockett	Ellen's Lion (1st, 8vo, ibds, 62p, 1-color, DJ/1.75)	Harper	(1959)	Johnson, Crockett	30-50	
Johnson, Crockett	Emperor's Gifts (1st {std}, 8vo, [32]p, color, DJ/3.00)	Holt, Rinehart	(1965)	Johnson, Crockett	30-50	
Johnson, Crockett	Frowning Prince (1st, 8vo, 32p, b/w, DJ/1.50)	Harper	(1959)	Johnson, Crockett	30-50	*
Johnson, Crockett	Harold & the Purple Crayon (1st, 16mo, ibds, [60]p, 1-color, DJ/1.50)	Harper	1955	Johnson, Crockett	150-250	R
Johnson, Crockett	Harold at the North Pole (1st, 24mo, 48p, 1-color, DJ/1.50)	Harper	1958	Johnson, Crockett	50-90	
Johnson, Crockett	Harold's ABC (1st, 24mo, [64]p, ibds, 1-color)	Harper	1963	Johnson, Crockett	50-90	
Johnson, Crockett	Harold's Circus (1st, 16mo, ibds, [61]p, 1-color, DJ/1.50)	Harper	1959	Johnson, Crockett	80-130	
Johnson, Crockett	Harold's Fairy Tale (1st, 24mo, [64]p, ibds, 1-color, DJ/1.95)	Harper	1956	Johnson, Crockett	50-85	*
Johnson, Crockett	Lion's Own Story (1st, 8vo, 63p, ipcb, fp 1-color, DJ/2.50)	Harper	(1963)	Johnson, Crockett	30-50	
Johnson, Crockett	Merry-Go-Round (1st, 8vo, unpag, color, DJ/1.50)	Harper	1958	Johnson, Crockett	30-50	
Johnson, Crockett	Picture for Harold's Room (1st, 8vo, 64p, ibds, 1-color, DJ/1.95)	Harper	(1960)	Johnson, Crockett	45-70	*
Johnson, Crockett	Terrible Terrifying Toby (1st, lg8vo, unpag, DJ/2.50)	Harper	1957	Johnson, Crockett	60-100	
Johnson, Crockett	Time for Spring (1st, 8vo, 29p, fp b/w, DJ/1.50)	Harper	1957	Johnson, Crockett	30-50	
Johnson, Crockett	Who's Upside Down? (1st, lg8vo, [24]p, ipcb, b/w, DJ/1.75)	W.R. Scott	1952	Johnson, Crockett	60-95	
Johnson, Doris	Su An (1st {std}, sm8vo, 30p, b/w, DJ/3.50)	Follett	(1968)	Weisgard, Leonard	30-50	
Johnson, Edna	Anthology of Children's Literature (1st, 4to, 917p, 15cp, pep, DJ/5.00)	Houghton	1940	Wyeth, N.C.	250-400	
Johnson, Edward (ed)	Private Memoirs of Madame Roland (1st, 12mo, 381p, teg, cvr by...)	McClurg	1900	Armstrong, Margaret	35-60	
Johnson, Elizabeth	All in Free but Janey (1st {std}, lg8vo, 31p, color, DJ/3.95)	Little/Brown	(1968)	Hyman, Trina S.	30-50	
Johnson, Elizabeth	Stuck with Luck (1st {std}, 8vo, 88p, b/w, DJ/3.50)	Little/Brown	(1967)	Hyman, Trina S.	30-50	
Johnson, Elizabeth	Three-in-One Prince (1st {std}, lg8vo, 58p, fp color, DJ/2.75)	Little/Brown	(1961)	Solbert, Ronni	25-40	*
Johnson, Emilie F.	Little Book of Prayers (1st, 16mo, [47]p, 1-color, pep, DJ/1.00)	Viking	1941	Petershams	55-80	
Johnson, Emilie F.	Umbrella Bird & other Verses (1st, lg8vo, 83p, col frn, color, DJ/1.00)	Falmouth Pub.	(1939)	Malcher, Lucretia	30-45	
Johnson, Enid	Runaway Balboa (1st {std}, 4to, [41]p, ibds, color, pep, DJ/2.00)	Harper	1938	Peck, Anne M.	40-65	*
Johnson, Enid	Three J's (1st, 8vo, 63p, fp b/w, pep, DJ/1.50)	J. Messner	(1952)	Sari	50-80	*
Johnson, Florence	Christmas ABC (1st, sm8vo, ibds, unpag, color, LGB/#478)	Golden Press	1962	Wilkin, Eloise B.	30-50	
Johnson, Gerald W.	America Grows Up (1st, 8vo, 223p, grey cl, fp b/w, DJ/3.75)	Wm. Morrow	1960	Fisher, Leonard	30-50	
Johnson, Gerald W.	America is Born (1st, lg8vo, 254p, red cl, b/w, DJ/3.95, NH)	Wm. Morrow	1959	Fisher, Leonard	50-85	R
Johnson, Gerald W.	America Moves Forward (1st, 8vo, 256p, blue cl, fp b/w, DJ/3.95, NH)	Wm. Morrow	1960	Fisher, Leonard	40-65	
Johnson, Gerald W.	British Empire (1st, 8vo, 158p, b/w, DJ/4.25)	Wm. Morrow	(1969)	Fisher, Leonard	20-35	
Johnson, Gerald W.	Franklin D. Roosevelt Portrait of a Great Man (1st, lg8vo, 192p, DJ/3.75)	Wm. Morrow	1967	Fisher, Leonard	25-40	
Johnson, Gerald W.	Little Night-Music (1st {std}, 8vo, gilt, 125p, b/w, DJ/1.50)	Harper	1937	Yardley, Richard	80-130	
Johnson, Gerald W.	Pattern for Liberty (1st, ob4to, gilt, 146p, fp color, DJ/7.50)	McGraw-Hill	(1952)	Various	50-80	
Johnson, Gerald W.	Story of Man's Work (1st, 8vo, 245p, uncut, fp b/w)	Minton Balch	1925	Kappel, Philip	30-50	*
Johnson, Gerald W.	Supreme Court (1st, 8vo, 127p, fp b/w, DJ/2.95)	Wm. Morrow	1962	Fisher, Leonard	50-75	R*
Johnson, Gerald W.	The Cabinet (1st, 8vo, 160p, fp b/w, DJ/3.50)	Wm. Morrow	1966	Fisher, Leonard	30-50	
Johnson, Gerald W.	The Congress (1st, 8vo, 128p, fp b/w, DJ/2.95)	Wm. Morrow	1963	Fisher, Leonard	30-50	
Johnson, Gerald W.	The Presidency (1st, 8vo, 128p, fp b/w, DJ/2.95)	Wm. Morrow	1962	Fisher, Leonard	30-50	
Johnson, J.P.	20 Years of Hus'ling (1st, 8vo, 664p, tan cl, 48 b/w)	Chi: Thompson	1900	Denslow, W.W.	100-165	
Johnson, James W.	God's Trombones (1st, 8vo, bds, gilt, 56p, 8pl, DJ)	Viking	1927	Douglas, Aaron	300-500	
Johnson, Laura E.	Teddy-Bear ABC (1st, sq4to, [55]p, color, pep)	Caldwell	(1907)	Sanford, Margaret L.	250-350	
Johnson, Margaret	Black Bruce (1st, 8vo, 154p, red cl, b/w, pep, DJ/1.75)	Harcourt	(1938)	Johnson, Margaret	125-200	
Johnson, Margaret	Polly & the Wishing Ring (1st, 12mo, 123p, 4cp)	Macmillan	1918	Pogany, Willy	70-100	
Johnson, Margaret	Tally-Ho (1st, lg8vo, 120p, b/w, pep, DJ/1.75)	Harcourt	(1936)	Johnson, Margaret	50-80	
Johnson, Margaret	What O'Clock Jingles (1st, ob8vo, ibds, [30]p, 27 b/w)	D. Lothrop Co.	(1887)	Johnson, Margaret	70-100	*
Johnson, Mary	Cat's Fairy Land... (1st, 12mo, 184p, gilt, b/w)	H. Carter	1900	(Photos)	120-200	
Johnson, Osa	Pantaloons (1st, 4to, ibds, 56p, color, pep, DJ/1.50)	Random	(1941)	Jansson, Arthur A.	70-120	
Johnson, Osa	Tarnish: True Story of a Lion Cub (1st, lg8vo, ibds, 59p, color, DJ/1.00)	Wilcox/Follett	(1944)	Jansson, Arthur A.	35-50	
Johnson, Owen	Tennessee Shad (1st, 12mo, red cl, 307p, 8pl, PPP)	Baker/Taylor	1911	Gruger, Frederic R.	80-120	

AUTHOR	TITLE	PUBLISHER	DATE	ARTIST	PRICE	LC
Johnson, Owen	The Varmint (1st, 12mo, 396p, green cl, 6pl, PPP)	Baker/Taylor	1910	Gruger, Frederic R.	60-100	
Johnson, Richard	Saint George & the Dragon (1st, lg8vo, [30]p, fp b/w, pep, DJ/1.00)	Scribner	1941	Maloy, Lois	30-50	
Johnson, Ryerson	Let's Walk up the Wall (1st, ob8vo, [48]p, fp 3-color, DJ/3.75)	Holiday House	(1967)	Cellini, Eva	30-45	
Johnson, Ryerson	Monkey & the Wild, Wild Wind (1st, 4to [40]p, fp col, pep, DJ/2.75, JABA)	Abelard-Schuman	1961	Lignell, Lois	30-50	
Johnson, Ryerson	Upstairs & Downstairs (1st, sq8vo, [40]p, fp 2-color, DJ/2.50)	Crowell	(1962)	Weil, Lisl	35-50	*
Johnson, Sally (ed)	Harper Book of Princes (1st, 8vo, 330p, b/w, DJ/4.95)	Harper	(1964)	Domanska, Janina	30-45	
Johnson, Sally (ed)	Princesses: 16 Stories about Princesses (1st, 8vo 318p, b/w, DJ/4.95, NYTBI)	Harper	(1962)	Montresor, Beni	60-90	*
Johnson, Siddie	Cat Hotel (1st {std}, 8vo, 132p, b/w, DJ/2.50)	Longmans	1955	Holland, Janice	30-50	
Johnson, Siddie	Rabbit Fires (1st {std}, lg ob8vo, 32p, b/w, pep)	TX: Highland Pr.	(1951)	Toepperwein, Emilie	50-80	*
Johnson, Siddie	Susan's Year (1st {std}, 8vo, uncut, 168p, b/w, pep, DJ/2.25)	Longmans	1948	Merriman, Anne	20-35	
Johnston, Annie F.	Georgina of the Rainbows (1st, sm8vo, gilt, 348p, col frn, 3pl)	NY: Britton	(1916)	Neill, John R.	70-100	
Johnston, Annie F.	Giant Scissors (1st, sm8vo, 201p, blue/gilt, teg, 8cp)	L.C. Page	1906	Merrill, Frank T.	30-50	
Johnston, Annie F.	It Was the Road to Jericho (1st {std}, sm8vo, [41]p, gilt, pep)	Britton	(1919)	Neill, John R.	50-80	
Johnston, Annie F.	Little Colonel (1st, 12mo, 102p, green/gilt, b/w, PPP)	J. Knight	1896	Barry, Etheldred B.	180-260	R
Johnston, Annie F.	Little Colonel's Knight Comes Riding (1st, 8vo, 318p, 8pl)	L.C. Page	1907	Barry, Etheldred B.	40-65	
Johnston, Annie F.	Mary Ware of Texas (1st, sm8vo, 385p, pict cl, 8pl)	L.C. Page	1910	Merrill, Frank T.	40-65	
Johnston, Annie F.	May Ware, Little Colonel's Chum (1st, sm8vo, 305p, tan cl, 8pl)	L.C. Page	1908	Barry, Etheldred B.	30-50	
Johnston, Annie F.	Mildred's Inheritance (1st, 12mo, blue cl, 74p, 10pl)	L.C. Page	1906	Horne, Diantha W.	40-65	
Johnston, Annie F.	Miss Santa Claus of the Pullman (1st, 8vo, 172p, gilt, col frn, 8pl)	Century	1913	Birch, Reginald	40-65	
Johnston, Annie F.	Ole Mammy's Torment (1st, 12mo, 118p, fp b/w)	L.C. Page	1897	Johnston/Sacker	70-125	
Johnston, Annie F.	Road of the Loving Heart (1st, sm8vo, gilt, 77p, pep, b/w)	L.C. Page	1922	Bromhall, Winifred	45-70	
Johnston, Annie F.	Story of Dago (1st, 12mo, 101p, 10pl)	L.C. Page	1900	Barry, Etheldred B.	40-65	
Johnston, Annie F.	Two Little Knights of Kentucky (1st, 8vo, 203p, blue/gilt, 8cp)	L.C. Page	1907	Brett, Harold M.	30-50	
Johnston, Harry	Pioneers in Canada (1st, 8vo, 328p, gilt, 8cp)	L: Blackie	1912	Wall-Cousins, E.	50-85	
Johnston, Isabel M.	Jeweled Toad (1st, lg8vo, 211p, ibds, 11cp)	Bobbs-Merrill	(1907)	Denslow, W.W.	500-750	
Johnston, Johanna	Eagle in Fact & Fiction (1st {std}, 8vo, 157p, b/w, DJ/3.25)	Harlin Quist	(1966)	Pinto, Ralph	25-40	
Johnston, Johanna	Edie Changes her Mind (1st, sm4to, 48p, fp 2-color, DJ/2.75)	Putnam	(1964)	Galdone, Paul	30-50	
Johnston, Johanna	Great Gravity the Cat (1st {std}, 8vo, 66p, b/w, DJ/2.50)	Knopf	1958	Wiese, Kurt	30-50	
Johnston, Johanna	Joan of Arc (1st {std}, lg4to, 88p, ibds, color, DJ/2.95)	Doubleday	1961	Mars, Witold T.	25-40	*
Johnston, Johanna	Penguins' Way (1st {std}, lg8vo, [44]p, 2-color, DJ/2.50)	Doubleday	1962	Weisgard, Leonard	30-45	*
Johnston, Johanna	Special Bravery (1st, 8vo, 94p, b/w, DJ/3.50)	Dodd	(1967)	Grifalconi, Ann	50-80	
Johnston, Johanna	Stories of the Norsemen (1st {std}, lg4to, 88p, color, DJ/2.95)	Garden City	1959	Mars, Witold T.	25-45	*
Johnston, Johanna	Story of Hannibal (1st {std}, lg4to, 67p, color, pep, DJ/2.95)	Garden City	(1960)	Mars, Witold T.	20-35	
Johnston, Johanna	Story of the Barber of Seville (1st, 4to, 61p, fp color, DJ/3.95)	Putnam	(1966)	Perl, Susan	25-40	
Johnston, Johanna	Sugarplum (1st, ob4to, [40]p, fp 2-color, dep, DJ/2.00)	Knopf	(1955)	Bileck, Marvin	50-80	R*
Johnston, Johanna	Supposings (1st, 4to, [32]p, fp 3-color, DJ/4.95)	Holiday House	(1967)	Sayers, Rudy	25-40	
Johnston, Johanna	That's Right, Edie (1st, 4to, 46p, fp 2-color, DJ/3.50)	Putnam	(1966)	Galdone, Paul	30-45	
Johnston, Johanna	Whale's Way (1st {std}, ob4to, 45p, color, DJ/2.95)	Doubleday	1965	Weisgard, Leonard	30-45	
Johnston, Mary	Long Roll (1st, 8vo, 683p, grey/gilt, 4cp, pep)	Houghton	1911	Wyeth, N.C.	40-65	
Johnston, Mary	Prisoners of Hope (1st, sm8vo, 378p, green/gilt)	Houghton	1898	Rogers, Bruce	60-100	
Johnston, Mary	To Have & to Hold (1st, 8vo, green cl, 403p, 8pl)	Houghton	1900	Various	40-70	
Johnston, Mary	To Have & to Hold (1st {this format}, lg8vo, 331p, 5cp)	Houghton	1931	Schoonover, Frank	30-50	
Johnston, Richard M.	Pearce Amerson's Will (1st, 12mo, teg, 275p, cvr by...)	Way & Williams	1898	Hazenplug, Frank	100-160	
Johnston, Richard M.	Widow Guthrie (1st, sm8vo, blue/gilt, 309p, 6pl, cep)	Appleton	1890	Kemble, Edward W.	35-60	*
Jones, DuPre	Adventures of Gremlin (1st {std}, 12mo, ibds, 112p, b/w, DJ/3.95)	Lippincott	(1966)	Gorey, Edward	100-150	
Jones, Eliz. O.	Big Susan (1st {std}, sq8vo, ibds, 83p, color, pep, DJ/2.00)	Macmillan	1947	Jones, Eliz. O.	55-80	
Jones, Eliz. O.	David: Bible Story with Pictures (1st, 4to, ibds, [64]p, color)	Macmillan	1937	Jones, Eliz. O.	40-60	*
Jones, Eliz. O.	Little Red Riding Hood (1st {A}, 8vo, ibds, [42]p, color, LGB/#42)	Simon/Schuster	(1948)	Jones, Eliz. O.	20-35	
Jones, Eliz. O.	Maminka's Children (1st, lg8vo, 107p, fp color, DJ/2.00)	Macmillan	1940	Jones, Eliz. O.	60-100	
Jones, Eliz. O.	Ragman of Paris & his Ragamuffins (1st, 8vo, 82p, fp 2-color, pep, DJ/1.50)	Oxford U. Pr.	(1937)	Jones, Eliz. O.	35-50	
Jones, Eliz. O.	Twig (1st, 8vo, 152p, fp 3-color, pep, DJ/2.00)	Macmillan	1942	Jones, Eliz. O.	200-300	
Jones, Harry	Prince Boo Hoo & Little Smuts (1st, sq8vo, 319p, teg, uncut, b/w)	L: Wells/Gard.	(1896)	Browne, Gordon	120-200	
Jones, Idwal	Chef's Holiday (1st {std}, sm8vo, 210p, b/w, DJ/3.00)	Longmans	1952	Duvoisin, Roger	40-65	
Jones, Idwal	Whistler's Van (1st, 8vo, 235p, b/w, pep, DJ/2.00, NH)	Viking	1936	Gay, Zhenya	50-80	
Jones, Inis	Peetie: Story of a Real Cat (1st {std}, 8vo, 90p, b/w, DJ/1.50)	McBride	(1935)	Wiese, Kurt	40-70	
Jones, Jessie O.	Little Child (1st, ob4to, ibds, 38p, pep, fp color, DJ/2.00)	Viking	1946	Jones, Eliz. O.	50-80	
Jones, Jessie O.	Secrets (1st, 8vo, 24p, fp color, DJ/2.00)	Viking	1945	Jones, Eliz. O.	30-50	
Jones, Jessie O.	Small Rain (1st, sm ob4to, ibds, [40]p, 1-color, pep, DJ/2.00, CH)	Viking	1943	Jones, Eliz. O.	60-100	
Jones, Jessie O. (ed)	Many Mansions (1st, lg8vo, 134p, 1-color, DJ/3.00)	Viking	1947	Ward, Lynd	30-50	
Jones, Jessie O. (ed)	This is the Way (1st, sm ob4to, 62p, 2-color, pep, DJ/3.00)	Viking	1951	Jones, Eliz. O.	40-65	
Jones, Mary A.	Tell Me About Heaven (1st {A}, 4to, 70p, color, pep, DJ/2.50)	Rand/McNally	(1956)	Cooper, Marjorie	20-35	
Jones, Mary A.	Tell Me About Prayer (1st {A}, 4to, 72p, color, pep, DJ/2.00)	Rand/McNally	(1948)	Grider, Dorothy	20-35	
Jones, Paul	Alphabet of Aviation (1st, lg8vo, blue cl, [62]p, gilt, 28 fp color)	Macrae Smith	(1928)	Shenton, Edward	140-225	*
Jones, Thomas O.	Minnie the Mermaid (1st, 16mo, [48]p, red cl, color, DJ/0.75)	NY: Oxford U.Pr.	(1939)	Jones, Eliz. O.	35-60	
Jones, Viola M.	Peter & Gretchen of Old Nuremberg (1st, 4to, p-o, 96p, color, pep, DJ/2.00)	Whitman	1935	Sewell, Helen	40-65	
Jones, Weyman	Edge of Two Worlds (1st {std}, 8vo, 143p, b/w, DJ/3.95)	Dial Press	(1968)	Kocsis, J.C.	25-40	
Jones, Wilfred	How the Derrick Works (1st, sm4to, black cl, 43p, 2-color, cep)	Macmillan	(1930)	Jones, Wilfred	60-100	
Joos, Dorothy H.	Golden Prince (1st, 4to, 129p, p-o, dp color, pep)	Duffield	1928	Wells, Rhea	40-65	
Jordan, Eliz. G.	May Iverson: Her Book (1st, 8vo, blue cl, 282p, p-o, 8pl)	Harper	1904	Harding, Charlotte	50-80	
Jordan, Mildred	I Won't, said the King (1st {std}, 8vo, 104p, color, DJ/2.00)	Knopf	1945	Duvoisin, Roger	45-70	
Jordan, Mildred	Shoo-Fly Pie (1st {std}, 8vo, 118p, dp color, pep, DJ/2.00)	Knopf	1944	Pitz, Henry C.	30-50	
Jordan, Nina	Mother Goose Handicraft (1st, sm8vo, 149p, fp b/w, DJ/2.00)	Harcourt	(1945)	Jordan, Nina	55-90	
Joseph, Alfred W.	Sondo: A Liberian Boy (1st, lg8vo, ibds, pep, 32p, fp b/w, DJ/1.00)	Whitman	(1936)	Magnie, Bernice	60-90	
Joslin, Sesyle	Baby Elephant & Secret Wishes (1st {std}, 12mo, ibds, 3-color, DJ/2.50)	Harcourt	(1962)	Weisgard, Leonard	40-65	
Joslin, Sesyle	Baby Elephant Goes to China (1st {std}, 12mo, [45]p, 1-color, DJ/2.50)	Harcourt	(1963)	Weisgard, Leonard	40-65	
Joslin, Sesyle	Baby Elephant's Baby Book (1st {std}, 12mo, [48]p, 1-color, DJ/2.50)	Harcourt	(1964)	Weisgard, Leonard	40-65	
Joslin, Sesyle	Baby Elephant's Trunk (1st {std}, 12mo, unpag, 1-color, DJ/2.50)	Harcourt	(1961)	Weisgard, Leonard	40-65	
Joslin, Sesyle	Brave Baby Elephant (1st {std}, 12mo, [48]p, color, DJ/2.50)	Harcourt	(1960)	Weisgard, Leonard	45-70	

AUTHOR	TITLE	PUBLISHER	DATE	ARTIST	PRICE	LC
Joslin, Sesyle	Doctor George Owl (1st {std}, 4to, 45p, color, DJ/3.75)	Houghton	(1970)	Weil, Lisl	25-40	
Joslin, Sesyle	Night They Stole the Alphabet (1st {std}, 8vo, 190p, DJ/3.95)	Harcourt	(1968)	Arno, Enrico	60-100	
Joslin, Sesyle	Please Share that Peanut (1st {std}, 8vo, [64]p, fp b/w, DJ/2.50, NYTBI)	Harcourt	(1965)	Taback, Simms	30-50	
Joslin, Sesyle	Senor Baby Elephant the Pirate (1st {std}, 12mo, unpag, 1-color, DJ/2.50)	Harcourt	(1962)	Weisgard, Leonard	30-50	
Joslin, Sesyle	There is a Dragon in my Bed (1st {std}, sq8vo, [64]p, fp b/w, DJ/2.25)	Harcourt	(1961)	Haas, Irene	50-80	R*
Joslin, Sesyle	What Do You Do, Dear? (1st, ob8vo, [48]p, color, DJ/2.75)	Young Scott	1961	Sendak, Maurice	130-180	
Joslin, Sesyle	What Do You Say, Dear? (1st, ob8vo, [48]p, 1-color, DJ/2.75, CH, NYTBI)	Young Scott	1958	Sendak, Maurice	250-350	
Joyce, James	Cat and the Devil (1st, 8vo, [48]p, color, pep, DJ/3.50)	Dodd	(1964)	Erdoes, Richard	100-175	R
Joyce, James	Cat and the Devil (1st UK, 8vo, 32p, color, DJ)	L: Faber	1965	Rose, Gerald	150-250	
Joyce, Robert	Stray Child (1st {std}, lg ob8vo, 38p, b/w)	Dutton	(1934)	Joyce, Robert	25-45	
Judah, Aaron	Pot of Gold (1st, 8vo, 62p, red cloth, fp b/w, DJ)	L: Faber	1959	Peake, Mervyn	60-100	
Judson, Clara I.	Abraham Lincoln (1st {this pub}, 8vo, 29p, color, DJ/1.00)	Follett	(1961)	Jackson, Polly	25-45	
Judson, Clara I.	Abraham Lincoln, Friend of People (1st, 8vo, 206p, fp color, dep, DJ/3.50)	Wilcox/Follett	(1950)	Frankenberg, Rbt.	30-50	
Judson, Clara I.	Alice Ann (1st, sm8vo, gilt, 300p, b/w, DJ/1.50)	Barse/Hopkins	(1928)	Foster, John M.	25-40	
Judson, Clara I.	Andrew Carnegie (1st, lg8vo, 157p, b/w, DJ/3.50)	Follett	(1964)	Savage, Steele	20-30	
Judson, Clara I.	Benjamin Franklin (1st, lg8vo, 204p, b/w, DJ/3.50)	Follett	(1957)	Frankenberg, Rbt.	25-35	
Judson, Clara I.	Billy Robin (1st, 12mo, ipcb, 76p, 10cp)	Rand/McNally	(1917)	Carr, Warner	30-50	
Judson, Clara I.	Boat Builder (1st, 8vo, tan cl, 121p, fp b/w, pep, DJ/1.50)	Scribner	1940	Sperry, Armstrong	30-50	
Judson, Clara I.	Christopher Columbus (1st, sm8vo, 29p, color, DJ)	Follett	(1960)	Jackson, Polly	25-45	
Judson, Clara I.	City Neighbor: Story of Jane Addams (1st, 8vo, 130p, b/w, DJ/2.50)	Scribner	1951	Ray, Ralph	20-30	
Judson, Clara I.	Donald McKay: Designer of Clipper Ships (1st, 8vo, 134p, DJ/1.75)	Scribner	1943	Cosgrave, John O.	30-45	
Judson, Clara I.	Flower Fairies (1st, lg8vo, p-o, pep, 93p, 6cp)	Rand/McNally	(1915)	Enright, Maginel W.	75-100	*
Judson, Clara I.	Garden Adventures of Tommy Tittlemouse (1st, sm8vo, 64p, color)	Rand/McNally	(1922)	Beem, Frances	30-50	
Judson, Clara I.	George Washington (1st, sm8vo, 29p, color, DJ/1.00)	Follett	(1961)	Patterson, Bob	20-35	
Judson, Clara I.	George Washington, Leader of the People (1st, lg8vo, 224p, b/w, DJ/3.50)	Wilcox/Follett	1951	Frankenberg, Rbt.	30-50	
Judson, Clara I.	Good-Night Stories (1st, 12mo, pict cl, 131p, b/w)	McClurg	1916	Wilson, Clara P.	25-45	*
Judson, Clara I.	Green Ginger Jar (1st, 8vo, green cl, 210p, fp b/w, pep, DJ/2.50)	Houghton	1949	Brown, Paul	50-85	
Judson, Clara I.	Lost Violin: They Came from Bohemia (1st, 8vo, 204p, b/w, pep, DJ/2.25)	Houghton	1947	Bradfield, Margaret	25-40	
Judson, Clara I.	Mary Jane's Friends in Holland (1st, sm8vo, 213p, b/w, pep, DJ/0.50)	Grosset/Dunlap	(1939)	Foster, Genevieve	20-30	
Judson, Clara I.	Michael's Victory (1st, 8vo, 192p, b/w, pep, DJ/2.00)	Houghton	1946	Wexler, Elmer	25-45	
Judson, Clara I.	Mighty Soo... (1st, lg8vo, 192p, b/w, DJ/3.50)	Follett	(1955)	Frankenberg, Rbt.	25-45	
Judson, Clara I.	Mr. Justice Holmes (1st, lg8vo, 192p, b/w, DJ/3.50, NH)	Follett	(1956)	Todd, Robert	75-100	*
Judson, Clara I.	People Who Come to Our House (1st {A}, 4to, 48p, color, DJ/1.00)	Rand/McNally	(1940)	Peters, Marjorie	30-50	
Judson, Clara I.	People Who Work in Country & City (1st {A}, sm4to, 94p, col, pep, DJ/2.00)	Rand/McNally	(1943)	Ward, Keith	40-60	
Judson, Clara I.	People Who Work Near our House (1st {A}, sm4to, 48p, ipcb, 2-col, DJ/1.00)	Rand/McNally	(1942)	Ward, Keith	40-60	*
Judson, Clara I.	Pioneer Girl (1st {A}, 8vo, ipcb, 80p, fp 1-color, pep, DJ/0.50)	Rand/McNally	(1939)	Foster, Genevieve	45-70	
Judson, Clara I.	Play Days (1st, 8vo, [39]p, ipcb, dep, b/w)	Grosset/Dunlap	(1937)	(Photos)	30-50	*
Judson, Clara I.	Railway Engineer (1st, 8vo, 171p, b/w pl, pep, DJ/1.50)	Scribner	(1941)	Simon, Eric M.	30-45	
Judson, Clara I.	Reaper Man (1st, 8vo, 156p, b/w, DJ/2.50)	Houghton	1948	Brown, Paul	80-130	
Judson, Clara I.	Soldier Doctor: Story of William Gorgas (1st, 8vo, 151p, b/w, DJ/1.60)	Scribner	1942	Doremus, Robert	30-45	
Judson, Clara I.	St. Lawrence Seaway (1st, 8vo, 160p, b/w, DJ/3.95)	Follett	(1959)	Bjorklund, Lorence	20-30	
Judson, Clara I.	Summer Time (1st, lg8vo, [44]p, color, DJ)	Broadman Press	(1948)	Jackson, Polly	30-50	
Judson, Clara I.	They Came from France (1st, 8vo, red cl, 245p, fp b/w, pep, DJ/2.00)	Houghton	1943	Lenski, Lois	60-95	
Judson, Clara I.	They Came from Scotland (1st, sm8vo, 198p, col frn, pep, DJ/2.00)	Houghton	1944	Reardon, Mary	25-45	
Judson, Clara I.	They Came from Sweden (1st, 8vo, 213p, b/w, pep, DJ/2.00)	Houghton	1942	Caswell, Edward	25-45	
Judson, Clara I.	Virginia Lee (1st, sm8vo, gilt, 308p, 4pl, DJ)	Barse/Hopkins	(1926)	Wrenn, Charles	30-45	
Judson, Clara I.	Yankee Clippers: Story of Donald McKay (1st, 8vo, 158p, b/w, DJ/3.50)	Follett	(1965)	Tashiro, Yukio	25-40	
Judson, Katherine	Old Crow Stories (1st, 8vo, 163p, blue cl, 6pl)	Little/Brown	1917	Bull, Charles L.	30-50	
June, Larry	Shadow's Holiday (1st {std}, lg8vo, gilt, [43]p, b/w, cep, DJ)	Farrar/Rinehart	(1931)	(Photos)	40-65	*
Jungman, B.	Holland (1st, lg8vo, gilt, teg, 212p, 75cp)	L: A&C Black	1904	Jungman, Nico W.	80-120	
Jupo, Frank	Atu, the Silent One (1st, ob8vo, [32]p, fp 2-color, DJ/3.75)	Holiday House	(1967)	Jupo, Frank	25-40	
Jupo, Frank	Up the Trail/Down the Street (1st {std}, 4to, ipcb, [38]p, color, DJ/2.75)	Macmillan	(1956)	Jupo, Frank	25-45	
Jupo, Frank	Wishing Shoe (1st AM, 8vo, 95p, fp b/w, DJ/2.50)	Abelard-Schuman	(1955)	Jupo, Frank	40-65	
Juster, Norton	Alberic the Wise (1st, 4to, 67p, gilt, b/w, DJ/3.50, NYTBI)	Pantheon	(1965)	Gnoli, Domenico	45-75	
Juster, Norton	Phantom Tollbooth (1st, 8vo, 255p, blue cl, b/w, pep, DJ/3.95)	Epstein/Carroll	(1961)	Feiffer, Jules	400-600	
Juster, Norton	Phantom Tollbooth (1st UK, 8vo, 256p, bds, b/w, DJ)	L: Collins	1962	Feiffer, Jules	250-400	
Justus, May	At the Foot of Windy Low (1st, 8vo, green cl, 80p, 10cp, pep)	Volland	(1930)	Dudley, Carrie	50-80	
Justus, May	Banjo Billy and Mr. Bones (1st, 8vo, 63p, p-o, fp color, pep, DJ/1.50)	Whitman	1944	Chisholm, Christine	20-30	
Justus, May	Fiddle Away (1st, sq8vo, [28]p, ipcb, col frn, DJ/0.50)	Grosset/Dunlap	(1942)	Berry, Erick	30-45	
Justus, May	Gabby Gaffer (1st, 8vo, green/gilt, 80p, 10cp, pep)	Volland	(1929)	Dudley, Carrie	50-80	
Justus, May	Here Comes Mary Ellen (1st, 8vo, 140p, col frn, b/w, DJ/1.50)	Lippincott	(1940)	Finger, Helen	30-45	
Justus, May	Honey Jane (1st {std}, 8vo, 202p, cp, pep, DJ/2.00)	Doubleday/Doran	1935	Smith, Charles	20-35	
Justus, May	House in No-End Hollow (1st {std}, 8vo, 286p, col frn, pep, DJ/2.00)	Doubleday/Doran	1938	Berry, Erick	30-50	
Justus, May	Mr. Songcatcher & Co. (1st {std}, 8vo, 237p, 2-color, DJ/2.00)	Doubleday/Doran	1940	Simon, Howard	20-35	
Justus, May	Near Side and Far (1st {std}, 8vo, 148p, fp b/w, pep)	Suttonhouse	(1936)	Mallon, Grace	30-50	
Justus, May	New Boy in School (1st, 8vo, 56p, b/w, DJ/2.95)	Hastings House	(1963)	Payne, Joan B.	45-70	
Justus, May	New Home for Billy (1st, lg8vo, 55p, b/w, pep, DJ/3.25)	Hastings House	(1966)	Payne, Joan B.	30-50	
Justus, May	Sammy (1st, lg8vo, p-o, 47p, color, pep, DJ/2.00)	Whitman	1946	Chisholm, Christine	25-40	
Justus, May	Susie (1st, 8vo, 46p, p-o, color, pep, DJ/1.50)	Whitman	1947	Chisholm, Christine	20-30	
Juta, Jan	Look Out for the Ostriches! (1st {std}, 8vo, 177p, b/w, DJ/2.50)	Knopf	1949	Pitz, Henry C.	25-45	
Kaberry, Charles J.	Book of Baby Dogs (1st, 4to, bds, 120p, p-o, 19 ticp)	L: H. Frowde	(1914)	Detmold, Edward J.	300-400	
Kaberry, Charles J.	Our Little Neighbors (4to, pcb, gilt, 105p, 12 ticp)	L: Oxford U.Pr.	(1921)	Detmold, Edward J.	250-400	
Kaeser, Hildegarde	Mimff-Robinson (1st, 8vo, grey/silver, 184p, b/w, DJ)	L: Oxford U.Pr.	1958	Ardizzone, Edward	70-120	
Kafka, Sherry	Big Enough (1st, 12mo, [32]p, 2-color, DJ/3.50)	Putnam	(1970)	Kuskin, Karla	40-65	*
Kahl, Virginia	Away Went Wolfgang (1st, sm ob4to, beige cl, [32]p, color, DJ/2.00)	Scribner	1954	Kahl, Virginia	50-80	R
Kahl, Virginia	Baron's Booty (1st, 4to, [32]p, 3-color, DJ/3.25)	Scribner	1963	Kahl, Virginia	40-65	*
Kahl, Virginia	Droopsi (1st, sm4to, [32]p, fp 3-color, DJ/2.50)	Scribner	1958	Kahl, Virginia	40-65	
Kahl, Virginia	Duchess Bakes a Cake (1st, 4to, [32]p, fp 2-color, DJ/2.00)	Scribner	1955	Kahl, Virginia	80-120	

AUTHOR	TITLE	PUBLISHER	DATE	ARTIST	PRICE	LC
Kahl, Virginia	Habits of Rabbits (1st, 4to, [32]p, b/w, DJ/2.50)	Scribner	1957	Kahl, Virginia	30-50	
Kahl, Virginia	Maxie (1st, ob4to, [32]p, 3-color, DJ/2.50)	Scribner	1956	Kahl, Virginia	40-65	
Kahl, Virginia	Perfect Pancake (1st, 4to, [32]p, 2-color, DJ/2.75)	Scribner	1960	Kahl, Virginia	40-65	
Kahl, Virginia	Plum Pudding for Christmas (1st, 4to, grey cl, unpag, color, DJ/2.50)	Scribner	(1956)	Kahl, Virginia	40-65	
Kahmann, Chesley	Carmen: Silent Partner (1st, sm8vo, 249p, uncut, b/w, pep)	Dodd	1934	Sperry, Armstrong	50-80	*
Kahmann, Chesley	Jasper the Gypsy Dog (1st, 8vo, yellow cl, 93p, b/w, pep, DJ/1.50)	J. Messner	(1938)	Wiese, Kurt	30-50	
Kahmann, Chesley	Sinfi and Little Gypsy Goat (1st {std}, sm4to, 70p, color, pep, DJ/1.50)	Random	(1940)	Mora, F. Luis	50-80	*
Kahmann, Chesley	Tara, Daughter of the Gypsies (1st {std}, 8vo, 288p, b/w, DJ/2.00)	Smith/Haas	1935	Mora, F. Luis	50-80	
Kahn, Joan	Seesaw (1st, 16mo, [24]p, b/w, DJ/1.95)	Harper	(1964)	Bonsall, Crosby	25-40	
Kaigh-Eustace, E.	Jungle Babies (1st, 8vo, 256p, black cl, p-o, color, pep)	Rand/McNally	(1930)	Bransom/Nelson	25-45	
Kalab, Theresa	Kokwa: Little Koala Bear (1st {std} lg8vo, [29]p, ibds, fp 1-color, DJ/1.00)	Longmans	(1940)	Kalab, Theresa	40-65	*
Kalashnikoff, N.	Jumper (1st, 8vo, blue/silver, 224p, b/w, DJ/2.75)	Scribner	1944	Shenton, Edward	30-50	
Kalashnikoff, N.	My Friend Yakub (1st, 8vo, 249p, fp b/w, DJ/2.75)	Scribner	(1953)	Rojankovsky, Feodor	30-50	
Kalashnikoff, N.	The Defender (1st, 8vo, 136p, tan cl, 8 fp b/w, DJ/2.00, NH)	Scribner	1951	Louden, C.& G.	60-90	
Kalashnikoff, N.	Toyon: Dog of the North (1st, 8vo, 246p, uncut, b/w, DJ/2.75)	Harper	(1950)	Marokvia, Artur	25-45	
Kalep, Elvy	Air Babies (1st, ob4to, [45]p, ibds, 22 fp color)	Denver: Bradford	(1936)	Kalep, Elvy	200-300	
Kalnay, Francis	Chucaro, Wild Pony of Pampa (1st {std}, 8vo, 126p, b/w, DJ/2.75, NH)	Harcourt	(1958)	DeMiskey, Julian	40-65	
Kalnay, Francis	Richest Boy in the World (1st {std}, 8vo, 92p, green cl, fp b/w, DJ/2.75)	Harcourt	(1959)	Mars, Witold T.	30-50	
Kalusky, Rebecca	Is it Blue as a Butterfly? (1st, 8vo, [30]p, color, cep, DJ/3.50)	Prentice-Hall	(1965)	Aliki	25-40	
Kane, Henry B.	Tale of a Wood (1st, lg8vo, 112p, fp b/w, pep, DJ/3.00, NYTBI)	Knopf	(1962)	(Photos)	20-35	*
Kane, Henry B.	Tale of the Whitefoot Mouse (1st, 8vo, [48]p, fp b/w, DJ/1.50)	Knopf	(1940)	(Photos)	30-50	*
Kantor, MacKinlay	Angleworms on Toast (1st, lg8vo, [32]p, color, ibds, DJ/1.50)	Coward	1942	Wiese, Kurt	60-100	
Kantor, MacKinley	Lobo (1st {std}, 8vo, 110p, bds, b/w, DJ/2.75)	World	(1957)	Layne, Irene	50-80	
Kantrowitz, Mildred	Maxie (1st, 8vo, [33]p fp color, DJ/3.50)	Parents Mag. Pr.	(1970)	McCully, Emily	50-85	
Kaplan, A.O.	Baby's Biography (1st, sm4to, AEG, 67p, gilt, color)	Brentano's	1891	Brundage, Frances	125-200	
Kapp, Paul (adap)	Cat Came Fiddling (1st {std}, sm sq4to, ibds, 80p, b/w, DJ/3.00)	Harcourt	(1956)	Haas, Irene	60-100	R
Karasz, Ilonka	Twelve Days of Christmas (1st, sm4to, [29]p, ibds, fp color, cep, DJ/1.50)	Harper	(1949)	Karasz, Ilonka	30-50	
Karazin, N.N.	Cranes Flying South (1st {std}, 8vo, 235p, blue cl, b/w, pep, DJ/2.50)	Doubleday/Doran	1931	Bock, Vera	30-50	
Kasdan, Sara	Love and Knishes (1st, 8vo, 191p, ipcb, b/w, DJ/3.50)	Vanguard Press	(1956)	Slobodkin, Louis	50-85	
Kasdan, Sara	Mazel Tov Y'All (1st, 8vo, 195p, b/w, DJ/4.95)	Vanguard Press	(1968)	Slobodkin, Louis	30-50	*
Kastner, Erich	Animal's Conference (1st AM, 4to, ibds, [62]p, color, DJ)	McKay	(1949)	Trier, Walter	120-180	
Kastner, Erich	Baron Munchausen (1st AM, sm4to, 68p, fp color, cep, DJ)	J. Messner	1957	Trier, Walter	50-75	
Kastner, Erich	Emil & the Detectives (1st AM {std}, 8vo, 224p, yellow cl, color)	Doubleday/Doran	1930	Trier, Walter	80-130	
Kastner, Erich	Emil & the Three Twins (1st UK, 8vo, 251p, ibds, 8 illus)	L: Cape	1935	Trier, Walter	80-125	
Kastner, Erich	Flying Classroom (1st UK, 8vo, 223p, ibds, 10 fp illus)	L: Cape	1934	Trier, Walter	75-100	
Kastner, Erich	Lisa and Lottie (1st AM {std}, 8vo, 137p, red cl, b/w, DJ/2.50)	Little/Brown	1951	Trier, Walter	35-50	
Kastner, Erich	Little Man (1st AM {std}, lg8vo, 183p, bds, b/w, DJ/3.95)	Knopf	(1966)	Schreiter, Rick	30-50	
Kastner, Erich	Puss in Boots (1st AM, 4to, ibds, 66p, fp color)	J. Messner	(1957)	Trier, Walter	60-90	
Kastner, Erich	The Simpletons (1st AM, 4to, 69p, fp color, cep, DJ)	J. Messner	1957	Lemke, Horst	35-50	
Kato, N. (tr.)	Children's Stories from Japanese Fairy Tales (1st, lg8vo, 134p, ibds, 10cp)	L: R. Tuck	[1918]	Theaker, Harry G.	100-170	
Kauffman, Reginald	Barbary Bo... (1st, 8vo, p-o, 261p, 5pl)	Penn	1929	Schoonover, Frank	30-60	
Kauffman, Reginald	Spanish Dollars (1st, 8vo, 299p, gilt, p-o, col frn, 7pl)	Penn	1925	Lee, Manning De V.	25-40	
Kauffman, Ruth	Three Little Kittens (12mo, blue cl, 63p, p-o, color, pep)	Platt/Munk	(1935)	Hoopes, Margaret	50-80	
Kaufmann, Alicia	No Room for Nicky (1st {std}, ob4to, [32]p, 2-color, DJ/3.95)	Hawthorn Books	(1969)	DeLarrea, Vicki	25-45	
Kay, Gertrude A.	Adventures in Geography (1st, 4to, 157p, orange cl, color, pep)	Volland	(1930)	Kay, Gertrude A.	45-75	
Kay, Gertrude A.	Adventures on our Street (1st, lg8vo, p-o, 130p, 4cp, pep)	McKay	(1925)	Kay, Gertrude A.	60-90	
Kay, Gertrude A.	Book of Seven Wishes (1st, 8vo, 224p, blue cl, 4cp, pep)	Moffat	1917	Kay, Gertrude A.	60-100	
Kay, Gertrude A.	Fairy Who Believed in Human Beings (1st, 8vo, 169p, 4cp)	Moffat	1918	Kay, Gertrude A.	80-120	
Kay, Gertrude A.	Friends of Jimmy (1st, lg8vo, ibds, [95]p, color, pep)	Volland	(1926)	Kay, Gertrude A.	60-100	
Kay, Gertrude A.	Helping the Weatherman (1st, 8vo, ibds, unpag, color, pep)	Volland	(1920)	Kay, Gertrude A.	60-95	
Kay, Gertrude A.	Jolly Old Shadow Man (1st, 12mo, ibds, [39]p, color, pep)	Volland	(1920)	Kay, Gertrude A.	70-100	
Kay, Gertrude A.	Peter, Patter & Pixie (1st, lg4to, ibds, 22p, 5cp)	McBride	1931	Kay, Gertrude A.	70-100	
Kay, Gertrude A.	Us Kids at the Circus (1st, 8vo, ibds, 120p, color, pep)	Volland	(1927)	Kay, Gertrude A.	70-100	*
Kay, Gertrude A.	When the Sandman Comes (1st, 8vo, 183p, p-o, pep, 4cp)	Moffat	1916	Kay, Gertrude A.	60-90	
Kay, Helen	City Springtime (1st, 4to, 48p, fp color, DJ/2.75)	Hastings House	(1957)	Cooney, Barbara	60-90	*
Kay, Helen	Magic Mitt (1st, sm4to, 54p, fp b/w, DJ/2.75)	Hastings House	(1959)	Hartman, C.L.	30-50	*
Kay, Helen	One Mitten Lewis (1st, 4to, ibds, [32]p, color, DJ/2.00)	Lothrop, Lee	(1955)	Werth, Kurt	50-80	
Kay, Helen	Snow Birthday (1st {std}, ob4to, 46p, fp color, DJ/2.50)	Ariel	(1955)	Cooney, Barbara	60-90	*
Kay, Mara	In Place of Katia (1st, 8vo, 224p, DJ/3.25)	Scribner	(1963)	Domanska, Janina	30-50	
Kaye, Mollie	Potter Pinner Meadow (1st, sq4to, [48]p, ibds, color)	L: Collins	1937	Tempest, Margaret	60-90	
Kaye, Mollie	Willow Witches Brook (1st, 12mo, ibds, 46p, color)	L: Collins	(1944)	Tempest, Margaret	60-85	
Kazin, Alfred	Walker in the City (1st {std}, 8vo, 176p, b/w, DJ/4.50)	Harcourt	(1951)	Bileck, Marvin	30-50	
Kearns, Frank	Rin Tin Tin (1st, [Cozy Corner Bk.], sq8vo, ipcb, [24]p, color, pep)	Whitman	1953	Armstrong, Samuel	30-50	
Keating, Norma	Mr. Chu (1st {std}, sm8vo, 34p, 3-color, DJ/3.75)	Macmillan	(1965)	Bryson, Bernarda	25-40	
Keats, Ezra J.	God is in the Mountain (1st {std}, ob8vo, [44]p, bds 1-color, pep, DJ/3.95)	Holt, Rinehart	(1966)	Keats, Ezra J.	40-65	
Keats, Ezra J.	Goggles (1st {std}, ob8vo, [32]p, color, pep, DJ/3.95, CH)	Macmillan	(1969)	Keats, Ezra J.	50-80	
Keats, Ezra J.	Hi, Cat! (1st {std}, sq8vo, [35]p, ibds, color, DJ/4.50)	Macmillan	(1970)	Keats, Ezra J.	50-80	
Keats, Ezra J.	Jennie's Hat (1st, lg ob8vo, unpag, color, DJ/3.95)	Harper	(1966)	Keats, Ezra J.	50-80	
Keats, Ezra J.	John Henry: American Legend (1st, 4to, [31]p, fp color, cep, DJ/3.50)	Pantheon	(1965)	Keats, Ezra J.	45-70	
Keats, Ezra J.	Letter to Amy (1st, ob8vo, [36]p, color, DJ/3.95)	Harper, Row	(1968)	Keats, Ezra J.	50-80	R
Keats, Ezra J.	My Dog is Lost! (1st, lg8vo, beige cl, [48]p, 1-color, DJ/2.75)	Crowell	(1960)	Keats, Ezra J.	35-50	
Keats, Ezra J.	Peter's Chair (1st, ob8vo, [33]p, color, DJ/3.95)	Harper	(1967)	Keats, Ezra J.	50-80	
Keats, Ezra J.	Snowy Day (1st, ob8vo, 32p, color, dep, DJ/3.00, CM)	Viking	(1962)	Keats, Ezra J.	80-140	R
Keats, Ezra J.	Whistle for Willie (1st, ob8vo, ibds, 33p, fp color, dep, DJ/3.50)	Viking	(1964)	Keats, Ezra J.	50-80	R
Keats, John	Isabella... (1st, 4to, teg, gilt, 8pl)	L: Kegan Paul	1898	MacDougall, W.B.	170-240	
Keats, John	Isabella... (1st, 12mo, 42p, gilt, uncut, 6 ticp)	L: Foulis	1907	King, Jessie	100-175	
Keats, John	Naughty Boy, a Poem (1st, 12mo, 31p, grey cl, 2-color, DJ/2.25)	Viking	(1965)	Keats, Ezra J.	40-65	
Keats, Mark	Sancho & Stubborn Mule (1st, ob12mo, ipcb, [41]p, 2-color, pep, DJ/1.00)	W.R. Scott	(1944)	Eichenberg, Fritz	40-65	

AUTHOR	TITLE	PUBLISHER	DATE	ARTIST	PRICE	LC

AUTHOR	TITLE	PUBLISHER	DATE	ARTIST	PRICE	LC
Keeler, David B.	Memoirs of Simple Simon (1st, 4to, [56]p, color)	R.H. Russell	(1901)	Vandevort, C.S.	250-400	
Keen, Ralph H.	Little Ape (1st [1st bk.], 8vo, yellow cl, 68p, 4pl & cvr by...)	L: Hendersons	(1921)	Austen, John	145-200	
Keeping, Charles	Alfie Finds Other Side of World (1st AM {std}, ob4to, [32]p, color, DJ/3.95)	F. Watts	(1968)	Keeping, Charles	40-65	*
Keeping, Charles	Charley, Charlotte & Golden Canary (1st, 4to, [32]p, ibds, color, DJ, KGM)	L: Oxford U.Pr.	1967	Keeping, Charles	100-150	
Keeping, Charles	Christmas Story (1st AM, 4to, [24]p, fp 2-color, DJ/3.95)	F. Watts	1968	Keeping, Charles	40-65	
Keeping, Charles	Joseph's Yard (1st AM {std}, 4to, [32]p, color, DJ/4.95)	F. Watts	1969	Keeping, Charles	40-70	
Keeping, Charles	Shaun & the Cart Horse (1st AM {std}, ob4to, [32]p, color, DJ/3.95)	F. Watts	(1966)	Keeping, Charles	40-65	
Keeping, Charles	Through the Window (1st AM {std}, ob4to, [32]p, color, DJ/4.95)	F. Watts	1970	Keeping, Charles	60-90	
Keeping, Charles	Tinker Tailor Folk Song Tales (1st AM {std}, 4to, [48]p, col, pep, DJ/4.50)	World	1969	Keeping, Charles	30-50	
Keeshan, Robert	She Loves Me, She Loves Me Not (1st, 24mo, unpag, ibds, color, DJ/1.95)	Harper	(1963)	Sendak, Maurice	200-300	
Keiro	Mephistopheles (8vo, 158p, green/gilt, 4pl)	L: Jarrold	(1907)	Wain, Louis	200-300	
Keiser, Melanie E.	God Returns to Vuelta Abajo (1st, lg8vo, 149p, rust/gilt, p-o, 1-color)	W.R. Scott	(1936)	Low, Joseph	80-120	R*
Keith, Eros	Rrra-ah (1st {std}, 4to, [32]p, color, DJ/4.95)	Bradbury Press	(1969)	Keith, Eros	30-50	*
Keith, Harold V.	Boy's Life of Will Rogers (1st, 8vo, 271p, pep, fp b/w, DJ/2.00)	Crowell	(1937)	Woerner, Karl	25-40	
Keith, Harold V.	Komantcia (1st, 8vo, 299p, b/w, DJ/3.95)	Crowell	(1965)	Keeping, Charles	20-35	
Keith, Harold V.	Pair of Captains (1st {std}, 8vo, 100p, b/w, DJ/2.50)	Crowell	(1951)	Woodbury, Mabel	25-40	*
Keith, Harold V.	Rifles for Watie (1st {std}, 8vo, 332p, DJ/3.75, NM)	Crowell	(1957)	No Illustrations	80-120	R
Keith, Harold V.	Shotgun Shaw: A Baseball Story (1st, 8vo, 163p, b/w, DJ/2.00)	Crowell	(1949)	Woodbury, Mabel	25-40	*
Keller, Frances	Contented Little Pussy Cat (1st, 4to, [52]p, ibds, color)	Platt/Munk	(1949)	Werber/Laslo	25-40	
Keller, Frances	Curious Little Owl (1st, sm4to, [48]p, ipcb, color, pep, DJ/1.50)	Platt/Munk	(1957)	Werber/Laslo	25-40	
Kellock, Harold	Down in the Grass (1st, 12mo, 247p, uncut, col frn, 25 fp b/w)	Coward	1929	Wiese, Kurt	70-100	
Kellogg, Steven	Wicked Kings of Bloon (1st, sq8vo, [32]p, fp color, cep, DJ/4.50)	Prentice-Hall	(1970)	Kellogg, Steven	50-85	
Kellogg, Vernon L.	Nuova or the New Bee (1st, 8vo, 150p, col frn, 14pl, pep)	Houghton	1920	Winter, Milo	45-75	
Kelly, Arthur	Rosebud and Other Tales (1st, sm4to, 78p, 20 ticp)	L: T.F. Unwin	1909	Crane, Walter	200-300	
Kelly, Eric P.	At the Sign of the Golden Compass (1st, 8vo, gilt, 195p, 11pl, pep, DJ/2.50)	Macmillan	1938	Lufkin, Raymond	25-45	
Kelly, Eric P.	Blacksmith of Vilno (1st, 8vo, 184p, green cl, 3cp)	Macmillan	1930	Pruszynska, Angela	35-60	*
Kelly, Eric P.	Christmas Nightingale (1st, 8vo, red cl, 73p, 4 b/w)	Macmillan	1932	DeAngeli, Marguerite	30-50	
Kelly, Eric P.	From Star to Star: Story of Krakow (1st {std}, 8vo, 239p, gilt, DJ/2.00)	Lippincott	(1944)	Lee, Manning De V.	25-45	
Kelly, Eric P.	Girl Who Would Be Queen (1st, lg8vo, 201p, DJ/2.00, decor by...)	McClurg	1939	Bock, Vera	50-80	
Kelly, Eric P.	Golden Star of Halich (1st, 8vo, green cl, 215p, 3cp, fp b/w)	Macmillan	1931	Pruszynska, Angela	40-60	*
Kelly, Eric P.	Hand in the Picture (1st {std}, 8vo, 241p, b/w, DJ/2.50)	Lippincott	(1947)	Lorentowicz, Irena	25-40	
Kelly, Eric P.	In Clean Hay (1st {std}, 8vo, ibds, 31p, color, cep, DJ/1.25)	Macmillan	1953	Petershams	40-65	
Kelly, Eric P.	On the Staked Plain (1st, 8vo, 250p, b/w, DJ/2.00)	Macmillan	1940	Stein, Harve	25-40	
Kelly, Eric P.	Three Sides of Agiochook (1st, 8vo, 211p, b/w, pep, DJ/2.00)	Macmillan	1935	Appleton, LeRoy	25-45	
Kelly, Eric P.	Treasure Mountain (1st, 8vo, 211p, green cl, pep, b/w, DJ/2.00)	Macmillan	1937	Lufkin, Raymond	25-45	
Kelly, Eric P.	Trumpeter of Krakow (1st, 8vo, 218p, blue cl, 3cp, DJ/2.50, NM)	Macmillan	1928	Pruszynska, Angela	80-125	
Kelly, Eric P.	Trumpeter of Krakow (1st [new ed. std], lg8vo, 208p, b/w, DJ/3.95)	Macmillan	(1966)	Domanska, Janina	20-35	
Kelly, Ethel M.	When I was Little (1st, 8vo, p-o, 96p, fp color)	Rand/McNally	(1915)	Squire, Maud H.	60-90	
Kelly, Florence	Delafield Affair (1st, sm8vo, ibds, 422p, 4cp)	McClurg	1909	Dixon, Maynard	40-60	
Kelly, James P.	Prince Izon (1st, 8vo, 399p, brown cl, p-o, 5cp, pep)	McClurg	1910	Betts, H.& E.	50-80	
Kelly, R. Talbot	Egypt (1st, 8vo, gilt, teg, 246p, 75cp)	L: A&C Black	1902	Kelly, Robert G.T.	100-165	
Kelman, Janet H.	Stories from Chaucer (1st, 12mo, 114p, p-o, 8cp)	L: Jack	[1906]	Robinson, W. Heath	140-225	
Kelsey, Alice	I Give You my Colt (1st {std}, 8vo, 160p, b/w, DJ/2.75)	Longmans	1956	Torrey, Helen	25-40	
Kelsey, Alice	Once the Hodja (1st {std}, 12mo, 170p, b/w, pep, DJ/2.00)	Longmans	1943	Dobias, Frank	30-50	
Kelsey, Vera	Maria Rosa (1st {std}, lg ob4to, [38]p, fp color, pep, DJ/2.00)	Doubleday/Doran	1942	Portinari, Candido	60-100	
Kemble, Edward W.	Comical Coons (1st, ob4to, unpag, ibds, b/w)	R.H. Russell	1898	Kemble, Edward W.	300-450	
Kemble, Edward W.	Coon Alphabet (1st, sm4to, ibds, unpag, b/w)	R.H. Russell	1898	Kemble, Edward W.	450-650	
Kemble, Edward W.	Coontown's 400 (1st, 4to, [63]p, cloth, fp b/w)	NY: Life Pub.	1899	Kemble, Edward W.	350-500	
Kemble, Edward W.	Kemble's Coons (1st, lg ob4to, ibds, 31p, b/w)	R.H. Russell	1896	Kemble, Edward W.	400-600	
Kemble, Edward W.	Kemble's Pickaninnies (1st, lg ob4to, 31pl, b/w)	R.H. Russell	1901	Kemble, Edward W.	400-600	
Kemble, Edward W.	Kemble's Sketch Book (1st, lg ob8vo, tan buckram, 30pl)	R.H. Russell	1899	Kemble, Edward W.	250-400	
Kemble, Edward W.	Life's Book of Animals (1st, ob4to, 80p, buckram, b/w)	Doub./McClure	1898	Various	90-120	
Kemble, Edward W.	The Blackberries... (1st, lg ob4to, ibds, [36]p, 16cp)	R.H. Russell	1897	Kemble, Edward W.	500-800	
Kempis, Thomas	Imitation of Christ (1st, sm4to, 280p, teg, gilt, 274p, 8cp)	L: Chatto	1908	Flint, William R.	100-170	
Kempner, Carol	Nicholas (1st {std}, 4to, [25]p, fp color, DJ/4.50)	Simon/Schuster	(1968)	Kempner, Carol	30-50	*
Kempson, Frederick C.	Sad End of Erica's Blackamoor (1st, ob folio, ibds, 39p, b/w)	L: E. Arnold	1903	Kempson, F.C.	200-300	
Kempton, Kenneth P.	Dragon's Thunder (1st, 8vo, 239p, col frn, b/w, pep)	Little/Brown	1931	Jones, Wilfred	20-35	
Kempton, Kenneth P.	Loot of the Flying Dragon (1st, 8vo, 269p, col frn, b/w, pep)	Little/Brown	1930	Jones, Wilfred	25-45	
Kendall, Carol S.	Big Splash (1st, 8vo, 217p, b/w, DJ/3.00)	Viking	(1960)	Obligado, Lilian	30-50	
Kendall, Carol S.	Gammage Cup (1st {std}, 8vo, 221p, blue cl, b/w, DJ/3.25, NH)	Harcourt	(1959)	Blegvad, Erik	40-65	
Kendall, Carol S.	Other Side of the Tunnel (1st, 8vo, 192p, b/w, DJ/2.75)	Abelard-Schuman	(1957)	Buchanan, Lilian	30-50	
Kendall, Carol S.	Whisper of Glocken (1st {std}, 8vo, 256p, yellow cl, b/w, DJ/3.50)	Harcourt	(1965)	Gobbato, Imero	40-65	R*
Kendall, Lace	Little Smoke (1st, lg8vo, unpag, ibds, b/w, DJ/2.75)	Coward	(1961)	Savitt, Sam	25-45	
Kennan, George	Tragedy of Pelee (1st, 8vo, 257p, teg, gilt, 7pl)	Outlook	1902	Varian, George	50-80	
Kennedy, Howard A.	New World Fairy Book (1st, 8vo, 354p, gilt, teg, uncut, 9pl)	L: Dent	1904	Millar, H.R.	80-120	*
Kennedy, Mary	Jenny (1st, 8vo, 153p, green cl, 11 fp b/w, DJ/2.50)	Lothrop, Lee	(1954)	Adams, Adrienne	30-55	
Kennedy, Mary	Surprise to the Children (1st {std}, sm sq4to, 88p, ibds, 6cp)	Doubleday/Doran	1933	Dowd, James H.	50-85	
Kennedy, Mary	Violets are Blue (1st, 8vo, 154p, blue cl, fp b/w, DJ/2.00)	Lothrop, Lee	(1951)	Stone, Helen	25-45	
Kennedy, Mildred	Forest Beyond the Woodlands (1st, 8vo, 152p, pcb, 14pl)	Knopf	1921	Knowlton, Vianna	80-120	
Kennell, Ruth E.	Vanya of the Streets (1st {std}, 8vo, 208p, uncut, b/w, pep, DJ/2.00)	Harper	1931	Perts, Michael	70-125	
Kenny, Herbert A.	Dear Dolphin (1st {std}, 8vo, 174p, blue cl, b/w, DJ/3.95)	Random	(1967)	Oechsli, Kelly	30-45	
Kent, Kathleen	Daddy Long-Legs (1st, 4to, [30]p, ibds, 6cp, pep)	L: Gale/Polden	[1917]	Cowham, Hilda	90-140	
Kent, Louise A.	Brookline Trunk (1st, 8vo, 306p, b/w, pep, DJ/3.00)	Houghton	1955	Cooney, Barbara	60-100	
Kent, Louise A.	Douglas of Porcupine (1st, 8vo, 320p, col frn, pep)	Houghton	1931	Grose, Helen M.	25-45	*
Kent, Louise A.	Red Rajah (1st, sm8vo, 290p, blue cl, 6 fp b/w, pep)	Houghton	1933	Wiese, Kurt	30-50	*
Kent, Louise A.	Two Children of Tyre (1st, 8vo, 233p, col frn, b/w, pep)	Houghton	1932	Wolcott, Elizabeth	20-35	
Kent, Rockwell	It's Me O Lord... (1st, lg8vo, gilt, 617p, color, DJ/10.00)	Dodd	(1955)	Kent, Rockwell	70-125	
Kent, Rockwell	N by E (1st, 8vo, white cl, 281p, b/w, DJ/3.50)	Brewer/Warren	1930	Kent, Rockwell	90-120	

AUTHOR	TITLE	PUBLISHER	DATE	ARTIST	PRICE	LC
Kent, Rockwell	Northern Christmas (1st, 12mo, [32]p, ipcb, 1-color, DJ/0.50)	A.A. Group	(1941)	Kent, Rockwell	50-75	
Kent, Rockwell	On Earth Peace... (1st, 16mo, [24]p, ibds, 1-color)	A.A. Group	(1942)	Kent, Rockwell	40-60	
Kent, Rockwell	Rockwellkentiana (1st {std}, 4to, 64p, col frn, blue cl, DJ/3.75)	Harcourt	1933	Kent, Rockwell	90-120	
Kent, Rockwell	Salamina (1st {std}, 8vo, blue/silver, 336p, 23pl, DJ/3.75)	Harcourt	1935	Kent, Rockwell	100-170	R
Kent, Rockwell	This is my Own (1st {std}, lg8vo, cream cl, 393p, fp b/w, DJ/3.50)	Duell, Sloan	(1940)	Kent, Rockwell	120-180	
Kent, Rockwell	Voyaging: Southward... (1st, 4to, yellow cl, teg, 184p, b/w, pep)	Putnam	1924	Kent, Rockwell	120-200	
Kent, Rockwell	Wilderness (1st, 4to, teg, 217p, grey/gilt, b/w, pep)	Putnam	1920	Kent, Rockwell	125-200	
Kenward, James	Suburban Child (1st, 8vo, 140p, white ipcb, 11 b/w, DJ)	L: Cambridge	1955	Ardizzone, Edward	50-80	
Kenyon, Charles R.	Argonauts of the Amazon (1st, 8vo, blue/gilt, 305p, 6pl)	L: Chambers	1901	Rackham, Arthur	200-300	
Kepes, Juliet A.	Birds (1st, 4to, [53]p, b/w, DJ/4.95, NYTBI)	NY: Walker	1968	Kepes, Juliet A.	40-65	
Kepes, Juliet A.	Five Little Monkeys (1st {1st bk}, sm4to, 32p, col, pep, DJ/2.50, CH, NYT)	Houghton	1952	Kepes, Juliet A.	70-100	
Kepes, Juliet A.	Frogs Merry (1st, lg ob8vo, [32]p, color, DJ/2.95)	Pantheon	(1961)	Kepes, Juliet A.	25-40	
Kepes, Juliet A.	Lady Bird, Quickly (1st {std}, lg ob8vo, 47p, color, DJ/3.00)	Little/Brown	(1964)	Kepes, Juliet A.	25-40	
Kepes, Juliet A.	Seed that Peacock Planted (1st {std}, lg8vo, 38p, color, DJ/3.50)	Little/Brown	(1967)	Kepes, Juliet A.	25-40	
Kepes, Juliet A.	Two Little Birds & Three (1st, lg8vo, 62p, fp 1-color, DJ/2.50, NYTBI)	Houghton	1960	Kepes, Juliet A.	75-125	R*
Kerina, Jane	African Crafts (1st, 4to, 64p, 1-color)	Lion Press	(1970)	Feelings, Tom	45-70	*
Kernahan, John C.	Bow-Wow Book (1st, 4to, 84p, ipcb, b/w pl)	L: J. Nesbit	1912	Wood, Lawson	60-90	
Kerr, Estelle	Little Sam in Volendam (1st, lg8vo, 32p)	Moffat	1908	Kerr, Estelle	80-120	
Kessel, Joseph	The Lion (1st {illus ed. std}, 4to, 186p, fp color, DJ/3.95)	Knopf	(1962)	Johnson, Harper	20-30	
Kesselman, Wendy	Franz Tovey & the Rare Animals (1st {std}, 4to, [32]p, b/w, cep, DJ/3.25)	Harlin Quist	(1968)	Schmid, Eleonore	40-65	
Kessler, Ethel	All Aboard the Train (1st {std}, ob4to, [46]p, color, DJ/2.95)	Doubleday	1964	Kessler, Leonard	20-30	
Kessler, Ethel	Are You Square? (1st {std}, ob4to, [40]p, ipcb, color, pep, DJ/3.50)	Doubleday	1966	Kessler, Leonard	30-50	
Kessler, Ethel	Big Red Bus (1st {std}, ob4to, [32]p, ibds, 2-color, DJ/2.00, NYTBI)	Doubleday	1957	Kessler, Leonard	60-90	
Kessler, Ethel	Crunch, Crunch (1st {std}, sq8vo, unpag, color, DJ/1.50)	Doubleday	1955	Kessler, Leonard	30-50	
Kessler, Ethel	Day Daddy Stayed Home (1st {std}, lg8vo, [32]p, color, DJ/2.00)	Doubleday	1959	Kessler, Leonard	25-45	
Kessler, Ethel	Do Baby Bears Sit in Chairs? (1st {std}, sm4to, 32p, ibds, color, DJ/2.50)	Doubleday	1961	Kessler, E.& L.	30-45	
Kessler, Ethel	I Have Twenty Teeth - Do You? (1st, ob12mo, unpag, DJ/1.95)	Dodd	1959	Kessler, Leonard	30-45	*
Kessler, Ethel	Kim and Me (1st {std}, ob8vo, ipcb, [29]p, fp 2-color, pep, DJ/2.00)	Doubleday	1960	Kessler, Leonard	30-50	
Kessler, Ethel	Peek-a-Boo (1st {std}, lg8vo, [32]p, ipcb, 3-color, pep, DJ/2.00)	Doubleday	1956	Kessler, Leonard	30-50	
Kessler, Ethel	Plink, Plink! (1st {std}, ob8vo, ipcb, [29]p, 3-color, pep, DJ/1.50)	Doubleday	1954	Kessler, Leonard	25-45	
Kessler, Leonard	Kick, Pass & Run (1st, 8vo, 64p, 2-color, DJ/1.95)	Harper	1966	Kessler, Leonard	25-40	
Ketchum, Jean	Stick-in-the-Mud (1st, sm8vo, unpag, green cl, pep, 1-color, DJ/1.50, JABA)	W.R. Scott	(1953)	Ketchum, Fred	30-50	
Keto, Emma	Ting-Ling and Mee-Too (1st, 8vo, ipcb, [37]p, color, pep, DJ/0.50)	Grosset/Dunlap	1937	Keto, Emma	30-50	
Keto, Emma	Tonto and Pronto (1st, 8vo, [32]p, ipcb, color, pep, DJ/0.50)	Grosset/Dunlap	(1938)	Keto, Emma	30-50	*
Key, Alexander	Red Eagle (1st, 4to, 95p, ibds, pep, color)	Volland	(1930)	Key, Alexander	40-70	
Key, Alexander	With Daniel Boone on Carolina Trail (1st, 8vo, 223p, gilt, 1-color, DJ/2.00)	Winston	(1941)	Key, Alexander	25-40	
Key, Ted	Biggest Dog in the World (1st {std}, 8vo, 72p, fp b/w, pep, DJ/2.50)	Dutton	(1960)	Key, Ted	20-30	
Keyes, Angela M.	Five Senses (1st, 8vo, ivory cl, 252p, 5cp)	Moffat	1911	Smith, Jessie W.	280-400	
Keys, Leonora	Happy Dollies (lg8vo, [46]p, color)	Whitman	(1914)	Lee, Ella D.	90-120	
Keys, Leonora	Play Dollies (sm4to, 38p, ibds, color)	Whitman	(1927)	Lee, Ella D.	90-120	*
Kidd, Dudley	Bull of the Kraal (1st, 8vo, 302p, gilt, teg, uncut, 12cp)	L: A&C Black	1908	Goodall, Agnes M.	80-130	
Kidd, Will	Dickydidos (1st, folio, 94p, ibds, 22cp)	L: Richards	[1903]	Kidd, Will	300-450	*
Kilbourne, Charles E.	Baby Elephant & Zoo Man (1st, 8vo, p-o, color, pep)	Penn	1911	Longstreet, Hattie	90-150	*
Kilbourne, Charles E.	Baby Ostrich & Mr. Wise Owl (1st, 16mo, ipcb, p-o, 82p, color, pep)	Penn	1915	Longstreet, Hattie	100-160	R*
Kilbourne, Charles E.	Baby Reindeer & Silver Fox (1st, 16mo, ipcb, p-o, 82p, color, pep)	Penn	1916	Longstreet, Hattie	100-165	R
Killilea, Marie	Treasure on the Hill (1st, lg8vo, gilt, 155p, fp b/w, DJ/3.50)	Dodd	1960	Ford, Lauren	30-50	
Killilea, Marie	Wren (1st, lg8vo, 118p, b/w, DJ/3.00)	Dodd	(1954)	Riger, Bob	30-50	
Kilmer, Joyce	Trees (1st, 8vo, [24]p, ipcb, color, DJ)	Doran	(1925)	MacKinstry, Eliz.	60-100	
Kilvert, Cory	Kite Book (1st, 4to, [36]p, ipcb, p-o, fp color)	Dodd	1909	Kilvert, Cory	120-180	
Kim, Yong-Ik	Blue in the Seed (1st {std}, 8vo, 117p, b/w, DJ/3.95)	Little/Brown	(1964)	Marokvia, Artur	25-40	*
Kincaid, Charles A.	Deccan Nursery Tales (1st, 8vo, 135p, 8cp)	L: Macmillan	1914	Dhurandhar, M.V.	50-85	
Kinert, Reed	Little Helicopter (1st, sm8vo, [40]p, ipcb, color)	Macmillan	1947	Kinert, Reed	25-45	
King, Alexander	Great Ker-Plunk (1st {std}, ob4to, [48]p, fp 2-color, pep, DJ/2.95)	Simon/Schuster	1962	King, Robin	40-65	*
King, Alexander	Memoirs of a Certain Mouse (1st, lg8vo, 92p, fp b/w, pep, DJ/2.95)	McGraw-Hill	(1966)	Erdoes, Richard	30-50	*
King, Ben	Ben King's Southland Melodies (1st, 8vo, green cl, 128p, b/w)	Chi: Forbes	1911	(Photos)	150-220	
King, Ben	Jane Jones and Some Others (1st, 8vo, green/gilt, 94p, 16cp)	Chi: Forbes	1909	Williams, John A.	80-120	
King, Beulah	Ruffs & Pompons (1st, 8vo, 256p, col frn, 6pl, pep)	Little/Brown	1924	Day, Maurice	30-50	
King, Charles	Apache Princess (1st, 12mo, 328p, p-o, teg, 8pl)	Hobart	1903	Deming/Remington	80-140	
King, Charles	Apache Princess (1st, 12mo, 328p, p-o, teg, 8pl)	Hobart	1903	Remington/Deming	80-140	
King, Charles	Cadet Days (1st, 12mo, 293p, blue/gilt, 25pl, PPP)	Harper	1894	Zogbaum, Rufus F.	100-175	
King, Charles	Daughter of the Sioux (1st, sm8vo, 306p, teg, p-o, 4pl)	Hobart	1903	Remington, Frederic	60-90	
King, Charles	From School to Battlefield (1st, 8vo, beige/gilt, 322p, 6pl)	Lippincott	1899	Oakley, Violet	50-85	
King, Charles	Medal of Honor (1st, 12mo, p-o, teg, 348p, 3pl by...)	Hobart	1905	Deming, Edwin W.	35-60	*
King, Charles	To the Front (1st, sm8vo, ibds, 260p, 4pl)	Harper	1908	Remington, Frederic	70-100	*
King, Charles	Tonio, Son of Sierras (1st, 12mo, 338p, 4cp, 4pl)	Dillingham	(1906)	Post, Charles J.	30-50	
King, Edith H.	Adventures in Toyland (1st, 4to, blue/gilt, AEG, 152p, 8cp)	L: Blackie	[1897]	Woodward, Alice B.	170-240	
King, Elizabeth	New House that Jack Built (1st, 4to, ibds, [31]p, color, pep)	McBride	1932	Dennis, Alice	45-70	
King, Gordon (ed)	Herodotus (1st {std}, 8vo, buckram, 274p, 14pl, map, pep, DJ/2.50)	Doubleday/Doran	1929	Artzybasheff, Boris	75-100	
King, Jessie M.	Budding Life (1st, 8vo, unpag, wraps, 15pl)	L: Gowans/Gray	[1906]	King, Jessie	350-500	
King, Jessie M.	Dwellings of an Old World Town (8vo, 51p, wraps, 24 b/w)	L: Gowans/Gray	1909	King, Jessie	200-300	
King, Jessie M.	Glasgow: City of the West (1st, 8vo, wraps, [27]p, 24 ticp)	L: Foulis	1910	King, Jessie	150-250	
King, Jessie M.	Grey City of the North (1st, 8vo, 51p, wraps, 26pl)	L: Foulis	(1910)	King, Jessie	150-250	
King, Jessie M.	How Cinderella Was Able to Go to the Ball (1st, 8vo ibds, 57p teg, 16 ticp)	L: Foulis	(1924)	King, Jessie	600-800	
King, Jessie M.	Legends of Flowers (1st, sm8vo, gilt, teg, p-o, 168p, cvr & b/w by...)	L: Foulis	1908	King, Jessie	150-225	
King, Jessie M.	Little White Town of Never Weary (1st, 4to, 155p, 4 ticp, 16pl, cep)	L: Harrap	(1917)	King, Jessie	700-900	
King, Julius	Odie Seeks a Friend (1st, ob8vo, [32]p, ibds, b/w, pep)	Coward	(1934)	Wiese, Kurt	40-70	
King, Marian	Amnon, Lad of Palestine (1st, sm8vo, 96p, color, pep)	Houghton	1931	Enright, Elizabeth	40-65	
King, Marian	Kees (1st {std}, 4to, 79p, ibds, color, pep)	Harper	1930	Enright, Elizabeth	60-85	

AUTHOR	TITLE	PUBLISHER	DATE	ARTIST	PRICE	LC
King, Marian	Kees & Kleintje (1st, 4to, 80p, p-o, color, pep)	Whitman	(1934)	Enright, Elizabeth	50-80	
King, Marian	Piccolino (1st, 8vo, 32p, p-o, color, pep, DJ/1.00)	Whitman	1939	Smock, Nell S.	25-45	
King, Marian	Sean & Sheela (1st, lg8vo, p-o, 135p, dp color, pep, DJ/2.00)	Whitman	1937	Brock, Emma	30-50	
Kinglake, A.W.	Eothen (1st, 12mo, 305p, teg, uncut, blue cl, b/w)	L: Newnes	1898	Millar, H.R.	70-100	
Kinglake, A.W.	Eothen (1st AM, sm4to, 30p, teg, 12cp)	Lippincott	[1913]	Brangwyn, Frank	100-170	
Kingman, Lee	Best Christmas (1st {std}, sm8vo, 95p, b/w, cep, DJ/1.50)	Doubleday	(1949)	Cooney, Barbara	60-90	
Kingman, Lee	Flivver, the Heroic Horse (1st {std}, lg8vo, 75p, b/w, pep, DJ/2.50)	Doubleday	1958	Blegvad, Erik	30-45	
Kingman, Lee	Ilenka (1st, 4to, red cl, [48]p, color, pep, DJ/2.00)	Houghton/JLG	1945	Bare, Arnold E.	45-70	
Kingman, Lee	Magic Christmas Tree (1st {std}, lg8vo, 48p, color, pep, DJ/2.75)	Ariel	(1956)	Bettina	30-45	
Kingman, Lee	Mikko's Fortune (1st {std}, sm ob4to, blue cl, 46p, color, pep, DJ/2.75)	Ariel	(1955)	Bare, Arnold E.	50-80	
Kingman, Lee	Peter's Long Walk (1st {std}, sm ob4to, 47p, ibds, color, DJ/2.50)	Doubleday	1953	Cooney, Barbara	65-100	R
Kingman, Lee	Philippe's Hill (1st {std}, 8vo, 86p, b/w, DJ/2.00)	Doubleday	1950	Woodward, Hildegarde	30-45	*
Kingman, Lee	Pierre Pidgeon (1st, 4to, [48]p, color, DJ/2.00, CH)	Houghton	1943	Bare, Arnold E.	70-120	
Kingman, Lee	Quarry Adventure (1st {std}, 8vo, 209p, b/w, DJ/2.50)	Doubleday	1951	Cooney, Barbara	50-80	
Kingman, Lee	Rocky Summer (1st, 8vo, 209p, blue cl, b/w, DJ/2.50)	Houghton	1948	Cooney, Barbara	50-80	
Kingman, Lee	Secret Journey of the Silver Reindeer (1st {std}, 8vo, 93p, color, DJ/3.50)	Doubleday	(1968)	Ward, Lynd	30-45	
Kingman, Lee	Sheep Ahoy! (1st, 8vo, 68p, fp b/w, pep, DJ/2.75)	Houghton	1963	Weil, Lisl	25-45	
Kingsbury, Helen O.	All Aboard for Wonderland (1st, 4to, 190p, 4cp)	Moffat	1917	Kay, Gertrude A.	80-125	
Kingsley, Charles	Hereward the Wake (1st, 8vo, 196p, pcb, p-o, 8cp)	L: Jack	[1910]	Orr, Monro S.	75-100	*
Kingsley, Charles	Heroes/Greek Fairy Tales (1st, 8vo, 166p, 9 ticp)	L: Medici	1928	Flint, William R.	100-165	
Kingsley, Charles	The Heroes (1st, sm4to, blue cl, 186p, uncut, 24cp)	R.H. Russell	1901	Mars/Squire	200-285	R*
Kingsley, Charles	The Heroes (1st, 8vo, blue/gilt, AEG, 296p, 6cp, pep)	L: Nister	[1903]	Robinson, Thomas H.	80-120	
Kingsley, Charles	The Heroes (12mo, grey cl, p-o, 157p, 4cp, dep)	L: Blackie	[1907]	Dixon, Arthur A.	55-80	
Kingsley, Charles	The Heroes (1st, 8vo, 166p, uncut, gilt, teg, 12 ticp)	L: P.L. Warner	1914	Flint, William R.	80-125	
Kingsley, Charles	The Heroes (1st, 8vo, 221p, 8cp)	L: A&C Black	1915	Tawse, Sybil	40-70	
Kingsley, Charles	The Heroes (sm4to, 6cp, pep)	Doran	[1920]	Soper, George	40-60	
Kingsley, Charles	The Heroes (1st, 8vo, 212p, 16cp)	L: Macmillan	1928	Brock, Henry M.	60-90	*
Kingsley, Charles	The Heroes (1st, 8vo, 196p, fp 1-color, pep, DJ/2.00)	Macmillan	(1954)	Bock, Vera	30-50	R
Kingsley, Charles	Theseus (1st {std}, folio, ibds, 46p, color, DJ/2.95)	Macmillan	1964	Castellon, Federico	40-70	
Kingsley, Charles	Water Babies (1st, 8vo, 371p, blue/gilt, AEG, b/w, cep)	L: Macmillan	1885	Sambourne, Linley	120-200	
Kingsley, Charles	Water Babies (1st, sm8vo, 308p, gilt, b/w)	Stokes	1891	Gordon, Frederic C.	100-165	
Kingsley, Charles	Water Babies (1st [new ed.], 8vo, blue/gilt, 330p, b/w)	L: Macmillan	1894	Sambourne, Linley	90-125	
Kingsley, Charles	Water Babies (1st, 12mo, blue/gilt, teg, 295p, b/w)	Rand/McNally	(1900)	Phillips, Mary E.	40-65	
Kingsley, Charles	Water Babies (1st, lg8vo, 231p, 8cp, pep)	Wessels	1900	Wright, George	70-100	
Kingsley, Charles	Water Babies (1st, 8vo, 104p, b/w)	Saalfield	(1905)	Williams, Carll B.	35-60	*
Kingsley, Charles	Water Babies (1st, 24mo, 117p, green cl, uncut, 8 ticp)	Jack/Dutton	[1906]	Cameron, Katharine	40-60	*
Kingsley, Charles	Water Babies (1st, 8vo, green/gilt, AEG, 336p, 6cp)	Nister/Dutton	[1908]	Dixon, Arthur A.	200-300	
Kingsley, Charles	Water Babies (1st, 8vo, 284p, uncut, p-o, teg, 12cp, pep)	L: Dent	1908	Tarrant, Margaret	80-120	
Kingsley, Charles	Water Babies (1st, 4to, AEG, green/gilt, 32 ticp)	L: Macmillan	1909	Goble, Warwick	300-500	
Kingsley, Charles	Water Babies (1st, 12mo, red/gilt, 256p, 4cp)	L: Blackie	1909	Woodward, Alice B.	60-90	*
Kingsley, Charles	Water Babies (1st {this format}, 8vo, teg, 273p, gilt, 16cp)	L: Macmillan	1910	Goble, Warwick	180-250	
Kingsley, Charles	Water Babies (lg8vo, teg, 4cp)	Baker/Taylor	(1910)	Soper, George	40-60	
Kingsley, Charles	Water Babies (1st AM, 4to, gilt, uncut, p-o, teg, 246p, 8 ticp)	Stokes	[1911]	Cameron, Katharine	100-170	
Kingsley, Charles	Water Babies (1st, 12mo, 208p, b/w)	D.C. Heath	(1914)	Babbitt/Blossom	35-60	*
Kingsley, Charles	Water Babies (1st AM, 8vo, green cl, p-o, 320p, 8cp)	Houghton	(1915)	Robinson, W. Heath	300-500	
Kingsley, Charles	Water Babies (1st, 8vo, 319p, green/gilt, 8cp)	L: Constable	1915	Robinson, W. Heath	400-600	
Kingsley, Charles	Water Babies (1st, sm4to, 115p, red cl, 12cp, pep)	L: R. Tuck	[1916]	Attwell, Mabel L.	300-450	
Kingsley, Charles	Water Babies (1st {this format}, 12mo, gilt, 270p, p-o, 8cp, pep)	Dodd	1916	Smith, Jessie W.	140-225	*
Kingsley, Charles	Water Babies (1st, sm4to, p-o, teg, gilt, 362p, 12cp, pep)	Dodd	(1916)	Smith, Jessie W.	400-600	
Kingsley, Charles	Water Babies (1st, 8vo, 340p, grey cl, p-o, 48cp, pep)	L: Ward Lock	1916	Theaker, Harry G.	120-180	
Kingsley, Charles	Water Babies (1st, 12mo, 280p, b/w)	Ginn & Co.	(1916)	Young, Florence L.	30-50	*
Kingsley, Charles	Water Babies (1st, 8vo, teg, 316p, 8cp, pep)	Lippincott	1917	Kirk, Maria L.	80-120	
Kingsley, Charles	Water Babies (1st UK, 4to, 240p, gilt, 12 ticp)	L: Boots	[1918]	Smith, Jessie W.	280-350	
Kingsley, Charles	Water Babies (1st, 4to, teg, blue/gilt, 252p, pep, 16 ticp)	L: Oxford U.Pr.	[1920]	Jackson, A.E.	200-300	
Kingsley, Charles	Water Babies (1st AM, lg8vo, blue/gilt, p-o, 180p, 12cp, pep)	Nelson	[1924]	Anderson, Anne	150-220	
Kingsley, Charles	Water Babies (1st, lg8vo, yellow cl, p-o, 12cp)	L: Jack	(1924)	Anderson, Anne	200-300	
Kingsley, Charles	Water Babies (1st, 8vo, 282p, p-o, 8cp)	Winston	(1930)	Everett, Ethel	70-120	
Kingsley, Charles	Water Babies (1st, 4to, ibds, 125p, col frn, 1-color)	L: Collins	1936	Disney Studios	250-400	
Kingsley, Charles	Water Babies (1st, 4to, 56p, color, pep, DJ/2.50)	Duell, Sloan	(1946)	Collison, Marjory	30-50	
Kingsley, Charles	Westward Ho! (16mo, blue/gilt, 2 volumes, teg, uncut, b/w)	L: Macmillan	1896	Brock, Charles E.	60-90	
Kingsley, Charles	Westward Ho! (12mo, 589p, 15pl)	L: J. Long	1904	Copping, Harold	55-80	*
Kingsley, Charles	Westward Ho! (1st, lg8vo, 604p, p-o, 14cp, pep)	Jacobs	[1920]	Oakley, Thornton	70-100	
Kingsley, Charles	Westward Ho! (1st, lg8vo, 413p, gilt, p-o, 14cp, pep, SC)	Scribner	1920	Wyeth, N.C.	180-270	
Kingsley, Charles	Westward Ho! (1st, 12mo, 342p, col frn, b/w)	Macmillan	1930	Pitz, Henry C.	40-60	*
Kingsley, Florence M.	Glass House (1st, sm8vo, 312p, 4pl)	Dodd	1909	Stephens, Alice B.	30-50	*
Kingsley, Florence M.	Those Brewster Children (1st, 12mo, tan cl, 214p, 3pl)	Dodd	1910	Chamberlin, E.H.	25-40	*
Kingsley, Florence M.	Transfiguration of Miss Philura (1st, 16mo, 81p, beige cl, cvr by....)	Funk/Wagnalls	(1901)	Armstrong, Margaret	40-60	
Kinney, T.& M.	Dance: Its Place in Art & Life (1st, lg8vo, gilt, 334p, col frn, b/w)	Stokes	1914	Kinneys	50-80	
Kinsey, Elizabeth	This Cat Came to Stay (1st {std}, sm8vo, 157p, b/w, pep, DJ/2.50)	F. Watts	(1955)	Sibley, Don	70-100	*
Kipling, Rudyard	All the Mowgli Stories (1st {std} 8vo, 299p, col frn 9 fp b/w, pep, DJ/2.50)	Doubleday/Doran	1936	Wiese, Kurt	30-50	
Kipling, Rudyard	Almanac of 12 Sports (1st AM, 4to, [30]p, ipcb, 12cp)	R.H. Russell	1898	Nicholson, Wm.	400-650	
Kipling, Rudyard	Almanac of 12 Sports (1st, 4to, [30]p, ibds, 12cp)	L: Heinemann	1898	Nicholson, Wm.	400-650	
Kipling, Rudyard	Brushwood Boy (1st, 8vo, blue/gilt, teg, uncut, 119p, b/w, pep)	Doub./McClure	1899	Lowell, Orson	120-180	
Kipling, Rudyard	Brushwood Boy (1st, 8vo, 91p, grey/gilt, teg, 12cp)	L: Macmillan	1907	Townsend, F.H.	70-100	
Kipling, Rudyard	Brushwood Boy (1st AM, 8vo, 73p, gilt, p-o, teg, 12cp)	Doubleday/Page	1907	Townsend, F.H.	60-100	
Kipling, Rudyard	Butterfly that Stamped (1st, 8vo, [28]p, ibds, color, pep)	Garden City	(1947)	Rojankovsky, Feodor	25-45	
Kipling, Rudyard	Captains Courageous (1st, sm8vo, 245p, blue/gilt, AEG, fp b/w)	L: Macmillan	1897	Taber, I.W.	500-700	
Kipling, Rudyard	Captains Courageous (1st AM, 8vo, green/gilt, 323p, teg, 21pl)	Century	1897	Taber, I.W.	400-600	

AUTHOR: 120

AUTHOR	TITLE	PUBLISHER	DATE	ARTIST	PRICE	LC
Kipling, Rudyard	Collected Verse of... (1st, sm4to, red/gilt, 392p, teg, 17 ticp)	Doubleday/Page	1910	Robinson, W. Heath	200-300	
Kipling, Rudyard	Dead King (1st, 8vo, 48p, grey/gilt, designs by...)	L: Hodder	(1910)	Robinson, W. Heath	140-225	
Kipling, Rudyard	East of Suez (1st, 4to, 72p, blue/gilt, 10cp)	L: Macmillan	1931	Maxwell, Donald	90-120	
Kipling, Rudyard	Elephant's Child (1st, lg8vo, ibds, [28]p, color, DJ/0.50)	Garden City	(1942)	Rojankovsky, Feodor	30-50	
Kipling, Rudyard	Elephant's Child (1st {std}, ob4to, 48p, color, cep, DJ/3.95)	Follett	(1969)	Kampmann, Ulla	25-35	
Kipling, Rudyard	His Apologies (1st {std}, 8vo, ibds, p-o, 17p, b/w)	Doubleday/Doran	1932	Aldin, Cecil	90-130	
Kipling, Rudyard	How the Camel Got his Hump (1st {std}, lg8vo, [28]p, ibds, color, pep)	Garden City	(1942)	Rojankovsky, Feodor	30-50	
Kipling, Rudyard	How the Leopard Got his Spots (1st, lg8vo, ibds, [28]p, color)	Garden City	(1942)	Rojankovsky, Feodor	35-50	
Kipling, Rudyard	How the Rhinoceros Got his Skin (1st, lg8vo, ibds, [31]p, color)	Garden City	(1942)	Rojankovsky, Feodor	35-50	
Kipling, Rudyard	Indian Tales (1st AM, 8vo, teg, gilt, 750p, 16pl)	Caldwell	(1899)	Various	100-160	
Kipling, Rudyard	Jungle Book (1st, 8vo, blue/gilt, AEG, 212p, b/w)	L: Macmillan	1894	Kipling, J.L.	400-600	
Kipling, Rudyard	Jungle Book (1st, 8vo, 314p, red/gilt, teg, 16cp)	L: Macmillan	1908	Detmold, Edward J.	250-400	
Kipling, Rudyard	Jungle Book (1st AM, 8vo, green/gilt, teg, 351p, 16cp, pep)	Century	1913	Detmold, Edward J.	200-300	
Kipling, Rudyard	Jungle Book (1st, 8vo, green/gilt, 303p, uncut, col frn, 18pl)	Doubleday/Doran	1932	Wiese, Kurt	45-70	*
Kipling, Rudyard	Just So Stories... (1st AM, lg8vo, green cl, 249p, b/w)	Doubleday/Page	1902	Kipling, Rudyard	350-500	R
Kipling, Rudyard	Just So Stories... (1st, sq4to, red/white, 249p, 22pl)	L: Macmillan	1902	Kipling, Rudyard	800-1200	
Kipling, Rudyard	Kim (1st AM, 8vo, green/gilt, teg, 460p, uncut, 10pl)	Doubleday/Page	1901	Kipling, J.L.	200-300	
Kipling, Rudyard	Puck of Pook's Hill (1st, 8vo, 306p, gilt, teg, 20pl)	L: Macmillan	1906	Millar, H.R.	200-300	
Kipling, Rudyard	Puck of Pook's Hill (1st AM, 8vo, green/gilt, teg, 277p, 4cp)	Doubleday/Page	1906	Rackham, Arthur	100-150	
Kipling, Rudyard	Rewards & Fairies (1st, 8vo, red/gilt, teg, 338p, 4pl)	L: Macmillan	1910	Craig, Frank	100-160	
Kipling, Rudyard	Sea & Sussex (1st, 4to, 94p, blue/gilt, teg, 24 ticp)	L: Macmillan	1926	Maxwell, Donald	120-200	
Kipling, Rudyard	Sea & Sussex (1st AM {std}, 4to, 94p, teg, blue cl, 24 ticp)	Doubleday/Page	1926	Maxwell, Donald	100-160	
Kipling, Rudyard	Second Jungle Book (1st, 8vo, blue/gilt, AEG, 238p, b/w)	L: Macmillan	1895	Kipling, J.L.	400-600	
Kipling, Rudyard	Seven Seas (1st {illus ed}, 8vo, teg, uncut, 209p, 8pl)	Appleton	1905	Unknown	50-80	
Kipling, Rudyard	Soldier Tales (1st, 8vo, AEG, 172p, blue/gilt, 21pl)	L: Macmillan	1896	Hartrick, A.S.	200-300	
Kipling, Rudyard	Song of the English (1st AM, 4to, [124]p, red/gilt, 30 ticp)	Doubleday/Page	(1909)	Robinson, W. Heath	400-600	
Kipling, Rudyard	Song of the English (1st, lg4to, [124]p, 91p, 30 ticp)	L: Hodder	[1909]	Robinson, W. Heath	450-650	
Kipling, Rudyard	Songs of the Sea (1st, sm4to, 99p, blue/gilt, teg, uncut, 12cp)	L: Macmillan	1927	Maxwell, Donald	80-125	
Kipling, Rudyard	Tales of India (1st, lg8vo, p-o, 320p, black cl, 5cp, pep, WS)	Rand/McNally	(1935)	Strayer, Paul	50-80	
Kipling, Rudyard	Tales of the Punjab (1st, 8vo, 359p, black/gilt, 5pl)	L: Macmillan	1894	Kipling, J.L.	200-300	
Kipling, Rudyard	Teem: A Treasure-Hunter (1st {std}, 12mo, 46p, b/w, DJ/1.00, frn by...)	Doubleday/Doran	1938	Kirmse, Marguerite	60-90	R
Kipling, Rudyard	They (1st, 8vo, 80p, white/gilt, [160]p, 15cp)	L: Macmillan	1905	Townsend, F.H.	120-200	
Kipling, Rudyard	They (1st AM, 8vo, [160]p, p-o, teg, uncut, 15cp)	Doubleday/Page	1906	Townsend, F.H.	80-125	
Kipling, Rudyard	They and Brushwood Boy (1st, 8vo, 160p, red/gilt, teg, 27cp)	L: Macmillan	1925	Townsend, F.H.	45-70	
Kipling, Rudyard	Wee Willie Winkie (1st, 12mo, ibds, color)	Macmillan	1927	Hader, B.& E.	60-100	
Kipling, Rudyard	With the Night Mail (1st, 8vo, teg, blue cl, 77p, pep, 4cp)	Doubleday/Page	1909	Leyendecker, F.X.	170-220	
Kirk, Victorine	Mickey & the Monkeys (1st, sm4to, 175p, col frn, b/w, pep)	Viking	1927	Rule, Christopher	40-60	
Kirkpatrick, Oliver	Naja the Snake & Mangus the Mongoose (1st {std}, ob4to, 40p, col, DJ/4.50)	Doubleday	(1970)	Richardson, Enid	30-50	*
Kirkwood, Edith B.	Animal Children (1st, 8vo, yellow ipcb, p-o, 96p, pep, color)	Volland	(1913)	Ross, M.T.	100-180	
Kirn, Ann	Beeswax Catches a Thief (1st {std}, ob4to, [48]p, ibds, color, DJ/3.95)	Norton	(1968)	Kirn, Ann	30-50	
Kirn, Ann	Full of Wonder (1st {std}, 8vo, [30]p, 2-color, DJ/2.75, NYTBI)	World	(1959)	Kirn, Ann	30-50	
Kirn, Ann	I Spy (1st {std}, 8vo, [32]p, color, DJ/2.95)	Norton	(1965)	Kirn, Ann	25-45	
Kirn, Ann	Leopard on a String (1st {std}, sq4to, [30]p, 3-color, DJ/2.75)	World	(1959)	Kirn, Ann	40-70	
Kirn, Ann	Let's Look at Tracks (1st, 8vo, 48p, fp 3-color, DJ)	Putnam	(1969)	Kirn, Ann	30-45	*
Kirn, Ann	Peacock and the Crow (1st, sq sm8vo, [32]p, color, DJ/3.95)	Four Winds Pr.	(1969)	Kirn, Ann	30-50	
Kirn, Ann	Tale of a Crocodile (1st {std}, sm ob4to, [32]p, color, DJ/3.75)	Norton	(1968)	Kirn, Ann	30-50	*
Kirn, Ann	Tinkie (1st {std}, lg narrow 4to, [30]p, fp 2-color, cep, DJ/2.75)	World	(1960)	Kirn, Ann	30-50	
Kirn, Ann	Tip for Tap (1st {std}, lg8vo, [32]p, fp 3-color, DJ)	Norton	(1970)	Kirn, Ann	50-80	
Kiser, Martha G.	Rainbow for Me (1st, 8vo, 126p, 5 fp b/w, DJ/2.00)	Random	(1948)	Wilkin, Eloise B.	70-100	
Kiser, Martha G.	Sunshine for Merrily (1st, 8vo, 130p, b/w, DJ/2.00)	Random	(1949)	Wilkin, Eloise B.	60-90	*
Kiser, Samuel E.	Love Sonnets of an Office Boy (1st, 16mo, ibds, 42p)	Chi: Forbes	1902	McCutcheon, J.T.	30-50	*
Kissin, Rita	Gramp's Desert Chick (1st, ob4to, ibds, [36]p, fp 2-color, pep, DJ/2.00)	Reynal/Hitchcock	(1946)	Sari	40-70	
Kissin, Rita	Pete the Pelican (1st, lg8vo, 31p, p-o, b/w, pep, DJ/1.00)	Lippincott	(1937)	Stolper, Joel	55-80	*
Kitt, Tamara	Boy Who Fooled the Giant (1st, 8vo, ibds, 61p, color)	Grosset/Dunlap	1963	Russell, William	25-40	*
Kitt, Tamara	Jake (1st, sm4to, [41]p, fp 2-color, dep, DJ/3.75)	Abelard-Schuman	(1969)	Turkle, Brinton	40-65	
Kitt, Tamara	Sam and the Impossible Thing (1st {std}, ob4to, [40]p, color, DJ/3.25)	Norton	(1967)	Turkle, Brinton	40-65	*
Kitt, Tamara	Special Birthday/Someone Very Special (1st {std}, 12mo, unpag, col, DJ/2.95)	Norton	(1966)	Turkle, Brinton	30-50	*
Kitty Cat	Tabbykin Town in School & at Play (1st, lg8vo, 12p, wraps, p-o, color)	L: Faulkner	[1920]	Wain, Louis	500-800	
Kiviat, Esther	Paji (1st {std}, sm4to, 56p, color, DJ/2.00)	McGraw-Hill	(1946)	Price, Harold	55-80	
Kiyooka, Chiyono	Chiyo's Return (1st {std}, 8vo, 342p, pep, DJ/2.00)	Doubleday/Doran	1935	Tagawa, Bunji	30-45	
Kjelgaard, Jim	Big Red (1st, sm8vo, 231p, tan cl, b/w, pep, DJ/2.00)	Holiday House	(1945)	Kuhn, Bob	25-40	
Kjelgaard, Jim	Boomerang Hunter (1st, 8vo, 172p, b/w, DJ/2.95)	Holiday House	(1960)	Mars, Witold T.	80-120	
Kjelgaard, Jim	Buckskin Brigade (1st, 8vo, 310p, b/w, pep, DJ/2.50)	Holiday House	(1947)	Ray, Ralph	30-50	
Kjelgaard, Jim	Chip the Dam Builder (1st, sm8vo, 233p, b/w, pep, DJ/2.50)	Holiday House	(1950)	Ray, Ralph	30-50	
Kjelgaard, Jim	Coyote Song (1st, 8vo, 174p, b/w, DJ/4.00)	Dodd	(1969)	MacLean, Robert	50-85	*
Kjelgaard, Jim	Duck-Footed Hound (1st, 8vo, 184p, b/w, DJ/2.95)	Crowell	(1960)	Simont, Marc	50-80	
Kjelgaard, Jim	Fire-Hunter (1st, 8vo, 217p, tan cl, b/w, pep, DJ/2.50)	Holiday House	(1951)	Ray, Ralph	30-50	
Kjelgaard, Jim	Forest Patrol (1st [1st bk.], 8vo, 293p, rust cl, fp b/w, DJ/2.00)	Holiday House	(1941)	Palazzo, Tony	60-100	
Kjelgaard, Jim	Haunt Fox (1st, sm8vo, 220p, brown cl, b/w, pep, DJ/2.50)	Holiday House	(1954)	Rounds, Glen	45-60	R
Kjelgaard, Jim	Kalak of the Ice (1st, sm8vo, 201p, b/w, DJ/2.50)	Holiday House	(1949)	Kuhn, Bob	150-220	
Kjelgaard, Jim	Lion Hound (1st, 8vo, 216p, b/w, DJ/2.75)	Holiday House	(1955)	Landau, Jacob	60-100	
Kjelgaard, Jim	Rebel Siege (1st, 8vo, 221p, b/w, DJ/2.00)	Holiday House	(1943)	Wilson, Charles B.	30-50	
Kjelgaard, Jim	Snow Dog (1st, 8vo, 236p, olive cl, b/w, pep, DJ/2.50)	Holiday House	(1948)	Landau, Jacob	40-65	
Kjelgaard, Jim	Stormy (1st, sm8vo, 190p, grey cl, pep, DJ/2.95)	Holiday House	(1959)	Darling, Louis	25-45	
Kjelgaard, Jim	Swamp Cat (1st, 8vo, 175p, b/w, DJ/3.00)	Dodd	(1957)	Shenton, Edward	50-80	
Klein, Charles	Music Master (1st, sm8vo, 341p, p-o, 4cp)	Dodd	1909	Rae, John	30-50	
Klein, Leonore	Henri's Walk to Paris (1st, 4to, unpag, color, DJ/3.75)	W.R. Scott	(1962)	Bass, Saul	65-100	
Klem, Grace	Mike and his Neighbors (1st {std}, ob8vo, ibds, [28]p, color, DJ/0.75)	Doubleday/Doran	1941	Klem, Grace	35-50	*

AUTHOR	TITLE	PUBLISHER	DATE	ARTIST	PRICE	LC
Knatchbull-Hugessen	Mountain-Sprite's Kingdom (1st, sm8vo, 372p, red/gilt, b/w, pep)	L: Routledge	1881	Griset, Ernest H.	80-125	
Knatchbull-Hugessen	Princess with Pea-Green Nose (1st, 12mo, 114p, col frn, pep)	Harper	1927	Cocks, Myra	30-50	
Knecht, Klara	Wild Animals as I Know Them (1st, lg4to, ibds, 90p, 12 fp color)	Saalfield	(1933)	Thorne, Diana	50-80	
Kneeland, Clarissa A.	Smuggler's Island (1st, 8vo, red cl, 355p, b/w, PPPa)	Houghton	1915	Goldsmith, Wallace	70-120	R*
Knevels, Gertrude	Wonderful Bed (1st, 8vo, 229p, 4cp)	Bobbs-Merrill	(1912)	Chamberlin, Emily H.	40-60	*
Knibbs, Henry H.	Tang of Life (1st, sm8vo, 393p, 4cp)	Houghton	1918	Smith, E. Boyd	40-60	
Knight, Hilary	Hilary Knight's Mother Goose (1st, lg4to, ibds, 62p, color, BGB)	Golden Press	1962	Knight, Hilary	45-70	
Knight, Hilary	Sylvia the Sloth (1st, 12mo, [32]p, pep, b/w, DJ/3.50)	Harper	(1969)	Knight, Hilary	40-65	
Knight, Hilary	Where's Wallace? (1st, sq8vo, ibds, 40p, color, DJ/3.50)	Harper	1964	Knight, Hilary	25-40	
Knight, M. Forster	Mr. Tittlewit's Holiday (1st, 8vo, 153p, col frn, b/w, pep, DJ/1.50)	Lippincott	(1940)	Knight, M. Forster	30-45	
Knight, Marjorie	Alexander's Christmas Eve (1st {std}, 8vo, 92p, color, pep, DJ/1.75)	Dutton	1938	Simon, Howard	30-50	
Knight, Marjorie	Land of Lost Handkerchiefs (1st {std}, 8vo, 92p, fp color, DJ/2.50)	Dutton	1954	Fry Rosalie	25-45	
Knight, Mary	Fox that Wanted 9 Golden Tales (1st {std}, 12mo, 94p, b/w, cep, DJ/3.95)	Macmillan	(1969)	Bryan, Brigitte	30-50	
Knight, Ruth A.	Brave Companions (1st {std}, 8vo, blue cl, 215p, col frn, DJ/2.00)	Doubleday/Doran	1945	Ward, Lynd	40-65	
Knight, Ruth A.	Friend in the Dark (1st, lg8vo, 64p, b/w pl, DJ/1.00)	Grosset/Dunlap	(1937)	Dennis, Morgan	40-65	*
Knight, Ruth A.	Halfway to Heaven (1st, 8vo, 184p, col frn, DJ/2.75)	Whittlesey	(1952)	Dennis, Wesley	25-40	
Knipe, A.A.	Cavalier Maid (1st, sm8vo, 255p, 6pl)	Macmillan	1919	Knipe, Emilie B.	30-50	
Knipe, A.A.	Everybody's Washington (1st, lg8vo, 282p, gilt, uncut, p-o, 7cp, pep)	Dodd	1931	Schaeffer, Mead	35-60	
Knipe, A.A.	Luck of Denewood (1st, sm8vo, 359p, brown cl, b/w)	Century	1921	Knipe, Emilie B.	35-60	
Knipe, A.A.	Remember Rhymes (1st, 4to, brown/gilt, 80p, 4cp, pep)	Penn	1914	Knipe, Emilie B.	90-120	
Knipe, E.& A.	Lucky Sixpence (1st, sm8vo, 408p, 4pl, PPPa)	Century	1912	Becher, Arthur E.	200-300	
Knipe, E.B.	Mayflower Maid (1st, 8vo, 297p, blue cl, 4pl)	Century	1920	Knipe, Emilie B.	35-60	
Knobel, E.	When Little Thoughts Go Rhyming (1st, 8vo, p-o, 96p, 10cp)	Rand/McNally	(1916)	Enright, Maginel W.	70-120	
Knott, M.O.	Gone Away with O'Malley (1st {std}, 8vo, red cl, 280p, b/w, pep, DJ/3.00)	Doubleday/Doran	1944	Brown, Paul	70-100	
Knowles, Horace J.	Peeps into Fairyland (1st, lg4to, 89p, tan/gilt, 6cp, pep)	L: Butterworth	(1924)	Knowles, Horace J.	600-850	
Knowles, J. (arr.)	King Arthur & his Knights (1st, 8vo, 340p, 8cp)	L: Warne	(1912)	Speed, Lancelot	75-100	
Knowles, Robert E.	Dawn at Shanty Bay (1st, 8vo, green/gilt, 156p, col frn, dep)	Revell	(1907)	McClure, Griselda M.	35-60	
Knox, Esther M.	Flags of Dawn (1st {std}, sm8vo, 298p, 10pl, DJ/2.00)	Little/Brown	1944	Lawson, Marie A.	30-50	
Knox, Esther M.	Swift Flies the Falcon (1st {std}, lg8vo, 245p, b/w, pep, DJ/2.00)	Winston	1939	King, Ruth	25-45	
Knox, Kathleen	Fairy Gifts (sm8vo, ibds, 128p, 4pl by...)	Dutton	[1882]	Greenaway, Kate	170-250	
Kobler, John	Afternoon in the Attic (1st, 4to, 135p, black cl, b/w, DJ/3.75)	Dodd	1950	Addams, Charles	50-85	
Koch, Dorothy	Gone is My Goose (1st, lg8vo, green cl, [27]p, 1-color, cep, DJ/2.25)	Holiday House	(1956)	Lee, Doris	45-70	R*
Koch, Dorothy	I Play at the Beach (1st, lg8vo, blue cl, [28]p, color, pep, DJ/2.50)	Holiday House	1955	Rojankovsky, Feodor	65-100	*
Koch, Dorothy	Let it Rain (1st, 4to, [27]p, green cl, color, cep, DJ)	Holiday House	(1959)	Stone, Helen	30-50	
Koch, Dorothy	Monkeys are Funny that Way (1st, narrow 4to, [25]p, fp 2-color, DJ/2.75)	Holiday House	1962	Freeman, Don	40-65	
Koch, Dorothy	When the Cows Got Out (1st, 8vo, [33]p, b/w, pep, DJ/2.50)	Holiday House	(1958)	Lantz, Paul	25-40	*
Koch, Katharine	Katie Meets Buffalo Bill (1st, lg8vo, [28]p, ibds, dep, DJ/0.50)	Grosset/Dunlap	(1947)	Paull, Grace	50-80	
Koenig, Richard	Seven Special Cats (1st {std}, 8vo, 57p, orange cl, b/w, DJ/2.75)	World	(1961)	Bacon, Peggy	30-50	
Koffler, Camilla	Little Elephant (1st {std}, lg4to, [30]p, ibds, cep, photos by...)	Harper	1956	Ylla	60-90	R*
Kohn, Bernice	Beachcomber's Book (1st, ob8vo, 96p, fp b/w, DJ/3.75)	Viking	(1970)	Wheatley, Arobelle	25-35	
Kohn, Bernice	One Day it Rained Cats and Dogs (1st, 8vo, [32]p, fp 1-color, DJ/2.50)	Coward	(1965)	Aliki	30-50	
Konigsburg, E.L.	About the B'nai Bagels (1st {std}, 8vo, 172p, blue/gilt, b/w, cep, DJ/4.25)	Atheneum	1969	Konigsburg, E.L.	45-70	R
Konigsburg, E.L.	From Mixed-Up Files/Mrs. B. Frankweiler (1st {std} 8vo 162p DJ/3.95, NM)	Atheneum	1967	Konigsburg, E.L.	100-175	
Konigsburg, E.L.	Jennifer, Hecate, Macbeth.... (1st {std}, 8vo, 117p, b/w, DJ, NH)	Atheneum	1967	Konigsburg, E.L.	65-100	
Konody, Paul G.	Art of Walter Crane (1st, folio, teg, 147p, 16cp)	L: G. Bell	1902	Crane, Walter	300-500	
Konopnicka, Maria	Golden Seed (1st, 8vo, [48]p, color, DJ/3.50)	Scribner	(1962)	Domanska, Janina	25-45	
Kossak-Szczucka, Z.	Troubles of a Gnome (1st, 4to, ibds, p-o, 102p, 8cp)	L: A&C Black	1928	Folkard, Charles	160-240	
Kotzwinkle, William	Day the Gang Got Rich (1st {std}, ob4to, [29]p, color, DJ/3.50)	Viking	(1970)	Servello, Joe	50-80	
Kotzwinkle, William	Elephant Boy (1st {std}, 4to, 43p, fp 2-color, cep, DJ/3.95)	Farrar, Straus	(1970)	Servello, Joe	45-70	
Kotzwinkle, William	Ship that Came Down the Gutter (1st, sq8vo, [23]p, fp color, DJ/4.50)	Pantheon	1970	Servello, Joe	30-50	
Kozisek, Josef	Forest Story (1st, 4to, ibds, [58]p, color, pep)	Macmillan	1929	Mates, Rudolf	250-350	
Kozisek, Josef	Magic Flutes (1st, lg ob4to, [56]p, ibds, color)	L: Longmans	1929	Mates, Rudolf	350-500	
Krag, Martha A.	Martha-Jane: Nursery Nonsense (1st, ob4to, [24]p, black pgs, AEG, cep)	Bowen-Merrill	1897	Keep, Virginia	140-225	
Krahn, Fernando	First Peko-Neko Bird (1st {std}, sq8vo, [46]p, fp b/w, DJ/3.95)	Simon/Schuster	(1969)	Krahn, Fernando	30-50	
Krahn, Fernando	Flying Saucer Full of Spaghetti (1st {std}, sq12mo, [29]p, color, DJ/3.95)	Dutton	(1970)	Krahn, Fernando	30-45	
Krahn, Fernando	Gustavus and Stop (1st {std}, lg8vo, [40]p, color, DJ/4.50)	Dutton	(1969)	Krahn, Fernando	25-40	
Krahn, Fernando	Hildegarde & Maximilian (1st {std}, 12mo, [41]p, 2-color, DJ/3.50)	Delacorte Pr.	(1970)	Krahn, Fernando	30-45	
Krahn, Fernando	Journeys of Sebastian (1st {std}, ob12mo, [121]p, color, DJ/3.95)	Delacorte Pr.	(1968)	Krahn, Fernando	30-50	
Krahn, Fernando	Life of Numbers (1st {std}, sq8vo, [47]p, color, DJ/3.95)	Simon/Schuster	(1970)	Krahn, Fernando	30-50	
Krahn, Fernando	Uncle Timothy's Traviata (1st {std}, ob4to, [32]p, color, pep, DJ/3.95)	Delacorte Pr.	(1967)	Krahn, Fernando	30-50	
Krakemsides, Baron	Careless Chicken (1st, sq12mo, 47p, p-o, fp color)	L: Warne	(1924)	Neilson, Harry B.	45-70	
Kramer, Nora	Cozy Hour Story Book (1st, 4to, 63p, yellow cl, color, pep, DJ/2.95)	Random	1960	Weisgard, Leonard	45-70	
Kramer, Nora	Storybook (1st, lg8vo, 160p, b/w, cep, DJ/2.95)	J. Messner	(1955)	Krush, Beth & Joe	45-75	
Krasilovsky, Phyllis	Benny's Flag (1st {std}, 4to, [40]p, b/w, DJ/2.50)	World	(1960)	Mars, Witold T.	25-45	
Krasilovsky, Phyllis	Cow Who Fell in the Canal (1st {std}, ob4to, [34]p, color, DJ/2.75)	Doubleday	1957	Spier, Peter E.	45-70	R*
Krasilovsky, Phyllis	Girl Who was a Cowboy (1st {std}, sm8vo, 31p, 1-color, DJ/2.75)	Doubleday	(1965)	Szekeres, Cyndy	20-30	
Krasilovsky, Phyllis	Man Who Didn't Wash his Dishes (1st {std}, sm4to, [33]p, ibds, col, DJ/1.50)	Doubleday	(1950)	Cooney, Barbara	45-70	
Krasilovsky, Phyllis	Scaredy Cat (1st {std}, 8vo, unpag, color, DJ/2.00)	Macmillan	1959	Ninon	30-50	
Krasilovsky, Phyllis	Shy Little Girl (1st {std}, 8vo, 31p, color, DJ/3.75)	Houghton	1970	Hyman, Trina S.	60-100	
Krasilovsky, Phyllis	Susan Sometimes (1st {std}, 12mo, 31p, ibds, 3-color, DJ/1.95)	Macmillan	1962	Giventer, Abbi	25-40	
Krasilovsky, Phyllis	Very Little Boy (1st {std}, 8vo, [32]p, color, DJ/1.95)	Doubleday	(1962)	Ninon	30-50	
Krasilovsky, Phyllis	Very Little Girl (1st {std}, 8vo, ibds, unpag, 2-color, DJ/1.50)	Doubleday	(1953)	Ninon	30-50	
Kraus, Robert	All the Mice Came (1st, sm ob4to, ibds, [32]p, b/w, DJ/1.75)	Harper	(1955)	Kraus, Robert	70-100	
Kraus, Robert	Amanda Remembers (1st, 4to, ipcb, 32p, fp color, DJ/3.50)	Harper	(1965)	Kraus, Robert	30-50	
Kraus, Robert	Daddy Long Ears (1st, 12mo, [32]p, color, DJ/3.50)	Windmill Books	(1970)	Kraus, Robert	30-50	
Kraus, Robert	First Robin (1st, 24mo, 48p, ibds, color, DJ/1.99)	Harper	(1965)	Partch, Virgil	25-35	
Kraus, Robert	Hello Hippopotamus (1st, lg8vo, [32]p, color, DJ/3.95)	Windmill Books	(1969)	Kraus, Robert	40-65	
Kraus, Robert	I, Mouse (1st, 12mo, ibds, 32p, b/w, DJ/1.75)	Harper	(1958)	Kraus, Robert	50-85	

AUTHOR: 122

AUTHOR	TITLE	PUBLISHER	DATE	ARTIST	PRICE	LC
Kraus, Robert	Junior, the Spoiled Cat (1st, 4to, [32]p, b/w, pep, DJ/2.00)	Oxford U. Pr.	1955	Kraus, Robert	30-50	
Kraus, Robert	Ladybug, Ladybug (1st, ob4to, ipcb, [30]p, b/w, DJ/1.75)	Harper	(1957)	Kraus, Robert	30-50	
Kraus, Robert	Little Giant (1st, 12mo, [32]p, color, cep, DJ/2.50)	Harper	(1967)	Kraus, Robert	25-45	*
Kraus, Robert	Littlest Rabbit (1st, 8vo, 32p, ipcb, 2-color, DJ/1.95)	Harper	(1961)	Kraus, Robert	20-30	
Kraus, Robert	Miranda's Beautiful Dream (1st, 8vo, [32]p, ibds, fp 3-color, DJ/1.95)	Harper	(1964)	Kraus, Robert	20-35	
Kraus, Robert	My Son the Mouse (1st, ob12mo, ipcb, [32]p, 1-color, DJ/1.95)	Harper	1966	Kraus, Robert	30-45	
Kraus, Robert	Penguin's Pal (1st, 8vo, ibds, 31p, 2-color, DJ/2.50)	Harper	(1964)	Kraus, Robert	20-35	
Kraus, Robert	Trouble with Spider (1st, 8vo, 32p, color, cep, DJ/1.95)	Harper	(1962)	Kraus, Robert	30-50	
Kraus, Robert	Unidentified Flying Elephant (1st {std}, lg4to, [30]p, fp color, DJ/4.95)	Windmill Books	(1968)	Darrow, Whitney	30-50	
Kraus, Robert	Whose Mouse are You? (1st {std}, 4to, [36]p, color, pep, DJ/4.95)	Macmillan	(1970)	Aruego, Jose	40-65	*
Krauss, Ruth	Backward Day (1st, 8vo, ibds, [31]p, color, DJ/1.50)	Harper	1950	Simont, Marc	50-85	
Krauss, Ruth	Bears (1st, 4to, [23]p, ibds, 1-color, cep, DJ/1.00)	Harper	(1948)	Rowand, Phyllis	80-120	
Krauss, Ruth	Big World & Little House (1st, sm4to, ibds, [41]p, color, pep, DJ/2.00)	NY: Schuman	1949	Simont, Marc	70-130	R
Krauss, Ruth	Birthday Party (1st, ob12mo, [23]p, dep, color, DJ/1.50, NYTBI)	Harper	1957	Sendak, Maurice	200-300	R
Krauss, Ruth	Bouquet of Littles (1st, 12mo, ipcb, [22]p, color, DJ/2.50)	Harper	(1963)	Flora, Jane	25-45	
Krauss, Ruth	Bundle Book (1st, lg ob8vo, ipcb, [32]p, pep, color, DJ/1.75)	Harper	(1951)	Stone, Helen	60-100	
Krauss, Ruth	Cantilever Rainbow (1st, 8vo, [46]p, 1-color, pep, DJ/2.95)	Pantheon	(1965)	Frasconi, Antonio	40-65	
Krauss, Ruth	Carrot Seed (1st, sm8vo, olive cl, [25]p, fp 2-color, cep, DJ/1.00)	Harper	1945	Johnson, Crockett	50-80	
Krauss, Ruth	Charlotte & White Horse (1st, 16mo, ibds, [20]p, color, dep, DJ/2.00)	Harper	(1955)	Sendak, Maurice	180-250	
Krauss, Ruth	Good Man & his Good Wife (1st, 8vo, [32]p, fp 2-color, DJ/1.50)	Harper	1944	Reinhardt, Adolph	250-400	
Krauss, Ruth	Good Man & his Good Wife (1st, 8vo, 30p, 1-color, DJ/1.95)	Harper	(1962)	Simont, Marc	100-160	
Krauss, Ruth	Great Duffy (1st, sm4to, ibds, [32]p, color, DJ/1.75)	Harper	(1946)	Richter, Mischa	100-165	
Krauss, Ruth	Growing Story (1st, 4to, ibds, [32]p, color, DJ/2.00)	Harper	(1947)	Rowand, Phyllis	60-90	
Krauss, Ruth	Happy Day (1st, lg4to, ipcb, [33]p, b/w, DJ/1.75, CH)	Harper	1949	Simont, Marc	80-130	
Krauss, Ruth	Hole is to Dig (1st, 12mo, [48]p, ibds, green pep, DJ/1.50, NYTBI)	Harper	(1952)	Sendak, Maurice	250-400	R
Krauss, Ruth	How to Make an Earthquake (1st {std}, 8vo, 28p, ipcb, 1-color, DJ/1.75)	Harper	(1954)	Johnson, Crockett	50-85	
Krauss, Ruth	I Want to Paint My Bathroom Blue (1st, 8vo, [22]p col, cep, DJ/2.50, NYTBI)	Harper	1956	Sendak, Maurice	200-300	R
Krauss, Ruth	I Write It (1st, 12mo, [32]p, ibds, color, DJ/2.50)	Harper	(1970)	Chalmers, Mary	40-65	
Krauss, Ruth	I'll Be You & You Be Me (1st, lg8vo, ibds, pep, [38]p, b/w, DJ/1.75, NYTBI)	Harper	(1954)	Sendak, Maurice	250-350	R
Krauss, Ruth	Is This You? (1st, 12mo, ipcb, [40]p, 1-color, cep, DJ/1.50)	W.R. Scott	1955	Johnson, Crockett	50-85	R
Krauss, Ruth	Mama, I Wish I Was Snow (1st {std}, ob8vo, [28]p, color, cep, DJ/2.50)	Atheneum	1962	Raskin, Ellen	50-85	
Krauss, Ruth	Monkey Day (1st, lg4to, ibds, [26]p, fp 1-color, DJ/2.50)	Harper	(1957)	Rowand, Phyllis	60-90	
Krauss, Ruth	Moon or a Button (1st, 12mo, [48]p, ipcb, b/w, DJ/1.50)	Harper	(1959)	Charlip, Remy	60-100	
Krauss, Ruth	Open House for Butterflies (1st, 16mo, ibds, [46]p, pep, b/w, DJ/1.50, NYT)	Harper	(1960)	Sendak, Maurice	200-320	R
Krauss, Ruth	Somebody Else's Nut Tree (1st, sm4to, ibds, 43p, fp b/w, DJ/2.00)	Harper	(1958)	Sendak, Maurice	180-240	
Krauss, Ruth	This Thumbprint (1st, 12mo, [30]p, 1-color, cep, DJ/1.95)	Harper	(1967)	Krauss, Ruth	25-40	
Krauss, Ruth	Very Special House (1st, sm4to, ibds, [22]p, 1-color, DJ/1.75, CH)	Harper	(1953)	Sendak, Maurice	250-400	R
Krauss, Ruth	What a Fine Day for.... (1st, ob8vo, [40]p, black/gilt, color, DJ/3.50)	Parents Mag. Pr.	(1967)	Charlip, Remy	40-65	
Kravetz, Nathan	Horse of Another Color (1st {std}, 8vo, 57p, color, DJ/2.95)	Little/Brown	(1962)	Perl, Susan	25-40	
Kravetz, Nathan	Monkey's Tale (1st {std}, 8vo, 57p, color, DJ/2.75)	Little/Brown	1964	Perl, Susan	25-40	
Kredenser, Gail	ABC of Bumptious Beasts (1st {std}, lg8vo, 56p, b/w, pep, DJ/3.75)	Harlin Quist	(1966)	Mack, Stanley	25-40	
Krehbiel, Henry E.	How to Listen to Music (1st, 12mo, 361p, gilt)	Scribner	1897	Armstrong, Margaret	55-80	
Krementz, Jill	Sweet Pea (1st {std}, 4to, 94p, b/w, DJ/4.50)	Harcourt	(1969)	(Photos)	50-85	
Kreymborg, Alfred	Funnybone Alley (1st, 4to, teg, 269p, gilt, 7 ticp, pep)	Macaulay	(1927)	Artzybasheff, Boris	100-160	
Kristoffersen, Eva	Bee in Her Bonnet (1st, 8vo, 168p, b/w, pep, DJ/2.00)	Crowell	1944	Sewell, Helen	30-50	
Kristoffersen, Eva	Hans Christian of Elsinore (1st, sq4to, 80p, pep, color, DJ/2.00)	Whitman	1937	Collin, Hedvig	55-80	
Kristoffersen, Eva	Merry Matchmakers (1st, 8vo, 95p, ibds, color, pep, DJ/2.00)	Whitman	1940	Collin, Hedvig	30-50	
Kroeber, Theodora	Ishi, Last of his Tribe (1st, 8vo, 209p, b/w, pep, DJ/3.95)	Parnassus Press	(1964)	Robbins, Ruth	30-50	
Krueger, Kermit	Golden Swans (1st, 4to, gilt, 32p, fp color, cep, DJ/3.95)	World	(1969)	Young, Ed	60-90	R*
Krumgold, Joseph	And Now Miguel (1st {std}, 8vo, 245p, b/w, pep, DJ/2.75, NM)	Crowell	(1953)	Charlot, Jean	100-165	
Krumgold, Joseph	Henry 3 (1st {std}, 8vo, gilt, 268p, fp b/w, pep, DJ/4.75)	Atheneum	1967	Smith, Alvin	20-35	
Krumgold, Joseph	Most Terrible Turk (1st, 8vo, 40p, b/w, DJ/3.75)	Crowell	(1969)	Hampshire, Michael	20-30	
Krumgold, Joseph	Onion John (1st {std}, 8vo, 248p, b/w, DJ/3.00, NM)	Crowell	(1959)	Shimin, Symeon	80-125	
Krumgold, Joseph	Sweeny's Adventure (1st, 4to, [40]p, ibds, color, pep, DJ/1.00)	Random	(1942)	Gergely, Tibor	40-70	
Krutch, Joseph W.	Most Wonderful Animals that Never Were (1st {std}, 8vo, 187p, gilt, DJ/3.75)	Houghton	1969	Baynes, Pauline	80-140	
Kubinyi, Laszlo	Cat and the Flying Machine (1st {std}, 8vo, 48p, fp b/w, DJ/3.95)	Simon/Schuster	(1970)	Kubinyi, Laszlo	25-40	
Kubinyi, Laszlo	Zeki and the Talking Cat (1st {std}, lg8vo, 47p, b/w, DJ/3.95)	Simon/Schuster	1970	Kubinyi, Laszlo	25-40	
Kubota, Hikoho	Golden Footprints (1st {std}, 8vo, 50p, blue cl, 1-color, DJ/2.95)	World	(1960)	Yashima, Taro	80-120	R
Kuebler, Katharine	Hansel the Gander (1st, 8vo, 45p, green cl, 8 fp color, pep)	Wm. Morrow	(1930)	Bischoff, Ilse	25-45	
Kuh, Charlotte	The Deliveryman (1st, 16mo, ibds, [42]p, color)	Macmillan	1929	Wiese, Kurt	40-65	
Kuh, Charlotte	The Engineer (1st, 16mo, [42]p, ibds, color)	Macmillan	1929	Wiese, Kurt	40-65	
Kuh, Charlotte	The Fireman (1st, 16mo, [42]p, ibds, color)	Macmillan	1929	Wiese, Kurt	40-65	
Kuh, Charlotte	The Motorman (1st, 16mo, [42]p, ibds, color)	Macmillan	1929	Wiese, Kurt	40-65	
Kuh, Charlotte	The Policeman (1st, 16mo, [42]p, ibds, color)	Macmillan	1929	Wiese, Kurt	45-60	
Kuh, Charlotte	Train, a Boat & an Island (1st, sq8vo, 89p, col frn, b/w)	Macmillan	1932	Dobias, Frank	30-50	
Kuhns, Oscar	Switzerland (2nd, 8vo, blue/gilt, 294p)	Crowell	(1910)	Armstrong, Margaret	40-60	
Kumin, Maxine	Beach Before Breakfast (1st, ob8vo, grey cl, 46p, color, DJ/3.50)	Putnam	(1964)	Weisgard, Leonard	50-80	R
Kumin, Maxine	Follow the Fall (1st, 8vo, 48p, color, DJ/2.50)	Putnam	(1961)	Marokvia, Artur	50-80	*
Kumin, Maxine	Speedy Digs Downside Up (1st, 8vo, 43p, fp 2-color, DJ/2.75)	Putnam	1964	Keats, Ezra J.	30-45	
Kummer, Frederic	Courage Over the Andes (1st, 8vo, 251p, col frn, fp b/w, pep, DJ/2.00)	Winston	(1940)	Sperry, Armstrong	30-45	
Kummer, Frederic	Leif Erikson the Lucky (1st, 8vo, 245p, col frn, b/w, pep, DJ/2.00)	Winston	(1939)	Price, Norman	25-40	
Kunhardt, Dorothy	Billy the Barber (1st, 12mo, 47p, color, DJ/1.95)	Harper	1961	DuBois, W.P.	40-65	
Kunhardt, Dorothy	Brave Mr. Buckingham (1st, sm sq8vo, [63]p, fp 1-color, DJ/1.00)	Harcourt	(1935)	Kunhardt, Dorothy	100-165	
Kunhardt, Dorothy	Gas Station Gus (1st, 12mo, 65p, ipcb, 1-color, DJ/1.95)	Harper	(1962)	Domanska, Janina	30-50	
Kunhardt, Dorothy	Junket is Nice (1st, sm ob4to, ibds, [63]p, 1-color)	Harcourt	1933	Kunhardt, Dorothy	200-300	
Kunhardt, Dorothy	Little Ones (1st, sm4to, red cl, 78p, color, pep, DJ/2.00)	Viking	1935	Wiese, Kurt	60-90	
Kunhardt, Dorothy	Lucky Mrs. Ticklefeather (1st, sm ob4to, ibds, [63]p, 1-color, DJ/1.25)	Harcourt	1935	Kunhardt, Dorothy	100-160	
Kunhardt, Dorothy	Now Open the Box (1st, sm ob4to, [61]p, ipcb, color)	Harcourt	1934	Kunhardt, Dorothy	100-160	

AUTHOR	TITLE	PUBLISHER	DATE	ARTIST	PRICE	LC
Kunhardt, Dorothy	Once there was a Little Boy (1st, lg8vo, 66p, fp color, DJ/2.50)	Viking	1946	Sewell, Helen	40-70	
Kunhardt, Dorothy	Wise Old Aard-Vark (1st, ob4to, ibds, 62p, 1-color, DJ/1.00)	Viking	1936	Kunhardt, Dorothy	120-180	
Kunos, Ignacz	Forty-Four Turkish Fairy Tales (1st, 4to, tan cl, teg, 363p, 16 ticp)	L: Harrap	[1913]	Pogany, Willy	250-400	
Kunos, Ignacz	Turkish Fairy Tales... (1st, lg8vo, gilt, 275p, teg, 9pl)	L: Lawrence	1896	Levetus, Celia	80-140	
Kusan, Ivan	Koko and the Ghosts (1st AM {std}, 8vo, 215p, b/w, DJ/3.75)	Harcourt	(1966)	Galdone, Paul	20-35	
Kuskin, Karla	ABCDEFGHIJKLMNOPQR... (1st, 24mo, [56]p, ipcb, color, pep, DJ/3.75)	Harper	(1963)	Kuskin, Karla	30-50	*
Kuskin, Karla	Alexander Soames (1st, 8vo, [48]p, 1-color, DJ/1.95)	Harper	(1962)	Kuskin, Karla	30-50	
Kuskin, Karla	All Sizes of Noises (1st, ob8vo, ipcb, [32]p, 3-color, DJ/1.95)	Harper	(1962)	Kuskin, Karla	30-45	
Kuskin, Karla	Animals and the Ark (1st, lg ob8vo, ipcb, [32]p, fp 3-color, DJ/2.50)	Harper	(1958)	Kuskin, Karla	30-50	
Kuskin, Karla	Bear Who Saw Spring (1st, 4to, ipcb, [47]p, 3-color, DJ/2.50)	Harper	(1961)	Kuskin, Karla	30-50	
Kuskin, Karla	In the Flaky Frosty Morning (1st, 8vo, ipcb, [26]p, fp 2-col, dep, DJ/3.95)	Harper	1969	Kuskin, Karla	30-50	
Kuskin, Karla	In the Middle of the Trees (1st, lg4to, 38p, 2-color, DJ/2.50)	Harper	(1958)	Kuskin, Karla	60-100	R
Kuskin, Karla	James & the Rain (1st, sq8vo, [38]p, ibds, 2-color, DJ/2.25)	Harper	(1957)	Kuskin, Karla	30-50	
Kuskin, Karla	Just Like Everyone Else (1st, 24mo, [32]p, fp 1-color, DJ/1.50)	Harper	(1959)	Kuskin, Karla	40-65	
Kuskin, Karla	Roar & More (1st [1st bk.], ob8vo, [45]p, fp 2-color, DJ/2.00)	Harper	(1956)	Kuskin, Karla	70-120	R
Kuskin, Karla	Rose on My Cake (1st, 4to, [42]p, ibds, b/w, DJ/2.50)	Harper	(1964)	Kuskin, Karla	30-45	
Kuskin, Karla	Sand and Snow (1st, ob12mo, ipcb, [32]p, fp color, cep, DJ/2.50)	Harper	(1965)	Kuskin, Karla	30-50	*
Kuskin, Karla	Square as a House (1st, ob8vo, [23]p, fp 2-color, DJ/2.50)	Harper	(1960)	Kuskin, Karla	40-65	
Kuskin, Karla	Walk the Mouse Girls Took (1st, 8vo, 32p, ibds, color, DJ/2.50)	Harper	(1967)	Kuskin, Karla	30-45	
Kuskin, Karla	Watson, Smartest Dog in the USA (1st, lg ob4to, [32]p, color, DJ/3.50)	Harper	(1968)	Kuskin, Karla	30-50	
Kuskin, Karla	Which Horse is William? (1st, ob8vo, [30]p, 2-color, DJ/1.95)	Harper	(1959)	Kuskin, Karla	30-45	
Kyle, Anne D.	Apprentice of Florence (1st, 8vo, 276p, b/w, pep, NH)	Houghton	1933	Berry, Erick	40-65	
Kyle, Anne D.	Prince of the Pale Mountains (1st, sm8vo, 250p, col frn, pep)	Houghton	1929	Barney, Maginel W.	30-50	*
Kyle, Anne D.	Red Sky over Rome (1st, 8vo, 260p, 8pl, DJ/2.00)	Houghton	1938	DeAngeli, Marguerite	40-60	*
Kyle, Elisabeth	Lost Karin (1st AM, 8vo, 266p, b/w, pep, DJ/2.50)	Houghton	1948	Unwin, Nora S.	50-80	
Kyne, Peter B.	Cappy Ricks (1st, sm8vo, 349p, 4pl)	H.K. Fly	(1916)	Dunn/Fischer	60-90	*
Kyne, Peter B.	Kindred of the Dust (1st, sm8vo, 376p, 4pl)	Cosmopolitan	1920	Cornwell, Dean	30-50	
Kyne, Peter B.	Long Chance (1st, sm8vo, black/gilt, 313p, 4cp)	H.K. Fly	1914	Johnson, F. Tenny	60-100	
Kyne, Peter B.	Three Godfathers (1st, 8vo, gilt, 95p, 4pl)	Doran	(1913)	Dixon, Maynard	50-80	
Kyne, Peter B.	Valley of the Giants (1st, sm8vo, 388p, col frn, b/w)	Doubleday	1918	Cornwell, Dean	30-50	*
Kyser, Halsa A.	Little Cumsee in Dixie (1st {std}, sm8vo, 158p, b/w, pep, DJ/1.50)	Longmans	1938	Berry, Erick	50-80	*
L'Engle, Madeleine	Arm of the Starfish (1st {std}, 8vo, 243p, uncut, DJ/3.50)	Ariel	(1965)	No Illustrations	60-90	
L'Engle, Madeleine	Dance in the Desert (1st {std}, 8vo, [55]p, color, gilt, pep, DJ/4.95)	Farrar, Straus	(1969)	Shimin, Symeon	60-90	
L'Engle, Madeleine	Journey with Jonah: One Act Play (1st {std}, 8vo, 63p, b/w, DJ/3.75)	Farrar, Straus	(1967)	Fisher, Leonard	60-90	
L'Engle, Madeleine	Twenty-Four Days before Christmas (1st {std}, lg8vo, 56p, color, DJ/3.25)	Ariel	(1964)	Inga	50-85	
L'Engle, Madeleine	Wrinkle in Time (1st {std}, 8vo, 211p, DJ/3.25, NM)	Ariel	(1962)	No Illustrations	75-125	R
L'Hommedieu, Dorothy	Leo, the Little St. Bernard (1st {std}, 8vo, 62p, color, DJ/2.00)	Lippincott	(1948)	Kirmse, Marguerite	60-90	
L'Hommedieu, Dorothy	Nipper the Little Bull Pup (1st {std}, 8vo, ibds, 58p, color, DJ/2.00)	Lippincott	(1943)	Kirmse, Marguerite	40-65	
L'Hommedieu, Dorothy	Robbie, Brave Little Collie (1st {std}, 8vo, 60p, ibds, color, DJ/2.00)	Lippincott	(1946)	Kirmse, Marguerite	60-90	
L'Hommedieu, Dorothy	Rusty, Little Red Dachshund (1st, 8vo, 55p, color, pep, DJ/1.50)	Lippincott	1940	Kirmse, Marguerite	50-80	
L'Hommedieu, Dorothy	Scampy the Little Black Cocker (1st, sm4to, ibds, 62p, pep, color, DJ/1.50)	Lippincott	(1939)	Kirmse, Marguerite	70-100	
L'Hommedieu, Dorothy	Tyke, the Little Mutt (1st {std}, sq8vo, ibds, 63p, color, DJ/2.00)	Lippincott	(1949)	Kirmse, Marguerite	45-70	
La Farge, Phyllis	Jane's Silver Chair (1st, 8vo, 31p, fp 2-color, cep, DJ/3.75)	Knopf	(1969)	Jacques, Robin	30-45	*
La Fontaine, J.	Fables in Rhyme for Little Folks (1st, 8vo, 94p, ibds, color)	Volland	(1918)	Rae, John	80-120	
La Fontaine, J.	Fables of Jean De La Fontaine (1st, 8vo, 469p, 12pl)	L: Heinemann	1933	Gooden, Stephen	100-160	
La Fontaine, J.	Fables of La Fontaine (1st, 4to, 304p, teg, gilt, 24pl)	L: Nimmo	1884	Delierre, A.	250-400	
La Fontaine, J.	Fables of La Fontaine (1st {std}, 4to, ibds, 60p, color, DJ/3.25)	Doubleday	(1964)	Scarry, Richard	65-100	
La Fontaine, J.	Hare & the Tortoise (1st AM, 4to, pink cl, unpag, color, DJ/3.95)	F. Watts	(1967)	Wildsmith, Brian	70-100	R
La Fontaine, J.	Hundred Fables of La Fontaine (1st, 8vo, green cl, 202p, fp b/w)	L: John Lane	1900	Billinghurst, Percy	120-180	
La Fontaine, J.	La Fontaine's Fables (1st, sm ob4to, ibds, [64]p, color)	L: T. Nelson	1905	Bull/Park	160-240	
La Fontaine, J.	Lion and the Rat (1st AM, 4to, [32]p, fp color, cep, DJ/3.95)	F. Watts	(1963)	Wildsmith, Brian	70-100	
La Fontaine, J.	North Wind and the Sun (1st AM, 4to, [32]p, color, cep, DJ/3.95)	F. Watts	1964	Wildsmith, Brian	60-90	
La Fontaine, J.	Rich Man and the Shoemaker (1st AM, 4to, [32]p, fp color, cep, DJ/3.95)	F. Watts	(1965)	Wildsmith, Brian	50-80	
La Prade, E.	Alice in Orchestralia (1st {std}, sm8vo, 171p, 1-color frn, b/w)	Doubleday/Page	1925	Snell, Carroll	40-65	
La Rue, Mabel G.	Billy Bang Book (1st, 12mo, 176p, 2-color)	Macmillan	1927	Petershams	40-70	*
La Rue, Mabel G.	Cats for the Tooseys (1st, lg4to, 40p, ipcb, b/w, DJ/1.00)	Nelson	1939	Wiese, Kurt	50-80	
La Rue, Mabel G.	Good-Time Book (1st, 12mo, 111p, 2-color, cep)	Macmillan	1931	Peck, A. Gladys	30-50	*
La Rue, Mabel G.	Hoot-Owl (1st, 12mo, blue cl, 207p, 2-color, pep)	Macmillan	1936	Seredy, Kate	35-60	*
La Rue, Mabel G.	Letter to Popsey (1st, sq8vo, [28]p, ibds, color, pep, DJ/0.50)	Grosset/Dunlap	1942	Lenski, Lois	60-100	
La Rue, Mabel G.	Little Indians (1st, 12mo, 170p, color)	Macmillan	1930	Petershams	40-65	
La Rue, Mabel G.	Tooseys (1st, 8vo, yellow cl, 127p, fp b/w, DJ/1.50)	Nelson	1938	Wiese, Kurt	30-50	*
La Rue, Mabel G.	Under the Story Tree (1st, 12mo, 139p, color)	Macmillan	1923	Petershams	50-80	*
La Rue, Mabel G.	Zip the Toy Mule (1st, sm4to, 46p, 6cp, pep)	Macmillan	1932	Petershams	50-80	
Laboulaye, E.R.	Laboulaye's Fairy Book (1st, lg8vo, 199p, p-o, 12cp, pep)	Harper	(1920)	McCandlish, Edward	70-100	
Laboulaye, E.R.	Laboulaye's Fairy Book (1st, 8vo, 363p, black cl, p-o, b/w)	Harper	(1925)	Potter, Edna	35-60	*
Laboulaye, E.R.	Laboulaye's Fairy Tales (1st, 8vo, 335p, green/gilt, 6cp, pep)	L: Nister	[1908]	Dixon, Arthur A.	100-185	
Laboulaye, E.R.	Last Fairy Tales (1st AM, 12mo, 382p, gilt, fp b/w)	Harper	1885	Various	80-130	
Lacey, Marion	Picture Book of Musical Instruments (1st, 4to, ibds, 55p, b/w, DJ/2.00)	Lothrop, Lee	(1942)	Weisgard, Leonard	45-70	
Lackey, Eunice	Lucky Blacky (1st {std}, 8vo, 118p, 2-color, pep, DJ/2.50, NYTBI)	F. Watts	(1953)	Greene, Winifred	30-50	
Ladas, Alexis	Seal that Couldn't Swim (1st {std}, lg8vo, 55p, blue cl, 3-color, DJ/2.75)	Little/Brown	(1959)	Simont, Marc	40-65	
Lady Frazer	Singing Wood (1st, 8vo, 144p, col frn, b/w)	L: A&C Black	1931	Brock, Henry M.	40-60	
Lagerlof, Selma	Christ Legends (1st, 8vo, 244p, blue cl, b/w)	L: E. Mathews	1930	Knowles, Horace J.	40-65	
Lagerlof, Selma	Further Adventures of Nils (1st {Engl lang.}, 12mo, 339p, 15pl)	Doubleday/Page	1911	Heiberg, Astri W.	90-120	*
Lagerlof, Selma	Wonderful Adventures of Nils (1st AM, 8vo, 430p, 8pl, pep)	Doubleday/Page	1907	Heartt, Harold	100-180	
Lagerlof, Selma	Wonderful Adventures of Nils (1st, lg8vo, 263p, 24cp, pep)	Doubleday/Page	1913	Frye, Mary H.	120-200	
Lagerlof, Selma	Wonderful Adventures of Nils (1st, lg8vo, 539p, b/w, pep, DJ/5.00)	Pantheon	(1947)	Baumhauer, Hans	30-50	
Laing, Alexander	Cadaver of Gideon Wyck (1st, 8vo, 376p, frn by...)	Farrar/Rinehart	1934	Ward, Lynd	50-75	
Laing, Alexander (ed)	Haunted Omnibus (1st, 8vo, 848p, fp b/w)	Farrar/Rinehart	(1937)	Ward, Lynd	70-120	

AUTHOR: 124

AUTHOR	TITLE	PUBLISHER	DATE	ARTIST	PRICE	LC
Laing, Allan M.	Prayers & Graces (1st, sq12mo, 64p, blue/gilt, 30 b/w, DJ)	L: Gollancz	1944	Peake, Mervyn	80-120	
Laing, Frederick	Why Heimdall Blew His Horn (1st, lg8vo, 96p, color)	Silver Burdette	(1969)	Dillon, L.& D.	40-65	
Laird, Helene	Nancy Keeps House (1st {std}, 8vo, 189p, b/w, DJ/2.00)	World	(1947)	Sari	25-40	
Laird, Rowena	Stuffy (1st, 4to, [32]p, p-o, color, DJ/2.00)	Wm. Morrow	1945	Laird, Rowena	30-50	
Lamb, Charles	Adventures of Ulysses (1st, 4to, 117p, uncut, 16cp, cep)	R.H. Russell	1902	Mars/Squire	200-320	
Lamb, Charles	Dissertation Upon a Roast Pig (1st, 16mo, 19p, pcb, p-o, 1-color)	(Concord)	(1903)	Bradley, Will	100-165	
Lamb, Charles	Essays of Elia (8vo, green/gilt, teg, uncut, 310p, woodcuts)	L: Methuen	1902	Jones, Garth	40-60	
Lamb, Charles	Last Essays of Elia (1st, 12mo, 254p, teg, uncut)	L: Dent	1900	Brock, Charles E.	50-80	
Lamb, Charles	Mrs. Leicester's School (1st, sq8vo, 128p, ibds, 20cp)	L: Dent	1899	Green, Winifred	90-120	
Lamb, Charles	Mrs. Leicester's School (1st, 8vo, 125p, blue cl, 5pl)	L: Wells/Gard.	(1904)	Brock, Charles E.	30-50	
Lamb, Charles	Tales from Shakespeare (1st, 8vo, 362p, blue/gilt, teg, 15pl)	L: Freemantle	1899	Bell, Robert A.	70-100	
Lamb, Charles	Tales from Shakespeare (lg8vo, AEG, 319p, gilt, 6cp, pep)	L: Nister	[1901]	Paget, Walter	100-150	
Lamb, Charles	Tales from Shakespeare (1st, 8vo, red cl, 296p, 16pl)	L: Sands	[1902]	Robinson, W. Heath	140-225	*
Lamb, Charles	Tales from Shakespeare (1st, sm8vo, 363p, gilt, teg, 24pl)	L: G. Bell	1903	Shaw, Byam	60-90	
Lamb, Charles	Tales from Shakespeare (1st AM, 4to, 324p, gilt, teg, 20cp)	Scribner	[1905]	Price, Norman	70-100	
Lamb, Charles	Tales from Shakespeare (1st AM, 8vo, gilt, 304p, teg, 12cp, pep)	Dent/Dutton	1909	Rackham, Arthur	225-300	
Lamb, Charles	Tales from Shakespeare (1st, 8vo, 304p, gilt, teg, 12cp, pep)	L: Dent	1909	Rackham, Arthur	300-395	
Lamb, Charles	Tales from Shakespeare (1st, lg8vo, 242p, ipcb, gilt, 16 ticp)	L: Rbt. Scott	1915	Mulliner, May	100-150	
Lamb, Charles	Tales from Shakespeare (1st, 8vo, gilt, 366p, fp b/w)	Harper	(1918)	Rhead, Louis	40-70	
Lamb, Charles	Tales from Shakespeare (1st, 8vo, 472p, blue cl, p-o, 48cp)	L: Ward Lock	1919	Jackson, A.E.	60-90	
Lamb, Charles	Tales from Shakespeare (1st, lg8vo, gilt, teg, 377p, p-o, pep, 11cp)	McKay	1922	Green, Eliz. S.	125-200	
Lamb, Charles	Tales from Shakespeare (1st, 8vo, 308p, teg, gilt, 12cp)	L: Warne	1923	Pape, Frank	80-125	
Lamb, Charles	Tales from Shakespeare (1st, sm8vo, 375p, blue cl, 4cp, pep)	Macmillan	1923	Petershams	55-80	
Lamb, Charles	Tales from Shakespeare (1st, 8vo, p-o, 323p, 12pl)	Winston	(1924)	Godwin, Frank	35-60	
Lamb, Charles	Tales from Shakespeare (lg8vo, 323p, 14cp, pep)	Baker/Taylor	[1924]	Soper, George	30-50	
Lamb, Charles	Tales from Shakespeare (1st, 8vo, 346p, p-o, 6cp)	Houghton	1925	Elwell, Robert F.	30-50	
Lamb, Charles	Tales from Shakespeare (1st, 8vo, 296p, color, pep, DJ/1.00)	Garden City	1939	Kredel, Fritz	30-50	
Lamb, Dean I.	Incurable Filibuster (1st, 8vo, 298p, uncut, b/w, pep)	Farrar/Rinehart	(1934)	Brown, Paul	50-80	*
Lamb, Harold	Kirdy (1st {std}, sm8vo, red cl, uncut, 276p, frn & pep by...)	Doubleday/Doran	1933	Artzybasheff, Boris	40-65	
Lamb, Peter O.	Sign of the Buffalo Skull (1st, 12mo, 288p, 14 b/w)	Stokes	1932	Daugherty, James	25-45	
Lamb, Tom	Jolly Kid Alphabet (1st, lg ob4to, ibds, color)	Volland	[1930]	Lamb, Tom	225-325	
Lamb, Tom	Tale of Bingo (1st, 8vo, ibds, 120p, color)	Volland	(1927)	Lamb, Tom	75-100	*
Lambert, Clara	Story of Alaska (1st {std}, sq4to, ibds, [40]p, color, pep, DJ/1.50)	Harper	(1940)	DeWitt, C.H.	60-100	
Lambert, Emily	Man Who Drew Cats (1st, ob4to, ipcb, [32]p, 3-color, DJ/2.00)	Harper	(1957)	Lambert, Saul	30-45	*
Lambert, H.G.C.	Peter Pixie at Play (4to, ibds, p-o, 6cp, pep)	L: Gale/Polden	[1910]	Lambert, M.	200-270	*
Lambert, Janet	Candy Kane (1st {std}, 8vo, 184p, b/w, DJ/2.00)	Dutton	1943	Paflin, Roberta	100-160	
Lambert, Janet	Glory Be! (1st {std}, 8vo, 207p, b/w, DJ/2.00)	Dutton	1943	Ishmael, Woodi	120-180	
Lambert, Janet	Just Jenifer (1st {std}, sm8vo, 187p, b/w, DJ/2.25)	Dutton	1945	Paflin, Roberta	120-180	
Lambert, Janet	Star-Spangled Summer (1st {std}, 8vo, 281p, b/w, pep, DJ/2.00)	Dutton	1941	James, Sandra	100-165	
Lamkey, Rosemary	Lonely Dwarf (1st, 8vo, 49p, fp color, pep, DJ/1.00)	Henry Holt & Co.	(1939)	Lamkey, Rosemary	60-85	
Lampman, Evelyn	Bounces of Cynthiann' (1st {std}, 8vo, 260p, b/w, DJ/2.50)	Doubleday	1950	Paull, Grace	25-45	*
Lampman, Evelyn	City Under the Back Steps (1st {std}, 8vo, 210p, b/w, DJ/2.95)	Doubleday	1960	Valintcourt, Honore	25-40	*
Lampman, Evelyn	Crazy Creek (1st {std}, 8vo, 213p, b/w, DJ/2.50)	Doubleday	1948	Paull, Grace	20-35	*
Lampman, Evelyn	Mrs. Updaisy (1st {std}, 8vo, 215p, fp b/w, DJ/3.25)	Doubleday	(1963)	Szekeres, Cyndy	25-40	
Lampman, Evelyn	Navaho Sister (1st {std}, 8vo, 191p, b/w, DJ/2.75)	Doubleday	(1956)	Lantz, Paul	30-45	
Lampman, Evelyn	Rusty's Space Ship (1st {std}, 8vo, 240p, b/w, DJ/2.95)	Doubleday	1957	Krigstein, Bernard	25-45	*
Lampman, Evelyn	Shy Stegosaurus of Cricket Creek (1st {std}, 8vo, 220p, b/w, DJ/2.75)	Doubleday	1955	Buel, Robert	70-120	
Lampman, Evelyn	Shy Stegosaurus of Indian Springs (1st {std} 8vo, 232p, gilt, b/w, DJ/2.75)	Doubleday	(1962)	Galdone, Paul	80-120	
Lampman, Evelyn	Tilted Sombrero (1st {std}, 8vo, 264p, gilt, b/w, DJ/3.50)	Doubleday	1966	Cruz, Ray	30-45	
Lampman, Evelyn	Treasure Mountain (1st {std}, 8vo, 207p, b/w, DJ/2.50)	Doubleday	1949	Bennett, Richard	20-35	*
Lampman, Evelyn	Tree Wagon (1st {std}, 8vo, 253p, b/w, DJ/2.75)	Doubleday	1953	Frankenberg, Rbt.	25-45	
Lamport, Felicia	Cultural Slag (1st {std}, 8vo, 136p, b/w, DJ/3.95)	Houghton	1966	Gorey, Edward	50-80	
Lamport, Felicia	Cultural Slag (1st UK, 8vo, 136p, b/w, DJ)	L: Gollancz	1967	Gorey, Edward	65-90	
Lamport, Felicia	Scrap Irony (1st {std}, 8vo, 126p, b/w, DJ/3.00)	Houghton	1961	Gorey, Edward	70-100	
Lamprey, Louise	Children of Ancient Britain (1st, 12mo, 222p, fp b/w)	Little/Brown	1921	Petershams	40-60	*
Lamprey, Louise	Long Ago People (1st, 12mo, 222p, fp b/w)	Little/Brown	1921	Petershams	40-60	*
Lamprey, Louise	Tomahawk Trail (1st, 8vo, 313p, gilt, 4cp, pep)	Stokes	1934	Good, Stafford	30-45	
Lamprey, Louise	Treasure Valley (1st, 8vo, 337p, yellow cl, p-o, 4cp, pep)	Wm. Morrow	(1928)	Freeman, Margaret	30-50	*
Landon, Margaret	Anna and the King of Siam (1st, 8vo, 391p, gilt, b/w, DJ/3.75)	John Day	1944	Ayer, Margaret	50-80	
Lane, Margaret	Tale of Beatrix Potter (1st, 8vo, gilt, 162p, 4cp, 16 b/w, DJ/3.50)	Warne	(1946)	Potter, Beatrix	100-160	
Lang, Andrew	Animal Story Book (1st, 12mo, AEG, 400p, blue/gilt, b/w, cep)	L: Longmans	1896	Ford, H.J.	150-250	
Lang, Andrew	Blue Fairy Book (1st, 12mo, 390p, blue/gilt, AEG, fp b/w, cep)	L: Longmans	1889	Ford/Hood	850-1300	
Lang, Andrew	Blue Fairy Book (1st, 8vo, teg, p-o, black/gilt, 16cp)	McKay	(1921)	Godwin, Frank	80-150	
Lang, Andrew	Blue Fairy Book (1st, 8vo, 428p, p-o, 6cp, cep)	Macrae Smith	(1926)	Lee, Manning De V.	30-50	
Lang, Andrew	Blue Fairy Book (1st, 8vo, 372p, gilt, 2-color frn, b/w, pep, DJ/2.00)	Longmans	(1948)	Kutcher, Ben	30-50	
Lang, Andrew	Blue Poetry Book (1st, 12mo, blue/gilt, AEG, 243p, 12pl, cep)	L: Longmans	1891	Ford, H.J.	170-240	
Lang, Andrew	Book of Dreams & Ghosts (1st, sm8vo, 303p, gilt, teg, cvr by...)	L: Longmans	1897	Woodroffe, Paul	100-175	
Lang, Andrew	Book of Princes & Princesses (1st, 12mo, gilt, 361p, AEG, 8cp)	L: Longmans	1908	Ford, H.J.	180-240	
Lang, Andrew	Book of Romance (1st, 12mo, AEG, 384p, gilt, 8cp, pep)	L: Longmans	1902	Ford, H.J.	180-240	
Lang, Andrew	Brown Fairy Book (1st, 8vo, AEG, 350p, 8cp, 22pl, pep)	L: Longmans	1904	Ford, H.J.	250-400	
Lang, Andrew	Conquest of Montezuma's Empire (1st {std}, sm8vo, 235p, 8pl, pep, DJ/1.50)	Longmans	1928	Daugherty, James	30-50	
Lang, Andrew	Crimson Fairy Book (1st, 12mo, gilt, AEG, 371p, 8cp, pep)	L: Longmans	1903	Ford, H.J.	250-400	
Lang, Andrew	Disentanglers (1st, 12mo, 418p, AEG, 7pl, cep)	L: Longmans	1902	Ford, H.J.	120-180	
Lang, Andrew	Gold of Fairnilee (1st, 4to, gilt, teg, 86p, uncut, 13cp)	L: Arrowsmith	(1888)	Lemann, E.A.	200-300	
Lang, Andrew	Green Fairy Book (1st, 12mo, AEG, 366p, gilt, b/w, cep)	L: Longmans	1892	Ford, H.J.	300-450	
Lang, Andrew	Grey Fairy Book (1st, 12mo, AEG, 387p, 32pl, cep)	L: Longmans	1900	Ford, H.J.	250-400	
Lang, Andrew	Johnny Nut & Golden Goose (1st, 4to, 45p, teg, gilt, col frn, b/w, cep)	L: Longmans	1887	Lynen, Amedee	250-350	
Lang, Andrew	Lilac Fairy Book (1st, 12mo, 369p, gilt, AEG, 6cp)	L: Longmans	1910	Ford, H.J.	250-400	

AUTHOR	TITLE	PUBLISHER	DATE	ARTIST	PRICE	LC
Lang, Andrew	Little Wildrose (1st, 12mo, 258p, blue/gilt, col frn, 19 b/w, pep)	L: Longmans	1906	Ford, H.J.	100-170	
Lang, Andrew	My Own Fairy Book (1st, sm8vo, 402p, rust cl, p-o, pep, 4cp)	McKay	(1927)	Kay, Gertrude A.	60-90	
Lang, Andrew	Nursery Rhyme Book (1st, 8vo, AEG, 288p, green/gilt, fp b/w, pep)	L: Warne	1897	Brooke, L. Leslie	150-225	
Lang, Andrew	Olive Fairy Book (1st, 12mo, AEG, 336p, 8cp, pep)	L: Longmans	1907	Ford, H.J.	250-400	
Lang, Andrew	Orange Fairy Book (1st, 12mo, orange/gilt, 358p, AEG, 8cp)	L: Longmans	1906	Ford, H.J.	250-400	
Lang, Andrew	Pink Fairy Book (1st, 12mo, gilt, AEG, 360p, b/w, cep)	L: Longmans	1897	Ford, H.J.	250-400	
Lang, Andrew	Prince Prigio (1st, sm8vo, 144p, gilt, 9 fp b/w, pep)	L: Arrowsmith	1889	Browne, Gordon	120-180	
Lang, Andrew	Prince Prigio (1st {std}, sq8vo, green cl, 108p, b/w, pep, DJ/1.75)	Little/Brown	1942	Lawson, Robert	100-160	
Lang, Andrew	Prince Ricardo of Pantouflia (1st, 12mo, 204p, gilt, 12pl)	L: Arrowsmith	(1893)	Browne, Gordon	130-200	
Lang, Andrew	Princess Nobody (1st, lg8vo, ibds, 56p, color, pep)	L: Longmans	(1884)	Doyle, Richard	400-600	
Lang, Andrew	Red Book of Animal Stories (1st, 12mo, gilt, AEG, 379p, 33pl)	L: Longmans	1899	Ford, H.J.	160-240	
Lang, Andrew	Red Fairy Book (1st, 12mo, red/gilt, AEG, 367p, b/w)	L: Longmans	1890	Ford/Speed	500-800	
Lang, Andrew	Red Fairy Book (1st, lg8vo, 285p, p-o, teg, red cl, 8cp, pep)	McKay	(1924)	Tenggren, Gustaf	200-300	
Lang, Andrew	Red Fairy Book (1st, sm8vo, 399p, p-o, 7cp, pep)	Macrae Smith	[1927]	Lee, Manning De V.	60-90	
Lang, Andrew	Red Fairy Book (1st, 8vo, 386p, gilt, p-o, 4cp)	Winston	(1930)	Richardson, F.	40-70	
Lang, Andrew	Red Fairy Book (1st [new ed.], 8vo, 364p, color, DJ/2.00)	Longmans	(1948)	Simont, Marc	30-50	*
Lang, Andrew	Red Romance Book (1st, 12mo, 366p, AEG, 8cp, 28pl, pep)	L: Longmans	1905	Ford, H.J.	140-225	
Lang, Andrew	Red True Story Book (1st, 12mo, gilt, 419p, AEG, 19pl, pep)	L: Longmans	1895	Ford, H.J.	200-320	
Lang, Andrew	Rose Fairy Book (1st {std}, 8vo, 212p, pink/gilt, 9cp, DJ/2.50)	Longmans	(1948)	Bock, Vera	40-65	
Lang, Andrew	Story of the Golden Fleece (1st, 8vo, 93p, 6pl)	Altemus	(1903)	Thompson, Mills	75-100	*
Lang, Andrew	Strange Story Book (1st, lg8vo, teg, gilt, 312p, 12cp)	L: Longmans	1913	Ford, H.J.	250-350	
Lang, Andrew	Tales of a Fairy Court (1st, 8vo, 108p, gilt, AEG, 12cp)	L: Collins	(1907)	Dixon, Arthur A.	170-240	
Lang, Andrew	Tales of Troy & Greece (1st, sm8vo, 302p, teg, uncut, 16pl)	L: Longmans	1907	Ford, H.J.	80-140	
Lang, Andrew	Tartan Tales (1st {std}, sm8vo, 301p, black cl, 8pl, pep, DJ/1.50)	Longmans	1928	Blaine, Mahlon	50-85	
Lang, Andrew	True Story Book (1st, 8vo, blue/gilt, 337p, AEG, 9pl, cep)	L: Longmans	1893	Various	200-300	
Lang, Andrew	Trusty John... (1st, sm8vo, maroon/gilt, 258p, col frn, 14pl)	L: Longmans	1906	Ford, H.J.	150-225	
Lang, Andrew	Violet Fairy Book (1st, 12mo, AEG, 388p, 8cp, cep)	L: Longmans	1901	Ford, H.J.	250-400	
Lang, Andrew	Yellow Fairy Book (1st, 12mo, AEG, 321p, 22pl, cep)	L: Longmans	1894	Ford, H.J.	220-320	
Lang, Andrew (ed)	Fairy Nurse & other Stories (1st, 12mo, 192p, gilt, col frn, b/w)	L: Longmans	1923	Ford, H.J.	45-70	
Lang, Andrew (ed)	History of Whittington (new ed., 8vo, 160p, fp b/w)	L: Longmans	1898	Ford/Hood	70-100	
Lang, Don	Nibs: Orphan Deer of the Adirondacks (1st, 8vo, 66p, b/w, DJ/0.50)	Grosset/Dunlap	(1942)	Wiese, Kurt	30-45	*
Lang, Don	Strawberry Roan (1st, 8vo, 218p, b/w, DJ/2.00)	NY: Oxford U.Pr.	1946	Howe, Gertrude	30-50	
Lang, Don	Tramp: The Sheep Dog (1st, sq8vo, [28]p, ibds, color, pep, DJ/0.50)	Grosset/Dunlap	(1938)	Wiese, Kurt	45-60	
Lang, Jeanie	Book of Myths (1st, 8vo, gilt, 340p, teg, uncut, 20cp)	L: Jack	1914	Stratton, Helen	100-160	
Lang, Jeanie	Stories from the Illiad (12mo, 119p, p-o, 8cp)	L: Jack	[1905]	Robinson, W. Heath	45-65	
Lang, Leonora B.	All Sorts of Stories Book (1st, 12mo, AEG, 377p, gilt, 5cp)	L: Longmans	1911	Ford, H.J.	200-325	
Lang, Leonora B.	Book of Saints & Heroes (1st, 8vo, blue/gilt, teg, 351p, 12cp)	L: Longmans	1912	Ford, H.J.	120-170	
Lang, Leonora B.	Red Book of Heroes (1st, 8vo, 368p, red/gilt, AEG, 8cp)	L: Longmans	1909	Mills, A. Wallis	140-220	
Langer, Susanne	Cruise of the Little Dipper (1st, 12mo, 176p, gilt, 5cp, pep)	NY: Norcross	(1923)	Sewell, Helen	120-180	
Langford, George	Stories of the First American Animals (1st, lg8vo, p-o, gilt, 5cp)	Boni/Liveright	(1923)	Mahon, Ty	55-80	*
Langley, Noel	Tale of the Land of Green Ginger (1st AM, lg4to, 143p, color, DJ/2.50)	Wm. Morrow	1938	Langley, Noel	280-400	
Langstaff, John	Frog Went A-Courtin' (1st {std}, 4to, [32]p, color, pep, DJ/2.50, CM)	Harcourt	(1955)	Rojankovsky, Feodor	140-200	R
Langstaff, John	Ol' Dan Tucker (1st {std}, sm4to, [33]p, color, cep, DJ/2.95)	Harcourt	(1963)	Krush, Joe	30-50	
Langstaff, John	Over in the Meadow (1st {std}, 4to, unpag, color, pep, DJ/2.75)	Harcourt	(1957)	Rojankovsky, Feodor	45-70	
Langstaff, John	Swapping Boy (1st {std}, sm4to, [32]p, color, pep, DJ/2.95)	Harcourt	(1960)	Krush, Beth & Joe	30-50	
Langton, Jane	Diamond in the Window (1st, 8vo, ibds, 242p, b/w, DJ/2.95)	Harper	1962	Blegvad, Erik	50-80	
Langton, Jane	Majesty of Grace (1st, 8vo, 190p, b/w, DJ/2.95)	Harper	(1961)	Langton, Jane	35-50	
Langton, Jane	Swing in the Summerhouse (1st, 8vo, ipcb, 185p, b/w, DJ/3.95)	Harper	(1967)	Blegvad, Erik	60-95	
Lanier, Sidney	Boy's Mabinogion (1st, 8vo, 361p, gilt, 12pl, cep, PPPa)	Scribner	1881	Fredericks, Alfred	150-250	
Lanier, Sidney	Knightly Legends of Wales (1st, 8vo, 361p, red/gilt, 12pl, cep)	Scribner	1901	Fredericks, Alfred	40-65	
Lansdale, M.H.	Chateaux of Touraine (1st, 4to, 363p, uncut, teg, gilt, 16cp)	Century	1906	Guerin, Jules	75-100	
Lansdown, Brenda	Galumph (1st, sq8vo, 48p, yellow cl, fp 2-color, DJ/3.00)	Houghton	1963	Crichlow, Ernest	25-45	*
Lansing, Elisabeth H.	Deer Mountain Hideaway (1st {std}, 8vo, 153p, b/w, DJ/2.50)	Crowell	(1953)	Simont, Marc	25-40	*
Lansing, Elisabeth H.	Deer River Raft (1st {std}, 8vo, 191p, b/w, DJ/2.50)	Crowell	(1955)	Simont, Marc	25-40	*
Lansing, Elisabeth H.	Jubilant for Sure (1st {std}, sm8vo, green cl, 148p, fp b/w, DJ/2.50)	Crowell	(1954)	Keats, Ezra J.	70-120	R
Lansing, Elisabeth H.	Lulu's Window (1st {std}, 8vo, 148p, fp b/w, DJ/2.50)	Crowell	(1954)	Paull, Grace	30-50	*
Lansing, Elisabeth H.	Pony that Kept a Secret (1st {std}, 8vo, 117p, b/w, pep, DJ/2.00)	Crowell	(1952)	Cooney, Barbara	40-65	
Lansing, Elisabeth H.	Pony that Ran Away (1st {std}, sm8vo, 149p, red cl, b/w, dep, DJ/2.00)	Crowell	(1951)	Cooney, Barbara	60-100	R
Lansing, Elisabeth H.	Pony Worth his Salt (1st {std}, 8vo, 168p, b/w, pep, DJ/2.00)	Crowell	1953	Cooney, Barbara	45-70	
Lansing, Elisabeth H.	Secret of Dark Entry (1st {std}, 8vo, 186p, b/w, DJ/3.00)	Crowell	(1961)	Shortall, Leonard	20-30	
Lansing, Elisabeth H.	Shoot for a Mule (1st {std}, 8vo, 121p, b/w, DJ/2.00)	Crowell	(1951)	Suba, Susanne	30-50	
Lansing, Elisabeth H.	Small Circus (1st, 8vo, 150p, b/w, DJ/2.50)	Crowell	(1957)	Krush, Beth & Joe	25-45	
Lansing, Elisabeth H.	Sure Thing for Shep (1st {std}, sm8vo, red cl, 177p, b/w, DJ/2.50)	Coward	(1956)	Keats, Ezra J.	35-60	
Lansing, Marion	Magic Gold (1st, 8vo, 302p, col frn, b/w, pep)	Little/Brown	1928	McIntosh, Frank	25-40	
Lansing, Marion	Man's Long Climb (1st, 8vo, 154p, b/w, pep, DJ/1.75)	Little/Brown	1933	Horvath, Ferdinand	40-65	*
Lansing, Marion	Nicholas Arnold, Toolmaker (1st {std}, 8vo, 277p, b/w pl, DJ/1.00)	Doubleday/Doran	1941	Sperry, Armstrong	30-50	*
Lardner, Ring	Bib Ballads (1st {1st bk.}, 8vo, teg, brown/gilt, [63]p, 2-color)	Volland	(1915)	Fox, Fontaine	200-280	R
Lardner, Ring	Big Town (1st, sm8vo, 244p, green cl, 5 tip-in pl)	Bobbs-Merrill	(1921)	Preston, May W.	100-165	
Lardner, Ring	Gullible's Travels (1st, sm8vo, blue cl, 255p, col frn, pep)	Bobbs-Merrill	(1917)	Preston, May W.	120-170	
Lardner, Ring	Story of a Wonder Man (1st, sm8vo, gilt, 151p, green cl, b/w)	Scribner	1927	Freeman, Margaret	70-120	
Larken, Edmund P.	Sea-Prince (1st, 12mo, blue/gilt, teg, 340p, b/w, dep)	L: Jarrold	1899	Bayes, Jessie M.	100-150	
Larned, William T.	American Indian Fairy Tales (1st, lg8vo, ibds, [88]p, color, pep)	Volland	(1921)	Rae, John	120-185	
Larned, William T.	Fairy Tales From France (1st, lg8vo, ibds, [93]p, color, pep)	Volland	(1920)	Rae, John	100-170	
Larom, Henry	Mountain Pony (1st {std}, 8vo, 240p, b/w, pep, DJ/2.00)	Whittlesey	(1946)	Santee, Ross	30-50	
Larrick, Nancy	Piping Down the Valleys Wild (1st {std}, 8vo, 247p, b/w, cep, DJ/4.95)	Delacorte Pr.	(1968)	Raskin, Ellen	20-35	
Larrimore, Lida	Blossoming of Patricia-The-Less (1st, 8vo, 253p, p-o, 4cp, pep)	Penn	1924	Price, Hattie L.	50-80	
Larson, Jean R.	Jack Tar (1st, 8vo, 76p, b/w, DJ/3.95)	Macrae Smith	(1970)	Mayer, Mercer	20-35	
Larson, Jean R.	Palace in Bagdad (1st, sm4to, 94p, b/w, DJ/3.50)	Scribner	(1966)	Yamaguchi, Marianne	30-45	*

AUTHOR	TITLE	PUBLISHER	DATE	ARTIST	PRICE	LC
Larson, Jean R.	Silkspinners (1st, 8vo, 93p, b/w, DJ/3.95)	Scribner	(1967)	Shulevitz, Uri	25-40	
Laskowski, Jerzy	Dragon Liked Smoked Fish (1st, 4to, [32]p, fp 3-color, DJ/3.95)	Seabury Press	(1967)	Domanska, Janina	30-50	
Laskowski, Jerzy	Master of the Royal Cats (1st, 4to, [32]p, color, DJ/3.50)	Seabury Press	(1965)	Domanska, Janina	30-45	*
Lasky, Muriel	Proud Little Kitten (1st, 4to, ibds, 32p, color)	Universal Books	1944	Erika	30-50	
Latham, Barbara	Perrito's Pup (1st {std}, lg ob8vo, ibds, [32]p, color, DJ/1.25)	Knopf	(1946)	Latham, Barbara	50-80	*
Latham, Jean L.	Aladdin (1st, 8vo, [32]p, ipcb, color, DJ/1.95)	Bobbs-Merrill	1961	Ramirez, Pablo	30-50	
Latham, Jean L.	Ali Baba (1st, 8vo, [32]p, ipcb, color, DJ/1.95)	Bobbs-Merrill	1961	Ramirez, Pablo	30-50	
Latham, Jean L.	Anchor's Aweigh... (1st, 8vo, 273p, b/w, DJ/4.50)	Harper	(1968)	Keith, Eros	40-65	
Latham, Jean L.	Carry On, Mr. Bowditch (1st, 8vo, green cl, 251p, fp b/w, DJ/2.75, NM)	Houghton	1955	Cosgrave, John O.	70-120	
Latham, Jean L.	Columbia: Power House of North America (1st, 8vo, 96p, color, DJ)	Garrard Pub.	(1967)	Kilem, Fred	30-50	
Latham, Jean L.	Cuckoo that Couldn't Count (1st {std}, 8vo, ibds, [32]p, fp color, DJ/2.50)	Macmillan	1961	Chwast, Jacqueline	30-50	
Latham, Jean L.	David Glasgow Faragut: Our First Admiral (1st, 8vo, 80p, color, DJ)	Garrard Pub.	(1967)	Frame, Paul	30-50	
Latham, Jean L.	Dog that Lost his Family (1st {std}, 8vo, [32]p, fp 2-color, DJ/2.50)	Macmillan	1961	Kuskin, Karla	30-50	
Latham, Jean L.	Drake: The Man they Called a Pirate (1st, 8vo, 278p, b/w, DJ/2.95)	Harper	(1960)	Chapman, Fred T.	30-50	
Latham, Jean L.	Eli Whitney (1st, 8vo, 80p, fp 3-color, DJ/2.50)	Garrard Pub.	(1963)	Cary	30-50	
Latham, Jean L.	Far Voyager: Story of James Cook (1st, 8vo, 242p, b/w, DJ/4.50)	Harper	(1970)	Suecklen, Karl	30-50	
Latham, Jean L.	Frightened Hero (1st {std}, sm8vo, 97p, 1-color, pep, DJ/3.50)	Chilton Books	(1965)	Latham, Barbara	30-50	
Latham, Jean L.	Jack the Giant-Killer (1st, 8vo, [32]p, p-o, color, DJ/1.95)	Bobbs-Merrill	1961	Ramierz, Pablo	30-50	
Latham, Jean L.	Man of the Monitor: Story of John Ericsson (1st, 8vo, 231p, b/w, DJ/3.50)	Harper	(1962)	Fisher, Leonard	30-50	
Latham, Jean L.	Man Who Never Snoozed (1st {std}, 8vo, [32]p, 2-color, DJ/2.50)	Macmillan	1961	Greenwald, Sheila	40-65	
Latham, Jean L.	Medals for Morse: Artist & Inventor (1st {std}, 8vo, 192p, 1-color, DJ/1.75)	Aladdin	1954	Gorsline, Douglas	30-50	
Latham, Jean L.	Nutcracker (1st, 8vo, [32]p, p-o, color, DJ/1.95)	Bobbs-Merrill	1961	Carreas, Jose	30-50	
Latham, Jean L.	On Stage, Mr. Jefferson! (1st {std}, 8vo, 266p, grey cl, DJ/2.95)	Harper	(1958)	Shenton, Edward	30-50	
Latham, Jean L.	Puss in Boots (1st, 8vo, [32]p, p-o, fp color, DJ/1.95)	Bobbs-Merrill	1961	Ramirez, Pablo	30-50	
Latham, Jean L.	Story of Eli Whitney (1st {std}, 8vo, 192p, b/w, DJ/1.75)	Aladdin	1953	Kredel, Fritz	45-70	
Latham, Jean L.	This Dear-Bought Land (1st {std}, 8vo, 246p, b/w, DJ/2.75)	Harper	(1957)	Landau, Jacob	30-50	
Latham, Jean L.	Trail Blazer of the Seas (1st, 8vo, 245p, b/w, DJ/2.75)	Houghton	1956	Mays, Victor	40-70	
Latham, Jean L.	When Homer Honked (1st {std}, 8vo, [32]p, 1-color, DJ/2.50)	Macmillan	1961	Szekeres, Cyndy	30-45	
Latham, Jean L.	Young Man in a Hurry (1st, 8vo, 238p, b/w, DJ/2.95)	Harper	(1958)	Mays, Victor	30-45	
Lathbury, M.A.	April Skies (1st, 4to, ibds, [25]p, 12 chromos)	Worthington	1889	Lathbury, M.A.	100-175	
Lathbury, M.A.	Idyls of the Months (4to, ibds, gilt, unpag, AEG, 14 chromos)	L: Routledge	(1885)	Lathbury, M.A.	250-400	
Lathbury, M.A.	Ring-a-Round-a-Rosy (4to, ibds, 13 chromos)	Worthington	1885	Lathbury, M.A.	125-200	
Lathrop, Dorothy	Angel in the Woods (1st {std}, 8vo, red cl, [48]p, fp b/w, cep, DJ/2.00)	Macmillan	1947	Lathrop, Dorothy	60-100	
Lathrop, Dorothy	Bouncing Betsy (1st, lg ob8vo, [41]p, 16pl, DJ/1.50)	Macmillan	1936	Lathrop, Dorothy	60-100	
Lathrop, Dorothy	Colt from Moon Mountain (1st, 8vo, [62]p, b/w, pep, DJ/1.75)	Macmillan	1941	Lathrop, Dorothy	140-200	
Lathrop, Dorothy	Dog in the Tapestry Garden (1st {std}, 8vo, ipcb, 42p, fp b/w, DJ/2.50)	Macmillan	1962	Lathrop, Dorothy	60-90	
Lathrop, Dorothy	Fairy Circus (1st {1st bk.}, lg ob8vo, gilt, 67p, 8cp, 12pl, NH)	Macmillan	1931	Lathrop, Dorothy	200-300	
Lathrop, Dorothy	Follow the Brook (1st {std}, sm4to, blue cl, 40p, fp b/w, DJ/3.25)	Macmillan	(1960)	Lathrop, Dorothy	70-120	
Lathrop, Dorothy	Hide and Go Seek (1st, sm4to, grey cl, [40]p, fp b/w, pep, DJ/1.75)	Macmillan	1938	Lathrop, Dorothy	80-130	
Lathrop, Dorothy	Let Them Live (1st {std}, 8vo, orange cl, 80p, fp b/w, cep, DJ/2.00)	Macmillan	1951	Lathrop, Dorothy	70-120	
Lathrop, Dorothy	Little White Goat (1st, ob4to, 59p, col frn, 15pl, pep)	Macmillan	1933	Lathrop, Dorothy	100-160	
Lathrop, Dorothy	Littlest Mouse (1st {std}, sm8vo, ibds, 32p, b/w, DJ/2.25)	Macmillan	(1955)	Lathrop, Dorothy	60-90	
Lathrop, Dorothy	Lost Merry-Go-Round (1st, sq8vo, 104p, col frn, 10pl, pep)	Macmillan	1934	Lathrop, Dorothy	120-170	
Lathrop, Dorothy	Presents for Lupe (1st, sm sq4to, orange cl, [40]p, color, dep, DJ/2.00)	Macmillan	1940	Lathrop, Dorothy	60-100	
Lathrop, Dorothy	Puffy & Seven Leaf Clover (1st {std}, 8vo, 34p, 2-color, cep, DJ/2.50)	Macmillan	(1954)	Lathrop, Dorothy	50-90	
Lathrop, Dorothy	Puppies for Keeps (1st {std}, lg ob8vo, brown cl, [40]p, color, DJ/2.00)	Macmillan	1943	Lathrop, Dorothy	80-145	
Lathrop, Dorothy	Skittle-Skattle Monkey (1st, lg8vo, red cl, [48]p, fp b/w, DJ/1.75)	Macmillan	1945	Lathrop, Dorothy	100-150	
Lathrop, Dorothy	Snail Who Ran (1st, 16mo, green cl, 57p, col frn, fp b/w)	Stokes	1934	Lathrop, Dorothy	50-90	
Lathrop, Dorothy	Who Goes There? (1st, sm ob4to, [40]p, 16 fp b/w, pep, DJ/1.50)	Macmillan	1935	Lathrop, Dorothy	100-165	
Lathrop, West	Juneau: Sleigh Dog (1st {std}, 8vo, 279p, blue/silver, b/w, DJ/2.00)	Random	(1942)	Wiese, Kurt	25-40	
Lattimore, Eleanor	Bayou Boy (1st {std}, 4to, 128p, b/w, pep, DJ/2.00)	Wm. Morrow	1946	Lattimore, Eleanor	80-130	
Lattimore, Eleanor	Bells for a Chinese Donkey (1st, 8vo, 126p, pep, DJ/2.00)	Wm. Morrow	1951	Lattimore, Eleanor	40-65	
Lattimore, Eleanor	Bittern's Nest (1st, 8vo, 127p, b/w, DJ/2.75)	Wm. Morrow	1962	Lattimore, Eleanor	40-65	*
Lattimore, Eleanor	Christopher and his Turtle (1st, 8vo, 126p, pep, DJ/2.00)	Wm. Morrow	1950	Lattimore, Eleanor	40-70	
Lattimore, Eleanor	Clever Cat (1st, sm8vo, 113p, b/w pl, pep, DJ/1.50)	Harcourt	1936	Lattimore, Eleanor	60-90	*
Lattimore, Eleanor	Cousin Melinda (1st, 8vo, 128p, b/w, pep, DJ/2.75)	Wm. Morrow	1961	Lattimore, Eleanor	30-50	
Lattimore, Eleanor	Davy of the Everglades (1st, 8vo, 127p, b/w, pep, DJ/2.00)	Wm. Morrow	1949	Lattimore, Eleanor	30-50	*
Lattimore, Eleanor	Deborah's White Winter (1st, 8vo, 124p, b/w, DJ/2.00)	Wm. Morrow	1949	Lattimore, Eleanor	25-45	
Lattimore, Eleanor	Happiness for Kimi (1st, 8vo, 126p, b/w, DJ/2.50)	Wm. Morrow	1958	Lattimore, Eleanor	25-45	
Lattimore, Eleanor	Holly in the Snow (1st, 8vo, 125p, b/w, pep, DJ/2.25)	Wm. Morrow	1954	Lattimore, Eleanor	30-45	
Lattimore, Eleanor	Indigo Hill (1st, 8vo, 128p, pep, DJ/2.00)	Wm. Morrow	1950	Lattimore, Eleanor	30-45	
Lattimore, Eleanor	Jasper (1st, 8vo, 128p, b/w, DJ/2.00)	Wm. Morrow	1953	Lattimore, Eleanor	30-50	
Lattimore, Eleanor	Jeremy's Isle (1st, 8vo, 123p, fp b/w, pep, DJ/2.00)	Wm. Morrow	1947	Lattimore, Eleanor	40-65	
Lattimore, Eleanor	Jerry and the Pusa (1st, 8vo, 197p, uncut, fp b/w, pep)	Harcourt	(1932)	Lattimore, Eleanor	200-300	
Lattimore, Eleanor	Junior, Colored Boy of Charleston (1st, 8vo, 129p, dep, fp b/w, DJ/2.00)	Harcourt	(1938)	Lattimore, Eleanor	75-125	
Lattimore, Eleanor	Little Pear (1st {1st bk.}, 8vo, 144p, uncut, fp b/w, pep)	Harcourt	(1931)	Lattimore, Eleanor	180-250	
Lattimore, Eleanor	Little Pear and his Friends (1st, 8vo, 178p, red cl, fp b/w, pep)	Harcourt	(1934)	Lattimore, Eleanor	100-170	
Lattimore, Eleanor	Little Pear and the Rabbits (1st, 8vo, 125p, b/w, pep, DJ/2.50)	Wm. Morrow	(1956)	Lattimore, Eleanor	50-85	*
Lattimore, Eleanor	Lost Leopard (1st, sm ob8vo, orange cl, 104p, 8cp, pep, DJ/2.00)	Harcourt	(1935)	Lattimore, Eleanor	60-90	
Lattimore, Eleanor	Molly in the Middle (1st, 8vo, 127p, b/w, pep, DJ/2.25)	Wm. Morrow	1956	Lattimore, Eleanor	30-50	
Lattimore, Eleanor	Peachblossom (1st, 8vo, 96p, fp b/w, pep, DJ/2.00)	Harcourt	(1943)	Lattimore, Eleanor	40-65	*
Lattimore, Eleanor	Questions of Lifu (1st, 8vo, 104p, 1-color, DJ/2.00)	Harcourt	(1942)	Lattimore, Eleanor	45-70	
Lattimore, Eleanor	Seven Crowns (1st, sm8vo, 189p, green cl, fp b/w, pep)	Harcourt	(1933)	Lattimore, Eleanor	180-240	
Lattimore, Eleanor	Turkistan Reunion (1st, 8vo, 296p, orange cl, 14pl, pep, DJ/2.75)	Hurst/Blackett	(1935)	(Photos)	120-200	*
Lau, Josephine	Cheeky: A Prairie Dog (1st, lg8vo, 62p, p-o, color, pep, DJ/1.50)	Whitman	1937	Wiese, Kurt	40-65	
Lauber, Patricia	Runaway Flea Circus (1st {std}, 8vo, 72p, 1-color, DJ/1.95)	Random	(1958)	Barnes, Catherine	20-35	
Laughlin, Clara E.	Felicity (1st, sm8vo, green/gilt, 426p, 4cp)	Scribner	1907	Stephens, Alice B.	30-50	
Laughlin, Elmer O.	Johnnie (1st, 12mo, 227p, teg, uncut)	Bowen-Merrill	1898	(Photos)	30-50	

AUTHOR	TITLE	PUBLISHER	DATE	ARTIST	PRICE	LC
Laune, Paul	Thirsty Pony (1st, 4to, [31]p, ibds, color, pep, DJ/0.50)	Grosset/Dunlap	(1940)	Laune, Paul	25-40	
Lauring, Paul	Stone Daggers (1st AM {std}, 8vo, 160p, b/w, DJ/3.50)	Macmillan	(1964)	Ohlsson, Ib	40-65	
Lawless, Emily	Book of Gilly (1st, 8vo, 298p, blue/gilt, teg, uncut, 4pl)	L: Smith Elder	1906	Brooke, L. Leslie	80-125	
Lawrence, C.H.	Santa Claus in Toyland (1st, 4to, 96p, ibds, 8cp, 12pl)	Reilly/Britton	(1915)	Lawrence, C.H.	140-220	
Lawrence, Jacob	Harriet & the Promised Land (1st {std}, lg4to, [32]p, color, DJ/5.95, NYTBI)	Windmill Books	(1968)	Lawrence, Jacob	250-350	R
Lawrence, John	Giant of Grabbist (1st AM, 4to, [32]p, ibds, color, DJ/3.95)	NY: David White	1969	Lawrence, John	45-70	
Lawrence, John	Pope Leo's Elephant (1st AM {std}, 12mo, [32]p, color, DJ/3.95)	World	(1970)	Lawrence, John	25-40	*
Lawrence, Josephine	Man in the Moon Stories... (1st, 4to, 121p, gilt, p-o, 8cp, pep)	Cupples/Leon	(1922)	Gruelle, Johnny	200-300	
Lawrence, Josephine	Rainbow Hill (1st, sm8vo, 312p, blue bds, 4pl)	Cupples/Leon	1924	Gooch, Thelma	20-30	
Lawrence, Mildred	Crissy at the Wheel (1st {std}, 8vo, 200p, DJ/2.50)	Harcourt	(1952)	Bileck, Marvin	25-45	*
Lawrence, Mildred	Peachtree Island (1st, 8vo, 224p, fp b/w, DJ/2.25)	Harcourt	(1948)	Stevens, Mary	50-80	
Lawson, Ellsworth	Euphrosyne & her Golden Book (1st, 8vo, 141p, green/gilt, cvr by...)	Herbert Stone	1901	Hazenplug, Frank	35-50	
Lawson, Lizzie	Christmas Roses (lg8vo, [31]p, ibds, 10 chromos, pep)	Nister/Dutton	[1880]	Lawson, Lizzie	170-240	
Lawson, Marie A.	Dragon John (1st, 8vo, 51p, green cl, 2-color, dep, DJ/1.50)	Viking	1943	Lawson, Marie A.	50-90	
Lawson, Marie A.	Hail Columbia (1st {std}, lg8vo, 387p, 7cp, 2-color, pep)	Doubleday/Doran	1931	Lawson, Marie A.	40-65	
Lawson, Marie A.	Sea is Blue (1st, 8vo, 126p, pep, 11 fp 1-color, DJ/2.00)	Viking	1946	Lawson, Marie A.	50-80	
Lawson, Robert	At that Time (1st, lg8vo, 127p, b/w, DJ/2.50)	Viking	1947	Lawson, Robert	60-90	
Lawson, Robert	Ben & Me (1st {std}, sq8vo, 114p, brown cl, b/w, pep, DJ/1.75)	Little/Brown	1939	Lawson, Robert	200-300	R
Lawson, Robert	Captain Kidd's Cat (1st {std}, 8vo, 151p, green cl, b/w, DJ/3.00)	Little/Brown	(1956)	Lawson, Robert	80-145	
Lawson, Robert	Country Colic (1st {std}, sq8vo, 66p, beige cl, b/w, pep, DJ/1.75)	Little/Brown	1944	Lawson, Robert	50-85	
Lawson, Robert	Edward, Hoppy & Joe (1st, 8vo, 122p, fp b/w, pep, DJ/2.50)	Knopf	(1952)	Lawson, Robert	150-225	
Lawson, Robert	Fabulous Flight (1st {std}, lg8vo, 152p, green cl, b/w, pep, DJ/2.75)	Little/Brown	1949	Lawson, Robert	70-120	
Lawson, Robert	Great Wheel (1st, lg8vo, 188p, pep, b/w, green cl, DJ/3.00, NH)	Viking	(1957)	Lawson, Robert	80-120	
Lawson, Robert	I Discover Columbus (1st {std}, 8vo, blue cl, 110p, b/w, pep, DJ/1.75)	Little/Brown	1941	Lawson, Robert	100-170	
Lawson, Robert	McWhinney's Jaunt (1st {std}, sq8vo, 77p, cloth, fp b/w, DJ/2.50)	Little/Brown	1951	Lawson, Robert	80-140	
Lawson, Robert	Mr. Revere & I (1st {std}, 8vo, 152p, b/w, pep, DJ/3.00)	Little/Brown	(1953)	Lawson, Robert	80-125	R
Lawson, Robert	Mr. Twigg's Mistake (1st {std}, 8vo, 143p, aqua cl, b/w, pep, DJ/2.50)	Little/Brown	1947	Lawson, Robert	80-125	
Lawson, Robert	Mr. Wilmer (1st {std}, sm8vo, 218p, beige cl, b/w, DJ/2.00)	Little/Brown	1945	Lawson, Robert	70-100	
Lawson, Robert	Rabbit Hill (1st, lg8vo, 128p, 1-color, pep, DJ/2.50, NM)	Viking	1944	Lawson, Robert	140-220	R
Lawson, Robert	Robbut: Tale of Tails (1st, 4to, ibds, 94p, b/w, pep, DJ/2.50)	Viking	1948	Lawson, Robert	80-140	
Lawson, Robert	Smeller Martin (1st, lg8vo, green cl, 157p, fp b/w, DJ/2.50)	Viking	1950	Lawson, Robert	60-100	
Lawson, Robert	They Were Strong & Good (1st, 4to, [68]p, fp b/w, pep, DJ/1.50, CM)	Viking	1940	Lawson, Robert	170-250	
Lawson, Robert	Tough Winter (1st, lg8vo, 128p, blue/silver, b/w, pep, DJ/3.00)	Viking	1954	Lawson, Robert	80-125	
Lawson, Robert	Watchwords of Liberty (1st {std}, sm4to, 115p, b/w, pep, DJ/2.00)	Little/Brown	1943	Lawson, Robert	60-100	
Layard, Arthur	Harriet Hare (1st, 16mo, grey bds, 88p, p-o, 20cp)	L: Nisbet	[1907]	Layard, Arthur	70-100	
Layard, George S.	Cruikshank's Portraits of Himself (1st, 8vo, 98p, 17pl)	L: Spencer	1897	Cruikshank, George	120-180	
Layard, George S.	Suppressed Plates... (1st, 8vo, 254p, gilt, b/w)	L: A&C Black	1907	Various	140-200	
Le Guin, Ursula K.	Wizard of Earthsea (1st, 8vo, 205p, fp b/w, cep, DJ/3.95)	Parnassus Press	(1968)	Robbins, Ruth	150-225	
Le Marchand, Jacques	Adventures of Ulysses (1st, lg4to, 48p, fp color, pep, DJ/3.95)	Criterion Bks.	(1960)	Francois, Andre	40-65	*
LeBaron, Grace	Twixt You & Me (1st, 12mo, 296p, decorations by...)	Little/Brown	1898	Pyle, Katharine	40-60	*
LeBaron, Grace	Twixt You & Me (1st, 12mo, 296p, 5pl by...)	Little/Brown	1898	Thompson, E.B.	40-60	*
LeBlanc, Georgette	Children's Blue Bird (1st, 8vo, ibds, 172p, 12cp)	L: Methuen	1913	Rothenstein, Albert	80-120	
LeCain, Errol	Cabbage Princess (1st, 4to, unpag, ibds, color, pep, DJ)	L: Faber	1969	LeCain, Errol	70-100	
LeFanu, J. Sheridan	In a Glass Darkly (1st {1st illus bk.}, 8vo, black/gilt, 382p, b/w)	L: P. Davies	1929	Ardizzone, Edward	150-250	
LeFevre, A.	Odd One (1st, sq8vo, uncut, 142p, b/w)	Revell	1898	Lathbury, M.A.	35-60	*
LeFevre, A.	Puzzling Pair (1st, sq8vo, 144p, b/w)	Revell	1898	Lance, Eveline	25-40	*
LeGallienne, Eva	Flossie & Bossie (1st {std}, sm8vo, 210p, 30 fp b/w, DJ/2.00)	Harper	(1949)	Williams, Garth	60-100	R
LeGallienne, R.	Maker of Rainbows (1st, 8vo, 104p, gilt, teg, p-o, 2cp, 3pl)	Harper	1912	Green, Eliz. S.	120-200	R
LeGallienne, R.	Mr. Sun & Mrs. Moon (1st, folio, bds, [62]p, 12pl)	R.H. Russell	1902	Unknown	220-280	R
LeGallienne, R.	October Vagabonds (1st, 8vo, ipcb, teg, gilt, 201p, col frn, pep)	Kennerley	1910	Fogarty, Thomas	55-90	R
LeGallienne, R.	Old Country House (1st, 4to, bds, teg, 144p, 6pl)	Harper	1902	Green, Eliz. S.	120-200	
LeGallienne, R.	Perseus & Andromeda (1st, 8vo, teg, gilt, p-o, uncut, 53p, 6pl)	R.H. Russell	1902	Various	50-90	R
LeGallienne, R.	Prose Fancies (1st AM, 12mo, gilt, 201p, cvr by...)	Herbert Stone	1896	Hazenplug, Frank	70-100	
LeGallienne, R.	Quest of the Golden Girl (1st, sm8vo, green/gilt, 308p, teg, cvr by...)	J. Lane	1896	Bradley, Will	90-120	
LeGallienne, R.	Romance of Perfume (1st, sm4to, 46p, ipcb, 8cp)	R. Hadnut	1928	Barbier, George	75-120	
LeGallienne, R.	Romance of Zion Chapel (1st {std}, sm8vo, 297p, teg, cvr by...)	J. Lane	1898	Bradley, Will	100-165	
LeGallienne, R.	Wagner's Tristan & Isolde (1st, 4to, 358p, black/gilt, teg, 7cp)	Stokes	(1909)	Williams, George A.	120-200	
LeGallienne, R.	Young Lives (1st, sm8vo, teg, 386p, cvr by...)	J. Lane	1899	Bradley, Will	100-145	
LeMair, H.W.	Auntie's Little Rhyme Book (ob 16mo, ibds, [26]p, 10 color)	Augener/McKay	[1918]	LeMair, H.W.	140-225	
LeMair, H.W.	Baby's Little Rhyme Book (ob 12mo, ibds, [28]p, 10 color)	L: Augener	[1920]	LeMair, H.W.	125-200	
LeMair, H.W.	Daddy's Little Rhyme Book (ob 16mo, ibds, [28]p, 10 color)	L: Augener	[1920]	LeMair, H.W.	130-200	
LeMair, H.W.	Granny's Little Rhyme Book (ob16mo, [28]p, ibds, 12 color)	L: Augener	(1912)	LeMair, H.W.	125-200	
LeMair, H.W.	Mother's Little Rhyme Book (ob 16mo, ibds, [28]p, color)	McKay	[1915]	LeMair, H.W.	120-170	
LeMair, H.W.	Nursie's Little Rhyme Book. (ob16mo, ibds, [26]p, 10 color)	Augener/McKay	[1915]	LeMair, H.W.	140-220	
LeSieg, Theo	Come Over to My House (1st, 8vo, 63p, ibds, color, pep, DJ/1.95)	Beginner Books	(1966)	Erdoes, Richard	40-65	*
LeSieg, Theo	Eye Book (1st, 8vo, [29]p, ibds, color, pep, DJ/1.95)	Beginner Books	(1968)	McKie, Roy	40-65	*
LeSieg, Theo	I Wish that I Had Duck Feet (1st, 8vo, 64p, ibds, fp color, cep, DJ/1.95)	Beginner Books	(1965)	Tobey, Barney	40-65	*
LeSieg, Theo	Ten Apples Up on Top! (1st, 8vo, 59p, ibds, 2-color, pep, DJ/1.95)	Beginner Books	(1961)	McKie, Roy	40-65	*
LeSueur, Meridel	Little Brother of the Wilderness (1st {std}, 8vo, 68p, fp color, DJ/2.50)	Knopf	1947	Alden, Betty	50-75	
LeSueur, Meridel	Nancy Hanks of Wilderness Road (1st {std}, 8vo, 88p, color, DJ/2.50)	Knopf	(1949)	Alden, Betty	40-65	*
LeWitt, Jan	The Vegetabull (1st {std}, 4to, ibds, [32]p, color, DJ/3.00)	Harcourt	1956	LeWitt, Jan	70-130	*
Lea, John	Magic Knocker (1st, sm4to, ibds, color)	Stokes	[1914]	Cowham, Hilda	100-150	
Lea, John	Queerie at the Pole (1st, 4to, ibds, 82p, 16cp)	L: A. Melrose	1911	Sinclair, James R.	250-350	
Lea, John	Willie Wimple's Adventures (1st, 4to, ibds, 16cp)	L: T.F. Unwin	(1908)	Cowham, Hilda	225-350	
Leach, Maria	How the People Sang the Mountains Up (1st, lg8vo, 159p, b/w, DJ/3.75)	Viking	(1967)	Rounds, Glen	20-30	
Leach, Maria	Luck Book (1st {std}, 8vo, 111p, b/w, DJ/2.95)	World	(1964)	Werth, Kurt	20-35	
Leach, Maria	Noodles, Nitwits and Numskulls (1st {std}, sm4to, 96p, b/w, DJ/2.95)	World	(1961)	Werth, Kurt	25-40	*
Leach, Maria	Rainbow Book of American Folk Tales (1st {std}, 4to, 318p, color)	World	(1958)	Simont, Marc	50-85	

AUTHOR	TITLE	PUBLISHER	DATE	ARTIST	PRICE	LC
Leach, Maria	Riddle Me, Riddle Me, Ree (1st {std}, lg8vo, 142p, DJ/3.95)	Viking	(1970)	Wiesner, William	25-40	
Leacock, Stephen B.	Nonsense Novels (1st, 8vo, 176p, grey bds, gilt, 8 color)	L: J. Lane	1921	Kettelwell, John	70-100	
Leaf, Munro	Boo, Who Used to be Scared of the Dark (1st, 4to, [40]p, ibds, color, pep)	Random	1948	Hunter, Frances T.	100-160	
Leaf, Munro	Fair Play (1st, 4to, 94p, blue cl, b/w, DJ/1.50)	Stokes	1939	Leaf, Munro	70-100	
Leaf, Munro	Ferdinand the Bull (4to, wraps, 31p, color)	Whitman	(1936)	Disney Studios	170-250	
Leaf, Munro	Ferdinand the Bull (1st, 4to, [8]p, stiff wraps, color)	Whitman	(1938)	Disney Studios	120-180	R
Leaf, Munro	Ferdinand the Bull (1st {this pub}, ob8vo, [14]p, wraps, 6 color)	Dell	1938	Disney Studios	100-165	
Leaf, Munro	Flock of Watchbirds (1st {std}, sm8vo, [42]p, red cl, color, DJ/1.50)	Lippincott	(1946)	Leaf, Munro	40-65	
Leaf, Munro	Gordon the Goat (1st {std}, 8vo, green cl, 48p, color, DJ/1.00)	Lippincott	(1944)	Leaf, Munro	60-90	
Leaf, Munro	John Henry Davis (1st, 8vo, 56p, red/black, color, pep, DJ/1.00)	Stokes	1940	Leaf, Munro	50-80	
Leaf, Munro	Listen Little Girl (1st, 8vo, 196p, DJ/1.50, decor by...)	Stokes	1938	Rose, Dick	40-60	
Leaf, Munro	Lucky You (1st {std}, 4to, 47p, red cl, b/w, DJ/2.25)	Lippincott	(1955)	Leaf, Munro	30-50	
Leaf, Munro	Manners Can be Fun (1st, sm4to, 45p, b/w, pep, DJ/1.25)	Stokes	1936	Leaf, Munro	100-150	
Leaf, Munro	Noodle (1st, sm ob4to, brown cl, [48]p, fp 1-color, pep, DJ/1.50)	Stokes	1937	Bemelmans, Ludwig	250-350	
Leaf, Munro	Robert Francis Weatherbee (1st, 12mo, 75p, blue cl, color, DJ/1.00)	Stokes	1935	Leaf, Munro	65-90	
Leaf, Munro	Sam and the Superdroop (1st, 8vo, 122p, b/w, DJ/1.50)	Viking	1948	Leaf, Munro	80-120	
Leaf, Munro	Story of Ferdinand (1st, 8vo, ibds, [81]p, b/w, pep, DJ/1.00)	Viking	1936	Lawson, Robert	900-1400	R
Leaf, Munro	Story of Simpson & Sampson (1st, sm4to, [64]p, blue cl, b/w pep, DJ/1.50)	Viking	1941	Lawson, Robert	120-200	
Leaf, Munro	This is Ann, She's Dying to Meet You (1st, 24mo, [36]p, wraps, 1-color)	DC: U.S. GPO	(1943)	Seuss, Dr.	650-800	
Leaf, Munro	Turnabout (1st {std}, 8vo, [34]p, 2-color, DJ/3.75)	Lippincott	1967	Leaf, Munro	30-50	
Leaf, Munro	Wee Gillis (1st, 4to, ipcb, [71]p, 33 fp b/w, pep, DJ/1.50, CH)	Viking	1938	Lawson, Robert	150-250	R
Leamy, Edmund	Fairy Minstrel of Glenmalure (1st, sm8vo, 92p, p-o, 4cp)	D. Fitzgerald	(1913)	Casseau, Vera	50-85	*
Leamy, Edmund	Fairy Minstrel of Glenmalure ([school ed.], sm8vo, 92p, b/w)	Longmans	1937	Bennett, Richard	30-50	*
Leanard, Rachel	Funny Bunny (1st, folio, ibds, [25]p, color, BGB)	Simon/Schuster	(1950)	Provensen, A.& M.	80-130	
Lear, Edward	Alphabet Book (1st, ob8vo, ibds, [55]p, color, pep)	Reilly/Britton	(1915)	Richardson, F.	120-165	
Lear, Edward	Dong with a Luminous Nose (1st, ob8vo, [46]p, b/w, DJ/2.95, NYTBI)	Young Scott	(1969)	Gorey, Edward	70-120	R
Lear, Edward	Duck & the Kangaroo (1st, 12mo, [56]p, pep, color)	Western Printing	(1932)	Ward, Keith	55-80	*
Lear, Edward	Four Little Children/Went around World (1st {std}, 4to, [32]p, 1-col, pep)	Harlin Quist	1967	Mack, Stanley	30-50	*
Lear, Edward	Four Little Children/Went around World (1st {std}, 8vo, 44p, DJ/3.95)	Macmillan	(1968)	Lobel, Arnold	30-50	
Lear, Edward	Lear's Nonsense Verses (1st, 4to, [42]p, color, DJ/1.25)	Grosset/Dunlap	(1967)	Ungerer, Tomi	45-70	*
Lear, Edward	Limericks by Lear (1st {std}, 4to, unpag, fp color, DJ/3.95)	World	(1965)	Ehlert, Lois	25-40	
Lear, Edward	New Vestments (1st {std}, 8vo, [32]p, color, ibds, DJ/3.95)	Bradbury Press	(1970)	Lobel, Arnold	30-45	
Lear, Edward	Nonsense Songs (1st, 8vo, AEG, [148]p, gilt, 14cp, pep)	L: Warne	[1900]	Brooke, L. Leslie	170-240	
Lear, Edward	Owl & the Pussycat (1st, ob8vo, [56]p, color, pep)	Whitman	(1932)	Ward, Keith	35-60	*
Lear, Edward	Owl & the Pussycat (1st {std}, 8vo, 26p, color, DJ/2.95)	Little/Brown	(1961)	Cooney, Barbara	40-65	*
Lear, Edward	Owl & the Pussycat (1st {std}, 12mo, gilt, unpag, color, pep, DJ/1.75)	Doubleday	1961	DuBois, W.P.	30-50	*
Lear, Edward	Owl & the Pussycat (1st {std}, 4to, [34]p, ibds, color, DJ/3.95)	Follett	1969	Maxey, Dale	25-40	
Lear, Edward	Pelican Chorus (1st, sq8vo, [63]p, ibds, p-o, 7cp)	L: Warne	(1899)	Brooke, L. Leslie	100-175	
Lear, Edward	Pelican Chorus (1st, 8vo, [41]p, gilt, color, pep, DJ/2.95)	Parents Mag. Pr.	(1967)	Berson, Harold	25-40	
Lear, Edward	Quangle Wangle's Hat (1st, 4to, [32]p, color, DJ, KGM)	L: Heinemann	(1969)	Oxenbury, Helen	60-90	
Lear, Edward	Quangle Wangle's Hat (1st AM, 4to, [32]p, color, pep, DJ/4.95, KGM)	F. Watts	(1970)	Oxenbury, Helen	50-85	
Lear, Edward	Scroobius Pip (1st, lg4to, [28]p, fp color, pep, DJ/3.95)	Harper	(1968)	Burkert, Nancy	40-65	
Lear, Edward	Story of the Four Little Children... (1st, 4to, [32]p, b/w, DJ/2.95)	Harlin Quist	1967	Mack, Stanley	50-80	
Lear, Edward	The Jumblies (1st, sq8vo, [64]p, ibds, p-o, 14cp, pep)	L: Warne	(1900)	Brooke, L. Leslie	120-170	
Lear, Edward	The Jumblies (1st, ob8vo, [48]p, tan cl, b/w, DJ/2.95)	Young Scott	(1968)	Gorey, Edward	60-90	
Lear, Edward	Two Old Bachelors (1st, 4to, [32]p, fp 2-color, pep, DJ/2.50)	Whittlesey	(1962)	Galdone, Paul	40-60	R*
Learnard, Rachel	Lucky Pete (1st, 8vo, 158p, fp b/w, DJ/2.50)	Abelard-Schuman	1954	Fiammenghi, Gioia	30-45	*
Learnard, Rachel	Mrs. Roo and the Bunnies (1st, lg8vo, 29p, color, pep, DJ/2.25)	Houghton	1953	Funk, Tom	50-80	
Leavens, Evelyn	Boswell's Life of Boswell (1st, 4to, [26]p, ibds, DJ/1.95)	Simon/Schuster	(1958)	Leavens, Evelyn	30-45	*
Leavitt, Ann H.	Three Little Indians (1st, 8vo, ipcb, [36]p, fp color, DJ/0.50)	Rand/McNally	1937	Holling, H.C. & L.	40-70	
Lebeck, Oskar	Diary of Terwilliger Jellico (1st, lg8vo, ibds, [48]p, color, pep, DJ/0.50)	Grosset/Dunlap	1935	Lebeck, Oskar	40-60	
Lebedev, Vladimir	Lion & the Ox (1st, sq4to, 35p, b/w, DJ/1.25)	Macmillan	1932	Lebedev, Vladimir	30-45	
Lecky, E.	Here, There, Everywhere (1st, 4to, unpag)	L: R. Tuck	(1890)	(Chromos)	100-165	
Lecky, Prescott	Play-Book of Words (1st, 4to, [72]p, fp 1-color)	Stokes	1933	Hader, B.& E.	50-85	
Lederer, Joe	Fafan in China (1st, 8vo, 137p, green cl, b/w, pep, DJ/2.00)	Holiday House	(1939)	Sanderson, William	25-40	*
Lederer, William J.	Story of Pink Jade (1st {std}, 8vo, 83p, b/w, pep, DJ/2.95)	Norton	(1966)	Victor, Joan B.	25-40	*
Lederer, William J.	Timothy's Song (1st {std}, sm8vo, gilt, 41p, b/w, DJ/2.95)	Norton	(1965)	Ardizzone, Edward	50-85	
Lee, Agnes	Round Rabbit (1st, 12mo, brown cl, 52p, 6pl)	Copeland & Day	1898	O'Neill, Rose	200-325	
Lee, Al	Tommy Toodles (1st, 8vo, p-o, blue cl, 192p, 26pl)	Harper	1896	Newell, Peter	180-240	
Lee, Ella D.	Ever Living Fairy Tales (lg8vo, blue/gilt, p-o, 18cp)	Donohue	1924	Lee, Ella D.	50-80	*
Lee, Frank H.	Children's King Arthur (1st, 8vo, 77p)	L: Harrap	1935	Appleton, Honor C.	55-80	*
Lee, Holme	Legends from Fairyland (1st, 8vo, 276p, blue/gilt, 17pl, pep)	L: Chatto	1907	Knowles, R.L.	200-300	
Lee, Jennette	Happy Island (1st, 12mo, 330p, frn by...)	Century	1910	Schoonover, Frank	25-40	
Lee, Melicent	Chang Chee (1st {std}, 8vo, 137p, b/w, pep, DJ/1.50)	Harper	1939	Bannon, Laura	40-65	*
Lee, Melicent	Marcos, Mountain Boy of Mexico (1st, sm4to, p-o, 79p, color, pep, DJ/2.00)	Whitman	1937	Hader, B.& E.	40-60	
Lee, Melicent	Pablo and Petra (1st, 8vo, 152p, col frn, b/w, pep)	Crowell	(1934)	Lee, Leslie W.	25-45	
Lee, Vernon	Ballet of the Nations (1st AM, 4to, ibds, 24p, uncut, 1-color)	Putnam	1915	Armfield, Maxwell	100-165	R*
Leekley, Thomas	World of Manabozho (1st, lg8vo, 128p, DJ/3.50)	Vanguard Press	(1965)	Kimball, Yeffe	25-45	
Leet, Frank R.	Animal Caravan (1st, lg4to, 60p, ibds, 12 fp color)	Saalfield	(1930)	Peat, Fern B.	70-125	
Leet, Frank R.	Christmas Carols (1st, 4to, ibds, [70]p, gilt, pep)	Saalfield	(1937)	Peat, Fern B.	60-90	
Leet, Frank R.	Hop, Skip & Jump (1st, 4to, ibds, 34p, 6cp)	Saalfield	1936	Peat, Fern B.	70-100	
Leet, Frank R.	Purr & Miew (1st, 4to, ibds, 60p, 12 fp color)	Saalfield	(1931)	Peat, Fern B.	70-100	
Leet, Frank R.	To the Circus the Children Go (ob folio, wraps, color)	Saalfield	1931	Kay, Gertrude A.	50-85	
Lefevre, Felicite	Cock, Mouse & Little Red Hen (1st AM, 8vo, 103p, 24cp)	Jacobs	(1907)	Sarg, Tony	180-270	
Lefevre, Felicite	Cock, Mouse & Little Red Hen (1st, 8vo, 103p, 24cp)	L: Richards	1907	Sarg, Tony	225-350	
Lefevre, Felicite	Cock, Mouse & Little Red Hen (ob folio, wraps, color)	Saalfield	1931	Peat, Fern B.	60-100	
Lefevre, Felicite	Fiddle Diddle Dee (1st, sm8vo, orange cl, [63]p, fp color, pep)	Greenberg	(1928)	Barney, Maginel W.	70-130	
Lefevre, Felicite	Little Henry and the Tiger (1st {std}, 8vo, ipcb, [41]p, color, pep)	Harper	1931	Berry, Erick	40-65	

AUTHOR	TITLE	PUBLISHER	DATE	ARTIST	PRICE	LC
Lefevre, Felicite	Soldier Boy (1st, sm8vo, [64]p, orange cl, color, pep)	Greenberg	(1926)	Sarg, Tony	60-100	
Lefferts, Sara T.	Mr. Cinnamon Bear (1st, sq16mo, ibds, [47]p, color)	Bassette Co.	(1907)	Bacquet, Louise	120-200	
Lefferts, Sara T.	Pansy Wedding (1st, sq16mo, ipcb, 86p, color, pep)	Cupples/Leon	(1909)	Smith, Wuanita	60-100	
Lefferts, Sara T.	Patriotic Jubilee (1st, sq16mo, ipcb, 84p, color, pep)	Cupples/Leon	(1910)	Smith, Wuanita	60-100	
Leichman, Seymour	Boy Who Could Sing Pictures (1st {std}, 4to, 59p, 2-color, DJ/3.50)	Doubleday	(1968)	Leichman, Seymour	25-45	
Leigh, Mabel C.	Love Songs & Verses (1st, sm4to, 65p, teg, 4pl)	L: Humphreys	1913	Robinson, Gordon	60-100	
Leighton (ed.)	Fleur & Blanchefleur (1st, sm4to, 61p, 37 color)	L: O'Connor	(1922)	Brickdale, E.F.	60-100	
Leighton, Clare	Country Matters (1st AM, 4to, 159p, gilt, 70 wood engravings, DJ/3.00)	Macmillan	1937	Leighton, Clare	100-160	R
Leighton, Clare	Farmer's Year... (1st, ob folio, 54p, gilt, 12 fp woodcuts, pep)	L: Collins	1933	Leighton, Clare	200-300	
Leighton, Clare	Four Hedges... (1st AM, 4to, 167p, blue cl, wood engravings, DJ/3.00)	Macmillan	1935	Leighton, Clare	80-125	
Leighton, Clare	Musical Box (1st {std}, ob4to, [32]p, ibds, color)	L: Longmans	(1932)	Leighton, Clare	130-185	
Leighton, Clare	Sometime Never (1st, lg8vo, 178p, b/w, pep, DJ/3.50)	Macmillan	1939	Leighton, Clare	55-80	
Leighton, Clare	Southern Harvest (1st UK, 4to, 123p, blue/gilt, b/w, DJ)	L: Gollancz	1943	Leighton, Clare	60-90	
Leighton, Clare	Where Land Meets Sea (1st, sm4to, 202p, 4 fp b/w, DJ/4.00)	Rinehart	(1954)	Leighton, Clare	70-125	
Leighton, Clare	Wood that Came Back (1st, ob4to, [33]p, ibds, 2-color)	L: Nicholson	(1934)	Leighton, Clare	100-165	
Leighton, Mary	Three Chums (1st, 8vo, 144p, red cl, col frn, 3pl, DJ/1.50)	Chapman/Grimes	(1939)	Tarrant, Margaret	50-90	
Leighton, Robert	Olaf the Glorious (1st, sm8vo, gilt, 350p, 8 fp b/w)	L: Blackie	1895	Peacock, Ralph	70-100	
Leighton, Robert	Olaf the Glorious (1st, sm8vo, 208p, col frn, 6 fp b/w, pep)	Macmillan	1929	Pitz, Henry C.	25-45	
Leighton, Robert	Wreck of the Golden Fleece (1st, 8vo, 352p, green cl, 6pl)	L: Blackie	(1893)	Brangwyn, Frank	80-130	
Leister, Mary	Silent Concert (1st {std}, ob4to, [32]p, gilt, cep, color, DJ/5.95)	Bobbs-Merrill	(1970)	Mitsuhashi, Yoko	30-50	
Lemon, Mark	Enchanted Doll (1st, 8vo, 64p, p-o, 4cp)	L: Jack	[1915]	Woodroffe, Paul	40-70	*
Lemonnier, Camille	Birds & Beasts (1st, 8vo, gilt, teg, 196p, 6cp)	L: G. Allen	(1911)	Detmold, Edward J.	170-240	
Lenotre, Therese	Mystery of Dog Flip (1st, sm8vo, 190p, b/w, dep, DJ/1.75)	Stokes	1939	Eichenberg, Fritz	30-50	
Lenski, Lois	A-Going to the Westward (1st, 8vo, 370p, uncut, b/w, pep, DJ/2.00)	Stokes	1937	Lenski, Lois	90-140	
Lenski, Lois	Alphabet People (1st {std}, lg8vo, 104p, p-o, blue cl, color, pep)	Harper	1928	Lenski, Lois	100-160	
Lenski, Lois	Animals for Me (1st, ob16mo, [48]p, fp 2-color, cep, DJ/0.75)	Oxford U. Pr.	(1941)	Lenski, Lois	60-90	
Lenski, Lois	Arabella & Her Aunts (1st, 16mo, p-o, 115p, 5cp, cep)	Stokes	1932	Lenski, Lois	100-170	
Lenski, Lois	Bayou Suzette (1st {std}, 8vo, 207p, map, fp b/w, pep, DJ/2.00)	Stokes	1943	Lenski, Lois	100-175	
Lenski, Lois	Benny & His Penny (1st, ob4to, blue cl, [32]p, color)	Knopf	1931	Lenski, Lois	120-170	
Lenski, Lois	Berries in the Scoop (1st {std}, 8vo, 124p, red cl, b/w, DJ/2.25)	Lippincott	(1956)	Lenski, Lois	80-140	
Lenski, Lois	Big Little Davy (1st, ob16mo, 48p, fp 2-color, pep, DJ/1.50)	Oxford U. Pr.	1956	Lenski, Lois	60-90	
Lenski, Lois	Blue Ridge Billy (1st {std}, 8vo, 203p, b/w, pep, DJ/2.50)	Lippincott	(1946)	Lenski, Lois	70-120	
Lenski, Lois	Blueberry Corners (1st, 8vo, blue/gilt, 209p, b/w, pep, DJ/2.00)	Stokes	1940	Lenski, Lois	80-140	
Lenski, Lois	Boom Town Boy (1st {std}, 8vo, 177p, fp b/w, pep, DJ/2.50)	Lippincott	1948	Lenski, Lois	80-140	
Lenski, Lois	Bound Girl of Cobble Hill (1st, 8vo, 292p, uncut, b/w, dep, DJ/2.25)	Stokes	1938	Lenski, Lois	70-120	
Lenski, Lois	Coal Camp Girl (1st {std}, 8vo, 173p, b/w, pep, DJ/3.95)	Lippincott	(1959)	Lenski, Lois	60-90	
Lenski, Lois	Corn-Farm Boy (1st {std}, 8vo, 179p, b/w, pep, DJ/3.00)	Lippincott	(1954)	Lenski, Lois	60-95	
Lenski, Lois	Cotton in My Sack (1st {std}, 8vo, 191p, dp b/w, pep, DJ/2.50)	Lippincott	(1949)	Lenski, Lois	80-125	
Lenski, Lois	Cowboy Small (1st, 12mo, [48]p, fp color, pep, DJ/1.00)	Oxford U. Pr.	(1949)	Lenski, Lois	70-120	
Lenski, Lois	Davy and His Dog (1st, ob16mo, 38p, fp 2-color, pep, DJ/1.50)	Oxford U. Pr.	1957	Lenski, Lois	50-80	
Lenski, Lois	Davy Goes Places (1st, ob16mo, 46p, fp 2-color, pep, DJ/1.75)	H.Z. Walck	1961	Lenski, Lois	50-80	
Lenski, Lois	Davy's Day (1st, ob 16mo, [48]p, color, DJ/0.75)	Oxford U. Pr.	(1943)	Lenski, Lois	50-80	
Lenski, Lois	Debbie and Her Dolls (1st, ob16mo, 48p, fp color, DJ/3.00)	H.Z. Walck	(1970)	Lenski, Lois	50-85	
Lenski, Lois	Debbie and Her Family (1st, ob16mo, 46p, fp color, DJ/3.00)	H.Z. Walck	(1969)	Lenski, Lois	50-85	
Lenski, Lois	Debbie and Her Grandma (1st, ob16mo, 48p, fp color, DJ/2.50)	H.Z. Walck	1967	Lenski, Lois	50-85	
Lenski, Lois	Debbie Goes to Nursery School (1st, ob16mo, 48p, color, DJ/3.00)	H.Z. Walck	(1970)	Lenski, Lois	50-85	
Lenski, Lois	Debbie Herself (1st, ob16mo, 46p, fp color, DJ/3.00)	H.Z. Walck	(1969)	Lenski, Lois	50-85	
Lenski, Lois	Deer Valley Girl (1st {std}, 8vo, 145p, fp b/w, DJ/3.95)	Lippincott	1968	Lenski, Lois	80-120	
Lenski, Lois	Dog Came to School (1st, ob16mo, 46p, 2-color, pep, DJ/1.50)	Oxford U. Pr.	1955	Lenski, Lois	60-95	
Lenski, Lois	Easter Rabbit's Parade (1st, lg8vo, ipcb, [31]p, 3-color, pep, DJ/1.00)	Oxford U. Pr.	(1936)	Lenski, Lois	200-300	
Lenski, Lois	Flood Friday (1st {std}, 8vo, 96p, b/w, DJ/2.50)	Lippincott	1956	Lenski, Lois	100-175	
Lenski, Lois	Gooseberry Garden (1st {std}, ob8vo, ipcb, [32]p, color, pep)	Harper	1934	Lenski, Lois	100-165	
Lenski, Lois	Grandmother Tippytoe (1st, lg8vo, p-o, 104p, 8cp, dep)	Stokes	1931	Lenski, Lois	100-165	
Lenski, Lois	High-Rise Secret (1st {std}, sm8vo, 152p, b/w, DJ/3.50)	Lippincott	(1966)	Lenski, Lois	50-80	
Lenski, Lois	Houseboat Girl (1st {std}, 8vo, 175p, bds, b/w, DJ/3.00)	Lippincott	1957	Lenski, Lois	80-125	
Lenski, Lois	I Like Winter (1st, sq24mo, [48]p, 2-color, DJ/1.00)	Oxford U. Pr.	(1950)	Lenski, Lois	70-120	
Lenski, Lois	Indian Captive (1st, 8vo, 269p, pep, color, DJ/2.00, NH)	Stokes	1941	Lenski, Lois	70-120	
Lenski, Lois	Jack Horner's Pie (1st, lg8vo, 83p, gilt, color)	Harper	1927	Lenski, Lois	100-175	
Lenski, Lois	Johnny Goes to the Fair (1st, ob8vo, [32]p, yellow cl, color)	Minton Balch	1932	Lenski, Lois	80-130	
Lenski, Lois	Judy's Journey (1st {std}, 8vo, 212p, b/w, pep, DJ/2.50)	Lippincott	1947	Lenski, Lois	70-120	
Lenski, Lois	Let's Play House (1st, ob8vo, [40]p, fp 2-color, dep, DJ/1.00)	Oxford U. Pr.	1944	Lenski, Lois	80-125	
Lenski, Lois	Life I Live: Collected Poems (1st, 8vo, 238p, gilt, b/w, DJ/7.50)	H.Z. Walck	1965	Lenski, Lois	100-175	
Lenski, Lois	Little Airplane (1st, sq12mo, [48]p, 1-color, pep, DJ/0.75)	Oxford U. Pr.	(1938)	Lenski, Lois	100-165	
Lenski, Lois	Little Auto (1st, sq12mo, [48]p, 1-color, pep)	Oxford U. Pr.	(1934)	Lenski, Lois	80-140	
Lenski, Lois	Little Baby Ann (1st, sq12mo, [47]p, color, pep)	Oxford U. Pr.	(1935)	Lenski, Lois	80-140	
Lenski, Lois	Little Family (1st {std}, sq24mo, ibds, [48]p, color, dep)	Doubleday/Doran	1932	Lenski, Lois	80-140	
Lenski, Lois	Little Farm (1st, sq12mo, [48]p, color, pep, DJ/0.75)	Oxford U. Pr.	(1942)	Lenski, Lois	80-130	
Lenski, Lois	Little Fire Engine (1st, ob8vo, red/gilt, [46]p, 1-color, pep, DJ/1.00)	Oxford U. Pr.	1946	Lenski, Lois	70-120	
Lenski, Lois	Little Girl of 1900 (1st, 8vo, 218p, p-o, col frn, 9pl, pep)	Stokes	1928	Lenski, Lois	100-165	R
Lenski, Lois	Little Sail Boat (1st, sq12mo, [48]p, color, pep)	Oxford U. Pr.	(1937)	Lenski, Lois	70-125	
Lenski, Lois	Little Sioux Girl (1st {std}, 8vo, 128p, b/w, DJ/2.75)	Lippincott	1958	Lenski, Lois	70-100	
Lenski, Lois	Little Train (1st, ob8vo, [48]p, color, pep, DJ/0.75)	Oxford U. Pr.	(1940)	Lenski, Lois	100-160	
Lenski, Lois	Lois Lenski's Christmas Stories (1st {std}, lg8vo, 152p, gilt b/w, DJ/3.95)	Lippincott	(1968)	Lenski, Lois	80-120	
Lenski, Lois	Mama Hattie's Girl (1st {std}, 8vo, 182p, pep, b/w, DJ/3.00)	Lippincott	(1953)	Lenski, Lois	80-135	
Lenski, Lois	Mr. and Mrs. Noah (1st, ob16mo, [48]p, fp color, pep, DJ/1.00)	Crowell	(1948)	Lenski, Lois	50-85	*
Lenski, Lois	Now It's Fall (1st, ob24mo, [48]p, ibds, color, DJ/1.00)	Oxford U. Pr.	(1948)	Lenski, Lois	100-160	
Lenski, Lois	Ocean-Born Mary (1st, sm8vo, 388p, fp b/w, pep, DJ/2.00)	Stokes	1939	Lenski, Lois	100-165	
Lenski, Lois	On a Summer Day (1st, sq16mo, [36]p, color, pep, DJ/1.25)	Oxford U. Pr.	(1953)	Lenski, Lois	70-100	

AUTHOR	TITLE	PUBLISHER	DATE	ARTIST	PRICE	LC
Lenski, Lois	Papa Small (1st, sq12mo, [46]p, 1-color, pep, DJ/1.25)	Oxford U. Pr.	1951	Lenski, Lois	60-90	
Lenski, Lois	Peanuts for Billy Ben (1st {std}, 8vo, 128p, 1-color, DJ/2.00)	Lippincott	1952	Lenski, Lois	70-125	
Lenski, Lois	Phebe Fairchild (1st, sm8vo, 316p, rust/gilt, b/w, dep, DJ/2.00, NH)	Stokes	1936	Lenski, Lois	100-165	
Lenski, Lois	Policeman Small (1st, 12mo, [48]p, fp 1-color, pep, DJ/2.25)	H.Z. Walck	1962	Lenski, Lois	50-85	
Lenski, Lois	Prairie School (1st {std}, 8vo, 196p, fp b/w, pep, DJ/2.75)	Lippincott	(1951)	Lenski, Lois	60-100	
Lenski, Lois	Project Boy (1st {std}, 8vo, 128p, b/w, cep, DJ/2.00)	Lippincott	1954	Lenski, Lois	70-100	
Lenski, Lois	Puritan Adventure (1st {std}, sm8vo, gilt, 223p, 2-color, DJ/2.00)	Lippincott	1944	Lenski, Lois	100-150	
Lenski, Lois	San Francisco Boy (1st {std}, 8vo, 176p, b/w, pep, DJ/3.00)	Lippincott	(1955)	Lenski, Lois	80-125	
Lenski, Lois	Shoo-Fly Girl (1st {std}, 8vo, 176p, b/w, pep, DJ/3.95)	Lippincott	(1963)	Lenski, Lois	70-120	
Lenski, Lois	Skipping Village (1st, sm4to, 179p, blue cl, 4cp, 3pl, pep)	Stokes	1927	Lenski, Lois	175-250	
Lenski, Lois	Spinach-Boy (1st, 12mo, 91p, p-o, 6cp, pep)	Stokes	1930	Lenski, Lois	80-120	
Lenski, Lois	Spring is Here (1st, ob12mo, [48]p, yellow cl, color, cep, DJ/0.75)	Oxford U. Pr.	(1945)	Lenski, Lois	70-125	
Lenski, Lois	Strawberry Girl (1st {std}, 8vo, 194p, green/gilt, b/w, dep, DJ/2.50, NM)	Lippincott	(1945)	Lenski, Lois	300-450	R
Lenski, Lois	Sugarplum House (1st {std}, lg ob8vo, ipcb, 31p, 2-color, DJ/1.00)	Harper	1935	Lenski, Lois	100-170	
Lenski, Lois	Surprise for Davy (1st, ob16mo, [48]p, fp 3-color, cep, DJ/1.00)	Oxford U. Pr.	1947	Lenski, Lois	60-100	
Lenski, Lois	Surprise for Mother (1st, sq12mo, 91p, yellow cl, col frn, b/w)	Stokes	1934	Lenski, Lois	50-80	
Lenski, Lois	Susie Mariar (1st, ob8vo, [43]p, 3-color, dep, DJ/1.00)	NY: Oxford U.Pr.	(1939)	Lenski, Lois	100-165	
Lenski, Lois	Texas Tomboy (1st {std}, 8vo, 180p, b/w, pep, DJ/2.50)	Lippincott	(1950)	Lenski, Lois	80-130	
Lenski, Lois	To Be a Logger (1st {std}, 8vo, 174p, b/w, pep, DJ/3.95)	Lippincott	1967	Lenski, Lois	70-100	
Lenski, Lois	Two Brothers & their Animal Friends (1st, ob12mo, 122p, p-o, 12 color, pep)	Stokes	1929	Lenski, Lois	120-200	
Lenski, Lois	Two Brothers & their Baby Sister (1st, ob12mo, 121p, p-o, 12cp, pep)	Stokes	1930	Lenski, Lois	120-200	
Lenski, Lois	Washington Picture Book (1st, ob4to, ibds, [32]p, color, pep)	Coward	1930	Lenski, Lois	120-180	
Lenski, Lois	We Live in the City (1st {std}, 8vo, 128p, blue cl, b/w, cep, DJ/2.00)	Lippincott	1954	Lenski, Lois	80-125	
Lenski, Lois	Wonder City: Picture Book of New York (1st, ob4to, [32]p, 2-color, pep)	Coward	1929	Lenski, Lois	140-200	
Lent, Blair	From King Boggen's Hall to Nothing-At-All (1st {std}, sq8vo, 44p, DJ/3.95)	Little/Brown	(1967)	Lent, Blair	30-50	
Lent, Blair	John Tabor's Ride (1st {std}, sq8vo, 48p, color, DJ/3.75)	Little/Brown	(1966)	Lent, Blair	30-50	
Lent, Blair	Pistachio (1st {std}, 4to, 30p, color, DJ/2.95)	Little/Brown	(1964)	Lent, Blair	40-65	
Lent, Henry B.	Air Pilot (1st, sq16mo, [42]p, color, pep)	Macmillan	1937	Hauman, G.& D.	35-60	
Lent, Henry B.	Bus Driver (1st, sq16mo, [42]p, color, pep)	Macmillan	1937	Winslow, Earle	35-60	*
Lent, Henry B.	Diggers and Builders (1st, 8vo, 68p, silhouettes)	Macmillan	1931	Lent, Henry B.	60-100	
Lent, Henry B.	Grindstone Farm (1st, 8vo, 127p, b/w, DJ/1.75)	Macmillan	1935	Bronson, Wilfrid	30-45	
Lent, Henry B.	The Captain (1st, sq16mo, [42]p, color, pep)	Macmillan	1937	Winslow, Earle	35-60	*
Lent, Henry B.	The Farmer (1st, sq16mo, ipcb, [42]p, color, pep)	Macmillan	1937	Hader, B.& E.	40-60	
Lent, Henry B.	The Storekeeper (1st, sq16mo, [42]p, color, pep)	Macmillan	1937	Hauman, G.& D.	35-60	
Leodhas, Sorche	All in the Morning Early (1st {std}, ob8vo, [30]p, 2-color, DJ/3.50, CH)	Holt, Rinehart	(1963)	Ness, Evaline	80-135	R
Leodhas, Sorche	Always Room for One More (1st {std}, ob8vo, [31]p, 2-color, DJ/3.00, CM)	Holt, Rinehart	(1965)	Hogrogian, Nonny	100-160	R*
Leodhas, Sorche	By Loch and Lin (1st {std}, 8vo, 130p, fp b/w, DJ/4.95)	Holt, Rinehart	(1969)	Bock, Vera	30-50	
Leodhas, Sorche	Claymore and Kilt (1st {std}, lg8vo, 157p, ibds, gilt, fp b/w, DJ/3.95)	Holt, Rinehart	(1967)	Dillon, L.& D.	30-50	
Leodhas, Sorche	Gaelic Ghosts (1st {std}, lg8vo, 110p, green bds, woodcuts, DJ/3.50)	Holt, Rinehart	(1963)	Hogrogian, Nonny	40-65	
Leodhas, Sorche	Ghosts Go Haunting (1st {std}, lg8vo, 128p, blue bds, b/w, DJ/3.75)	Holt, Rinehart	(1965)	Hogrogian, Nonny	30-50	
Leodhas, Sorche	Golden Summer (1st {std}, 8vo, 205p, b/w, DJ/2.00)	Harper	(1942)	Watson, Aldren A.	30-50	*
Leodhas, Sorche	Heather and Broom (1st {std}, 8vo, 128p, b/w, DJ/3.25)	Holt, Rinehart	(1960)	Joerns, Consuelo	30-50	
Leodhas, Sorche	Kellyburn Braes (1st {std}, lg8vo, [30]p, ibds, 3-color, DJ/3.95)	Holt, Rinehart	(1968)	Ness, Evaline	30-45	
Leodhas, Sorche	Laird of Cockpen (1st {std}, 8vo, [32]p, ibds, color, DJ/3.95)	Holt, Rinehart	(1969)	Adams, Adrienne	30-50	
Leodhas, Sorche	Scottish Songbook (1st {std}, ob4to, 63p, 1-color, DJ/4.50)	Holt, Rinehart	(1969)	Ness, Evaline	30-50	
Leodhas, Sorche	Sea-Spell and Moor-Magic (1st {std}, 8vo, ibds, 207p, 10 fp b/w, DJ/4.95)	Holt, Rinehart	(1968)	Bock, Vera	30-45	
Leodhas, Sorche	Thistle and Thyme... (1st {std}, 8vo, 143p, ibds, b/w, DJ/3.50, NH)	Holt, Rinehart	(1962)	Ness, Evaline	50-80	*
Leonard, Mary F.	How the Two Ends Met (1st, sm8vo, 97p, 4pl)	Crowell	(1903)	Falls, Charles B.	55-80	*
Leonard, Mary F.	Susan Grows Up (1st, 8vo, 307p, 8pl)	Crowell	(1914)	Elmer, Rachel R.	25-40	*
Leonard, Nellie	Grandfather Whiskers, M.D. (1st {std}, sm8vo, 216p, b/w, DJ/2.00)	Crowell	1953	Cooney, Barbara	100-165	
Leonard, Nellie	Graymouse Family (1st, sm8vo, 209p, b/w, DJ/2.00)	Crowell	(1950)	Cooney, Barbara	50-80	R
LesTina, Dorothy	Flag Day (1st, 8vo, [38]p, 2-color, DJ/2.95)	Crowell	(1965)	Emberley, Ed	35-60	
Leskov, Nicholas	Steel Flea (1st [rev. ed.], 8vo, 56p, color, cep, DJ/2.95)	Harper	(1964)	Domanska, Janina	30-45	*
Lester, Carol E.	To Make a Duck Happy (1st {std}, 8vo, uncut, 148p, b/w, pep, DJ/4.95)	Harper	(1969)	Rojankovsky, Feodor	20-35	*
Lester, Julius B.	Black Folktales (1st, 8vo, 159p, fp b/w, cep, DJ/4.50)	R.W. Baron	1969	Feelings, Tom	60-95	
Lester, Julius B.	To Be a Slave (1st {std}, 8vo, 160p, black/gilt, b/w, DJ/3.95, NH)	Dial Press	(1968)	Feelings, Tom	80-140	
Levenson, Dorothy	Magic Carousel (1st, sm ob4to, [36]p, color, dep, DJ/3.50)	Parents Mag. Pr.	(1967)	Forberg, Ati	25-40	
Lever, Charles	Charles O'Malley... (1st, 8vo, 628p, uncut, red/gilt, 16pl)	L: Service	1897	Rackham, Arthur	150-225	
Lever, Charles	Templelogue Lever (1st, 4to, AEG, green cl, 631p, 32cp)	NY: Pollard	1880	Browne, H.K.	160-200	
Levine, Edna S.	Little Nemo in Slumberland (1st, 12mo, ibds, [63]p, 12 fp color)	Rand/McNally	(1941)	McCay, Winsor	80-125	
Levine, Rhoda	Harrison Loved his Umbrella (1st {std}, sq12mo, [46]p, 3-color, cep, DJ)	Atheneum	1964	Kuskin, Karla	30-45	
Levine, Rhoda	He Was There from Day We Moved In (1st, 12mo, [24]p, color, cep, DJ/2.95)	Harlin Quist	(1968)	Gorey, Edward	60-95	
Levine, Rhoda	Herbert Situation (1st {std}, ob4to, 32p, gilt, color, DJ/3.95)	Harlin Quist	1969	Ross, Larry	25-45	
Levine, Rhoda	Quiet Story (1st {std}, sq24mo, [32]p, 1-color, cep, DJ/1.95)	Atheneum	1963	Richards, Rosalie	25-35	
Levine, Rhoda	Three Ladies Beside the Sea (1st {std}, ob8vo, [32]p, color, cep, DJ)	Atheneum	1963	Gorey, Edward	60-90	
Levy, Harry	Not Over Ten Inches High (1st, 8vo, 48p, fp b/w, cep, DJ/3.95)	McGraw-Hill	(1968)	Grossman, Nancy	40-65	*
Levy, Mimi C.	Corrie and the Yankee (1st, 8vo, 189p, blue cl, b/w, DJ/3.00)	Viking	(1958)	Crichlow, Ernest	30-50	
Levy, Newman	Opera Guyed (1st, lg8vo, 87p, b/w, DJ)	Knopf	1923	Irvin, Rea	45-80	
Levy, Newman	Saturday to Monday (1st, sm8vo, uncut, 79p, ipcb, fp b/w)	Knopf	1930	Held, John	50-80	
Lewicki, Lillian	Golden Book of Christmas Tales (1st {A}, folio, 28p, ipcb, color, BGB)	Simon/Schuster	(1956)	Lewicki, James	60-90	R
Lewis, Alfred H.	Black Lion Inn (1st, sm8vo, 380p, yellow cl, 16pl)	R.H. Russell	1903	Remington, Frederic	80-140	
Lewis, Alfred H.	Peggy O'Neal (1st, 12mo, uncut, 494p, 4cp)	Drexel Biddle	1903	Hutt, Henry	35-60	
Lewis, Alfred H.	Sandburrs (1st, 12mo, 318p, 16pl)	Stokes	(1900)	Taylor, H. Weston	50-80	
Lewis, Alfred H.	The Throwback (1st, 12mo, 347p, green/gilt, 4cp)	Outing	1906	Wyeth, N.C.	60-100	
Lewis, Alfred H.	Wolfville (1st, 12mo, red cl, 337p, 18pl)	Stokes	(1897)	Remington, Frederic	120-200	
Lewis, Alfred H.	Wolfville Days (1st, 12mo, 311p, frn by...)	Stokes	(1902)	Remington, Frederic	80-125	
Lewis, Alfred H.	Wolfville Folks (1st, 12mo, 321p, frn by...)	Appleton	1908	Dunton, W. Herbert	80-125	
Lewis, Alice H.	Day after Tomorrow (1st, 8vo, 117p, b/w, cep, DJ/2.50)	Friendship Pr.	(1956)	Wiese, Kurt	25-40	*

AUTHOR	TITLE	PUBLISHER	DATE	ARTIST	PRICE	LC
Lewis, Beth H.	Blue Mountain (1st {std}, lg8vo, blue cl, 59p, fp b/w, dep, DJ/2.25)	Knopf	1956	Adams, Adrienne	35-50	
Lewis, C.S.	Horse & his Boy (1st, sm8vo, grey/silver, 199p, b/w, pep, DJ)	L: G. Bles	(1954)	Baynes, Pauline	500-700	
Lewis, C.S.	Last Battle (1st AM {std}, sm8vo, 174p, blue cl, b/w, DJ/2.75)	Macmillan	(1956)	Baynes, Pauline	350-500	R
Lewis, C.S.	Last Battle (1st, 8vo, blue cl, 184p, b/w, DJ, CgM)	L: G. Bles	1956	Baynes, Pauline	500-700	
Lewis, C.S.	Lion, the Witch & the Wardrobe (1st, 8vo, green/silver, col frn, b/w, DJ)	L: G. Bles	(1950)	Baynes, Pauline	900-1300	
Lewis, C.S.	Lion, the Witch & the Wardrobe (1st AM {std}, 8vo, 154p, b/w, DJ/2.50)	Macmillan	1950	Baynes, Pauline	700-1000	
Lewis, C.S.	Magician's Nephew (1st, 8vo, 183p, green cl, b/w, DJ)	L: Bodley Head	1955	Baynes, Pauline	800-1000	
Lewis, C.S.	Magician's Nephew (1st AM {std}, sm8vo, 167p, green cl, b/w, DJ/2.75)	Macmillan	(1955)	Baynes, Pauline	700-1000	
Lewis, C.S.	Prince Caspian (1st, 8vo, 194p, b/w, DJ)	L: G. Bles	(1951)	Baynes, Pauline	600-850	
Lewis, C.S.	Prince Caspian (1st AM {std}, sm8vo, 186p, green cl, 4 fp b/w, DJ/2.50)	Macmillan	1951	Baynes, Pauline	500-700	
Lewis, C.S.	Silver Chair (1st AM {std}, sm8vo, 208p, blue cl, 4 fp b/w, DJ/2.75)	Macmillan	1953	Baynes, Pauline	300-500	
Lewis, C.S.	Voyage of the Dawn Treader (1st AM {std}, sm8vo, 210p, b/w, DJ/2.75)	Macmillan	1952	Baynes, Pauline	500-700	
Lewis, C.S.	Voyage of the Dawn Treader (1st, 8vo, 223p, fp b/w, DJ)	L: G. Bles	(1952)	Baynes, Pauline	700-900	
Lewis, Caroline	Clara in Blunderland (1st, 8vo, 150p, green cl, 4pl)	L: Heinemann	1902	S.R.	100-165	
Lewis, Claudia	Straps the Cat (1st, 12mo, 141p, rust cl, fp b/w, DJ/2.50)	W.R. Scott	(1957)	Ruhtenberg, Cornelis	30-50	
Lewis, Claudia	When I Go to the Moon (1st {std}, 4to, [32]p, fp color, DJ/3.00)	Macmillan	1961	Weisgard, Leonard	30-50	*
Lewis, D.B.W.	Stuffed Owl (1st AM, sm8vo, bds, p-o, 236p, 6pl, pep)	Coward	(1930)	Beerbohm, Max	30-50	
Lewis, Eliz. F.	China Quest (1st, 8vo, 301p, gilt, 4cp, pep, DJ/2.00)	Winston	(1937)	Wiese, Kurt	30-50	
Lewis, Eliz. F.	Ho-Ming, Girl of New China (1st, 8vo, 266p, gilt, pep, 4cp)	Winston	1934	Wiese, Kurt	30-50	
Lewis, Eliz. F.	Portraits from a Chinese Scroll (1st {std}, 8vo, 267p, gilt, 1-col, DJ/2.50)	Winston	(1938)	Stout, Virginia	25-40	
Lewis, Eliz. F.	To Beat a Tiger, One Needs a Brother's Help (1st {std}, 8vo, 215p, DJ/2.95)	Winston	(1956)	Huehnergarth, John	20-35	
Lewis, Eliz. F.	When the Typhoon Blows (1st, 8vo, 273p, orange cl, col frn, pep, DJ/2.00)	Winston	(1942)	Wiese, Kurt	30-50	
Lewis, Eliz. F.	Young Fu of the Upper Yangtze (1st, 8vo, 265p, black cl, 4cp, pep, NM)	Winston	1932	Wiese, Kurt	60-100	R
Lewis, Emily W.	Next-Door Morelands (1st, sm8vo, 342p, 4pl)	Little/Brown	1907	Aherns, E.W.	25-40	*
Lewis, Hilda	Ship that Flew (1st, 8vo, 320p, b/w, DJ)	L: Oxford U.Pr.	1939	Lavrin, Nora	100-165	*
Lewis, Janet	Keiko's Bubble (1st {std}, lg8vo, 62p, b/w, DJ/2.50)	Doubleday	1961	Mizumura, Kazue	40-65	
Lewis, Lorna	Puppy & the Cat (1st, sq8vo, 44p, fp b/w, DJ/0.50)	Grosset/Dunlap	(1940)	Dawson, Lucy	25-40	
Lewis, Richard	In a Spring Garden (1st, 4to, [31]p, fp color, pep, DJ/3.95)	Dial Press	(1965)	Keats, Ezra J.	50-80	R
Lewis, Richard W.	Summer Adventure (1st, 8vo, 105p, fp b/w, DJ/2.95)	Harper	(1962)	Lewis, Richard	50-80	*
Lewisohn, Ludwig	Last Days of Shylock (1st, 8vo, 221p, b/w pl)	Harper	1931	Szyk, Arthur	40-70	
Lewiton, Mina	Candita's Choice (1st, sm8vo, 184p, DJ/2.95)	Harper	(1959)	Simon, Howard	30-50	
Lexau, Joan M.	Archimedes Takes a Bath (1st, 8vo, 56p, b/w, DJ/3.50)	Crowell	(1969)	Murdocca, Salvatore	30-45	
Lexau, Joan M.	Benjie (1st, sm ob4to, [38]p, fp b/w, DJ/3.00)	Dial Press	(1964)	Bolognese, Don	30-50	
Lexau, Joan M.	Benjie on His Own (1st {std}, sm ob4to, ipcb, [38]p, fp b/w, DJ/3.95)	Dial Press	(1970)	Bolognese, Don	30-50	*
Lexau, Joan M.	Cathy is Company (1st, 8vo, [34]p, 2-color, pep, DJ/2.50)	Dial Press	(1961)	Aliki	25-40	*
Lexau, Joan M.	Crocodile & Hen (1st, ob4to, [32]p, color, DJ/3.95)	Harper	(1969)	Sandin, Joan	20-35	*
Lexau, Joan M.	Every Day a Dragon (1st, 12mo, 32p, b/w, DJ/1.95)	Harper	(1967)	Shecter, Ben	20-25	*
Lexau, Joan M.	Finders Keepers, Losers Weepers (1st, 8vo, [36]p, 3-color, pep, DJ/3.25)	Lippincott	(1967)	DePaola, Tomie	25-40	
Lexau, Joan M.	I Should have Stayed in Bed (1st, 8vo, 48p, color, DJ/2.50)	Harper	(1965)	Hoff, Syd	20-25	*
Lexau, Joan M.	It All Began with Drip, Drip, Drip (1st {std}, ob4to, [41]p, color, DJ/4.25)	McCall Pub.	(1970)	Sandin, Joan	30-45	*
Lexau, Joan M.	Jose's Christmas Secret (1st, lg8vo, 54p, fp b/w, pep, DJ/2.95)	Dial Press	(1963)	Bolognese, Don	25-40	
Lexau, Joan M.	Kite Over 10th Avenue (1st {std}, 8vo, 94p, gilt, 1-color, cep, DJ/2.95)	Doubleday	(1967)	Shimin, Symeon	30-45	
Lexau, Joan M.	Maria (1st {std}, 4to, [32]p, color, DJ/2.95)	Dial Press	(1964)	Crichlow, Ernest	40-65	*
Lexau, Joan M.	Millicent's Ghost (1st, 8vo, [32]p, 2-color, pep, DJ/2.75)	Dial Press	(1962)	Shecter, Ben	20-30	*
Lexau, Joan M.	More Beautiful than Flowers (1st, 8vo, [26]p, fp color, DJ/2.95)	Lippincott	(1966)	Bolognese, Don	25-40	*
Lexau, Joan M.	Olaf is Late (1st, 8vo, [32]p, fp 1-color, pep, DJ/2.75)	Dial Press	(1963)	Weiss, Harvey	20-35	
Lexau, Joan M.	Olaf Reads (1st [1st bk.], 8vo, 53p, 3-color, pep, DJ/2.75)	Dial Press	(1961)	Weiss, Harvey	30-50	
Lexau, Joan M.	Rooftop Mystery (1st, 8vo, 64p, color, DJ/2.50)	Harper	(1968)	Hoff, Syd	25-45	
Lexau, Joan M.	Striped Ice Cream (1st {std}, 8vo, 95p, b/w, DJ/3.25)	Lippincott	(1968)	Wilson, John	25-40	*
Lexau, Joan M.	That's Good, That's Bad (1st, sm ob4to, [40]p, fp color, DJ/3.25)	Dial Press	1963	Aliki	30-50	
Ley, Madeleine	Enchanted Eve (1st, 4to, [52]p, blue cl, 1-color, pep, DJ/2.50)	Howell/Soskin	(1946)	LeGrand, Edy	30-45	
Leydenfrost, Robert	Other Side of the Mountain (1st, 4to, [28]p, fp 3-color, DJ/4.50)	Macmillan	(1968)	Leydenfrost, Rbt.	25-45	
Li, Ling-ai	Children of the Sun in Hawaii (1st, 8vo, 80p, color, pep)	D.C. Heath	(1944)	Yap, Weda	35-50	*
Liang, Yen	Dee-Dee's Birthday (1st, sq12mo, [32]p, fp 3-color, DJ/1.75)	NY: Oxford U.Pr.	1952	Liang, Yen	25-45	
Liang, Yen	The Skyscraper (1st, 4to, 48p, blue cl, fp 1-color, DJ/2.95)	Lippincott	(1958)	Liang, Yen	20-35	*
Lida	Bruin the Brown Bear (1st {std}, 4to, ibds, [32]p, color, pep)	Harper	1937	Rojankovsky, Feodor	50-85	
Lida	Cuckoo (1st {std}, 4to, ibds, [32]p, pep, color, DJ/1.25)	Harper	1942	Rojankovsky, Feodor	60-100	
Lida	Little French Farm (1st {std}, 4to, ibds, [26]p, color, pep, DJ/1.00)	Harper	1939	Guertik, Helene	120-180	
Lida	Plouf the Little Wild Duck (1st, 4to, ibds, [40]p, color, pep)	Harper	1936	Rojankovsky, Feodor	50-85	
Lida	Pompom (1st, sq4to, ibds, [38]p, color, pep, DJ/1.00)	Harper	1936	Rojankovsky, Feodor	50-80	
Lida	Scuff the Seal (1st {std}, 4to, ibds, [32]p, color, pep)	Harper	1937	Rojankovsky, Feodor	50-80	
Lida	Spiky the Hedgehog (1st {std}, 4to, ibds, [34]p, color, pep, DJ/1.00)	Harper	1938	Rojankovsky, Feodor	80-125	
Lida	The Kingfisher (1st {std}, sm sq4to, ibds, [32]p, pep, color, DJ/1.00)	Harper	1940	Rojankovsky, Feodor	70-100	
Liddell, Mary	Little Machinery (1st, 8vo, 62p, ibds, color)	Doubleday/Page	(1926)	Liddell, Mary	120-200	
Lide, Alice A.	Aztec Drums (1st {std}, sm8vo, 142p, blue cl, fp b/w, pep, DJ)	Longmans	1938	Sanchez, Carlos M.	30-50	
Lide, Alice A.	Inemak: Little Greenlander (1st, sm8vo, 148p, blue cl, fp b/w)	Rand/McNally	(1927)	Clarke, William W.	25-45	*
Lide, Alice A.	Ood-Le-Uk: Wanderer (1st, sm8vo, 265p, col frn, 9 fp b/w, pep, NH)	Little/Brown	1930	Lufkin, Raymond	45-70	
Lide, Alice A.	Pearls of Fortune (1st, sm8vo, 276p, col frn, 11 fp b/w, dep)	Little/Brown	1931	Cheney, Philip	25-40	*
Lide, Alice A.	Princess of Yucatan (1st {std}, 12mo, tan cl, 187p, b/w, pep, DJ/1.75)	Longmans	1939	Sanchez, Carlos M.	30-50	
Lide, Alice A.	Thord Firetooth (1st, 8vo, 226p, b/w, pep, DJ/2.00)	Lothrop, Lee	1937	Pitz, Henry C.	25-40	
Lide, Alice A.	Yinka-Tu the Yak (1st, 4to, ibds, 63p, color, pep, DJ/2.00)	Viking	1938	Wiese, Kurt	60-90	
Lie, Haakon	Ekorn (1st, sm8vo, 150p, fp color)	Laidlaw	1931	Wiese, Kurt	40-65	*
Liers, Emil	Otter's Story (1st, 8vo, blue cl, 191p, fp b/w, DJ/2.50)	Viking	1953	Palazzo, Tony	55-80	R
Lifton, Betty	Cock and the Ghost Cat (1st {std}, lg8vo, 34p, 1-color, DJ/3.50)	Atheneum	1965	Akino, Fuku	30-45	
Lifton, Betty	Dwarf Pine Tree (1st {std}, lg8vo, 37p, color, DJ/3.50)	Atheneum	1963	Akino, Fuku	50-80	R
Lifton, Betty	Joji and the Amanojaku (1st {std}, sm4to, [64]p, fp b/w, DJ/2.75)	Norton	(1965)	Mitsui, Eiichi	40-65	*
Lifton, Betty	Joji and the Dragon (1st, 4to, [64]p, fp b/w, DJ/2.50)	Wm. Morrow	1957	Mitsui, Eiichi	30-50	*
Lifton, Betty	Kap the Kappa (1st, sm4to, [64]p, b/w, DJ/2.75)	Wm. Morrow	1960	Mitsui, Eiichi	30-45	*

AUTHOR	TITLE	PUBLISHER	DATE	ARTIST	PRICE	LC
Lifton, Betty	Rice-Cake Rabbit (1st {std}, sm4to, [62]p, fp b/w, DJ/2.75)	Norton	(1966)	Mitsui, Eiichi	30-45	*
Lifton, Betty	Secret Seller (1st {std}, 4to, [42]p, fp color, DJ/3.95)	Norton	(1967)	Delessert, Etienne	45-70	
Liggett, Thomas	Pigeon, Fly Home! (1st, 8vo, 189p, tan cl, b/w, pep, DJ/2.75)	Holiday House	(1956)	Simont, Marc	25-40	*
Lightfoot, Beryl H.	Jolly Jack Horner (1st, 8vo, 64p, p-o, 4cp, pep)	Whitman	(1916)	Rosenkrans, Eliz.	35-60	
Lilly, Jean	Hundred Tuftys (1st {std}, sm4to, [32]p, ipcb, 2-color, pep, DJ/1.50)	Dutton	(1940)	Gergely, Tibor	70-100	
Lin, Yutang	With Love and Irony (1st, 8vo, 291p, b/w, DJ/2.75)	John Day	(1940)	Wiese, Kurt	40-65	
Lincoln, Joseph C.	Cape Cod Ballads (1st [1st bk.], 8vo, yellow/gilt, 198p, b/w)	NJ: Brandt	1902	Kemble, Edward W.	100-150	
Lincoln, Victoria	Everyhow Remarkable (1st, 8vo, [32]p, b/w, cep, DJ/3.50)	Crowell-Collier	(1967)	Jeffers, Susan	20-35	*
Lindberg, Maja	Karl's Journey to the Moon (4to, ibds, 28p, 14 fp color)	Harper	[1927]	Lindberg, Maja	150-225	
Linde, Gunnell	White Stone (1st AM {std}, 8vo, 185p, b/w, DJ/3.25)	Harcourt	(1964)	Gobbato, Imero	30-50	
Linderman, Frank B.	Blackfeet Indians (1st, lg4to, 65p, ibds, 49 color, DJ/3.50)	(St. Paul)	1935	Reiss, Winold	350-500	
Linderman, Frank B.	How It Came About Stories (1st, 8vo, 221p, p-o, 6cp)	Scribner	1921	Boog, Carle M.	160-250	
Linderman, Frank B.	Indian Old-Man Stories (1st, 8vo, gilt, p-o, 169p, 9cp)	Scribner	1920	Russell, Charles M.	160-250	
Linderman, Frank B.	Indian Why Stories (1st, 8vo, maroon/gilt, p-o, 236p, 8cp)	Scribner	1915	Russell, Charles M.	160-250	
Linderman, Frank B.	Kootenai Why Stories (1st, 8vo, 166p, blue cl, 4cp)	Scribner	1926	Bull, Charles L.	100-165	
Linderman, Frank B.	Red Mother (1st, 8vo, 256p, green/gilt, b/w, pep)	John Day	(1932)	Stoops, Herbert M.	100-165	
Lindgren, Astrid	Bill Bergson & White Rose Rescue (1st, 8vo, 215p, b/w, DJ/3.50)	Viking	(1965)	Freeman, Don	50-80	
Lindgren, Astrid	Bill Bergson Lives Dangerously (1st, sm8vo, 214p, b/w, pep, DJ/2.50)	Viking	1954	Freeman, Don	60-100	
Lindgren, Astrid	Cherry Time at Bullerby (1st UK, 12mo, cloth, 93p, DJ)	L: Methuen	1964	Wikland, Ilon	30-50	
Lindgren, Astrid	Children of Noisy Village (1st, 8vo, 124p, b/w, DJ/2.50)	Viking	(1962)	Wikland, Ilon	60-90	
Lindgren, Astrid	Children on Troublemaker Street (1st {std}, 8vo, 102p, b/w, DJ/3.25)	Macmillan	(1964)	Wikland, Ilon	50-80	
Lindgren, Astrid	Christmas in Noisy Village (1st AM, ob4to, 30p, green cl, color, DJ/3.00)	Viking	(1964)	Wikland, Ilon	60-100	
Lindgren, Astrid	Christmas in the Stable (1st, ob4to, [28]p, fp color, DJ/2.95)	Coward	(1962)	Wiberg, Harald	60-100	
Lindgren, Astrid	Emil in the Soup Tureen (1st AM {std}, 8vo, 126p, b/w, DJ/3.95)	Follett	(1970)	Berg, Bjorn	50-85	
Lindgren, Astrid	Happy Times in Noisy Village (1st AM, 8vo, 122p, b/w, DJ/2.50)	Viking	1963	Wikland, Ilon	60-90	
Lindgren, Astrid	Kati in Italy (1st, 8vo, 152p, color, DJ/2.50)	Grosset/Dunlap	(1961)	Dupuy, Daniel	40-65	
Lindgren, Astrid	Kati in Paris (1st, 8vo, 152p, color, DJ/2.50)	Grosset/Dunlap	(1961)	Dupuy, Daniel	40-65	
Lindgren, Astrid	Lotta on Troublemaker Street (1st AM, 8vo, 57p, DJ/3.50)	Macmillan	1963	Wikland, Ilon	50-85	
Lindgren, Astrid	Madicken (1st UK, 8vo, 142p, b/w, DJ)	L: Oxford U.Pr.	1963	Wikland, Ilon	50-85	
Lindgren, Astrid	Mio, my Son (1st, 8vo, 179p, blue cl, fp b/w, DJ/2.50)	Viking	(1956)	Wikland, Ilon	70-120	*
Lindgren, Astrid	Mischievous Meg (1st, sm8vo, 139p, fp b/w, DJ/2.75)	Viking	(1962)	Domanska, Janina	60-90	
Lindgren, Astrid	Pippi Goes on Board (1st, 8vo, 140p, b/w, DJ/2.00)	Viking	1957	Glanzman, Louis	60-100	
Lindgren, Astrid	Pippi in the South Seas (1st, 8vo, 126p, b/w, DJ/2.00)	Viking	(1959)	Glanzman, Louis	50-80	
Lindgren, Astrid	Pippi Longstocking (1st, 8vo, 158p, b/w, DJ/2.00)	Viking	1950	Glanzman, Louis	80-140	
Lindgren, Astrid	Rasmus & the Vagabond (1st, 8vo, 192p, b/w, DJ/2.75)	Viking	(1960)	Palmquist, Eric	60-100	
Lindgren, Astrid	Seacrow Island (1st AM {std}, 8vo, 287p, b/w, DJ/5.95)	Viking	1969	Hales, Robert	50-85	
Lindgren, Astrid	Skrallan and the Pirates (1st {std}, lg4to, 48p, color, DJ/4.95)	Doubleday	(1969)	Deler/Hallgren	50-80	
Lindgren, Astrid	Springtime in Noisy Village (1st, ob4to, ibds, 28p, fp color, DJ/3.50)	Viking	(1966)	Wikland, Ilon	60-90	
Lindgren, Astrid	The Tomten (1st UK, ob4to, [30]p, color)	L: Constable	1962	Wiberg, Harald	50-85	
Lindgren, Astrid	Tomten and the Fox (1st AM, ob4to, [32]p, fp color, DJ/3.50)	Coward	1966	Wiberg, Harald	60-90	
Lindgren, Barbo	Hilding's Summer (1st AM {std}, 8vo, 138p, b/w, DJ/3.75)	Macmillan	(1967)	Tusan, Stan	20-30	
Lindman, Maj	Dear Little Deer (1st, sm4to, [27]p, p-o, color, DJ)	Whitman	(1953)	Lindman, Maj	100-160	
Lindman, Maj	Fire Eye (1st, ob4to, ipcb, 32p, color, DJ/1.50)	Whitman	1948	Lindman, Maj	70-100	
Lindman, Maj	Flicka, Ricka, Dicka & Little Dog (1st, lg8vo, p-o, [27]p, color, DJ/1.00)	Whitman	1946	Lindman, Maj	80-130	
Lindman, Maj	Flicka, Ricka, Dicka & Three Kittens (1st, lg8vo, [27]p, p-o, fp color)	Whitman	1941	Lindman, Maj	80-120	
Lindman, Maj	Sailboat Time (1st, 4to, [27]p, p-o, fp color, pep)	Whitman	(1951)	Lindman, Maj	60-100	
Lindman, Maj	Snipp, Snapp, Snurr & Buttered Bread (1st, sm4to, ibds, p-o, [23]p, color)	Whitman	1934	Lindman, Maj	70-120	
Lindman, Maj	Snipp, Snapp, Snurr & Gingerbread (1st, lg8vo, p-o, ibds, [23]p, color, pep)	Whitman	1936	Lindman, Maj	75-120	
Lindman, Maj	Snipp, Snapp, Snurr & the Red Shoes (1st, sm4to, [24]p, bds, p-o, col, pep)	Whitman	1936	Lindman, Maj	90-125	
Lindman, Maj	Snowboot, Son of Fire Eye (1st, ob4to, 26p, ipcb, color)	Whitman	(1950)	Lindman, Maj	60-100	
Lindquist, Jennie	Crystal Tree (1st, 8vo, 297p, ibds, fp b/w, cep, DJ/3.95)	Harper	(1966)	Chalmers, Mary	30-50	
Lindquist, Jennie	Golden Name Day (1st, 8vo, blue cl, 247p, pep, b/w, DJ/2.75, NH)	Harper	(1955)	Williams, Garth	80-135	R
Lindquist, Jennie	Little Silver House (1st, sm8vo, 213p, green cl, fp b/w, DJ/2.75)	Harper	(1959)	Williams, Garth	50-85	
Lindquist, Willis	Burma Boy (1st, 8vo, 93p, fp b/w, DJ/2.00)	Whittlesey	1953	Nicolas	40-65	R
Lindsay, Christina	Little Italian Cookbook (1st, 4to, 128p, color)	NY: Walker	(1968)	Parnall, Peter	25-45	*
Lindsay, Maud	Bobby & the Big Road (1st, 12mo, 112p, blue cl, 16cp, pep)	Lothrop, Lee	(1920)	Young, Florence L.	50-85	
Lindsay, Maud	Jock Barefoot (1st, 8vo, 177p, fp b/w, DJ/1.50)	Lothrop, Lee	1939	Linton, Jane	75-125	
Lindsay, Maud	Joyous Guests (1st, lg8vo, 208p, 13cp, pep)	Lothrop, Lee	(1921)	Berger, William M.	60-90	
Lindsay, Maud	Joyous Travelers (1st, 8vo, 157p, blue/gilt, col frn, pep)	Lothrop, Lee	(1919)	Berger, William M.	60-90	
Lindsay, Maud	Little Missy (1st, sq8vo, 188p, 8cp, pep)	Lothrop, Lee	(1922)	Young, Florence L.	70-100	
Lindsay, Maud	Posey & the Pedlar (1st, sm8vo, tan cl, 186p, fp b/w, DJ/1.50)	Lothrop, Lee	1938	Credle, Ellis	70-120	
Lindsay, Maud	Silverfoot (1st, sq8vo, 223p, 8cp, pep)	Lothrop, Lee	(1924)	Young, Florence L.	60-90	
Lindsay, Maud	Story-Teller (1st, sm sq8vo, 117p, 12cp)	Lothrop, Lee	(1915)	Young, Florence L.	60-90	
Lindsay, Maud	Toy Shop (1st, 12mo, 158p, col frn, b/w, pep)	Lothrop, Lee	(1926)	Young, Florence L.	50-80	
Lindsay, Merrill	One Hundred Great Guns (1st, folio, gilt, 379p, color, pep, DJ)	NY: Walker	(1967)	Parnall, Peter	80-125	
Lindsay, Norman	Magic Pudding (1st AM, 8vo, orange cl, [159]p, b/w, DJ/1.50)	Farrar/Rinehart	[1936]	Lindsay, Norman	100-165	
Lindsay, Vachel	Johnny Appleseed (1st, 12mo, green cl, 144p, color, DJ/1.00)	Macmillan	1928	Richards, George M.	50-80	
Lindsey, William	Apples of Istakhar (1st, sm8vo, 100p, brown/gilt, cvr by...)	Copeland & Day	1895	Goodhue, B.G.	70-120	
Lindsey, William	Curtain of Forgetfulness (1st, lg8vo, 31p, 11 ticp)	Houghton	1923	Paul, Evelyn	80-120	
Lindsey, William	Severed Mantle (1st, lg8vo, 452p, 7cp)	Houghton	1909	Keller, Arthur I.	25-45	
Lines, Kathleen	Dick Whittington (1st, 8vo, 42p, color, DJ)	L: Bodley Head	(1970)	Ardizzone, Edward	50-85	
Lines, Kathleen	Dick Whittington (1st AM, 8vo, 42p, color, DJ/4.75)	H.Z. Walck	(1970)	Ardizzone, Edward	60-90	
Lines, Kathleen	Lavender's Blue (1st AM, 4to, 180p, blue/gilt, color, pep, DJ/6.00)	F. Watts	(1956)	Jones, Harold	80-120	R
Linklater, Eric	Pirates in the Deep Green Sea (1st, 8vo, 397p, gilt, b/w, pep, DJ/2.75)	Macmillan	1949	Reeves, William	50-80	*
Linklater, Eric	Wind on the Moon (1st, 12mo, 363p, fp b/w, DJ, CgM)	L: Macmillan	1944	Bentley, Nicolas	50-80	
Linnell, Olive	Autumn Songs with Music (4to, bds, p-o, 12 ticp)	L: Blackie	[1920]	Barker, Cicely M.	130-200	
Linnell, Olive	Spring Songs with Music (4to, bds, p-o, 12 ticp)	L: Blackie	[1920]	Barker, Cicely M.	120-200	
Lionni, Leo	Alexander and the Wind-Up Mouse (1st, 4to, [30]p, color, DJ/3.95, CH)	Pantheon	(1969)	Lionni, Leo	40-65	

AUTHOR	TITLE	PUBLISHER	DATE	ARTIST	PRICE	LC
Lionni, Leo	Alphabet Tree (1st, 4to, ibds, [33]p, color, pep, DJ)	Pantheon	(1968)	Lionni, Leo	60-100	
Lionni, Leo	Biggest House in the World (1st, 4to, [30]p, fp color, DJ/3.50)	Pantheon	1968	Lionni, Leo	45-70	
Lionni, Leo	Fish is Fish (1st, 4to, [32]p, color, DJ)	Pantheon	(1970)	Lionni, Leo	40-60	
Lionni, Leo	Frederick (1st, 4to, [32]p, color, pep, DJ/3.50, CH, NYTBI)	Pantheon	(1967)	Lionni, Leo	65-100	
Lionni, Leo	Inch by Inch (1st, sq4to, ipcb, unpag, color, pep, DJ/3.50, CH, NYTBI)	Obolensky	(1960)	Lionni, Leo	140-200	R
Lionni, Leo	Little Blue & Little Yellow (1st, sq8vo, ibds, [40]p, col, DJ/2.95, NYTBI)	Obolensky	(1959)	Lionni, Leo	200-300	R
Lionni, Leo	On My Beach there are Many Pebbles (1st, ob4to, [32]p, fp b/w, DJ/3.50)	Obolensky	(1961)	Lionni, Leo	60-100	R
Lionni, Leo	Swimmy (1st, 4to, [31]p, ibds, color, dep, DJ/3.50, CH, NYTBI)	Pantheon	(1963)	Lionni, Leo	65-100	R
Lionni, Leo	Tico and the Golden Wings (1st, 4to, ibds, [34]p, fp, color, cep, DJ/3.50)	Pantheon	1964	Lionni, Leo	60-90	
Lipkind, Will	Billy the Kid (1st {std}, 4to, unpag, color, DJ/3.25)	Harcourt	(1961)	Nicolas	30-50	*
Lipkind, Will	Boy and the Forest (1st {std}, 4to, [40]p, fp 3-color, DJ/3.25)	Harcourt	1964	Nicolas	30-50	*
Lipkind, Will	Boy of the Islands (1st {std}, 8vo, 55p, fp b/w, DJ/2.50)	Harcourt	(1954)	Nicolas	30-45	
Lipkind, Will	Boy with a Harpoon (1st {std}, 8vo, ibds, 58p, b/w, DJ/2.25)	Harcourt	(1952)	Nicolas	30-45	
Lipkind, Will	Chaga (1st {std}, 4to, [40]p, fp color, DJ/2.50, NYTBI)	Harcourt	(1955)	Nicolas	30-50	
Lipkind, Will	Christmas Bunny (1st {std}, 4to, [49]p, green cl, color, pep, DJ/2.50)	Harcourt	(1953)	Nicolas	70-120	R
Lipkind, Will	Circus Ruckus (1st {std}, 4to, [48]p, fp 3-color, DJ/2.75, NYTBI)	Harcourt	(1954)	Nicolas	50-90	R
Lipkind, Will	Even Steven (1st {std}, 4to, unpag, ibds, 2-color, DJ/2.25)	Harcourt	(1952)	Nicolas	40-65	
Lipkind, Will	Finders Keepers (1st {std}, 4to, [32]p, pep, 28 color, DJ/2.00, CM)	Harcourt	(1951)	Nicolas	80-120	
Lipkind, Will	Four-Leaf Clover (1st {std}, 4to, [32]p, color, DJ/3.00)	Harcourt	(1959)	Nicolas	45-70	
Lipkind, Will	Little Tiny Rooster (1st {std}, 4to, [30]p, fp 3-color, DJ/3.25)	Harcourt	(1960)	Nicolas	45-70	
Lipkind, Will	Magic Feather Duster (1st {std}, [38]p, 2-color, pep, DJ/3.25, NYTBI)	Harcourt	(1958)	Nicolas	50-80	R
Lipkind, Will	Nubber Bear (1st {std}, 4to, [36]p, ibds, DJ/3.25)	Harcourt	(1966)	Duvoisin, Roger	50-85	
Lipkind, Will	Perry the Imp (1st {std}, 4to, [38]p, fp 3-color, DJ/2.95)	Harcourt	1956	Nicolas	50-80	R*
Lipkind, Will	Professor Bull's Umbrella (1st, 4to, [38]p, color, pep, DJ/2.50)	Viking	1954	Schreiber, Georges	30-50	
Lipkind, Will	Russet and the Two Reds (1st {std}, 4to, [32]p, 2-color, DJ/3.25)	Harcourt	(1962)	Nicolas	30-50	
Lipkind, Will	Sleepyhead (1st {std}, 4to, green cl, [38]p, 2-color, pep, DJ/3.00)	Harcourt	(1957)	Nicolas	60-90	
Lipkind, Will	Two Reds (1st {std}, 4to, [48]p, color, pep, DJ/2.00, CH)	Harcourt	(1950)	Nicolas	80-120	R
Lipman, Michael	Chatterlings in Wordland (8vo, orange cl, 112p, color, pep)	Wise-Parlow	(1935)	Lipman, Michael	40-70	
Lipman, Michael	The Chatterlings (1st, lg8vo, 96p, ibds, color, pep)	Volland	(1928)	Lipman, Michael	60-100	R
Lippincott, J.W.	Black Wings (1st {std}, sm8vo, 143p, blue cl, col frn, pep, DJ/2.50)	Lippincott	(1947)	Hunt, Lynn B.	50-80	
Lippincott, J.W.	Bun, a Wild Rabbit (1st, 12mo, 124p, p-o, 12pl)	Penn	1918	(Photos)	30-50	
Lippincott, J.W.	Gray Squirrel (1st, 12mo, 144p, p-o, 7pl)	Penn	1921	(Photos)	30-50	
Lippincott, J.W.	Phantom Deer (1st {std}, sm8vo, blue cl, 192p, 1 dp cp, 4pl, DJ/3.00)	Lippincott	(1954)	Bransom, Paul	30-50	
Lippincott, J.W.	Red Roan Pony (1st, 8vo, 320p, red cl, col frn, 4pl, pep)	Penn	(1934)	Hunt, Lynn B.	55-80	*
Lippincott, J.W.	Red Roan Pony (1st {new ed}, sm8vo, 218p, red cl, 1 dp col, 6pl, DJ/2.50)	Lippincott	(1951)	Anderson, C.W.	30-50	
Lippincott, J.W.	Wahoo Bobcat (1st {std}, 8vo, 207p, 1 dp color, 4 dp b/w, DJ/2.50)	Lippincott	(1950)	Bransom, Paul	60-90	
Lippincott, J.W.	Wilderness Champion (1st {std}, lg8vo, 195p, 6 dp b/w, 5pl, cep, DJ/2.50)	Lippincott	(1944)	Bransom, Paul	45-70	
Lippincott, J.W.	Wolf King (1st, 8vo, 316p, col frn, 4pl, pep)	Penn	(1933)	Bransom, Paul	30-50	
Lippman, Peter J.	New at the Zoo (1st, sm ob4to, 31p, 2-color, DJ/3.50)	Harper	(1969)	Lippman, Peter	25-40	
Lippman, Peter J.	Plunkety Plunk (1st {std}, 4to, [46]p, color, cep, DJ/3.25, NYTBI)	Ariel	(1963)	Lippman, Peter	30-50	
Lippmann, Julie M.	Dearie Dot and the Dog (1st, sm8vo, 194p, 5pl)	Penn	1903	Winner, Margaret	25-40	*
Lippmann, Julie M.	Dreamland (1st, sm8vo, green/gilt, 211p, 5pl, dep)	Penn	1901	Betts, Anna W.	30-45	
Lippmann, Julie M.	Jock O'Dreams (1st, 8vo, 211p, gilt, b/w)	Roberts Bros.	1891	McDermott, Jessie	40-70	
Lippmann, Julie M.	Sweet P's (1st, 12mo, 192p, 5pl, pep)	Penn	1902	Waugh, Ida	30-50	
Lips, Julius	Tents in the Wilderness (1st, 8vo, 297p, b/w, pep, DJ/2.25)	Stokes	1942	Wiese, Kurt	25-45	
Litchfield, Sarah	Hello, Alaska! (1st, narrow 8vo, p-o, 31p, color, pep, DJ/1.25)	Whitman	1945	Wiese, Kurt	30-45	
Litsey, E. Carl	Race of the Swift (1st, sm8vo, gilt, uncut, 151p, 4pl)	Little/Brown	1905	Bull, Charles L.	25-40	*
Little, Frances	Little Sister Snow (1st, 12mo, 141p, p-o, 12cp, pep)	Century	1909	Kataoka, Genjiro	40-65	
Little, Jean	Look Through My Window (1st, 8vo, 258p, fp b/w, DJ/3.95)	Harper	(1970)	Sandin, Joan	25-45	
Little, Jean	Mine for Keeps (1st {std}, 8vo, 186p, b/w, DJ/3.75)	Little/Brown	(1962)	Parker, Lewis	25-45	
Little, Jean	Spring Begins in March (1st {std}, 8vo, 156p, b/w, DJ/3.95)	Little/Brown	(1966)	Parker, Lewis	25-45	
Littledale, Harold	Alexander (1st, sm4to, [43]p, ipcb, color, pep, DJ/2.75)	Parents Mag. Pr.	1964	Vroman, Tom	30-50	
Littlefield, Wm. J.	Seventh Son of a Seventh Son (1st, 8vo, 190p, fp b/w, DJ/3.50)	Lothrop, Lee	(1959)	Berson, Harold	50-80	
Littlefield, Wm. J.	Whiskers of Ho Ho (1st, lg sq8vo, [32]p, fp color, pep, DJ/2.75)	Lothrop, Lee	1958	Bobri, Vladimir	30-50	
Littlewood, Letty	Bower Book of Simple Poems.... (1st, 8vo, 267p, red cl, 10cp, pep)	L: O'Connor	(1922)	Appleton, Honor C.	100-165	
Littlewood, Samuel R.	Child of the Sea (1st, 8vo, gilt, 196p, 8cp, pep)	L: Simpkin	1915	Appleton, Honor C.	40-60	*
Littlewood, Samuel R.	Valentine and Orson (1st, 4to, 143p, p-o, 8cp, pep)	L: Simpkin	1919	Anderson, Florence	100-170	
Lively, Penelope	Astercote (1st [1st bk.], 8vo, gilt, 156p, b/w, DJ)	L: Heinemann	1970	Maitland, Antony	70-120	
Livingston, Myra C.	Crazy Flight (1st {std}, 8vo, 48p, b/w, DJ/3.50)	Harcourt	(1969)	Spanfeller, James	25-35	
Livingston, Myra C.	Moon and a Star (1st {std}, 12mo, 48p, b/w, DJ/2.50)	Harcourt	(1965)	Shahn, Judith	20-35	*
Livingston, Myra C.	Old Mrs. Twindlytart (1st {std}, 8vo, 48p, b/w, DJ/2.75)	Harcourt	(1967)	Arno, Enrico	20-35	
Livingston, Myra C.	See What I Found (1st {std}, 12mo, [32]p, b/w, DJ/1.95)	Harcourt	(1962)	Blegvad, Erik	20-35	
Livingston, Myra C.	Whispers (1st {std}, 12mo, 48p, b/w, DJ/2.25)	Harcourt	(1958)	Chwast, Jacqueline	30-45	
Livingston, Myra C.	Wide Awake (1st {std}, 12mo, 48p, b/w, DJ/2.25)	Harcourt	(1959)	Chwast, Jacqueline	20-30	*
Livingston, Richard	The Hunkendunkens (1st {std}, ob8vo, [36]p, color, DJ/3.25)	Harcourt	(1968)	Pincus, Harriet	30-45	
Lloyd, John U.	Red-Head (1st, 8vo, teg, gilt, 208p, 10 fp b/w)	Dodd	1903	Birch, Reginald	40-65	
Lloyd, John U.	Right Side of the Car (1st, 8vo, 59p, teg, green/gilt, cvr by...)	Badger	1897	Hapgood, T.B.	60-100	
Lloyd, John U.	Scroggins (1st, sm8vo, 119p, gilt, teg, 4pl)	Dodd	1904	Birch, Reginald	40-65	
Lloyd, John U.	Stringtown on the Pike (1st, sm8vo, 414p, tan cl, p-o, b/w)	Dodd	1900	(Photos)	40-70	
Lloyd, Marion	Penny & Peter of the Island (1st, 4to, [60]p, fp 1-color, pep, DJ/2.00)	J. Messner	(1941)	Tait, Agnes	30-50	*
Lloyd, Nelson M.	Soldier of the Valley (1st, 12mo, red/gilt, 335p, 34 fp b/w)	Scribner	1904	Frost, A.B.	30-50	
Lloyd, Trevor	Sky Highways: Geography from the Air (1st, 4to, 61p, color, DJ/2.50)	Houghton	1945	Sperry, Armstrong	30-50	
Lobe, Mira	Grandma in the Apple Tree (1st, lg8vo, 94p, fp b/w, DJ/4.95)	McGraw-Hill	(1970)	Brown, Judith	20-35	*
Lobel, Anita	Potatoes, Potatoes (1st, ob4to, [40]p, ibds, fp 2-color, DJ/2.95)	Harper	(1967)	Lobel, Anita	30-50	
Lobel, Anita	Seamstress of Salzburg (1st, ob4to, [49]p, fp color, cep, DJ/4.50)	Harper	(1970)	Lobel, Anita	30-50	
Lobel, Anita	Sven's Bridge (1st, ob8vo, ibds, [32]p, color, cep, DJ/2.95, NYTBI)	Harper	(1965)	Lobel, Anita	40-65	
Lobel, Anita	Troll Music (1st, 4to, ibds, [32]p, fp color, DJ/2.95)	Harper	(1966)	Lobel, Anita	30-50	
Lobel, Anita	Under a Mushroom (1st, sm sq8vo, ibds, [40]p, fp b/w, DJ/3.95)	Harper	(1970)	Lobel, Anita	30-50	

AUTHOR	TITLE	PUBLISHER	DATE	ARTIST	PRICE	LC
Lobel, Arnold	Bears of the Air (1st, lg8vo, [32]p, ibds, 1-color, cep, DJ/2.50)	Harper	(1965)	Lobel, Arnold	30-50	
Lobel, Arnold	Frog and Toad are Friends (1st, 8vo, ibds, 64p, color, DJ/2.50, CH)	Harper	(1970)	Lobel, Arnold	50-80	
Lobel, Arnold	Giant John (1st, 4to, [32]p, ibds, fp 2-color, DJ/2.95)	Harper	1964	Lobel, Arnold	45-70	
Lobel, Arnold	Great Blueness & other Predicaments (1st, 4to, ibds, [32]p, color, DJ/3.95)	Harper	1968	Lobel, Arnold	50-80	
Lobel, Arnold	Holiday for Mister Muster (1st {std}, ob4to, [32]p, 1-color, DJ/2.75, NYT)	Harper	(1963)	Lobel, Arnold	30-50	
Lobel, Arnold	Lucille (1st, 8vo, 64p, color, DJ/1.95)	Harper	(1964)	Lobel, Arnold	30-50	*
Lobel, Arnold	Martha the Movie Mouse (1st, 4to, [32]p, ibds, color, cep, DJ/2.95)	Harper	(1966)	Lobel, Arnold	45-70	
Lobel, Arnold	Prince Bertram the Bad (1st {std}, 4to, [32]p, color, DJ/2.95)	Harper	(1963)	Lobel, Arnold	40-65	
Lobel, Arnold	Small Pig (1st, 8vo, 63p, 2-color, DJ/2.50)	Harper	(1969)	Lobel, Arnold	30-50	
Lobel, Arnold	Zoo for Mister Muster (1st, sm ob4to, [32]p, ibds, 1-color, cep, DJ/2.75)	Harper	(1962)	Lobel, Arnold	40-65	
Locke, Alain L. (ed)	New Negro (1st, 8vo, ipcb, 445p, col frn, b/w)	A. & C. Boni	1925	Reiss, Winold	400-600	
Locke, Elsie	Runaway Settlers (1st AM {std}, 8vo, 190p, b/w, DJ/3.75)	Dutton	(1966)	Maitland, Antony	30-50	*
Locke, William J.	Beloved Vagabond (1st, 8vo, 267p, 16cp)	L: John Lane	1922	Dulac, Jean	80-120	
Locke, William J.	Christmas Mystery (1st, 8vo, 54p, green/gilt, 4pl, dep)	NY: John Lane	1910	Campbell, Blendon	75-100	*
Locke, William J.	Christmas Mystery (1st UK, 4to, 37p, orange cl, 6cp)	L: John Lane	1922	Lendon, Warwick W.	35-60	*
Locke, William J.	Fortunate Youth (1st, 12mo, 352p, green/gilt, cvr by...)	NY: John Lane	1914	Hazenplug, Frank	35-60	
Locke, William J.	Fortunate Youth (1st, 12mo, 352p, green/gilt, 8pl by...)	NY: John Lane	1914	Keller, Arthur I.	35-60	
Locke, William J.	Golden Journey of Mr. Paradyne (1st AM, 8vo, ibds, 53p, 8cp, pep)	Dodd	1924	Foster, Marcia L.	55-80	*
Locke, William J.	Story of the Three Wise Men (1st, 8vo, 38p, gilt, 6cp)	L: John Lane	1922	Lendon, Warwick W.	40-60	
Locker, Mrs. F.	What the Blackbird Said (1st, sq8vo, 87p, gilt, fp b/w)	L: Routledge	1881	Caldecott, Randolph	100-170	
Lockhart, Caroline	Lady Doc (1st, 8vo, tan cloth, 339p, 4pl)	Lippincott	1912	Hoskins, Gayle	30-50	
Lockhart, Caroline	Man from the Bitter Roots (1st, 8vo, 327p, red/gilt, 3cp)	Lippincott	1915	Hoskins, Gayle	40-65	
Lockridge, Frances	Cat Who Rode Cows (1st {std}, 8vo, yellow cl, 36p, b/w, DJ/2.25)	Lippincott	(1955)	Bacon, Peggy	45-70	
Lockridge, Frances	Cats & People (1st {std}, 8vo, 286p, b/w, DJ/3.50)	Lippincott	(1950)	Stone, Helen	30-50	
Lockridge, Frances	Nameless Cat (1st {std}, 8vo, 78p, green cl, b/w, DJ/2.25)	Lippincott	(1954)	Bacon, Peggy	30-50	*
Lockridge, Frances	Proud Cat (1st {std}, 8vo, 95p, b/w, DJ/2.25)	Lippincott	(1951)	Blaisdell, Elinore	30-45	
Lockyer, A.M.	Robbers of Squeak (1st, lg ob8vo, [32]p, ibds, chromos)	L: Marcus Ward	[1890]	Lockyer, A.M.	100-165	
Lofting, Hugh	Dr. Dolittle & Green Canary (1st {std}, 8vo, 276p, col frn, pep, DJ/2.75)	Lippincott	(1950)	Lofting, Hugh	100-175	
Lofting, Hugh	Dr. Dolittle & Secret Lake (1st {std}, 8vo, 366p pep, p-o col frn, DJ/3.00)	Lippincott	(1948)	Lofting, Hugh	100-175	
Lofting, Hugh	Dr. Dolittle in the Moon (1st, 8vo, p-o, 307p, col frn, pep)	Stokes	(1928)	Lofting, Hugh	100-175	
Lofting, Hugh	Dr. Dolittle's Birthday Bk. (1st, sq12mo gilt [216]p, col frn, dep, DJ/1.75)	Stokes	(1935)	Lofting, Hugh	200-300	
Lofting, Hugh	Dr. Dolittle's Caravan (1st {std}, 8vo, 342p, p-o, col frn, pep)	Stokes	(1926)	Lofting, Hugh	100-175	
Lofting, Hugh	Dr. Dolittle's Circus (1st, 8vo, 379p, p-o, col frn, pep)	Stokes	(1924)	Lofting, Hugh	100-175	
Lofting, Hugh	Dr. Dolittle's Garden (1st, 8vo, 327p, p-o, col frn, pep)	Stokes	(1927)	Lofting, Hugh	100-175	
Lofting, Hugh	Dr. Dolittle's Post Office (1st, 8vo, 359p, col frn, pep)	Stokes	(1923)	Lofting, Hugh	100-175	
Lofting, Hugh	Dr. Dolittle's Puddleby Advens (1st {std} 8vo, 241p, pep, col frn, DJ/3.00)	Lippincott	(1952)	Lofting, Hugh	100-175	
Lofting, Hugh	Dr. Dolittle's Return (1st, 8vo, p-o, 273p, col frn, b/w, pep)	Stokes	1933	Lofting, Hugh	100-175	
Lofting, Hugh	Dr. Dolittle's Zoo (1st, 8vo, grey cl, p-o, 338p, col frn, pep)	Stokes	(1925)	Lofting, Hugh	100-175	
Lofting, Hugh	Gub Gub's Book (1st, sm8vo, 185p, p-o, 2cp, 6pl, pep)	Stokes	(1932)	Lofting, Hugh	100-185	
Lofting, Hugh	Noisy Nora (1st, 16mo, [53]p, pink cl, p-o, pep, color)	Stokes	(1929)	Lofting, Hugh	100-170	
Lofting, Hugh	Porridge Poetry (1st, ob12mo, [96]p, p-o, yellow cl, color)	Stokes	(1924)	Lofting, Hugh	120-180	
Lofting, Hugh	Story of Dr. Dolittle (1st, 8vo, p-o, 180p, col frn, b/w, pep, PPP)	Stokes	1920	Lofting, Hugh	300-500	
Lofting, Hugh	Story of Mrs. Tubbs (1st, sm ob8vo, p-o, [95]p, color)	Stokes	(1923)	Lofting, Hugh	200-300	
Lofting, Hugh	Tommy, Tilly & Mrs. Tubbs (1st UK, ob12mo, 72p, ibds, color)	L: J. Cape	(1937)	Lofting, Hugh	90-140	
Lofting, Hugh	Twilight of Magic (1st, 8vo, p-o, 303p, col frn, b/w, pep)	Stokes	1930	Lenski, Lois	100-175	
Lofting, Hugh	Voyages of Doctor Dolittle (1st, 12mo, p-o, 364p, 2cp, pep, NM)	Stokes	1922	Lofting, Hugh	120-185	
Loken, Anna B.	Colt from the Dark Forest (1st, 8vo, 127p, b/w, DJ/3.00)	Lothrop, Lee	(1959)	Bolognese, Don	20-30	
London, Jack	Abysmal Brute (1st, 12mo, 169p, frn by...)	Century	1913	Grant, Gordon	250-400	
London, Jack	Before Adam (1st, 8vo, brown cl, 242p, uncut, 8cp)	Macmillan	1907	Bull, Charles L.	150-250	
London, Jack	Call of the Wild (1st, 8vo, teg, 231p, green/gilt, 10cp, pep, PPP)	Macmillan	1903	Bull/Goodwin	500-700	
London, Jack	Call of the Wild (1st, 8vo, 254p, p-o, blue cl, 16cp, pep)	Macmillan	1912	Bransom, Paul	200-300	
London, Jack	Children of the Frost (1st, sm8vo, 261p, blue cl, 8pl)	Macmillan	1902	Reay, Raphael M.	425-600	
London, Jack	Cruise of the Snark (1st, 8vo, 340p, teg, p-o, blue/gilt, col frn)	Macmillan	1911	(Photos)	300-450	
London, Jack	Daughter of the Snows (1st, 12mo, 334p, gilt, 4cp)	Lippincott	1902	Yohn, F.C.	350-500	
London, Jack	John Barleycorn (1st, 8vo, 343p, gilt, 8pl)	Century	1913	Dunn, Harvey T.	250-400	
London, Jack	People of the Abyss (1st, lg8vo, 319p, gilt, teg, uncut, 19pl)	Macmillan	1903	(Photos)	350-500	
London, Jack	Scarlet Plague (1st, 8vo, 181p, gilt, b/w, pep)	Macmillan	1915	Grant, Gordon	250-400	
London, Jack	Sea Wolf (1st, 8vo, blue/gilt, teg, 366p, 6pl)	Macmillan	1904	Aylward, W.J.	400-600	
London, Jack	Smoke Bellew (1st, 8vo, blue cl, 385p, 8pl)	Century	1912	Monahan, P.J.	250-350	
London, Jack	Son of the Sun (1st, 8vo, blue cl, 333p, 3pl)	Doubleday/Page	1912	Fischer, Anton O.	300-450	
London, Jack	Tales of the Fish Patrol (1st, 8vo, teg, 243p, map, 7pl)	Macmillan	1905	Varian, George	250-450	
London, Jack	The Game (1st, 8vo, 182p, teg, uncut, col frn, 5pl)	Macmillan	1905	Hutt, Henry	450-650	
London, Jack	The Road (1st, 8vo, grey/gilt, teg, 224p)	Macmillan	1907	(Photos)	400-600	
London, Jack	Valley of the Moon (1st, 8vo, orange/gilt, 530p, col frn by...)	Macmillan	1913	Harper, George	200-300	
London, Jack	White Fang (1st, 8vo, blue cl, 328p, 8cp, PPP)	Macmillan	1906	Bull, Charles L.	300-450	
Long, John L.	Billy Boy (1st, sm8vo, blue cl, 74p, teg, p-o, uncut, 4pl, pep)	Dodd	1906	Smith, Jessie W.	160-220	
Long, John L.	Felice (1st, sm8vo, 156p, frn by...)	Moffat	1908	Flagg, James M.	25-40	*
Long, John L.	Madame Butterfly (1st, 8vo, teg, gilt, 152p, uncut, 16pl)	Century	1903	Abbott, C.Y.	45-70	
Long, John L.	Seffy (1st, sm8vo, 144p, green/gilt, 8cp)	Bobbs-Merrill	(1905)	Williams, C.D.	30-50	
Long, John L.	War (1st, 12mo, red/gilt, 371p, 4cp)	Bobbs-Merrill	(1913)	Wyeth, N.C.	60-100	
Long, Laura	Square Sails & Spice Islands (1st {std}, 8vo, 249p, b/w, pep, DJ/2.50)	Longmans	1945	Falls, Charles B.	30-50	
Long, Olive M.	The Lollipops (1st, ob8vo, ipcb, [28]p, b/w)	R.H. Russell	1901	Long, Olive M.	120-180	*
Long, William J.	Brier-Patch Philosophy (1st, 12mo, 296p, teg, col frn, 4pl)	Ginn & Co.	1906	Copeland, Charles	35-60	
Long, William J.	How Animals Talk (1st, lg8vo, green/gilt, teg, 301p, 8cp)	Harper	(1919)	Copeland, Charles	40-65	
Long, William J.	Mother Nature (1st {std}, lg8vo, green/gilt, 330p, 8cp)	Harper	(1923)	Bull, Charles L.	40-60	
Long, William J.	Northern Trails (1st, 8vo, teg, 390p, gilt, col frn, b/w)	Ginn & Co.	1905	Copeland, Charles	30-50	
Long, William J.	Wood-Folk Comedies (1st, lg8vo, green/gilt, 307p, 8cp)	Harper	(1920)	Bull, Charles L.	45-70	
Longfellow, H.W.	Children's Longfellow (1st, lg8vo, 334p, p-o, 8cp)	Houghton	1908	Various	50-80	*

AUTHOR	TITLE	PUBLISHER	DATE	ARTIST	PRICE	LC
Longfellow, H.W.	Courtship of Miles Standish (1st, lg8vo, 152p, grey/gilt, 8cp, pep)	Bobbs-Merrill	(1903)	Christy, Howard C.	60-100	
Longfellow, H.W.	Courtship of Miles Standish (1st, lg8vo, 148p, gilt, p-o, 8cp, pep)	Houghton	1920	Wyeth, N.C.	170-240	
Longfellow, H.W.	Evangeline (1st, 8vo, 143p, teg, gilt, 5cp by...)	Houghton	1897	Oakley, Violet	200-300	
Longfellow, H.W.	Evangeline (1st, 8vo, 143p, teg, gilt, 5cp by...)	Houghton	1897	Smith, Jessie W.	200-300	
Longfellow, H.W.	Evangeline (1st, lg8vo, red/gilt, 132p, 6cp)	Bobbs-Merrill	(1905)	Christy, Howard C.	50-85	
Longfellow, H.W.	Evangeline (1st, sm8vo, teg, p-o, 172p, pep)	Reilly/Britton	(1909)	Neill, John R.	80-125	
Longfellow, H.W.	Evangeline (1st, lg8vo, gilt, p-o, 260p, 11cp)	Stokes	(1913)	Kirk, Maria L.	120-180	*
Longfellow, H.W.	Golden Legend (1st, 4to, green/gilt, teg, 153p, 25 ticp)	L: Hodder	[1910]	Meteyard, Sidney	125-200	
Longfellow, H.W.	Golden Legend (1st AM, 4to, 153p, gilt, 25 ticp)	Doran	[1912]	Meteyard, Sidney	120-180	
Longfellow, H.W.	Hanging of the Crane (1st, 8vo, [60]p, teg, p-o, 12cp)	Houghton	1907	Keller, Arthur I.	40-70	
Longfellow, H.W.	Hiawatha (1st, 8vo, suede/gilt, 242p, teg, 23pl)	Houghton	1891	Remington, Frederic	250-350	
Longfellow, H.W.	Hiawatha (1st, lg8vo, p-o, gilt, 189p, 16cp)	Bobbs-Merrill	(1906)	Fisher, Harrison	120-200	
Longfellow, H.W.	Hiawatha (lg8vo, p-o, 193p, 9pl by...)	Riverside	1908	Remington, Frederic	120-180	
Longfellow, H.W.	Hiawatha (1st, 8vo, p-o, 208p, teg, 1-color, pep)	Reilly/Britton	(1909)	Neill, John R.	80-140	
Longfellow, H.W.	Hiawatha (1st, lg8vo, gilt, 313p, p-o, 11cp, pep)	Stokes	(1910)	Kirk, Maria L.	100-175	
Longfellow, H.W.	Hiawatha (1st, lg8vo, 245p, p-o, buckram)	Rand/McNally	(1911)	(Photos)	100-165	
Longfellow, H.W.	Hiawatha (1st, red/gilt, 8vo, teg, 242p, p-o by...)	Houghton	1911	Parrish, Maxfield	400-600	
Longfellow, H.W.	Hiawatha (1st, 8vo, teg, red/gilt, 242p, b/w illus by...)	Houghton	1911	Remington, Frederic	400-600	
Longfellow, H.W.	Hiawatha (1st, 8vo, red/gilt, teg, 242p, frn by...)	Houghton	1911	Wyeth, N.C.	400-600	
Longfellow, H.W.	Hiawatha (1st, 4to, ibds, [68]p, fp color, pep, DJ/1.00)	Random	1951	Sperry, Armstrong	40-60	
Longfellow, H.W.	Skeleton in Armor (1st, lg8vo, [31]p, fp color, DJ/3.50)	Prentice-Hall	(1963)	Kennedy, Paul	20-35	*
Longstreth, Joseph	Little Big Feather (1st, 4to, [40]p, color, pep, DJ/2.50, NYTBI)	Abelard-Schuman	(1956)	Borten, Helen	40-65	
Loomis, Charles B.	Just Rhymes (1st, sm8vo, ibds, 70p, b/w)	R.H. Russell	1899	Cory, Fanny	75-100	
Loomis, Charles B.	Little Maude & her Mama (1st, 12mo, 43p, brown cl, 4pl)	Doubleday/Page	1909	Loomis, Chester B.	40-65	
Loomis, Charles B.	More Cheerful Americans (1st, 8vo, green/gilt, 284p, 12pl)	Henry Holt & Co.	1904	Various	30-50	
Loomis, Charles B.	Yankee Enchantments (1st, 8vo, 328p, gilt, 20 fp b/w, pep)	McClure	1900	Cory, Fanny	70-100	
Loomis, Ruth	Mrs. Purdy's Children (1st {std}, 8vo, 178p, fp b/w, cep, DJ/4.50)	Dial Press	(1970)	Kellogg, Steven	30-50	
Lopshire, Robert M.	I Am Better than You (1st, 8vo, 64p, ibds, fp color, DJ/2.50)	Harper	(1968)	Lopshire, Robert	25-40	
Lord Brabourne	Friends & Foes from Fairy Land (1st AM, 8vo, yellow cl, 367p)	Little/Brown	1886	Sambourne, Linley	100-180	
Lord Byron	Don Juan (1st, lg8vo, 17 woodcuts, 408p, buckram)	L: John Lane	(1926)	Austen, John	60-90	
Lord Dunsany	Book of Wonder (1st, 8vo, 98p, brown pcb, p-o, 10pl)	L: Heinemann	1912	Sime, Sidney	250-350	
Lord Dunsany	Dreamer's Tales (1st, sm8vo, 252p, blue/gilt, teg, uncut, 9pl)	L: G. Allen	1910	Sime, Sidney	160-220	
Lord Dunsany	Gods of Pegana (1st, 8vo, 94p, grey bds, uncut, 8pl)	L: E. Mathews	1905	Sime, Sidney	250-350	
Lord Dunsany	Sword of Welleran (1st, 4to, 243p, green/gilt, teg, 10pl)	L: G. Allen	1908	Sime, Sidney	150-225	
Lord Dunsany	Time & the Gods (1st AM, 8vo, bds, 179p, p-o, 10pl)	Bos: J.W. Luce	[1913]	Sime, Sidney	80-140	
Lord, Nancy	My Dog and I (1st, sm4to, 31p, fp 2-color, pep, DJ/2.25)	Whittlesey	1958	Galdone, Paul	40-65	
Lorimer, D.& E.	Persian Tales (1st, 8vo, gilt, 354p, 16cp, 8pl)	L: Macmillan	1919	Roberts, Hilda	45-70	
Lorimer, George H.	False Gods (1st, 8vo, gilt, p-o, 91p, 4pl)	Appleton	1906	Leyendecker, J.C.	40-65	
Lothar, Ernest	Door Opens (1st AM {std}, 12mo, 188p, b/w, DJ/2.00)	Doubleday/Doran	1945	Williams, Garth	30-50	
Loti, Pierre	Romance of a Child (1st, 8vo, 179p, teg, gilt, cvr by...)	Rand/McNally	1897	Denslow, W.W.	55-80	
Loud, Marian V.	Picnic on a Pyramid (1st, 8vo, 114p, grey cl, 4pl)	Saalfield	1904	Loud, Marian V.	80-125	
Lounsberry, Alice	Frank & Bessie's Forester (1st, sm8vo, 191p, p-o & frn by...)	Stokes	(1912)	Kirk, Maria L.	35-60	
Love, Edwin M.	Rocking Island (1st, lg8vo, p-o, 182p, purple/gilt, 6cp, 12pl, pep)	Nelson	(1927)	Love, Edwin M.	50-85	
Lovelace, Maud H.	Betsy and Joe (1st, 8vo, 256p, b/w, DJ/2.50)	Crowell	(1948)	Neville, Vera	100-165	
Lovelace, Maud H.	Betsy and the Great World (1st {std}, 8vo, 305p, b/w, DJ/2.50)	Crowell	1952	Neville, Vera	250-400	
Lovelace, Maud H.	Betsy in Spite of Herself (1st {std}, 8vo, 272p, b/w, DJ/2.50)	Crowell	(1946)	Neville, Vera	100-165	*
Lovelace, Maud H.	Betsy's Wedding (1st, 8vo, 241p, b/w, DJ/2.75)	Crowell	(1955)	Neville, Vera	200-300	
Lovelace, Maud H.	Betsy-Tacy (1st, 8vo, 112p, pink cl, b/w, pep, DJ/2.00)	Crowell	1940	Lenski, Lois	120-170	
Lovelace, Maud H.	Betsy-Tacy and Tib (1st, 8vo, 127p, b/w, DJ/2.00)	Crowell	1941	Lenski, Lois	150-200	
Lovelace, Maud H.	Down Town: Betsy-Tacy Story (1st, 8vo, 180p, b/w, DJ/2.00)	Crowell	1943	Lenski, Lois	80-140	
Lovelace, Maud H.	Emily of Deep Valley (1st {std}, 8vo, green cl, 257p, b/w, DJ/2.50)	Crowell	(1950)	Neville, Vera	100-170	
Lovelace, Maud H.	Golden Wedge (1st {std}, 8vo, 189p, color, DJ/2.00)	Crowell	(1942)	Chase, Charlotte	100-165	
Lovelace, Maud H.	Over the Big Hill (1st, 8vo, 171p, b/w, pep, DJ/2.00)	Crowell	1942	Lenski, Lois	100-170	
Lovelace, Maud H.	Trees Kneel at Christmas (1st {std}, sm8vo, 127p, b/w, pep, DJ/2.50)	Crowell	1951	Howe, Gertrude	140-200	
Lovelace, Maud H.	Tune is in the Tree (1st, 8vo, 177p, fp b/w, pep, DJ/2.50)	Crowell	(1950)	Wilkin, Eloise B.	100-160	
Lovelace, Maud H.	Valentine Box (1st, 8vo, [45]p, fp b/w, DJ/3.50)	Crowell	(1966)	Fetz, Ingrid	40-65	
Lovelace, Maud H.	Winona's Pony Cart (1st {std}, 8vo, 117p, b/w, DJ/2.00)	Crowell	(1953)	Neville, Vera	200-300	*
Lovelace, Richard	Songs & Sonnets (1st, sm8vo, 57p, uncut, 1-color)	R.H. Russell	1901	Unknown	80-120	*
Loveland, Mrs. S.	Illustrated Bible Story Book (1st, lg4to, 126p, p-o, 12cp, pep)	Rand/McNally	(1923)	Winter, Milo	60-90	
Lovell, Dorothy A.	Silvanus Goes to Sea (1st, lg ob8vo, blue ibds, [26]p, 12 color)	L: Faber	(1943)	Bentley, Nicolas	60-95	
Lovell, Lucille	Walcott Twins (1st, sm8vo, 211p, 5pl)	Penn	1900	Waugh, Ida	30-50	
Lover, Samuel	Handy Andy (1st, 12mo, 523p, blue/gilt, AEG, pep, 40pl)	L: Macmillan	1896	Brock, Henry M.	70-100	
Low, Elizabeth	Snug in the Snow (1st {std}, 8vo, 63p, color, DJ/2.95)	Little/Brown	(1963)	Solbert, Ronni	25-40	*
Low, Frances H.	Little Men in Scarlet (1st, 8vo, 237p, green/gilt, b/w)	L: Jarrold	1896	Guthrie, James J.	50-85	
Low, Frances H.	Queen Victoria's Dolls (1st, 4to, [86]p, gilt, AEG, 39cp)	L: Newnes	1894	Wright, Alan	250-400	
Low, Joseph	Adam's Book of Odd Creatures (1st {std}, sm ob4to, [32]p, DJ/3.50)	Atheneum	(1962)	Low, Joseph	30-50	*
Low, Joseph	Smiling Duke (1st, ob4to, ibds, 30p, color, DJ/3.25)	Houghton	1963	Low, Joseph	25-45	
Low, Joseph	There was a Wise Crow (1st {std}, ob4to, [32]p, color, DJ/3.95)	Follett	(1969)	Low, Joseph	25-45	
Lowe, Edith	Cookie, the Rabbit (1st, narrow 4to, [24]p, ibds, color, pep)	Garden City	(1949)	Eckart, Frances	30-50	
Lowe, Edith	Little Bear Who Wanted Friends (1st, narrow 4to, ibds, [24]p, color, pep)	Garden City	(1949)	Eckart, Frances	30-50	
Lowe, Samuel E.	In the Court of King Arthur (1st, 8vo, 223p, blue cl, p-o, 6cp, pep)	Western Printing	(1918)	O'Keefe, Neil	50-80	
Lowe, Samuel E.	New Story of Peter Rabbit (1st, 16mo, tan bds, unpag, 8cp, pep)	Whitman	1926	Wright, Alan	80-120	
Lowell, James R.	The Courtin' (1st, 8vo, teg, bds/gilt, [58]p, color, pep)	Houghton	1909	Keller, Arthur I.	35-60	
Lowell, Joan	Cradle of the Deep (1st, lg8vo, 261p, pep, b/w)	Simon/Schuster	1929	Wiese, Kurt	40-65	
Lownsbery, Eloise	Boy Knight of Rheims (1st, 8vo, 332p, col frn, gilt, b/w, pep)	Houghton	1927	Wolcott, Elizabeth	25-45	
Lownsbery, Eloise	Camel for a Throne (1st, 8vo, 305p, b/w, DJ/2.50)	Houghton	1941	Wolcott, Elizabeth	20-35	*
Lownsbery, Eloise	Out of the Flame (1st {std}, sm8vo, 352p, pep, b/w, NH)	NY: Longmans	1931	Wolcott, Elizabeth	50-85	*
Lowrey, Janette S.	Day in the Jungle (1st {A}, sm8vo, ibds, [42]p, color, pep, LGB/#18)	Simon/Schuster	1943	Gergely, Tibor	40-60	*

AUTHOR	TITLE	PUBLISHER	DATE	ARTIST	PRICE	LC
Lowrey, Janette S.	Lavender Cat (1st {std}, 8vo, 180p, b/w, DJ/2.00)	Harper	(1944)	Busoni, Rafaello	25-40	
Lowrey, Janette S.	Mr. Heff & Mr. Ho (1st, 8vo, 148p, fp b/w, DJ/2.50)	Harper	(1952)	Bacon, Peggy	25-40	
Lowrey, Janette S.	Poky Little Puppy (1st {A}, 12mo, [42]p, ibds, color, LGB/#8)	Simon/Schuster	1942	Tenggren, Gustaf	40-60	
Lowrey, Janette S.	Silver Dollar (1st {std}, lg4to, ibds, [48]p, pep, DJ/1.50)	Harper	1940	Latham, Barbara	45-70	*
Lowrey, Janette S.	The Bird (1st, 4to, 32p, color, ibds, pep, DJ/2.00)	Harper	1947	Merida, Carlos	50-85	
Lowry, H.D.	Make-Believe (1st, 8vo, 177p, teg, green/gilt, b/w)	L: John Lane	1896	Robinson, Charles	100-160	
Lucas, E.V.	All the World Over (1st, ob4to, gilt, 30ff, ibds, 30cp)	L: Richards	1898	Farmiloe, Edith	150-250	
Lucas, E.V.	Another Book of Verses for Children (1st AM, 8vo, 431p, 18pl)	Macmillan	1907	Bedford, Francis D.	60-90	
Lucas, E.V.	As the Bee Sucks (1st, 8vo, 169p, pink cl, b/w, DJ)	L: Methuen	(1937)	Shepard, Ernest H.	30-50	
Lucas, E.V.	Book of Shops (1st, ob4to, ipcb, 24cp)	L: Richards	1899	Bedford, Francis D.	200-270	
Lucas, E.V.	Cat Book (1st, 16mo, 121p, fp b/w)	L: G. Richards	1900	Smith, H. Officer	50-85	
Lucas, E.V.	Cat Book (1st, lg8vo, 37p, ibds, b/w)	Harper	1927	Sullivan, Pat	60-90	
Lucas, E.V.	Edwin A. Abbey (1st AM, 8vo, 2 vols, pcb)	Scribner	1921	Abbey, Edwin A.	120-200	
Lucas, E.V.	Forgotten Tales of Long Ago (1st, 8vo, gilt, 424p, teg, col frn, 22pl)	L: Wells/Gard.	1906	Bedford, Francis D.	100-165	
Lucas, E.V.	Forgotten Tales of Long Ago (1st AM, 8vo, 424p, teg, gilt, fp b/w)	Stokes	(1906)	Bedford, Francis D.	70-125	
Lucas, E.V.	Four & Twenty Toilers (1st AM, ob4to, 103p, blue cl, p-o, 24cp)	McDevitt/Wilson	[1900]	Bedford, Francis D.	200-300	
Lucas, E.V.	Mr. Punch's Country Songs (1st, lg4to, 92p, ibds, p-o, b/w)	L: Methuen	1928	Shepard, Ernest H.	100-165	
Lucas, E.V.	Old Fashioned Tales (1st, 8vo, teg, 389p, gilt, col frn, b/w)	L: Wells/Gard.	[1905]	Bedford, Francis D.	80-120	
Lucas, E.V.	Open Road (1st, 4to, blue/gilt, 301p, teg, 16ticp)	Henry Holt & Co.	1913	Shepperson, Claude	100-160	
Lucas, E.V.	Playtime & Company (1st, 4to, ibds, b/w, 95p, pep, DJ)	L: Methuen	(1925)	Shepard, Ernest H.	120-200	
Lucas, E.V.	The Slowcoach (1st AM, 8vo, 367p, p-o, frn by...)	Macmillan	1910	Hood, George	40-60	
Lucas, E.V.	The Slowcoach (1st, 8vo, brown cl, 284p, 16cp, pep)	L: Wells/Gard.	(1910)	Wheelhouse, Mary V.	45-80	
Lucas, E.V.	Visit to London (1st, 4to, ipcb, 118p, 24cp)	L: Methuen	1902	Bedford, Francis D.	120-200	
Lucas, E.V.	Visit to London (1st AM, 4to, ibds, 118p, 24cp)	Brentano's	[1902]	Bedford, Francis D.	100-165	
Ludins, Ryah	Wonder Rock (1st, ob8vo, [40]p, ibds, 2-color)	Coward	1931	Ludins, Ryah	80-125	
Ludmann, Oscar	Hansi the Stork (1st, ob8vo, p-o, 62p, fp color)	Whitman	(1932)	Brock, Emma	40-70	
Lummis, Charles F.	Enchanted Burro (1st, sm8vo, 277p, teg, 15pl)	Way & Williams	1897	Corwin, C.A.	60-100	
Lummis, Charles F.	Gold Fish of Gran Chimu (1st, 12mo, gilt, 126p, teg, 7pl)	Lamson/Wolffe	1896	Sandham, Henry	100-175	
Lummis, Charles F.	King of the Broncos (1st, 12mo, 254p, red/gilt, photos, cvr by)	Scribner	1897	Armstrong, Margaret	80-130	
Lummis, Charles F.	Land of Poco Tiempo (1st, 8vo, 310p, orange/gilt, cvr by...)	Scribner	1893	Armstrong, Margaret	100-160	
Lummis, Charles F.	Pueblo Indian Folk Stories (new ed., 12mo, 257p, b/w)	Appleton	1920	Edwards, George W.	40-65	
Lund, Doris	Attic of the Wind (1st, 4to, [38]p, color, pep, DJ/2.95)	Parents Mag. Pr.	(1966)	Forberg, Ati	25-40	
Lunn, Janet	Twin Spell (1st, 8vo, 158p, pcb, fp b/w, DJ/3.95)	Harper	(1969)	McCully, Emily	40-65	*
Lupprian, Hildegard	Honey Land (1st, 4to, [30]p, ibds, color)	McLoughlin	1927	Lupprian, Hildegard	100-160	
Lustig, Sonia	Roses of the Winds (1st {std}, sm8vo, 275p, col frn, pep, b/w)	Doubleday/Page	1926	Artzybasheff, Boris	40-70	
Lyall, Edna	Autobiography of a Slander (1st, 8vo, blue/gilt, AEG, 146p, b/w)	L: Longmans	1892	Speed, Lancelot	60-100	
Lyall, Mary C.	Cubies' ABC (1st, sm ob8vo, p-o, 56p, color)	Putnam	1913	Lyall, Earl H.	200-300	
Lyle, Eugene P.	Lone Star (1st, 8vo, p-o, 431p, 4pl)	Doubleday/Page	1907	Goodwin, Philip R.	35-60	
Lyle, Eugene P.	The Missourian (1st, sm8vo, 519p, 8pl)	Doubleday/Page	1905	Haskell, Ernest	30-60	
Lyle, G.M.	Little Travelers in Wales (1st, 8vo, p-o, 127p, gilt, b/w, pep)	Whitman	1929	Frazee, Hazel	30-50	
Lyman, Betty K.	Peter-Pan Twins are Glad to Help (sm4to, ibds, 12p, color)	Whitman	1928	Chase, Rhoda	35-60	
Lyman, Betty K.	Playtime for the Peter-Pan Twins (1st, 4to, ibds, fp color, pep)	Whitman	1928	Chase, Rhoda	30-50	
Lyman, Edward B.	Me'ow Jones (1st, sm8vo, p-o, 91p, 5cp, pep)	Doran	(1917)	Daniels, Julia	40-65	
Lynch, Lorenzo	Hot Dog Man (1st {std}, ob4to, [24]p, color, DJ/5.00)	Bobbs-Merrill	(1970)	Lynch, Lorenzo	30-50	
Lynch, Maude B.	Henry the Navigator (1st, sm8vo, yellow cl, 72p, 4 fp b/w, pep, DJ/0.60)	NY: Nelson	1935	Artzybasheff, Boris	45-70	
Lynch, Patricia	Brogeen and the Bronze Lizard (1st AM {std}, 8vo, 180p, b/w, DJ/4.95)	Macmillan	(1970)	Vestal, Herman B.	30-45	
Lynch, Patricia	Donkey Goes Visiting (1st {std}, 8vo, 229p, 4cp, b/w, pep, DJ/2.00)	Dutton	(1936)	Altendorf, George	45-70	
Lynch, Patricia	Grey Goose of Kilnevin (1st {std}, sm8vo, 285p, col frn, fp b/w, DJ/2.00)	Dutton	1940	Keating, John	30-50	*
Lynch, Patricia	King of the Tinkers (1st {std}, sm8vo, 240p, 8cp, DJ/2.00)	Dutton	1938	Lloyd, Katharine	40-65	
Lynch, Patricia	Turf-Cutter's Donkey (1st AM {std}, sm8vo, 245p, 5cp, dep, DJ/2.00)	Dutton	1935	Yeats, Jack B.	80-120	
Lynde, Francis	Taming of Red Butte Western (1st, 12mo, 410p, 4pl)	Scribner	1910	Dixon, Maynard	30-50	
Lyon, Elinor	Runaway Home (1st, 8vo, 192p, b/w, DJ/2.50)	Viking	1953	Price, Christine	30-45	
Lyons, A. Neil	Simple Simon... (1st, 8vo, 344p, red/gilt, 8pl)	L: John Lane	1914	Peto, G.E.	40-60	
Lyons, A. Neil	Tom, Dick and Harriet (1st, 8vo, 254p, green cl, b/w)	L: Cresset Pr.	(1937)	Ardizzone, Edward	150-225	
Lyons, Dorothy	Blue Smoke (1st {std}, 8vo, 244p, b/w, DJ/2.75)	Harcourt	(1953)	Dennis, Wesley	50-85	
Lyons, Dorothy	Copper Khan (1st {std}, 8vo, 232p, tan cl, b/w, DJ/2.50)	Harcourt	(1950)	Dennis, Wesley	100-150	
Lyons, Dorothy	Golden Sovereign (1st {std}, 8vo, 259p, fp b/w, DJ/2.00)	Harcourt	(1946)	Dennis, Wesley	90-145	*
Lyons, Dorothy	Harlequin Hullabaloo (1st {std}, 8vo, 264p, b/w, DJ/2.50)	Harcourt	(1949)	Dennis, Wesley	70-100	
Lyons, Dorothy	Midnight Moon (1st, 8vo, 276p, b/w, DJ/2.00)	Harcourt	(1941)	Nims, W.C.	100-165	*
Lyons, Dorothy	Silver Birch (1st, 8vo, 308p, b/w, DJ/2.00)	Harcourt	(1939)	Taylor, John A.	80-140	
Lyons, Dorothy	Smoke Rings (1st {std}, 8vo, 222p, DJ/3.25, frn by...)	Harcourt	1960	Dennis, Wesley	100-165	
Lystad, Mary	Millicent the Monster (1st, sq8vo, [32]p, fp color, dep, DJ/3.25)	Harlin Quist	(1968)	Chess, Victoria	20-30	
Lytton, Edward B.	Last Days of Pompeii (1st, lg8vo, p-o, 425p, 9cp, pep, SC)	Scribner	1926	Yohn, F.C.	70-120	
Mabie, Hamilton W.	Book of Christmas (1st, 12mo, 369p, gilt, 12pl)	Macmillan	1909	Edwards, George W.	50-75	
Mabie, Hamilton W.	Fairy Tales Every Child Should Know (1st, sm8vo, 370p, pep, b/w)	Doubleday/Page	1905	Ostertag, Blanche	100-160	
Mabie, Hamilton W.	Fairy Tales Every Child Should Know (1st, 8vo, 266p, p-o, 8cp)	Doubleday/Page	1915	Frye, Mary H.	60-100	
Mabie, Hamilton W.	In Arcady (1st, 8vo, 128p, teg, green/gilt, 4pl, pep)	Dodd	1903	Low, Will H.	40-65	
Mabie, Hamilton W.	Myths Every Child Should Know (1st, lg8vo, p-o, 224p, 11cp)	Doubleday/Page	1914	Frye, Mary H.	60-90	
Mabie, Hamilton W.	Norse Stories (1st, 8vo, green/gilt, 250p, 10cp)	Dodd	1901	Wright, George	80-130	
Mabie, Hamilton W.	Under The Trees (1st, 8vo, teg, 165p, green/gilt, 6pl, pep)	Dodd	1902	Hinton, Charles L.	40-60	
Mabie, Peter	A to Z Book (lg4to, wraps, color)	Whitman	1929	Mabie, Peter	100-160	
Mabie, Peter	Gingerbread Stories (1st, ob4to, ibds, [42]p, color, pep)	Whitman	(1931)	Mabie, Peter	80-130	
MacArthur, David	Thunderbolt Men (1st, 8vo, blue/gilt, 229p, fp b/w, DJ)	L: P. Lunn	1947	Stobbs, William	30-50	
MacDonald, Betty	Hello, Mrs. Piggle-Wiggle (1st {std}, 8vo, green cl, 119p, col, DJ/2.50)	Lippincott	(1957)	Knight, Hilary	150-220	
MacDonald, Betty	Mrs. Piggle-Wiggle (1st {std}, sm8vo, 119p, blue cl, b/w, DJ/2.00)	Lippincott	(1947)	Bennett, Richard	150-220	
MacDonald, Betty	Mrs. Piggle-Wiggle's Farm (1st {std}, 8vo, 128p, b/w, DJ/2.00)	Lippincott	(1954)	Sendak, Maurice	250-400	
MacDonald, Betty	Mrs. Piggle-Wiggle's Magic (1st {std}, 8vo, 126p, col frn, b/w, DJ/2.00)	Lippincott	(1949)	Wiese, Kurt	100-165	
MacDonald, Betty	Nancy and Plum (1st {std}, 8vo, 190p, b/w, DJ/2.50)	Lippincott	(1952)	Hopkins, Hildegarde	150-250	

AUTHOR	TITLE	PUBLISHER	DATE	ARTIST	PRICE	LC
MacDonald, Eliz. R.	Little Canadian Cousin (1st, sm8vo, 129p, 6pl)	L.C. Page	1904	Bridgman, L.J.	30-50	
MacDonald, George	Back of the North Wind (new ed., 12mo, 378p, grey/gilt, cep, b/w)	L: Blackie	[1886]	Hughes, Arthur	60-100	
MacDonald, George	Back of the North Wind (1st, 8vo, 378p, gilt, frn & cvr by...)	L: Blackie	(1899)	Housman, Laurence	160-240	
MacDonald, George	Back of the North Wind (1st, 8vo, 352p, gilt, pep, teg, 12cp)	Lippincott	1909	Kirk, Maria L.	90-120	
MacDonald, George	Back of the North Wind (1st AM, 8vo, blue cl, teg, p-o, 12 fp color)	Caldwell	[1911]	Pape, Frank	80-140	
MacDonald, George	Back of the North Wind (1st, 8vo, 391p, p-o, 12cp)	L: Blackie	1911	Pape, Frank	120-170	
MacDonald, George	Back of the North Wind (new ed., 8vo, 126p, 6cp)	Lippincott	(1914)	Kirk, Maria L.	25-45	
MacDonald, George	Back of the North Wind (1st, 4to, p-o, teg, 342p, 8cp, pep)	McKay	1919	Smith, Jessie W.	140-220	
MacDonald, George	Back of the North Wind (1st AM, 8vo, 376p, 12pl, col frn, pep)	NY: Macmillan	(1924)	Bedford, Francis D.	70-125	
MacDonald, George	Back of the North Wind (1st, 8vo, p-o, 326p, 4cp)	McKay	(1926)	Kay, Gertrude A.	60-90	
MacDonald, George	Dealings with Fairies (1st AM, 8vo, 284p, gilt)	NY: Routledge	1891	Brooke, L. Leslie	700-1000	
MacDonald, George	Fairy Fleet (1st, 8vo, [52]p, pattern cl, 1-color, DJ/1.25)	Holiday House	1936	Van Veen, Stuyvesant	60-90	R
MacDonald, George	Fairy Tales (1st [new ed.], lg8vo, 435p, gilt, 12 b/w)	L: Fifield	1904	Hughes, Arthur	160-240	
MacDonald, George	Golden Key (1st {std}, 12mo, 85p, gilt, fp b/w, DJ/3.95)	Farrar, Straus	(1967)	Sendak, Maurice	100-170	R
MacDonald, George	Gutta-Percha Willie (1st, 12mo, 212p, blue/gilt, cvr by...)	L: Blackie	[1900]	Housman, Laurence	100-165	
MacDonald, George	Gutta-Percha Willie (1st, 12mo, blue cl, 212p, 8pl by...)	L: Blackie	[1900]	Hughes, Arthur	100-165	
MacDonald, George	Light Princess (1st, sm8vo, 192p, gilt, 3pl, cep)	L: Blackie	(1890)	Brooke, L. Leslie	200-325	
MacDonald, George	Light Princess (1st, 8vo, 305p, tan cl, 7 fp b/w)	Putnam	(1893)	Humphrey, Maud	200-300	
MacDonald, George	Light Princess (1st, 12mo, 133p, col frn, 12pl, pep)	Macmillan	1926	Lathrop, Dorothy	70-100	
MacDonald, George	Light Princess (1st, 4to, ibds, 48p, color, pep, DJ/3.50)	Crowell	(1962)	DuBois, W.P.	45-70	
MacDonald, George	Light Princess (1st, sm8vo, 110p, blue/gilt, fp b/w, DJ/3.95, NYTBI)	Farrar, Straus	(1969)	Sendak, Maurice	100-165	
MacDonald, George	Lost Princess (1st, 8vo, 258p, blue/gilt, 6pl)	L: Wells/Gard.	(1895)	Walker, Arthur G.	180-250	
MacDonald, George	Magic Crook (1st, 8vo, teg, 273p, b/w)	L: Fifield	1911	Hughes, Arthur	100-170	
MacDonald, George	Phantastes (1st, sm8vo, 280p, aqua cloth, 14pl)	L: Chatto	1894	Bell, John	300-425	
MacDonald, George	Phantastes (1st [new ed], 8vo, 320p, blue/gilt, uncut, teg, 33 b/w)	L: A. Fifield	1905	Hughes, Arthur	300-450	
MacDonald, George	Phantastes (8vo, 320p, blue/gilt, uncut, teg, b/w)	L: Dent	[1910]	Hughes, Arthur	200-300	
MacDonald, George	Princess & Curdie (1st, 8vo, 304p, blue/gilt, 31 b/w, cep)	L: Blackie	1900	Stratton, Helen	125-180	
MacDonald, George	Princess & Curdie (1st, 8vo, teg, 305p, gilt, 12cp)	Lippincott	1908	Kirk, Maria L.	80-120	
MacDonald, George	Princess & Curdie (new ed., 8vo, 320p, p-o, gilt, teg, 12cp, pep)	L: Blackie	1912	Stratton, Helen	90-140	
MacDonald, George	Princess & Curdie (1st, sm8vo, p-o, 274p, 4cp, pep)	McKay	[1926]	Kay, Gertrude A.	50-80	
MacDonald, George	Princess & Curdie (1st, sm8vo, p-o, 265p, gilt, col frn, 12pl, pep)	Macmillan	1927	Lathrop, Dorothy	100-175	
MacDonald, George	Princess & Curdie (1st, 8vo, 238p, tan cl, 8cp, DJ)	L: Dent	(1949)	Folkard, Charles	40-65	
MacDonald, George	Princess & Curdie (1st, 8vo, 240p, 1-color, DJ/2.00)	Macmillan	(1954)	Unwin, Nora S.	30-60	*
MacDonald, George	Princess & the Goblin (1st, 8vo, 313p, aqua/gilt, cep, cvr by..)	L: Blackie	1900	Housman, Laurence	125-180	
MacDonald, George	Princess & the Goblin (1st, 8vo, 313p, aqua/gilt, cep, 30 b/w by..)	L: Blackie	1900	Hughes, Arthur	120-200	
MacDonald, George	Princess & the Goblin (1st, 8vo, red/gilt, 305p, teg, pep, 12cp)	Lippincott	1907	Kirk, Maria L.	120-180	
MacDonald, George	Princess & the Goblin (1st AM, 8vo, 308p, teg, blue/gilt, p-o, 12cp)	Caldwell	[1911]	Stratton, Helen	160-220	
MacDonald, George	Princess & the Goblin (1st, 8vo, teg, 308p, p-o, gilt, 12cp)	L: Blackie	1911	Stratton, Helen	170-250	
MacDonald, George	Princess & the Goblin (1st, 4to, gilt, p-o, teg, 203p, 8cp, pep)	McKay	1920	Smith, Jessie W.	160-240	
MacDonald, George	Princess & the Goblin (1st, 12mo, 267p, blue/gilt, col frn)	Macmillan	1926	Bedford, Francis D.	80-120	
MacDonald, George	Princess & the Goblin (1st, 12mo, 251p, blue cl, p-o, col frn)	Saalfield	(1927)	Brundage, Frances	30-50	
MacDonald, George	Princess & the Goblin (1st, lg8vo, 271p, 4cp)	Doubleday/Doran	1928	MacKinstry, Eliz.	70-100	
MacDonald, George	Princess & the Goblin (1st, 8vo, olive cl, 249p, 1-color, pep, DJ/2.00)	Macmillan	(1951)	Unwin, Nora S.	30-50	
MacDonald, George	Princess and Curdie (1st AM, 8vo, 255p, gilt, 11 b/w)	Lippincott	1883	Allen, James	160-225	
MacDonald, George	Ronald Bannerman's Boyhood (1st, 8vo, 335p, teg, p-o, gilt, 12cp)	L: Blackie	(1911)	Wheelhouse, Mary V.	90-145	
MacDonald, George	Rough Shaking (1st, 8vo, 384p, red/gilt, 12pl)	L: Blackie	1891	Parkinson, W.A.	185-265	
MacDonald, Golden	Big Dog, Little Dog (1st, lg sq8vo, [36]p, red cl, b/w, dep, DJ/1.25)	Doubleday/Doran	(1943)	Weisgard, Leonard	60-90	
MacDonald, Golden	Little Island (1st {std}, sm ob4to, [42]p, ibds, color, pep, DJ/2.50, CM)	Doubleday	1946	Weisgard, Leonard	120-180	R
MacDonald, Golden	Little Lost Lamb (1st {std}, 4to, 48p, ibds, color, pep, DJ/2.00, CH)	Doubleday/Doran	1945	Weisgard, Leonard	100-160	
MacDonald, Golden	Red Light Green Light (1st {std}, sm ob4to, ibds, [40]p, col, cep, DJ/2.00)	Doubleday/Doran	(1944)	Weisgard, Leonard	80-120	R
MacDonald, Golden	Whistle for the Train (1st {std}, ob4to, [28]p, fp 3-color, pep, DJ/2.50)	Doubleday	1956	Weisgard, Leonard	50-80	
MacDonald, Greville	Billy Barnicoat (1st AM, 8vo, 230p, col frn, fp b/w)	Dutton	1923	Bedford, Francis D.	50-80	
MacDonald, Greville	Count Billy (1st {std}, 8vo, 246p, gilt, uncut, col frn, 6pl)	Dutton	1928	Bedford, Francis D.	50-80	
MacDonald, L.	Babies' Classics (1st, 4to, 79p, blue/gilt, b/w)	L: Longmans	1904	Hughes, Arthur	120-200	
MacDonald, Ray	Mad Scientist (1st, 8vo, blue cl, 242p, 8pl)	NY: Cochrane	1908	Bunnell, Charles B.	75-100	*
MacDonald, Zillah	Eileen's Adventures in Wonderland (1st, 8vo, p-o, 241p, col frn)	Stokes	(1920)	Hay, Stuart	100-170	*
MacDonell, Anne	Italian Fairy Book (1st, 8vo, 403p, green/gilt, col frn, 1-color)	L: T.F. Unwin	(1911)	Williams, Morris M.	220-300	
MacDonell, Anne	Italian Fairy Book (1st AM, 8vo, gilt, 307p, col frn, 17 fp b/w, pep)	Stokes	[1911]	Williams, Morris M.	165-250	
MacDonough, Glen	Babes in Toyland (1st, lg8vo, 180p, tan cloth, 7cp, pep)	Fox Duffield	1904	Betts, Ethel F.	180-270	
MacDonough, Glen	Babes in Toyland (2nd, 8vo, aqua cl, 180p, p-o, 7cp)	Macaulay	(1924)	Betts, Ethel F.	100-160	
MacFall, Haldane	Book of Lovat Claud Fraser (1st, 4to, ipcb, 183p, 8cp)	L: Dent	1923	Fraser, Claud L.	120-200	
MacGrath, Harold	Best Man (1st, 8vo, 207p, green/gilt, p-o, 8pl)	Bobbs-Merrill	(1907)	Grefe, Will	25-40	
MacGrath, Harold	Carpet from Bagdad (1st, 12mo, 390p, olive cl, 5cp)	Bobbs-Merrill	(1911)	Castaigne, Andre	30-50	
MacGrath, Harold	Half a Rogue (1st, 12mo, red cl, 449p, p-o, 4pl)	Bobbs-Merrill	(1906)	Fisher, Harrison	25-40	
MacGrath, Harold	Man on the Box (1st, sm8vo, 361p, aqua cloth, cvr by...)	Bobbs-Merrill	(1904)	Armstrong, Margaret	25-40	
MacGregor, Barrington	King Longbeard (1st, 8vo, 262p, blue/gilt, 12 fp b/w)	L: John Lane	1898	Robinson, Charles	200-280	
MacGregor, Ellen	Miss Pickerell and the Geiger Counter (1st, 8vo, 123p, b/w, DJ/2.25)	Whittlesey	(1953)	Galdone, Paul	40-65	
MacGregor, Ellen	Miss Pickerell Goes to Mars (1st, sm8vo, red cl, 128p, fp b/w, DJ/2.25)	Whittlesey	(1951)	Galdone, Paul	45-70	
MacGregor, Ellen	Miss Pickerell Goes to the Arctic (1st, 8vo, 126p, b/w, DJ/2.25)	Whittlesey	(1954)	Galdone, Paul	30-45	
MacGregor, Ellen	Miss Pickerell Goes Undersea (1st, 8vo, 128p, b/w, DJ/2.25)	Whittlesey	(1953)	Galdone, Paul	30-45	
MacGregor, Ellen	Mr. Ferguson of the Fire Department (1st, 4to, 32p, 2-color, dpep, DJ/2.25)	Whittlesey	(1956)	Galdone, Paul	30-45	
MacGregor, Ellen	Mr. Pringle and Mister Buttonhouse (1st, 4to, 32p, fp color, dep, DJ/2.00)	Whittlesey	(1957)	Galdone, Paul	30-50	
MacGregor, Ellen	Theodore Turtle (1st, sm4to, green cl, 32p, color, dep, DJ/2.00)	Whittlesey	1955	Galdone, Paul	50-85	
MacGregor, Ellen	Tommy & the Telephone (1st, 8vo, [32]p, p-o, color, pep, DJ/1.25)	Whitman	1947	Selover, Zabeth	30-50	
MacGregor, Mary	Pilgrim's Progress told to Children (24mo, 120p, p-o, 8cp)	L: Jack	[1910]	Shaw, Byam	25-40	
MacGregor, Mary	Romance of the Netherlands (1st, 8vo, teg, 344p, uncut, 12cp)	Jack/Stokes	1907	McCormick, A.D.	60-90	
MacGregor, Mary	Stories of King Arthur's Knights (12mo, 155p, ipcb, 8 ticp)	L: Jack	(1909)	Cameron, Katharine	80-120	
MacGregor, Mary	Story of France (1st AM, lg8vo, gilt, 508p, 20cp)	Stokes	[1920]	Rainey, William	40-60	

AUTHOR	TITLE	PUBLISHER	DATE	ARTIST	PRICE	LC
MacHarg, Wm. B.	Let's Pretend... (1st, 8vo, 80p, ibds, fp color)	Volland	1914	Butler, Bonnibel	80-140	
MacIntyre, Carlyle F.	Pig that Ate Truffles (1st, sm ob4to, ibds, [25]p, color, pep, DJ/2.95)	Golden Press	(1963)	Obligado, Lilian	50-80	*
MacKay, Helen	Stories for Pictures (1st, 8vo, ibds, uncut, teg, 168p, 8cp, pep)	Duffield	1912	Walker, Dugald S.	80-120	
MacKay, Malcolm S.	Cow Range & Hunting Trail (1st, 8vo, gilt, 243p, 3pl by...)	Putnam	1925	Russell, Charles M.	300-500	
MacKay, Margaret	Flowered Donkey (1st, 91p, b/w, DJ/2.25)	John Day	(1950)	Wiese, Kurt	25-45	
MacKay, Margaret	Poetic Parrot (1st, 8vo, 96p, b/w, DJ/2.50)	John Day	(1951)	Wiese, Kurt	20-35	
MacKaye, David L.	Far Distant Bugle (1st {std}, 8vo, 264p, b/w, DJ/2.50)	Longmans	1948	Johnson, Avery	30-45	*
MacKaye, Percy	Tall Tales of Kentucky Mountains (1st, 8vo, 185p, ipcb, p-o, col frn, b/w)	Doran	(1926)	MacKinstry, Eliz.	40-65	
MacKellar, William	Wee Joseph (1st, 8vo, 76p, fp b/w, pep, DJ/2.50)	Whittlesey	(1957)	Keats, Ezra J.	30-45	
MacKinstry, Eliz.	Fairy Alphabet (1st, lg8vo, [59]p, ibds, 26pl)	Viking	1933	MacKinstry, Eliz.	100-175	
MacKinstry, Eliz.	Puck in Pasture (1st {std}, 8vo, ibds, 79p, pep, b/w)	Doubleday/Page	1925	MacKinstry, Eliz.	40-60	
MacLaren, Ian	Doctor of the Old School (1st {this fmt.}, 209p, bds, gilt, AEG, b/w)	L: Hodder	1895	Gordon, Frederic C.	60-100	
MacLaren, Ian	Our Neighbors (1st, sm8vo, 341p, gilt, cvr by...)	Dodd	1903	Falls, Charles B.	25-45	
MacLellan, Esther	Suzy and the Dog School (1st {std}, 8vo, 46p, b/w, pep, DJ/1.75)	Ariel	1953	Bradfield, Margaret	30-45	*
MacLeod, Fiona	Hills of Ruel (1st AM, sm4to, gilt, teg, 92p, pep, 8 ticp)	Duffield	1921	Lawrence, Margery	90-120	
MacLeod, Fiona	Mountain Lovers (1st, 8vo, 241p, blue/white, uncut, cvr by...)	L: John Lane	1895	Beardsley, Aubrey	60-100	
MacManus, Seamus	Donegal Wonder Book (1st, 8vo, green/gilt, 283p, b/w)	Stokes	1926	Stevens, William	120-200	
MacManus, Seumas	Donegal Fairy Stories (1st, sm8vo, 256p, 34pl)	McClure	1900	VerBeck, Frank	80-130	
MacManus, Seumas	Well O'the World's End (1st, 8vo, 189p, b/w, DJ/2.00)	Macmillan	1939	Bennett, Richard	65-100	
MacMillan, Cyrus	Canadian Wonder Tales (1st, sm4to, 199p, 17pl, pep)	L: John Lane	1918	Sheringham, George	100-170	
MacMillan, Miriam	Etuk: The Eskimo Hunter (1st, 8vo, 177p, b/w, DJ/2.75)	Dodd	(1950)	Wiese, Kurt	50-85	
MacMunn, George F.	Armies of India (1st, 8vo, blue/gilt, 224p, teg, 72cp)	L: A&C Black	1911	Lovett, Alfred C.	150-225	
MacNeice, Louis	Penny that Rolled Away (1st, sq12mo, 37p, ipcb, b/w, cep, DJ/2.25)	Putnam	(1954)	Bileck, Marvin	40-65	R
MacNeil, Marion	Monty Marine (1st, sq12mo, [48]p, 3-color, pep, DJ/1.00)	Oxford U. Pr.	(1943)	Dobias, Frank	40-70	*
MacNeil, Marion	Soldier Sammy (1st AM, sq12mo, [48]p, 3-color, pep, DJ/1.00)	Oxford U. Pr.	(1942)	Doane, Pelagie	40-65	
MacPherson, J.F.	Children For Ever (1st, 8vo, 352p, 16 color)	L: John Long	1908	Sarg, Tony	120-200	
MacPherson, Margaret	Australia Calling (1st, 8vo, 199p, b/w, DJ/2.50)	Dodd	1946	Wiese, Kurt	25-45	
Macaulay, Thomas B.	Lays of Ancient Rome (1st AM, black/gilt, teg, 180p, 13 ticp)	Longmans	1929	Cox, Elijah A.	60-90	
Macauley, Charles R.	Fantasma Land (1st, 8vo, brown/gilt, 204p, b/w)	Bobbs-Merrill	(1904)	Macauley, Charles R.	60-100	
Macgregor, Angusine	Maxims for Mice (1st AM, sq8vo, p-o, unpag, color, pep)	Dodge	[1910]	Macgregor, Angusine	180-300	
Macgregor, Angusine	Story of Snips (1st, lg ob8vo, ibds, [46]p, fp color)	L: Blackie	[1909]	Macgregor, Angusine	150-225	
Machen, Arthur	Great God Pan & Inmost Light (1st AM, 12mo, 234p, gilt, cvr by...)	Roberts Bros.	1894	Beardsley, Aubrey	170-240	
Machetanz, Sara	Puppy Named Gih (1st, sm4to, [32]p, fp 2-color, DJ/2.75)	Scribner	(1957)	Machetanz, Fred	30-50	
Machray, Robert	Night Side of London (1st, 8vo, yellow cl, 300p, b/w)	Lippincott	1902	Browne, Tom	35-60	
Mack, Robert E.	All Around the Clock (8vo, ibds, 64p, AEG, 23 chromos)	Dutton	[1895]	Bennett, Harriet	200-300	
Mack, Robert E.	Little Bright Eyes (1st, sm4to, unpag, ipcb, chromos)	L: Nister	1890	Mack/Bennett	80-125	
Mack, Robert E.	Old Father Christmas (4to, ibds, unpag, 14 chromos)	Nister/Dutton	(1888)	Lawson, Lizzie	200-350	
Mack, Robert E.	Old Father Santa Claus (4to, ibds, [40]p, 14 chromos)	Nister/Dutton	[1885]	Lawson, Lizzie	200-300	
Mack, Robert E.	Old Father Time & his 12 Children (1st, 4to, ibds, unpag, chromos)	L: Nister	[1890]	Bennett, Harriet	120-200	
Mack, Robert E.	Queen of the Meadow (lg8vo, ipcb, 16 chromos)	Dutton	[1885]	Bennett, Harriet	150-225	
Mack, Robert E.	Under the Mistletoe (lg8vo, ibds, [40]p, 14 chromos)	Nister/Dutton	[1890]	Lawson, Lizzie	120-200	
Mack, Robert E.	When All is Young (1st, 4to, unpag, ibds, chromos)	Nister/Dutton	[1888]	Bennett, Harriet	120-200	
Mackall, Lawton	Poodle-Oodle on Doodle Farm (1st, ob12mo, p-o, 137p, color, pep)	Stokes	1929	Wiese, Kurt	60-90	R
Mackenzie, Compton	Kensington Rhymes (1st, sm4to, pcb, gilt, 87p, uncut, 9cp)	L: M. Secker	1912	Monsell, J.R.	100-165	
Mackenzie, Compton	Santa Claus in Summer (1st, 8vo, 298p, b/w)	L: Constable	1924	Watson, A.H.	50-80	
Mackenzie, Donald A.	Indian Fairy Stories (1st, 8vo, 200p, 8pl)	L: Blackie	1915	Armfield, Maxwell	50-80	
Mackenzie, Donald A.	Indian Myth & Legend (1st, 8vo, 463p, teg, gilt, 8cp, 32pl)	L: Gresham	1913	Goble, Warwick	170-240	
Mackie, Pauline B.	Flight of Rosy Dawn (1st, 12mo, 98p, b/w)	L.C. Page	1903	Bruce, Josephine	30-50	*
Macleod, Mary	Book of King Arthur (1st {std}, 8vo, blue cl, 324p, color, DJ)	Lippincott	(1949)	Pitz, Henry C.	35-60	*
Macleod, Mary	King Arthur & Noble Knights (1st, 8vo, 418p, teg, gilt, 35 fp b/w)	L: Wells/Gard.	(1900)	Walker, Arthur G.	150-240	
Macleod, Mary	King Arthur & Noble Knights (1st AM, 8vo, 417p, teg, gilt, 35 fp b/w)	Stokes	[1900]	Walker, Arthur G.	150-220	
Macleod, Mary	Red Cross Knight & Sir Guyan (1st, 8vo, 128p)	L: Wells/Gard.	1908	Walker, Arthur G.	40-60	*
Macmillan, Cyrus	Canadian Fairy Tales (1st, sm4to, 203p 12cp, 14pl, pep)	Dodd	1922	Foster, Marcia L.	80-125	
Macvane, Edith	Adventures of Joujou (1st, sq8vo, 302p, teg, p-o, 15cp, pep)	Lippincott	1906	VerBeck, Frank	100-160	
Macy, S.B.	Book of the Kingdom (1st, lg8vo, 388p, gilt, col frn, fp b/w)	L: Longmans	1912	Robinson, Thomas H.	80-120	*
Macy, S.B.	From Slavery to Freedom (1st, 4to, 299p, green/gilt, 8cp, pep)	L: Longmans	1910	Robinson/Sarg	200-300	
Macy, S.B.	From Slavery to Freedom (1st, 4to, 299p, green/gilt, 8cp, pep)	L: Longmans	1910	Sarg/Robinson	200-300	
Madariaga, Salvador	Sir Bob (1st {std}, lg8vo, 202p, fp b/w)	Harcourt	(1930)	Ward, Lynd	35-60	*
Madison, Janet (comp)	Sweethearts Always (1st, 8vo, 232p, grey/gilt, teg, uncut, 12pl)	Reilly/Britton	1906	Hall, H. Putnam	85-120	
Madison, Janet (comp)	Sweethearts Always (2nd, 8vo, 210p, green/gilt, 8cp)	Reilly/Britton	1907	Manning, Fred S.	50-80	
Madison, Lucy F.	Captain Kitty Colonial (1st, 8vo, blue cl, 309p, p-o, col frn)	Penn	1923	Davis, Marguerite	25-45	*
Madison, Lucy F.	Joan of Arc (1st, lg8vo, 389p, p-o, blue/gilt, 8cp, pep)	Penn	1918	Schoonover, Frank	60-90	
Madison, Lucy F.	Lafayette (1st, lg8vo, p-o, 371p, blue cl, 8cp, pep)	Penn	1921	Schoonover, Frank	60-90	
Madison, Lucy F.	Lincoln (1st, lg8vo, p-o, 368p, 8cp, pep)	Penn	1928	Schoonover, Frank	60-90	
Madison, Lucy F.	Washington (1st, lg8vo, blue/gilt, p-o, 399p, 8cp, pep)	Penn	1925	Schoonover, Frank	60-90	
Maeterlinck, Maurice	Blue Bird (1st AM, 4to, teg, blue/gilt, 211p, 25 ticp)	Dodd	1911	Robinson, F. Cayley	120-200	
Maeterlinck, Maurice	Children's Blue Bird (1st, 4to, p-o, 182p, teg, 19pl)	Dodd	1913	Paus, Herbert	100-160	
Maeterlinck, Maurice	Hours of Gladness (1st, 4to, 181p, uncut, white/gilt, 20 ticp)	L: G. Allen	(1912)	Detmold, Edward J.	400-600	
Maeterlinck, Maurice	Life of the Bee (1st, 4to, 232p, uncut, white/gilt, teg, 13 ticp)	L: G. Allen	1911	Detmold, Edward J.	300-500	
Maeterlinck, Maurice	Life of the Bee (1st AM, 4to, 262p, teg, green/gilt, 13 ticp)	Dodd	1912	Detmold, Edward J.	250-400	
Maeterlinck, Maurice	My Dog (1st, 8vo, 64p, teg, gilt, p-o, 6cp)	L: G. Allen	1913	Aldin, Cecil	150-220	
Maeterlinck, Maurice	News of Spring (1st AM, 4to, green/gilt, uncut, 213p, teg, 20 ticp)	Dodd	1913	Detmold, Edward J.	400-600	
Maeterlinck, Maurice	Old Fashioned Flowers (1st, sm8vo, 105p, 6cp)	Dodd	1905	Falls, Charles B.	45-70	
Maeterlinck, Maurice	Our Friend the Dog (1st AM, 8vo, 67p, gilt, 6cp)	Dodd	1913	Aldin, Cecil	180-250	
Maeterlinck, Maurice	The Swarm (1st, 8vo, green cl, p-o, 113p, frn by...)	Dodd	1906	Euwer, Anthony	30-50	
Maeterlinck, Maurice	Tyltyl (1st, 4to, blue/gilt, p-o, 159p, 8 ticp, pep)	Dodd	1920	Paus, Herbert	120-185	
Maeterlinck, Maurice	Tyltyl (1st UK, sm4to, p-o, 159p, blue/gilt, 8 ticp, pep)	L: Methuen	(1921)	Paus, Herbert	100-165	
Maeterlinck, Maurice	Visions of Spring... (1st, 4to, teg, 213p, gilt, 20 ticp)	Dodd	1913	Detmold, Edward J.	400-600	

AUTHOR	TITLE	PUBLISHER	DATE	ARTIST	PRICE	LC
Magoon, Marian	Little Dusty Foot (1st {std}, 8vo, 239p, b/w, pep, DJ/2.50)	Longmans	1948	Price, Christine	25-45	
Magruder, Julia	Child Amy (1st, 8vo, 302p, red/gilt, 7pl)	Lothrop Pub.	(1894)	Armstrong, Helen	35-60	
Magruder, Julia	Miss Ayr of Virginia (1st, 12mo, green cl, 395p, cvr by..)	Herbert Stone	1896	Kimbrough, F.R.	70-100	
Magruder, Julia	Princess Sonia (1st, 12mo, teg, gilt, 225p, 19pl)	Century	1895	Gibson, Charles D.	60-100	
Magruder, Julia	Sunny Southerner (1st, 12mo, 194p, teg, b/w pl)	L.C. Page	1901	Hubbell, Henry S.	25-40	
Magruder, Julia	The Violet (1st, sm8vo, teg, 210p, 11pl)	Longmans	1896	Gibson, Charles D.	50-80	
Mahy, Margaret	Dragon of an Ordinary Family (1st, ob4to, [41]p, color, KGM)	L: Heinemann	1969	Oxenbury, Helen	70-125	
Maiden, Cecil	Beginning with Mrs. McBee (1st, lg8vo, [46]p, fp color, cep, DJ/3.00)	Vanguard Press	(1960)	Knight, Hilary	60-90	
Maiden, Cecil	Speaking of Mrs. McCluskie (1st, 8vo, 43p, 3-color, DJ/3.00)	Vanguard Press	(1962)	Knight, Hilary	60-90	
Major, Charles	Dorothy Vernon of Haddon Hall (1st, 8vo, 369p, blue/gilt, col frn)	Macmillan	1902	Christy, Howard C.	30-50	
Major, Charles	Forest Hearth (1st, sm8vo, teg, green/gilt, 354p, 8pl)	Macmillan	1903	DeLand, Clyde O.	30-50	
Makower, Stanley	Mirror of Music (1st, 8vo, 179p, uncut, cvr by...)	L: John Lane	1895	Beardsley, Aubrey	80-120	
Malcolm, Fiona	My Fairyland: Child's Own Visions (1st, 4to, 85p, grey ibds, 4 ticp)	L: Harrap	1916	Anderson, Florence	120-200	
Malcolmson, Anne	Song of Robin Hood (1st, 4to, 123p, color, DJ/5.00, CH)	Houghton	1947	Burton, Virginia L.	120-180	
Malcolmson, Anne	Yankee Doodle's Cousins (1st, sm4to, 267p, red cl, fp b/w, pep, DJ/2.50)	Houghton	1941	McCloskey, Robert	100-165	R
Malcolmson, David	Yipe (1st {std}, 8vo, 112p, red cl, b/w, DJ/2.75)	Little/Brown	(1955)	Dennis, Morgan	25-45	*
Malet, Lucas	Golden Galleon (1st, 12mo, grey/gilt, 158p, 6cp)	L: Hodder	(1910)	Brock, Charles E.	35-50	
Malet, Lucas	Little Peter (1st, 8vo, grey/gilt, 168p, pep, 9pl)	L: Kegan Paul	1888	Hardy, Paul	80-125	
Malet, Lucas	Little Peter (1st {new ed.}, sm4to, 175p, teg, white cl, uncut, 8 ticp)	L: H. Frowde	1909	Brock, Charles E.	60-90	
Malkus, Alida S.	Amazon: River of Promise (1st, lg8vo, 128p, DJ/5.95)	McGraw-Hill	(1970)	Leepin, Bruno	20-30	
Malkus, Alida S.	Animals of the High Andes (1st, 8vo, 160p, DJ/3.50)	Abelard-Schuman	(1965)	Osmond, Edward	20-35	
Malkus, Alida S.	Caravans to Sante Fe (1st {std}, 12mo, 289p, b/w)	Harper	1928	Lawson, Marie A.	35-60	*
Malkus, Alida S.	Citadel of a Hundred Stairways (1st, 8vo, 234p, col frn, pep, DJ/2.00)	Winston	(1941)	Pitz, Henry C.	20-35	
Malkus, Alida S.	Colt of Destiny... (1st {std}, 8vo, 244p, b/w, DJ/2.50)	Winston	(1950)	Lee, Manning De V.	25-40	
Malkus, Alida S.	Dark Star of Itza (1st {std}, 8vo, 217p, brown cl, 6 fp b/w, NH)	Harcourt	(1930)	Houser, Lowell	50-85	*
Malkus, Alida S.	Dragon Fly of Zuni (1st, 8vo, 213p, uncut, fp b/w, pep)	Harcourt	(1928)	Berry, Erick	30-60	*
Malkus, Alida S.	Eastward Sweeps the Current (1st, 8vo, 394p, b/w, pep, DJ/2.00)	Winston	(1937)	Sweeney, Dan	20-30	
Malkus, Alida S.	Fifth for the King (1st {std}, sm8vo, 250p, col frn, b/w)	Harper	1931	Berry, Erick	20-30	
Malkus, Alida S.	Little Giant of the North (1st {std}, 8vo, 178p, b/w, pep, DJ/1.50)	Winston	(1952)	Barnum, Jay H.	25-40	
Malkus, Alida S.	Meadows in the Sea (1st {std}, 8vo, 71p, dp color, DJ/2.75)	World	(1960)	Cosgrove, Mildred	40-65	
Malkus, Alida S.	Pirates' Port: Tale of Old New York (1st {std}, 12mo, 251p, col frn, pep)	Harper	(1929)	Justis, Lyle	25-45	
Malkus, Alida S.	Raquel of the Ranch Country (1st, sm8vo, 314p, b/w pl)	Harcourt	(1927)	Avison, George	30-45	*
Malkus, Alida S.	Sidi: Boy of the Desert (1st {std}, 8vo, 210p, b/w, DJ/2.95)	Winston	(1956)	Lee, Manning De V.	20-35	*
Malkus, Alida S.	Silver Llama (1st, lg8vo, 107p, fp color, pep, DJ/2.00)	Winston	(1939)	Malkus, Alida S.	30-50	
Malkus, Alida S.	Spindle Imp (1st, sm8vo, pink cl, 176p, uncut, fp b/w, pep)	Harcourt	(1931)	Berry, Erick	35-60	
Malkus, Alida S.	Stone Knife Boy (1st, 8vo, 270p, b/w pl, pep)	Harcourt	(1933)	Stoops, Herbert M.	30-45	
Malkus, Alida S.	Story of Good Queen Bess (1st, 8vo, 177p, b/w, DJ/1.50)	Grosset/Dunlap	(1953)	Gorsline, Douglas	20-30	*
Malkus, Alida S.	Story of Louis Pasteur (1st, 8vo, 178p, b/w, DJ/1.50)	Grosset/Dunlap	(1952)	Spier, Jo	25-40	
Malkus, Alida S.	Story of Winston Churchill (1st, 8vo, 181p, b/w, DJ/1.95)	Grosset/Dunlap	(1957)	Vestal, Herman B.	25-35	
Malkus, Alida S.	There Really Was a Hiawatha (1st, 8vo, 180p, b/w, pep, DJ/2.95)	Grosset/Dunlap	1963	Neilson, Jon	30-50	*
Malkus, Alida S.	Timber Line (1st, 8vo, 247p, b/w, pep)	Harcourt	(1929)	King, Ruth	25-40	
Malkus, Alida S.	We Were There at Battle of Gettysburg (1st, 8vo, 176p, b/w, pep, DJ/1.75)	Grosset/Dunlap	(1955)	Vosburgh, Leonard	20-35	
Malkus, Alida S.	Young Inca Prince (1st {std}, 8vo, 246p, b/w, pep, DJ/3.00)	Knopf	1957	Moyers, William	25-40	
Mallett, Beatrice	Playmates (4to, ibds, 16 fp color)	L: R. Tuck	[1910]	Mallett, Beatrice	200-350	
Mallison, Clare	Wooster-Poosters (1st, ob4to, p-o, 88p, 15cp, pep)	Stokes	(1931)	Mallison, Clare	150-220	
Malloch, Douglas	Little Hop Skipper (1st, 8vo, 99p, blue cl, col frn)	Doran	(1926)	Green, Eliz. S.	35-60	
Malloch, Douglas	Someone to Care (1st, sq16mo, [22]p, ibds, color)	Volland	(1920)	Unknown	35-60	
Malmberg, Bertil	Ake & his World (1st, 8vo, 176p, red/gilt, uncut, fp b/w, DJ/2.00)	Farrar/Rinehart	(1940)	Cooney, Barbara	100-165	
Malone, Henry	Lost Fairy Tales (1st, 8vo, gilt, 288p, 8cp)	L: C.H. Kelly	(1915)	Robinson, Gordon	80-125	
Malone, Mary	Here's Howie (1st, 8vo, 173p, uncut, b/w, DJ/3.00)	Dodd	1962	Wiese, Kurt	25-40	
Malory, Thomas	Arthur Pendragon of Britain (1st, 8vo, 542p, uncut, 4pl, pep, DJ/5.00)	Putnam	(1943)	Wyeth, Andrew	170-250	*
Malory, Thomas	Boy's King Arthur (1st, 8vo, 403p, gilt, 12pl, cep)	Scribner	1880	Kappes, Alfred	120-200	
Malory, Thomas	Boy's King Arthur (1st, lg8vo, p-o, teg, 321p, 14cp, pep, SC)	Scribner	1917	Wyeth, N.C.	200-300	
Malory, Thomas	King Arthur & his Knights (1st, lg8vo, p-o, 256p, pep, 4cp)	Winston	(1927)	Godwin, Frank	30-50	
Malory, Thomas	King Arthur... (1st, 12mo, 64p, green wraps, fp b/w)	Penn	1908	LeFanu, B.	40-60	*
Malory, Thomas	King Arthur... (1st, 12mo, 335p, gilt, cp)	Macmillan	1916	Thomson, Rodney	40-60	*
Malory, Thomas	Le Morte D'Arthur (1st, lg8vo, gilt, teg, 2 volumes, 36cp)	L: P.L. Warner	(1920)	Flint, William R.	200-300	
Malory, Thomas	Le Morte D'Arthur (lg8vo, 531p, red/gilt, teg, 24cp)	Hale-Cushman	(1927)	Flint, William R.	120-180	*
Malory, Thomas	Malory's King Arthur (1st, 8vo, 421p, cp, pep)	Baker/Taylor	(1911)	Birch, Reginald	70-100	*
Malory, Thomas	Story of Sir Galahad (1st, 8vo, 223p, tan cl, 7cp, pep)	Dutton	(1908)	Chapman, William E.	45-70	
Malory, Thomas	Women of Morte Darthur (1st, 8vo, 251p, gilt, 4cp)	L: Methuen	1927	Alexander, A.D.	50-80	
Malot, Hector	Adventures of Perrine (1st, lg8vo, 284p, black cl, p-o, 5cp, pep, WS)	Rand/McNally	(1932)	Winter, Milo	50-80	
Malot, Hector	Adventures of Remi (1st, lg8vo, p-o, 492p, gilt, pep, 8cp, WS)	Rand/McNally	(1925)	Schaeffer, Mead	40-70	
Malot, Hector	Nobody's Boy (1st AM, 8vo, 372p, green/gilt, p-o, 4cp)	Cupples/Leon	1916	Gruelle, Johnny	60-100	
Malot, Hector	Nobody's Boy (1st, lg8vo, p-o, 308p, 8cp, pep)	Cupples/Leon	(1930)	Gooch, Thelma	45-70	
Maloy, Lois	Arabella of the Merry-Go-Round (1st, lg ob8vo, [64]p, color, DJ/1.50)	Scribner	1935	Maloy, Lois	30-50	
Maloy, Lois	Tea Party in Plumpudding Street (1st, 8vo, ibds, [54]p, 1-color, pep)	Grosset/Dunlap	(1946)	Maloy, Lois	30-50	
Maloy, Lois	Wooden Shoes in America (1st, sm ob4to, [72]p, color, DJ/1.75)	Scribner	(1940)	Maloy, Lois	50-85	*
Malvern, Gladys	Dancing Star (1st, lg8vo, 280p, b/w, pep, DJ/2.50)	J. Messner	1942	Suba, Susanne	30-50	
Mamin-Siberiak, D.N.	Verotchka's Tales (1st, 8vo, pink/gilt, uncut, 190p, 10pl, dep)	Dutton	(1922)	Artzybasheff, Boris	60-95	
Mandal, Sant Ram	Happy Flute (1st, lg8vo, 54p, tan cl, 10 fp b/w, pep, DJ/1.50)	Stokes	1939	Lathrop, Dorothy	80-130	
Maniates, Belle	Little Boy Bear (1st, 12mo, blue/white, 54p, 5pl)	Pilgrim Press	(1917)	Warren, Elizabeth	25-40	
Maniates, Belle	Our Next-Door Neighbors (1st, sm8vo, 280p, 12 fp b/w)	Little/Brown	1917	Sarg, Tony	30-55	
Mann, Peggy	Boy with a Billion Pets (1st, sq8vo, [44]p, 2-color, DJ)	Coward	(1968)	Galdone, Paul	25-40	
Mann, Thomas	Christmas Poem (1st, sm8vo, wraps, [8]p, 1-color)	Equinox	1932	Ward, Lynd	50-80	*
Manners, Robert	Cuba & other Verse (1st, 12mo, 155p, uncut, gilt, teg, cvr by...)	Way & Williams	1898	Hazenplug, Frank	125-200	
Manning, Anne	Household of Sir Thomas More (1st, 12mo, 185p, teg, 24cp, dep)	L: J.M. Dent	1906	Brock, Charles E.	45-75	
Manning, William	Child's Dream of the Zoo (sq4to, 24p, wraps)	L: Routledge	1889	Griset, Ernest H.	90-120	

AUTHOR	TITLE	PUBLISHER	DATE	ARTIST	PRICE	LC
Manning-Sanders, Ruth	Book of Dwarfs (1st AM {std}, lg8vo, 127p, b/w, DJ/3.50)	Dutton	(1964)	Jacques, Robin	30-50	
Manning-Sanders, Ruth	Book of Ghosts & Goblins (1st AM {std}, lg8vo, 126p, DJ/3.95)	Dutton	(1969)	Jacques, Robin	30-50	
Manning-Sanders, Ruth	Book of Giants (1st {std}, 8vo, 124p, col frn, b/w, DJ)	L: Methuen	1962	Jacques, Robin	30-50	
Manning-Sanders, Ruth	Book of Mermaids (1st AM {std}, 8vo, 127p, b/w, DJ/3.75)	Dutton	(1968)	Jacques, Robin	40-65	
Manning-Sanders, Ruth	Book of Princes and Princesses (1st, lg8vo, 127p, ibds, col frn, b/w)	L: Methuen	(1969)	Jacques, Robin	30-50	
Manning-Sanders, Ruth	Bundle of Ballads (1st AM, 8vo, 245p, b/w, DJ/3.00, KGM)	Lippincott	(1959)	Stobbs, William	30-50	
Manning-Sanders, Ruth	Jonnikin and the Flying Basket (1st, 8vo, 152p, 8cp, DJ)	L: Oxford U.Pr.	1969	Ambrus, Victor	20-35	
Manning-Sanders, Ruth	Peter & the Piskies (1st AM, 8vo, 215p, b/w, DJ)	NY: Roy	(1958)	Briggs, Raymond	30-50	
Mansfield, Katherine	Stories by Katherine Mansfield (1st, 4to, 215p, DJ/4.00, designs by...)	Knopf	1930	Gay, Zhenya	40-65	
Mansfield, Richard	Blown Away (1st, 12mo, 180p, teg, cvr by...)	L.C. Page	1897	McManus, Blanche	60-100	
Mansion, Horace	Old English Nursery Songs (1st, 4to, ibds, p-o, 6cp)	L: Harrap	[1921]	Anderson, Anne	125-200	
Mansion, Horace	Old English Nursery Songs (1st AM, 4to, 87p, ibds, p-o, 6cp)	Brentano's	[1921]	Anderson, Anne	150-220	
Mantle, Winifred	Tinker's Castle (1st {std}, 8vo, 222p, b/w, DJ/3.75)	Holt, Rinehart	(1964)	Werth, Kurt	20-35	
Manzi, Alberto	White Boy (1st {std}, 8vo, 202p, fp b/w, DJ/3.95)	Macmillan	1963	Molina, Charles	25-40	*
Marais, Josef	Koos the Hottentot (1st {std}, 8vo, ibds, 188p, color, DJ/2.50)	Knopf	1945	Stahlhut, Henry	70-125	R
Marc, Elizabeth	Doris & David All Alone (1st, 8vo, 259p, red/gilt, 4cp, pep)	L: Hutchinson	[1922]	Robinson, Charles	90-120	
March, Eleanor S.	Little White Barbara (1st, 24mo, green cl, 95p, 24cp)	L: Richards	1902	March, Eleanor S.	250-400	
March, Eleanor S.	Three Naughty Elves (1st, ob4to, 37p, ibds, color)	L: Liberty	[1903]	Evans, E.	200-300	*
Marchant, Bessie	Captives of the Kaid (1st, 8vo, 208p, 4cp, pep)	L: Collins	[1904]	Goble, Warwick	40-65	*
Marcher, Marion W.	Monarch Butterfly (1st, 8vo, 42p, green cl, 2-color, DJ/2.00)	Holiday House	(1954)	Latham, Barbara	60-90	R
Marchioness/London	Magic Ink Spot (1st, 8vo, 208p, 16cp)	L: Macmillan	1928	Brock, E./Stewart	90-120	*
Marcy, Mary E.	Rhymes of Early Jungle Folk (1st, lg8vo, 124p, woodcuts, pep)	Chi: Kerr	1922	Esherick, Wharton H.	80-125	
Margalit, Avi	Hebrew Alphabet Book (1st, ob4to, [25]p, color, DJ/2.95)	Funk/Wagnalls	(1968)	Margalit, Avi	50-80	*
Margo, Jan	Make-Believe Parade (1st, 8vo, ipcb, unpag, color)	Wonder Books	(1949)	Wilkin, Eloise B.	60-90	*
Margolis, Ellen	Idy, the Fox-Chasing Cow (1st {std}, 8vo, 64p, b/w, DJ/2.95)	World	(1962)	Werth, Kurt	25-40	*
Marguulies, John	Gold Steps, Stone Steps (1st, 4to, [30]p, color, DJ)	Harlin Quist	1969	Lambert, J.K.	40-60	
Mariana	Doki the Lonely Papoose (1st, lg8vo, unpag, color, DJ/2.50)	Lothrop, Lee	(1955)	Mariana	30-45	
Mariana	Hotspur (1st, 12mo, ibds, [40]p, fp color, DJ/1.25)	Lothrop, Lee	(1953)	Mariana	45-70	
Mariana	Journey of Bangwell Put (1st, sm4to, [38]p, color, DJ/3.50)	Lothrop, Lee	(1965)	Mariana	60-85	
Mariana	Miss Flora McFlimsey & Baby New Year (1st, 12mo, ibds, unpag, DJ/1.00)	Lothrop, Lee	(1951)	Mariana	60-90	
Mariana	Miss Flora McFlimsey & Little Laughing Water (1st 12mo [32]p, col, DJ/1.25)	Lothrop, Lee	(1954)	Mariana	60-90	
Mariana	Miss Flora McFlimsey's Easter Bonnet (1st sq12mo ibds, [40]p, col, DJ/1.00)	Lothrop, Lee	(1951)	Mariana	60-90	
Maril, Lee	Mr. Bunny Paints the Eggs (1st, ob4to, ibds, [28]p, color, DJ/1.00)	Roy Pub. Co.	(1945)	Lorentowicz, Irena	40-65	*
Marino, Dorothy	Buzzy Bear Goes South (1st {std}, sm4to, [33]p, 1-color, pep, DJ/2.95)	F. Watts	1961	Marino, Dorothy	30-50	
Marino, Dorothy	Good-Bye Thunderstorm (1st, ob8vo, [36]p, 3-color, DJ/2.25)	Lippincott	1958	Marino, Dorothy	30-45	
Marino, Dorothy	Little Angela and her Puppy (1st {std}, ob8vo, [40]p, 1-color, DJ/2.00)	Lippincott	(1954)	Marino, Dorothy	40-65	
Marino, Josef	Hi! Ho! Pinocchio (1st, 4to, 127p, col frn, p-o, b/w, cep, DJ/1.00)	Reilly/Lee	(1940)	Donahey, William	200-300	
Marion	Mummy's Bedtime Story Book (1st, folio, 55p, ipcb, 12cp, pep)	L: C. Palmer	(1929)	King, Jessie	1500-2500	
Marion, Francis	Truant Tricycle (1st, 4to, ipcb, [25]p, color, pep, DJ/1.00)	Hollow Tree Hse.	1948	Crandall, C. Leslie	60-90	
Mariotti, Jean	Tales of Poindi (1st, 4to, 64p, green/gilt, b/w, DJ/2.50)	Domino Press	(1938)	Rojankovsky, Feodor	80-130	
Markham, Edwin	Man With the Hoe... (1st, 8vo, 114p, gilt, teg, b/w)	Doub./McClure	1900	Pyle, Howard	90-120	
Marks, Gerald	Sing a Song of Safety (1st, lg4to, 71p, spiral wraps, fp 3-color)	NY: I. Caesar	1937	O'Neill, Rose	60-100	
Marks, Jeannette	Cheerful Cricket... (1st, 4to, [124]p, green cl, dep, color)	Small/Maynard	1907	Brown, Edith	120-200	R
Marks, Jeannette	Children in the Wood Stories (1st, sm8vo, 141p, p-o, 6cp)	Milton Bradley	1919	Burd, Clara M.	25-40	
Marks, Jeannette	Through Welsh Doorways (1st, 8vo, 244p, rust/gilt, 4pl)	Houghton	1909	Betts, Anna W.	30-50	
Marks, Mickey	What Can I Buy? (1st, 8vo, [33]p, 1-color, pep, DJ/2.50)	Dial Press	1962	Aliki	30-45	
Marokvia, Mireille	French School for Paul (1st AM, 4to, ipcb, 47p, 2-color, DJ/3.50)	Lippincott	(1963)	Marokvia, Artur	30-45	*
Marokvia, Mireille	Jannot, a French Rabbit (1st AM, sm4to, 46p, fp color, DJ/3.00)	Lippincott	1959	Marokvia, Artur	30-50	
Marquand, John	Haven's End (1st, 8vo, 341p, uncut, b/w)	Little/Brown	1933	Lawson, Robert	50-80	
Marquand, Josephine	Chi Ming & the Writing Lesson (1st AM, 4to, [32]p, fp color, DJ/4.95)	F. Watts	1970	Binder, Pearl	30-45	
Marquand, Josephine	Chi Ming and the Tiger Kitten (1st AM, 4to, [32]p, fp color, DJ/3.95)	F. Watts	(1965)	Binder, Pearl	30-45	
Marquis, Don	Archy Does His Part (1st {std}, 12mo, p-o, 269p, b/w, pep, DJ/2.00)	Doubleday/Doran	1935	Herriman, George	70-120	
Marquis, Don	Danny's Own Story (1st, 8vo, green cl, 333p, p-o, 16pl)	Doubleday/Page	1912	Kemble, Edward W.	120-200	
Marquis, Don	Noah an' Jonah an' Cap'n John Smith (1st, 12mo, 157p, b/w)	Appleton	1921	Sarg, Tony	25-45	
Marriott, Crittenden	Sally Castleton, Southerner (1st, sm8vo, uncut, 312p, col frn, 5pl)	Lippincott	1913	Wyeth, N.C.	70-125	
Marryat, Frederick	Children of the New Forest (1st, 8vo, 397p, p-o, 8cp)	Henry Holt & Co.	1911	Smith, E. Boyd	75-100	
Marryat, Frederick	Children of the New Forest (1st, lg8vo, black cl, p-o, 9cp, pep, SC)	Scribner	1927	Good, Stafford	80-120	
Marryat, Frederick	Children of the New Forest (1st, 8vo, 322p, green cl, 10 fp b/w)	Macmillan	1930	Ward, Lynd	40-60	
Marryat, Frederick	Jacob Faithful (1st, 8vo, blue/gilt, 416p, AEG, b/w, dep)	L: Macmillan	1895	Brock, Henry M.	60-90	
Marryat, Frederick	Japhet in Search of a Father (1st, 12mo, blue/gilt, 401p, AEG, 14pl, pep)	L: Macmillan	1895	Brock, Henry M.	80-120	
Marryat, Frederick	King's Own (1st, 12mo, blue cl, AEG, 429p, 40pl, pep)	L: Macmillan	1896	Townsend, F.H.	50-80	
Marryat, Frederick	King's Own (1st, 8vo, 451p, 6pl)	L: Oxford U.Pr.	1907	Goble, Warwick	100-165	
Marryat, Frederick	Masterman Ready (1st, lg8vo, gilt, 403p, p-o, 6cp)	Harper	1928	Rae, John	35-60	
Marryat, Frederick	Newton Foster (1st, 12mo, 393p, blue/gilt, 40 b/w, pep)	L: Macmillan	1897	Sullivan, Edmund J.	55-80	
Marryat, Frederick	Snarleyyow (1st, sm8vo, 405p, blue/gilt, AEG, fp b/w)	L: Macmillan	1897	Millar, H.R.	55-80	
Marsh, Edith	Trillium Hill (1st, 8vo, 159p, DJ/2.50, pep & DJ by...)	Lothrop, Lee	(1955)	Duvoisin, Roger	30-45	*
Marsh, George	Sled Trails and White Waters (1st, lg8vo, 298p, gilt, p-o, col frn, 9pl)	Penn	1929	Schoonover, Frank	30-50	
Marsh, George	Toilers of the Trails (1st, lg8vo, p-o, 245p, col frn, 8pl)	Penn	1921	Schoonover, Frank	35-60	
Marsh, Lewis	Tales of the Fairies (1st, 8vo, gilt, 5cp, 7 b/w)	L: Hodder	[1912]	Govey, Lilian	150-220	
Marsh, Lewis	Tales of the Homeland (1st, 8vo, buckram, 199p, 6cp)	L: Hodder	[1911]	Robinson, Thomas H.	75-100	*
Marshall, Archibald	Peggy in Toyland (1st, 8vo, ipcb, 277p, b/w, pep)	Dodd	1920	Barton, Helen M.	40-60	*
Marshall, Archibald	The Dragon (1st AM {std}, lgob8vo, [32]p, color, DJ/3.25)	Dutton	(1967)	Ardizzone, Edward	30-50	
Marshall, Bernard G.	Cedric the Forester (1st, 8vo, 278p, 18pl, NH)	Appleton	1921	Williams, J. Scott	80-130	
Marshall, Caroline	Girl Ranchers of San Coulee (1st, 12mo, 322p, 4pl)	Penn	1897	Waugh, Ida	35-60	
Marshall, Caroline	Two Wyoming Girls (1st, 12mo, 329p, brown/gilt, b/w)	Penn	1899	Waugh, Ida	30-50	*
Marshall, Catherine	Friends with God (1st, 4to, 48p, 2-color, DJ/2.00)	Whittlesey	1956	Cooney, Barbara	30-50	
Marshall, Catherine	Julie's Heritage (1st {std}, 8vo, 231p, b/w, DJ/3.00)	Longmans	1957	Johnson, Harper	20-30	
Marshall, Dean	Dig for a Treasure (1st {std}, 8vo, 188p, b/w, pep, DJ/2.50)	Dutton	1949	Price, Christine	100-170	

AUTHOR	TITLE	PUBLISHER	DATE	ARTIST	PRICE	LC
Marshall, Dean	House for Elizabeth (1st {std}, 8vo, 219p, fp b/w, dep, DJ/2.00)	Dutton	1941	Kalab, Theresa	120-180	
Marshall, Dean	Invisible Island (1st {std}, 8vo, 191p, fp b/w, pep, DJ/2.50)	Dutton	1948	Price, Christine	70-100	
Marshall, Dean	Silver Robin (1st {std}, 8vo, 246p, b/w, pep, DJ/2.50)	Dutton	1947	Dobias/McGuckin	120-200	
Marshall, Dean	Wish on the Moon (1st {std}, 8vo, 192p, b/w, DJ/2.50)	Dutton	1951	Morse, Dorothy B.	200-300	
Marshall, Helen L.	New Mexican Boy (1st, 8vo, 85p, 9 fp color, cep, DJ/2.00)	Holiday House	(1940)	Rush, Olive	30-50	
Marshall, Henrietta	Our Empire Story (1st AM, lg8vo, gilt, teg, 493p, 8cp, maps)	Stokes	(1908)	Skelton, Joseph R.	60-100	
Marshall, Peter	Let's Keep Christmas (1st, 12mo, ibds, [32]p, 2-color, pep, DJ/1.50)	McGraw-Hill	1953	Cooney, Barbara	40-65	
Martens, Frederick H.	Fairy Tales from Orient (1st, 8vo, 293p, blue cl, 4cp, pep)	McBride	1923	Hood, George	60-90	
Martin, Bill	Adam's Balm (1st, 8vo, [32]p, color, cep)	CA: Bowmar	(1970)	Foreman, Michael	30-50	*
Martin, Charles M.	Orphans of the Range (1st, 8vo, 192p, blue cl, fp b/w, DJ/2.00)	Viking	1950	Barnum, Jay H.	30-50	
Martin, Dahris	Little Lamb (1st {std}, ob4to, [32]p, color, pep, DJ/1.50)	Harper	1938	Somppi, Lilly	45-70	*
Martin, Dahris	Wonder Cat (1st, 8vo, 59p, 1-color, DJ/1.75)	Crowell	1942	Watson, Aldren A.	20-35	
Martin, Edward S.	Cousin Anthony and I (1st, 12mo, 255p, green cl, cvr by...)	Scribner	1895	Armstrong, Margaret	30-60	
Martin, Edward S.	Lucid Intervals (1st, 12mo, 263p, teg, blue cl, 6pl)	Harper	1900	Stilwell, Sarah	55-80	
Martin, Edward S.	Luxury of Children (1st, lg8vo, 213p, green/gilt, p-o, teg, 8cp)	Harper	1904	Stilwell, Sarah	70-100	
Martin, Fran	Nine Tales of Coyote (1st, 8vo, 60p, fp color, pep, DJ/2.00)	Harper	(1950)	McEntee, Dorothy	30-45	
Martin, H.R.	His Courtship (1st, 8vo, uncut, 322p, 4pl)	McClure	1907	Stephens, Alice B.	30-50	*
Martin, John	Children's Munchausen (1st, lg8vo, 185p, p-o, gilt, 8cp)	Houghton	1921	Ross, Gordon	60-100	
Martin, John	Prayers for Little Men & Women (1st, 8vo, 96p, gilt, 6 ticp)	Harper	1912	Rae, John	60-80	
Martin, Judith	Tree Angel (1st, sq12mo, [49]p, 3-color, cep, DJ/1.95)	Knopf	(1962)	Charlip, Remy	50-80	
Martin, Patricia	Abraham Lincoln (1st, 8vo, 64p, color, DJ/1.95)	Putnam	(1964)	Schrotter, Gustav	20-30	
Martin, Patricia	Andrew Jackson (1st, 8vo, 62p, color, DJ)	Putnam	(1966)	Tamer, Salem	20-30	
Martin, Patricia	Benjie Goes into Business (1st, 4to, [30]p, 2-color, DJ/2.75)	Putnam	(1961)	Galdone, Paul	30-45	*
Martin, Patricia	Birthday Present (1st {A}, sm8vo, 47p, fp 3-color, DJ/2.25)	Abingdon Press	(1963)	Locke, Margot	25-40	
Martin, Patricia	Bony Pony (1st, 4to, 44p, color, DJ/2.75)	Putnam	(1965)	Dines, Glen	20-35	*
Martin, Patricia	Broomtail Bronc (1st {A}, 8vo, 64p, b/w, pep, DJ/2.50)	Abingdon Press	(1965)	Locke, Margot	25-40	*
Martin, Patricia	Calvin and the Cub Scouts (1st, sm4to, 47p, color, DJ/3.00)	Putnam	(1964)	Hamil, Tom	30-45	
Martin, Patricia	Chandler Chipmunk's Flying Lesson (1st {A}, lg8vo, 64p, color, DJ/2.50)	Abingdon Press	(1960)	Locke, Margot	20-35	
Martin, Patricia	Daniel Boone (1st, 8vo, 62p, color, DJ/1.95)	Putnam	(1965)	Dines, Glen	25-40	
Martin, Patricia	Dog and the Boat Boy (1st, 4to, 44p, color, DJ)	Putnam	(1969)	Thollander, Earl	20-35	
Martin, Patricia	Dolls from Cheyenne (1st, 8vo, 38p, color, DJ)	Putnam	(1967)	Almquist, Don	25-40	
Martin, Patricia	Eskimos: People of Alaska (1st, 8vo, 64p, color, DJ)	Parents Mag. Pr.	(1970)	Frankenberg, Rbt.	25-40	
Martin, Patricia	Friend of Miguel (1st, 8vo, 45p, color, DJ/2.95)	Rand/McNally	1967	Genia	25-40	
Martin, Patricia	Grandma's Gun (1st, 8vo, [47]p, color, DJ/3.50)	Golden Gate	(1968)	Corey, Robert	25-40	
Martin, Patricia	Greedy One (1st {A}, 8vo, 64p, color, DJ/2.95)	Rand/McNally	(1964)	Mizumura, Kazue	25-40	
Martin, Patricia	Happy Piper and the Goat (1st, 8vo, 38p, color, DJ/2.75)	Lothrop, Lee	(1960)	Werth, Kurt	20-30	
Martin, Patricia	Indians: The First Americans (1st, 8vo, 64p, color, DJ)	Parents Mag. Pr.	(1970)	Frankenberg, Rbt.	25-40	
Martin, Patricia	Jacqueline Kennedy Onassis (1st, 8vo, 62p, color, DJ)	Putnam	(1969)	Frame, Paul	25-35	
Martin, Patricia	James Madison (1st, 8vo, 63p, color, DJ)	Putnam	(1970)	Cuffari, Richard	25-35	
Martin, Patricia	Jefferson Davis (1st, 8vo, 63p, color, DJ)	Putnam	(1966)	Tamer, Salem	25-35	*
Martin, Patricia	John Fitzgerald Kennedy (1st, 8vo, 64p, color, DJ/1.95)	Putnam	(1964)	Frame, Paul	25-40	*
Martin, Patricia	John Marshall (1st, 8vo, 63p, color, DJ)	Putnam	(1967)	Tamer, Salem	25-35	
Martin, Patricia	Jump Frog Jump (1st, sm4to, 47p, color, DJ/2.75)	Putnam	(1965)	Thollander, Earl	25-35	
Martin, Patricia	Kumi and the Pearl (1st, 4to, 45p, color, DJ)	Putnam	1968	Hamil, Tom	20-35	
Martin, Patricia	Little Brown Hen (1st, 8vo, 23p, 1-color, pep, DJ/2.50)	Crowell	(1960)	Johnson, Harper	30-55	
Martin, Patricia	Little Two and the Peach Tree (1st {std}, 8vo, 39p, 1-color, DJ/2.75)	Atheneum	1963	Berg, Joan	25-40	
Martin, Patricia	Long Ago Christmas (1st, ob4to, ibds, 31p, 2-color)	Putnam	(1968)	Orbaan, Albert	20-30	
Martin, Patricia	Mrs. Grumble and Fire Engine Number 7 (1st, 4to, 48p, color, DJ)	Putnam	(1966)	Thollander, Earl	40-65	
Martin, Patricia	No, No Rosina (1st, 8vo, 48p, color, DJ/2.75)	Putnam	(1964)	Thollander, Earl	20-35	*
Martin, Patricia	One Special Dog (1st, 8vo, 48p, color, DJ/3.95)	Rand/McNally	1968	Hawkinson, Lucy	25-35	
Martin, Patricia	Pocahontas (1st, 8vo, 63p, color, DJ/1.95)	Putnam	(1964)	Takajian, Portia	20-35	
Martin, Patricia	Pointed Brush (1st, sm4to, red cl, [36]p, color, pep, DJ/2.75)	Lothrop, Lee	1959	Duvoisin, Roger	30-50	
Martin, Patricia	Pumpkin Patch (1st, 8vo, 47p, color, DJ/2.75)	Putnam	(1966)	Hamil, Tom	20-35	
Martin, Patricia	Raccoon and Mrs. McGinnis (1st, 8vo, 45p, fp 1-color, pep, DJ/2.00)	Putnam	(1961)	Weisgard, Leonard	30-45	
Martin, Patricia	Rice Bowl Pet (1st, sm4to, [36]p, fp 2-color, dep, DJ/3.50)	Crowell	(1962)	Keats, Ezra J.	30-45	
Martin, Patricia	Rolling the Cheese (1st {std}, ob4to, [46]p, fp 2-color, cep, DJ/3.95)	Atheneum	1966	Raible, Alton	25-40	
Martin, Patricia	Show and Tell (1st, 8vo, 48p, fp 2-color, DJ/2.00)	Putnam	(1962)	Hamil, Tom	25-45	
Martin, Patricia	Sing, Sailor, Sing (1st, sm ob4to, [30]p, fp 2-color, cep, DJ/3.50)	Golden Gate	(1966)	Booth, Graham	20-35	
Martin, Patricia	Suzu and the Bride Doll (1st {A}, 8vo, [48]p, color, pep, DJ/2.75)	Rand/McNally	1960	Mizumura, Kazue	30-50	
Martin, Patricia	Sylvester Jones & Voice in the Forest (1st, 4to, [32]p, 2-color, DJ/2.75)	Lothrop, Lee	(1958)	Weisgard, Leonard	30-50	
Martin, Patricia	That Cat! 1-2-3 (1st, sm ob4to, [48]p, color, DJ)	Putnam	1969	Unada	25-35	
Martin, Patricia	There Goes the Tiger! (1st, 8vo, [48]p, color, DJ)	Putnam	1970	Hamil, Tom	20-35	
Martin, Patricia	Trina's Boxcar (1st, 8vo, 112p, fp 3-color, pep, DJ/3.25)	Abingdon Press	(1967)	Jefferson, Robert	25-40	
Martin, Patricia	Woody's Big Trouble (1st, 4to, 46p, fp 2-color)	Putnam	(1967)	Galdone, Paul	20-30	
Martin, Patricia	Zachary Taylor (1st, 8vo, 62p, color, DJ)	Putnam	(1969)	Mawicke, Tran	20-35	
Martin, Sarah C.	Comic Adventures of Old Mother Hubbard & her Dog (1st, sm8vo, [32]p, DJ)	Bradbury Press	(1968)	Lobel, Arnold	30-50	R
Martin, Sarah C.	Old Mother Hubbard and Her Dog (1st, ob4to, 32p, color, DJ/2.25)	Whittlesey	(1960)	Galdone, Paul	30-50	
Martineau, Harriet	Feats on the Fiord (1st, 8vo, 301p, blue/gilt, col frn, pep)	Macmillan	1924	Artzybasheff, Boris	40-65	
Martineau, Harriet	Feats on the Fjord (1st, 16mo, blue cl, teg, 237p, col frn)	L: Dent	1899	Rackham, Arthur	170-240	
Martineau, Harriet	Feats on the Fjord (1st AM, 12mo, p-o, 128p, 8cp)	Dutton	[1914]	Rackham, Arthur	100-160	
Martinengo-Cesaresco	Fairies' Fountain (1st, 8vo, 268p, blue/gilt, col frn, 15pl)	L: A. Fairbairns	1908	Robinson, Charles	200-285	
Marton, Gregory	Boy & his Friend the Blizzard (1st {std} sm8vo, 126p, 2-color, pep, DJ/3.50)	Harper	(1962)	Wildsmith, Brian	30-45	
Marvel, Ik.	Reveries of a Bachelor (1st, 8vo, 338p, blue cl, 17cp)	Bobbs-Merrill	(1906)	Ashe, E.M.	25-40	
Marzetti, Ada C.	In the Land of Nod (1st, 8vo, 81p, red/gilt, b/w)	L: Griffith	1887	Gould, F. Carruthers	70-120	*
Marzials, Theo	Pan Pipes (1st, lg ob4to, tan ibds, 51p, dep, color)	L: Routledge	1883	Crane, Walter	200-300	
Masani, Shakuntala	Nehru's Story (1st, 8vo, 81p, 2-color, cep, DJ/2.50)	NY: Oxford U.Pr.	1949	Masani, Shakuntala	40-70	R
Masefield, John	Book of Discoveries (1st, 8vo, 354p, teg, 53 b/w, pep)	L: Wells/Gard.	1910	Browne, Gordon	60-100	R
Masefield, John	Jim Davis (1st, 8vo, blue/gilt, p-o, 226p, 8cp)	Stokes	1924	Schaeffer, Mead	35-60	*

AUTHOR	TITLE	PUBLISHER	DATE	ARTIST	PRICE	LC
Masefield, John	Martin Hyde (1st, 8vo, 303p, teg, green cl, uncut, 16pl)	L: Wells/Gard.	1910	Dugdale, Thomas C.	60-90	
Masefield, John	Midnight Folk (1st, 4to, 282p, blue/gilt, 6cp, pep)	L: Heinemann	(1931)	Hilder, Rowland	120-175	
Masefield, John	Reynard the Fox (1st, 4to, gilt, 116p, uncut, 4cp, 12pl)	L: Heinemann	1921	Armour, George D.	90-120	
Masefield, John	Reynard the Fox (1st AM, 4to, green/gilt, 339p, 4cp)	Macmillan	1921	Armour, George D.	70-100	
Masefield, John	Reynard the Fox (1st, lg8vo, ibds, [94]p, color, pep)	Volland	(1925)	Rae, John	75-100	
Masefield, John	Right Royal (1st AM, 8vo, black/gilt, 116p, 4cp)	Macmillan	1922	Aldin, Cecil	150-225	
Masereel, Franz	Passionate Journey (1st AM, 8vo, [190]p, fp woodcuts, DJ)	NY: Lear Pub.	(1948)	Masereel, Franz	80-125	*
Mason, Arthur	Fossil Fountain (1st {std}, 8vo, 198p, col frn, 4pl, pep)	Doubleday/Doran	1928	Van Everen, Jay	20-30	
Mason, Arthur	From the Horn of the Moon (1st {std}, lg8vo, 259p, blue cl, b/w, pep)	Doubleday/Doran	1931	Lawson, Robert	70-125	
Mason, Arthur	Roving Lobster (1st {std}, 8vo, 132p, green cl, 10 fp b/w, cep)	Doubleday/Doran	1931	Lawson, Robert	80-120	
Mason, Arthur	Wee Men of Ballywooden (1st {std}, lg8vo, 266p, pep, 4pl)	Doubleday/Doran	1930	Lawson, Robert	100-165	
Mason, Arthur	Wee Men of Ballywooden (1st {this pub}, 8vo, p-o, 266p, 4pl, pep)	Garden City	(1937)	Lawson, Robert	50-80	
Mason, Edith H.	Great Plan (1st, 8vo, green/white, 308p, 5pl)	McClurg	1913	St. John, J. Allen	70-100	
Mason, Eugene (tr)	Old-World Love Stories (1st, 8vo, 282p, gilt, teg, 8 ticp)	L: J.M. Dent	1913	Knowles, R.L.	170-240	
Mason, Francis E.	Daddy Gander (1st, 4to, ibds, [90]p, color)	NY: F.E. Mason	(1900)	Spedon	80-140	
Mason, George	Snip and Snap and the Lost Baby (1st, 16mo, ibds, unpag, color)	Volland	(1914)	Lee/Hardy	50-80	
Mason, Miriam E.	Broomtail - Brother of Lightning (1st {std}, 8vo, 135p, b/w, DJ/2.00)	Macmillan	1952	Moyers, William	50-80	
Mason, Miriam E.	Dan Beard, Boy Scout (1st {std}, 8vo, 192p, b/w, DJ/1.75)	Bobbs-Merrill	(1953)	Laune, Paul	25-45	*
Mason, Miriam E.	Hominy and his Blunt-Nosed Arrow (1st {std}, 8vo, 145p, b/w, DJ/1.75)	Macmillan	1950	Hauman, G.& D.	25-40	
Mason, Miriam E.	Hoppity (1st {std}, 8vo, 76p, fp 1-color, cep, DJ/1.50)	Macmillan	1947	Wiese, Kurt	30-45	
Mason, Miriam E.	Lion for Patsy (1st {std}, lg8vo, ibds, [32]p, color, DJ/1.50)	McKay	(1947)	Neville, Vera	60-90	*
Mason, Miriam E.	Little Jonathan (1st {std}, 8vo, 128p, b/w, DJ/1.25)	Macmillan	1944	Hauman, G.& D.	120-180	
Mason, Miriam E.	Major and his Camels (1st {std}, 8vo, 130p, b/w, DJ/2.00)	Macmillan	(1953)	Gay, Zhenya	25-40	
Mason, Miriam E.	Middle Sister (1st {std}, 8vo, 160p, b/w, DJ/1.75)	Macmillan	1947	Paull, Grace	25-45	*
Mason, Miriam E.	Miss Posy Longlegs (1st {std}, 8vo, 54p, 1-color, DJ/2.00)	Macmillan	(1955)	Petershams	40-65	
Mason, Miriam E.	Pony Called Lightning (1st {std}, 8vo, 142p, b/w, DJ/1.75)	Macmillan	1948	Anderson, C.W.	50-80	*
Mason, Miriam E.	Sara and the Winter Gift (1st {std}, 8vo, 152p, fp b/w, DJ/4.50)	Macmillan	(1968)	Frame, Paul	30-50	
Mason, Miriam E.	Smiling Hill Farm (1st, 8vo, 311p, pep, 1-color)	Ginn & Co.	(1937)	Seredy, Kate	80-130	
Mason, Miriam E.	Sugarbush Family (1st {std}, 8vo, 137p, b/w, DJ/2.00)	Macmillan	1954	Gay, Zhenya	25-45	
Mason, Miriam E.	Susannah: Pioneer Cow (1st, 8vo, yellow cl, 151p, 1-color, cep, DJ/1.25)	Macmillan	1941	Petershams	40-65	
Mason, Miriam E.	Three Ships Came Sailing In (1st {std}, 8vo, 246p, b/w, DJ/2.50)	Bobbs-Merrill	(1950)	John, Charles V.	40-65	*
Mason, Miriam E.	Timothy has Ideas (1st {std}, 8vo, 127p, blue cl, fp b/w, DJ/1.50)	Macmillan	1943	Hader, B.& E.	40-65	
Mason, Miriam E.	Yours with Love, Kate (1st, 8vo, 277p, b/w, DJ/3.00)	Houghton	1952	Cooney, Barbara	40-70	
Mason, Walt	Uncle Walt (1st, 8vo, brown cl, teg, 189p, cvr by...)	Chi: Adams	1910	Bradley, Will	80-120	
Massey, Jeanne	Littlest Witch (1st, sm ob4to, [33]p, orange cl, 2-color, DJ)	Knopf	(1959)	Adams, Adrienne	50-85	
Massie, Diane R.	Baby Beebee Bird (1st, ob8vo, ipcb, [32]p, 3-color, cep, DJ/2.75)	Harper	(1963)	Massie, Diane R.	20-35	
Massie, Diane R.	King Henry the Mouse (1st {std}, 8vo, 65p, b/w, cep, DJ/3.50)	Atheneum	1968	Massie, Diane R.	25-40	*
Massie, Diane R.	Monstrous Glisson Glop (1st, lg8vo, [39]p, color, DJ/3.95)	Parents Mag. Pr.	(1970)	Massie, Diane R.	20-35	
Massie, Diane R.	Tiny Pin (1st, sm ob8vo, 31p, color, DJ/2.95)	Harper	(1964)	Massie, Diane R.	25-40	*
Masson, Thomas L.	Corner in Women (1st, 8vo, teg, ipcb, gilt, 332p, cvr by...)	Moffat	1905	Gibson, Charles D.	35-60	
Masters, Edgar L.	The Sangamon (1st, 8vo, 258p, fp b/w, pep, DJ/2.50)	Farrar/Rinehart	(1942)	Ward, Lynd	50-80	
Matheson, Annie	As Months Go By (4to, ibds, fp color)	L: R. Tuck	[1900]	Hughes, E.R.	180-250	
Matheson, Annie	Songs of Love & Praise (1st, 8vo, unpag, gilt, designs by...)	L: J.M. Dent	1907	Robinson, Charles	75-100	*
Matheson, John	Needle in the Haystack (1st, sq8vo, 189p, ibds, 8cp, pep)	Wm. Morrow	1930	D'Aulaire, E. Parin	70-100	
Mathews, Frances A.	My Lady Peggy Goes to Town (1st, 12mo, teg, 338p, 8pl)	Bowen-Merrill	1901	Fisher, Harrison	40-65	
Mathews, Joanna H.	Belle's Pink Boots (1st, AEG, green/gilt, 16cp)	Dutton	1881	Waugh, Ida	180-280	
Mathis, Sharon B.	Brooklyn Story (1st [1st bk.] {std}, sm8vo, 56p, b/w)	NY: Hill & Wang	1970	Bible, Charles	60-90	
Matsuno, Masako	Chie and the Sports Day (1st AM {std}, ob8vo, [28]p, color, DJ/3.00)	World	(1965)	Mizumura, Kazue	70-100	
Matsuno, Masako	Pair of Red Clogs (1st {std}, lg ob8vo, [28]p, color, DJ/3.00)	World	(1960)	Mizumura, Kazue	80-125	
Matsuno, Masako	Taro and the Tofu (1st AM {std}, sm4to, [26]p, fp color, DJ/3.00)	World	(1962)	Mizumura, Kazue	70-120	*
Matsutani, Miyoko	Crane Maiden (1st, 4to, [32]p, color, DJ/3.50)	Parents Mag. Pr.	(1968)	Iwasaki, Chihiro	25-40	
Matsutani, Miyoko	Fisherman Under the Sea (1st, 4to, 32p, color, DJ/3.50)	Parents Mag. Pr.	(1969)	Iwasaki, Chihiro	25-40	
Matthews, Brander	Poems of American Patriotism (1st, lg8vo, 222p, p-o, 14cp, pep, SC)	Scribner	1922	Wyeth, N.C.	250-350	
Matthews, Harry B.	Happy Day Fair (folio, ibds, color)	McLoughlin	(1908)	Matthews, Harry B.	200-320	
Matzdorff, Hyde	Limpy: Tale of a Monkey Hero (1st, 8vo, 87p, fp b/w, DJ/2.50)	John Day	(1957)	Wiese, Kurt	30-45	
Maud, Constance E.	Wagner's Heroes (1st, 8vo, 284p, black/silver, 8pl)	L: E. Arnold	1895	Fell, H. Granville	55-80	
Maugham, W. Somerset	Princess September (1st {std}, 8vo, [38]p, 2-color, DJ)	Harcourt	(1969)	Ayer, Jacqueline	30-50	
Maugham, W. Somerset	Princess September & Nightingale (1st, sm4to, [31]p, color, pep, DJ/2.50)	Oxford U. Pr.	(1939)	Jones, Richard	60-90	
Maunder, Irene	Plain Princess (1st, 4to, 95p, brown cl, 14pl, dep)	L: Longmans	1905	Taylor/Baxter	100-160	
Maunder, Irene	Songs of Happy Children (12mo, 110p, teg, b/w)	L: Clark	[1908]	Robinson, Charles	60-90	
Maurois, Andre	Battle of France (1st {std}, 8vo, 210p, 8 fp b/w, DJ)	L: John Lane	1940	Ardizzone, Edward	45-70	
Maurois, Andre	Country of 36000 Wishes (1st AM, 4to, ibds, 66p, 11cp, pep)	Appleton	1930	Segur, Adrienne	100-185	R
Maurois, Andre	Fatapoufs & Thinifers (1st, 4to, pep, blue cl, 92p, color, DJ/2.00)	Henry Holt & Co.	(1940)	Bruller, Jean	60-100	
Maurois, Andre	Fattypuffs & Thinifers (1st AM {std}, sm4to, 87p, b/w, DJ/3.95)	Knopf	(1969)	Wegner, Fritz	40-65	
Maurois, Andre	Frederic Chopin (1st {std}, 8vo, 91p, 13 fp color, pep, DJ/1.75)	Harper	(1942)	Shinn, Everett	50-80	
Maury, Jean W.	Old Raven's World (1st, 8vo, 281p, col frn, 6pl, pep)	Little/Brown	1931	Kutcher, Ben	20-35	
Mauzey, Merritt	Cotton Farm Boy (1st, 4to, 79p, fp b/w, cep, DJ/2.50)	H. Schuman	(1953)	Mauzey, Merritt	35-50	
Mauzey, Merritt	Salt Boy (1st, 4to, 60p, fp b/w, DJ/3.00)	Abelard-Schuman	(1963)	Mauzey, Merritt	25-45	*
Mavor, William	English Spelling Book (1st, 12mo, grey bds, 108p, b/w)	L: Routledge	1885	Greenaway, Kate	180-260	
Max, Peter	Peter Max Land of Blue (1st, 4to, ibds, [32]p, color, pep)	F. Watts	(1970)	Max, Peter	60-100	
Max, Peter	Peter Max Land of Red (1st, 4to, ibds, [32]p, color, pep)	F. Watts	(1970)	Max, Peter	60-100	
Max, Peter	Peter Max Land of Yellow (1st, 4to, [31]p, ibds, color, pep)	F. Watts	1970	Max, Peter	60-100	
Maxwell, Donald	Excursions in Color (1st, lg8vo, blue/gilt, 118p, 89 illus)	L: Cassell	1927	Maxwell, Donald	90-160	
Maxwell, Donald	New Lights O'London (1st, lg8vo, 158p, blue/gilt, color)	L: H. Jenkins	1926	Maxwell, Donald	70-100	
Maxwell, Donald	Wembley in Colour (1st, 4to, bds, 112p, 37cp)	L: Longmans	1924	Maxwell, Donald	75-100	
Maxwell, G.S.	Just Beyond London (1st, 8vo, 280p, 18pl)	L: Methuen	1927	Maxwell, Donald	50-80	
Maxwell, William	Heavenly Tenants (1st, 8vo, blue cl, 56p, 1-color, pep, DJ/2.00, NH)	Harper	(1946)	Karasz, Ilonka	120-200	R
May, Charles P.	Box Turtle Lives in Armor (1st, sm8vo, 42p, 2-color, cep, DJ/2.50)	Holiday House	(1960)	Castle, Jane	25-40	*

AUTHOR	TITLE	PUBLISHER	DATE	ARTIST	PRICE	LC
May, Charles P.	High-Noon Rocket (1st, ob8vo, [39]p, fp 1-color, DJ/2.95)	Holiday House	(1966)	Turkle, Brinton	30-50	
May, Elizabeth	Flower Babies (1st, 4to, [100]p, ibds, fp color)	Saalfield	(1905)	Rockwell, Ida M.	250-350	
May, Julian	Before the Indians (1st, 4to, [40]p, color, DJ/3.95)	Holiday House	(1969)	Shimin, Symeon	30-45	
May, Julian	First Living Things (1st, 4to, [40]p, color, DJ/4.50)	Holiday House	(1970)	Berelson, Howard	25-40	
May, Julian	First Men (1st, sq8vo, [48]p, b/w, DJ/3.95)	Holiday House	(1968)	Bjorklund, Lorence	20-35	
May, Julian	Horses, how They Came to Be (1st, sq8vo, [36]p, color, DJ/3.75)	Holiday House	(1968)	Bjorklund, Lorence	20-35	
May, Julian	Why Birds Migrate (1st, ob8vo, [36]p, color, DJ/4.95)	Holiday House	(1970)	Reneson, Chet	20-35	
May, Robert	Benny the Bunny Liked Beans (1st {std}, 8vo, [25]p, ibds, color, DJ/0.50)	Knopf	(1940)	Hubbell, Harriet	30-50	
Mayakovsky, Vladimir	Timothy's Horse (1st ob4to, [29]p, fp color, cep, DJ, NYTBI)	Pantheon	(1970)	Constantini, Flavio	60-90	*
Maybank, Thomas	Mirth by Maybank (1st, ob4to, ibds, b/w)	L: Ward Lock	(1937)	Maybank, Thomas	80-120	
Mayberry, Genevieve	Eskimo of Little Diomede (1st, 8vo, 31p, color, DJ/1.50)	Follett	(1961)	Mars, Witold T.	25-40	
Mayer, Henry	Adventures of a Japanese Doll (1st, ob4to, 127p, ibds, 30cp)	L: Richards	1901	Mayer, Henry	500-700	
Mayer, Henry	In Laughland (1st, folio, [58]p)	R.H. Russell	1899	Mayer, Henry	350-500	
Mayer, Henry	Trip to Toyland (lg ob4to, ibds, 127p, 30 fp color)	L: Richards	1900	Mayer, Henry	250-350	
Mayer, Mercer	Boy, a Dog, and a Frog (1st {std}, 32mo, [32]p, ibds, DJ/1.95)	Dial Press	(1967)	Mayer, Mercer	25-40	
Mayer, Mercer	Frog, Where are You? (1st {std}, 32mo, [32]p, ibds, DJ/2.50)	Dial Press	(1969)	Mayer, Mercer	25-40	
Mayer, Mercer	Special Trick (1st {std}, sq8vo, 33p, color, pep, DJ/4.50)	Dial Press	(1970)	Mayer, Mercer	50-85	
Mayer, Mercer	There's a Nightmare in My Closet (1st {std}, 4to, [30]p, 2-col, cep DJ/3.50)	Dial Press	(1968)	Mayer, Mercer	50-85	
Mayne, William	Blue Boat (1st AM {std}, 8vo, 173p, b/w, DJ/2.95)	Dutton	1960	Spence, Geraldine	50-80	
Mayne, William	Chorister's Cake (1st, 8vo, 160p, b/w, DJ)	L: Oxford U.Pr.	1956	Hodges, C. Walter	60-90	
Mayne, William	Day Without Wind (1st AM, sm4to, 59p, fp 1-color, DJ/3.50)	Dutton	(1964)	Gill, Margery	30-45	*
Mayne, William	Glass Ball (1st AM {std}, sm4to, 63p, fp 1-color, DJ/2.95)	Dutton	(1962)	Duchesne, Janet	20-35	
Mayne, William	Grass Rope (1st {std}, 8vo, 166p, b/w, DJ, CgM)	L: Oxford U.Pr.	1957	Lamb, Lynton	40-65	
Mayne, William	Old Zion (1st AM {std}, sm4to, 64p, 1-color, DJ/3.95)	Dutton	(1967)	Gill, Margery	25-40	
Mayne, William	Plot Night (1st AM {std}, 8vo, 126p, b/w, DJ)	Dutton	(1968)	Duchesne, Janet	25-40	*
Mayne, William	Ravensgill (1st AM {std}, 8vo, 174p, DJ/4.25 by...)	Dutton	(1970)	Gorey, Edward	30-45	
Mayne, William	Rolling Season (1st, 8vo, 175p, bds, b/w, DJ)	L: Oxford U.Pr.	1960	Brooker, Christopher	30-45	
Mayne, William	Swarm in May (1st, 8vo, 199p, b/w, pep, DJ)	L: Oxford U.Pr.	1955	Hodges, C. Walter	80-130	
Mayne, William	The Changeling (1st AM {std}, 8vo, 153p, b/w, DJ/3.00)	Dutton	(1963)	Ambrus, Victor	45-70	
Mayne, William	Underground Alley (1st {std}, 8vo, 168p, b/w, DJ)	L: Oxford U.Pr.	1958	Foster, Marcia L.	40-65	
Mayne, William	Whistling Rufus (1st AM {std}, 8vo, 120p, b/w, DJ/3.00)	Dutton	(1965)	Briggs, Raymond	25-40	
Mayne, William	William Mayne's Book of Giants (1st AM {std}, 8vo, 215p, b/w, DJ/4.95)	Dutton	(1969)	Briggs, Raymond	30-50	*
Mayol, Lurline B.	Jiji Lou (1st, sm4to, p-o, 142p, blue cl, 8 fp color, dep)	Saalfield	1928	Peat, Fern B.	50-80	
Mayol, Lurline B.	Story of a Happy Doll (4to, ibds, 142p, 1cp)	Saalfield	1928	Peat, Fern B.	40-60	
Mazer, Sonia	Yossele's Holiday & Brave Maccabees (1st {std}, sm4to, ibds, 60p, b/w, pep)	Doubleday/Doran	1934	Mazer, Sonia	50-85	*
McBride, Mary M.	How Dear to My Heart (1st {std}, 8vo, 196p, b/w, DJ/2.00)	Macmillan	1940	Hader, Elmer	30-50	
McCabe, Olivia	Rose Fairies (1st, lg8vo, 159p, p-o, green cl, 12cp, pep)	Rand/McNally	(1911)	Dunlap, Hope	120-170	
McCall, Sidney	Truth Dexter (1st, 8vo, 375p, blue cloth, frn by...)	Little/Brown	1903	Smith, Jessie W.	35-60	
McCann, Rebecca	Children's Cheerful Cherub (1st, 12mo, ibds, [63]p, color, pep)	Covici Friede	(1932)	McCann, Rebecca	45-65	
McCarter, Margaret	Corner Stone (1st, 8vo, 100p, wraps, col frn, b/w, pep)	McClurg	1915	St. John, J. Allen	40-65	
McCleery, William	Wolf Story (1st {std}, 12mo, 82p, red cl, p-o, col frn, DJ/2.00)	Knopf	1947	Chappell, Warren	60-100	R
McClelland, Hugh	Magic Lasso (1st, lg8vo, DJ)	St. Martin's	(1963)	McClelland, Hugh	30-45	
McClintock, Marshall	Fly Went By (1st {std}, 8vo, ibds, 62p, color, pep, DJ/1.95)	Beginner Books	(1958)	Siebel, Fritz	60-100	
McClintock, Marshall	Story of New England (1st {std}, 4to, ibds, 39p, color, pep, DJ/1.50)	Harper	1941	DeWitt, C.H.	60-100	
McClintock, Marshall	Story of the Mississippi (1st {std}, 4to, ibds, 39p, color, pep, DJ/1.50)	Harper	1941	DeWitt, C.H.	50-80	
McClintock, Marshall	What Have I Got? (1st, 8vo, ibds, 32p, fp color, DJ/1.50)	Harper	(1961)	Kessler, Leonard	50-80	
McCloskey, Robert	Blueberries for Sal (1st, ob4to, 54p, fp 1-color, DJ/2.00, CH)	Viking	1948	McCloskey, Robert	140-200	
McCloskey, Robert	Burt Dow, Deep-Water Man (1st, lg4to, 63p, green cl, color, DJ/4.00)	Viking	(1963)	McCloskey, Robert	100-165	
McCloskey, Robert	Centerburg Tales (1st, 8vo, 190p, fp 1-color, DJ/2.50)	Viking	1951	McCloskey, Robert	80-120	
McCloskey, Robert	Homer Price (1st, lg8vo, 149p, blue cloth, sepia, DJ/2.00)	Viking	1943	McCloskey, Robert	120-180	R
McCloskey, Robert	Lentil (1st {1st bk.}, lg4to, beige cl, fp b/w, [61]p, pep, DJ/2.00)	Viking	1940	McCloskey, Robert	140-225	R
McCloskey, Robert	Make Way for Ducklings (1st, lg4to, [70]p, 1-color, pep, DJ/2.00, CM)	Viking	1941	McCloskey, Robert	200-300	R
McCloskey, Robert	One Morning in Maine (1st, lg4to, 64p, grey cl, pep, DJ/2.50, CH)	Viking	1952	McCloskey, Robert	250-350	
McCloskey, Robert	Time of Wonder (1st, lg4to, 63p, blue cl, color, DJ/3.50, CM)	Viking	(1957)	McCloskey, Robert	250-350	R
McConnell, Margaret	Bobo the Barrage Balloon (1st, lg8vo, 36p, ipcb, 1-color, pep, DJ/1.50)	Lothrop, Lee	1943	Gergely, Tibor	40-65	
McCool, Henry C.	Old Farm Fairies (1st, 8vo, 392p, woodcuts)	L: Hodder	1895	Various	70-100	*
McCord, David	Every Time I Climb a Tree (1st {std}, 4to, [48]p, color, cep, DJ/3.95)	Little/Brown	(1967)	Simont, Marc	60-90	R*
McCord, David	Far and Few (1st {std}, 8vo, 99p, gilt, b/w, DJ/2.50)	Little/Brown	(1952)	Kane, Henry B.	30-50	
McCord, David	For Me to Say (1st {std}, 8vo, 100p, b/w, DJ/4.50)	Little/Brown	(1970)	Kane, Henry B.	20-30	
McCord, David	Take Sky (1st {std}, 8vo, 107p, fp b/w, DJ/3.50)	Little/Brown	(1962)	Kane, Henry B.	50-80	R
McCoy, Neely	Jupie the Wise Old Owl (1st, 8vo, 95p, 3cp, pep)	Macmillan	1931	McCoy, Neely	25-45	
McCracken, Harold	Biggest Bear on Earth (1st, sm4to, 114p, col frn, 6pl, cep, DJ/2.00)	Stokes	(1943)	Bransom, Paul	40-65	
McCracken, Harold	Flaming Bear (1st {std}, 8vo, 222p, b/w, DJ/2.50)	Lippincott	(1951)	Bransom, Paul	40-65	*
McCracken, Harold	Last of the Sea Otters (1st, sm4to, 99p, col frn, fp b/w, pep, DJ/2.00)	Stokes	1942	Bransom, Paul	40-65	
McCracken, Harold	Son of the Walrus King (1st {std}, sm4to, 128p, col frn, DJ/2.50)	Lippincott	(1944)	Hunt, Lynn B.	40-65	
McCracken, Harold	Winning of the West (1st {std}, lg4to, ibds, 64p, color, DJ/2.00)	Garden City	1955	Ames, Lee	30-50	
McCracken, Russell	Gentle Giraffe (1st {std}, sm4to, ibds, 31p, color, DJ/1.00)	Rand/McNally	(1945)	Suba, Susanne	45-70	
McCracken, Russell	Mystery of Carmen the Cow (1st, sm4to, ibds, 31p, 3-color, DJ/1.00)	Rand/McNally	1946	Suba, Susanne	45-70	
McCrea, James & Ruth	King's Procession (1st {std}, lg ob8vo, [30]p, color, DJ/3.25)	Atheneum	1963	McCrea, J.& R.	30-50	
McCrea, James & Ruth	Magic Tree (1st {std}, lg sq8vo, [30]p, 2-color, DJ)	Atheneum	1965	McCrea, J.& R.	40-65	R
McCready, Thomas L.	Adventures of a Beagle (1st, 8vo, [48]p, fp color, pep, DJ/2.75)	Ariel	(1959)	Tudor, Tasha	200-300	
McCready, Thomas L.	Biggity Bantam (1st, sq8vo, yellow cl, 49p, color, cep, DJ/2.50)	Ariel	(1954)	Tudor, Tasha	140-220	
McCready, Thomas L.	Increase Rabbit (1st, sq8vo, yellow cl, unpag, color, pep, DJ/2.75)	Ariel	(1958)	Tudor, Tasha	300-500	
McCready, Thomas L.	Mr. Stubbs (1st, sm8vo, 48p, red cl, color, pep, DJ/2.50)	Ariel	(1956)	Tudor, Tasha	180-240	
McCready, Thomas L.	Pekin White (1st, sm8vo, green cl, 49p, color, pep, DJ/2.50)	Ariel	(1955)	Tudor, Tasha	300-500	
McCullough, John	At Our House (1st, sm4to, [41]p, ibds, 1-color, DJ/1.25)	W.R. Scott	1943	Duvoisin, Roger	30-50	
McCullough, John	Dark is Dark (1st, lg8vo, [34]p, ibds, color, cep, DJ/1.50)	W.R. Scott	1947	Shaw, Charles G.	30-50	
McCullough, John	Good Work! What Will You be when You Grow Up? (1st, 4to, [40]p, color)	W.R. Scott	1948	Ipcar, Dahlov	30-45	*

AUTHOR	TITLE	PUBLISHER	DATE	ARTIST	PRICE	LC
McCutcheon, George B.	Beverly of Graustark (1st, 8vo, blue cl, 357p, 5cp)	Dodd	1904	Fisher, Harrison	25-40	
McCutcheon, George B.	Butterfly Man (1st, sm8vo, teg, 121p, lavender cl, 4cp)	Dodd	1910	Fisher, Harrison	25-40	
McCutcheon, George B.	Cowardice Court (1st, 12mo, 140p, p-o, 5cp)	Dodd	1906	Fisher, Harrison	40-65	
McCutcheon, George B.	Daughter of Anderson Crow (1st, 8vo, 346p, col frn, 14pl)	Dodd	1907	Justice, B. Martin	30-50	
McCutcheon, George B.	Day of the Dog (1st, 8vo, red/gilt, 137p, 5cp, pep)	Dodd	1904	Fisher, Harrison	40-60	
McCutcheon, George B.	Husbands of Edith (1st, 12mo, 126p, 5cp)	Dodd	1908	Fisher, Harrison	30-50	
McCutcheon, George B.	Jane Cable (1st, sm8vo, 336p, p-o, 5cp)	Dodd	1906	Fisher, Harrison	25-45	
McCutcheon, George B.	Man from Brodneys (1st, 8vo, p-o, 355p, 4cp)	Dodd	1908	Fisher, Harrison	25-45	
McCutcheon, George B.	Nedra (1st, sm8vo, 343p, p-o, 5cp)	Dodd	1905	Fisher, Harrison	25-45	
McCutcheon, George B.	Purple Parasol (1st, 8vo, green/gilt, 108p, 5cp)	Dodd	1905	Fisher, Harrison	40-70	
McCutcheon, George B.	The Alternative (1st, 8vo, teg, p-o, 119p, 4cp, pep)	Dodd	1909	Fisher, Harrison	30-50	
McCutcheon, George B.	The Sherrods (1st, sm8vo, 343p, cvr by...)	Dodd	1903	Armstrong, Margaret	30-50	
McCutcheon, George B.	What's His Name? (1st, 12mo, 243p, 4cp)	Dodd	1911	Fisher, Harrison	30-50	
McCutcheon, John T.	Congressman Pumphrey (1st, 8vo, 126p, b/w)	Bobbs-Merrill	(1907)	McCutcheon, J.T.	25-40	*
McDevitt, Jean	Mr. Apple's Family (1st {std}, 8vo, 118p, fp color, DJ/2.00)	Doubleday	1950	Ninon	25-45	*
McDevitt, Jean	No, No, Taffy (1st {std}, ob4to, ibds, 47p, 2-color, DJ/2.50)	Doubleday	1952	Gag, Flavia	45-70	*
McDonald, Lucile S.	Sheker's Lucky Piece (1st, 8vo, 79p, fp color, pep, DJ/1.75)	Oxford U. Pr.	(1941)	Yap, Weda	40-65	
McDougall, Walter	Rambillicus Book (1st, lg8vo, 239p, 20pl)	Jacobs	(1903)	McDougall, Walter	80-130	*
McElhone, Helen K.	Secrets of the Elves (1st, sq 12mo, green cloth, p-o, color)	Devin-Adair	1913	Wheelan, A.R.	140-220	
McElhone, Helen K.	Surprise Book (1st, lg ob4to, yellow cl, 33pl)	Stokes	1901	Wheelan, A.R.	140-220	
McElrath, Frances	The Rustler (1st, 8vo, 425p, 7pl)	Funk/Wagnalls	1902	Deming, Edwin W.	60-90	
McElravy, May F.	Tortilla Girl (1st, sm4to, 26p, p-o, 46p, pep, color, DJ/1.25)	Whitman	1946	Bannon, Laura	40-65	
McElroy, Margaret	Adventures of Johnny T. Bear (1st, 12mo, 105p, color, pep)	Dutton	(1926)	Daugherty, James	40-65	
McEvoy, Joseph P.	Bam Bam Clock (1st, sq12mo, ibds, [38]p, color, pep)	Volland	(1920)	Gruelle, Johnny	100-165	
McEvoy, Joseph P.	Slams of Life... (1st, sm4to, 127p, uncut, 10 p b/w, cep)	Volland	(1919)	King, Frank	75-100	*
McEwen, Catherine	Away We Go! (1st {std}, 8vo, 111p, color, pep, DJ/2.50)	Crowell	(1956)	Cooney, Barbara	60-100	*
McFarlane, Arthur E.	Great Bear Island (1st, sm8vo, 290p, 8pl)	Houghton	1911	Fogarty, Thomas	30-50	
McGaw, Jessie B.	How Medicine Man Cured Paleface Women (1st, ob4to, [62]p, 1-col, DJ/2.75)	W.R. Scott	(1956)	McGaw, Jessie B.	40-60	*
McGinley, Phyllis	All Around the Town (1st {std}, sm4to, ibds, [63]p, fp color, DJ/2.00, CH)	Lippincott	(1948)	Stone, Helen	80-140	
McGinley, Phyllis	Blunderbus (1st {std}, sm4to, 47p, yellow cl, 1-color, DJ/2.00)	Lippincott	(1951)	Wiesner, William	35-60	*
McGinley, Phyllis	Girl and her Room (1st {std}, ob4to, [38]p, fp 1-color, dep, DJ/2.95)	F. Watts	1963	Forberg, Ati	30-50	*
McGinley, Phyllis	Horse Who had Picture in Paper (1st {std}, sm4to, 48p, color, DJ/2.00)	Lippincott	(1951)	Stone, Helen	40-65	*
McGinley, Phyllis	Horse Who Lived Upstairs (1st {std}, sm4to, [48]p, color, DJ/2.00)	Lippincott	(1944)	Stone, Helen	45-70	
McGinley, Phyllis	Lucy McLockett (1st, sm4to, [32]p, color, DJ/3.00)	Lippincott	(1959)	Stone, Helen	60-90	
McGinley, Phyllis	Merry Christmas, Happy New Year (1st, 8vo, bds, 48p, 3-color, DJ/2.50)	Viking	(1958)	Karasz, Ilonka	30-50	
McGinley, Phyllis	Mince Pie and Mistletoe (1st, 8vo, [32]p, fp 2-color, DJ/2.95)	Lippincott	(1961)	Berson, Harold	25-45	
McGinley, Phyllis	Most Wonderful Doll in the World (1st, 8vo, 61p, color, cep, DJ/1.75, CH)	Lippincott	(1950)	Stone, Helen	60-90	
McGinley, Phyllis	Name for Kitty (1st {A}, sm8vo, ibds, [28]p, color, LGB/#55)	Simon/Schuster	(1948)	Rojankovsky, Feodor	20-35	
McGinley, Phyllis	On the Contrary (1st {std}, sm8vo, 119p, gilt, b/w)	Doubleday/Doran	1934	McGinley, Phyllis	30-50	*
McGinley, Phyllis	Plain Princess (1st {std}, 8vo, gilt, 62p, color, DJ/1.50)	Lippincott	(1945)	Stone, Helen	30-50	
McGinley, Phyllis	Short Walk from the Station (1st, 8vo, 175p, b/w, DJ/2.75)	Viking	1951	Macdonald, Roberta	30-50	
McGinley, Phyllis	The B Book (1st {std}, 4to, ibds, [64]p, b/w, cep)	Crowell-Collier	(1962)	Jones, Robert	60-100	
McGinley, Phyllis	Wonderful Time (1st {std}, 4to, 47p, b/w, DJ/3.50, NYTBI)	Lippincott	(1966)	Alcorn, John	30-45	
McGinley, Phyllis	Wreath of Christmas Legends (1st {std}, ob8vo, 62p, ibds, b/w, DJ/3.95)	Macmillan	(1967)	Weisgard, Leonard	30-45	
McGinley, Phyllis	Year Without a Santa Claus (1st, sm4to, tan cl, [32]p, color, cep, DJ/3.00)	Lippincott	1957	Werth, Kurt	30-50	
McGovern, Ann	Black is Beautiful (1st, ob8vo, [40]p, fp b/w, cep, DJ/3.50)	Four Winds Pr.	(1969)	(Photos)	80-120	
McGovern, Ann	If You Grew Up with Abraham Lincoln (1st, ob8vo, 79p, color, pep, DJ/2.95)	Four Winds Pr.	(1966)	Turkle, Brinton	30-50	
McGovern, Ann	If You Lived in Colonial Times (1st, ob8vo, 79p, color, pep, DJ/2.95)	Four Winds Pr.	(1966)	Turkle, Brinton	30-50	
McGovern, Ann	Too Much Noise (1st, sm ob4to, 44p, fp 3-color, cep, DJ/3.25)	Houghton	1967	Taback, Simms	30-50	
McGovern, Ann	Zoo, Where Are You? (1st, 4to, [20]p, color, pep, DJ/3.50)	Harper, Row	1964	Keats, Ezra J.	30-50	
McGovern, Mary H.	Fifty Famous Fairy Tales (1st, 8vo, 254p, 7cp)	Whitman	(1917)	Lee, Ella D.	60-100	*
McGowen, Tom	Apple Strudel Soldier (1st {std}, 4to, 48p, fp color, DJ/3.95)	Follett	(1968)	Johnson, John	30-50	
McGowen, Tom	Biggest Toot in Toozelburg (1st, 8vo, [30]p, fp 3-color, DJ/4.95)	Reilly/Lee	(1970)	Appleyard, Dev	50-80	
McGowen, Tom	Dragon Stew (1st {A & std}, 8vo, 31p, color, DJ/1.95)	Follett	(1969)	Hyman, Trina S.	100-165	
McGowen, Tom	Hammet and the Highlanders (1st {std}, 8vo, 47p, b/w, DJ/3.50)	Follett	(1970)	Stone, David	40-65	*
McGowen, Tom	Sir Machinery (1st {std}, 8vo, 155p, fp b/w, DJ)	Follett	(1970)	Hyman, Trina S.	140-200	
McGraw, Eloise J.	Golden Goblet (1st, 8vo, 248p, DJ/3.50, NH)	Coward	(1961)	No Illustrations	40-65	
McGraw, Eloise J.	Mara (1st, 8vo, 279p, DJ/3.00)	Coward	(1953)	No Illustrations	50-80	
McGraw, Eloise J.	Merry Go Round in Oz (1st, lg8vo, 303p, fp b/w, pep, DJ/3.95)	Reilly/Lee	(1963)	Martin, Dick	350-500	
McGraw, Eloise J.	Moccasin Trail (1st, 8vo, 247p, DJ/2.75, NH, b/w frn by...)	Coward	1952	Galdone, Paul	30-50	
McGraw, Eloise J.	Sawdust in his Shoes (1st, 8vo, 264p, col frn, b/w, pep, DJ/2.50)	Coward	(1950)	Crowell, Pers	200-300	
McGregor, Dion	Dream World of Dion McGregor (1st, 8vo, ibds, 213p, fp b/w, DJ/3.95)	Bernard Geis	(1964)	Gorey, Edward	60-100	
McHargue, Georgess	Baker & the Basilisk (1st {std}, ob4to, 31p, color, DJ/4.50)	Bobbs-Merrill	(1970)	Quackenbush, Rbt.	25-40	
McIlvaine, Jane	Cammie's Challenge (1st {std}, 8vo, 244p, b/w, DJ/3.50)	Bobbs-Merrill	(1962)	Dennis, Wesley	25-40	
McIlwraith, Jean N.	Curious Career of Roderick Campbell (1st, sm8vo, 287p, 4pl)	Houghton	1901	Schoonover, Frank	25-45	
McIntyre, John T.	In the Rockies with Kit Carson (1st, sm8vo, p-o, 220p, b/w)	Penn	1913	Boyer, Ralph L.	30-50	
McKay (ed.)	Tale of the Cauldron (1st, ob8vo, 64p, ibds, 16cp)	MacLeod	1927	Browne, Gordon	70-100	
McKee, David	Elmer, Story of a Patchwork Elephant (1st, lg8vo, [45]p, color, DJ/4.50)	McGraw-Hill	(1968)	McKee, David	25-45	
McKelvey, Gertrude	Stories to Live By (1st, 12mo, 62p, b/w, cep, DJ/0.75)	Winston	(1943)	Doane, Pelagie	20-35	
McKenna, Dolores	Adventures of a Wee Mouse (1st, 8vo, ipcb, [30]p, p-o, 6cp, pep)	Stokes/Saalfield	(1921)	Bennett, Ruth H.	30-50	
McKenna, Dolores	Adventures of the Bunny-Boys (16mo, green bds, 42p, p-o, 6cp, pep)	Stokes/Saalfield	(1921)	Bennett, Ruth H.	40-65	
McKenney, John	Tackroom Tattles (1st, 8vo, 230p, beige cl, fp b/w, cep)	Scribner	1934	Brown, Paul	60-100	
McKim, Audrey	Andy and the Gopher (1st {std}, 8vo, 119p, b/w, DJ/2.75)	Little/Brown	(1959)	Solbert, Ronni	20-30	
McKinley, Charles	Harriett (1st, sm4to, 44p, 1-color, pep, DJ/2.00)	Viking	1946	DuBois, W.P.	80-130	R
McKown, Gretchen	All the Days Were Antonia's (1st, 8vo, 268p, fp b/w, pep, DJ/2.00)	Viking	1939	Gay, Zhenya	40-65	
McKown, Robin	Boy Who Woke Up in Madagascar (1st, 8vo, 221p, fp b/w, DJ)	Putnam	(1967)	Quackenbush, Rbt.	25-35	
McKown, Robin	Rakoto & the Drongo Bird (1st, 4to, 52p, fp color, cep, DJ/3.95)	Lothrop, Lee	(1966)	Quackenbush, Rbt.	25-40	*
McKown, Wendell	Me an' Pete (1st {std}, sm8vo, 88p, b/w pl)	Doubleday/Doran	1934	Wiese, Kurt	25-40	

AUTHOR	TITLE	PUBLISHER	DATE	ARTIST	PRICE	LC
McLeod, Emilie	One Snail and Me (1st {std}, sm ob4to, 32p, color, DJ/2.95)	Little/Brown	1961	Lorraine, Walter	30-50	
McLeod, Emilie	Seven Remarkable Bears (1st, sq8vo, 46p, blue cl, fp 2-col, pep, DJ/2.50)	Houghton	1954	Kepes, Juliet A.	45-70	
McMahon, Jo	Deenie Folks and Friends of Theirs (1st, 8vo, ibds, unpag, color, pep)	Volland	(1925)	Gee, John	70-100	
McManus, Blanche	Bachelor Ballads (1st, 8vo, beige cl, 159p, color)	New Amsterdam	1898	McManus, Blanche	60-90	
McManus, Blanche	Calendar of Omar Khayaam (4to, ibds, dep, color)	L.C. Page	1904	McManus, Blanche	80-120	*
McManus, Blanche	Little Dutch Cousin (1st, 12mo, 99p, 6pl)	L.C. Page	1906	McManus, Blanche	25-45	*
McManus, Blanche	Little French Cousin (1st, sm8vo, 116p, 6pl)	L.C. Page	1905	McManus, Blanche	25-45	*
McManus, Blanche	Little Hindu Cousin (1st, sm8vo, 103p, 6pl)	L.C. Page	1907	McManus, Blanche	25-45	*
McManus, Blanche	Little Scotish Cousin (1st, sm8vo, 95p, 6pl)	L.C. Page	1906	McManus, Blanche	25-45	*
McMeekin, Isabel	Journey Cake (1st, 8vo, 231p, b/w, DJ/2.00)	J. Messner	1942	Panesis, Nicholas	25-45	*
McNagny, Bob	Noah's Nightmare (1st, 4to, p-o, [67]p, 30cp)	Bobbs-Merrill	(1926)	McNagny, Bob	65-100	
McNamara, John F.	Playing Airplane (1st, ob8vo, 128p, col frn, b/w, pep)	Macmillan	1930	Unknown	60-90	
McNeely, Marian H.	Jumping-Off Place (1st {std}, sm8vo, 308p, b/w, pep, NH)	Longmans	1929	Siegel, William	55-80	*
McNeely, Marian H.	Rusty Ruston (1st {std}, 12mo, green cl, 293p, col frn, 5pl, dep)	Longmans	1928	Burns, Eloise	50-85	*
McNeely, Marian H.	Way to Glory (1st {std}, 8vo, 240p, b/w)	Longmans	1932	Esley, Joan	35-60	*
McNeely, Marian H.	Winning Out (1st {std}, 12mo, 308p, b/w)	Longmans	1931	Price, Hattie L.	35-60	*
McNeer, May	Alaska Gold Rush (1st {std}, 8vo, 186p, 1-color, pep, DJ/1.95)	Random	(1960)	Ward, Lynd	25-45	
McNeer, May	America's Abraham Lincoln (1st, lg8vo, 119p, blue cl, fp color, DJ/3.50)	Houghton	1957	Ward, Lynd	50-75	R
McNeer, May	America's Mark Twain (1st, lg8vo, 159p, dp color, DJ/3.75)	Houghton	1962	Ward, Lynd	30-50	
McNeer, May	American Indian Story (1st {std}, 4to, 95p, fp color, pep, DJ/4.25)	Ariel	(1963)	Ward, Lynd	30-50	
McNeer, May	Armed with Courage (1st, lg8vo, 112p, blue/silver, b/w, pep, DJ/2.50)	Abingdon Press	(1957)	Ward, Lynd	40-65	
McNeer, May	California Gold Rush (1st {std}, 8vo, 184p, 2-color, pep, DJ/1.50)	Random	1950	Ward, Lynd	25-40	
McNeer, May	Canadian Story (1st {std}, 4to, 96p, fp color, pep, DJ/4.25)	Ariel	(1958)	Ward, Lynd	30-45	
McNeer, May	Give Me Freedom (1st, lg8vo, 128p, fp b/w, DJ/3.00)	Abingdon Press	(1964)	Ward, Lynd	30-45	
McNeer, May	Gold Rush (1st, 8vo, ibds, 31p, color, pep, DJ/0.50)	Grosset/Dunlap	(1944)	Ward, Lynd	40-65	
McNeer, May	Golden Flash (1st, 8vo, 227p, pep, color, DJ/3.00)	Viking	1947	Ward, Lynd	30-50	
McNeer, May	John Wesley (1st, lg8vo, 96p, fp color, pep, DJ/2.50)	Abingdon Press	1951	Ward, Lynd	30-50	
McNeer, May	Little Baptiste (1st, lg8vo, [50]p, 1-color, DJ/2.50)	Houghton	1954	Ward, Lynd	30-45	
McNeer, May	Martin Luther (1st, lg8vo, 95p, rust cl, pep, color, DJ/2.50)	Abingdon Press	(1953)	Ward, Lynd	55-80	R
McNeer, May	Mexican Story (1st {std}, 4to, 96p, fp color, pep, DJ/3.95)	Ariel	(1953)	Ward, Lynd	40-65	R
McNeer, May	My Friend Mac (1st, lg8vo, 78p, 1-color, DJ/2.75)	Houghton	1960	Ward, Lynd	30-50	
McNeer, May	Prince Bantam (1st, lg8vo, 229p, aqua cl, col frn, 15 fp b/w)	Macmillan	1929	Ward, Lynd	40-60	
McNeer, May	Stop Tim! (1st, ob8vo, ibds, [39]p, 2-color, pep)	Farrar/Rinehart	1930	Ward, Lynd	55-80	
McNeer, May	Story of California (1st {std}, 4to, [32]p, ibds, color, pep, DJ/1.50)	Harper	1944	DeWitt, C.H.	60-90	
McNeer, May	Story of the Great Plains (1st {std}, 4to, ibds, 32p, color, pep, DJ/1.50)	Harper	(1943)	DeWitt, C.H.	35-50	
McNeer, May	Story of the South-West (1st, sq4to, ibds, [32]p, color, pep, DJ/1.75)	Harper	(1948)	DeWitt, C.H.	60-90	
McNeer, May	Tales from the Crescent Moon (1st, lg8vo, 306p, blue/silver, 6cp, DJ)	Farrar/Rinehart	(1930)	Lederer, Charlotte	40-60	
McNeer, May	Tinka Minka & Linka (1st, 8vo, 30p, yellow cl, cep, fp color)	Knopf	1931	Lederer, Charlotte	50-85	
McNeer, May	Up a Crooked River (1st, 8vo, 222p, b/w, pep, DJ/2.50)	Viking	1952	Ward, Lynd	25-45	
McNeer, May	Waif Maid (1st, 8vo, p-o, 212p, col frn, woodcuts, cep)	Macmillan	1930	Ward, Lynd	40-60	
McNeer, May	Wolf of Lambs Lane (1st {std}, lg8vo, 64p, 2-color, DJ/3.50)	Houghton	1967	Ward, Lynd	30-50	
McNeil, Everett	Dickon Bend-The-Bow (1st, lg8vo, 126p, fp color, pep)	Saalfield	1903	Wagner, Rob	80-130	
McNeil, Everett	Lost Treasure Cave (1st, 8vo, tan cl, 352p, 8pl)	Dutton	1905	Cary, William M.	35-60	
McNeil, Everett	With Kit Carson in the Rockies (1st, 8vo, 333p, 5pl)	Dutton	(1909)	Hutchinson	30-50	
McNeil, Marion	Blue Elephant and the Pink Pig (1st, 4to, [40]p, ibds, color, pep)	Saalfield	(1931)	Francoise	120-180	
McNeil, Marion	Children Across the Sea (1st, ob folio, wraps, unpag, color)	Saalfield	1931	Scott, Janet L.	150-225	
McNeil, Marion	Little Green Cart (1st, 4to, ibds, [38]p, color, pep)	Saalfield	(1931)	Francoise	45-60	
McNeil, Marion	Round the Mulberry Bush (1st, 4to, ibds, 32p, 8cp)	Saalfield	1933	Peat, Fern B.	60-100	
McNeill, James	Double Knights (1st, 8vo, 128p, fp b/w, DJ/3.50)	H.Z. Walck	1964	Dimson, Theo	30-50	
McNulty, Faith	When a Boy Goes to Bed at Night (1st, 4to, [32]p, 2-color, pep, DJ/3.00)	Knopf	(1963)	Weisgard, Leonard	30-50	
McNulty, Faith	When a Boy Wakes Up in the Morning (1st, 4to, [32]p, 2-color, dep, DJ/2.95)	Knopf	(1962)	Weisgard, Leonard	30-45	
McNulty, Faith	Wholly Cats (1st {std}, 8vo, 208p, b/w, DJ/3.50)	Bobbs-Merrill	(1962)	Bacon, Peggy	25-40	
McSpadden, J.W.	Robin Hood & his Merry Outlaws (1st, 8vo, green cl, 320p, teg, 12cp)	Crowell	(1923)	Stewart, Allan	40-60	*
McSpadden, J.W.	Robin Hood & his Merry Outlaws (1st {std}, 8vo, 285p, color, DJ/1.25, RC)	World	1946	Slobodkin, Louis	55-80	*
McSpadden, J.W.	Stories From Wagner (8vo, [new ed.], 282p, cvr by...)	Crowell	(1914)	Armstrong, Margaret	35-60	
McVickar, H.W.	Evolution of Woman (1st, sm4to, [94]p, teg, uncut, 1-color)	Harper	1896	McVickar, H.W.	40-65	
Meade, Julian R.	Peter by the Sea (1st {std}, 8vo, 146p, b/w, pep, DJ/1.50)	Doubleday/Doran	1940	Paull, Grace	35-45	
Meade, Julian R.	Teeny & the Tall Man (1st {std}, 8vo, 155p, col frn, b/w, pep, DJ/2.00)	Doubleday/Doran	1936	Paull, Grace	25-40	
Meade, L.T.	Band of Mirth (8vo, 320p, 4cp)	L: Chambers	(1917)	Attwell, Mabel L.	60-90	
Meade, L.T.	Bunch of Cousins (1st, 8vo, 220p, 4pl, cep)	L: Chambers	1911	Cowham, Hilda	50-80	*
Meade, L.T.	Daddy's Girl (1st, 8vo, 340p, blue cl, teg, b/w)	L: G. Newnes	1901	Browne, Gordon	30-50	*
Meader, Stephen W.	Away to Sea (1st, 8vo, 233p, 9pl, DJ/2.50)	Harcourt	(1931)	Balmer, Clinton	70-120	
Meader, Stephen W.	Bat: Story of a Bull Terrier (1st, 8vo, 273p, b/w pl, DJ/2.00)	Harcourt	(1939)	Shenton, Edward	80-140	
Meader, Stephen W.	Behind the Ranges (1st {std}, 8vo, 222p, b/w, pep, DJ/2.50)	Harcourt	(1947)	Shenton, Edward	120-185	
Meader, Stephen W.	Black Buccaneer (1st, lg8vo, black/gilt, 269p, 8cp, pep)	Harcourt	(1920)	Schaeffer, Mead	70-100	
Meader, Stephen W.	Blow for Liberty (1st {std}, 8vo, 187p, tan cl, pep, DJ/3.50)	Harcourt	(1965)	Mays, Victor	85-130	
Meader, Stephen W.	Blueberry Mountain (1st, 8vo, 309p, b/w pl, pep, DJ/2.00)	Harcourt	(1941)	Shenton, Edward	100-165	
Meader, Stephen W.	Boy with a Pack (1st, 8vo, 297p, brown cl, b/w, pep, DJ/2.00, NH)	Harcourt	(1939)	Shenton, Edward	100-170	
Meader, Stephen W.	Buckboard Stranger (1st, 8vo, 213p, b/w, DJ/2.75)	Harcourt	(1954)	Shenton, Edward	100-160	
Meader, Stephen W.	Buffalo and Beaver (1st {std}, 8vo, 189p, b/w, DJ/2.95)	Harcourt	(1960)	Beck, Charles	100-160	
Meader, Stephen W.	Bulldozer (1st {std}, 8vo, 239p, b/w, DJ/2.50)	Harcourt	(1951)	Schmidt, Edwin	130-175	
Meader, Stephen W.	Cape May Packet (1st {std}, 8vo, 218p, tan cl, DJ/4.50)	Harcourt	(1969)	Frankenberg, Rbt.	70-125	
Meader, Stephen W.	Cedar's Boy (1st {std}, 8vo, 234p, b/w, DJ/2.50)	Harcourt	(1949)	Townsend, Lee	70-120	
Meader, Stephen W.	Clear for Action! (1st, 8vo, 323p, fp b/w, pep, DJ/2.00)	Harcourt	(1940)	Beaudouin, Frank	120-165	
Meader, Stephen W.	Commodore's Cup (1st {std}, 8vo, 222p, b/w, pep, DJ/2.50)	Harcourt	(1958)	Sibley, Don	100-165	
Meader, Stephen W.	Down the Big River (1st, sm8vo, 270p, b/w pl, DJ)	Harcourt	(1924)	Meader, Stephen	120-165	
Meader, Stephen W.	Everglades Adventure (1st {std}, 8vo, 192p, b/w, DJ/2.75)	Harcourt	(1957)	Beck, Charles	100-170	
Meader, Stephen W.	Fish Hawk's Nest (1st {std}, 8vo, 236p, b/w, pep, DJ/2.50)	Harcourt	(1952)	Shenton, Edward	100-170	

AUTHOR: 146

AUTHOR	TITLE	PUBLISHER	DATE	ARTIST	PRICE	LC
Meader, Stephen W.	Guns for the Saratoga (1st {std}, 8vo, 207p, b/w, DJ/2.75)	Harcourt	(1955)	Cosgrave, John O.	100-170	
Meader, Stephen W.	Jonathan Goes West (1st {std}, 8vo, 241p, b/w, DJ/2.25)	Harcourt	(1946)	Shenton, Edward	120-185	
Meader, Stephen W.	Keep 'Em Rolling (1st {std}, 8vo, 192p, b/w, DJ/3.50)	Harcourt	(1967)	Savitt, Al	80-120	
Meader, Stephen W.	King of the Hills (1st, 8vo, 250p, b/w, DJ/2.00)	Harcourt	(1933)	Townsend, Lee	120-180	
Meader, Stephen W.	Lonesome End (1st {std}, 8vo, 190p, b/w, DJ/3.50)	Harcourt	(1968)	Butterfield, Ned	80-120	
Meader, Stephen W.	Long Trains Roll (1st, 8vo, 259p, black cl, b/w, DJ/2.00)	Harcourt	(1944)	Shenton, Edward	80-120	
Meader, Stephen W.	Longshanks (1st, 12mo, 243p, b/w pl)	Harcourt	(1928)	Caswell, Edward	70-100	
Meader, Stephen W.	Lumberjack (1st, 8vo, 277p, b/w pl, pep, DJ/2.00)	Harcourt	(1934)	Pitz, Henry C.	80-135	
Meader, Stephen W.	Muddy Road to Glory (1st {std}, 8vo, 190p, b/w, DJ/3.50)	Harcourt	(1963)	Hughes, George	80-125	
Meader, Stephen W.	Phantom of the Blockade (1st {std}, 8vo, 190p, red cl, b/w, DJ/3.25)	Harcourt	(1962)	Mays, Victor	70-100	
Meader, Stephen W.	Red Horse Hill (1st {std}, 8vo, 244p, b/w pl, pep)	Harcourt	(1930)	Townsend, Lee	70-100	
Meader, Stephen W.	River of the Wolves (1st {std}, 8vo, 248p, b/w, DJ/2.50)	Harcourt	(1948)	Shenton, Edward	80-120	
Meader, Stephen W.	Sabre Pilot (1st {std}, 8vo, 173p, b/w, DJ/2.75)	Harcourt	(1956)	Polgreen, John	70-120	
Meader, Stephen W.	Sea Snake (1st, 8vo, 255p, b/w, pep, DJ/2.00)	Harcourt	(1943)	Shenton, Edward	80-135	
Meader, Stephen W.	Shadow in the Pines (1st, 8vo, 281p, b/w, pep, DJ/2.00)	Harcourt	(1942)	Shenton, Edward	80-135	
Meader, Stephen W.	Skippy's Family (1st {std}, 8vo, 153p, b/w, DJ/2.00)	Harcourt	(1945)	Korn, Elizabeth	80-140	
Meader, Stephen W.	Snow on Blueberry Mountain (1st {std}, 8vo, 189p, b/w, DJ/3.25)	Harcourt	(1961)	Sibley, Don	80-125	
Meader, Stephen W.	Sparkplug of the Hornets (1st {std}, 8vo, 245p, b/w, DJ/2.75)	Harcourt	(1953)	Sibley, Don	80-120	
Meader, Stephen W.	Stranger on Big Hickory (1st {std}, 8vo, 186p, b/w, DJ/3.50)	Harcourt	(1964)	Lambo, Don	70-100	
Meader, Stephen W.	T-Model Tommy (1st, 8vo, 305p, b/w pl, DJ/2.00)	Harcourt	(1938)	Shenton, Edward	120-180	
Meader, Stephen W.	Topsail Island Treasure (1st {std}, 8vo, 189p, b/w, DJ/3.50)	Harcourt	(1966)	Brown, Marbury	120-185	
Meader, Stephen W.	Voyage of the Javelin (1st {std}, 8vo, 189p, b/w, DJ/2.95)	Harcourt	(1959)	Cosgrave, John O.	100-165	
Meader, Stephen W.	Whaler 'Round the Horn (1st {std}, 8vo, 244p, b/w, pep, DJ/2.50)	Harcourt	(1950)	Shenton, Edward	80-120	
Meader, Stephen W.	Who Rides in the Dark? (1st, sm8vo, 281p, b/w, pep, DJ/2.00)	Harcourt	(1937)	MacDonald, James	80-130	
Meader, Stephen W.	Wild Pony Island (1st {std}, 8vo, 192p, b/w, DJ/2.95)	Harcourt	(1959)	Beck, Charles	100-170	
Meader, Stephen W.	Will to Win and other Stories (1st, 8vo, 300p, b/w, DJ/2.00)	Harcourt	1936	Gincano, John	120-185	
Meadowcroft, Enid	Abraham Lincoln (1st, lg8vo, 191p, fp b/w, DJ/2.00)	Crowell	(1942)	Wiese, Kurt	30-45	
Meadowcroft, Enid	Adventures of Peter Whiffen (1st, 8vo, 148p, b/w, pep, DJ/1.50)	Crowell	(1936)	Bennetts, Beatrice	20-35	
Meadowcroft, Enid	Along the Erie Towpath (1st, 8vo, 227p, fp color, pep, DJ/2.00)	Crowell	(1940)	Ninon	30-50	
Meadowcroft, Enid	By Secret Railway (1st, 8vo, 275p, b/w, pep, DJ/3.00)	Crowell	(1948)	Pitz, Henry C.	30-50	
Meadowcroft, Enid	First Year (1st [new ed.], 8vo, 153p, b/w, pep, DJ/2.00)	Crowell	(1946)	Paull, Grace	20-30	*
Meadowcroft, Enid	Scarab for Luck: Story of Ancient Egypt (1st, 8vo, 229p, fp b/w, DJ/3.75)	Crowell	(1964)	Weisgard, Leonard	30-45	
Means, Florence C.	Across the Fruited Plain (1st, sm8vo, 113p, fp b/w, cep, DJ/1.00)	Friendship Pr.	(1940)	Smalley, Janet	30-50	
Means, Florence C.	Alicia (1st, 8vo, 266p, b/w, DJ/2.75)	Houghton	1953	Barss, William	20-30	
Means, Florence C.	Assorted Sisters (1st, 8vo, 250p, 4 fp 2-color, DJ/2.50)	Houghton	1947	Blair, Helen	30-50	
Means, Florence C.	At the End of Nowhere (1st, 8vo, 232p, white cl, 12pl, DJ/2.00)	Houghton	1940	Hendrickson, David	30-50	*
Means, Florence C.	Borrowed Brother (1st, 8vo, blue cl, 239p, b/w, DJ/3.00)	Houghton	1958	Morse, Dorothy B.	30-50	
Means, Florence C.	Bowlful of Stars (1st, 8vo, green cl, 247p, b/w, pep)	Houghton	1934	Pitz, Henry C.	30-50	*
Means, Florence C.	Candle in the Mist (1st, sm8vo, 252p, blue cl, pep, 4pl)	Houghton	1931	DeAngeli, Marguerite	40-65	
Means, Florence C.	Carver's George (1st, 8vo, 176p, b/w, DJ/2.50)	Houghton	1952	Stein, Harve	25-40	
Means, Florence C.	Dusky Day: A College Story (1st, 8vo, 271p, b/w, pep)	Houghton	1933	Lee, Manning De V.	25-40	
Means, Florence C.	Emmy & the Blue Door (1st, 8vo, yellow cl, 217p, b/w, DJ/3.00)	Houghton	1959	Nicholas, Frank	25-45	
Means, Florence C.	Great Day in the Morning (1st, 8vo, red cl, 182p, 6cp, pep, DJ/2.00)	Houghton	1946	Blair, Helen	30-50	
Means, Florence C.	Hetty of the Grande Deluxe (1st, 8vo, grey cl, 188p, 8cp, pep, DJ/2.50)	Houghton	1951	Blair, Helen	30-50	
Means, Florence C.	House Under the Hill (1st, 8vo, 184p, 8 fp 1-color, pep, DJ/2.50)	Houghton	1949	Blair, Helen	30-50	
Means, Florence C.	Knock at the Door, Emmy (1st, 8vo, 240p, tan cl, b/w, DJ/2.75)	Houghton	1956	Lantz, Paul	30-50	
Means, Florence C.	Moved-Outers (1st, 12mo, 154p, orange cl, 5cp, pep, DJ/2.00, NH)	Houghton	1945	Blair, Helen	80-140	
Means, Florence C.	Penny for Luck: Story of the Rockies (1st, 8vo, 232p, fp b/w, DJ/2.00)	Houghton	1935	Quinn, Paul	30-45	
Means, Florence C.	Peter of the Mesa (1st, sm8vo, p-o, 120p, fp b/w, DJ/1.00)	Friendship Pr.	(1944)	Smalley, Janet	25-45	
Means, Florence C.	Rains Will Come (1st, 8vo, 241p, green cl, b/w, DJ/2.50)	Houghton	1954	Kabotie, Fred	30-60	
Means, Florence C.	Ranch and Ring (1st, sm8vo, tan cl, 260p, fp b/w, pep)	Houghton	1932	Peck, Henry J.	25-45	
Means, Florence C.	Shadow Over Wide Ruin (1st, 8vo, 227p, 6 fp 1-color, pep, DJ/2.00)	Houghton	1942	Bjorklund, Lorence	25-45	
Means, Florence C.	Shuttered Windows (1st, 8vo, 206p, 8pl, DJ/2.00)	Houghton	1938	Sperry, Armstrong	45-60	
Means, Florence C.	Silver Fleece (1st {std}, 8vo, 213p, b/w, cep, DJ/2.50)	Winston	(1950)	Schmidt, Edwin	20-35	
Means, Florence C.	Singing Wood: College Story (1st, 8vo, 241p, b/w, DJ/2.00)	Houghton	1937	Lee, Manning De V.	50-80	*
Means, Florence C.	Tangled Waters (1st, 8vo, 212p, col frn, DJ/2.00)	Houghton	1936	Stoops, Herbert M.	25-45	
Means, Florence C.	Whispering Girl (1st, 8vo, 225p, col frn, pep, DJ/2.00)	Houghton	1941	Howard, Oscar	20-35	
Means, Philip A.	Tupak of the Incas (1st, lg8vo, 136p, b/w, DJ/2.00)	Scribner	1942	Herget, H.M.	30-45	*
Medary, Marjorie	Joan & the Three Deer (1st {std}, 8vo, 160p, b/w, DJ/2.00)	Random	(1939)	Wiese, Kurt	30-50	
Medary, Marjorie	Topgallant: A Herring Gull (1st {std}, 8vo, 159p, p-o, pep, b/w, DJ/1.75)	Smith/Haas	(1935)	Ward, Lynd	50-85	
Mee, John	Three Little Frogs (1st, 8vo, ibds, color, pep)	Volland	(1924)	Rae, John	60-90	
Meeker, Col. S.P.	Pierre of the Big Top (1st, 8vo, 208p, DJ/3.00)	Dodd	1956	Wiese, Kurt	40-65	
Meeks, Esther	Jeff and Mr. James' Pond (1st, 8vo, [35]p, color, DJ/2.95)	Lothrop, Lee	(1962)	Galdone, Paul	30-45	*
Mehdevi, Alexander	Bungling Pedro & other Majorcan Tales (1st {std}, 8vo, 117p, b/w, DJ/4.50)	Knopf	(1970)	Bodor, Isabel	20-35	
Meigs, Cornelia L.	Call of the Mountain (1st {std}, 8vo, 258p, 9 fp 1-color, DJ/2.00)	Little/Brown	1940	Daugherty, James	30-55	
Meigs, Cornelia L.	Clearing Weather (1st, 8vo, blue cl, 312p, 3cp, pep, NH)	Little/Brown	1928	Dobias, Frank	60-90	
Meigs, Cornelia L.	Covered Bridge (1st, sq8vo, 145p, blue cl, col frn, b/w, DJ/2.00)	Macmillan	1936	DeAngeli, Marguerite	40-60	
Meigs, Cornelia L.	Crooked Apple Tree (1st, 8vo, 300p, col frn, fp b/w)	Little/Brown	1929	Grose, Helen M.	20-30	
Meigs, Cornelia L.	Dutch Colt (1st {std}, 8vo, 121p, b/w, DJ/2.00)	Macmillan	1952	Hauman, G.& D.	25-40	
Meigs, Cornelia L.	Fair Wind to Virginia (1st {std}, 8vo, blue cl, 198p, b/w, DJ/2.75)	Macmillan	1955	Wonsetler, Jon	30-50	
Meigs, Cornelia L.	Helga and the White Peacock (1st, sm8vo, gilt, 81p, frn by...)	Macmillan	1922	Bigham, Ruth	30-50	
Meigs, Cornelia L.	Invincible Louisa (1st, sm8vo, 260p, red cl, 16pl, NM)	Little/Brown	1933	(Photos)	60-100	R
Meigs, Cornelia L.	Kingdom of the Winding Road (1st, sm8vo, blue cl, 238p, 6cp)	Macmillan	1915	White, Frances	50-80	
Meigs, Cornelia L.	Master Simon's Garden (1st, 8vo, 320p, blue cl, col frn, pep)	Macmillan	1929	Rae, John	60-90	R
Meigs, Cornelia L.	Mother Makes Christmas (1st, sq8vo, ibds, [28]p, pep, 14 color, DJ/0.50)	Grosset/Dunlap	1940	Lenski, Lois	70-120	
Meigs, Cornelia L.	Mystery at the Red House (1st {std}, 8vo, 158p, red cl, b/w, DJ/3.00)	Macmillan	1961	MacLean, Robert	25-40	
Meigs, Cornelia L.	New Moon (1st, sm8vo, blue/gilt, 251p, col frn by...)	Macmillan	1924	DeAngeli, Marguerite	35-50	
Meigs, Cornelia L.	Pool of Stars (1st, 8vo, 203p, blue cl, pep, col frn)	Macmillan	1929	Rae, John	25-40	*

AUTHOR	TITLE	PUBLISHER	DATE	ARTIST	PRICE	LC
Meigs, Cornelia L.	Railroad West (1st {std}, sm8vo, 326p, 1-color, pep, DJ/2.00)	Little/Brown	1937	Bencker, Helen	25-45	
Meigs, Cornelia L.	Rain on the Roof (1st, sm8vo, 308p, b/w, dep)	Macmillan	1925	Price, Edith B.	70-100	
Meigs, Cornelia L.	Scarlet Oak (1st, 8vo, 198p, col frn, pep, 8pl, DJ/2.00)	Macmillan	1938	Jones, Eliz. O.	35-60	
Meigs, Cornelia L.	Swift Rivers (1st, 8vo, black cl, p-o, 269p, 6cp, pep, DJ/2.00)	Little/Brown	1937	Hurd, Peter	35-60	*
Meigs, Cornelia L.	Trade Wind (1st, 8vo, 309p, black cl, p-o, 8cp, pep)	Little/Brown	1927	Pitz, Henry C.	30-45	
Meigs, Cornelia L.	Vanished Island (1st {std}, 8vo, 258p, b/w, DJ/2.00)	Macmillan	1941	Bayley, Dorothy	25-40	
Meigs, Cornelia L.	Wild Geese Flying (1st {std}, 8vo, 194p, b/w, DJ/2.75)	Macmillan	1957	Geer, Charles	20-35	
Meigs, Cornelia L.	Willow Whistle (1st, ob8vo, 144p, yellow cl, col frn, 10pl)	Macmillan	1931	Smith, E. Boyd	200-300	R
Meigs, Cornelia L.	Wind in the Chimney (1st, 8vo, 144p, blue cl, col frn, 8pl, cep)	Macmillan	1934	Mansfield, Louise	25-40	
Meigs, Cornelia L.	Windy Hill (1st, sm8vo, 210p, frontis, NH)	Macmillan	1921	Unknown	60-90	
Meigs, Cornelia L.	Wonderful Locomotive (1st, ob8vo, gilt, 104p, 3cp, pep, DJ/2.00)	Macmillan	1928	Hader, B.& E.	80-130	
Melcher, Marguerite	Why Don't You Draw a Dog (1st {std}, 8vo, 28p, fp color, DJ/2.95)	Little/Brown	(1962)	Zemach, Margot	30-50	*
Melville, Herman	Billy Bud, Foretopman (1st, 8vo, 126p, fp b/w, DJ/2.95)	F. Watts	(1968)	Quackenbush, Rbt.	20-30	*
Melville, Herman	Moby Dick (1st, lg8vo, p-o, 540p, black/gilt, teg, 12cp, pep)	Dodd	1922	Schaeffer, Mead	50-85	
Melville, Herman	Moby Dick (1st, 12mo, 822p, black/silver, b/w, DJ)	Random	1930	Kent, Rockwell	350-500	
Melville, Herman	Moby Dick (1st, lg8vo, 414p, black/gilt, p-o, 15cp, pep)	Winston	(1931)	Fischer, Anton O.	35-60	
Melville, Herman	Omoo (1st, lg8vo, teg, 299p, black/gilt, 8cp, pep)	Dodd	1924	Schaeffer, Mead	70-125	
Melville, Herman	Typee (lg8vo, black cl, teg, 283p, 8cp, pep)	Dodd	(1923)	Schaeffer, Mead	60-90	
Memling, Carl	Amazing Advens/Dennis the Menace (1st, 4to, ibds, [62]p, color, pep, DJ/1.95)	Random	(1961)	Holley, Lee	30-50	*
Memling, Carl	I Can Count (1st, folio, ibds, [24]p, fp color, pep)	Golden Press	1963	Rojankovsky, Feodor	40-65	*
Memling, Carl	Little Bear's Mother (1st {std}, 4to, [41]p, 3-color, DJ/2.75)	Ariel	1959	Fern, Gene	30-45	
Memling, Carl	Riddles, Riddles from A to Z (1st {A}, 8vo, [24]p, ibds, color, LGB/#490)	Golden Press	(1962)	Schart, Trina	35-50	
Mencken, H.L.	Christmas Story (1st {std}, sq12mo, [31]p, p-o, pep, color, DJ/1.00)	Knopf	1946	Crawford, Bill	60-90	
Mencken, H.L.	Europe After 8:15 (1st, sm8vo, gilt, 222p, 8pl)	J. Lane	1914	Benton, Thomas H.	100-150	
Mendel, Florence	Little Polish Cousin (1st, 12mo, 147p, 6pl)	L.C. Page	1912	O'Brien, Harriet	30-50	*
Mendes, Catulle	Fairy Spinning Wheel (1st, sq8vo, 146p, 14 fp b/w)	Badger	1898	Peabody, Marion L.	120-170	*
Mendoza, George	Are You my Friend? (1st, 8vo, [31]p, color, DJ/4.95)	Prentice-Hall	(1970)	Bozzo, Frank	25-40	
Mendoza, George	Beastly Alphabet (1st, ob4to, [30]p, color, DJ/3.95)	Grosset/Dunlap	(1969)	Low, Joseph	30-50	
Mendoza, George	Crack in the Wall (1st {std}, lg8vo, 54p, b/w, DJ/3.95)	Dial Press	(1968)	Mayer, Mercer	25-45	
Mendoza, George	Digger Wasp (1st {std}, ob8vo, 48p, b/w, DJ/3.95)	Dial Press	(1969)	Zallinger, Jean	25-40	
Mendoza, George	Flowers & Grasses & Weeds (1st, ob4to, ibds, [33]p, 2-color, dep, DJ/4.50)	Funk/Wagnalls	(1968)	Low, Joseph	20-35	
Mendoza, George	Good Luck Spider (1st {std}, 8vo, 47p, b/w, DJ/3.50)	Doubleday	(1970)	Wilson, Galan	25-40	
Mendoza, George	Gwot! Horribly Funny Hairticklers (1st, 8vo, 37p, fp b/w, DJ/2.95)	Harper	(1967)	Kellogg, Steven	70-120	
Mendoza, George	Herman's Hat (1st {std}, ob4to, [48]p, color, DJ/4.50)	Doubleday	(1969)	Parnall, Peter	30-50	
Mendoza, George	Marcel Marceau Alphabet Book (1st {std}, 4to, [63]p, color, pep, DJ/5.95)	Doubleday	(1970)	(Photos)	40-70	
Mendoza, George	Mist Men (1st {std}, lg8vo, 45p, cep, DJ/3.95, b/w decor by...)	Doubleday	(1970)	Bacon, Paul	25-45	*
Mendoza, George	Piece of String (1st {std}, 4to, 34p, 1-color, pep, DJ/3.50)	Obolensky	(1966)	Koplin, Norma J.	25-45	
Mendoza, George	Practical Man (1st, 12mo, [32]p, b/w, DJ/2.95)	Lothrop, Lee	(1968)	Gobbato, Imero	25-40	
Mendoza, George	Starfish Trilogy (1st {1}, 8vo, bds, 44p, color, cep, DJ)	Funk/Wagnalls	(1969)	Forberg, Ati	25-45	
Mendoza, George	The Gillygoofang (1st, ob4to, ipcb, [32]p, fp color, cep, DJ)	Dial Press	1968	Mayer, Mercer	30-45	
Mendoza, George	The Inspector (1st {std}, ob8vo, [48]p, color, DJ/3.95)	Doubleday	(1970)	Parnall, Peter	30-45	
Mendoza, George	Wart Snake in a Fig Tree (1st {std}, 8vo, ibds, [32]p, color, cep, DJ/3.95)	Dial Press	(1968)	Delessert, Etienne	30-50	
Mendoza, George	World from My Window (1st, 4to, [102]p, color, DJ/4.95)	Hawthorn Books	(1969)	Mendoza, George	20-30	
Menotti, Gian-Carlo	Amahl & Night Visitors (1st, lg8vo, 86p, bds, 17 color, pep, DJ/2.75)	Whittlesey	(1952)	Duvoisin, Roger	50-80	
Menotti, Gian-Carlo	Help, Help, the Golobolinks (1st, sm4to, ibds, [56]p, color, DJ/4.95, NYT)	McGraw-Hill	(1970)	Glaser, Milton	50-80	*
Menotti, Gian-Carlo	Last Savage (1st lg4to, 45p, dp color, b/w, cep, DJ/5.95)	NY Graphic Soc.	(1964)	Montresor, Beni	45-70	
Menpes, Dorothy	World Pictures (1st AM, 8vo, gilt, teg, 332p, color)	R.H. Russell	1902	Menpes, Mortimer	80-120	*
Menpes, Mortimer	Brittany (1st, 8vo, gilt, 254p, teg, 75cp)	L: A&C Black	1912	Menpes, Mortimer	80-120	
Menpes, Mortimer	Japan (1st, lg8vo, 207p, teg, blue/gilt, 75cp)	L: A&C Black	1905	Menpes, Mortimer	80-120	
Menpes, Mortimer	Rembrandt (1st, 4to, 50p, teg, gilt, 16cp)	L: A&C Black	1905	Menpes, Mortimer	90-150	
Menpes, Mortimer	World's Children (1st, 8vo, teg, 246p, blue/gilt, 100cp)	L: A&C Black	1903	Menpes, Mortimer	100-170	
Meredith, George	Jump to Glory Jane (1st, 8vo, ipcb, teg, designs by...)	L: Swan	1892	Housman, Laurence	120-200	
Meredith, Nicolete	King of the Kerry Fair (1st, 8vo, 56p, 1-color woodcuts, DJ/2.50)	Crowell	(1960)	Hogrogian, Nonny	40-65	
Meredith, Owen	Lucille (1st, 8vo, 382p, red/gilt, teg, cvr by...)	Stokes	(1897)	Bradley, Will	70-100	
Meredith, Owen	Lucille (1st, 8vo, teg, 12cp by...)	Stokes	(1897)	Lemaire, Madeleine	70-100	
Merimee, Prosper	Carmen (1st, 4to, 204p, red/gilt, teg, pep, 16cp)	L: Hutchinson	[1916]	Bull, Rene	250-350	
Merimee, Prosper	Carmen (1st AM, 4to, 204p, teg, red/gilt, 16cp, pep)	Hearst	[1916]	Bull, Rene	200-300	
Merington, Marguerite	Captain Lettarblair (1st, 8vo, aqua/gilt, 212p, cvr by...)	Bobbs-Merrill	(1906)	Armstrong, Margaret	35-60	
Meriwether, Lee	Afloat and Ashore on the Mediterranean (1st, sm8vo, brown/gilt, 363p)	Scribner	1892	Armstrong, Margaret	35-60	
Merriam, Eve	Catch a Little Rhyme (1st {std}, lg8vo, 51p, b/w, DJ/3.50)	Atheneum	1966	Gobbato, Imero	20-30	
Merriam, Eve	Epaminondas (1st {std}, 8vo, 32p, fp 1-color, DJ/3.95)	Follett	(1968)	Hyman, Trina S.	150-220	
Merriam, Eve	Finding a Poem (1st {std}, 8vo, 68p, fp b/w, cep, DJ, NYTBI)	Atheneum	1970	Chwast, Seymour	30-45	*
Merriam, Eve	Funny Town (1st {std}, lg4to, 63p, ibds, fp color, cep)	Crowell-Collier	1963	Ness, Evaline	45-70	
Merriam, Eve	Gaggle of Geese (1st, sm4to, yellow cl, [31]p, fp 2-color, pep, DJ)	Knopf	(1960)	Galdone, Paul	50-80	*
Merriam, Eve	It Doesn't Always Have to Rhyme (1st {std}, 8vo, 83p, DJ/3.25)	Atheneum	1964	Spooner, Malcolm	20-30	
Merriam, Eve	Mommies at Work (1st, 4to, [38]p, color, cep, DJ/3.00)	Knopf	(1961)	Montresor, Beni	50-80	R
Merriam, Eve	Story of Ben Franklin (1st, 8vo, 78p, green cl, fp 1-color, DJ)	Four Winds Pr.	(1965)	Turkle, Brinton	40-65	*
Merriam, Eve	There is No Rhyme for Silver (1st {std}, 8vo, 70p, b/w, DJ/3.25)	Atheneum	1962	Schindelman, Joseph	30-45	
Merrill, Jean	Black Sheep (1st, lg8vo, 73p, fp 1-color, cep, DJ/3.95)	Pantheon	(1969)	Solbert, Ronni	25-40	
Merrill, Jean	Blue's Broken Heart (1st, 8vo, [24]p, 1-color, pep, DJ/2.25)	Whittlesey	1960	Solbert, Ronni	25-45	
Merrill, Jean	Boxes (1st, 4to, [32]p, fp 3-color, pep, DJ/2.50)	Coward	(1953)	Solbert, Ronni	30-50	
Merrill, Jean	Elephant Who Liked to Smash Small Cars (1st, ob4to, [32]p, color, DJ/3.50)	Pantheon	(1967)	Solbert, Ronni	60-100	*
Merrill, Jean	Emily Emerson's Moon (1st {std}, 8vo, 32p, 2-color, DJ/2.75)	Little/Brown	(1960)	Solbert, Ronni	25-40	*
Merrill, Jean	Henry, the Hand-Painted Mouse (1st, sm4to, [40]p, ibds, b/w, cep, DJ/1.75)	Coward	(1951)	Solbert, Ronni	30-50	*
Merrill, Jean	Pushcart War (1st, 8vo, 222p, fp b/w, DJ/3.95)	W.R. Scott	(1964)	Solbert, Ronni	40-70	R*
Merrill, Jean	Shan's Lucky Knife (1st, sm4to, [48]p, 2-color, DJ)	W.R. Scott	1960	Solbert, Ronni	30-50	
Merrill, Jean	Superlative Horse (1st, lg8vo, 79p, 1-color, DJ/3.00)	W.R. Scott	(1961)	Solbert, Ronni	25-40	*
Merrill, Jean	The Woover (1st, 8vo, 31p, fp 1-color, cep, DJ/2.00)	Coward	(1952)	Solbert, Ronni	25-40	*

AUTHOR	TITLE	PUBLISHER	DATE	ARTIST	PRICE	LC
Merrill, Jean	Tree House of Jimmy Domino (1st, ob4to, [38]p, 1-color, pep, DJ/2.50)	NY: Oxford U.Pr.	(1955)	Solbert, Ronni	30-45	*
Merrill, Margaret	Bears in My Kitchen (1st, 8vo, 249p, b/w, DJ/3.95)	McGraw-Hill	(1956)	Graboff, Abner	50-80	
Merriman, Henry S.	Dross (1st, 12mo, 54p, teg, cvr by...)	Herbert Stone	1899	Hazenplug, Frank	70-100	
Merriman, Henry S.	Grey Lady (1st, 8vo, blue/gilt, 342p, 12pl)	L: Smith Elder	1897	Rackham, Arthur	250-350	
Merriman, Henry S.	Money Spinner (1st, sm8vo, 242p, gilt, 12pl)	L: Smith Elder	1896	Rackham, Arthur	250-350	
Merritt, Abraham	Moon Pool (1st, sm8vo, 433p, gilt, frn by...)	Putnam	1919	Coll, Joseph C.	100-175	
Merryman, Mildred P.	Bonbon & Bonbonette (1st, 8vo, 96p, p-o, color, pep)	Rand/McNally	1924	Cadie, V. Eliz.	80-130	
Merryman, Mildred P.	Daddy Domino (1st {std}, 8vo, ibds, 6 fp color, pep)	Volland	(1929)	Scott, Janet L.	80-140	
Merryman, Mildred P.	Mr. Wubbles Bubbles (1st, 12mo, spiral bds, [44]p, color)	Saalfield	1936	Cadie, V. Eliz.	60-90	
Merryman, Mildred P.	Quack! Said Jerusha (1st, lg8vo, ibds, [50]p, 1-color, pep)	Sears	(1930)	Phipps, Mary	140-200	
Merwin, Decie	Pink-Tails (1st, 8vo, 103p, 1-color, DJ/2.00)	NY: Oxford U.Pr.	1950	Merwin, Decie	25-45	
Merwin, Samuel	Road Builders (1st, sm8vo, 313p, 10pl, pep)	Macmillan	1905	Masters, F.B.	30-50	
Merwin, Samuel	Silk (1st, 12mo, 266p, red/gilt, pep, col frn by...)	Houghton	1923	Wyeth, N.C.	40-60	
Messer, Clarence J.	Next-Night Stories (1st, 12mo, 261p, 8pl)	Lothrop, Lee	1912	Bridgman, L.J.	30-50	
Metcalf, Suzanne	Annabel (1st [1], 12mo, 231p, grey/gilt, p-o, 6pl)	Reilly/Britton	(1906)	Hall, H. Putnam	600-800	
Metcalf, Suzanne	Annabel (2nd, 8vo, 213p, green cl, 3pl)	Reilly/Britton	(1912)	Nuyttens, Joseph P.	180-270	
Metcalfe, Francis	Side Show Studies (1st, 12mo, 232p, b/w)	Outing	1906	Herford, Oliver	40-65	
Meyer, Ann	Nibby (1st, ob4to, 31p, p-o, 1-color, pep, DJ/2.25)	Coward	(1952)	Wiese, Kurt	50-80	*
Meyer, Edith P.	Tim Chick (1st, sm sq4to, 42p, p-o, color)	Rand/McNally	1932	Ward, Keith	40-60	
Meyer, Franklyn	Me & Caleb (1st {std}, 8vo, 160p, b/w, DJ/3.25)	Follett	(1962)	Smith, Lawrence	140-200	
Meyer, Lucy	Mary North (1st, 8vo, 339p, cvr by...)	Revell	(1903)	Hazenplug, Frank	55-80	*
Meyers, Susan	Cabin on the Fjord (1st {std}, 8vo, 128p, b/w, DJ/3.50)	Doubleday	(1968)	Hyman, Trina S.	25-45	
Meynell, Alice	Flower of the Mind (1st, sm8vo, green/gilt, 348p, cvr by...)	L: Richards	1897	Housman, Laurence	70-100	
Meynell, Alice	The Children (1st, 12mo, gilt, 96p, title page by...)	L: John Lane	1897	Robinson, Charles	80-120	
Michael, A.C.	Artist in Spain (1st, 4to, rust cl, 205p, 26 ticp)	L: Hodder	[1920]	Michael, A.C.	80-125	
Michael, Maurice	German Folk and Fairy Tales (1st AM {std}, 8vo, 189p, fp b/w, DJ/2.75)	Putnam	(1963)	Jauss, Anne M.	30-45	
Michelson, Miriam	Anthony Overman (1st, 8vo, 330p, 5pl)	Doubleday/Page	1906	Clay, John Cecil	25-40	*
Michelson, Miriam	In The Bishop's Carriage (1st, 8vo, red cl, 280p, 6pl)	Bobbs-Merrill	(1904)	Fisher, Harrison	25-40	
Michelson, Miriam	Michael Thwaites's Wife (1st, 8vo, red cl, 402p, 3cp)	Doubleday/Page	1909	Phillips, Coles	25-40	
Miers, Earl S.	Ball of Fire (1st {std}, 8vo, 220p, b/w, DJ/2.50)	World	(1956)	Galdone, Paul	20-30	
Miers, Earl S.	Billy Yank and Johnny Reb (1st, 8vo, 256p, b/w, DJ/3.50)	Rand/McNally	(1959)	Vosburgh, Leonard	25-40	
Miers, Earl S.	Monkey Shines (1st {std}, 8vo, 207p, b/w, DJ/2.50)	World	(1952)	Galdone, Paul	20-30	
Miers, Earl S.	Rainbow Book of American History (1st {std}, 4to, 319p, color, DJ/4.95)	World	(1955)	Daugherty, James	60-90	R
Miers, Earl S.	Touchdown Trouble (1st {std}, 8vo, 221p, b/w, DJ/2.50)	World	(1953)	Galdone, Paul	20-30	
Mighels, Philip V.	Chatwit the Man-Talk Bird (1st, sm8vo, blue cl, 265p, b/w)	Harper	1906	Mighels, Philip W.	30-50	
Mighels, Philip V.	Furnace of Gold (1st, sm8vo, 402p, p-o, 12pl)	D. Fitzgerald	(1910)	Marchand, J.N.	25-40	
Mijatovich, Elodie	Serbian Fairy Tales (1st, 8vo, gilt, 204p, 8cp)	L: Heinemann	(1917)	Stanley, Sidney	80-125	
Mijatovich, Elodie	Serbian Fairy Tales (1st AM, 8vo, black cl, 204p, 8cp, 8pl)	McBride	1918	Stanley, Sidney	75-100	
Mikhalkov, Sergei	Let's Fight (1st AM, lg8vo, [54]p, fp color, cep, DJ/3.50)	Pantheon	(1968)	Foreman, Michael	30-45	
Miles, Betty	Day of Summer (1st, 8vo, [31]p, fp color, cep, DJ)	Knopf	1960	Charlip, Remy	50-80	
Miles, Betty	Day of Winter (1st, 8vo, [32]p, color, cep, DJ/2.75)	Knopf	1961	Charlip, Remy	50-80	
Miles, Betty	What is the World? (1st, 4to, [40]p, fp color, dep, DJ/3.00)	Knopf	(1958)	Charlip, Remy	50-80	
Miles, Miska	Apricot ABC (1st {std}, sq8vo, [32]p, color, DJ)	Little/Brown	(1969)	Parnall, Peter	25-40	
Miles, Miska	Dusty and the Fiddlers (1st {std}, 8vo, 52p, b/w, DJ/2.95)	Little/Brown	(1962)	Blegvad, Erik	25-40	
Miles, Miska	Eddie's Bear (1st {std}, sq8vo, 43p, color, DJ/3.95)	Little/Brown	(1970)	Schoenherr, John	25-40	
Miles, Miska	Fox and the Fire (1st {std}, ob4to, 40p, color, DJ/3.50)	Little/Brown	(1966)	Schoenherr, John	25-40	
Miles, Miska	Gertrude's Pocket (1st {std}, 8vo, 55p, fp b/w, DJ/3.95)	Little/Brown	(1970)	McCully, Emily	25-40	
Miles, Miska	Hoagie's Rifle Gun (1st {std}, 8vo, 40p, fp b/w, DJ/3.50)	Little/Brown	(1970)	Schoenherr, John	25-40	
Miles, Miska	Kickapoo (1st {std}, 8vo, 54p, b/w, DJ/2.75)	Little/Brown	(1961)	Dennis, Wesley	30-45	
Miles, Miska	Mississippi Possum (1st {std}, lg8vo, 41p, 2-color, DJ/3.00)	Little/Brown	(1965)	Schoenherr, John	40-65	
Miles, Miska	Nobody's Cat (1st {std}, ob8vo, 43p, 2-color, DJ/3.75)	Little/Brown	(1969)	Schoenherr, John	30-45	
Miles, Miska	Pieces of Home (1st {std}, 8vo, 60p, b/w, DJ/3.25)	Little/Brown	(1967)	Ambrus, Victor	25-40	
Miles, Miska	Pony in the Schoolhouse (1st {std}, 8vo, 60p, b/w, DJ/2.95)	Little/Brown	(1964)	Blegvad, Erik	20-30	
Miles, Miska	Rabbit Garden (1st {std}, 4to, 40p, b/w, DJ/3.50)	Little/Brown	(1967)	Schoenherr, John	25-40	
Miles, Miska	See a White Horse (1st {std}, 8vo, 38p, b/w, DJ/2.75)	Little/Brown	(1963)	Dennis, Wesley	25-40	
Miles, Miska	Teacher's Pet (1st {std}, lg8vo, 54p, b/w, DJ/3.25)	Little/Brown	(1966)	Lassell, Fen	20-30	
Miles, Miska	Uncle Fonzo's Ford (1st {std}, 8vo, 54p, b/w, DJ/3.25)	Little/Brown	(1968)	Watson, Wendy	20-35	
Milhous, Katherine	Appolonia's Valentine (1st, sm4to, red cl, [32]p, color, DJ/2.00)	Scribner	(1954)	Milhous, Katherine	70-120	R
Milhous, Katherine	Corporal Keeperupper (1st, sm8vo, 62p, ipcb, color, DJ/1.00)	Scribner	1943	Milhous, Katherine	30-50	
Milhous, Katherine	Egg Tree (1st, sm4to, [32]p, aqua cl, color, DJ/2.00, CM)	Scribner	(1950)	Milhous, Katherine	150-250	R
Milhous, Katherine	First Christmas Crib (1st, 12mo, ibds, 47p, fp color, DJ/1.00)	Scribner	1944	Milhous, Katherine	50-90	
Milhous, Katherine	Herodia the Lovely Puppet (1st, 8vo, 193p, red cl, pep, 7cp, DJ/2.00)	Scribner	1942	Milhous, Katherine	60-100	R
Milhous, Katherine	Lovina (1st, lg ob8vo, [48]p, red cl, color, DJ/1.50)	Scribner	(1940)	Milhous, Katherine	50-85	
Milhous, Katherine	Patrick & the Golden Slippers (1st {std}, 4to, [32]p, color, cep, DJ/2.00)	Scribner	1951	Milhous, Katherine	30-50	
Milhous, Katherine	Snow Over Bethlehem (1st, 8vo, 98p, pep, 3 dp color, DJ/2.00)	Scribner	1945	Milhous, Katherine	40-70	
Milhous, Katherine	Through These Arches (1st, ob4to, 96p, fp 2-color, DJ/4.50)	Lippincott	1964	Milhous, Katherine	50-80	R
Milhous, Katherine	With Bells On: A Christmas Story (1st, 4to, [32]p, fp 2-color, DJ/2.00)	Scribner	(1955)	Milhous, Katherine	40-70	R
Milius, Winifred	Here Comes Daddy (1st, lg ob8vo, spiral ipcb, [22]p, color)	W.R. Scott	1944	Milius, Winifred	40-60	*
Millar, H.R.	Dreamland Express (1st AM, ob4to, 56p, ibds, 14cp)	Dodd	(1927)	Millar, H.R.	170-250	
Millay, Edna St. V.	Princess Marries the Page (1st {std}, lg8vo, 50p, bds, col frn)	Harper	1932	Paget-Fredericks, J.	80-140	R
Millen, Muriel	Wild West Bill Rides Home (1st, 8vo, 32p, p-o, fp color, pep, DJ/1.00)	Whitman	1946	Wiese, Kurt	30-50	
Miller, Alice D.	Calderon's Prisoner (1st, 8vo, olive/gilt, 294p, cvr by...)	Scribner	1903	Armstrong, Margaret	40-65	
Miller, Alice D.	Modern Obstacle (1st, sm8vo, 273p, blue/gilt, cvr by...)	Scribner	1903	Armstrong, Margaret	100-165	
Miller, Arthur	Jane's Blanket (1st {std}, 4to, 64p, ibds, fp 1-color, cep)	Crowell-Collier	(1963)	Parker, Al	200-300	
Miller, Diane D.	Story of Walt Disney (1st {std}, 8vo, ibds, 247p, DJ/3.95)	Holt	(1957)	(Photos)	300-500	
Miller, Edna	Mouseskin's Family (1st, lg8vo, [32]p, color, cep, DJ/4.95)	Prentice-Hall	(1969)	Miller, Edna	20-35	
Miller, Edna	Mouseskin's Woodland Sleepers (1st, 8vo, [32]p, color, cep, DJ/4.50)	Prentice-Hall	(1970)	Miller, Edna	20-30	
Miller, Elizabeth	The Yoke (1st, 12mo, 616p, blue/gilt, cvr by...)	Bobbs-Merrill	(1904)	Armstrong, Margaret	35-60	

AUTHOR	TITLE	PUBLISHER	DATE	ARTIST	PRICE	LC
Miller, Elizabeth C.	Children of Mountain Eagle (1st {std}, sm8vo, 328p, 3cp, pep)	Doubleday/Doran	1927	Petershams	35-60	*
Miller, Elizabeth C.	Pran of Albania (1st {std}, 8vo, 257p, col frn, pep, NH)	Doubleday/Doran	1929	Petershams	60-100	
Miller, Elizabeth C.	Young Trajan (1st {std}, 8vo, 232p, black cl, pep, col frn)	Doubleday/Doran	1931	Petershams	30-50	*
Miller, James R.	Glimpses of Heavenly Life (1st, sm8vo, 32p, cvr by...)	Crowell	(1908)	Armstrong, Margaret	35-60	
Miller, Jane	Jimmy the Groceryman (1st, sm8vo, 88p, blue cl, color, pep)	Houghton	(1934)	Hader, B.& E.	70-120	
Miller, Janet	Sammy & Silverband (1st, 8vo, 236p, col frn, 9pl)	Houghton	1931	Berry, Erick	20-35	
Miller, Leo E.	Adrift on the Amazon (1st, 8vo, 263p, olive cl, 4pl)	Scribner	1923	Rogers, W.A.	30-50	*
Miller, Leo E.	Hidden People (1st, 8vo, 321p, 8pl)	Scribner	1920	Bransom, Paul	30-50	*
Miller, Leo E.	In the Tiger's Lair (1st, 8vo, 252p, 4pl)	Scribner	1921	Bransom, Paul	30-50	
Miller, Lisa	Sound (1st, 8vo, [46]p, fp 2-color, DJ/2.95)	Coward	(1965)	DePaola, Tomie	30-45	
Miller, Margaret	Knights, Beasts & Wonder (1st AM, 8vo, 127p, 3-color, DJ/3.95)	NY: David White	(1969)	Keeping, Charles	25-40	
Miller, Mary B.	All Aboard: Poems (1st {std}, 8vo, 47p, 1-color, cep, DJ/2.75, NYTBI)	Pantheon	(1958)	Sokol, Bill	30-50	
Miller, Mary B.	Give a Guess (1st, 8vo, blue cl, [32]p, 1-color, dep, DJ/2.50)	Pantheon	1957	Kepes, Juliet A.	60-100	R*
Miller, Mary B.	Listen -- the Birds (1st, 8vo, 46p, 3-color, DJ/3.00, NYTBI)	Pantheon	(1961)	Ness, Evaline	30-50	
Miller, Mary B.	Menagerie (1st, sq8vo, 124p, col frn, 8pl, pep)	Macmillan	1928	Sewell, Helen	35-60	
Miller, Olive B.	Come Play with Me (1st, sm8vo, ibds, [38]p, color, pep)	Volland	(1918)	Browne, Carmen L.	100-160	*
Miller, Olive B.	Little Pictures of Japan (1st, 4to, 191p, p-o, pep, color)	Book House	(1925)	Sturges, Katharine	50-80	
Miller, Olive B.	Nursery Friends from France (1st, 4to, 190p, gilt, p-o, color, pep)	Book House	(1925)	Petershams	40-65	
Miller, Olive B.	Sunny Rhymes/Happy Children (1st, 8vo, ibds, [40]p, pep, color)	Volland	(1917)	Browne, Carmen L.	60-90	*
Miller, Olive B.	Tales Told in Holland (1st, 4to, 190p, p-o, pep, gilt, color)	Book House	(1926)	Petershams	50-85	
Miller, Olive B.	Whisk Away on a Sunbeam (1st, lg8vo, [93]p, pep, ibds, color)	Volland	(1919)	Enright, Maginel W.	90-150	
Miller, Olive Thorne	Kristy's Rainy Day Picnic (1st, 12mo, 235p, p-o, 4cp, pep)	Houghton	1906	Farnsworth, Ethel	30-50	
Miller, Warren	Goings on at Little Wishful (1st {std}, ob4to, [30]p, 2-col, cep, DJ/2.75)	Little/Brown	(1959)	Sorel, Edward	70-100	R
Miller, Warren	King Carlo of Capri (1st {std}, sm4to, [32]p, 2-color, pep, DJ/2.95)	Harcourt	(1958)	Sorel, Edward	70-100	R
Miller, Warren	Pablo Paints a Picture (1st {std}, ob4to [28]p, 1-color, pep, DJ/2.75, NYT)	Little/Brown	(1959)	Sorel, Edward	60-90	
Miller, Warren H.	Lone Woodsman (1st {std}, 8vo, 230p, col frn, pep, DJ/2.00)	Winston	(1943)	Collins, Kreigh	50-80	*
Mills, Enos A.	Animal Trainer (1st, ob8vo, 31p, p-o, 6cp)	Duffield	1910	Vimar, Auguste	70-100	
Mills, Enos A.	In Beaver World (1st, 8vo, 228p, olive cl, 19pl, pep)	Houghton	1913	(Photos)	70-100	
Mills, Enos A.	Watched by Wild Animals (1st {std}, 8vo, 243p, 4pl by...)	Doubleday/Page	1922	James, Will	50-80	
Mills, Enos A.	Wild Animal Homesteads (1st {std}, 8vo, 259p, b/w pl)	Doubleday/Page	1923	James, Will	60-85	
Mills, Freya	Susan's Surprise (1st, 8vo, [31]p, color, pep, DJ/1.50)	Oxford U. Pr.	1946	Sheldon, Marian	30-45	
Mills, G.R.	Talking Dolls (1st, 4to, [96]p, color, pep)	Greenberg	(1930)	Sarg, Tony	80-130	
Mills, Weymer J.	Caroline of Courtlandt Street (1st, 8vo, 291p, gilt, teg, 6cp)	Harper	1905	Betts, Anna W.	60-80	
Mills, Weymer J.	Girl I Left Behind Me (1st, 4to, 90p, teg, p-o, 11cp, pep)	Dodd	1910	Rae, John	100-175	
Mills, Weymer J.	Through the Gates of Old Romance (1st, sm8vo, 281p, teg, b/w)	Lippincott	1903	Rae, John	30-50	
Mills, Weymer J.	Van Rensselaers of Old Manhattan (1st, 8vo, p-o, 215p, 5cp)	Stokes	(1907)	Rae, John	30-50	
Mills, Winifred H.	Marionettes, Masks & Shadows (1st {std}, lg8vo, 270p, col frn, b/w)	Doubleday/Page	1927	Bell, Corydon	40-60	*
Milne, A.A.	Christopher Robin Birthday Book (1st, 16mo, 215p, orange/gilt, b/w)	L: Methuen	(1930)	Shepard, Ernest H.	300-450	
Milne, A.A.	Christopher Robin Story Book (1st, sm8vo, 171p, blue/gilt, b/w)	L: Methuen	(1929)	Shepard, Ernest H.	300-400	
Milne, A.A.	Christopher Robin Story Book (1st AM, sm8vo, gilt, 171p, b/w)	Dutton	(1929)	Shepard, Ernest H.	250-400	
Milne, A.A.	Christopher Robin Verses (1st, 8vo, 210p, blue/gilt, 12cp)	L: Methuen	(1932)	Shepard, Ernest H.	200-300	
Milne, A.A.	Christopher Robin Verses (1st AM {std}, 8vo, 210p, 12cp)	Dutton	(1932)	Shepard, Ernest H.	140-225	*
Milne, A.A.	Gallery of Children (1st AM, 4to, 105p, p-o, gilt, 12cp)	McKay	(1925)	LeMair, H.W.	120-200	
Milne, A.A.	Gallery of Children (1st, lg4to, p-o, 105p, 12cp)	L: Stan. Paul	(1925)	LeMair, H.W.	200-300	
Milne, A.A.	Gallery of Children (1st AM {this fmt}, 12mo, 125p, b/w, DJ)	McKay	[1939]	Watson, A.H.	65-100	
Milne, A.A.	House at Pooh Corner (1st [1], 12mo, 178p, teg, pink/gilt, b/w, pep)	L: Methuen	(1928)	Shepard, Ernest H.	450-650	
Milne, A.A.	King's Breakfast (1st, lg8vo, bds, 17p, b/w, DJ)	L: Methuen	(1925)	Shepard, Ernest H.	140-200	
Milne, A.A.	Magic Hill (1st {this pub}, 4to, 40p, ibds, 8 fp color, pep)	Grosset/Dunlap	(1937)	Sewell, Helen	90-160	
Milne, A.A.	Now We Are Six (1st, 12mo, 103p, maroon/gilt, teg, b/w, pep)	L: Methuen	(1927)	Shepard, Ernest H.	450-650	
Milne, A.A.	Now We Are Six (1st AM, sm8vo, buckram, 103p, gilt, b/w)	Dutton	(1927)	Shepard, Ernest H.	250-400	
Milne, A.A.	Old Sailor (1st AM, lg8vo, ipcb, [23]p, 1-color, pep, DJ/0.50)	Dutton	(1947)	Shepard, Ernest H.	100-160	*
Milne, A.A.	Once On a Time (1st, 8vo, 316p, blue cl, p-o, col frn, 4pl)	L: Hodder	(1917)	Brock, Henry M.	200-300	
Milne, A.A.	Once On a Time (1st, 12mo, gilt, 269p, col frn, pep)	L: Hodder	[1925]	Robinson, Charles	180-250	
Milne, A.A.	Once On a Time (1st AM, sm8vo, 358p, gilt, col frn, pep)	Putnam	1922	Robinson, Charles	150-225	
Milne, A.A.	Prince Rabbit & Princess Who Could Not Laugh (1st {std} 4to 72p color DJ)	Dutton	(1966)	Shepard, Mary	40-65	
Milne, A.A.	Princess & the Apple Tree (1st, 4to, ibds, 40p, 8 fp color, pep, DJ/1.00)	Grosset/Dunlap	(1937)	Sewell, Helen	80-120	
Milne, A.A.	Sneezles (1st AM, lg sq8vo, ibds, [23]p, 2-color, pep, DJ/0.50)	Dutton	(1947)	Shepard, Ernest H.	80-120	
Milne, A.A.	Teddy Bear & other Songs (1st AM, lg4to, bds, p-o, 43p, b/w)	Dutton	(1926)	Shepard, Ernest H.	140-225	
Milne, A.A.	Teddy Bear & other Songs (1st, lg4to, bds, p-o, 43p, b/w)	L: Methuen	(1926)	Shepard, Ernest H.	130-200	
Milne, A.A.	Very Young Verses (1st, sm8vo, 88p, blue cl, 6pl)	L: Methuen	(1929)	Shepard, Ernest H.	120-180	*
Milne, A.A.	When We Were Very Young (1st AM, 12mo, 100p, red/gilt, b/w, pep)	Dutton	(1924)	Shepard, Ernest H.	350-500	
Milne, A.A.	When We Were Very Young (1st, 12mo, 100p, gilt, AEG, b/w)	L: Methuen	(1924)	Shepard, Ernest H.	500-700	
Milne, A.A.	Winnie-the-Pooh (1st, 12mo, 158p, gilt, teg, b/w, pep)	L: Methuen	(1926)	Shepard, Ernest H.	700-1000	
Milne, A.A.	Winnie-the-Pooh (1st AM, 12mo, 158p, gilt, b/w, pep)	Dutton	(1926)	Shepard, Ernest H.	500-700	
Milne, A.A. (intro)	Fun & Fantasy (1st, lg4to, 87p, ibds, color)	L: Methuen	(1927)	Shepard, Ernest H.	180-270	
Milne, James	Travels in Hope (1st, sm4to, 190p, blue cl, 22ticp)	L: Hodder	[1926]	Maxwell, Donald	100-150	
Milne-Home, M.P.	Mama's Black Nurse Stories (1st, 12mo, 131p, grey/gilt, 6 fp b/w)	L: Blackwood	1890	Milne-Home, M.P.	130-200	
Milton, John	Comus (1st, 12mo, 83p, teg, gilt, 10pl)	L: Routledge	1906	King, Jessie	350-500	
Milton, John	Comus (1st AM, sm4to, teg, green/gilt, 76p, 24 ticp, pep)	Doubleday/Page	[1921]	Rackham, Arthur	200-285	
Miltoun, Francis	Automobilist Abroad (1st, 8vo, 381p, gilt, teg, p-o, col frn, pep)	L.C. Page	1907	McManus, Blanche	70-125	
Miltoun, Francis	Castles & Chateaux of Touraine (1st, 8vo, 347p, teg, gilt, 39pl, pep)	L.C. Page	1906	McManus, Blanche	40-60	
Miltoun, Francis	Rambles on the Riviera (1st, 8vo, teg, 434p, 32pl)	L.C. Page	1906	McManus, Blanche	35-60	
Minarik, Else H.	Cat and Dog (1st, 8vo, ibds, 32p, fp 2-color, DJ/1.50)	Harper	(1960)	Siebel, Fritz	30-50	
Minarik, Else H.	Father Bear Comes Home (1st, 8vo, ibds, 62p, color, DJ/1.95, NYTBI)	Harper	(1959)	Sendak, Maurice	150-220	
Minarik, Else H.	Kiss for Little Bear (1st, 8vo, 32p, ibds, color, DJ/2.50, NYTBI)	Harper	(1968)	Sendak, Maurice	180-260	
Minarik, Else H.	Little Bear (1st, 8vo, 63p, ibds, color, DJ/2.50)	Harper	(1957)	Sendak, Maurice	200-300	R
Minarik, Else H.	Little Bear's Friend (1st, 8vo, 57p, ibds, fp 2-color, DJ/1.95)	Harper	(1960)	Sendak, Maurice	150-220	R
Minarik, Else H.	Little Bear's Visit (1st, 8vo, 64p, ibds, color, DJ/1.95, CH)	Harper	(1961)	Sendak, Maurice	150-220	

AUTHOR	TITLE	PUBLISHER	DATE	ARTIST	PRICE	LC
Minarik, Else H.	Little Giant Girl & Elf Boy (1st, 8vo, [31]p, ibds, color, DJ/2.95)	Harper	1963	Williams, Garth	70-120	
Minarik, Else H.	No Fighting! No Biting! (1st, 8vo, 62p, b/w, DJ/2.50)	Harper	1958	Sendak, Maurice	200-300	
Minarik, Else H.	Winds that Come from Far Away (1st, 8vo, 32p, b/w, DJ/2.50)	Harper	(1964)	Berg, Joan	25-40	
Mincieli, Rose	Harlequin (1st, 4to, 75p, bds, 1-color, DJ)	Knopf	1968	Zemach, Margot	50-80	
Mincieli, Rose	Old Neapolitan Fairy Tales (1st, 4to, 123p, fp b/w, gilt, cep, DJ/3.25)	Knopf	(1963)	Montresor, Beni	40-65	
Mincieli, Rose	Pulcinella (1st {std}, 4to, [34]p, color, DJ/2.95)	Knopf	(1960)	Low, Joseph	30-50	
Minnion, W.J.	Topsy Turvey (1st, 4to, 72p, bds, gilt, 5 fp 2-color)	L: Connoisseur	1913	Robinson, Charles	300-400	
Mirza, Youel B.	Children of the Housetops (1st {std}, sm8vo, 248p, col frn, b/w)	Doubleday/Doran	1931	Dobias, Frank	30-50	
Mirza, Youel B.	Myself when Young (1st {std}, 8vo, 260p, col frn)	Doubleday/Doran	1929	Nadejen, Theodore	40-65	
Mirza, Youel B.	Rug that Went to Mecca (1st, 8vo, red/gilt, 60p, 5 fp b/w, DJ/1.00)	Stokes	1939	Artzybasheff, Boris	50-80	
Mirza, Youel B.	Son of the Sword (1st, 8vo, black cl, 211p, pep, designs by...)	Viking	1934	Artzybasheff, Boris	45-70	
Mirza, Youel B.	Young Tentmaker (1st, 8vo, 192p, b/w, pep, DJ/2.00)	Lothrop, Lee	1935	Jones, Wilfred	25-40	
Misch, Robert J.	At Daddy's Office (1st {std}, sm4to, ibds, [32]p, color, DJ/1.50)	Knopf	(1946)	Duvoisin, Roger	60-95	
Mitchell, Edith	Betty, Bobby & Bubbles (1st, 12mo, ibds, [40]p, pep, color)	Volland	(1921)	Scott, Janet L.	70-100	
Mitchell, Edith	Otherside Book (1st, 4to, ipcb, [36]p, color)	Reilly/Britton	(1915)	Mitchell, Edith	70-120	*
Mitchell, Edmund	Chickabiddy Stories (1st, 8vo, 150p, p-o, 4 ticp)	L: Wells/Gard.	(1899)	Barham, Sybil	100-165	
Mitchell, George W.	Kernel Cob & Little Miss Sweetclover (1st, 8vo, ibds, [96]p, color, pep)	Volland	(1918)	Sarg, Tony	100-160	
Mitchell, George W.	Little Babs (1st, 12mo, unpag, ibds, pep, color)	Volland	(1919)	Henderson, Arthur	80-135	
Mitchell, John A.	Amos Judd (1st, 12mo, teg, 252p, 8cp)	Scribner	1901	Keller, Arthur I.	25-40	
Mitchell, John A.	Drowsy (1st [1], sm8vo, blue/gilt, 301p, 19pl)	Stokes	(1917)	Macdonall, Agnus	35-60	
Mitchell, John A.	Romance of the Moon (1st, ob12mo, [32]p, gilt, 1-color, dep)	Henry Holt & Co.	1886	Mitchell, John A.	60-90	*
Mitchell, Lebbeus	Bobby in Search of/Birthday (1st, 12mo, pcb, 64p, p-o, gilt, b/w)	Volland	1916	Nuyttens, Joseph P.	40-60	
Mitchell, Lucy S.	Guess What's in the Grass (1st, sm ob4to, ibds, [30]p, 2-col, pep, DJ/1.50)	W.R. Scott	1945	Glannon, Edward J.	60-90	
Mitchell, Lucy S.	Red, White & Blue Auto (1st, ob8vo, ibds, [33]p, color, DJ/1.00)	W.R. Scott	1943	Gergely, Tibor	60-100	
Mitchell, Muriel M.	Adventures of Nip & Tuck (1st, 8vo, 40p, pep, ipcb, color)	Volland	(1927)	Ellsworth, Mary	70-125	
Mitchell, S. Weir	Adventures of Francois (1st, 8vo, 321p, orange cl, 15pl)	Century	1898	Castaigne, Andre	40-60	
Mitchell, S. Weir	Mr. Kris Kringle (1st, sm8vo, teg, 105p, 5cp)	Jacobs	1893	DeLand, Clyde O.	120-200	R
Mitchell, S. Weir	Red City (1st, 8vo, 421p, p-o, 10pl)	Century	1908	Keller, Arthur I.	25-40	
Mitchison, Naomi	Rib of the Green Umbrella (1st, 8vo, 160p, b/w, DJ)	L: Collins	1960	Ardizzone, Edward	45-70	
Mitchison, Naomi	The Hostages (1st AM, 8vo, 332p, 16 fp b/w)	Harcourt	(1931)	Southby, Logi	25-40	*
Mitford, Mary R.	Our Village (1st, sm8vo, 256p, AEG, green/gilt, b/w, cep)	L: Macmillan	1893	Thomson, Hugh	60-100	
Mitford, Mary R.	Our Village (1st, lg8vo, green/gilt, 256p, teg, 16 ticp)	L: Macmillan	1910	Rawlings, Alfred	90-120	
Mitton, G.E.	Scenery of London (1st, 8vo, 223p, gilt, teg, 75cp)	L: A&C Black	1905	Marshall, Herbert	120-200	
Mizumura, Kazue	Emperor Penguins (1st, sq4to, 35p, color, DJ/3.50)	Crowell	(1969)	Mizumura, Kazue	50-85	
Mizumura, Kazue	I See the Winds (1st, sm ob8vo, 35p, fp color, DJ)	Crowell	(1966)	Mizumura, Kazue	45-70	
Mizumura, Kazue	If I Were a Mother (1st, 4to, [32]p, color, DJ/3.95)	Crowell	(1968)	Mizumura, Kazue	45-70	
Mizumura, Kazue	Way of an Ant (1st, narrow 4to, [34]p, fp color, DJ/3.95)	Crowell	(1970)	Mizumura, Kazue	30-45	
Mockler, Geraldine	Little Girl from Next Door (1st, 8vo, 160p, 2pl by...)	L: Blackie	1896	Brooke, L. Leslie	60-90	*
Mockler, Geraldine	Spring Fairies & Sea Fairies (1st, sm8vo, 192p, red/gilt, b/w)	L: G. Allen	1897	Benson, Nellie	100-150	
Moe, Louis M.	Kylle Kluk (1st AM, ob4to, [24]p, orange cl, 11 fp color)	NY: Laidlaw	[1931]	Moe, Louis M.	130-225	*
Moe, Louis M.	Peter Kroak (1st AM, ob4to, [17]p, p-o, 8 fp color, cep)	Whitman	1932	Moe, Louis M.	150-220	*
Moe, Louis M.	Vain Pussy Cat (1st, sm ob4to, ipcb, [32]p, b/w, cep)	Coward	(1929)	Moe, Louis M.	125-200	*
Moe, Virginia	Animal Inn (1st, lg8vo, grey cl, 174p, b/w, DJ/2.50)	Houghton	1946	Winter, Milo	25-40	
Moerleim, G.	Trip Around the World (1st, 4to, AEG, red/gilt, 100 chromos)	Burgheim	1880	Unknown	170-240	
Moery, Robert	Kevin (1st {std}, 4to, [32]p, 2-color, DJ/4.75)	Bradbury Press	1970	Keith, Eros	30-45	
Moeschlin, Elsa	Little Boy with Big Apples (1st AM, 4to, ibds, [23]p, color)	Coward	[1932]	Moeschlin, Elsa	90-140	
Moeschlin, Elsa	Red Horse (1st AM, sm4to, ibds, 19p, color, cep, DJ/1.75)	Coward	[1929]	Moeschlin, Elsa	80-120	
Moffat, Alfred	Little Songs of Long Ago (1st, ob4to, 64p, gilt, p-o, 32 fp color)	L: Augener	(1912)	LeMair, H.W.	150-220	
Moffat, Alfred	Our Old Nursery Rhymes (1st, ob4to, 63p, gilt, p-o, 30 fp color)	L: Augener	(1911)	LeMair, H.W.	150-220	
Mohan, Beverly	Punia and the King of the Sharks (1st, 4to, [32]p, color, DJ/2.50)	Follett	(1964)	Bolognese, Don	25-40	
Molarsky, Osmond	Song of the Empty Bottles (1st, lg8vo, [55]p, color, pep, DJ/3.75)	H.Z. Walck	1968	Feelings, Tom	40-65	
Molarsky, Osmond	Where the Good Luck Was (1st, lg8vo, 63p, fp b/w, DJ/4.25)	H.Z. Walck	(1970)	Fetz, Ingrid	30-45	*
Molesworth, Mrs.	Adventures of Herr Baby (1st, lg8vo, red/gilt, 171p, 13pl, dep)	L: Macmillan	1881	Crane, Walter	100-160	
Molesworth, Mrs.	Bewitched Lamp (1st, 12mo, 128p, frn by...)	L: Chambers	1891	Barnes, Robert	40-70	*
Molesworth, Mrs.	Carved Lions (1st, 8vo, 195p, blue cl, 7pl)	Macmillan	1895	Brooke, L. Leslie	80-130	
Molesworth, Mrs.	Children of the Castle (1st, 12mo, 196p, gilt, cep, b/w & cvr by...)	L: Macmillan	1890	Crane, Walter	80-120	
Molesworth, Mrs.	Christmas Child (1st, 12mo, 223p, gilt, 7pl, cep)	L: Macmillan	1880	Crane, Walter	120-200	
Molesworth, Mrs.	Christmas Posy (1st, 12mo, 215p, gilt, cep, b/w, cvr by...)	Macmillan	1888	Crane, Walter	80-120	
Molesworth, Mrs.	Christmas-Tree Land (1st, 12mo, 223p, red/gilt, 8pl)	L: Macmillan	1884	Crane, Walter	120-170	
Molesworth, Mrs.	Cozy Corner Stories (1st, sm4to, ibds, 12 chromos)	L: Nister	(1895)	Bennett, Harriet	120-200	
Molesworth, Mrs.	Cuckoo Clock (12mo, 242p, blue cl, 8pl)	L: Macmillan	1905	Crane, Walter	40-70	
Molesworth, Mrs.	Cuckoo Clock (1st, 8vo, teg, red/gilt, 283p, pep, 8cp)	Lippincott	1914	Kirk, Maria L.	40-60	*
Molesworth, Mrs.	Cuckoo Clock (1st, 8vo, 196p, 16cp, pep)	L: Macmillan	1931	Brock, Charles E.	50-80	
Molesworth, Mrs.	Enchanted Garden: Fairy Stories (1st, 16mo, 221p, teg, b/w)	L: T.F. Unwin	1892	Hennessey, Wm. J.	60-90	
Molesworth, Mrs.	Fairies Afield (1st, 8vo, 252p, gilt, teg, 8pl)	L: Macmillan	1911	Hammond, Gertrude D.	60-100	
Molesworth, Mrs.	Fairies of Sorts (1st, 8vo, gilt, 249p, AEG, 8pl)	L: Macmillan	1908	Hammond, Gertrude D.	100-150	*
Molesworth, Mrs.	February Boys (1st, 8vo, 266p, gilt, 8cp)	L: Chambers	1909	Attwell, Mabel L.	60-100	*
Molesworth, Mrs.	Four Winds Farm (1st, 8vo, blue cl, 180p, 6pl)	L: Macmillan	1886	Crane, Walter	100-170	
Molesworth, Mrs.	Girls & I (1st, 12mo, orange cl, 192p, 7pl, cep)	L: Macmillan	1892	Brooke, L. Leslie	80-120	
Molesworth, Mrs.	Grim House (1st, 8vo, 289p, teg, 6pl)	L: J: Nisbet	1899	Goble, Warwick	80-120	*
Molesworth, Mrs.	Hermy, Story of a Little Girl (1st, sm8vo, 248p, gilt, 17pl)	L: Chambers	1898	Baumer, Lewis	40-65	
Molesworth, Mrs.	House that Grew (1st, 12mo, 206p, orange/gilt, 7pl)	L: Macmillan	1900	Woodward, Alice B.	75-100	
Molesworth, Mrs.	Imogen (1st, 12mo, 272p, gilt, 4pl)	L: Chambers	1892	Bone, Herbert A.	30-50	
Molesworth, Mrs.	Jasper, a Story for Children (1st, 12mo, 236p, red/gilt, 8pl)	L: Macmillan	1906	Hammond, Gertrude D.	30-50	
Molesworth, Mrs.	Little Miss Peggy (1st, 12mo, red cl, 195p, 12pl)	L: Macmillan	1887	Crane, Walter	85-130	
Molesworth, Mrs.	Lucky Ducks (1st, 8vo, 96p, blue/gilt, color, pep)	L: SPCK	[1891]	Morgan, Walter J.	40-70	*
Molesworth, Mrs.	Magic Nuts (1st, 8vo, 194p, orange/gilt, 7pl)	L: Macmillan	1898	Pitman, R.M.M.	55-80	
Molesworth, Mrs.	Mary (1st, 8vo, 180p, gilt, 7pl)	L: Macmillan	1893	Brooke, L. Leslie	75-100	*

AUTHOR	TITLE	PUBLISHER	DATE	ARTIST	PRICE	LC
Molesworth, Mrs.	Miss Mouse & her Boys (1st, 8vo, green/gilt, 198p, 7pl)	L: Macmillan	1897	Brooke, L. Leslie	40-60	
Molesworth, Mrs.	My New Home (1st, 8vo, red cl, 207p, 7 fp b/w & cvr by...)	L: Macmillan	1894	Brooke, L. Leslie	50-80	
Molesworth, Mrs.	Next-Door House (1st, 8vo, 226p, grey/gilt, 6pl)	L: Chambers	1893	Hatherell, William	40-60	*
Molesworth, Mrs.	Nurse Heatherdale's Story (1st, 12mo, 202p, red/gilt, cep, 7pl)	L: Macmillan	1891	Brooke, L. Leslie	70-120	
Molesworth, Mrs.	Old Pincushion (1st AM, 8vo, 271p, brown cl, 8cp)	Dutton	[1910]	Attwell, Mabel L.	50-80	
Molesworth, Mrs.	Old Pincushion (1st, 8vo, 271p, 8cp)	L: Chambers	1910	Attwell, Mabel L.	75-100	*
Molesworth, Mrs.	Olivia (1st, 12mo, 456p, 8pl)	L: Chambers	1895	Barnes, Robert	35-60	
Molesworth, Mrs.	Oriel Window (1st, 8vo, 182p, 7pl)	Macmillan	1896	Brooke, L. Leslie	70-100	
Molesworth, Mrs.	Palace in the Garden (1st, 8vo, 298p, white/gilt, b/w)	L: Hatchard	1887	Bennett, Harriet	75-100	*
Molesworth, Mrs.	Peterkin (1st, sm8vo, 198p, orange/gilt, 8pl)	L: Macmillan	1902	Millar, H.R.	40-60	
Molesworth, Mrs.	Rectory Children (1st, 8vo, gilt, 212p, 7pl)	L: Macmillan	1889	Crane, Walter	70-100	
Molesworth, Mrs.	Rosy (1st, sm8vo, red/gilt, 204p, 8pl, cep)	L: Macmillan	1882	Crane, Walter	90-120	
Molesworth, Mrs.	Ruby Ring (1st, 8vo, 213p, orange cl, 8pl)	L: Macmillan	1904	Pitman, R.M.M.	50-80	
Molesworth, Mrs.	Sheila's Mystery (1st, sm8vo, 198p, 7pl)	L: Macmillan	1895	Brooke, L. Leslie	50-85	*
Molesworth, Mrs.	Stories by Mrs. Molesworth (1st, 4to, p-o, green cl, 353p, 8cp)	Duffield	1922	Cooke, Edna	70-100	
Molesworth, Mrs.	Studies & Stories (1st, 8vo, 256p, gilt, uncut, pep, frn by...)	L: A.D. Innes	1893	Crane, Walter	150-200	
Molesworth, Mrs.	Tales Told in the Twilight (1st, 8vo, 152p, ibds, chromos)	Nister/Dutton	[1911]	Various	70-120	
Molesworth, Mrs.	This & That (1st, 12mo, 212p, orange/gilt, 8pl)	L: Macmillan	1899	Thomson, Hugh	60-80	
Molesworth, Mrs.	Three Witches (1st, 8vo, 278p, blue cl, 14pl)	L: Chambers	1900	Baumer, Lewis	40-60	*
Molesworth, Mrs.	Two Little Waifs (1st, 8vo, gilt, 216p, 7pl)	L: Macmillan	(1883)	Crane, Walter	120-180	
Molesworth, Mrs.	US: An Old Fashioned Story (1st, 8vo, red/gilt, 240p, 7pl)	L: Macmillan	1885	Crane, Walter	80-120	
Molesworth, Olive	Sunny Land Stories (1st, lg8vo, [72]p, ibds, 6cp)	L: Nister	[1907]	Bennett, Harriet	100-150	
Molloy, Anne	Blanche of the Blueberry Barrens (1st, 8vo, 168p, fp b/w, dep, DJ/2.95)	Hastings House	(1959)	Thomson, Arline K.	30-50	
Molloy, Anne	Celia's Lighthouse (1st, 8vo, 248p, fp b/w, DJ/2.50)	Houghton	1949	Koering, Ursula	40-65	*
Molloy, Anne	Decky's Secret (1st, 8vo, 120p, fp color, DJ/2.00)	Houghton	1944	Hauman, G.& D.	25-45	
Molloy, Anne	Lucy's Christmas (1st, lg8vo, 46p, red cl, color, DJ/2.00)	Houghton	1950	Cosgrave, John O.	25-45	
Molloy, Anne	Monkey's Fist (1st, 8vo, 227p, 1-color, DJ/2.50)	Houghton	1953	Tolford, Joshua	30-50	
Molloy, Anne	Shaun and the Boat (1st, lg8vo, 43p, green bds, 3-color, pep, DJ/3.50)	Hastings House	(1965)	Cooney, Barbara	45-70	
Molloy, Anne	Shooting Star Farm (1st, 8vo, 231p, b/w, dep, DJ/2.50)	Houghton	1946	Cooney, Barbara	60-100	
Molloy, Anne	The Pigeoneers (1st, lg8vo, 180p, grey cl, woodcuts, dep, DJ/2.50)	Houghton	1947	Converse, Elizabeth	30-50	
Molloy, Anne	Uncle Andy's Island (1st, 8vo, 243p, b/w, DJ/2.50)	Houghton	1950	Tolford, Joshua	30-45	
Molnar, Ferenc	Blue-Eyed Lady (1st, sm4to, blue cl, 46p, color, pep, DJ/2.00)	Viking	1942	Sewell, Helen	40-60	
Monath, Norman	Songs of the Pogo (1st, 4to, 152p, bds, color, pep, DJ/3.95)	Simon/Schuster	1956	Kelly, Walt	70-100	
Moncrieff, Ascott	Surrey (1st, 8vo, blue/gilt, 252p, teg, 75cp)	L: A&C Black	1906	Palmer, Sutton	80-120	
Monjo, Ferdinand N.	Drinking Gourd (1st, 8vo, 62p, color, DJ/2.50)	Harper	(1970)	Brenner, Fred	30-45	
Monjo, Ferdinand N.	Indian Summer (1st, 8vo, 62p, ibds, color, DJ/2.50)	Harper	(1968)	Lobel, Anita	30-45	
Monjo, Ferdinand N.	One Bad Thing About Father (1st, 8vo, ibds, 62p, fp 2-color, DJ/2.50)	Harper	(1970)	Negri, Rocco	25-40	
Monjo, Ferdinand N.	Pirates in Panama (1st {std}, lg8vo, 59p, fp 1-color, DJ/4.50)	Simon/Schuster	(1970)	Tripp, Wallace	40-65	
Monrad, Jean	How Many Kisses Good Night? (1st, lg ob8vo, ibds, [20]p, color, DJ/1.00)	W.R. Scott	1949	Bloch, Lucienne	30-50	
Monreal, Guy	Teletrips of Alala (1st, sq4to, [36]p, fp color, DJ, NYTBI)	Harlin Quist	1970	Claveloux, Nicole	50-80	
Monro, W.D.	India's Gods & Heroes (1st AM, 8vo, uncut, 237p, 16cp)	Crowell	(1910)	Paul, Evelyn	70-100	
Monroe, Harriet	Columbian Ode (1st, 12mo, 23p, wraps, cvr by...)	Chi: W.I. Way	1893	Bradley, Will	220-350	
Monroe, Harriet	Dance of the Seasons (1st, 8vo, 20p, wraps, cvr & ti page by..)	R.F. Seymour	1911	Bradley, Will	100-170	R
Monsell, Helen	Paddy's Christmas (1st {std}, ob8vo, [48]p, ibds, fp 2-color, DJ/1.00)	Knopf	1942	Wiese, Kurt	40-70	
Monsell, J.R.	Hooded Crow (1st, 8vo, [48]p, yellow cl, 1-color)	L: Blackwell	[1926]	Monsell, J.R.	70-100	*
Monsell, J.R.	Pink Knight (1st, 16mo, 95p, 24cp)	L: Richards	1901	Monsell, J.R.	150-225	
Montalba, Anthony R.	Doyle Fairy Book (1st, 12mo, 582p, red/gilt, AEG, 36pl)	L: Dean	1890	Doyle, Richard	250-350	
Montefiore	Friend and Foe (8vo, ipcb, 107p)	Dutton	(1898)	5 Chromos	100-170	
Montgomery, F.T.	Billy Whiskers at the Fair (1st, lg8vo, ibds, 163p, cp)	Saalfield	(1909)	DeBebian, Arthur	70-120	
Montgomery, F.T.	Billy Whiskers in an Aeroplane (1st, lg8vo, 219p, 6cp)	Saalfield	(1912)	White, Constance	200-300	*
Montgomery, F.T.	Billy Whiskers in Panama (1st, lg8vo, 168p, color)	Saalfield	(1914)	White, Constance	100-165	
Montgomery, F.T.	Billy Whiskers in the South (1st, lg8vo, green/gilt, 148p, 6cp)	Saalfield	(1917)	Fitzgerald, Will	70-130	
Montgomery, F.T.	Billy Whiskers in Town (1st, lg8vo, 200p, color)	Saalfield	(1913)	White, Constance	70-120	
Montgomery, F.T.	Billy Whiskers' Grandchildren (1st, lg8vo, 152p, 6cp)	Saalfield	(1909)	Von Hofsten, H.	80-125	
Montgomery, F.T.	Billy Whiskers' Kids (1st, sq8vo, 134p, gilt, 6cp)	Saalfield	(1903)	Fry, W.H.	70-120	
Montgomery, F.T.	Cats & Kitts (1st, 8vo, 63p, p-o, 6cp)	Brewer/Barse	(1908)	Von Hofsten, H.	70-100	*
Montgomery, F.T.	Christmas with Santa Claus (1st, lg8vo, 154p, color)	Saalfield	(1905)	Hallock, Ruth M.	70-120	
Montgomery, F.T.	Horses & Colts (1st, 8vo, 62p, red cl, p-o, 8cp)	Barse/Hopkins	(1911)	Von Hofsten, H.	45-70	
Montgomery, F.T.	On a Lark to the Planets (1st, 12mo, blue/silver, 180p, 7cp)	Saalfield	1904	Elrod, Winifred D.	200-300	
Montgomery, F.T.	Wonderful Electric Elephant (1st, 8vo, 253p, 50pl)	Saalfield	1903	Coolidge, C.M.	70-100	*
Montgomery, F.T.	Zip: Adventures of a Frisky Fox Terrier (1st, 8vo, 77p, ipcb, 4cp)	Saalfield	(1917)	Higgins, Violet M.	60-100	*
Montgomery, Lucy M.	Anne of Avonlea (1st, sm8vo, 367p, p-o, green cl, col frn)	L.C. Page	1909	Gibbs, George	300-500	
Montgomery, Lucy M.	Anne of Green Gables (1st, sm8vo, 429p, p-o, gilt, 8pl, PPP)	L.C. Page	1908	Claus, M.A.	2000-3000	
Montgomery, Lucy M.	Anne of Ingleside (1st, 12mo, 323p, col frn, DJ/2.00)	Stokes	1939	John, Charles V.	75-125	
Montgomery, Lucy M.	Anne of the Island (1st, sm8vo, 326p, col frn & p-o)	L.C. Page	1915	Taylor, H. Weston	200-300	
Montgomery, Lucy M.	Anne's House of Dreams (1st, 8vo, 346p, gilt, p-o, col frn)	Stokes	(1917)	Kirk, Maria L.	180-250	
Montgomery, Lucy M.	Chronicles of Avonlea (1st, sm8vo, 306p, p-o, gilt, col frn)	L.C. Page	1912	Gibbs, George	250-400	
Montgomery, Lucy M.	Emily Climbs (1st, sm8vo, green cl, 312p, col frn & p-o by)	Stokes	1925	Kirk, Maria L.	150-250	
Montgomery, Lucy M.	Emily of New Moon (1st, sm8vo, 351p, col frn & p-o by...)	Stokes	1923	Kirk, Maria L.	120-200	
Montgomery, Lucy M.	Emily's Quest (1st, sm8vo, 310p, green cl, p-o & col frn by...)	Stokes	1927	Kirk, Maria L.	120-200	
Montgomery, Lucy M.	Further Chronicles of Avonlea (1st, sm8vo, 301p, 6pl)	L.C. Page	1920	Goss, John	100-170	
Montgomery, Lucy M.	Golden Road (1st, sm8vo, 369p, p-o, gilt, col frn)	L.C. Page	1913	Gibbs, George	160-220	
Montgomery, Lucy M.	Jane of Lantern Hill (1st, sm8vo, 297p, gilt, col frn, DJ/2.00)	Stokes	1937	Costello, Louise	100-170	
Montgomery, Lucy M.	Kilmeny of the Orchard (1st, sm8vo, 256p, p-o, 4cp)	L.C. Page	1910	Gibbs, George	200-300	
Montgomery, Lucy M.	Magic for Marigold (1st, sm8vo, 328p, p-o, col frn)	Stokes	1929	Shoemaker, Edna C.	150-225	
Montgomery, Lucy M.	Mistress Pat (1st, 12mo, 338p, col frn, DJ/2.00)	Stokes	1935	Lawson, Marie A.	150-220	
Montgomery, Lucy M.	Pat of Silver Bush (1st, sm8vo, 329p, col frn)	Stokes	1933	Cooke, Edna	140-200	
Montgomery, Lucy M.	Rainbow Valley (1st, sm8vo, 341p, col frn & p-o by...)	Stokes	1919	Kirk, Maria L.	100-180	

AUTHOR	TITLE	PUBLISHER	DATE	ARTIST	PRICE	LC
Montgomery, Lucy M.	Rilla of Ingleside (1st, sm8vo, gilt, 370p, p-o, col frn)	Stokes	(1921)	Kirk, Maria L.	150-225	
Montgomery, Lucy M.	Story Girl (1st, sm8vo, 365p, gilt, p-o, col frn)	L.C. Page	1911	Gibbs, George	150-225	
Montgomery, R.	Amikuk (1st {std}, 8vo, 204p, b/w, DJ/2.75)	World	(1955)	Nonnast, Marie	25-35	*
Montgomery, R.	Beaver Water (1st {std}, 8vo, 214p, b/w, DJ/2.75)	World	(1956)	Doremus, Robert	20-35	*
Montgomery, R.	Big Brownie (1st, 8vo, 222p, b/w, DJ/2.00)	Henry Holt & Co.	(1944)	Landau, Jacob	25-40	*
Montgomery, R.	Broken Fang (1st, 8vo, red cl, 186p, 10cp, pep)	Donohue	(1935)	Hunt, Lynn B.	45-70	*
Montgomery, R.	Claim Jumpers of Marble Canyon (1st {std}, 8vo, 179p, b/w, DJ/2.50)	Knopf	1956	Moyers, William	20-30	
Montgomery, R.	Corey's Sea Monster (1st, sm8vo, 159p, fp b/w, DJ/3.75)	World	(1969)	Kidder, Harvey	25-35	
Montgomery, R.	Crazy Kill Range (1st {std}, 8vo, 192p, b/w, DJ/2.95)	World	(1963)	Bjorklund, Lorence	20-30	
Montgomery, R.	Ghost Town Adventure (1st, 12mo, 252p, dp pl, pep, DJ/2.00)	Henry Holt & Co.	(1942)	Sherman, Russell	25-40	
Montgomery, R.	Golden Stallion & Mysterious Feud (1st {std}, sm8vo, 180p, b/w, DJ/3.95)	Little/Brown	(1967)	Michini, Albert	40-65	
Montgomery, R.	Golden Stallion and the Wolf Dog (1st {std}, sm8vo, 210p, b/w, DJ/3.00)	Little/Brown	(1958)	Leason, Percy	25-40	
Montgomery, R.	Golden Stallion's Advens at Redstone (1st {std}, sm8vo, 198p, b/w DJ/3.00)	Little/Brown	(1959)	Leason, Percy	25-40	
Montgomery, R.	Golden Stallion's Revenge (1st {std}, sm8vo, 242p, b/w, DJ/2.75)	Little/Brown	(1953)	Giguere, George	25-40	
Montgomery, R.	Gray Wolf (1st, 8vo, 185p, col frn, DJ/2.25)	Houghton	1938	Abbott, Jacob	25-40	*
Montgomery, R.	Hill Ranch (1st {std}, 8vo, green cl, 200p, uncut, b/w, DJ/2.50)	Doubleday	(1951)	Cooney, Barbara	30-50	
Montgomery, R.	Hurricane Yank (1st, 8vo, 250p, col frn, b/w, DJ/2.00)	McKay	(1942)	Shimer, James	25-40	
Montgomery, R.	Husky: Co-Pilot of the Pilgrim (1st, sm8vo, 271p, b/w, DJ/2.00)	Holt	1942	Landau, Jacob	20-35	
Montgomery, R.	Iceblink (1st, sm8vo, 288p, b/w, pep, DJ/2.00)	Holt	1941	Freund, Rudolf	20-35	
Montgomery, R.	In Happy Hollow (1st {std}, lg8vo, 128p, fp b/w, DJ/2.50)	Doubleday	1958	Berson, Harold	20-35	
Montgomery, R.	Kildee House (1st {std}, 8vo, 209p, gilt, b/w, DJ/2.50, NH)	Doubleday	(1949)	Cooney, Barbara	70-100	R
Montgomery, R.	King of the Castle (1st {std}, 8vo, 60p, 1-color, DJ/2.95)	World	(1961)	Pedersen, Russell	30-45	
Montgomery, R.	Kinkajou on the Town (1st, 8vo, 159p, b/w, DJ/3.75)	World	(1967)	Bjorklund, Lorence	20-30	
Montgomery, R.	Klepty (1st {std}, 8vo, 83p, b/w, DJ/2.95)	Duell, Sloan	(1961)	Hecathorn, Polly	20-30	
Montgomery, R.	McGonnigle's Lake (1st {std}, 8vo, 219p, fp b/w, DJ/2.50)	Doubleday	(1953)	Mackenzie, Garry	25-35	
Montgomery, R.	McNulty's Holiday (1st {std}, 8vo, 150p, b/w, DJ/3.50)	Duell, Sloan	(1963)	Geer, Charles	20-30	*
Montgomery, R.	Midnight (1st, sm8vo, 275p, b/w, DJ/2.00)	Henry Holt & Co.	(1940)	Abbott, Jacob	25-45	*
Montgomery, R.	Mister Jim (1st {std}, 8vo, 219p, b/w, DJ/2.75)	World	(1957)	Galdone, Paul	30-50	
Montgomery, R.	Mystery of Crystal Canyon (1st {std}, 8vo, 216p, b/w, DJ/2.50)	Winston	(1951)	Oughton, Taylor	20-30	
Montgomery, R.	Mystery of the Turquoise Frog (1st, sm8vo, 187p, b/w, DJ/2.25)	J. Messner	(1946)	McGee, Millard	20-35	
Montgomery, R.	Out of the Sun (1st, 8vo, 254p, b/w, DJ/2.00)	McKay	1943	Knight, Clayton	20-30	
Montgomery, R.	Rough Riders Ho! (1st, 8vo, 228p, b/w, DJ/1.00)	McKay	(1946)	Wittmack, E.F.	20-30	
Montgomery, R.	Sea Raiders Ho! (1st, 8vo, 224p, b/w, DJ/2.00)	McKay	(1945)	Wittmack, E.F.	20-30	
Montgomery, R.	Silver Hills (1st {std}, 8vo, 213p, b/w, DJ/3.00)	World	(1958)	Frankenberg, Rbt.	20-30	
Montgomery, R.	Snowman (1st {std}, 8vo, 130p, b/w, DJ/3.50)	Duell, Sloan	(1962)	(Photos)	30-45	
Montgomery, R.	Stan Ball of the Rangers (1st, 8vo, 250p, col frn, DJ/1.00)	McKay	1941	Abbott, Jacob	20-35	
Montgomery, R.	Thornbush Jungle (1st {std}, 8vo, 159p, b/w, DJ/3.50)	World	(1966)	Bjorklund, Lorence	20-30	
Montgomery, R.	Thunderboats Ho! (1st, 8vo, 256p, col frn, DJ/2.00)	McKay	(1945)	Wittmack, E.F.	25-40	
Montgomery, R.	Tim's Mountain (1st {std}, 8vo, 218p, b/w, DJ/2.95)	World	(1959)	DeMiskey, Julian	20-30	
Montgomery, R.	Timberline Tales (1st {std}, 8vo, 264p, col frn, b/w, DJ/1.00)	McKay	(1939)	Abbott, Jacob	20-30	
Montgomery, R.	Troopers Three (1st {std}, 8vo, 233p, col frn, pep)	Doubleday/Doran	1932	Gay, Zhenya	25-40	*
Montgomery, R.	Wapiti the Elk (1st {std}, 8vo, 186p, b/w, DJ/2.50)	Little/Brown	(1952)	Christensen, G.D.	25-45	
Montgomery, R.	War Wings (1st, 8vo, 224p, col frn, DJ/2.00)	McKay	(1943)	Knight, Clayton	20-35	
Montgomery, R.	White Mountaineer (1st {std}, 8vo, 177p, b/w, DJ/2.75)	Little/Brown	1953	Christensen, G.D.	20-35	
Montgomery, R.	Whitetail: Story of a Prairie Dog (1st {std}, 8vo, 64p, b/w, DJ/2.50)	World	(1958)	Nonnast, Marie	20-35	
Montgomery, R.	Yellow Eyes (1st, 8vo, 243p, b/w, pep, DJ/2.00)	Caxton Press	1937	Cram, L.D.	50-80	*
Montresor, Beni	A for Angel: Beni Montresor's ABC... (1st, ob4to, [39]p, 3-color, cep, DJ)	Knopf	(1969)	Montresor, Beni	50-85	
Montresor, Beni	House of Flowers, House of Stars (1st {std} 4to, [40]p color, cep, DJ/3.50)	Knopf	(1962)	Montresor, Beni	50-85	
Montresor, Beni	I Saw a Ship A-Sailing (1st, 4to, [38]p 2-color, cep, DJ/3.95)	Knopf	1967	Montresor, Beni	60-90	
Montresor, Beni	Witches of Venice (1st, 4to, [40]p, 1-color, DJ/3.25)	Knopf	(1963)	Montresor, Beni	50-80	
Moodey, Marion M.	Here Comes the Peddler! (1st, lg8vo, ipcb, [32]p, b/w, cep, DJ/1.50)	Holiday House	(1947)	Markham, Kyra	30-50	
Moodie, Susanna	Roughing It in the Bush (1st, 8vo, 568p, uncut, teg, 17 ticp)	L: G. Bell	1913	Stewart, R.A.	60-90	
Moon, Carl	Painted Moccasin (1st, 8vo, 318p, green/gilt, col frn, pep)	Stokes	1931	Moon, Carl	70-120	
Moon, Grace P.	Arrow of Tee-May (1st {std}, 8vo, 284p, col frn, b/w, pep)	Doubleday/Doran	1931	Moon, Carl	50-80	
Moon, Grace P.	Book of Nah-Wee (1st {std}, sm sq4to, 59p, ibds, color, pep)	Doubleday/Doran	1932	Moon, Carl	50-80	
Moon, Grace P.	Chi-Wee (1st, 8vo, uncut, 239p, col frn, fp b/w, pep)	Doubleday/Page	1925	Moon, Carl	30-50	
Moon, Grace P.	Chi-Wee and Loki (1st {std}, 8vo, 208p, tan cl, col frn, 18pl)	Doubleday/Page	1926	Moon, Carl	50-80	
Moon, Grace P.	Daughter of Thunder (1st, sm8vo, 184p, col frn, pep, DJ/2.00)	Macmillan	1942	Moon, Carl	50-80	
Moon, Grace P.	Far-Away Desert (1st {std}, sm8vo, 261p, color, pep)	Doubleday/Doran	1932	Moon, Carl	40-65	
Moon, Grace P.	Indian Legends in Rhyme (1st, sm4to, p-o, 54p, 5cp)	Stokes	(1917)	Moon, Carl	70-125	
Moon, Grace P.	Lost Indian Magic (1st, sm8vo, 301p, p-o, 8cp, pep)	Stokes	(1918)	Moon, Carl	80-125	
Moon, Grace P.	Magic Trail (1st {std}, sm8vo, 234p, col frn, 13pl, pep)	Doubleday/Doran	1929	Moon, Carl	50-80	
Moon, Grace P.	Missing Katchina (1st {std}, 8vo, 286p, col frn, b/w, pep)	Doubleday/Doran	1930	Moon, Carl	40-65	
Moon, Grace P.	Nadita (1st {std}, 8vo, 274p, col frn, 16pl, pep)	Doubleday/Doran	1927	Moon, Carl	45-70	
Moon, Grace P.	One Little Indian (1st, lg8vo, [32]p, p-o, fp color, pep, DJ/2.00)	Whitman	1950	Moon, Carl	45-70	
Moon, Grace P.	Runaway Papoose (1st {std}, 8vo, 264p, col frn, b/w, pep, NH)	Doubleday/Doran	1928	Moon, Carl	40-60	
Moon, Grace P.	Shanty Ann (1st, 8vo, 200p, col frn, DJ/2.00)	Stokes	1935	Moon, Carl	45-70	
Moon, Grace P.	Singing Sands (1st {std}, 8vo, 245p, col frn, b/w, pep, DJ/2.00)	Doubleday/Doran	1936	Moon, Carl	40-65	
Moon, Grace P.	Solita (1st {std}, 8vo, tan cl, 241p, col frn, b/w, pep, DJ/2.00)	Doubleday/Doran	1938	Moon, Carl	60-90	
Moon, Grace P.	Tita of Mexico (1st, sm8vo, 213p, col frn, 4pl, pep)	Stokes	1934	Moon, Carl	40-65	
Moon, Grace P.	White Indian (1st {std}, sm8vo, 221p, col frn, b/w, pep, DJ/2.00)	Doubleday/Doran	1937	Moon, Carl	45-70	
Moon, Grace P.	Wongo & the Wise Old Crow (1st, 8vo, 188p, pep, gilt, col frn)	Reilly/Lee	(1923)	Moon, Carl	50-80	
Moon, Sheila	Knee Deep in Thunder (1st {std}, lg8vo, 307p, b/w, DJ/4.95, NYTBI)	Atheneum	1967	Parnall, Peter	30-50	
Moorat, Joseph	Thirty Old-Time Nursery Songs (1st, lg4to, 32p, ibds, color, pep)	L: Jack	[1895]	Woodroffe, Paul	200-300	
Moorat, Joseph	Ye Booke of Nursery Rhymes (1st, lg ob4to, [47]p, ipcb, b/w)	L: G. Bell	(1895)	Woodroffe, Paul	160-240	
Moorat, Joseph	Ye Second Book of Nursery Rhymes (1st, ob4to, ipcb, 54p, b/w)	L: G. Allen	1896	Woodroffe, Paul	100-175	
Moore, Ann C.	Nicholas (1st, 12mo, red/gilt, 331p, col frn, pep, NH)	Putnam	1924	Van Everen, Jay	70-100	
Moore, Ann C.	Nicholas & Golden Goose (1st, 12mo, 259p, blue/gilt, color, pep)	Putnam	1932	Van Everen, Jay	40-65	

AUTHOR	TITLE	PUBLISHER	DATE	ARTIST	PRICE	LC
Moore, Clement C.	Night Before Christmas (8vo, [24]p, pep, 12 chromos)	L: Nister	[1885]	Lawson, Lizzie	100-170	*
Moore, Clement C.	Night Before Christmas (4to, ibds)	McLoughlin	[1888]	16 Chromos	300-500	
Moore, Clement C.	Night Before Christmas (4to, wraps, [14]p, color)	McLoughlin	1896	(Color Lithos)	300-500	
Moore, Clement C.	Night Before Christmas (1st, ob8vo, [32]p, ibds, 12cp, pep)	Houghton	(1912)	Smith, Jessie W.	200-300	
Moore, Clement C.	Night Before Christmas (folio, wraps, color)	Saalfield	[1915]	Brundage, Frances	80-120	
Moore, Clement C.	Night Before Christmas (folio, wraps {shape bk}, color)	NY: Stecher	(1917)	Price, Margaret E.	90-140	
Moore, Clement C.	Night Before Christmas (1st, 4to, ibds, [26]p, color)	Dutton	1928	MacKinstry, Eliz.	100-170	R
Moore, Clement C.	Night Before Christmas (folio, wraps, unpag, color)	Saalfield	(1932)	Peat, Fern B.	65-100	
Moore, Clement C.	Night Before Christmas (1st AM, 8vo, p-o, 37p, 4cp, pep)	Lippincott	[1932]	Rackham, Arthur	170-250	
Moore, Clement C.	Night Before Christmas (1st, sm4to, ibds, fp color)	L: Collins	1934	Disney Studios	140-200	
Moore, Clement C.	Night Before Christmas (1st, 8vo, [32]p, color, pep, DJ/0.50)	Grosset/Dunlap	(1935)	Fanchette	60-100	
Moore, Clement C.	Night Before Christmas (4to, [16]p, wraps, color)	Whitman	(1935)	Ward, Keith	60-90	
Moore, Clement C.	Night Before Christmas (1st {std}, lg8vo, ibds, [43]p, color, DJ/1.50)	Harcourt	(1937)	Birch, Reginald	90-160	R
Moore, Clement C.	Night Before Christmas (1st, 24mo, ibds, [37]p, color)	Holiday House	(1937)	Bischoff, Ilse	80-130	R
Moore, Clement C.	Night Before Christmas (1st, lg4to, [24]p, ipcb, color, pep, DJ/0.50)	Grosset/Dunlap	1937	Gooch, Thelma	100-150	R
Moore, Clement C.	Night Before Christmas (1st, 4to, [33]p, ipcb, color, pep)	Whitman	(1937)	Newton, Ruth	60-90	R*
Moore, Clement C.	Night Before Christmas (16mo, ibds, 62p, color)	Rand/McNally	(1938)	Biers, C.	25-40	
Moore, Clement C.	Night Before Christmas (4to, wraps, [12]p, color)	Whitman	1939	Ward, Keith	50-80	
Moore, Clement C.	Night Before Christmas (1st, folio, ipcb, [18]p, color)	Whitman	1940	Madsen, Eleanora	50-80	
Moore, Clement C.	Night Before Christmas (1st, sm4to, [24]p, ibds, color, DJ/1.25)	Winston	(1942)	Shinn, Everett	70-100	
Moore, Clement C.	Night Before Christmas (4to, [16]p, wraps, fp color)	Whitman	(1943)	Taylor, Ethel	30-50	*
Moore, Clement C.	Night Before Christmas (1st, lg8vo, ibds, [16]p, color, DJ/1.00)	Dutton	(1944)	Paflin, Roberta	50-80	
Moore, Clement C.	Night Before Christmas (1st, lg8vo, ibds, [22]p, color, pep)	Grosset/Dunlap	(1948)	Dorcas	50-85	
Moore, Clement C.	Night Before Christmas (1st, 4to, ibds, [25]p, color, pep, DJ/1.00)	Wilcox/Follett	1949	Friend, Esther	35-60	
Moore, Clement C.	Night Before Christmas (1st, lg4to, ibds, [28]p, color, pep, DJ/1.00)	Grosset/Dunlap	1949	Weisgard, Leonard	65-100	
Moore, Clement C.	Night Before Christmas (1st, 4to, ibds, unpag, color, BGB)	Simon/Schuster	(1951)	Tenggren, Gustaf	100-165	
Moore, Clement C.	Night Before Christmas (1st, folio, ibds, [32]p, color, pep, DJ/1.50)	Garden City	1954	Duvoisin, Roger	120-200	R
Moore, Clement C.	Night Before Christmas (1st, 4to, ibds, color, pep)	Grosset/Dunlap	(1961)	Fujikawa, Gyo	60-100	
Moore, Clement C.	Night Before Christmas (1st, 8vo, [64]p, red/gilt, fp 2-color)	Harlin Quist	1964	Perl, Susan	30-50	
Moore, Clement C.	Visit from Santa Claus (4to, ibds, 12cp, 24p)	Stokes/Allen	1887	Gerson, Virginia	200-270	
Moore, Clement C.	Visit from St. Nicholas (1st, 8vo, ibds, 9p, 3 woodcuts by...)	Atl. Monthly Pr.	1921	Ivins, Florence	80-120	
Moore, Clement C.	Visit from St. Nicholas (1st, 8vo, ibds, 9p, designed by....)	Atl. Monthly Pr.	1921	Rogers, Bruce	80-120	
Moore, Clement C.	Visit from St. Nicholas (1st, 16mo, 53p, gilt, pep, color)	Macmillan	1925	Whittemore, C.	50-80	R*
Moore, Clement C.	Visit from St. Nicholas (1st, ob8vo, ibds, [18]p, color)	Hawthorn House	(1937)	Angelo, Valenti	70-100	R
Moore, Clement C.	Visit from St. Nicholas (1st, 24mo, [42]p, ibds, pep, color)	Macmillan	1937	Hader, B.& E.	50-85	R
Moore, Clement C.	Visit from St. Nicholas (1st, ob8vo, [32]p, color, DJ/2.95)	McGraw-Hill	(1968)	Galdone, Paul	30-50	*
Moore, Colleen	Enchanted Castle (1st, 4to, 63p, ibds, 6 fp 1-color, cep)	Garden City	1935	Lawson, Marie A.	60-100	
Moore, David	End of Black Dog (1st, 8vo, 198p, b/w, DJ/2.50)	Crowell	(1949)	Pitz, Henry C.	25-40	
Moore, Elaine T.	Winning Your Spurs (1st {std}, 4to, 123p, b/w, DJ/4.75)	Little/Brown	(1954)	Brown, Paul	100-165	*
Moore, Frank F.	Impudent Comedian (1st, sm8vo, green cl, teg, 274p, 10pl)	Herbert Stone	1897	Sauber, Robert	60-90	
Moore, Hannah	Deeds of Daring done by Girls (1st, sm8vo, 300p, 6cp)	Stokes	(1906)	Gunn, Archie	25-40	*
Moore, Ida C.	Lucky Orphan (1st, 8vo, 122p, fp b/w, pep, DJ/2.00)	Scribner	(1947)	Robertson, Primrose	20-30	
Moore, Janet G.	Many Ways of Seeing (1st, 4to, 141p, color, DJ/7.95, NH)	World	(1968)	Various	80-130	
Moore, John T.	Cinnamon Seed (1st, 8vo, 48p, fp 1-color, DJ/3.25)	Houghton	1967	Hyman, Trina S.	50-85	
Moore, Lilian	I Feel the Same Way (1st {std}, 12mo, [32]p, color, cep, DJ/3.25)	Atheneum	1967	Quackenbush, Rbt.	20-30	*
Moore, Lilian	Junk Day on Juniper Street (1st, 8vo, 71p, 1-color, DJ/3.95)	Parents Mag. Pr.	(1969)	Lobel, Arnold	20-30	
Moore, Lilian	Magic Spectacles (1st, 8vo, 70p, fp 1-color, DJ/2.95)	Parents Mag. Pr.	(1965)	Lobel, Arnold	20-30	
Moore, Lilian	Old Rosie, the Horse Nobody Understood (1st, 4to, 33p, fp 1-color, DJ/1.95)	Random	(1960)	Shortall, Leonard	30-50	
Moore, Lilian	Once Upon a Season (1st, 8vo, 96p, 1-color, DJ/2.75)	Abingdon Press	(1962)	Fiammenghi, Gioia	30-45	
Moore, Lilian	Papa Albert (1st {std}, ob4to, [48]p, color, DJ/3.95)	Atheneum	1964	Fiammenghi, Gioia	25-40	*
Moore, Lilian	Terrible Mr. Twitmeyer (1st {std}, 8vo, 62p, fp b/w, pep, DJ/2.00)	Random	(1952)	Shortall, Leonard	30-45	*
Moore, Marianne	Puss in Boots, Sleeping Beauty & Cinderella (1st {std}, 8vo, 46p, color)	L: Macmillan	1963	Karlin, Eugene	30-50	
Moore, Merrill	Case-Record from a Sonnetorium (1st, 8vo, grey/red, unpag, b/w, DJ/1.50)	NY: Twayne	(1951)	Gorey, Edward	120-200	
Moore, Merrill	Illegitimate Sonnets (1st {1st illus}, 8vo, gilt, 125p, pep, DJ/2.75)	NY: Twayne	(1950)	Gorey, Edward	160-250	
Moore, Nancy	Unhappy Hippopotamus (1st, 4to, 44p, ibds, fp 1-color, DJ/2.75, NYTBI)	Vanguard Press	(1957)	Leight, Edward	40-65	
Moore, Thomas	Lalla Rookh (1st, sm4to, 179p, red/gilt, uncut, 16pl, pep)	MacVeagh/Dial	1930	Kutcher, Ben	55-80	
Moran, Jim	Sophocles the Hyena (1st, sm4to, red cl, 48p, 2-color, DJ/2.25)	Whittlesey	(1954)	Duvoisin, Roger	60-100	
Moray, Ann	Gervase (1st, sm8vo, 93p, b/w, DJ/4.50)	Wm. Morrow	1970	Rosier, Lydia	20-30	
Mord, W.	Four Champions of Great Britain & Ireland (1st, 4to, ibds, 16cp)	L: T.F. Unwin	[1905]	Robinson, Charles	250-350	
Mordvinoff, Nicolas	Bear's Land (1st, 8vo, [48]p, ibds, 2-color, DJ/2.50)	Coward	(1955)	Nicolas	45-70	*
Mordvinoff, Nicolas	Coral Island (1st {std}, 8vo, [41]p, ibds, color, DJ/2.75)	Doubleday	(1957)	Nicolas	40-65	
Morel, Eve (comp)	Fairy Tales & Fables (1st, lg4to, 124p, color, pep)	Grosset/Dunlap	(1970)	Fujikawa, Gyo	50-80	
Morey, Walter	Angry Waters (1st {std}, 8vo, 224p, b/w, DJ/4.95)	Dutton	(1969)	Cuffari, Richard	20-35	
Morey, Walter	Gentle Ben (1st {std}, 8vo, 191p, fp b/w, DJ/3.95)	Dutton	(1965)	Schoenherr, John	40-70	
Morey, Walter	Home is the North (1st {std}, 8vo, 223p, b/w, DJ/3.95)	Dutton	(1967)	Shore, Robert	20-35	
Morey, Walter	Kavik the Wolf Dog (1st {std}, 8vo, 192p, b/w, DJ/4.50)	Dutton	(1968)	Parnall, Peter	25-40	
Morgan, Alice	Boy Who Brought Christmas (1st, 12mo, 139p, 4cp)	Doubleday/Page	1911	Jackson, John E.	60-100	*
Morgan, Carol	Hunt for the Yule Log (1st, 8vo, 159p, b/w, DJ/2.75)	Abelard-Schuman	(1957)	Wildsmith, Brian	20-35	
Morgan, Harriet	Island Impossible (1st, 12mo, gilt, 206p, 5pl)	Little/Brown	1899	Pyle, Katharine	70-100	
Morgan, Helen	Meet Mary Kate (1st, 8vo, 61p, DJ)	L: Faber	1963	Hughes, Shirley	40-65	*
Morgan, Helen	Satchkin Patchkin (1st AM, 8vo, 64p, fp b/w, DJ/3.95)	Macrae Smith	(1970)	Hughes, Shirley	70-100	
Morgan, Nina	Prairie Star (1st, 8vo, 189p, b/w, DJ/2.75)	Viking	1955	Henneberger, Rbt.	25-40	
Morgenstern, Eliz.	Little Gardeners (1st AM, sm sq4to, 14p, p-o, color)	Whitman	1933	Bantzer, Marigard	60-90	*
Morier, James	Adventures of Hajji Baba (1st, 12mo, 456p, gilt, fp b/w)	L: Macmillan	1895	Millar, H.R.	60-90	
Morier, James	Hajji Baba of Ispahan (1st, 2volumes, tan/gilt, cvr by..)	Stone/Kimball	1895	Hazenplug, Frank	70-100	
Morier, James	Hajji Baba of Ispahan (1st, 4to, 403p, gilt, color, DJ/3.50)	Random	1937	Baldridge, Cyrus L.	40-60	
Morley, Charles	Peter, a Cat O' One Tail (1st AM, 8vo, 110p, ibds, b/w)	Putnam	1892	Wain, Louis	250-350	
Morley, Christopher	Don't Open Until Christmas (1st {std}, 8vo, ibds, 26p, b/w)	Doubleday/Doran	1931	Willard, Howard	25-45	*

AUTHOR	TITLE	PUBLISHER	DATE	ARTIST	PRICE	LC
Morley, Christopher	Goldfish Under the Ice (1st {std}, sm8vo, 69p, 14 b/w, cep, DJ/1.00)	Doubleday/Doran	1932	Wiese, Kurt	50-85	
Morley, Christopher	Where the Blue Begins (1st AM, smo, blue/gilt, teg, 227p, 4cp, pep)	Doubleday/Page	(1922)	Rackham, Arthur	200-300	
Morris, Alice T.	Child's Book of Empire (1st, 4to, unpag)	L: Blackie	[1914]	Robinson, Charles	170-240	*
Morris, Alice T.	Elephant's Apology (1st, sm8vo, AEG, 152p, blue/gilt, b/w, cep)	L: Blackie	1899	Woodward, Alice B.	100-160	
Morris, Alice T.	Old Friends and New Fables (1st, 4to, 52p, p-o, 21 ticp)	L: Blackie	1916	Park, Carton M.	160-245	
Morris, Alice T.	Old Friends and New Fables (1st AM, 4to, p-o, 52p, 21 ticp)	Dodge	[1916]	Park, Carton M.	170-220	
Morris, Alice T.	Troubles of Tatters (1st, lg8vo, 155p, gilt, 8 fp b/w, cep)	L: Blackie	[1898]	Woodward, Alice B.	80-120	
Morris, Ann A.	Digging in Yucatan (1st {std}, lg8vo, 279p, pep, b/w)	Doubleday/Doran	1931	Charlot, Jean	55-80	*
Morris, Clara	Trouble Woman (1st, 12mo, 58p, cvr by…)	Funk/Wagnalls	1904	Armstrong, Margaret	40-60	*
Morris, Constance	Behind Moroccan Walls (1st, lg4to, 239p, 20pl, cep)	Macmillan	1931	Artzybasheff, Boris	75-100	
Morris, Cora	Gypsy Story-Teller (1st {std}, 8vo, 206p, col frn, 16 b/w, pep)	Macmillan	1931	Dobias, Frank	45-70	*
Morris, Ethelberta	Ameliaranne Bridesmaid (1st, 8vo, ibds, unpag, p-o, color)	L: Harrap	(1946)	Pearse, Susan B.	50-85	
Morris, Ethelberta	Ameliaranne's Moving-Day (1st, 8vo, ibds, [60]p, color, DJ)	L: Harrap	(1950)	Pearse, Susan B.	55-80	
Morris, Gouverneur	Voice in the Rice (1st, 12mo, 158p, 6cp)	Dodd	1910	Leyendecker, J.C.	60-80	
Morris, James	Upstairs Donkey (1st, 8vo, 126p, b/w, DJ/3.00)	Pantheon	(1961)	Baynes, Pauline	50-80	
Morris, Kenneth	Book of Three Dragons (1st {std}, 4to, gilt, 206p, 8pl, pep)	Longmans	(1930)	Horvath, Ferdinand	90-120	R
Morris, M.	Reign of William and Mary (ob4to, ibds, p-o, 8cp)	Nister/Dutton	[1908]	Morris, M.	280-350	
Morris, Margaretta	Bryn Mawr Stories (1st, 8vo, 296p, teg, green/gilt, illus by…)	Jacobs	(1901)	Green, Eliz. S.	60-100	
Morris, Margaretta	Bryn Mawr Stories (1st, 8vo, 296p, teg, green/gilt, cvr by…)	Jacobs	(1901)	Leyendecker, J.C.	60-100	
Morris, Phyllis	Adventures of Willy & Nilly (1st, sm8vo, tan cl, 8cp, 7pl)	L: John Lane	1921	Cowham, Hilda	200-300	
Morris, William	Defense of Guenevere (1st, 8vo, teg, 310p, red/gilt, 24pl)	L: John Lane	1904	King, Jessie	500-700	
Morris, William	Doom of King Acrisius (1st, 8vo, teg, uncut, 82p, 11pl)	R.H. Russell	1902	Burne-Jones, Edward	100-160	
Morris, William	Early Poems of… (1st, 4to, blue/gilt, teg, 194p, 16 ticp, pep)	L: Blackie	1914	Harrison, Florence	180-260	
Morris, William	Early Poems of… (1st AM, 4to, 194p, teg, 16 ticp)	Dodge	(1914)	Harrison, Florence	140-225	
Morris, William	History of Over Sea (1st, 4to, 28p, ipcb, 1-color)	R.H. Russell	1902	Rhead, Louis	140-200	
Morris, William	Life and Death of Jason (1st, lg8vo, 332p, blue cl, 6cp)	Swarthmore Pr.	(1915)	Armfield, Maxwell	80-130	
Morris, William	Pygmalion & the Image (1st, 8vo, white/gilt, teg, 34p, 5pl)	R.H. Russell	1903	Burne-Jones, Edward	80-120	
Morris, William	Wolf's Head & the Queen (1st, 8vo, 243p, gilt, p-o, col frn, 13pl, pep)	Scribner	1931	Grofe, Nelson	60-100	
Morrison, Lucile P.	Doll Dreams (1st, 8vo, p-o, 121p, fp b/w, pep)	Hollycrofters	(1932)	Various	120-200	
Morrison, Mary J.	Stories True & Fancies New (1st, 8vo, 208p, 11pl)	Estes & Lauriat	(1898)	Bridgman, L.J.	70-100	*
Morrison, Sean	Is That a Happy Hippopotamus? (1st, 8vo, [46]p, fp 2-color, DJ/3.75)	Crowell	(1966)	Aliki	25-40	
Morrow, Elizabeth	Beast, Bird & Fish (1st {std}, 4to, [59]p, color, pep)	Knopf	1933	D'Harnoncourt, R.	100-165	
Morrow, Elizabeth	My Favorite Age (1st, sm8vo, 220p, green cl, fp b/w, cep, DJ/2.00)	Macmillan	1943	Suba, Susanne	30-50	
Morrow, Elizabeth	Painted Pig (1st, 4to, ipcb, 32p, fp color, pep)	Knopf	1930	D'Harnoncourt, R.	100-170	R
Morrow, Elizabeth	Pint of Judgment (1st {std}, 24mo, ibds, 43p, dep, DJ/0.50)	Knopf	(1939)	Suba, Susanne	30-50	
Morrow, Elizabeth	Rabbit's Nest (1st {std}, 24mo, 43p, ipcb, 1-color, pep, DJ/0.50)	Macmillan	1940	Willard, Howard	35-50	
Morrow, Elizabeth	Shannon (1st {std}, 24mo, ipcb, 68p, fp b/w, DJ/0.50)	Macmillan	1941	Torrey, Helen	25-45	
Morrow, Honore	Ship's Monkey (1st, 8vo, 188p, fp color, pep, DJ/2.00)	Wm. Morrow	1933	Grant, Gordon	25-40	
Morrow, Suzanne	Inatuck's Friend (1st {std}, 4to, 48p, color, DJ/3.50)	Little/Brown	(1968)	Raskin, Ellen	30-45	
Morrow, W.C.	Lentala of the South Seas (1st, 8vo, grey cl, 278p, p-o, 7cp)	Stokes	(1908)	Dixon, Maynard	70-100	
Morse, Elizabeth	Chang of the Siamese Jungle (1st {std}, sm8vo, 195p, b/w, pep)	Dutton	(1930)	Berry, Erick	25-45	*
Morse, Elizabeth	Siamese Cat (1st, sm8vo, 62p, b/w, pep, DJ/1.50)	Dutton	(1929)	Seymour, Ruth	30-50	
Morse, Evangeline	Brown Rabbit, Her Story (1st {std}, 8vo, 191p, b/w, DJ/3.50)	Follett	(1967)	Martin, David S.	25-45	
Morse, Livingston B.	Road to Nowhere (1st, 12mo, 236p, color)	Harper	1900	Morse, Edna	55-80	*
Morse, Samuel	All in a Suitcase (1st {std}, lg ob8vo, 48p, color, DJ/3.75)	Little/Brown	(1966)	Cooney, Barbara	50-80	
Morse, Samuel	Sea Sums (1st {std}, lg ob8vo, 32p, color, DJ/4.50)	Little/Brown	(1970)	Akino, Fuku	25-40	
Morshead, O.F.	Everybody's Pepys (1st, 8vo, blue cl, 615p, b/w, pep)	Harcourt	1926	Shepard, Ernest H.	40-65	
Morton, Elizabeth	Rags the Firehouse Dog (1st {std}, 4to, 38p, 1-color, DJ/2.00)	Winston	(1952)	Dennis, Morgan	30-50	*
Morton, John B.	Who's Who in the Zoo (1st, 4to, 173p, 4cp)	L: Eyre/Spotts.	1933	Aldin, Cecil	90-120	
Mosel, Arlene	Tikki-Tikki Tembo (1st {std}, sm4to, ibds, [45]p, color, DJ/4.50)	Holt, Rinehart	(1968)	Lent, Blair	45-60	
Moses, Horace S.	Here Comes the Circus (1st, lg8vo, 47p, color, DJ/1.75)	Houghton	1941	Suba, Susanne	40-65	
Moses, Montrose (ed)	Treasury of Plays for Children (1st, 8vo, 550p, col frn, 8pl, pep)	Little/Brown	1921	Sarg, Tony	60-100	
Mother Goose	And So My Garden Grows (1st {std}, ob8vo, [44]p, ibds, color, DJ/3.95)	Doubleday	1969	Spier, Peter E.	30-50	
Mother Goose	Animal Mother Goose… (1st, 8vo, 168p, grey cl, b/w, pep)	Lothrop	(1921)	(Photos)	120-170	*
Mother Goose	Baby's Mother Goose (1st, sq16mo, [16]p, color, pep)	Grosset/Dunlap	1938	Stearns, Sharon	55-80	*
Mother Goose	Boyd Smith Mother Goose (1st, 4to, red/gilt, 223p, 20cp)	Putnam	(1919)	Smith, E. Boyd	200-300	
Mother Goose	Charles Addams Mother Goose (1st, 4to, [54]p, color, cep, DJ/4.95)	Windmill Books	(1967)	Addams, Charles	80-125	
Mother Goose	Children's Mother Goose (1st, 4to, 120p, p-o, 12cp, pep)	Reilly/Lee	(1921)	Donahey, William	300-450	
Mother Goose	Chinese Mother Goose Rhymes (1st {std}, ob4to, [48]p, color, DJ/3.95)	World	(1968)	Young, Ed	40-70	*
Mother Goose	Complete Mother Goose (1st, lg8vo, 227p, 11cp)	Stokes	(1909)	Betts, Ethel F.	200-280	
Mother Goose	Crooked Man (1st {std}, 12mo, [56]p, fp 1-color, pep)	Longmans	(1940)	Barto, Emily N.	30-45	
Mother Goose	Denslow's Mother Goose (1st [1], 4to, ibds, [96]p, color, pep)	McClure	1901	Denslow, W.W.	500-750	R
Mother Goose	Disney's Mother Goose (1st, folio, ibds, [28]p, color, GGB)	Simon/Schuster	(1949)	Disney Studios	100-170	*
Mother Goose	Ella Dolbear Lee Mother Goose (1st, sm4to, 280p, 24cp, pep)	Donohue	(1918)	Lee, Ella D.	120-200	
Mother Goose	Everychild's Mother Goose (1st, 12mo, 308p, 64 fp 1-color)	Macmillan	1918	Wilson, Edith R.	60-100	*
Mother Goose	Familiar Rhymes of Mother Goose (1st, 8vo, 30cp, pcb)	L: Nister	1888	Loomis, Chester B.	200-300	
Mother Goose	Fanny Cory Mother Goose (1st, 4to, gilt, p-o, 74p, 12cp, pep)	Bobbs-Merrill	(1913)	Cory, Fanny	170-260	R
Mother Goose	Favorite Mother Goose Rhymes (4to, ibds, color)	Platt/Munk	(1937)	Eulalie	50-80	
Mother Goose	Favorite Nursery Rhymes (1st, 4to, 47p, 6cp)	Stokes	(1906)	Betts, Ethel F.	130-200	*
Mother Goose	Gay Mother Goose (1st, 4to, beige cl, 63p, fp color, DJ/1.75)	Scribner	(1938)	Francoise	80-125	
Mother Goose	Golden Mother Goose (1st, folio, ibds, 96p, color, GGB)	Simon/Schuster	(1948)	Provensen, A.& M.	90-160	*
Mother Goose	Humpty Dumpty (1st, sq12mo, ibds)	Macmillan	1927	Richards, George M.	80-120	
Mother Goose	Hurrah, We're Outward Bound! (1st {std}, ob8vo, [41]p, ipcb, col, DJ/3.95)	Doubleday	(1968)	Spier, Peter E.	25-40	
Mother Goose	Jessie W. Smith Mother Goose (1st, ob4to, 173p, p-o, 12cp, 5pl, pep)	Dodd	(1914)	Smith, Jessie W.	600-800	
Mother Goose	Jolly Mother Goose (1st, folio, [66]p, p-o, 19cp)	Rand/McNally	(1916)	Wright, Blanche F.	100-170	
Mother Goose	Little Mother Goose (1st, sm4to, bds, p-o, [30]p, 16cp)	McBride	1915	Pogany, Willy	225-320	
Mother Goose	Little Mother Goose (1st, ob8vo, p-o, 176p, gilt, 12cp)	Dodd	(1918)	Smith, Jessie W.	250-400	
Mother Goose	Littlefolks' Mother Goose (1st, 4to, 158p, p-o, 7cp, pep)	Sears	(1926)	Rule, Christopher	70-100	

AUTHOR	TITLE	PUBLISHER	DATE	ARTIST	PRICE	LC
Mother Goose	Lois Lenski's Mother Goose (1st, 8vo, 83p, fp 2-color)	Harper	(1936)	Lenski, Lois	80-120	
Mother Goose	London Bridge is Falling Down (1st {std}, ob4to, 32p, color, DJ)	Little/Brown	(1967)	Ness, Evaline	30-50	
Mother Goose	London Bridge is Falling Down (1st {std} ob8vo ibds, [41]p, color, DJ/3.95)	Doubleday	(1967)	Spier, Peter E.	40-70	R
Mother Goose	Masha's Stuffed Mother Goose (1st {std}, 4to, ibds, 64p, color, DJ/1.00)	Garden City	1946	Masha	60-90	*
Mother Goose	Mickey Mouse & Mother Goose (1st, 8vo, ibds, 136p, color, pep)	Whitman	(1937)	Disney Studios	250-350	
Mother Goose	Most Popular Mother Goose Songs (1st, ob4to, 44p, ipcb, 39cp)	NY: Hinds	(1915)	Hill, Mabel B.	160-240	
Mother Goose	Mother Goose (1st, 12mo, yellow ibds, 48p, fp color, cep)	L: Routledge	[1881]	Greenaway, Kate	400-600	
Mother Goose	Mother Goose (4to, ibds, [48]p, color)	McLoughlin	[1882]	Greenaway, Kate	200-300	
Mother Goose	Mother Goose (1st, 4to, ibds, 24cp)	Stokes	1891	Humphrey, Maud	500-750	
Mother Goose	Mother Goose (1st, 8vo, [64]p, color)	McLoughlin	(1909)	Bennett, C.H.	100-150	R
Mother Goose	Mother Goose (1st, sm4to, grey cl, 159p, 13 ticp, pep)	L: Heinemann	(1913)	Rackham, Arthur	400-600	R
Mother Goose	Mother Goose (1st AM, lg8vo, blue/gilt, p-o, 262p, 13cp)	Century	1913	Rackham, Arthur	450-600	R
Mother Goose	Mother Goose (1st, 4to, teg, 255p, 16cp)	L: Harrap	(1915)	Orr, Monro S.	180-240	
Mother Goose	Mother Goose (1st AM, lg8vo, 255p, 16cp)	McKay	(1915)	Orr, Monro S.	100-160	*
Mother Goose	Mother Goose (1st, lg4to, grey/gilt, [119]p, p-o, color)	Volland	(1915)	Richardson, F.	180-260	
Mother Goose	Mother Goose (1st, 4to, ibds, 74p, 16cp, DJ)	L: Coker	(1920)	Tarrant, Margaret	120-160	
Mother Goose	Mother Goose (1st {std}, lg4to, 96p, black cl, color, pep)	Doubleday/Page	1924	Falls, Charles B.	120-200	
Mother Goose	Mother Goose (1st AM, 12mo, 125p, color)	Dent/Dutton	(1927)	Chadburn, Mabel	50-80	*
Mother Goose	Mother Goose (1st, lg4to, ipcb, [60]p, p-o, 8cp)	Saalfield	(1929)	Peat, Fern B.	80-130	
Mother Goose	Mother Goose (1st AM, 8vo, 340p, 8cp)	Dutton	(1932)	Folkard, Charles	120-180	
Mother Goose	Mother Goose (1st, 4to, 224p, ibds, 12pl)	L: Harrap	1932	Tawse, Sybil	90-120	
Mother Goose	Mother Goose (1st, lg4to, [28]p, 12 fp color, pep)	Whitman	(1934)	Newton/Horn	90-120	*
Mother Goose	Mother Goose (1st, folio, 144p, yellow cl, color, pep)	Heritage Press	(1936)	Duvoisin, Roger	100-160	R
Mother Goose	Mother Goose (1st, lg4to, p-o, 113p, color, pep)	Saalfield	(1938)	Lohman, Fred D.	75-100	*
Mother Goose	Mother Goose (1st, 32mo, [41]p, color, pep)	Holiday House	(1939)	Ives, Ruth	55-80	*
Mother Goose	Mother Goose (1st, lg8vo, ibds, [52]p, color, pep)	Random	(1940)	Doane, Pelagie	45-80	*
Mother Goose	Mother Goose (1st, 4to, 136p, color, pep, DJ/2.00)	Little/Brown	1940	Tenggren, Gustaf	100-170	
Mother Goose	Mother Goose (1st, sm4to, ipcb, 380p, color, pep)	Whitman	(1941)	Snow, Dorothea J.	35-60	*
Mother Goose	Mother Goose (1st {new ed}, 4to, ipcb, 112p, color, pep, DJ/2.50)	Heritage Press	(1943)	Duvoisin, Roger	60-90	*
Mother Goose	Mother Goose (1st, sm sq8vo, green cl, 87p, color, pep, DJ/2.00, CH)	NY: Oxford U.Pr.	(1944)	Tudor, Tasha	250-400	
Mother Goose	Mother Goose (1st, 12mo, [53]p, wraps, color)	Whitman	1944	Weihs, Erika	35-60	*
Mother Goose	Mother Goose (1st, lg8vo, [40]p, color)	Wonder Books	(1946)	Hirsch, Joseph	55-80	*
Mother Goose	Mother Goose (1st, 12mo, [52]p, 2-color)	Whitman	1950	Vaughan, E.F.	35-60	*
Mother Goose	Mother Goose & her Goslings (1st, lg8vo, 125p, color)	Chi: Stanton	(1918)	Higgins, Violet M.	75-100	*
Mother Goose	Mother Goose & Nursery Rhymes (1st {std}, 4to, 57p, color, DJ/4.95, CH)	Atheneum	1963	Reed, Philip	60-100	R
Mother Goose	Mother Goose ABC (4to, 14p, wraps, color)	Donohue	(1913)	Brundage, Frances	75-100	*
Mother Goose	Mother Goose Book (ob4to, red cl, p-o, 11cp)	Whitman	(1915)	Perkins, Lucy F.	90-140	
Mother Goose	Mother Goose Book of Rhymes (narrow folio, wraps, color)	Stecher	1927	Price, Margaret E.	55-80	
Mother Goose	Mother Goose in Holland (1st, 4to, 90p, color)	Jacobs	(1912)	Post, May A.	120-200	*
Mother Goose	Mother Goose in Silhouettes (1st, sq16mo, 78p, b/w)	Houghton	1907	Buffam, Katharine G.	80-125	
Mother Goose	Mother Goose in Song & Rhyme (1st, 4to, 87p, 2-color, pep)	C.E. Graham	(1930)	Burd, Clara M.	40-60	*
Mother Goose	Mother Goose Jungle Book (1st, 4to, 63p, color)	Madison Book Co.	1903	Von Hofsten, H.	70-120	*
Mother Goose	Mother Goose Nursery Almanac (1st {std}, folio, ibds, 88p, color, DJ/2.50)	Garden City	1960	Palazzo, Tony	90-160	*
Mother Goose	Mother Goose Nursery Rhymes (1st, sm8vo, 320p, col frn, b/w)	Lippincott	1900	Opper, Frederick B.	60-100	*
Mother Goose	Mother Goose Nursery Rhymes (1st AM, 8vo, 363p, 24cp)	Dodge	(1909)	Hassall, John	150-225	
Mother Goose	Mother Goose Nursery Rhymes (1st, 8vo, gilt, 364p, 24cp)	L: Blackie	1909	Hassall, John	150-200	
Mother Goose	Mother Goose Nursery Rhymes (4to, ibds, 16 fp color)	L: R. Tuck	[1910]	Attwell, Mabel L.	220-300	
Mother Goose	Mother Goose Nursery Rhymes (1st {this pub}, sq8vo, 136p, b/w)	Platt/Peck	(1912)	McManus, Blanche	70-100	
Mother Goose	Mother Goose Nursery Rhymes (4to, ibds, 128p, 16cp)	L: Jack	[1915]	Orr, Jack	170-220	
Mother Goose	Mother Goose Nursery Rhymes (1st, 8vo, 159p, ibds, color)	L: A&C Black	(1919)	Folkard, Charles	150-225	
Mother Goose	Mother Goose Nursery Rhymes (1st, 8vo, 256p, color, pep)	Winston	(1928)	Greene, Julia	35-60	*
Mother Goose	Mother Goose Nursery Rhymes (1st, 8vo, 159p)	L: Collins	[1928]	Robinson, Charles	80-120	*
Mother Goose	Mother Goose Nursery Rhymes (1st, 4to, 176p, 24cp)	L: Ward Lock	[1929]	Tarrant, Margaret	90-120	*
Mother Goose	Mother Goose Nursery Rhymes (1st, 8vo, red/gilt, 385p, 11cp, pep)	Cupples/Leon	(1930)	Cooke, Edna	60-100	
Mother Goose	Mother Goose Nursery Tales (12mo, 91p, green cl, p-o, color)	Altemus	(1904)	Neill, John R.	100-165	
Mother Goose	Mother Goose Nursery Tales (1st, 4to, 219p, 16cp, pep)	L: A&C Black	(1923)	Folkard, Charles	150-220	
Mother Goose	Mother Goose Picture Book (1st, 12mo, 119p, color, pep)	S. Gabriel	(1939)	Deane, Elsie	55-80	*
Mother Goose	Mother Goose Rhymes (1st, 8vo, p-o, 199p, b/w)	Baker/Tayler	1911	Knowles, Machan	100-160	*
Mother Goose	Mother Goose Rhymes (1st, 8vo, 206p, cp)	NY: Noble	1917	Knowles, Machan	90-150	R*
Mother Goose	Mother Goose Rhymes (1st, 4to, p-o, [120]p, 8cp, pep)	Platt/Munk	(1931)	Lenski/Eulalie	50-80	
Mother Goose	Mother Goose Rhymes (1st, 4to, red cl, [83]p, color, pep, DJ/1.25)	Platt/Munk	(1940)	Austin, Margot	80-120	*
Mother Goose	Mother Goose Rhymes (1st, 12mo, ipcb, [62]p, fp color)	Rand/McNally	(1942)	Wedde, Junice	40-60	*
Mother Goose	Mother Goose Riddle Rhymes (1st {std}, 8vo, [46]p, color, DJ/2.50, NYTBI)	Harcourt	(1953)	Low, Joseph	30-50	R*
Mother Goose	Mother Goose Song Book (1st, folio, ibds)	A.& C. Boni	(1926)	Harshberger, Mac	200-300	
Mother Goose	Mother Goose Song Book (1st, ob4to, 100p, color)	Garden City	(1948)	Smith, Marion F.	90-160	*
Mother Goose	Mother Goose Stories (folio, ibds, 76p, 14 fp color)	L: Collins	[1928]	Newton, Ruth	60-90	
Mother Goose	Mother Goose: Best Known Rhymes (1st, lg4to, ibds, [34]p, color)	Saalfield	1933	Peat, Fern B.	80-120	
Mother Goose	Mother Goose: Her Book (1st, lg8vo, 48p, color)	Duffield	(1906)	Smith, Harry L.	60-100	*
Mother Goose	Mother Goose: Her Own Book (1st, folio, [55]p, color, pep)	Reilly/Lee	(1932)	Royt, Mary	120-200	*
Mother Goose	Mother Goose: Her Rhymes (lg8vo, blue cl, 142p, 6 ticp, pep)	Saalfield	(1915)	Matthews, Harry B.	100-165	
Mother Goose	Mother Goose: Her Rhymes & Riddles (1st, 4to, ipcb, [16]p, color, pep)	Saalfield	1939	Peat, Fern B.	75-100	*
Mother Goose	My First Mother Goose (1st, lg8vo, ipcb, [32]p, color, pep, DJ/1.00)	Wilcox/Follett	(1946)	Gehr, Mary	50-80	*
Mother Goose	New Mother Goose Pictures (1st, sq4to, ibds)	Russell	1898	Loomis, Chester B.	170-240	
Mother Goose	Nursery Rhymes from Mother Goose (1st, lg4to, [48]p, color)	Scribner	1907	Wiederseim, Grace	150-220	
Mother Goose	Nursery Rhymes from Mother Goose (sm8vo, 111p, color)	Scribner	1916	Drayton, Grace	160-240	*
Mother Goose	Old Mother Goose in a New Dress (1st, ob4to, [45]p, color, pep)	NY: Laidlaw	1932	Hall, Douglas	120-170	*
Mother Goose	Old Mother Goose Nursery Rhyme Book (16mo, 96p, 24 color, ibds)	T. Nelson	[1920]	Anderson, Anne	80-120	
Mother Goose	Old Mother Goose... (lg4to, p-o, 144p, red cl, 24cp, pep)	T. Nelson	[1926]	Anderson, Anne	170-240	

AUTHOR	TITLE	PUBLISHER	DATE	ARTIST	PRICE	LC
Mother Goose	Original Melodies from... (1st, lg8vo, green cl, 96p, color, cep, DJ/1.25)	Phi: Davis Co.	(1938)	Deming, Kathryn O.	100-170	
Mother Goose	Picture Book of Mother Goose (1st, lg sq8vo, [151]p, color, pep)	Coward	(1930)	Hader, B.& E.	200-300	
Mother Goose	Piper's Son (1st {std}, 16mo, blue cl, [56]p, fp b/w, pep, DJ/0.85)	Longmans	(1942)	Barto, Emily N.	40-65	
Mother Goose	Rainbow Mother Goose (1st, 8vo, 160p, 8cp, pep, DJ/1.00, RC)	World	(1947)	Cassel, Lili	50-80	R
Mother Goose	Real Mother Goose (1st, lg4to, [132]p, color, pep)	Rand/McNally	(1916)	Wright, Blanche F.	100-170	*
Mother Goose	Real Mother Goose (lg4to, p-o, gilt, color, pep)	Rand/McNally	(1928)	Winter, Milo	70-120	
Mother Goose	Real Mother Goose ([new ed.], lg4to, 134p, color, DJ/2.00)	Rand/McNally	(1941)	Wright, Blanche F.	50-80	*
Mother Goose	Romney Gay Mother Goose (1st, sq4to, ipcb, 56p, color, pep)	Grosset/Dunlap	(1936)	Gay, Romney	65-90	
Mother Goose	Songs from Mother Goose (1st, 4to, 83p, color)	Macmillan	1920	Enright, Maginel W.	120-180	*
Mother Goose	Stokes Wonder Book of Mother Goose (1st, 4to, 240p, 24cp, pep)	Stokes	(1919)	Choate/Curtis	60-90	
Mother Goose	Tall Book of Mother Goose (1st {std}, lg4to, 120p, ibds, color, pep)	Harper	(1942)	Rojankovsky, Feodor	80-140	
Mother Goose	Teenie Weenie Man's Mother Goose (1st, 4to, 126p, 12cp, pep)	Reilly/Lee	(1921)	Donahey, William	200-300	
Mother Goose	Tiny Book of Nursery Rhymes (1st, 12mo, ipcb, 61p, color, pep)	Harter	(1934)	Van Nortwick, C.	40-60	*
Mother Goose	To Market! To Market! (1st, ob8vo, [41]p, color, DJ/3.50)	Doubleday	(1967)	Spier, Peter E.	60-90	*
Mother Goose	Tom, Tom the Piper's Son (1st, ob4to, 32p, color, DJ/2.50)	Whittlesey	1964	Galdone, Paul	40-70	R*
Mother Goose	Toni Frissell's Mother Goose (1st, sm4to, ibds, 94p, fp b/w, pep)	Harper	(1948)	(Photos)	80-130	
Mother Goose	True Mother Goose (1st, lg8vo, 138p)	Lamson/Wolffe	1896	McManus, Blanche	120-185	R*
Mother Goose	True Mother Goose (1st, lg8vo, 138p, b/w)	Mansfield/Wes.	1899	McManus, Blanche	100-175	*
Mother Goose	Willy Pogany's Mother Goose (1st, lg8vo, [152]p, teg, gilt, color, pep)	Nelson	(1928)	Pogany, Willy	250-400	
Mott, Lawrence	White Darkness (1st, 12mo, blue cl, 308p, 3pl by...)	Outing	1907	Schoonover, Frank	35-60	
Moulton, Louise C.	Arthur O'Shaughnessy (1st, 12mo, 120p, gilt, teg, cvr by...)	Stone/Kimball	1894	Hallowell, G.H.	80-120	
Moulton, Louise C.	In Childhood's Country (1st, 8vo, tan cl, 69p, uncut, 9pl, pep)	Copeland & Day	1896	Reed, Ethel	200-300	R
Mourat, Joseph	Humpty Dumpty & other Songs (1st, sq4to, ibds, 32p, 7 fp b/w)	L: Blackwell	1920	Woodroffe, Paul	200-285	
Mowat, Farley	Black Joke (1st AM {std}, 8vo, 218p, b/w, DJ/3.75)	Little/Brown	(1963)	Mays, Victor	40-65	
Mowat, Farley	Dog Who Wouldn't Be (1st {std}, 8vo, 238p, DJ/3.95)	Little/Brown	(1957)	Galdone, Paul	30-45	
Mowat, Farley	Lost in the Barrens (1st {std}, 8vo, 244p, b/w, DJ/3.00)	Little/Brown	(1956)	Geer, Charles	45-70	
Mowat, Farley	Owls in the Family (1st {std}, 8vo, 103p, b/w, DJ/2.95)	Little/Brown	(1961)	Frankenberg, Rbt.	25-45	
Mowbray, John	Dismal Jimmy of the Fourth (1st, 8vo, 215p, p-o, col frn, 3pl)	L: Cassell	1928	Brock, Henry M.	30-50	*
Mrs. Valentine	Shakespearian Tales in Verse for Children (4to, gilt, AEG, 109p, chromos)	Armstrong/Warne	[1882]	Andre, R.	450-600	
Muehl, Lois B.	Hidden Year of Devlin Bates (1st, 8vo, 138p, fp b/w, DJ/3.25)	Holiday House	(1967)	Martinez, John	20-30	
Muehl, Lois B.	My Name Is... (1st, sm8vo, tan cl, [55]p, 2-color, DJ)	Holiday House	(1959)	Watson, Aldren A.	25-45	
Muhlenweg, Fritz	Big Tiger and Christian (1st, 8vo, yellow cl, 592p, b/w, pep, DJ/4.95)	Pantheon	(1952)	Busoni, Rafaello	120-200	
Muir, John	Stickeen... (1st, 12mo, tan cl, [73]p, designs, PPPa)	Houghton	1909	Rogers, Bruce	120-200	
Mukerji, Dhan G.	Bunny, Hound and Clown (1st {std}, 8vo, gilt, 124p, b/w, pep, DJ/2.50)	Dutton	(1931)	Wiese, Kurt	25-45	
Mukerji, Dhan G.	Chief of the Herd (1st {std}, 8vo, 168p, 6pl, pep)	Dutton	(1929)	Blaine, Mahlon	30-45	
Mukerji, Dhan G.	Fierce Face (1st {std}, 8vo, 77p, green cl, pep, DJ/1.00)	Dutton	1936	Lathrop, Dorothy	100-150	
Mukerji, Dhan G.	Gay Neck (1st, 8vo, 197p, t.e. blue, gilt, b/w, pep, DJ, NM)	Dutton	(1927)	Artzybasheff, Boris	100-165	R
Mukerji, Dhan G.	Ghond the Hunter (1st {std}, 8vo, gilt, 204p, 3 dp pl, pep, DJ/2.50)	Dutton	(1928)	Artzybasheff, Boris	80-125	
Mukerji, Dhan G.	Hari: The Jungle Lad (1st, 8vo, 220p, b/w)	Dutton	(1924)	Steinmetz, Morgan	20-30	
Mukerji, Dhan G.	Jungle Beasts and Men (1st, 8vo, 160p, col frn, b/w)	Dutton	(1923)	Allen, J.E.	25-40	
Mukerji, Dhan G.	Kari: The Elephant (1st, 8vo, 135p, b/w)	Dutton	(1922)	Allen, J.E.	20-30	
Mukerji, Dhan G.	Master Monkey (1st {std}, 8vo, aqua/gilt, 261p, pep, 5pl)	Dutton	(1932)	Weber, Florence	35-60	*
Mukerji, Dhan G.	Rama, Hero of India (1st {std}, 8vo, red/gilt, 219p, dep)	Dutton	(1930)	D'Aulaire, E. Parin	70-100	
Mulets, Lenore E.	Stories of the Little Fishes (1st, 8vo, 288p, 6pl)	L.C. Page	1905	Schneider, Sophie	25-40	*
Mulford, Clarence	Bar 20 (1st [1st bk.], sm8vo, 382p, 2pl by...)	Outing	1907	Wyeth, N.C.	250-400	
Mulford, Clarence	Bar-20 Days (1st, 8vo, 412p, 4cp)	McClurg	1911	Dixon, Maynard	200-300	
Mulford, Clarence	Buck Peters, Ranchman (1st, 8vo, 367p, 4cp)	McClurg	1912	Dixon, Maynard	200-300	
Mulford, Clarence	Coming of Cassidy (1st, 8vo, 438p, 5cp)	McClurg	1913	Dixon, Maynard	200-300	
Mulford, Clarence	Hopalong Cassidy (1st, 8vo, 392p, ipcb, 5cp)	McClurg	1910	Dixon, Maynard	250-350	
Mulford, Clarence	Hopalong Cassidy Returns (1st, sm8vo, 310p, color)	Doubleday/Page	1924	Schuyler, Remington	80-130	
Mulford, Clarence	The Orphan (1st, sm8vo, 399p, 4cp)	Outing	1908	True, Allen	100-165	
Muller, Charles G.	How they Carried the Goods (1st, lg8vo, 318p, 4cp, 9pl)	Sears	(1932)	Tenggren, Gustaf	40-60	
Muller, F. Max	Memories... (1st [new ed], 8vo, 135p, teg, gilt, p-o, 8pl)	McClurg	1902	Ostertag, Blanche	40-60	
Muller, F. Max	Memories... (2nd, lg8vo, 135p, blue/gilt, teg, cvr by...)	McClurg	1906	Armstrong, Margaret	100-170	
Munari, Bruno	Birthday Present (1st AM, lg4to, unpag, ibds, color, DJ/2.00)	World	(1959)	Munari, Bruno	80-125	
Munari, Bruno	Bruno Munari's ABC (1st AM {std}, lg4to, [48]p, color, DJ/3.50, NYTBI)	World	(1960)	Munari, Bruno	100-175	
Munari, Bruno	Bruno Munari's Zoo (1st AM {std}, 4to, ibds, unpag, color, DJ/3.50)	World	(1963)	Munari, Bruno	75-125	
Munari, Bruno	Circus in the Mist (1st AM {std}, sq8vo, ibds, [57]p, color, DJ/4.50, NYT)	World	(1969)	Munari, Bruno	70-120	
Munari, Bruno	Jimmy has Lost his Cap, Where Can it Be? (1st AM lg4to unpag col, DJ/2.00)	World	(1959)	Munari, Bruno	70-100	
Munari, Bruno	Tic, Tac, and Toc (1st AM, folio, ibds, unpag, DJ/2.00)	World	(1957)	Munari, Bruno	75-125	
Munari, Bruno	Who's There? Open the Door! (1st AM, folio, ibds, unpag, color, DJ/2.00)	World	(1957)	Munari, Bruno	70-120	
Mundy, Talbot	Hira Singh (1st, sm8vo, green cl, 308p, 6pl)	Bobbs-Merrill	(1918)	Coll, Joseph C.	70-100	
Mundy, Talbot	Ivory Trail (1st, sm8vo, 411p, 6pl)	Bobbs-Merrill	(1919)	Coll, Joseph C.	70-100	
Mundy, Talbot	King of the Khyber Rifles (1st, 8vo, 395p, 7 pl b/w, gilt)	Bobbs-Merrill	(1916)	Coll, Joseph C.	100-175	
Munkittrick, R.K.	Farming (1st, 8vo, green pcb, [102]p, 1-color)	Harper	1891	Frost, A.B.	90-120	R
Munkittrick, R.K.	Moon Prince & Other Nabobs (1st, 12mo, 340p, aqua/gilt, b/w)	Harper	1893	Various	55-80	*
Munro, E.S.	Topsy-Turvey Tales (1st, lg8vo, 180p, 6cp, 16 b/w)	L: John Lane	1923	Robinson, W. Heath	180-270	
Munroe, Kirk	At War with Pontiac (1st, 12mo, 320p, grey/gilt, 8pl)	Scribner	1895	Finnemore, J.	30-50	
Munroe, Kirk	Blue Dragon (1st, 12mo, 268p, grey cl, 7pl)	Harper	1904	Mears, W.E.	35-60	
Munroe, Kirk	Brethren of the Coast (1st, 12mo, 303p, 8pl)	Scribner	1900	Zogbaum, Rufus F.	50-85	*
Munroe, Kirk	Copper Princess (1st, 12mo, 237p, 12pl)	Harper	1898	Rogers, W.A.	40-70	
Munroe, Kirk	Coral Ship (1st, sm8vo, 261p, 14pl)	Putnam	1893	Unknown	30-50	
Munroe, Kirk	Flamingo Feather (1st {std}, lg8vo, 222p, p-o, gilt, 10pl, pep)	Harper	(1923)	Schoonover, Frank	50-80	
Munroe, Kirk	Forward March (1st, 12mo, 254p, 20pl)	Harper	1899	(Photos)	50-80	*
Munroe, Kirk	Fur-Seal's Tooth (1st, 12mo, 267p, green cl, b/w)	Harper	1894	Rogers, W.A.	70-100	
Munroe, Kirk	Golden Days of '49 (1st, sm8vo, 351p, col frn, pep)	Dodd	1924	Crump, Leslie	40-65	R
Munroe, Kirk	Ready Rangers (1st, sm8vo, 334p, red cl, 6pl)	Lothrop Pub.	(1897)	Rogers, W.A.	40-60	
Munroe, Kirk	Rick Dale (1st, 12mo, 282p, 19pl)	Harper	1899	Rogers, W.A.	30-50	

AUTHOR	TITLE	PUBLISHER	DATE	ARTIST	PRICE	LC
Munroe, Kirk	Son of Satsuma (1st, 12mo, green cl, 306p, 8pl)	Scribner	1901	Zogbaum, Rufus F.	40-70	
Munroe, Kirk	Under the Great Bear (1st, 12mo, 313p, 12pl)	Doubleday/Page	1900	Giles, Howard	35-60	*
Munroe, Kirk	White Conquerors (1st, 12mo, 326p, uncut, gilt, 8pl)	Harper	1893	Stacey, Walter S.	40-60	
Munson, Nelson	Who's Who in Tony Sarg's Zoo (1st, 4to, ibds, [34]p, fp color, pep)	McLoughlin	1937	Sarg, Tony	140-200	
Murai, Gensai	Kibun Daizin (1st, 12mo, 164p, 12pl)	Century	1904	Varian, George	35-60	*
Murphey, Eleanor A.	Nihal (1st, lg8vo, aqua cl, 39p, fp 2-color, DJ/3.00)	Crowell	(1960)	Keats, Ezra J.	45-75	
Murphy, Marguerite	Necklace of Jewels (1st, sm8vo, 123p, blue/gilt, 8pl)	L.C. Page	1918	Goss, John	20-30	
Murphy, Nettie S.	Isn't It So? (1st, sm8vo, 92p, b/w)	Lippincott	1902	Coll, Joseph C.	70-120	
Murphy, Robert	Warm-Hearted Polar Bear (1st {std}, 4to, 47p, blue cl, color, DJ/2.95)	Little/Brown	(1957)	Slobodkin, Louis	35-50	
Murphy, Ruby B.	Who's Who in Mother Goose Land (1st, 12mo, [31]p, ibds, 1-color)	Rand/McNally	1935	Combet, Fernande	35-60	
Murphy, Shirley R.	Elmo Doolan & Search for Golden Mouse (1st {std}, 8vo, 125p, b/w, DJ/4.25)	Viking	(1970)	Kredel, Fritz	20-35	
Murray, Gilbert	Airplane Spider (1st, 12mo, grey cl, 86p, p-o, 7cp)	Little/Brown	1920	Cady, Harrison	120-180	*
Murray, Gilbert	Airplane Spider (1st UK, 8vo, 86p, tan bds, p-o, 7cp)	L: A&C Black	1921	Cady, Harrison	120-180	
Murray, Hilda	Flower Legends for Children (1st, ob4to, ibds, 63p, 14cp, pep)	L: Longmans	1901	Eland, John S.	120-200	
Musselman, M.M.	I Married a Redhead (1st, sm8vo, 244p, b/w, DJ/3.00)	Crowell	(1949)	Galdone, Paul	30-45	
Musson, Bennet	Maisie & her Dog Snip in Fairyland (1st, 8vo, 165p, 8cp)	Harper	1903	Cory, Fanny	70-120	
Muter, Gladys N.	Duck's Adventure (1st, sm sq4to, color)	Volland	(1927)	Unknown	55-80	*
Muter, Gladys N.	Little Bim the Circus Boy (1st, ob folio, color)	Volland	(1924)	Scott, Janet L.	140-220	*
Muter, Gladys N.	Mother Let Me Do It (1st {std}, 12mo, ibds, [36]p, color)	Volland	(1925)	Barney, Maginel W.	55-80	*
Muter, Gladys N.	Told in Our Neighborhood (1st, sm8vo, ibds, color)	Volland	(1925)	Foster, Marcia L.	40-60	*
Mutt, Eugenie	Fairy Tales from Baltic Shores (1st, lg8vo, p-o, 382p, pep, 8cp)	Penn	(1930)	Berkowitz, Jeannette	60-90	
Myers, Grace	Fishing Cat (1st, ob8vo, yellow cl, [24]p, 1-color, pep, DJ/1.25)	Abingdon Press	1953	Galdone, Paul	30-50	
Myers, Jane P.	Stories of Enchantment (1st, 12mo, 215p, b/w)	McClurg	1901	Richards, Harriet R.	25-40	
Myers, Madeleine	Pulling Strings (1st {std}, 8vo, 228p, DJ/2.50)	Holt	(1954)	Adams, Adrienne	25-40	
Myers, Walter	Where Does the Day Go? (1st, sm ob4to, [40]p, fp color, DJ/3.50)	Parents Mag. Pr.	(1969)	Carty, Leo	50-80	*
Myller, Rolf	Rolling Round (1st {std}, 8vo, [34]p, 1-color, DJ/2.95)	Atheneum	1963	Myller, Rolf	25-40	
Myrick, Mildred	Ants are Fun (1st, 8vo, 63p, color, DJ/2.50)	Harper	(1968)	Lobel, Arnold	25-40	
Myrick, Mildred	Secret Three (1st, 8vo, ibds, 64p, 2-color, DJ/1.95)	Harper	(1963)	Lobel, Arnold	25-45	
N/A	100 Best Fairy Tales (folio, ibds, 123p, 8cp, DJ)	Whitman	(1937)	Anderson, Anne	120-180	
N/A	A Carol: Good King Wenceslas (4to, [26]p, wraps, p-o, 12 ticp)	L: L.B. Hill	[1920]	King, Jessie	500-800	
N/A	Adventures of Jack (narrow folio, wraps, [16]p, color)	Stecher	1921	Brundage, Frances	50-80	
N/A	Adventures of Mr. Mouse (lg4to, ibds, [48]p, 16 fp color)	L: Collins	[1918]	Greenwood, W.E.	90-165	
N/A	Aladdin (1st, 16mo, 61p, pep)	L: J.M. Dent	1895	Heath, Sidney H.	45-80	*
N/A	Aladdin (1st, sq4to, wraps, [15]p, chromos)	McLoughlin	1898	Unknown	45-80	*
N/A	Aladdin (1st, lg8vo, red cl, 39p, 8cp)	L: John Lane	1924	Beaman, S.G.H.	100-165	
N/A	Aladdin (1st AM, sm4to, 39p, 8cp)	McBride	1925	Beaman, S.G.H.	100-150	
N/A	Aladdin & his Wonderful Lamp (1st, 4to, [17]p, color, DJ)	Macmillan	1935	MacKinstry, Eliz.	100-170	R
N/A	Aladdin and his Wonderful Lamp (12mo, 38p, color, pep)	NY: Nelson	1928	Anderson, Anne	55-80	
N/A	Ali Baba & Aladdin (1st, 4to, 128p, ibds, 8cp)	L: Harrap	1918	Mackenzie, Thomas B.	200-300	
N/A	Ali Baba and the Forty Thieves (12mo, ibds, 4cp)	Nelson	[1920]	Anderson, Anne	65-90	
N/A	All About Story Book (1st, sq4to, 63p, orange/gilt, color)	Cupples/Leon	(1929)	Various	80-120	*
N/A	All About the Fairies (16mo, wraps, 5 fp color, b/w)	L: Swain	[1920]	Attwell, Mabel L.	180-220	
N/A	All About the Three Bears (12mo, bds, p-o, 47p, color)	Cupples/Leon	(1914)	Hartley, Dick	60-90	
N/A	All Shakespeare's Tales (1st, lg8vo, gilt, p-o, 453p, 11cp)	Stokes	(1911)	Kirk, Maria L.	125-200	
N/A	All the Best Nursery Stories & Rhymes (4to, red cl, 6 dp color, 24cp)	L: Blackie	[1908]	Hassall, John	180-225	
N/A	American Stage of Today (1st, folio, [86]p, ipcb, b/w designs by...)	Collier	(1910)	Bradley, Will	120-200	
N/A	Animal Alphabet (4to, 24p, color, wraps, pep)	Whitman	[1930]	Cady, Harrison	120-200	*
N/A	Animals on the Farm (1st, 4to, linen, [20]p, 8cp)	Saalfield	1936	Burd, Clara M.	30-50	
N/A	Arabian Nights (1st, 12mo, 424p, AEG, blue/gilt, b/w, cep)	L: Longmans	1898	Ford, H.J.	400-600	
N/A	Arabian Nights (1st, 4to, 472p, green cl, b/w)	L: Newnes	1899	Various	120-160	*
N/A	Arabian Nights (1st, 8vo, 501p, 4cp by...)	L: Routledge	1904	Cooper, Alfred W.	140-200	
N/A	Arabian Nights (1st, 8vo, 501p, cvr by...)	L: Routledge	1904	King, Jessie	140-200	
N/A	Arabian Nights (1st, 8vo, gilt, AEG, 328p, 6cp, pep)	Nister/Dutton	[1907]	Paget, Walter	120-180	
N/A	Arabian Nights (1st, lg8vo, 435p)	L: Constable	(1908)	Various	75-100	*
N/A	Arabian Nights (1st, lg8vo, 339p, teg, p-o, 12cp, pep, SC)	Scribner	1909	Parrish, Maxfield	180-240	R
N/A	Arabian Nights (1st, 12mo, 318p, col frn, 7pl)	Baker/Taylor	1910	Emerson/D'Emo	30-50	*
N/A	Arabian Nights (8vo, 352p, 29cp)	L: Blackie	[1910]	Stratton, Helen	55-90	*
N/A	Arabian Nights (8vo, 435p, gilt, col frn)	Dodge	(1910)	Various	25-45	*
N/A	Arabian Nights (1st AM, sm4to, p-o, 299p, teg, 20 ticp)	Dodd	1912	Bull, Rene	250-400	
N/A	Arabian Nights (1st, sm4to, 299p, p-o, gilt, 20 ticp)	L: Constable	1912	Bull, Rene	300-500	
N/A	Arabian Nights (1st, 8vo, 412p, teg, gilt, 12cp)	L: A&C Black	(1913)	Folkard, Charles	150-220	
N/A	Arabian Nights (1st AM, 8vo, 294p, 15cp)	Henry Holt & Co.	1913	Orr, Monro S.	75-100	
N/A	Arabian Nights (1st, lg8vo, teg, 294p, gilt, 15cp)	L: Harrap	1913	Orr, Monro S.	90-120	
N/A	Arabian Nights (1st, 8vo, 295p, 6cp)	L: Allen/Unwin	(1913)	Soper, George	70-100	
N/A	Arabian Nights (1st, lg8vo, 293p, p-o, 16cp, pep, WS)	Rand/McNally	(1914)	Winter, Milo	70-100	
N/A	Arabian Nights (8vo, 299p, green cl, p-o, 7 ticp, later)	L: Constable	[1917]	Bull, Rene	150-220	
N/A	Arabian Nights (1st, sm8vo, p-o, 420p, 7cp, pep)	Jacobs	[1918]	Lister, W.H.	30-50	
N/A	Arabian Nights (1st, sm8vo, 371p, col frn, b/w)	Macmillan	1923	Pape, Eric	60-90	
N/A	Arabian Nights (1st, 8vo, 257p, 4cp, b/w)	Winston	(1924)	Bolton, Adelaide H.	25-40	*
N/A	Arabian Nights (1st, 4to, 240p, teg, white/gilt, 12 ticp)	L: Hodder	(1924)	Detmold, Edward J.	500-700	
N/A	Arabian Nights (1st AM, lg8vo, blue/gilt, 297p, p-o, 12 ticp)	Dodd	(1925)	Detmold, Edward J.	400-650	
N/A	Arabian Nights (1st, lg8vo, 242p, gilt, col frn, pep)	Sears	(1928)	Becker, Charlotte	30-50	
N/A	Arabian Nights (1st, 4to, 308p, black cl, p-o, 16cp, pep)	Penn	(1928)	Sterrett, Virginia	250-400	R
N/A	Arabian Nights (1st, 12mo, grey cl, 402p, 11 fp b/w)	Appleton-Century	(1936)	Artzybasheff, Boris	50-80	*
N/A	Arabian Nights (1st, 8vo, 308p)	Longmans	1946	Bock, Vera	35-60	*
N/A	Arabian Nights (1st, lg8vo, 327p, fp color)	Grosset/Dunlap	(1946)	Goodenow, Earle	30-50	*
N/A	Arabian Nights (1st, 8vo, 348p, 16cp, DJ)	L: Blackie	1957	Baynes, Pauline	40-65	
N/A	Arabian Nights' Entertainment (1st, 8vo, 430p, p-o, 4cp, pep)	Harper	(1916)	Rhead, Louis	50-80	

AUTHOR	TITLE	PUBLISHER	DATE	ARTIST	PRICE	LC
N/A	Around the House (1st, 4to, ibds, 96p, 63 illus)	Worthington	1888	Greenaway, Kate	100-160	
N/A	Around the World with Santa Claus (lg4to, ibds, 14 chromos)	McLoughlin	1896	Andre, R.	300-500	
N/A	Aucassin & Nicolette (1st, 12mo, 103p, teg, vellum, 4pl)	L: J. Murray	(1902)	Housman, Laurence	140-200	
N/A	Aucassin & Nicolette (1st, 8vo, 91p, teg, vellum/gilt, 12pl)	L: Routledge	1905	James, Gilbert	80-120	
N/A	Aucassin & Nicolette (1st, 8vo, 72p, color)	Dent/Dutton	1910	Armfield, Maxwell	60-80	*
N/A	Aucassin & Nicolette (1st, lg8vo, 131p, teg, 6cp)	L: A&C Black	1911	Anderson, Anne	90-160	
N/A	Aucassin & Nicolette (1st, lg4to, teg, [138]p, gilt, 3 ticp, 14pl)	L: Melrose	1914	Smith, Eileen L.	120-180	
N/A	Aucassin & Nicolette (1st, 4to, 120p, p-o, teg, 13 ticp)	L: Harrap	[1917]	Paul, Evelyn	130-200	
N/A	Aucassin & Nicolette (1st AM, 4to, p-o, unpag, 13 ticp)	Brentano's	[1917]	Paul, Evelyn	100-145	
N/A	Aucassin & Nicolette (1st, narrow 12mo, 106p, color)	Holiday House	1936	Simpson, Maxwell	70-100	R*
N/A	Aunt Louisa's Choice Present (sq4to, AEG)	Warne	(1880)	24 Chromos	100-165	
N/A	Babes in the Wood (4to, ibds, p-o, 12cp)	L: Blackie	[1910]	Adams, Frank	150-220	
N/A	Baby's Animal Book (sm8vo, ibds, 10cp)	Platt/Munk	1929	Eulalie	55-80	
N/A	Baby's Birthday Book (sq16mo, ibds, A.E. pink, color)	L: Marcus Ward	[1885]	Greenaway, Kate	170-240	
N/A	Baby's Book (4to, ibds, 16 fp color)	L: R. Tuck	[1915]	Attwell, Mabel L.	250-350	
N/A	Baby's Record (1st, 4to, green/silver, 12cp)	Stokes	1898	Humphrey, Maud	500-700	
N/A	Banbury Cross... (1st, 8vo, unpag, red cl, 29pl)	L: Dent	1893	Woodward, Alice B.	55-80	*
N/A	Beauty & the Beast (4to, wraps, 6cp)	L: Warne	[1895]	Brock, Henry M.	100-160	
N/A	Beauty & the Beast Picture Book (4to, yellow cl, 24cp)	Dodd	[1915]	Crane, Walter	120-180	*
N/A	Bedtime Story Book (lg4to, wraps, 16cp)	L: Birn Bros.	(1943)	Wood, Lawson	150-225	
N/A	Bettina's Bonnet (sq12mo, ibds, 10 fp color)	Hearst	1915	Drayton, Grace	120-180	*
N/A	Betty's Painting Book (sq4to, stiff wraps, color)	NY: Stecher	1917	Price, Margaret E.	65-90	
N/A	Book for Little People (4to, ibds, 16 chromos)	L: Nister	[1890]	Hardy, E. Stuart	250-400	
N/A	Book of Fairy Tales (1st, 4to, gilt, unpag, pep, 24cp)	L: Warne	[1914]	Brock, Henry M.	250-400	
N/A	Book of New Fairy Tales (4to, grey bds, p-o, [72]p, 7cp by...)	Dodge	[1910]	Dixon, Arthur A.	80-120	
N/A	Book of Pets (lg4to, ibds, 12cp by...)	L: Gardner	1897	Humphrey, Maud	425-600	
N/A	Book of Pets (lg4to, ibds, 12cp by...)	L: Gardner	1897	Tucker, Eliz. S.	425-600	
N/A	Book of Sweethearts (1st, lg4to, [32]p, p-o, 8cp)	Bobbs-Merrill	(1908)	Various	140-200	
N/A	Breman Band (1st, 16mo, [42]p, ibds, color, pep)	Macmillan	1927	Dobias, Frank	50-85	
N/A	Briar Rose Book of Old Fairy Tales (4to, p-o, 159p, 11cp, pep)	L: Jack	[1915]	Anderson, Anne	150-225	
N/A	Bride's Book (4to, white/gilt, 4cp by...)	Stokes	1900	Humphrey, Maud	350-500	
N/A	Bumps & Thumps (sq4to, pict tan cloth, color)	Caldwell	(1903)	Bridgman, L.J.	100-170	
N/A	Chicken Little & Little Half Chick (1st, sq12mo, ibds, color)	Macmillan	1927	Hader, B.& E.	55-80	*
N/A	Children All (4to, ibds)	D. Lothrop Co.	(1898)	6 Chromos	120-180	
N/A	Children at Play in Many Lands (1st, lg ob4to, [16]p, color)	Volland	1922	Rae, John	100-150	
N/A	Children's Story Garden (1st, sm8vo, 247p, blue cl, col frn, 9pl)	Lippincott	1920	Wireman, K.& E.	45-70	
N/A	Christmas Card (8vo, wraps, 8cp)	Dutton	1883	Waugh, Ida	100-175	
N/A	Cinderella (sm4to, ipcb)	Dutton	(1890)	5 Chromos	120-180	
N/A	Cinderella (16mo, ibds, cp)	Reilly/Britton	1907	Bell, Robert A.	75-100	
N/A	Cinderella (1st, 8vo, p-o, 57p, color, pep)	Reilly/Britton	(1908)	Neill, John R.	80-140	
N/A	Cinderella (1st, 4to, [10]p, wraps, color)	Rand/McNally	(1912)	Wright, Blanche F.	100-150	
N/A	Cinderella (4to, ipcb, teg, 62p, gilt, 12 ticp)	L: Hodder	[1915]	Sowerby, Millicent	200-300	
N/A	Cinderella (4to, ibds, color)	L: Gale/Polden	[1917]	Wain, Louis	700-1000	
N/A	Cinderella (1st AM, 4to, ibds, 100p, DJ)	Lippincott	(1919)	Rackham, Arthur	200-300	
N/A	Cinderella (sm folio, 16p, wraps, 8cp)	Harter	(1931)	Peat, Fern B.	50-80	
N/A	Cinderella (1st, 4to, blue cl, [17]p, color, DJ/1.75)	Macmillan	1934	Sewell, Helen	80-130	R
N/A	Cinderella (folio, [22]p, color)	Whitman	1935	Bennett, Juanita C.	40-60	*
N/A	Cinderella (1st, 24mo, [41]p, ipcb, 2-color)	Holiday House	[1938]	Scott, Hilda	55-80	
N/A	Cinderella (1st, 4to, ibds, [32]p, color, pep)	Garden City	1938	Weisgard, Leonard	80-140	
N/A	Cinderella (1st, lg8vo, [16]p, color, pep)	Grosset/Dunlap	(1939)	Stenberg-Masolle, A.	40-60	*
N/A	Cinderella (1st, lg8vo, ibds, [33]p, color)	Wilcox/Follett	(1948)	Stolberg, Doris	35-60	*
N/A	Cinderella (1st, sm ob4to, unpag, fp color, DJ/3.50)	Knopf	(1965)	Montresor, Beni	80-130	
N/A	Cinderella's Picture Book (1st, 4to, 8cp)	J. Lane	(1897)	Crane, Walter	140-200	
N/A	Cock Robin (1st, ob8vo, [30]p, color, DJ/3.25)	Scribner	(1965)	Cooney, Barbara	45-70	*
N/A	Comin' Thro the Rye (1st, lg8vo, p-o, 6cp)	Bobbs-Merrill	(1909)	Underwood, C.F.	50-80	
N/A	Cuddly-Kitty Book (1st, 8vo, tan cl, p-o, 12cp)	Nelson	[1915]	Anderson/Wright	150-220	
N/A	Daisy Days (4to, ipcb)	Fiske Co.	1890	(Chromos)	120-180	
N/A	Dandy-Andy Book (lg8vo, 24p, p-o, 12cp)	Nelson	[1907]	Anderson, Anne	120-170	
N/A	Diamond Fairy Book (1st, 8vo, 310p, gilt, AEG, b/w, dep)	L: Hutchinson	(1897)	Millar, H.R.	120-180	
N/A	Diamonds & Toads (4to, linen wraps, 6cp)	McLoughlin	[1875]	Greenaway, Kate	200-270	
N/A	Dick Whittington & his Cat (4to, ibds, color)	L: Hodder	[1910]	Hassall, John	100-160	
N/A	Dick Whittington & his Cat (1st, 24mo, ipcb, [38]p, 2-color)	Holiday House	1937	Eichenberg, Fritz	75-100	R*
N/A	Dick Whittington & his Cat (1st, 4to, ibds, [32]p, 1-color, DJ/1.75, CH)	Scribner	1950	Brown, Marcia	100-165	R
N/A	Dodge's Red Picture Book (8vo, red bds, p-o, fp color, cep)	Dodge	[1912]	Hassall, John	160-220	
N/A	Droll Doings (1st, lg4to, [64]p, ibds, 40 color)	L: Blackie	[1900]	Neilson, Harry B.	140-200	
N/A	Early Work of Aubrey Beardsley (1st, lg4to, 157p, teg, uncut)	L: John Lane	1899	Beardsley, Aubrey	250-400	
N/A	Everyman & other Plays (1st, 4to, black cl, 201p, 18cp, pep)	L: Chapman	1925	Austen, John	100-165	
N/A	Fair Women from Vogue (4to, 28p, tan buckram, b/w)	Fashion Co.	1894	Armstrong, Margaret	140-220	
N/A	Fairy Ship (lg sq4to, wraps, 12p)	J. Lane	(1890)	Crane, Walter	100-160	
N/A	Fairy Tale Omnibus (1st, 4to, 182p, red cl, col frn, 4cp)	L: Collins	[1915]	Anderson, Anne	75-100	*
N/A	Fairy Tales in Other Lands (1st, 12mo, 96p, ibds, 4cp)	L: Cassell	[1925]	Folkard, Charles	80-120	
N/A	Fairy Tales/Arabian Nights (1st, 12mo, 287p, col frn, 12pl)	L: Dent	1899	Robinson, Thomas H.	75-100	*
N/A	Faithful Friends (4to, pict red cl, 6pl by...)	L: Blackie	[1913]	Rackham, Arthur	280-350	
N/A	Famous Love Songs (1st, lg8vo, blue cl, p-o, 17cp)	Bobbs-Merrill	(1909)	Underwood, C.F.	70-100	
N/A	Father Tuck's Bird ABC (4to, wraps, [14]p, 4cp)	L: R. Tuck	1895	Unknown	100-150	
N/A	Father Tuck's Dog Show (lg ob4to, wraps)	L: R. Tuck	[1895]	4 Chromos	120-165	
N/A	Favorite Fairy Tales (1st, 8vo, 355p, gilt, teg, 16pl)	Harper	1907	Newell, Peter	200-300	
N/A	Favorite Fairy Tales (1st, folio, ibds, [28]p, color, GGB)	Simon/Schuster	(1949)	Rojankovsky, Feodor	55-80	*

AUTHOR	TITLE	PUBLISHER	DATE	ARTIST	PRICE	LC
N/A	Favourite Fairy Tales (lg4to, ibds, 16 color)	L: Nelson	[1929]	Anderson, Anne	80-120	
N/A	Foolish Fox (1st, 16mo, ibds, p-o, 92p, color)	Altemus	(1904)	Neill, John R.	60-100	R
N/A	Four Feet by Two (lg8vo, ibds, 72p)	L: Nister	[1890]	8 Chromos	125-200	
N/A	Fox Went Out on Chilly Night (1st {std}, ob4to, [32]p, color, DJ/2.95, CH)	Doubleday	1961	Spier, Peter E.	30-50	
N/A	Frog He Would a Wooing Go (1st AM, 12mo, blue bds, color, pep, DJ)	Follett	1969	Stobbs, William	30-45	
N/A	Fun for the Little Ones (4to, ibds, [36]p, t-i col frn, fp b/w)	L: Nister	[1900]	Wain, Louis	180-250	
N/A	Funny Bunny ABC (1st AM, folio, p-o, color)	NY: Sully	[1912]	Anderson, Anne	160-250	
N/A	Funny Little Darkies (1st, sq4to, wraps, 6cp)	McLoughlin	[1890]	(Lithos)	280-400	
N/A	Gillyflower Garden Book (1st, lg8vo, [48]p, p-o, 12cp)	L: Nelson	[1915]	Anderson, Anne	150-220	
N/A	Gingerbread Boy (ob12mo, 32p, bds, p-o)	Winston	(1918)	Richardson, F.	40-60	
N/A	Gingerbread Boy (folio, wraps, 16 color)	Whitman	(1941)	Peat, Fern B.	50-80	
N/A	Golden Fairy Book (1st, lg8vo, 312p, AEG, b/w, gilt)	L: Hutchinson	[1890]	Millar, H.R.	100-175	
N/A	Golden Goose (1st, sq16mo, ibds, [42]p, color)	Macmillan	1928	Seaman, Mary L.	60-100	
N/A	Golden Goose Book (1st, sq4to, green cl, unpag, 8cp)	L: Warne	(1905)	Brooke, L. Leslie	125-200	
N/A	Golden Ship... (1st, 8vo, 98p, green bds, gilt, b/w)	(London)	1900	Woodward/Bell	140-200	*
N/A	Goldilocks (folio, wraps, color)	Saalfield	1919	Brundage, Frances	55-80	
N/A	Goldilocks & Three Bears (1st, ob4to, [14]p, color)	McLoughlin	1943	McKean, E.C.	45-80	*
N/A	Goody Two Shoes (folio, wraps, shape book)	McLoughlin	1897	6 Chromos	150-250	
N/A	Great Big Animal Book (1st, folio, [22]p, ibds, color, pep, GGB/#468)	Simon/Schuster	1950	Rojankovsky, Feodor	40-60	
N/A	Happy Day Begins (lg sq4to, wraps, [12]p, color)	Saalfield	1931	Scott, Janet L.	70-100	
N/A	Happy Times (4to, ibds, 8 fp color)	L: R. Tuck	[1900]	Wain, Louis	750-1000	
N/A	Henny Penny (1st, narrow ob4to, [32]p, 3-color, DJ/3.50)	Seabury Press	1968	Galdone, Paul	30-50	
N/A	History of Ali Baba (1st, 24mo, 63p, b/w)	L: J.M. Dent	1895	Fell, H. Granville	75-100	*
N/A	History of Cinderella (1st, 24mo, 63p, gilt, teg, uncut, 14pl)	L: J.M. Dent	1894	Fell, H. Granville	100-160	
N/A	History of Simple Simon (1st, smob4to, [32]p, fp 2-color, dep, DJ/2.75)	McGraw-Hill	(1966)	Galdone, Paul	30-50	
N/A	Homes in the Wilderness (1st, 8vo, 74p, p-o, maps)	W.R. Scott	(1939)	Stewart, Mary W.	60-90	
N/A	Hop O' My Thumb (4to, wraps, 8cp)	L: Warne	[1910]	Brock, Henry M.	70-100	
N/A	House that Jack Built (1st {std} 4to, [32]p, 3-color dep, DJ/3.00, CH, NYT)	Harcourt	(1958)	Frasconi, Antonio	100-170	R
N/A	House that Jack Built (1st, sm ob4to, 32p, fp 2-color, pep, DJ/2.25)	Whittlesey	(1961)	Galdone, Paul	30-45	
N/A	Humpty-Dumpty (4to, wraps, fp color)	L: Blackie	[1910]	Hassall, John	70-100	
N/A	Ideal Heads (1st, folio, brown/gilt, AEG, 20cp)	Sunshine	1890	Various	350-500	
N/A	Indian Fairy Book (1st, 8vo, 303p, 8cp, pep)	Stokes	(1916)	Choate/Curtis	80-120	
N/A	Irish Fairy Tales (1st, 12mo, 236p, 2pl)	L: T.F. Unwin	1892	Yeats, Jack B.	300-450	
N/A	Isn't it Funny (4to, ibds)	L: Nister	1895	(Chromos)	250-350	
N/A	Jack & the Beanstalk (1st, 12mo, [31]p, color)	NY: Sully	(1920)	Stecher, William	35-60	*
N/A	Jack & the Beanstalk (1st, sq16mo, ibds, color, pep)	Macmillan	1927	Dobias, Frank	50-85	
N/A	Jack & the Beanstalk (1st, 24mo, ibds, [39]p, decor by...)	Holiday House	(1935)	Parker, Arvilla	70-100	R*
N/A	Jack Frost Arrives on Butternut Hill (1st, 12mo, ibds, color, pep)	Whitman	(1929)	Cady, Harrison	80-125	
N/A	Jack the Giant Killer (1st, 24mo, 82p, teg, uncut, 12pl, pep)	L: J.M. Dent	1894	Bell, Robert A.	70-120	
N/A	Jingle Book (1st, sm ob8vo, ibds, color)	L: Nister	(1905)	Monsell, J.R.	40-65	
N/A	Jolly Old Sports (folio, ibds, p-o, 36cp)	L: Blackie	[1912]	Adams, Frank	170-240	
N/A	Just for Fun... (1st, 4to, 64p, blue cl, fp b/w, pep, DJ/1.00)	Rand/McNally	(1940)	Lawson, Robert	80-130	
N/A	King Albert's Book (1st, 4to, 187p, pcb, 17 ticp)	L: Hodder	(1914)	Various	120-185	
N/A	Kittens (1st, folio, [12]p, wraps, 6cp)	Saalfield	1937	Peat, Fern B.	55-80	
N/A	Kriss Kringle (4to, stiff wraps, [16]p, color)	McLoughlin	1897	(Chromos)	200-300	
N/A	Land of Enchantment (1st, 4to, 144p, olive/gilt, 14pl)	L: Cassell	1907	Rackham, Arthur	250-315	
N/A	Liberty Belles (1st, folio, [56]p, brown/gilt, 8cp)	Bobbs-Merrill	(1912)	Christy, Howard C.	250-400	
N/A	Little Bo Peep (4to, ipcb, [12]p, color)	L: Warne	[1906]	Brooke, L. Leslie	70-125	
N/A	Little Dutch Book (1st, 4to, ibds, [48]p)	McLoughlin	1909	(Chromos)	200-300	
N/A	Little Golden Hair & the Three Bears (1st, 16mo, 111p, bds, p-o, fp color)	L: Nisbet	1904	Batchelor, Anne	160-240	
N/A	Little Housekeepers (folio, wraps, 8cp)	Saalfield	1934	Peat, Fern B.	55-80	
N/A	Little People's Book of Airships (ob4to, ibds, [32]p)	L: Nister	[1905]	(Chromos)	250-400	
N/A	Little Plays for Little People (1st, ob4to, 56p, fp 1-color, DJ/3.50)	Parents Mag. Pr.	(1965)	Vogel, Ilse-Margret	30-50	*
N/A	Little Rabbit (1st, 8vo, [48]p, b/w, pep)	Whitman	(1934)	Livings, Bess	30-45	
N/A	Little Red Riding Hood (16mo, ibds, 57p, fp color)	Reilly/Britton	(1908)	Neill, John R.	70-100	
N/A	Little Snow Drop (1st, 8vo, 10p, wraps, 4 fp color)	Sam Gabriel	1911	Robinson, Gordon	30-50	
N/A	Little Tom Tucker (1st, sm ob4to, [39]p, fp color, DJ/4.50)	McGraw-Hill	(1970)	Galdone, Paul	30-45	
N/A	Love Songs Old & New (1st, sm4to, p-o, unpag, 18cp)	Bobbs-Merrill	(1909)	Underwood, C.F.	70-100	
N/A	Lovely Woman (1st, 4to, [50]p, p-o, 9cp)	Bobbs-Merrill	(1910)	Various	150-225	
N/A	Man in the Moon (1st, 4to, bds, 31p, p-o, 12cp, pep)	L: Blackie	[1918]	Harrison, Florence	200-300	
N/A	May & November Correspondence (1st, lg8vo, 24p, bds, p-o & frn by...)	Houghton	1928	Green, Eliz. S.	40-60	
N/A	Merry Children's Nursery Rhymes (1st, 4to, ipcb, t-i frn)	L: Nister	[1890]	Various	90-120	
N/A	Merry Times (4to, ipcb, AEG)	Fiske Co.	1890	8 Chromos	100-160	
N/A	Miss Lovemouse's Letters (1st, ob4to, 21p, wraps, fp b/w)	L: T. Nelson	1896	Wain, Louis	300-500	
N/A	Mother Hubbard's Book of Rhymes (4to, ibds, p-o, 16cp)	L: Blackie	[1915]	Adams, Frank	180-250	
N/A	Mr. Miacca, an English Folktale (1st {std}, ob4to, [32]p, color, DJ/3.75)	Holt, Rinehart	(1967)	Ness, Evaline	30-50	
N/A	My High School Days (1st, 8vo, teg, green/gilt, color)	Caldwell	(1908)	Bridgman, L.J.	70-90	
N/A	New Story of Little Black Sambo (16mo, grey bds, unpag, color, pep)	Whitman	1926	Thurston/Vetsch	100-165	
N/A	Night Before Christmas & Jingles (sq8vo, 48p, p-o, 12cp by...)	Hurst	(1908)	Morgan, Ike	130-200	*
N/A	No Place Like Home (ob4to, ibds, [22]p)	Nims & Knight	1891	6 Chromos	100-180	
N/A	Nursery Rhyme Picture Book (1st, 4to, ipcb, [32]p, p-o, 16cp, pep)	L: Warne	[1905]	Brooke, L. Leslie	150-220	
N/A	Nursery Rhymes (1st, 8vo, 340p, blue/gilt, p-o, 44cp, pep)	L: Ward Lock	1914	Tarrant, Margaret	200-300	
N/A	Nursery Rhymes (1st, 16mo, grey bds, 48p, p-o, 8cp, pep)	L: Warne	[1917]	Brooke, L. Leslie	70-100	
N/A	Nursery Rhymes (1st, 4to, 46p, ibds, 23 color)	L: Jack	(1919)	Fraser, Claud L.	120-200	
N/A	Nursery Rhymes & Fables (8vo, ibds, 64p, fp color)	L: SPCK	[1910]	Morgan, Walter J.	100-165	
N/A	Odyssey of Homer (1st AM, 8vo, 332p, teg, gilt, 20cp)	Hale-Cushman	(1930)	Flint, William R.	100-160	*
N/A	Old English Songs (1st, sm8vo, 163p, AEG, green/gilt)	L: Macmillan	1894	Thomson, Hugh	60-90	
N/A	Old English Songs & Ballads (1st, lg4to, 198p, 24 ticp)	L: Hodder	[1915]	Brickdale, E.F.	200-300	

AUTHOR	TITLE	PUBLISHER	DATE	ARTIST	PRICE	LC
N/A	Old English Songs & Dances (1st, sm folio, [62]p, ibds, color)	L: Longmans	1902	Robertson, W.G.	350-500	
N/A	Old English Songs & Dances (folio, ibds, color)	L: Hamish	[1910]	Robertson, W.G.	250-350	
N/A	Old Fairy Tales (1st, 4to, [32]p, gilt, 11cp)	L: Warne	(1914)	Brock, Henry M.	150-225	R
N/A	Old King Cole's Book of Nursery Rhymes (4to, ibds, fp color)	L: Macmillan	[1906]	Shaw, Byam	200-300	
N/A	Old Mother Hubbard (4to, ibds, 12cp)	L: Blackie	[1900]	Adams, Frank	120-180	
N/A	Old Nursery Rhymes (4to, 142p, beige cl, 24cp)	L: Nelson	1933	Wood, Lawson	200-300	
N/A	Old Nursery Stories & Rhymes (4to, ibds)	L: Bkackie	[1907]	Hassall, John	180-250	
N/A	Old Songs in French & English (1st, 4to, p-o, 63p, 24cp)	Penn	1923	Cramer, Rie	120-180	
N/A	Old Time Rhymes (1st, lg4to, gilt, 36 ticp, pep)	L: Blackie	1913	Adams, Frank	350-500	
N/A	Old Woman & her Pig (1st, 24mo, [41]p, ibds, 1-color)	Holiday House	[1937]	Tinker, Jack H.	40-70	
N/A	Orange Tree (12mo, [16]p, bds, fp 1-color)	L: Hodder	[1909]	Anderson, Anne	60-100	
N/A	Oranges & Lemons (1st, 4to, [26]p, wraps, 8cp)	L: Warne	[1913]	Brooke, L. Leslie	120-180	
N/A	Oriental Fairy Tales (1st, 8vo, p-o, 627p, gilt, 16 ticp)	Duffield	1923	Cramer, Rie	120-200	
N/A	Our Amateur Circus (1st, ob8vo, [48]p, black/gilt, color)	Harper	1892	McVickar, H.W.	300-450	
N/A	Our Darlings (4to, 288p, ibds, 24 ticp, pep)	L: J.F. Shaw	[1905]	Watkins, Jessie	100-165	
N/A	Peter Pan's ABC (8vo, ibds, p-o, gilt, 25cp)	L: H. Frowde	[1912]	White, Flora	200-320	
N/A	Peter Pickle and his Dog Fido (1st, ob4to, ibds, [20]p, color)	L: D. Nutt	(1906)	Cowham, Hilda	150-225	
N/A	Picture & Rhyme Book (folio, wraps, 20 color)	Saalfield	1941	Peat, Fern B.	70-100	
N/A	Picture Story Book (folio, [18]p, wraps, shape bk., 12 color)	Saalfield	1929	Peat, Fern B.	50-80	
N/A	Plain Jane (1st, 16mo, 95p, green stripe cl, color)	L: G. Richards	1903	Fry, G.M.C.	130-175	
N/A	Poems for Galloping (1st, 8vo, [25]p, fp color, pep, DJ)	Holt, Rinehart	1963	Quackenbush, Rbt.	20-35	*
N/A	Prince Ahmed & the Fairy Perie Banou (1st, 8vo, 118p, bds, p-o, 5cp)	L: Gay/Hancock	(1915)	Robinson, Charles	180-250	
N/A	Puss in Boots (4to, cloth, p-o, 8cp)	Warne	[1900]	Brock, Henry M.	70-100	
N/A	Puss in Boots (1st, 24mo, [38]p, ibds, color, pep)	Holiday House	1936	Eichenberg, Fritz	60-90	
N/A	Puss in Boots (1st, sq16mo, [41]p, color, pep)	Macmillan	1937	Dobias, Frank	70-100	*
N/A	Puss in Boots (1st, 16mo, [59]p, fp color)	McLoughlin	(1941)	Sari	25-40	*
N/A	Queen Mab's Fairy Realm (1st, 8vo, AEG, 310p, gilt, 27pl, pep)	L: G. Newnes	1901	Various	200-270	
N/A	Read to Me Storybook (1st, 8vo, 146p, b/w, cep, DJ/2.00)	Crowell	(1947)	Lenski, Lois	45-70	
N/A	Rhymes of Old Times (1st, 8vo, 107p, teg, 16 ticp, pep)	L: Medici	1925	Tarrant, Margaret	70-120	
N/A	Ride a Cock-Horse (1st, 4to, 29p, ibds, fp color)	L: Chatto	1940	Peake, Mervyn	350-500	
N/A	Robber Kitten (1st, 16mo, 96p, gilt, color)	Altemus	(1904)	Neill, John R.	75-100	
N/A	Robin Hood (1st, lg8vo, olive cl, 115p, 12cp)	Stokes	(1906)	Perkins, Lucy F.	60-90	
N/A	Robin Hood (1st, lg8vo, green/gilt, p-o, teg, 362p, 8cp, pep)	McKay	1917	Wyeth, N.C.	175-250	
N/A	Romance of Tristam & Isoude (1st, 4to, teg, 12cp, pep)	Brentano's	(1920)	Paul, Evelyn	150-200	
N/A	Santa Claus Picture Book (4to, ibds, 12cp)	McLoughlin	1901	(Chromos)	250-400	
N/A	Santa Claus Up-to-Date (4to, stiff wraps, fp color)	McLoughlin	1906	(Chromos)	250-350	
N/A	Santa's Footprints (1st, sm8vo, 154p, uncut, red/gilt, fp b/w, DJ/2.00)	Aladdin	1948	Price, Christine	80-140	
N/A	Scampers and Scrapes (1st, sm4to, [20]p, color)	L: T. Nelson	1905	Hassall, John	60-100	*
N/A	Seven Voyages of Sinbad (1st, 12mo, 71p, ipcb, color)	Holiday House	1939	Reed, Philip	70-100	R*
N/A	Seven Voyages of Sinbad the Sailor (1st AM, sm4to, 71p, 8cp)	McBride	1926	Beaman, S.G.H.	100-170	R
N/A	Seven Voyages of Sinbad the Sailor (1st {std}, 8vo, 58p, color, DJ/3.25)	Atheneum	1962	Reed, Philip	45-70	
N/A	Siegfried & Kriemhild (8vo, 96p, p-o, 8cp, pep)	Dana Estes	[1905]	Pape, Frank	120-175	
N/A	Silly Hare (sm4to, ipcb)	McLoughlin	[1893]	4 Chromos	75-100	
N/A	Simple Addition (lg8vo, p-o, blue cl, [16]p)	McLoughlin	[1880]	21 Chromos	200-300	
N/A	Sinbad the Sailor (1st, 8vo, 279p)	L: Lawrence	1896	Strang/Clark	60-90	*
N/A	Sinbad the Sailor (1st, lg4to, 223p, gilt, bds, p-o, 23 ticp)	L: Hodder	[1914]	Dulac, Edmund	500-700	
N/A	Sing a Song of Sixpence (4to, ibds, 12cp)	L: Blackie	[1912]	Adams, Frank	150-220	
N/A	Sister Susie and the Twins (4to, shape book, wraps, 1-color)	L: Valentine	[1914]	Attwell, Mabel L.	150-225	
N/A	Sleeping Beauty (1st, 8vo, [6]p, linen wraps, color)	Sam Gabriel	(1908)	Robinson, Gordon	70-100	
N/A	Sleeping Beauty (1st, 12mo, ibds, 40p, color, pep)	NY: Nelson	1928	Anderson, Anne	60-90	
N/A	Sleeping Beauty Picture Book (4to, 24cp)	Dodd	[1915]	Evans, E.	120-200	
N/A	Snow White & Rose Red (sq4to, wraps, [16]p, color)	Stecher	1929	Brundage, Frances	40-60	
N/A	Some British Ballads (1st, 4to, 170p, blue/gilt, 16 ticp)	L: Constable	1919	Rackham, Arthur	180-240	
N/A	Some Old Nursery Tales (lg8vo, ibds, 98p, 12cp)	L: Blackie	[1920]	Adams, Frank	120-200	
N/A	Songs of Bryn Mawr College (1st, lg ob4to, 137p, p-o, ibds, b/w, dep)	C.W. Beck	1903	Green, Eliz. S.	125-180	
N/A	Stories from Arabian Nights (lg8vo, 205p, 8cp, pep, later)	Garden City	[1932]	Dulac, Edmund	75-100	
N/A	Stories from Aunt Judy (1st, 8vo, teg, uncut, 268p, 8cp, pep)	L: Bell	1913	Everett, Ethel	50-85	
N/A	Stories from the Odyssey (16mo, 118p, brown/gilt, p-o)	L: Jack	[1910]	Robinson, W. Heath	80-120	*
N/A	Stories Merry and Wise (4to, ibds)	McLoughlin	[1898]	6 Chromos	150-250	
N/A	Story Book (4to, ibds, 248p, 6cp)	Whitman	[1930]	Attwell, Mabel L.	150-220	
N/A	Story of Aladdin (1st AM, 4to, yellow cl, 110p, 1-color)	Knopf	1928	Kettelwell, John	100-160	
N/A	Story of Little Red Hen (1st, folio, red ipcb, [16]p, b/w)	Whitman	(1935)	Ward, Keith	90-140	*
N/A	Story of Old Dame Trot and her Pig (4to, ibds, 12 color)	L: Blackie	[1908]	Adams, Frank	100-145	
N/A	Story of Simple Simon (1st AM, 4to, ibds, p-o, 12cp)	Dodge	[1920]	Adams, Frank	140-185	
N/A	Story of Simple Simon (1st, 4to, ibds, 12cp)	L: Blackie	[1920]	Adams, Frank	150-240	
N/A	Story of the American Firemen (folio, ibds)	McLoughlin	1909	4 Chromos	250-400	
N/A	Tale of Little Priscilla Purr (16mo, red bds, p-o, 13cp, pep)	L: Valentine	[1915]	Wain, Louis	300-450	
N/A	Tale of the Little Bunnies (1st, 4to, wraps, shape book, color)	S. Gabriel	1914	Brundage, Frances	70-125	
N/A	Tales & Talks About Animals (4to, 29cp, pcb, p-o)	Caldwell	[1901]	Unknown	60-100	*
N/A	Tales from Arabian Nights (1st, 8vo, 128p, p-o, 8cp)	L: Dent	[1914]	Robinson/Curtis	120-170	*
N/A	Tales from Arabian Nights (sm4to, 190p, gilt, 20 ticp, later)	L: Hodder	[1920]	Dulac, Edmund	170-220	
N/A	Tales from Arabian Nights (1st, lg8vo, 340p, 48cp)	L: Ward Lock	1920	Jackson, A.E.	80-120	*
N/A	Tall Book of Nursery Tales (1st, narrow 4to, ibds, 120p, color, DJ/1.00)	A.& W. Guild	(1944)	Rojankovsky, Feodor	70-100	*
N/A	Three Bears (12mo, [16]p, linen, color)	McLoughlin	1888	Andre, R.	100-160	*
N/A	Three Bears (4to, wraps, 8cp)	L: Warne	[1900]	Brooke, L. Leslie	100-180	
N/A	Three Bears (12mo, 63p, color)	Rand/McNally	(1937)	Price, Margaret E.	35-60	*
N/A	Three Bears (1st, sq4to, [18]p, color, pep)	Grosset/Dunlap	(1938)	Tedder, Elizabeth	30-50	*
N/A	Three Billy Goats Gruff (1st, sq16mo, ibds, color)	Macmillan	1927	Dobias, Frank	40-65	

AUTHOR	TITLE	PUBLISHER	DATE	ARTIST	PRICE	LC
N/A	Three Little Kittens (4to, wraps)	McLoughlin	[1880]	6 Chromos	130-200	
N/A	Three Little Kittens (lg4to, ibds)	L: Nister	[1890]	5 Chromos	60-90	
N/A	Three Little Kittens (1st, 16mo, [42]p, ibds, color)	Macmillan	1928	Wiese, Kurt	40-60	
N/A	Three Little Kittens (1st, 12mo, ipcb, [32]p, fp 1-color)	Rand/McNally	1938	Brice, Tony	25-40	*
N/A	Three Little Kittens (1st, 4to, ipcb, [16]p, color, dep)	Saalfield	1940	Peat, Fern B.	50-80	
N/A	Three Little Kittens (1st, sm8vo, ibds, [42]p, color, LGB)	Simon/Schuster	1942	Masha	25-40	R
N/A	Three Little Pigs (tall 4to, ibds, color)	L: Blackie	[1925]	Adams, Frank	90-120	
N/A	Three Little Pigs (1st, ob8vo, [48]p, color, pep)	Whitman	(1933)	Jordan, Susan	30-60	*
N/A	Three Little Pigs (folio, wraps, 16p, color)	Saalfield	1933	Peat, Fern B.	50-80	
N/A	Three Little Pigs (1st, 12mo, ipcb, [47]p, fp color)	Rand/McNally	1941	Brice, Tony	25-45	*
N/A	Three Little Pigs in Verse (1st, 8vo, 32p, color, pep, DJ/2.50)	Viking	(1962)	DuBois, W.P.	50-80	R
N/A	Told in the Twilight (1st, 8vo, 93p, tan cloth, 9pl, pep)	Herrick	(1898)	McManus, Blanche	75-100	
N/A	Tom the Piper's Son (4to, ibds, [32]p, 12cp, pep)	L: Blackie	[1920]	Adams, Frank	90-120	
N/A	Tot & Tim (1st, lg4to, [52]p, ibds, 16cp)	L: Collins	[1918]	Marsh, H.G.C.	200-300	
N/A	Twelve Dancing Princesses (1st, 8vo, ipcb, gilt, unpag, color, DJ/3.95)	Holt, Rinehart	(1966)	Adams, Adrienne	25-45	
N/A	Two Jolly Mariners (1st, lg ob8vo, [52]p, ibds, 24 fp color)	L: Blackie	(1915)	Orr, Stewart	150-220	
N/A	Two Well-Worn Shoe Stories (1st, ob folio, ibds, color)	L: Sands	1899	Aldin/Hassall	300-500	
N/A	Wedding Bells (4to, blue/silver, AE silver, 4 chromos)	L: R. Tuck	[1900]	Brundage, Frances	150-225	
N/A	Wee Wee Woman (ob16mo, bds, p-o, 32p, fp color)	Winston	(1918)	Richardson, F.	45-70	
N/A	Whose Little Kitty are You? (folio, ibds, color)	NY: S. Gabriel	1913	Brundage, Frances	130-200	
N/A	Wishing Penny (1st, 8vo, 69p, fp 1-color, cep, DJ/2.95)	Parents Mag. Pr.	(1967)	Lobel, Anita	30-50	
N/A	Wonder Stories from Herodotus (1st, 8vo, 163p, 12cp)	Harper	1900	Fell, H. Granville	100-150	
N/A	Wonderful Kittens (sq4to, ibds, 5cp)	Worthington	1883	Weir, H.	150-220	
N/A	World's Fairy Book (1st, lg8vo, 256p, 12cp)	L: Harrap	(1930)	Orr, Monro S.	120-170	
N/A	Yankee Doodle (4to, wraps, 6 chromos by...)	McLoughlin	[1880]	Nast, Thomas	250-400	
N/A	Young Folks Birthday Book (sq12mo, 188p, fp color)	L: Hills & Co.	[1905]	Aldin, Cecil	120-170	*
N/A	Yours Truly (ob folio, ibds, b/w)	(NY)	1907	Various	100-170	
Nakano, Hirotaka	Elephant Blue (1st AM, 4to, 31p, color, cep, DJ/4.50)	Bobbs-Merrill	(1970)	Nakano, Hirotaka	40-65	*
Nakatani, Chiyoko	Day Chiro Was Lost (1st AM, ob4to, ipcb, 29p, fp color, cep, DJ/3.75)	World	(1969)	Nakatani, Chiyoko	30-50	*
Nakatani, Chiyoko	Fumio and the Dolphins (1st AM {std}, 4to, [42]p, color, DJ/4.95)	World	1970	Nakatani, Chiyoko	30-50	
Napjus, Alice	Freddie Found a Frog (1st, 12mo, [27]p, color, DJ/4.95)	Van Nostrand	(1969)	Ford, George	25-40	*
Nash, Dorothy	Moon Baby (1st, 4to, ibds, p-o, 87p, 9 ticp)	L: Jarrold	[1917]	Nash/Rudge	120-180	*
Nash, Ogden	Adventures of Isabel (1st {std}, 4to, 32p, 3-color, DJ/2.75)	Little/Brown	(1963)	Lorraine, Walter	200-300	R*
Nash, Ogden	Animal Garden (1st, sq8vo, [48]p, dp 1-color, DJ/3.95)	NY: M. Evans	(1965)	Knight, Hilary	40-65	
Nash, Ogden	Bad Parents' Garden of Verse (1st, 8vo, 132p, b/w, DJ/2.00)	Simon/Schuster	1936	Birch, Reginald	40-65	
Nash, Ogden	Boy & his Room (1st {std}, yellow cl, unpag, b/w, DJ/2.95)	F. Watts	(1963)	Smith, Lawrence	40-65	
Nash, Ogden	Boy is a Boy (1st {std}, sm4to, unpag, 1-color, DJ/2.95)	F. Watts	(1960)	Shilstone, Arthur	40-65	R
Nash, Ogden	Christmas that Almost Wasn't (1st {std}, lg8vo, 63p, 8 fp color, DJ/3.50)	Little/Brown	(1957)	Nash, Linell	50-80	
Nash, Ogden	Cricket of Carador (1st {std}-{1st bk}, sm8vo, 165p, col frn, b/w, pep)	Doubleday/Page	1925	Rule, Christopher	80-145	
Nash, Ogden	Cruise of the Aardvark (1st {std}, 8vo, unpag, b/w, DJ/3.95)	M. Evans	1967	Watson, Wendy	30-50	*
Nash, Ogden	Custard the Dragon & Wicked Knight (1st {std}, 8vo, 47p, color, DJ/2.75)	Little/Brown	(1961)	Linell	50-80	R
Nash, Ogden	Everyone but Thee and Me (1st {std}, sm8vo, 171p, b/w, DJ/3.95)	Little/Brown	(1962)	Alcorn, John	40-65	
Nash, Ogden	Girls are Silly (1st {std}, ob4to, [38]p, 1-color, pep, DJ/2.95)	F. Watts	(1961)	Smith, Lawrence	50-80	R
Nash, Ogden	Happy Days (1st, 8vo, 161p, p-o, fp b/w)	Simon/Schuster	1933	Soglow, Otto	80-120	
Nash, Ogden	Hard Lines (1st [1st bk.], 12mo, 99p, gilt, b/w)	Simon/Schuster	1931	Soglow, Otto	80-130	
Nash, Ogden	Musical Zoo (1st {std}, 4to, 47p, cloth, b/w, DJ/2.50)	Little/Brown	1947	Owen, Frank	60-90	
Nash, Ogden	New Nutcracker Suite (1st {std}, sm4to, 48p, color, cep, DJ/3.50)	Little/Brown	(1962)	Chermayeff, Ivan	60-90	R
Nash, Ogden	Parents Keep Out (1st {std}, 8vo, 187p, b/w, DJ/2.75)	Little/Brown	1951	Corrigan, Barbara	50-85	R*
Nash, Ogden	Primrose Path (1st, 8vo, 354p, gilt, b/w, DJ/2.50)	Simon/Schuster	1935	Soglow, Otto	60-90	
Nash, Ogden	Santa Go Home (1st {std}, 8vo, 56p, green cl, 2-color, DJ/4.95)	Little/Brown	(1967)	Osborn, Robert	40-65	
Nash, Ogden	Untold Adventures of Santa Claus (1st {std}, lg8vo, 47p, color, DJ/2.95)	Little/Brown	(1964)	Lorraine, Walter	40-65	
Nash, Ogden	You Can't Get There from Here (1st {std}, 12mo, gilt, 190p, b/w, DJ/3.75)	Little/Brown	(1957)	Sendak, Maurice	120-200	
Nash, Thomas	Spring Song (1st, 8vo, unpag, wraps, teg, 16 color)	L: J.M. Dent	1898	Brooke, L. Leslie	80-125	
Nast, Elsa R.	Farm Story (1st {std}, 4to, ibds, [40]p, color, pep, DJ/1.00)	Harper	(1946)	Masha	35-50	
Nast, Elsa R.	Little Steps (1st, lg8vo, ibds, [36]p, color, pep, DJ/0.50)	Grosset/Dunlap	1947	Doane, Pelagie	30-45	
Nast, Elsa R.	Our Puppy (1st {A}, 8vo, ibds, [28]p, color, LGB/#56)	Simon/Schuster	(1948)	Rojankovsky, Feodor	25-40	
Nast, Thomas	Christmas Drawings for the Human Race (1st, 4to, [67]p, fp b/w)	Harper	1890	Nast, Thomas	450-600	
Nathan, Dorothy	Month Brothers (1st {std}, 8vo, 95p, b/w, DJ/3.95)	Dutton	(1967)	Shulevitz, Uri	30-45	
Nathan, Robert	Fiddler in Barly (1st, 8vo, 137p, 6 woodcuts, DJ)	L: Heinemann	1927	Leighton, Clare	50-80	
Nathan, Robert	Jonah (1st, sm8vo, 212p, 5 engravings)	Knopf	1934	Artzybasheff, Boris	40-65	
Nathan, Robert	Snowflake & the Starfish (1st {std}, 8vo, 68p, fp 2-color, pep, DJ/2.95)	Knopf	(1959)	Weisgard, Leonard	40-70	
Nathan, Robert	Tapiola's Brave Regiment (1st {std}, 8vo, 137p, b/w, pep, DJ/1.75)	Knopf	1941	Wiese, Kurt	25-40	
Nay, Carol	Timmy Rides the China Clipper (1st, 8vo, 94p, p-o, color, pep)	Whitman	1939	Nay, Carol	20-30	
Naylor, James B.	Witch Crow & Barney Bylow (1st, lg8vo, ipcb, 118p, 6cp)	Saalfield	1906	Williams, Carll B.	50-85	
Naylor, Phyllis	Galloping Goat & other Stories (1st, 8vo, 112p, fp color, DJ/3.50)	Abingdon Press	(1965)	Jefferson, Robert	20-35	
Naylor, Phyllis	To Make a Wee Moon (1st {std}, 8vo, 190p, b/w, DJ/3.95)	Follett	(1969)	Krush, Beth & Joe	20-35	
Neale, Dr.	Good King Wenceslas (1st, sm4to, ipcb, [32]p, 6 woodcuts)	Cornish Bros.	1895	Gaskin, Arthur J.	150-250	
Neally, Amy	Baby Days... (1st, 4to, gilt, AEG, 6 chromos)	Dutton	[1890]	Waugh, Ida	200-320	
Neidlinger, Wm. H.	Owl and the Woodchuck (1st, lg8vo, [56]p, ibds, 4cp)	Rand/McNally	(1901)	Bobbett, Walter	50-85	
Neidlinger, Wm. H.	Small Songs for Small Singers (1st, lg4to, 57p, ibds, color)	NY: Schirmer	1896	Bobbett, Walter	50-90	
Neikirk, Mabel O.	Oscar the Trained Seal (1st, ob4to, ibds, [24]p, color, dep, DJ/0.50)	Grosset/Dunlap	(1940)	Dobias, Frank	60-90	
Neill, John R.	Lucky Bucky in Oz (1st [1], 8vo, 289p, p-o, blue cl, b/w, pep, DJ/1.50)	Reilly/Lee	(1942)	Neill, John R.	400-650	
Neill, John R.	Scalawagons of Oz (1st, lg8vo, 309p, p-o, b/w, pep, DJ/1.50)	Reilly/Lee	(1941)	Neill, John R.	500-700	
Neill, John R.	Wonder City of Oz (1st [1], 8vo, p-o, 318p, b/w, pep, DJ/1.50)	Reilly/Lee	(1940)	Neill, John R.	350-500	
Nella	Prince Babillon (1st, 8vo, 131p, uncut, gilt, color)	Kennerley	[1910]	Robinson, Charles	160-225	
Nelson, Margaret W.	Pinky Finds a Home (1st, 12mo, 118p, ibds, col frn, DJ/1.75)	Holiday House	(1940)	Heyneman, Anne	25-45	
Nelson, Mary J.	Fun with Music (1st, sm4to, 47p, color, DJ/1.50)	Whitman	1941	Barnett, G.& O.	30-45	
Nelson, Rhoda	High Timber (1st, sm8vo, 280p, b/w, DJ/2.00)	Crowell	(1941)	Boyle, Mildred	30-50	*

AUTHOR	TITLE	PUBLISHER	DATE	ARTIST	PRICE	LC
Nelson, Rhoda	Wagon Train West (1st, 8vo, 224p, 4cp, fp b/w, pep, DJ/2.00)	Crowell	1939	Blaidsell, Elinore	30-45	
Nerman, Einar	Fairy Tales from the North (1st {std}, lg8vo, 128p, 8cp, pep, DJ/3.00)	Knopf	1946	Nerman, Einar R.	35-50	
Nesbit, Edith	As Happy as a King (1st, ob8vo, unpag)	L: Marcus Ward	[1896]	Praeger, Sophia R.	100-165	
Nesbit, Edith	Bastable Children (1st {this fmt}, 8vo, 293p, col frn, DJ)	Coward	(1929)	Browne/Blam	50-80	
Nesbit, Edith	Book of Dogs (1st, obsm4to, 55p, b/w)	Dutton	1898	Austen, Winifred	200-300	*
Nesbit, Edith	Book of Dragons (1st, 8vo, 290p, gilt, teg, 8 fp color by...)	L: Harper	1901	Fell, H. Granville	450-600	
Nesbit, Edith	Book of Dragons (1st, 8vo, teg, 290p, blue/gilt, 16 b/w by...)	L: Harper	1901	Millar, H.R.	450-600	
Nesbit, Edith	Cat Tales (1st, 12mo, 62p, grey cl, 4 fp color)	Nister/Dutton	[1904]	Watkin, Isabel	140-200	
Nesbit, Edith	Children's Shakespeare (1st AM, 8vo, gilt, 76p, ibds, 11 fp b/w)	Altemus	(1900)	Brundage, Frances	75-100	
Nesbit, Edith	Children's Shakespeare (1st, lg8vo, 128p, fp b/w, DJ/2.00)	Random	(1938)	Klep, Rolf	60-90	*
Nesbit, Edith	Daphne of Fitzroy Street (1st AM, 12mo, 417p, col frn by..)	Doubleday/Page	1909	Cootes, F. Graham	80-145	
Nesbit, Edith	Enchanted Castle (1st, 8vo, teg, 352p, red/gilt, 46pl)	L: T.F. Unwin	1907	Millar, H.R.	300-400	
Nesbit, Edith	Enchanted Castle (1st AM, 12mo, 297p, 8pl)	Harper	1908	Millar, H.R.	250-350	
Nesbit, Edith	Five Children (1st, 8vo, 306p, col frn)	Coward	1930	Millar/Blam	60-100	
Nesbit, Edith	Five Children and It (1st, 8vo, 301p, teg, red/gilt, 46pl)	L: T.F. Unwin	1902	Millar, H.R.	200-300	
Nesbit, Edith	Five of Us & Madeline (1st, sm8vo, 310p, red cl, col frn, 6pl)	L: T.F. Unwin	1925	Unwin, Nora S.	125-180	
Nesbit, Edith	Harding's Luck (1st, 8vo, 281p, gilt, teg, 16 fp b/w)	L: Hodder	1909	Millar, H.R.	250-350	
Nesbit, Edith	Harding's Luck (1st AM, 12mo, green cl, 308p, 16pl)	Stokes	(1910)	Millar, H.R.	180-280	
Nesbit, Edith	House of Arden (1st, 8vo, 349p, teg, red/gilt, 33 fp b/w)	L: T.F. Unwin	1908	Millar, H.R.	250-400	
Nesbit, Edith	House of Arden (1st AM, 12mo, 349p, gilt, 33 fp b/w)	Dutton	1909	Millar, H.R.	200-300	
Nesbit, Edith	Incomplete Amorist (1st AM, 8vo, p-o, 356p, 8pl)	Doubleday/Page	1906	Underwood, C.F.	100-165	
Nesbit, Edith	Long Ago When I was Young (1st AM, 8vo, 127p, b/w, DJ/5.95)	F. Watts	(1966)	Ardizzone, Edward	50-85	
Nesbit, Edith	Long Ago When I was Young (1st, 8vo, 127p, b/w, DJ)	L: Whiting	1966	Ardizzone, Edward	60-90	
Nesbit, Edith	Magic City (1st, 12mo, red/gilt, teg, 333p, 26pl)	L: Macmillan	1910	Millar, H.R.	300-450	
Nesbit, Edith	Magic World (1st, 12mo, teg, 280p, red/gilt, 24pl)	L: Macmillan	1912	Millar, H.R.	300-425	
Nesbit, Edith	New Treasure Seekers (1st, 8vo, red/gilt, 328p, teg, 33 fp b/w)	L: T.F. Unwin	1904	Browne/Baumer	180-240	
Nesbit, Edith	Nine Unlikely Tales for Children (1st, 8vo, gilt, 279p, b/w)	L: T.F. Unwin	1901	Bowley/Millar	160-250	
Nesbit, Edith	Oswald Bastable & Others (1st, 12mo, teg, 369p, gilt, 22pl)	L: Wells/Gard.	(1905)	Brock/Millar	250-400	
Nesbit, Edith	Phoenix & the Carpet (1st, lg8vo, teg, blue/gilt, 321p, col frn, b/w)	L: Newnes	(1904)	Millar, H.R.	300-425	
Nesbit, Edith	Pomander of Verse (1st, sm8vo, gilt, teg, 88p, cvr by..)	J. Lane	1895	Housman, Laurence	130-170	
Nesbit, Edith	Pug Peter (1st, 4to, 64p, teg, blue cloth, color)	L: A. Cooke	(1905)	Rountree, Harry	200-300	
Nesbit, Edith	Pussy & Doggy Tales (1st, 12mo, 132p, 1-color title pg, b/w)	L: J.M. Dent	1899	Kemp-Welch, Lucy	160-240	*
Nesbit, Edith	Railway Children (1st, 8vo, 309p, uncut, teg, gilt, 20pl)	L: Wells/Gard.	(1906)	Brock, Charles E.	250-450	
Nesbit, Edith	Red House (1st AM, 12mo, 274p, green cl, b/w)	Harper	1902	Keller, Arthur I.	90-150	
Nesbit, Edith	Royal Children of English History (1st, 4to, 94p, AEG, 10cp)	L: R. Tuck	(1896)	Brundage/Bowley	180-260	
Nesbit, Edith	Story of Five Rebellious Dolls (1st, ob folio, ibds, 8cp, pep)	L: Nister	(1904)	Hardy, E. Stuart	350-500	
Nesbit, Edith	Story of the Amulet (1st, 12mo, teg, 374p, red/gilt, 48pl)	L: T.F. Unwin	1906	Millar, H.R.	250-350	
Nesbit, Edith	Story of the Treasure Seekers (1st, 8vo, 296p, AEG, 17pl)	L: T.F. Unwin	1899	Browne/Baumer	280-350	
Nesbit, Edith	The Wouldbegoods (1st AM, sm8vo, gilt, 313p, 16pl)	Harper	1901	Birch, Reginald	180-250	
Nesbit, Edith	The Wouldbegoods (1st, sm8vo, red/gilt, 331p, teg, 18pl)	L: T.F. Unwin	(1901)	Buckland, Arthur H.	200-300	
Nesbit, Edith	These Little Ones (1st, 8vo, gilt, 210p, teg, 10pl)	L: G. Allen	1909	Pryse, Gerald S.	160-240	
Nesbit, Edith	Wet Magic (1st, 12mo, teg, red/gilt, 274p, 12pl)	L: T. Laurie	(1913)	Millar, H.R.	160-220	
Nesbit, Edith	Wonderful Garden (1st, 8vo, teg, 402p, red/gilt, 26 fp b/w)	L: Macmillan	1911	Millar, H.R.	200-300	
Nesbit, Wilbur D.	A Friend or Two (1st, 16mo, [14]p, ibds, color)	Volland	(1910)	Unknown	75-100	*
Nesbit, Wilbur D.	As Children Do (1st, 12mo, ibds, 96p, pep, decor by...)	Volland	(1929)	Friend, Ellery	55-80	
Nesbit, Wilbur D.	Friend O'Mine (1st, 12mo, ipcb, [12]p, color)	Volland	(1912)	Myers, Marie H.	45-80	*
Nesbit, Wilbur D.	In Tumbledown Town (1st, sm8vo, unpag, ibds, color, pep)	Volland	(1926)	Gee, John	60-100	
Nesbit, Wilbur D.	Jolly Kid Book (1st, ob4to, ibds, [12]p, color)	Volland	(1926)	Meyers, M.H.	160-240	
Nesbit, Wilbur D.	Just Because of You (1st, 12mo, ibds, color)	Volland	(1925)	Myers, Marie H.	40-60	*
Nesbit, Wilbur D.	Land of Make-Believe (1st, 8vo, green cl, 98p, 5pl)	Harper	1907	Various	35-60	*
Nesbit, Wilbur D.	Oh Skin-nay! (1st, ob folio, [125]p, illus)	Volland	(1913)	Briggs, C.A.	80-125	
Nesbit, Wilbur D.	Sermons in Song (1st, 12mo, ibds, 96p, 1-color, pep)	Volland	(1929)	Unknown	35-60	*
Nesbit, Wilbur D.	Trail to Boyland (1st, sm8vo, tan/gilt, uncut, 163p, 5pl)	Bobbs-Merrill	(1904)	Vawter, J. Will	35-60	*
Nesbit, Wilbur D.	When a Feller Needs a Friend (1st, 4to, ibds, [96]p, 2-color)	Volland	(1914)	Briggs, C.A.	90-145	*
Nesbitt, Philip	Nicholas Needlefoot (1st, 8vo, ibds, [32]p, 1-color, DJ/1.00)	Wilcox/Follett	1944	Nesbitt, Philip	50-80	
Nesbitt, Philip	Trum Peter's Tea-Party (1st, lg8vo, [31]p, 2-color)	Coward	1931	Nesbitt, Philip	30-50	
Ness, Evaline M.	Double Discovery (1st, 4to, [32]p, 3-color, DJ/3.25, NYTBI)	Scribner	(1965)	Ness, Evaline	30-50	
Ness, Evaline M.	Exactly Alike (1st, ob4to, [32]p, 3-color, DJ/3.50, NYTBI)	Scribner	1964	Ness, Evaline	30-50	
Ness, Evaline M.	Gift for Sula Sula (1st, 4to, [31]p, fp 3-color, DJ/3.25)	Scribner	1963	Ness, Evaline	50-80	
Ness, Evaline M.	Girl and the Goatherd (1st {std}, 4to, [32]p, color, DJ/4.25)	Dutton	(1970)	Ness, Evaline	40-65	
Ness, Evaline M.	Josefina February (1st, 4to, [32]p, fp 3-color, DJ/3.25)	Scribner	1963	Ness, Evaline	50-85	R
Ness, Evaline M.	Long, Broad and Quickeye (1st, 4to, [39]p, color, pep, DJ/3.95)	Scribner	(1969)	Ness, Evaline	30-50	
Ness, Evaline M.	Pavo and the Princess (1st, 4to, [32]p, fp color, DJ/3.25)	Scribner	1964	Ness, Evaline	30-50	
Ness, Evaline M.	Sam, Bangs & Moonshine (1st {std}, 4to, [41]p, 2-color, pep, DJ/3.95, CM)	Holt, Rinehart	(1966)	Ness, Evaline	150-225	
Neumeyer, Peter	Why We have Day and Night (1st, ob8vo, ibds, [38]p, color, DJ/3.50)	Young Scott	(1970)	Gorey, Edward	60-85	
Neville, Emily C.	It's Like this, Cat (1st {std}, 8vo, ibds, 180p, b/w, DJ/3.50, NM)	Harper	(1963)	Weiss, Emil	50-80	R
Neville, Emily C.	Seventeenth Street Gang (1st, 8vo, 148p, b/w, DJ/3.50)	Harper	(1966)	McCully, Emily	30-50	*
Neville, Emily C.	Traveler from a Small Kingdom (1st, 8vo, 197p, b/w, DJ/3.50)	Harper	(1968)	Mocniak, George	20-35	
Neville, Mary	First and Last Annual Pet Parade (1st, lg ob8vo, [46]p, b/w, cep, DJ/3.50)	Pantheon	(1968)	Chwast, Jacqueline	30-50	*
Neville, Mary	Woody and Me (1st, lg8vo, [60]p, b/w, DJ/2.95)	Pantheon	(1966)	Solbert, Ronni	25-45	
Nevins, Albert J.	Adventures of Pancho of Peru (1st, 8vo, 246p, gilt, b/w, DJ/2.75)	Dodd	1953	Wiese, Kurt	25-40	*
New, Catherine M.	Woman Reigns (1st, 12mo, 112p, gilt, teg, uncut, cvr by..)	Bowen-Merrill	1895	Rogers, Bruce	30-50	
Newberry, Clare T.	April's Kittens (1st {std}, 4to, [32]p, gilt, color, pep, DJ/1.75, CH)	Harper	1940	Newberry, Clare T.	120-180	
Newberry, Clare T.	Babette (1st {std}, lg8vo, ibds, 32p, pep, color, DJ/1.50)	Harper	1937	Newberry, Clare T.	85-140	
Newberry, Clare T.	Barkis (1st {std}, lg ob8vo, 31p, color, pep, DJ/1.75, CH)	Harper	1938	Newberry, Clare T.	120-180	
Newberry, Clare T.	Cousin Toby (1st {std}, lg8vo, [32]p, yellow bds, pep, DJ/1.60)	Harper	1939	Newberry, Clare T.	100-165	
Newberry, Clare T.	Frosty (1st, 8vo, 92p, fp b/w, DJ/2.50)	Harper	(1961)	Newberry, Clare T.	40-70	
Newberry, Clare T.	Herbert the Lion (1st, ob4to, [41]p, pep, color, DJ/2.00)	Brewer/Warren	1931	Newberry, Clare T.	180-300	

AUTHOR	TITLE	PUBLISHER	DATE	ARTIST	PRICE	LC
Newberry, Clare T.	Herbert the Lion (1st {this pub-std}, ob4to, ibds [64]p, pep, col, DJ/2.00)	Harper	1939	Newberry, Clare T.	150-250	
Newberry, Clare T.	Ice Cream for Two (1st, 8vo, 58p, 2-color, cep, DJ/2.50)	Harper	(1953)	Newberry, Clare T.	45-70	
Newberry, Clare T.	Kitten's ABC (1st {std}, folio, ibds, [36]p, color, DJ/2.00)	Harper	(1946)	Newberry, Clare T.	80-125	
Newberry, Clare T.	Lambert's Bargain (1st {std}, lg8vo, 31p, b/w, pep, DJ/1.00)	Harper	1941	Newberry, Clare T.	80-120	
Newberry, Clare T.	Marshmallow (1st {std}, lg ob4to, [31]p, color, DJ/1.75, CH)	Harper	(1942)	Newberry, Clare T.	100-165	
Newberry, Clare T.	Mittens (1st {std}, lg8vo, ibds, [28]p, pep, 12cp, DJ/1.50)	Harper	1936	Newberry, Clare T.	70-120	
Newberry, Clare T.	Pandora (1st {std}, folio, ibds, p-o, [35]p, b/w, DJ/1.75)	Harper	(1944)	Newberry, Clare T.	80-140	
Newberry, Clare T.	Percy, Polly and Pete (1st, lg ob8vo, ibds, [30]p, color, DJ/2.00)	Harper	(1952)	Newberry, Clare T.	50-80	
Newberry, Clare T.	Smudge (1st, 8vo, ibds, [32]p, 1-color, pep, DJ/1.75)	Harper	1948	Newberry, Clare T.	65-90	R
Newberry, Clare T.	T-Bone the Baby-Sitter (1st, lg ob8vo, ibds, [30]p, color pep, DJ/1.75, CH)	Harper	1950	Newberry, Clare T.	120-200	
Newberry, Clare T.	Widget (1st, lg ob8vo, unpag, 1-color, DJ/2.50)	Harper	(1958)	Newberry, Clare T.	60-90	
Newberry, Fanny E.	Everyday Honor (1st, 12mo, 429p, b/w)	Jacobs	1898	Waugh, Ida	25-45	*
Newbolt, Henry J.	Book of the Happy Warrior (1st, sm8vo, blue/gilt, 284p, 8cp)	L: Longmans	1917	Ford, H.J.	65-90	
Newbolt, Henry J.	Drake's Drum... (1st, 4to, green cl, 143p, 12 ticp, pep)	L: Hodder	[1914]	McCormick, A.D.	100-165	
Newbolt, Henry J.	Taken From the Enemy (1st [new ed], 8vo, gilt, teg, 170p, p-o, 8cp)	L: Chatto	1911	Leake, Gerald	30-60	
Newcomb, Covelle	Cortez the Conqueror (1st, folio, 106p, fp 1-color, DJ/3.00)	Random	(1947)	Rojankovsky, Feodor	70-100	
Newell, David M.	American Animals (1st, 8vo, blue cl, 80p, 10cp, pep)	Volland	(1929)	Newell, David	70-120	
Newell, Hope	Cinder Ike (1st, 8vo, 121p, b/w, DJ/1.75)	NY: Nelson	1942	Peck, Anne M.	30-50	*
Newell, Hope	Steppin & Family (1st, 8vo, 198p, color, pep, DJ/2.00)	NY: Oxford U.Pr.	(1942)	Peck, Anne M.	65-90	
Newell, Peter	Hole Book (1st, 8vo, p-o, [51]p, blue cloth, 24 fp color, PPP)	Harper	(1908)	Newell, Peter	300-500	R
Newell, Peter	Peter Newell's Pictures & Rhymes (1st, ob8vo, tan cl, p-o, 50pl)	Harper	1899	Newell, Peter	200-300	
Newell, Peter	Rocket Book (1st, lg8vo, [48]p, p-o, 23 fp color)	Harper	(1912)	Newell, Peter	300-500	R
Newell, Peter	Shadow Show (1st, ob8vo, ipcb, 72p, color)	Century	1896	Newell, Peter	280-350	
Newell, Peter	Slant Book (1st, 8vo, [47]p, ibds, 22 fp color)	Harper	(1910)	Newell, Peter	250-400	R
Newell, Peter	Topsys & Turvys (1st, lg ob8vo, bds, p-o, 31cp)	Century	1893	Newell, Peter	250-400	
Newell, Peter	Topsys & Turvys Number 2 (1st, lg ob8vo, ipcb, 69p, color)	Century	(1894)	Newell, Peter	250-400	
Newman, Carol	Strella's Children (1st {std}, lg ob8vo, 40p, fp b/w, DJ/3.50)	Atheneum	1966	Krahn, Fernando	30-50	
Newman, Gertrude	Delicia and Adolphus (1st, 8vo, [33]p, ipcb, b/w, pep, DJ/0.50)	Rand/McNally	(1938)	(Photos)	40-70	
Newman, Gertrude	Story of Delicia (1st, 8vo, [61]p, ipcb, b/w)	Rand/McNally	(1935)	(Photos)	40-70	
Newman, Isidora	Fairy Flowers (1st AM, 8vo, ibds, 196p, 15 ticp, pep)	Henry Holt & Co.	(1926)	Pogany, Willy	250-350	
Newman, Isidora	Fairy Flowers (1st, 4to, ibds, 160p, 15 ticp, pep)	L: H. Milford	(1926)	Pogany, Willy	200-300	
Newman, Isidora	Flowers, Facts & Fables (1st, 4to, 141p, ibds, 7cp, cep)	NY: Snellgrove	1937	Pogany, Willy	120-170	
Newman, Isidora	Legend of the Lilac (1st, 4to, ibds, [23]p, 4cp)	Whitman	1926	Pogany, Willy	60-90	
Newman, Isidora	Legend of the Tulip... (1st, 4to, [24]p, ibds, 5cp)	Whitman	(1926)	Pogany, Willy	60-90	
Newman, Isidora	Shades of Blue (8vo, blue/silver, 96p, 16cp)	NY: Harrison Co.	(1927)	Fouts, Herbert E.	70-100	
Newman, Isidora	Wee Miss Violet... (1st, 4to, ibds, unpag, 4cp)	Whitman	(1926)	Pogany, Willy	50-80	
Newman, Robert	Boy Who Could Fly (1st {std}, 8vo, 121p, fp b/w, cep, DJ)	Atheneum	1967	Sagsoorian, Paul	30-50	*
Newman, Robert	Merlin's Mistake (1st {std}, 8vo, 237p, b/w, DJ/5.25)	Atheneum	1970	Lebenson, Richard	20-30	
Newton, Ruth E.	Kittens and Puppies (1st, linen wraps, [12]p, color)	Whitman	1940	Newton, Ruth	20-35	
Neyhart, Louise A.	Henry's Lincoln (1st, lg8vo, 49p, ipcb, 9 fp b/w, pep, DJ/1.50)	Holiday House	(1945)	Wilson, Charles B.	50-80	R
Nicholds, Elizabeth	Thunder Hill (1st {std}, 8vo, 248p, b/w, DJ/3.00)	Doubleday	1953	Spier, Peter E.	35-50	
Nichols, Beverly	Book of Old Ballads (1st, 4to, 279p, brown/gilt, 16cp, pep)	L: Hutchinson	1934	Brock, Henry M.	100-175	
Nichols, Beverly	Cats' XYZ (1st AM, lg8vo, ibds, 128p, fp color, pep, DJ/3.50)	Dutton	(1961)	Sayer, Derrick	30-50	
Nichols, Beverly	Mountain of Magic (1st, 8vo, 302p, col frn, b/w, DJ)	L: J. Cape	1950	Fortnum, Peggy	30-50	
Nichols, Beverly	Stream that Stood Still (1st, 8vo, 218p, gilt, b/w, pep, DJ)	L: J. Cape	(1948)	Kennedy, Richard	30-50	
Nichols, Beverly	Thatched Roof (1st, 8vo, 285p, red cl, b/w, pep)	L: J. Cape	1933	Whistler, Rex	30-45	
Nichols, Ruth	A Walk Out of the World (1st {std}, 8vo, 192p, b/w, DJ/4.25)	Harcourt	(1969)	Hyman, Trina S.	30-50	
Nichols, William T.	Making Good (1st, sm8vo, 293p, p-o, gilt, color)	Appleton	1915	Varian, George	20-30	
Nicholson, Meredith	Hoosier Chronicle (1st, sm8vo, 606p, brown/gilt, 4cp)	Houghton	1912	Yohn, F.C.	25-40	
Nicholson, Meredith	House of a Thousand Candles (1st, 8vo, 382p, 7cp)	Bobbs-Merrill	(1905)	Christy, Howard C.	25-40	
Nicholson, Meredith	Little Brown Jug at Kildare (1st, sm8vo, blue cl, 422p, 5pl)	Bobbs-Merrill	(1908)	Flagg, James M.	25-40	
Nicholson, Meredith	Lords of High Decision (1st, sm8vo, 503p, 4cp)	Doubleday/Page	1909	Keller, Arthur I.	25-40	*
Nicholson, Meredith	Main Chance (1st, 12mo, 419p, 6pl)	Bobbs-Merrill	(1903)	Fisher, Harrison	20-30	
Nicholson, Meredith	Reversible Santa Claus (1st, sm8vo, blue cl, 176p, 4cp, dep)	Houghton	1917	Minard, Florence	30-50	
Nicholson, Meredith	Siege of the Seven Suitors (1st, sm8vo, green cl, 401p, col frn)	Houghton	1910	Phillips, Coles	40-65	
Nicholson, Meredith	The Poet (1st, 8vo, teg, 189p, blue/gilt, cep, 4cp)	Houghton	1914	Booth, Franklin	45-70	
Nicholson, Meredith	The Poet (1st, 8vo, teg, 189p, 4cp & designs by...)	Houghton	1914	Dwiggins, W.A.	45-70	
Nicholson, Meredith	Zelda Dameron (1st, 12mo, 411p, cvr by...)	Bobbs-Merrill	(1904)	Armstrong, Margaret	35-60	
Nicholson, Meredith	Zelda Dameron (1st, 12mo, 411p, 8cp by...)	Bobbs-Merrill	(1904)	Clay, John Cecil	35-60	
Nicholson, William	An Alphabet (1st, folio, ipcb, 26cp)	L: Heinemann	1898	Nicholson, Wm.	500-700	
Nicholson, William	An Alphabet (1st AM, folio, ibds, 26cp)	R.H. Russell	1898	Nicholson, Wm.	500-700	
Nicholson, William	Book of Blokes (1st, sm8vo, [60]p, green/gilt)	L: Faber	[1929]	Nicholson, Wm.	500-700	
Nicholson, William	Clever Bill (1st AM, ob sm4to, yellow bds, 23p, color)	Doubleday/Page	[1926]	Nicholson, Wm.	425-600	
Nicholson, William	Clever Bill (1st, ob4to, [23]p, yellow ipcb, 21p, color)	L: Heinemann	[1926]	Nicholson, Wm.	500-700	
Nicholson, William	Pirate Twins (1st AM, ob8vo, 28p, ibds, color)	Coward	[1929]	Nicholson, Wm.	275-450	
Nicholson, William	Pirate Twins (1st, ob4to, 28p, ibds, 32p, fp color, pep)	L: Faber	[1929]	Nicholson, Wm.	400-600	
Niebuhr	Greek Heroes (12mo, 96p, p-o, teg, blue/gilt, 4cp)	L: Cassell	1910	Rackham, Arthur	180-260	
Nightingale, Madeleine	Tony-O'-Dreams (1st, lg8vo, p-o, 160p, 8 ticp, pep)	L: Blackwell	1919	Nightingale, C.T.	70-100	*
Ninon	Kit Koala (1st, 8vo, [32]p, ipcb, fp 1-color, pep, DJ/1.25)	Rinehart	(1948)	Ninon	40-65	
Nisbet, John	Our Forests & Woodlands (1st, 8vo, teg, gilt, 340p, b/w, pep)	L: J.M. Dent	1900	Rackham, Arthur	100-165	
Nixon-Roulet	Little Spanish Cousin (1st, sm8vo, 125p, 6pl)	L.C. Page	1906	McManus, Blanche	30-50	
Noble, Thomas T.	Round of Carols (1st {std}, 4to, red/gilt, 72p, b/w, pep, DJ/2.00)	Oxford U. Pr.	1935	Sewell, Helen	40-65	
Noble-Ives, Sarah	Key to Betsy's Heart (1st, 12mo, 225p, green cl, 4pl)	Macmillan	1916	Noble-Ives, Sarah	25-40	
Noble-Ives, Sarah	Songs of the Shining Way (1st, 8vo, tan ipcb, 45p, fp b/w)	R.H. Russell	1899	Noble-Ives, Sarah	75-100	*
Noble-Ives, Sarah	Story of Teddy the Bear (1st, lg4to, [42]p, ibds, 5cp)	McLoughlin	[1907]	Noble-Ives, Sarah	180-250	
Nodier, Charles	Luck of the Bean Rows (1st, lg8vo, 60p, ibds, 28 color)	L: O'Connor	(1921)	Fraser, Claud L.	120-185	
Nodier, Charles	Woodcutter's Dog (1st, lg8vo, 18p, p-o, bds, 12 color)	L: O'Connor	(1921)	Fraser, Claud L.	100-165	
Nolen, Eleanor W.	Shipment for Susannah (1st, 8vo, 82p, b/w, DJ/1.25)	Nelson	1938	Berry, Erick	50-80	

AUTHOR	TITLE	PUBLISHER	DATE	ARTIST	PRICE	LC
Nordhoff, Charles	Bounty Trilogy (1st, 8vo, 903p, 12cp, pep, DJ/3.50)	Little/Brown	1940	Wyeth, N.C.	180-250	
Nordstrom, Ursula	Secret Language (1st, 8vo, 167p, b/w, DJ/2.75)	Harper	1960	Chalmers, Mary	80-120	
Norman	Elfin Rhymes (1st AM, sm4to, unpag, 40 color)	Stokes	(1900)	Park, Carton M.	140-240	
Norman	Elfin Rhymes (1st, 4to, unpag, 40 color)	L: Gay & Bird	1900	Park, Carton M.	200-300	
Norman	Ten Little Boer Boys (1sst, ob4to, unpag, ibds, 14cp)	L: Dean	[1900]	Forrest, A.S.	170-240	
Norman, Charles	Crumb that Walked: More about Jane Jonquil (1st, 8vo, 52p, fp b/w, DJ/1.75)	Harper	(1951)	Graham, Margaret B.	30-45	
Norman, Charles	Hunch, Munch and Crunch (1st, 8vo, 46p, fp b/w, DJ/2.00)	Harper	(1952)	Graham, Margaret B.	30-45	*
Norman, Charles	Mr. Upstairs and Mr. Downstairs (1st, 8vo, 52p, fp b/w, DJ/1.75)	Harper	(1950)	Graham, Margaret B.	30-45	*
Norris, Charles G.	Zest (1st {std}, 8vo, 445p, pict cl, frn by...)	Doubleday/Doran	1933	Kent, Rockwell	40-60	
Norris, Faith	Kim of Korea (1st, 8vo, 157p, b/w, DJ/2.75)	J. Messner	(1955)	Wiese, Kurt	25-40	
Norris, Frank	Deal in Wheat (1st, 8vo, 272p, red/gilt, teg, 4pl)	Doubleday/Page	1903	Remington, Frederic	60-90	
Norris, Gunilla	Good Morrow (1st {std}, 8vo, 92p, b/w, DJ/3.75)	Atheneum	1969	Robinson, Chas.	20-35	
Norris, June	Dotzie the Dancey Duck (1st, sq8vo, ibds, color)	Volland	(1927)	Tower, Lew	55-80	*
Norris, June	Katherine the Komical Kow (1st, 12mo, ibds, unpag, color, pep)	Volland	(1926)	Tower, Lew	60-90	
North, Sterling	Abe Lincoln: Log Cabin to White House (1st {std}, 8vo, 184p, pep, DJ/1.50)	Random	(1956)	Ames, Lee	25-40	
North, Sterling	Birthday of Little Jesus (1st {std}, 4to, ipcb, 1-color, pep, DJ/2.50)	Grosset/Dunlap	(1952)	Angelo, Valenti	65-90	
North, Sterling	Five Little Bears (1st, 8vo, ipcb, [32]p, 1-color, pep, DJ/0.50)	Rand/McNally	(1935)	Frazee/Biers	50-85	
North, Sterling	Greased Lightning (1st, sm4to, [93]p, dp color, pep, DJ/2.00)	Winston	(1940)	Wiese, Kurt	60-90	
North, Sterling	Hurry, Spring! (1st {std}, 8vo, 58p, b/w, DJ/3.75)	Dutton	(1966)	Burger, Carl	20-30	
North, Sterling	Little Rascal (1st {std}, 8vo, 78p, b/w, DJ/3.50)	Dutton	(1965)	Burger, Carl	20-30	
North, Sterling	Mark Twain and the River (1st, 8vo, 184p, 1-color, DJ/1.95)	Houghton	1961	Mays, Victor	20-30	
North, Sterling	Midnight & Jeremiah (1st {std}, 8vo, 125p, tan cl, color, pep, DJ/2.00)	Winston	(1943)	Wiese, Kurt	30-50	
North, Sterling	Rascal... (1st {std}, 8vo, 189p, pcb, gilt, b/w, pep, DJ/3.95, NH)	Dutton	1963	Schoenherr, John	60-90	R
North, Sterling	So Red the Nose (1st, sm8vo, pink cl, [72]p, fp b/w, DJ/1.00)	Farrar/Rinehart	(1935)	Nelson, Roy C.	50-80	
North, Sterling	Son of the Lamp Maker (1st, 8vo, 60p, 1-color, pep, DJ/2.00)	Rand/McNally	(1956)	Lee, Manning De V.	20-30	
North, Sterling	The Wolfling (1st {std}, 8vo, ibds, 223p, fp b/w, DJ/5.95)	Dutton	1969	Schoenherr, John	25-40	
North, Sterling	Thoreau of Walden Pond (1st, 8vo, 183p, b/w, DJ/1.95)	Houghton	1959	Stein, Harve	20-30	
North, Sterling	Zipper ABC Book (1st, 12mo, ipcb, [59]p, 2-color)	Rand/McNally	(1937)	Ward, Keith	60-100	R*
Northrup, Mili	Watch Cat (1st {std}, ob4to, [32]p, color, DJ/3.50)	Bobbs-Merrill	(1968)	Zanazanian, Adrina	45-70	
Norton, Alice	Rogue Reynard (1st, lg8vo, 96p, b/w, pep, DJ/2.50)	Houghton	1947	Bannon, Laura	150-220	
Norton, Andre	Fur Magic (1st, 8vo, 174p, fp b/w, DJ/3.95)	World	(1968)	Kaufmann, John	70-120	
Norton, Andre	Huon of the Horn (1st {std}, 8vo, 208p, b/w, DJ/2.75)	Harcourt	1951	Krush, Joe	100-175	
Norton, Andre	Octagon Magic (1st, 8vo, 189p, fp b/w, DJ/3.95)	World	(1967)	Conner, Mac	150-250	
Norton, Andre	Prince Commands (1st {std}, sm8vo, 268p red cl, fp b/w)	Appleton-Century	1934	Seredy, Kate	200-300	*
Norton, Andre	Ralestone Luck (1st, sm8vo, 296p, fp b/w, DJ/2.00)	Appleton-Century	1938	Reid, James	500-700	*
Norton, Andre	Scarface (1st, 8vo, 263p, black cl, p-o, b/w, DJ/2.75)	Harcourt	(1948)	Bjorklund, Lorence	200-300	
Norton, Andre	Star Man's Son, 2250 A.D. (1st {std}, 8vo, 248p, b/w, DJ/2.75)	Harcourt	(1952)	Nicolas	500-700	
Norton, Andre	Steel Magic (1st {std}, 8vo, 155p, blue cl, b/w, DJ/3.50)	World	(1965)	Jacques, Robin	100-150	
Norton, Andre	Sword in Sheath (1st {std}, 8vo, 246p, b/w, DJ/2.50)	Harcourt	(1949)	Bjorklund, Lorence	250-400	
Norton, Andre	Sword is Drawn (1st, 8vo, 180p, col frn, 4 fp b/w, pep, DJ/2.00)	Houghton	1944	Coburn, Duncan	250-400	
Norton, Andre	Yankee Privateer (1st {std}, 8vo, 300p, b/w, DJ/2.75)	World	(1955)	Vosburgh, Leonard	200-300	*
Norton, Mary	Bed-Knob & Broomstick (1st AM {std}, sm8vo, blue cl, 189p, b/w, DJ/3.00)	Harcourt	(1957)	Blegvad, Erik	80-140	
Norton, Mary	Bonfires and Broomsticks (1st, 8vo, 119p, pep, b/w, DJ)	L: Dent	(1947)	Adshead, Mary	150-225	
Norton, Mary	Borrowers Afield (1st AM {std}, 8vo, 215p, green cl, b/w, DJ/2.50)	Harcourt	(1955)	Krush, Beth & Joe	120-185	R
Norton, Mary	Borrowers Afloat (1st AM {std}, 8vo, 191p, b/w, DJ/2.75)	Harcourt	(1959)	Krush, Beth & Joe	100-165	
Norton, Mary	Borrowers Afloat (1st, sm8vo, 176p, blue cl, col frn, b/w, DJ)	L: Dent	(1959)	Stanley, Diana	120-200	
Norton, Mary	Borrowers Aloft (1st AM {std}, 8vo, 193p, fp b/w, DJ/2.95)	Harcourt	(1961)	Krush, Beth & Joe	100-175	R
Norton, Mary	Magic Bed-Knob (1st {1st bk}, 4to, ibds, [48]p, fp color, pep, DJ/1.75)	Hyperion Press	(1943)	Peirce, Waldo	200-300	
Norton, Mary	The Borrowers (1st, 8vo, 159p, b/w, DJ, CgM)	L: J.M. Dent	(1952)	Stanley, Diana	250-400	
Norton, Mary	The Borrowers (1st AM {std}, 8vo, 180p, blue cl, b/w, DJ/2.50, CgM)	Harcourt	(1953)	Krush, Beth & Joe	180-250	
Norwood, Edwin P.	Adventures of Diggeldy Dan (1st, 8vo, p-o, 240p, 8cp)	Little/Brown	1922	Peyton, A. Conway	40-65	
Norwood, Edwin P.	Davy Winkle in Circusland (1st, 8vo, 202p, tan cl, col frn)	Little/Brown	1926	Peyton, A. Conway	40-65	
Norwood, Edwin P.	Friends of Diggeldy Dan (1st, 8vo, 215p, p-o, 8cp)	Little/Brown	1924	Peyton, A. Conway	40-65	
Norwood, Edwin P.	In the Land of Diggeldy Dan (1st, 8vo, p-o, 226p, 8cp)	Little/Brown	1923	Peyton, A. Conway	40-65	
Noseworthy, F.	Land of Play (1st, 4to, 128p, p-o, blue cl, 10cp)	Cupples/Leon	(1911)	Kirk, Maria L.	80-120	
Novinger, Virginia	Tommy on Time (1st, lg8vo, [28]p, p-o, fp color, pep, DJ/1.50)	Whitman	(1952)	Evans, Katherine	25-45	
Noyes, Alfred	Forty Singing Seamen (1st, 8vo, ipcb, 124p, 6cp, pep)	Stokes	(1930)	MacKinstry, Eliz.	55-80	
Noyes, Alfred	Sherwood (1st, 8vo, 225p, black/gilt, p-o, 4cp)	Stokes	1911	Nichols, Spencer B.	35-60	*
Noyes, Alfred (ed)	Magic Casement (1st, 8vo, teg, uncut, 391p, gilt, b/w)	L: Chapman	[1908]	Reid, Stephen	50-80	
Nuckel, Otto	Destiny (1st AM, 8vo, [414]p, red cl, woodcuts)	Farrar/Rinehart	(1930)	Nuckel, Otto	100-165	
Nura	All Aboard: We Are Off (1st, 4to, [40]p, fp color, DJ/2.50)	Studio Pub.	(1944)	Nura	100-165	
Nura	Kitten Who Listened (1st, 4to, ibds, 30p, 1-color, pep, DJ/1.50)	Harper	(1950)	Nura	40-65	*
Nura	Mitty Children Fix Things (1st, 4to, gilt, [40]p, fp color, DJ/2.50)	American Studio	(1946)	Nura	50-80	
Nura	Nura's Garden of Betty & Booth (1st, 4to, [50]p, ibds, fp color, DJ/2.00)	Wm. Morrow	1935	Nura	50-80	
Nusbaum, Aileen	Seven Cities of Cibola (1st, 8vo, 167p, 6 dp cp, pep)	Putnam	1926	Finnan, Margaret	50-90	
Nusbaum, Aileen	Zuni Indian Tales (1st, 8vo, 167p, gilt, dp color, pep)	Putnam	1926	Finnan, Margaret	50-80	*
Nusbaum, Deric	Deric in Mesa Verde (1st, 8vo, 166p, 22pl, pep)	Putnam	1926	(Photos)	30-50	
Nyce, Vera	Adventures of Greyfur Family (1st, 16mo, 76p, 24cp, pep)	Lippincott	(1917)	Nyce, Helen	50-80	
Nyce, Vera	Greyfur's Neighbors (1st, 16mo, 76p, 24cp)	Lippincott	(1917)	Nyce, Helen	55-80	*
Nye, Edgar W.	Guest at the Ludlow (1st, sm8vo, red/gilt, 272p, teg, 21pl)	Bowen-Merrill	1897	Braunhold, L.	30-50	
Nye, Harry	Home is If You Find It (1st {std}, 12mo, 251p, b/w, DJ/2.00)	Doubleday	1947	Galdone, Paul	30-50	
Nye, Robert	March Has Horse's Ears (1st AM {std}, 8vo, 88p, fp b/w, cep, DJ/3.75)	Hill & Wang	(1967)	Maas, Dorothy	60-90	R*
O'Brien, Jack	Corporal Corey... (1st, 8vo, 276p, col frn, DJ/2.00)	Winston	(1936)	Wiese, Kurt	40-65	
O'Brien, Jack	King and the Princess (1st, sm ob4to, ibds, [24]p, color, pep, DJ/0.50)	Grosset/Dunlap	1940	Wiese, Kurt	30-50	
O'Brien, Jack	Return of Silver Chief (1st {std}, 8vo, 211p, col frn, b/w, DJ/2.00)	Winston	(1943)	Wiese, Kurt	30-45	
O'Brien, Jack	Silver Chief (1st, 8vo, blue/silver, 218p, col frn, 14pl, pep)	Winston	(1933)	Wiese, Kurt	40-65	
O'Brien, Jack	Silver Chief to the Rescue (1st, 8vo, 235p, fp color, pep, DJ/2.00)	Winston	(1937)	Wiese, Kurt	45-70	
O'Brien, Jack	Valiant, Dog of the Timberline (1st, 8vo, 218p, col frn, 5cp, pep, DJ/2.00)	Winston	(1935)	Wiese, Kurt	40-65	

AUTHOR	TITLE	PUBLISHER	DATE	ARTIST	PRICE	LC
O'Brien, Robert	Silver Crown (1st {std}, 8vo, 274p, fp b/w, DJ/4.95)	Atheneum	1968	Payson, Dale	100-175	
O'Clery, Helen (comp)	Mermaid Reader (1st {std}, 8vo, 193p, b/w, DJ/4.95)	F. Watts	(1964)	Arno, Enrico	60-90	
O'Cluny, Thomas	Merry Multifleet & the Mounting Multicorps (1st, 8vo, 206p, 16 illus)	L: J.M. Dent	1904	Robinson, W. Heath	120-170	*
O'Connor, Edwin	Benjy, a Ferocious Fairy Tale (1st {std}, 8vo, 143p, color, cep, DJ/4.00)	Little/Brown	(1957)	Forberg, Ati	30-45	
O'Connor, Winfield	Jockeys, Crooks and Kings (1st, 8vo, 219p, b/w decor by...)	NY: Cape/Smith	1930	Ward, Lynd	60-90	*
O'Day, James	Daddy Long Legs Fun Songs (1st, folio, [68]p, ibds, color)	Chi: Witmark	1900	Keller, Edgar	140-220	
O'Dell, Scott	Black Pearl (1st {std}, 8vo, 140p, black/gilt, fp b/w, cep, DJ/3.25, NH)	Houghton	1967	Johnson, Milton	40-65	
O'Dell, Scott	Dark Canoe (1st {std}, 8vo, 165p, green cl, b/w, cep, DJ/3.50)	Houghton	1968	Johnson, Milton	30-50	
O'Dell, Scott	Island of the Blue Dolphins (1st, 8vo, 184p, uncut, DJ/2.75, NM)	Houghton	1960	No Illustrations	100-175	R
O'Dell, Scott	Journey to Jericho (1st {std}, lg8vo, 40p, 2-color, DJ/3.75)	Houghton	1969	Weisgard, Leonard	40-65	
O'Dell, Scott	King's Fifth (1st {std}, 8vo, 264p, b/w, DJ/3.95, NH)	Houghton	1966	Bryant, Samuel	40-65	
O'Dell, Scott	Sing Down the Moon (1st {std}, 8vo, 137p, DJ/3.75, NH)	Houghton	1970	No Illustrations	60-90	
O'Donnell, T.C.	Ladder of Ricketty Rungs (1st, 8vo, ibds, [85]p, color, pep)	Volland	(1923)	Scott, Janet L.	80-120	
O'Faolain, Eileen	Children of the Salmon (1st {std}, 8vo, 349p, fp b/w, DJ/6.75)	Little/Brown	(1965)	Hyman, Trina S.	40-65	
O'Faolain, Eileen	Miss Pennyfeather & the Pooka (1st {std}, lg8vo, 154p, 1-col, cep, DJ/2.00)	Random	(1946)	Watson, Aldren A.	30-50	
O'Hara, Mary	My Friend Flicka (1st, 8vo, 349p, col frn, 14pl, DJ/2.50)	Lippincott	1941	Curry, John S.	55-80	
O'Malley, Frank W.	War-Whirl in Washington (1st, sm8vo, 298p, grey cl, 16pl)	Century	1918	Sarg, Tony	40-60	
O'Neill, George	Tomorrow's House (1st {std}, sq8vo, purple cl, 159p, b/w, pep)	Dutton	1930	O'Neill, Rose	70-100	
O'Neill, Hester	Picture Story of the Philippines (1st, 4to, [49]p, 3-color, pep, DJ/2.50)	McKay	1948	Koering, Ursula	30-50	
O'Neill, Mary	Ali (1st {std}, lg8vo, 122p, b/w, DJ/3.95)	Atheneum	1968	Barberis, Juan	20-30	*
O'Neill, Mary	Anna Amelia's Apteryx (1st {std}, sm8vo, unpag, color, DJ/2.95)	Doubleday	1966	Groedel, Burt	30-45	*
O'Neill, Mary	Fingers are Always Bringing Me News (1st {std}, 8vo, 40p, 2-color, DJ/3.50)	Doubleday	(1969)	Bolognese, Don	25-45	
O'Neill, Mary	Hailstones & Halibut Bones (1st {std}, 8vo, 59p, bds, pep, color, DJ/2.95)	Doubleday	1961	Weisgard, Leonard	40-65	
O'Neill, Mary	People I'd Like to Keep (1st {std}, lg8vo, 64p, color, DJ/2.95)	Doubleday	1964	Galdone, Paul	20-30	
O'Neill, Mary	Poor Merlo (1st {std}, ob8vo, [48]p, color, DJ/3.95)	Atheneum	1967	Piussi-Campbell, J.	30-50	*
O'Neill, Mary	Take a Number (1st {std}, lg8vo, 63p, fp 3-color, cep, DJ/3.95)	Doubleday	(1968)	Nagy, Al	30-50	R
O'Neill, Mary	What is that Sound! (1st {std}, 8vo, 54p, b/w, DJ/3.50)	Atheneum	1966	Ehlert, Lois	20-30	*
O'Neill, Mary	White Palace (1st, 4to, aqua cl, [48]p, fp color, DJ/3.95)	Crowell	(1966)	Hogrogian, Nonny	40-65	
O'Neill, Mary	Winds (1st {std}, ob8vo, [64]p, fp color, DJ/5.95)	Doubleday	1970	Barkley, James	30-45	
O'Neill, Moira	Elf-Errant (1st, 8vo, teg, 109p, pink/gilt, 7pl)	L: Lawrence/Bul.	1895	Britten, William E.	80-120	
O'Neill, Rose	Garda (1st {std}, sm8vo, blue cl, 305p, pep, DJ/2.50)	Doubleday/Doran	1929	O'Neill, Rose	100-150	
O'Neill, Rose	Goblin Woman (1st {std}, 8vo, 345p, b/w, pep)	Doubleday/Doran	1930	O'Neill, Rose	50-80	
O'Neill, Rose	Kewpie Kutouts (1st, 4to, bds, p-o, 48p, pep, color)	Stokes	(1914)	O'Neill, Rose	800-1100	
O'Neill, Rose	Kewpie Primer (1st, sq8vo, 118p, color, cep)	Stokes	(1916)	O'Neill, Rose	400-600	
O'Neill, Rose	Kewpies & Dotty Darling (1st, 4to, 88p, tan bds, p-o, 1-color, pep)	Doran	(1912)	O'Neill, Rose	600-900	
O'Neill, Rose	Kewpies & Dotty Darling (4to, p-o, tan bds, 79p, 1-color, pep)	Stokes	(1912)	O'Neill, Rose	500-700	R
O'Neill, Rose	Kewpies & Runaway Baby (1st {std}, 8vo, 111p, red cl, color, cep)	Doubleday/Doran	1928	O'Neill, Rose	250-400	
O'Neill, Rose	Kewpies: Their Book (1st, lg4to, tan bds, p-o, 80p, 1-color, dep)	Stokes	(1913)	O'Neill, Rose	500-700	R
O'Neill, Rose	Lady in the White Veil (1st, 12mo, blue cl, 350p, col frn, 4pl)	Harper	1909	O'Neill, Rose	90-140	
O'Neill, Rose	Loves of Edwy (1st, sm8vo, tan cl, 432p, b/w)	Lothrop Pub.	(1904)	O'Neill, Rose	60-100	
O'Neill, Rose	Master-Mistress (1st, 8vo, maroon bds, 227p, 9pl)	Knopf	1922	O'Neill, Rose	70-120	
O'Reilly, John	The Glob (1st, 8vo, 63p, b/w, pep, DJ/1.50)	Viking	1952	Kelly, Walt	50-85	
O'Sullivan, Vincent	Book of Bargains (1st, 8vo, 185p, frn by...)	L: Smithers	1896	Beardsley, Aubrey	80-125	
Oakes, Vanya	Bamboo Gate (1st {std}, 8vo, 157p, red cl, b/w, DJ/2.00)	Macmillan	1946	Kingman, Dong	30-50	*
Oakes, Vanya	Willy Wong, American (1st, 8vo, 174p, fp b/w, pep, DJ/2.50)	J. Messner	(1951)	Yap, Weda	25-40	
Obligado, George	Gaucho Boy (1st, 8vo, 63p, b/w, DJ/2.50)	Viking	(1961)	Obligado, Lilian	20-30	
Obligado, George	Magic Butterfly (1st, folio, 62p, ibds, color, pep)	Golden Press	(1963)	Fontana, Ugo	50-90	
Obligado, George	Warrior & the Princess (1st, 4to, ibds, [60]p, color, pep)	Golden Press	1961	DeGaspari, Giorgi	50-80	
Offit, Sidney	Adventures of Homer Fink (1st, 8vo, 181p, b/w, DJ/3.50)	St. Martin's	(1966)	Galdone, Paul	20-30	
Offit, Sidney	Boy Who Made a Million (1st, 8vo, 148p, b/w, DJ/3.95)	St. Martin's	(1968)	Mayer, Mercer	25-40	
Ogburn, Charlton	Big Caesar (1st, 8vo, 118p, b/w, DJ/2.75)	Houghton	1958	Krush, Joe	25-45	*
Ogburn, Charlton	The Bridge (1st, lg8vo, 68p, fp 2-color, DJ/2.75)	Houghton	1957	Ness, Evaline	70-100	R
Ogburn, Charlton	White Falcon (1st, 8vo, tan/silver, 51p, b/w, pep, DJ/2.25)	Houghton	1955	Bryson, Bernarda	65-90	R
Ogden, Ruth	Little Homespun (1st, 12mo, 127p, 15pl)	Stokes	(1897)	Humphrey, Maud	140-200	
Ogden, Ruth	Little Pierre & Big Peter (1st, 8vo, gilt, p-o, 367p, 5cp, pep)	Stokes	(1915)	Kirk, Maria L.	60-100	
Ogden, Ruth	Little Queen of Hearts (1st, 8vo, 232p, 15 fp b/w, gilt)	Stokes	(1893)	Ogden, Henry A.	40-60	*
Ogden, Ruth	Loyal Little Redcoat (1st, 8vo, 217p, gilt, b/w, PPPa)	Stokes	1890	Ogden, Henry A.	70-125	
Olcott, F.J.	Book of Elves & Fairies (1st, 8vo, 303p, p-o, 3cp by...)	Houghton	1918	Winter, Milo	90-120	
Olcott, F.J.	Book of Elves & Fairies (1st UK, 8vo, 303p, 3cp by...)	L: Harrap	1919	Winter, Milo	80-120	*
Olcott, F.J.	Go! Champions of Light (1st, 8vo, 226p, b/w, pep, DJ/1.75)	Revell	(1933)	Walker, Dugald S.	50-80	
Olcott, F.J.	Red Indian Fairy Book (1st, 8vo, 338p, col frn, 5pl)	Houghton	1917	Richardson, F.	120-200	
Olcott, F.J.	Wonder Tales from Baltic Wizards (1st {std}, sm8vo, 234p col frn, pep)	Longmans	1928	Candell, Victor G.	40-65	
Olcott, F.J.	Wonder Tales from China Seas (1st, 8vo, 238p, col frn, b/w, pep)	Longmans	1925	Walker, Dugald S.	50-80	
Olcott, F.J.	Wonderful Garden (1st, 12mo, 483p, p-o, 4cp)	Houghton	1919	Winter, Milo	70-90	
Olcott, F.J. (ed)	Adventures of Haroun Er Raschid (1st, 8vo, 363p, gilt, col frn)	Henry Holt & Co.	1923	Pogany, Willy	55-80	*
Olcott, F.J. (ed)	Bible Stories to Read & Tell (1st, 8vo, blue cl, 486p, 8cp)	Houghton	1916	Pogany, Willy	70-100	
Olcott, F.J. (ed)	More Tales of the Arabian Nights (1st, 8vo, 274p, red/gilt, 12cp)	Henry Holt & Co.	1915	Pogany, Willy	120-180	
Olcott, F.J. (ed)	Tales of the Persian Genii (1st, 8vo, gilt, pep, 225p, 4cp)	Houghton	(1917)	Pogany, Willy	70-100	
Olcott, F.J. (ed)	Tales of the Persian Genii (1st UK, 8vo, grey cl, 225p, 4cp)	L: Harrap	1919	Pogany, Willy	70-100	
Olcott, F.J. (ed)	Wonder Tales from Goblin Hills (1st {std}, 8vo, 268p, col frn, pep)	NY: Longmans	1930	Sichel, Harold	40-60	*
Olcott, F.J. (ed)	Wonder Tales from Pirate Isles (1st {std}, 8vo, 256p, col frn, b/w, pep)	NY: Longmans	1927	Rosse, Herman	40-60	*
Olcott, F.J. (ed)	Wonder Tales from Windmill Lands (1st, 8vo, 238p, col frn, pep, DJ)	L: Longmans	1926	Rosse, Herman	55-90	
Olcott, Julia	Happy Surprises (1st, 8vo, p-o, gilt, 163p, color, pep)	Whitman	1929	Hubbard, Eleanore	30-50	
Oldrin, John	Eight Rings on his Tail (1st, 4to, 79p, b/w, DJ/2.50)	Viking	1956	Wiese, Kurt	20-35	
Oldrin, John	Round Meadow (1st, 4to, 80p, fp 1-color, DJ/2.50)	Viking	1951	Wiese, Kurt	20-35	
Olds, Elizabeth	Big Fire (1st, lg sq8vo, red cl, [32]p, color, pep, DJ/2.00)	Houghton	1945	Olds, Elizabeth	40-65	
Olds, Elizabeth	Deep Treasure: Story of Oil (1st, 4to, [36]p, fp color, DJ/3.00)	Houghton	1958	Olds, Elizabeth	30-50	
Olds, Elizabeth	Feather Mountain (1st, lg ob8vo, aqua cl, 27p, color, pep, DJ/2.00, CH)	Houghton	1951	Olds, Elizabeth	65-90	

AUTHOR	TITLE	PUBLISHER	DATE	ARTIST	PRICE	LC
Olds, Elizabeth	Little Una (1st, 4to, [28]p, fp color, DJ/3.25)	Scribner	(1963)	Olds, Elizabeth	30-50	
Olds, Elizabeth	Plop Plop Ploppie (1st, 4to, [30]p, 3-color, DJ/2.95)	Scribner	(1962)	Olds, Elizabeth	30-50	
Olds, Elizabeth	Riding the Rails (1st, lg ob8vo, 43p, color, dep, DJ/2.50)	Houghton	1948	Olds, Elizabeth	40-60	*
Olds, Helen D.	What Will I Wear? (1st, 8vo, [33]p, 1-color, pep, DJ/2.50)	Knopf	(1961)	Weil, Lisl	20-35	
Oleson, Claire	For Pepita, An Orange Tree (1st {std}, 4to, ibds, [44]p, col, cep, DJ/3.50)	Doubleday	(1967)	Tomes, Margot	30-45	*
Ollivant, Alfred	Redcoat Captain (1st, 8vo, 203p, fp b/w)	L: J. Murray	1907	Robertson, W.G.	45-70	
Olmsted, Millicent	Land of Never Was (1st, 8vo, p-o, 148p, 12cp, pep)	Jacobs	(1908)	Knipe, Helen A.	70-120	
Olmsted, Millicent	Land of Really True (1st, 8vo, p-o, 187p, 12cp, pep)	Jacobs	(1909)	Knipe, Helen A.	70-120	
Olsen, Aileen	Bernadine & the Water Bucket (1st, 4to, unpag, color, pep, DJ/2.95)	Abelard-Schuman	1966	Langner, Nola	25-45	
Olsen, Aileen	Big Fish (1st, 8vo, 47p, orange cl, b/w, DJ/3.95)	Lothrop, Lee	(1970)	Gobbato, Imero	30-50	*
Omar Khayyam	Rubaiyat of Omar Khayyam (folio, teg, brown/gilt, unpag, 56pl, pep)	Houghton	1884	Vedder, Elihu	400-600	
Omar Khayyam	Rubaiyat of Omar Khayyam (3rd, sm4to, brown/gilt, b/w)	Houghton	1894	Vedder, Elihu	90-140	
Omar Khayyam	Rubaiyat of Omar Khayyam (1st, 16mo, green ipcb, 61p, b/w)	R.H. Russell	(1897)	Bradley, Will	100-170	
Omar Khayyam	Rubaiyat of Omar Khayyam (1st, 4to, uncut, green/gilt, 43p, b/w)	L: Macmillan	1898	MacDougall, W.B.	120-185	
Omar Khayyam	Rubaiyat of Omar Khayyam (1st, 8vo, 65p)	L: John Lane	1901	Cole, Herbert	80-120	*
Omar Khayyam	Rubaiyat of Omar Khayyam (1st, 8vo, 33p)	L: G. Bell	1902	Bell, Robert A.	75-100	*
Omar Khayyam	Rubaiyat of Omar Khayyam (1st, 8vo, 25p, 12 illus)	L: A. Moring	1903	McManus, Blanche	75-120	*
Omar Khayyam	Rubaiyat of Omar Khayyam (1st AM, 4to, teg, unpag, blue/gilt, 28 ticp)	Dodge	(1905)	(Photos)	120-200	
Omar Khayyam	Rubaiyat of Omar Khayyam (1st, sm4to, 135p, grey cl, 5cp)	L: Gibbings	1906	Brangwyn, Frank	120-180	
Omar Khayyam	Rubaiyat of Omar Khayyam (1st {this pub}, 12mo, 159p, color)	L.C. Page	1907	McManus, Blanche	40-60	*
Omar Khayyam	Rubaiyat of Omar Khayyam (1st, 12mo, 147p, AEG, blue/gilt, 5 fp color)	Nister/Dutton	[1907]	Robinson, Thomas H.	80-120	
Omar Khayyam	Rubaiyat of Omar Khayyam (1st, lg4to, white/gilt, unpag, 20 ticp)	L: Hodder	[1909]	Dulac, Edmund	400-600	
Omar Khayyam	Rubaiyat of Omar Khayyam (1st, 4to, 203p, teg, 16cp)	L: A&C Black	1909	James, Gilbert	120-200	
Omar Khayyam	Rubaiyat of Omar Khayyam (8vo, teg, 160p, 12pl)	Elder	1909	James, Gilbert	40-60	
Omar Khayyam	Rubaiyat of Omar Khayyam (1st AM, 4to, ibds, teg, 96p, 24 ticp)	Crowell	(1909)	Pogany, Willy	250-400	
Omar Khayyam	Rubaiyat of Omar Khayyam (1st, 4to, ibds, teg, gilt, 24 ticp, pep)	L: Harrap	(1909)	Pogany, Willy	300-450	
Omar Khayyam	Rubaiyat of Omar Khayyam (1st, 12mo, beige/gilt, teg, 69p, 8 ticp, pep)	L: Foulis	(1910)	Brangwyn, Frank	100-160	
Omar Khayyam	Rubaiyat of Omar Khayyam (32mo, leather, teg, 86p, 3 ticp)	L: Collins	[1910]	Robinson, Charles	75-100	
Omar Khayyam	Rubaiyat of Omar Khayyam (1st, 4to, p-o, teg, [76]p, b/w)	NY: A. Harriman	1911	Hall, Isabel H.	120-200	*
Omar Khayyam	Rubaiyat of Omar Khayyam (8vo, blue/gilt, 110p, 8cp)	L: Foulis	1913	Brangwyn, Frank	80-130	
Omar Khayyam	Rubaiyat of Omar Khayyam (1st, 4to, blue/gilt, [88]p, 10 ticp)	L: Hodder	[1913]	Bull, Rene	425-600	
Omar Khayyam	Rubaiyat of Omar Khayyam (1st AM, 4to, red/gilt, unpag, teg, col frn)	Dutton	(1913)	Sullivan, Edmund J.	100-170	
Omar Khayyam	Rubaiyat of Omar Khayyam (1st, 4to, red/gilt, unpag, teg, uncut, col frn)	L: Methuen	1913	Sullivan, Edmund J.	120-180	
Omar Khayyam	Rubaiyat of Omar Khayyam (4to, gilt, uncut, buckram, 15 ticp)	L: Foulis	(1919)	Brangwyn, Frank	130-200	
Omar Khayyam	Rubaiyat of Omar Khayyam (1st AM, 4to, p-o, gilt, 6 ticp, 32 tipl)	Dodd	[1920]	Balfour, Ronald E.	320-425	
Omar Khayyam	Rubaiyat of Omar Khayyam (1st, 4to, bds, p-o, 6 ticp, 32 tipl)	L: Constable	1920	Balfour, Ronald E.	350-500	
Omar Khayyam	Rubaiyat of Omar Khayyam (lg8vo, green/gilt, 4 color, pep)	L: Sampson Low	[1920]	Brangwyn, Frank	60-100	
Omar Khayyam	Rubaiyat of Omar Khayyam (lg8vo, 96p, green/gilt, teg, 12 ticp)	Crowell	[1920]	Pogany, Willy	200-300	
Omar Khayyam	Rubaiyat of Omar Khayyam (1st, 8vo, 63p, 7 ticp)	L: L.B. Hill	(1920)	Tagore, A.N.	120-170	*
Omar Khayyam	Rubaiyat of Omar Khayyam (1st, 16mo, ipcb, gilt, 86p, 8cp)	Harper	1921	Jones, Wilfred	50-80	
Omar Khayyam	Rubaiyat of Omar Khayyam (1st AM, 4to, ibds, gilt, 20 fp color)	Dutton	(1922)	Fish, Anne H.	250-400	
Omar Khayyam	Rubaiyat of Omar Khayyam (1st, 4to, gilt, uncut, 108p, ibds, 19pl, dep)	L: Bodley Head	(1922)	Fish, Anne H.	500-800	
Omar Khayyam	Rubaiyat of Omar Khayyam (1st, 8vo, 159p, 8cp)	L: Kegan Paul	(1923)	Weston, H.	55-80	*
Omar Khayyam	Rubaiyat of Omar Khayyam (1st, 4to, 128p, gilt, 12 ticp)	L: L.B. Hill	[1925]	Palmer, Doris M.	170-240	
Omar Khayyam	Rubaiyat of Omar Khayyam (1st, 4to, 56p, 4 ticp)	L: Collins	(1929)	Robinson, Charles	120-200	*
Omar Khayyam	Rubaiyat of Omar Khayyam (1st {this pub.}, lg8vo, 197p, cp)	Doubleday/Doran	1930	Dulac, Edmund	50-80	
Omar Khayyam	Rubaiyat of Omar Khayyam (1st [new ed.], 4to, 171p, gilt, teg, 12 ticp)	L: Harrap	(1930)	Pogany, Willy	175-250	
Omar Khayyam	Rubaiyat of Omar Khayyam (sm4to, unpag, black/gilt, 7cp)	World	(1938)	Abdullah Kar, Hemzeh	60-90	
Omar Khayyam	Rubaiyat of Omar Khayyam (1st, 12mo, 64p, 4 ticp)	L: Harrap	1940	Gooden, Stephen	30-50	
Omar Khayyam	Rubaiyat of Omar Khayyam (4to, blue ibds, gilt, [40]p, 8 ticp)	Heritage Press	1940	Szyk, Arthur	160-225	
Omar Khayyam	Rubaiyat of Omar Khayyam (1st, lg8vo, 149p, gilt, color, pep)	Random	(1947)	Sayah, Mahmoud	45-70	
Omond, George W.	Belgium (1st, sm4to, 390p, black/gilt, 77cp)	L: A&C Black	1908	Forestier, Amedee	100-175	
Orcutt, William D.	Princess Kallisto (1st, 4to, 138p, ibds, 6 fp color)	Little/Brown	1902	Amsden, Harriette	150-220	
Orcutt, William D.	Princess Kallisto (1st UK, 4to, 139p, 6 fp color, pep)	L: Jack	1905	Amsden, Harriette	140-220	
Orcutt, William D.	Princess Kallisto (1st [this pub.], 8vo, 139p, p-o, 6 fp color)	Harper	(1911)	Amsden, Harriette	70-120	
Orgel, Doris	Cindy's Sad and Happy Tree (1st, 8vo, [40]p, fp 1-color, cep, DJ/3.50)	Knopf	(1967)	Forberg, Ati	25-40	
Orgel, Doris	Cindy's Snowdrops (1st, 8vo, [38]p, 1-color, cep, DJ/3.25)	Knopf	(1966)	Forberg, Ati	25-40	
Orgel, Doris	Good-Byes of Magnus Marmalade (1st, 8vo, 32p, b/w, DJ/2.75)	Putnam	(1966)	Blegvad, Erik	20-35	
Orgel, Doris	In a Forgotten Place (1st, 8vo, 144p, b/w, cep, DJ/3.95)	Knopf	(1967)	McMullan, Jim	20-35	
Orgel, Doris	Merry, Rose & Christmas-Tree June (1st, 8vo, 77p, fp b/w, DJ/3.95)	Knopf	(1969)	Gorey, Edward	75-120	
Orgel, Doris	Next Door to Xanadu (1st, 8vo, 160p, b/w, DJ/3.95)	Harper	(1969)	Payson, Dale	25-35	*
Orgel, Doris	On the Sand Dune (1st, ob8vo, 30p, fp 1-color, DJ/3.50)	Harper	(1968)	Weisgard, Leonard	40-65	
Orgel, Doris	Phoebe and the Prince (1st, ob 12mo, 31p, b/w, DJ)	Putnam	(1969)	Blegvad, Erik	20-35	
Orgel, Doris	Sarah's Room (1st, 24mo, 46p, ibds, color, DJ/1.95)	Harper	(1963)	Sendak, Maurice	150-220	
Orgel, Doris	The Uproar (1st, 4to, [40]p, 3-color, DJ/4.95)	McGraw-Hill	(1970)	Lobel, Anita	30-50	
Orgel, Doris	Whose Turtle? (1st, 4to, [46]p, gilt, fp b/w, DJ/3.95)	World	(1968)	Alexander, Martha	30-45	*
Ormondroyd, Edward	Broderick (1st, ob8vo, [32]p, color, dep, DJ/3.50)	Parnassus Press	(1969)	Larrecq, John	30-45	
Ormondroyd, Edward	David and the Phoenix (1st, 8vo, 173p, b/w, DJ/2.75)	Follett	1957	Raysor, Joan	100-165	
Ormondroyd, Edward	Michael, the Upstairs Dog (1st {std}, ob4to, [40]p, 1-color, cep, DJ/3.50)	Dial Press	(1967)	Szekeres, Cyndy	50-80	*
Ormondroyd, Edward	Tale of Alain (1st, lg8vo, 94p, b/w, DJ/2.75)	Follett	(1960)	Frankenberg, Rbt.	50-80	*
Ormondroyd, Edward	Theodore (1st, ob12mo, [33]p, fp 2-color, dep, DJ/3.25)	Parnassus Press	(1966)	Larrecq, John	50-75	*
Ormondroyd, Edward	Time at the Top (1st, 8vo, 176p, b/w, DJ/2.95)	Parnassus Press	(1963)	Bach, Peggie	80-120	
Orr, Aileen	Miss Manners (1st, 8vo, 99p, AEG, blue cl, 26cp)	L: A. Melrose	1909	Hassall, John	200-300	
Orr, Monro S.	The Alphabet (1st, 4to, ibds, [60]p, 26cp)	L: J.M. Dent	1931	Orr, Monro S.	145-225	
Ort, Jane	Mr. Mogo Mouse (1st, 12mo, ibds, 39p, color, pep)	Volland	(1930)	Ort, Jane	60-100	
Orton, Helen F.	Little Lost Pigs (1st, ob12mo, 96p, color)	Stokes	1925	Price, Luxor	60-100	
Orton, Helen F.	Twin Lambs (1st, ob12mo, 106p, 6cp)	Stokes	1931	Flack, Marjorie	30-50	*
Orton, Ruth	Pepito the Colt (1st, ob4to, ibds, 36p, b/w, pep)	Houghton	1933	Thorne, Diana	50-80	*

AUTHOR	TITLE	PUBLISHER	DATE	ARTIST	PRICE	LC
Osborne, Maurice M.	Ondine (1st, lg8vo, 75p, 2-color, DJ/2.75)	Houghton	1960	Ness, Evaline	25-45	
Osborne, Maurice M.	Rudi and the Mayor of Naples (1st, 8vo, 48p, b/w, DJ/2.50)	Houghton	1958	Low, Joseph	20-35	
Osborne, Nancy C.	Good Wind & Good Water (1st, 8vo, 248p, red cl, b/w, pep, DJ/2.00)	Viking	1934	Wiese, Kurt	25-45	
Osbourne, M. (ed.)	Favorite Fairy Tales (1st, lg8vo, 365p, p-o, b/w & pep by...)	Penn	(1930)	Berkowitz, Jeannette	100-175	
Osbourne, M. (ed.)	Favorite Fairy Tales (1st, lg8vo, 365p, p-o, 20cp by...)	Penn	(1930)	Cramer, Rie	100-175	
Osmond, Edward	Valley Grows Up (1st, 4to, ibds, 81p, 10 dp color, CgM)	L: Oxford U.Pr.	1953	Osmond, Edward	50-80	
Osswald, Edith	Come Play House (1st {A}, sm8vo, ibds, [42]p, color, LGB/#44)	Simon/Schuster	(1948)	Wilkin, Eloise B.	50-80	*
Ostrander, Fannie	Baby Goose: His Adventures (1st, lg8vo, ibds, unpag, color)	Laird & Lee	(1900)	Hirchert, R.W.	80-120	*
Ostrander, Fannie	Gift of the Magic Staff (1st, 8vo, 221p, green cl, 8pl)	Revell	(1902)	Dwiggens, Will	50-80	
Ostrander, Fannie	Goose Family Tales (1st, sq8vo, 87p, gilt, color)	Conkey	(1905)	Carqueville, Will	100-160	
Otis, James	Boy's Revolt (1st, 8vo, 193p, 16pl)	Estes & Lauriat	(1894)	Hooper, Will P.	40-70	
Otis, James	Fighting for the Empire (1st, 8vo, 466p, 8pl)	Dana Estes	(1900)	Merrill, Frank T.	40-60	
Otis, James	Jenny Wren's Boarding House (1st, 8vo, blue/gilt, 173p, 12pl, pep, PPP)	Estes & Lauriat	(1893)	Rogers, W.A.	120-180	
Otis, James	Old Ben (1st, 12mo, ipcb, 188p, 7pl)	Harper	1911	Noble-Ives, Sarah	30-50	
Otis, James	Princess & Joe Potter (1st, sq8vo, 249p, 7pl)	Estes & Lauriat	(1898)	Oakley, Violet	80-120	
Otis, James	Teddy & Carrots (1st, 8vo, 225p, 18pl, pep)	Estes & Lauriat	(1896)	Rogers, W.A.	45-70	
Otis, James	Tim & Tip (1st, 16mo, 179p, 13 fp b/w, dep)	Harper	1883	Rogers, W.A.	80-140	R
Otis, James	Toby Tyler (1st, sq8vo, 265p, brown/gilt, 21 fp b/w, PPP)	Harper	1881	Rogers, W.A.	160-240	
Otis, James	Toby Tyler (1st, 8vo, 212p, p-o, fp color, pep, DJ/1.00)	Winston	1937	Shinn, Everett	30-50	
Otis, James	Toby Tyler (1st, 8vo, 223p, col frn, b/w, pep)	Jr. Deluxe Ed.	(1958)	Weisgard, Leonard	20-30	
Otsuka, Yuzo	Suho and the White Horse (1st AM {std}, ob4to, [48]p, color, DJ/5.00)	Bobbs-Merrill	(1969)	Akaba, Suekichi	30-50	
Ott, John	Peter Pumpkin (1st {std}, ob4to, [43]p, fp 3-color, dep, DJ/3.25)	Doubleday	1963	Chermayeff, Ivan	50-80	
Ottley, Reginald	Boy Alone (1st AM {std}, 8vo, 191p, b/w, DJ/3.50)	Harcourt	(1966)	Pearson, Clyde	25-40	
Otto, Margaret G.	Cocoa (1st {std}, 8vo, 90p, b/w, DJ/2.00)	Holt	(1953)	Spier, Peter E.	30-50	*
Otto, Margaret G.	Great Aunt Victoria's House (1st {std}, 8vo, yellow cl, 120p, DJ/2.50)	Holt	(1957)	Adams, Adrienne	30-45	
Otto, Margaret G.	Little Brown Horse (1st, 8vo, [30]p, fp 1-color, dep, DJ/2.50)	Knopf	(1959)	Cooney, Barbara	60-90	
Otto, Margaret G.	Man in the Moon (1st {std}, sm8vo, green cl, 128p, fp b/w, DJ/2.50)	Holt	(1957)	Galdone, Paul	40-65	
Otto, Margaret G.	Pumpkin, Ginger & Spice (1st {std}, sm8vo, 116p, yellow cl, b/w, DJ/2.00)	Holt	(1954)	Cooney, Barbara	60-90	
Otto, Margaret G.	Roly-Poly Snowman (1st {std}, 8vo, blue cl, 83p, fp b/w, DJ/2.00)	Holt	(1954)	Suba, Susanne	40-65	
Otto, Margaret G.	Stephen's Train (1st {std}, ob4to, unpag, 1-color, DJ/2.00)	Holt	1953	Stevens, Mary	25-45	
Otto, Margaret G.	Syrup (1st {std}, 8vo, 159p, b/w, DJ/2.50)	Holt	(1956)	Jackson, Polly	70-100	
Otto, Margaret G.	Three Little Dachshunds (1st {std}, lg ob8vo, [25]p, color, DJ)	Holt, Rinehart	1963	Cooney, Barbara	50-85	*
Oursler, Fulton	String of Blue Beads (1st {std}, 12mo, ibds, [32]p, color, DJ/1.50)	Doubleday	1956	Lonette, Reisie	30-50	
Outhwaite, Annie R.	Fairyland (1st AM, folio, 165p, 19cp, pep)	Stokes	1929	Outhwaite, Ida R.	900-1500	
Outhwaite, Grenbry	Enchanted Forest (1st, 4to, 93p, gilt, pep, 16 ticp, 15pl)	L: A&C Black	1921	Outhwaite, Ida R.	700-1000	
Outhwaite, I. & A.	Little Green Road to Fairyland (1st, 4to, 103p, bds, p-o, 8cp)	L: A&C Black	1922	Outhwaite, Ida R.	700-1000	
Outhwaite, I. & A.	Little Green Road to Fairyland (1st AM, 4to, ibds, 102p, 8cp, pep)	Dutton	[1922]	Outhwaite, Ida R.	600-900	
Outhwaite, Ida R.	Blossom: A Fairy Story (1st, sm4to, p-o, bds/gilt, 94p, 8cp, pep)	L: A&C Black	(1928)	Outhwaite, Ida R.	700-900	
Outhwaite, Ida R.	Bunny & Brownie (1st UK, sm4to, 99p, ibds, 8cp, 8pl, p-o, pep)	L: A&C Black	(1930)	Outhwaite, Ida R.	600-900	
Outhwaite, Ida R.	Fairyland (1st UK, lg4to, blue cl, 128p, 16cp, pep)	L: A&C Black	(1931)	Outhwaite, Ida R.	900-1400	
Outhwaite, Ida R.	Little Fairy Sister (1st, 4to, gilt, ibds, 8cp, 8pl)	L: A&C Black	1923	Outhwaite, Ida R.	800-1000	
Outhwaite, Ida R.	Little Fairy Sister (2nd, 4to, 91p, 8cp, pep)	L: A&C Black	1929	Outhwaite, Ida R.	250-400	
Outhwaite, Ida R.	Sixpence to Spend (1st, 4to, 92p, bds, 5 ticp)	Angus/Robertson	1935	Outhwaite, Ida R.	425-600	
Overbeck, Alice	Sven the Wise & Svea the Kind (1st, 8vo, 171p, 2cp, b/w, pep)	Harper	1932	Tenggren, Gustaf	60-85	
Overton, Gwendolen	Anne Carmel (1st, sm8vo, 335p, teg, 6pl)	Macmillan	1903	Keller, Arthur I.	30-50	
Ovington, Mary W.	Hazel (1st, 8vo, 162p, b/w)	NY: Crisis Pub	(1913)	Roseland, Harry	150-200	*
Ovington, Mary W.	Zeke (1st, sm8vo, blue cl, 205p, uncut, b/w)	Harcourt	(1931)	Davis, Natalie H.	80-130	
Owen, Betty M.	Wreath of Carols (1st, 8vo, 84p, 1-color, cep, DJ/3.95)	Four Winds Pr.	(1966)	Hyman, Trina S.	50-85	*
Owen, Caroline D.	Seth Way (1st, sm8vo, 413p, col frn)	Houghton	1917	Booth, Franklin	40-65	
Owen, Dora	Book of Fairy Poetry (1st, 4to, 180p, grey cl, 16 ticp, pep)	L: Longmans	1920	Goble, Warwick	350-500	
Owen, Mary A.	Old Rabbit the Voodoo (1st, 8vo, blue/gilt, 310p, uncut, b/w)	L: T.F. Unwin	1893	Wain, Louis	250-400	
Owen, Mary A.	Voodoo Tales (1st, 8vo, 310p, b/w)	Putnam	1893	Wain/Owen	300-500	
Owen, Ruth	Castle in Silver Wood (1st, 8vo, 181p, blue cl, col frn, pep, DJ/2.00)	Dodd	1939	Simont, Marc	30-50	
Owens, Harry J.	Scandalous Advens. of Reynard the Fox (1st {std}, 8vo, 115p, b/w, DJ/3.00)	Knopf	1945	Ward, Keith	45-65	
Owsley, Jennifer	Handy Guide to Grownups (1st {std}, 8vo, [40]p, ipcb, 1-col, pep, DJ/1.00)	Random	(1950)	Graham, Margaret B.	25-40	*
Oxenham, Elsie J.	Goblin Island (1st, 8vo, 316p, AEG, p-o, col frn, pep)	L: Collins	[1907]	Robinson, Thomas H.	150-225	
Oxley, James M.	Family on Wheels (1st AM, sm8vo, 219p, 4pl)	Crowell	(1905)	Smith, E. Boyd	30-50	
Oxley, James M.	Fife & Drum at Louisburg (1st, 12mo, 307p, 4pl)	Little/Brown	1899	DeLand, Clyde O.	30-50	
Pace, Mildred M.	Friend of Animals (1st, 8vo, 125p, pink cl, fp b/w, DJ/1.60)	Scribner	1942	Brown, Paul	80-140	
Pace, Mildred M.	Juliette Low (1st, 8vo, 186p, b/w, DJ/2.00)	Scribner	1947	Castle, Jane	20-30	
Pace, Mildred M.	Old Bones, the Wonder Horse (1st, 8vo, 119p, fp b/w, pep, DJ/2.95)	Whittlesey	(1955)	Dennis, Wesley	25-40	
Pack, Robert	How to Catch a Crocodile (1st, ob4to, [38]p, fp color, cep, DJ/3.25)	Knopf	(1964)	Langner, Nola	30-50	*
Packard, Andrew	Mr. Spindles and the Spiders (1st {std}, sm4to, [32]p, 1-color, DJ/3.00)	Macmillan	1961	Slobodkin, Louis	40-65	
Page, Margaret	In Childhood Land (1st, 4to, [116]p, ibds, color)	Saalfield	1903	Greenland, Katharine	130-200	
Page, Thomas N.	Bred in the Bone (1st, 8vo, 274p, teg, 8pl)	Scribner	1904	Fisher, Harrison	30-50	
Page, Thomas N.	Captured Santa Claus (1st, 12mo, 81p, teg, 4cp)	Scribner	1902	Jacobs, William L.	35-60	
Page, Thomas N.	Gordon Keith (1st, sm8vo, blue/gilt, 548p, b/w)	Scribner	1903	Armstrong, Margaret	40-70	
Page, Thomas N.	John Marvel, Assistant (1st, 12mo, 573p, green cl, 8pl)	Scribner	1909	Flagg, James M.	25-40	
Page, Thomas N.	Old Gentleman of the Black Stock (1st, 12mo, 170p, teg, 7cp)	Scribner	1900	Christy, Howard C.	40-65	
Page, Thomas N.	On Newfound River (1st, sm8vo, 286p, blue/gilt, teg, 4cp)	Scribner	1906	Jackson, John E.	25-45	
Page, Thomas N.	Pastime Stories (1st, 12mo, grey cl, 220p, fp b/w)	Harper	1894	Frost, A.B.	45-70	
Page, Thomas N.	Santa Claus's Partner (1st, 12mo, red/gilt, 177p, teg, 8cp)	Scribner	1899	Glackens, William	35-60	
Page, Thomas N.	Social Life in Old Virginia (1st, 8vo, teg, 109p, green/gilt)	Scribner	1897	Armstrong, Margaret	55-80	
Page, Thomas N.	Tommy Trot's Visit to Santa Claus (1st, 8vo, 98p, uncut, 6cp)	Scribner	1908	Anderson, Victor C.	45-70	
Page, Thomas N.	Two Little Confederates (1st, sm4to, 189p, gilt, p-o, col frn)	Scribner	1932	Thomason, John W.	70-120	
Page, Thomas N.	Two Prisoners (1st, 8vo, 82p, teg, gilt, 5cp)	R.H. Russell	1903	Keep, Virginia	30-50	
Page, Thomas N.	Under the Crust (1st, 8vo, 307p, green/gilt, cvr by...)	Scribner	1907	Armstrong, Margaret	40-65	
Page, Valerie K.	Pi Gal (1st, lg8vo, 127p, fp b/w, DJ/3.95)	Dodd	(1970)	Callaert, Jacques	20-30	

AUTHOR	TITLE	PUBLISHER	DATE	ARTIST	PRICE	LC
Paget, John O.	Hunting (1st, 8vo, 287p, blue/gilt, teg, b/w, pep)	L: Dent	1900	Rackham, Arthur	140-200	
Paget-Fredericks, J.	Green-Pipes (1st {1st bk.}, lg4to, 50p, green/gilt, 6cp, pep)	Macmillan	1929	Paget-Fredericks, J.	80-140	
Paget-Fredericks, J.	Miss Pert's Christmas Tree (1st, 4to, red/gilt, 24p, 6cp, pep)	Macmillan	1929	Paget-Fredericks, J.	80-140	
Pain, Eva	Stories Barry Told Me (1st, 8vo, ibds, 94p, color)	L: Longmans	1927	Darwin, Mrs. Bernard	90-150	
Paine, Albert B.	Arkansaw Bear (1st, 8vo, 118p, ibds, b/w)	R.H. Russell	1898	VerBeck, Frank	200-300	
Paine, Albert B.	Beacon Prize Medals (1st, 12mo, 325p, 6pl)	Baker/Taylor	1899	Wright/Huestis	40-60	*
Paine, Albert B.	Great White Way (1st, sm8vo, blue cl, teg, 327p, 6pl)	J.F. Taylor	1901	Rosenmeyer, B.J.	90-120	
Paine, Albert B.	Hollow Tree (1st, lg8vo, 128p, ibds, b/w, PPP)	R.H. Russell	1898	Conde, J.M.	200-300	
Paine, Albert B.	Hollow Tree Nights & Days (1st, 8vo, 290p, green cl, b/w)	Harper	(1916)	Conde, J.M.	40-65	
Paine, Albert B.	Hollow Tree Snowed-In Book (1st, 8vo, cloth, 285p, b/w)	Harper	1910	Conde, J.M.	200-300	
Paine, Albert B.	In the Deep Woods (1st, lg8vo, 134p, ipcb, 52pl)	R.H. Russell	1899	Conde, J.M.	220-300	
Paine, Albert B.	Mr. Crow & the Whitewash (1st, 12mo, 120p, p-o, gilt, b/w)	Harper	(1917)	Conde, J.M.	60-100	
Paine, Albert B.	Mr. Rabbit's Wedding (1st, sm8vo, gilt, p-o, 123p, fp b/w)	Harper	(1917)	Conde, J.M.	60-100	
Paine, Albert B.	Tent Dwellers (1st, 8vo, uncut, 272p, b/w)	Outing	1908	Watson, Hy	150-220	
Paine, Ralph D.	Blackbeard Buccaneer (1st, 8vo, 309p, gilt, p-o, col frn 5pl)	Penn	1922	Schoonover, Frank	35-60	
Palazzo, Tony	Amerigo, the Wandering Tortoise (1st {std}, 4to, 56p, color, DJ/2.95)	Duell, Sloan	(1965)	Palazzo, Tony	20-35	
Palazzo, Tony	Animal Babies (1st {std}, lg4to, ibds, gilt, 88p, color, DJ/2.50)	Garden City	1960	Palazzo, Tony	30-50	*
Palazzo, Tony	Animal Folk Tales of America (1st {std}, lg4to, ibds, 88p, color, DJ/2.95)	Doubleday	1961	Palazzo, Tony	30-45	
Palazzo, Tony	Bianco and the New World (1st, 4to, 64p, green cl, b/w, pep, DJ/2.75)	Viking	(1957)	Palazzo, Tony	30-50	
Palazzo, Tony	Bird Alphabet (1st {std}, 4to, ibds, [58]p, color, pep, DJ/2.95)	Duell, Sloan	(1966)	Palazzo, Tony	30-45	
Palazzo, Tony	Cat Alphabet (1st {std}, 4to, ibds, [56]p, color, pep, DJ/2.95)	Duell, Sloan	(1966)	Palazzo, Tony	30-45	
Palazzo, Tony	Charley the Horse (1st, sq4to, 56p, color, pep, DJ/2.50)	Viking	1950	Palazzo, Tony	40-65	
Palazzo, Tony	Did You Say Dogs? (1st, lg8vo, 43p, color, DJ/2.50)	Garrard Pub.	(1964)	Palazzo, Tony	25-45	
Palazzo, Tony	Dinosaur Alphabet (1st {std}, 4to, unpag, color, DJ/2.95)	Duell, Sloan	(1963)	Palazzo, Tony	25-45	
Palazzo, Tony	Elephant Alphabet (1st, 4to, [41]p, color, pep, DJ/2.95)	Duell, Sloan	(1961)	Palazzo, Tony	30-45	
Palazzo, Tony	Federico the Flying Squirrel (1st, 4to, 54p, ipcb, color, pep, DJ/2.50)	Viking	1951	Palazzo, Tony	40-65	
Palazzo, Tony	Fireman: Save My Cat! (1st, sm4to, [42]p, fp color, DJ/2.95)	Abelard-Schuman	1964	Palazzo, Tony	30-50	*
Palazzo, Tony	Giant Nursery Book (1st, lg4to, ibds, 188p, color, pep, DJ/3.95)	Garden City	1957	Palazzo, Tony	55-80	*
Palazzo, Tony	Golden Girl (1st, lg8vo, 43p, color, pep, DJ/2.50)	Garrard Pub.	(1963)	Palazzo, Tony	25-40	
Palazzo, Tony	Goldilocks & the Three Bears (1st {std}, 4to, ibds, [34]p, color, DJ/1.00)	Garden City	1959	Palazzo, Tony	25-45	
Palazzo, Tony	Great Othello (1st, sm ob4to, 48p, blue cl, 1-color, DJ/2.00)	Viking	1952	Palazzo, Tony	40-65	
Palazzo, Tony	Henny-Penny and Chicken Little (1st {std}, 4to, unpag, color, pep, DJ/1.00)	Garden City	1960	Palazzo, Tony	30-50	
Palazzo, Tony	Jan and the Reindeer (1st, lg8vo, 42p, color, pep, DJ/2.50)	Garrard Pub.	(1963)	Palazzo, Tony	25-40	
Palazzo, Tony	Let's Go to the Circus (1st {std}, lg4to, 88p, ibds, color, pep, DJ/2.95)	Doubleday	1961	Palazzo, Tony	25-40	
Palazzo, Tony	Let's Go to the Jungle (1st {std}, lg4to, 88p, ibds, color, pep, DJ/2.95)	Doubleday	(1962)	Palazzo, Tony	25-40	
Palazzo, Tony	Monkey Alphabet (1st {std}, 4to, [54]p, ibds, color, pep, DJ/2.50)	Duell, Sloan	1962	Palazzo, Tony	30-50	
Palazzo, Tony	Mr. Whistle's Secret (1st, sm4to, 52p, fp color, DJ/2.50)	Viking	1953	Palazzo, Tony	25-45	
Palazzo, Tony	Noah's Ark (1st, lg4to, ibds, [88]p, color, pep, DJ/2.50)	Garden City	(1955)	Palazzo, Tony	40-65	
Palazzo, Tony	Pig for Tom (1st, lg8vo, 42p, color, pep, DJ/2.50)	Garrard Pub.	(1963)	Palazzo, Tony	25-40	
Palazzo, Tony	Ramona Knew What She Wanted (1st, sm4to, [41]p, 2-color, pep, DJ/2.95)	Abelard-Schuman	(1964)	Palazzo, Tony	30-50	
Palazzo, Tony	Secret of Alexander's Horse (1st {std}, 4to, [42]p, ibds, color, DJ/2.95)	Duell, Sloan	(1965)	Palazzo, Tony	25-45	
Palazzo, Tony	Simple Simon (1st {std}, 4to, unpag, ibds, color, DJ/1.00)	Garden City	1959	Palazzo, Tony	30-45	
Palazzo, Tony	Story of Snowmand (1st {std}, 4to, [60]p, 2-color, ipcb, DJ/2.50)	Duell, Sloan	1962	Palazzo, Tony	25-40	
Palazzo, Tony	Susie the Cat (1st, 4to, 50p, color, pep, DJ/2.50)	Viking	1949	Palazzo, Tony	30-50	
Palazzo, Tony	Tales of Don Quixote (1st, lg4to, 84p, dp 2-color, DJ/2.95)	Garden City	1958	Palazzo, Tony	30-45	
Palazzo, Tony	Thai, Kao and Tone: Elephant Story (1st, 4to, [41]p, 1-color, pep, DJ/2.95)	Abelard-Schuman	(1966)	Palazzo, Tony	30-45	
Palazzo, Tony	Three Little Kittens (1st {std}, 4to, [32]p, ibds, color, pep, DJ/1.25)	Doubleday	1961	Palazzo, Tony	25-40	
Palazzo, Tony	Waldo the Wood Chuck (1st {std}, 4to, [42]p, color, DJ/2.95)	Duell, Sloan	(1964)	Palazzo, Tony	40-65	
Paley, Claudia	Benjamin the True (1st {std}, 8vo, 88p, color, DJ/3.75)	Little/Brown	(1969)	Hyman, Trina S.	30-45	
Palgrave, Francis T.	Golden Treasury of Songs & Lyrics (1st, 8vo, 366p, teg, uncut, 25 ticp)	L: Dent	1907	Bell, Robert A.	200-300	
Palgrave, Francis T.	Golden Treasury of Songs & Lyrics (1st, lg8vo, p-o, 373p, pep, 8cp)	Duffield	1911	Parrish, Maxfield	200-300	
Palgrave, Francis T.	Golden Treasury of Songs & Lyrics (8vo, yellow cl, 459p, 12 tipc)	Hodder	[1915]	Brickdale, E.F.	90-120	
Palm, Amy	Wanda and Greta at Broby Farm (1st {std}, 8vo, 198p, 6cp, pep)	Longmans	1930	McIntosh, Frank	30-45	*
Palmer, C. Everard	Cloud with the Silver Lining (1st AM {std}, 8vo, gilt, 164p, b/w, DJ/3.95)	Pantheon	(1967)	Acs, Laszlo	20-35	
Palmer, Candida	Snow Storm Before Christmas (1st, 8vo, ibds, 32p, b/w, DJ/2.75)	Lippincott	(1965)	Hall, Tom	50-80	
Palmer, Elizabeth	Give Me a River (1st, 8vo, 152p, dp color, DJ/1.75)	Scribner	1939	Holberg, Richard	40-65	
Palmer, Elizabeth	Good Old Clipsy (1st, 8vo, 194p, tan cl, fp 1-color, DJ/1.75)	Scribner	1941	Brown, Paul	60-100	
Palmer, Elizabeth	Nightingale House (1st, 8vo, 122p, orange cl, b/w, DJ/1.75)	Scribner	1937	Peters, Marjorie	20-30	
Palmer, Elizabeth	Up the River to Danger (1st, 8vo, 183p, b/w, DJ/1.75)	Scribner	1940	Holberg, Richard	25-40	
Palmer, Ernest C.	Young Blackbird (1st, 8vo, 62p, b/w, DJ)	L: Allan Wingate	1953	Peake, Mervyn	50-80	
Palmer, Frederick	The Vagabond (1st, sm8vo, 476p, 6pl)	Scribner	1903	Fisher, Harrison	25-40	
Palmer, G. (tr)	Odyssey of Homer (1st, 4to, red/gilt, 314p, p-o, 16cp, pep)	Houghton	1929	Wyeth, N.C.	250-350	
Palmer, H. Marion	Three Caballeros (1st, 4to, ibds, 56p, fp color, pep, DJ/1.25)	Random	(1944)	Disney Studios	350-500	
Palmer, Helen	I Was Kissed by a Seal at the Zoo (1st, lg8vo, ibds, 62p, DJ/1.95)	Beginner Books	1962	(Photos)	50-80	*
Palmer, Robin	Mickey Never Fails (1st, 8vo, 102p, color, pep, DJ/1.00)	D.C. Heath	(1939)	Disney Studios	75-120	
Palmer, Robin	The Barkingtons (1st, 8vo, 112p, grey cl, 2-color, pep, DJ/2.00)	Harper	(1948)	Gag, Flavia	30-50	*
Palmer, Robin	Wings of the Morning (1st, sq8vo, [29]p, color, DJ/3.75)	H.Z. Walck	1968	Palazzo, Tony	20-35	
Palmer, Winthrop	American Songs for Children (1st, ob4to, 64p, b/w)	Macmillan	1931	Cady, Harrison	70-125	
Paltenghi, Madalena	Honey on a Raft (1st, sm4to, ibds, [36]p, 15 fp b/w, pep, DJ/0.50)	Garden City	(1941)	Anderson, C.W.	50-80	
Paltenghi, Madalena	Honey the City Bear (1st, sm4to, 31p, ipcb, 14 fp b/w, DJ/0.50)	Grosset/Dunlap	1937	Anderson, C.W.	50-80	
Paltenghi, Madalena	Remus Goes to Town (1st, sm4to, 29p, ipcb, 15 fp b/w, DJ/0.50)	Grosset/Dunlap	1938	Anderson, C.W.	60-90	
Paltenghi, Madalena	Rumpus Rabbit (1st {std}, narrow 4to, 25p, green cl, b/w, DJ/1.50)	Harper	1939	Anderson, C.W.	80-135	
Paltock, Robert	Life & Adventures of Peter Wilkins (1st, lg8vo, 342p, gilt, 17cp, pep)	Dent/Dutton	1928	Bawden, Edward	100-165	
Pancoast, Morris H.	Rejuvenation of Mama & Papa Goose (1st, lg4to, ipcb, [84]p, color)	NY: Britton	(1916)	Pancoast, Morris H.	180-280	*
Panetta, George	Sea Beach Express (1st, lg8vo, 64p, fp b/w, DJ/3.95)	Harper	(1966)	McCully, Emily	45-70	
Pape, Lee	First Doll in the World (1st, 4to, [30]p, ibds, fp 2-color, DJ/2.75)	Lothrop, Lee	1961	Weisgard, Leonard	50-85	
Paquin, Samuel S.	Garden Fairies (1st, 8vo, 179p, p-o, 4cp)	Moffat	1908	Chamberlin, E.H.	100-165	
Paradis, Marjorie	Timmy and the Tiger (1st {std}, 8vo, 246p, fp b/w, DJ/2.50)	Harper	(1952)	Simont, Marc	30-50	

AUTHOR	TITLE	PUBLISHER	DATE	ARTIST	PRICE	LC
Paramore, Edward	Ballad of Yukon Jake (1st, 12mo, [42]p, 2pl, pcb)	Coward	1928	Kent, Rockwell	60-90	
Pardee, Lucius C.	Folk of the Woods (1st, lg8vo, gilt, p-o, 129p, teg, 10cp, pep)	Doubleday/Page	1913	Bull, Charles L.	40-70	
Parish, Helen R.	At the Palace Gates (1st, sm4to, ipcb, 64p, fp 2-color, pep, DJ/2.00)	Viking	1949	Politi, Leo	70-125	
Parish, Helen R.	Our Lady of Guadalupe (1st, sm4to, 48p, 6 dp color, DJ/3.00)	Viking	1955	Charlot, Jean	70-100	
Parish, Peggy	Amelia Bedelia (1st, 8vo, 64p, ipcb, fp 3-color, DJ/1.95)	Harper	(1966)	Siebel, Fritz	20-30	
Parish, Peggy	Beastly Circus (1st {std}, 12mo, [48]p, fp 1-color, DJ/3.95)	Simon/Schuster	(1969)	Parnall, Peter	25-40	
Parish, Peggy	Good Hunting, Little Indian (1st, lg ob8vo, [32]p, color, DJ/3.00)	Young Scott	1962	Weisgard, Leonard	40-65	
Parish, Peggy	Granny & the Desperadoes (1st {std}, 8vo, 40p, color, DJ/4.50)	Macmillan	(1970)	Kellogg, Steven	45-70	*
Parish, Peggy	Granny and the Indians (1st {std}, 8vo, 39p, color, DJ/3.95)	Macmillan	(1969)	Turkle, Brinton	25-40	
Parish, Peggy	Jumper Goes to School (1st {std}, ob4to, [29]p, color, DJ/3.95)	Simon/Schuster	(1969)	Szekeres, Cyndy	20-30	
Parish, Peggy	Let's Be Early Settlers with Daniel Boone (1st, 8vo, 96p, b/w, DJ/2.95)	Harper	(1967)	Lobel, Arnold	25-40	
Parish, Peggy	Let's Be Indians (1st, 8vo, 96p, b/w, DJ/2.75)	Harper	(1962)	Lobel, Arnold	20-35	
Parish, Peggy	Little Indian (1st, ob8vo, [32]p, color, DJ/3.95)	Simon/Schuster	(1968)	Johnson, John	20-35	*
Parish, Peggy	My Golden Book of Manners (1st, folio, [24]p, ibds, color)	Golden Press	1962	Scarry, Richard	30-50	*
Parish, Peggy	Ootah's Lucky Day (1st, 8vo, 63p, color, DJ/2.50)	Harper	(1970)	Funai, Mamoru	20-25	*
Parish, Peggy	Snapping Turtle's All Wrong Day (1st {std}, ob8vo, [34]p, color, DJ/3.95)	Simon/Schuster	(1970)	Johnson, John	20-30	*
Parish, Peggy	Thank You, Amelia Bedelia (1st, 8vo, [32]p, color, DJ/1.95)	Harper	(1964)	Siebel, Fritz	20-30	*
Parish, Peggy	Willy is my Brother (1st, ob8vo, [48]p, color, DJ/3.50)	W.R. Scott	(1963)	Hughes, Shirley	25-40	*
Park, Carton M.	Alphabet of Animals (1st, 4to, ibds, 105p, 26 fp color)	L: Blackie	1899	Park, Carton M.	180-260	
Parker, Arthur C.	Skunny Wundy (1st, lg8vo, p-o, 262p, 7 ticp, pep)	Doran	(1926)	Crawford, Will	70-130	
Parker, B.	A's and the K's (lg ob4to, ibds, 12 dp color)	L: Chambers	[1910]	Parker, N.	450-600	
Parker, B.	Arctic Orphans (1st, ob folio, ibds, color, pep)	L: Chambers	[1910]	Parker, N.	400-650	
Parker, B.	Cinderella at the Zoo (lg4to, ibds, 16 chromos)	L: Chambers	[1900]	Parker, B.	400-600	
Parker, B.	Funny Bunnies (lg ob4to, ibds, unpag, 12cp)	L: Chambers	[1905]	Parker, N.	400-650	
Parker, B.	History of the Hoppers (lg4to, ibds, color)	Chambers/Stokes	[1908]	Parker, N.	400-600	
Parker, B.	Hole & Corner Book (lg ob4to, ibds, 12 fp chromos, pep)	L: Chambers	[1910]	Parker, N.	450-600	
Parker, B.	Lays of the Grays (lg ob4to, ibds, color, pep)	L: Chambers	[1908]	Parker, N.	450-600	
Parker, B.& N.	Larder Lodge (lg ob4to, ibds, 14 fp color)	L: Chambers	[1910]	Parker, N.	400-600	
Parker, Dorothy	High Society (1st, lg4to, ipcb, 65p, fp b/w, pep)	Putnam	(1920)	Fish, Anne H.	120-200	*
Parker, Edgar	Rogue's Gallery (1st, 4to, 62p, fp b/w, DJ/3.95)	Pantheon	(1969)	Parker, Edgar	20-35	
Parker, Elinor	Here and There... (1st {std}, 8vo, 170p, b/w, DJ/4.50)	Crowell	(1967)	Spier, Peter E.	30-45	*
Parker, Elinor	Singing and the Gold (1st {std}, 4to, 230p, b/w woodcuts, DJ/3.75)	Crowell	(1962)	Leighton, Clare	25-45	
Parker, Elinor	Some Dogs (1st, sm4to, ibds, 48p, fp color, DJ/2.50)	Pantheon	(1950)	Jauss, Anne M.	25-45	
Parker, Frances	Hope Hathaway (1st, sm8vo, 408p, green cl, 9pl)	C.M. Clark	1904	Russell, Charles M.	80-125	
Parker, Gilbert	Lane that Had No Turning (1st, lg8vo, 215p, teg, uncut, 7pl, pep)	Doubleday/Page	1902	Schoonover, Frank	35-60	
Parker, Gilbert	March of the White Guard (1st, 12mo, gilt, 133p, b/w)	Fenno	1902	Starkweather, W.	30-50	
Parker, Gilbert	Money Master (1st, 12mo, green/gilt, 360p, 6pl)	Harper	1915	Castaigne, Andre	30-50	
Parker, Gilbert	Northern Lights (1st, 12mo, green/gilt, 352p, 16pl)	Harper	1909	Various	35-60	
Parker, Gilbert	The Weavers (1st, sm8vo, 530p, olive/gilt, 8pl)	Harper	1907	Castaigne, Andre	25-40	
Parker, Gilbert	When Valmond Came to Pontiac (1st, 12mo, teg, green/gilt, 222p)	Stone/Kimball	1895	Rogers, Bruce	70-120	
Parker, Louis N.	Pomander Walk (1st, 8vo, 267p, 16pl)	J. Lane	1911	Williams, J. Scott	60-90	
Parkes, William T.	Spook Ballads (1st, 12mo, 246p, brown/gilt, b/w, cep)	L: Simpkin	1895	Parkes, William T.	70-100	
Parkman, Francis	Oregon Trail (1st, 8vo, teg, gilt, 411p, 10pl)	Little/Brown	1892	Remington, Frederic	250-400	
Parkman, Francis	Oregon Trail (1st, 8vo, 364p, p-o, 5cp, pep)	Little/Brown	1925	Wyeth, N.C.	130-200	
Parkman, Francis	Oregon Trail (1st, 8vo, 385p, color, pep, DJ/3.00)	Farrar/Rinehart	(1931)	Daugherty, James	45-70	
Parkman, Francis	Oregon Trail (1st, lg8vo, 388p, black cl, p-o, 4cp, pep)	Winston	(1931)	Jackson, William H.	45-70	
Parkman, Francis	Oregon Trail (1st, 8vo, 328p, 13cp, DJ/5.00)	Doubleday	1946	Benton, Thomas H.	25-40	
Parks, Gale T.	Here Comes Daddy (1st, ob8vo, ibds, unpag, color, DJ/1.00)	W.R. Scott	1951	Gropper, William	60-100	
Parrish, A.& D.	Dream Coach (1st, 8vo, 143p, blue/gilt, fp b/w, pep, NH)	Macmillan	1924	Parrish, A.& D.	70-120	
Parrish, A.& D.	Floating Island (1st {std}, lg8vo, p-o, 265p, 13pl, NH)	Harper	(1930)	Parrish, Anne	80-140	R
Parrish, A.& D.	Knee-High to a Grasshopper (1st, 8vo, yellow cl, 209p, b/w, pep)	Macmillan	1923	Parrish, A.& D.	45-75	
Parrish, Anne	Story of Appleby Capple (1st, lg4to, 184p, pep, b/w, DJ/2.75, NH)	Harper	(1950)	Parrish, Anne	70-120	
Parrish, Randall	Air Pilot (1st, 8vo, 318p, p-o, 3cp)	McClurg	1913	Underwood, C.F.	30-60	
Parrish, Randall	Beth Norvell (1st, 8vo, 341p, tan cl, col frn by...)	McClurg	1907	Wyeth, N.C.	60-90	
Parrish, Randall	Bob Hampton of Placer (1st, 8vo, 383p, 4cp)	McClurg	1906	Keller, Arthur I.	25-40	
Parrish, Randall	Don MacGrath (1st, 8vo, 269p, 5pl)	McClurg	1910	Norton, John W.	30-50	
Parrish, Randall	Great Plains (1st, 8vo, 399p, 32pl)	McClurg	1907	(Engravings)	50-85	
Parrish, Randall	Keith of the Border (1st, 8vo, 362p, 4cp)	McClurg	1910	Dunton, W. Herbert	35-60	
Parrish, Randall	Last Voyage of the Donna Isabel (1st, 8vo, blue cl, 366p, 4cp)	McClurg	1908	True, Allen	30-45	
Parrish, Randall	Love Under Fire (1st, 8vo, 400p, 5cp)	McClurg	1911	Kimball, Alonzo	25-40	*
Parrish, Randall	Maid of the Forest (1st, 8vo, 427p, 5cp)	McClurg	1913	Schoonover, Frank	30-50	
Parrish, Randall	My Lady of the South (1st, 8vo, 360p, tan cl, 4cp)	McClurg	1909	Kimball, Alonzo	25-40	
Parrish, Randall	Prisoners of Chance (1st, 8vo, yellow cl, 423p, 4cp)	McClurg	1908	Kinneys	30-50	
Parrish, Randall	Sword of the Old Frontier (1st, 8vo, 407p, tan cl, 4cp)	McClurg	1905	Yohn, F.C.	30-50	
Parrish, Randall	When Wilderness was King (1st, 8vo, 388p, uncut, 6cp, dep)	McClurg	1904	Kinneys	25-40	
Parry, David M.	Scarlet Empire (1st, sm8vo, red/gilt, 400p, 10pl)	Bobbs-Merrill	(1906)	Wall, Hermann C.	65-100	
Parry, Edward A.	Butterscotia... (1st, 8vo, blue/gilt, uncut, 170p, map, 6pl)	L: D. Nutt	1896	MacGregor, Archie	180-270	
Parry, Edward A.	First Book of Krab (1st, lg8vo, green cl, 132p, uncut, b/w)	L: D. Nutt	1897	MacGregor, Archie	125-200	
Parry, Edward A.	Gamble Gold (1st, sq8vo, ibds, 248p, AEG, gilt, 15pl)	L: Hutchinson	1907	Furniss, Harry	60-80	
Parry, Edward A.	Katawampus: Its Treatment & Cure (1st, 8vo, green cl, 96p, b/w)	L: D. Nutt	1895	MacGregor, Archie	120-200	
Parry, Edward A.	Scarlet Herring (1st, 8vo, 253p, uncut, green/gilt, fp b/w, AEG)	L: Smith Elder	1899	Rusden, Athelstan	75-150	
Parsons, Arthur	Horn that Stopped the Band (1st {std}, 4to, [48]p, b/w, dep, DJ/2.50)	F. Watts	1954	Ward, Lynd	50-80	R
Parsons, Frances T.	According to Season... (1st, sm8vo, 197p, green/gilt, cvr by...)	Scribner	1902	Armstrong, Margaret	35-60	*
Parsons, Frances T.	How to Know the Ferns (1st, 8vo, brown/gilt, 215p)	Scribner	1899	Armstrong, Margaret	55-80	
Parsons, Geoffrey	Stream of History (1st, lg8vo, 590p, gilt, b/w, pep)	Scribner	1928	Daugherty, James	35-60	
Parton, Ethel	Lost Locket (1st, 8vo, 317p, b/w, pep, DJ/2.00)	Viking	1940	Platt, Margaret	30-50	
Parton, Ethel	Melissa Ann (1st {std}, 8vo, 280p, col frn, fp b/w)	Doubleday/Doran	1931	Lawson, Marie A.	40-65	
Parton, Ethel	Mule of the Parthenon (1st {std}, 8vo, 243p, blue cl, col frn, b/w, DJ)	Doubleday/Doran	1932	Gay, Zhenya	30-50	

AUTHOR	TITLE	PUBLISHER	DATE	ARTIST	PRICE	LC
Parton, Ethel	Penelope Ellen (1st, 8vo, 300p, b/w, pep, DJ/2.00)	Viking	1936	Platt, Margaret	25-45	
Parton, Ethel	Tabitha Mary (1st, 8vo, 244p, col frn, 4 dp b/w, pep)	Viking	1933	Platt, Margaret	30-45	
Paschang, Adolph	Dragon Treasure (1st {std}, sm8vo, 265p, 5 fp b/w, pep)	Longmans	1932	Wiese, Kurt	30-50	
Pasma, Henry K.	Enchanted Sword (1st {std}, sm8vo, 275p, 6 fp b/w, pep)	Longmans	1932	Westmacott, Bernard	25-40	
Patch, Edith M.	Holiday Hill (1st, sq8vo, 135p, pep, b/w)	Macmillan	1931	(Photos)	30-50	
Patri, Angelo	Pinocchio in America (1st {std}, 8vo, 255p, col frn, 17pl, pep)	Doubleday/Doran	1928	Liddell, Mary	60-90	
Pattee, Fred L.	House of the Black Ring (1st, sm8vo, 324p, cvr by...)	Henry Holt & Co.	1905	Stuart, Bertha	60-90	
Patterson, R.F.	Mein Rant (1st, 8vo, 69p, tan cl, b/w)	L: Blackie	1940	Robinson, W. Heath	80-140	
Pauli, Hertha	Golden Door (1st {std}, 8vo, 155p, b/w, pep, DJ/2.50)	Knopf	1949	Wiese, Kurt	60-80	
Pauli, Hertha	Little Town of Bethlehem (1st {std} 12mo, [44]p, gilt, color, pep, DJ/2.50)	Duell, Sloan	(1963)	Kredel, Fritz	25-40	
Pauli, Hertha	Most Beautiful House... (1st {std}, 8vo, 114p, color, DJ/2.50)	Knopf	1949	Wiese, Kurt	30-50	
Paull, Grace	Four Friends (1st, 8vo, [48]p, 2-color, pep)	Grosset/Dunlap	1935	Paull, Grace	30-50	
Paull, Grace	Freddy the Curious Cat (1st {std}, ob4to, unpag, color, pep, DJ/2.75)	Doubleday	1958	Paull, Grace	30-50	
Paull, Grace	Gloomy the Camel (1st, 12mo, [40]p, ibds, color, pep, DJ/1.50)	Viking	1938	Paull, Grace	25-45	
Paull, Grace	Horse to Ride (1st {std}, sq8vo, [32]p, ibds, color, DJ/1.25)	Doubleday	1949	Paull, Grace	30-50	
Paull, Grace	Little Twin (1st {std}, sq8vo, ipcb, 29p, 2-color, pep, DJ/1.50)	Doubleday	(1953)	Paull, Grace	30-50	*
Paull, Grace	Pancakes for Breakfast (1st {std}, ob4to, ibds, [28]p, color, DJ/1.75)	Doubleday	1946	Paull, Grace	40-65	
Paull, Grace	Peanut Butter's Slide (1st, 8vo, ibds, [32]p, fp 3-color, DJ/1.00)	Viking	1939	Paull, Grace	30-50	*
Paull, Grace	Raspberry Patch (1st {std}, sm4to, ibds, [25]p, color, pep, DJ/1.50)	Doubleday/Doran	1941	Paull, Grace	30-50	
Paull, Grace	Squash for the Fair (1st {std}, 4to, ibds, [24]p, color, DJ/1.50)	Doubleday/Doran	1943	Paull, Grace	30-50	
Paxon, Mary	Mary Paxon, her Book (1st {std}, 8vo, 98p, ipcb, b/w)	Doubleday/Doran	1931	Doane, Pelagie	25-40	
Payne, Emmy	Katy No-Pocket (1st, 4to, [32]p, color, pep, DJ/2.00)	Houghton	1944	Rey, Hans A.	100-160	
Payne, Joan B.	Magnificent Milo (1st, 4to, 64p, b/w, DJ/2.75)	Hastings House	(1958)	Payne, Joan B.	40-65	
Payne, Joan B.	The Raven & other Fairy Tales (1st, 4to, 52p, 1-color, DJ/4.95)	Hastings House	(1969)	Payne, Joan B.	40-65	
Peabody, Josephine	Book of the Little Past (1st, sm4to, 50p, p-o, pcb, 6cp)	Houghton	1908	Green, Eliz. S.	80-120	
Peabody, Josephine	The Wayfarers (1st [1st bk.], sm8vo, 83p, gilt, cvr by...)	Copeland & Day	1898	Peabody, Marion L.	70-100	
Peacock, Thomas L.	Gryll Grange (1st, sm8vo, 292p, gilt, uncut, AEG, b/w)	L: Macmillan	1896	Townsend, F.H.	55-80	
Peacock, Thomas L.	Headlong Hall and Nightmare Abbey (1st, sm8vo, 243p, gilt, 40 fp b/w, pep)	L: Macmillan	1896	Millar, H.R.	40-65	
Peacock, Thomas L.	Maid Marian & Crotchet Castle (1st, 12mo, AEG, gilt, 321p, dep)	L: Macmillan	1895	Townsend, F.H.	75-100	
Peacock, Thomas L.	Melincourt (1st, sm8vo, 326p, AEG, gilt, 40 illus)	L: Macmillan	1896	Townsend, F.H.	75-100	
Peacock, Thomas L.	Misfortunes of Elphin & Rhododaphne (1st, 12mo, AEG, 262p, gilt, b/w)	L: Macmillan	1897	Townsend, F.H.	50-85	
Peacocke, Isabel M.	My Friend Phil (1st, 8vo, p-o, 320p, 6cp)	L: Ward Lock	1915	Tarrant, Margaret	60-90	*
Peake, Elmore E.	House of Hawley (1st, 8vo, 341p, cvr by...)	Appleton	1905	Armstrong, Margaret	35-60	*
Peake, Mervyn	Captain Slaughterboard Drops Anchor (1st, 4to, 48p, cloth, color, DJ)	L: Eyre/Spotts.	1945	Peake, Mervyn	300-500	
Peake, Mervyn	Figures of Speech (1st, lg8vo, fp b/w, gilt, [58]p, DJ)	L: Gollancz	(1954)	Peake, Mervyn	150-220	
Peake, Mervyn	Mr. Pye (1st, 8vo, 278p, blue/gilt, b/w, DJ)	L: Heinemann	(1953)	Peake, Mervyn	150-225	
Peake, Mervyn	Rhymes without Reason (1st, 8vo, 39p, yellow cl, 16 fp color, DJ)	L: Eyre/Spotts.	1944	Peake, Mervyn	200-300	
Peake, Mervyn	Shapes & Sounds (1st, 8vo, 23p, pcb, DJ)	L: Chatto	1941	Peake, Mervyn	200-300	
Peake, Mervyn	Titus Groan (1st AM, 8vo, 430p, b/w, DJ/3.00)	Reynal/Hitchcock	(1946)	Peake, Mervyn	250-400	
Pearce, Philippa	Dog So Small (1st AM {std}, 8vo, 142p, b/w, DJ/2.95)	Lippincott	(1963)	Maitland, Antony	25-40	
Pearce, Philippa	Minnow on the Say (1st, 8vo, 241p, blue cl, b/w, DJ)	L: Oxford U.Pr.	(1955)	Ardizzone, Edward	70-100	
Pearce, Philippa	Mrs. Cockle's Cat (1st AM {std}, 4to, [32]p, b/w, DJ/3.00, KGM)	Lippincott	(1961)	Maitland, Antony	30-50	
Pearce, Philippa	Tom's Midnight Garden (1st, 8vo, 229p, b/w, DJ, CgM)	L: Oxford U.Pr.	1958	Einzig, Susan	70-100	
Pearson, Edmund L.	Voyage of the Hoppergrass (1st, sm8vo, 348p, b/w, PPPa)	Macmillan	1913	Fogarty, Thomas	80-125	R
Peart, Hendry	Red Falcons of Tremoine (1st {std}, 8vo, 244p, fp b/w, cep, DJ/3.00)	Knopf	(1956)	Brevannes, Maurice	20-35	*
Peary, Josephine	Children of the Arctic (1st, sm4to, cloth, 120p, p-o)	Stokes	(1903)	(Photos)	120-200	
Peary, Josephine	Snow Baby (1st, sm4to, p-o, 84p, b/w, PPP)	Stokes	(1901)	(Photos)	150-225	R
Peary, Marie A.	Little Tooktoo (1st, 8vo, ibds, 62p, pep, 5cp)	Wm. Morrow	(1930)	Wiese, Kurt	50-80	*
Pease, Eleanor F.	Gay Pippo (1st, sm4to, p-o, 80p, color, pep)	Whitman	1936	Wiese, Kurt	50-80	
Pease, Eleanor F.	Jolly Little Clown (1st, lg8vo, p-o, gilt, 126p, pep, color)	Whitman	(1927)	Hetherington, M.L.	30-55	
Pease, Howard	Foghorns (1st {std}, 8vo, uncut, 295p, pep, DJ/2.00)	Doubleday/Doran	1937	Fischer, Anton O.	80-130	
Pease, Howard	Gypsy Caravan (1st {std}, 8vo, 254p, col frn, pep)	Doubleday/Doran	1930	Wood, Harrie	80-125	
Pease, Howard	Jinx Ship (1st {std}, 8vo, uncut, 324p, col frn, pep)	Doubleday/Page	1927	Blaine, Mahlon	80-125	
Pease, Howard	Jungle River (1st {std}, 8vo, 295p, col frn, pep, DJ/2.00)	Doubleday/Doran	1938	Sperry, Armstrong	70-125	
Pease, Howard	Tattooed Man (1st {std}, sm8vo, 332p, col frn, b/w)	Doubleday/Page	1926	Blaine, Mahlon	70-100	
Pease, Howard	Thunderbolt House (1st {std}, sm8vo, 287p, b/w, pep, DJ/2.00)	Doubleday/Doran	1944	Sperry, Armstrong	80-125	
Pease, Josephine	Nimbo (1st, 8vo, p-o, 64p, color)	Whitman	(1934)	Young, Eleanor M.	100-165	
Pease, Leonora	Child You Used to Be (1st, 8vo, 198p, 10pl, pep)	McClurg	1909	Perkins, Lucy F.	45-70	
Pease, Leonora	Dollies in Happy-Land (1st, lg8vo, pict cl, [45]p, color)	Whitman	(1914)	Lee, Ella D.	100-160	
Pease, Leonora	Four & Twenty Dollies (1st, sm sq4to, 94p, ibds, color)	Hamming	(1914)	Lee, Ella D.	80-140	
Peat, Fern B.	Magnificent Squeak (1st, 8vo, ibds, 42p, color)	Saalfield	(1929)	Peat, Fern B.	50-80	
Peat, Fern B.	Rags (1st, lg4to, [12]p, wraps, color)	Saalfield	1929	Peat, Fern B.	60-100	
Peat, Fern B.	Stories Children Like (1st, lg4to, [34]p, ibds, 8cp)	Saalfield	1933	Peat, Fern B.	50-85	
Peattie, Donald C.	Almanac for Moderns (1st, 8vo, 396p, b/w, DJ/3.00)	Putnam	(1935)	Ward, Lynd	50-85	
Peattie, Donald C.	Book of Hours (1st, 8vo, 246p, 202p, b/w, DJ/2.50, cvr by...)	Putnam	1937	Ward, Lynd	40-60	*
Peattie, Donald C.	Child's Story of the World (1st, sq8vo, [148]p, color, pep, DJ/2.00)	Simon/Schuster	1937	Averill, Naomi	70-100	
Peattie, Donald C.	Journey into America (1st, 8vo, 276p, color, pep, DJ/3.00)	Houghton	1943	Ward, Lynd	30-50	
Peattie, Donald C.	Story of America (1st, sq8vo, [24]p, ibds, color, pep, DJ/0.50)	Grosset/Dunlap	1937	Averill, Naomi	35-50	
Peattie, Donald C.	Story of Ancient Civilization (1st, sq8vo, [24]p, ibds, color, pep, DJ/0.50)	Grosset/Dunlap	1937	Averill, Naomi	35-50	
Peattie, Donald C.	Story of the First Men (1st, sq8vo, ibds, [24]p, color, pep, DJ/0.50)	Grosset/Dunlap	1937	Averill, Naomi	30-50	
Peattie, Elia W.	Azalea at Sunset Gap (1st, sm8vo, tan cl, 286p, 4pl)	Reilly/Britton	(1914)	Nuyttens, Joseph P.	30-50	*
Peattie, Elia W.	Edda & the Oak (1st, sq8vo, 134p, p-o)	Rand/McNally	(1911)	Merrill, Katharine	30-50	
Peattie, Elia W.	Mountain Woman (1st, 12mo, 251p, teg, cvr by...)	Way & Williams	1896	Rogers, Bruce	100-175	
Peattie, Elia W.	Pippins and Cheese (1st, 12mo, 282p, teg, uncut, cvr by...)	Way & Williams	1897	Hazenplug, Frank	80-120	
Peck, Anne M.	Manoel & the Morning Star (1st {std}, 8vo, 31p, ipcb, color, pep, DJ/1.75)	Harper	(1943)	Peck, Anne M.	25-40	
Peck, George W.	Peck's Bad Boy & his Chums (ob4to, stiff wraps, color)	Chi: Stanton	1908	McDougall, Walter	250-350	
Peck, Harry T.	Hilda and the Wishes (1st, sm8vo, 240p, 8pl)	Dodd	1907	Leonard, M.E.	35-60	*
Peck, Leigh	Don Coyote (1st, sm4to, 78p, color, cep, DJ/2.00)	Houghton	1942	Burton, Virginia L.	60-90	

AUTHOR	TITLE	PUBLISHER	DATE	ARTIST	PRICE	LC
Peck, Leigh	Pecos Bill & Lightning (1st, lg8vo, 68p, color, cep, DJ/1.75)	Houghton	1940	Wiese, Kurt	50-80	
Peck, Theodora A.	Sword of Dundee (1st, sm8vo, 398p, p-o, col frn, 6pl)	Duffield	1908	Rae, John	30-45	
Peckinpah, Betty	Coco is Coming (1st, sm4to, [26]p, fp color, cep, DJ/2.50)	Lothrop, Lee	1956	Mariana	40-65	*
Pedley, Muriel	Land of Goodness Knows Where (1st, 8vo, 117p, col frn, b/w)	L: Newnes	(1923)	Knowles, Horace J.	100-150	
Peedie, Jean M.	Donald in Numberland (1st, 8vo, ipcb, [64]p, color, dep)	R.D. Henkle	(1927)	Hader, B.& E.	100-160	
Peeples, Edwin A.	Blue Boy (1st, 8vo, 176p, b/w, DJ/3.00)	Houghton	1964	Shenton, Edward	30-50	
Peet, Bill	Buford, the Little Bighorn (1st, sm sq4to, 46p, fp color, DJ/3.25)	Houghton	1967	Peet, Bill	30-50	
Peet, Bill	Capyboppy (1st {std}, 8vo, 62p, color, DJ/3.00)	Houghton	1966	Peet, Bill	30-50	
Peet, Bill	Chester, the Worldly Pig (1st, sm sq4to, 48p, fp color, DJ/3.25)	Houghton	1965	Peet, Bill	30-50	
Peet, Bill	Ella (1st, sm sq4to, 48p, fp color, DJ/3.25)	Houghton	1964	Peet, Bill	30-50	
Peet, Bill	Farewell to Shady Glade (1st, lg8vo, 38p, color, pep, DJ/3.25)	Houghton	1966	Peet, Bill	30-50	
Peet, Bill	Fly Homer, Fly (1st {std}, lg8vo, 60p, color, DJ/4.50)	Houghton	1969	Peet, Bill	50-75	
Peet, Bill	Hubert's Hair-Raising Adventure (1st, 4to, color, 38p, DJ/3.00)	Houghton	1959	Peet, Bill	35-50	
Peet, Bill	Huge Harold (1st, sm sq4to, [45]p, fp color, DJ/3.00)	Houghton	1961	Peet, Bill	35-50	
Peet, Bill	Jennifer & Josephine (1st, sm sq4to, 46p, fp color, DJ/3.25)	Houghton	1967	Peet, Bill	35-50	*
Peet, Bill	Kermit the Hermit (1st {std}, sm sq4to, 48p, fp color, DJ/3.25)	Houghton	1965	Peet, Bill	35-50	
Peet, Bill	Pinkish, Purplish, Bluish Egg (1st, sm sq4to, 46p, fp color, DJ/3.25)	Houghton	1963	Peet, Bill	35-50	
Peet, Bill	Randy's Dandy Lions (1st, sm sq4to, 48p, fp color, DJ/3.00)	Houghton	1964	Peet, Bill	35-50	
Peet, Bill	Smokey (1st, sm sq4to, 38p, fp color, pep, DJ/3.00)	Houghton	1962	Peet, Bill	35-50	
Peet, Bill	Whingdingdilly (1st {std}, sm4to, 60p, color, cep, DJ/4.95)	Houghton	1970	Peet, Bill	50-75	
Peet, Bill	Wump World (1st {std}, lg8vo, 44p, color, cep, DJ/3.95)	Houghton	1970	Peet, Bill	35-50	
Peet, Creighton	Defending America (1st {std}, 8vo, 160p, color, pep, DJ/1.50)	Harper	(1941)	Kredel, Fritz	30-50	
Peltier, Florence	Through the Rainbow (1st, 8vo, blue cl, p-o, 117p, 7cp)	Revell	(1917)	Wilson, Clara P.	60-100	
Pemberton, Max	House Under the Sea (1st AM, sm8vo, 346p, brown/gilt, 8pl)	Appleton	1902	Forestier, Amedee	35-60	
Pemberton, Max	Pro Patria (1st, 8vo, 316p, red/gilt, 16pl)	L: Ward Lock	1901	Forestier, Amedee	60-100	
Pender, Lydia	Barnaby and the Horses (1st, sm4to, [40]p, color, pep, DJ/2.75)	Abelard-Schuman	1961	Evers, Alie	30-50	
Penfield, Edward	Big Book of Horses & Goats (1st, ob folio, [24]p, color)	R.H. Russell	1901	Penfield, Edward	300-500	*
Penfield, Edward	Holland Sketches (1st, lg8vo, 147p, ibds, 34 ticp, pep)	Scribner	1907	Penfield, Edward	150-225	
Penfield, Edward	Spanish Sketches (1st, lg8vo, 146p, yellow bds, 27 ticp, pep)	Scribner	1911	Penfield, Edward	150-225	
Penn, Ruth B.	Mommies are for Loving (1st, ob8vo, [32]p, 2-color, DJ/1.95)	Putnam	1962	Emberley, Ed	25-40	
Pennell, Eliz. R.	Our House (1st, 8vo, ipcb, 373p, 10pl)	Houghton	1912	Pennell, Joseph	50-85	
Pennell, Eliz. R.	Over the Alps on a Bicycle (1st, 8vo, 110p, 18 fp b/w)	L: T.F. Unwin	1898	Pennell, Joseph	80-130	
Pennell, Eliz. R.	To Gypsyland (1st, sm8vo, pink cl, 240p, fp b/w)	L: T.F. Unwin	1893	Pennell, Joseph	60-100	
Pennell, Joseph	Adventures of an Illustrator (1st, lg4to, buckram/gilt, 372p, col frn)	Little/Brown	1925	Pennell, Joseph	100-185	
Pennell, Joseph	French Cathedrals (1st AM, 4to, 424p, teg, 38pl)	Century	1909	Pennell, Joseph	70-125	
Pennell, Joseph	Jew at Home (1st, 12mo, red/gilt, 105p, b/w)	Appleton	1892	Pennell, Joseph	200-300	
Pennell, Joseph	Our Philadelphia (1st, sm4to, red/gilt, 552p, teg, b/w)	Lippincott	1914	Pennell, Joseph	60-90	
Pennell, Joseph	Pictures of Panama Canal (1st, sm4to, [56]p, brown cl, p-o, 28pl)	Lippincott	1912	Pennell, Joseph	60-100	
Pennell, Joseph	Play in Provence (1st, sm8vo, tan cl, teg, uncut, 202p, b/w)	Century	1892	Pennell, Joseph	80-125	
Pennell, Joseph	Wonder of Work (1st, sm4to, [226]p, brown cl, p-o, 52pl)	Lippincott	1916	Pennell, Joseph	70-100	
Penney, Grace	Tales of the Cheyennes (1st, lg8vo, 117p, b/w, DJ/2.25)	Houghton	1953	West, Walter	20-35	
Percival, Olive	Mexico City: Idler's Note-Book (1st, 12mo, 208p, cvr & designs by...)	Herbert Stone	1901	Hazenplug, Frank	100-170	
Perera, Lydia	Frisky (1st, sm8vo, [46]p, red cl, color, cep, DJ/2.25)	Holiday House	1955	Liebman, Oscar	25-40	
Perez, Luis	El Coyote the Rebel (1st {std}, sm8vo, orange cl, 233p, b/w, DJ/2.75)	Henry Holt & Co.	(1947)	Politi, Leo	50-80	
Perez-Guerra, A.	Poppy, Adventures of a Fairy (1st, lg8vo, ibds, 80p, pep, b/w)	Rand/McNally	(1931)	West, Benton	100-160	*
Perez-Guerra, A.	Poppy, Adventures of a Fairy (12mo, [62]p, ibds, 16 color)	Rand/McNally	(1942)	Barclay, Betsy	40-60	*
Perkins, Al	King Midas and the Golden Touch (1st, 8vo, ibds, 62p, fp color, pep, DJ)	Beginner Books	(1969)	Berson, Harold	30-45	*
Perkins, Eleanor E.	News from Notown (1st, sm4to, 108p, b/w)	Houghton	1919	Perkins, Lucy F.	40-60	
Perkins, Lucy F.	American Twins of the Revolution (1st, 8vo, 208p, pep, b/w)	Houghton	1926	Perkins, Lucy F.	35-60	*
Perkins, Lucy F.	Belgian Twins (1st, 8vo, brown cl, 198p, b/w, pep)	Houghton	1917	Perkins, Lucy F.	40-70	R
Perkins, Lucy F.	Book of Joys (1st, lg8vo, 212p, green cl, uncut, p-o, 5cp)	McClurg	1907	Perkins, Lucy F.	50-80	
Perkins, Lucy F.	Cave Twins (1st, 8vo, 164p, b/w)	Houghton	1916	Perkins, Lucy F.	40-60	*
Perkins, Lucy F.	Chinese Twins (1st, sm8vo, yellow cl, 166p, col frn, b/w, DJ/1.75)	Houghton	1935	Perkins, Lucy F.	50-80	
Perkins, Lucy F.	Cornelia (1st, sm8vo, 202p, 8pl)	Houghton	1919	Perkins, Lucy F.	30-50	
Perkins, Lucy F.	Dutch Twins (1st, 8vo, 190p, b/w, PPPa)	Houghton	1911	Perkins, Lucy F.	75-120	
Perkins, Lucy F.	Filipino Twins (1st, 8vo, 150p, b/w)	Houghton	1923	Perkins, Lucy F.	35-60	
Perkins, Lucy F.	French Twins (1st, 8vo, blue cl, 202p, b/w, pep)	Houghton	1918	Perkins, Lucy F.	40-60	
Perkins, Lucy F.	Indian Twins (1st, 8vo, 203p, b/w)	Houghton	1930	Perkins, Lucy F.	35-50	
Perkins, Lucy F.	Irish Twins (1st, 8vo, 206p, b/w)	Houghton	1913	Perkins, Lucy F.	35-50	
Perkins, Lucy F.	Italian Twins (1st, 8vo, green cl, 149p, b/w, pep)	Houghton	1920	Perkins, Lucy F.	30-50	
Perkins, Lucy F.	Japanese Twins (1st, 8vo, 178p, beige cl, b/w, pep)	Houghton	1912	Perkins, Lucy F.	35-60	
Perkins, Lucy F.	Mexican Twins (1st, 8vo, tan cl, 186p, b/w)	Houghton	1915	Perkins, Lucy F.	30-50	
Perkins, Lucy F.	Mr. Chick: his Travels & Adventures (1st, ob4to, 117p, p-o, fp b/w)	Houghton	1926	Perkins, Lucy F.	45-70	
Perkins, Lucy F.	Pickaninny Twins (1st, 8vo, 152p, tan cl, b/w, pep)	Houghton	1931	Perkins, Lucy F.	120-180	
Perkins, Lucy F.	Puritan Twins (1st, 8vo, 179p, pep, b/w)	Houghton	1921	Perkins, Lucy F.	30-50	
Perkins, Lucy F.	Spartan Twins (1st, 12mo, 161p, b/w)	Houghton	1920	Perkins, Lucy F.	35-60	
Perkins, Lucy F.	Swiss Twins (1st, 8vo, 132p, brown cl, b/w, pep)	Houghton	1922	Perkins, Lucy F.	35-60	
Perkins, Marlin	Zooparade (1st {A}, 4to, beige cl, 94p, 16 fp color, pep, DJ/2.95)	Rand/McNally	(1954)	Bransom, Paul	55-80	
Perrault, Charles	Bluebeard & other Fairy Tales (1st {std}, folio, ibds, 38p, color, DJ/2.95)	Macmillan	1964	Lambert, Saul	30-50	*
Perrault, Charles	Cinderella (1st, sm4to, [32]p, gilt, color, DJ/2.00, CM)	Scribner	(1954)	Brown, Marcia	150-220	
Perrault, Charles	Cinderella (1st, lg8vo, unpag, color, DJ/1.50)	World	(1965)	Ramirez, Pablo	20-30	
Perrault, Charles	Fairy Garland (1st, lg8vo, 251p, 12 ticp)	L: Cassell	(1928)	Dulac, Edmund	170-240	
Perrault, Charles	Fairy Garland (1st AM, lg8vo, blue/gilt, 251p, p-o, 12 ticp)	Scribner	(1929)	Dulac, Edmund	150-220	
Perrault, Charles	Fairy Tales (1st, sm4to, p-o, 107p, 12cp)	L: Simpkin	(1911)	Appleton, Honor C.	140-200	
Perrault, Charles	Fairy Tales (1st, 12mo, brown/gilt, p-o, 128p, 8cp)	L: Dent	(1913)	Robinson, Charles	160-225	
Perrault, Charles	Fairy Tales (1st, sm4to, blue bds, p-o, color)	L: Selwyn/Blount	1922	Austen, John	55-80	*
Perrault, Charles	Fairy Tales (1st AM, 4to, blue/gilt, 160p, 12cp, 12pl)	Dodge	[1922]	Clarke, Harry	400-600	
Perrault, Charles	Fairy Tales (1st, 4to, blue/gilt, 160p, 12cp, 12pl)	L: Harrap	(1922)	Clarke, Harry	500-700	

AUTHOR	TITLE	PUBLISHER	DATE	ARTIST	PRICE	LC
Perrault, Charles	Favorite Fairy Tales with New Pictures (1st, 4to, ibds, [25]p, color)	Stokes	1892	Humphrey, Maud	350-500	
Perrault, Charles	Ideal Fairy Tales (1st, 4to, [62]p, ibds)	McLoughlin	(1897)	16 Chromos	160-225	
Perrault, Charles	Old Time Stories (1st AM, 4to, 200p, p-o, gilt, 6 ticp)	Dodd	(1921)	Robinson, W. Heath	250-400	
Perrault, Charles	Old-Time Stories (1st, 4to, red/gilt, 200p, 6 ticp)	L: Constable	1921	Robinson, W. Heath	350-500	
Perrault, Charles	Once Upon a Time (1st, sm4to, 115p, 8cp)	L: O'Connor	1922	Sinclair, Helen	90-160	*
Perrault, Charles	Puss in Boots (1st, 4to, [30]p, color, pep, DJ/2.00, CH)	Scribner	(1952)	Brown, Marcia	120-170	R
Perrault, Charles	Puss in Boots (1st AM {std}, sm ob4to, [25]p, color, DJ/3.95)	World	1969	Wilkinson, Barry	25-40	
Perrault, Charles	Puss in Boots (1st {std}, 4to, 34p, color, DJ/4.95)	Doubleday	(1970)	Noonan, Julia	25-40	
Perrault, Charles	Sleeping Beauty (1st, 4to, teg, blue/gilt, 12cp)	Dodge	[1922]	Clarke, Harry	300-450	
Perrault, Charles	Story of Blue-Beard (1st, 8vo, green cl, teg, 61p, b/w)	L: Lawrence	1895	Southall, Joseph	65-90	
Perrault, Charles	Tales of Past Times... (1st, sq8vo, blue bds, 63p, p-o, color)	L: Selwyn	(1922)	Austen, John	90-120	
Perrault, Charles	Tom Thumb (1st AM, 8vo, 10p, wraps, 4 fp color)	Sam Gabriel	(1911)	Robinson, Gordon	25-45	
Perrine, Mary	Nannabah's Friend (1st {std}, 8vo, [23]p, color, DJ/3.75)	Houghton	1970	Weisgard, Leonard	40-70	
Perrine, Mary	Salt Boy (1st {std}, 4to, 31p, 2-color, cep, DJ/3.25)	Houghton	1968	Weisgard, Leonard	45-70	R
Perry, Bliss	Plated City (1st, 12mo, brown cl, 397p)	Scribner	1895	Armstrong, Margaret	30-50	*
Perry, Bliss	Salem Kittredge (1st, 12mo, 291p, yellow/gilt, cvr by...)	Scribner	1894	Armstrong, Margaret	25-45	
Perry, Catherine	Island of Enchantment (1st, 4to, 157p, 10 tipl, pep)	L: Hutchinson	[1926]	Bromhall, Winifred	60-90	*
Perry, Francis F.	Their Hearts' Desire (1st, lg8vo, teg, 152p, 6cp, dep)	Dodd	1909	Fisher, Harrison	70-100	
Perry, Nora	Another Flock of Girls (1st, sq8vo, 194p, green/gilt, b/w)	Little/Brown	1890	Birch/Copeland	50-80	
Perry, Nora	Flock of Girls & Boys (1st, sm8vo, 323p, grey/gilt, 9pl)	Little/Brown	1895	Parker, C.T.	35-60	
Perry, Stella G.	Angel of Christmas (1st, 12mo, 112p, p-o, 4cp)	Stokes	1917	Kirk, Maria L.	40-70	
Perry, Stella G.	Kind Adventure (1st, 12mo, 318p, green cl, p-o, 4cp)	Stokes	(1914)	Kirk, Maria L.	55-80	
Pertwee, Rowland	Islanders (1st, 8vo, gilt, 267p, b/w, pep, DJ/3.00)	Bobbs-Merrill	(1956)	Shepard, Ernest H.	30-55	
Peterkin, Julia	Plantation Christmas (1st, sm8vo, red cl, 26p, p-o, 1-color)	Houghton	1934	Hendrickson, David	50-80	
Peters, Fritz	Book of the Year (1st {std}, 8vo, 52p, 12 fp b/w, DJ/2.50)	Harper	(1950)	Karasz, Ilonka	30-45	
Petersham, Maud	American ABC (1st, lg8vo, [56]p, gilt, color, cep, DJ/2.00, CH)	Macmillan	1941	Petershams	100-160	
Petersham, Maud	Auntie & Celia Jane & Miki (1st {std}, sm4to, ibds, [64]p, color, NH)	Doubleday/Doran	1932	Petershams	100-160	R*
Petersham, Maud	Box with Red Wheels (1st, sm4to, ibds, [32]p, color, DJ/1.50)	Macmillan	(1949)	Petershams	60-100	*
Petersham, Maud	Christ Child (1st {std}, 4to, ibds, [62]p, color, pep)	Doubleday/Doran	(1931)	Petershams	80-125	R
Petersham, Maud	Circus Baby (1st, sm4to, ibds, [32]p, color, DJ/1.50)	Macmillan	(1950)	Petershams	80-120	
Petersham, Maud	Get-A-Way & Harry Janos (1st, 4to, ibds, p-o, [64]p, 14cp)	Viking	1933	Petershams	140-200	
Petersham, Maud	Joseph and his Brothers (1st, lg8vo, [32]p, color, pep, DJ/0.90)	Winston	1938	Petershams	40-65	
Petersham, Maud	Miki (1st {std}, sm4to, [63]p, ibds, color, pep)	Doubleday/Doran	1929	Petershams	80-125	
Petersham, Maud	Miki & Mary... (1st, 4to, ibds, [64]p, color, pep, DJ/2.50)	Viking	1934	Petershams	80-120	R
Petersham, Maud	Moses (1st, lg8vo, blue cl, [32]p, color, pep, DJ/0.90)	Winston	1938	Petershams	60-90	
Petersham, Maud	Off to Bed (1st {std}, 4to, [30]p, color, DJ/2.25)	Macmillan	(1954)	Petershams	50-80	
Petersham, Maud	Peppernuts (1st {std}, 8vo, 62p, 1-color, DJ/2.50)	Macmillan	(1958)	Petershams	30-50	
Petersham, Maud	Rooster Crows (1st, sm4to, [64]p, tan cl, color, cep, DJ/2.00, CM)	Macmillan	1945	Petershams	85-140	R
Petersham, Maud	Ruth (1st, lg8vo, blue/gilt, [32]p, pep, 8 fp color, DJ/0.90)	Winston	1938	Petershams	50-80	
Petersham, Maud	Shepherd Psalm (1st {std}, 8vo, 27p, ibds, color, DJ/2.50)	Macmillan	1962	Petersham, Maud	25-40	
Petersham, Maud	Stories from the Old Testament (1st, lg8vo, [128]p, color, pep, DJ/2.75)	Winston	1938	Petershams	40-65	
Petersham, Maud	Story Book of Clothes (1st, sq8vo, [32]p, p-o, yellow cl, color)	Winston	1933	Petershams	30-50	
Petersham, Maud	Story Book of Cotton (1st, sq8vo, [32]p, p-o, color, DJ/0.50)	Winston	1939	Petershams	30-50	
Petershams	America's Stamps... (1st, 4to, 144p, 3 fp color, DJ/3.50)	Macmillan	1947	Petershams	60-90	
Petershams	Ark of Father Noah & Mother Noah (1st {std}, sq4to, ibds, color, pep)	Doubleday/Doran	1930	Petershams	70-120	R
Petershams	Boy Who Had no Heart (1st {std}, sm4to, ibds, [30]p, color, DJ/2.75)	Macmillan	(1955)	Petershams	70-100	
Petershams	Silver Mace (1st {std}, sm4to, ibds, 38p, fp color, DJ/2.75)	Macmillan	(1956)	Petershams	50-80	
Petershams	Story Book of Iron and Steel (1st, sq8vo, p-o, [32]p, color, cep, DJ/0.60)	Winston	1935	Petershams	30-50	
Peterson, Barbara	Whitefoot Mouse (1st, 8vo, 52p, red cl, 2-color, pep, DJ)	Holiday House	(1959)	Peterson, Russell	25-40	
Peterson, Hans	Brownie (1st AM, 24mo, [32]p, color, DJ/1.50)	Lothrop, Lee	(1965)	Galdone, Paul	20-35	*
Peterson, Hans	Erik & the Christmas Horse (1st AM {std}, ob4to, [32]p, color, DJ/3.95)	Lothrop, Lee	(1970)	Wikland, Ilon	45-70	*
Peterson, Hans	Liselott and the Goloff (1st AM {std}, 8vo, 157p, b/w, DJ/3.50)	Coward	(1964)	Galdone, Paul	20-35	
Peterson, Hans	Magnus & the Wagon Horse (1st AM {std}, 8vo, 138p, b/w, DJ/3.25)	Pantheon	(1966)	Wikland, Ilon	20-35	
Peterson, Hans	When Peter Was Lost in the Forest (1st AM, ob4to, [32]p, fp color, DJ)	Coward	1970	Wiberg, Harald	50-80	*
Peterson, Henry	Dulcibel (1st, 12mo, grey cl, 402p, teg, p-o, 3cp)	Winston	1907	Pyle, Howard	50-80	
Peterson, Maud H.	Potter and the Clay (1st, sm8vo, green/gilt, 348p, teg, 4pl)	Lothrop Pub.	1901	Harding, Charlotte	30-50	
Peterson, Phyllis	Log Cabin in the Forest (1st, lg8vo, 24p, 2-color, dep, DJ/2.00)	Houghton	1954	Forberg, Ati	30-50	R*
Peto, Gladys	China Cow (1st, 4to, p-o, 129p, black/gilt, 8cp)	Houghton	[1926]	Peto, Gladys	80-120	
Peto, Gladys	Gladys Peto's Children's Book (lg8vo, ibds, 7cp)	L: Routledge	[1930]	Peto, Gladys	70-100	*
Peto, Gladys	Twilight Stories (1st, 4to, ibds, unpag, 8cp)	L: J.F. Shaw	[1932]	Peto, Gladys	90-140	*
Petrovitch, W.	Hero Tales & Legends of Serbians (1st, 4to, 394p, uncut, teg, 32cp)	L: Harrap	1914	James, Gilbert	80-125	
Petry, Ann	Drugstore Cat (1st, lg8vo, 87p, red cl, fp b/w, pep, DJ/2.00)	Crowell	1949	Suba, Susanne	250-400	
Petry, Ann	Legends of the Saints (1st, lg8vo, 47p, fp color, dep, DJ/4.50)	Crowell	(1970)	Rockwell, Anne	80-130	
Peyton, Kathleen M.	Edge of the Cloud (1st, 8vo, 166p, b/w, DJ, CgM)	L: Oxford U.Pr.	1969	Ambrus, Victor	40-65	
Peyton, Kathleen M.	Flambards (1st AM {std}, 8vo, 206p, b/w, DJ/3.95)	World	(1968)	Ambrus, Victor	30-45	
Peyton, Kathleen M.	Plan for Birdsmarsh (1st AM {std}, 8vo, 240p, green cl, b/w, DJ/3.75)	World	(1966)	Ambrus, Victor	25-40	
Peyton, Kathleen M.	Sea Fever (1st AM {std}, 8vo, 240p, b/w, DJ/3.50)	World	(1963)	Ambrus, Victor	25-40	
Peyton, Kathleen M.	Thunder in the Sky (1st AM {std}, 8vo, 158p, b/w, DJ/3.75)	World	(1967)	Ambrus, Victor	25-40	
Pezet, A. Washington	Aristokia (1st, 8vo, 214p, blue/gilt, 8pl)	Century	1919	Sarg, Tony	40-65	
Phelan, Mary K.	Midnight Alarm: Story of Paul Revere's Ride (1st, 8vo, 131p, b/w, DJ/4.50)	Crowell	(1968)	Weisgard, Leonard	25-40	*
Phelan, Mary K.	Mother's Day (1st, 8vo, [40]p, color, DJ/2.95)	Crowell	(1965)	Aliki	30-50	
Phelan, Mary K.	White House (1st {std}, 8vo, unpag, 3-color, DJ/2.50)	Holt, Rinehart	(1962)	Emberley, Ed	25-40	
Phelps, Eliz. S.	Avery... (1st, 12mo, 238p, gilt)	Houghton	1902	Rogers, Bruce	30-50	
Phelps, Eliz. S.	Supply at St. Agatha's (1st, sm8vo, 38p, uncut, teg, 2pl by...)	Houghton	1896	Smith, E. Boyd	35-60	
Philbrook, Elizabeth	Far From Marlborough Street (1st, 8vo, 302p, b/w, DJ/2.00)	Viking	1944	Torrey, Marjorie	30-50	
Philbrook, Elizabeth	Hobo Hill (1st, lg8vo, 96p, fp b/w, DJ/2.50)	Viking	1954	Freeman, Don	25-40	
Phillips, Coles	Gallery of Girls (1st, 4to, p-o, [88]p, green cl, 39cp)	Century	1911	Phillips, Coles	450-650	
Phillips, Coles	Young Man's Fancy (1st, 4to, [47]p, gilt, 19cp)	Bobbs-Merrill	(1912)	Phillips, Coles	450-650	

| --- | --- | --- | --- | --- | --- | --- |
Phillips, David G.	Golden Fleece (1st, sm8vo, 326p, b/w)	McClure	1903	Fisher, Harrison	20-35	*
Phillips, David G.	The Cost (1st, sm8vo, 402p, grey/gilt, 16pl)	Bobbs-Merrill	(1904)	Fisher, Harrison	30-50	
Phillips, Ethel C.	Calico (1st, 8vo, 139p, col frn, b/w, DJ/2.00)	Houghton	1937	Barney, Maginel W.	40-65	
Phillips, Ethel C.	Gay Madelon (1st, 8vo, 142p, 4cp)	Houghton	1931	Bischoff, Ilse	30-45	
Phillips, Ethel C.	Jeanne-Marie and her Golden Bird (1st, 8vo, 112p, 7pl)	Houghton	1934	Blair, Helen	100-160	
Phillips, Ethel C.	Little Rag Doll (1st, 8vo, p-o, 173p, 4cp, pep)	Houghton	1930	Lenski, Lois	70-125	
Phillips, Ethel C.	Little Sally Waters (1st, 8vo, 143p, color, pep)	Houghton	1926	Butler, Edith F.	40-65	
Phillips, Ethel C.	Name for Obed (1st, sm4to, 117p, 1-color, pep, DJ/2.00)	Houghton	1941	Lenski, Lois	80-125	
Phillips, Ethel C.	Peter Peppercorn (1st, sm4to, 148p, pep, color, DJ/2.00)	Houghton	1939	Bischoff, Ilse	30-50	
Phillips, Ethel C.	Pyxie, Little Boy of the Pines (1st, 8vo, 164p, fp color, pep)	Houghton	1932	Barney, Maginel W.	30-50	
Phillips, Ethel C.	Santa Claus Brownies (1st, 8vo, 139p, col frn, pep)	Houghton	1928	Unknown	30-45	
Phillips, Ethel C.	Wee Ann (1st, 12mo, 134p, 4cp, pep)	Houghton	1919	Butler, Edith F.	30-50	
Phillips, Henry W.	The Pets (1st, 12mo, 47p, tan cl, 5pl)	McClure	1906	Frost, A.B.	30-50	
Phillips, J.	Trip to Fairyland (1st, sq8vo, [53]p, gilt)	Conkey	(1905)	Carqueville, Will	100-160	
Phillips, Jay C.	Plantation Sketches (1st, ob folio, [58]p, brown ibds, b/w)	R.H. Russell	1899	Phillips, Jay C.	250-400	
Phillips, Mary E.	Tommy Tregennis (1st, lg8vo, gilt, uncut, teg, 209p, 7cp)	L: Constable	1912	Wheelhouse, Mary V.	60-100	*
Phillpotts, Eden	Dish of Apples (1st, sm4to, lavender cl, teg, 75p, 3 ticp, pep)	Hodder	[1921]	Rackham, Arthur	300-400	
Phillpotts, Eden	Flint Heart (1st AM, 8vo, 334p, 16cp)	Dutton	(1910)	Folkard, Charles	80-120	
Phillpotts, Eden	Flint Heart (1st, 8vo, 310p, teg, gilt, 16cp)	L: Smith Elder	1910	Folkard, Charles	100-160	
Phillpotts, Eden	Girl & The Faun (1st, sm4to, 78p, 4cp)	L: Cecil Palmer	1916	Brangwyn, Frank	120-170	
Phillpotts, Eden	Girl & The Faun (1st AM, sm4to, pict cl, 78p, 4cp)	Lippincott	1917	Brangwyn, Frank	100-160	
Phillpotts, Eden	Nancy Owlett (1st AM, 8vo, 262p, gilt, 8cp)	NY: Macmillan	1933	Brock, Charles E.	25-40	
Phipps, Mary	All About Patsy (1st {std}, 8vo, red cl, 136p, 16cp, 38pl, pep)	Doubleday/Doran	1930	Phipps, Mary	120-180	
Phipps, Mary	Liza Jane & the Kinkies (1st, 4to, ibds, [90]p, color, pep)	Sears	(1929)	Phipps, Mary	250-350	
Phipson, Joan	Family Conspiracy (1st AM {std}, 8vo, 224p, blue cl, b/w, DJ/3.50)	Harcourt	(1964)	Horder, Margaret	20-35	
Phleger, Fred	Ann Can Fly (1st {std}, 8vo, 63p, color, pep, DJ/1.95)	Beginner Books	(1959)	Lopshire, Robert	45-70	
Phleger, Fred	Red Tag Comes Back (1st, 8vo, ipcb, 64p, fp 2-color, DJ/1.95)	Harper	(1961)	Lobel, Arnold	30-45	
Phleger, Fred	Whales Go By (1st {std}, lg8vo, ipcb, 62p, p-o, pep, color, DJ/1.95)	Random	(1959)	Galdone, Paul	50-85	
Piatti, Celestino	Animal ABC (1st AM {std}, ob4to, [26]p, color, DJ/4.50, NYTBI)	Atheneum	1966	Piatti, Celestino	40-70	
Piatti, Celestino	Happy Owls (1st AM {std}, ob4to, [32]p, ibds, color, DJ/4.50, NYTBI)	Atheneum	1964	Piatti, Celestino	40-70	
Picard, Barbara	Faun & the Woodcutter's Daughter (1st AM, 8vo, 255p, b/w, DJ/3.50)	Criterion Bks.	(1964)	Stewart, Charles	25-40	
Picard, Barbara	Lady of the Linden Tree (1st AM {std}, 8vo, 214p, b/w, DJ/3.50)	Criterion Bks.	1962	Stewart, Charles	30-45	
Picard, Barbara	Mermaid & the Simpleton (1st AM, 8vo, 254p, fp b/w, pep, DJ)	Criterion Bks.	(1970)	Gough, Philip	40-65	*
Picard, Barbara	Ransom for a Knight (1st AM, 8vo, 314p, b/w, DJ/4.50)	H.Z. Walck	(1967)	Hodges, C. Walter	50-80	*
Pickard, William B.	Adventures of Alcassim (1st, 8vo, 352p, red/gilt, fp b/w)	L: J. Cape	1936	DeBosschere, Jean	40-65	
Pickett, George E.	Heart of a Soldier (1st, 8vo, 215p, pcb, uncut, b/w)	NY: Moyle	(1913)	Booth, Franklin	60-90	
Pidgin, Charles F.	Blennerhassett (1st, sm8vo, 442p, blue cl, teg, 12pl)	C.M. Clark	1901	Stephens, Charles H.	25-40	
Pier, Arthur S.	Boys of St. Timothy's (1st, sm8vo, 284p, gilt, 3pl, PPPa)	Scribner	1904	Wyeth, N.C.	70-100	
Pierson, Clara D.	Among the Farmyard People (1st, 12mo, teg, uncut, 245p, 11pl)	Dutton	1899	Gordon, Frederic C.	60-90	
Pierson, Clara D.	Among the Forest People (1st, 12mo, teg, 219p, gilt)	Dutton	(1898)	Gordon, Frederic C.	60-90	
Pierson, Clara D.	Among the Meadow People (1st, 12mo, 127p, gilt, teg, b/w, uncut)	Dutton	1897	Gordon, Frederic C.	60-90	
Pierson, Clara D.	Among the Night People (1st, 12mo, 221p, teg, 11pl)	Dutton	(1902)	Gordon, Frederic C.	60-90	
Pierson, Clara D.	Among the Pond People (1st, 12mo, 210p, teg, 12 b/w)	Dutton	1901	Gordon, Frederic C.	60-90	
Pierson, Clara D.	Plucky Allens (1st, sm8vo, green/gilt, 327p, 5 fp b/w)	Dutton	(1925)	Daugherty, James	30-50	
Pierson, Clara D.	Tales of a Poultry Farm (1st, sm8vo, 195p, gilt, 9pl)	Dutton	1904	Pierson, Clara D.	70-120	
Pilkington, Francis	Shamrock and Spear (1st {std}, 8vo, 177p, b/w, DJ/4.50)	Holt, Rinehart	(1968)	Dillon, L.& D.	35-50	
Pine, F.W. (ed.)	Franklin's Autobiography (1st, lg8vo, green cl, 341p, 10cp)	Henry Holt & Co.	1916	Smith, E. Boyd	60-100	
Pine, Tillie S.	Africans Knew (1st, sm4to, 28p, 3-color, DJ/3.50)	McGraw-Hill	(1967)	Grifalconi, Ann	40-65	
Pine, Tillie S.	Chinese Knew (1st, 4to, 32p, 2-color, DJ/2.50)	Whittlesey	(1958)	Keats, Ezra J.	35-50	
Pine, Tillie S.	Egyptians Knew (1st, 4to, 30p, 2-color, DJ/2.95)	Whittlesey	(1962)	Keats, Ezra J.	35-50	
Pine, Tillie S.	Eskimos Knew (1st, 4to, 32p, 2-color, DJ/2.75)	Whittlesey	(1962)	Keats, Ezra J.	35-50	
Pine, Tillie S.	Indians Knew (1st, sm4to, teal cl, 32p, 2-color, pep, DJ/2.00)	Whittlesey	(1957)	Keats, Ezra J.	45-70	
Pine, Tillie S.	Pilgrims Knew (1st, 4to, 32p, 2-color, DJ/2.00)	Whittlesey	(1957)	Keats, Ezra J.	30-50	
Piper, Watty	Brimful Book (1st, 4to, [74]p, p-o, color, pep)	Platt/Munk	(1929)	Eulalie	60-100	
Piper, Watty	Children of Other Lands (1st, lg4to, [85]p, p-o, orange cl, fp color)	Platt/Munk	(1933)	Holling, Holling C.	60-90	
Piper, Watty	Ginger Bread Boy (1st, 4to, ibds, [40]p, p-o, color, pep)	Platt/Munk	(1927)	Eulalie	60-90	R
Piper, Watty	Little Folks of Other Lands (1st, lg4to, [80]p, gilt, p-o, color, pep)	Platt/Munk	(1929)	Holling, Holling C.	70-100	
Piper, Watty	Tick-Tock Tales (1st, 4to, [118]p, gilt, col frn, b/w, pep)	Platt/Munk	(1931)	Lenski/Eulalie	80-120	
Piper, Watty (ed)	Animal Story Book (1st, folio, [73]p, p-o, fp color, pep, DJ/2.50)	Platt/Munk	(1954)	Dennis, Wesley	30-50	
Piper, Watty (ed)	Famous Rhymes/Mother Goose (4to, blue/gilt, p-o, color)	Platt/Munk	(1923)	Various	50-80	
Piper, Watty (ed)	Jolly Rhymes of Mother Goose (1st, 12mo, [118]p, col frn)	Platt/Munk	(1932)	Lenski, Lois	60-100	
Piper, Watty (ed)	Little Engine that Could (1st, 8vo, [25]p, p-o, color, pep)	Platt/Munk	(1930)	Lenski, Lois	70-100	
Piper, Watty (ed)	Road in Storyland (1st, lg4to, [106]p, color, pep)	Platt/Munk	(1932)	Holling, Holling C.	50-85	
Piper, Watty (ed)	Stories Children Love (lg4to, green cl, p-o, [71]p, color, cep)	Platt/Munk	(1933)	Lenski/Eulalie	70-100	
Piper, Watty (ed)	Tales from Storyland (1st, lg4to, p-o, [80]p, color)	Platt/Munk	(1941)	Hauman, G.& D.	60-90	
Pitman, Norman	Chinese Fairy Tales (1st, sm8vo, 230p, uncut, fp 1-color, pep)	Crowell	(1945)	Yap, Weda	40-60	*
Pitman, Norman	Chinese Wonder Book (1st, ob8vo, 219p, ibds, 12cp)	L: J.M. Dent	1919	Chu-T'ang, Li	60-100	
Pitts, Lilla B.	First Grade Book (lg4to, 206p, red cl, 4 fp color by...)	Ginn & Co.	(1949)	Wilkin, Eloise B.	50-85	*
Plant, Richard	S.O.S. Geneva (1st, 8vo, 246p, b/w, DJ/2.00)	Viking	1939	DuBois, W.P.	120-170	
Plasmati, Valdine	Algernon and the Pigeons (1st, 4to, 37p, fp 1-color, DJ/2.50)	Viking	(1963)	Mizumura, Kazue	25-35	
Platt, Rutherford	River of Life (1st, 8vo, 309p, b/w, DJ/5.00)	Simon/Schuster	1956	Bryson, Bernarda	25-40	
Pleasonton, Louise	Fairyland of Opera (1st, 8vo, 240p, p-o, col frn, b/w, pep)	Penn	1923	Price, Hattie L.	40-65	
Plenn, Doris T.	Green Song (1st {std}, 8vo, 126p, b/w, DJ/2.50)	McKay	(1954)	Galdone, Paul	25-45	
Plimpton, George	Rabbit's Umbrella (1st, 8vo, 159p, yellow cl, b/w, pep, DJ/2.75)	Viking	1955	DuBois, W.P.	80-140	
Plotz, Helen	Imagination's Other Place (1st, 8vo, 200p, fp b/w, DJ/3.50)	Crowell	(1955)	Leighton, Clare	30-50	
Plotz, Helen	Untune the Sky (1st {std}, 8vo, 162p, b/w, DJ/3.50)	Crowell	(1957)	Leighton, Clare	70-120	
Plotz, Helen (comp)	Earth is the Lord's (1st {std}, 8vo, 223p, b/w, DJ/5.00)	Crowell	(1965)	Leighton, Clare	30-45	*
Plummer, Mary W.	Chronicles of the Cid (1st, sm8vo, 155p, 10pl)	Henry Holt & Co.	1910	McVickar, H.W.	60-100	*

AUTHOR	TITLE	PUBLISHER	DATE	ARTIST	PRICE	LC
Poe, Edgar A.	Poems of Edgar Allan Poe (1st, 8vo, 225p, olive/gilt, teg, b/w)	L: G. Bell	1900	Robinson, W. Heath	350-500	
Poe, Edgar A.	Poetical Works of Edgar A. Poe (1st AM, 4to, 192p, bds, 28cp)	Doran	[1921]	Dulac, Edmund	250-350	
Poe, Edgar A.	Selected Tales of Mystery (1st AM, 4to, 334p, teg, 16cp)	Lippincott	1909	Shaw, Byam	100-165	
Poe, Edgar A.	Tales of Mystery... (1st, 8vo, 416p)	L: A. Pearson	1905	McCormick, A.D.	75-100	*
Poe, Edgar A.	Tales of Mystery... (1st AM, 4to, p-o, 8 ticp, 24pl)	Brentano's	[1919]	Clarke, Harry	425-600	
Poe, Edgar A.	Tales of Mystery... (1st, 4to, 383p, p-o, teg, 8 ticp, 24pl)	L: Harrap	1919	Clarke, Harry	500-700	
Poe, Edgar A.	Tales of Mystery... (1st {this pub}, 4to, p-o, 412p, 8 ticp)	Tudor	1933	Clarke, Harry	180-250	
Poe, Edgar A.	Tales of Mystery... (1st AM, 4to, gilt, 318p, 12cp, pep)	Lippincott	[1935]	Rackham, Arthur	250-350	
Poe, Edgar A.	Tales of Mystery... (1st, 4to, 318p, gilt, 12cp, pep)	L: Harrap	(1935)	Rackham, Arthur	250-400	
Poe, Edgar A.	The Bells... (1st, 4to, teg, green/gilt, pep, 28 ticp)	L: Hodder	(1912)	Dulac, Edmund	300-450	
Poe, Edgar A.	The Raven (1st, folio, gilt, 23p, AEG, engravings by...)	Harper	1884	Dore, Gustave	200-300	
Poe, Edgar A.	The Raven (1st, sm8vo, 110p, b/w pl, pep)	Reilly/Britton	(1910)	Neill, John R.	120-170	
Pogany, Elaine	Peterkin (1st, sm4to, ibds, [75]p, 14 fp color, pep, DJ/1.00)	McKay	1940	Pogany, Willy	130-200	
Pogany, Nebby	Hungarian Fairy Book (1st, 8vo, 287p, blue/gilt, col frn)	L: T.F. Unwin	(1913)	Pogany, Willy	125-200	
Pogany, Nebby	Magyar Fairy Tales (1st {std}, 8vo, green/gilt, 268p, b/w, pep)	Dutton	(1930)	Pogany, Willy	100-170	R
Pohlmann, Lilton	Myrtle Albertine's Song (1st {std}, 8vo, 218p, b/w, DJ/3.00)	Coward	(1958)	Blegvad, Erik	25-45	
Politi, Leo	Boat for Peppe (1st, 4to, [32]p, fp color, DJ/2.00)	Scribner	1950	Politi, Leo	80-125	
Politi, Leo	Butterflies Come (1st, sm4to, yellow cl, [31]p, color, DJ/2.75)	Scribner	(1957)	Politi, Leo	120-200	
Politi, Leo	Juanita (1st, sm4to, ibds, [31]p, color, DJ/2.00, CH)	Scribner	1948	Politi, Leo	150-220	
Politi, Leo	Lito and the Clown (1st, 4to, [31]p, fp color, DJ/3.25)	Scribner	(1964)	Politi, Leo	70-100	
Politi, Leo	Little Leo (1st, sm4to, [30]p, color, DJ/2.00)	Scribner	1951	Politi, Leo	150-220	
Politi, Leo	Little Pancho (1st {1st book}, 16mo, [40]p, ibds, color, pep, DJ/0.50)	Viking	1938	Politi, Leo	150-220	
Politi, Leo	Mieko (1st, lg4to, [31]p, fp color, DJ/4.95)	Golden Gate	(1969)	Politi, Leo	60-90	
Politi, Leo	Mission Bell (1st, ob8vo, [32]p, blue cl, color, DJ/2.25)	Scribner	1953	Politi, Leo	80-125	
Politi, Leo	Moy, Moy (1st, sm4to, [31]p, fp color, DJ/2.95)	Scribner	(1960)	Politi, Leo	100-150	
Politi, Leo	Pedro, Angel of Olvera Street (1st, 8vo, [32]p, color, DJ/1.75, CH)	Scribner	1946	Politi, Leo	125-220	
Politi, Leo	Piccolo's Prank (1st, 4to, [32]p, fp color, DJ/3.25)	Scribner	(1965)	Politi, Leo	90-150	
Politi, Leo	Rosa (1st, 4to, [38]p, fp color, DJ/3.25)	Scribner	(1963)	Politi, Leo	100-165	R
Politi, Leo	Song of the Swallows (1st, sm4to, [32]p, color, DJ/2.00, CM)	Scribner	1949	Politi, Leo	120-200	R
Politi, Leo	St. Francis & the Animals (1st, sm4to, beige cl, [32]p, dp color, DJ/2.95)	Scribner	1959	Politi, Leo	100-165	
Polland, Madeleine	Beorn the Proud (1st AM, 8vo, 176p, fp b/w, DJ/3.00)	Holt, Rinehart	(1962)	Stobbs, William	40-60	*
Polland, Madeleine	Children of the Red King (1st AM {std}, 8vo, 159p, b/w, DJ/3.00)	Holt, Rinehart	(1961)	Macarthur-Onslow, A.	20-30	
Polland, Madeleine	To Tell My People (1st {std}, 8vo, 209p, b/w, DJ/4.50)	Holt, Rinehart	(1968)	Powers, Richard	30-45	*
Pollard, Alfred (ed)	Romance of King Arthur (1st AM, lg8vo, 517p, green/gilt, 16cp)	Macmillan	1917	Rackham, Arthur	250-400	
Pollard, Eliza F.	Little Chief (1st, sm8vo, teg, uncut, 236p, 6pl)	L: Nister	(1901)	Robinson, Thomas H.	35-60	
Pollard, Josephine	Boston Tea Party (1st, lg8vo, ipcb, [32]p, color)	Dodd	1882	McVickar, H.W.	90-140	
Pollard, Josephine	Elfin-Land (1st, ob folio, [40]p, ibds, chromos, dep)	G.W. Harlan	(1882)	Satterlee, Walter	160-240	
Pollard, Percival	Posters in Miniature (1st, 8vo, [255]p, 250pl)	R.H. Russell	1896	Various	200-300	
Pollock, Katherine	Sly Mongoose (1st, 8vo, 78p, b/w, pep, DJ/1.75)	Scribner	1943	Wiese, Kurt	30-45	
Pollock, Nellie	Belgian Playmates (sq12mo, 122p, red cl, col frn, 4pl)	L: Gay/Hancock	[1918]	Folkard, Charles	80-120	
Pomerantz, Charlotte	Ask the Windy Sea (1st, 4to, [32]p, color, DJ/3.95)	Young Scott	(1968)	Grossman/Siegel	20-35	*
Pomerantz, Charlotte	Bear Who Couldn't Sleep (1st, sm4to, [30]p, fp color, pep, DJ/2.95)	Wm. Morrow	1965	Wohlberg, Meg	25-45	*
Pomerantz, Charlotte	Moon Pony (1st, sq4to, [32]p, fp color, DJ/3.95)	Young Scott	(1967)	Trezzo, Loretta	30-45	
Pomerantz, Charlotte	Why You Look Like You... (1st, 8vo, 64p, fp 2-color, cep, DJ/3.95)	Young Scott	(1969)	Jeffers/Wells	40-65	*
Pons, Helene	Story of Vania (1st, ob4to, 24p, color, pep, DJ/3.50)	Viking	(1963)	Pons, Helene	30-50	
Ponsot, Georges	Romance of the River (1st AM, 8vo, green/gilt, 290p, col frn)	Dodd	(1924)	Detmold, Edward J.	35-60	*
Ponsot, Marie	Fairy Tale Book (1st, folio, ibds, 156p, color, GGB)	Simon/Schuster	(1958)	Segur, Adrienne	200-300	
Ponsot, Marie (tran)	Snow Queen (1st, folio, 136p, ibds, fp color, DGB)	Golden Press	(1961)	Segur, Adrienne	120-200	
Pool, Maria L.	Chums (1st, 8vo, 241p, 4pl)	L.C. Page	1900	Bridgman, L.J.	30-50	
Pool, Maria L.	Little Bermuda (1st, 8vo, 163p, 4pl)	L.C. Page	1899	Bridgman, L.J.	25-45	
Pool, Maria L.	Mrs. Gerald (1st, 12mo, 339p, orange/silver, 13pl)	Harper	1896	Rogers, W.A.	25-45	
Pool, Maria L.	Red-Bridge Neighborhood (1st, 12mo, gilt, 369p, 13pl)	Harper	1898	Carleton, Clifford	25-45	
Poole, Josephine	Moon Eyes (1st AM {std}, 8vo, 151p, b/w, DJ/4.25)	Little/Brown	(1967)	Hyman, Trina S.	40-65	
Pope, Alexander	Rape of the Lock (1st, lg8vo, 47p, blue/gilt, AEG, 7pl)	L: Smithers	1896	Beardsley, Aubrey	350-500	
Pope, Edith	Biggety Chameleon (1st, ob8vo, [32]p, fp 3-color, cep, DJ/1.50)	Scribner	1946	Grider, Dorothy	30-50	
Pope, Elizabeth M.	Sherwood Ring (1st, 8vo, tan cl, 266p, fp b/w, DJ/3.00)	Houghton	1958	Ness, Evaline	50-80	R
Pope, Jessie	Babes & Beasts (1st, 8vo, ibds, unpag, color)	L: Blackie	[1912]	Robinson, Charles	180-270	*
Pope, Jessie	Babes & Birds (1st AM, 8vo, ibds, unpag, 17cp)	Caldwell	(1910)	Robinson, Charles	180-270	
Pope, Jessie	Babes & Birds (1st, 8vo, ibds, unpag, 17cp)	L: Blackie	[1910]	Robinson, Charles	200-300	
Pope, Jessie	Babes and Beasts (1st AM, 8vo, ibds, unpag, color)	Caldwell	(1912)	Robinson, Charles	180-250	
Pope, Jessie	Baby Scouts (1st, ob 16mo, unpag)	L: Blackie	[1911]	Robinson, Charles	150-200	*
Pope, Jessie	Bobbity Flop (1st, ob8vo, unpag, ibds, 24pl)	L: Blackie	[1912]	Macgregor, Angusine	80-125	
Pope, Jessie	Bunny Book (1st, 4to, [36]p, ibds, color)	L: Blackie	[1909]	Macgregor, Angusine	80-130	
Pope, Jessie	Cat Scouts (1st, sm4to, ibds, [48]p, fp b/w, pep, 6cp)	L: Blackie	[1912]	Wain, Louis	600-900	
Pope, Jessie	Story of Flip & Fuzzy (1st AM, 8vo, ibds, color)	Dodge	[1910]	Macgregor, Angusine	200-300	
Pope, Jessie	Three Jolly Huntsmen (4to, ibds, 12 color)	L: Blackie	[1912]	Adams, Frank	100-145	
Porter, Eleanor	Cross Currents (1st, 12mo, 207p, 4pl)	W.A. Wilde	(1907)	Stecher, William	30-50	*
Porter, Eleanor	Pollyanna (1st, sm8vo, 310p, pink/gilt, 8pl, PPP)	L.C. Page	1913	Mulford, Stockton	300-500	
Porter, Eleanor	Pollyanna (1st UK, sm8vo, blue/gilt, p-o, 310p, 8pl)	L: I. Pitman	1913	Mulford, Stockton	100-165	
Porter, Eleanor	Pollyanna (1st {this pub.}, 8vo, 255p, 8pl)	L: Harrap	1938	Tawse, Sybil	55-80	*
Porter, Eleanor	Pollyanna Grows Up (1st, sm8vo, 308p, gilt, 8pl)	L.C. Page	1915	Taylor, H. Weston	45-70	
Porter, Eleanor	Turn of the Tide (1st, sm8vo, 306p, 4pl)	W.A. Wilde	(1908)	Merrill, Frank T.	30-50	*
Porter, Jane	Biffy Buffalo (1st, 8vo, 63p, color, pep, DJ/2.00)	Wm. Morrow	1942	Smalley, Janet	50-80	
Porter, Katherine A.	Christmas Story (1st {std}, sq16mo, [32]p, ibds, fp b/w, pep, DJ/2.95)	Delacorte Pr.	(1967)	Shahn, Ben	50-80	R
Porter, Laura S.	Little Long Ago (1st, 8vo, 470p, b/w, pep)	Dutton	1927	Barney, Maginel W.	30-50	*
Porter, Rose	Charm of Birds (1st, 12mo, gilt, 206p, teg, cvr by...)	Herrick	(1897)	McManus, Blanche	40-60	
Porter, Sheena	Nordy Bank (1st, 8vo, gilt, 144p, b/w, DJ, CgM)	L: Oxford U.Pr.	1964	Macarthur-Onslow, A.	70-100	*
Posey, Anita	Rings and Things (1st {std}, 8vo, 32p, fp 1-color, DJ/2.95)	Crowell-Collier	(1967)	Maas, Julie	25-40	

AUTHOR	TITLE	PUBLISHER	DATE	ARTIST	PRICE	LC
Post, Emily	Flight of a Moth (1st, sm8vo, 253p, cvr by...)	Dodd	1904	Falls, Charles B.	40-65	
Postgate, Oliver	Ice Dragon (1st, 24mo, 48p, color, DJ/2.95)	Holiday House	(1968)	Firmin, Peter	30-45	
Postgate, Oliver	King of the Nogs (1st, 24mo, 48p, color, DJ/2.95)	Holiday House	(1968)	Firmin, Peter	30-45	
Postgate, Oliver	Nogbad and the Elephants (1st, 8vo, 47p, fp 2-color, pep, DJ/3.50)	NY: David White	(1967)	Firmin, Peter	40-65	
Postgate, Oliver	Noggin and the Moon Mouse (1st, 8vo, 47p, fp 2-color, pep, DJ/3.50)	NY: David White	(1967)	Firmin, Peter	40-65	
Poston, Martha L.	Ching-Li (1st, 8vo, 40p, color, pep, DJ/1.50)	T. Nelson	(1941)	Yap, Weda	35-50	*
Pothast-Gimberg, C.	Corso the Donkey (1st AM {std}, 8vo, 123p, b/w, DJ)	Dutton	(1963)	Ver Beek, Elly	25-40	
Potter, Beatrix	All About Peter Rabbit (16mo, 47p, bds, p-o, 8cp)	Cupples/Leon	(1914)	Hartley, Dick	60-100	
Potter, Beatrix	Appley Dapply's Nursery Rhymes (1st, 16mo, [52]p, ibds, 15cp)	L: Warne	[1917]	Potter, Beatrix	500-750	
Potter, Beatrix	Cecily Parsley's Nursery Rhymes (1st, 16mo, orange bds, p-o, 15cp)	L: Warne	(1922)	Potter, Beatrix	500-700	
Potter, Beatrix	Fairy Caravan (1st, 8vo, green/gilt, p-o, 225p, 6cp)	McKay	(1929)	Potter, Beatrix	400-600	
Potter, Beatrix	Ginger & Pickles (1st, 12mo, 52p, bds, p-o, 10cp, pep)	L: Warne	1909	Potter, Beatrix	500-700	R
Potter, Beatrix	Peter Rabbit (folio, wraps, [12]p, fp color)	C.E. Graham	[1914]	Brundage, Frances	100-165	
Potter, Beatrix	Peter Rabbit (1st, 4to, unpag, color, DJ/1.00)	Grosset/Dunlap	1955	Weisgard, Leonard	50-80	
Potter, Beatrix	Peter Rabbit Story Book (lg8vo, 62p, p-o, col frn)	Platt/Munk	(1935)	Willis, Bess G.	80-120	*
Potter, Beatrix	Pie & Patty Pan (1st, 12mo, 52p, p-o, bds, 10cp)	L: Warne	1905	Potter, Beatrix	500-700	
Potter, Beatrix	Roly Poly Pudding (1st, lg8vo, 69p, p-o, 18cp)	L: Warne	1908	Potter, Beatrix	500-700	
Potter, Beatrix	Sister Anne (1st, sm8vo, 154p, gilt, b/w)	McKay	(1932)	Sturges, Katharine	400-600	
Potter, Beatrix	Story of Miss Moppet (1st, 16mo, bds, p-o, 14cp)	L: Warne	1906	Potter, Beatrix	700-950	
Potter, Beatrix	Story of Peter Rabbit (1st, 24mo, p-o, ibds)	Reilly/Britton	(1911)	Neill, John R.	100-165	
Potter, Beatrix	Story of Peter Rabbit (1st, 8vo, green cl, p-o, color)	Whitman	(1924)	Cochran, J.T.	70-125	
Potter, Beatrix	Story of Peter Rabbit (16mo, ibds, [58]p, color)	Whitman	(1932)	Jordan, Nina	60-100	
Potter, Beatrix	Tailor of Gloucester (1st, 16mo, green bds, 85p, p-o, 27cp)	L: Warne	1903	Potter, Beatrix	500-750	
Potter, Beatrix	Tale of Benjamin Bunny (1st, 16mo, 85p, p-o, tan bds, color, pep)	L: Warne	1904	Potter, Beatrix	600-800	
Potter, Beatrix	Tale of Flopsy Bunnies (1st, sm8vo, 85p, bds, p-o, 27cp, pep)	L: Warne	1909	Potter, Beatrix	500-750	R
Potter, Beatrix	Tale of Jemima Puddle Duck (1st, sq16mo, grey bds, p-o, 85p, color, pep)	L: Warne	1908	Potter, Beatrix	500-700	
Potter, Beatrix	Tale of Johnny Town Mouse (1st, 16mo, 85p, bds, p-o)	L: Warne	1918	Potter, Beatrix	400-600	
Potter, Beatrix	Tale of Little Pig Robinson (1st AM, 8vo, p-o, 141p, 6cp, pep)	McKay	(1930)	Potter, Beatrix	250-350	
Potter, Beatrix	Tale of Little Pig Robinson (1st, sq8vo, 141p, p-o, gilt, 6cp)	L: Warne	(1930)	Potter, Beatrix	300-450	
Potter, Beatrix	Tale of Mr. Jeremy Fisher (1st, 24mo, red bds, 85p, p-o, color)	L: Warne	1906	Potter, Beatrix	500-750	
Potter, Beatrix	Tale of Mr. Tod (1st, 16mo, grey bds, p-o, 94p, color)	L: Warne	1912	Potter, Beatrix	500-750	R
Potter, Beatrix	Tale of Mrs. Tiggy-Winkle (1st, 16mo, grey bds, 85p, p-o, color)	L: Warne	1905	Potter, Beatrix	500-700	
Potter, Beatrix	Tale of Mrs. Tittlemouse (1st, 24mo, bds, 85p, p-o, 28cp)	L: Warne	1910	Potter, Beatrix	500-700	
Potter, Beatrix	Tale of Peter Rabbit (1st {trade}, 16mo, 97p, grey bds, p-o 31cp)	L: Warne	(1902)	Potter, Beatrix	700-900	
Potter, Beatrix	Tale of Peter Rabbit (1st {this pub}, 16mo, 127p, green cl, 31cp)	Altemus	1904	Potter, Beatrix	300-500	R*
Potter, Beatrix	Tale of Peter Rabbit (12mo, yellow cl, p-o, color)	Hurst	(1908)	Anderson, S.W.	80-120	*
Potter, Beatrix	Tale of Peter Rabbit (12mo, grey bds, [56]p, fp color, pep)	Saalfield	(1916)	Albert, Virginia	50-80	
Potter, Beatrix	Tale of Peter Rabbit (lg4to, wraps, 8 color)	Harter	1931	Peat, Fern B.	75-120	
Potter, Beatrix	Tale of Pigling Bland (1st, 16mo, 94p, bds, p-o, 15cp, pep)	L: Warne	1913	Potter, Beatrix	450-600	
Potter, Beatrix	Tale of Squirrel Nutkin (1st, 16mo, grey bds, p-o, 27cp)	L: Warne	1903	Potter, Beatrix	425-600	R
Potter, Beatrix	Tale of the Faithful Dove (1st, 24mo, ibds, [47]p, fp color)	L: Warne	(1970)	Angel, Marie	60-90	
Potter, Beatrix	Tale of Timmy Tiptoes (1st, sq16mo, 85p, brown bds, p-o, color)	L: Warne	1911	Potter, Beatrix	425-600	
Potter, Beatrix	Tale of Tom Kitten (1st, 16mo, green bds, 85p, p-o, color)	L: Warne	1907	Potter, Beatrix	450-650	
Potter, Beatrix	Tale of Two Bad Mice (1st, 16mo, bds, p-o, 85p, color, pep)	L: Warne	1904	Potter, Beatrix	600-800	
Potter, Beatrix	Wag by Wall (1st {std}, 16mo, [30]p, buckram, p-o, t-i frn, DJ/1.50)	Horn Book	1944	Lankes, Julius J.	180-250	
Potter, Charles F.	More Tongue Tanglers & a Rigamarole (1st {std}, 12mo, 42p, color, DJ/2.95)	World	(1964)	Wiesner, William	50-80	R
Potter, Mary A.	Mathematics for Success (1st, 8vo, 439p, b/w)	Ginn & Co.	(1952)	Lawson, Robert	50-80	*
Potter, Mary K.	Love in Art (1st, 12mo, 260p, gilt, teg, cvr by...)	L.C. Page	1898	Armstrong, Margaret	40-65	
Potter, Mary K.	Peggy's Trial (1st, 12mo, 97p, b/w)	L.C. Page	1901	Barry, Etheldred B.	25-45	
Potter, Miriam C.	Captain Sandman (1st, 8vo, 233p, uncut, b/w, pep)	Dutton	(1926)	Balcom, Sophia T.	40-70	
Potter, Miriam C.	Goofy Mrs. Goose (1st {std}, sm8vo, 122p, b/w, DJ/2.95)	Lippincott	(1963)	Potter, Miriam C.	100-160	
Potter, Miriam C.	Hello, Mrs. Goose (1st {std}, sm8vo, 150p, b/w, DJ/2.00)	Lippincott	1947	Potter, Miriam C.	100-150	
Potter, Miriam C.	Mrs. Goose and Three Ducks (1st, 12mo, 114p, color, pep, DJ/1.25)	Stokes	1936	Potter, Miriam C.	100-170	
Potter, Miriam C.	Sally Gabble & the Fairies (1st, 12mo, 87p, col frn, b/w, DJ/1.00)	Macmillan	1929	Sewell, Helen	80-120	
Potter, Miriam C.	The Gigglequicks (1st, 12mo, ibds, unpag, color, pep)	Volland	(1918)	Sarg, Tony	90-135	*
Potter, Miriam C.	The Littlebits (1st {std}, sm8vo, grey cl, 129p, b/w, DJ/1.75)	Lippincott	(1951)	Potter, Miriam C.	120-170	
Potter, Miriam C.	Timmy Mouse (1st, 16mo, [32]p, ibds, color, pep)	Rand/McNally	1951	Brice, Tony	50-80	
Potter, Russell	Little Red Ferry Boat (1st, 8vo, 50p, fp 2-color, pep, DJ/2.00)	Henry Holt & Co.	(1947)	Hill, Marjorie	30-45	*
Potter, Stephen	Squawky, Advens. of a Clasperchoice (1st, sm4to, 48p, 2-color, DJ/3.75)	Lippincott	1964	Him, George	30-45	*
Poulsson, Emilie	Finger Plays for Nursery & Kindergarten (1st, lg8vo, 80p, gilt, b/w)	D. Lothrop Co.	1893	Bridgman, L.J.	60-100	
Poulsson, Emilie	In the Child's World (1st, sq8vo, 443p, b/w, pep)	Milton Bradley	1893	Bridgman, L.J.	70-100	
Pourrat, Henri	Treasury of French Tales (1st, 8vo, 239p, ibds, fp b/w, DJ/3.00)	Houghton	1954	Baynes, Pauline	30-50	
Powell, Fern	Porcupine and the Tiger (1st, sm ob4to, [32]p, fp 3-color, cep, DJ/3.75)	Lothrop, Lee	1969	Pinkney, Jerry	30-45	
Powell, Miriam	Jareb (1st {std}, sm8vo, grey cl, 241p, b/w, cep, DJ/2.50)	Crowell	(1952)	Simont, Marc	30-50	
Powell, R.S.	Phyllis in Bohemia (1st, 12mo, 233p, teg, cvr by...)	Herbert Stone	1897	Hazenplug, Frank	45-70	
Power, Phyllis	Legends from the Outback (1st, 8vo, 127p, col frn, DJ)	L: J.M. Dent	(1958)	Outhwaite, Ida R.	120-170	
Power, Rhoda	How it Happened (1st, lg8vo, beige cl, 188p, 12pl)	Cambridge U. Pr.	1930	Parker, Agnes M.	55-80	*
Powers, Alfred	Long Way to Frisco (1st {std}, 8vo, 181p, b/w, DJ/2.50)	Little/Brown	1951	Daugherty, James	30-50	
Powers, Tom	Scotch Circus (1st, 8vo, 95p, col frn, 3 dp color)	Houghton	1934	Lenski, Lois	100-165	
Powers, Tom	Virgin with Butterflies (1st {std}, 8vo, 188p, black cl, b/w, DJ/2.50)	Bobbs-Merrill	(1945)	Duvoisin, Roger	45-70	
Powys, Llewelyn	Impassioned Clay (1st {std}, 8vo, bds, 120p, tp-in frn, DJ/2.00)	Longmans	1931	Ward, Lynd	120-170	
Powys, Llewelyn	Twelve Months (1st UK, sm4to, 88p, uncut, gilt, b/w, DJ)	L: John Lane	(1936)	Gibbings, Robert	70-100	
Praed, Winthrop M.	Every-Day Characters (1st, 4to, white cl, 74p, b/w)	L: Kegan Paul	1898	Aldin, Cecil	300-500	
Praeger, Sophia R.	Adventures of Three Bold Bears (ob4to, ibds, 48p)	L: Longmans	1897	Praeger, Sophia R.	120-200	
Praeger, Sophia R.	Little Twin Dragons (1st, ob4to, 60p, ibds)	L: Longmans	1900	Praeger, Sophia R.	120-185	
Pratt, Alice	Animal Babies (1st, 8vo, 148p, ibds, color, DJ/1.75)	Beacon Press	(1941)	Wiese, Kurt	25-40	
Pratt, Alice	Animals of a Sage Brush Ranch (1st, lg8vo, p-o, 208p, 3cp, pep)	Rand/McNally	(1931)	Wiese, Kurt	50-80	
Pratt, Anna	Friends from My Garden (1st, 8vo, AEG, 128p, white/gilt, 12cp)	Stokes	1890	Hill, Laura C.	165-220	

AUTHOR	TITLE	PUBLISHER	DATE	ARTIST	PRICE	LC
Pratt, Charles S.	Baby's Lullaby Book (folio, [64]p, 16 t-i chromos, dep)	Prang Co.	1888	Taylor, W.L.	450-600	
Pratt, Charles S.	Buz-Buz (1st, sm8vo, 102p, fp b/w)	Lothrop Pub.	1898	Bridgman, L.J.	60-90	
Pratt, Charles S.	Bye O' Baby Ballads (lg8vo, [61]p, ipcb, 14 chromos)	D. Lothrop Co.	1886	Hassam, F. Childe	280-400	
Pratt, Davis	Magic Animals of Japan (1st ob4to, [32]p, color, dep, DJ/3.95)	Parnassus Press	1967	Kula, Elsa	40-65	
Pratt, Ella	Happy Children (1st, lg4to, 64p, ibds, 8cp)	Crowell	(1896)	McCullough, Wm. A.	120-200	
Pratt, Lucy	Ezekiel (1st, 12mo, 254p, red cl, 16pl)	Doubleday/Page	1909	Steele, Frederic D.	60-100	
Pratt, Lucy	Ezekiel Expands (1st, 8vo, tan cl, 228p, 6pl)	Houghton	1914	Kemble, Edward W.	100-165	
Pratt, Margaret	Flash of Washington Square (1st, 4to, green cl, [29]p, dp color, DJ/2.00)	Lothrop, Lee	1954	Duvoisin, Roger	50-80	
Pratt, Margaret	Successful Secretary (1st, sm8vo, 144p, p-o, 15 fp b/w, DJ/2.00)	Lothrop, Lee	(1946)	Duvoisin, Roger	50-80	
Pratt, Margaret	Talking Typewriter (1st {std}, sm4to, ibds, 38p, color, pep, DJ/1.00)	Lothrop, Lee	(1940)	Gergely, Tibor	50-80	
Prelutsky, Jack	Gopher in the Garden (1st {std}, 4to, [32]p, 3-color, DJ/3.95)	Macmillan	(1967)	Leydenfrost, Rbt.	25-40	*
Prelutsky, Jack	Lazy Blackbird (1st AM {std}, ob4to, [28]p, ibds, fp color, DJ/3.95)	Macmillan	(1969)	Janosch	30-45	
Prelutsky, Jack	Terrible Tiger (1st {std}, 4to, [38]p, color, DJ/4.95)	Macmillan	(1970)	Lobel, Arnold	30-50	
Prelutsky, Jack	Three Saxon Nobles (1st AM {std}, lg4to, [23]p, color, DJ/3.95)	Macmillan	(1969)	Rubin, Eva	25-40	
Prelutsky, Jack	Toucans Two (1st {std}, 8vo, [32]p, color, DJ/4.95)	Macmillan	(1970)	Aruego, Jose	25-40	
Prendergast, Mabel	Little Yellow Duckling (1st, ob4to, ibds, 18 fp color)	Cooke/Stokes	(1907)	Prendergast, Mabel	180-260	
Prentiss, Lois (comp)	Dickens' Year Book (1st, 8vo, [147]p, tan bds, p-o, b/w)	McClurg	1913	Groesbeck, Dan S.	80-130	
Preston, Edna M.	Monkey in the Jungle (1st, sq4to, [32]p, fp color, cep, DJ/4.95)	Viking	(1968)	Hurd, Clement	25-40	
Preston, Edna M.	One Dark Night (1st, ob8vo, [28]p, fp 1-color, DJ/3.50)	Viking	(1969)	Werth, Kurt	30-45	*
Preston, Edna M.	Pop Corn and Ma Goodness (1st, ob8vo, [35]p, fp color, DJ/4.50, CH)	Viking	(1969)	Parker, Robert	60-100	
Preston, Edna M.	Toolittle (1st, lg8vo, 47p, fp 1-color, DJ/2.95)	Viking	(1969)	Servello, Joe	25-45	
Preston, Hayter	House of Vanities (1st, 12mo, 59p, bds, b/w)	L: John Lane	1922	Fraser, Claud L.	60-90	
Preston, Hayter	Windmills (1st, 4to, yellow cl, 125p, uncut, 16cp, dep)	Lane/Dodd	(1923)	Brangwyn, Frank	150-220	
Preston, Tom	Peek-A-Boo Twins (1st, 4to, tan bds, p-o, 12cp)	L: H. Frowde	[1915]	Preston, Chloe	300-450	
Preston, Tom	Peek-a-Boo's Holiday (4to, ibds, 18cp)	Frowde/Hodder	[1915]	Preston, Chloe	350-500	
Preussler, Otfried	Little Ghost (1st AM, 8vo, 126p, b/w, DJ/2.95)	Abelard-Schuman	(1967)	Tripp, F.J.	20-30	
Preussler, Otfried	Robber Hotzenplotz (1st AM, 8vo, 128p, b/w, DJ/3.00)	Abelard-Schuman	(1965)	Tripp, F.J.	20-30	
Price, Christine	Dragon and the Book (1st {std}, 8vo, 196p, b/w, DJ/2.75)	Longmans	1953	Price, Christine	25-40	
Price, Christine	One is God: Two Old Counting Songs (1st, ob4to, [48]p, color, DJ/4.95)	Warne	(1970)	Price, Christine	40-65	*
Price, Christine	Three Golden Nobles (1st {std}, 89vo, 239p, b/w, pep, DJ/2.75)	Longmans	(1951)	Price, Christine	20-35	
Price, Christine	Valiant Chattee-Maker (1st, sq8vo, [43]p, 2-color, pep, DJ/2.95)	Warne	(1965)	Price, Christine	25-40	
Price, Edith B.	Four Winds (1st, 8vo, 181p, col frn, b/w, pep)	Stokes	1927	Price, Edith B.	25-40	
Price, Eleanor C.	Adventures of King Arthur (1st, sm4to, ibds, 153p, 8cp, p-o)	L: Coker	1931	Wheelwright, Rowland	40-60	*
Price, Luxor	The Quoks (1st, 4to, 62p, p-o, red cl, color, pep)	Stokes	1924	Price, Luxor	180-270	
Price, Margaret E.	Angora Twinnies (4to, wraps, [12]p, shape book, color)	Stecher	1919	Price, Margaret E.	60-90	
Price, Margaret E.	Betty Fairy Book (folio, [14]p, wraps, shape book, color)	Stecher	1915	Price, Margaret E.	60-90	
Price, Margaret E.	Child's Book of Myths (1st, 4to, blue cl, p-o, 112p, 6cp)	Rand/McNally	(1924)	Price, Margaret E.	60-90	
Price, Margaret E.	Down Comes the Wilderness (1st {std}, 8vo, 212p, b/w, pep, DJ/1.75)	Harper	1937	Price, Margaret E.	25-45	
Price, Margaret E.	Enchantment Tales for Children (1st, 4to, 118p, p-o, color, pep)	Rand/McNally	(1926)	Price, Margaret E.	70-100	
Price, Margaret E.	Land of Nod (folio, wraps, [12]p, shape book, color)	Stecher	1916	Price, Margaret E.	50-80	
Price, Margaret E.	Legends of the Seven Seas (1st {std}, 8vo, 168p, gilt, col frn, pep)	Harper	1929	Price, Margaret E.	40-65	
Price, Margaret E.	Manger Babe (folio, [14]p, wraps, shape bk., color)	Stecher	1916	Price, Margaret E.	55-80	
Price, Margaret E.	Monkey-Do (1st {std}, 8vo, 149p, b/w, pep)	Harper	1934	Price, Margaret E.	30-50	
Price, Margaret E.	Mota & the Monkey Tree (1st {std}, 8vo, 146p, b/w, pep, DJ/1.50)	Harper	1935	Price, Margaret E.	40-65	
Price, Margaret E.	Myths & Enchantment Tales (1st, lg8vo, 160p, color, DJ/1.00)	Rand/McNally	(1935)	Price, Margaret E.	50-80	
Price, Margaret E.	Visit to Santa Claus (sm4to, wraps, [16]p, color)	Stecher	[1915]	Price, Margaret E.	70-100	
Price, Margaret E.	Windy Shore (1st {std}, lg8vo, brown cl, 181p, col frn, 18pl, pep)	Harper	1930	Price, Margaret E.	50-85	
Price, Olive M.	Donkey for the King (1st, sm8vo, 73p, fp 1-color, DJ/2.00)	Whittlesey	(1945)	Angelo, Valenti	30-50	*
Price, Pattie	Bantu Tales (1st {std}, 8vo, ibds, 64p, 3-color, pep, DJ/1.00)	Dutton	1938	Smith, Desmond	40-65	
Prieto, Mariana	When the Monkeys wore Sombreros (1st, ob4to, 36p, fp color, dep, DJ/3.50)	Harvey House	(1969)	Quackenbush, Rbt.	30-50	*
Prince Ahmed	Flying Carpet (1st, 4to, [48]p, color, DJ/3.00)	Scribner	(1956)	Brown, Marcia	50-80	R
Priolo, Pauline	Piccolina and the Easter Bells (1st {std}, sm ob4to, 48p, color, DJ/3.00)	Little/Brown	(1962)	Fava, Rita	30-50	*
Prishvin, Mikhail	Treasure Trove of the Sun (1st, 4to, 80p, color, pep, DJ/2.75)	Viking	1952	Rojankovsky, Feodor	60-100	R
Pritchard, Myron T.	Upward Path (1st, sm8vo, 255p)	Harcourt	(1920)	Wheeler, Laura	80-120	
Procter, E.H.	Rabbit's Day in Town (1st, 4to, ibds, [48]p, 20 fp color)	L: Blackie	[1908]	Corbould, Walton	140-220	*
Proctor, Beth	Tale of a Lucky Dog (1st, lg8vo, [59]p, fp color)	Jordan Pub. Co.	(1924)	Turpin, Fay	40-65	*
Proddow, Penelope	Dionysos & the Pirates (1st {std}, 4to, ibds, [40]p, color, DJ/4.95)	Doubleday	(1970)	Cooney, Barbara	50-80	R
Proddow, Penelope	Spirit of Spring (1st {std}, 8vo, 133p, b/w, DJ/4.75)	Bradbury Press	(1970)	Jeffers, Susan	25-40	
Prokofieff, Serge	Peter & the Wolf (1st {std}, sm ob4to, [32]p, p-o, color, DJ/2.00)	Knopf	(1940)	Chappell, Warren	80-125	
Prokofieff, Serge	Peter & the Wolf (1st {std}, lg4to, ibds, 88p, color, pep, DJ/2.95)	Doubleday	1961	Palazzo, Tony	40-65	
Proudfit, Isabel	Come & See the Bottle Family (1st, sq12mo, ibds, 38p, color, DJ/0.50)	McKay	(1938)	Whitehead, Caroline	30-50	
Proudfit, Isabel	Come & See the Broom Closet Family (1st, sq12mo, ibds, [38]p, color)	McKay	(1938)	Whitehead, Caroline	35-50	
Proudfit, Isabel	Come and See the Pencil Box Family (1st, 12mo, ibds, [38]p, color)	McKay	(1945)	Matson, Caroline	30-50	
Proudfit, Isabel	Treasure Hunter (1st, lg8vo, 206p, uncut, dp b/w, dep, DJ/2.50)	J. Messner	(1939)	Gramatky, Hardie	75-100	*
Provensen, A.& M.	Animal Fair (1st {A}, folio, 76p, ibds, color, pep, GGB, NYTBI)	Simon/Schuster	1952	Provensen, A.& M.	50-80	
Provensen, A.& M.	What is a Color? (1st, 4to, 32p, ibds, color, DJ/2.95, BGB)	Golden Press	(1967)	Provensen, A.& M.	50-85	
Provensen, A.& M.	Who's in the Egg? (1st, lg4to, ibds, 32p, color, cep)	Golden Press	1970	Provensen, A.& M.	50-85	
Provines, Mary V.	Liz'beth Ann's Goat (1st, 4to, 40p, ipcb, color, DJ/2.00)	Viking	1947	Paull, Grace	30-50	
Proysen, Alf	Pepperpot in the Magic Wood (1st AM {std}, 8vo, 86p, bds, b/w, DJ/3.50)	Pantheon	1968	Berg, Bjorn	25-40	
Prud'Hommeaux, Rene	Sunken Forest (1st, 8vo, 248p, b/w, pep, DJ/2.50)	Viking	1949	Busoni, Rafaello	25-40	
Pugh, Edwin W.	Tony Drum (1st, sm8vo, 225p, tan cl, 10cp)	Henry Holt & Co.	1898	Nicholson, Wm.	120-180	
Puner, Helen	Daddies: What They Do All Day (1st, 4to, [34]p, ibds, color, DJ/1.75)	Lothrop, Lee	1946	Duvoisin, Roger	50-85	
Puner, Helen	Sitter Who Didn't Sit (1st, sm4to, ibds, [26]p, color, pep, DJ/1.50)	Lothrop, Lee	1949	Duvoisin, Roger	50-80	
Purnell, Idella	Talking Bird (1st, sq8vo, 95p, col frn, 9pl, pep)	Macmillan	1930	Dehlsen, Frances P.	25-45	
Pushkin, Alexander	Golden Cockerel (1st, lg4to, red/gilt, [48]p, 12cp, pep, DJ/2.50)	NY: Nelson	1938	Pogany, Willy	150-250	
Putnam, George H.	Little Gingerbread Man (1st, 8vo, 20p, fp color, pep)	Putnam	(1910)	Herbert, Robert	60-90	R*
Putnam, Nina W.	Adventures in the Open (1st, sm8vo, ibds, color)	Volland	(1918)	Dodge, Katharine S.	55-80	*
Putnam, Nina W.	Sunny Bunny (1st, 8vo, ibds, [42]p, color, pep)	Volland	(1918)	Gruelle, Johnny	120-185	

AUTHOR	TITLE	PUBLISHER	DATE	ARTIST	PRICE	LC
Putnam, Nina W.	Winkle, Twinkle & Lollypop (1st, 8vo, ibds, [95]p, fp color, pep)	Volland	(1918)	Dodge, Katharine S.	70-120	
Puzo, Mario	Runaway Summer of Davie Shaw (1st, 8vo, 186p, b/w, DJ/2.95)	Platt/Munk	(1966)	Sherwood, Stewart	50-80	
Pycraft, W.P.	Animal Why Book (1st AM, sm4to, 90p, p-o, 31 ticp)	Stokes	[1910]	Noble, Edwin	200-300	
Pycraft, W.P.	Pads, Paws & Claws (1st, 4to, ibds, 123p, p-o, 32 ticp)	L: Wells/Gard.	(1911)	Noble, Edwin	200-300	
Pyle, Howard	Book of American Spirit (1st {std}, lg4to, 344p, ibds, p-o, 23cp)	Harper	1923	Pyle, Howard	250-350	
Pyle, Howard	Book of Pirates (1st, lg4to, 247p, bds, gilt, p-o, 11cp, 25pl)	Harper	1921	Pyle, Howard	250-350	R
Pyle, Howard	Champions of the Round Table (1st lg8vo, tan/gilt, 328p, b/w)	Scribner	1905	Pyle, Howard	220-300	R
Pyle, Howard	Garden Behind the Moon (1st, 8vo, green/gilt, 192p, 10pl)	Scribner	1895	Pyle, Howard	150-225	
Pyle, Howard	Jack Ballister's Fortunes (1st, 8vo, 420p, 14pl)	Harper	1895	Pyle, Howard	90-140	
Pyle, Howard	Men of Iron (1st, 8vo, 328p, red cl, teg, 15pl)	Harper	1892	Pyle, Howard	160-240	
Pyle, Howard	Merry Adventures of Robin Hood (1st, 4to, leather/gilt, 296p, 23 fp b/w)	Scribner	1883	Pyle, Howard	700-950	R
Pyle, Howard	Modern Aladdin (1st, 8vo, 205p, blue/gilt, b/w)	Harper	1892	Pyle, Howard	160-240	
Pyle, Howard	Otto of the Silver Hand (1st, lg8vo, olive/gilt, 173p, fp b/w, PPP)	Scribner	1888	Pyle, Howard	250-400	
Pyle, Howard	Pepper and Salt (1st, 4to, tan/gilt, 121p, b/w)	Harper	1886	Pyle, Howard	300-450	
Pyle, Howard	Price of Blood (1st, 8vo, ipcb, 98p, A.E. red, 6cp)	Badger	1899	Pyle, Howard	160-240	R
Pyle, Howard	Rose of Paradise (1st, 12mo, green/gilt, 231p, 8pl)	Harper	1888	Pyle, Howard	125-180	
Pyle, Howard	Ruby of Kishmoor (1st, 8vo, teg, 74p, gilt, 10cp)	Harper	1908	Pyle, Howard	130-200	R
Pyle, Howard	Stolen Treasure (1st, 12mo, 253p, orange cl, p-o, 8pl)	Harper	1907	Pyle, Howard	100-150	
Pyle, Howard	Story of Jack Ballister's Fortunes (1st, 8vo, 420p, 14pl)	Century	1895	Pyle, Howard	170-240	
Pyle, Howard	Story of King Arthur... (1st, lg8vo, tan/gilt, 313p, b/w, cep)	Scribner	1903	Pyle, Howard	250-400	
Pyle, Howard	Story of Sir Lancelot (1st, lg8vo, 340p, tan/gilt, b/w)	Scribner	1907	Pyle, Howard	180-250	
Pyle, Howard	Story of the Grail (1st, lg8vo, 258p, tan/gilt, b/w)	Scribner	1910	Pyle, Howard	170-240	R
Pyle, Howard	Twilight Land (1st, 8vo, 438p, gilt, b/w)	Harper	1895	Pyle, Howard	140-200	
Pyle, Howard	Wonder Clock (1st, sm4to, grey cl, 318p, b/w)	Harper	1888	Pyle, Howard	250-350	
Pyle, Howard	Yankee Doodle (1st, 4to, 31p, ibds, 8 fp color)	Dodd	1881	Pyle, Howard	400-650	
Pyle, Katharine	As the Goose Flies (1st, sm8vo, 183p, gilt, 6pl)	Little/Brown	1901	Pyle, Katharine	50-80	
Pyle, Katharine	Black-Eyed Puppy (1st, 8vo, 89p, p-o, 12cp)	Dutton	1923	Pyle, Katharine	60-100	
Pyle, Katharine	Careless Jane (1st, 12mo, green cl, 110p, b/w)	Dutton	(1902)	Pyle, Katharine	45-70	
Pyle, Katharine	Charlemagne & his Knights (1st, 8vo, gilt, 302p, col frn, 7pl)	Lippincott	(1932)	Pyle, Katharine	50-85	
Pyle, Katharine	Childhood (1st, sm4to, ibds, 46p, 21cp)	Dutton	(1904)	Stilwell, Sarah	160-240	
Pyle, Katharine	Christmas Angel (1st, 12mo, green/gilt, teg, 136p, 6pl)	Little/Brown	1900	Pyle, Katharine	70-100	
Pyle, Katharine	Counterpane Fairy (1st [1st bk.], 8vo, green/gilt, uncut, teg, 191p, b/w)	Dutton	1898	Pyle, Katharine	300-450	
Pyle, Katharine	Fairy Tales from Far & Near (1st, 8vo, green cl, 274p, 7cp)	Little/Brown	1922	Pyle, Katharine	70-120	
Pyle, Katharine	Fairy Tales from India (1st, lg8vo, 229p, red/gilt, 12cp, pep)	Lippincott	1926	Pyle, Katharine	70-120	
Pyle, Katharine	Fairy Tales from Many Lands (1st, 8vo, 316p, col frn)	Dutton	(1911)	Pyle, Katharine	70-120	
Pyle, Katharine	In the Green Forest (1st, lg8vo, green cl, 171p, 5pl)	Little/Brown	1902	Pyle, Katharine	60-90	
Pyle, Katharine	Katherine Pyle's Book of Fairy Tales (1st, 8vo, 338p, col frn, 28pl)	Dutton	(1925)	Pyle, Katharine	120-200	
Pyle, Katharine	Lazy Matilda... (1st, 8vo, 173p, blue cl, b/w)	Dutton	(1921)	Pyle, Katharine	35-60	*
Pyle, Katharine	Mother's Nursery Tales (1st, lg8vo, gilt, 376p, 7cp, pep)	Dutton	(1918)	Pyle, Katharine	100-180	
Pyle, Katharine	Nancy Rutledge (1st, 8vo, 206p, 6pl)	Little/Brown	1906	Pyle, Katharine	55-80	
Pyle, Katharine	Rabbit Witch (1st, lg ob8vo, 81p, 1-color)	Dutton	(1895)	Pyle, Katharine	200-300	
Pyle, Katharine	Six Little Ducklings (1st, 8vo, green cl, p-o, 99p, 24pl, pep)	Dodd	1915	Pyle, Katharine	90-145	
Pyle, Katharine	Tales from Greek Mythology (1st, 8vo, blue cl, 312p, 12pl)	Lippincott	1928	Pyle, Katharine	60-90	
Pyle, Katharine	Tales from Norse Mythology (1st, lg8vo, 256p, 8cp, pep)	Lippincott	(1930)	Pyle, Katharine	55-80	
Pyle, Katharine	Tales of Folk & Fairies (1st, 8vo, blue cl, 288p, 6cp)	Little/Brown	1919	Pyle, Katharine	100-165	
Pyle, Katharine	Tales of Two Bunnies (1st, 8vo, 87p, red cl, b/w, pep)	Dutton	(1913)	Pyle, Katharine	80-120	
Pyle, Katharine	Tales of Wonder & Magic (1st, sm8vo, green cl, 314p, 8cp)	Little/Brown	1920	Pyle, Katharine	65-90	
Pyle, Katharine	Two Little Mice (1st, 8vo, 108p, grey cl, p-o, 16pl, pep)	Dodd	1917	Pyle, Katharine	80-125	
Pyle, Katharine	Where the Wind Blows (1st, 4to, 120p, p-o, 11cp)	R.H. Russell	1902	Day, Bertha C.	200-300	
Pyle, Katharine	Where the Wind Blows (1st {this pub.}, 8vo, 295p, 10pl)	Dutton	(1910)	Day, Bertha C.	50-85	
Pyle, Katharine	Wonder Tales Retold (1st, 8vo, green/gilt, 322p, 8cp)	Little/Brown	1916	Pyle, Katharine	100-165	
Pyle/Porter	Theodora (1st, 12mo, 271p, 4pl)	Little/Brown	1907	McCullough, Wm. A.	35-60	*
Pyrnelle, Louise C.	Diddie, Dumps & Tot (1st, 12mo, green cl, 217p, 12 fp b/w, PPP)	Harper	1882	Unknown	250-400	
Pyrnelle, Louise C.	Diddie, Dumps & Tot (1st, 8vo, 214p, col frn, cp)	Harper	1930	Kay, Gertrude A.	50-80	
Quackenbush, Robert	Poems for Counting (1st, 8vo, [24]p, color, pep, DJ)	Holt, Rinehart	(1963)	Quackenbush, Rbt.	20-35	*
Queen Marie	Dreamer of Dreams (1st, lg8vo, 181p, grey/gilt, 6 ticp)	L: Hodder	[1915]	Dulac, Edmund	275-400	
Queen Marie	Lost Princess (sm4to, red cl, 159p, 6 ticp, pep)	L: Warne	[1915]	Attwell, Mabel L.	80-120	
Queen Marie	Magic Doll of Roumania (1st, 8vo, p-o, 319p, 10cp)	Stokes	1929	Petershams	90-145	
Queen Marie	Stealers of Light (1st, 4to, blue/gilt, 190p, 2 ticp)	L: Hodder	1916	Dulac, Edmund	250-350	
Quick, Herbert	In the Fairyland of America (1st, 8vo, green cl, 190p, p-o, b/w)	Stokes	(1901)	Deming, Edwin W.	120-200	
Quick, Herbert	Vandemark's Folly (1st, 12mo, gilt, 420p, 8pl)	Bobbs-Merrill	(1922)	Wyeth, N.C.	30-50	
Quick, Herbert	Virginia of the Air Lanes (1st, sm8vo, blue cl, 424p, 5pl)	Bobbs-Merrill	(1909)	Leigh, William R.	40-65	
Quigg, Jane	Crispin's Acres (1st, 8vo, 112p, b/w, DJ/1.50)	NY: Oxford U.Pr.	(1941)	Howe, Gertrude	45-70	
Quigg, Jane	Fun for Freddy (1st, 8vo, 106p, green cl, b/w, DJ/2.75)	NY: Oxford U.Pr.	(1953)	Cooney, Barbara	60-90	
Quigg, Jane	Hickory Lane (1st, 8vo, 62p, grey cl, b/w, DJ/1.00)	NY: T. Nelson	1938	Ninon	50-85	
Quigg, Jane	Jean & Jon are Six (1st, 8vo, 54p, 1-color, pep, DJ/1.50)	Nelson	1936	Gay, Romney	30-50	
Quigg, Jane	Jenny Jones and Skid (1st, 8vo, 99p, green cl, fp b/w, DJ/2.00)	NY: Oxford U.Pr.	1947	Wilkin, Eloise B.	70-100	
Quigg, Jane	Jiggy Likes Nantucket (1st, 8vo, 96p, fp 1-color, DJ/2.75)	NY: Oxford U.Pr.	1954	Gay, Zhenya	30-50	*
Quigg, Jane	Judy and her Turtle Osmond (1st {std}, 8vo, 35p, fp 1-color, DJ/2.75)	Macmillan	1960	Bacon, Peggy	30-50	R*
Quigg, Jane	Looking for Lucky (1st, 8vo, ibds, 29p, 2-color, pep, DJ/1.00)	Howell/Soskin	1946	Moran, Connie	40-70	*
Quigg, Jane	Polly Peters (1st, 8vo, 77p, 8 fp 1-color, DJ/1.25)	Oxford U. Pr.	(1942)	Doane, Pelagie	25-45	
Quigg, Jane	Trolling with Susie Bennett (1st {std}, 8vo, ibds, 28p, b/w, DJ/2.25)	Macmillan	1961	Bacon, Peggy	30-45	
Quigley, Lillian	Blind Men and the Elephant (1st, sm4to, [25]p, color, DJ/2.95)	Scribner	(1959)	Holland, Janice	25-45	
Quiller-Couch, A.	Fairy Tales from Far & Near (1st, 12mo, teg, 192p)	L: Cassell	1895	Millar, H.R.	120-180	*
Quiller-Couch, A.	In Powder & Crinoline (1st, 4to, 164p, ibds, teg, gilt, 24 ticp)	L: Hodder	[1913]	Nielsen, Kay	750-1000	
Quiller-Couch, A.	Roll Call of Honor (1st, lg8vo, p-o, 348p, 9cp)	Nelson	[1911]	Almond, William D.	55-80	
Quiller-Couch, A.	Sleeping Beauty... (1st, 4to, 129p, gilt, 30 ticp)	L: Hodder	(1910)	Dulac, Edmund	400-600	
Quiller-Couch, A.	Sleeping Beauty... (1st AM, lg4to, 129p, maroon/gilt, 30 ticp)	NY: Hodder	[1910]	Dulac, Edmund	300-500	

AUTHOR	TITLE	PUBLISHER	DATE	ARTIST	PRICE	LC
Quiller-Couch, A.	Sleeping Beauty... (8vo, 196p, black cl, p-o, 8cp, pep)	Garden City	[1932]	Dulac, Edmund	50-90	
Quiller-Couch, A.	Splendid Spur (1st, lg8vo, orange cl, 274p, p-o, 15cp)	Doran	(1927)	Daugherty, James	35-50	
Quiller-Couch, A.	Splendid Spur (1st {this pub.}, lg8vo, p-o, 274p, 4cp, pep)	Garden City	1937	Daugherty, James	35-60	*
Quiller-Couch, A.	Treasure Book of Children's Verse (4to, 336p, teg, gilt, 20 ticp, pep)	L: Hodder	[1911]	Gray, Millicent E.	100-170	
Quiller-Couch, A.	Twelve Dancing Princesses (1st AM, lg8vo, gilt, 244p, 16 ticp, pep)	Doran	[1923]	Nielsen, Kay	400-650	
Quiller-Couch, A.	Twelve Dancing Princesses (lg8vo, 244p, 16cp, pep)	Doubleday/Doran	1930	Nielsen, Kay	125-200	
Quiller-Couch, Mabel	Pair of Red Polls (1st, 8vo, 190p, 6pl)	L: Jack	(1905)	Cowham, Hilda	50-80	*
Quiller-Couch, Mabel	Troublesome Ursula (1st, 8vo, blue/gilt, p-o, 311p, 8pl)	L: Chambers	1907	Attwell, Mabel L.	80-125	
Quilp, Jocelyn	Baron Verdigris (1st, 8vo, 214p, cvr & frn by...)	L: Henry Co.	1894	Beardsley, Aubrey	70-120	
Raabe, Martha	Little Lost Sioux (1st, 8vo, 30p, p-o, color, pep, DJ/1.25)	Whitman	(1942)	Howe, Oscar	40-70	
Rabelais	Wise Fool (1st {std}, 4to, ibds, [32]p, color, DJ/3.95)	Random	(1968)	Galdone, Paul	25-40	
Rackham, Arthur	Arthur Rackham Fairy Book (1st, lg8vo, red cl, 287p, 8cp, pep)	L: Harrap	(1933)	Rackham, Arthur	200-300	
Rackham, Arthur	Fairy Book (1st {std}, 8vo, 111p, blue/gilt, 11cp)	Doubleday/Page	1923	Rackham, Arthur	180-250	
Rackham, Arthur	Rackham's Book of Pictures (1st, 4to, grey/gilt, 44 ticp)	L: Heinemann	(1913)	Rackham, Arthur	400-600	
Radcliffe, Winifred	Saint's Garden (1st, sm8vo, 150p, green/gilt, 8pl)	L: SPCK	1927	Robinson, Charles	120-185	
Radford, Dollie	Songs for Somebody (1st, 8vo, ibds, 28p, 6cp)	L: D. Nutt	1893	Bradley, Gertrude	200-300	
Radlov, Nicholas	Cautious Carp (1st, ob4to, ibds, [48]p, color, DJ/1.50)	Coward	(1938)	Radlov, Nicholas	60-100	
Rae, John	Big Family (1st, ob4to, 50p, color)	Dodd	1916	Rae, John	100-165	
Rae, John	Granny Goose (1st, 4to, [48]p, ibds, 21 fp color, pep)	Volland	(1926)	Rae, John	180-260	
Rae, John	Grasshopper Green and the Meadow Mice (1st, 12mo, ibds, [40]p, color)	Volland	(1922)	Rae, John	75-100	
Rae, John	Lucy Locket... (1st, 8vo, 120p, ibds, color)	Volland	(1928)	Rae, John	70-100	
Rae, John	New Adventures of Alice (1st, lg8vo, ibds, 158p gilt, 12cp, pep)	Volland	(1917)	Rae, John	125-200	
Rae, John	Why: Reflections for Children (1st, lg8vo, unpag, blue cl, p-o, color)	Dodd	1910	Rae, John	200-300	
Raftery, Gerald	Twenty-Dollar Horse (1st, 8vo, 192p, b/w, DJ/2.75)	J. Messner	(1955)	Safran, Bernard	30-50	*
Rahr, Ruth	Journey of the Toys (1st, 4to, 87p, p-o, blue cl, pep, color)	(Wisconsin)	(1934)	Ertz, Bruno	65-90	
Raiker, Alice M.	Brontos and the Tootle-Bird (4to, green cl, p-o, 16 fp color)	Valentine	[1904]	Wood, Lawson	400-600	
Raiker, Alice M.	Dulcibella & the Fairies (1st, 4to, green bds, 54p, p-o, 13cp)	L: C. Faulkner	[1919]	Miller, Hilda T.	200-300	
Raine, William M.	Brand Blotters (1st, sm8vo, 348p, 2pl)	Dillingham	1912	Rowe, Clarence	40-65	
Raine, William M.	Daughter of Raasay (1st [1st bk.], 12mo, 311p, cvr by...)	Stokes	(1902)	Bradley, Will	120-180	*
Raine, William M.	Wyoming (1st, sm8vo, 353p, 4pl)	Dillingham	1908	Rowe, Clarence	40-60	
Rains, Marie C.	Lazy Liza Lizard (1st, 8vo, 182p, gilt, fp 2-color, pep, DJ/2.00)	Winston	(1938)	Neville, Vera	300-500	
Rains, Marie C.	Lazy Liza Lizard's Tricks (1st {std}, 8vo, 119p, b/w, DJ/2.00)	Winston	(1953)	Neville, Vera	200-300	
Raleigh, Francis	Ralph Somerby at Panama (1st, sm8vo, 305p, p-o, 10pl, pep)	L.C. Page	1913	Bull/Edwards	25-40	
Ralph, Julian	Dixie (1st, lg8vo, 411p, gilt, b/w)	Harper	1896	Various	60-100	
Ralph, Julian	On Canada's Frontier (1st, 8vo, 325p, 60 illus by...)	Harper	1892	Remington, Frederic	150-250	
Ramal, Walter	Songs of Childhood (1st, 16mo, 106p, teg, gilt, frn by...)	L: Longmans	1902	Doyle, Richard	350-500	
Ramsay, Tamara	Toy Workshop in Land of Silvery Blue (1st AM, 4to, p-o, [31]p, color, cep)	Whitman	1932	Ramsay, Tamara	60-100	
Ramsden, Evelyn (ed)	Singing Town (1st AM, 8vo, 97p, ibds, color, pep, DJ/2.75)	Macmillan	1959	Egner, Thorbjorn	20-35	
Ramsden, Helen G.	Smile Within a Tear (1st, sm8vo, 251p, blue/gilt, 8pl)	L: Hutchinson	1897	Newcombe, Bertha	60-100	
Rand, Ann	Did a Bear Just Walk There? (1st {std}, 4to, [27]p, color, DJ/3.75)	Harcourt	(1966)	Birnbaum, Abe	60-90	
Rand, Ann	Edward and the Horse (1st {std}, 4to, [30]p, color, pep, DJ/3.00)	Harcourt	(1961)	Eskell, Olle	60-100	
Rand, Ann	I Know a Lot of Things (1st {std}, 4to, [32]p, color, cep, DJ/2.75, NYTBI)	Harcourt	(1956)	Rand, Paul	200-300	R
Rand, Ann	Listen! Listen! (1st {std}, 4to, 31p, color, DJ/4.25)	Harcourt	(1970)	Rand, Paul	80-130	
Rand, Ann	Little 1 (1st, 4to, ibds, unpag, color, DJ/3.25)	Harcourt	(1962)	Rand, Paul	150-225	
Rand, Ann	Little River (1st {std}, sm ob4to, ibds, [32]p, color, pep, DJ/2.95)	Harcourt	(1959)	Rojankovsky, Feodor	75-125	
Rand, Ann	So Small (1st {std}, sq12mo, [48]p, fp color, DJ/2.95)	Harcourt	(1962)	Rojankovsky, Feodor	80-125	
Rand, Ann	Sparkle & Spin (1st {std}, sm4to, [30]p, color, dep, DJ/2.95, NYTBI)	Harcourt	(1957)	Rand, Paul	250-350	R
Rand, Ann	Umbrellas, Hats & Wheels (1st {std}, 4to, [31]p, color, DJ/3.25, NYTBI)	Harcourt	(1961)	Snyder, Jerome	80-135	
Randall, Jane	When Toys Could Talk (1st, 4to, [16]p, spiral-bound, 6 fp color)	Saalfield	1939	Peat, Fern B.	80-130	
Randall, Janet	Miracle of Sage Valley (1st {std}, 8vo, 185p, DJ/2.75, b/w decor by...)	NY: Longmans	1958	Turkle, Brinton	40-65	*
Randolph, Althea	Bouquet of Rhymes for Children (1st, folio, ibds, 6cp)	Bonnell/Silver	(1909)	Whitney, Isabel	140-220	*
Randolph, Jane	Circus in Peter's Closet (1st, 8vo, blue cl, 48p, 3-color, pep, DJ/2.50)	Crowell	(1955)	Freeman, Don	40-70	
Randolph, Vance	Who Blowed Up the Church House? (1st, 8vo, 232p, b/w, DJ/3.50)	Columbia U. Pr.	1952	Rounds, Glen	50-80	
Rands, William B.	Lilliput Lyrics (1st, 12mo, 330p, gilt, col frn, b/w, pep)	L: John Lane	1899	Robinson, Charles	100-160	
Rankin, Louise S.	Daughter of the Mountains (1st, lg8vo, 191p, fp b/w, pep, DJ/2.50, NH)	Viking	1948	Wiese, Kurt	60-100	R
Rankin, Louise S.	Gentling of Jonathan (1st, 8vo, 223p, green cl, b/w, pep, DJ/2.50)	Viking	1950	Townsend, Lee	30-50	
Ranking, Boyd M.	Flowers & Fancies (1st, 24mo, 186p, 4 color)	L: Marcus Ward	1882	Greenaway, Kate	200-285	
Ransom, Will	Little Dutchy... (1st, 4to, 79p, ibds, 12 ticp)	L: Harrap	(1925)	Cramer, Rie	130-180	
Ransome, Arthur	Aladdin & his Wonderful Lamp (1st, 4to, [128]p, 12 ticp)	L: J. Nisbet	[1919]	Mackenzie, Thomas B.	300-450	
Ransome, Arthur	Aladdin & his Wonderful Lamp (1st AM, sm4to, [128]p, 12ticp pep)	Brentano's	[1920]	Mackenzie, Thomas B.	250-350	
Ransome, Arthur	Big Six (1st AM, 8vo, 353p, b/w, DJ/2.00)	Macmillan	1941	Ransome, Arthur	70-100	
Ransome, Arthur	Bohemia in London (1st AM, 8vo, 293p, teg, uncut, 16pl)	Dodd	1907	Taylor, Fred	70-125	
Ransome, Arthur	Coot Club (1st AM, 8vo, 342p, 1-color, DJ/2.00)	Lippincott	(1935)	Ransome/Carter	70-125	
Ransome, Arthur	Fool of the World & Flying Ship (1st, ob4to, [48]p, color, pep, DJ/4.50, CM)	Farrar, Straus	(1968)	Shulevitz, Uri	60-100	R
Ransome, Arthur	Missee Lee (1st, 8vo, 336p, gilt, b/w, pep, DJ)	L: J. Cape	1941	Ransome, Arthur	200-300	
Ransome, Arthur	Old Peter's Russian Tales (1st, 8vo, 334p, 6cp, pep)	L: Jack	1916	Mitrokhin, Dmitri	100-165	
Ransome, Arthur	Old Peter's Russian Tales (1st {this pub}, 12mo, 334p, 7cp, DJ)	L: Nelson	[1938]	Mitrokhin, Dmitri	75-100	*
Ransome, Arthur	Peter Duck (1st AM, 8vo, 427p, b/w, pep)	Lippincott	1933	Carter, Helene	40-70	
Ransome, Arthur	Pigeon Post (1st, 8vo, 383p, b/w, pep, DJ, CgM)	L: J. Cape	(1936)	Ransome, Arthur	160-240	
Ransome, Arthur	Secret Water (1st AM, 8vo, 363p, b/w, pep, DJ/2.00)	Macmillan	1940	Ransome, Arthur	30-45	
Ransome, Arthur	Swallowdale (1st AM, 8vo, 393p, b/w, pep)	Lippincott	1932	Carter, Helene	60-90	
Ransome, Arthur	Swallows & Amazons (1st AM, 8vo, green cl, 343p, b/w, pep, DJ/2.00)	Lippincott	1931	Carter, Helene	70-120	R
Raphael, Arthur	Great Jug (1st, 8vo, 136p, col frn, b/w, DJ/1.00)	Reilly/Lee	(1936)	Benton, Clifford	70-125	
Raskin, Ellen	A & The (1st {std}, lg8vo, [32]p, color, DJ/4.95)	Atheneum	1970	Raskin, Ellen	30-50	
Raskin, Ellen	And It Rained (1st {std}, 8vo, [48]p, color, DJ/3.75)	Atheneum	1969	Raskin, Ellen	30-50	
Raskin, Ellen	Ghost in a Four-Room Apartment (1st {std}, 12mo, [48]p, color, DJ/3.75)	Atheneum	1969	Raskin, Ellen	30-50	
Raskin, Ellen	Nothing Ever Happens/my Block (1st {std}, ob8vo, unpag, col, DJ/2.95, NYT)	Atheneum	1966	Raskin, Ellen	45-70	
Raskin, Ellen	Silly Songs and Sad (1st, sq8vo, [48]p, fp color, DJ/3.75)	Crowell	(1967)	Raskin, Ellen	30-50	

AUTHOR	TITLE	PUBLISHER	DATE	ARTIST	PRICE	LC
Raskin, Ellen	Spectacles (1st {std}, ob12mo, [48]p, color, DJ/3.50, NYTBI)	Atheneum	1968	Raskin, Ellen	60-100	R
Rasmussen, K.	People of the Frozen North (1st UK, 4to, 358p, 12cp)	L: Trubner	1908	Moltke, H.	120-180	
Ratel, Simonne	The Weathercock (1st AM, 8vo, 84p, color, DJ/1.75)	Appleton-Century	1939	Mittelman, Gertrude	20-35	
Ratzesberger, Anna	Ali Hassan of Hamadan (1st, 8vo, 95p, p-o, 12cp, pep)	Whitman	(1933)	Akbar, Ali	50-85	
Ratzesberger, Anna	Camel Bells (1st, 4to, ipcb, 80p, color, pep, DJ/2.00)	Whitman	1935	Wiese, Kurt	50-85	
Ratzesberger, Anna	Donkey Beads (1st, lg8vo, 62p, p-o, pep, color, DJ/1.50)	Whitman	1938	Wiese, Kurt	80-125	
Ratzesberger, Anna	Jasmine: A Story of Present Day Persia (1st, 8vo, 286p, 6cp, pep, DJ/2.00)	Whitman	1937	Wiese, Kurt	30-50	
Rau, Margaret	Band of the Red Hand (1st {std}, 8vo, 250p, b/w, DJ/2.00)	Knopf	1938	Low, Joseph	25-40	
Rawlings, Marjorie K.	Cross Creek (1st, 8vo, 368p, gilt, b/w, pep, DJ/2.50)	Scribner	1942	Shenton, Edward	150-250	
Rawlings, Marjorie K.	Cross Creek Cookery (1st, 8vo, 230p, color, pep, DJ/2.50)	Scribner	1942	Camp, Robert	120-200	
Rawlings, Marjorie K.	Secret River (1st, 8vo, [57]p, b/w, brown pages, DJ/2.50, NH)	Scribner	(1955)	Weisgard, Leonard	150-225	R
Rawlings, Marjorie K.	The Yearling (1st, 8vo, 428p, beige cl, b/w, DJ/2.50)	Scribner	1938	Shenton, Edward	400-600	
Rawlings, Marjorie K.	The Yearling (1st {Pulitzer ed.}, 8vo, 400p, 14cp, DJ)	Scribner	1939	Wyeth, N.C.	175-275	
Rawlings, Marjorie K.	The Yearling (1st {this fmt}, lg8vo, 400p, p-o, 12cp, pep, SC)	Scribner	1940	Wyeth, N.C.	160-240	
Ray, Anna C.	Half a Dozen Boys (1st, 8vo, 318p, 18pl)	Crowell	(1895)	Merrill, Frank T.	30-45	*
Ray, Anna C.	Hearts & Creeds (1st, sm8vo, 320p, 4pl)	Little/Brown	1906	Stephens, Alice B.	30-50	
Ray, Anna C.	Janet: Her Winter in Quebec (1st, 12mo, blue cl, 370p, 4pl)	Little/Brown	1906	Stephens, Alice B.	30-50	
Ray, Anna C.	Nathalie's Chum (1st, 12mo, 289p, 6pl)	Little/Brown	1902	Thompson, E.B.	30-50	
Ray, Anna C.	Nathalie's Sister (1st, 12mo, gilt, 290p, 6pl)	Little/Brown	1904	Stephens, Alice B.	35-60	*
Ray, Anna C.	Playground Toni (1st, 8vo, ipcb, 136p, 4pl)	Crowell	(1900)	(Photos)	25-40	
Ray, Anna C.	Sidney: Summer on St. Lawrence (1st, 12mo, 332p, blue/gilt, 4pl)	Little/Brown	1905	Stephens, Alice B.	35-60	
Ray, Anna C.	Ursula's Freshman (1st, 12mo, 303p, 6pl)	Little/Brown	1903	Richards, Harriet R.	30-50	
Ray, Wade	Train to Spain (1st, 4to, [38]p, fp dp color, cep, DJ/2.95)	Knopf	(1963)	Ray, Wade	25-40	
Raymond, Evelyn	Boys & Girls of Brantham (1st, sm8vo, 283p, grey/gilt, 6pl)	Little/Brown	1899	Barry, Etheldred B.	30-50	*
Raymond, Evelyn	The Whirligig (1st, 12mo, 351p, 6pl)	Penn	1905	Rollins, R.	35-60	*
Raymond, Louise	Child's Story of the Nativity (1st, lg4to, [36]p, ibds, color, pep, DJ/1.50)	Random	1943	Masha	40-65	
Raymond, Margaret T.	Roberta Goes Adventuring (1st, 8vo, ibds, 96p, color, pep)	Volland	(1931)	Campbell, Eleanor	60-90	
Raymond, Walter	Charity Chance (1st, 12mo, 256p, cvr by..)	Dodd	1896	McManus, Blanche	25-40	*
Raymond, Walter	Rebels of the New South (1st, sm8vo, 294p, 5pl)	C.H. Kerr	1905	Ball, Percy B.	60-95	
Raymond, Walter	Tryphena In Love... (1st, 12mo, gilt, teg, 295p, col frn, 12pl)	L: Dent	1912	Brock, Charles E.	50-80	
Rayner, Emma	Free to Serve (2nd, 8vo, 434p, cover art by..)	Copeland & Day	1897	Parrish, Maxfield	125-200	
Razzell, Arthur	Circles and Curves (1st AM {std}, 8vo, 47p, color, DJ/2.50)	Doubleday	(1969)	Raskin, Ellen	30-50	
Razzell, Arthur	Probability: Science of Chance (1st AM {std}, 8vo, 47p, color, DJ/2.50)	Doubleday	(1967)	Raskin, Ellen	30-50	
Razzell, Arthur	Symmetry (1st AM {std}, 8vo, 47p, color, DJ/2.50)	Doubleday	(1968)	Raskin, Ellen	30-45	
Razzell, Arthur	This is 4: Idea of a Number (1st AM {std}, 8vo, 47p, color, DJ/2.50)	Doubleday	(1967)	Raskin, Ellen	30-50	
Razzell, Arthur	Three and the Shape of Three (1st {std}, 8vo, 47p, color, DJ/2.50)	Doubleday	(1969)	Raskin, Ellen	30-45	
Read, Elfreida	Magical Egg (1st AM {std}, 12mo, 95p, aqua cl, pep, fp b/w, DJ/3.25)	Lippincott	(1965)	Green, Alison	30-45	*
Read, Helen S.	My Blue Book (1st, sq8vo, [166]p, fp color, pep)	Scribner	1931	Lee, Eleanor	60-90	*
Read, Herbert	This Way Delight (1st, lg8vo, 155p, b/w, pep, DJ/3.50)	Pantheon	(1956)	Kepes, Juliet A.	25-45	
Read, Miss	Village School (1st [1st bk.] {std}, 8vo, ipcb, 238p, fp b/w, pep, DJ/3.00)	Houghton	1956	Goodall, John S.	40-70	
Read, Opie	Arkansas Planter (1st, 8vo, teg, 315p, cvr by...)	Rand/McNally	(1896)	Denslow, W.W.	60-90	
Read, Opie	Bolanyo (1st, 12mo, tan cl, teg, 309p, uncut, cvr by...)	Way & Williams	1897	Parrish, Maxfield	200-320	
Read, Opie	Waters of Caney Fork (1st, 8vo, 287p, cvr by...)	Rand/McNally	1898	Denslow, W.W.	45-70	
Reade, Charles	Cloister & Hearth (1st, 4to, 663p, violet/gilt, teg, 20cp)	L: Chatto	1909	Shaw, Byam	60-90	
Reade, Charles	Peg Woffington (1st AM, 12mo, green/gilt, 298p, AEG, b/w)	Doub./McClure	1899	Thomson, Hugh	60-90	
Reade, Charles	Peg Woffington (1st, 12mo, 298p, green/gilt, AEG, b/w)	L: G. Allen	1899	Thomson, Hugh	75-100	
Reader, Ethel	Story of the Little Merman (1st, 8vo, 274p)	L: Macmillan	1909	Pape, Frank	30-50	*
Rechnitzer, F.E.	Jinks of Jayson Valley (1st {std}, 8vo, 216p, b/w, DJ/2.00)	Winston	1950	Kirmse, Marguerite	25-40	
Reck, Alma	Clocks Tell the Time (1st, 8vo, 48p, 2-color, DJ/2.75)	Scribner	(1960)	Domanska, Janina	25-40	
Redford, Polly	Christmas Bower (1st {std}, 8vo, 192p, b/w, DJ/3.95)	Dutton	1967	Gorey, Edward	30-50	
Redman, Sylvia	Do You Want to Hear a Secret? (1st, 4to, [28]p, fp 2-color, DJ/2.75)	Lothrop, Lee	(1960)	Weisgard, Leonard	35-50	*
Reed, Helen L.	Amy in Acadia (1st, 8vo, 344p, blue cl, 6pl)	Little/Brown	1905	Pyle, Katharine	50-80	
Reed, Helen L.	Brenda's Bargain (1st, 8vo, 251p, 6pl)	Little/Brown	1903	Thompson, E.B.	35-60	
Reed, Helen L.	Brenda's Cousin at Radcliffe (1st, 8vo, 318p, 5pl)	Little/Brown	1902	Stephens, Alice B.	35-60	*
Reed, Helen L.	Brenda's Summer at Rockley (1st, 8vo, blue/gilt, 376p, 5pl)	Little/Brown	1901	Smith, Jessie W.	200-300	
Reed, Helen L.	Brenda's Ward (1st, 8vo, 340p, 6pl)	Little/Brown	1906	Merrill, Frank T.	40-70	
Reed, Helen L.	Brenda, Her School & her Club (1st, sm8vo, 328p, gilt, 5pl)	Little/Brown	1900	Smith, Jessie W.	160-220	
Reed, Langford	Book of Nonsense Verse (1st AM, lg8vo, 159p, 26 b/w, DJ)	Putnam	1926	Bateman, Henry M.	30-50	
Reed, Langford	Sausages & Sundials (1st, lg8vo, 131p, ibds, b/w)	L: Jarrold	[1927]	Stimpson, Murdock	35-60	
Reed, Myrtle	Book of Clever Beasts (1st, 8vo, p-o, 231p, col frn, 8pl)	Putnam	1904	Newell, Peter	100-165	
Reed, Myrtle	Old Rose and Silver (1st, 8vo, 364p, teg, lavender/gilt, cvr by...)	Putnam	1909	Armstrong, Margaret	35-60	
Reed, Myrtle	Pickaback Songs (1st, 4to, [70]p, ibds, pep, color)	Putnam	1903	Morgan, Ike	350-500	
Reed, Myrtle	Weaver of Dreams (1st, 8vo, teg, 374p, blue/gilt)	Putnam	1911	Armstrong, Margaret	35-60	
Reed, Myrtle	White Shield (1st, 8vo, 343p, lavender/gilt, teg)	Putnam	1912	Armstrong, Margaret	35-60	
Reely, Mary K.	Blue Mittens (1st, 8vo, 153p, green cl, b/w, pep, DJ/2.00)	Grosset/Dunlap	1935	Wiese, Kurt	35-60	*
Reely, Mary K.	Seatmates (1st, 8vo, 237p, fp b/w, pep, DJ/2.00)	F. Watts	(1949)	Wilkin, Eloise B.	60-100	
Rees, Ennis	Brer Rabbit and his Tricks (1st, lg ob8vo, [48]p, 2-color, DJ/3.95)	Young Scott	(1967)	Gorey, Edward	80-125	R
Rees, Ennis	More of Brer Rabbit's Tricks (1st, ob8vo, [48]p, ibds, 2-color, DJ/3.95)	Young Scott	(1968)	Gorey, Edward	60-90	
Reesink, Maryke	Golden Treasure (1st AM {std}, 4to, [32]p, fp color, cep, DJ/3.95)	Harcourt	(1968)	Tol, Jaap	35-60	
Reeves, James	Angel and the Donkey (1st, lg ob8vo, [32]p, color, DJ)	L: Hamilton	1969	Ardizzone, Edward	40-65	
Reeves, James	Angel and the Donkey (1st AM, lg ob8vo, [32]p, color, DJ/4.50)	McGraw-Hill	(1970)	Ardizzone, Edward	30-50	
Reeves, James	Blackbird in the Lilac (1st, 8vo, blue/silver, 95p, b/w, DJ)	L: Oxford U.Pr.	1952	Ardizzone, Edward	50-80	
Reeves, James	Exploits of Don Quixote (1st AM, 8vo, 219p, fp color, DJ)	H.Z. Walck	1960	Ardizzone, Edward	30-50	
Reeves, James	Pigeons and Princesses (1st, 8vo, 113p, b/w, DJ)	L: Heinemann	(1956)	Ardizzone, Edward	50-85	*
Reeves, James	Prefabulous Animiles (1st, 8vo, 56p, blue/gilt, b/w, DJ)	L: Heinemann	(1957)	Ardizzone, Edward	60-85	
Reeves, James	Ragged Robin (1st AM {std}, sm8vo, unpag, color, DJ/3.75)	Dutton	1961	Paton, Jane	20-30	
Reeves, James	Rhyming Will (1st AM, sm ob4to, [32]p, color, DJ/3.50)	McGraw-Hill	(1968)	Ardizzone, Edward	30-45	
Reeves, James	Sailor Rumbelow (1st AM {std}, 8vo, 221p, b/w, DJ/3.75)	Dutton	1962	Ardizzone, Edward	30-50	*

AUTHOR	TITLE	PUBLISHER	DATE	ARTIST	PRICE	LC
Reeves, James	Secret Shoemakers (1st AM, 8vo, 96p, b/w, DJ/3.25)	Abelard-Schuman	1966	Ardizzone, Edward	30-50	
Reeves, James	Story of Jackie Thimble (1st {std}, 12mo, 31p, b/w, DJ/1.95)	Dutton	(1964)	Ardizzone, Edward	30-50	
Reeves, James	Titus in Trouble (1st, 4to, ibds, unpag, 46 color, DJ)	L: Bodley Head	(1959)	Ardizzone, Edward	120-180	R
Reeves, James	Trojan Horse (1st AM, 4to, [32]p, fp color, DJ/4.95)	F. Watts	1969	Turska, Krystyna	40-70	*
Reeves, James	Wandering Moon (1st AM {std}, 8vo, 73p, b/w, DJ/2.50)	Dutton	1960	Ardizzone, Edward	45-70	
Reeves, William P.	New Zealand (1st, 8vo, gilt, teg, 241p, 75cp)	L: A&C Black	1908	Wright, F.& W.	100-165	
Reid, Alastair	Allth (1st, lg8vo, 51p, 1-color, DJ/3.00)	Houghton	1958	Lorraine, Walter	50-85	R*
Reid, Alastair	I Will Tell You of a Town (1st, 8vo, 36p, fp 3-color, DJ/2.25, NYTBI)	Houghton	1956	Lorraine, Walter	50-80	
Reid, Alastair	Ounce, Dice, Trice (1st {std}, 4to, 57p, fp b/w, DJ/3.50)	Little/Brown	(1958)	Shahn, Ben	60-90	R
Reid, Alastair	Supposing (1st {std}, lg8vo, 48p, 2-color, DJ/3.00)	Little/Brown	(1960)	Birnbaum, Abe	20-35	
Reid, Barbara	Carlo's Cricket (1st, sm4to, 58p, color, DJ/3.50)	McGraw-Hill	1967	Grifalconi, Ann	25-45	
Reid, Carol M.	Toys at Play (1st, sq4to, wraps, 14p, color)	Whitman	1937	(Photos)	80-130	
Reid, K.E.J.	Book of Wedding Days (1st, 4to, red/silver, t.e. silver, [108]p)	L: Longmans	1889	Crane, Walter	280-350	
Reid, Lionel	Miss Carlotta (1st, ob4to, [48]p, color, pep, DJ/1.25)	Oxford U. Pr.	(1936)	Denison, Richard	40-65	*
Reid, Sydney	How Sing Found the World is Round (1st, 12mo, [40]p, ibds, color)	Volland	(1921)	Dodge, Katharine S.	80-120	*
Reid, Sydney	Josey & the Chipmunk (1st, sm8vo, 301p, 17pl)	Century	1900	Cory, Fanny	40-65	
Reinheimer, Sophie	Flower Heaven (1st AM, 4to, ibds, [16]p, color, cep)	Harper	1931	Wenz-Vietor, Else	120-180	
Reiss, John J.	Colors (1st {std}, 4to, [32]p, 2-color, DJ/4.95)	Bradbury Press	(1969)	Reiss, John	40-70	
Reit, Seymour	Round Things Everywhere (1st, 4to, [32]p, DJ, color photos by...)	McGraw-Hill	(1969)	Basen, Carol	30-50	
Remington, Frederic	Crooked Trails (1st, 8vo, 150p, tan cloth, 49pl)	Harper	1898	Remington, Frederic	200-320	
Remington, Frederic	Done in the Open (1st, folio, [90]p, ibds, 70 b/w)	R.H. Russell	1902	Remington, Frederic	650-850	
Remington, Frederic	Drawings (1st, ob folio, ibds, 60pl)	R.H. Russell	1897	Remington, Frederic	700-1000	
Remington, Frederic	Frontier Sketches (1st, lgob4to, AEG, white pcb, 15pl)	Werner Co.	1898	Remington, Frederic	800-1200	
Remington, Frederic	John Ermine of the Yellowstone (1st, 8vo, brown cl, 271p, teg, 7pl)	Macmillan	1902	Remington, Frederic	160-225	
Remington, Frederic	Men with The Bark On (1st, 12mo, 209p, tan/gilt, 32pl)	Harper	1900	Remington, Frederic	200-300	
Remington, Frederic	Pony Tracks (1st {1st bk.}, 8vo, tan/gilt, 269p, 70 illus)	Harper	1895	Remington, Frederic	400-650	
Remington, Frederic	Stories of Peace & War (1st, 16mo, blue cl, 98p, 2pl)	Harper	1899	Remington, Frederic	140-200	
Remington, Frederic	Sundown Leflare (1st, 12mo, brown/gilt, 115p, 12pl)	Harper	1899	Remington, Frederic	200-300	
Remington, Frederic	Way of an Indian (1st, 8vo, red cl, 251p, p-o, 14pl)	Fox Duffield	1906	Remington, Frederic	160-240	
Renick, Marion	Big Basketball Prize (1st, 4to, [32]p, color, DJ/3.25)	Scribner	1963	Galdone, Paul	25-40	
Renick, Marion	Boy at Bat (1st, 4to, [32]p, fp color, DJ/2.95)	Scribner	(1961)	Galdone, Paul	30-45	*
Reno, Esther W.	Pick the Vegetables (1st, 4to, [18]p, wraps, color)	Lothrop, Lee	1944	Weisgard, Leonard	70-100	*
Reno, Esther W.	Pup Called Cinderella (1st {std}, 8vo, [32]p, ibds, 1-color, b/w, DJ/1.25)	Bobbs-Merrill	(1939)	Weisgard, Leonard	60-100	
Repplier, Agnes	Fireside Sphinx (1st, 12mo, teg, 305p, gilt, 4pl)	Houghton	1901	Bonsall, Eliz. F.	30-50	
Resnick, William S.	Dragon Ship (1st, 8vo, 214p, col frn, DJ/2.75)	Coward	1942	Busoni, Rafaello	30-50	
Ressner, Phil	August Explains (1st, 4to, [32]p, ibds, fp 2-color DJ/2.50)	Harper	(1963)	Bonsall, Crosby	40-65	*
Ressner, Phil	Dudley Pippin (1st, 8vo, 46p, fp b/w, cep, DJ/2.50)	Harper	(1965)	Lobel, Arnold	30-50	
Retan, Walter	Snowplow that Tried to Go South (1st {std}, 4to, [31]p, 2-color, DJ/1.75)	Aladdin	(1950)	Resko, John	30-50	*
Retner, Beth	Tired Trolley Car (1st {std}, 8vo, 158p, green cl, 4cp, dep)	Doubleday/Page	1926	Millard, C.E.	25-45	
Rey, Hans A.	Anybody at Home? (1st AM, ob8vo, [24]p, wraps, color)	Houghton	1942	Rey, Hans A.	120-180	
Rey, Hans A.	Au Clair de la Lune (1st, ob4to, spiral bds, [32]p, fp color)	Greystone Press	(1941)	Rey, Hans A.	250-350	
Rey, Hans A.	Cecily G. & the 9 Monkeys (1st AM, 4to, 31p, color, DJ/2.00)	Houghton	1942	Rey, Hans A.	140-200	
Rey, Hans A.	Curious George (1st, sm4to, [55]p, color, pep, DJ/2.00)	Houghton	1941	Rey, Hans A.	200-300	
Rey, Hans A.	Curious George Gets a Medal (1st, 4to, 47p, 1-color, DJ/3.25, NYTBI)	Houghton	1957	Rey, Hans A.	100-170	
Rey, Hans A.	Curious George Learns the Alphabet (1st, lg8vo, 72p, color, pep, DJ/3.25)	Houghton	1963	Rey, Hans A.	70-125	*
Rey, Hans A.	Curious George Rides a Bike (1st, 4to, 45p, color, DJ/2.75)	Houghton	1952	Rey, Hans A.	100-160	*
Rey, Hans A.	Curious George Takes a Job (1st, 4to, 47p, color, pep, DJ/2.50)	Houghton	1947	Rey, Hans A.	120-180	
Rey, Hans A.	Elizabite (1st {std}, sm4to, ipcb, [32]p, color, DJ/1.50)	Harper	(1942)	Rey, Hans A.	120-180	
Rey, Hans A.	Humpty Dumpty... (1st {std}, ob4to, [23]p, color, DJ/1.00)	Harper	(1943)	Rey, Hans A.	100-160	
Rey, Hans A.	Look for the Letters (1st, lg ob8vo, [56]p, ibds, color, DJ/2.00)	Harper	(1945)	Rey, Hans A.	120-200	
Rey, Hans A.	Raffy & the 9 Monkeys (1st, lg4to, 31p, ibds, color)	L: Chatto	1939	Rey, Hans A.	100-150	
Rey, Hans A.	The Stars: New Way to See Them (1st, 4to, blue cl, 143p, 2-color, DJ/4.00)	Houghton	1952	Rey, Hans A.	60-90	
Rey, Hans A.	Tit for Tat (1st {std}, sq4to, ipcb, [30]p, color, DJ/1.50)	Harper	(1942)	Rey, Hans A.	150-225	
Rey, Hans A.	Zebrology (1st, ob8vo, wraps, color)	L: Chatto	[1937]	Rey, Hans A.	150-200	
Rey, Hans A.	Zozo (1st UK, 4to, stiff wraps)	L: Chatto	(1942)	Rey, Hans A.	220-300	
Rey, Margret E.	Billy's Picture (1st, sm4to, ibds, [22]p, 2-color, DJ/1.00)	Harper	(1948)	Rey, Hans A.	90-130	
Rey, Margret E.	Curious George Goes to the Hospital (1st, lg8vo, 48p, fp color, DJ/3.25)	Houghton	1966	Rey, Hans A.	50-80	*
Rey, Margret E.	Pretzel (1st {std}-[1st bk.], sm4to, [30]p, color, DJ/1.75)	Harper	(1944)	Rey, Hans A.	200-300	
Rey, Margret E.	Pretzel & the Puppies (1st {std}, sm4to, ibds, [30]p, color, DJ/1.00)	Harper	(1946)	Rey, Hans A.	140-200	
Rey, Margret E.	Spotty (1st, sm4to, [30]p, ibds, p-o, color, DJ/1.75)	Harper	(1945)	Rey, Hans A.	80-125	
Reyher, Rebecca	My Mother/Most Beautiful Woman i/t World (1st, 8vo, [39]p, color, DJ, CH)	Howell/Soskin	(1945)	Gannett, Ruth C.	60-100	*
Reynier, Marguerite	Wild Animals at Home (sq4to, wraps, [16]p, color)	A.& W. Guild	(1934)	Rojankovsky, Feodor	35-60	
Reynolds, Barbara	Hamlet and Brownswiggle (1st, 8vo, 203p, b/w, DJ/2.50)	Scribner	1954	Henneberger, Rbt.	30-45	*
Reynolds, Barbara	Pepper (1st, 8vo, grey cl, 169p, fp b/w, DJ/2.00)	Scribner	(1952)	Cooney, Barbara	45-70	
Reynolds, Jessica	Jessica's Journal (1st {std}, 8vo, 191p, b/w, DJ/3.00)	Holt	(1958)	Spier, Peter E.	25-40	
Reynolds, Marjorie	Horse Called Mystery (1st, 8vo, 205p, fp b/w, DJ/2.95)	Harper	(1964)	Dennis, Wesley	30-45	*
Rhead, George W.	Treatment of Drapery in Art (1st, 8vo, 119p, 32pl, cvr by...)	L: G. Bell	1904	Crane, Walter	120-170	
Rhead, Louis	Robin Hood (1st, 8vo, black cl, 285p, p-o, col frn, b/w)	Harper	1912	Rhead, Louis	65-90	
Rhinehart, Susan	Something Old, Something New (1st, 8vo, ibds, 32p, 2-color, DJ/1.95)	Harper	(1961)	Lobel, Arnold	35-50	
Rhoads, Dorothy	Bright Feather (1st {std}, 8vo, 196p, uncut, pep, col frn, b/w)	Doubleday/Doran	1932	Houser, Lowell	25-45	
Rhoads, Dorothy	Corn Grows Ripe (1st, sm4to, 88p, pep, 1-color, DJ/2.75, NH)	Viking	1956	Charlot, Jean	70-100	
Rhoads, Dorothy	Story of Chan Yuc (1st {std}, sq8vo, [45]p, ibds, color, DJ/1.50)	Doubleday/Doran	1941	Charlot, Jean	80-125	
Rhodes, Eugene M.	Desire of the Moth (1st, 12mo, 149p, 2pl)	Henry Holt & Co.	1916	Dunn, Harvey T.	100-170	
Rhodes, Eugene M.	West is West (1st, 8vo, 304p, black cloth, frn by...)	H.K. Fly	(1917)	Dunn, Harvey T.	100-165	
Rhys, Ernest (ed.)	English Fairy Book (1st, 8vo, 318p, gilt, col frn, 1-color, pep)	L: T.F. Unwin	1912	Whitney, Frederic C.	50-90	
Rhys, Ernest (ed.)	English Fairy Tales (12mo, p-o, 474p, gilt, 8cp)	Dutton	1906	Cole, Herbert	60-90	
Rhys, Ernest (ed.)	Fairy-Gold (1st, 8vo, 474p, 12cp)	L: J.M. Dent	1906	Cole, Herbert	70-120	
Rhys, Grace (ed.)	Children's Garland of Verse (1st, 8vo, 296p, 8cp)	L: J.M. Dent	1921	Robinson, Charles	150-220	*

AUTHOR	TITLE	PUBLISHER	DATE	ARTIST	PRICE	LC
Rhys, Grace (ed.)	Fairy Gifts (1st, 12mo, 61p, uncut, teg, gilt, 16pl)	L: J.M. Dent	1895	Fell, H. Granville	70-100	
Rhys, Grace (ed.)	Magic Wood Beyond the World (1st, 8vo, ibds, 4cp)	L: Harrap	1931	Tarrant, Margaret	50-80	
Rhys, Mimpsy	Mr. Hermit Crab (1st, 8vo, green cl, 190p, col frn, 6pl, pep)	Macmillan	1929	Sewell, Helen	30-50	
Rice, Alice H.	Captain June (1st, 8vo, blue cl, 120p, 8pl)	Century	1907	Weldon, C.D.	25-45	
Rice, Alice H.	Lovey Mary (1st, 8vo, teg, uncut, 236p, 24pl)	Century	1903	Shinn, Florence S.	25-40	
Rice, Alice H.	Romance of Billy-Goat Hill (1st, 12mo, green/gilt, 404p, 8pl)	Century	1912	Wright, George	30-45	
Rice, Ethel	Wiggle & Waggle (1st, 4to, bds, [28]p, p-o, color, pep, DJ/1.25)	NY: S. Gabriel	(1939)	Kay, Albert	55-80	
Rice, Inez	Long, Long Time (1st, sm4to, [32]p, fp 3-color, DJ/3.50)	Lothrop, Lee	1964	Quackenbush, Rbt.	25-45	*
Rice, Inez	March Wind (1st, 4to, [30]p, fp color, pep, DJ/2.75)	Lothrop, Lee	(1957)	Bobri, Vladimir	50-80	R
Rice, Inez	Tree this Tall (1st, lg8vo, [32]p, 3-color, DJ/3.95)	Wm. Morrow	(1970)	Smith, Alvin	30-50	
Rice, Rebecca	Giles of the Star (1st, 8vo, 350p, 6cp, pep, DJ/2.00)	Lothrop, Lee	(1928)	Berger, William M.	40-65	
Rich, Edwin G.	Hans the Eskimo (1st, 8vo, 287p, blue cl, p-o, b/w)	Houghton	1934	Kent, Rockwell	40-70	
Rich, Edwin G.	Why-So Stories (1st, sm8vo, gilt, 207p, col frn, b/w)	Small/Maynard	(1918)	Copeland, Charles	30-50	*
Richards, Anna M.	New Alice in the Old Wonderland (1st, 12mo, 309p, teg, red/gilt, b/w)	Lippincott	1895	Richards, Anna M.	160-220	
Richards, Dorothy	Adventures in an Old Shoe House (1st, 12mo, 30p, ibds, 6cp)	L: Faber	(1948)	Thomas, Elsie	40-60	
Richards, Dorothy	Roma Rabbit's Picnic (1st, 16mo, 30p, ibds, 6cp)	L: Faber	1948	Thomas, Elsie	40-60	
Richards, Laura E.	Captain January (1st, sq8vo, teg, 133p, gilt, b/w)	Estes & Lauriat	1893	Merrill, Frank T.	55-80	*
Richards, Laura E.	Fairy Operettas (1st, 12mo, 119p, col frn, b/w)	Little/Brown	1916	Bassett, Mary R.	80-135	
Richards, Laura E.	Five Mice in a Mousetrap (8vo, 228p, cloth, b/w, dep)	Estes & Lauriat	(1880)	Greenaway, Kate	100-165	
Richards, Laura E.	Golden Windows (1st, 8vo, 123p, green/gilt, teg, 5pl)	Little/Brown	1903	Becher, Arthur E.	50-80	
Richards, Laura E.	Isla Heron (1st, 8vo, 109p, fp b/w)	Estes & Lauriat	(1896)	Merrill, Frank T.	20-35	
Richards, Laura E.	Joyous Story of Toto (1st, 12mo, 226p, fp b/w)	Roberts Bros.	1885	Garrett, E.H.	30-50	
Richards, Laura E.	Merry-Go-Round (1st, sm8vo, 113p, p-o, b/w, DJ/1.50)	Appleton-Century	1935	Lefferts, Winfred E.	30-50	*
Richards, Laura E.	Mrs. Tree (1st, 12mo, ipcb, 282p, teg, 4pl)	Dana Estes	(1902)	Merrill, Frank T.	40-65	
Richards, Laura E.	Peggy (1st, 12mo, 308p, 8pl)	Dana Estes	(1899)	Barry, Etheldred B.	25-40	
Richards, Laura E.	Quicksilver Sue (1st, 12mo, 177p, 7pl)	Century	1899	Stevens, W.D.	20-35	
Richards, Laura E.	Silver Crown (1st, 8vo, 105p, teg, grey/gilt, cvr by...)	Little/Brown	1906	Smith, Jessie W.	60-90	
Richards, Laura E.	The Piccolo (1st, lg8vo, 121p, color, pep)	Dana Estes	(1906)	Various	30-50	*
Richards, Laura E.	Tirra Lirra (1st, 8vo, 194p, col frn, pep, DJ/2.50, NH)	Little/Brown	1932	Davis, Marguerite	45-70	
Richardson, Alfred	King of the Grizzlies (1st, sm8vo, 242p, p-o, col frn, b/w, pep)	Rand/McNally	(1925)	Wildering, Walter	30-50	
Richardson, Emmeline	Doors... (1st, 8vo, 160p, 12cp)	L: Headley	[1909]	Richardson, Emmeline	140-200	*
Richardson, Emmeline	Songs of Near & Far Away (1st, 4to, tan cl, 80p, color)	L: Cassell	1900	Richardson, Emmeline	120-180	*
Richardson, Emmeline	Sun, Moon & Stars... (1st, 4to, green cl, unpag, b/w)	L: Bodley Head	1899	Richardson, Emmeline	120-185	
Richardson, Frederick	Book for Children (1st, ob4to, 107p, pep, p-o, 35cp, DJ/1.50)	Donohue	(1938)	Richardson, F.	90-120	
Richardson, Frederick	Book of Drawings (1st, folio, [106]p, grey bds, b/w)	Lakeside Pr.	1899	Richardson, F.	425-600	
Richardson, Myra	Sheep Wagon Family (1st {std}, 8vo, 217p, fp b/w, pep, DJ/2.00)	McBride	1941	Wilkin, Eloise B.	65-100	*
Richardson, W.C.F.	India Rubber Jack (1st, 16mo, blue cl, [124]p, 28 color)	L: Swan/Sonn.	[1902]	Sichel, Gerald	120-180	
Richelson, Geraldine	What is a Child? (1st {std}, sq12mo, [32]p, color, DJ/2.95)	Harlin Quist	(1966)	Johnson, John	25-45	
Richmond, Grace S.	On Christmas Day in the Evening (1st, 12mo, 76p, white bds, 4cp)	Doubleday/Page	1910	Relyea, Charles M.	30-50	
Richter, Conrad	Light in the Forest (1st {std}, lg8vo, 176p, fp b/w, cep, DJ/4.95)	Knopf	1966	Chappell, Warren	30-50	*
Richter, Conrad	Over the Blue Mountain (1st, 8vo, 81p, b/w, cep, DJ/3.75)	Knopf	(1967)	Danska, Herbert	20-30	*
Richter, Mischa	Eric and Matilda (1st, 4to, ibds, 32p, 2-color, DJ/2.95)	Harper	(1967)	Richter, Mischa	25-45	
Rickert, Edith	Blacksmith & the Birds (1st {std}, 12mo, 46p, orange cl, pep, b/w)	Doubleday/Doran	1928	Daugherty, James	30-50	
Rideout, Henry M.	Lola the Bear (1st, 8vo, 159p, gilt, col frn, 3pl, DJ/1.75)	Duffield	1928	Ward, Lynd	50-80	
Riesenberg, Felix	Balboa, Swordsman & Conquistador (1st, 8vo, 178p, color, pep, DJ/1.50)	Random	(1956)	Rojankovsky, Feodor	30-45	*
Rietveld, Jane	ABC Molly (1st {std}, 8vo, 89p, b/w, DJ/3.00)	Norton	(1966)	Rietveld, Jane	20-35	
Rietveld, Jane	Monkey Island (1st, 4to, 54p, 1-color, DJ/2.75)	Viking	(1963)	Rietveld, Jane	30-45	*
Rietveld, Jane	Nicky's Bugle (1st, 4to, 56p, ibds, b/w, dep, DJ/2.00)	Viking	1947	Rietveld, Jane	40-65	
Rietveld, Jane	Wild Dog (1st, 8vo, 189p, b/w, DJ/2.50)	Wilcox/Follett	(1953)	Rietveld, Jane	20-35	*
Rieu, E.V.	Flattered Flying Fish (1st AM {std}, sm8vo, 101p, b/w, DJ/2.95)	Dutton	(1962)	Shepard, Ernest H.	35-50	
Rigby, Douglas	Moustachio (1st, 4to, [31]p, ibds, 1-color, DJ/1.50)	Harper	(1947)	Duvoisin, Roger	70-125	
Riggs, Renee	Animal Stories from Eskimo Land (1st, 12mo, 113p, 2-color)	Stokes	1923	Hood, George	30-45	
Righter, Linwood	Junior Starke, Poundman (1st {std}, 8vo, 306p, col frn, pep)	Doubleday/Doran	1928	Lee, Manning De V.	20-35	
Rihbany, Abraham M.	Christ Story for Boys & Girls (1st, 8vo, gilt, p-o, 239p, 4cp)	Houghton	(1923)	Tenggren, Gustaf	55-80	
Riis, Jacob A.	Children of the Tenements (1st, sm8vo, green cl, 387p, 8pl)	Macmillan	1903	Various	70-120	
Riley, Alice C.	Voyage of the Wishbone Boat (1st, lg8vo, ipcb, 205p, fp color, pep)	Caldwell	(1907)	Bridgman, L.J.	100-165	
Riley, James W.	All the Year Round (1st, 4to, gilt, ibds, [30]p, p-o, 12cp)	Bobbs-Merrill	(1912)	Baumann, Gustave	300-450	R
Riley, James W.	Book of Joyous Children (1st, 8vo, gilt, teg, 176p, uncut, b/w)	Scribner	1902	Vawter, J. Will	50-85	
Riley, James W.	Boy Lives on our Farm (1st, sq4to, p-o, [18]p, 5cp)	Bobbs-Merrill	(1908)	Betts, Ethel F.	120-170	
Riley, James W.	Boys of the Old Glee Club (1st, lg8vo, [56]p, 13pl)	Bobbs-Merrill	(1907)	Vawter, J. Will	60-100	R
Riley, James W.	Defective Santa Claus (1st, 12mo, green/gilt, 77p, cvr by...)	Bobbs-Merrill	(1904)	Armstrong, Margaret	70-120	R
Riley, James W.	Defective Santa Claus (1st, 12mo, green/gilt, 77p, b/w)	Bobbs-Merrill	(1904)	Vawter, J. Will	70-120	R
Riley, James W.	Discouraging Model (1st, lg8vo, ipcb, [12]p, color)	Bobbs-Merrill	(1914)	Christy, Howard C.	90-120	R*
Riley, James W.	Flying Islands of the Night (1st, sm4to, bds, 124p, gilt, 16 ticp pep)	Bobbs-Merrill	(1913)	Booth, Franklin	125-200	R
Riley, James W.	Good-Bye Jim (1st, sq8vo, gilt, [33]p, 11cp, pep)	Bobbs-Merrill	(1913)	Christy, Howard C.	60-90	
Riley, James W.	Host of Children (1st, lg8vo, p-o, 189p, brown/gilt, 16cp, pep)	Bobbs-Merrill	(1920)	Betts, Ethel F.	200-300	R
Riley, James W.	Old Sweetheart of Mine (1st, sm ob4to, ibds, [26]p, AEG, color)	Bowen-Merrill	1891	(Chromos)	150-225	
Riley, James W.	Old Sweetheart of Mine (1st, 8vo, gilt, [94]p, p-o, 19pl, pep)	Bobbs-Merrill	(1902)	Christy, Howard C.	80-135	
Riley, James W.	Orphant Annie Book (1st, sq folio, [30]p, ibds, 8cp)	Bobbs-Merrill	(1908)	Betts, Ethel F.	170-240	
Riley, James W.	Poems Here at Home (1st, 8vo, green cl, 187p, teg, b/w)	Century	1893	Kemble, Edward W.	80-125	
Riley, James W.	Poems of Childhood (1st, 8vo, [36]p, ibds, color, pep, DJ/0.50)	Grosset/Dunlap	(1943)	Shinn, Everett	30-50	
Riley, James W.	Raggedy Man (1st, sq4to, [30]p, p-o, 8cp)	Bobbs-Merrill	(1907)	Betts, Ethel F.	180-240	R
Riley, James W.	Riley Baby Book (1st, 8vo, [35]p, red/gilt, t-i col frn)	Bobbs-Merrill	(1913)	Cotton, William	120-180	R
Riley, James W.	Riley Child Verse (1st, lg8vo, p-o, 58p, 8cp)	Bobbs-Merrill	(1906)	Betts, Ethel F.	120-200	R
Riley, James W.	Riley Fairy Tales (1st, lg8vo, 96p, p-o, color)	Bobbs-Merrill	(1923)	Vawter, J. Will	140-200	
Riley, James W.	Riley Roses (1st, lg8vo, [30]p, green/gilt, 8cp)	Bobbs-Merrill	(1909)	Christy, Howard C.	70-120	
Riley, James W.	Rubaiyat of Doc Sifers (1st, 12mo, teg, 211p, green/gilt)	Century	1897	Relyea, Charles M.	60-100	R
Riley, James W.	Runaway Boy (1st, lg8vo, p-o, red cl, [40]p, pep, 8cp)	Bobbs-Merrill	(1906)	Betts, Ethel F.	120-180	

|---|---|---|---|---|---|---|
Riley, James W.	The Rose (1st, sm4to, ibds, [16]p, color)	Bobbs-Merrill	(1914)	Christy, Howard C.	60-90	
Riley, James W.	While the Heart Beats Young (1st, lg8vo, 110p, p-o, 16cp, dep)	Bobbs-Merrill	(1906)	Betts, Ethel F.	120-200	
Riley, Louise	Train for Tiger Lily (1st, 8vo, 186p, fp b/w, pep, DJ/2.50)	Viking	1954	Price, Christine	40-65	R*
Rinder, Frank	Old World Japan (1st, 8vo, blue/gilt, teg, uncut, 195p, fp b/w, pep)	L: G. Allen	1895	Robinson, Thomas H.	100-180	
Rinehart, Mary R.	Amazing Adventures of Letitia Carberry (1st, sm8vo, 344p, green cl, 10pl)	Bobbs-Merrill	(1911)	Christy, Howard C.	50-80	
Rinehart, Mary R.	Amazing Interlude (1st, sm8vo, 317p, 4pl)	Doran	(1918)	Kinneys	30-50	
Rinehart, Mary R.	Circular Staircase (1st, 12mo, 362p, 7pl)	Bobbs-Merrill	(1908)	Lester, Ralph	80-130	
Rinehart, Mary R.	Man in the Lower Ten (1st, 8vo, green cl, 372p, 5cp)	Bobbs-Merrill	(1909)	Christy, Howard C.	100-165	
Rinehart, Mary R.	Tish (1st, sm8vo, 371p, 9cp)	Houghton	1916	Preston, May W.	30-50	
Rinehart, Mary R.	Truce of God (1st, 8vo, 96p, gilt, col frn, pep)	Doran	(1920)	Sichel, Harold	25-40	
Rinehart, Mary R.	When a Man Marries (1st, 12mo, 353p, 5cp)	Bobbs-Merrill	(1909)	Fisher, Harrison	40-65	
Rinehart, Mary R.	Where There's a Will (1st, sm8vo, blue/gilt, 352p, 5pl)	Bobbs-Merrill	(1912)	Wilson, F. Vaux	30-50	
Rinehart, Mary R.	Window at the White Cat (1st, sm8vo, 378p, 4pl)	Bobbs-Merrill	(1910)	Keller, Arthur I.	30-50	
Ring, Barbara	Peik (1st, sm8vo, 268p, 15 fp b/w, cep)	Little/Brown	1932	Lawson, Robert	60-90	
Rinkoff, Barbara	Elbert the Mind Reader (1st, 8vo, 112p, b/w, DJ/3.25)	Lothrop, Lee	(1967)	Galdone, Paul	40-70	
Rinkoff, Barbara	Headed for Trouble (1st {std}, lg8vo, 119p, b/w, DJ/4.50)	Knopf	(1970)	Bolognese, Don	20-30	
Rinkoff, Barbara	Pretzel Hero (1st, 4to, [32]p, fp color, DJ/3.95)	Parents Mag. Pr.	(1970)	Mikolaycak, Charles	20-35	
Rinkoff, Barbara	Rutherford T. Finds 21B (1st, 8vo, [47]p, fp 2-color, DJ)	Putnam	(1970)	DePaola, Tomie	30-50	
Rinkoff, Barbara	Troublesome Tuba (1st, 8vo, 80p, fp b/w, DJ/3.25)	Lothrop, Lee	(1967)	Turkle, Brinton	25-45	*
Rion, H.	Smiling Road (1st, 8vo, green cl, 191p, 10pl)	E.J. Clode	(1910)	VerBeck, Frank	30-50	*
Ripley, Sherman	Raggedies in Fairy Land (1st, 4to, 96p, p-o, 3cp, pep)	Rand/McNally	(1930)	Cady, Harrison	150-220	
Ripley, Sherman	Raggedy Animal Book (1st, 4to, p-o, 96p, fp color, pep)	Rand/McNally	(1928)	Cady, Harrison	150-250	
Rippey, Sarah C.	Goody-Naughty Book (1st, 12mo, tan cl, p-o, [62]p, color)	Rand/McNally	(1913)	Wright, Blanche F.	50-85	
Rippey, Sarah C.	Sunny-Sulky Book (1st, sm8vo, [40]p, p-o, 12cp)	Rand/McNally	(1915)	Wright, Blanche F.	45-80	
Risley, Eleanor	Abandoned Orchard (1st, 8vo, 284p, b/w)	Little/Brown	1932	Wiese, Kurt	25-40	*
Ritchie, Barbara	To Catch a Mongoose (1st AM, 4to, 61p, fp color, DJ/3.75)	Parnassus Press	(1963)	Thollander, Earl	25-40	*
Ritchie, Jean	Singing Family of the Cumberlands (1st, 8vo, grn cl, 282p, b/w, DJ/4.00)	NY: Oxford U.Pr.	1955	Sendak, Maurice	200-300	
Ritchie, Rita	Pirates of Samarkand (1st {std}, 8vo, 158p, b/w, DJ/3.75)	Norton	(1967)	Jacques, Robin	30-45	
Ritter, Elizabeth	You Never Can Tell (1st, lg sq8vo, ibds, [28]p, fp color, pep, DJ/0.50)	Grosset/Dunlap	(1947)	Holland, Marion	80-120	
Rives, Amelia	Athelwold (1st, 12mo, uncut, 118p, 8pl)	Harper	1893	Gow, M.	80-120	
Rives, Amelia	Damsel Errant (1st, 16mo, teg, 211p, uncut, 4pl)	Lippincott	1898	Oakley, Violet	90-120	*
Rives, Hallie E.	Valiants of Virginia (1st, 8vo, red/gilt, 432p)	Bobbs-Merrill	(1912)	Armstrong, Margaret	25-45	
Rix, Herbert	Prince Pimpernel (1st, 8vo, 141p, 8cp)	L: Duckworth	1909	Pape, Frank	100-160	
Robbins, Louis	Dutch Doll Ditties (1st, 4to, 23p, grey bds, p-o, b/w)	L: Longmans	1904	(Photos)	90-120	
Robbins, Ruth	Baboushka & Three Kings (1st sq12mo, [28]p, col, pep, DJ/2.50, CM, NYT)	Parnassus Press	(1960)	Sidjakov, Nicolas	100-165	R*
Robbins, Ruth	Emperor & the Drummer Boy (1st, lg8vo, [38]p, fp color, DJ/3.25, NYTBI)	Parnassus Press	(1962)	Sidjakov, Nicolas	60-90	*
Robbins, Ruth	Harlequin and Mother Goose (1st, 4to, 32p, color, DJ/3.75)	Parnassus Press	(1965)	Sidjakov, Nicolas	45-70	
Roberts, Chas. G.D.	Earth's Enigmas (1st, 12mo, 285p, red/gilt, 10pl)	L.C. Page	1903	Bull, Charles L.	70-120	
Roberts, Chas. G.D.	Fleet of the Furtive (1st, sm8vo, 384p, gilt, pep, frn by...)	Macmillan	1913	Bransom, Paul	20-30	
Roberts, Chas. G.D.	Haunters of the Silences (1st, 8vo, 316p, gilt, b/w, pep)	L.C. Page	1907	Bull, Charles L.	50-75	
Roberts, Chas. G.D.	Hoof and Claw (1st AM, 8vo, 291p, 8pl)	NY: Macmillan	1914	Bransom, Paul	40-65	
Roberts, Chas. G.D.	Kindred of the Wild (1st, 8vo, 374p, green/gilt, teg, 50pl)	L.C. Page	1902	Bull, Charles L.	50-80	
Roberts, Chas. G.D.	Red Fox (1st, 8vo, uncut, 340p, teg, 48pl)	L.C. Page	1905	Bull, Charles L.	50-80	
Roberts, Chas. G.D.	Secret Trails (1st, 12mo, 212p, green/gilt, 8pl)	Macmillan	1916	Bransom, Paul	30-50	
Roberts, Chas. G.D.	Watchers of the Trails (1st, 8vo, uncut, 361p, 48pl, pep)	L.C. Page	1904	Bull, Charles L.	50-85	
Roberts, Chas. G.D.	Young Acadian (1st, 12mo, 139p, 6pl)	L.C. Page	1907	McManus, Blanche	30-50	*
Roberts, Elizabeth M.	Time of Man (1st, 8vo, 397p, p-o, fp woodcuts, DJ/5.00)	Viking	1945	Leighton, Clare	60-100	
Roberts, Elizabeth M.	Under the Tree (1st, lg8vo, p-o, 85p, col frn, b/w)	Viking	1930	Bedford, Francis D.	30-50	
Roberts, Irma	Jungle Twins (1st {std}, 8vo, 127p, ibds, fp 1-color, DJ/2.25)	Coward	(1951)	Wiese, Kurt	25-45	
Roberts, Kenneth L.	Trending into Maine (1st, lg8vo, 394p, tan cl, 14cp, pep, DJ/4.00)	Little/Brown	1938	Wyeth, N.C.	175-250	
Roberts, Theodore G.	Flying Plover (1st, sm8vo, 125p, tan cl, 6pl, cvr by...)	L.C. Page	1909	Bull, Charles L.	40-60	
Roberts, Theodore G.	Red Feathers (1st, sm8vo, p-o, 325p, col frn, 10pl, pep)	L.C. Page	1907	Bull, Charles L.	40-65	
Robertson, Dorothy	Fairy Tales from Viet Nam (1st, lg8vo, 93p, b/w, DJ/3.50)	Dodd	(1968)	Mars, Witold T.	30-50	*
Robertson, Keith	Dog Next Door (1st, 8vo, 222p, pep, DJ/2.50)	Viking	1950	Dennis, Morgan	25-40	*
Robertson, Keith	Henry Reed's Baby-Sitting Service (1st, 8vo, 204p, color, DJ/3.50)	Viking	(1966)	McCloskey, Robert	70-100	
Robertson, Keith	Henry Reed's Big Show (1st {std}, 8vo, 206p, color, DJ/4.50)	Viking	(1970)	McCloskey, Robert	50-80	
Robertson, Keith	Henry Reed's Journey (1st, 8vo, 220p, color, DJ/3.25)	Viking	(1963)	McCloskey, Robert	50-80	
Robertson, Keith	Henry Reed, Inc. (1st, 8vo, 239p, b/w, DJ/3.00)	Viking	(1958)	McCloskey, Robert	60-90	R
Robertson, Keith	If Wishes Were Horses (1st {std}, 8vo, 246p, b/w, DJ/2.95)	Harper	(1958)	Kennedy, Paul	30-50	
Robertson, Keith	Missing Brother (1st, 8vo, 220p, orange cl, b/w, DJ/2.50)	Viking	1950	Busoni, Rafaello	30-50	
Robertson, Keith	Pilgrim Goose (1st, lg8vo, 80p, b/w, pep, DJ/2.00)	Viking	1956	Berry, Erick	25-40	
Robertson, Keith	Ticktock and Jim (1st {std}, 8vo, 240p, b/w, DJ/2.50)	Winston	(1948)	Dennis, Wesley	25-45	*
Robertson, Lilian	Runaway Rocking Horse (1st, ob4to, [32]p, 3-color, DJ/2.00)	Harcourt	(1948)	Robertson, Lillian	60-100	*
Robertson, W.G.	Baby's Day Book (1st, lg8vo, 127p, grey cl, col frn, b/w)	L: John Lane	1908	Robertson, W.G.	170-240	
Robertson, W.G.	Gold, Frankincense & Myrrh (1st, 4to, blue cl, 152p, 12cp)	L: John Lane	1907	Robertson, W.G.	200-300	
Robertson, W.G.	Masque of May Morning (1st, 4to, green cl, 62p, 12cp)	L: John Lane	1904	Robertson, W.G.	250-350	
Robertson, W.G.	Pan's Garden (1st, 8vo, 530p, gilt, b/w woodcuts)	L: Macmillan	1912	Robertson, W.G.	140-200	
Robertson, W.G.	Pinkie & the Fairies (1st, 12mo, 146p, 6 fp b/w)	L: Heinemann	1909	Robertson, W.G.	180-260	
Robertson, W.G.	Slippers of Cinderella (1st, 12mo, 130p)	L: Heinemann	1919	Robertson, W.G.	70-100	*
Robertson, W.G.	Year of Songs for a Baby in a Garden (1st, 8vo, 111p, fp b/w)	L: John Lane	1906	Robertson, W.G.	200-300	
Robida, Albert	Treasure of Carcassone (1st {std}, sm8vo, 213p, col frn, 7pl, pep)	Longmans	1928	Lathrop, Dorothy	50-80	
Robins, Elizabeth	Prudence & Peter... (1st, sm8vo, 244p, grey cl, p-o, b/w)	Wm. Morrow	(1928)	Lenski, Lois	60-100	
Robins, Elizabeth	Under the Southern Cross (1st, 8vo, teg, p-o, 234p, 4cp, pep)	Stokes	(1907)	Rae, John	35-60	
Robinson, Barbara	Across from Indian Shore (1st, 8vo, 158p, fp b/w, DJ/3.50)	Lothrop, Lee	(1962)	Ness, Evaline	25-40	
Robinson, Barbara	Trace through the Forest (1st, 8vo, 219p, b/w, DJ/3.50)	Lothrop, Lee	(1965)	Ness, Evaline	25-40	
Robinson, Charles	Black Bunnies (1st, 16mo, [56]p, blue/gilt, fp silhouettes, pep)	L: Blackie	[1907]	Robinson, Charles	400-650	
Robinson, Charles	Black Doggies (16mo, red cloth, silhouettes)	L: Blackie	[1907]	Robinson, Charles	300-425	
Robinson, Charles	Silly Submarine (1st, ob16mo, ibds, 30 fp color, pep)	L: Blackie	[1906]	Robinson, Charles	200-320	

AUTHOR	TITLE	PUBLISHER	DATE	ARTIST	PRICE	LC
Robinson, Charles	Ten Little Babies (sm4to, ibds, pep, color)	L: SPCK	[1905]	Robinson, Charles	500-700	
Robinson, Charles	Ten Little Puppy Dogs (1st, ob4to, green cl, fp b/w)	L: Sands	1902	Aldin, Cecil	600-800	
Robinson, Edith	Captain of the School (1st, sm8vo, 258p, grey cl, 15pl)	Little/Brown	1901	Stephens, Alice B.	25-45	
Robinson, Edith	Little Puritan Rebel (1st, 12mo, 135p, blue/gilt, b/w)	L.C. Page	1898	Sacker, Amy	30-50	
Robinson, Edith	Loyal Little Maid (1st, 12mo, 79p, b/w illus)	J. Knight	1897	Sacker, Amy	25-40	
Robinson, Edwin A.	Children of the Night (1st, 12mo, 123p, tan cl, cvr by...)	Badger	1897	Hapgood, T.B.	200-300	
Robinson, Geraldine	Toy Bearkins Christmas (12mo, 32cp)	L: Nister	[1915]	Petherick, Rosa	130-180	
Robinson, Gertrude	Chee-Chee's Brother (1st {std}, sm4to, green cl, 40p, fp b/w, pep, DJ/1.50)	Dutton	(1937)	Latimer, Glenna M.	30-50	
Robinson, Gertrude	White Heron Feather (1st {std}, 12mo, orange cl, 299p, b/w, pep)	Harper	(1930)	Berry, Erick	30-60	*
Robinson, Mabel L.	All by Ourselves (1st, sm8vo, 254p, decor by...)	Dutton	(1924)	Wright, Mary S.	25-40	*
Robinson, Mabel L.	All the Year Round (1st {std}, 8vo, 150p, b/w, DJ/2.50)	Harper	(1954)	Watson, Aldren A.	20-30	*
Robinson, Mabel L.	Back-Seat Driver (1st, 8vo, 68p, fp b/w, DJ/2.00)	Random	(1949)	Shortall, Leonard	30-50	*
Robinson, Mabel L.	Bright Island (1st, 8vo, 268p, silver cl, b/w, pep, DJ/2.00, NH)	Random	(1937)	Ward, Lynd	60-90	
Robinson, Mabel L.	King Arthur and His Knights (1st, 8vo, 174p, 1-color, DJ/1.50)	Random	(1953)	Gorsline, Douglas	30-50	*
Robinson, Mabel L.	Little Lucia's School (1st, 12mo, 138p, fp b/w, pep)	Dutton	(1926)	Balcom, Sophia T.	25-40	*
Robinson, Mabel L.	Riley Goes to Obedience School (1st, 8vo, 80p, fp b/w, DJ/2.50)	Random	(1956)	Shortall, Leonard	25-40	
Robinson, Mabel L.	Robin & Angus (1st, 8vo, green cl, 186p, col frn, fp b/w)	Macmillan	1931	Wilkin, Eloise B.	40-65	*
Robinson, Mabel L.	Robin & Tito (1st, 8vo, 192p, col frn, b/w)	Macmillan	1930	Burns, Eloise	25-40	*
Robinson, Mabel L.	Robin and Heather (1st, 8vo, 214p, col frn, b/w)	Macmillan	1932	Vibberts, Eunice	20-30	
Robinson, Mabel L.	Runner of the Mountain Tops (1st {std}, 8vo, blue/gilt, col, DJ/3.00, NH)	Random	(1939)	Ward, Lynd	60-100	
Robinson, Mabel L.	Sarah's Daikin (1st, sm8vo, 271p, green/gilt, uncut, b/w)	Dutton	(1927)	Brown, Julie	25-40	*
Robinson, Mabel L.	Skipper Riley: Terrier Dog (1st, 8vo, 90p, b/w, DJ/2.50)	Random	(1955)	Shortall, Leonard	25-45	
Robinson, Mabel L.	Strong Wings (1st {std}, 8vo, 249p, blue cl, b/w, DJ/2.75)	Random	(1951)	Ward, Lynd	35-50	
Robinson, Mary Y.	Songs of the Trees (1st, lg4to, 125p, ibds, 2-color)	Bobbs-Merrill	(1903)	Robinson, Mary Y.	140-200	
Robinson, Philip S.	Bubble and Squeak (1st, 8vo, 230p, green cl, teg, 15pl)	L: Ibister	1902	Aldin/Shepherd	70-125	*
Robinson, Selma	City Child (1st, 8vo, red/gilt, 64p, b/w, DJ/2.00)	Farrar/Rinehart	1931	Kent, Rockwell	70-125	
Robinson, Tom P.	Buttons (1st, lg4to, [63]p, red cl, p-o, b/w, DJ/2.00)	Viking	1938	Bacon, Peggy	50-80	
Robinson, Tom P.	Greylock & the Robins (1st, sm4to, 32p, ibds, color, DJ/2.00)	Viking	1946	Lawson, Robert	80-140	
Robinson, Tom P.	In & Out (1st, lg8vo, 140p, color, pep, DJ/2.50)	Viking	1943	DeAngeli, Marguerite	50-85	
Robinson, Tom P.	Lost Dog Jerry (1st, 8vo, 191p, brown cl, b/w, DJ/2.50)	Viking	1952	Dennis, Morgan	25-45	
Robinson, Tom P.	Mr. Red Squirrel (1st, sm4to, ibds, [32]p, color, pep, DJ/1.50)	Viking	1943	Wiese, Kurt	30-50	
Robinson, Tom P.	Pete (1st, 8vo, 139p, b/w, DJ/2.00)	Viking	1941	Dennis, Morgan	30-50	*
Robinson, Tom P.	Trigger John's Son (1st, 8vo, 284p, b/w, DJ/2.50)	Viking	1949	McCloskey, Robert	60-90	
Robinson, Veronica	David in Silence (1st, 8vo, 126p, fp b/w, DJ/3.25)	Lippincott	1966	Ambrus, Victor	25-45	
Robinson, W. Heath	Absurdities (1st, lg4to, 96p, ibds, fp b/w illus)	L: Hutchinson	[1934]	Robinson, W. Heath	125-200	
Robinson, W. Heath	Adventures of Uncle Lubin (1st, sm4to, 117p, col frn, fp b/w, pep)	L: Richards	1902	Robinson, W. Heath	2000-3000	
Robinson, W. Heath	Adventures of Uncle Lubin (1st AM, 8vo, 117p, green cl, b/w)	Brentano's	1902	Robinson, W. Heath	1000-1600	
Robinson, W. Heath	Adventures of Uncle Lubin (new ed, sm4to, 114p, ibds, col frn, 7 b/w, DJ)	L: Chatto	(1934)	Robinson, W. Heath	200-300	
Robinson, W. Heath	Bill the Minder (1st AM, 4to, p-o, 254p, gilt, 16 ticp)	Henry Holt & Co.	1912	Robinson, W. Heath	450-600	
Robinson, W. Heath	Bill the Minder (1st, 4to, green/gilt, 255p, p-o, 16 ticp)	L: Constable	1912	Robinson, W. Heath	500-700	
Robinson, W. Heath	Book of Goblins (1st, 4to, 239p, blue/gilt, 7cp)	L: Hutchinson	(1934)	Robinson, W. Heath	400-600	
Robinson, W. Heath	Child's Arabian Nights (1st, 4to, ibds, 84p, 12cp)	L: Richards	1903	Robinson, W. Heath	700-1000	
Robinson, W. Heath	Humours of Golf (1st AM, 4to, ibds, 50p, b/w)	Dodd	1923	Robinson, W. Heath	250-350	
Robinson, W. Heath	Hunlikely! (1st, sm4to, ibds, 24pl)	L: Duckworth	(1916)	Robinson, W. Heath	125-200	
Robinson, W. Heath	Jamboree of Laughter (1st, 4to, [24]p, p-o, wraps)	L: Jones & Co.	[1918]	Robinson, W. Heath	250-400	
Robinson, W. Heath	Railway Ribaldry (1st, 4to, [96]p, wraps, 88 fp b/w)	G.W. Railway	1935	Robinson, W. Heath	160-220	
Robinson, W. Heath	Some Frightful War Pictures (1st, folio, [54]p, 24 fp b/w, pep)	L: Duckworth	(1915)	Robinson, W. Heath	200-300	
Robinson, William H.	Golden Palace of Neverland (1st, sm8vo, green cl, 307p, 6cp)	Dutton	1907	Davidson, Clara D.	60-90	
Robinson, William W.	Elephants (1st {std}, lg4to, 43p, b/w, DJ/1.75)	Harper	1935	Robinson, Irene	30-50	
Roche, A.K.	Clever Turtle (1st, ob8vo, [32]p, fp 2-color, cep, DJ/4.50)	Prentice-Hall	(1969)	Roche, A.K.	35-50	*
Roche, James J.	Her Majesty's King (1st, 12mo, 149p, 8cp)	R.H. Russell	1902	Herford, Oliver	65-90	
Roche, James J.	Sorrows of Sap'ed (1st, 8vo, uncut, 195p, p-o, 8cp)	Harper	1904	Mears, W.E.	25-40	
Rockwell, Anne	Filippo's Dome (1st {std}, lg8vo, 82p, fp b/w, DJ)	Atheneum	1967	Rockwell, Anne	30-45	
Rockwell, Anne	Olly's Polliwogs (1st {std}, 4to, [57]p, color, DJ/3.95)	Doubleday	(1970)	Rockwell, Harlow	30-50	*
Rockwell, Anne	Stolen Necklace (1st, sm4to, [32]p, color, cep, DJ/3.95)	World	(1968)	Rockwell, Anne	30-45	
Rockwell, Anne	Temple on a Hill (1st {std}, lg8vo, 108p, b/w, cep, DJ/3.95)	Atheneum	1969	Rockwell, Anne	50-80	R*
Rockwell, Anne	Wonderful Eggs of Furicchia (1st, 4to, [32]p, fp color, cep, DJ/3.95)	World	(1969)	Rockwell, Anne	30-45	
Rockwell, Norman	Willie Was Different (1st, sm4to, cloth, [48]p, color, DJ/3.95)	Funk/Wagnalls	(1969)	Rockwell, Norman	140-200	
Rockwood, Roy	Through Space to Mars (1st, sm8vo, 248p, blue cl, 4pl)	Cupples/Leon	(1910)	Kuser, G.M.	65-90	
Rodgers, Carolyn	Pirate's Loot (1st, 8vo, yellow cl, 282p, 30 fp 1-color)	Sears	(1931)	Tenggren, Gustaf	55-80	
Rodgers, Mary	Rotten Book (1st, 8vo, [32]p, b/w, DJ/2.50)	Harper	(1969)	Kellogg, Steven	40-65	
Rodman, Maia	Market Day for 'Ti Andre (1st, 4to, 48p, b/w, DJ/2.00)	Viking	1952	Bigaud, Wilson	50-80	
Roethke, Theodore	I Am! Says the Lamb (1st {std}, 8vo, ibds, 70p, b/w, DJ/2.50)	Doubleday	1961	Leydenfrost, Rbt.	150-225	
Roethke, Theodore	Party at the Zoo (1st {std}, 4to, ibds, 62p, fp color, cep)	Crowell-Collier	(1963)	Swiller, Al	80-130	
Rogers, Cameron	Drake's Quest (1st, sm8vo, 284p, col frn)	Doubleday/Page	1927	Daugherty, James	25-45	
Rogers, Elizabeth	Angela of Angel Court (1st {std}, 8vo, 116p, green cl, b/w, pep, DJ/2.00)	Crowell	(1954)	Adams, Adrienne	30-50	*
Rogers, Frances	Indigo Treasure (1st, sm8vo, 291p, col frn, DJ/2.00)	Stokes	(1941)	Lenski, Lois	80-120	
Rogerson, Sidney	Both Sides of the Road (1st, 4to, red cl, 183p, 23cp)	L: Collins	1949	Tunnicliffe, C.F.	55-80	
Rohmer, Albert	Ivan the Iron Horse (1st, 12mo, 31p, 2-color, DJ/1.25)	Whitman	1944	Rohmer, Albert	35-50	
Rojankovsky, Feodor	Animals in the Zoo (1st, 4to, unpag, color, pep, DJ/3.95)	Knopf	(1962)	Rojankovsky, Feodor	70-120	R
Rojankovsky, Feodor	Animals on the Farm (1st, 4to, [32]p, color, pep, DJ/2.95)	Knopf	(1967)	Rojankovsky, Feodor	70-120	
Rollins Philip A.	Gone Haywire (1st, 8vo, 269p, 4 dp b/w, DJ/2.00)	Scribner	1939	Hurd, Peter	40-65	
Rollins, Charlene	Christmas Gif' (1st, lg8vo, 119p, fp b/w, cep, DJ/4.95)	Follett	(1963)	O'Sullivan, Tom	50-85	
Rollins, Philip A.	Jinglebob (1st, lg8vo, black cl, 263p, p-o, 4cp, pep, SC)	Scribner	1930	Wyeth, N.C.	250-350	
Rook, Clarence	Hooligan Nights (1st, 8vo, 289p, rust cl, col frn by...)	L: Richards	1899	Nicholson, Wm.	60-100	*
Roosevelt, Eleanor	Christmas (1st {std}, 24mo, ibds, 42p, 8 fp b/w, dep, DJ/0.50)	Knopf	1940	Kredel, Fritz	30-50	
Roosevelt, Theodore	Ranch Life & the Hunting Trail (1st, 4to, tan/gilt, 186p, AEG, b/w)	Century	(1888)	Remington, Frederic	175-240	
Root, Charlet	Feast of Lamps (1st, lg8vo, 75p, p-o, pep, color, DJ/2.00)	Whitman	1938	Duvoisin, Roger	70-125	

AUTHOR: 184

AUTHOR	TITLE	PUBLISHER	DATE	ARTIST	PRICE	LC
Roscoe, William	Butterfly's Ball & Grasshopper's Feast (1st, ob4to, [32]p, color, DJ/3.50)	McGraw-Hill	(1967)	Bolognese, Don	30-50	
Rose, Elizabeth	Old Winkle and the Seagulls (1st, 8vo, unpag, color, DJ, KGM)	L: Faber	1960	Rose, Gerald	50-85	*
Roselli, Auro	Cats of the Eiffel Tower (1st {std}, 8vo, 44p, color, DJ/3.25)	Delacorte Pr.	(1967)	DeBrunhoff, Laurent	45-70	
Rosen, Sidney	Doctor Paracelsus (1st {std}, 8vo, 214p, b/w, DJ/3.50)	Little/Brown	(1959)	Busoni, Rafaello	20-35	*
Rosen, Winifred	Marvin's Manhole (1st {std}, 4to, ipcb, [32]p, fp color, cep, DJ/3.95)	Dial Press	(1970)	Wells, Rosemary	30-45	
Rosenblum, Robert	Eight Lights: Story of Chanukah (1st {std}, 4to, 94p, 2-color, DJ/4.95)	Doubleday	1967	Weil, Shraga	30-50	
Rosenquist, Fingal	Nipper Shiffer's Donkey (1st, 8vo, 141p, uncut, b/w, DJ/2.50)	Harper	(1955)	Bileck, Marvin	40-65	
Rosenthal, Leonard	Kingdom of the Pearl (1st AM, 4to, 152p, teg, bds, p-o, 10 ticp)	Brentano's	[1920]	Dulac, Edmund	450-650	
Rosman, Alice G.	Jock the Scot (1st, lg8vo, gilt, 204p, p-o, 7cp, pep)	Minton Balch	(1930)	Esley, Joan	40-65	
Ross, Diana	Old Perisher (1st, sm4to, [32]p, ibds, color, DJ)	L: Faber	(1965)	Ardizzone, Edward	70-100	
Ross, Eulalie (ed)	Blue Rose (1st {std}, 8vo, 186p, DJ/3.50)	Harcourt	(1966)	Arno, Enrico	20-30	
Ross, Geraldine	Elf Who Didn't Believe in Himself (1st, lg8vo, 32p, color, DJ/2.95)	Steck-Vaughn	(1966)	Werth, Kurt	30-50	
Ross, Margaret I.	Back of Time (1st {std}, 8vo, 271p, pep, b/w)	Harper	1932	Wiese, Kurt	30-50	
Ross, Margaret I.	Morgan's Fourth Son (1st {std}, 8vo, 252p, uncut, 6pl, DJ/2.00)	Harper	(1940)	Daugherty, James	30-50	
Ross, Nancy W.	Heroines of the Early West (1st, 8vo, 182p, b/w, pep, DJ/1.95)	Random	(1960)	Galdone, Paul	20-30	
Ross, Patricia	Hungry Moon (1st {std}, sm4to, 72p, color, DJ/3.00)	Knopf	1946	Merida, Carlos	80-130	
Ross, Patricia	Magic Forest (1st {std}, 8vo, 128p, color, DJ/2.50)	Knopf	1948	Merida, Carlos	120-170	
Ross, Robert B.	Aubrey Beardsley (1st, 12mo, 112p, teg, gilt, 16pl)	L: John Lane	1909	Beardsley, Aubrey	60-100	
Rossetti, Christina	Goblin Market (1st, sm8vo, AEG, 63p, olive/gilt, 12pl)	L: Macmillan	1893	Housman, Laurence	500-700	
Rossetti, Christina	Goblin Market (1st, lg8vo, ibds, 79p, 8cp)	L: Blackie	1923	Harrison, Florence	150-220	
Rossetti, Christina	Goblin Market (1st, 8vo, wraps, 43p, 4cp, pep)	L: Harrap	(1933)	Rackham, Arthur	200-300	
Rossetti, Christina	Goblin Market (1st AM, 8vo, 42p, p-o, red cl, 4cp, pep)	Lippincott	[1933]	Rackham, Arthur	150-250	
Rossetti, Christina	Goblin Market (1st {std}, ob8vo, ipcb, 32p, color, DJ/4.95)	Dutton	(1970)	Raskin, Ellen	40-65	R
Rossetti, Christina	Maude: Prose & Verse (1st, 12mo, 122p, red pcb, title pg by ..)	Herbert Stone	1897	Hazenplug, Frank	50-80	
Rossetti, Christina	Pageant & other Poems (1st, 8vo, 198p, blue/gilt)	L: Macmillan	1881	Rossetti, Daniel G.	200-300	
Rossetti, Christina	Poems by Christina Rossetti (1st, 4to, gilt, teg, 369p, 36 ticp, pep)	L: Blackie	[1910]	Harrison, Florence	350-500	
Rossetti, Christina	Poems by Christina Rossetti (1st AM, 4to, teg, 369p, 36 ticp)	Dana Estes	[1910]	Harrison, Florence	300-450	
Rossetti, Christina	Prince's Progress (1st, 8vo, gilt, 146p, teg, fp b/w)	L: A. Melrose	[1900]	Sandheim, May	75-120	
Rossetti, Christina	Shorter Poems of Christina Rossetti (1st, 4to, 79p, ibds, 8cp, pep)	L: Blackie	[1920]	Harrison, Florence	70-125	
Rossetti, Christina	Sing Song (1st [new ed.], 12mo, AEG, 135p, gilt, b/w)	L: Macmillan	1893	Hughes, Arthur	120-200	
Rossetti, Christina	Sing-Song (1st, 16mo, green cl, 122p, b/w, pep)	Macmillan	1924	Davis, Marguerite	30-50	
Rossetti, Dante G.	Blessed Damozel (1st, 8vo, 54p, gilt, teg, uncut)	L: Duckworth	1898	MacDougall, W.B.	130-200	
Rossetti, Dante G.	Pictures & Poems (1st, folio, gilt, teg, [54]p, 14 tipl)	R.H. Russell	1899	Rossetti, Dante G.	300-450	*
Rossini, Gioacchino	Cinderella: From the Opera (1st, ob4to, [32]p, fp color, DJ/3.50)	Knopf	(1965)	Montresor, Beni	40-65	R
Rostand, Edmond	Story of Chanticleer (1st AM, 8vo, 144p, 12cp)	Stokes	(1913)	Shepherd, J.A.	60-90	
Rostand, Edmond	Story of Chanticleer (1st, 8vo, 144p, gilt, 12cp, pep)	L: Heinemann	1913	Shepherd, J.A.	75-100	
Rosvall, Toivo D.	Very Stupid Folk (1st {std}, 12mo, cloth, 52p, b/w, DJ/1.00)	Dutton	1938	Gergely, Tibor	30-45	
Rothberg, Abraham	Boy and the Dolphin (1st {std}, 8vo, 85p, fp b/w, DJ/4.25)	Norton	(1969)	Gobbato, Imero	40-65	
Rounds, Glen	Blind Colt (1st, lg8vo, blue cl, [80]p, color, DJ/2.00)	Holiday House	(1941)	Rounds, Glen	30-50	
Rounds, Glen	Buffalo Harvest (1st, 8vo, 141p, b/w, pep, DJ/2.25)	Holiday House	(1952)	Rounds, Glen	20-35	
Rounds, Glen	Lumbercamp (1st, sm8vo, wood bds, 116p, b/w, pep)	Holiday House	1937	Rounds, Glen	45-70	
Rounds, Glen	Ol' Paul, Mighty Logger (1st, 12mo, beige cl, 132p, b/w, pep, DJ/2.00)	Holiday House	1936	Rounds, Glen	50-85	R
Rounds, Glen	Pay Dirt (1st, 12mo, 148p, b/w, pep, DJ/2.00)	Holiday House	(1938)	Rounds, Glen	30-50	
Rounds, Glen	Prairie Schooners (1st, lg8vo, 95p, b/w, cep, DJ/3.75)	Holiday House	(1968)	Rounds, Glen	30-45	R
Rounds, Glen	Rain in the Woods (1st {std}, lg8vo, 95p, b/w, DJ/3.00)	World	(1964)	Rounds, Glen	20-30	
Rounds, Glen	Rodeo: Bulls, Broncs & Buckaroos (1st, 8vo, 157p, b/w, pep, DJ/2.25)	Holiday House	(1949)	Rounds, Glen	25-40	
Rounds, Glen	Snake Tree (1st {std}, lg8vo, 95p, b/w, DJ/3.50)	World	(1966)	Rounds, Glen	20-30	
Rounds, Glen	Stolen Pony (1st, lg8vo, [96]p, b/w, DJ/3.95)	Holiday House	(1969)	Rounds, Glen	20-35	
Rounds, Glen	Strawberry Roan (1st, ob4to, [48]p, 2-color, cep, DJ/4.50)	Golden Gate	(1970)	Rounds, Glen	25-40	
Rounds, Glen	Treeless Plains (1st, lg8vo, 95p, b/w, DJ/3.75)	Holiday House	(1967)	Rounds, Glen	20-35	
Rounds, Glen	Whitey & Jinglebob (1st, sq8vo, [28]p, ibds, pep, color, DJ/0.50)	Grosset/Dunlap	(1946)	Rounds, Glen	35-50	
Rounds, Glen	Whitey & the Blizzard (1st, sm8vo, blue cl, 31p, b/w, cep, DJ/1.25)	Holiday House	(1952)	Rounds, Glen	30-50	
Rounds, Glen	Whitey & the Colt Killer (1st, 8vo, 90p, b/w, DJ/2.50)	Holiday House	(1962)	Rounds, Glen	20-30	*
Rounds, Glen	Whitey & the Rustlers (1st, sm8vo, 32p, b/w, DJ/1.25)	Holiday House	(1951)	Rounds, Glen	25-40	
Rounds, Glen	Whitey Looks for a Job (1st, lg8vo, [28]p, ibds, color, pep, DJ/0.50)	Grosset/Dunlap	(1944)	Rounds, Glen	40-65	
Rounds, Glen	Whitey's First Roundup (1st, lg8vo, [28]p, ibds, color, DJ/0.50)	Grosset/Dunlap	(1942)	Rounds, Glen	35-50	
Rounds, Glen	Whitey's New Saddle (1st, 8vo, 92p, b/w, DJ/2.50)	Holiday House	(1963)	Rounds, Glen	20-30	
Rounds, Glen	Whitey's Sunday Horse (1st, lg8vo, [28]p, ibds, color, pep, DJ/0.50)	Grosset/Dunlap	1943	Rounds, Glen	40-65	
Rounds, Glen	Wild Horses of the Red Desert (1st, ob4to, [48]p, 3-color, cep, DJ/4.95)	Holiday House	(1969)	Rounds, Glen	25-40	
Rounds, Glen	Wild Orphan (1st, lg8vo, [75]p, b/w, cep, DJ/2.95)	Holiday House	(1961)	Rounds, Glen	25-45	
Rountree, Harry	Adventures of Mabel (1st AM, sm4to, 223p, 8cp)	Dodd	1916	Rountree, Harry	60-90	
Rountree, Harry	Peter Pink-Eye (1st AM, 8vo, p-o, 85p, 8cp)	Dana Estes	(1908)	Rountree, Harry	55-90	
Rountree, Harry	Rountree's Ridiculous Rabbits (1st AM, 8vo, unpag, ibds, 5 cp, b/w)	LeRoy Phillips	[1915]	Rountree, Harry	200-300	
Rourke, Constance	Davy Crockett (1st, 8vo, green cl, 276p, 8pl, pep, DJ/2.50, NH)	Harcourt	(1934)	MacDonald, James	40-65	
Rourke, Thomas	Stallion from the North (1st, sm8vo, 266p, pep)	Farrar/Rinehart	(1932)	Ward, Lynd	30-45	
Rouse, W.H.D.	Giant Crab (1st, 8vo, 134p, 7pl)	L: D. Nutt	1897	Robinson, W. Heath	180-265	
Rouse, W.H.D.	Talking Thrush (8vo, 8pl, cvr by...)	L: Dent	1902	Robinson, W. Heath	200-300	
Rousseau, Victor	Messiah of the Cylinder (1st, sm8vo, green/gilt, 319p, 11pl)	McClurg	1917	Coll, Joseph C.	100-175	
Rowand, Phyllis	Cats Who Stayed for Dinner (1st, 8vo, ipcb, [41]p, color, pep)	Wonder Books	(1951)	Burchard, Peter	35-50	
Rowand, Phyllis	Day After Yesterday (1st {std}, lg8vo, 54p, fp 2-color, DJ/2.50)	Little/Brown	(1953)	Rowand, Phyllis	40-65	
Rowand, Phyllis	Every Day in the Year (1st {std}, sm4to, 26p, fp 2-color, DJ/2.75)	Little/Brown	(1959)	Rowand, Phyllis	30-45	
Rowand, Phyllis	It is Night (1st, 4to, [32]p, ibds, fp 2-color, dep, DJ/1.75)	Harper	(1953)	Rowand, Phyllis	30-50	
Rowand, Phyllis	Watch the Birdie! (1st, lg8vo, ipcb, [40]p, fp 1-color, DJ/1.50)	W.R. Scott	1947	Rowand, Phyllis	60-100	
Rowe, Dorothy	Begging Deer (1st, sm8vo, 109p, tan cl, 8cp, pep)	Macmillan	1928	Ward, Lynd	35-60	*
Rowe, Dorothy	Rabbit Lantern (1st, 8vo, 98p, 8cp, pep)	Macmillan	1925	Tang, Ling Jui	30-45	
Rowe, Dorothy	Traveling Shops (1st, sm8vo, yellow cl, 109p, col frn, pep)	Macmillan	1929	Ward, Lynd	30-60	*
Rowe, Nellie	Crystal Locket (1st, lg8vo, 143p, ipcb, 10cp, pep)	Whitman	1935	Enright, Elizabeth	35-50	
Rowland, Eva E.	In & Out of the Nursery (1st, ob folio, [62]p)	R.H. Russell	(1900)	Eickmeyer, Rudolf	350-500	

AUTHOR	TITLE	PUBLISHER	DATE	ARTIST	PRICE	LC
Rowland, Henry C.	Countess Diane (1st, sm8vo, 149p, uncut, p-o, 5cp, pep)	Dodd	1908	Rae, John	40-60	
Rowland, Sydney	Beckoning Road (1st, sm8vo, 471p, color, pep)	Winston	(1931)	Petershams	30-50	
Rowland, Sydney	Rich Cargoes (1st, sm8vo, 449p, fp 1-color, pep)	Winston	(1931)	Petershams	30-50	
Rowland, Sydney	Wings of Adventure (1st, sm8vo, 500p, color, pep)	Winston	(1931)	Petershams	30-50	
Rowley, Anthony	Sunday in Autumn (1st, 4to, 31p, ibds, color)	L.W. Singer	1967	Quackenbush, Rbt.	20-35	*
Rowntree, Lester	Ronnie (1st, 8vo, 188p, b/w, DJ/2.50)	Viking	1952	Perceval, Don	25-45	*
Rowsell, Mary	Pedlar & His Dog (8vo, green cl, p-o, 156p, 4cp)	L: Blackie	[1912]	Pape, Frank	50-80	
Roy, Claude	Very Obliging Flowers (1st, ob4to, ibds, 38p, color, DJ/3.95, NYTBI)	Grove Press	(1968)	LeFoll, Alain	50-80	*
Ruck-Pauquet, Gina	Little Hedgehog (1st AM, sm4to, [36]p, color, DJ/2.75)	Hastings House	(1959)	Richter, Marianne	40-65	
Ruding, Walter	Evil Motherhood (1st, 8vo, blue/gilt, 99p, uncut, frn by...)	L: E. Mathews	1896	Beardsley, Aubrey	120-200	
Rudolph, Marguerita	I am Your Misfortune (1st, 4to, [32]p, fp color, cep, DJ/3.50)	Seabury Press	(1968)	Gobbato, Imero	40-65	*
Rudolph, Marguerita	Look at Me (1st, ob12mo, [38]p, color, DJ/2.75)	McGraw-Hill	(1967)	Kuskin, Karla	25-45	
Rue, Flora	Cocoa Dancer (1st, 4to, 27p, p-o, fp color, pep, DJ/1.25)	Whitman	1945	Blackwood, Gladys	60-90	
Rugh, Belle Dorman	Crystal Mountain (1st [1st bk.], 8vo, 208p, b/w, DJ/2.75)	Houghton	1955	Shepard, Ernest H.	50-85	R
Rugoff, Milton	Hurly Burly & the Knights (1st AM, 4to, ibds, 31p, color, DJ/1.95, NYTBI)	Platt/Munk	(1963)	Luzzati, Emanuele	45-70	
Rugoff, Milton (ed)	Harvest of World Folk Tales (1st, 8vo, 734p, b/w, DJ/3.95)	Viking	1949	Low, Joseph	30-50	*
Rukeyser, Muriel	Come Back, Paul (1st, 4to, [32]p, ibds, 3-color, pep, DJ/2.50)	Harper	(1955)	Rukeyser, Muriel	50-85	R*
Rukeyser, Muriel	I Go Out (1st, 4to, [32]p, ipcb, color, DJ/2.95)	Harper	1961	Kessler, Leonard	50-80	R*
Rumsey, Mirian	Seal of Frog Island (1st, 8vo, 48p, fp b/w, DJ/2.50)	Wm. Morrow	1961	Johnson, Harper	30-50	
Runbeck, Margaret	Our Miss Boo (1st, 8vo, 226p, b/w, DJ/2.00)	Appleton-Century	1942	Bacon, Peggy	30-50	
Running, Corinne	When Coyote Walked the Earth (1st {std}, 8vo, 71p, b/w, DJ/2.00)	Henry Holt & Co.	(1949)	Bennett, Richard	45-70	*
Runyon, Damon	In Our Town (1st, 8vo, 120p, uncut, fp b/w, DJ/2.00)	NY: Creative Age	(1946)	Williams, Garth	40-65	
Rush, William M.	Duff, Story of a Bear (1st {std}, 8vo, 149p, b/w, DJ/2.25)	Longmans	1950	Christensen, G.D.	25-45	
Ruskin, John	King of the Golden River (ob8vo, 43p, cloth, chromo frn)	McLoughlin	(1905)	Davis, G.A.	60-90	
Ruskin, John	King of the Golden River (1st, 8vo, wraps, 47p, 4cp, pep)	L: Harrap	(1932)	Rackham, Arthur	200-270	
Ruskin, John	King of the Golden River (1st AM, 8vo, red cl, 47p, p-o, 4cp)	Lippincott	(1932)	Rackham, Arthur	140-220	
Ruskin, John	King of the Golden River (1st {std}, 8vo, 113p, color, pep, DJ/1.25, RC)	World	(1946)	Kredel, Fritz	25-40	
Ruskin, John (ed.)	Dame Wiggin of Lee (1st, 12mo, 20p, gilt)	L: G. Allen	1885	Greenaway, Kate	150-200	
Russ, Patrick	Caesar: Life Story of a Panda Leopard (1st, 8vo, 88p, col frn, b/w)	Putnam	(1930)	Rountree, Harry	30-45	
Russell, Arthur	Snowy for Luck (1st, 8vo, p-o, 128p, col frn, pep)	Whitman	1934	Wiese, Kurt	30-50	
Russell, Charles M.	Good Medicine (1st [trade ed], 4to, 162p, tan cl, col frn, pep)	Doubleday/Doran	(1930)	Russell, Charles M.	120-200	
Russell, Charles M.	Trails Plowed Under (1st {std}, 4to, 210p, 5 dp cp)	Doubleday/Page	1927	Russell, Charles M.	120-200	
Russell, Dorothy	Betty's Diary (1st, 8vo, 261p, gilt, p-o, 5cp)	L: Blackie	[1914]	Appleton, Honor C.	60-90	
Russell, Franklin	The Honeybees (1st, 4to, [34]p, fp color, pep, DJ/3.95, NYTBI)	Knopf	(1967)	Portal, Colette	30-50	*
Russell, Helen R.	Clarion the Killdeer (1st {std}, 8vo, 60p, DJ/3.95)	Hawthorn House	(1970)	Hamberger, John	20-30	
Russell, Mary A.	April Baby's Book of Tunes (1st, sq8vo, tan cl, 75p, 16cp)	L: Macmillan	1900	Greenaway, Kate	250-350	
Russell, Robert H.	Delft Cat (1st, 16mo, 71p, uncut, b/w)	R.H. Russell	1896	Smith, F. Berkeley	80-120	*
Russell, Solveig	Lines and Shapes (1st, 8vo, 31p, b/w, DJ/2.75)	H.Z. Walck	1965	Spilka, Arnold	30-45	
Russell, Solveig	The Mushmen (1st, 8vo, 94p, b/w, DJ/3.50)	Dodd	1968	Gobbato, Imero	30-50	
Russell, Solveig	What Good is a Tail? (1st {std}, 4to, [32]p, 3-color, DJ/2.50)	Bobbs-Merrill	(1962)	Keats, Ezra J.	30-50	
Russell, Solveig	Which is Which (1st, 4to, 30p, color, DJ/3.50)	Prentice-Hall	(1966)	Haley, Gail E.	25-40	
Russell, Walter	Bending of the Twig (1st, 8vo, 297p, teg, p-o, cvr by...)	Dodd	1903	Richards, Anna M.	80-140	
Russell, William C.	Lady Maud (1st {this pub}, 8vo, 312p, b/w pl)	Fenno	(1896)	Shute, A.B.	100-175	*
Russell, William C.	Rose Island (1st, sm8vo, 359p, teg, cvr by...)	Herbert Stone	1899	Hazenplug, Frank	50-80	
Russell, William C.	Tragedy of Ida Noble (1st UK, 8vo, 315p, blue buckram, b/w)	L: Hutchinson	1893	Hopkins, Everard	70-100	
Russell, William C.	Two Captains (1st UK, 8vo, 372p, cloth, b/w)	L: Sampson Low	1897	Rosenmeyer, B.J.	75-100	
Ruthley, Cecily	Tale of the Tabby Twins (1st, 16mo, bds, p-o, fp color)	L: Valentine	(1920)	Wain, Louis	500-700	
Ruy-Vidal, Francois	Secret Journey of Hugo the Brat (1st AM sq8vo, [32]p, color, DJ/3.75, NYT)	Harlin Quist	(1969)	Claveloux, Nicole	50-85	
Ryan, Marah E.	Druid Path (1st, 8vo, 321p, green/gilt, b/w, uncut)	McClurg	1917	Vreeland, Will	60-90	
Ryan, Marah E.	Flute of the Gods (1st, 8vo, 338p, uncut, p-o, pep, 24 photo plates by...)	Stokes	(1909)	Curtis, Edward	250-400	
Ryan, Marah E.	House of the Dawn (1st, 8vo, 407p, 4pl, pep)	McClurg	1914	Booth, Hanson	45-70	
Rydberg, Ernie	Dark of the Cave (1st, 8vo, 118p, fp b/w, DJ/2.95)	McKay	1965	Kidwell, Carl	70-100	
Ryder, Arthur	Twenty-Two Goblins (1st, 8vo, 220p, 20cp)	L: Dent	1917	Nahl, Perham	70-100	*
Ryland, Lee	Gordon & the Glockenspiel (1st, 4to, [26]p, ibds, color)	Whitman	1966	Walters, Audrey	20-30	
Sabatini, Rafael	Captain Blood (1st, 12mo, black cl, 356p, col frn by...)	Houghton	1922	Wyeth, N.C.	80-140	*
Sabin, Edwin L.	Beaufort Chums (1st, sm8vo, 281p, 4pl)	Crowell	1905	Copeland, Charles	30-55	
Sabin, Edwin L.	Gold Seekers of '49 (1st, sm8vo, 335p, tan cl, col frn, 4pl by)	Lippincott	1915	Stephens, Charles H.	60-100	R*
Sabin, Edwin L.	Gold! (1st, 8vo, 336p, fp color, pep)	Macrae-Smith	1929	Hargens, Charles	30-50	
Sabin, Edwin L.	Magic Mashie (1st, sm8vo, 210p, frn by...)	A. Wessels	1902	Phillips, Jay C.	250-350	*
Sabin, Edwin L.	Old Jim Badger on the Moccasin Trail (1st, 8vo, 316p, 4cp)	Crowell	(1928)	Hastings, Howard	25-45	
Sabin, Edwin L.	On the Plains with Custer (1st, sm8vo, 308p, tan cl, 5cp)	Lippincott	1913	Stephens, Charles H.	25-45	
Sabin, Edwin L.	Pirate Waters (1st, 8vo, 338p, b/w, pep, DJ/2.00)	Lippincott	(1941)	Ward, Lynd	40-65	
Sabin, Edwin L.	Range & Trail (1st, 8vo, 445p, 8pl)	Crowell	(1910)	Rowe, Clarence	50-85	
Sabin, Edwin L.	When You Were a Boy (1st, sm8vo, 302p, green cl, b/w)	Baker/Taylor	(1905)	Steele, Frederic D.	30-50	
Sabin, Elbridge H.	Magical Man of Mirth (1st, 8vo, p-o, 233p, 8cp, pep)	Jacobs	(1910)	Knipe, Helen A.	100-150	
Sabin, Elbridge H.	Prince Trixie (1st, lg8vo, 142p, p-o, 8cp)	Rand/McNally	(1914)	Beem, Frances	100-165	
Sabin, Elbridge H.	Queen of the City of Mirth (1st, 8vo, p-o, 164p, 8cp, pep)	Jacobs	(1911)	Knipe, Helen A.	100-165	
Sabin, Elbridge H.	Stella's Adventures in Starland (1st, 8vo, 210p, 9pl)	Small/Maynard	1907	Brown, Edith	80-130	
Sacher-Masoch, L.	Jewish Tales (1st, 12mo, 317p, beige/gilt, cvr by...)	McClurg	1894	Armstrong, Margaret	60-100	*
Sachs, Marilyn	Amy and Laura (1st {std}, 8vo, 189p, b/w, DJ/3.25)	Doubleday	(1966)	Sugarman, Tracy	20-25	
Sachs, Marilyn	Amy Moves In (1st {std}, 8vo, 191p, b/w, DJ/2.95)	Doubleday	(1964)	Brown, Judith	20-25	
Sachs, Marilyn	Laura's Luck (1st {std}, 8vo, 181p, b/w, DJ/3.25)	Doubleday	(1965)	Ohlsson, Ib	20-30	*
Sachs, Marilyn	Marv (1st {std}, 8vo, 160p, b/w, DJ/3.95)	Doubleday	(1970)	Glanzman, Louis	20-35	
Sachs, Marilyn	Peter and Veronica (1st {std}, 8vo, 174p, b/w, DJ/3.95)	Doubleday	(1969)	Glanzman, Louis	20-35	
Sachs, Marilyn	Veronica Ganz (1st {std}, 8vo, 156p, b/w, DJ/3.50)	Doubleday	(1968)	Glanzman, Louis	20-35	
Sackett, Rose M.	Cousin from Clare (1st, sm8vo, 270p, green cl, 4pl)	Macmillan	1932	DeAngeli, Marguerite	30-50	
Sackville, Margaret	Dream Pedlar (1st, sm4to, 184p, blue/gilt, 16 ticp)	L: Simpkin	(1914)	Anderson, Florence	200-300	
Sackville, Margaret	Travelling Companions... (1st, lg8vo, 132p, blue/gilt, 12cp)	L: Simpkin	(1915)	Anderson, Florence	250-400	

AUTHOR	TITLE	PUBLISHER	DATE	ARTIST	PRICE	LC
Sadler, Marie C.	Mamma's Angel Child (1st, 8vo, ibds, p-o, 115p, fp color)	Rand/McNally	(1915)	Ross, M.T.	140-200	
Sage, Agnes C.	Little Colonial Dame (1st, 8vo, 197p, 16pl)	Stokes	(1898)	Humphrey, Maud	60-90	
Sage, Agnes C.	Two Girls of Old New Jersey (1st, 8vo, 195p, 16pl)	Stokes	(1912)	Connah, D.J.	30-50	
Sage, Betty	Rhymes of If & Why (1st, 4to, 31p, ibds, 4cp)	Duffield	1927	Robinson, Boardman	80-125	
Sage, Betty	Rhymes of Real Children (1st, sq4to, 32p, ibds, 6cp)	Fox/Duffield	1903	Smith, Jessie W.	300-450	
Sage, Juniper	Man in the Manhole & Fix-It-Men (1st, lg8vo, ipcb, [40]p, color, DJ/1.50)	W.R. Scott	1946	Ballantine, Bill	30-50	
Sage, Michael	Careful Carlos (1st, ob8vo, [30]p, b/w, DJ/2.25)	Holiday House	(1967)	Spilka, Arnold	25-40	
Sage, Michael	Tree and Me (1st, lg8vo, [29]p, fp color, DJ/4.25)	H.Z. Walck	(1970)	Spilka, Arnold	25-40	
Saint, Lawrence B.	Knight of the Cross (1st, 8vo, 220p, gilt, uncut, p-o, teg, 7 ticp)	Jacobs	(1914)	Saint, Lawrence B.	25-40	
Saint-Cecere, Gilles	Piruwayu and the Rainbow (1st {std}, 4to, 47p, color, DJ)	L: Oxford U.Pr.	1958	Bettina	30-50	
Saint-Exupery, A.	Flight to Arras (1st AM, 8vo, 255p, 13pl, pep, DJ/2.75)	Reynal/Hitchcock	(1942)	Lamotte, Bernard	300-500	
Saint-Exupery, A.	Little Prince (1st AM, sq8vo, 91p, color, DJ/2.50)	Reynal/Hitchcock	(1943)	Saint-Exupery, A.	800-1400	
Saint-Exupery, A.	Southern Mail (1st AM, 8vo, 253p, pep, 1-color lithos by...)	Smith/Haas	1933	Ward, Lynd	80-130	
Saint-Exupery, A.	Wind, Sand & Stars (1st AM, 8vo, 306p, pep, 1-color designs, DJ/2.75)	Reynal/Hitchcock	(1939)	Cosgrave, John O.	150-250	*
Saleh, Harold	Even Tiny Ants Must Sleep (1st, sm ob4to, [31]p, fp 3-color, pep, DJ/3.25)	McGraw-Hill	(1967)	Pinkney, Jerry	40-65	*
Salten, Felix	Bambi's Children (1st {std}, sm8vo, 315p, green cl, b/w, DJ/2.50)	Bobbs-Merrill	(1939)	Pinner, Erna	80-140	
Salten, Felix	Bambi's Children (1st, 8vo, [32]p, ibds, color, DJ/0.50)	Grosset/Dunlap	(1948)	Kuhn, Bob	25-45	
Salten, Felix	Bambi's Children (1st, 4to, 63p, ibds, fp color, pep, DJ/1.00)	Random	(1950)	Erickson, Phoebe	25-45	
Salten, Felix	Bambi's Children (1st, 8vo, [41]p, ipcb, color)	Wonder Books	(1951)	Bartlett, William	20-30	
Salten, Felix	Bambi: Life in the Woods (1st AM {std}, 12mo, 293p, green/gilt, b/w, pep)	Simon/Schuster	1928	Wiese, Kurt	120-200	R
Salten, Felix	Bambi: Life in the Woods (1st {std}, 8vo, 190p, fp 1-color, cep, DJ/4.95)	Simon/Schuster	(1970)	Cooney, Barbara	30-50	
Salten, Felix	Favorite Animal Stories (1st, 8vo, orange cl, 243p, b/w, DJ/3.00)	J. Messner	(1948)	Eichenberg, Fritz	30-50	
Salten, Felix	Hound of Florence (1st, 8vo, 236p, gilt, b/w)	Simon/Schuster	1930	Wiese, Kurt	30-50	
Salten, Felix	Perri (1st {std}, 8vo, 228p, b/w, DJ/2.50)	Bobbs-Merrill	(1938)	Jungnickel, L.H.	65-90	
Salten, Felix	Renni the Rescuer (1st {std}, 8vo, 326p, b/w, DJ/2.50)	Bobbs-Merrill	1940	Thorne, Diana	40-60	
Sampson, Emma S.	Miss Minerva's Scallywags (1st, 12mo, red cl, 321p, b/w)	Reilly/Lee	(1927)	Donahey, William	50-85	
Sampson, Martin	Good Giant (1st, 8vo, 218p, col frn, 10pl, pep)	Houghton	1928	Hilton	40-60	*
Samson, Anne S.	Lines, Spines & Porcupines (1st {std}, lg8vo, [64]p, 2-color, DJ/3.50)	Doubleday	(1969)	Samson, Anne	25-40	
Samstag, Nicholas	Kay-Kay Comes Home (1st, ob8vo, wraps, [44]p, fp b/w, DJ)	NY: Valentin	1952	Shahn, Ben	65-100	
Samstag, Nicholas	Kay-Kay Comes Home (1st {this pub} {std}, 8vo, bds 47p, b/w DJ/2.95, NYT)	Obolensky	(1962)	Shahn, Ben	30-50	
Sandburg, Carl	Abe Lincoln Grows Up (1st, lg8vo, 222p, b/w, pep)	Harcourt	1928	Daugherty, James	30-50	
Sandburg, Carl	Early Moon (1st {std}, lg8vo, 136p, b/w)	Harcourt	(1930)	Daugherty, James	70-120	*
Sandburg, Carl	Prairie-Town Boy (1st, 8vo, 179p, b/w, DJ/2.75)	Harcourt	(1955)	Krush, Joe	30-50	
Sandburg, Carl	Rootabaga Country (1st, 4to, 259p, col frn, 16 b/w, pep)	Harcourt	(1929)	Bacon, Peggy	80-125	
Sandburg, Carl	Rootabaga Pigeons (1st, 8vo, blue cl, 218p, col frn)	Harcourt	(1923)	Petershams	80-120	R
Sandburg, Carl	Rootabaga Stories (1st, 8vo, 230p, blue cl, col frn, PPP)	Harcourt	(1922)	Petershams	100-165	R
Sandburg, Carl	Wedding Procession/Rag Doll & Broomhandle (1st {std}, ob4to, [30]p, color)	Harcourt	(1967)	Pincus, Harriet	40-65	
Sandburg, Carl	Wind Song (1st {std}, 8vo, 127p, b/w, DJ/3.00)	Harcourt	(1960)	Smith, William A.	30-50	
Sandburg, Helga	Anna and the Baby Buzzard (1st {std}, 8vo, [48]p, color, DJ/4.75)	Dutton	(1970)	Turkle, Brinton	30-50	
Sandburg, Helga	Bo & the Old Donkey (1st {std}, sm4to, unpag, 2-color, DJ/3.50)	Dial Press	(1965)	Morton, Marian	25-45	
Sandburg, Helga	Gingerbread (1st, 8vo, 192p, b/w, DJ/3.50)	Dial Press	1964	Geer, Charles	45-70	
Sandburg, Helga	Joel & the Wild Goose (1st, ob4to, [34]p, ibds, fp color, pep, DJ/3.50)	Dial Press	1963	Daly, Thomas	50-75	R
Sanders, Martha	Alexander & the Magic Mouse (1st, 4to, 44p, fp color, cep, DJ/3.95)	Amer. Heritage	1969	Fix, Phillippe	80-120	
Sandoz, Maurice	House Without Windows (1st, sm4to, 101p, gilt, 7cp, DJ)	L: W. Campion	1950	Dali, Salvador	200-300	
Sandoz, Maurice	On the Verge (1st {std}, 4to, 127p, col frn, cep, DJ/4.50)	Doubleday	1950	Dali, Salvador	170-240	
Sandoz, Maurice	The Maze (1st {std}, 8vo, 110p, gilt, uncut, 13pl, DJ/2.50)	Doubleday/Doran	1945	Dali, Salvador	160-245	
Sandwell, Helen B.	Valley of Color Days (1st, 8vo, tan cl, 299p, 6cp, pep)	Little/Brown	1924	Preston, Alice B.	55-80	
Sandys, Ruth	Numerous Names Nimbly Narrated (1st, 4to, ibds, [58]p, color)	L: Oxford U.Pr.	(1930)	Sandys, Ruth	170-240	
Sanford, Wendy	Puma & the Pearl (1st, lg ob8vo, [39]p, 1-color, DJ/3.50)	Walker	(1962)	Forberg, Ati	25-40	*
Sapte, William	By the Way Ballads (1st, 8vo, 153p, b/w)	L: Sands	1901	Reynolds/Hassall	30-50	
Sarg, Tony	Tony Sarg's Book of Animals (4to, green ibds, color, pep)	Greenberg	(1925)	Sarg, Tony	100-150	
Sarg, Tony	Tony Sarg's Book of Tricks (1st, 4to, ibds, [96]p, color, pep)	Greenberg	(1928)	Sarg, Tony	80-120	
Sarg, Tony	Tony Sarg's New York (1st, lg4to, p-o, [60]p, 24cp)	Greenberg	1926	Sarg, Tony	140-200	
Sarg, Tony	Tony Sarg's Wonder Zoo (1st, ob12mo, ibds, [30]p, color)	Greenberg	(1925)	Sarg, Tony	50-80	
Sarg, Tony	Where is Tommy? (1st, sm ob4to, [20]p, ipcb, color)	Greenberg	(1932)	Sarg, Tony	70-120	
Sargant, Alice	Crystal Ball (1st, 8vo, uncut, 119p, 10 fp b/w)	L: G. Bell	(1894)	Florence, Mary S.	150-225	
Sargent, Robert	Adventurous Moth (1st {std}, 4to, [32]p, 2-color, DJ/3.50)	Simon/Schuster	(1968)	Sargent, Robert	25-45	
Saroyan, William	Me (1st, 4to, [64]p, ibds, color)	Crowell-Collier	(1963)	Tinkelman, Murray	80-120	
Saroyan, William	My Name is Aram (1st {std}, 8vo, 220p, col frn, b/w, DJ/2.50)	Harcourt	(1940)	Freeman, Don	70-100	
Sasek, Miroslav	This is New York (1st, lg4to, ibds, 60p, color, DJ/3.00, NYTBI)	Macmillan	(1960)	Sasek, Miroslav	80-120	
Sasek, Miroslav	This is Paris (1st, lg4to, ibds, 60p, color, DJ/3.00)	Macmillan	(1959)	Sasek, Miroslav	60-100	
Sassoon, Siegfried	Memoirs of a Fox Hunting Man (1st AM, lg8vo, 296p, 7pl)	Coward	1929	Nicholson, Wm.	90-140	
Sauer, Julia L.	Fog Magic (1st, 8vo, grey cl, 107p, b/w frn, pep, DJ/2.00, NH)	Viking	1943	Ward, Lynd	60-100	R
Sauer, Julia L.	Light at Tern Rock (1st, sm4to, 62p, pep, brown illus, DJ/2.50, NH)	Viking	1951	Schreiber, Georges	80-120	R*
Sauer, Julia L.	Mike's House (1st, sm4to, red cl, 31p, 2-color, pep, DJ/2.50)	Viking	1954	Freeman, Don	45-70	
Saunders, Louise	Knave of Hearts (1st {hardback}, folio, 46p, p-o, color, pep)	Scribner	1925	Parrish, Maxfield	900-1400	
Saunders, Marshall	Alpatok (1st, 12mo, tan cl, 51p, b/w)	L.C. Page	1906	Horne, Diantha W.	25-40	*
Saunders, Marshall	Beautiful Joe's Paradise (1st, sm8vo, red/gilt, p-o, 365p, 15pl, pep)	L.C. Page	1902	Bull, Charles L.	120-200	
Saunders, Marshall	Nita (1st, 12mo, 77p, b/w)	L.C. Page	1904	Barry, Etheldred B.	25-40	*
Saunders, Phyllis	Flame Flower (1st, lg8vo, purple cl, 127p, p-o, 4cp)	L: Butterworth	1922	Miller, Hilda T.	70-125	
Sautriax [Rabelais]	Gargantua (1st, ob folio, 52p, ibds, 6cp)	Duffield	1921	Leroy, Adrien	120-200	*
Savery, Constance	Enemy Brothers (1st {std}, 8vo, 313p, DJ/2.50, b/w decor by...)	Longmans	1943	Pitz, Henry C.	40-65	
Savery, Constance	Good Ship Red Lily (1st {std}, 8vo, 197p, b/w, pep, DJ/2.25)	Longmans	1944	Walker, Nedda	50-80	
Savery, Constance	Magic in My Shoes (1st {std}, 8vo, 152p, b/w, DJ/2.75)	Longmans	1958	Price, Christine	40-65	*
Savery, Constance	Moonshine in Candle Light (1st {std}, sm8vo, 149p, fp b/w, pep, DJ/1.75)	Longmans	1937	Birch, Reginald	40-65	*
Savery, Constance	Pippin's House (1st {std}, sm8vo, 207p, 6 fp b/w, pep)	Longmans	1931	Bowman, Charlot	60-90	*
Savery, Constance	Reb and the Redcoats (1st {std}, 8vo, 241p, b/w, DJ/3.75)	Longmans	1961	Brock, Vera	30-50	
Savery, Constance	Welcome Santza (1st {std}, 8vo, 166p, b/w, DJ/2.75)	Longmans	1956	Torrey, Helen	30-50	

AUTHOR	TITLE	PUBLISHER	DATE	ARTIST	PRICE	LC
Sawyer, Edith A.	Christmas Maker's Club (1st, 8vo, 275p, 6pl)	L.C. Page	1908	Williamson	25-40	*
Sawyer, Edith A.	Elsa's Gift Home (1st, 8vo, 229p, 6pl)	L.C. Page	1911	Nosworthy, Florence	25-40	*
Sawyer, Ruth	Christmas Anna Angel (1st, 8vo, 48p, color, pep, DJ/2.00, CH)	Viking	1944	Seredy, Kate	80-120	
Sawyer, Ruth	Cottage for Betsy (1st {std}, 8vo, 120p, yellow cl, b/w, DJ/2.50)	Harper	(1954)	Bock, Vera	25-35	
Sawyer, Ruth	Daddles: Story of a Plain Hound-Dog (1st {std}, 8vo, 99p, b/w, DJ/3.50)	Little/Brown	(1964)	Frankenberg, Rbt.	20-35	
Sawyer, Ruth	Doctor Danny (1st, sm8vo, 410p, ibds, pep, 8pl)	Harper	1918	Williams, J. Scott	40-65	
Sawyer, Ruth	Enchanted Schoolhouse (1st, lg8vo, green cl, 128p, fp b/w, pep, DJ/2.50)	Viking	1956	Troy, Hugh	30-50	
Sawyer, Ruth	Journey Cake, Ho! (1st, 4to, 45p, 2-color, pep, DJ/2.50, CH)	Viking	1953	McCloskey, Robert	250-350	R
Sawyer, Ruth	Joy to the World (1st {std}, 8vo, 102p, fp 1-color, DJ/3.95)	Little/Brown	(1966)	Hyman, Trina S.	30-50	
Sawyer, Ruth	Least One (1st, sm4to, 88p, 2-color, pep, DJ/2.00)	Viking	1941	Politi, Leo	70-100	
Sawyer, Ruth	Leerie (1st, 12mo, 309p, 4pl)	Harper	(1920)	Balmer, Clinton	30-50	
Sawyer, Ruth	Little Red Horse (1st, 8vo, 108p, brown cl, pep, color, DJ/2.50)	Viking	1950	Barnum, Jay H.	50-80	
Sawyer, Ruth	Long Christmas (1st, 4to, 200p, buckram, 1-color, dep, DJ/2.50)	Viking	1941	Angelo, Valenti	40-60	
Sawyer, Ruth	Maggie Rose: Her Birthday Christmas (1st {std}, 12mo, 151p, b/w, DJ/2.00)	Harper	1952	Sendak, Maurice	180-250	
Sawyer, Ruth	Old Con and Patrick (1st, 8vo, 137p, col frn, b/w, DJ/2.00)	Viking	1946	O'Toole, Cathal	30-50	
Sawyer, Ruth	Picture Tales from Spain (1st, ob12mo, 132p, b/w, DJ/1.25)	Stokes	1936	Sanchez, Carlos M.	40-65	
Sawyer, Ruth	Primrose Ring (1st, 12mo, 186p, 6pl)	Harper	(1915)	Munsell, Fanny	40-65	
Sawyer, Ruth	Roller Skates (1st, lg8vo, 186p, 1-color, pep, DJ/2.00, NM)	Viking	1936	Angelo, Valenti	85-140	R
Sawyer, Ruth	Silver Sixpence (1st, sm8vo, blue cl, 331p, 4pl)	Harper	1921	Crank, James H.	20-30	*
Sawyer, Ruth	Tale of the Enchanted Bunnies (1st {std}, lg8vo, 137p, p-o, fp color)	Harper	(1923)	Sawyer, Ruth	60-100	
Sawyer, Ruth	This Way to Christmas (1st, 12mo, 165p, gilt, frn by...)	Harper	(1916)	Rockwell, Norman	55-80	*
Sawyer, Ruth	This Way to Christmas (1st, lg8vo, ibds, 175p, 10cp, pep)	Harper	1924	Barney, Maginel W.	90-145	
Sawyer, Ruth	Tono Antonio (1st, 8vo, 132p, red/gilt, 8 fp b/w, pep)	Viking	1934	Mora, F. Luis	30-50	*
Sawyer, Ruth	Year of Jubilo (1st, 8vo, 266p, b/w, pep, DJ/2.00)	Viking	1940	Shenton, Edward	30-45	
Sawyer, Ruth	Year of the Christmas Dragon (1st, lg8vo, red cl, 88p, b/w, pep, DJ/2.50)	Viking	(1960)	Troy, Hugh	30-50	
Saxe, John	Blind Men and the Elephants (1st, smob4to, [48]p, fp 2-color, DJ/2.50)	Whittlesey	(1963)	Galdone, Paul	20-35	
Saxon, Gladys	Sea Beach Adventure (1st {std}, 8vo, 190p, b/w, DJ/2.75)	Holt	(1956)	Galdone, Paul	25-40	
Sayers, Frances C.	Blue Bonnets for Lucinda (1st, sm sq8vo, ibds, [30]p, color, pep)	Viking	1934	Sewell, Helen	50-85	
Sayers, Frances C.	Ginny and Custard (1st, 8vo, 128p, b/w, pep, DJ/2.00)	Viking	1951	Evans, Eileen	30-45	
Sayers, Frances C.	Mr. Tidy Paws (1st, 8vo, ibds, 64p, b/w, pep, DJ/1.50)	Viking	1935	Gay, Zhenya	50-80	
Sayers, Frances C.	Sally Tait (1st, 8vo, 126p, b/w, pep, DJ/2.00)	Viking	1948	Evans, Eileen	25-45	
Sayers, Frances C.	Tag-Along Tooloo (1st, lg8vo, 87p, pep, 8 fp color, DJ/1.50)	Viking	1941	Sewell, Helen	40-65	
Scarry, Patricia	Jeremy Mouse Book (1st, lg sq4to, 64p, fp color, cep, DJ/3.95)	Amer. Heritage	1969	Knight, Hilary	65-100	
Scarry, Patricia	My Dolly and Me (1st {A}, sm8vo, ibds, [24]p, color, LGB/#418)	Golden Press	1960	Wilkin, Eloise B.	50-80	*
Scarry, Patricia	My Snuggly Bunny (1st {A}, sm8vo, [24]p, ibds, color, LGB/#250)	Simon/Schuster	1956	Wilkin, Eloise B.	40-65	
Scarry, Richard	Great Big Schoolhouse (1st, folio, 69p, color)	Random	(1969)	Scarry, Richard	50-85	*
Scarry, Richard	What Do People Do All Day? (1st, folio, 95p, color, pep)	Random	1968	Scarry, Richard	60-90	
Schaad, Hans	Gunpowder Tower (1st AM {std}, ob folio, ibds, unpag, color, DJ/3.75)	Harcourt	(1967)	Schaad, Hans	25-45	
Schackburg, Richard	Yankee Doodle (1st, ob4to, [30]p, fp 3-color, pep, DJ/3.75)	Prentice-Hall	(1965)	Emberley, Ed	30-50	
Schackne, Stewart	Rowena the Skating Cow (1st, sm4to, [61]p, tan cl, 28 fp color, DJ/1.50)	Scribner	1940	Eichenberg, Fritz	65-100	
Schaefer, Jack W.	Old Ramon (1st, 8vo, 102p, b/w, uncut, DJ/2.50, NH)	Houghton	1960	West, Harold	120-200	
Schaefer, Jack W.	Shane (1st, sm8vo, 214p, DJ/2.50)	Houghton	1949	No Illustrations	600-800	
Schaefer, Jack W.	Shane (1st {illus. ed}, 8vo, 214p, 16 fp b/w, DJ/2.75)	Houghton	1954	McCormack, John	200-300	
Schaefer, Jack W.	Stubby Pringle's Christmas (1st, 8vo, 43p, 2-color, cep, DJ/2.75)	Houghton	1964	Bjorklund, Lorence	120-180	
Schaefer, Jack W.	The Mavericks (1st, 8vo, 184p, b/w, DJ/3.25)	Houghton	1967	Bjorklund, Lorence	120-180	
Schaefer, Jack W.	The Plainsmen (1st, 8vo, uncut, 252p, b/w, cep, DJ/3.25)	Houghton	1963	Bjorklund, Lorence	120-180	
Schaeffler, Ursula	Thief and the Blue Rose (1st AM {std}, 4to, [25]p, ibds, color, DJ/4.25)	Harcourt	(1967)	Schaeffler, Ursula	40-65	
Scharen, Beatrix	Gigin and Till (1st AM {std}, ob4to, [27]p, 2-color, DJ/4.95)	Atheneum	1969	Scharen, Beatrix	25-45	
Schatz, Letta	A Rhinoceros? Preposterous! (1st, ob4to, 32p, color, DJ/2.50)	Steck-Vaughn	(1965)	Emberley, Ed	30-45	
Schatz, Letta	Bola and the Oba's Drummers (1st, 8vo, 156p, b/w, pep, DJ/4.50)	McGraw-Hill	(1967)	Feelings, Tom	30-50	*
Schatz, Letta	Extraordinary Tug-of-War (1st AM {std}, ob4to, 48p, fp color, DJ/3.95)	Follett	(1968)	Burningham, John	30-50	
Schatz, Letta	Taiwo and her Twin (1st, lg8vo, 128p, b/w, DJ/2.95)	McGraw-Hill	1964	Fax, Elton C.	20-30	
Schatz, Letta	When Will my Birthday Be? (1st, lg8vo, 31p, 2-color, pep, DJ/2.50)	McGraw-Hill	1962	Bergere, Richard	25-45	
Schatz, Letta	Whiskers, My Cat (1st, sm4to, 32p, fp 1-color, DJ/3.50)	McGraw-Hill	(1967)	Galdone, Paul	50-80	
Schauffler, Rbt. H.	Romantic America (1st, 4to, 339p, gilt, teg, col frn by...)	Century	1913	Parrish, Maxfield	100-170	
Scheer, George	Cherokee Animal Tales (1st, 8vo, 79p, fp b/w, DJ/3.50)	Holiday House	(1968)	Frankenberg, Rbt.	25-45	
Scheer, Julian	Rain Makes Applesauce (1st, 4to, [30]p, fp color, DJ/4.95, CH, NYTBI)	Holiday House	1964	Bileck, Marvin	70-100	
Scheer, Julian	Upside Down Day (1st, lg8vo, [32]p, fp color, DJ/3.95)	Holiday House	1968	Oechsli, Kelly	30-50	
Scheffer, Victor	Little Calf (1st, 8vo, 140p, green cl, 1-color, DJ)	Scribner	(1970)	Fisher, Leonard	30-50	
Schick, Eleanor	5A and 7B (1st {std}, ob4to, [32]p, fp b/w, ipcb, DJ/2.95)	Macmillan	(1967)	Schick, Eleanor	30-50	
Schick, Eleanor	City in the Summer (1st {std}, ob4to, [32]p, color, DJ/4.50)	Macmillan	(1969)	Schick, Eleanor	30-50	
Schick, Eleanor	City in the Winter (1st {std}, ob4to, [32]p, color, DJ/4.95)	Macmillan	(1970)	Schick, Eleanor	30-50	
Schick, Eleanor	Dancing School (1st, ob12mo, ipcb, [32]p, b/w, DJ/2.25)	Harper	(1966)	Schick, Eleanor	30-50	
Schick, Eleanor	I'm Going to the Ocean (1st {std}, ob8vo, [30]p, fp b/w, DJ/2.50)	Macmillan	(1966)	Schick, Eleanor	30-50	
Schick, Eleanor	Katie Goes to Camp (1st, ob4to, [32]p, b/w, DJ/3.50)	Macmillan	(1968)	Schick, Eleanor	30-50	
Schick, Eleanor	Little School at Cottonwood Corners (1st, ob8vo, [32]p, b/w, DJ/2.25)	Harper	(1965)	Schick, Eleanor	30-50	
Schick, Eleanor	Making Friends (1st {std}, 8vo, [32]p, 1-color, cep, DJ/3.95)	Macmillan	(1969)	Schick, Eleanor	30-50	
Schick, Eleanor	Peggy's New Brother (1st {std}, 8vo, [32]p, color, DJ/4.50)	Macmillan	(1970)	Schick, Eleanor	30-50	
Schick, Eleanor	Surprise in the Forest (1st, ob24mo, [32]p, ibds, b/w, DJ/1.95)	Harper	(1964)	Schick, Eleanor	30-50	
Schickel, Richard	Gentle Knight (1st AM {std}, 8vo, 58p, 1-color, pep, DJ/2.75)	Abelard-Schuman	1964	Blake, Quentin	25-40	
Schiller, Barbara	Erec and Enid (1st {std}, 8vo, 45p, 1-color, DJ/4.25)	Dutton	(1970)	Forberg, Ati	30-45	
Schiller, Barbara	Kitchen Knight (1st {std}, 8vo, 64p, color, DJ/3.50)	Holt, Rinehart	(1965)	Hogrogian, Nonny	30-45	
Schiller, Barbara	White Rat's Tale (1st {std}, 8vo, [32]p, color, DJ/3.50)	Holt, Rinehart	(1967)	Adams, Adrienne	30-50	
Schlein, Miriam	Amazing Mr. Pelgrew (1st, sm4to, [42]p, fp 3-color, pep, DJ/2.50)	Abelard-Schuman	1957	Weiss, Harvey	25-45	
Schlein, Miriam	Best Place (1st, 8vo, [32]p, fp color, DJ/3.50)	Whitman	(1968)	Merkling, Erica	25-40	*
Schlein, Miriam	Big Cheese (1st, sm4to, white cl, [48]p, 2-color, DJ/2.95)	W.R. Scott	1958	Low, Joseph	30-50	
Schlein, Miriam	Big Green Thing (1st, 8vo, 60p, color)	Grosset/Dunlap	(1963)	Dauber, Elizabeth	20-35	
Schlein, Miriam	Big Talk (1st, lg sq8vo, olive cl, [36]p, 2-color, pep, DJ/2.25)	W.R. Scott	1955	Weiss, Harvey	30-50	

AUTHOR: 188

AUTHOR	TITLE	PUBLISHER	DATE	ARTIST	PRICE	LC
Schlein, Miriam	Billy, the Littlest One (1st, sq12mo, [34]p, fp color, DJ/2.75)	Whitman	(1966)	Hawkinson, Lucy	20-35	
Schlein, Miriam	Bumblebee's Secret (1st, sq8vo, 51p, fp color, pep, DJ/2.50)	Abelard-Schuman	(1958)	Weiss, Harvey	30-45	
Schlein, Miriam	Deer in the Snow (1st, 4to, [42]p, fp 3-color, pep, DJ/2.50)	Abelard-Schuman	1956	Kessler, Leonard	30-50	*
Schlein, Miriam	Elephant Herd (1st, lg8vo, ipcb, [40]p, 1-color, cep, DJ/2.00)	W.R. Scott	1954	Shimin, Symeon	30-50	
Schlein, Miriam	Fast is Not a Ladybug (1st, sm8vo, ipcb [34]p, 1-col, pep, DJ/1.75, NYTBI)	W.R. Scott	(1953)	Kessler, Leonard	30-50	
Schlein, Miriam	Fisherman's Day (1st, lg8vo, [32]p, color, DJ/2.00)	Whitman	1959	Weiss, Harvey	20-35	*
Schlein, Miriam	Four Little Foxes (1st, sm4to, ipcb, unpag, color, pep, DJ/2.00)	W.R. Scott	1953	Quintanilla, Luis	50-85	
Schlein, Miriam	Go With the Sun (1st, lg8vo, ipcb, [40]p, fp 2-color, pep, DJ/2.00)	W.R. Scott	1952	Shimin, Symeon	25-40	
Schlein, Miriam	Heavy is a Hippopotamus (1st sm8vo, ipcb unpag, 1-col, pep, DJ/1.75, NYTBI)	W.R. Scott	1954	Kessler, Leonard	50-80	R
Schlein, Miriam	Henry's Ride (1st, 8vo, [24]p, color, DJ/1.50)	Abingdon Press	1956	Earle, Vana	20-25	
Schlein, Miriam	Here Comes Night (1st, lg8vo, p-o, [32]p, fp color, pep, DJ/2.00)	Whitman	(1957)	Weiss, Harvey	25-40	
Schlein, Miriam	Home: the Tale of a Mouse (1st, sq8vo, [58]p, fp 2-color, dep, DJ/2.50)	Abelard-Schuman	1958	Johnson, Harper	30-45	
Schlein, Miriam	How Do You Travel? (1st, 8vo, unpag, color, DJ/1.50)	Abingdon Press	1954	Galdone, Paul	25-40	
Schlein, Miriam	It's About Time (1st, sm8vo, [41]p, ipcb, 1-color, pep, DJ/2.00)	W.R. Scott	1955	Kessler, Leonard	30-50	
Schlein, Miriam	Kittens, Cubs & Babies (1st, sm4to, green cl, [48]p, color, DJ)	W.R. Scott	1959	Charlot, Jean	120-200	
Schlein, Miriam	Laurie's New Brother (1st, 4to, unpag, color, pep, DJ/2.75)	Abelard-Schuman	1961	Donald, Elizabeth	20-30	
Schlein, Miriam	Lazy Day (1st, ob8vo, [38]p, fp 2-color, DJ/2.00)	W.R. Scott	1955	Weiss, Harvey	25-40	
Schlein, Miriam	Little Rabbit the High Jumper (1st, 8vo, [46]p, 2-color, DJ/2.25)	W.R. Scott	1957	Sherman, Theresa	30-50	
Schlein, Miriam	Little Red-Nose (1st, 4to, [42]p, fp 2-color, pep, DJ/2.50)	Abelard-Schuman	1955	Duvoisin, Roger	30-50	
Schlein, Miriam	Oomi, the New Hunter (1st, 8vo, 109p, b/w, DJ/2.50)	Abelard-Schuman	(1955)	Mason, George F.	20-30	
Schlein, Miriam	Shapes (1st, sq8vo, ibds, [33]p, color, DJ/1.75)	W.R. Scott	1952	Berman, Sam	40-65	
Schlein, Miriam	Sun Looks Down (1st, 4to, [42]p, fp color, pep, DJ/2.50, NYTBI)	Abelard-Schuman	(1954)	Graboff, Abner	50-85	R*
Schlein, Miriam	When Will the World be Mine? (1st, 4to, unpag, pep, color, DJ/2.25, CH)	W.R. Scott	(1953)	Charlot, Jean	100-170	
Schloat, G. Warren	Wonderful Egg (1st, 4to, [48]p, b/w, DJ/2.25)	Scribner	(1952)	(Photos)	30-50	
Schmid, Eleonore	Horns Everywhere (1st, sq8vo, [32]p, fp color, cep, DJ/3.95)	Harlin Quist	1968	Schmid, Eleonore	45-70	
Schmidt, Sarah L.	New Land (1st, sm8vo, 317p, brown cl, 9 fp b/w, pep, NH)	McBride	1933	Dobias, Frank	40-65	
Schmidt, Sarah L.	Ranching on Eagle Eye (1st {std}, 12mo, 374p, pep, DJ/2.00)	McBride	(1936)	Laune, Paul	30-50	*
Schmidt, Sarah L.	Secret of Silver Peak (1st, sm8vo, 334p, rust cl, b/w, DJ/2.00)	Random	(1938)	Kreis, Hans	30-50	*
Schmidt, Sarah L.	Shadow over Winding Ranch (1st, 8vo, 298p, beige cl, b/w, DJ/2.00)	Random	(1940)	Busoni, Rafaello	35-60	*
Schmitt, Gladys	Boris the Lopsided Bear (1st {std}, 8vo, 32p, fp b/w, DJ/2.95)	Collier Books	(1966)	Kuskin, Karla	30-50	
Schneider, E.B. (adap)	King Arthur & Knights of Roundtable (1st, 4to ibds unpag, col, pep DJ/1.00)	Random	1954	Barnum, Jay H.	30-50	
Schneider, Herman	Follow the Sunset (1st {std}, 4to, ibds, 43p, color, cep, DJ/2.75)	Doubleday	(1952)	Corcos, Lucille	70-125	R
Schneider, Herman	How Big is Big? (1st {this fmt}, sm4to, ibds, [40]p, color, DJ/1.75)	W.R. Scott	1950	Shimin, Symeon	30-60	*
Schneider, Herman	Let's Look Under the City (1st, sm8vo, grey cl, 70p, 1-color, DJ/2.00)	W.R. Scott	(1954)	Ballantine, Bill	25-45	
Schneider, Herman	Now Try This (1st, sm4to, ibds, 40p, 1-color, DJ/1.50)	W.R. Scott	(1947)	Ballantine, Bill	30-50	
Schneider, Nina	Hercules: Gentle Giant (1st, sm4to, ibds, [40]p, dp 2-color, pep)	Roy Publishers	(1947)	Werth, Kurt	45-70	*
Schneider, Nina	Hercules: Gentle Giant (1st {std}, ob4to, [48]p, fp 1-color, cep, DJ/3.95)	Hawthorn Books	(1969)	DePaola, Tomie	30-45	
Schneider, Nina	Let's Find Out (1st, lg8vo, ibds, 38p, color, DJ/1.50)	W.R. Scott	(1946)	Bendick, Jeanne	50-80	
Schneider, Nina	Let's Look Inside your House (1st, lg8vo, ibds, 39p, color, DJ/1.50)	W.R. Scott	(1948)	Ivins, Barbara	40-60	
Schneider, Nina	While Susie Sleeps (1st, sm4to, [32]p, ibds, color, DJ/1.50)	W.R. Scott	(1948)	Wilson, Dagmar	40-65	
Schoenherr, John	The Barn (1st {std}, sm4to, 40p, b/w, pep, DJ/3.50)	Little/Brown	(1968)	Schoenherr, John	25-40	*
Schrank, Joseph	Seldom & the Golden Cheese (1st, 8vo, 160p, uncut, col frn, 7pl, pep)	Dodd	1933	Tenggren, Gustaf	150-250	
Schreiber, Georges	Bambino Goes Home (1st, 4to, 29p, fp color, pep, DJ/3.00)	Viking	(1959)	Schreiber, Georges	50-85	
Schreiber, Georges	Bambino the Clown (1st, 4to, 30p, ipcb, color, pep, DJ/2.00, CH)	Viking	1947	Schreiber, Georges	80-140	
Schultz, James W.	Gold Dust (1st, 8vo, 243p, b/w, DJ/2.00)	Houghton	1934	Mulford, Stockton	40-60	
Schultz, James W.	In the Great Apache Forest (1st, 8vo, 225p, green cl, 4pl)	Houghton	1920	Cue, Harold	30-50	*
Schultz, James W.	Lone Bull's Mistake (1st, 8vo, 207p, p-o, 4pl)	Houghton	1918	Varian, George	70-120	
Schultz, James W.	Plumed Snake Medicine (1st, 8vo, 244p, p-o, 4pl)	Houghton	1924	Varian, George	70-100	
Schultz, James W.	Quest of the Fish-Dog Skin (1st, 8vo, 219p, tan cl, p-o, 4pl)	Houghton	1913	Varian, George	70-100	
Schultz, James W.	Seizer of Eagles (1st, sm8vo, 230p, brown cl, 4pl)	Houghton	1922	Schoonover, Frank	30-50	
Schultz, James W.	Sinopah, the Indian Boy (1st, 8vo, 154p, 4pl)	Houghton	1913	Smith, E. Boyd	45-70	
Schultz, James W.	Skull Head the Terrible (1st, sm8vo, 208p, brown cl, 4pl, pep)	Houghton	1929	Schoonover, Frank	30-50	*
Schultz, James W.	With the Indians in the Rockies (1st, 8vo, p-o, 227p, 6pl)	Houghton	1912	Varian, George	70-100	
Schultz, James W.	With the Indians in the Rockies (1st, lg8vo, 252p, p-o, 4cp)	Houghton	1925	Brett, Harold M.	30-50	
Schulz, Charles	Charlie Brown Christmas (1st {std}, sq8vo, 42p, color, DJ/2.50)	World	(1965)	Schulz, Charles	30-50	
Schulz, Charles	Snoopy and the Red Baron (1st {std}, 8vo, [64]p, b/w, DJ/2.00)	Holt, Rinehart	(1966)	Schulz, Charles	35-50	
Schwalje, Earl	Cezar and the Music-Maker (1st {std}, 8vo, 77p, fp 2-color, DJ/2.50)	Knopf	1951	Nicolas	25-45	
Schwalje, Marjory	Mr. Angelo (1st, sm4to, unpag, ipcb, 20 dp color, DJ/2.75)	Abelard-Schuman	(1960)	Graboff, Abner	30-45	
Schwartz, Elizabeth R.	Cottontail Rabbit (1st, 8vo, 45p, olive cl, 2-color, cep, DJ/2.00)	Holiday House	(1957)	Schwartz, Charles	30-50	
Schwartz, Elizabeth R.	When Water Animals are Babies (1st, 4to, [36]p, color, DJ/4.50)	Holiday House	(1970)	Schwartz, Charles	20-35	
Schwartz, Evgeny	Tale of Stolen Time (1st, ob8vo, [32]p, 1-color, dep, DJ/3.75)	Prentice-Hall	1966	Hogrogian, Nonny	25-45	
Schwartz, Julius	I Know a Magic House (1st, sm4to, 32p, 2-color, pep, DJ/2.00)	Whittlesey	(1956)	Simont, Marc	25-45	
Schwartz, Julius	Now I Know (1st, 4to, 32p, 2-color, pep, DJ/2.00)	Whittlesey	(1955)	Simont, Marc	30-50	
Schwarzman, Marg.	Steel (1st, lg ob8vo, ibds, [28]p, color)	Western Printing	1937	Luykx, Th. D.	30-50	
Schwatka, Fred	Children of the Cold (1st, 12mo, 212p, gilt, b/w)	NY: Cassell	(1886)	Bobbett, Walter	100-165	
Schweitzer, Byrd B.	Amigo (1st {std}, 4to, 41p, color, DJ/3.95)	Macmillan	1963	Williams, Garth	50-85	
Schweitzer, Byrd B.	Chinese Bug (1st, 4to, 48p, gilt, dp color, DJ/3.50)	Houghton	1968	Darwin, Beatrice	30-50	
Schweitzer, Byrd B.	Man Who Talked to a Tree (1st {std}, sm4to, [47]p, color, DJ/4.50)	Dutton	(1968)	Shimin, Symeon	40-70	
Schweitzer, Byrd B.	One Small Blue Bead (1st {std}, 4to, 40p, 2-color, DJ/3.50)	Macmillan	(1965)	Shimin, Symeon	35-50	
Schwetzky, Otto	Peter Teeter Stories (1st, ob4to, [63]p, ipcb, color, pep)	Chi: Thompson	1905	Garman, R.H.	100-160	
Schwimmer, Rosika	Tisza Tales (1st {std}, lg8vo, 225p, blue/gilt, 8cp, pep, DJ/5.00)	Doubleday/Doran	1928	Pogany, Willy	100-170	
Scoppettone, Sandra	Suzuki Beane (1st {std}, 4to, 95p, ibds, b/w, DJ/2.50)	Doubleday	1961	Fitzhugh, Louise	150-220	
Scott, Ann H.	Big Cowboy Western (1st, sm4to, [28]p, color, cep, DJ/2.95)	Lothrop, Lee	(1965)	Lewis, Richard	50-80	*
Scott, Ann H.	Let's Catch a Monster (1st, sm4to, [44]p, 2-color, DJ/3.50)	Lothrop, Lee	(1967)	Hall, Tom	25-45	*
Scott, Ann H.	Sam (1st, 4to, [33]p, 1-color, DJ/3.95)	McGraw-Hill	(1967)	Shimin, Symeon	50-80	R*
Scott, Anna M.	Flower Babies' Book (1st, 8vo, 78p, ibds, color)	Rand/McNally	(1914)	Ross, M.T.	120-180	
Scott, Anna M.	Year with the Fairies (1st, 4to, ibds, [100]p, color, pep)	Volland	(1914)	Ross, M.T.	200-300	
Scott, Barbara	Tales of Raindrop, Cloud Fairy (1st {std}, 8vo, 55p, fp 2-color, DJ/2.95)	Vantage Press	1968	Scott, Barbara	30-50	

AUTHOR	TITLE	PUBLISHER	DATE	ARTIST	PRICE	LC
Scott, Florence E.	Kindergarten Limericks (1st, sm4to, [59]p, 27cp)	Hurst	(1915)	Scott, Arthur O.	160-240	*
Scott, Gabriel	Kari (1st {std}, 8vo, 242p, blue cl, uncut, col frn, 7pl, pep)	Doubleday/Doran	1931	D'Aulaire, E. Parin	30-50	
Scott, Janet L.	Round the World We Sail (ob4to, [16]p, ibds, color)	Volland/Buzza	[1930]	Scott, Janet L.	120-165	
Scott, Janet L.	Round the World We Sail (1st, sq4to, spiral bds, [16]p, color, pep)	Saalfield	1939	Scott, Janet L.	50-80	
Scott, Lena B.	Dawn Boy of the Pueblos (1st, 8vo, 198p, 4cp, DJ/2.00)	Winston	1935	Kihn, W. Langdon	30-50	
Scott, Lucy M.	Dewdrops from Fairyland (1st, 8vo, 91p, 9cp, pep)	L: Warne	(1912)	Carse, A. Duncan	85-130	
Scott, Michael	Tom Cringle's Log (1st, 8vo, 569p, AEG, blue/gilt, 42 b/w)	L: Macmillan	1895	Symington, J.A.	40-60	
Scott, Michael	Tom Cringle's Log (1st, lg8vo, black/gilt, 384p, p-o, 7cp, pep)	Dodd	1927	Schaeffer, Mead	50-80	
Scott, Rochelle	Colors, Colors All Around (1st, lg8vo, [41]p, ipcb, color, pep, DJ/1.95)	Grosset/Dunlap	(1965)	Kessler, Leonard	40-65	*
Scott, Sally	Benjie & his Family (1st {std}, 8vo, yellow cl, [62]p, fp b/w, DJ/2.00)	Harcourt	(1952)	Krush, Beth	25-45	
Scott, Sally	Binky's Fire (1st {std}, 8vo, [54]p, fp b/w, DJ/1.75)	Harcourt	(1952)	Krush, Beth	25-40	*
Scott, Sally	Bitsy (1st {std}, 8vo, 41p, b/w, DJ/2.25)	Harcourt	(1957)	Krush, Beth	25-40	*
Scott, Sally	Bobby & his Band (1st {std}, 8vo, [46]p, fp b/w, DJ/2.00)	Harcourt	(1954)	Krush, Beth	25-40	*
Scott, Sally	Brand New Kitten (1st {std}, 8vo, 54p, fp b/w, DJ/2.25)	Harcourt	(1956)	Krush, Beth	25-40	*
Scott, Sally	Chica (1st {std}, 8vo, 114p, rust cl, fp b/w, DJ/2.25)	Harcourt	(1954)	Krush, Joe	25-45	
Scott, Sally	Jenny & the Wonderful Jeep (1st {std}, 8vo, 47p, b/w, DJ/2.50)	Harcourt	(1963)	Krush, Beth	25-40	
Scott, Sally	Judy's Baby (1st {std}, 8vo, 45p, b/w, DJ/1.75)	Harcourt	1949	Toan, Jane	20-30	*
Scott, Sally	Judy's Summer Adventure (1st {std}, 8vo, 61p, b/w, DJ/2.50)	Harcourt	(1960)	Krush, Beth	20-30	*
Scott, Sally	Little Wiener (1st {std}, 8vo, ibds, [48]p, b/w, DJ/1.75)	Harcourt	(1951)	Krush, Beth	30-50	*
Scott, Sally	Molly & the Tool Shed (1st, 8vo, ibds, 40p, b/w, DJ/1.50)	Harcourt	(1943)	Segner, Ellen	20-35	*
Scott, Sally	Mr. Doodle (1st, 8vo, 45p, fp b/w, DJ/1.75)	Harcourt	(1947)	Krush, Beth	25-45	*
Scott, Sally	Rip & Royal (1st {std}, 8vo, 58p, tan cl, b/w, DJ/1.75)	Harcourt	(1950)	Krush, Beth	30-60	*
Scott, Sally	Silly Billy (1st, 8vo, [48]p, b/w, DJ/1.50)	Harcourt	(1945)	Hartwell, Marjorie	20-30	*
Scott, Sally	Sue Ann's Busy Day (1st, 8vo, [57]p, b/w, DJ/1.75)	Harcourt	(1948)	Chastain, Madye L.	20-35	*
Scott, Sally	Sunny Jim the Uppity Kitten (1st {std}, 8vo, 46p, b/w, DJ/2.50)	Harcourt	(1962)	Krush, Beth	25-45	
Scott, Sally	There was Timmy! (1st {std}, 8vo, 46p, b/w, DJ/2.25)	Harcourt	(1959)	Krush, Beth	20-30	*
Scott, Sally	Tinker Takes a Walk (1st {std}, 8vo, 62p, b/w, DJ/2.25)	Harcourt	(1958)	Krush, Beth	20-30	
Scott, Sally	Tippy (1st {std}, 8vo, [48]p, b/w, DJ/1.75)	Harcourt	(1950)	Krush, Beth	20-30	*
Scott, Sally	What Susan Wanted (1st {std}, sm8vo, pink cl, 36p, fp b/w, DJ/2.00)	Harcourt	(1956)	Krush, Beth	30-50	
Scott, Walter	Ivanhoe (1st, 8vo, blue/gilt, 523p, teg, uncut, 12cp, pep)	L: Dent	1899	Brock, Charles E.	70-100	
Scott, Walter	Ivanhoe (1st, sm8vo, 346p, 4cp)	Appleton	1910	Unknown	25-45	*
Scott, Walter	Ivanhoe (1st, 8vo, red cl, 676p, teg, 16cp)	Houghton	1913	Smith, E. Boyd	100-160	
Scott, Walter	Ivanhoe (1st, 12mo, 336p, 10cp, pep)	Row, Peterson	(1914)	Cole, Clarence L.	30-50	*
Scott, Walter	Ivanhoe (1st AM, 8vo, 564p, 12cp)	Lippincott/Jack	[1915]	Greiffenhagen, M.	50-80	*
Scott, Walter	Ivanhoe (1st, lg8vo, p-o, 637p, blue/gilt, 14cp, pep, WS)	Rand/McNally	(1918)	Winter, Milo	60-100	
Scott, Walter	Ivanhoe (1st, lg8vo, gilt, teg, 12cp)	McKay	[1920]	Greiffenhagen, M.	30-45	
Scott, Walter	Ivanhoe (1st, lg8vo, 515p, p-o, blue/gilt, 10cp, pep)	Harper	1922	Schoonover, Frank	60-90	
Scott, Walter	Ivanhoe (1st, 8vo, red cl, 469p, uncut, 6pl)	Sears	(1928)	Pitz, Henry C.	30-50	*
Scott, Walter	Kenilworth (1st, 4to, teg, red/gilt, 551p, uncut, 12cp)	L: Jack	(1920)	Ford, H.J.	120-200	
Scott, Walter	Lady of the Lake (1st, 12mo, 236p, gilt, b/w)	L: Service/Paton	1898	Brock, Charles E.	30-50	
Scott, Walter	Lady of the Lake (1st, 4to, [79]p, green/gilt, 13cp)	Bobbs-Merrill	(1910)	Christy, Howard C.	100-175	
Scott, Walter	Quentin Durward (1st, sm8vo, 348p, 4cp)	Appleton	1910	Varian, George	25-45	*
Scott, Walter	Quentin Durward (1st, lg8vo, 422p, gilt, p-o, 13cp, pep, SC)	Scribner	1923	Chambers, C.B.	80-120	
Scott, Walter	Quentin Durward (1st, lg8vo, uncut, 499p, 16cp)	Dodd	1923	Tarrant, Percy	35-60	*
Scott, William R.	Apple that Jack Ate (1st, sm ob4to, ipcb, [25]p, color, dep, DJ/1.50)	W.R. Scott	1951	Shaw, Charles G.	45-70	
Scott, William R.	This is the Milk that Jack Drank (1st, sm ob4to, ipcb, [24]p, color)	W.R. Scott	1944	Shaw, Charles G.	40-65	
Scott, William R.	Water that Jack Drank (1st, sm ob4to, ipcb, [24]p, color, pep, DJ/1.50)	W.R. Scott	1950	Shaw, Charles G.	45-70	
Scott-Gatty, Alfred	I Wonder Why? (1st, lg4to, 72p, bds, p-o, 16 ticp)	L: Collins	1920	Robertson, W.G.	125-200	
Scovel, Myra	Buffalo & the Bell (1st, sm8vo, 127p, b/w, wraps)	Friendship Pr.	(1963)	Keats, Ezra J.	40-65	*
Scoville, Samuel	Lords of the Wild (1st, sm8vo, green cl, 246p, 4pl, pep)	Wm. Morrow	1928	Bull, Charles L.	25-45	
Scribner, Grace	American Pilgrimage (1st, 12mo, 89p, 4 woodcuts)	Vanguard Press	(1927)	Ward, Lynd	55-80	*
Scripps, Harriet J.	Little Handful (1st, 8vo, 224p, ibds, 4pl)	L: Blackie	(1894)	Brooke, L. Leslie	80-125	
Scudder, Horace E.	Children's Book (sm4to, 444p, p-o by…)	Houghton	(1909)	Parrish, Maxfield	50-80	
Scull, Florence	Bear Teeth for Courage (1st, 8vo, 163p, fp b/w, DJ/3.75)	Van Nostrand	(1964)	Lent, Blair	40-65	*
Seabrook, Katie	Colette & Baba in Timbuctoo (1st {std}, 8vo, 168p, frn by…)	Coward	(1933)	Berry, Erick	25-40	*
Seabrook, Katie	Gao of the Ivory Coast (1st, 8vo, 121p, col frn, 4pl)	Coward	(1931)	D'Aulaire, E. Parin	50-80	
Seaman, Augusta	Book of Mysteries (1st {std}, sm8vo, 224p, col frn, b/w)	Doubleday/Doran	1929	Wiese, Kurt	30-50	*
Seaman, Louise	Brave Bantam (1st {std}, 8vo, green cl, 48p, b/w, pep, DJ/1.00)	Macmillan	1946	Sewell, Helen	30-50	
Seaman, Louise	Mr. Peck's Pets (1st {std}, 8vo, ibds, 96p, b/w, pep, DJ/2.00)	Macmillan	1947	Hader, B.& E.	30-50	
Sears, Paul M.	Barn Swallow (1st, 8vo, 45p, fp 2-color, cep, DJ/2.00)	Holiday House	(1955)	Ferguson, Walter	20-35	
Sears, Paul M.	Downy Woodpecker (1st, 8vo, 43p, 2-color, cep, DJ/2.00)	Holiday House	(1953)	Latham, Barbara	25-45	
Sears, Paul M.	Firefly (1st, sm8vo, 37p, green cl, 2-color, pep, DJ/2.00)	Holiday House	1956	Rounds, Glen	25-45	
Sears, Paul M.	Tree Frog (1st, 8vo, 45p, green cl, 2-color, DJ/2.00)	Holiday House	(1954)	Latham, Barbara	50-80	R
Seawell, Molly E.	Betty at Fort Blizzard (1st, 8vo, 224p, teg, p-o, 4cp)	Lippincott	1916	Frederick, Edmund	25-40	
Seawell, Molly E.	Chateau of Montplaisir (1st, 8vo, uncut, 245p, blue cl, cvr by…)	Appleton	1906	Armstrong, Margaret	30-50	
Seawell, Molly E.	Fortunes of Fifi (1st, 8vo, 239p, cvr by…)	Bobbs-Merrill	(1903)	Armstrong, Margaret	30-50	
Seawell, Molly E.	Francezka (1st, sm8vo, 466p, green/gilt, cvr by…)	Bobbs-Merrill	(1902)	Armstrong, Margaret	35-60	
Seawell, Molly E.	Francezka (1st, sm8vo, 466p, green/gilt, 7pl by…)	Bobbs-Merrill	(1902)	Fisher, Harrison	35-60	
Seawell, Molly E.	House of Egremont (1st, sm8vo, 515p, gilt, 6pl)	Scribner	1900	Relyea, Charles M.	20-30	
Seawell, Molly E.	Loves of Lady Arabella (1st, 8vo, p-o, 244p, 12cp)	Bobbs-Merrill	(1906)	Underwood, C.F.	25-40	
Seawell, Molly E.	Midshipman Paulding (1st, sm8vo, 133p, gilt, b/w)	Appleton	1891	Edwards, George W.	40-60	
Seawell, Molly E.	Papa Bouchard (1st, 12mo, 261p, uncut, teg, b/w)	Scribner	1901	Glackens, William	25-40	
Seccombe, Lieut.	Good Old Story of Cinderella (1st AM, sm4to, 48p, gilt, 12cp)	NY: Armstrong	(1882)	Seccombe, Lieut.	120-175	*
Sechrist, Eliz. H.	Rufie Had a Monkey! (1st, lg8vo, [46]p, red cl, b/w, cep, DJ/1.00)	McKay	(1939)	Janeway, Hestermary	100-170	*
Sedberry, J. Hamilton	Under the Flag of the Cross (1st, sm8vo, 472p, blue/gilt, 10pl)	C.M. Clark	1908	Kirkpatrick, W.	70-100	
Sedgwick, Anne D.	Dull Miss Archinard (1st, 12mo, 287p, beige/gilt, cvr by…)	Scribner	1898	Armstrong, Margaret	35-60	*
Sedlacek, Hanus	Nursery Rhymes from Bohemia (1st AM, lg4to, [24]p, ibds, color, pep)	McBride	1929	Mates, Rudolf	150-225	
Seeger, Elizabeth	Five Brothers (1st, 8vo, 300p, b/w, DJ/3.75)	John Day	(1948)	Baldridge, Cyrus L.	25-40	

AUTHOR	TITLE	PUBLISHER	DATE	ARTIST	PRICE	LC
Seeger, Elizabeth	Five Sons of King Pandu (1st, 8vo, 340p, fp color, DJ/6.95)	W.R. Scott	(1967)	Laite, Gordon	30-50	
Seeger, Elizabeth	Pageant of Chinese History (1st {std}, 8vo, 386p, b/w, pep, NH)	Longmans	1934	Watkins, Bernard	45-70	
Seeger, Elizabeth	The Ramayana (1st, lg8vo, 244p, fp color, DJ/6.95)	W.R. Scott	(1969)	Laite, Gordon	20-30	
Seeger, Ruth C.	Animal Folk Songs for Children (1st {std}, 4to, gilt, 80p, b/w, DJ/2.50)	Doubleday	1950	Cooney, Barbara	60-90	
Seeger, Ruth C.	Let's Build a Railroad (1st {std}, 4to, ibds, [32]p, color, DJ/2.50)	Aladdin	(1954)	Funk, Tom	30-50	
Seegmiller, Wilhelmia	Hand Clasp (1st, narrow 16mo, [8]p)	Volland	(1911)	Unknown	50-80	*
Seegmiller, Wilhelmia	Journeys in Storyland (1st, sm8vo, [120]p, pep, color)	Houghton	1922	Enright, Maginel W.	55-80	*
Seegmiller, Wilhelmia	Little Rhymes for Little Readers (1st, lg4to, p-o, 81p, fp color, pep)	Rand/McNally	(1903)	Hallock, Ruth M.	80-125	
Seeman, Elizabeth	In the Arms of the Mountain (1st, 8vo, 251p, b/w, DJ/4.00)	Crown	(1961)	Rounds, Glen	20-35	
Sefton, Harriet L.	Dream Imp & Others (1st, 4to, 96p, red/gilt, 10cp)	L: Bickers	[1912]	MacQuigg, Gertrude	140-220	
Segal, E.A.	Ring and a Riddle (1st {std}, sm4to, 65p, col frn, 1-color, DJ/2.00)	Lippincott	(1944)	Bock, Vera	30-50	
Segal, Lore	Tell Me a Mitzi (1st {std}, ob4to, [40]p, color, DJ/4.95)	Farrar, Straus	(1970)	Pincus, Harriet	30-50	
Segovia, Gertrudis	Spanish Fairy Book (1st, 8vo, 321p, gilt, 8cp, pep)	Stokes	(1918)	Hood, George	100-165	
Seidelman, James	14th Dragon (1st, ob4to, [31]p, fp color, cep, DJ/3.95)	Harlin Quist	(1968)	Various	50-85	
Seidler, Ann	Bendemolena (1st {std}, sm4to, 31p, color, pep, DJ/2.95)	Follett	(1967)	Martin, Richard	30-50	
Seidler, Rosalie	Grumpus and the Venetian Cat (1st {std}, sm4to, 39p, color, DJ/3.50)	Atheneum	1964	Seidler, Rosalie	30-50	
Seidlin, Oskar	Green Wagons (1st, 8vo, 130p, b/w, DJ/2.00)	Houghton	1943	Cooney, Barbara	40-65	*
Seidman, Mitzi	Who Woke the Sun? (1st {std}, 12mo, [31]p, fp color, DJ/1.95)	Macmillan	(1960)	Kuskin, Karla	30-50	
Seitz, Don C.	The Buccaneers (1st, 8vo, p-o, teg, 52p, frn by...)	Harper	1912	Pyle, Howard	60-100	
Selden, George	Cricket in Times Square (1st, lg8vo, 151p, fp b/w, DJ/3.50, NH)	Ariel	(1960)	Williams, Garth	70-100	
Selden, George	Dog that Could Swim Underwater (1st, 8vo, grey cl, 126p, b/w, DJ/2.50)	Viking	1956	Dennis, Morgan	30-50	
Selden, George	Dunkard (1st, 8vo, 47p, 1-color, cep, DJ/2.95)	Harper	(1968)	Lippman, Peter	20-25	
Selden, George	Garden Under the Sea (1st, 8vo, 190p, b/w, DJ/2.75)	Viking	(1957)	Mackenzie, Garry	20-30	
Selden, George	Heinrich Schliemann (1st {std}, lg8vo, unpag, 2-color, DJ/2.95)	Macmillan	(1964)	Bjorklund, Lorence	25-40	
Selden, George	I See What I See! (1st {std}, sm ob4to, [46]p, color, DJ/3.50)	Ariel	(1962)	Galster, Robert	20-30	
Selden, George	Mice, the Monks & the Christmas Tree (1st {std}, 8vo, 31p, color, DJ/2.95)	Macmillan	1963	Balet, Jan B.	40-65	
Selden, George	Oscar Lobster's Fair Exchange (1st, 12mo, 172p, b/w, cep, DJ/3.95)	Harper	(1966)	Lippman, Peter	30-50	
Selden, George	Sir Arthur Evans... (1st {std}, 8vo, 35p, color, DJ/2.95)	Macmillan	(1964)	Ames, Lee	20-35	
Selden, George	Tucker's Countryside (1st {std}, 8vo, 166p, b/w, DJ/3.95)	Farrar, Straus	(1969)	Williams, Garth	30-50	
Selsam, Millicent	A Time for Sleep (1st, sm8vo, [57]p, DJ/2.00)	W.R. Scott	1953	Ludwig, Helen	30-45	
Selsam, Millicent	All About Eggs (1st, sm8vo, [62]p, 3-color, DJ/2.00)	W.R. Scott	1952	Ludwig, Helen	30-50	
Selsam, Millicent	All Kinds of Babies (1st, ob8vo, [40]p, 2-color, DJ/3.75)	Four Winds Pr.	(1969)	Shimin, Symeon	25-40	*
Selsam, Millicent	Benny's Animals & How He Put them in Order (1st, 8vo, 60p, color, DJ/1.95)	Harper	(1966)	Lobel, Arnold	25-40	
Selsam, Millicent	Birth of an Island (1st, lg8vo, 48p, 2-color, DJ/2.50)	Harper	(1959)	Lubell, Winifred	20-30	*
Selsam, Millicent	Greg's Microscope (1st, 8vo, 64p, color, DJ/1.95)	Harper	(1963)	Lobel, Arnold	20-35	
Selsam, Millicent	How to Be a Nature Detective (1st, lg8vo, 46p, fp color, DJ/2.95)	Harper	(1966)	Keats, Ezra J.	30-50	
Selsam, Millicent	Let's Get Turtles (1st, 8vo, 62p, color, DJ/1.95)	Harper	(1965)	Lobel, Arnold	20-30	
Selsam, Millicent	Nature Detective (1st, ob8vo, [48]p, color, DJ)	W.R. Scott	1958	Sherman, Theresa	30-45	
Selsam, Millicent	See Along the Shore (1st, 8vo, ipcb, [48]p, color, cep, DJ/2.95)	Harper	1961	Weisgard, Leonard	30-45	
Selsam, Millicent	Seeds & More Seeds (1st, 8vo, ibds, 60p, 2-color, DJ/2.50)	Harper	(1959)	Ungerer, Tomi	50-80	
Selsam, Millicent	Terry and the Caterpillars (1st, 8vo, 64p, color, DJ/1.95)	Harper	(1962)	Lobel, Arnold	30-50	
Selsam, Millicent	Tony's Birds (1st, 8vo, 64p, 3-color, DJ/1.95)	Harper	(1961)	Werth, Kurt	20-30	
Selsam, Millicent	Underwater Zoos (1st, 8vo, 96p, b/w, DJ/2.75)	Wm. Morrow	1961	Elgin, Kathleen	25-40	
Seltzer, Charles A.	Range Boss (1st, sm8vo, green cl, 333p, 4pl)	McClurg	1916	Schoonover, Frank	60-100	
Seltzer, Charles A.	Range Riders (1st, 8vo, 310p, b/w)	Outing	1911	Rowe, Clarence	60-100	
Semple, Daisy	Tommy & Jane & the Birds (1st, lg8vo, p-o, 94p, color, pep)	Saalfield	(1929)	Peat, Fern B.	55-90	
Sendak, Jack	Circus Girl (1st, lg8vo, beige cl, [30]p, color, DJ/2.50)	Harper	1957	Sendak, Maurice	180-260	R
Sendak, Jack	Happy Rain (1st, sm4to, 40p, blue cl, 8 fp b/w, DJ/2.50)	Harper	(1956)	Sendak, Maurice	350-500	R
Sendak, Jack	King of the Hermits (1st {std}, 8vo, red cl, 105p, b/w, DJ/3.75)	Farrar, Straus	(1966)	Zemach, Margot	40-65	
Sendak, Jack	Martze (1st, 8vo, 70p, b/w, DJ/3.50)	Farrar, Straus	(1968)	Miller, Mitchell	30-50	*
Sendak, Jack	Second Witch (1st, 8vo, 94p, fp b/w, DJ/2.95)	Harper	(1965)	Shulevitz, Uri	30-45	
Sendak, Maurice	Fantasy Sketches (1st, 4to, [28]p, wraps, b/w)	Rosenbach Found.	1970	Sendak, Maurice	100-170	
Sendak, Maurice	Hector the Protector (1st, ob8vo, [52]p, ibds, color, pep, DJ/4.25)	Harper	(1965)	Sendak, Maurice	100-170	
Sendak, Maurice	Higglety Pigglety Pop! (1st 12mo, p-o, gilt fp 1-color, 69p, cep, DJ/4.95)	Harper	(1967)	Sendak, Maurice	180-250	R
Sendak, Maurice	In the Night Kitchen (1st, 4to, p-o, [40]p, color, DJ/4.95, CH, NYTBI)	Harper	(1970)	Sendak, Maurice	250-400	
Sendak, Maurice	Kenny's Window (1st, lg sq8vo, tan cl, [62]p, 1-color, DJ/2.00)	Harper	(1956)	Sendak, Maurice	350-500	R
Sendak, Maurice	Sign on Rosie's Door (1st, 8vo, grey cl, 47p, 2-color, DJ/2.50)	Harper	(1960)	Sendak, Maurice	250-400	R
Sendak, Maurice	Very Far Away (1st, 8vo, green cl, cep, 52p, color, DJ/2.00)	Harper	(1957)	Sendak, Maurice	220-300	R
Sendak, Maurice	Where the Wild Things Are (1st 4to [40]p, ibds col, dep, DJ/3.50, CM, NYT)	Harper	1963	Sendak, Maurice	800-1200	R
Serage, Nancy	Prince Who Gave up a Throne (1st, 8vo, 62p, fp b/w, DJ/3.50)	Crowell	(1966)	Mizumura, Kazue	30-50	
Seredy, Kate	Brand-New Uncle (1st, 8vo, 142p, 1-color, DJ/3.00)	Viking	(1961)	Seredy, Kate	50-80	
Seredy, Kate	Chestry Oak (1st, 8vo, 236p, red cl, fp b/w, DJ/2.50)	Viking	1948	Seredy, Kate	75-120	
Seredy, Kate	Good Master (1st, sq8vo, 211p, b/w, pep, DJ/2.00, NH)	Viking	1935	Seredy, Kate	70-120	R
Seredy, Kate	Gypsy (1st, 4to, 62p, cloth, 29pl, DJ/3.00)	Viking	1951	Seredy, Kate	70-100	
Seredy, Kate	Lazy Tinka (1st, 8vo, 56p, fp color, pep, DJ/2.75)	Viking	(1962)	Seredy, Kate	60-90	
Seredy, Kate	Listening (1st, 8vo, gilt, 157p, pep, 18pl, DJ/2.00)	Viking	1936	Seredy, Kate	60-100	
Seredy, Kate	Open Gate (1st, 8vo, blue cl, 280p, fp b/w, pep, DJ/2.50)	Viking	1943	Seredy, Kate	50-80	
Seredy, Kate	Philomena (1st, lg8vo, 95p, b/w, pep, DJ/2.75)	Viking	1955	Seredy, Kate	50-80	
Seredy, Kate	Singing Tree (1st, 8vo, 247p, color, 32 fp b/w, pep, DJ/2.50, NH)	Viking	1940	Seredy, Kate	80-120	
Seredy, Kate	Tenement Tree (1st, 4to, 96p, fp b/w, pep, DJ/3.00)	Viking	(1959)	Seredy, Kate	60-90	
Seredy, Kate	Tree for Peter (1st, lg8vo, 102p, 1-color, DJ/2.00)	Viking	1941	Seredy, Kate	120-200	
Seredy, Kate	White Stag (1st, lg8vo, 95p, gilt, b/w, pep, DJ/2.00, NM)	Viking	1937	Seredy, Kate	120-185	R
Serraillier, Ian	Robin and his Merry Men (1st, 4to, 64p, fp color, DJ/4.50)	H.Z. Walck	(1970)	Ambrus, Victor	35-50	
Serraillier, Ian	Silver Sword (1st AM, 8vo, 187p, b/w, DJ/3.50)	Criterion Bks.	(1959)	Hodges, C. Walter	25-45	
Service, Robert W.	Rhymes of a Red Cross Man (1st, 8vo, 192p, red/gilt, 8cp)	Barse/Hopkins	1916	Wrenn, Charles	30-50	
Service, Robert W.	Trail of Ninety-Eight (1st, sm8vo, 514p, 4pl)	Dodd	1911	Dixon, Maynard	45-70	
Serviss, Garrett P.	Columbus of Space (1st, sm8vo, 298p, green cl, 4pl)	Appleton	1911	Heath, Howard	140-240	
Serviss, Garrett P.	Second Deluge (1st, sm8vo, 399p, aqua cl, 4pl)	McBride	1912	Varian, George	170-240	

AUTHOR	TITLE	PUBLISHER	DATE	ARTIST	PRICE	LC
Serwer, Blanche L.	Let's Steal the Moon (1st {std}, lg8vo, gilt, 88p, color, DJ/3.95)	Little/Brown	(1970)	Hyman, Trina S.	60-90	
Seton, Ernest T.	Animal Heroes (1st, 8vo, green/gilt, 362p, teg, 19p)	Scribner	1905	Seton, Ernest T.	120-180	
Seton, Ernest T.	Arctic Prairies (1st, lg8vo, 415p, green/gilt, uncut, b/w)	Scribner	1911	(Photos)	170-250	R
Seton, Ernest T.	Biography of a Grizzly (1st, sq8vo, 167p, 12 tipl, cep)	Century	1900	Seton, Ernest T.	75-120	
Seton, Ernest T.	Biography of a Silver Fox (1st, sm8vo, blue cl, 209p, 10pl)	Century	1909	Seton, Ernest T.	50-80	
Seton, Ernest T.	Bird Portraits (1st, lg4to, 40p, green cl, 20pl)	Ginn & Co.	1901	Seton, Ernest T.	140-200	
Seton, Ernest T.	Book of Woodcraft (1st, 8vo, 567p, green/gilt, b/w)	Doubleday/Page	1912	Seton, Ernest T.	80-125	
Seton, Ernest T.	Krag & Johnny Bear (1st, sm8vo, 141p, b/w pl)	Scribner	1902	Seton, Ernest T.	70-100	
Seton, Ernest T.	Lives of the Hunted (1st, 8vo, 360p, green/gilt, teg, b/w)	Scribner	1901	Seton, Ernest T.	100-165	
Seton, Ernest T.	Monarch the Big Bear of Tallac (1st, 8vo, 214p, blue/gilt, p-o, 8pl)	Scribner	1904	Seton, Ernest T.	80-125	
Seton, Ernest T.	Preacher of Cedar Mountain (1st, 8vo, 426p, gilt, col frn by...)	Doubleday/Page	1917	Rowe, Clarence	60-90	
Seton, Ernest T.	Rolf in the Woods (1st, 8vo, 437p, green/gilt, 12pl)	Doubleday/Page	1911	Seton, Ernest T.	120-200	
Seton, Ernest T.	Studies in Art Anatomy of Animals (1st, folio, teg, green/gilt, 96p, 49pl)	L: Macmillan	1896	Seton, Ernest T.	500-800	
Seton, Ernest T.	Trail of the Sandhill Stag (1st, 8vo, teg, 93p, gilt, col frn)	Scribner	1899	Seton, Ernest T.	80-125	
Seton, Ernest T.	Two Little Savages (1st, 8vo, grey/gilt, 552p, 29pl, pep)	Doubleday/Page	1903	Seton, Ernest T.	80-145	
Seton, Ernest T.	Wild Animal Play for Children (1st, sm8vo, green cl, 79p, b/w)	Doubleday/Page	1900	Seton, Ernest T.	100-150	
Seton, Ernest T.	Wild Animals at Home (1st, 8vo, 226p, gilt, b/w)	Doubleday/Page	1913	Seton, Ernest T.	120-170	
Seton, Ernest T.	Wild Animals I Have Known (1st, 8vo, gilt, teg, 359p, b/w, PPP)	Scribner	1898	Seton, Ernest T.	150-220	
Seton, Ernest T.	Woodmyth & Fable (1st, 8vo, 181p, red/gilt, b/w)	Century	1905	Seton, Ernest T.	120-165	
Seton, Grace G.	Nimrod's Wife (1st, 8vo, 406p, teg, 18pl)	Doubleday/Page	1907	Seton, Ernest T.	60-100	
Seton, Grace G.	Woman Tenderfoot (1st, 8vo, 361p, teg, b/w)	Doubleday/Page	1900	Seton, Ernest T.	80-130	
Setoun, Gabriel	Child World (1st, 12mo, AEG, gilt, 174p, uncut, 14pl)	L: John Lane	1896	Robinson, Charles	150-220	
Seuss, Dr.	500 Hats/Bartholomew Cubbins (1st, 4to, ibds, [47]p, pep, 1-color, DJ/1.50)	Vanguard Press	(1938)	Seuss, Dr.	700-1000	R
Seuss, Dr.	And to Think/I Saw It on Mulberry Street (1st, 4to, [32]p, ibds pep)	Vanguard Press	1937	Seuss, Dr.	500-800	R
Seuss, Dr.	Bartholomew & the Oobleck (1st, lg4to, [48]p, blue ibds, pep, DJ/2.00, CH)	Random	(1949)	Seuss, Dr.	500-750	
Seuss, Dr.	Cat in the Hat (1st, lg8vo, 61p, ipcb, 2-color, pep, DJ/2.00)	Random	(1957)	Seuss, Dr.	600-900	R
Seuss, Dr.	Cat in the Hat Comes Back (1st {std}, lg8vo, ibds 61p, color, pep, DJ/1.95)	Beginner Books	(1958)	Seuss, Dr.	400-650	
Seuss, Dr.	Cat in the Hat Songbook (1st, 4to, ibds, [64]p, color, pep, DJ/2.95)	Random	(1967)	Seuss, Dr.	250-400	
Seuss, Dr.	Dr. Seuss's ABC (1st, 8vo, ibds, 63p, color, DJ/1.95)	Beginner Books	(1963)	Seuss, Dr.	250-400	
Seuss, Dr.	Dr. Seuss's Sleep Book (1st, 4to, ibds, [56]p, color, DJ/2.95)	Random	(1962)	Seuss, Dr.	400-650	
Seuss, Dr.	Foot Book (1st, 8vo, ibds, [32]p, color, DJ/1.95)	Beginner Books	(1968)	Seuss, Dr.	250-400	
Seuss, Dr.	Fox in Socks (1st, 8vo, ibds, 61p, color, pep, DJ/1.95)	Beginner Books	(1965)	Seuss, Dr.	250-400	
Seuss, Dr.	Green Eggs & Ham (1st, lg8vo, 62p, ibds, color, DJ/1.95)	Beginner Books	1960	Seuss, Dr.	300-450	
Seuss, Dr.	Happy Birthday to You! (1st, lg4to, [57]p, ibds, color, pep, DJ/2.95)	Random	(1959)	Seuss, Dr.	500-700	
Seuss, Dr.	Hop on Pop (1st, 8vo, 64p, color, DJ/1.95)	Beginner Books	1963	Seuss, Dr.	250-400	
Seuss, Dr.	Horton Hatches the Egg (1st {std}, 4to, [55]p, fp 2-color)	Random	(1940)	Seuss, Dr.	450-600	
Seuss, Dr.	Horton Hears a Who! (1st, 4to, [68]p, ibds, fp 2-color, pep, DJ/2.50)	Random	(1954)	Seuss, Dr.	500-800	
Seuss, Dr.	How the Grinch Stole Christmas (1st, lg4to ibds [62]p, 1-color, pep DJ/2.50)	Random	1957	Seuss, Dr.	800-1200	
Seuss, Dr.	I Can Lick 30 Tigers Today... (1st, 4to, ibds, [65]p, color, pep, DJ/2.95)	Random	(1969)	Seuss, Dr.	300-450	
Seuss, Dr.	I Had Trouble Getting to Solla Sollew (1st, 4to, ibds, color, pep, DJ/2.95)	Random	(1965)	Seuss, Dr.	500-700	
Seuss, Dr.	If I Ran the Circus (1st, lg4to, [64]p, ibds, 3-color, pep, DJ/2.50)	Random	(1956)	Seuss, Dr.	450-650	
Seuss, Dr.	If I Ran the Zoo (1st, lg4to, ibds, [56]p, color, pep, DJ/2.00, CH)	Random	(1950)	Seuss, Dr.	450-650	
Seuss, Dr.	King's Stilts (1st, lg4to, [48]p, 1-color, cep)	Random	(1939)	Seuss, Dr.	500-800	
Seuss, Dr.	McElligot's Pool (1st, 4to, [56]p, green cl, color, pep, DJ/2.50, CH)	Random	(1947)	Seuss, Dr.	600-900	
Seuss, Dr.	Mr. Brown Can Moo: Can You? (1st, 8vo, [27]p, color, pep, DJ)	Random	(1970)	Seuss, Dr.	250-450	
Seuss, Dr.	On Beyond Zebra! (1st, 4to, ibds, unpag, color, DJ/2.50)	Random	(1955)	Seuss, Dr.	500-700	
Seuss, Dr.	One Fish Two Fish Red Fish Blue Fish (1st, lg8vo, 62p, ipcb, col, DJ/1.95)	Beginner Books	1960	Seuss, Dr.	400-650	
Seuss, Dr.	Scrambled Eggs Super (1st, lg4to, ibds, [52]p, color, pep, DJ/2.50)	Random	(1953)	Seuss, Dr.	400-650	
Seuss, Dr.	Seven Lady Godivas (1st {std}, sm4to, [80]p, fp 1-color, pep, DJ)	Random	(1939)	Seuss, Dr.	800-1200	
Seuss, Dr.	Sneetches and other Stories (1st, 4to, ibds, 65p, color, DJ/2.95)	Random	1961	Seuss, Dr.	300-450	
Seuss, Dr.	Thidwick the Big-Hearted Moose (1st, 4to, ibds, [40]p, color, pep, DJ/2.00)	Random	(1948)	Seuss, Dr.	500-750	
Seuss, Dr.	Yertle the Turtle (1st, 4to, ibds, [80]p, fp 2-color, pep, DJ/2.95)	Random	(1958)	Seuss, Dr.	500-700	
Sewell, A.A.	Ballad of the Prince (1st, lg4to, unpag, 12pl, pep)	R.H. Russell	1900	Sewell, A.A.	180-250	
Sewell, Anna	Black Beauty (1st UK, sm4to, gilt, 229p, b/w)	L: Jarrold	1894	Beer, John	100-145	
Sewell, Anna	Black Beauty (1st, sm8vo, 200p, grey/silver, 22 illus)	NY: Hovendon	1894	Toaspern, H.	200-300	
Sewell, Anna	Black Beauty (1st, sm8vo, 262p, 19pl)	L.C. Page	1902	Austin/Toaspern	80-125	
Sewell, Anna	Black Beauty (1st, 12mo, 319p, b/w)	Rand/McNally	(1904)	Copeland, Charles	45-70	
Sewell, Anna	Black Beauty (1st, 8vo, 96p, p-o, b/w)	Saalfield	(1905)	Miller, Harry L.	35-60	*
Sewell, Anna	Black Beauty (1st, 8vo, p-o, 261p, color)	Dodge	(1907)	Pancoast, C.W.	50-85	
Sewell, Anna	Black Beauty (1st, sm8vo, 45p, 6cp, pep)	Brewer/Barse	(1907)	Von Hofsten, H.	40-70	
Sewell, Anna	Black Beauty (sm8vo, red cl, 58p, p-o, color)	Reilly/Britton	1908	Neill, John R.	70-100	
Sewell, Anna	Black Beauty (1st, 8vo, 295p, 12cp)	Jacobs	(1910)	Scrivener, M.	50-80	
Sewell, Anna	Black Beauty (8vo, p-o, 357p, 20 fp color)	Platt/Peck	(1911)	Burke, J.M.	60-90	
Sewell, Anna	Black Beauty (1st, lg8vo, 278p, teg, p-o, 12cp)	Barse/Hopkins	(1911)	Dickey, Robert L.	40-60	*
Sewell, Anna	Black Beauty (1st, 4to, blue/gilt, 291p, 18 ticp, pep)	L: Jarrold	[1912]	Aldin, Cecil	250-350	
Sewell, Anna	Black Beauty (1st AM, 8vo, 291p, 18 ticp, pep)	Stokes	[1913]	Aldin, Cecil	200-300	
Sewell, Anna	Black Beauty (1st, 8vo, 224p, blue/gilt, 24cp, pep)	L: J.M. Dent	1915	Kemp-Welch, Lucy	100-160	
Sewell, Anna	Black Beauty (1st, lg8vo, p-o, 239p, 4cp, 13pl, pep)	Dodd	1923	Pyle, Katharine	100-160	
Sewell, Anna	Black Beauty (1st, lg8vo, 244p, p-o, gilt, col frn, 1-color, pep)	Sears	(1926)	McMann, Jessica S.	40-60	*
Sewell, Anna	Black Beauty (1st, 8vo, green/gilt, p-o, 297p, 4cp, pep)	Winston	(1927)	Prittie, Edwin J.	35-60	
Sewell, Anna	Black Beauty (1st, 8vo, p-o, 234p, col frn, b/w)	Saalfield	(1924)	Williams, Florence	25-45	*
Sewell, Anna	Black Beauty (1st, 8vo, 224p, 8cp)	L: Bell	1931	Woodward, Alice B.	55-80	
Sewell, Anna	Black Beauty (Special Ed., sm8vo, 288p, 45p, pep, 10cp, DJ/2.00)	Grosset/Dunlap	(1945)	Eichenberg, Fritz	45-70	R
Sewell, Anna	Black Beauty (1st, 8vo, 315p, color, pep, DJ/1.25, RC)	World	(1946)	Dennis, Wesley	25-45	
Sewell, Anna	Black Beauty (1st, 4to, 62p, ibds, color, pep, DJ)	Random	1949	Erickson, Phoebe	40-60	*
Sewell, Anna	Black Beauty (1st, lg ob8vo, [128]p, fp b/w, DJ/3.00)	Scribner	(1952)	Brown, Paul	120-200	*
Sewell, Daisy	About Fairies.... (1st, sq8vo, ibds, 76p, 5cp)	L: Allenson	[1930]	McConnell, Jeannie	120-180	
Sewell, Daisy	Visions in Fairyland (1st, sq8vo, ibds, 69p, 3cp)	L: Allenson	[1930]	McConnell, Jeannie	100-170	

AUTHOR: 192

AUTHOR	TITLE	PUBLISHER	DATE	ARTIST	PRICE	LC
Sewell, Helen	ABC for Everyday (1st, 4to, ipcb, [28]p, pep, 2-color)	Macmillan	1930	Sewell, Helen	120-180	R*
Sewell, Helen	Belinda the Mouse (1st, sq12mo, grey cl, [61]p, color, DJ/1.25)	Oxford U. Pr.	(1944)	Sewell, Helen	40-65	
Sewell, Helen	Birthdays for Robin (1st, sq12mo, [46]p, grey cl, fp 3-color, DJ/1.00)	Macmillan	1943	Sewell, Helen	30-50	
Sewell, Helen	Blue Barns (1st, sm sq4to, [46]p, b/w, DJ/1.75)	Macmillan	1933	Sewell, Helen	80-120	R
Sewell, Helen	Head for Happy (1st, ob4to, [56]p, p-o, pep, DJ/2.50)	Macmillan	1931	Sewell, Helen	80-120	
Sewell, Helen	Jimmy & Jemima (1st, 8vo, [47]p, p-o, color, DJ/1.00)	Macmillan	1940	Sewell, Helen	40-60	
Sewell, Helen	Ming & Mehitable (1st, 16mo, yellow cl, [60]p, dep, color, DJ/0.75)	Macmillan	1936	Sewell, Helen	30-50	
Sewell, Helen	Peggy & the Pony (1st, sq8vo, blue cl, [47]p, 2-color, DJ/1.25)	Oxford U. Pr.	(1936)	Sewell, Helen	55-90	
Sewell, Helen	Peggy & the Pup (1st, sq8vo, [46]p, beige cl, fp 2-color, DJ/1.25)	Oxford U. Pr.	(1941)	Sewell, Helen	35-60	*
Sewell, Helen	Three Tall Tales (1st {std}, sq4to, ibds, [40]p, color, DJ/1.50)	Macmillan	1947	Sewell, Helen	50-80	
Sewell, Helen	Words to the Wise (1st, ob8vo, [64]p, 1-color, tan cl, dep)	Dodd	(1932)	Sewell, Helen	40-65	
Seyfert, Ella	Little Amish Schoolhouse (1st, lg8vo, 136p, dp color, pep, DJ/2.00)	Crowell	1939	Ninon	30-50	*
Shackelford, L.T.	As I See It (1st {std}, ob8vo, 96p, b/w, DJ/1.50)	Knopf	1943	Shackelford, L.T.	50-80	
Shaffer, Robert	Skeeter: Story of an Arabian Gazelle (1st, 8vo, 192p, b/w, DJ/2.75)	Dodd	(1952)	Wiese, Kurt	30-50	*
Shakespeare, Wm.	As You Like It (1st, 4to, ibds, 143p, gilt, 40 ticp)	L: Hodder	[1909]	Thomson, Hugh	125-200	
Shakespeare, Wm.	As You Like It (1st, 4to, 111p, red cl, p-o, 6 ticp)	L: Jackson	1930	Austen, John	80-120	
Shakespeare, Wm.	Comedy of the Twelfth Night (1st, 4to, 144p, green/gilt, 40 ticp)	L: Hodder	[1908]	Robinson, W. Heath	200-325	
Shakespeare, Wm.	Hamlet (1st, lg4to, 165p, gilt, 30 ticp)	L: Hodder	[1900]	Simmonds, W.G.	250-400	
Shakespeare, Wm.	Hamlet (1st, 4to, 175p, black bds, gilt, 35 b/w)	L: Selwyn/Blount	(1922)	Austen, John	220-300	
Shakespeare, Wm.	Hamlet (1st AM, 4to, black bds, b/w)	Dutton	(1922)	Austen, John	140-200	
Shakespeare, Wm.	Macbeth (1st {std}, lg8vo, black bds, 125p, 12 fp b/w, pep)	Garden City	1946	Dali, Salvador	200-300	
Shakespeare, Wm.	Merchant of Venice (1st, lg8vo, gilt, 143p, 36 ticp)	L: Hodder	[1909]	Linton, James D.	100-180	
Shakespeare, Wm.	Merry Wives of Windsor (1st, 4to, teg, gilt, 172p, 40 ticp)	L: Heinemann	1910	Thomson, Hugh	200-300	
Shakespeare, Wm.	Merry Wives of Windsor (1st AM, 4to, 170p, red/gilt, teg, 40 ticp)	Stokes	(1910)	Thomson, Hugh	165-250	
Shakespeare, Wm.	MidSummer Night's Dream (1st, sq8vo, green/gilt, teg, 128p, pep)	L: Dent	1895	Bell, Robert A.	100-160	
Shakespeare, Wm.	MidSummer Night's Dream (1st, sm4to, p-o, 93p, 12cp, pep)	Stokes	(1907)	Perkins, Lucy F.	120-180	
Shakespeare, Wm.	MidSummer Night's Dream (1st, lg8vo, 134p, grey/gilt, 40 ticp)	L: Heinemann	1908	Rackham, Arthur	425-600	
Shakespeare, Wm.	MidSummer Night's Dream (1st AM, 4to, 187p, teg, gilt, 12 ticp)	Henry Holt & Co.	1914	Robinson, W. Heath	350-450	
Shakespeare, Wm.	MidSummer Night's Dream (1st, lg4to, 187p, gilt, 12 ticp)	L: Constable	1914	Robinson, W. Heath	400-600	
Shakespeare, Wm.	Romeo & Juliet (1st, 4to, 95p, purple cl, 8 ticp)	L: Batsford	1936	Messel, Oliver	80-120	*
Shakespeare, Wm.	Songs (1st, 12mo, 140p, uncut, green/gilt, teg, 11pl)	J. Lane	1901	Ospovat, Henry	60-80	
Shakespeare, Wm.	Songs & Sonnets (1st AM, 4to, 240p, blue/gilt, 12 ticp, pep)	McKay	[1915]	Robinson, Charles	250-400	
Shakespeare, Wm.	Songs & Sonnets (1st, lg8vo, 240p, blue/gilt, 12 ticp, pep)	L: Duckworth	(1915)	Robinson, Charles	350-500	
Shakespeare, Wm.	The Tempest (4to, teg, 106p, uncut, b/w, pep)	L: Freemantle	1901	Bell, Robert A.	80-120	
Shakespeare, Wm.	The Tempest (1st, 4to, blue/gilt, 144p, 40 ticp)	L: Hodder	[1908]	Dulac, Edmund	350-500	
Shakespeare, Wm.	The Tempest (1st, 4to, gilt, teg, 130p, 20 ticp, pep)	L: Chapman	1908	Woodroffe, Paul	170-240	
Shakespeare, Wm.	The Tempest (1st AM, 4to, grey/gilt, 20 ticp)	Doubleday/Page	(1926)	Rackham, Arthur	250-350	
Shakespeare, Wm.	The Tempest (1st, sm4to, olive/gilt, 185p, 20 ticp)	L: Heinemann	1926	Rackham, Arthur	350-500	
Shakespeare, Wm.	Under the Greenwood Tree (1st, 4to, black/gilt, 51p, color, DJ)	NY: Oxford U.Pr.	[1940]	Weisgard, Leonard	45-65	
Shakespeare, Wm.	Venus & Adonis (1st, 4to, red/gilt, 112p, pep, 12cp)	Macveagh/Dial	1930	Kutcher, Ben	35-60	*
Shakespeare, Wm.	Winter's Tale (1st, sm4to, 98p, gilt, 12cp, pep, DJ)	L: Dent	(1922)	Armfield, Maxwell	90-140	
Shane, Ruth & Harold	New Baby (1st {A}, sm8vo, [42]p, ibds, color, LGB/#41)	Simon/Schuster	1948	Wilkin, Eloise B.	30-50	
Shane, Ruth & Harold	The Twins (1st {A}, 12mo, ibds, [28]p, color, LGB/#227)	Simon/Schuster	(1955)	Wilkin, Eloise B.	70-100	
Shank, Margarethe	Coffee Train (1st {std}, sm8vo, 285p, b/w, DJ/3.50)	Doubleday	1953	Lonette, Reisie	20-35	
Shankland, Frank	Bird Book (1st, 4to, 60p, ibds, 8 fp color)	Saalfield	(1931)	Peat, Fern B.	50-80	
Shankland, Frank	Friends of the Forest (1st, lg4to, ibds, 92p, color)	Saalfield	(1932)	Peat, Fern B.	40-65	
Shannon, Monica	California Fairy Tales (1st {std}, sm8vo, 298p, cp, pep)	Doubleday/Page	1926	Millard, C.E.	50-80	
Shannon, Monica	Dobry (1st, lg8vo, 176p, grey cl, col frn, pep, DJ/2.00, NM)	Viking	1934	Katchamakoff, A.	100-165	R
Shannon, Monica	Eyes for the Dark (1st {std}, 8vo, 311p, 4cp, 15pl, pep)	Doubleday/Doran	1928	Millard, C.E.	35-60	
Shannon, Monica	Goose Grass Rhymes (1st {std}, sm8vo, 155p, col frn, b/w, pep)	Doubleday/Doran	1930	Brown, Neva K.	40-60	*
Shannon, Monica	Tawnymore (1st {std}, sm8vo, 254p, col frn, fp b/w, pep)	Doubleday/Doran	1931	Charlot, Jean	80-130	
Shapiro, Irwin	John Henry & Double-Jointed Steam Drill (1st, lg8vo, [55]p, b/w, DJ/1.50)	J. Messner	(1945)	Daugherty, James	30-50	
Shapiro, Irwin	Yankee Thunder (1st, 8vo, 205p, gilt, b/w, DJ/2.50)	J. Messner	(1944)	Daugherty, James	35-60	
Shapp, Martha	Let's Find Out about Summer (1st, 8vo, 42p, color, DJ/2.50)	F. Watts	1963	DePaola, Tomie	25-40	
Sharfman, Amalie	Beagle Named Bertram (1st, 8vo, 166p, b/w, DJ/2.50)	Crowell	(1954)	Palazzo, Tony	30-45	
Sharmat, Marjorie	Gladys told Me to Meet her Here (1st, 4to, ibds, 31p, color, pep, DJ/3.95)	Harper	(1970)	Frascino, Edward	30-50	*
Sharmat, Marjorie	Goodnight Andrew, Goodnight Craig (1st, 12mo, 32p, color, DJ/2.95)	Harper	(1969)	Chalmers, Mary	25-40	
Sharmat, Marjorie	Rex (1st, sm ob4to, 32p, fp 2-color, pep, DJ/3.50)	Harper	(1967)	McCully, Emily	30-50	
Sharp, Dallas L.	Roof & Meadow (1st, sm8vo, green cl, 281p, b/w)	Century	1904	Horsfall, Bruce	25-45	
Sharp, Edith L.	Nkwala (1st {std}, 8vo, 125p, b/w, DJ/3.00)	Little/Brown	(1958)	Winter, William	30-50	R*
Sharp, Evelyn	All the Way to Fairyland (1st, 8vo, 196p, 8cp & cvr by...)	L/NY: Longmans	1898	Dearmer, Mabel	200-300	
Sharp, Evelyn	At the Relton Arms (1st, 12mo, 182p, gilt, uncut, design by..)	L: John Lane	1895	Beardsley, Aubrey	80-130	
Sharp, Evelyn	Child's Christmas (1st, lg8vo, 227p, orange/gilt, AEG, 38 color)	L: Blackie	(1906)	Robinson, Charles	400-600	
Sharp, Evelyn	Child's Christmas (1st AM, lg8vo, teg, gilt, 227p, color, pep)	Caldwell	[1907]	Robinson, Charles	300-500	
Sharp, Evelyn	Hill that Fell Down (1st, 8vo, green/gilt, 275p)	L: Blackie	1909	Browne, Gordon	80-120	
Sharp, Evelyn	Micky... (1st, 8vo, 240p)	L: Macmillan	1905	Brock, Henry M.	40-60	*
Sharp, Evelyn	Other Side of the Sun (1st, 12mo, 188p, 8cp)	L: John Lane	1900	Syrett, Nellie	150-250	
Sharp, Evelyn	Round the World to Wympland (1st, sm8vo, 235p, 8pl)	L: John Lane	1901	Woodward, Alice B.	80-120	
Sharp, Evelyn	Story of the Weathercock (1st AM, 4to, 258p, teg, red/gilt, 16cp)	Caldwell	[1907]	Robinson, Charles	200-300	
Sharp, Evelyn	Story of the Weathercock (1st, 4to, 258p, red/gilt, AEG, 16cp, pep)	L: Blackie	(1907)	Robinson, Charles	200-300	
Sharp, Evelyn	What Happened at Christmas (1st, 4to, unpag)	L: Blackie	[1915]	Robinson, Charles	125-200	*
Sharp, Evelyn	Wymps & other Fairy Tales (1st, 8vo, 190p, 8cp)	NY: J. Lane	1897	Dearmer, Mabel	250-350	
Sharp, Evelyn	Youngest Girl in the School (1st, 8vo, 326p)	L: Macmillan	1901	Brock, Charles E.	40-60	*
Sharp, Margery	Lost at the Fair (1st {std}, sm8vo, 57p, fp 2-color, DJ/2.95)	Little/Brown	(1965)	Fry, Rosalind	25-40	
Sharp, Margery	Melisande (1st {std}, 4to, [88]p, fp b/w, DJ/2.95)	Little/Brown	(1960)	McKie, Roy	25-40	
Sharp, Margery	Miss Bianca (1st {std}, 8vo, 138p, grey cl, fp b/w, DJ)	L: Collins	1962	Williams, Garth	50-85	
Sharp, Margery	Miss Bianca in the Orient (1st AM {std}, 8vo, 144p, gilt, b/w, DJ/4.95)	Little/Brown	(1970)	Blegvad, Erik	40-65	
Sharp, Margery	Miss Bianca in the Salt Mines (1st AM {std}, 8vo, 148p, b/w, DJ/3.95)	Little/Brown	(1966)	Williams, Garth	50-80	R

AUTHOR	TITLE	PUBLISHER	DATE	ARTIST	PRICE	LC
Sharp, Margery	Rescuers: a Fantasy (1st, 8vo, green/gilt, 158p, b/w, DJ)	L: Collins	1959	Brook, Judith	170-250	
Sharp, Margery	Rescuers: a Fantasy (1st AM {std}, 8vo, blue cl, 149p, b/w, DJ/3.50)	Little/Brown	(1959)	Williams, Garth	140-220	
Sharp, Margery	The Turret (1st AM {std}, 8vo, 138p, fp b/w, DJ/3.95)	Little/Brown	(1963)	Williams, Garth	60-100	R
Sharts, Joseph W.	Romance of a Rogue (1st, sm8vo, 249p, designs by...)	Herbert Stone	1902	Hazenplug, Frank	50-80	
Shaw, Charles G.	Blue Guess Book (1st, 8vo, ipcb, [48]p, color, DJ/1.00)	W.R. Scott	(1942)	Shaw, Charles G.	50-80	
Shaw, Charles G.	Giant of Central Park (1st, lg8vo, ipcb, [64]p, fp b/w, DJ/1.50)	W.R. Scott	(1940)	Shaw, Charles G.	50-80	
Shaw, Charles G.	Guess Book (1st, 8vo, [48]p, ipcb, color, DJ/1.00)	W.R. Scott	(1941)	Shaw, Charles G.	50-80	
Shaw, George B.	St. Joan (1st, folio, ibds, 182p, p-o, teg, 16 ticp, 1/750)	L: Constable	(1924)	Ricketts, Charles	200-300	
Shaw, Richard	Budd's Noisy Wagon (1st, ob8vo, [32]p, fp 3-color, DJ/2.95)	NY: Warne	(1968)	Galdone, Paul	45-70	
Shay, Frank	Drawn from the Wood (1st, 8vo, 186p, b/w, DJ)	Macaulay	(1929)	Held, John	70-120	
Shay, Frank	More Pious Friends (1st, 8vo, 192p, b/w)	Macaulay	(1927)	Held, John	60-100	
Shecter, Ben	Conrad's Castle (1st, sm4to, [32]p, color, DJ/3.50)	Harper	(1967)	Shecter, Ben	30-50	
Shecter, Ben	Partouche Plants a Seed (1st, ob8vo, ipcb, 32p, 2-color, DJ/2.50)	Harper	(1966)	Shecter, Ben	25-45	*
Sheehy, Emma	Molly and the Golden Wedding (1st {std}, 8vo, 159p, b/w, DJ/2.50)	Holt	(1956)	Henneberger, Rbt.	20-30	
Sheffield, Rena C.	Golden Hollow (1st, sm8vo, 214p, col frn, cvr by...)	NY: John Lane	1913	Hazenplug, Frank	50-85	
Shelby, Annie B.	Lullaby Book (1st, 8vo, blue/gilt, 183p, col frn by...)	Duffield	1921	Smith, Jessie W.	80-125	
Sheldon, Charles	Crucifixion of Philip Strong (1st, 12mo, 267p, gray/gilt, cvr by...)	McClurg	1894	Armstrong, Margaret	30-50	*
Shelley, Mary W.	Frankenstein (1st, lg8vo, 259p, 15 b/w)	Smith/Haas	1934	Ward, Lynd	180-250	
Shelley, Percy B.	Poems of Shelley (1st, 16mo, 244p, teg, purple/gilt, 8cp)	L: Jack	(1907)	King, Jessie	150-250	
Shelley, Percy B.	Sensitive Plant (1st, 8vo, gilt, 60p, teg, uncut, 12pl)	L: Aldine House	1898	Housman, Laurence	150-220	
Shelley, Percy B.	Sensitive Plant (1st AM, 4to, 127p, gilt, teg, 18 ticp)	Heinemann/Lipp.	[1911]	Robinson, Charles	300-450	
Shemin, Margaretha	Mrs. Herring (1st, 8vo, 192p, b/w, DJ/3.95)	Lothrop, Lee	(1967)	Quackenbush, Rbt.	20-35	
Shemin, Margarteha	Little Riders (1st, lg8vo, 60p, b/w, DJ/3.00)	Coward	(1963)	Spier, Peter E.	30-50	*
Shenton, Edward	Riders of the Winds (1st, lg8vo, 205p, gilt, 16cp, pep, DJ/2.50)	Macrae Smith	(1929)	Shenton, Edward	50-80	
Shepard, Birse	Cat Next Door (1st, 8vo, 64p, fp b/w, pep, DJ/1.50)	Oxford U. Pr.	(1943)	Doane, Pelagie	20-30	
Shepard, Ernest	Ben and Brock (1st AM {std}, sm8vo, 91p, gilt, b/w, DJ/2.95)	Doubleday	(1966)	Shepard, Ernest H.	30-50	
Shepard, Ernest	Betsy and Joe (1st AM {std}, 12mo, 78p, b/w, DJ/3.25)	Dutton	(1967)	Shepard, Ernest H.	50-80	
Shepard, Odell	Pedlar's Progress (1st, lg8vo, 546p, 5pl, DJ/3.75)	Little/Brown	1937	Robillard, Conrad	30-50	
Shephard, Esther	Paul Bunyan (1st, 8vo, gilt, 234p, fp b/w)	Harcourt	(1924)	Kent, Rockwell	90-120	
Shepherd, J.A.	Zig Zag Fables (1st, ob4to, 36p, ibds, color)	L: Gardner	1897	Shepherd, J.A.	170-240	
Shepperd, Eli	Plantation Songs for My Lady's Banjo (1st, lg8vo, 150p, 25pl)	R.H. Russell	1901	(Photos)	250-400	
Sheridan, Richard B.	School for Scandal (1st, 4to, gilt, teg, 196p, 25 ticp, pep)	L: Hodder	(1911)	Thomson, Hugh	180-250	
Sheridan, Richard B.	The Duenna (1st, lg8vo, 105p, bds, gilt, 12cp)	L: Constable	1925	Sheringham, George	60-90	
Sheridan, Richard B.	The Rivals (1st, 8vo, 365p, b/w)	(London)	1896	Sullivan, Edmund J.	70-100	
Sheridan, Richard B.	The Rivals (1st, 8vo, 131p, 17pl, cvr by...)	Crowell	(1907)	Armstrong, Margaret	40-60	
Sherlock, Philip	Anansi the Spider Man (1st {std}, 8vo, green cl, 112p, b/w, DJ/2.50)	Crowell	(1954)	Brown, Marcia	80-140	R
Sherman, Fanny J.	Admiral Wags of USS Lexington (1st {std}, sm4to, 84p, 1-color, DJ/2.25)	Dodd	1943	Brown, Paul	70-120	
Sherman, Frank D.	Little Folk Lyrics (1st, sm8vo, 140p, green cl, teg, designs by...)	Houghton	1897	Rogers, Bruce	30-50	
Sherman, Henry	Children's Bible (1st, lg8vo, 329p, black cl, p-o, 15cp, pep, SC)	Scribner	1922	Various	100-165	
Sherman, James W.	Quart of Moonlight (1st, sm8vo, 147p, blue cl, b/w)	Little/Brown	1928	Gee, John	25-45	
Sherman, Nancy	Gwendolyn & Weathercock (1st, ob4to, unpag, ibds color, pep, DJ/3.50, NYT)	Golden Press	1963	Sorel, Edward	120-200	
Sherman, Nancy	Gwendolyn, the Miracle Hen (1st, ob4to, [25]p, ibds, color, pep, DJ/2.95)	Golden Press	1961	Sorel, Edward	120-200	R
Sherman, Nancy	Miss Agatha's Lark (1st {std}, 4to, [32]p, color, DJ/3.50)	Bobbs-Merrill	(1968)	Vasiliu, Mircea	30-45	*
Sherman, Stuart P.	Critical Woodcuts (1st, 8vo, 348p, 15 fp b/w, DJ)	Scribner	1926	Zadig, Bertrand	55-80	
Sherratt, J.H.L.	Goblin Gobblers (1st, ob8vo, 64p, bds, p-o, 10cp)	L: Warne	(1910)	Crombie, Charles E.	140-225	
Sherrill, Dorothy	Little White Teddy Bear... (1st {std}, 12mo, [62]p, color)	Farrar/Rinehart	(1931)	Sherrill, Dorothy	70-90	
Sherrill, Dorothy	Story of a Little Duck (1st, 12mo, [50]p, ibds, color)	Merrill	(1934)	Sherrill, Dorothy	60-80	
Sherrill, Dorothy	Story of Roly & Poly (1st {std}, 24mo, [63]p, fp color, cep, DJ/1.50)	Crowell	(1952)	Sherrill, Dorothy	50-80	
Sherwood, E. Hugh	Bobbie Bubbles (1st, sq8vo, 78p, ibds, color)	Rand/McNally	(1916)	Sherwood, E. Hugh	70-100	
Sherwood, E. Hugh	Jack Jingling in Jungleland (1st, lg ob8vo, 80p, ibds, fp color)	Rand/McNally	(1918)	Sherwood, E. Hugh	100-170	
Sherwood, Lorraine	Old Abe, American Eagle (1st, sm8vo, 60p, ibds, color, DJ/1.50)	Scribner	1946	Milhous, Katherine	50-80	
Sherwood, Mary M.	Fairchild Family (sq8vo, 111p, gilt, p-o, 8cp)	Dutton	(1908)	Beale, Evelyn	55-80	
Sherwood, Mary M.	Prince Por Quoi (1st, 12mo, 211p, designs by...)	Houghton	1907	Rogers, Bruce	25-45	
Sherwood, Merriam	Road to Cathay (1st, lg8vo, 251p, gilt, col frn, pep)	Macmillan	1928	Siegel, William	25-45	
Shetter, Stella C.	When Grandma Was a Little Girl (1st, 12mo, 250p, p-o, 4cp)	Rand/McNally	(1926)	Gregory, Dorothy L.	25-40	
Shideler, Ross (tran)	Staffan (1st, 12mo, [25]p, grey cl, color, DJ/3.25)	Parnassus Press	(1970)	Sidjakov, Nicolas	35-50	*
Shiel, Matthew P.	Lord of the Sea (1st AM, 12mo, 474p, blue cl, frn by...)	Stokes	(1901)	Russell, Walter	150-250	
Shiel, Matthew P.	Shapes in the Fire (1st AM, 12mo, 324p, blue cl, cvr & ti page by..)	Roberts Bros.	1896	Beardsley, Aubrey	180-240	
Shipman, Nell	Kurly Kew & Tree-Princess (1st, sm8vo, 200p, orange cl, 6cp, pep)	MacVeagh/Dial	1930	Ellender, Elizabeth	35-60	*
Shippen, Kath. B.	Andrew Carnegie & the Age of Steel (1st {std}, 8vo, 183p, b/w, DJ/1.95)	Random	(1958)	Barth, Ernest	20-35	
Shippen, Kath. B.	Big Mose (1st {std}, 8vo, grey cl, 90p, b/w, DJ/2.00)	Harper	(1953)	Graham, Margaret B.	40-65	
Shippen, Kath. B.	Bridle for Pegasus (1st, lg8vo, 192p, b/w, DJ/3.50)	Viking	1951	Falls, Charles B.	25-40	
Shippen, Kath. B.	Great Heritage (1st, lg8vo, 230p, yellow cl, b/w, pep, DJ/3.50)	Viking	1947	Falls, Charles B.	30-55	
Shippen, Kath. B.	I Know a City: Story of New York' Growth (1st, 8vo, 192p, b/w, DJ/2.75)	Viking	1954	King, Robin	20-35	*
Shippen, Kath. B.	Lightfoot: Story of an Indian Boy (1st, 8vo, 122p, b/w, DJ/2.00)	Viking	1950	Two-Arrows, Tom	30-50	*
Shippen, Kath. B.	Men of Medicine (1st, 8vo, 220p, b/w, DJ/3.50)	Viking	(1957)	Ravielli, Anthony	25-40	*
Shippen, Kath. B.	Men, Microscopes & Living Things (1st, 8vo, grn cl, fp b/w, DJ/3.00, NH)	Viking	1955	Ravielli, Anthony	50-80	R
Shippen, Kath. B.	Moses (1st, 8vo, blue cl, 132p, DJ/2.00, frn by...)	Harper	(1949)	Cassel, Lili	35-60	
Shippen, Kath. B.	Mr. Bell Invents the Telephone (1st, 8vo, 183p, 2-color, DJ/1.50)	Random	(1952)	Floethe, Richard	30-50	
Shippen, Kath. B.	New Found World (1st, lg8vo, 262p, blue cl, b/w, pep, DJ/3.50, NH)	Viking	1945	Falls, Charles B.	45-70	
Shippen, Kath. B.	Portals to the Past (1st, 8vo, 255p, b/w, DJ/4.50)	Viking	(1963)	Silverman, Mel	25-40	*
Shirk, Jeannette C.	Bela the Juggler (1st {std}, lg8vo, green cl, 66p, 2-color, pep, DJ/1.75)	Suttonhouse	(1936)	Finger, Helen	45-70	
Shirk, Jeannette C.	Mr. Baxter's Dandelion Garden (1st {std}, 4to, 58p, fp b/w, dep, DJ/1.50)	Dutton	1940	Shirk, Jeanette C.	30-50	
Shirley, Edward	Reggie & I (1st, 4to, 64p, ibds, 8cp)	L: T. Nelson	[1910]	Hassall, John	180-260	
Shirley, Edward	The Twins (4to, 63p, ibds, 24cp)	L: Nelson	[1905]	Hassall, John	160-240	
Sholl, Anna M.	Faery Tales of Weir (1st, 8vo, 172p, purple/gilt, col frn, pep)	Dutton	(1918)	Pyle, Katharine	70-100	
Short, Wayne	Cheechakoes (1st {std}, 8vo, 244p, b/w, DJ/4.95)	Random	(1964)	Parnall, Peter	25-45	*
Shortall, Leonard	Andy, the Dog Walker (1st, 8vo, 48p, 2-color, pep, DJ/2.95)	Wm. Morrow	(1968)	Shortall, Leonard	20-35	*

AUTHOR	TITLE	PUBLISHER	DATE	ARTIST	PRICE	LC
Shortall, Leonard	Peter in Grand Central Station (1st, 8vo, 46p, color, DJ/3.25)	Wm. Morrow	(1969)	Shortall, Leonard	20-35	
Shotwell, Louisa	Roosevelt Grady (1st {std}, 8vo, 151p, b/w, DJ/2.95)	World	(1963)	Burchard, Peter	25-40	
Showalter, Jean B.	Around the Corner (1st {std}, 4to, [30]p, 3-color, pep, DJ/2.95)	Doubleday	(1965)	Duvoisin, Roger	35-50	
Showalter, Jean B.	Donkey Ride (1st {std}, ob4to, [40]p, color, DJ/3.95)	Doubleday	(1967)	Ungerer, Tomi	30-50	
Showers, Paul	Columbus Day (1st, 8vo, [40]p, fp 2-color, DJ/2.95)	Crowell	(1965)	Emberley, Ed	25-40	
Showers, Paul	Follow Your Nose (1st, ob8vo, [40]p, fp 2-color, DJ/2.50)	Crowell	1963	Galdone, Paul	25-40	
Showers, Paul	In the Night (1st, ob8vo, [38]p, fp 2-color, DJ/1.95, CH)	Crowell	(1961)	Keats, Ezra J.	50-85	*
Showers, Paul	Listening Walk (1st, ob8vo, [38]p, fp 2-color, DJ/2.50)	Crowell	(1961)	Aliki	20-30	*
Showers, Paul	Look at Your Eyes (1st, ob8vo, [30]p, color, DJ)	Crowell	(1962)	Galdone, Paul	25-40	
Showers, Paul	What Happened to a Hamburger? (1st, ob8vo, 33p, color, DJ/3.75)	Crowell	(1970)	Rockwell, Anne	25-40	
Showers, Paul	Your Skin and Mine (1st, sq8vo, [36]p, 2-color, DJ/2.95)	Crowell	(1965)	Galdone, Paul	30-45	
Shuck, Professor H.	Medieval Stories (1st, 8vo, brown cl, 8pl, pep)	L: Sands	1902	Robinson, W. Heath	120-180	
Shuldham, Edward B.	Pictures from Birdland (1st {1st bk.}, 4to, ibds, 24cp)	L: Dent	1899	Detmold, Edward J.	600-850	
Shulevitz, Uri	Moon in My Room (1st {std}, [1st bk.], 8vo, [30]p, color, DJ/2.50)	Harper	1963	Shulevitz, Uri	60-90	
Shulevitz, Uri	One Monday Morning (1st, 4to, [46]p, color, DJ)	Scribner	(1967)	Shulevitz, Uri	30-50	
Shulevitz, Uri	Rain Rain Rivers (1st, ob4to, [32]p, fp 2-color, pep, DJ/4.50)	Farrar, Straus	(1969)	Shulevitz, Uri	60-90	R*
Shura, Mary F.	Mary's Marvelous Mouse (1st, 8vo, [30]p, 2-color, pep, DJ/2.75)	Knopf	(1962)	Adams, Adrienne	30-50	
Shura, Mary F.	Nearsighted Knight (1st {std}, 8vo, 111p, fp b/w, DJ/3.25)	Knopf	(1964)	Adams, Adrienne	25-45	
Shura, Mary F.	Shoe Full of Shamrock (1st {std}, sm4to, 64p, b/w, DJ/3.75)	Atheneum	1965	Bodecker, N.M.	20-30	
Shura, Mary F.	Tale of Middle Length (1st {std}, 8vo, 105p, green cl, b/w, DJ/3.50)	Atheneum	1966	Parnall, Peter	25-35	
Shurtleff, Bertrand	Awol the Courier (1st {std}, 8vo, 272p, b/w, DJ/2.50)	Bobbs-Merrill	(1951)	Thorne, Diana	40-65	*
Shute, Henry A.	Brite & Fair (1st, sm8vo, 286p, b/w, pep, DJ/4.50)	Noone House	1968	Tudor, Tasha	70-100	
Shute, Henry A.	Farming It (1st, 12mo, 248p, gilt, 16pl)	Houghton	1909	Birch, Reginald	30-50	
Shute, Henry A.	Real Diary of a Real Boy (1st, sm8vo, 194p, red cl, 12 b/w, DJ/3.95)	R.R. Smith Co.	(1967)	Tudor, Tasha	70-100	
Shuttlesworth, Dorothy	ABC of Buses (1st {std}, ob4to, ipcb, fp 3-color, cep, DJ/3.25)	Doubleday	(1965)	Shortall, Leonard	40-65	*
Sickels, Evelyn	Pet Parade (1st, sq12mo, ipcb, 64p, color, pep)	Scribner	1935	Potter, Edna	30-45	
Sickels, Evelyn	That Boy Johnny! (1st, 8vo, 120p, b/w, DJ/2.00)	Scribner	(1952)	Martinez, Jean	30-50	*
Sicotte, Virginia	Riot of Quiet (1st {std}, 12mo, [32]p, color, DJ/2.95)	Holt, Rinehart	(1969)	Ardizzone, Edward	40-65	
Siddiqui, Ashraf	Bhombal Dass (1st {std}, sm4to, [28]p, color, DJ/2.75)	Macmillan	(1959)	Hamil, Tom	40-65	*
Siddiqui, Ashraf	Toontoony Pie (1st {std}, 8vo, 158p, b/w, DJ/3.50)	World	(1961)	Fairservis, Jan	20-30	
Sidgwick, Frank (ed)	Ballads & Lyrics of Love (1st, lg8vo, teg, 178p, uncut, 10cp)	L: Chatto	1908	Shaw, Byam	70-100	
Sidgwick, Frank (ed)	Legendary Ballads (1st, lg8vo, 180p, red/gilt, uncut, teg, 10cp)	L: Chatto	1908	Shaw, Byam	70-100	
Sidney, Margaret	Ballad of the Lost Hare (1st, ob4to, ibds, [44]p, color)	D. Lothrop Co.	1882	9 Chromos	150-225	R
Sidney, Margaret	Ben Pepper (1st, sm8vo, 474p, green/gilt, 6pl)	Lothrop Pub.	1905	Wireman, Eugenie	100-160	
Sidney, Margaret	Child's Day Book (1st, 4to, ibds, [32]p)	D. Lothrop Co.	1893	5 Chromos	100-170	
Sidney, Margaret	Five Little Peppers in Little Brown House (1st, sm8vo, 434p, gilt, 8pl)	Lothrop, Lee	1907	Heyer, Hermann	100-160	
Sidney, Margaret	Five Little Peppers Midway (1st, 12mo, 512p, gilt, 20pl)	D. Lothrop Co.	(1890)	Taylor, W.L.	70-100	
Sidney, Margaret	Our Davie Pepper (1st, sm8vo, 492p, green/gilt, 6 tipl)	Lothrop, Lee	(1916)	Stephens, Alice B.	60-100	
Sidney, Margaret	Phronsie Pepper (1st, sm8vo, 437p, green/gilt, b/w)	Lothrop, Lee	1897	McDermott, Jessie	70-120	
Sidney, Margaret	Stories Polly Pepper Told (1st, 12mo, green/gilt, 469p, b/w)	Lothrop Pub.	1899	McDermott/Barry	100-165	
Sidney, Margaret (cmp)	Lullabies and Jingles (1st, sm4to, ibds, 32p)	D. Lothrop Co.	1893	(5 Chromos)	100-160	
Siebe, Josephine	Kasperle's Adventures (1st, lg sq8vo, pink cl, 199p, 6cp, pep)	Macmillan	1929	Dobias, Frank	30-50	
Siegel, William	Around the World in a Mailbag (1st, 8vo, ibds, [30]p, color, pep)	McBride	1932	Siegel, William	40-60	*
Siepmann, Jane	Lion on Scott Street (1st, 12mo, ibds, [32]p, 2-color, DJ/1.75)	Oxford U. Pr.	(1952)	Hurd, Clement	25-40	*
Sigerson, Dora	Do-Well & Do-Little (1st, 8vo, 210p, p-o, 4cp)	L: Cassell	(1913)	Woodward, Alice B.	70-100	
Sigsgaard, Jens	Nils All Alone (1st AM, 8vo, [47]p, fp color, DJ/1.75)	Oxford U. Pr.	1947	Ungermann, Arne	30-50	
Silberrad, Una L.	Good Comrade (1st, 12mo, 365p, blue/gilt, col frn, 3pl)	Doubleday/Page	1907	Betts, Anna Whelan	25-40	*
Sill, Louise M.	Sunnyfield (1st, 8vo, 228p, 4pl)	Harper	1909	Robinson, Rachael	30-50	
Sill, S.C.	Reminiscences/Chest of Drawers (1st, sm8vo, [40]p, AEG, 6pl)	Lippincott	1900	Smith, Jessie W.	100-165	
Silverberg, Robert	Lost Race of Mars (1st {std}, 8vo, 120p, b/w, DJ/2.95)	Winston	(1960)	Kessler, Leonard	40-65	
Silverman, Mel	Good-for-Nothing Burro (1st {std}, 8vo, [39]p, 1-color, pep, DJ/2.50)	World	1958	Silverman, Mel	20-35	
Silverman, Mel	Hymie's Fiddle (1st {std}, sm4to, 46p, b/w, DJ/2.50)	World	(1960)	Silverman, Mel	25-45	
Silverstein, Shel	Giving Tree (1st, 8vo, [57]p, ibds, b/w, DJ/2.50)	Harper	(1964)	Silverstein, Shel	70-100	
Silverstein, Shel	Take Ten (1st [1st bk.], 12mo, ibds, [126]p, b/w)	Stars & Stripes	1955	Silverstein, Shel	150-250	
Silverstein, Shel	Uncle Shelby's a Giraffe and a Half (1st, 4to, unpag, b/w, DJ/2.95)	Harper	(1964)	Silverstein, Shel	50-85	
Silverstein, Shel	Uncle Shelby's ABZ Book (1st {std}, 4to, [76]p, wraps, b/w)	Simon/Schuster	1961	Silverstein, Shel	60-100	
Silverstein, Shel	Uncle Shelby's Story of Lafcadio (1st {std}, 8vo, [100]p, b/w, DJ/2.95)	Harper	1963	Silverstein, Shel	50-85	
Silverstein, Shel	Uncle Shelby's Zoo... (1st {std}, 8vo, [62]p, color, DJ/3.95)	Simon/Schuster	(1964)	Silverstein, Shel	60-90	
Silverstein, Shel	Who Wants a Cheap Rhinoceros? (1st, ob8vo, [48]p, fp b/w, DJ/2.00)	Macmillan	1964	Silverstein, Shel	60-90	*
Simbari, Nicola	Gennarino (1st, 4to, [32]p, fp color, DJ/3.95)	Lippincott	(1962)	Simbari, Nicola	40-65	*
Sime, Sidney H.	Bogey Beasts (1st, 4to, ibds, 62p, 15pl)	L: Goodwin	(1923)	Sime, Sidney	275-450	
Simmons, Ellie	Mary the Mouse Champion (1st, 8vo, [32]p, b/w, DJ/2.75)	McKay	(1963)	Simmons, Ellie	25-40	
Simmons, Henry B.	Jingle Jangle Rhyme Book (1st, ob4to, [38]p, ibds, 18cp)	Stokes	1898	Simmons, Henry B.	150-220	
Simon, Ellen	Critter Book (1st, sm ob4to, ibds, [48]p, color, DJ/1.50)	Holiday House	(1940)	Simon, Ellen	45-70	
Simon, Norma	Baby House (1st, lg8vo, mauve cl, [25]p, 1-color, dep, DJ/2.00)	Lippincott	1955	Adams, Adrienne	40-65	
Simon, Norma	Daddy Days (1st, 4to, [40]p, color, dep, DJ/2.50, NYTBI)	Abelard-Schuman	(1958)	Graboff, Abner	30-50	
Simon, Norma	Tree For Me (1st, lg8vo, green cl, [26]p, 1-color, dep, DJ/2.00)	Lippincott	(1956)	Stone, Helen	30-50	
Simon, Norma	Wet World (1st [1st bk.], 8vo, [25]p, fp 1-color, pep, DJ/2.00, NYTBI)	Lippincott	(1954)	Miller, Jane	30-45	*
Simon, Norma	What Do I Do? (1st, lg8vo, [40]p, 2-color, DJ/3.50)	Whitman	(1969)	Lasker, Joe	20-35	
Simon, Shirley	Best Friend (1st, 8vo, 191p, b/w, DJ/3.50)	Lothrop, Lee	(1964)	Lonette, Reisie	25-45	*
Simon, Sidney	Armadillo Who Had No Shell (1st {std}, ob8vo, ipcb, 32p, color, DJ/3.25)	Norton	(1966)	Lorraine, Walter	25-40	
Simon, Sidney	Henry the Uncatchable Mouse (1st {std}, ob8vo, [40]p, 1-col, pep, DJ/2.95)	Norton	(1964)	Langner, Nola	30-50	
Simont, Marc	Afternoon in Spain (1st, 8vo, 64p, ibds, color, DJ/3.95)	Wm. Morrow	1965	Simont, Marc	25-40	
Simont, Marc	Contest at Paca (1st, 8vo, ibds, 60p, 3-color, DJ/2.00)	Harper	(1959)	Simont, Marc	25-40	
Simont, Marc	How Come Elephants? (1st, 12mo, [44]p, fp 2-color, cep, DJ/2.50)	Harper	1965	Simont, Marc	30-50	
Simont, Marc	How to Get to First Base (1st, 8vo, [62]p, wraps, b/w)	Schuman	(1952)	Simont, Marc	25-40	
Simont, Marc	Lovely Summer (1st, sm4to, blue cl, [46]p, b/w, DJ/2.00)	Harper	(1952)	Simont, Marc	60-90	
Simont, Marc	Mimi (1st, 8vo, beige cl, 55p, b/w, DJ/2.00)	Harper	(1954)	Simont, Marc	45-60	

AUTHOR	TITLE	PUBLISHER	DATE	ARTIST	PRICE	LC
Simont, Marc	Opera Souffle: 60 Pictures in Bravura (1st, 4to, [89]p, b/w, pep, DJ/2.50)	Schuman	(1950)	Simont, Marc	30-50	
Simont, Marc	Plumber Out of the Sea (1st, lg8vo, ipcb, 39p, 2-color, pep, DJ/2.00)	Harper	(1955)	Simont, Marc	45-70	
Simont, Marc	Polly's Oats (1st, sm4to, [46]p, fp b/w, DJ/1.75)	Harper	(1951)	Simont, Marc	40-65	
Sinclair, Bertrand	North of Fifty-Three (1st, sm8vo, 345p, 4pl)	Little/Brown	1914	Fischer, Anton O.	30-50	
Sinclair, Bertrand	Raw Gold (1st, sm8vo, 311p, 4pl)	Dillingham	1908	Rowe, Clarence	40-60	
Sinclair, Harry D.	Out of the Silent North (1st, 12mo, 304p, frn by...)	Macaulay	1923	Johnson, F. Tenny	60-90	
Sinclair, May	Immortal Moment (1st, sm8vo, 315p, white cl, 4pl)	Doubleday/Page	1908	Phillips, Coles	35-60	
Sinclair, May	Judgment of Eve (1st, sm8vo, 122p, uncut, 8pl)	Harper	1908	Adams, J.W.	25-40	*
Sinclair, May	The Creators (1st, sm8vo, 517p, b/w)	Century	1910	Keller, Arthur I.	25-40	
Sinclair, May	Uncanny Stories (1st AM, sm8vo, red/gilt, 362p, 21pl)	NY: Macmillan	1923	DeBosschere, Jean	100-160	
Sinclair, Upton	The Gnomobile (1st, 8vo, tan cl, 181p, b/w, DJ/1.50)	Farrar/Rinehart	(1936)	Cosgrave, John O.	140-200	
Sinclair, Upton	The Gnomobile (1st [this pub.], 8vo, 191p, color, DJ/3.50)	Bobbs-Merrill	1962	Tillard, Marcel	80-120	
Singer, Caroline	Ali Lives in Iran (1st, 4to, 71p, color, pep)	Holiday House	1937	Baldridge, Cyrus L.	25-45	*
Singer, Caroline	Boomba Lives in Africa (1st, sm4to, ibds, [64]p, color, pep, DJ/1.75)	Holiday House	1935	Baldridge, Cyrus L.	35-60	
Singer, Caroline	Half the World is Isfahan (1st, lg4to, ibds, 153p, 6 fp color, pep)	NY: Oxford U.Pr.	1936	Baldridge, Cyrus L.	90-160	R
Singer, Caroline	Santa Claus Comes to America (1st {std}, 4to, [32]p, ibds, color, DJ/1.00)	Knopf	1942	Baldridge, Cyrus L.	40-70	
Singer, Caroline	Turn to the East (1st, folio, 71p, ipcb, color)	Minton Balch	1926	Baldridge, Cyrus L.	70-120	
Singer, Isaac B.	Day of Pleasure (1st {std}, 8vo, 227p, fp b/w, DJ/4.50)	Farrar, Straus	(1969)	(Photos)	50-80	R*
Singer, Isaac B.	Elijah the Slave (1st {std}, 4to, [31]p, color, purple cl, pep, DJ/4.95)	Farrar, Straus	(1970)	Frasconi, Antonio	60-100	
Singer, Isaac B.	Fearsome Inn (1st, 8vo, [46]p, color, DJ, NH)	Scribner	(1967)	Hogrogian, Nonny	40-70	
Singer, Isaac B.	Joseph and Koza (1st {std}, lg4to, [38]p, fp 2-color, DJ/4.95)	Farrar, Straus	(1970)	Shimin, Symeon	40-65	
Singer, Isaac B.	Mazel and Shlimazel (1st, ob4to, 42p, red cl, fp color, cep, DJ/4.50)	Farrar, Straus	(1967)	Zemach, Margot	50-80	R
Singer, Isaac B.	When Shlemiel Went to Warsaw (1st, 8vo, 115p, fp b/w, DJ/4.50, NH)	Farrar, Straus	(1968)	Zemach, Margot	60-90	
Singer, Isaac B.	Zlateh the Goat (1st, 8vo, gilt, 90p, fp b/w, DJ/4.50, NH, NYTBI)	Harper	(1966)	Sendak, Maurice	120-200	
Singleton, Esther	Golden Rod Fairy Book (1st, 8vo, blue/gilt, 342p, pep, 16cp)	Dodd	1903	Falls, Charles B.	150-220	
Singleton, Esther	Wild Flower Fairy Book (1st, 8vo, gilt, 354p, teg, pep, 16cp)	Dodd	1905	Falls, Charles B.	150-225	
Singmaster, Elsie	Bred in the Bone (1st, 8vo, green/gilt, 300p, 6pl)	Houghton	1925	Green, Eliz. S.	35-60	
Singmaster, Elsie	Isle of Que (1st {std}, 8vo, 152p, DJ/2.25, designs by...)	Longmans	(1948)	Hader, Elmer	45-65	
Singmaster, Elsie	Little Money Ahead (1st, sm8vo, 194p, b/w pl)	Houghton	1930	Rogers, Hubert	200-300	
Singmaster, Elsie	Loving Heart (1st, 8vo, 244p, col frn, DJ/2.00)	Houghton	1937	Rogers, Hubert	80-120	
Singmaster, Elsie	Rifles for Washington (1st, 8vo, 321p, color title page, b/w, DJ/2.25)	Houghton	1938	Schoonover, Frank	25-45	
Singmaster, Elsie	Swords of Steel (1st, 8vo, 262p, b/w, pep, NH)	Houghton	1933	Hendrickson, David	40-60	*
Singmaster, Elsie	When Sarah Saved the Day (1st, 12mo, 135p, pink cl, 4pl)	Houghton	1909	Becher, Arthur E.	25-40	
Singmaster, Elsie	You Make Your Own Luck (1st {std}, 8vo, 255p, b/w pl)	Longmans	1929	Westmacott, Bernard	25-40	
Singmaster, Elsie	Young Ravenels (1st, 12mo, 214p, blue/gilt, 9pl)	Houghton	1932	Price, Hattie L.	25-45	*
Sitomer, Mindel	What is Symmetry? (1st, ob8vo, 33p, color, DJ/3.75)	Crowell	(1970)	Emberley, Ed	30-45	
Skaar, Grace M.	All About Dogs, Dogs, Dogs (1st, lg ob8vo, wraps, [20]p, color)	Young Scott	1947	Skaar, Grace M.	60-90	
Skaar, Grace M.	Boy and his Horse (1st, 8vo, 141p, b/w, DJ/2.95)	Young Scott	(1958)	Skaar, Grace M.	50-80	
Skaar, Grace M.	Little Red House (1st, ob8vo, [32]p, fp 2-color, DJ/2.00)	Young Scott	1955	Skaar, Grace M.	30-50	
Skaar, Grace M.	Nothing But Cats, Cats, Cats (1st, ob8vo, ipcb, [20]p, color)	Young Scott	1947	Skaar, Grace M.	70-120	
Skaar, Grace M.	Very Little Dog (1st, ob8vo, [20]p, ipcb, 2-color, DJ/1.00)	Young Scott	1949	Skaar, Grace M.	70-100	
Skaar, Grace M.	What Do they Say! (1st, ob8vo, ibds, [20]p, color, DJ/1.00)	W.R. Scott	1950	Skaar, Grace M.	70-100	
Skariatina, Irina	Little Era in Old Russia (1st {std}, 8vo, 392p, b/w, pep)	Bobbs-Merrill	(1934)	Baldridge, Cyrus L.	30-50	*
Skelding, Susie B.	Flowers from Dell and Bower (1st, 8vo, 128p, brown/gilt, AEG)	White/Stokes	1886	12 Chromos	120-180	
Skelding, Susie B.	Flowers from Glade and Garden (1st, lg8vo, [128]p, AEG, gilt)	White/Stokes	1884	12 Chromos	120-170	
Skinner, Ada M.	Child's Book of Country Stories (1st, lg8vo, gilt, 265p, p-o, 4cp)	Duffield	1925	Smith, Jessie W.	180-250	
Skinner, Ada M.	Child's Book of Country Stories (1st {this pub}, 8vo, p-o, 4cp)	Dial	1935	Smith, Jessie W.	90-120	
Skinner, Ada M.	Child's Book of Modern Stories (1st, lg8vo, gilt p-o, 340p, 8cp)	Duffield	1920	Smith, Jessie W.	160-240	
Skinner, Ada M.	Child's Book of Modern Stories (4to, gilt, 341p, p-o, 8cp)	Dial	1935	Smith, Jessie W.	80-120	
Skinner, Ada M.	Children's Plays (1st, sm8vo, 269p, color)	Appleton	1919	Pogany, Willy	80-125	
Skinner, Ada M.	Emerald Story Book (1st, sm8vo, 371p, col frn by...)	Duffield	1915	Parrish, Maxfield	100-135	
Skinner, Ada M.	Little Child's Book of Stories (1st, lg8vo, 258p, gilt, 8cp, pep)	Duffield	1922	Smith, Jessie W.	180-270	*
Skinner, Ada M.	Topaz Story Book (1st, 12mo, 381p, col frn by...)	Duffield	1917	Parrish, Maxfield	100-150	
Skinner, Ada M.	Turquoise Story Book (1st, sm8vo, 409p, blue cl, col frn by...)	Duffield	1918	Parrish, Maxfield	100-150	
Skinner, Ada M.	Very Little Child's Book of Stories (1st, lg8vo, 232p, gilt, 8cp)	Duffield	1923	Smith, Jessie W.	180-270	*
Skinner, Charles M.	Do-Nothing Days (1st, 12mo, 219p, teg, frn by...)	Lippincott	1899	Oakley, Violet	90-120	
Skinner, Charles M.	With Feet to the Earth (1st, 12mo, 231p, teg, frn by...)	Lippincott	1899	Oakley, Violet	100-150	
Skinner, Constance	Debby Barnes, Trader (1st, 8vo, 244p, col frn, b/w, pep)	Macmillan	1932	Rae, John	30-45	
Skipper, Mervyn	Fooling of King Alexander (1st AM {std}, 4to, 30p, 2-color, DJ/4.50)	Atheneum	1967	Chapman, Gaynor	25-45	
Skirrow, Desmond	Case of the Silver Egg (1st {std}, 8vo, 239p, b/w, DJ/3.95)	Doubleday	(1968)	Jacques, Robin	20-35	*
Skorpen, Liesel	All the Lassies (1st {std}, ob8vo, [32]p, 3-color, cep, DJ/3.50)	Dial Press	(1970)	Scott, Bruce M.	80-130	
Skorpen, Liesel	If I Had a Lion (1st, ob8vo, 32p, ibds, color, DJ/2.50)	Harper	(1967)	Landshoff, Ursula	50-85	
Skorpen, Liesel	Outside My Window (1st, 12mo, 32p, color, DJ/2.50)	Harper	(1968)	Mayer, Mercer	30-50	
Skorpen, Liesel	That Mean Man (1st, 4to, 32p, fp color, DJ/2.95)	Harper	(1968)	McCully, Emily	50-80	*
Slade, Irene (comp)	Ring of Bells (1st, 8vo, 129p, b/w, DJ)	L: J. Murray	(1962)	Ardizzone, Edward	30-50	
Sleater, William	Angry Moon (1st {std}, sq8vo, blue cl, 45p, color, DJ/4.95, CH)	Little/Brown	(1970)	Lent, Blair	70-125	
Sleigh, Barbara	Carbonel, King of Cats (1st AM {std}, 8vo, 253p, b/w, DJ/2.75)	Bobbs-Merrill	(1957)	Drummond, Violet	200-300	
Sleigh, Barbara	Kingdom of Carbonel (1st AM, 8vo, blue cl, 287p, fp b/w, DJ/3.50)	Bobbs-Merrill	(1960)	Leonard, D.M.	150-225	
Sleigh, Barbara	No One Must Know (1st AM, 8vo, 192p, DJ/3.50)	Bobbs-Merrill	(1963)	No Illustrations	40-65	
Sleigh, Barbara	North of Nowhere (1st AM {std}, 8vo, 223p, b/w, DJ)	Coward	(1966)	Ambrus, Victor	70-100	
Sleight, Charles L.	Prince of the Pin Elves (1st, 12mo, 159p, b/w)	L.C. Page	1897	Sacker, Amy	70-100	
Sloane, Eric	ABC Book of Early Americana (1st {std}, 4to, gilt, [68]p, b/w, DJ/2.95)	Doubleday	(1963)	Sloane, Eric	35-50	
Sloane, Eric	Return to Taos (1st, 4to, 120p, 4cp, DJ/6.50)	Funk/Wagnalls	(1960)	Sloane, Eric	45-60	
Sloane, Eric	Reverence for Wood (1st, 4to, 110p, b/w, DJ/6.50)	Wilfred Funk	(1965)	Sloane, Eric	45-60	
Sloane, Eric	Second Barrel (1st, 4to, 104p, fp b/w, DJ/5.95)	Funk/Wagnalls	(1969)	Sloane, Eric	45-60	
Sloane, Eric	Sound of Bells (1st {std}, lg8vo, 58p, b/w, DJ/2.75)	Doubleday	(1966)	Sloane, Eric	60-90	
Slobodkin, Florence	Cowboy Twins (1st, 4to, [28]p, color, DJ/2.95)	Vanguard Press	1960	Slobodkin, Louis	30-50	
Slobodkin, Florence	Mr. Papadilly and Willy (1st, 4to, [38]p, fp color, cep, DJ/3.50)	Vanguard Press	(1964)	Slobodkin, Louis	40-65	*

AUTHOR	TITLE	PUBLISHER	DATE	ARTIST	PRICE	LC
Slobodkin, Florence	Sarah Somebody (1st, 8vo, 71p, 1-color, DJ/3.95)	Vanguard Press	(1970)	Slobodkin, Louis	35-50	
Slobodkin, Florence	Too Many Mittens (1st, 4to, [32]p, blue cl, fp 3-color, DJ/2.75)	Vanguard Press	(1958)	Slobodkin, Louis	40-65	
Slobodkin, Louis	Adventures of Arab (1st, lg8vo, 128p, color, cep, DJ/2.50)	Macmillan	1946	Slobodkin, Louis	45-70	
Slobodkin, Louis	Amiable Giant (1st {std}, sm4to, 33p, color, DJ/2.75)	Macmillan	(1955)	Slobodkin, Louis	40-65	
Slobodkin, Louis	Big Circus April 1st (1st {std}, sm8vo, 90p, b/w, cep, DJ/2.25)	Macmillan	(1953)	Slobodkin, Louis	30-50	
Slobodkin, Louis	Bixxy & the Secret Message (1st {std}, 8vo, 94p, b/w, pep, DJ/2.00)	Macmillan	1949	Slobodkin, Louis	30-45	
Slobodkin, Louis	Clear the Track for Michael's Magic Train (1st ob8vo [48]p, color, DJ/1.50)	Macmillan	(1945)	Slobodkin, Louis	30-50	
Slobodkin, Louis	Colette and the Princess (1st {std}, 4to, 46p, color, DJ/3.50)	Dutton	(1965)	Slobodkin, Louis	30-50	
Slobodkin, Louis	Dinny & Danny (1st {std}, sm4to, ibds, [30]p, color, pep, DJ/2.00)	Macmillan	(1951)	Slobodkin, Louis	40-65	
Slobodkin, Louis	Excuse Me! Certainly! (1st, sm4to, [32]p, color, DJ/2.75)	Vanguard Press	(1959)	Slobodkin, Louis	30-50	
Slobodkin, Louis	First Book of Drawing (1st {std}, 8vo, 68p, b/w, DJ/1.95)	F. Watts	1958	Slobodkin, Louis	25-40	
Slobodkin, Louis	Friendly Animals (1st, ob4to, [25]p, ibds, 2-color, DJ/1.50)	Vanguard Press	1944	Slobodkin, Louis	60-90	
Slobodkin, Louis	Gogo: French Seagull (1st {std}, 4to, [46]p, fp color, DJ)	Macmillan	(1960)	Slobodkin, Louis	50-80	
Slobodkin, Louis	Good Place to Hide (1st {std}, lg8vo, 29p, color, DJ/2.50)	Macmillan	(1961)	Slobodkin, Louis	30-50	
Slobodkin, Louis	Horse with the High-Heeled Shoes (1st, 4to, 30p, fp color, DJ/2.50)	Vanguard Press	(1954)	Slobodkin, Louis	30-50	
Slobodkin, Louis	Hustle & Bustle (1st, sm ob4to, [36]p, 1-color, DJ/1.50)	Macmillan	1948	Slobodkin, Louis	50-80	
Slobodkin, Louis	Late Cuckoo (1st, sm4to, [38]p, fp color, cep, DJ/3.00)	Vanguard Press	(1962)	Slobodkin, Louis	30-50	
Slobodkin, Louis	Little Mermaid Who Could Not Sing (1st {std}, sm4to, 38p, color, DJ/2.75)	Macmillan	(1956)	Slobodkin, Louis	40-65	
Slobodkin, Louis	Luigi and the Long-Nosed Soldier (1st {std}, 4to, 32p, 2-color, DJ/2.95)	Macmillan	(1963)	Slobodkin, Louis	30-50	
Slobodkin, Louis	Magic Michael (1st, ob8vo, ibds, [48]p, 2-color, cep, DJ/1.50)	Macmillan	(1944)	Slobodkin, Louis	60-90	
Slobodkin, Louis	Melvin the Moose Child (1st {std}, sm4to, 32p, color, DJ/2.50)	Macmillan	(1957)	Slobodkin, Louis	30-50	
Slobodkin, Louis	Millions & Millions & Millions! (1st, 4to, picb, [32]p, color, pep, DJ/2.50)	Vanguard Press	(1955)	Slobodkin, Louis	30-50	
Slobodkin, Louis	Moon Blossom and the Golden Penny (1st, 8vo, [61]p, fp color, cep, DJ/3.25)	Vanguard Press	(1963)	Slobodkin, Louis	30-45	
Slobodkin, Louis	Mr. Mushroom (1st {std}, sq16mo, picb, [32]p, color, DJ/1.25)	Macmillan	(1950)	Slobodkin, Louis	30-50	
Slobodkin, Louis	Mr. Petersand's Cats & Kittens (1st {std}, 8vo, 63p, col, cep, DJ/2.25)	Macmillan	(1954)	Slobodkin, Louis	30-50	
Slobodkin, Louis	Nomi and the Lovely Animals (1st, 8vo, [32]p, color, cep, DJ/2.50)	Vanguard Press	(1960)	Slobodkin, Louis	50-80	
Slobodkin, Louis	One is Good, but Two are Better (1st, 4to, [23]p, color, pep, DJ/2.50)	Vanguard Press	1956	Slobodkin, Louis	40-65	
Slobodkin, Louis	Our Friendly Friends (1st, ob4to, ibds, [27]p, 2-color, pep, DJ/2.00)	Vanguard Press	(1951)	Slobodkin, Louis	40-65	
Slobodkin, Louis	Polka-Dot Goat (1st {std}, 4to, 34p, 2-color, DJ/2.95)	Macmillan	(1964)	Slobodkin, Louis	35-50	
Slobodkin, Louis	Read About the Busman (1st, 8vo, 70p, 1-color, DJ/2.65)	F. Watts	(1967)	Slobodkin, Louis	30-45	
Slobodkin, Louis	Read About the Fireman (1st, 8vo, 71p, 1-color, DJ/2.65)	F. Watts	(1967)	Slobodkin, Louis	30-45	
Slobodkin, Louis	Read About the Policeman (1st, 8vo, 168p, 1-color, DJ/2.65)	F. Watts	(1966)	Slobodkin, Louis	30-45	
Slobodkin, Louis	Read About the Postman (1st, 8vo, 67p, 1-color, DJ/2.65)	F. Watts	(1966)	Slobodkin, Louis	30-45	
Slobodkin, Louis	Round-Trip Space Ship (1st {std}, sm8vo, 167p, b/w, DJ/4.50)	Macmillan	(1968)	Slobodkin, Louis	80-130	
Slobodkin, Louis	Seaweed Hat (1st, 8vo, ibds, [48]p, color, DJ/2.00)	Macmillan	1947	Slobodkin, Louis	40-65	
Slobodkin, Louis	Space Ship Returns to Apple Tree (1st {std}, 8vo, 128p, b/w, DJ/2.50)	Macmillan	(1958)	Slobodkin, Louis	100-160	
Slobodkin, Louis	Space Ship Under Apple Tree (1st {std}, 8vo, 116p, blue cl, b/w, DJ/2.50)	Macmillan	(1952)	Slobodkin, Louis	100-175	
Slobodkin, Louis	Thank You, You're Welcome (1st, ob4to, [30]p, color, dep, DJ/2.75)	Vanguard Press	(1957)	Slobodkin, Louis	30-50	
Slobodkin, Louis	Three-Seated Space Ship (1st {std}, 8vo, 126p, b/w, DJ/2.75)	Macmillan	1962	Slobodkin, Louis	70-120	
Slobodkin, Louis	Trick or Treat (1st {std}, 4to, [29]p, fp 3-color, DJ/2.25)	Macmillan	(1959)	Slobodkin, Louis	30-55	
Slobodkin, Louis	Up High and Down Low (1st {std}, sm4to, [32]p, color, DJ/2.50)	Macmillan	(1960)	Slobodkin, Louis	25-45	
Slobodkin, Louis	Wide-Awake Owl (1st {std}, sm4to, [32]p, color, DJ/2.50)	Macmillan	(1958)	Slobodkin, Louis	30-50	
Slobodkin, Louis	Yasu and the Strangers (1st {std}, ob4to, 34p, color, DJ/2.95)	Macmillan	(1965)	Slobodkin, Louis	30-45	
Slobodkina, Esphyr	Boris and his Balalaika (1st, sm4to, [42]p, color, DJ/2.95)	Abelard-Schuman	1964	Bobri, Vladimir	25-40	
Slobodkina, Esphyr	Caps for Sale (1st, 8vo, ibds, [43]p, color, pep, DJ/1.00)	W.R. Scott	1940	Slobodkina, Esphyr	40-65	
Slobodkina, Esphyr	Flame, the Breeze & the Shadow (1st {std}, lg8vo, 62p, fp color, DJ/3.95)	Rand/McNally	1969	Slobodkina, Esphyr	25-40	
Slobodkina, Esphyr	Jack and Jim (1st, sm4to, [42]p, color, DJ/2.75)	Abelard-Schuman	1961	Slobodkina, Esphyr	25-40	
Slobodkina, Esphyr	Little Dinghy (1st, 4to, [41]p, color, DJ/2.50)	Abelard-Schuman	(1958)	Slobodkina, Esphyr	30-50	
Slobodkina, Esphyr	Pinky and the Petunias (1st, 4to, [39]p, fp color, pep, DJ/2.75)	Abelard-Schuman	(1959)	Slobodkina, Esphyr	40-70	*
Slobodkina, Esphyr	Wonderful Feast (1st, lg sq8vo, picb, [26]p, color, DJ/2.00)	Lothrop, Lee	1955	Slobodkina, Esphyr	40-65	
Slocum, Rosalie	Breakfast with the Clowns (1st, 8vo, ibds, [32]p, color, DJ/1.00)	Viking	1937	Slocum, Rosalie	40-65	
Slocum, Rosalie	Key to New York (1st {std}, 8vo, 312p, b/w, pep, DJ/2.00)	Harper	1939	Slocum, Rosalie	40-65	
Small, Ernest	Baba Yaga (1st, 4to, 48p, fp 3-color, cep, DJ/3.50)	Houghton	(1966)	Lent, Blair	30-50	
Smalley, Janet	Animals Came In (1st, 8vo, [88]p, ibds, 2-color, pep)	Wm. Morrow	(1930)	Smalley, Janet	60-90	
Smalley, Janet	Do You Know about Fishes? (1st, narrow ob8vo, 45p, ibds, color, pep)	Wm. Morrow	(1936)	Smalley, Janet	50-80	
Smalley, Janet	Do You Know? (1st, narrow ob8vo, 44p, color, pep)	Wm. Morrow	(1934)	Smalley, Janet	50-80	
Smalley, Janet	How It All Began (1st, 8vo, ibds, 94p, color)	Wm. Morrow	(1932)	Smalley, Janet	50-80	
Smalley, Janet	Now and Then... (1st, 8vo, 91p, ibds, color, pep)	Wm. Morrow	(1931)	Smalley, Janet	70-120	
Smalley, Janet	Plum to Plum Jam (1st, 8vo, 87p, ibds, color, pep)	Wm. Morrow	(1929)	Smalley, Janet	70-120	
Smalley, Janet	Rice to Rice Pudding (1st, smsq8vo, 85p, ibds, color, pep)	Wm. Morrow	(1928)	Smalley, Janet	70-120	
Smaridge, Norah	Peter's Tent (1st, 8vo, [32]p, fp 1-color, DJ/2.50)	Viking	(1965)	Turkle, Brinton	30-50	
Smaridge, Norah	What a Silly Thing to Do (1st {std}, 8vo, [38]p, 2-color, DJ/2.50)	Abingdon Press	(1967)	Perl, Susan	25-40	
Smeaton, William H.	Mystery of the Pacific (1st, 8vo, 335p, red/gilt, 8pl)	L: Blackie	1899	Paget, Walter	70-100	
Smedley, A. Constance	Wizards of Ryetown (1st, 12mo, gilt, 273p, b/w)	Henry Holt & Co.	1905	Macgregor, Angusine	60-90	
Smith, Agnes	Edge of the Forest (1st, 8vo, 192p, DJ/3.00, b/w decor by...)	Viking	(1959)	Moynihan, Roberta	60-90	
Smith, Arthur C.	Turquoise Cup (1st, 8vo, blue bds, 209p, frn by...)	Scribner	1903	Parrish, Maxfield	100-150	
Smith, C.M. (tran)	Queen Bee (1st, 8vo, 125p, gilt, pep, 2cp by...)	L: Nelson	1907	Dulac, Edmund	160-225	
Smith, Dodie	Hundred and One Dalmatians (1st AM, 8vo, 199p, b/w, DJ/2.75)	Viking	(1957)	Grahame-Johnstone	200-300	
Smith, Dodie	Starlight Barking (1st AM {std}, 8vo, 156p, b/w, DJ/3.95)	Simon/Schuster	(1967)	Grahame-Johnstone	100-165	
Smith, E. Boyd	After they Came Out of the Ark (1st, ob4to, ibds, 48p, 22cp)	Putnam	(1918)	Smith, E. Boyd	250-350	
Smith, E. Boyd	Chicken World (1st, ob4to, ibds, [28]p, color)	Putnam	1910	Smith, E. Boyd	250-350	
Smith, E. Boyd	Circus & All About It (1st, 4to, p-o, 62p, 16cp, pep)	Stokes	(1909)	Smith, E. Boyd	250-350	
Smith, E. Boyd	Early Life of Mr. Man before Noah (1st, ob4to, ibds, [50]p, 23cp, pep)	Houghton	1914	Smith, E. Boyd	250-400	
Smith, E. Boyd	Fun in the Radio World (1st, ob4to, [30]p, p-o, 12cp, pep)	Stokes	1923	Smith, E. Boyd	250-350	
Smith, E. Boyd	In the Land of Make-Believe (1st, sm ob4to, ibds, [28]p, 12cp, pep)	Henry Holt & Co.	(1916)	Smith, E. Boyd	250-400	R
Smith, E. Boyd	Lions 'n' Elephants & Everything (1st, ob4to, [32]p, ibds, 12cp)	Putnam	(1929)	Smith, E. Boyd	250-350	
Smith, E. Boyd	My Village (1st [1st bk], 12mo, teg, 325p, b/w)	Scribner	1896	Smith, E. Boyd	90-120	
Smith, E. Boyd	Pocahontas & Captain Smith (1st, lg ob4to, ibds, [56]p, color, pep)	Houghton	1906	Smith, E. Boyd	250-400	

AUTHOR	TITLE	PUBLISHER	DATE	ARTIST	PRICE	LC
Smith, E. Boyd	Railroad Book (1st, ob4to, [28]p, p-o, 12cp, pep)	Houghton	1913	Smith, E. Boyd	250-400	R
Smith, E. Boyd	Santa Claus & All About Him (1st, ob4to, ibds, 62p, 16 fp color, pep)	Stokes	(1908)	Smith, E. Boyd	250-400	
Smith, E. Boyd	Seashore Book (1st, ob4to, [30]p, ibds, 12cp, pep)	Houghton	1912	Smith, E. Boyd	250-350	R
Smith, E. Boyd	So Long Ago (1st, lg8vo, green cl, 36p, color, DJ/2.00)	Houghton	1944	Smith, E. Boyd	100-160	
Smith, E. Boyd	Story of Noah's Ark (1st, ob4to, ibds, [56]p, p-o, 26cp, pep)	Houghton	1905	Smith, E. Boyd	250-350	R
Smith, E. Boyd	Story of our Country (1st, ob4to, ibds, 44p, fp color)	Putnam	1920	Smith, E. Boyd	80-135	
Smith, Eleanor	Song Devices & Jingles (1st, lg sq8vo, 65p, 6cp)	Lothrop, Lee	(1920)	Young, Florence L.	30-50	*
Smith, Emma	Emily, the Traveling Guinea Pig (1st AM, 8vo, 76p, 8cp, DJ/2.75)	McDowell/Obl.	1959	Wigglesworth, Kath.	35-50	
Smith, Eugene C.	Kongo the Elephant (1st {std}, lg8vo, 78p, color, pep, DJ/2.00)	Knopf	(1939)	Vaughan, Anne	30-50	
Smith, F. Berkeley	Real Latin Quarter (1st, 8vo, 204p, b/w photos, frn by…)	Funk/Wagnalls	1901	Smith, F. Hopkinson	50-80	
Smith, Francis H.	Arm-Chair at the Inn (1st, sm8vo, green/gilt, uncut, 357p, 8pl)	Scribner	1912	Various	30-50	
Smith, Francis H.	Caleb West, Master Diver (1st, 12mo, gilt, 378p, 6pl by…)	Houghton	1898	Keller, Arthur I.	30-60	
Smith, Francis H.	Charcoals of New & Old New York (1st, 4to, 142p, bds, 23 tipl)	Doubleday/Page	1912	Smith, Francis H.	90-120	
Smith, Francis H.	Colonel Carter's Christmas (1st, 8vo, teg, gilt, 159p, 8cp)	Scribner	1903	Yohn, F.C.	25-40	
Smith, Francis H.	Day at Laguerre's… (1st, 8vo, tan cl, 190p, teg)	Houghton	1892	Smith, Francis H.	70-120	
Smith, Francis H.	Fortunes of Oliver Horn (1st, smo, green/gilt, uncut, 552p, b/w)	Scribner	1902	Clark, Walter A.	25-40	
Smith, Francis H.	Gondola Days (1st, 12mo, 205p, red/gilt, cvr by…)	Houghton	1897	Rogers, Bruce	50-80	
Smith, Francis H.	In Dickens' London (1st, 4to, bds, 199p, teg, 22 tipl)	Scribner	1914	Smith, Francis H.	75-100	
Smith, Francis H.	Old Lines & New in Black & White (1st, ob folio, [28]p, p-o, 12pl)	Houghton	1886	Smith, Francis H.	125-200	*
Smith, Francis H.	Other Fellow (1st, 8vo, teg, 218p)	Houghton	1899	Rogers, Bruce	30-50	
Smith, Francis H.	Outdoor Sketching (1st, sm8vo, pcb, 145p, 3pl)	Scribner	1915	Smith, Francis H.	30-60	
Smith, Francis H.	Romance of an Old Fashioned Gentleman (1st, 8vo, 213p, teg, 5cp)	Scribner	1907	Keller, Arthur I.	25-40	
Smith, Francis H.	Tom Grogan (1st, 12mo, 246p, teg, 19pl)	Houghton	1896	Reinhart, C.S.	30-50	
Smith, Francis H.	Wood Fire in No.3 (1st, sm8vo, 298p, teg, uncut, 9cp)	Scribner	1905	Kimball, Alonzo	25-40	
Smith, Gertrude	Arabella & Araminta Stories (1st, sq8vo, 103p, uncut, 15pl, PPPa)	Copeland & Day	1895	Reed, Ethel	350-500	
Smith, Gertrude	Arabella & Araminta Stories (8vo, 103p, 15pl, pep, later)	Small/Maynard	1903	Reed, Ethel	100-180	
Smith, Gertrude	Beautiful Story of Doris & Julie (1st, lg sq8vo, 167p, 14cp)	Harper	1901	Mears, W.E.	75-100	*
Smith, Gertrude	Boys of Marmiton Prairie (1st, sm8vo, gilt, 262p, 5pl)	Little/Brown	1899	Day, Bertha C.	30-50	*
Smith, Gertrude	Jolly Polly Stories (1st, lg sq8vo, 99p, b/w)	Small/Maynard	1918	Drake, Elise D.	30-50	
Smith, Gertrude	Little Girl & Phillip (1st, lg sq8vo, 187p, 8cp)	Harper	1902	Robinson, Rachael	50-80	*
Smith, Gertrude	Little Mother and Georgie (1st, sq8vo, beige cl, 150p, 12cp)	Harper	1905	'DD'	60-90	*
Smith, Gertrude	Little Precious (1st, 8vo, 146p, 15cp)	Harper	1904	'DD'	55-80	
Smith, Gertrude	Loveable Tales of Janey, Josey & Joe (1st, 4to, green cl, 157p, 16cp)	Harper	1902	Mars, E.	80-120	
Smith, Gertrude	Roggie & Reggie Stories (1st, 8vo, 95p, 15cp)	Harper	1900	Mars/Squire	75-100	*
Smith, Gertrude	Stories of Peter & Ellen (1st, 8vo, 137p, 15cp)	Harper	1903	Mars/Squire	75-100	*
Smith, Gertrude	When Roggie and Reggie were Five (1st, sq8vo, 169p, 8cp)	Harper	1909	Adams, Henreitta	60-90	
Smith, Gertrude	Wonderful Stories of Jane & John (1st, 8vo, 74p, 10cp)	Herbert Stone	1899	Woods, Alice	100-150	
Smith, Harriet L.	Pollyanna of the Orange Blossoms (1st, sm8vo, p-o, 313p, 6pl)	L.C. Page	1924	Taylor, H. Weston	30-50	
Smith, Harriet L.	Pollyanna's Jewels (1st, sm8vo, 328p, blue cl, p-o, 6pl)	L.C. Page	(1925)	Taylor, H. Weston	30-50	
Smith, Helen	Laughing Matter (1st, 8vo, 166p, b/w, DJ/2.50)	Scribner	1949	Wiese, Kurt	20-35	
Smith, Irene	Down the Road with Johnny (1st, 8vo, 64p, fp b/w, pep, DJ/1.75)	Whittlesey	(1951)	Wiese, Kurt	30-50	
Smith, Irene	Lucky Days for Johnny (1st, 8vo, 64p, fp b/w, pep, DJ/1.75)	Whittlesey	(1950)	Wiese, Kurt	30-50	
Smith, Jessie W.	Child's Book of Old Verses (1st, lg8vo, p-o, teg, 124p, 10cp, pep)	Duffield	1910	Smith, Jessie W.	200-300	
Smith, Laura R.	Good-Night Stories (1st, lg8vo, 120p, ipcb, 8cp by…)	Chi: Stanton	(1921)	Burd, Clara M.	50-80	
Smith, Laura R.	Pixie in the House (1st, sm8vo, 123p, pep)	McClurg	1915	Wilson, Clara P.	30-50	*
Smith, Laura R.	Runaway Bunny (1st, sm8vo, 128p, pep, color)	Chi: Flanagan	1923	Dulin, Dorothy	35-60	
Smith, Lawrence B.	Fur or Feather (1st, 4to, 144p, fp b/w, DJ/4.00)	Scribner	1946	Brown, Paul	80-140	
Smith, Linell	Auction Pony (1st {std}, 8vo, 117p, yellow cl, fp b/w, DJ/3.75)	Little/Brown	(1965)	Bacon, Peggy	30-50	
Smith, Linell	Miranda & the Cat (1st {std}, 8vo, ipcb, 43p, b/w, DJ/2.75)	Little/Brown	(1963)	Bacon, Peggy	30-50	
Smith, Mabell S.	Twenty Centuries of Paris (1st, 8vo, blue/gilt, 400p, cvr by…)	Crowell	(1913)	Armstrong, Margaret	50-80	
Smith, Mary P.W.	Boy Captive of Old Deerfield (1st, 8vo, 295p, p-o, 6cp, gilt, pep)	Little/Brown	1929	Schoonover, Frank	30-50	*
Smith, Mary P.W.	Young Puritans in Captivity (1st, 12mo, grey cl, 323p, 6pl, dep)	Little/Brown	1899	Smith, Jessie W.	120-200	
Smith, Mary P.W.	Young Puritans of Old Hadley (1st, 12mo, 345p, gilt, 5pl, dep)	Roberts Bros.	1897	Bridgman, L.J.	45-70	
Smith, Nora A.	Adventures of a Doll (1st, 8vo, p-o, 64p, color)	McClure	1907	Groesbeck, Dan S.	35-60	
Smith, Nora A.	Boys & Girls of Bookland (1st, lg4to, p-o, 100p, 11cp, cep)	Cosmopolitan	1923	Smith, Jessie W.	125-200	
Smith, Nora A.	Boys & Girls of Bookland (lg4to, 100p, brown pcb, 11cp, later)	McKay	(1923)	Smith, Jessie W.	120-200	
Smith, Pamela C.	Annancy Stories (1st, folio, 79p, ibds, b/w)	R.H. Russell	1899	Smith, Pamela	200-300	
Smith, Pamela C.	Golden Vanity & Green Bed (1st, folio, [26]p, p-o, green cl, 12cp)	Doub./McClure	1899	Smith, Pamela	250-350	
Smith, Richard G.	Ancient Tales & Folklore of Japan (1st, 8vo, gilt, teg, 361p, 62cp)	L: A&C Black	1908	Mo-No-Yuki	250-400	
Smith, Robert P.	Jack Mack (1st, 8vo, ipcb, [29]p, color, DJ/2.50)	Coward	(1960)	Blegvad, Erik	30-50	
Smith, Robert P.	When I am Big (1st, 8vo, 32p, fp color, cep, DJ/2.50)	Harper	(1965)	Hoban, Lillian	30-50	
Smith, Ruth (ed)	Tree of Life (1st, lg8vo, 496p, blue cl, fp b/w, DJ/5.00)	Viking	1942	Artzybasheff, Boris	60-100	R*
Smith, Susan C.	Christmas Tree in the Woods (1st, sq12mo, [38]p, color, pep)	Minton Balch	(1932)	Sewell, Helen	35-60	*
Smith, Susan C.	Tranquilina's Paradise (1st, lg4to, 34p, color, pep)	Minton Balch	(1930)	Handforth, Thomas	75-120	R
Smith, Thorne	Lazy Bear Lane (1st {std}, 8vo, 240p, green cl, pep, b/w, DJ/2.00)	Doubleday/Doran	1931	Shanks, George	120-185	
Smith, Wallace	Little Tigress (1st, 8vo, 209p, teg, 15pl, pep)	Putnam	1923	Smith, Wallace	30-50	
Smith, William J.	Boy Blue's Book of Beasts (1st {std}, 8vo, 58p, fp 1-color, cep, DJ/2.75)	Little/Brown	(1957)	Kepes, Juliet A.	80-120	R
Smith, William J.	Ho for a Hat! (1st {std}, lg narrow 4to, 47p, color, cep, DJ/3.25)	Little/Brown	(1964)	Chermayeff, Ivan	30-50	*
Smith, William J.	If I Had a Boat (1st {std}, ob8vo, [32]p, fp color, cep, DJ/2.95)	Macmillan	(1966)	Bolognese, Don	40-65	R*
Smith, William J.	Laughing Time (1st {std}, 8vo, 54p, yellow cl, fp 1-color, cep, DJ/2.50)	Little/Brown	(1955)	Kepes, Juliet A.	80-125	R
Smith, William J.	Poems from France (1st, 8vo, 226p, b/w, DJ/4.50)	Crowell	(1967)	Duvoisin, Roger	30-50	*
Smith, William J.	Puptents & Pebbles (1st {std}, 4to, yellow cl, 32p, color, pep, DJ/2.75)	Little/Brown	(1959)	Kepes, Juliet A.	80-125	R
Smith, William J.	Typewriter Town (1st {std}, lg8vo, 32p, 3-color, dep, DJ/2.95)	Dutton	(1960)	Smith, William J.	60-85	R
Smith, William J.	What Did I See? (1st {std}, 4to, [61]p, ibds, fp b/w, cep)	Crowell-Collier	(1962)	Almquist, Don	60-100	R
Smither, Ethel	First to Be Called Christians (1st {A}, 8vo, 80p, fp color, pep, DJ/1.50)	Abingdon Press	(1955)	Wiese, Kurt	30-50	
Smither, Ethel	Stories of Jesus (1st, 24mo, 80p, fp color, pep, DJ/1.50)	Abingdon Press	(1954)	Wiese, Kurt	30-50	
Smucker, Barbara	Wigwam in the City (1st {std}, 8vo, 154p, b/w, DJ)	Dutton	(1966)	Miret, Gil	25-40	
Smythe, Gladys	Fairy Scales (1st, 4to, 101p, white cl, p-o, 10cp)	L: Jack	(1917)	Patricchio, C.	140-200	

AUTHOR	TITLE	PUBLISHER	DATE	ARTIST	PRICE	LC
Snedeker, Caroline D.	Beckoning Road (1st {std}, 8vo, 326p, col frn)	Doubleday/Doran	1929	Lee, Manning De V.	25-40	
Snedeker, Caroline D.	Black Arrowhead (1st {std}, 8vo, 279p, col frn, pep)	Doubleday/Doran	1929	Lee, Manning De V.	25-40	
Snedeker, Caroline D.	Downright Dencey (1st {std}, 8vo, 314p, col frn, pep, NH)	Doubleday/Doran	1927	Barney, Maginel W.	60-90	
Snedeker, Caroline D.	Forgotten Daughter (1st {std}, 8vo, 309p, col frn, 3pl, pep, NH)	Doubleday/Doran	1933	Lathrop, Dorothy	100-160	
Snedeker, Caroline D.	Luke's Quest (1st {std}, sm8vo, blue cl, 208p, uncut, b/w, DJ/2.00)	Doubleday	1947	Unwin, Nora S.	30-50	
Snedeker, Caroline D.	Lysis Goes to the Play (1st {std}, lg8vo, 61p, fp b/w, DJ/3.00)	Lothrop, Lee	(1962)	Lonette, Reisie	40-65	
Snedeker, Caroline D.	Perilous Seat (1st {std}, sm8vo, 314p, frn by...)	Doubleday/Page	1923	Lee, Manning De V.	30-50	
Snedeker, Caroline D.	Theras & his Town (1st {std}, sm8vo, 252p, pep, 4pl)	Doubleday/Page	1924	Haring, Mary W.	80-125	
Snedeker, Caroline D.	Town of the Fearless (1st {std}, 8vo, 351p, col frn, 12 fp b/w, pep)	Doubleday/Doran	1931	Lee Manning De V.	30-50	
Snedeker, Caroline D.	Triumph for Flavius (1st, lg8vo, 87p, b/w, DJ/3.00)	Lothrop, Lee	(1955)	Rogers, Cedric	20-35	*
Snedeker, Caroline D.	Uncharted Ways (1st {std}, 8vo, 340p, 14pl, pep, DJ/2.00)	Doubleday/Doran	1935	Lee, Manning De V.	25-45	
Snedeker, Caroline D.	White Isle (1st {std}, 8vo, 271p, pep, b/w pl, DJ/2.00)	Doubleday/Doran	1940	Kredel, Fritz	30-50	
Snell, Roy J.	Eskimo Island & Penguin Land (1st, 8vo, [256]p, cloth, p-o by...)	Whitman	1928	Winter, Milo	30-50	
Snell, Roy J.	Told Beneath the Northern Lights (1st, 8vo, 238p, col frn, 4 b/w)	Little/Brown	1925	Hooper, Florence	70-100	
Snow, Jack	Magical Mimics in Oz (1st, 8vo, grey cl, p-o, 243p, b/w, pep, DJ/2.00)	Reilly/Lee	(1946)	Kramer, Frank	350-500	
Snow, Jack	Shaggy Man of Oz (1st, lg8vo, grey cl, p-o, 254p, b/w, pep, DJ/2.00)	Reilly/Lee	(1949)	Kramer, Frank	350-500	
Snow, Jack	Who's Who in Oz (1st, lg8vo, 277p, gilt, 1-color, pep, DJ/3.75)	Reilly/Lee	(1954)	Various	250-400	
Snowden, James H.	Wonderful Night (1st, 12mo, blue cl, 95p, p-o, designs by...)	Macmillan	1919	Petershams	30-55	
Snyder, Anne	50000 Names for Jeff (1st {std}, 8vo, 70p, fp b/w, cep, DJ)	Holt, Rinehart	(1969)	Carty, Leo	40-65	
Snyder, Fairmont	Lovely Garden (1st, 12mo, ibds, [38]p, color, pep)	Volland	(1919)	Rae, John	70-100	
Snyder, Fairmont	Rhymes for Kindly Children (1st, lg8vo, ibds, [95]p, color, pep)	Volland	(1916)	Gruelle, Johnny	120-180	R
Snyder, Madeline	My Book of Parties (1st {std}, 8vo, 191p, col frn)	Doubleday/Doran	1928	Berry, Erick	20-30	
Snyder, Zilpha K.	Black and Blue Magic (1st {std}, 8vo, 186p, b/w, DJ/3.95)	Atheneum	1966	Holtan, Gene	40-65	
Snyder, Zilpha K.	Egypt Game (1st {std}, 8vo, 215p, yellow cl, b/w, DJ/3.95, NH)	Atheneum	1967	Raible, Alton	50-85	*
Snyder, Zilpha K.	Eyes in the Fishbowl (1st {std}, 8vo, 168p, b/w, DJ/3.95)	Atheneum	1968	Raible, Alton	40-65	
Snyder, Zilpha K.	Season of Ponies (1st {std}, 8vo, 133p, b/w, DJ/3.25)	Atheneum	1964	Raible, Alton	30-45	
Snyder, Zilpha K.	The Changeling (1st {std}, 8vo, 220p, yellow cl, cep, DJ/5.25)	Atheneum	1970	Raible, Alton	30-50	
Snyder, Zilpha K.	Today is Saturday (1st {std}, ob8vo, 56p, DJ/3.75, b/w photos by...)	Atheneum	1969	Arms, John	30-50	
Snyder, Zilpha K.	Velvet Room (1st {std}, 8vo, 216p, b/w, cep, DJ/3.95)	Atheneum	1965	Raible, Alton	30-50	
Sobol, Donald J.	Double Quest (1st {std}, 8vo, 240p, b/w, DJ/2.95)	F. Watts	1957	Rethi, Lili	25-45	*
Sobol, Donald J.	Greta the Strong (1st {std}, 8vo, 158p, b/w, DJ/4.95)	Follett	(1970)	Hyman, Trina S.	30-45	
Sobol, Donald J.	Lost Dispatch (1st {std}, 8vo, 173p, b/w, DJ/2.95)	F. Watts	(1958)	Palumbo, Anthony	20-35	
Sobol, Donald J.	Secret Agents Four (1st, sm8vo, 142p, b/w, DJ)	Four Winds Pr.	(1967)	Shortall, Leonard	20-30	
Sobol, Ken	Clock Museum (1st, sm4to, 48p, color, DJ/3.75)	McGraw-Hill	(1967)	Pinkney, Jerry	30-50	
Softly, Barbara	Magic People Around the World (1st AM {std}, sq8vo, [48]p, 1-color, DJ/3.50)	Holt, Rinehart	(1970)	Bock, Vera	30-50	*
Softly, Barbara	Place Mill (1st AM, 8vo, 190p, b/w, DJ/3.25)	St. Martin's	1963	Hughes, Shirley	20-30	*
Softly, Barbara	Plain Jane (1st AM, 8vo, 256p, b/w, DJ/3.25)	St. Martin's	1962	Hughes, Shirley	20-30	
Soglow, Otto	Little King (1st, 4to, [67]p, yellow cl, b/w, DJ/2.00)	Farrar/Rinehart	(1933)	Soglow, Otto	70-125	
Somervell, Arthur	Singing Time (1st, 4to, ibds, p-o, 48p, b/w)	L: Constable	1899	Brooke, L. Leslie	120-200	
Somerville, William	The Chase (1st, lg sq8vo, 87p, gilt, teg, 9 fp b/w)	L: Redway	1896	Thomson, Hugh	70-100	
Sommerfelt, Aimee	Road to Agra (1st AM {std}, 8vo, 191p, b/w, DJ/3.50, JABA)	Criterion Bks.	(1961)	Aas, Ulf	30-45	
Sommerfelt, Aimee	White Bungalow (1st AM {std}, 8vo, 126p, b/w, DJ/3.00)	Criterion Bks.	(1964)	Aas, Ulf	25-45	
Sonneborn, Ruth	Friday Night is Papa Night (1st {std}, 8vo, [31]p, 2-color, DJ/3.00)	Viking	(1970)	McCully, Emily	30-50	
Sonneborn, Ruth	Lollipop Party (1st, sq8vo, ipcb, [32]p, fp 1-color, DJ/2.75)	Viking	(1967)	Turkle, Brinton	30-45	
Sonneborn, Ruth	Seven in a Bed (1st, sq8vo, [31]p, fp color, DJ/2.95)	Viking	(1968)	Freeman, Don	30-45	
Sorensen, Virginia	Curious Missie (1st {std}, 8vo, 208p, b/w, DJ/2.75)	Harcourt	(1953)	Miller, Marilyn	30-50	
Sorensen, Virginia	House Next Door: Utah, 1896 (1st, 8vo, 223p, b/w, pep, DJ/3.00)	Scribner	(1954)	Cassel, Lili	20-30	*
Sorensen, Virginia	Lotte's Locket (1st {std}, sm8vo, 253p, b/w, DJ/3.50)	Harcourt	(1964)	Rocker, Fermin	25-40	*
Sorensen, Virginia	Miracles on Maple Hill (1st {std}, 8vo, 180p, b/w, DJ/2.95, NM)	Harcourt	(1956)	Krush, Beth & Joe	60-100	R
Sorensen, Virginia	Plain Girl (1st {std}, 8vo, 151p, b/w, DJ/2.50)	Harcourt	(1955)	Geer, Charles	25-45	
Sotomayor, Antonio	Khasa Goes to the Fiesta (1st {std}, 4to, 57p, color, DJ/3.25)	Doubleday	(1967)	Sotomayor, Antonio	20-35	
Soule, Jean	Scuttle, the Stowaway Mouse (1st, ob4to, [41]p, color, pep, DJ/3.50)	Parents Mag. Pr.	(1969)	Remington, Barbara	25-40	
Sousa, John P.	Fifth String (1st, 8vo, green cl, 124p, teg, b/w pl)	Bowen-Merrill	(1902)	Christy, Howard C.	30-50	
Sousa, John P.	Pipetown Sandy (1st, 8vo, brown/gilt, 383p, cvr by...)	Bobbs-Merrill	(1905)	Armstrong, Margaret	30-50	
Southwart, Elizabeth	Password to Fairyland (1st, 4to, 186p, tan cl, 8cp, pep)	L: Simpkin	[1920]	Anderson, Florence	250-400	
Southwold, Stephen	Book of Animal Tales (1st AM, lg8vo, ibds, 286p, 8cp)	Crowell	(1929)	Appleton, Honor C.	65-100	
Southwold, Stephen	Book of Animal Tales (1st, lg8vo, 286p, ibds, 8cp)	L: Harrap	1929	Appleton, Honor C.	70-100	*
Southwold, Stephen	Three by Candlelight (sm8vo, 128p, blue/gilt, 2cp)	L: Collins	[1920]	Anderson, Anne	50-80	
Sowerby, Githa	Bonnie Book (1st, 8vo, p-o, 12cp)	L: Oxford U.Pr.	1918	Sowerby, Millicent	150-220	
Sowerby, Githa	Childhood (4to, bds, gilt, 12cp)	L: Chatto	(1907)	Sowerby, Millicent	200-300	
Sowerby, Githa	Dainty Book (1st, sq8vo, ibds, unpag, 12cp)	Hodder	[1915]	Sowerby, Millicent	120-180	
Sowerby, Githa	Gay Book (1st {this pub.}, 8vo, [29]p, ibds, 12 fp color)	A.& W. Guild	(1935)	Sowerby, Millicent	35-60	
Sowerby, Githa	Glad Book (1st {this pub}, 8vo, [29]p, ibds, 12 fp color)	A.& W. Guild	(1935)	Sowerby, Millicent	35-60	
Sowerby, Githa	Little Stories for Little People (1st, lg8vo, 72p)	L: H. Frowde	[1910]	Sowerby, Millicent	75-100	*
Sowerby, Githa	Merry Book (1st, sm sq4to, white bds, 12cp)	L: Hodder	[1911]	Sowerby, Millicent	150-220	
Sowerby, Githa	Poems of Childhood (1st, 4to, 46p, teg, ibds, gilt, 12 ticp, dep)	L: H. Frowde	[1912]	Sowerby, Millicent	200-300	
Sowerby, Githa	The Bumbletoes (1st, 12mo, ibds, 60p, 12cp)	L: Chatto	1907	Sowerby, Millicent	160-250	
Sowerby, Githa	Wise Book (1st AM, 12mo, ipcb, 13cp)	Dent/Dutton	1906	Sowerby, Millicent	120-175	
Sowerby, Githa	Yesterday's Children (1st AM, 4to, 47p, p-o, 12cp)	Duffield	1909	Sowerby, Millicent	80-120	
Sowerby, Millicent	Childhood (1st AM, lg8vo, 44p, p-o, 12cp)	Duffield	1907	Sowerby, Millicent	140-200	
Sowers, Phyllis A.	Dhan of the Pearl Country (1st, lg8vo, p-o, 125p, color, pep, DJ/2.00)	Whitman	1939	Ayer, Margaret	45-70	
Sowers, Phyllis A.	Elephant Boy of the Teak Forest (1st, 8vo, 169p, DJ/2.50)	J. Messner	(1949)	Ayer, Margaret	30-45	
Sowers, Phyllis A.	Sons of the Dragon (1st, 8vo, 285p, yellow cl, 4cp, pep, DJ/2.00)	Whitman	1942	Ayer, Margaret	25-45	
Spaeth, Sigmund	Maxims to Music (1st {std}, 4to, 64p, color, DJ/2.00)	McBride	1939	Sarg, Tony	130-180	
Spark, Muriel	Very Fine Clock (1st AM, ob8vo, [32]p, fp b/w, pep, DJ/3.95)	Knopf	(1968)	Gorey, Edward	60-90	
Sparrow, Walter S.	Book of Bridges (1st, 4to, gilt, 415p, teg, uncut, 36cp)	L: John Lane	1915	Brangwyn, Frank	100-170	
Sparrow, Walter S.	Frank Brangwyn: His Work (1st, sm4to, gilt, 258p, teg, 20cp)	L: Kegan Paul	1910	Brangwyn, Frank	100-175	
Sparrow, Walter S.	Prints & Drawings of Frank Brangwyn (1st, 4to, 287p, gilt, 50pl)	L: John Lane	1919	Brangwyn, Frank	150-250	

AUTHOR	TITLE	PUBLISHER	DATE	ARTIST	PRICE	LC
Speare, Elizabeth G.	Bronze Bow (1st, 8vo, 255p, DJ/3.25, NM)	Houghton	1961	No Illustrations	80-120	
Speare, Elizabeth G.	Calico Captive (1st, 8vo, red cl, 274p, b/w, DJ/3.50)	Houghton	1957	Mars, Witold T.	25-45	
Spearman, Frank	Nan of Music Mountain (1st, 12mo, green/gilt, 430p, 4cp)	Scribner	1916	Wyeth, N.C.	70-125	
Spearman, Frank	Robert Kimberly (1st, sm8vo, 437p, gilt, 4cp)	Scribner	1911	Flagg, James M.	25-40	
Spearman, Frank	Whispering Smith (1st, 12mo, red cl, 421p, 4cp)	Scribner	1906	Wyeth, N.C.	80-140	
Speed, Flora	The Limbersnigs (1st, 4to, 75p, 4cp, dep)	L: Lawrence/Jell	(1896)	Speed, Lancelot	80-125	
Spellman, John W.	Beautiful Blue Jay (1st {std}, lg8vo, 101p, b/w, DJ/3.50)	Little/Brown	(1967)	Pinkney, Jerry	30-50	
Spence, Lewis	Myths of Babylonia & Assyria (1st AM, 8vo, teg, 411p, 8cp)	Stokes	[1915]	Paul, Evelyn	90-120	
Spencer, Ann	Cat Who Tasted Cinnamon Toast (1st {std}, 4to, 68p, ibds, b/w, DJ/4.95)	Knopf	1968	Spencer, Ann	30-45	
Spencer, Cornelia	Made in China (1st {std}, 8vo, 258p, 8cp, DJ/3.50)	Knopf	1943	Wiese, Kurt	30-50	*
Spencer, Cornelia	Three Sisters (1st, 8vo, blue/silver, 279p, b/w, DJ/2.00)	John Day	(1939)	Wiese, Kurt	40-65	*
Spender, Stephen	Magic Flute (1st, sm ob4to, [44]p, fp color, cep, DJ/3.95, NYTBI)	Putnam	(1966)	Montresor, Beni	60-90	
Spenser, Edmund	Shepheard's Calendar (1st, 8vo, ibds, gilt, 118p, 12pl, pep)	L: Harper	1898	Crane, Walter	400-600	
Spenser, Edmund	Una & Red Cross Knight (1st, 8vo, teg, 264p, ipcb, col frn)	L: J.M. Dent	1905	Robinson, Thomas H.	70-125	
Sperry, Armstrong	All About the Arctic and Antarctic (1st, 8vo, 146p, color, pep, DJ/1.95)	Random	(1957)	Sperry, Armstrong	20-30	
Sperry, Armstrong	All About the Jungle (1st {std}, 8vo, 141p, color, pep, DJ/1.95)	Random	(1959)	Sperry, Armstrong	20-30	
Sperry, Armstrong	All Sail Set (1st, sm4to, 175p, pep, b/w, DJ/2.00, NH)	Winston	(1935)	Sperry, Armstrong	50-80	R
Sperry, Armstrong	Amazon: River Sea of Brazil (1st, 8vo, 96p, 1-color, pep, DJ/2.50)	Garrard Pub.	(1961)	Sperry, Armstrong	30-50	
Sperry, Armstrong	Bamboo: The Grass Tree (1st, sm8vo, [47]p, 1-color, pep, DJ/1.00)	Macmillan	1942	Sperry, Armstrong	60-100	
Sperry, Armstrong	Black Falcon (1st {std}, 8vo, 218p, b/w, DJ/2.50)	Winston	(1949)	Sperry, Armstrong	25-40	
Sperry, Armstrong	Boy Who Was Afraid (1st UK, 8vo, 95p, b/w, pep, DJ)	L: John Lane	1942	Sperry, Armstrong	30-45	
Sperry, Armstrong	Call it Courage (1st, 8vo, 95p, beige cl, 1-color, pep, DJ/1.75, NM)	Macmillan	1940	Sperry, Armstrong	80-130	R
Sperry, Armstrong	Coconut: Wonder Tree (1st, 8vo, blue cl, [47]p, 1-color, pep, DJ/1.00)	Macmillan	1942	Sperry, Armstrong	30-50	
Sperry, Armstrong	Danger to the Windward (1st {std}, 8vo, 241p, b/w, DJ/2.50)	Winston	(1947)	Sperry, Armstrong	30-45	
Sperry, Armstrong	Frozen Fire (1st {std}, 8vo, 192p, green cl, b/w, DJ/2.75)	Doubleday	(1956)	Sperry, Armstrong	25-45	
Sperry, Armstrong	Hull-Down for Action (1st {std}, 8vo, 213p, pep, DJ/2.00)	Doubleday/Doran	1945	Sperry, Armstrong	40-70	
Sperry, Armstrong	John Paul Jones: Fighting Sailor (1st, 8vo, 180p, fp b/w, pep, DJ/1.50)	Random	(1953)	Sperry, Armstrong	50-80	R*
Sperry, Armstrong	Little Eagle: A Navaho Boy (1st, lg8vo, 102p, color, pep, DJ/2.00)	Winston	(1938)	Sperry, Armstrong	50-80	
Sperry, Armstrong	One Day with Jambi in Sumatra (1st, sm4to, ibds, [65]p, fp color, pep)	Winston	(1934)	Sperry, Armstrong	45-70	R
Sperry, Armstrong	One Day with Manu (1st [1st bk.], sm4to, ibds, [64]p, color, pep)	Winston	(1933)	Sperry, Armstrong	60-90	R
Sperry, Armstrong	One Day with Tuktu (1st, sm4to [66]p, blue/gilt, 10 dp color, pep, DJ/2.00)	Winston	1935	Sperry, Armstrong	60-90	
Sperry, Armstrong	Pacific Islands Speaking (1st {std}, 8vo, 220p, b/w, DJ/3.00)	Macmillan	1955	Sperry, Armstrong	25-40	
Sperry, Armstrong	Rain Forest (1st, 8vo, 190p, green cl, pep, fp 1-color, DJ/2.50)	Macmillan	1947	Sperry, Armstrong	40-65	
Sperry, Armstrong	River of the West (1st {std}, 8vo, 182p, b/w, DJ/1.50)	Winston	(1952)	Pitz, Henry C.	20-35	
Sperry, Armstrong	South of Cape Horn... (1st {std}, 8vo, 180p, b/w, DJ/2.95)	Winston	(1958)	Sperry, Armstrong	40-60	*
Sperry, Armstrong	Storm Canvas (1st {std}, 8vo, pep, 301p, col frn, pep, DJ/2.50)	Winston	(1944)	Sperry, Armstrong	30-50	
Sperry, Armstrong	Thunder Country (1st {std}, 8vo, 150p, b/w, DJ/2.75)	Macmillan	1952	Sperry, Armstrong	25-40	
Sperry, Armstrong	Voyages of Christopher Columbus (1st, 8vo, 186p, color, pep, DJ/1.50)	Random	(1950)	Sperry, Armstrong	30-50	
Sperry, Armstrong	Wagons Westward (1st, 8vo, 276p, orange cl, pep, b/w, DJ/2.00)	Winston	1936	Sperry, Armstrong	30-50	
Spicer, Marion D.	Rainbows (1st, 12mo, 41p, white cl, p-o, b/w, pep)	L: A. Melrose	1913	Robinson, Charles	100-165	
Spiegel, Doris	Danny and Company 92 (1st, ob8vo, ibds, [32]p, color, DJ/1.00)	Coward	(1945)	Spiegel, Doris	40-70	*
Spiegelberg, Flora	Princess Goldenhair & the Wonderful Flower (1st, 8vo, 176p, p-o, 8cp)	Rand/McNally	(1915)	Winter, Milo	100-165	
Spiegelberg, Flora	Princess Goldenhair & the Wonderful Flower (8vo, 176p, green cl, p-o, 8cp)	World	(1932)	Winter, Milo	50-85	
Spielmann, M.H.	Child of the Air (1st, 8vo, blue/gilt, 125p, teg, 6cp, pep)	L: Duckworth	1910	Wilhelm, M.H.C.	70-120	
Spielmann, M.H.	Hugh Thomson: His Art (1st, lg8vo, 269p, gilt, 12cp)	L: A&C Black	1931	Thomson, Hugh	100-170	
Spielmann, M.H.	Kate Greenaway (1st, lg8vo, blue cl, 301p, 52cp)	L: A&C Black	1905	Greenaway, Kate	120-180	
Spielmann, M.H.	Littledom Castle (1st, sm8vo, 377p, gilt, col & b/w, AEG)	L: Routledge	1903	Various	350-450	
Spielmann, M.H.	Love Family (1st, 8vo, ibds, 63p, 12cp)	L: G. Allen	(1908)	Park, Carton M.	100-180	
Spielmann, M.H.	My Son & I (1st, 8vo, red/gilt, teg, 307p, uncut, col frn, 9pl)	L: G. Allen	1908	Thomson, Hugh	60-90	
Spielmann, M.H.	Rainbow Book (1st, 8vo, 289p, teg, red/gilt, col frn, 15pl, pep)	L: Chatto	1909	Various	250-400	
Spier, Peter E.	Erie Canal (1st {std}, ob4to, ibds, [36]p, color, DJ/4.50)	Doubleday	(1970)	Spier, Peter E.	50-85	R*
Spier, Peter E.	Of Dikes and Windmills (1st {std}, 4to, 187p, color, DJ/5.95)	Doubleday	(1969)	Spier, Peter E.	50-80	R
Spilka, Arnold	Lion I Can Do Without (1st, ob4to, [40]p, fp 1-color, cep, DJ/3.50)	H.Z. Walck	1964	Spilka, Arnold	30-45	*
Spilka, Arnold	Whom Shall I Marry? (1st, 8vo, pink cl, [33]p, 1-color, DJ)	Holiday House	1960	Spilka, Arnold	25-45	
Spina, Paul	Tree Grew & Birds Flew (1st, ob4to, [40]p, gilt, fp 3-color, DJ/2.95)	Harlin Quist	(1967)	Spina, Paul	30-50	
Spofford, Harriet	Fairy Changeling (1st, 8vo, 75p, 20pl)	Badger	1911	Cory, Fanny	80-140	
Spofford, Harriet	Maid He Married (1st, 16mo, blue cl, 210p, teg, frn by...)	Stone/Kimball	1899	Oakley, Violet	80-125	
Spurr, Harry A.	Bachelor Ballads (1st, sm8vo, 194p, teg, green cl)	L: Greening	1899	Hassall, John	55-80	
Spyri, Johanna	Cornelli... (1st {Gift ed.}, lg8vo, teg, 275p, p-o, pep, 14 ticp)	Lippincott	1921	Kirk, Maria L.	70-100	
Spyri, Johanna	Dora (1st, 8vo, red/gilt, 216p, 8cp)	Lippincott	(1924)	Kirk, Maria L.	35-60	*
Spyri, Johanna	Erick and Sally (1st, 8vo, 173p, gilt, teg, 3cp)	Bos: Beacon Pr.	1921	Unknown	40-65	
Spyri, Johanna	Eveli (1st, 8vo, red/gilt, 272p, 8cp, pep)	Lippincott	(1926)	Greer, Blanche	30-50	
Spyri, Johanna	Gritli's Children (1st {Gift ed.}, lg8vo, 264p, p-o, teg, 14cp, pep)	Lippincott	(1924)	Kirk, Maria L.	80-120	
Spyri, Johanna	Heidi (1st {this pub}, 12mo, red cl, 338p, b/w pl)	Crowell	(1902)	Unknown	30-50	*
Spyri, Johanna	Heidi (1st, 8vo, 219p, gilt, teg, uncut, 13 fp color)	Dent/Dutton	(1909)	Lawson, Lizzie	30-50	*
Spyri, Johanna	Heidi (1st, 8vo, red/gilt, 318p, 8cp)	Lippincott	1915	Kirk, Maria L.	60-90	
Spyri, Johanna	Heidi (4to, p-o, 240p, 8cp)	Whitman	(1916)	Carsey, Ann	80-120	
Spyri, Johanna	Heidi (1st {Gift ed.}, sm4to, gilt, 318p, teg, 14 ticp, pep)	Lippincott	(1919)	Kirk, Maria L.	100-165	
Spyri, Johanna	Heidi (1st, lg8vo, 368p, p-o, gilt, pep, 8cp, WS)	Rand/McNally	(1921)	Enright, Maginel W.	50-80	
Spyri, Johanna	Heidi (1st, lg8vo, 380p, teg, p-o, blue cl, 10cp, pep)	McKay	1922	Smith, Jessie W.	140-200	
Spyri, Johanna	Heidi (1st, 8vo, green/gilt, 356p, p-o, 8cp, pep)	McKay	(1923)	Anderson, Anne	80-130	
Spyri, Johanna	Heidi (1st, 8vo, 356p, blue cl, p-o, 4cp)	Houghton	1923	Tenggren, Gustaf	60-100	
Spyri, Johanna	Heidi (1st UK, 8vo, 328p, 8cp)	L: Harrap	1924	Anderson, Anne	75-100	*
Spyri, Johanna	Heidi (1st, 8vo, 307p, p-o, col frn, b/w)	Saalfield	(1924)	Brundage, Frances	25-40	
Spyri, Johanna	Heidi (1st, 8vo, gilt, p-o, 290p, 4cp, pep)	Winston	(1924)	Burd, Clara M.	30-50	
Spyri, Johanna	Heidi (1st, 8vo, 284p, p-o, 1-color, pep)	Whitman	(1924)	Higgins, Violet M.	35-60	*
Spyri, Johanna	Heidi (1st, lg8vo, 333p, col frn, 23pl, p-o)	Harper	(1925)	Rhead, Louis	30-50	*
Spyri, Johanna	Heidi (1st, 12mo, 305p, p-o, gilt, 7 fp color)	Macrae Smith	(1925)	Shoemaker, Edna C.	40-65	

AUTHOR: 200

AUTHOR	TITLE	PUBLISHER	DATE	ARTIST	PRICE	LC
Spyri, Johanna	Heidi (1st, lg8vo, 243p, col frn, 1-color)	Sears	(1926)	Welling, G.	25-40	*
Spyri, Johanna	Heidi (1st, 8vo, 433p, pep, 12cp)	Crowell	(1927)	Whittemore, C.	30-50	*
Spyri, Johanna	Heidi (1st, 8vo, blue cl, p-o, 319p, 4cp, pep)	Garden City	1932	Petershams	40-60	
Spyri, Johanna	Heidi (1st, lg4to, 284p, ibds, col frn, b/w, pep)	Whitman	(1934)	Vernon, Ethel	40-60	
Spyri, Johanna	Heidi (1st {std}, 8vo, 334p, color, DJ/1.25, RC)	World	(1946)	Weisgard, Leonard	30-50	R*
Spyri, Johanna	Little Singer (1st, 8vo, 272p, red/gilt, col frn, 7pl, pep)	Lippincott	(1926)	Greer, Blanche	25-40	
Spyri, Johanna	Mazli (1st {Gift ed.}, lg8vo, 320p, teg, p-o, 14cp, pep)	Lippincott	(1923)	Kirk, Maria L.	90-120	
Spyri, Johanna	Moni the Goat Boy (1st, 12mo, 43p, 3cp, pep)	Crowell	(1914)	Unknown	30-50	
Spyri, Johanna	Moni the Goat Boy (1st, 12mo, red cl, 72p, 4cp)	Lippincott	1916	Kirk, Maria L.	40-60	*
Spyri, Johanna	New Year's Carol (1st, 12mo, ipcb, 34p, col frn, 3pl)	Houghton	(1924)	Wesson, G.E.	30-45	
Spyri, Johanna	Peppino (1st, 12mo, 114p, red cl, 4cp)	Lippincott	(1926)	Greer, Blanche	35-60	*
Spyri, Johanna	Shirley Temple in Heidi (1st, 8vo, 404p, b/w)	Saalfield	(1937)	(Photos)	75-100	*
Spyri, Johanna	Story of Rico (1st, 8vo, 163p, blue cl, 3cp)	Beacon Press	(1921)	Greene, Julia	35-60	*
Spyri, Johanna	Tiss - A Little Alpine Waif (1st, sm8vo, 78p, col frn, pep)	Crowell	(1921)	Carlson, George	30-50	
Spyri, Johanna	Vinzi (1st AM, 8vo, 296p, red cl, 8cp, pep)	Lippincott	1923	Kirk, Maria L.	30-50	
Spyri, Johanna	What Sami Sings with the Birds (1st, 8vo, 90p, blue cl, 3cp, pep)	Crowell	(1917)	Copeland, Charles	25-40	
Squier, Emma-Lindsay	Wild Heart (1st, sm8vo, green cl, 220p, b/w)	Cosmopolitan	1922	Bransom, Paul	30-60	
Squire, Charles	Celtic Myth & Legend (1st, 8vo, 446p, teg, gilt, 4cp)	L: Gresham	[1912]	Various	100-180	
Squire, John (ed)	Cheddar Gorge (1st, 4to, 181p, yellow/gilt, fp b/w)	L: Collins	(1937)	Shepard, Ernest H.	60-100	*
Squire, Robert	World Wonderful (1st, 8vo, 201p, 10 fp b/w)	L: D. Nutt	1898	MacGregor, Archie	50-80	*
Squires, Frederick	Architec-tonics (1st {1st bk.}, 12mo, gilt, 172p, col frn)	Comstock Co.	1914	Kent, Rockwell	300-500	R
Srivastava, Jane	Weighing and Balancing (1st, ob8vo, ibds, 32p, 2-color, DJ/3.75)	Crowell	(1970)	Aliki	30-50	
St. Francis of Assisi	Song of the Sun (1st {std}, sq8vo, [32]p, 11 fp color, pep, DJ)	Macmillan	1952	Jones, Eliz. O.	40-60	
St. John, J. Allen	Face in the Pool (1st, 4to, 156p, grey/gilt, 4cp)	McClurg	1905	St. John, J. Allen	120-180	
St. Mars, F.	Pinion & Paw (1st, sm8vo, green cl, 296p, 12pl)	L: Chambers	1919	Rountree, Harry	55-80	*
Stables, Gordon	Boy's Book of Battleships (lg4to, ibds, 64p, 16 color)	L: Blackie	[1909]	Robinson, Charles	125-200	
Stables, Gordon	City at the Pole (1st, 8vo, blue cl, 352p, 8pl)	L: J. Nisbet	1906	Pearse, Alfred	60-90	
Stables, Gordon	Young Peggy McQueen (1st, 8vo, 152p, gilt, 4cp)	L: Collins	1903	Goble, Warwick	80-120	
Stacpoole, H.D.	Blue Lagoon (1st, 8vo, blue/gilt, uncut, 326p, 13 ticp)	L: T.F. Unwin	1910	Pogany, Willy	250-400	
Stacpoole, H.D.	Pierrette (1st, 8vo, 294p, teg, fp b/w)	L: John Lane	1900	Robinson, Charles	150-225	
Stacpoole, H.D.	Pierrot! (1st, 8vo, red cl, 163p, uncut, pep, cvr & title page by...)	L: John Lane	1896	Beardsley, Aubrey	75-100	*
Stacpoole, H.D.	Poppyland (1st, lg8vo, 219p, blue/gilt, 17cp, pep)	L: Bodley Head	1914	Pearce, Leighton	140-220	
Stafford, Jean	Elephi (1st {std}, sm8vo, 76p, b/w, DJ/3.50)	Ariel	1962	Blegvad, Erik	40-65	
Stafford, Kay	Ling Tang & the Lucky Cricket (1st, 4to, 80p, red cl, color, DJ/2.00)	Whittlesey	(1944)	Zibold, Louise	35-50	
Stafford, Marie A.	Muskox: Little Tootoo's Friend (1st, 8vo, 64p, color, pep)	Wm. Morrow	(1931)	Wiese, Kurt	55-80	*
Stafford, Marie A.	Ootah and his Puppy (1st, 8vo, 64p, 2-color, pep)	D.C. Heath	1942	Wiese, Kurt	25-40	
Stahl, Ben	Blackbeard's Ghost (1st {std}, lg8vo, 184p, fp b/w, cep, DJ/3.50)	Houghton	1965	Stahl, Ben	60-100	R
Stamm, Claus	Three Strong Women (1st, 8vo, 47p, fp 1-color, dep, DJ/2.50)	Viking	(1962)	Mizumura, Kazue	60-100	R
Stamm, Claus	Very Special Badgers (1st, ob4to, 40p, fp b/w, pep, DJ/2.25)	Viking	(1960)	Mizumura, Kazue	30-50	
Standon, Anna	Singing Rhinoceros (1st AM, sm4to, [32]p, fp color, DJ/3.00)	Coward	(1963)	Standon, Edward	30-50	
Stang, Wendy	Hubert (1st {std}, 24mo, [31]p, color, pep, DJ/1.95, NYTBI)	Harlin Quist	(1967)	Anderson, Robert	50-85	
Stanley, H.M.	London Street Arabs (1st, 4to, 67p, green cl, AEG, 28pl)	L: Cassell	1890	Tennant, Dudley	120-170	
Stanovsky, Vladislav	Fairy Tale Tree (1st, lg8vo, 452p, color, DJ/4.95)	Putnam	(1961)	Kolibal, Stanislav	45-70	
Stanovsky, Vladislav	The Firebird (1st, 8vo, 64p, color, DJ)	L: J.M. Dent	1969	Manasek, Ludek	35-50	
Stapp, Emilie B.	Bread & Lasses (1st, 8vo, tan cl, 94p, 6pl)	(DeMoines)	1902	Monahan, P.J.	30-60	
Stapp, Emilie B.	Uncle Peter-Heathen (1st, 8vo, 285p, 10cp)	McKay	(1912)	Macy, Harriet	25-40	
Starbird, Kaye	Don't Ever Cross a Crocodile (1st, 8vo, 62p, b/w, DJ/2.95)	Lippincott	(1963)	Dalton, Kit	20-30	*
Starbird, Kaye	Pheasant on a Route Seven (1st {std}, 8vo, 74p, fp b/w, cep, DJ/3.50)	Lippincott	(1968)	DeLarrea, Victoria	40-65	R*
Starbird, Kaye	Speaking of Cows (1st, 8vo, 70p, b/w, DJ/2.95)	Lippincott	(1960)	Fava, Rita	25-45	
Starkie, Walter	Don Gypsy (1st, 8vo, orange/gilt, 525p, frn by...)	L: J. Murray	(1936)	Rackham, Arthur	60-100	
Starkie, Walter	Spanish Raggle-Taggle (1st, 8vo, 488p, red/gilt, frn by...)	L: J. Murray	(1934)	Rackham, Arthur	70-125	
Staunton, Schuyler	Daughters of Destiny (1st [1], sm8vo, p-o, gilt, 319p, 8cp)	Reilly/Britton	(1906)	Peirce/DeLay	220-300	
Staunton, Schuyler	Fate of a Crown (1st, sm8vo, 306p, red/gilt, 6pl)	Reilly/Britton	(1905)	Sheffer, G.C.	350-500	
Staver, Mary W.	New & True (1st, sm4to, 136p, green/gilt, 4pl, dep)	Lee & Shepard	1892	Various	180-250	
Stawell, Mrs. R.	Fairies I Have Met (1st, 8vo, green cl, 117p, 8cp)	L: John Lane	[1907]	Dulac, Edmund	250-400	
Stawell, Mrs. R.	Fairies I Have Met (8vo, 117p, blue/gilt, 8cp)	L: Hodder	[1910]	Dulac, Edmund	250-350	
Stawell, Mrs. R.	Fairy of Old Spain... (1st AM, 8vo, beige/gilt, 134p, teg, 6cp)	Dent/Dutton	1912	Pape, Frank	65-120	
Stawell, Mrs. R.	My Days with the Fairies (1st, 4to, 169p, red/gilt, 8 ticp)	L: Hodder	[1913]	Dulac, Edmund	350-500	
Stawell, R. (ed.)	Fabre's Book of Insects (1st AM, 4to, 271p, green/gilt, 12 ticp)	Dodd	1921	Detmold, Edward J.	200-300	
Stawell, R. (ed.)	Fabre's Book of Insects (1st {this pub.}, 4to, 271p, 12 ticp)	Tudor	1935	Detmold, Edward J.	100-150	
Steadman, Ralph	Little Red Computer (1st AM, 4to, [32]p, color, DJ/4.50)	McGraw-Hill	(1969)	Steadman, Ralph	40-65	
Stearns, Monroe	Kasimir's Journey (1st, 4to, [35]p, fp color, DJ/3.00, NYTBI)	Lippincott	1957	Reidel, Marlene	45-70	
Steedman, Amy	Apple Pie... (8vo, 111p, AEG, gilt, p-o, 8cp)	L: Jack	[1908]	Beale, Evelyn	30-50	
Steedman, Amy	Legends & Stories of Italy... (1st, lg8vo, 188p, teg ibds, gilt, 12 ticp)	L: Jack	[1909]	Cameron, Katharine	120-200	
Steedman, Amy	Madonna of the Goldfinch (1st, 8vo, 194p, uncut, 8 ticp)	L: Jack	[1917]	Steedman, E.M.	60-90	
Steedman, Amy	Margot and the Golden Fish (1st, sm8vo, 96p, AEG, p-o, 8cp)	L: Jack	[1908]	Spooner, M.D.	50-80	
Steedman, Amy	Our Island Saints (1st AM, 8vo, p-o, teg, 178p, 8 ticp)	Putnam	(1912)	Spooner, M.D.	50-90	
Steedman, Amy	Stories from Grimm... (16mo, 116p, p-o, 8cp)	Jack/Dutton	[1908]	Rountree, Harry	60-90	
Steedman, C.M.	Child's Life of Jesus (1st, 8vo, 423p, white/gilt, 30cp, pep)	L: Jack	[1906]	Woodroffe, Paul	100-180	
Steedman, Charles J.	Bucking the Sagebrush (1st, 8vo, 270p, map, teg, 9pl)	Putnam	1904	Russell, Charles M.	300-500	
Steel, Flora A.	Adventures of Akbar (1st AM, 8vo, 204p, gilt, 8cp)	Stokes	(1913)	Shaw, Byam	80-120	
Steel, Flora A.	Adventures of Akbar (1st, 8vo, 204p, gilt, 8cp)	L: Heinemann	1913	Shaw, Byam	80-120	
Steel, Flora A.	English Fairy Tales (1st AM, 8vo, red/gilt, 363p, 16cp, pep)	Macmillan	1918	Rackham, Arthur	200-285	R
Steele, Mary Q.	Journey Outside (1st, lg8vo, 143p, brown cl, dp b/w, DJ/4.50, NH)	Viking	(1969)	Negri, Rocco	30-50	
Steele, Mary Q.	Secret of Crossbone Hill (1st {std}, 8vo, 183p, b/w, DJ/2.95)	World	(1959)	Stevens, Mary	20-30	*
Steele, Richard	Perverse Widow (1st, 16mo, 31p, bds, p-o, teg, 3 ticp)	L: Heinemann	1909	Aldin, Cecil	100-160	
Steele, Richard	Perverse Widow (1st AM, 12mo, teg, ibds, p-o, 3 ticp)	Dent/Dutton	1909	Aldin, Cecil	85-130	
Steele, Robert	Story of Alexander (1st, lg8vo, 226p, uncut, 6pl)	L: D. Nutt	1894	Mason, Fred	80-125	

AUTHOR	TITLE	PUBLISHER	DATE	ARTIST	PRICE	LC
Steele, Robert (ed)	Russian Garland (1st, 8vo, 243p, 6cp)	McBride	1916	De Rosciszewski, R.	200-300	*
Steele, Robert (tr)	Renaud of Montauban (1st, 8vo, 284p, gilt, uncut 10 fp b/w)	L: G. Allen	1897	Mason, Fred	70-100	
Steele, William O.	Andy Jackson's Water Well (1st {std}, 8vo, 80p, fp b/w, DJ/2.75)	Harcourt	(1959)	Ramus, Michael	20-30	
Steele, William O.	Buffalo Knife (1st {std}, 8vo, 177p, b/w, DJ/2.25)	Harcourt	(1952)	Galdone, Paul	25-40	*
Steele, William O.	Daniel Boone's Echo (1st {std}, 8vo, 78p, b/w, DJ/2.50)	Harcourt	(1957)	Nicolas	25-40	
Steele, William O.	Davy Crockett's Earthquake (1st {std}, 8vo, 63p, fp b/w, DJ/2.25)	Harcourt	(1956)	Nicolas	25-40	
Steele, William O.	DeSoto, Child of the Sun: Search for Gold (1st {std}, 8vo, 190p, DJ/1.75)	Aladdin	1956	Bjorklund, Lorence	20-30	
Steele, William O.	Far Frontier (1st {std}, 8vo, 185p, fp b/w, DJ/2.95)	Harcourt	(1959)	Galdone, Paul	20-30	
Steele, William O.	Flaming Arrows (1st {std}, 8vo, 178p, b/w, DJ/2.75)	Harcourt	(1957)	Galdone, Paul	30-60	*
Steele, William O.	Francis Marion, Young Swamp Fox (1st {std}, sm8vo, 192p, b/w, DJ/1.75)	Bobbs-Merrill	(1954)	Gringhuis, Dirk	20-30	
Steele, William O.	Golden Root (1st {std}, sm8vo, ibds, 76p, fp b/w, DJ/1.75)	Aladdin	1951	Kredel, Fritz	30-50	*
Steele, William O.	Hound Dog Zip to the Rescue (1st, 8vo, 62p, color)	Garrard Pub.	1970	Korach, Mimi	20-25	
Steele, William O.	John Sevier, Pioneer Boy (1st {std}, sm8vo, 192p, b/w, DJ/1.75)	Bobbs-Merrill	(1953)	James, Sandra	20-30	
Steele, William O.	Lone Hunt (1st {std}, 8vo, 176p, b/w, DJ/2.75)	Harcourt	(1956)	Galdone, Paul	20-35	
Steele, William O.	No-Name Man of the Mountain (1st {std}, 8vo, 79p, b/w, DJ/2.95)	Harcourt	(1964)	Davis, Jack	20-35	
Steele, William O.	Over-Mountain Boy (1st {std}, 8vo, 192p, b/w, pep, DJ/1.75)	Aladdin	1952	Kredel, Fritz	20-30	
Steele, William O.	Perilous Road (1st {std}, 8vo, 191p, blue cl, b/w, DJ/2.95, NH, JABA)	Harcourt	(1958)	Galdone, Paul	40-65	
Steele, William O.	Spooky Thing (1st {std}, 8vo, 80p, fp b/w, DJ/2.75)	Harcourt	(1960)	Coker, Paul	20-30	
Steele, William O.	Story of Daniel Boone (1st, 8vo, 175p, b/w, DJ/1.50)	Grosset/Dunlap	(1953)	Baumgartner, Warren	20-35	
Steele, William O.	Story of Leif Ericson (1st, 8vo, 181p, b/w, DJ/1.50)	Grosset/Dunlap	(1954)	Lape, Panas	20-35	
Steele, William O.	Tomahawks and Trouble (1st {std}, 8vo, 213p, b/w, DJ/2.50)	Harcourt	1955	Galdone, Paul	20-30	
Steele, William O.	Trail through Danger (1st {std}, 8vo, 184p, b/w, DJ/3.25)	Harcourt	(1965)	Beck, Charles	20-35	
Steele, William O.	We Were There on the Oregon Trail (1st, 8vo, 182p, b/w, DJ/1.95)	Grosset/Dunlap	(1955)	Vaughn, Frank	20-30	
Steele, William O.	Wilderness Journey (1st {std}, sm8vo, aqua cl, 209p, b/w, DJ/2.50)	Harcourt	(1953)	Galdone, Paul	25-40	
Steele, William O.	Winter Danger (1st {std}, 8vo, 183p, grey cl, b/w, DJ/2.25)	Harcourt	(1954)	Galdone, Paul	25-40	
Steele, William O.	Year of the Bloody Sevens (1st {std}, 8vo, 187p, fp b/w, DJ/3.25)	Harcourt	(1963)	Beck, Charles	20-30	
Steen, Elizabeth	Red Jungle Boy (1st, lg sq8vo, 82p, fp 2-color, pep, DJ/2.00)	Harcourt	(1937)	Steen, Elizabeth	30-50	
Steen, Margarite	Stallion (sm8vo, 315p, 1-color title page by....)	Little/Brown	1933	Ward, Lynd	25-40	
Steffens, Lincoln	Boy on Horseback (1st, 8vo, 258p, b/w, DJ/2.00)	Harcourt	(1935)	Tousey, Sanford	30-50	*
Steig, William	About People (1st {std}, 8vo, 105p, buckram, b/w, DJ/2.50)	Random	(1939)	Steig, William	70-120	*
Steig, William	Agony in the Kindergarten (1st {std}, lg8vo, [124]p, bds, b/w, DJ/1.50)	Duell, Sloan	(1950)	Steig, William	80-120	*
Steig, William	All Embarrassed (1st {std}, 8vo, 101p, b/w, DJ/2.00)	Duell, Sloan	(1944)	Steig, William	60-90	
Steig, William	Bad Island (1st {std}, lg4to, [32]p, fp color, DJ/5.95)	Windmill Books	(1969)	Steig, William	50-80	
Steig, William	Bad Speller (1st {std}, sq12mo, ipcb, [48]p, b/w, DJ)	Windmill Books	1970	Steig, William	40-65	
Steig, William	CDB! (1st, sq12mo, [48]p, ibds, b/w, DJ/2.95)	Windmill Books	1968	Steig, William	30-50	
Steig, William	Continuous Performance (1st {std}, lg8vo, 95p, b/w, DJ/1.95)	Duell, Sloan	(1963)	Steig, William	30-50	*
Steig, William	Dreams of Glory (1st {std}, lg8vo, 147p, b/w, DJ/2.95)	Knopf	(1953)	Steig, William	50-85	
Steig, William	Eye for Elephants (1st, sq12mo, [48]p, 1-color, DJ/2.95)	Windmill Books	(1970)	Steig, William	30-50	
Steig, William	Lonely Ones (1st {std}, sm8vo, 102p, ibds, fp b/w, DJ/1.00)	Duell, Sloan	(1942)	Steig, William	85-140	
Steig, William	Man About Town (1st, 4to, [98]p, cartoons)	NY: Long/Smith	1932	Steig, William	80-125	
Steig, William	Persistent Faces (1st {std}, 12mo, brown cl, [186]p, b/w, DJ/1.50)	Duell, Sloan	(1945)	Steig, William	60-90	
Steig, William	Rejected Lovers (1st {std}, lg8vo, 152p, b/w, DJ/2.95)	Knopf	1951	Steig, William	45-70	
Steig, William	Roland the Minstrel Pig (1st, lg4to, 32p, color, cep, DJ/4.95)	Windmill Books	(1968)	Steig, William	70-100	R
Steig, William	Small Fry (1st, ob12mo, [128]p, b/w, DJ/1.50)	Duell, Sloan	(1944)	Steig, William	55-90	
Steig, William	Small Fry (1st {this fmt}, lg8vo, ipcb, [64]p, b/w, DJ/1.00)	Duell, Sloan	(1951)	Steig, William	45-70	
Steig, William	Sylvester & the Magic Pebble (1st, lg4to, ibds, [32]p, color, DJ/4.95, CM)	Windmill Books	(1969)	Steig, William	140-200	
Steig, William	Till Death Do Us Part (1st {std}, 8vo, [128]p, b/w, DJ/2.00)	Duell, Sloan	(1947)	Steig, William	50-80	
Stein, Evaleen	Child Songs of Cheer (1st, sm8vo, 120p, gilt, 4cp, pep)	Lothrop, Lee	(1918)	Inglis, Antoinette	30-50	*
Stein, Evaleen	Troubadour Tales (1st, sm8vo, 165p, gilt, col frn by...)	Bobbs-Merrill	(1903)	Parrish, Maxfield	100-150	
Stein, Gertrude	World is Round (1st, 4to, 67p, blue bds, color, DJ/2.50)	W.R. Scott	1939	Hurd, Clement	150-225	R
Steiner, Charlotte	ABC (1st, lg4to, [27]p, ibds, color, DJ/0.50)	F. Watts	1946	Steiner, Charlotte	50-80	
Steiner, Charlotte	Annie's ABC Kitten (1st, 4to, [31]p, color, cep, DJ/3.25)	Knopf	(1965)	Steiner, Charlotte	30-50	
Steiner, Charlotte	Big Laughing Book (1st, lg4to, ibds, [58]p, color, DJ/1.00)	Grosset/Dunlap	1949	Steiner, Charlotte	45-70	*
Steiner, Charlotte	Birthdays are for Everyone (1st {std}, sm8vo, 32p, color, DJ/2.95)	Doubleday	(1964)	Steiner, Charlotte	50-80	
Steiner, Charlotte	Daddy Comes Home (1st {std}, ob8vo, ibds, [24]p, 2-color, DJ/1.25)	Doubleday/Doran	1944	Steiner, Charlotte	30-50	
Steiner, Charlotte	Kiki & Muffy (1st {std}, ob8vo, ibds, [26]p, 2-color, cep, DJ/1.25)	Doubleday/Doran	1943	Steiner, Charlotte	60-90	
Steiner, Charlotte	Kiki Dances (1st {std}, ob8vo, ibds, [32]p, color, DJ/1.25)	Doubleday	(1949)	Steiner, Charlotte	60-90	
Steiner, Charlotte	Kiki is an Actress (1st {std}, lg8vo, unpag, ibds, color, DJ/2.00)	Doubleday	(1958)	Steiner, Charlotte	70-100	
Steiner, Charlotte	Kiki Skates (1st {std}, ob8vo, ibds, [34]p, color, DJ/1.25)	Doubleday	(1950)	Steiner, Charlotte	50-80	
Steiner, Charlotte	Kiki's Play House (1st {std}, ob4to, [29]p, color, DJ/2.50)	Doubleday	1962	Steiner, Charlotte	40-65	
Steiner, Charlotte	Listen to my Seashell (1st, ob4to, 32pg, color, pep, DJ)	Knopf	(1959)	Steiner, Charlotte	40-65	
Steiner, Charlotte	Lulu (1st {std}, sm ob4to, ibds, [38]p, color, DJ/1.00)	Doubleday/Doran	1939	Steiner, Charlotte	60-90	
Steiner, Charlotte	Lulu's Play School (1st {std}, ob8vo, ibds, [32]p, color, DJ/1.25)	Doubleday	(1948)	Steiner, Charlotte	45-70	*
Steiner, Charlotte	My Bunny Feels Soft (1st, ob4to, [33]p, color, DJ/2.75)	Knopf	(1958)	Steiner, Charlotte	50-80	
Steiner, Charlotte	My Slippers are Red (1st, ob4to, [32]p, color, pep, DJ/2.75)	Knopf	(1957)	Steiner, Charlotte	60-90	
Steiner, Charlotte	Patsy's Pet (1st {std}, ob8vo, ibds, [30]p, 2-color, DJ/1.50)	Doubleday	(1955)	Steiner, Charlotte	45-70	
Steiner, Charlotte	Pete and Peter (1st {std}, sq8vo, ipcb, [26]p, color, DJ/1.25)	Doubleday/Doran	1941	Steiner, Charlotte	60-90	
Steiner, Charlotte	Pete's Puppets (1st {std}, 8vo, unpag, ibds, color, DJ/1.25)	Doubleday	(1952)	Steiner, Charlotte	35-50	
Steiner, Charlotte	Polka Dot (1st {std}, ob8vo, ibds, [34]p, color, dep, DJ/1.25)	Doubleday	1947	Steiner, Charlotte	30-50	
Steiner, Charlotte	Red Riding Hood Goes Sledding (1st {std}, sq8vo, 26p, fp color, DJ/2.50)	Macmillan	1962	Steiner, Charlotte	30-45	
Steiner, Charlotte	Sleepy Quilt (1st {std}, sq12mo, [16]p, color, cep, DJ/1.00)	Doubleday/Doran	(1945)	Steiner, Charlotte	30-50	
Steiner, Charlotte	Wake Up! Wake Up! (1st, ob8vo, ibds, [25]p, color, DJ/0.50)	Grosset/Dunlap	(1946)	Steiner, Charlotte	30-50	
Steiner, Stan	Last Horse (1st {std}, 8vo, 71p, color, DJ/3.00)	Macmillan	(1961)	Yazz, Beatien	20-30	
Stephan, A. Condie	Fairy Tales of a Parrot (1st, 8vo, ibds, [90]p, 6 ticp, dep)	Nister/Dutton	(1892)	Ellis, Tristam	120-200	
Stephane, Nelly	Roland (1st AM, lg4to, [32]p, ipcb, fp 2-color, DJ/3.25, NYTBI)	Harcourt	(1958)	Francois, Andre	50-80	
Stephens, Charles A.	Grandfather's Broadaxe (1st, 8vo, 222p, b/w, DJ/3.95)	W.R. Scott	(1967)	Moriarty, Jerome	25-45	
Stephens, James	Crock of Gold (1st, 8vo, 298p, green/gilt, 6 fp 2-color, pep)	Macmillan	1922	Jones, Wilfred	40-65	
Stephens, James	Crock of Gold (1st, 8vo, 227p, red/gilt, 12cp)	L: Macmillan	1926	Mackenzie, Thomas B.	120-175	

AUTHOR	TITLE	PUBLISHER	DATE	ARTIST	PRICE	LC
Stephens, James	Deidre (1st {std}, 8vo, 202p, b/w, DJ/5.95)	Macmillan	(1970)	Hogrogian, Nonny	25-45	
Stephens, James	Irish Fairy Tales (1st, 8vo, 318p, green/gilt, 16cp)	L: Macmillan	1920	Rackham, Arthur	250-350	
Stephens, Robert N.	Captain Ravenshaw (1st, 12mo, 369p, teg, blue/gilt, 7pl)	L.C. Page	1901	Various	35-60	
Stephens, William	Hermit Crab Lives in a Shell (1st, 8vo, 46p, color, DJ/3.95)	Holiday House	(1969)	Sapieha, Christine	25-45	*
Stephens, William	Octopus Lives in the Ocean (1st, 8vo, 44p, color, DJ/3.50)	Holiday House	(1968)	D'Attilio, Anthony	30-45	*
Stephens, William	Sea Horse: Fish in Armor (1st, 8vo, 48p, color, DJ/3.50)	Holiday House	(1969)	D'Attilio, Anthony	25-45	
Stephenson, Dorothy	How to Scare a Lion (1st, 4to, 32p, fp color, DJ/2.95)	Follett	(1965)	Johnson, John	25-45	
Stephenson, Dorothy	Night it Rained Toys (1st, lg4to, 32p, fp color, DJ/2.95)	Follett	(1963)	Johnson, John	30-45	
Steptoe, John	Stevie (1st, 8vo, [24]p, fp color, cep, DJ/3.50)	Harper	(1969)	Steptoe, John	60-100	R
Steptoe, John	Uptown (1st, 8vo, [24]p, ipcb, color, DJ/3.50)	Harper	(1970)	Steptoe, John	65-90	
Sterling, Dorothy	Creatures of the Night (1st {std}, 8vo, 125p, blue bds, b/w, DJ/2.95)	Doubleday	(1960)	Lubell, Winifred	30-45	
Sterling, Dorothy	Forever Free (1st {std}, 8vo, 208p, b/w, DJ/2.95)	Doubleday	(1963)	Crichlow, Ernest	25-45	*
Sterling, Dorothy	Mary Jane (1st {std}, 8vo, 214p, fp b/w, DJ/2.75)	Doubleday	1959	Crichlow, Ernest	30-50	
Sterling, Helen	Horse that Takes Milk Around (1st, sq4to, [28]p, ipcb, color, pep, DJ/1.50)	F. Watts	1946	Hartwell, Marjorie	30-45	
Sterling, Sara H.	Lady of King Arthur's Court (1st, 8vo, teg, 262p, p-o, 5cp)	Jacobs	(1907)	Peck, Clara E.	60-95	
Sterling, Sara H.	Robin Hood & his Merry Men (8vo, brown cl, 118p, 7cp)	L: Coker	[1933]	Wheelwright, Rowland	35-60	*
Sterling, Sara H.	Shakespeare's Sweetheart (1st, 8vo, 282p, p-o, teg, 5pl, pep)	Jacobs	(1905)	Peck, Clara E.	40-70	
Stern, Arthur K.	Fairy Quackenbose (1st, 8vo, 123p, picb, uncut, 4pl)	Phi: Brown Bros.	1913	Iredell, R.W.	100-160	*
Stern, Gladys B.	Ugly Dachshund (1st, 8vo, 132p, b/w, DJ/1.75)	Macmillan	1938	Barker, Kathleen F.	30-50	
Sterne, Emma G.	All About Little Boy Blue (1st, 24mo, ibds, p-o, 48p, color)	Cupples/Leon	(1924)	Gooch, Thelma	50-80	
Sterne, Emma G.	All About Peter Pan (1st, 24mo, tan bds, 48p, p-o, 8cp)	Cupples/Leon	(1924)	Gooch, Thelma	50-80	
Sterne, Emma G.	Drums of Monmouth (1st, 8vo, 287p, aqua cl, uncut, b/w, pep, DJ/2.50)	Dodd	1935	Lawson, Robert	75-130	
Sterne, Emma G.	Miranda is a Princess (1st, 8vo, 221p, yellow cl, b/w, pep, DJ/1.75)	Dodd	1937	Lawson, Robert	70-125	
Sterne, Emma G.	Pirate of Chatham Square (1st, 8vo, 213p, b/w, pep, DJ/2.00)	Dodd	1939	Simont, Marc	25-45	
Sterne, Laurence	Sentimental Journey/France & Italy (1st, 12mo, 442p, blue/gilt, b/w, AEG)	L: Bliss Sands	1897	Robinson, Thomas H.	75-100	
Sterne, Laurence	Sentimental Journey/France & Italy (1st, 4to, gilt, teg, 12 ticp)	Putnam	1910	Hopkins, Everard	90-120	
Sterne, Laurence	Sentimental Journey/France & Italy (1st, lg8vo, 253p, black/gilt, 12 b/w)	Dodd	1929	Angelo, Valenti	50-80	
Stevens, Carla	Rabbit and Skunk & the Scary Rock (1st, ob8vo, [46]p, 1-color, DJ/2.75)	W.R. Scott	1962	Kraus, Robert	30-45	*
Stevens, D.K.	Ballads of the Be-Ba-Boes (1st, 4to, yellow cl, 100p)	Houghton	1913	Daland, Katharine	160-240	
Stevens, Eden V.	Abba (1st {std}, 8vo, 116p, fp b/w, cep, DJ/3.00)	Atheneum	1962	Stevens, Anthony	40-65	
Stevens, Eden V.	The Piper (1st {std}, 8vo, 85p, b/w, gilt, cep, DJ/3.95)	Atheneum	1964	Rocker, Fermin	30-50	
Stevens, Frank	Adventures in Hiveland (1st, 8vo, 227p, green/gilt, b/w)	L: Hutchinson	1903	Sargent, L.A.	140-220	
Stevens, Frank L.	Through Merrie England (1st, 8vo, green/gilt, teg, 214p, 12cp, pep)	L: Warne	(1928)	Bedford, Francis D.	80-120	
Stevens, James	Paul Bunyan (1st, 8vo, 245p, woodcuts by...)	Knopf	1925	Lewis, Allen	30-50	
Stevens, Thomas	Children of the World from A to Z (1st, 4to, [58]p, 26cp)	R.H. Russell	1903	Collins, A.H.	250-350	
Stevenson, Alice M.	Bridget's Fairies (1st, sm8vo, p-o, 131p, b/w)	L: R.T.S.	(1919)	Robinson, Charles	150-240	
Stevenson, John G.	Father Time Stories (1st, 8vo, ibds, 154p, 3cp, pep)	L: R.T.S.	(1921)	Robinson, Charles	140-200	
Stevenson, Rbt. L.	Black Arrow (1st, lg8vo, teg, p-o, 328p, 14cp, pep, SC)	Scribner	1916	Wyeth, N.C.	170-240	
Stevenson, Rbt. L.	Catriona (1st, 8vo, 357p, 4cp)	L: Cassell	(1915)	Michael, A.C.	50-80	
Stevenson, Rbt. L.	Child's Garden of Verses (1st, sm8vo, 137p, teg, uncut, gilt, b/w)	Scribner/Lane	1895	Robinson, Charles	250-350	R
Stevenson, Rbt. L.	Child's Garden of Verses (1st UK, 8vo, 136p, AEG, gilt, b/w)	L: John Lane	1895	Robinson, Charles	200-300	
Stevenson, Rbt. L.	Child's Garden of Verses (1st, 12mo, 107p, b/w)	L.C. Page	1900	Barry, Etheldred B.	30-50	*
Stevenson, Rbt. L.	Child's Garden of Verses (1st, lg sq4to, ibds, 115p, 12cp)	R.H. Russell	(1900)	Mars/Squire	400-600	
Stevenson, Rbt. L.	Child's Garden of Verses (1st {this pub}, 8vo, 94p, 9 fp color, b/w)	Rand/McNally	(1902)	Mars/Squire	80-125	
Stevenson, Rbt. L.	Child's Garden of Verses (1st, 8vo, blue cl, 110p, 21cp, pep)	Dodge	(1905)	Pease, Bessie C.	130-200	
Stevenson, Rbt. L.	Child's Garden of Verses (1st, lg8vo, p-o, 125p, teg uncut, 12cp, SC)	Scribner	1905	Smith, Jessie W.	170-245	
Stevenson, Rbt. L.	Child's Garden of Verses (1st, sm8vo, 131p, cp, pep)	Chi: Flanagan	(1908)	O'Reilly, E.D.	50-80	*
Stevenson, Rbt. L.	Child's Garden of Verses (1st {color ed.}, 8vo, gilt, teg, 8cp, pep)	L: Bodley Head	(1908)	Robinson, Charles	200-280	
Stevenson, Rbt. L.	Child's Garden of Verses (1st, 4to, blue/gilt, teg, 12ticp, pep)	L: Chatto	1908	Sowerby, Millicent	200-300	
Stevenson, Rbt. L.	Child's Garden of Verses (1st AM, 4to, 125p, teg, 12cp, pep)	Scribner	1908	Sowerby, Millicent	200-300	
Stevenson, Rbt. L.	Child's Garden of Verses (1st, sm4to, 91p, color)	McLoughlin	(1909)	Comstock, Enos B.	60-100	
Stevenson, Rbt. L.	Child's Garden of Verses (1st, 8vo, 115p, 8cp)	Scribner	1909	Storer, Florence	50-80	
Stevenson, Rbt. L.	Child's Garden of Verses (12mo, ibds, 92p)	Barse/Hopkins	[1910]	Von Hofsten, H.	40-60	
Stevenson, Rbt. L.	Child's Garden of Verses (12mo, 96p, col frn, fp b/w)	Donohue	(1916)	Sheldon, Marian	35-50	
Stevenson, Rbt. L.	Child's Garden of Verses (1st, 4to, p-o, 140p, color, pep)	Whitman	(1917)	Weage, Josephine	60-90	*
Stevenson, Rbt. L.	Child's Garden of Verses (1st, 4to, 96p, p-o, 8cp, pep)	Rand/McNally	(1919)	Hallock, Ruth M.	70-100	
Stevenson, Rbt. L.	Child's Garden of Verses (1st, 8vo, 191p, teg, gilt, 8cp)	Lippincott	1919	Kirk, Maria L.	100-160	
Stevenson, Rbt. L.	Child's Garden of Verses (16mo, bds, p-o, 127p, color)	Altemus	(1921)	Hoopes, Margaret	40-65	
Stevenson, Rbt. L.	Child's Garden of Verses (1st, 8vo, [306]p, col frn, b/w)	Saalfield	(1924)	Brundage, Frances	35-60	*
Stevenson, Rbt. L.	Child's Garden of Verses (1st, ob4to, p-o, 89p, gilt, 12cp, pep)	McKay	(1926)	LeMair, H.W.	225-325	
Stevenson, Rbt. L.	Child's Garden of Verses (1st, lg8vo, 243p, col frn, b/w, pep)	Sears	(1926)	Noe, Eva	30-50	*
Stevenson, Rbt. L.	Child's Garden of Verses (1st, 16mo, 121p, col frn, b/w)	Macmillan	1927	Davis, Marguerite	25-45	*
Stevenson, Rbt. L.	Child's Garden of Verses (1st, sm4to, 85p, p-o, 11 fp color, pep)	Platt/Munk	(1929)	Eulalie	55-80	
Stevenson, Rbt. L.	Child's Garden of Verses (1st, 4to, ibds, [36]p, 8 fp color)	Saalfield	(1930)	Burd, Clara M.	30-60	
Stevenson, Rbt. L.	Child's Garden of Verses (1st, 8vo, p-o, gilt, 127p, fp color, pep)	Whitman	(1930)	McCracken, James	30-50	*
Stevenson, Rbt. L.	Child's Garden of Verses (1st, 4to, 76p, color, pep)	C.E. Graham	(1930)	Pratt, J.C.	35-60	*
Stevenson, Rbt. L.	Child's Garden of Verses (1st, 12mo, 91p, b/w, pep)	Whitman	(1931)	Good, Paula R.	25-45	*
Stevenson, Rbt. L.	Child's Garden of Verses (1st UK, ob4to, ibds, pep, 71p, 12cp)	L: Harrap	(1931)	LeMair, H.W.	200-300	
Stevenson, Rbt. L.	Child's Garden of Verses (folio, ibds, 60p, color, pep)	Whitman	1932	Bennett, Juanita C.	50-80	
Stevenson, Rbt. L.	Child's Garden of Verses (1st {this fmt} ob8vo, [24]p, color, pep)	Grosset/Dunlap	1938	Bennett, Juanita C.	40-60	*
Stevenson, Rbt. L.	Child's Garden of Verses (1st, 4to, ibds, 89p, 7cp, pep)	Saalfield	(1940)	Peat, Fern B.	50-80	
Stevenson, Rbt. L.	Child's Garden of Verses (1st, 12mo, 68p, color)	Rand/McNally	(1942)	Brice, Tony	30-50	*
Stevenson, Rbt. L.	Child's Garden of Verses (1st, sq4to, ibds, [30]p, fp color, pep, DJ/1.00)	Garden City	1942	Doane, Pelagie	50-80	
Stevenson, Rbt. L.	Child's Garden of Verses (1st, 4to, 112p, ibds, color, DJ/2.50)	Heritage Press	1944	Duvoisin, Roger	40-60	*
Stevenson, Rbt. L.	Child's Garden of Verses (1st, 12mo, ipcb, b/w, pep)	Whitman	1947	Scott, Janet L.	30-50	*
Stevenson, Rbt. L.	Child's Garden of Verses (1st, 8vo 118p, grn cl, p-o, 15cp, pep, DJ/2.50)	Oxford U. Pr.	1947	Tudor, Tasha	200-300	
Stevenson, Rbt. L.	Child's Garden of Verses (1st, 4to, 76p, ibds, color, pep, BGB)	Simon/Schuster	(1951)	Provensen, A.&.M.	70-100	R
Stevenson, Rbt. L.	Child's Garden of Verses (1st AM {std}, 4to, ibds, 96p, color, DJ/5.95)	F. Watts	(1966)	Wildsmith, Brian	30-55	

AUTHOR	TITLE	PUBLISHER	DATE	ARTIST	PRICE	LC
Stevenson, Rbt. L.	David Balfour (1st, lg8vo, p-o, 356p, 9cp, pep, SC)	Scribner	1924	Wyeth, N.C.	200-300	
Stevenson, Rbt. L.	Dr. Jekyll & Mr. Hyde (1st, lg8vo, gilt, teg, 189p, 8pl)	Scott-Thaw	1904	Macauley, Charles R.	80-120	*
Stevenson, Rbt. L.	Dr. Jekyll & Mr. Hyde (1st AM, lg8vo, 136p, gilt, 8pl, pep)	Dodd	1930	Beaman, S.G.H.	100-165	
Stevenson, Rbt. L.	Dr. Jekyll & Mr. Hyde (1st [Movie ed.], 8vo, 234p)	Grosset/Dunlap	[1941]	(Photos)	80-145	*
Stevenson, Rbt. L.	Dr. Jekyll & Mr. Hyde (1st, 8vo, 148p, gilt, 12 fp b/w)	Folio Society	1948	Peake, Mervyn	80-120	
Stevenson, Rbt. L.	Ebb-Tide (1st, 12mo, 204p, gilt, cvr by...)	Stone/Kimball	1894	Meteyard, Thomas B.	90-150	
Stevenson, Rbt. L.	Fables (1st AM, 4to, maroon/gilt, teg, 83p, 20pl)	Scribner	1914	Herman, E.R.	100-165	
Stevenson, Rbt. L.	Kidnapped (1st, 8vo, 343p, 8cp)	L: Cassell	1913	Stott, W.R.S.	55-80	*
Stevenson, Rbt. L.	Kidnapped (1st, lg8vo, map, teg, 289p, 14cp, pep, SC)	Scribner	1913	Wyeth, N.C.	250-350	
Stevenson, Rbt. L.	Kidnapped (1st, sm8vo, p-o, 332p, 7cp, pep)	Jacobs	(1915)	Abbott, Elenore P.	50-80	
Stevenson, Rbt. L.	Kidnapped (1st, lg8vo, 262p, p-o, 8cp, WS)	Rand/McNally	(1916)	Winter, Milo	60-100	
Stevenson, Rbt. L.	Kidnapped (1st, lg8vo, gilt, 301p, p-o, col frn, b/w, pep)	Harper	(1921)	Rhead, Louis	30-60	*
Stevenson, Rbt. L.	Kidnapped (1st AM, sm8vo, 327p, blue cl, 16pl)	Macmillan	1925	Goble, Warwick	160-220	
Stevenson, Rbt. L.	Kidnapped (1st, 8vo, 348p, gilt, p-o, 4cp, 12pl, pep)	Winston	(1925)	Godwin, Frank	30-50	*
Stevenson, Rbt. L.	Kidnapped (1st, 8vo, 251p)	L: Macmillan	1928	Brock, Charles E.	55-80	*
Stevenson, Rbt. L.	Kidnapped (1st, 4to, 290p, tan/gilt, 12 ticp, pep)	L: Oxford U.Pr.	1930	Hilder, Rowland	65-100	
Stevenson, Rbt. L.	Kidnapped (1st, 16mo, 387p, b/w)	Macmillan	(1930)	Rowe, Clarence	30-50	*
Stevenson, Rbt. L.	Kidnapped (1st [special ed.], 8vo, 340p, fp color, pep, DJ/2.00)	Grosset/Dunlap	(1948)	Ward, Lynd	25-40	*
Stevenson, Rbt. L.	Master of Ballantrae (1st, 8vo, 349p, 12cp)	L: Cassell	1911	Paget, Walter	40-60	*
Stevenson, Rbt. L.	Master of Ballantrae (1st, 8vo, 259p)	L: Macmillan	1928	Brock, Henry M.	40-60	*
Stevenson, Rbt. L.	Merry Men (1st, 8vo, 266p)	L: Macmillan	1928	Millar, H.R.	35-60	*
Stevenson, Rbt. L.	Pavilion on the Links (1st, 8vo, 96p, gilt, col frn, fp b/w, pep)	L: Chatto	1913	Browne, Gordon	50-85	
Stevenson, Rbt. L.	Songs with Music of Child's Garden of Verses (1st, 4to, 55p, pcb, 12cp)	L: Jack	[1915]	Tarrant, Margaret	90-120	
Stevenson, Rbt. L.	St. Ives (1st, 8vo, 438p, brown/gilt, cvr by...)	Scribner	1897	Armstrong, Margaret	100-160	
Stevenson, Rbt. L.	Stevenson Song Book (1st, 4to, ibds, 119p, cvr by...)	Scribner	1897	Armstrong, Margaret	80-120	
Stevenson, Rbt. L.	Travels with a Donkey in the Cevennes (1st, 8vo, 189p, gilt, 8pl, pep)	L: John Lane	1931	Blampied, Edmund	90-120	
Stevenson, Rbt. L.	Treasure Island (1st AM, sm8vo, 292p, mustard cl, 4 fp b/w)	Roberts Bros.	1884	Merrill, Frank T.	350-500	
Stevenson, Rbt. L.	Treasure Island (1st AM, 12mo, 388p, fp b/w)	Scribner	1900	Paget, Walter	55-80	*
Stevenson, Rbt. L.	Treasure Island (1st, sm8vo, 292p, cp, pep)	Jacobs	(1911)	Abbott, Elenore P.	45-80	*
Stevenson, Rbt. L.	Treasure Island (1st, 8vo, 339p, 12cp)	L: Cassell	1911	Cameron, John	75-100	*
Stevenson, Rbt. L.	Treasure Island (1st, lg8vo, p-o, gilt, teg, 273p, 14cp, pep, SC)	Scribner	1911	Wyeth, N.C.	350-500	
Stevenson, Rbt. L.	Treasure Island (1st, 8vo, 288p, 35pl, pep)	Harper	(1915)	Rhead, Louis	40-60	*
Stevenson, Rbt. L.	Treasure Island (1st, lg8vo, 258p, p-o, cp, pep, WS)	Rand/McNally	(1915)	Winter, Milo	70-120	
Stevenson, Rbt. L.	Treasure Island (1st, sm8vo, 306p, 7cp, fp b/w)	Scribner	1918	Varian, George	60-100	*
Stevenson, Rbt. L.	Treasure Island (1st, sm8vo, 312p, blue cl, pep, 4cp)	L: Macmillan	1923	Goble, Warwick	100-165	
Stevenson, Rbt. L.	Treasure Island (1st, lg8vo, 230p, col frn, b/w, pep)	Saalfield	(1924)	Brundage, Frances	25-45	
Stevenson, Rbt. L.	Treasure Island (1st, 8vo, 304p, p-o, 3cp)	Winston	(1924)	Godwin, Frank	30-50	*
Stevenson, Rbt. L.	Treasure Island (1st, lg8vo, 241p, col frn)	Sears	(1926)	Kelsey, C.W.	30-50	*
Stevenson, Rbt. L.	Treasure Island (1st, 4to, 255p, brown/gilt, 12cp)	L: Benn	(1927)	Dulac, Edmund	200-300	
Stevenson, Rbt. L.	Treasure Island (1st AM, lg8vo, 287p, green/gilt, 12 ticp)	Doran	(1927)	Dulac, Edmund	180-220	
Stevenson, Rbt. L.	Treasure Island (1st {this pub}, 8vo, green cl, 287p, 8cp)	Garden City	[1930]	Dulac, Edmund	100-160	
Stevenson, Rbt. L.	Treasure Island (1st, sm4to, 228p, color, pep)	Grosset/Dunlap	(1930)	Justis, Lyle	40-60	*
Stevenson, Rbt. L.	Treasure Island (1st, 8vo, red/gilt, 252p, 10cp)	L: Muller	1934	Orr, Monro S.	100-160	
Stevenson, Rbt. L.	Treasure Island (1st, 8vo, 287p, color, pep, DJ/1.25, RC)	World	(1946)	Falls, Charles B.	30-50	*
Stevenson, Rbt. L.	Treasure Island (1st [special ed], lg8vo, 342p, color, DJ/2.00)	Grosset/Dunlap	(1947)	Price, Norman	30-50	
Stevenson, Rbt. L.	Treasure Island (1st, 8vo, 246p, gilt, 20 fp b/w, DJ)	L: Eyre/Spotts.	1949	Peake, Mervyn	130-200	
Stevenson, Rbt. L.	Weir of Hermiston (1st AM, 8vo, teg, gilt, 266p, cvr by...)	Scribner	1896	Armstrong, Margaret	55-80	
Stevenson, William	Bushbabies (1st {std}, 8vo, 278p, b/w, cep, DJ/3.50)	Houghton	1965	Ambrus, Victor	25-45	
Steward, Ray M.	Surprising Adventures of Man in the Moon (1st, sm4to, 142p, 12cp)	Lee & Shepard	(1903)	Bridgman, L.J.	150-225	
Stewart, Anna B.	Bibi the Baker's Horse (1st, 8vo, 190p, color, pep, DJ/2.00)	Lippincott	(1942)	Richter, Catherine	30-50	
Stewart, Anna B.	Gentlest Giant (1st {1st bk}, lg8vo, 142p, blue bds, color)	NY: Wayne	1915	Walker, Dugald S.	100-165	
Stewart, Anna B.	Gentlest Giant (1st {this pub}, 8vo, blue cl, 148p, uncut, b/w, dep)	McBride	1929	Walker, Dugald S.	50-85	
Stewart, Anna B.	Little Brother Goose (1st, 8vo, 107p, illus, pep)	McBride	1928	Fouse, Dorothea	40-65	
Stewart, Anna B.	Three White Cats of Avignon (1st {std}, 12mo, 167p, col frn, pep)	Doubleday/Doran	1929	Joyce, Robert	30-50	
Stewart, Anna B.	Two Young Corsicans (1st {std}, 8vo, 261p, color, DJ/2.00)	Lippincott	(1944)	Richter, Catherine	30-45	
Stewart, Anna B.	Young Miss Burney (1st {std}, 8vo, green/gilt, 270p, b/w, DJ/2.50)	Lippincott	1947	Stone, Helen	30-50	
Stewart, Elinore	Letters of a Woman Homesteader (1st, 12mo, 282p, 6pl)	Houghton	1914	Wyeth, N.C.	200-300	
Stewart, Grace B.	Good Fairy (1st, 8vo, 128p, gilt, 4cp)	Reilly/Lee	(1930)	Adams, P.B.	75-125	
Stewart, John	Key to the Kitchen (1st, sm4to, ipcb, [32]p, fp color, pep, DJ/3.95)	Lothrop, Lee	1970	Quackenbush, Rbt.	30-45	
Stewart, Mary	Once Upon a Time Tales (1st, 8vo, 275p, pep, 8cp)	Revell	(1912)	McClure, Griselda M.	40-65	
Stewart, Mary	Way to Wonderland (1st, lg8vo, 144p, gilt, 194p, p-o, 6cp, pep)	Dodd	(1917)	Smith, Jessie W.	180-260	
Stewart, Mary	Way to Wonderland (1st UK, lg8vo, 144p, blue/gilt, 6 ticp, pep)	L: Hodder	[1918]	Smith, Jessie W.	250-350	
Stickney, J.H.	Bird World (1st, 12mo, 214p, green cl, 10pl by...)	Ginn & Co.	1898	Seton, Ernest T.	100-160	*
Stigand, Chauncy H.	Black Tales for White Children (1st, 8vo, 200p, b/w)	L: Constable	(1914)	Hargrave, John G.	300-500	
Stilwell, Alison	Chin Ling & Chinese Cricket (1st {std}, sm4to, ibds, [48]p, color, DJ/2.25)	Macmillan	1947	Enright, Maginel W.	70-120	
Stilwell, Sarah	Musical Tree (1st, 4to, [66]p, tan cloth, fp color, pep)	Penn	1925	Stilwell, Sarah	70-120	
Stimson, Frederic J.	Mrs. Knollys (1st, sm8vo, 207p, green/gilt, teg)	Scribner	1897	Armstrong, Margaret	30-60	*
Stinetorf, Louise	Children of North Africa (1st {std}, 8vo, 189p, col frn, b/w, DJ/2.00)	Lippincott	(1943)	Dobias, Frank	25-45	*
Stinetorf, Louise	Musa the Shoemaker (1st {std}, 8vo, 183p, b/w, DJ/3.00)	Lippincott	(1959)	Johnson, Harper	20-35	*
Stirling, John	For a Little Child Like Me (1st, 8vo, 52p, blue cl, b/w, pep)	Scribner	1934	Knowles, Horace J.	30-50	
Stirling, Monica	Little Ballet Dancer (1st, lg8vo, ipcb, 61p, 2-color, pep, DJ/2.50)	Lothrop, Lee	1952	Stone, Helen	30-50	
Stitch, Wilhelmina	Little Book of Singing Rhymes (1st, 12mo, ibds, decor by...)	Volland	(1931)	Halstead, Muriel	50-80	
Stobbs, William	Story of the Three Bears (1st AM, lg ob8vo, 32p, fp 3-color, pep, DJ/2.75)	Whittlesey	1965	Stobbs, William	25-40	
Stockton, Frank	Adventures of Captain Horn (1st, sm8vo, green/gilt, 404p, cvr by...)	Scribner	1895	Armstrong, Margaret	30-50	
Stockton, Frank	Afield & Afloat (1st, sm8vo, teg, 422p, 12pl)	Scribner	1900	Newell, Peter	40-60	
Stockton, Frank	Associate Hermits (1st, 12mo, green/gilt, 257p, 9pl)	Harper	1899	Frost, A.B.	80-120	R
Stockton, Frank	Bee-Man of Orn (1st {std}, sq8vo, 44p, ibds, color, DJ/3.50)	Holt, Rinehart	(1964)	Sendak, Maurice	120-200	R
Stockton, Frank	Bicycle of Cathay (1st, sm8vo, green cl, 240p, 32pl)	Harper	1900	Lowell, Orson	50-80	

AUTHOR	TITLE	PUBLISHER	DATE	ARTIST	PRICE	LC
Stockton, Frank	Captain Chap (1st, sm8vo, 298p, tan cl, 6pl)	Lippincott	1897	Stephens, Charles H.	40-60	
Stockton, Frank	Fanciful Tales (1st, 12mo, maroon cl, 135p, cvr by…)	Scribner	1894	Armstrong, Margaret	75-100	*
Stockton, Frank	Floating Prince… (1st, 8vo, 199p, PPP, b/w)	Scribner	1881	Unknown	225-350	
Stockton, Frank	Girl at Cobhurst (1st, 12mo, green/gilt, teg, 408p, cvr by…)	Scribner	1898	Armstrong, Margaret	45-70	
Stockton, Frank	Great Stone of Sardis (1st, 12mo, 230p, teg, uncut, gilt, 52pl)	Harper	1898	Newell, Peter	80-130	R
Stockton, Frank	Griffin and the Minor Canon (1st {std}, 8vo, 55p, ibds, color, DJ/3.50)	Holt, Rinehart	(1963)	Sendak, Maurice	120-200	R
Stockton, Frank	John Gayther's Garden… (1st, sm8vo, green/gilt, uncut, teg, 365p)	Scribner	1902	Armstrong, Margaret	50-85	R
Stockton, Frank	Kate Bonnet (1st, 12mo, gilt, 420p, 8pl)	Appleton	1902	Keller/Potter	40-70	
Stockton, Frank	Mrs. Cliff's Yacht (1st, 12mo, 341p, 8pl, cvr by…)	Scribner	1896	Armstrong, Margaret	30-60	
Stockton, Frank	Pomona's Travels (1st [1], 12mo, 275p, teg, gilt, 10pl)	Scribner	(1894)	Frost, A.B.	70-100	
Stockton, Frank	Queen's Museum (1st, lg8vo, 219p, gilt, p-o, teg, 10cp, pep, SC)	Scribner	1906	Richardson, F.	150-220	
Stockton, Frank	Squirrel Inn (1st, sm8vo, 222p, teg, b/w)	Century	1891	Frost, A.B.	55-80	
Stockton, Frank	Storyteller's Pack (1st, sm8vo, 380p, gilt, 16pl, teg, cvr by…)	Scribner	1897	Armstrong, Margaret	60-100	
Stockton, Frank	Storyteller's Pack (1st, 8vo, 358p, fp b/w, pep, DJ/5.95)	Scribner	(1968)	Bryson, Bernarda	30-50	R*
Stoddard, Anne	Bingo is My Name (1st {std}, 8vo, [58], color)	Century	(1931)	Hader, B.& E.	50-80	
Stoddard, Anne	Good Little Dog (1st {std}, 8vo, ibds, [59]p, 16cp)	Century	(1930)	Hader, B.& E.	60-90	
Stoddard, Anne	Here Bingo! (1st {std}, sq8vo, ibds, [61]p, 16 fp color)	Century	(1932)	Hader, B.& E.	60-90	
Stoddard, Charles W.	Cruise Under the Crescent (1st, 8vo, 358p, cvr by…)	Rand/McNally	(1898)	Denslow, W.W.	50-80	*
Stoddard, William O.	Little Smoke (1st, 8vo, blue/gilt, 295p, 14pl, PPP)	Appleton	1891	Dellenbaugh, Fred	160-250	
Stokely, Edith K.	Bubbleloon (1st, lg8vo, 201p, blue/gilt, 6cp, pep)	Doran	(1926)	Porter, J. Erwin	80-125	
Stokely, Edith K.	Pantaloon (1st, lg8vo, 168p, orange cl, 6cp, pep)	Doran	(1927)	Kay, Gertrude A.	40-65	
Stokes, Hugh	Belgium (1st, lg4to, black/gilt, 143p, 52 fp b/w)	L: Kegan Paul	1916	Brangwyn, Frank	120-180	
Stokes, Vernon	Blobbs at the Sea Side (lg4to, 64p, ibds, 11 chromos, pep)	L: Chambers	[1908]	Stokes, Vernon	250-400	
Stolper, Joel	Patches (1st, 8vo, 100p, 1-color, DJ/1.75)	Harcourt	(1940)	Stolper, Joel	30-45	*
Stolz, Mary S.	Belling the Tiger (1st, 8vo, 64p, fp b/w, DJ/2.50, NH)	Harper	(1961)	Montresor, Beni	40-65	
Stolz, Mary S.	Bully of Barkham Street (1st {std}, 8vo, 194p, fp b/w, cep, DJ/3.50)	Harper	(1963)	Shortall, Leonard	25-40	
Stolz, Mary S.	Dog on Barkham Street (1st, 8vo, 184p, fp b/w, DJ/2.50)	Harper	(1960)	Shortall, Leonard	25-45	
Stolz, Mary S.	Dragons of the Queen (1st, 8vo, 47p, ibds, fp b/w, DJ/3.50)	Harper	(1969)	Frascino, Edward	20-30	
Stolz, Mary S.	Emmett's Pig (1st, 8vo, ibds, 61p, 2-color, DJ/2.50)	Harper	(1959)	Williams, Garth	50-80	
Stolz, Mary S.	Fredou (1st, 8vo, 118p, b/w, DJ/2.95)	Harper	(1962)	Ungerer, Tomi	25-40	
Stolz, Mary S.	Great Rebellion (1st, 8vo, 63p, fp b/w, DJ/2.50)	Harper	(1961)	Montresor, Beni	30-50	R
Stolz, Mary S.	Juan (1st, 8vo, 131p, fp b/w, DJ/3.95)	Harper	(1970)	Glanzman, Louis	30-50	R
Stolz, Mary S.	Leftover Elf (1st, 8vo, 57p, green cl, fp b/w, DJ/2.00)	Harper	(1952)	Bacon, Peggy	30-50	
Stolz, Mary S.	Maximilian's World (1st, 8vo, 57p, ibds, fp b/w, cep, DJ/2.95)	Harper	(1966)	Shulevitz, Uri	40-65	R
Stolz, Mary S.	Mystery of the Woods (1st, 8vo, 46p, fp 2-color, DJ/2.95)	Harper	(1964)	Shulevitz, Uri	30-50	
Stolz, Mary S.	Noonday Friends (1st, 8vo, 182p, b/w, DJ/3.50, NH)	Harper	(1965)	Glanzman, Louis	30-50	
Stolz, Mary S.	Pigeon Flight (1st, 8vo, 54p, fp b/w, DJ/2.50)	Harper	(1962)	Tinkelman, Murray	40-65	R
Stolz, Mary S.	Say Something (1st, 4to, ibds, [32]p, fp color, DJ/3.50)	Harper	(1968)	Frascino, Edward	30-45	
Stolz, Mary S.	Singular Hen & her Peculiar Children (1st, ob8vo, 48p, color, DJ/3.50)	Harper	(1969)	Frascino, Edward	25-45	*
Stolz, Mary S.	Siri the Conquistador (1st {std}, 8vo, 57p, b/w, DJ/2.50)	Harper	(1963)	Montresor, Beni	25-45	*
Stolz, Mary S.	Wonderful Terrible Time (1st, 8vo, 182p, fp b/w, DJ/3.95)	Harper	(1967)	Glanzman, Louis	25-45	
Stone, A. Harris	Last Free Bird (1st, ob4to, [30]p, fp color, pep, DJ/4.95)	Prentice-Hall	(1967)	Heins, Sheila	30-50	*
Stone, Amy W.	Going-on-Nine (1st, 8vo, 128p, 6 fp color, b/w, pep, DJ/2.00)	Lothrop, Lee	(1939)	Wilkin, Eloise B.	70-130	
Stone, Amy W.	Here's Juggins (1st, sm8vo, 162p, blue cl, 6cp, pep, DJ/2.00)	Lothrop, Lee	1936	Woodward, Hildegarde	40-65	
Stone, Amy W.	P-Penny & his Little Red Cart (1st, sm8vo, 165p, color, pep)	Lothrop, Lee	1934	Woodward, Hildegarde	50-80	
Stone, Caroline R.	Inga of Porcupine Mine (1st, sm8vo, 212p, blue cl, b/w, DJ/2.00)	Holiday House	(1942)	Simon, Ellen	25-45	
Stone, Eugenia	Robin Hood's Arrow (1st, lg8vo, 162p, b/w, DJ/2.50)	Wilcox/Follett	(1948)	Busoni, Rafaello	40-65	
Stone, Eugenia	Secret of the Bog (1st, sm8vo, 217p, b/w, cep, DJ/2.25)	Holiday House	(1948)	Price, Christine	25-40	
Stone, Eugenia	Squire for King Arthur (1st, lg8vo, 158p, fp b/w, DJ/2.95)	Follett	(1955)	Busoni, Rafaello	50-85	
Stone, Mary	Children's Stories that Never Grow Old (1st, 12mo, 312p, yellow cl, color)	Reilly/Britton	(1908)	Neill, John R.	100-165	
Stone, Stuart B.	Kingdom of Why (1st, lg8vo, green cl, 275p, p-o, 9pl)	Bobbs-Merrill	(1913)	Newell, Peter	200-300	
Stone, William S.	Pepe was the Saddest Bird (1st {std}, lg8vo, [62]p, ipcb, b/w, DJ/1.75)	Knopf	1944	Nicolas	80-125	R
Stone, William S.	Ship of Flame (1st {std}, 4to, 164p, bds, col frn, b/w, DJ/7.50)	Knopf	1945	Nicolas	60-100	R
Stone, William S.	Tahiti Landfall (1st, 8vo, 308p, b/w, DJ/3.50)	Wm. Morrow	1946	Nicolas	30-50	
Stone, William S.	Teri Taro from Bora Bora (1st {std}, 8vo, 133p, 8cp, pep, DJ/1.75)	Knopf	1940	Sperry, Armstrong	50-80	
Stone, William S.	Thunder Island (1st {std}, 8vo, 194p, 7cp, DJ/2.00)	Knopf	(1942)	Nicolas	40-65	
Stong, Philip D.	Beast Called an Elephant (1st, 8vo, 123p, b/w, DJ/2.75)	Dodd	1955	Wiese, Kurt	25-40	
Stong, Philip D.	Captain Kidd's Cow (1st, 8vo, 122p, color, DJ/2.50)	Dodd	1941	Wiese, Kurt	40-65	*
Stong, Philip D.	Censored, the Goat (1st, lg8vo, 78p, ibds, color, DJ/2.50)	Dodd	1945	Wiese, Kurt	50-80	*
Stong, Philip D.	Cowhand Goes to Town (1st {std}, sm4to, ibds, 85p, dp color, pep, DJ/2.50)	Dodd	1939	Wiese, Kurt	50-80	
Stong, Philip D.	Edgar: The 7:58 (1st, sm8vo, 101p, pep, b/w, DJ/1.50)	Farrar/Rinehart	1938	Lenski, Lois	80-125	
Stong, Philip D.	Farm Boy (1st {std}, sm4to, ibds, col frn, 80p, pep)	Doubleday/Doran	1934	Wiese, Kurt	50-80	
Stong, Philip D.	Forty Pounds of Gold (1st {std}, sm8vo, 218p, b/w, DJ/2.50)	Doubleday	1951	Shilstone, Arthur	25-45	
Stong, Philip D.	High Water (1st {std}, sm4to, ibds, 79p, color, pep, DJ/2.00)	Dodd	1937	Wiese, Kurt	50-80	
Stong, Philip D.	Hired Man's Elephant (1st, 8vo, 149p, beige cl, b/w, DJ/2.00)	Dodd	1939	Lee, Doris	30-50	
Stong, Philip D.	Hirum, the Hillbilly (1st, 8vo, 104p, b/w, DJ/2.75)	Dodd	1951	Wiese, Kurt	25-45	
Stong, Philip D.	Honk! the Moose (1st {std}, sm4to, ibds, 80p, color, pep, DJ/2.00, NH)	Dodd	1935	Wiese, Kurt	90-140	R
Stong, Philip D.	Horses and Americans (1st, 4to, 333p, col frn, DJ/5.00)	Stokes	1939	Wiese, Kurt	30-55	
Stong, Philip D.	Long Lane (1st, 8vo, 308p, b/w, DJ/2.50)	Farrar/Rinehart	(1939)	Warren, F.E.	25-45	*
Stong, Philip D.	Mike: Story of a Young Circus Acrobat (1st, 8vo, 126p, b/w, DJ/3.00)	Dodd	1957	Wiese, Kurt	30-50	
Stong, Philip D.	Missouri Canary (1st, lg8vo, 77p, ibds, color, DJ/2.50)	Dodd	1943	Wiese, Kurt	40-65	
Stong, Philip D.	No-Sitch: the Hound (1st {std}, sm4to, 80p, col frn, pep, DJ/2.00)	Dodd	1936	Wiese, Kurt	60-80	
Stong, Philip D.	Phil Stong's Big Book (1st, 8vo, 159p, 2-color, DJ/3.50)	Dodd	(1961)	Wiese, Kurt	25-45	*
Stong, Philip D.	Positive Pete (1st, sm4to, ibds, 64p, color, pep, DJ/2.75)	Dodd	1947	Wiese, Kurt	40-60	
Stong, Philip D.	Prince and the Porker (1st, lg8vo, 67p, ibds, color, DJ/2.75)	Dodd	1950	Wiese, Kurt	35-50	
Stong, Philip D.	Way Down Cellar (1st, 8vo, 159p, color, pep, DJ/2.50)	Dodd	1942	Wiese, Kurt	150-220	
Stong, Philip D.	Young Settler (1st {std}, sm4to, ibds, 80p, 20 fp color, pep, DJ/2.50)	Dodd	1938	Wiese, Kurt	60-90	
Stonier, George W.	Pictures on the Pavement (1st, 8vo, 214p, brown cl, b/w, pep, DJ)	L: M. Joseph	1955	Ardizzone, Edward	60-100	

AUTHOR	TITLE	PUBLISHER	DATE	ARTIST	PRICE	LC
Storm, Theodor	Immensee (1st, 8vo, 130p, olive cl, 9cp)	McClurg	1907	Armstrong, Margaret	100-160	
Stoutenburg, Adrien	American Tall Tales (1st, lg8vo, 112p, fp b/w, DJ/3.50)	Viking	(1966)	Powers, Richard	25-40	
Stoutenburg, Adrien	Crocodile's Mouth (1st, 4to, 64p, fp b/w, DJ/3.00)	Viking	(1966)	Rounds, Glen	30-50	
Stoutenburg, Adrien	Timber Line Treasure (1st, 8vo, 218p, b/w, DJ/2.50)	Westminster Pr.	(1951)	Turkle, Brinton	25-40	*
Stow, Edith	Nancy the Joyous (1st, sm8vo, 253p, col frn, decor by...)	Reilly/Britton	1914	Nuyttens, Joseph P.	40-60	
Stowe, Harriet B.	Uncle Tom's Cabin (1st, 8vo, 529p, gilt, illus by...)	L: Routledge	1897	Thomas, George H.	170-220	
Stowe, Harriet B.	Uncle Tom's Cabin (8vo, green cl, 531p, col frn, 16pl)	L: Nelson	[1900]	Forrest, A.S.	100-160	*
Stowe, Harriet B.	Uncle Tom's Cabin (1st, 8vo, 529p, gilt, cvr by...)	L: Routledge	1904	King, Jessie	170-220	
Stowe, Harriet B.	Uncle Tom's Cabin (1st, 8vo, 508p, 8cp)	L: A&C Black	1904	Vedder, Simon H.	80-120	*
Stowe, Harriet B.	Uncle Tom's Cabin (16mo, p-o, gilt, 115p, 8cp)	Jack/Dutton	[1908]	Forrest, A.S.	55-80	*
Stowe, Harriet B.	Uncle Tom's Cabin (brown cl, p-o, 12mo, 46p, 6 color)	Barse/Hopkins	[1915]	Von Hofsten, H.	60-90	*
Stowe, Harriet B.	Uncle Tom's Cabin (1st, lg8vo, 446p, fp b/w, pep)	E. McCann	(1929)	Daugherty, James	60-90	
Strack, Lilian H.	Swords and Iris (1st {std}, 8vo, 125p, col frn, fp b/w, pep, DJ/2.00)	Harper	1937	Tagawa, Bunji	60-100	
Strahorn, Carrie A.	15 Thousand Miles by Stage (1st, lg8vo, 673p, gilt, p-o, teg, 4cp)	Putnam	1911	Russell, Charles M.	500-800	
Strain, E.H.	School in Fairyland (1st, 8vo, green cl, 186p, 7pl)	L: T.F. Unwin	1896	Brooke, L. Leslie	120-200	
Stranathan, May	Silhouette Stories (1st, 8vo, 198p, brown cl, 14 fp b/w)	Moffat	1921	Taylor, Ethel C.	35-60	*
Strang, Herbert	Big Book of Fairy Stories (1st, 8vo, 191p, ibds, 4cp, pep)	L: H. Milford	(1929)	Watson, A.H.	80-120	
Strang, Herbert	Old Man of the Mountain (1st, 8vo, 322p, green/gilt, fp b/w by...)	L: H. Frowde	(1916)	Bull, Rene	75-100	
Strang, Herbert	Rose Book of the Fairies (4to, ibds, 6cp)	L: H. Milford	(1922)	Govey, Lilian	200-300	
Strang, Herbert	Rose Fairy Book (1st, 4to, 303p, p-o, pep, 12 ticp)	L: Hodder	(1912)	Govey, Lilian	250-350	
Strang, Herbert	What Baby Reads (1st AM, 12mo, bds, gilt, p-o, [32]p, 6cp)	NY: Hodder	[1910]	Sowerby, Millicent	100-160	
Strang, Mrs. H.	Our Old Fairy Stories (1st, 8vo, 223p, 4cp, b/w)	L: Oxford U.Pr.	(1930)	Watson, A.H.	30-50	
Strang, William	Book of Giants (1st, 8vo, 56p, 12pl)	L: Unicorn Press	1898	Strang, William	250-400	
Stratton, Clarence	Swords & Statues (1st, 8vo, 254p, col frn, 7 b/w, cep, DJ/2.00)	Winston	(1937)	Lawson, Robert	120-175	
Stratton, Elenore	Wild Pasture (1st {std}, 8vo, [32]p, fp 2-color, pep, DJ/1.50)	Harper	1940	Yap, Weda	30-45	*
Stratton-Porter, Gene	At the Foot of the Rainbow (1st, 8vo, 258p, yellow cl, 4cp)	Outing	1907	Kemp, Oliver	500-700	
Stratton-Porter, Gene	Birds of the Bible (1st, lg8vo, 469p, 81 illus, pep)	Jennings	(1909)	(Photos)	450-650	
Stratton-Porter, Gene	Daughter of the Land (1st, sm8vo, 475p, green cl, col frn)	Doubleday/Page	1918	Rogers, Frances	65-100	
Stratton-Porter, Gene	Fire Bird (1st {std}, 8vo, 71p, tan bds, pep, 3cp by...)	Doubleday/Page	1922	Grant, Gordon	280-400	
Stratton-Porter, Gene	Freckles (1st, 8vo, teg, 433p, uncut, 6pl, PPPa)	Doubleday/Page	1904	Crawford, E. Stetson	450-700	
Stratton-Porter, Gene	Friends In Feathers (1st, lg8vo, 335p, gilt, p-o, teg, b/w)	Doubleday/Page	1917	(Photos)	250-400	
Stratton-Porter, Gene	Girl of the Limberlost (1st, 8vo, 485p, 4pl, pep)	Doubleday/Page	1909	Benda, W.T.	250-400	
Stratton-Porter, Gene	Her Father's Daughter (1st, sm8vo, 486p, pep, col frn by...)	Doubleday/Page	1921	Summers, D.G.	100-180	
Stratton-Porter, Gene	Homing With Birds (1st, 8vo, 381p, brown cl)	Doubleday/Page	1919	(Photos)	150-225	
Stratton-Porter, Gene	Jesus of the Emerald (1st, lg8vo, [44]p, white bds, col frn)	Doubleday/Page	1923	Winchell, Everett	500-700	
Stratton-Porter, Gene	Keeper of the Bees (1st {std}, sm8vo, 515p, 4cp, pep)	Doubleday/Page	1925	Grant, Gordon	100-165	
Stratton-Porter, Gene	Laddie (1st, 8vo, 602p, blue cl, 4cp, pep)	Doubleday/Page	1913	Pfeifer, Herman	100-175	
Stratton-Porter, Gene	Magic Garden (1st {std}, sm8vo, 272p, pep, designs by...)	Doubleday/Page	1927	Thayer, Lee	120-170	
Stratton-Porter, Gene	Michael O'Halloran (1st, 8vo, 560p, green cl, 4pl, pep)	Doubleday/Page	1915	Rogers, Frances	50-85	
Stratton-Porter, Gene	Morning Face (1st, sm4to, 127p, blue/gilt, color & b/w)	Doubleday/Page	1916	(Photos)	250-350	
Stratton-Porter, Gene	Moths of the Limberlost (1st, 4to, tan/gilt, 370p, color, pep)	Doubleday/Page	1912	(Photos)	220-300	
Stratton-Porter, Gene	Music of the Wild (1st, lg8vo, 430p, green/gilt, b/w)	Jennings/Graham	(1910)	(Photos)	180-260	
Stratton-Porter, Gene	Song of the Cardinal (1st {1st bk.}, 8vo, red/gilt, 163p, 17pl)	Bobbs-Merrill	(1903)	(Photos)	200-300	
Stratton-Porter, Gene	Tales You Won't Believe (1st {std}, 8vo, 327p, grey cl, 23pl)	Doubleday/Page	1925	(Photos)	200-300	
Stratton-Porter, Gene	The Harvester (1st, 8vo, 564p, 4cp, pep)	Doubleday/Page	1911	Jacobs, William L.	60-90	
Stratton-Porter, Gene	What I Have Done with Birds (1st, lg8vo, 258p, green cl, p-o, 16 color)	Bobbs-Merrill	(1907)	(Photos)	250-400	
Stratton-Porter, Gene	White Flag (1st {std}, sm8vo, 483p, col frn, pep)	Doubleday/Page	1923	Lester, Ralph	100-150	
Streamer, Col. D.	Baby's Baedeker (1st, sm8vo, 56p, uncut, ibds, 9pl)	R.H. Russell	1902	Unknown	80-120	*
Streamer, Col. D.	Ruthless Rhymes for Heartless Homes (1st, sm8vo, 40p, ibds, b/w, pep)	R.H. Russell	1901	J.W.A.	90-120	
Streatfeild, Noel	Ballet Shoes (1st AM, 8vo, 294p, color, DJ/2.00)	Random	(1937)	Floethe, Richard	80-125	
Streatfeild, Noel	Circus is Coming (1st, sm8vo, 314p, b/w, CgM)	L: J.M. Dent	(1938)	Spurrier, Steven	50-85	
Streatfeild, Noel	Circus Shoes (1st {std}, 8vo, 401p, color, DJ/2.00)	Random	(1939)	Floethe, Richard	50-65	
Streatfeild, Noel	Dancing Shoes (1st {std}, 8vo, 273p, b/w, DJ)	Random	1957	Floethe, Richard	80-140	
Streatfeild, Noel	Dennis the Dragon (1st, 8vo, 32p)	L: Dent	1939	Streatfeild, Ruth	30-45	
Streatfeild, Noel	Family at Caldicott Place (1st AM {std}, 8vo, 177p, ibds, b/w, DJ/3.95)	Random	(1968)	Maxey, Betty	30-45	
Streatfeild, Noel	Fearless Treasure (1st, 8vo, 272p, b/w, DJ)	L: Joseph	1953	Braby, Dorothea	25-45	
Streatfeild, Noel	First Book of the Ballet (1st AM, sm4to, 93p, 2-color, DJ/1.75)	F. Watts	1953	Soyer, Moses	30-50	
Streatfeild, Noel	Growing Summer (1st, 8vo, blue cl, b/w, 223p, DJ)	L: Collins	1966	Ardizzone, Edward	30-50	
Streatfeild, Noel	Magic Summer (1st AM {std}, 8vo, 270p, b/w, cep, DJ/3.95)	Random	(1967)	Ardizzone, Edward	30-50	
Streatfeild, Noel	New Shoes (1st AM, 8vo, 314p, b/w, DJ/2.95)	Random	1960	Low, Vaike	30-50	
Streatfeild, Noel	Osbert (1st {std}, 8vo, 30p, ipcb, fp 2-color)	Rand/McNally	(1950)	Suba, Susanne	50-80	*
Streatfeild, Noel	Party Shoes (1st AM {std}, 8vo, 333p, grey cl, fp b/w, DJ/2.50)	Random	(1947)	Zinkeisen, Anna	30-50	
Streatfeild, Noel	Secret of the Lodge (1st {std}, 8vo, 233p, 7 fp 2-color, DJ/2.00)	Random	(1940)	Floethe, Richard	120-200	
Streatfeild, Noel	Stranger in Primrose Lane (1st {std}, 8vo, 338p, p-o, 7cp, DJ/2.00)	Random	(1941)	Floethe, Richard	100-160	*
Streatfeild, Noel	Tennis Shoes (1st, 8vo, 290p, 8 fp 2-color, DJ/2.00)	Random	(1938)	Floethe, Richard	120-200	
Streatfeild, Noel	Theater Shoes (1st {std}, 8vo, 282p, color, DJ/2.00)	Random	(1945)	Floethe, Richard	30-50	*
Streatfeild, Noel	Theatre Cat (1st {std}, lg8vo, ipcb, 30p, fp color, DJ/1.25)	Rand/McNally	(1951)	Suba, Susanne	45-65	R*
Street, Julia M.	Fiddler's Fancy (1st, 8vo, 157p, b/w, DJ/2.50)	Follett	(1955)	Sibley, Don	20-35	
Streeter, Edward	Mr. Robbins Rides Again (1st, 8vo, 155p, b/w, pep, DJ/3.00)	Harper	(1958)	Simont, Marc	25-45	
Strettell, Alma	Lullabies of Many Lands (1st, 4to, 127p, gilt, teg, uncut, b/w, dep)	L: G. Allen	1894	Harding, Emily J.	100-170	
Strickland, Harold	Juggernaut of the Rangers (1st, 8vo, 130p, b/w, DJ/2.50)	Dodd	1946	Brown, Paul	80-120	
Stringer, Arthur J.	Loom of Destiny (1st, 16mo, 208p, blue/silver, cvr by...)	Small/Maynard	1899	Peabody, Marion L.	55-90	*
Stroebe, C. (ed.)	Danish Fairy Book (1st, 8vo, blue cl, 218p, 6cp, pep)	Stokes	(1922)	Hood, George	70-120	
Stroebe, C. (ed.)	Norwegian Fairy Book (1st, 8vo, 304p, 6cp, pep)	Stokes	(1922)	Hood, George	50-90	
Strong, Charles	Ranger's Arctic Patrol (1st {std}, 8vo, 214p, b/w, DJ/2.50)	Winston	(1952)	Wiese, Kurt	25-40	*
Strong, L.A.G.	Henry of Agincourt (1st, 8vo, 160p, col frn, b/w, DJ)	L: Nelson	(1937)	Matthew, Jack	40-65	
Strong, L.A.G.	King Richard's Land (1st AM {std}, 12mo, 231p, col frn, b/w, pep, DJ/2.00)	Knopf	1934	Gay, Zhenya	40-65	
Strong, L.A.G.	Mr. Sheridan's Umbrella (1st, 8vo, 215p, col frn, fp b/w, DJ)	L: Nelson	(1935)	Hodges, C. Walter	30-50	

AUTHOR	TITLE	PUBLISHER	DATE	ARTIST	PRICE	LC
Strong, Rowland	Yoyo's Animal Friends (1st, 4to, 170p, teg, 3cp)	Dent/Dutton	1913	Flower, Noel	50-80	
Struther, Jan	Modern Struwwelpeter (1st, lg8vo, ibds, 37p, color)	L: Methuen	1936	Shepard, Ernest H.	200-300	
Struther, Jan	Sycamore Square (1st AM, 8vo, 63p, b/w, DJ/1.25)	Oxford U. Pr.	1932	Shepard, Ernest H.	45-60	
Struther, Jan	Sycamore Square (1st, 8vo, green/gilt, 63p, fp b/w)	L: Methuen	(1932)	Shepard, Ernest H.	50-80	
Stuart, Jesse	Old Ben (1st, 8vo, ipcb, 92p, fp b/w, DJ/3.95)	McGraw-Hill	(1970)	Cuffari, Richard	50-80	R*
Stuart, Jesse	Penny's Worth of Character (1st, 8vo, 61p, b/w, DJ/1.75)	Whittlesey	(1954)	Henneberger, Rbt.	60-90	
Stuart, Jesse	Red Mule (1st, 8vo, 123p, b/w, DJ/2.25)	Whittlesey	(1955)	Henneberger, Rbt.	60-90	*
Stuart, Mary	Pirate's Bridge (1st, ob4to, unpag, color, DJ/2.95)	Lothrop, Lee	1960	Lubell, Winifred	30-45	
Stuart, Ruth M.	Aunt Amity's Silver Wedding (1st, 12mo, green/gilt, 228p, b/w)	Century	1909	Frost, A.B.	35-60	
Stuart, Ruth M.	Carlotta's Intended (1st, 12mo, 277p, 11pl)	Harper	1894	Unknown	30-50	
Stuart, Ruth M.	Daddy'Do-Funny'sWisdom Jingles (1st, sm8vo, 95p, b/w, pep)	Century	1913	Clements, G.H.	120-200	R
Stuart, Ruth M.	George Washington Jones (1st, 12mo, 147p, 5pl)	Altemus	(1903)	Potthast, Edward	35-60	
Stuart, Ruth M.	Gobolinks (1st, ob8vo, ibds, 73p, b/w)	Century	1896	Unknown	100-165	
Stuart, Ruth M.	Golden Wedding (1st, 12mo, 366p, gilt, 8pl)	Harper	1893	Frost, A.B.	50-80	
Stuart, Ruth M.	Haunted Photograph (1st, 12mo, gilt, 168p, 10pl)	Century	1911	Various	60-100	
Stuart, Ruth M.	Holly & Pizen (1st, 12mo, gilt, 216p, 7pl)	Century	1899	Potthast, Edward	50-80	
Stuart, Ruth M.	In Simpkinsville (1st, 12mo, 244p, tan/gilt, 8pl)	Harper	1897	Various	50-80	
Stuart, Ruth M.	Moriah's Mourning (1st, 12mo, gilt, 218p, 8pl)	Harper	1898	Frost/Kemble	60-90	
Stuart, Ruth M.	Napoleon Jackson (1st, 12mo, 132p, red/gilt, 8pl)	Century	1902	Potthast, Edward	60-90	
Stuart, Ruth M.	River's Children (1st, 12mo, 179p, green/gilt, 5pl)	Century	1904	Edwards, Harry C.	45-70	
Stuart, Ruth M.	Second Wooing of Salina Sue (1st, 12mo, gilt, 236p, 12pl)	Harper	1905	Frost/Kemble	50-80	
Stuart, Ruth M.	Solomon Crow's Christmas Pockets (1st, 12mo, gilt, 201p, 14pl)	Harper	1897	Frost, A.B.	50-80	
Stuart, Ruth M.	Sonny's Father (1st, 12mo, teg, 240p, uncut, 2pl by...)	Century	1910	Smith, Jessie W.	70-100	
Stuart, Ruth M.	Sonny, A Christmas Guest (1st, sm8vo, 135p, teg, gilt, 13pl)	Century	1904	Cory, Fanny	40-65	
Stuart, Ruth M.	Story of Babette (1st, 12mo, 209p, beige/gilt, cvr by...)	Harper	1894	Armstrong, Margaret	40-60	*
Sturges, Katharine	Mimi, Momo and Miss Tabby Tibbs (1st, 12mo, ibds, [42]p, color)	Volland	(1927)	Sturges, Katharine	80-120	
Sturges, Lilian B.	Runaway Toys (1st, 12mo, [64]p, black cl, p-o, color)	Rand/McNally	(1920)	Sturges, Lilian B.	70-100	
Sturges, Lilian B.	Toys of Nuremberg (1st, sm8vo, p-o, [80]p, color)	Rand/McNally	(1915)	Sturges, Lilian B.	70-100	
Sturgis, Edith B.	My Busy Days (1st, folio, 50p, ibds, 8cp)	Appleton	1908	Hinchman, Margaretta	120-200	*
Sturton, Hugh	Zomo the Rabbit (1st {std}, lg8vo, 128p, b/w, DJ/3.95)	Atheneum	1966	Warner, Peter	25-40	
Stutters, Percival	How Percival Caught the Python (1st, sq24mo, [89]p, fp color)	Holiday House	(1937)	Stutters, Percival	50-85	
Stutters, Percival	How Percival Caught the Tiger (1st, sq24mo, [89]p, fp color)	Holiday House	(1936)	Stutters, Percival	50-85	
Suba, Susanne	Man with the Bushy Beard (1st {std}, ob4to, [35]p, color, DJ/4.95)	Viking	(1969)	Suba, Susanne	30-45	
Suba, Susanne	Monkeys and the Pedlar (1st {std}, ob4to, [32]p, color, DJ/5.95)	Viking	(1970)	Suba, Susanne	30-45	
Sublette, Clifford	Scarlet Cockerel (1st, 8vo, 293p, p-o, gilt, 6cp)	Little/Brown	1931	Schoonover, Frank	25-45	
Sudermann, Hermann	Magda (1st, 12mo, 161p, red/gilt, teg, uncut, cvr by...)	Lamson/Wolffe	1896	Rhead, Louis	80-120	
Sullivan, Frank	In One Ear (1st, 8vo, red/gilt, 169p, frn by...)	Viking	1933	Seuss, Dr.	150-225	
Sullivan, Thomas R.	Tom Sylvester (1st, 12mo, 428p, green/silver, cvr by...)	Scribner	1893	Armstrong, Margaret	30-45	
Summers, Clara	Sandy Sandman (1st, lg8vo, tan cl, p-o, 155p, 8cp, pep)	Whitman	(1917)	Scannell, Mae	40-70	
Surany, Anico	Covered Bridge (1st, ob4to, [33]p, color, DJ/3.25)	Holiday House	(1967)	Fisher, Leonard	25-40	
Surany, Anico	Etienne-Henri and Gri-Gri (1st, sq8vo, [35]p, color, DJ/4.50)	Holiday House	(1969)	Selig, Sylvie	25-40	
Surany, Anico	Golden Frog (1st, ob4to, [39]p, fp color, cep, DJ/3.00)	Putnam	(1963)	Fisher, Leonard	50-80	
Surany, Anico	Jungle Jumble (1st, 4to, 45p, 1-color, DJ/3.00)	Putnam	(1966)	Fisher, Leonard	40-65	
Surany, Anico	Kati and Kormos (1st, ob8vo, [39]p, fp 2-color, DJ/2.95)	Holiday House	(1966)	Fisher, Leonard	25-40	
Surany, Anico	Malachy's Gold (1st, 4to, [46]p, color, DJ/4.50)	Holiday House	(1968)	Fisher, Leonard	25-40	
Surany, Anico	Monsieur Jolicoeur's Umbrella (1st, 4to, [44]p, fp color, DJ/3.50)	Putnam	(1967)	Fisher, Leonard	40-65	*
Surany, Anico	Ride the Cold Wind (1st, 4to, [45]p, fp color, DJ/3.50)	Putnam	(1964)	Fisher, Leonard	50-80	R
Surtees, Robert S.	Handley Cross (1st, lg8vo, 2 vols, gilt, 24cp)	L: E. Arnold	[1910]	Aldin, Cecil	250-400	
Surtees, Robert S.	Hunting with Mr. Jorrocks (1st, 8vo, 186p, tan/gilt, color, DJ)	L: Oxford U.Pr.	1956	Ardizzone, Edward	60-100	
Surtees, Robert S.	Jorrock's on 'Unting (1st, 16mo, teg, bds, 32p, p-o, 3 ticp)	L: Heinemann	1909	Aldin, Cecil	140-220	
Sutcliff, Rosemary	Armourer's House (1st, 8vo, 235p, 11 fp b/w, pep, DJ/2.50)	L: Oxford U.Pr.	1951	Hodges, C. Walter	30-50	
Sutcliff, Rosemary	Brother Dusty-Feet (1st, 8vo, 231p, b/w, DJ)	L: Oxford U.Pr.	1952	Hodges, C. Walter	30-50	
Sutcliff, Rosemary	Dawn Wind (1st AM {std}, 8vo, 241p, b/w, DJ/3.75)	H.Z. Walck	1962	Keeping, Charles	25-45	
Sutcliff, Rosemary	Eagle of the Ninth (1st, 8vo, 255p, b/w, DJ)	H.Z. Walck	1961	Hodges, C. Walter	30-50	
Sutcliff, Rosemary	High Deeds of Finn MacCool (1st AM {std}, 8vo, 189p, b/w, DJ/3.95)	Dutton	(1967)	Charlton, Michael	30-50	
Sutcliff, Rosemary	Hound of Ulster (1st AM {std}, 8vo, 192p, b/w, DJ/3.50)	Dutton	(1963)	Ambrus, Victor	30-50	*
Sutcliff, Rosemary	Knight's Fee (1st AM, 8vo, 241p, fp b/w, DJ/3.50)	H.Z. Walck	1960	Keeping, Charles	35-50	
Sutcliff, Rosemary	Knight's Fee (1st, 8vo, 241p, fp b/w, DJ)	L: Oxford U.Pr.	1960	Keeping, Charles	50-75	
Sutcliff, Rosemary	Lantern Bearers (1st AM {std}, 8vo, 252p, b/w, DJ/3.50)	H.Z. Walck	1959	Keeping, Charles	60-90	
Sutcliff, Rosemary	Lantern Bearers (1st, 8vo, 252p, b/w, DJ, CgM)	L: Oxford U.Pr.	1959	Keeping, Charles	70-125	
Sutcliff, Rosemary	Queen Elizabeth Story (1st, 8vo, 208p, fp b/w, pep, DJ/2.00)	Oxford U. Pr.	1950	Hodges, C. Walter	30-50	*
Sutcliff, Rosemary	Shield Ring (1st AM {std}, 8vo, 215p, b/w, DJ/3.00)	H.Z. Walck	1957	Hodges, C. Walter	25-45	
Sutcliff, Rosemary	Silver Branch (1st AM {std}, 8vo, 215p, b/w, DJ/3.50)	H.Z. Walck	(1959)	Keeping, Charles	30-45	
Sutton, Adah L.	Mr. Bunny - His Book (4to, ipcb, 106p, color)	Saalfield	(1900)	Fry, W.H.	200-300	*
Sutton, Adah L.	Mushroom Fairies (1st, ob4to, ibds, 159p, 12cp)	Saalfield	(1910)	(Chromos)	225-300	R
Sutton, Adah L.	Teddy Bears (1st, lg8vo, 154p, ibds, 6cp)	Saalfield	1907	Schaffer, A.J.	250-400	
Sutton, Margaret	Magic Makers and Bramble Bush Man (1st, lg8vo, 114p, ipcb, b/w, pep)	Grosset/Dunlap	(1936)	Doane, Pelagie	50-85	
Swan, Oliver G.	Deep Water Days (1st, lg8vo, 506p, p-o, 11cp, pep)	Macrae Smith	(1929)	Various	60-90	
Swan, Oliver G.	Frontier Days (1st, lg8vo, 512p, 3cp by...)	Macrae Smith	(1928)	Schoonover, Frank	60-90	
Sweeney, James J.	Three Young Rats (1st {std}, lg4to, 130p, fp b/w, DJ/6.00)	NY: Valentin	(1944)	Calder, Alexander	60-90	R*
Sweetser, Kate D.	Book of Indian Braves (1st, lg8vo, 183p, p-o, col frn, 6pl)	Harper	1913	Williams, George A.	55-80	
Sweetser, Kate D.	Boys & Girls from George Eliot (1st, lg8vo, 212p, 8pl)	Duffield	1906	Williams, George A.	55-80	*
Sweetser, Kate D.	Boys & Girls from Thackeray (1st, lg8vo, 355p, p-o, 7pl)	Duffield	1907	Williams, George A.	45-70	
Sweetser, Kate D.	Ten Boys from Dickens (1st, lg8vo, 223p, uncut, b/w pl)	R.H. Russell	1901	Williams, George A.	60-100	
Sweetser, Kate D.	Ten Boys from History (1st, lg8vo, 210p, p-o, col frn, 3pl)	Duffield	1910	Williams, George A.	45-70	
Sweetser, Kate D.	Ten Girls from Dickens (1st, lg8vo, 236p, p-o, uncut, 11pl)	Baker/Taylor	1902	Williams, George A.	60-90	
Swenson, Juliet	Hawaii: Book to Begin On (1st {std}, 8vo, ipcb, [48]p, 3-color, DJ/2.50)	Holt, Rinehart	(1963)	Keats, Ezra J.	30-45	
Swift, Hildegarde H.	Edge of April: Biography of John Burroughs (1st, 8vo, 316p, b/w, DJ/3.95)	Wm. Morrow	1957	Ward, Lynd	30-45	

AUTHOR	TITLE	PUBLISHER	DATE	ARTIST	PRICE	LC
Swift, Hildegarde H.	From the Eagle's Wing (1st, 8vo, 287p, b/w, DJ/3.95)	Wm. Morrow	1962	Ward, Lynd	25-40	
Swift, Hildegarde H.	House by the Sea (1st, 8vo, 245p, blue cl, 8pl, pep, DJ/2.00)	Harcourt	(1938)	Ward, Lynd	40-60	
Swift, Hildegarde H.	Little Blacknose (1st, sm8vo, 149p, 2-color, pep, DJ/2.00, NH)	Harcourt	(1929)	Ward, Lynd	60-100	
Swift, Hildegarde H.	Little Red Lighthouse & Great Gray Bridge (1st, 8vo, [56]p, color, DJ/1.75)	Harcourt	(1942)	Ward, Lynd	40-65	
Swift, Hildegarde H.	North Star Shining (1st, 4to, 44p, 10 fp color, DJ/2.50)	Wm. Morrow	(1947)	Ward, Lynd	80-130	
Swift, Hildegarde H.	Railroad to Freedom (1st, 8vo, 364p, b/w, NH)	Harcourt	1932	Daugherty, James	50-80	
Swift, Jonathan	Directions to Servants (1st {std}, 8vo, bds, 126p, 2-color, DJ/4.95)	Pantheon	(1964)	Low, Joseph	30-50	
Swift, Jonathan	Gulliver's Travels (1st, 12mo, 381p, green/gilt, AEG, b/w)	Macmillan	1894	Brock, Charles E.	70-125	*
Swift, Jonathan	Gulliver's Travels (1st, 8vo, 414p, 12cp)	L: Routledge	1895	Wheeler, Edward J.	70-100	
Swift, Jonathan	Gulliver's Travels (1st, sm8vo, green cl, 355p, 27pl)	J. Lane	1900	Cole, Herbert	50-80	*
Swift, Jonathan	Gulliver's Travels (1st AM, 8vo, gilt, teg, 291p, 12cp, pep)	Dent/Dutton	1909	Rackham, Arthur	250-350	
Swift, Jonathan	Gulliver's Travels (1st, 8vo, 291p, gilt, teg, 12cp, pep)	L: Dent	1909	Rackham, Arthur	300-450	
Swift, Jonathan	Gulliver's Travels (1st, 8vo, blue/gilt, AEG, 332p, 6cp, pep)	Nister/Dutton	[1911]	Jackson, A.E.	80-125	
Swift, Jonathan	Gulliver's Travels (1st, sm8vo, 304p, cp, pep)	Doubleday/Page	1912	Groesbeck, Dan S.	25-45	
Swift, Jonathan	Gulliver's Travels (1st AM, 8vo, 235p, 8cp, pep)	Henry Holt & Co.	(1912)	Staynes, Percy A.	35-60	*
Swift, Jonathan	Gulliver's Travels (1st, 8vo, 235p, 8cp, pep)	L: Sidgwick	(1912)	Staynes, Percy A.	35-60	*
Swift, Jonathan	Gulliver's Travels (1st, lg8vo, 344p, gilt, p-o, 12cp, pep, WS)	Rand/McNally	(1912)	Winter, Milo	100-150	
Swift, Jonathan	Gulliver's Travels (1st, 8vo, 350p, col frn, b/w, pep)	Harper	1913	Rhead, Louis	35-60	*
Swift, Jonathan	Gulliver's Travels (1st, sm8vo, 296p, blue/gilt, 12cp, pep)	Macmillan	1917	Pogany, Willy	90-120	
Swift, Jonathan	Gulliver's Travels (1st, 8vo, 346p, brown/gilt, b/w)	L: Wells/Gard.	[1918]	Bull, Rene	160-220	
Swift, Jonathan	Gulliver's Travels (1st, 8vo, 221p, 8cp, pep)	Lippincott	1918	Kirk, Maria L.	50-85	
Swift, Jonathan	Gulliver's Travels (1st UK, 8vo, 296p, gilt, uncut, 12cp)	L: Harrap	1919	Pogany, Willy	80-120	
Swift, Jonathan	Gulliver's Travels (1st AM, 4to, 135p, blue/gilt, 4cp)	Dodd/Heinemann	[1920]	DeBosschere, Jean	160-240	
Swift, Jonathan	Gulliver's Travels (1st, sm8vo, 370p, cp)	Jacobs	[1923]	Smith, Wuanita	30-50	*
Swift, Jonathan	Gulliver's Travels (1st, lg8vo, 338p, p-o, 48cp)	L: Ward Lock	(1923)	Theaker, Harry G.	70-100	
Swift, Jonathan	Gulliver's Travels (1st, 8vo, 274p, p-o, gilt, 3cp, fp b/w, pep)	Winston	(1930)	Prittie, Edwin J.	30-50	
Swift, Jonathan	Gulliver's Travels (1st, lg8vo, green cl, 309p, 4cp)	Houghton	1931	Bacharach, Herman I.	30-50	*
Swift, Jonathan	Gulliver's Travels (1st, sm8vo, 64p)	Chi: Rockwell	1931	Stahl, Ben	55-80	*
Swift, Jonathan	Gulliver's Travels (1st, 8vo, 343p, b/w)	Heritage Press	1940	Eichenberg, Fritz	45-80	*
Swift, Jonathan	Gulliver's Travels (1st, lg8vo, 358p, 24 engravings, DJ/5.00)	NY: Crown	(1947)	Quintanilla, Luis	60-100	*
Swift, Jonathan	Gulliver's Travels (1st [special ed], 8vo, 306p, color, DJ/2.00)	Grosset/Dunlap	(1947)	Watson, Aldren A.	40-60	*
Swift, Jonathan	Gulliver's Travels (1st, 8vo, 272p, b/w, DJ)	Garden City	(1954)	Weisgard, Leonard	20-35	
Swift, Jonathan	Gulliver's Travels (1st, 8vo, 195p, fp 2-color, DJ)	L: Oxford U.Pr.	1955	Jacques, Robin	25-45	
Swinburne, A.C.	Selected Poems... (1st, 4to, black/gilt, 217p, 10pl, pep)	Lane/Dodd	(1928)	Clarke, Harry	300-500	
Swinburne, A.C.	Springtide of Life (1st AM, 4to, 132p, green cl, 8cp, pep)	Lippincott	1918	Rackham, Arthur	200-300	
Swinburne, A.C.	Springtide of Life (1st, 4to, green/gilt, 133p, 8cp, pep)	L: Heinemann	(1918)	Rackham, Arthur	225-300	
Swinburne, A.C.	Tale of Balen (1st AM, 8vo, 132p, olive/gilt, cvr by...)	Scribner	1896	Armstrong, Margaret	80-120	*
Swinnerton, Frank	Cats and Rosemary (1st {std}, 8vo, 182p, b/w, DJ/2.50)	Knopf	1948	Gay, Zhenya	25-45	
Swinnerton, James	Canyon Country Kiddies (1st {std}, 4to, blue cl, 74p, color)	Doubleday/Page	1923	Swinnerton, James	80-120	
Sykes, M'Cready	Poe's Run.... (1st, 8vo, teg, green cl, 84p, b/w)	Cannon Press	1904	Tarkington, Booth	40-60	
Sylva, Carmen	Legends from River & Mountain (1st, 8vo, blue/gilt, teg, 328p, fp b/w)	L: G. Allen	1896	Robinson, Thomas H.	90-120	
Sylva, Carmen	Lily of Life (1st, 4to, gilt, teg, 146p, p-o, 18 ticp)	L: Hodder	[1910]	Stratton, Helen	400-550	
Sylva, Carmen	Peeping Pansy (1st, 4to, red/gilt, 312p, 8 ticp)	L: Hodder	(1918)	Attwell, Mabel L.	400-600	
Sylva, Carmen	Real Queen's Fairy Book (8vo, 279p, gilt, col frn, b/w, pep)	L: G. Newnes	1901	Jones/Nelson	100-165	
Sylvester, Charles	Manny & Co. (1st, 8vo, ibds, [40]p, color)	Volland	1913	Dodge, Katharine S.	60-90	
Syme, Ronald	Columbus, Finder of the New World (1st, 8vo, 70p, dp b/w, DJ/2.00)	Wm. Morrow	1952	Stobbs, William	25-45	*
Symington, E.H.	By Light of Sun (1st, 8vo, 196p, buckram, DJ/2.00, fp woodcuts by...)	Putnam	1941	Leighton, Clare	40-65	
Symonds, John	Away to the Moon (1st, 8vo, 64p, b/w, pep, DJ/2.25)	Lippincott	(1956)	Bianco, Pamela	30-50	
Symonds, John	Elfrida and the Pig (1st, 4to, green cl, 48p, b/w, DJ)	L: Harrap	(1959)	Ardizzone, Edward	60-95	
Symonds, John	Elfrida and the Pig (1st AM, sm4to, 48p, b/w, DJ/2.95)	F. Watts	(1960)	Ardizzone, Edward	50-85	
Symonds, John	Grodge-Cat & the Window Cleaner (1st, 4to, 61p, fp 1-color, DJ/3.50)	Pantheon	(1965)	Francois, Andre	30-50	*
Symonds, John	In the Key of Blue (1st, 8vo, 302p, blue/gilt, cvr by...)	L: E. Mathews	1893	Ricketts, Charles	200-300	
Symonds, John	Magic Currant Bun (1st AM {std}, 8vo, ibds, 38p, 1-color, DJ/2.00, NYTBI)	Lippincott	(1952)	Francois, Andre	40-65	
Symonds, John	Tom and Tabby (1st AM {std}, 4to, ibds, [80]p, 1-color, DJ/4.95)	NY: Universe	(1964)	Francois, Andre	50-85	
Symonds, John	Travelers Three (1st {std}, 8vo, 48p, 2-color, DJ/2.75)	Lippincott	1953	Francois, Andre	30-50	
Symons, Arthur	Aubrey Beardsley (1st, lg8vo, 32p, bds, gilt, 6 b/w)	L: Unicorn Press	1898	Beardsley, Aubrey	170-240	
Syrett, Netta	Garden of Delight (1st, sq8vo, green/gilt, 218p, 10pl)	Hurst/Blackett	1898	Syrett, Nellie	70-120	*
Syrett, Netta	Godmother's Garden (1st, 8vo, 222p, ibds, color)	L: Blackie	[1918]	Harrison, Florence	70-130	
Syrett, Netta	Rachel & the Seven Wonders (1st, 8vo, 172p, p-o, 5cp, pep)	Stokes	(1923)	Mercer, Joyce	75-120	
Syrett, Netta	Tinkelly Winkle (1st AM, 8vo, 157p, green cl, 8cp)	Dodd	1923	Foster, Marcia L.	30-50	
Syrett, Netta	Toby & the Odd Beasts (1st, 8vo, 139p, blue cl, p-o, 5cp)	L: Butterworth	(1921)	Govey, Lilian	100-165	
Syrett, Netta	Vanishing Princess (1st, 8vo, blue cl, 93p, 10pl)	L: D. Nutt	(1910)	Robinson, Charles	120-180	*
Szekely, Sari	Marika (1st, sm4to, 62p, p-o, fp color, pep, DJ/1.50)	Whitman	1939	Gabor, Barbara	60-100	
Szyk, Arthur	New Order (1st, sm4to, [76]p, 8 fp color, DJ/1.50)	Putnam	(1941)	Szyk, Arthur	120-200	
Tabak, Mary N.	Fish is Not a Pet (1st, 4to, 32p, fp 2-color, DJ/2.50)	Whittlesey	(1959)	Duvoisin, Roger	50-80	*
Taber, Gladys	Daisy and Dobbin (1st, 8vo, [62]p, 2-color, DJ/2.00)	Macrae Smith	(1948)	Wiese, Kurt	25-45	*
Taber, Gladys	First Book of Dogs (1st, 8vo, 45p, color, pep, DJ/1.50)	F. Watts	(1949)	Kuhn, Bob	30-50	
Taber, Gladys	Stillmeadow Road (1st {std}, 8vo, 287p, b/w, DJ/4.95)	Lippincott	(1962)	Shenton, Edward	25-40	
Taggart, Marion A.	Pussy-Cat Town (1st, sm8vo, 245p, green/gilt, color, pep)	L.C. Page	1906	Chase, Rhoda	45-70	
Tagore, Rabindranath	Moon, for What Do You Wait? (1st {std}, sm ob8vo, [32]p, color, DJ)	Atheneum	1967	Bryan, Ashley	25-40	*
Tagore, Rabindranath	Stray Birds (1st, sm8vo, blue/gilt, 84p, col frn by...)	L: Macmillan	1917	Pogany, Willy	35-60	
Tague, Lola	Wonderful Merry Go Gound (1st, lg8vo, 46p, fp b/w, DJ/2.95)	Lothrop, Lee	(1961)	Werth, Kurt	20-30	
Talbot, Alfred J.	Pond Mermaid (1st, 4to, 48p)	L: Cassell	1929	Rountree, Harry	40-65	*
Tallant, Edith	Danny and Prue (1st, 8vo, 143p, blue cl, p-o, 2-color, pep, DJ/2.00)	Crowell	(1938)	Freund, Rudolf	30-50	
Tamburine, Jean	I Think I will Go to the Hospital (1st, 4to, cloth, 48p, 3-color, DJ/2.95)	Abingdon Press	(1965)	Tamburine, Jean	20-30	
Tappan, Eva M.	American Hero Stories (1st, 8vo, 301p, gilt, 4cp)	Houghton	1926	Schoonover, Frank	25-40	
Tappan, Eva M.	House with the Silver Door (1st, sm8vo, green cl, 184p, p-o, 4cp)	Houghton	1913	Chamberlin, E.H.	30-50	*
Tappan, Eva M.	Old Ballads in Prose (1st, 12mo, 228p, 4 b/w pl)	Houghton	1901	Cory, Fanny	35-50	

AUTHOR	TITLE	PUBLISHER	DATE	ARTIST	PRICE	LC
Tappan, Eva M.	Prince from Nowhere... (1st, sm8vo, 206p, blue cl, 8cp)	Houghton	1928	Nystrom, J.	30-50	*
Tappan, Eva M.	Robin Hood: His Book (1st, 8vo, tan cl, 267p, 6cp)	Little/Brown	1903	Harding, Charlotte	60-90	
Tarbell, Ida M.	Madame Roland (1st, sm8vo, 328p, blue/gilt, cvr by...)	Scribner	1896	Armstrong, Margaret	30-50	
Tarkington, Booth	Beasley's Christmas Party (1st, 8vo, 100p, gilt, color)	Harper	1909	Clements, Ruth S.	50-80	
Tarkington, Booth	Man from Home (1st, 8vo, 175p, tan cl, 7pl)	Harper	1908	(Photos)	60-90	
Tarkington, Booth	Penrod [1] (1st, sm8vo, p-o, 345p, blue cl, b/w, PPP)	Doubleday/Page	1914	Grant, Gordon	250-350	
Tarkington, Booth	Penrod & Sam (1st, sm8vo, 356p, green/gilt, 8pl, PPP)	Doubleday/Page	1916	Brehm, Worth	100-165	
Tarkington, Booth	Penrod Jashber (1st {std}, sm8vo, blue cl, 321p, b/w)	Doubleday/Doran	1929	Grant, Gordon	45-70	
Tarkington, Booth	Seventeen (1st, 12mo, 328p, orange/gilt, 12pl)	Harper	(1916)	Brown, Arthur W.	60-100	
Tarkington, Booth	Two Vanrevels (1st, sm8vo, 351p, green/gilt, teg, 7pl)	McClure	1902	Hutt, Henry	35-60	
Tarn, William W.	Treasure of Isle of Mist (1st, 8vo, green/gilt, 163p, fp 1-color)	L: P. Allan	1919	Macdonald, Somerled	80-125	
Tarn, William W.	Treasure of Isle of Mist (1st, 8vo, gilt, 184p, pep, b/w)	Putnam	(1934)	Lawson, Robert	60-90	
Tarrant, Margaret	Joan in Flowerland (1st, 8vo, 60p, blue cl, 16cp, pep, DJ)	L: Warne	(1935)	Tarrant, Margaret	250-350	
Tarrant, Margaret	Margaret Tarrant's Christmas Garland (1st, sq8vo, 125p, 19 ticp)	Hale-Cushman	(1942)	Tarrant, Margaret	55-80	*
Tarry, Ellen	Hezekiah Horton (1st, lg8vo, ibds, 39p, fp 1-color, pep, DJ/1.00)	Viking	1942	Harrington, Oliver	60-100	
Tarry, Ellen	Janie Belle (1st, 4to, [30]p, ibds, fp 1-color, DJ/0.50)	Garden City	1940	Sheldon, Marian	80-120	
Tarry, Ellen	My Dog Rinty (1st, lg8vo, [48]p, ibds, DJ/1.50, b/w photos by...)	Viking	1946	Alland, A.& A.	200-300	R
Tarry, Ellen	Runaway Elephant (1st, lg8vo, ipcb, 37p, fp 1-color, pep, DJ/1.50)	Viking	1950	Harrington, Oliver	80-140	R
Tashjian, Virginia	Once there Was and Was Not (1st {std}, 8vo, 85p, color, DJ/3.50)	Little/Brown	(1966)	Hogrogian, Nonny	30-50	
Tashlin, Frank	Bear that Wasn't (1st {std}, sm4to, [60]p, ibds, b/w, DJ/1.25)	Dutton	1946	Tashlin, Frank	25-40	
Tate, Elizabeth	Little Flower Girl (1st, lg8vo, aqua cl, [40]p, 3-color, pep, DJ/2.50)	Lothrop, Lee	(1956)	Stone, Helen	40-65	
Tate, Elizabeth	Little Teddy & the Big Sea (1st, 4to, [32]p, fp color, pep, DJ/2.50)	Lothrop, Lee	1954	Werth, Kurt	60-100	
Tavo, Gus	Hunt the Mountain Lion (1st {std}, 8vo, 209p, b/w, DJ/3.00)	Knopf	1959	Turkle, Brinton	30-50	
Taylor, Anne & Jane	Meddlesome Matty (1st, 8vo, 54p, ibds, color)	L: Bodley Head	1925	Payne, Wyndham	60-90	
Taylor, Anne & Jane	Meddlesome Matty (1st AM, 8vo, ibds, 54p, uncut, color)	Viking	1926	Payne, Wyndham	80-120	R
Taylor, Anne & Jane	Original Poems (2nd AM, 8vo, 415p, gilt, teg, tan cl, col frn)	Stokes	(1905)	Bedford, Francis D.	60-100	
Taylor, Anne & Jane	Original Poems (2nd, 8vo, 415p, teg, uncut, col frn)	L: Wells/Gard.	1905	Bedford, Francis D.	100-175	
Taylor, Bayard	Boys of Other Countries (1st, 8vo, gilt, 260p, col frn, b/w)	Putnam	1912	Coburn, Frederick S.	25-40	
Taylor, Bert L.	Well in the Wood (1st, 8vo, 191p, blue/gilt, 8pl)	Bobbs-Merrill	(1904)	Cory, Fanny	50-80	
Taylor, C. Bryson	Nicanor, Teller of Tales (1st, 8vo, p-o, 422p, pep, 5cp)	McClurg	1906	Kinneys	25-40	
Taylor, Deems	Fantasia (1st, folio, tan cloth, 158p, 15 ticp, pep, DJ/3.75)	Simon/Schuster	1940	Disney Studios	250-400	
Taylor, Don A.	Old Sam & the Horse Thieves (1st {std}, 8vo, 160p, fp b/w, DJ/3.50)	Follett	(1967)	Bjorklund, Lorence	25-40	
Taylor, Elizabeth	Mossy Trotter (1st AM {std}, 8vo, blue cl, 160p, DJ/3.25)	Harcourt	(1967)	Acs, Laszlo	20-35	
Taylor, Florance	Carrier Boy (1st, 8vo, 160p, b/w, DJ/2.50)	Abelard-Schuman	(1956)	Fisher, Leonard	25-40	
Taylor, Florance	With Fife and Drum (1st, 8vo, 129p, p-o, col frn, b/w, pep, DJ/1.50)	Whitman	1936	Young, Eleanor M.	30-50	
Taylor, Ida Scott	Baby's Book (sm4to, AEG, gilt, 4 chromos)	L: R. Tuck	[1898]	Brundage, Frances	100-180	
Taylor, Jane	Little Ann... (1st, lg8vo, ibds, 64p, color, cep)	L: Routledge	[1883]	Greenaway, Kate	300-450	
Taylor, Mary I.	Little Mistress Goodhope (1st, 12mo, gilt, p-o, 186p, col frn)	McClurg	1902	Smith, Jessie W.	250-350	
Taylor, Paul B.	Tippletappleteven Town (1st, sq8vo, [12]p, ibds, color, pep)	Henry Holt & Co.	(1931)	Taylor, P.B.	65-90	
Taylor, Sophie C.	Story of a Little Poet (1st, sm8vo, 390p, green cl, 8pl)	Little/Brown	1901	Stephens, Alice B.	30-50	
Taylor, Una	Early Italian Love Stories (1st, sm4to, 144p, 13 fp b/w)	L: Longmans	1899	Ford, H.J.	120-200	
Tazewell, Charles	Littlest Angel (1st, lg8vo, ibds, [28]p, color, pep, DJ/1.00)	Children's Press	(1946)	Evans, Katherine	60-100	
Tchaika, Florence	Trouble at Beaver Dam (1st, 8vo, 63p, fp 1-color, pep, DJ/1.60)	J. Messner	(1953)	Rojankovsky, Feodor	25-45	
Teal, Valentine	Angel Child (1st, sm8vo, ipcb, [40]p, color, pep, DJ/1.00)	Rand/McNally	1946	Doane, Pelagie	30-50	
Teal, Valentine	Little Woman Wanted Noise (1st, 8vo, [40]p, orange cl, b/w, pep, DJ/1.00)	Rand/McNally	(1943)	Lawson, Robert	80-120	
Teall, Edna A.	Batter and Spoon Fairies (1st {std}, 8vo, p-o, 279p, b/w, pep)	Harper	1929	Whittemore, C.	70-100	
Teasdale, Sara	Rainbow Gold (1st, 8vo, 267p, blue/gilt, col frn, b/w, pep)	Macmillan	1922	Walker, Dugald S.	50-80	
Teasdale, Sara	Stars Tonight (1st, 8vo, blue cl, p-o, 49p, col frn, 14 fp b/w)	Macmillan	1930	Lathrop, Dorothy	60-90	
Teilhet, Darwin	Skwee-Gee (1st {std}, 4to, ibds, [40]p, color, DJ/1.50)	Doubleday/Doran	1940	Gramatky, Hardie	60-100	
Tempski, Armine	Bright Spurs (1st, 12mo, 283p, peach cl, uncut, b/w, DJ/2.50)	Dodd	1946	Brown, Paul	60-90	
Tempski, Armine	Pam's Paradise Ranch (1st, 8vo, 333p, orange cl, uncut, pep, b/w, DJ/2.00)	Dodd	1940	Brown, Paul	50-85	
Tenggren, Gustaf	Tenggren's Story Book (1st {std}, folio, 89p, ibds, color, pep, GGB)	Simon/Schuster	1944	Tenggren, Gustaf	80-125	
Tennyson, Alfred	Charge of the Light Brigade (1st ob4to, ibds, [25]p, col, DJ/2.95, NYTBI)	Golden Press	1964	Provensen, A.& M.	45-70	
Tennyson, Alfred	Dream of Fair Women (1st AM, lg8vo, teg, 197p, gilt, b/w)	Page/Richards	1900	Sullivan, Edmund J.	100-165	
Tennyson, Alfred	Dream of Fair Women (1st, lg8vo, [96]p, p-o, 22cp)	Bobbs-Merrill	(1907)	Fisher, Harrison	200-300	
Tennyson, Alfred	Dream of Fair Women (lg8vo, p-o, 148p, 21cp)	Grosset/Dunlap	(1907)	Fisher, Harrison	180-250	
Tennyson, Alfred	Dream of Fair Women (8vo, grey bds, 79p, 8cp, pep)	L: Blackie	[1915]	Harrison, Florence	60-90	
Tennyson, Alfred	Geraint & Enid (1st, 16mo, blue/gilt, 4cp)	L: Jack	[1906]	Shaw, Byam	80-125	
Tennyson, Alfred	Guinevere... (1st, 4to, teg, 156p, gilt, 24 ticp)	L: Blackie	1912	Harrison, Florence	200-300	
Tennyson, Alfred	Guinevere... (1st AM, 4to, 156p, gilt, teg, 24 ticp)	Dana Estes	1912	Harrison, Florence	160-240	
Tennyson, Alfred	Idylls of the King (1st, lg4to, [114]p, gilt, uncut, 24 woodcuts)	R.H. Russell	1898	Rhead, Louis	150-250	
Tennyson, Alfred	Idylls of the King (1st, 4to, 174p, gilt, 21 ticp)	L: Hodder	(1911)	Brickdale, E.F.	200-300	
Tennyson, Alfred	Idylls of the King (1st, lg8vo, black cl, p-o, 394p, 12cp, pep)	Stokes	(1912)	Kirk, Maria L.	100-160	
Tennyson, Alfred	Lady of Shalott (1st, lg8vo, [64]p, blue/gilt, AEG, color, dep)	Dodd	(1881)	Pyle, Howard	350-500	
Tennyson, Alfred	Maud (1st, 8vo, teg, uncut, 107p, green/gilt, dep, 10cp)	Dodd	1905	Armstrong, Margaret	50-85	
Tennyson, Alfred	Maud (1st, sm4to, 103p, uncut, 8cp)	L: Macmillan	1922	Sullivan, Edmund J.	70-90	
Tennyson, Alfred	Morte d'Arthur (1st, sm4to, white bds/gilt, 24p, color)	L: Chatto	1912	Sangorski, Alberto	180-250	
Tennyson, Alfred	The Princess (1st, 4to, [95]p, brown/gilt, 14cp)	Bobbs-Merrill	(1911)	Christy, Howard C.	100-180	
Tennyson, H.	Jack & the Bean Stalk (1st, sq8vo, 70p, green cl, b/w)	L: Macmillan	1886	Caldecott, Randolph	170-240	
Teresah	A Doll, Two Children & Three Storks (1st AM {std}, 8vo, 178p, col frn)	Dutton	(1931)	Reetz, Wilhelm	30-50	
Terhune, Albert P.	Book of Famous Dogs (1st {std}, 8vo, 300p, b/w pl, DJ/2.75)	Doubleday/Doran	1937	Dickey, Robert L.	50-80	
Terhune, Albert P.	Caleb Conover, Railroader (1st, 12mo, green/gilt, 322p, 4cp)	A.& N. Assoc.	1907	Parker, Frank	80-140	
Terhune, Albert P.	Columbia Stories (1st {1st bk.}, sm8vo, 214p, b/w)	Dillingham	1897	Thornburgh, F.	120-200	*
Terhune, Albert P.	Dogs (1st, 4to, ipcb, 60p, col frn, fp b/w)	Saalfield	(1940)	Wiese, Kurt	45-70	
Terhune, Albert P.	Further Adventures of Lad (1st, sm8vo, 341p, col frn)	Doran	(1922)	Bull, Charles L.	80-120	
Terhune, Albert P.	Heart of a Dog (1st, 8vo, 249p, 8 ticp)	Doran	(1924)	Kirmse, Marguerite	70-100	
Terhune, Albert P.	Lochinvar Luck (1st, sm8vo, 309p, frn by...)	Doran	(1923)	Stinemetz, Morgan	60-100	
Terhune, Albert P.	My Friend the Dog (1st {std}, lg8vo, gilt, 317p, 8 ticp, pep)	Harper	1926	Kirmse, Marguerite	70-100	

AUTHOR	TITLE	PUBLISHER	DATE	ARTIST	PRICE	LC
Terhune, Albert P.	Real Tales of Real Dogs (1st, lg4to, ibds, 92p, b/w, DJ/1.00)	Saalfield	(1935)	Thorne, Diana	80-125	
Terhune, Albert P.	Story of Damon and Pythias (1st, 12mo, 307p, 30pl)	Grosset/Dunlap	(1915)	(Photos)	40-65	
Terhune, Albert P.	The Woman (1st, 12mo, 341p, gilt, 5pl)	Bobbs-Merrill	(1912)	King, W.B.	60-90	
Terhune, Albert P.	True Dog Stories (1st, 12mo, 60p, b/w)	Saalfield	1936	Thorne, Diana	50-80	
Terhune, Anice	Chinese Child's Day (1st, lg4to, 33p, ibds, 15 color)	NY: Schirmer	[1910]	Wheelan, A.R.	120-200	
Terhune, Anice	Dutch Ditties for Children (1st, lg4to, 31p, ibds, 15 color)	NY: Schirmer	[1910]	Wheelan, A.R.	100-170	
Terry, Richard R.	Old Rhymes with New Tunes (1st, 4to, ibds, 32p, b/w)	Longmans	1912	Pippet, Gabriel	55-80	*
Thacher, Lucy W.	Listening Child (1st, sm8vo, 405p, blue cl, col frn, 11pl, pep)	Macmillan	1924	Barnhart, Nancy	40-65	
Thackeray, Lance	Light Side of Egypt (1st, ob4to, ibds, [80]p, 36cp)	L: A&C Black	1908	Thackeray, Lance	125-200	
Thackeray, Wm. M.	Ballads & Songs (1st, 12mo, AEG, 276p, red/gilt, b/w)	L: Cassell	1896	Brock, Henry M.	60-100	
Thackeray, Wm. M.	Chronicle of the Drum (1st, 4to, AEG, 70p, brown/gilt, 32pl)	Scribner	1882	Various	150-225	
Thackeray, Wm. M.	History of Henry Esmond (1st, 8vo, 476p, gilt, teg, 12cp)	L: Dent	1898	Bedford, Francis D.	50-80	
Thackeray, Wm. M.	History of Henry Esmond (1st, 12mo, 402p, gilt, AEG, 50 b/w)	L: Macmillan	1905	Thomson, Hugh	60-100	
Thackeray, Wm. M.	Rose & the Ring (lg8vo, 159p, green cl, col frn, 12pl, pep)	Stokes	[1910]	Browne, Gordon	60-95	
Thackeray, Wm. M.	Rose & the Ring (1st AM, 4to, red/gilt, 128p, 12 ticp, pep)	Crowell	[1911]	Monsell, J.R.	100-160	
Thackeray, Wm. M.	Rose & the Ring (1st, sq8vo, 128p, gilt, teg, 12 ticp, pep)	L: Kegan Paul	1911	Monsell, J.R.	120-185	
Thackeray, Wm. M.	Rose & the Ring (lg8vo, 161p, p-o, 9cp, cep)	Brentano's	[1920]	Tinker, Jack H.	80-135	
Thackeray, Wm. M.	Vanity Fair (1st, 4to, 483p, p-o, teg, gilt, 20 ticp)	L: Hodder	[1913]	Baumer, Lewis	200-300	
Thaler, Mike	The Rainbow (1st {std}, ob8vo, [30]p, color, cep, DJ/2.95)	Harlin Quist	(1967)	Leake, Donald	30-50	
Thanet, Octave	Adventure in Photography (1st, 12mo, 179p, photos, cvr by…)	Scribner	1893	Armstrong, Margaret	200-300	
Thanet, Octave	Heart of Toil (1st sm8vo, teg, 215p, cvr by…)	Scribner	1898	Armstrong, Margaret	40-60	*
Thanet, Octave	Heart of Toil (1st, sm8vo, teg, 215p, 24pl by…)	Scribner	1898	Frost, A.B.	40-60	*
Thanet, Octave	Man of the Hour (1st, 12mo, green/gilt, 477p, cvr by…)	Bobbs-Merrill	(1905)	Armstrong, Margaret	30-50	
Thanet, Octave	Missionary Sheriff (1st, 12mo, 248p, blue/gilt, 15pl)	Harper	1897	Frost/Carleton	35-60	
Thanet, Octave	Slave to Duty (1st, 12mo, 221p, teg, frn by…)	Herbert Stone	1898	Oakley, Violet	60-100	
Thaxter, Celia	Idyls and Pastorals (1st, 8vo, AEG, 58p, gilt, 24pl)	D. Lothrop Co.	(1886)	Various	90-120	*
Thaxter, Celia	Island Garden (1st, lg8vo, 126p, white/gilt, teg, col frn, b/w)	Houghton	1894	Hassam, F. Childe	350-500	
Thayer, Ernest	Casey at the Bat (1st, 8vo, 32p, fp b/w, DJ/2.65, NYTBI)	F. Watts	(1964)	Fisher, Leonard	30-50	*
Thayer, Jane	Andy & Mr. Cunningham (1st, 8vo, 48p, color, DJ/3.25)	Wm. Morrow	(1969)	Wohlberg, Meg	20-30	
Thayer, Jane	Andy & the Runaway Horse (1st, 8vo, 48p, 2-color, pep, DJ/2.75)	Wm. Morrow	1963	Wohlberg, Meg	20-35	*
Thayer, Jane	Cat that Joined the Club (1st, lg8vo, [32]p, color, DJ/3.25)	Wm. Morrow	1967	Fleishman, Seymour	25-45	
Thayer, Jane	Charley and the New Car (1st, 8vo, 48p, 2-color, pep, DJ/2.25)	Wm. Morrow	1957	Barnum, Jay H.	25-45	
Thayer, Jane	Chicken in the Tunnel (1st, 8vo, 48p, fp 1-color, pep, DJ/2.00)	Wm. Morrow	1956	Palazzo, Tony	25-45	
Thayer, Jane	Contrary Little Quail (1st, 4to, [32]p, color, pep, DJ/3.25)	Wm. Morrow	(1968)	Wohlberg, Meg	20-35	
Thayer, Jane	Curious, Furious Chipmunk (1st, lg8vo, [32]p, color, DJ/3.50)	Wm. Morrow	(1969)	Fleishman, Seymour	25-45	
Thayer, Jane	Gus Was a Friendly Ghost (1st, lg8vo, [32]p, color, pep, DJ/2.75)	Wm. Morrow	1962	Fleishman, Seymour	25-45	*
Thayer, Jane	Horse with the Easter Bonnet (1st, 8vo, 48p, 2-color, DJ/2.00)	Wm. Morrow	1953	Barnum, Jay H.	25-45	
Thayer, Jane	I'm Not a Cat, Said Emerald (1st, lg8vo, [32]p, color, DJ/3.75)	Wm. Morrow	(1970)	Fleishman, Seymour	25-45	
Thayer, Jane	Little Mr. Greenthumb (1st, lg8vo, [32]p, fp 3-color, DJ/3.50)	Wm. Morrow	(1968)	Fleishman, Seymour	25-45	
Thayer, Jane	Mrs. Perrywinkle's Pets (1st, sm8vo, 45p, 2-color, dep, DJ/2.00)	Wm. Morrow	1955	Galdone, Paul	30-50	
Thayer, Jane	Outside Cat (1st, 4to, [34]p, color, pep, DJ/2.95)	Wm. Morrow	1957	Rojankovsky, Feodor	30-50	
Thayer, Jane	Popcorn Dragon (1st, 8vo, 48p, 3-color, DJ/2.00)	Wm. Morrow	1953	Barnum, Jay H.	30-50	
Thomajan, Puzant K.	Runaway House (1st, lg8vo, 45p, color, pep, DJ/1.50)	Rittenhouse	(1941)	Palazzo, Tony	30-50	
Thomas, Dorothy	Hi-Po the Hippo (1st {std}, folio, [48]p, ibds, color, DJ/3.00)	Random	(1942)	Gannett, Ruth C.	100-165	
Thomas, Dylan	Child's Christmas in Wales (1st, ob16mo, wraps, 5 fp b/w)	New Directions	(1959)	Raskin, Ellen	45-70	
Thomas, Dylan	Me and My Bike (1st AM, 4to, red cl, 53p, b/w, DJ/5.00)	McGraw-Hill	(1965)	Box, Leonora	65-90	
Thomas, Edith M.	Babes of the Nations (1st, lg8vo, [26]p, ibds, 12cp)	Stokes	1889	Humphrey, Maud	500-700	
Thomas, Edith M.	Children of Spring (4to, wraps, 3 chromos)	Stokes	1888	Humphrey, Maud	350-500	
Thomas, Edith M.	In Sunshine Land (1st, sm8vo, tan/silver, teg, 152p, b/w pl, cep)	Houghton	1894	Pyle, Katharine	60-90	
Thomas, Edith M.	Tiny Folk of Sunny Days (1st, sm4to, [14]p, 6cp)	Stokes	1889	Humphrey, Maud	300-500	
Thomas, Edith M.	Tiny Folk of Wintery Days (1st, sm4to, [14]p, 6cp)	Stokes	1889	Humphrey, Maud	300-500	
Thomas, Edith M.	Treasury of Stories, Jingles & Rhymes (1st, lg8vo, p-o, 251p, b/w)	Stokes	(1894)	Humphrey, Maud	300-425	
Thomas, Edith M.	Winter Swallow… (1st, 12mo, 120p, teg, p-o, green/gilt, cvr by…)	Scribner	1896	Armstrong, Margaret	70-125	
Thomas, Edward	Complete Fairy Tales (1st AM, 8vo, 94p, ibds, b/w, pep, DJ/3.95)	F. Watts	(1966)	Gill, Margery	40-65	
Thomas, Eleanor	Mr. Pearly of Pepper Pot Lane (1st, 8vo, 84p, fp color, DJ/1.50)	Scribner	(1939)	Becker, Charlotte	25-45	
Thomas, Lowell	Hero of Vincennes (1st, 8vo, 195p, p-o, pep)	Houghton	1929	Yohn, F.C.	35-50	
Thomas, Margaret L.	George Washington Lincoln Goes Around/World (1st, 8vo, p-o, 205p, pep)	NY: T. Nelson	(1927)	Pogany, Willy	80-120	*
Thomas, Philip	Flowers I Love (1st, 4to, 81p, 24cp)	L: Jack	(1916)	Cameron, Katharine	70-120	*
Thomason, John W.	Fix Bayonets! (1st, lg8vo, 245p, gilt, bds, p-o, col frn, b/w)	Scribner	1926	Thomason, John W.	70-125	
Thompson, Blanche J.	Bible Children (1st {std}, 8vo, ibds, [32]p, color, DJ/1.50)	Dodd	(1937)	Seredy, Kate	40-60	
Thompson, Blanche J.	Candle Burns for France (1st, 8vo, 80p, col frn, fp b/w, DJ/1.75)	Bruce Pub. Co.	(1946)	Seredy, Kate	40-60	
Thompson, Blanche J.	Golden Trumpets (1st, sm8vo, 163p, blue/gilt, 2-color)	Macmillan	1927	Torrey, Helen	30-50	
Thompson, Blanche J.	Oldest Story (1st, 8vo, 241p, b/w, DJ/2.50)	Bruce Pub. Co.	(1943)	Seredy, Kate	40-65	
Thompson, Blanche J.	With Harp and Lute (1st, sm8vo, 187p, fp b/w, DJ/1.25)	Macmillan	1935	Seredy, Kate	30-45	
Thompson, Charles M.	Calico Cat (1st, 12mo, green/gilt, 228p, 8pl)	Houghton	1908	Gruger, Frederic R.	40-60	
Thompson, Dorothy	Once on Christmas (1st, 24mo, ipcb, [44]p, pep, 6 fp b/w, DJ/0.50)	NY: Oxford U.Pr.	1938	Lenski, Lois	90-140	R
Thompson, Jeannette	Over Indian and Animal Trails (1st, 8vo, gilt, p-o, 263p, 8cp, pep)	Stokes	(1918)	Bransom, Paul	40-60	*
Thompson, K.L.	Ameliaranne at the Zoo (1st AM, 8vo, p-o, ibds, color)	McKay	[1936]	Pearse, Susan B.	50-80	
Thompson, Kay	Eloise (1st {std}, 4to, 65p, white cloth, color, pep, DJ/2.95)	Simon/Schuster	1955	Knight, Hilary	250-400	
Thompson, Kay	Eloise at Christmastime (1st {std}, 4to, red ibds, [52]p, color, DJ/3.50)	Random	(1958)	Knight, Hilary	250-400	
Thompson, Kay	Eloise in Moscow (1st {std}, 4to, [66]p, ibds, pep, color, DJ/3.75)	Simon/Schuster	1959	Knight, Hilary	250-400	
Thompson, Kay	Eloise in Paris (1st {std}, 4to, red pcb, [65]p, color, pep, DJ/3.50)	Simon/Schuster	1957	Knight, Hilary	250-400	
Thompson, Kay	Miss Pooky Peckinpaugh (1st {std}, 4to, ibds, [30]p, b/w, DJ/4.95)	Harper	(1970)	Eula, Joe	150-225	
Thompson, Mary W.	Blueberry Muffin (1st {std}, 8vo, 248p, b/w, DJ/2.00)	Longmans	(1942)	Berry, Erick	25-45	
Thompson, Mary W.	My Grandpa's Farm (1st, sm8vo, 184p, col frn)	Stokes	1929	Potter, Edna	20-35	
Thompson, Maurice	Alice of Old Vincennes (1st [1], 8vo, 419p, green/gilt, 6pl)	Bobbs-Merrill	(1900)	Yohn, F.C.	30-50	
Thompson, Maurice	Rosalynde's Lovers (1st, 8vo, p-o, 249p, gilt, teg, 11pl, dep)	Bowen-Merrill	1901	Peirson, G. Alden	25-40	
Thompson, Ruth P.	Captain Salt in Oz (1st, lg8vo, 306p, blue cl, p-o, b/w, pep, DJ/1.50)	Reilly/Lee	(1936)	Neill, John R.	400-650	

AUTHOR: 210

AUTHOR	TITLE	PUBLISHER	DATE	ARTIST	PRICE	LC
Thompson, Ruth P.	Cowardly Lion of Oz (1st [1], lg8vo, 291p, p-o, pep, 12cp)	Reilly/Lee	(1923)	Neill, John R.	400-600	
Thompson, Ruth P.	Curious Cruise of Captain Santa (1st, lg8vo, 124p, p-o, color)	Reilly/Lee	(1926)	Neill, John R.	300-500	
Thompson, Ruth P.	Giant Horse of Oz (1st, lg8vo, 283p, p-o, brown cl, pep, 12cp)	Reilly/Lee	(1928)	Neill, John R.	300-500	
Thompson, Ruth P.	Gnome King of Oz (1st, lg8vo, 282p, p-o, green cl, pep, 12cp)	Reilly/Lee	(1927)	Neill, John R.	400-600	
Thompson, Ruth P.	Grampa in Oz (1st, lg8vo, 271p, p-o, 12cp, pep)	Reilly/Lee	(1924)	Neill, John R.	350-500	
Thompson, Ruth P.	Handy Mandy in Oz (1st, lg8vo, 246p, blue cl, p-o, b/w, pep, DJ/1.50)	Reilly/Lee	(1937)	Neill, John R.	400-600	
Thompson, Ruth P.	Hungry Tiger of Oz (1st [1], 8vo, p-o, 261p, 12cp, pep)	Reilly/Lee	(1926)	Neill, John R.	350-500	
Thompson, Ruth P.	Jack Pumpkinhead of Oz (1st, 8vo, 252p p-o, 12cp, pep)	Reilly/Lee	(1929)	Neill, John R.	300-500	
Thompson, Ruth P.	Kabumpo in Oz (1st [1], lg8vo, blue cl, 297p, p-o, 12cp, pep)	Reilly/Lee	(1922)	Neill, John R.	350-500	
Thompson, Ruth P.	King Kojo (1st, lg8vo, red cl, p-o, 239p, 8cp, pep), DJ/1.50)	McKay	(1938)	Marge	250-350	
Thompson, Ruth P.	Lost King of Oz (1st, 8vo, p-o, 280p, 12cp, pep)	Reilly/Lee	(1925)	Neill, John R.	350-500	
Thompson, Ruth P.	Ojo in Oz (1st, 8vo, 304p, p-o, red cl, 12cp, pep)	Reilly/Lee	(1933)	Neill, John R.	300-500	
Thompson, Ruth P.	Ozoplaning with the Wizard of Oz (1st, lg8vo, 272p, p-o, pep, DJ/1.50)	Reilly/Lee	(1939)	Neill, John R.	400-600	
Thompson, Ruth P.	Perhappsy Chaps (1st [1st bk.], tall 8vo, [90]p, ibds, color, pep)	Volland	(1918)	Henderson, Arthur	400-600	
Thompson, Ruth P.	Pirates in Oz (1st [1], 8vo, green cl, p-o, 280p, 12cp, pep)	Reilly/Lee	(1931)	Neill, John R.	350-500	
Thompson, Ruth P.	Princess of Cozytown (1st, lg8vo, ibds, [96]p, color, pep)	Volland	(1922)	Scott, Janet L.	250-400	
Thompson, Ruth P.	Purple Prince of Oz (1st [1], lg8vo, p-o, 281p, 12cp, pep)	Reilly/Lee	(1932)	Neill, John R.	350-500	
Thompson, Ruth P.	Royal Book of Oz (1st [1], 8vo, 312p, grey cl, p-o, 12cp, pep)	Reilly/Lee	(1921)	Neill, John R.	300-450	
Thompson, Ruth P.	Silver Princess in Oz (1st, lg8vo, 255p, p-o, b/w, pep. DJ/1.50)	Reilly/Lee	(1938)	Neill, John R.	450-650	
Thompson, Ruth P.	Speedy in Oz (1st, lg8vo, p-o, 298p, blue cl, 12cp, pep)	Reilly/Lee	(1934)	Neill, John R.	350-500	
Thompson, Ruth P.	Wishing Horse of Oz (1st, lg8vo, grey cl, 298p, p-o, 12cp, DJ/1.50)	Reilly/Lee	(1935)	Neill, John R.	400-600	
Thompson, Ruth P.	Wonder Book (1st, sm4to, green cl, 217p, p-o, 7cp)	Reilly/Lee	(1929)	Donahey, William	200-300	
Thompson, Ruth P.	Yellow Knight of Oz (1st, 8vo, 275p, grey cl, p-o, 12cp, pep)	Reilly/Lee	(1930)	Neill, John R.	250-350	
Thompson, Vivian L.	Camp in the Yard (1st, 8vo, [32]p, b/w, pep, DJ/2.50)	Holiday House	1961	Turkle, Brinton	30-50	
Thompson, Vivian L.	Hawaiian Legends of Tricksters & Riddlers (1st, 8vo, 103p, color, DJ/4.50)	Holiday House	(1969)	Selig, Sylvie	60-100	
Thompson, Vivian L.	Hawaiian Myths of Earth, Sea & Sky (1st, 8vo, 83p, 2-color, DJ/3.00)	Holiday House	(1966)	Weisgard, Leonard	60-100	*
Thompson, Vivian L.	Horse that Liked Sandwiches (1st, 8vo, [48]p, fp 2-color, DJ/2.00)	Putnam	(1962)	Aliki	30-45	
Thompson, Vivian L.	Sad Day, Glad Day (1st, sm8vo, [40]p, b/w, DJ/2.50)	Holiday House	1962	Obligado, Lilian	30-50	
Thompson, William	Wigwam Wonder Tales (1st, sm8vo, 156p, b/w)	Scribner	1919	Boog, Carle M.	30-45	
Thompson, Wolfe	Circle of the Braves (1st, sm8vo, 257p, col frn, b/w)	Stokes	1931	Schuyler, Remington	25-45	
Thompson, Wolfe	Moccasins on the Trail (1st {std}, sm8vo, 298p, gilt, DJ/2.00)	Longmans	1935	Rodgers, Richard	30-50	
Thomson, Clara L.	Celtic Wonder World (1st, 8vo, 155p, b/w)	L: H. Marshall	1902	Conner, E.	70-100	
Thomson, Clara L.	Selections from LeMorte D'arthur (1st, 8vo, 240p)	L: H. Marshall	1902	Stratton, Helen	80-130	
Thomson, Hugh	Jack the Giant Killer (1st, sq8vo, [32]p, wraps, 16 color)	L: Macmillan	1898	Thomson, Hugh	200-350	
Thoreau, Henry D.	Cape Cod (1st, 8vo, gilt, teg, 319p, cvr by...)	Crowell	(1908)	Armstrong, Margaret	80-125	
Thoreau, Henry D.	Maine Woods (1st, 8vo, teg, 423p, green/gilt, b/w, cvr by...)	Crowell	(1909)	Armstrong, Margaret	70-120	
Thoreau, Henry D.	Men of Concord (1st, lg8vo, 255p, green/silver, 10cp, pep, DJ/4.50)	Houghton	1936	Wyeth, N.C.	250-400	
Thoreau, Henry D.	Week Along the Concord and Merrimack Rivers (1st, 8vo, gilt)	Crowell	(1911)	Armstrong, Margaret	40-60	
Thorne, Diana	Cats & More Cats (1st, 8vo, ibds, [32]p, 2-color, DJ/1.00)	Wilcox/Follett	1945	Thorne, Diana	30-45	
Thorne, Diana	Dog Book (1st, 4to, 89p, ibds, 12 fp color)	Saalfield	(1932)	Thorne, Diana	100-165	
Thorne, Diana	Peter the Goat (1st, sq8vo, ibds, [48]p, fp b/w, DJ/1.00)	McKay	(1940)	Thorne, Diana	30-50	
Thornley, G. (tr.)	Daphnis & Chloe (1st, 4to, 200p, gilt, buckram, 12cp)	L: G. Bles	1925	Austen, John	100-150	
Thurber, James	Further Fables of Our Time (1st {std}, 8vo, 174p, bds, gilt, b/w, DJ/3.50)	Simon/Schuster	1956	Thurber, James	65-100	
Thurber, James	Great Quillow (1st, 8vo, 54p, p-o, yellow cl, color, DJ/2.00)	Harcourt	(1944)	Lee, Doris	150-250	
Thurber, James	Many Moons (1st, sm4to, red cl, [47]p, color, pep, DJ/2.00, CM)	Harcourt	(1943)	Slobodkin, Louis	170-250	R
Thurber, James	Owl in the Attic (1st {std}, 8vo, 151p, yellow cl, b/w)	Harper	1931	Thurber, James	140-220	R
Thurber, James	Thirteen Clocks (1st, 8vo, ibds, 124p, color, pep, DJ/2.50)	Simon/Schuster	(1950)	Simont, Marc	120-200	R
Thurber, James	White Deer (1st, 8vo, green cl, 115p, color, DJ/2.50)	Harcourt	(1945)	Freeman, Don	150-225	
Thurber, James	Wonderful O. (1st {std}, 8vo, bds, 72p, 2-color, dep, DJ/3.50)	Simon/Schuster	(1957)	Simont, Marc	80-140	
Thurston, Clara B.	Discontented Stuffed Cat (1st, 4to, ibds, b/w)	Saalfield	(1910)	Thurston, Clara B.	150-225	
Thurston, Clara B.	Jingle of a Jap (1st, lg8vo, [64]p, p-o, color, pep)	Caldwell	(1906)	Thurston, Clara B.	100-165	
Thurston, Ernest T.	Open Window (1st, lg8vo, 287p, blue/gilt, 4cp, pep)	L: Chapman	1913	Robinson, Charles	120-175	
Thurston, Katherine	The Mystics (1st, sm8vo, black/gilt, 191p, 8pl)	Harper	1907	Gibbs, George	30-50	
Thwaite, Ann	Day with the Duke (1st AM {std}, lg8vo, [32]p, color, DJ/4.95)	World	1969	Him, George	30-50	
Thwaite, Ann	House in Turner Square (1st AM {std}, 8vo, 157p, DJ/2.95)	Harcourt	(1961)	Jacques, Robin	25-40	
Thwaites, Reuben G.	Down Historic Waterways (1st, sm8vo, gilt, 300p, cvr by...)	McClurg	1902	Hazenplug, Frank	60-90	
Tibber, Robert	Aristide (1st, 4to, ipcb, 61p, 1-color, DJ/3.50)	Dial Press	(1966)	Blake, Quentin	30-50	
Tice, Clara	ABC Dogs (1st, folio, ibds, [32]p, color, pep, DJ/2.00)	NY: Wilfred Funk	1940	Tice, Clara	200-300	
Tietjens, Eunice H.	Boy of the Desert (1st, 8vo, 182p, green cl, dep, fp b/w)	Coward	1928	Hollingsworth, W.	30-50	*
Tietjens, Eunice H.	Boy of the South Seas (1st, 8vo, 193p, 20 fp b/w, pep, NH)	Coward	(1931)	Sheldon, Marian	55-80	*
Tietjens, Eunice H.	Gingerbread Boy (1st, 16mo, ipcb, [57]p, color, pep)	Whitman	(1932)	Jordan, Nina	30-50	
Tietjens, Eunice H.	Jaw Breaker's Alphabet (1st, ob4to, ibds, [111]p, b/w, dep)	A. & C. Boni	1930	Post, Hermann	70-100	*
Tietjens, Eunice H.	Romance of Antar (1st, 8vo, 219p, gilt, fp b/w)	Coward	1929	Glanckoff, Sam	30-50	
Tileston, Mary W.	Chiquita (1st, 12mo, orange cl, 306p, col frn, 7pl)	Merrill	1902	(Photos)	30-50	
Tileston, Mary W.	Sugar & Spice & all that's Nice (1st, 12mo, red/gilt, 239p, b/w)	Little/Brown	(1910)	Various	35-60	*
Tileston, Mary W.	Sugar & Spice & all that's Nice (1st [revised], 8vo, red/gilt, 220p, 4cp)	Little/Brown	1928	Davis, Marguerite	35-60	
Tilney, Frederick C.	Robin Hood & his Merry Outlaws (12mo, green/gilt, 128p, p-o, 8cp)	Dent/Dutton	[1919]	Railton, Ione	35-60	*
Tilton, Dwight	Miss Petticoats (1st, 12mo, 377p, tan cl, teg, 7cp)	C.M. Clark	1902	Stephens, Charles H.	20-40	
Timlin, William M.	Ship that Sailed to Mars (1st, lg4to, gilt, 48p, ibds, 48 ticp)	L: Harrap	(1923)	Timlin, William M.	2000-3000	
Tippett, James S.	Christmas Magic (1st, 16mo, ibds, [40]p, fp color, pep)	Grosset/Dunlap	(1944)	Sewell, Helen	30-50	
Tippett, James S.	Counting the Days (1st {std}, 24mo, ibds, 66p, DJ/0.75)	Harper	(1940)	Wolcott, Elizabeth	25-45	*
Tippett, James S.	Shadow and the Stocking (1st {std}, 24mo, 50p, ibds, fp b/w, pep, DJ/0.75)	Harper	1937	Dennis, Morgan	30-50	
Tippett, James S.	Toys and Toy Makers (1st {std}, sm8vo, 144p, cp, pep)	Harper	1931	Enright, Elizabeth	25-35	
Titcomb, Margaret	Voyage of the Flying Bird (1st, 8vo, 236p, b/w, DJ/3.50)	Dodd	(1963)	Feher, Joseph	20-30	
Tittle, Walter	Colonial Holidays (1st, sm4to, gilt, teg, 73p, p-o, 22cp)	Doubleday/Page	1910	Tittle, Walter	60-90	
Tittle, Walter	First Nantucket Tea-Party (1st, sm4to, [82]p, teg, tan cl, p-o, 23cp)	Doubleday/Page	(1907)	Tittle, Walter	70-125	
Tittle, Walter	My Country (1st, lg4to, unpag, ipcb, chromos)	Tandy-Thomas	(1909)	Tittle, Walter	200-300	
Titus, Eve	Anatole (1st, sm4to, 32p, blue cl, color, DJ/2.00, CH)	Whittlesey	(1956)	Galdone, Paul	70-120	

AUTHOR	TITLE	PUBLISHER	DATE	ARTIST	PRICE	LC
Titus, Eve	Anatole & the Cat (1st, sm4to, 32p, red cl, color, DJ/2.25, CH)	Whittlesey	(1957)	Galdone, Paul	80-120	
Titus, Eve	Anatole and the Piano (1st, 4to, 32p, color, DJ/2.75)	McGraw-Hill	(1966)	Galdone, Paul	40-65	
Titus, Eve	Anatole and the Poodle (1st, 4to, 32p, fp 2-color, dep, DJ/2.75)	Whittlesey	(1965)	Galdone, Paul	40-65	
Titus, Eve	Anatole and the Robot (1st, 4to, 32p, fp 2-color, dep, DJ/2.50)	Whittlesey	(1960)	Galdone, Paul	40-65	
Titus, Eve	Anatole and the Thirty Thieves (1st, 4to, 32p, fp 2-color, DJ/4.50)	McGraw-Hill	(1969)	Galdone, Paul	40-65	
Titus, Eve	Anatole and the Toyshop (1st, 4to, 36p, color, DJ/4.50)	McGraw-Hill	(1970)	Galdone, Paul	30-50	
Titus, Eve	Anatole over Paris (1st, 4to, 32p, color, DJ/2.75)	Whittlesey	(1961)	Galdone, Paul	30-50	
Titus, Eve	Basil & the Lost Colony (1st, 8vo, 95p, b/w, DJ/2.95)	Whittlesey	(1964)	Galdone, Paul	30-50	
Titus, Eve	Basil of Baker Street (1st, 8vo, beige cl, 96p, b/w, DJ/2.75)	Whittlesey	(1958)	Galdone, Paul	40-70	
Titus, Eve	Mouse and the Lion (1st, 4to, unpag, 1-color, pep, DJ/2.75)	Parents Mag. Pr.	1962	Weisgard, Leonard	30-50	
Titus, Eve	Two Stonecutters (1st {std}, ob4to, [48]p, color, DJ/3.95)	Doubleday	(1967)	Mitsuhashi, Yoko	25-40	
Tobias, Doris G.	Zoo's Who (1st, ob4to, ibds, [28]p, 1-color, DJ/2.00)	Vanguard Press	1948	Smith, Barbara	30-50	
Todd, Ann	No Time for Funnies (1st, sm8vo, 54p, fp color, DJ/1.25)	Oxford U. Pr.	(1942)	Slocum, Rosalie	30-50	
Todd, Ann	Umbrella that Got Wet (1st, sm8vo, 55p, color, pep, DJ/1.25)	Oxford U. Pr.	(1938)	Slocum, Rosalie	35-50	
Todd, Mabel L.	Corona & Coronet (1st, 8vo, teg, 383p, green/gilt, designs by...)	Houghton	1898	Rogers, Bruce	125-200	
Todd, Ruthven	Space Cat (1st, sm8vo, 69p, blue cl, fp b/w, DJ/2.00)	Scribner	(1952)	Galdone, Paul	80-125	
Todd, Ruthven	Space Cat and the Kittens (1st, 8vo, 94p, b/w, DJ/2.50)	Scribner	(1958)	Galdone, Paul	70-100	
Todd, Ruthven	Space Cat Meets Mars (1st, 8vo, 72p, b/w, DJ/2.25)	Scribner	(1957)	Galdone, Paul	70-120	
Todd, Ruthven	Space Cat Visits Venus (1st, 8vo, 87p, fp b/w, DJ/2.00)	Scribner	(1955)	Galdone, Paul	70-125	
Todd, Ruthven	Tan's Fish (1st {std}, 8vo, 58p, color, DJ/2.75)	Little/Brown	(1958)	Sherman, Theresa	20-35	
Toland, M.B.M.	Legend Laymone (1st, 4to, 61p, gilt, teg, 10pl, dep)	Lippincott	1890	Various	75-100	*
Tolboom, Wanda	Shining Bird (1st {std}, 8vo, ibds, [48]p, color, DJ/2.25)	Aladdin	(1955)	Bruce, Robert	25-45	
Tolboom, Wanda	Tosie of the Far North (1st {std}, 4to, [64]p, 2-color, DJ/2.75)	Aladdin	1954	Bruce, Robert	30-50	
Tolkien, J.R.R.	Adventures of Tom Bombadil (1st, 4to, 61p, gilt, teg, 10pl, 3-color, DJ)	L: Allen/Unwin	(1962)	Baynes, Pauline	200-300	
Tolkien, J.R.R.	Farmer Giles of Ham (1st, 8vo, 78p, orange cl, 2 fp color, pep, DJ)	L: Allen/Unwin	1949	Baynes, Pauline	350-500	
Tolkien, J.R.R.	Farmer Giles of Ham (1st AM {std}, 8vo, blue cl, 79p, color, DJ/2.00)	Houghton	1950	Baynes, Pauline	250-400	
Tolkien, J.R.R.	Smith of Wootton Major (1st AM {std}, 12mo, 62p, b/w, cep, DJ/1.95)	Houghton	1967	Baynes, Pauline	80-125	
Tolkien, J.R.R.	The Hobbit (1st AM, sm8vo, 310p, beige cl, 4cp, pep, DJ)	Houghton	1938	Tolkien, J.R.R.	3000-5000	R
Tolstoy, Alexei	Great Big Enormous Turnip (1st AM, sm8vo, [34]p, color, DJ/3.95)	F. Watts	(1968)	Oxenbury, Helen	30-50	*
Tolstoy, Leo	Nikolenka's Childhood (1st, lg8vo, 173p, ibds, b/w, DJ/3.95)	Pantheon	(1963)	Sendak, Maurice	200-300	
Tomlins, William L.	Child's Garden of Song (1st, lg8vo, 72p, red/gilt, color)	McClurg	1895	Ricketts, Ella	120-185	
Tomlinson, Everett	Jersey Boy in the Revolution (1st, sm8vo, 428p, 4pl)	Houghton	1899	Schoonover, Frank	50-85	
Tomlinson, Everett	Scouting with Daniel Boone (1st, sm8vo, 303p, green cl, 8pl)	Doubleday/Page	1914	Rockwell, Norman	120-180	
Tomlinson, H.M.	Sea & the Jungle (1st, 8vo, 343p, green/gilt, 16 woodcuts)	L: Duckworth	1930	Leighton, Clare	60-100	
Tompkins, Jane	Black Bear Twins (1st {std}, 8vo, 112p, b/w, DJ/2.25)	Lippincott	(1952)	Wiese, Kurt	25-45	
Tompkins, Jane	Moo-Wee: The Musk-Ox (1st, 8vo, blue cl, 103p, 11 fp b/w, pep, DJ/1.50)	Stokes	1938	Wiese, Kurt	80-125	
Tompkins, Jane	Otter Twins (1st {std}, 8vo, 120p, b/w, DJ/2.50)	Lippincott	(1955)	Wiese, Kurt	25-40	
Tompkins, Jane	Penguin Twins (1st, 8vo, 116p, b/w, pep, DJ/2.00)	Stokes	1939	Wiese, Kurt	25-40	
Tompkins, Jane	Polar Bear Twins (1st, 8vo, 106p, b/w, DJ/1.50)	Stokes	1937	Wiese, Kurt	30-50	
Tompkins, Jane	Raccoon Twins (1st, 8vo, 126p, orange cl, b/w, pep, DJ/1.60)	Stokes	1942	Wiese, Kurt	30-50	
Tompkins, Jane	Red Squirrel Twins (1st {std}, 8vo, tan cl, 123p, b/w, DJ/2.25)	Stokes	(1950)	Wiese, Kurt	50-80	
Tompkins, Jane	Reindeer Twins (1st {std}, 8vo, 125p, b/w, DJ/2.65)	Lippincott	(1956)	Wiese, Kurt	25-45	
Tompkins, Jane	Snowshoe Twins (1st, 8vo, 118p, b/w, DJ/2.00)	Stokes	(1941)	Wiese, Kurt	30-45	*
Tompkins, Jane	Storks Fly Home (1st {std}, 8vo, 58p, col frn, b/w, DJ/1.50)	Stokes	(1943)	Gergely, Tibor	30-50	
Toogood, Cora C.	Child's Prayer (1st, lg8vo, [16]p, blue/gilt, col frn)	McKay	(1925)	Smith, Jessie W.	100-175	*
Toon, Gladys E.	Animal Story Book (1st, folio, 63p, ibds, 12cp)	Saalfield	(1928)	Burd, Clara M.	35-60	
Toon, Gladys E.	Ducky Dee (1st, 4to, ibds, unpag, 8cp)	Saalfield	1928	Burd, Clara M.	35-60	*
Tooze, Ruth	America (1st, lg8vo, 31p, color, DJ/2.00)	Viking	1956	Angelo, Valenti	40-60	
Tooze, Ruth	Nikkos of the Pink Pelican (1st, lg8vo, 64p, 2-color, DJ/2.75)	Viking	(1964)	Domanska, Janina	25-45	
Tooze, Ruth	Our Rice Village in Cambodia (1st, 8vo, 39p, 2-color, DJ/2.75)	Viking	(1963)	Keats, Ezra J.	25-40	
Tooze, Ruth	Silver from the Sea (1st, 8vo, 40p, fp 3-color, pep, DJ/2.75)	Viking	(1962)	Wiese, Kurt	30-50	
Topelius, Zacharias	Canute Whistlewinks... (1st {std}, 8vo, 271p, orange cl, 5cp, dep)	NY: Longmans	1927	McIntosh, Frank	50-80	
Torjesen, Elizabeth	Captain Ramsay's Daughter (1st, 8vo, 223p, blue cl, fp b/w, pep, DJ/2.50)	Lothrop, Lee	(1953)	Adams, Adrienne	30-50	
Torrey, Marjorie	Artie & the Princess (1st, lg8vo, 80p, green cl, 5cp, pep, DJ/2.00)	Howell/Soskin	(1945)	Torrey, Marjorie	25-45	
Torrey, Marjorie	Merriweathers (1st, 8vo, 254p, grey cl, b/w, DJ/2.50)	Viking	1949	Torrey, Marjorie	40-65	
Torrey, Marjorie	Penny (1st, lg8vo, 126p, fp color, pep, DJ/3.00)	Howell/Soskin	1944	Torrey, Marjorie	40-65	
Torrey, Marjorie	Three Little Chipmunks (1st, 4to, ipcb, [40]p, color, pep, DJ/1.00)	Grosset/Dunlap	(1947)	Torrey, Marjorie	50-85	
Totheroh, Dan	David Hotfoot (1st, 8vo, p-o, 246p, col frn, 4pl)	Doran	(1926)	Day, Maurice	30-50	
Totheroh, Dan	Last Dragon (1st, 8vo, 186p, 8cp, pep)	Doran	(1927)	Eadie, Eleanor	25-40	
Tousey, Sanford	Airplane Andy (1st {std}, ob8vo, 43p, ipcb, color, DJ/1.75)	Doubleday/Doran	1942	Tousey, Sanford	25-45	
Tousey, Sanford	Bob & the Railroad (1st {std}, lg8vo, ibds, 53p, pep, color, DJ/1.00)	Doubleday/Doran	1941	Tousey, Sanford	30-50	
Tousey, Sanford	Buffalo Bill (1st, lg8vo, [36]p, map, ibds, color, pep, DJ/0.50)	Rand/McNally	1938	Tousey, Sanford	30-50	
Tousey, Sanford	Chinky Joins the Circus (1st {std}, lg ob8vo, [56]p, ibds, color, DJ/1.00)	Doubleday/Doran	1938	Tousey, Sanford	45-70	
Tousey, Sanford	Chinky: Banker Pony (1st {std}, ob8vo, ibds, [56]p, color, pep)	Doubleday/Doran	1937	Tousey, Sanford	40-60	
Tousey, Sanford	Cowboy Tommy (1st {std}, lg ob8vo, ibds, [56]p, pep, color)	Doubleday/Doran	1932	Tousey, Sanford	35-60	
Tousey, Sanford	Cowboy Tommy's Roundup (1st {std}, lg ob8vo, [56]p, pep, color)	Doubleday/Doran	1934	Tousey, Sanford	40-60	*
Tousey, Sanford	Cowboys of America (1st, 8vo, [36]p, ibds, color)	Rand/McNally	1937	Tousey, Sanford	30-50	
Tousey, Sanford	Daniel Boone (1st, lg8vo, [36]p, map, color, DJ/0.50)	Rand/McNally	1939	Tousey, Sanford	35-60	*
Tousey, Sanford	Davy Crockett (1st, lg8vo, 48p, cloth, p-o, color, DJ/1.50)	Whitman	1948	Tousey, Sanford	30-50	
Tousey, Sanford	Dick & the Canal Boat (1st {std}, lg8vo, [41]p, ipcb, color, DJ/1.50)	Doubleday/Doran	1943	Tousey, Sanford	30-50	
Tousey, Sanford	Fisherman Tommy (1st, sm4to, 47p, pep, color, DJ/1.50)	Houghton	1940	Tousey, Sanford	40-65	
Tousey, Sanford	Indians & Cowboys (1st, lg8vo, [76]p, color, pep, DJ/1.00)	Rand/McNally	(1940)	Tousey, Sanford	30-50	
Tousey, Sanford	Indians of the Plains (1st, 8vo, ipcb, [36]p, 1-color, DJ/0.50)	Rand/McNally	1940	Tousey, Sanford	30-50	
Tousey, Sanford	Jack Finds Gold (1st {std}, 8vo, ibds, [36]p, 41p, 8 fp color, pep, DJ/1.50)	Doubleday	(1947)	Tousey, Sanford	30-50	
Tousey, Sanford	Jerry & Pony Express (1st {std}, ob8vo, [56]p, pep, color, DJ/1.00)	Doubleday/Doran	1936	Tousey, Sanford	30-50	
Tousey, Sanford	Little Bear's Pinto Pony (1st, lg8vo, 29p, p-o, col frn, DJ/1.00)	Whitman	1943	Tousey, Sanford	30-50	
Tousey, Sanford	Lumberjack Bill (1st, lg8vo, blue cl, 47p, color, pep, DJ/1.75)	Houghton	1943	Tousey, Sanford	40-65	
Tousey, Sanford	Ned & the Rustlers (1st, lg8vo, 32p, color, pep, DJ/1.00)	Whitman	1941	Tousey, Sanford	30-50	

AUTHOR	TITLE	PUBLISHER	DATE	ARTIST	PRICE	LC
Tousey, Sanford	Old Blue (1st, 8vo, p-o, 32p, fp color, pep, DJ/1.00)	Whitman	1942	Tousey, Sanford	30-50	
Tousey, Sanford	Stagecoach Sam (1st {std}, 8vo, ibds, 53p, color, pep, DJ/1.50)	Doubleday/Doran	1940	Tousey, Sanford	65-90	
Tousey, Sanford	Steamboat Billy (1st {std}, lg ob8vo, ibds, [56]p, color, pep, DJ/1.50)	Doubleday/Doran	1935	Tousey, Sanford	50-80	
Tousey, Sanford	Tinker Tim (1st {std}, 8vo, ibds, 41p, color, pep, DJ/1.50)	Doubleday	1946	Tousey, Sanford	35-60	
Tousey, Sanford	Treasure Cave (1st, lg8vo, 32p, orange cl, p-o, color, DJ/1.25)	Whitman	1946	Tousey, Sanford	30-50	
Tousey, Sanford	Trouble in the Gulch (1st, 8vo, p-o, 32p, fp color, pep, DJ/1.25)	Whitman	1944	Tousey, Sanford	35-60	
Tousey, Sanford	White Prince, the Arabian Horse (1st, 8vo, p-o, 32p, 2-color, DJ/1.25)	Whitman	1945	Tousey, Sanford	30-50	
Tousey, Sanford	Wild Bill Hickok - Frontier Marshall (1st, 8vo, 46p, p-o, color, DJ/1.50)	Whitman	(1952)	Tousey, Sanford	30-50	
Tovey, Doreen	Cats in Cahoots (1st AM {std}, 8vo, 147p, b/w, DJ/2.95)	Doubleday	1960	Wilson, Maurice	40-65	
Tovey, Doreen	Donkey Work (1st AM {std}, 8vo, 138p, b/w, DJ/3.50)	Doubleday	1963	Wilson, Maurice	30-50	
Tovey, Doreen	New Boy (1st AM, 8vo, 162p, b/w, DJ/4.95)	Norton	(1970)	Wilson, Maurice	40-65	
Tovey, Doreen	Raining Cats and Donkeys (1st AM, 8vo, 156p, b/w, DJ/4.50)	Norton	(1968)	Wilson, Maurice	40-65	
Towers, Alton	Billy Bunce... (1st, 4to, ibds, unpag, 17cp)	L: A. Cooke	(1907)	Rountree, Harry	250-350	
Towers, Alton	Bunny & Bobbie (1st, 4to, unpag)	Cooke/Stokes	[1907]	Various	80-120	*
Towers, Alton	Child's Aesop (1st AM, 16mo, red cl, 117p, color)	Stokes	[1902]	Billinghurst, Percy	80-120	*
Towne, Charles H.	Rise & Fall of Prohibition (1st, sm8vo, blue/gilt, 220p, 4pl)	Macmillan	1923	Newell, Peter	60-100	
Towne, Robert D.	Teddy Bears at the Circus (1st, 12mo, ibds, [12]p, color)	Reilly/Britton	(1907)	Bray, J.R.	80-120	
Towne, Robert D.	Teddy Bears Come to Life (1st, 12mo, ibds, unpag, color)	Reilly/Britton	(1907)	Bray, J.R.	100-160	
Towne, Robert D.	Teddy Bears in a Smashup (1st, 12mo, ibds, [16]p, color)	Reilly/Britton	(1907)	Sieber, C.A.	80-145	
Towne, Robert D.	Teddy Bears in Hot Water (1st, 12mo, [16]p, ibds, color)	Reilly/Britton	(1907)	Sieber, C.A.	80-145	
Towne, Robert D.	Teddy Bears on a Lark (1st, 12mo, ibds, [16]p, color)	Reilly/Britton	(1907)	Sieber, C.A.	80-145	
Towne, Robert D.	Teddy Bears on a Tobaggon (1st, 12mo, ibds, [12]p, color)	Reilly/Britton	(1907)	Bray, J.R.	100-150	
Townend, Jack	Railroad ABC (1st, ob24mo, ibds, [57]p, color, DJ/0.50)	F. Watts	1944	Budd, Denison	50-80	*
Townsend, J. David	Five Trials of the Pansy Bed (1st {std}, 8vo, 59p, fp b/w, cep, DJ/3.25)	Houghton	1967	Hyman, Trina S.	60-90	
Townsend, John R.	Pirate's Island (1st AM {std}, 8vo, 159p, b/w, DJ/3.75)	Lippincott	(1968)	Hall, Douglas	25-45	
Townsend, John R.	The Intruder (1st AM {std}, 8vo, 220p, b/w, DJ/4.50)	Lippincott	(1969)	Humphreys, Graham	25-40	
Townsend, Kenneth	Felix the Bald-Headed Lion (1st AM {std}, 8vo, [32]p, color, DJ/3.95)	Delacorte Pr.	(1968)	Townsend, Kenneth	20-30	
Townsend, Ralph M.	Journey to the Garden Gate (1st, lg8vo, p-o, gilt, 127p, 8cp, pep)	Houghton	1919	Winter, Milo	70-120	
Toye, William	How Summer Came to Canada (1st AM, 4to, 32p, color, DJ/3.95)	H.Z. Walck	1969	Cleaver, Elizabeth	30-50	
Toye, William	Mountain Goats of Temlaham (1st AM, 4to, 32p, color, DJ/3.95)	H.Z. Walck	1969	Cleaver, Elizabeth	30-50	
Tozer, Katharine	Mumfie's Magic Box (1st, 8vo, 221p, ibds, 8cp)	L: J. Murray	1938	Tozer, Katharine	40-65	
Trachsel, Myrtle	Elizabeth of the Mayflower (1st {std}, 8vo, 207p, b/w, pep, DJ/2.50)	Macmillan	1950	Godwin, Stephani	25-45	*
Tracy, Edward B.	King of the Stallions (1st, 8vo, orange cl, 241p, b/w, DJ/2.50)	Dodd	1947	Brown, Paul	60-100	
Tracy, Louis	American Emperor (1st AM, sm8vo, 424p, tan/gilt, 16pl)	Putnam	1897	Hope, E.S.	60-90	
Tracy, Louis	Final War (1st UK, sq8vo, 372p, grey/gilt, 16pl)	L: C. Pearson	1896	Sherie, Ernest F.	60-90	*
Tracy, Louis	Lost Provinces (1st, 8vo, 380p, olive/gilt, 12pl)	L: C. Pearson	1898	Piffard, Harold	55-80	*
Tracy, Louis	The Invaders (1st, 8vo, maroon cl, 428p, 4pl)	L: C. Pearson	1901	Wood, Lawson	75-100	*
Tracy, Louis	Wings of the Morning (1st, lg8vo, black/gilt, 320p, teg, 12cp)	E.J. Clode	(1924)	Schaeffer, Mead	35-60	
Tracy, Louis	Wings of the Morning (lg8vo, 319p, p-o, 4cp)	Winston	(1924)	Schaeffer, Mead	35-60	
Tracy, Thomas H.	Book of the Poodle (1st, 4to, gilt, 136p, b/w, DJ/5.00)	Viking	1950	Gag, Flavia	35-50	
Train, Arthur	Lost Gospel (1st, sm8vo, 77p, col frn)	Scribner	1925	Daugherty, James	20-35	
Travers, Georgia	Wily Woodchucks (1st, sm ob4to, ibds, [32]p, color, DJ/1.50)	Coward	(1946)	Gag, Flavia	50-80	
Travers, Pamela L.	Fox at the Manger (1st {std}, sm8vo, 75p, brown cl, b/w, DJ/3.00)	Norton	(1962)	Bewick, Thomas	80-120	
Travers, Pamela L.	Fox at the Manger (1st UK, 12mo, 75p, b/w, pep, DJ)	L: Collins	1963	Bewick, Thomas	70-100	
Travers, Pamela L.	I Go by Sea, I Go by Land (1st {std}, 8vo, 233p, b/w, DJ/2.00)	Harper	(1941)	Hermes, Gertrude	80-125	
Travers, Pamela L.	Mary Poppins (1st AM, 12mo, 206p, blue cl, b/w, pep, DJ/1.50)	Reynal/Hitchcock	(1934)	Shepard, Mary	250-400	R
Travers, Pamela L.	Mary Poppins Comes Back (1st AM, 12mo, 268p, grn cl, b/w, pep, DJ/1.50)	Reynal/Hitchcock	(1935)	Shepard, Mary	180-275	
Travers, Pamela L.	Mary Poppins Comes Back (1st, sm8vo, 303p, beige cl, b/w, DJ)	L: Lovat/Dicks	(1935)	Shepard, Mary	300-425	
Travers, Pamela L.	Mary Poppins from A to Z (1st {std}, sm sq8vo, [58]p, b/w, pep, DJ/2.95)	Harcourt	(1962)	Shepard, Mary	80-125	
Travers, Pamela L.	Mary Poppins in the Park (1st, sm8vo, 212p, brown/gilt, b/w, DJ)	L: P. Davies	1952	Shepard, Mary	180-260	
Travers, Pamela L.	Mary Poppins in the Park (1st AM {std}, 12mo, 235p, b/w, dep, DJ/2.50)	Harcourt	(1952)	Shepard, Mary	120-185	
Travers, Pamela L.	Mary Poppins Opens the Door (1st, sm8vo, 239p, grey cl, b/w, DJ/1.75)	Reynal/Hitchcock	(1943)	Shepard/Sims	100-165	
Treadgold, Mary	Heron Ride (1st {std}, 8vo, 192p, b/w, DJ)	L: J. Cape	1962	Ambrus, Victor	25-45	
Treadgold, Mary	No Ponies (1st, 8vo, 290p, fp b/w, DJ)	L: J. Cape	1946	Gervis, Ruth	25-45	
Treadgold, Mary	We Couldn't Leave Dinah (1st, 8vo, 272p, b/w, DJ, CgM)	L: J. Cape	1941	Tresilian, S.	80-125	*
Treadgold, Mary	Winter Princess (1st AM, 8vo, 112p, b/w, DJ/3.50)	Van Nostrand	(1964)	Falconer, Pearl	30-50	
Trease, Geoffrey	Bows Against the Barons (1st, 12mo, 152p, b/w, DJ)	L: M. Lawrence	1934	Boland, Michael	60-100	
Trease, Geoffrey	Secret Fiord (1st AM {std}, sm8vo, 241p, b/w, DJ/2.50)	Harcourt	(1950)	Krush, Joe	25-45	
Trease, Geoffrey	Trumpets in the West (1st AM {std}, 8vo, 239p, b/w, pep, DJ/2.50)	Harcourt	(1947)	Krush, Joe	30-50	
Treece, Henry	Dream Time (1st AM {std}, 8vo, 114p, fp b/w, DJ/3.95)	Meredith Press	(1967)	Keeping, Charles	45-70	
Treece, Henry	Horned Helmet (1st AM, 8vo, 118p, b/w, DJ/3.00)	Criterion Bks.	(1963)	Keeping, Charles	45-70	
Treece, Henry	Road to Miklagard (1st AM, 8vo, 254p, b/w, DJ/3.50)	Criterion Bks.	(1957)	Price, Christine	45-70	
Treece, Henry	Viking's Dawn (1st AM, 8vo, 252p, b/w, DJ/3.00)	Criterion Bks.	(1956)	Price, Christine	40-70	
Treece, Henry	Viking's Sunset (1st AM {std}, 8vo, 182p, b/w, DJ/3.50)	Criterion Bks.	(1961)	Price, Christine	40-70	
Treffinger, Carolyn	Jimmy's Shoes (1st, 12mo, red cl, 219p, pep, 3pl)	Penn	(1934)	Collings, R.C.	35-60	*
Treffinger, Carolyn	Li Lun: Lad of Courage (1st {A}, 8vo, 93p, 1-color, pep, DJ/2.50, NH)	Abingdon-Cokes.	(1947)	Wiese, Kurt	50-85	
Treffinger, Carolyn	Rag Doll Jane (1st, lg4to, 59p, ibds, 12cp)	Saalfield	(1930)	Peat, Fern B.	80-125	
Tregarthen, Enys	Doll Who Came Alive (1st, sq12mo, 75p, fp 3-color, DJ/2.00)	NY: J. Day	(1942)	Unwin, Nora S.	60-100	
Tregarthen, Enys	North Cornwall Fairies and Legends (1st, 8vo, 192p, teg, gilt, b/w)	L: Wells/Gard.	1906	Unknown	50-85	*
Tregarthen, Enys	White Ring (1st, sq8vo, 65p, fp b/w, DJ/2.00)	Harcourt	(1949)	Unwin, Nora S.	40-65	
Trent, Robbie	First Christmas (1st, 12mo, ipcb, [32]p, color, pep, DJ/1.00)	Harper	1948	Simont, Marc	40-65	
Trent, Robbie	To Church We Go (1st, sm4to, ibds, [28]p, color, DJ/1.25)	Wilcox/Follett	1948	Anglund, Joan W.	70-100	
Trent, Robbie	To Church We Go (1st {this artist}, 4to, [32]p, ibds, 1-color, DJ/2.00)	Follett	(1956)	Jones, Eliz. O.	40-65	
Tresselt, Alvin	An Elephant is Not a Cat (1st, 8vo, [46]p, color, DJ/2.95)	Parents Mag. Pr.	1962	Vroman, Tom	20-35	
Tresselt, Alvin	Autumn Harvest (1st, sm4to, ipcb, [25]p, color, pep, DJ/2.00)	Lothrop, Lee	1951	Duvoisin, Roger	40-65	
Tresselt, Alvin	Beaver Pond (1st, 4to, [32]p, fp color, pep, DJ/4.50)	Lothrop, Lee	1970	Duvoisin, Roger	50-80	
Tresselt, Alvin	Bonnie Bess, Weathervane Horse (1st, 4to, ibds, [25]p, color, DJ/1.75)	Lothrop, Lee	1949	Hafner, Marylin	30-50	*
Tresselt, Alvin	Follow the Road (1st, sm4to, unpag, color, DJ/2.50)	Lothrop, Lee	1953	Duvoisin, Roger	35-60	

AUTHOR	TITLE	PUBLISHER	DATE	ARTIST	PRICE	LC
Tresselt, Alvin	Follow the Wind (1st, sm4to, ibds, [26]p, color, DJ/2.00)	Lothrop, Lee	(1950)	Duvoisin, Roger	50-80	
Tresselt, Alvin	Frog in the Well (1st, sm4to, green cl, [32]p, color, pep, DJ/2.75)	Lothrop, Lee	1958	Duvoisin, Roger	50-80	
Tresselt, Alvin	Hi, Mister Robin! (1st, 4to, ibds, [26]p, color, pep, DJ/2.00)	Lothrop, Lee	1950	Duvoisin, Roger	60-90	
Tresselt, Alvin	Hide and Seek Fog (1st, lg8vo, [32]p, color, DJ/3.50, CH, NYTBI)	Lothrop, Lee	(1965)	Duvoisin, Roger	60-90	
Tresselt, Alvin	I Saw the Sea Come In (1st, sm4to, [28]p, color, pep, DJ/2.50)	Lothrop, Lee	1954	Duvoisin, Roger	45-70	
Tresselt, Alvin	It's Time Now! (1st, 4to, [32]p, fp color, pep, DJ/3.95)	Lothrop, Lee	(1969)	Duvoisin, Roger	40-65	*
Tresselt, Alvin	Johnny Maple-Leaf (1st, 4to, 28p, ibds, color, DJ/2.00)	Lothrop, Lee	1948	Duvoisin, Roger	45-70	*
Tresselt, Alvin	Legend of Willow Plate (1st, ob4to, [43]p, color, pep, DJ/3.50)	Parents Mag. Pr.	1968	Low, Joseph	50-80	R*
Tresselt, Alvin	Little Lost Squirrel (1st, folio, ibds, [26]p, color, pep, DJ/1.00)	Grosset/Dunlap	1950	Weisgard, Leonard	40-65	
Tresselt, Alvin	Rabbit Story (1st, sm4to, unpag, fp 1-color, DJ/2.50)	Lothrop, Lee	1957	Weisgard, Leonard	70-100	R
Tresselt, Alvin	Rain Drop Splash (1st, 4to, [29]p, ipcb, fp color, pep, DJ/1.50, CH)	Lothrop, Lee	(1946)	Weisgard, Leonard	120-200	R
Tresselt, Alvin	Smallest Elephant in the World (1st, 4to, [32]p, 3-color, pep, DJ)	Knopf	(1959)	Glaser, Milton	25-45	*
Tresselt, Alvin	Sun Up (1st, sm4to, ibds, pep, [25]p, color, DJ/2.00)	Lothrop, Lee	1949	Duvoisin, Roger	55-80	
Tresselt, Alvin	The Mitten (1st, sm4to, [32]p, color, DJ/2.95)	Lothrop, Lee	1964	Yaroslava	25-45	
Tresselt, Alvin	Timothy Robbins Climbs the Mountain (1st, 4to, [30]p, color, pep, DJ/2.75)	Lothrop, Lee	(1960)	Duvoisin, Roger	30-50	
Tresselt, Alvin	Under the Trees and Through the Grass (1st, 4to, [28]p, color, DJ/2.95)	Lothrop, Lee	1962	Duvoisin, Roger	30-50	
Tresselt, Alvin	Wake Up, City! (1st, 8vo, unpag, color, DJ/2.50)	Lothrop, Lee	1957	Duvoisin, Roger	30-50	
Tresselt, Alvin	Wake Up, Farm! (1st, 8vo, [33]p, color, DJ/2.50)	Lothrop, Lee	1955	Duvoisin, Roger	30-50	
Tresselt, Alvin	White Snow, Bright Snow (1st, 4to, ibds, 33p, color, DJ/2.00, CM)	Lothrop, Lee	(1947)	Duvoisin, Roger	100-165	R
Tresselt, Alvin	World in the Candy Egg (1st, lg ob8vo, [32]p, fp color, dep, DJ/3.75)	Lothrop, Lee	1967	Duvoisin, Roger	45-70	
Trevor, Meriol	Sun Slower, Sun Faster (1st, 8vo, blue cl, 217p, b/w, DJ)	NY: Sheed Ward	(1957)	Ardizzone, Edward	40-65	
Trez, Denise	Good Night Veronica (1st, 4to, 32p, yellow cl, fp color, DJ/3.95)	Viking	(1968)	Trez, D.& A.	20-35	*
Trez, Denise	Maila and the Flying Carpet (1st, 4to, [32]p, yellow cl, fp color, DJ)	Viking	(1969)	Trez, Alain	25-40	
Trickey, Edna	Billy Celebrates (1st, 8vo, [48]p, wraps, color)	United Church Pr	(1964)	Hyman, Trina S.	60-90	*
Trier, Walter	10 Little Negroes (1st, ob8vo, [32]p, ibds, color, pep)	L: Sylvan Press	1944	Trier, Walter	180-250	
Trimpey, Alice	Story of My Dolls (1st, 4to, 76p, ibds, b/w, pep, DJ/0.75)	Whitman	1935	Scott, Janet L.	60-90	
Trine, Ralph W.	In Tune with the Infinite (1st, 8vo, ibds, 254p, 8 ticp)	L: Foulis	(1926)	Robinson, F. Cayley	80-120	*
Tripp, Edward	Tin Fiddle (1st, lg ob8vo, pink cl, unpag, brown illus, cep, DJ/2.00)	NY: Oxford U.Pr.	1954	Sendak, Maurice	350-500	R
Tripp, Paul	Little Red Flower (1st {std}, ob8vo, [49]p, 2-color, pep, DJ/3.95)	Doubleday	1968	Hyman, Trina S.	80-125	*
Tripp, Paul	Strawman Who Smiled by Mistake (1st {std}, ob8vo, 40p, color, pep, DJ/3.95)	Doubleday	1967	Watson, Wendy	30-50	
Tripp, Paul	Tale of Tubby the Tuba (1st, ob8vo, ibds, [26]p, color, pep, DJ/2.00)	Vanguard Press	(1948)	Maas, George	70-100	*
Tripp, Paul	Vi-Daylin Book of Minnie the Mump (1st, 4to, 46p, 3-color)	OH: Ross Labs.	(1970)	Hyman, Trina S.	60-90	*
Tripp, Wallace	Tale of a Pig (1st, sm4to, 32p, color, DJ/3.50)	McGraw-Hill	(1968)	Tripp, Wallace	20-30	
Tritten, Charles	Heidi Grows Up (1st UK, 8vo, 256p, green cl, col frn, 19pl, pep)	L: Collins	(1939)	Doane, Pelagie	40-65	*
Troutbeck, G.E.	Westminster Abbey (1st, 16mo, 278p, 13pl)	L: Methuen	1900	Bedford, Francis D.	40-65	
Trowbridge, John T.	Pair of Madcaps (1st, 12mo, 359p, 8pl)	Lothrop, Lee	(1909)	Merrill, Frank T.	50-80	*
Troy, Hugh	Chippendale Dam (1st, sm4to, 45p, fp 2-color, DJ/1.50)	Oxford U. Pr.	1941	Troy, Hugh	50-85	
True, Barbara	Their First Igloo on Baffin Island (1st, 4to, [28]p, p-o, col, pep, DJ/1.00)	Whitman	1943	Blackwood, Gladys	25-45	
Tschiffely, Aime	Tale of Two Horses (1st AM, 8vo, 220p, pep, b/w, DJ/2.00)	Simon/Schuster	1935	Wiese, Kurt	30-50	
Tucker, Elizabeth S.	Baby and Me! (4to, [13]p, ibds)	Worthington	[1890]	6 Chromos	100-170	*
Tucker, Elizabeth S.	Baby Folk (1st, 4to, [26]p, ibds, 6cp)	Stokes	(1898)	Humphrey, Maud	250-400	
Tucker, Elizabeth S.	Book of Pets (1st, 4to, [48]p, ibds, 12cp)	Stokes	1893	Humphrey, Maud	600-800	
Tucker, Elizabeth S.	Bubbles (4to, 12p, ibds, 6cp)	Worthington	(1892)	Tucker, Eliz. S.	100-160	
Tucker, Elizabeth S.	Cats & Kittens (1st, lg4to, ibds, [26]p, 6 chromos)	Stokes	1895	Boston, Frederick	140-220	*
Tucker, Elizabeth S.	Children of Colonial Days (1st, lg4to, ibds, [74]p, 12cp)	Stokes	1894	Moran, E. Percy	180-270	*
Tucker, Elizabeth S.	Cup of Tea (ob4to, [22]p, ibds, chromos)	Worthington	1892	Tucker, Eliz. S.	120-200	
Tucker, Elizabeth S.	Favorite Pets (1st, 4to, [24]p, ibds, 12cp)	Stokes	1893	Tucker, Eliz. S.	120-170	
Tucker, Elizabeth S.	Little Belles & Beaux (1st, lg4to, [26]p, ibds, 6cp)	Stokes	1896	Brundage, Frances	200-300	
Tucker, Elizabeth S.	Little Grown-Ups (1st, 4to, [74]p, ibds, 12cp)	Stokes	1897	Humphrey, Maud	500-700	
Tucker, Elizabeth S.	Little Men & Maids (1st, 4to, ibds, [26]p, 6cp)	Stokes	1896	Brundage, Frances	200-300	*
Tucker, Elizabeth S.	Little Ways & Great Plays (4to, ibds, 12 chromos)	Worthington	1892	Tucker, Eliz. S.	150-220	
Tucker, Elizabeth S.	Littlest Ones (1st, lg4to, ibds, 12cp)	Stokes	1898	Humphrey, Maud	500-700	
Tucker, Elizabeth S.	Make-Believe Men & Women (1st, 4to, [26]p, ibds, 6cp)	Stokes	1897	Humphrey, Maud	400-600	
Tucker, Elizabeth S.	Old Youngsters (1st, lg4to, ibds, unpag, 6cp)	Stokes	1897	Humphrey, Maud	500-800	
Tucker, Elizabeth S.	Rhymes & Stories of Olden Times (1st, lg4to, ibds, [26]p, 6cp)	Stokes	1894	Moran, E. Percy	140-225	*
Tucker, Elizabeth S.	Royal Little People (1st, 4to, unpag, ibds, 12cp)	Stokes	(1895)	Tucker, Eliz. S.	120-170	
Tudor, Bethany	Skiddycock Pond (1st, ob8vo, [31]p, ibds, fp color, pep, DJ/2.75)	Lippincott	(1965)	Tudor, Bethany	60-90	
Tudor, Tasha	1 Is One (1st, lg ob8vo, unpag, pep, pink cl, color, DJ/2.75, CH)	NY: Oxford U.Pr.	1956	Tudor, Tasha	200-300	
Tudor, Tasha	A is for Annabelle (1st, lg ob8vo, unpag, grn/gilt, 27 col, pep, DJ/2.50)	NY: Oxford U.Pr.	1954	Tudor, Tasha	180-260	
Tudor, Tasha	Alexander the Gander (1st, 24mo, green cl, [47]p, color, pep, DJ/0.75)	Oxford U. Pr.	(1939)	Tudor, Tasha	300-450	
Tudor, Tasha	Amanda & the Bear (1st, 12mo, unpag, p-o, blue cl, color, dep, DJ/1.75)	NY: Oxford U.Pr.	1951	Tudor, Tasha	200-300	
Tudor, Tasha	Around the Year (1st, lg ob8vo, [54]p, cloth, color, DJ/3.00)	NY: Oxford U.Pr.	1957	Tudor, Tasha	150-250	R
Tudor, Tasha	Becky's Birthday (1st, 8vo, 47p, yellow cl, color, DJ/3.00)	Viking	(1960)	Tudor, Tasha	170-240	
Tudor, Tasha	Becky's Christmas (1st, 4to, 45p, color, pep, DJ/3.00)	Viking	(1961)	Tudor, Tasha	200-300	
Tudor, Tasha	County Fair (1st, 24mo, [47]p, red/white, pep, DJ/0.75)	Oxford U. Pr.	1940	Tudor, Tasha	350-500	
Tudor, Tasha	Doll's Christmas (1st, sq12mo, red cl, [29]p, pep, p-o, color, DJ/1.50)	NY: Oxford U.Pr.	1950	Tudor, Tasha	250-400	
Tudor, Tasha	Dorcas Porkus (1st, 24mo, [35]p, orange cl, color, DJ/0.75)	NY: Oxford U.Pr.	(1942)	Tudor, Tasha	300-500	
Tudor, Tasha	Edgar Allan Crow (1st, 12mo, gilt, p-o, unpag, fp color, pep, DJ/1.75)	Oxford U. Pr.	1953	Tudor, Tasha	250-400	
Tudor, Tasha	First Delights (1st, 8vo, ibds, [32]p, color, pep, DJ/2.50)	Platt/Munk	(1966)	Tudor, Tasha	80-145	
Tudor, Tasha	First Poems of Childhood (1st, 8vo, gilt, 45p, color, cep, DJ/1.95)	Platt/Munk	(1967)	Tudor, Tasha	140-200	
Tudor, Tasha	Linsey Woolsey (1st, sq24mo, [43]p, yellow bds, color, DJ/0.75)	NY: Oxford U.Pr.	1946	Tudor, Tasha	350-500	
Tudor, Tasha	Pumpkin Moonshine (1st, 24mo, blue cl, [41]p, color, pep, DJ/0.75)	Oxford U. Pr.	(1938)	Tudor, Tasha	300-500	R
Tudor, Tasha	Snow Before Christmas (1st, sq12mo, [37]p, pep, p-o, color, DJ/1.00)	NY: Oxford U.Pr.	1941	Tudor, Tasha	300-500	
Tudor, Tasha	Tale for Easter (1st, sq12mo, [33]p, dep, p-o, color, DJ/1.00)	NY: Oxford U.Pr.	1941	Tudor, Tasha	250-400	
Tudor, Tasha	Tasha Tudor's Favorite Stories (1st {std}, sm4to, 131p, ibds, col, DJ/3.95)	Lippincott	(1965)	Tudor, Tasha	100-165	
Tudor, Tasha	Thistly B. (1st, sq12mo, [27]p, red bds, p-o, color, DJ/1.50)	NY: Oxford U.Pr.	1949	Tudor, Tasha	200-300	
Tudor, Tasha	White Goose (1st, sq12mo, grey cl, p-o, [27]p, color, DJ/1.00)	Oxford U. Pr.	(1943)	Tudor, Tasha	250-400	
Tudor, Tasha (comp)	Wings from the Wind (1st {std}, lg8vo, 119p, color, DJ/3.95)	Lippincott	(1964)	Tudor, Tasha	120-200	

AUTHOR	TITLE	PUBLISHER	DATE	ARTIST	PRICE	LC
Tudor, Tasha (ed)	Take Joy! Tasha Tudor Christmas Book (1st, ob4to, 157p, color, DJ/4.95)	World	(1966)	Tudor, Tasha	100-165	
Tudor, Tasha (ed)	Tasha Tudor Book of Fairy Tales (1st, lg4to, 92p, color, DJ/3.95)	Platt/Munk	(1961)	Tudor, Tasha	140-185	
Tufts, Georgia	Catrina & the Cats (1st, sm4to, [38]p, fp color, DJ/2.75)	Lothrop, Lee	(1959)	Tufts, Georgia	30-45	
Tunis, Edwin B.	Frontier Living (1st {std}, lg4to, 165p, ibds, b/w, DJ/5.95, NH)	World	(1961)	Tunis, Edwin B.	50-80	
Tunis, Edwin B.	Indians (1st {std}, lg4to, 157p, ipcb, b/w, DJ/4.95)	World	(1959)	Tunis, Edwin B.	60-90	R
Tunis, Edwin B.	Oars, Sails & Steam (1st {std}, lg4to, 78p, ivory cl, b/w, DJ/3.50)	World	(1952)	Tunis, Edwin B.	50-90	R
Tunis, Edwin B.	Shaw's Fortune (1st, ob4to, 63p, fp b/w, DJ/3.95, NYTBI)	World	(1966)	Tunis, Edwin B.	30-50	
Tunis, John R.	All-American (1st, 8vo, 245p, b/w, pep, DJ/2.00)	Harcourt	(1942)	Walleen, Hans A.	20-35	
Tunis, John R.	Buddy and the Old Pro (1st, 8vo, 189p, b/w, DJ/2.50)	Wm. Morrow	1955	Barnum, Jay H.	50-85	*
Tunis, John R.	Champion's Choice (1st, 8vo, 300p, fp b/w, DJ/2.00)	Harcourt	(1940)	Barnum, Jay H.	20-35	
Tunis, John R.	Iron Duke (1st, 8vo, 276p, b/w, pep, DJ/2.00)	Harcourt	(1938)	Bull, Johan	20-35	
Tunis, John R.	Kid from Tomkinsville (1st, 8vo, 355p, fp b/w, DJ/2.00)	Harcourt	(1940)	Barnum, Jay H.	20-35	
Tunis, John R.	World Series (1st, sm8vo, 318p, blue cl, 24pl, pep, DJ/2.00)	Harcourt	(1941)	Barnum, Jay H.	30-50	
Turkle, Brinton	Fiddler of High Lonesome (1st, 4to, 44p, fp 1-color, DJ/3.50)	Viking	(1968)	Turkle, Brinton	30-50	
Turkle, Brinton	Magic of Millicent Musgrave (1st, 4to, ibds, [40]p, 1-color, pep, DJ/3.50)	Viking	(1967)	Turkle, Brinton	30-45	
Turkle, Brinton	Mooncoin Castle (1st {std}, lg8vo, 141p, b/w, DJ/3.95)	Viking	(1970)	Turkle, Brinton	30-50	
Turkle, Brinton	Obadiah the Bold (1st, ob8vo, [36]p, fp color, DJ/3.50)	Viking	(1965)	Turkle, Brinton	30-50	
Turkle, Brinton	Sky Dog (1st, lg8vo, [31]p, fp 2-color, DJ/3.95)	Viking	(1969)	Turkle, Brinton	25-45	*
Turkle, Brinton	Thy Friend Obadiah (1st, ob8vo, [37]p, fp color, DJ/3.95, CH)	Viking	(1969)	Turkle, Brinton	50-80	R*
Turnbull, Agnes S.	George (1st, 8vo, 94p, b/w, cep, DJ/3.00)	Houghton	1965	Hyman, Trina S.	40-65	*
Turner, Nancy B.	Magpie Lane (1st, sm8vo, 88p, orange cl, silhouettes, dep)	Harcourt	(1927)	Merwin, Decie	30-60	*
Turner, Nancy B.	Ray Coon to the Rescue (1st, lg8vo, 80p, ipcb, b/w, pep)	Rand/McNally	(1931)	Ward, Keith	55-90	*
Turner, Nancy B.	When it Rained Cats & Dogs (1st {std}, 4to, ibds, [32]p, color, DJ/1.00)	Lippincott	(1946)	Gergely, Tibor	60-100	R
Turner, Nancy B.	Zodiac Town (1st, 8vo, 131p, gilt, 13 b/w, pep)	Atl. Monthly Pr.	(1921)	Bromhall, Winifred	35-60	
Turner, Philip	Grange at High Force (1st, 8vo, 220p, b/w, DJ, CgM)	L: Oxford U.Pr.	1965	Papas, William	60-95	
Turner, Thyra	Christmas House... (1st, 12mo, ibds, 25p, 14 color, DJ/1.00)	Scribner	1943	Gag, Flavia	80-120	
Turngren, Ellen	Shadows into Mist (1st {std}, 8vo, 207p, b/w, DJ/2.75)	Longmans	1958	Bock, Vera	20-35	
Turpin, Edna	Littling of Gaywood (1st, 12mo, 265p, pep, b/w, DJ/2.00)	Random	(1939)	Eichenberg, Fritz	35-55	
Twain, Mark	$30000 Bequest (1st, 8vo, 522p, red/gilt, 8pl)	Harper	1906	Unknown	200-300	
Twain, Mark	Adventures of Huckleberry Finn (1st, 4to, 346p, gilt, 8 ticp, box)	Heritage Press	(1940)	Rockwell, Norman	90-120	
Twain, Mark	Adventures of Tom Sawyer (1st, 8vo, 264p, p-o, 4cp, pep)	Winston	(1931)	Hurd, Peter	45-70	
Twain, Mark	Adventures of Tom Sawyer (1st, 4to, 284p, 8 ticp, box)	Heritage Press	(1937)	Rockwell, Norman	90-120	
Twain, Mark	Adventures of Tom Sawyer (1st {std}, 8vo, 302p, col frn, fp b/w, pep)	World	(1946)	Slobodkin, Louis	25-40	
Twain, Mark	American Claimant (1st, 8vo, 277p, green/gilt, b/w)	Webster	1892	Beard, Dan	350-500	
Twain, Mark	Dog's Tale (1st AM, 8vo, red cl, teg, 36p, 4cp)	Harper	1904	Smedley, W.T.	120-200	
Twain, Mark	Double-Barrelled Detective Story (1st, 8vo, red/gilt, teg, uncut, 7pl)	Harper	1902	Hitchcock, Lucius	150-250	
Twain, Mark	Eve's Diary (1st, 8vo, 109p, red cloth, b/w)	Harper	1906	Ralph, Lester	120-185	
Twain, Mark	Extracts from Adam's Diary (1st, 8vo, red cl, 89p, b/w)	Harper	1904	Strothmann, F.	200-300	
Twain, Mark	Horse's Tale (1st, 8vo, red cl, 152p, 5pl)	Harper	1907	Hitchcock, Lucius	120-200	
Twain, Mark	Huckleberry Finn (1st, lg8vo, p-o, 421p, col frn, b/w)	Harper	(1923)	Brehm, Worth	30-50	
Twain, Mark	Jumping Frog (1st, 8vo, 65p, 11pl)	Harper	1903	Strothmann, F.	70-120	
Twain, Mark	Mysterious Stranger (1st, lg8vo, 151p, gilt, teg, p-o, 7cp)	Harper	(1916)	Wyeth, N.C.	200-300	
Twain, Mark	Prince & the Pauper (1st, 8vo, 285p, gilt, 8cp, pep)	Harper	1909	Hatherell, William	40-60	
Twain, Mark	Prince & the Pauper (1st, 8vo, teg, 284p, gilt, uncut, p-o, 7cp)	Harper	(1917)	Booth, Franklin	60-90	
Twain, Mark	Prince & the Pauper (1st, 8vo, 274p, p-o, gilt, color, pep, DJ)	Winston	(1937)	Lawson, Robert	80-140	
Twain, Mark	St. Joan of Arc (1st, lg8vo, black/gilt, 32p, p-o, 4 ticp, pep)	Harper	(1919)	Pyle, Howard	140-200	
Twain, Mark	Tom Sawyer Abroad (1st, 8vo, 219p, white/gilt, b/w)	NY: Webster	1894	Beard, Dan	350-500	
Tworkov, Jack	Camel Who Took a Walk (1st {std}, 4to, [32]p, ibds, 2-color, DJ/2.00)	Aladdin	(1951)	Duvoisin, Roger	60-90	
Tworkov, Jack	Tigers Don't Bite (1st {std}, 4to, ibds, [32]p, fp 1-color, DJ/2.25)	Dutton	(1956)	Duvoisin, Roger	50-80	
Tybout, Ella M.	Poketown People (1st, 8vo, 356p, 6cp)	Lippincott	1904	VerBeck/Moore	100-170	
Tyler, Anna C.	Twenty-Four Unusual Stories (1st, 12mo, 328p, fp b/w)	Harcourt	1921	Petershams	40-65	
Tyman, Loretta	Julio (1st, 8vo, beige cl, 176p, fp b/w, DJ/2.50)	Abelard-Schuman	(1955)	Charlot, Jean	45-70	
Tynan, Katharine	Little Book of Courtesies (1st, 12mo, teg, 57p, gilt, col frn)	L: Dent	1906	Robinson, Charles	80-120	
Tyrell, Eleanor	How I Tamed the Wild Squirrels (1st, sq8vo, 111p, pep, p-o, 6cp)	L: Nelson	[1918]	Appleton, Honor C.	70-100	
Tyrell, Eleanor	More About the Squirrels (1st, sq8vo, 111p, pep, p-o, 6cp)	L: Nelson	[1918]	Appleton, Honor C.	60-100	
Uchida, Yoshiko	Dancing Kettle (1st {std}, 8vo, 174p, b/w, DJ/2.25)	Harcourt	(1949)	Jones, Richard	25-40	*
Uchida, Yoshiko	Forever Christmas Tree (1st, lg8vo, gilt, [46]p, fp 1-color, DJ/2.95)	Scribner	(1963)	Mizumura, Kazue	40-65	
Uchida, Yoshiko	Full Circle (1st, 8vo, 135p, b/w, DJ/2.50)	Friendship Pr.	(1957)	Uchida, Yoshiko	30-50	
Uchida, Yoshiko	In-Between Miya (1st, 8vo, 128p, fp b/w, cep, DJ/3.25)	Scribner	(1967)	Bennett, Susan	25-45	
Uchida, Yoshiko	Magic Listening Cap (1st {std}, 8vo, 146p, b/w, DJ/2.50)	Harcourt	(1955)	Uchida, Yoshiko	30-45	
Uchida, Yoshiko	Makoto, the Smallest Boy (1st, 8vo, 41p, b/w, DJ/3.75)	Crowell	(1970)	Shirakawa, Akihito	30-50	*
Uchida, Yoshiko	Mik and the Prowler (1st {std}, 8vo, 122p, b/w, DJ/2.95)	Harcourt	(1960)	Hutchinson, Wm.	30-50	
Uchida, Yoshiko	New Friends for Susan (1st, sm8vo, 185p, b/w, DJ/2.00)	Scribner	1951	Sugimoto, Henry	40-65	
Uchida, Yoshiko	Sea of Gold (1st AM, lg8vo, 136p, b/w, DJ/3.50)	Scribner	(1965)	Yamaguchi, Marianne	30-50	
Uchida, Yoshiko	Sumi & the Goat and the Tokyo Express (1st, 8vo, [48]p, color, DJ/3.95)	Scribner	(1969)	Mizumura, Kazue	30-50	
Uchida, Yoshiko	Sumi's Prize (1st, lg8vo, [48]p, 1-color, DJ/3.25)	Scribner	(1964)	Mizumura, Kazue	30-50	
Uchida, Yoshiko	Sumi's Special Happening (1st, lg8vo, [46]p, fp color, DJ/3.50)	Scribner	(1966)	Mizumura, Kazue	30-50	
Uchida, Yoshiko	Takao and Grandfather's Sword (1st {std}, 8vo, 127p, b/w, DJ/2.50)	Harcourt	(1958)	Hutchinson, Wm.	30-50	
Uden, Grant	Dictionary of Chivalry (1st, 8vo, 352p, color, DJ, KGM)	L: Longmans	1968	Baynes, Pauline	50-80	*
Udry, Janice M.	Glenda (1st, lg8vo, 55p, b/w, DJ/3.50)	Harper	(1969)	Simont, Marc	25-40	*
Udry, Janice M.	If You're a Bear (1st, 12mo, [32]p, color, DJ/2.95)	Whitman	(1967)	Merkling, Erica	20-35	
Udry, Janice M.	Let's Be Enemies (1st, 24mo, [32]p, 3-color, DJ/1.95)	Harper	1961	Sendak, Maurice	80-135	
Udry, Janice M.	Mary Ann's Mud Day (1st, 16mo, 29p, color, DJ/2.50)	Harper	(1967)	Alexander, Martha	20-30	
Udry, Janice M.	Mean Mouse & other Mean Stories (1st, ob8vo, unpag, ibds, 1-color, DJ/2.50)	Harper	(1962)	Young, Ed	30-50	
Udry, Janice M.	Moon Jumpers (1st, sm4to, ibds, [31]p, 7 dp color, DJ/2.50, CH)	Harper	(1959)	Sendak, Maurice	300-450	
Udry, Janice M.	Sunflower Garden (1st, ob4to, 37p, fp 3-color, pep, DJ/3.95)	Harvey House	(1969)	Darwin, Beatrice	50-80	
Udry, Janice M.	Theodore's Parents (1st, sm4to, [30]p, green cl, color, DJ/2.75)	Lothrop, Lee	(1958)	Adams, Adrienne	55-80	*
Udry, Janice M.	Tree is Nice (1st, 4to, ibds, [30]p, fp color, DJ/2.50, CM)	Harper	1956	Simont, Marc	130-180	R

AUTHOR	TITLE	PUBLISHER	DATE	ARTIST	PRICE	LC
Udry, Janice M.	What Mary Jo Shared (1st, lg8vo, unpag, color, pep, DJ/2.95)	Whitman	(1966)	Mill, Eleanor	20-30	*
Ullman, James R.	Banner in the Sky (1st {std}, 8vo, 252p, pep, DJ/2.75, NH)	Lippincott	(1954)	No Illustrations	40-65	
Uncle Frank	Uncle Frank's Visit to Fairy-Land (1st, 12mo, 241p, b/w)	Doub./McClure	1897	Stevens, W.D.	200-300	*
Uncle Milton	Bennie & Jennie (ob8vo, ibds, fp color)	Cupples/Leon	1907	Wall, Bernhardt	65-90	
Uncle Milton	Little Karl (1st, lg8vo, unpag, 8 fp color)	Cupples/Leon	1908	Wall, Bernhardt	50-80	*
Underdown, E.	Gateway to Romance (1st, 4to, 299p, teg, 16cp, pep)	L: Nelson	[1909]	Various	90-120	
Underdown, E.	Gateway to Spenser (1st, 8vo, teg, 399p, 16cp, pep)	L: Nelson	[1911]	Pape, Frank	80-130	
Underdown, E.	Stories from Chaucer (1st, 12mo, p-o, 157p, 8cp)	T. Nelson	1913	Anderson, Anne	55-80	
Underhill, Andrew F.	Goochy Goggles & Pollywog Named Woggles (1st, lg8vo, [93]p, ibds, color)	McLoughlin	(1926)	Sturges, Katharine	50-80	
Underhill, Zoe (ed)	Dwarf's Tailor... (1st, lg8vo, 260p, p-o by...)	Harper	(1924)	Gaze, Harold	40-65	
Underwood, C.F.	American Types (1st, 4to, p-o, red cl, 16cp)	Stokes	(1912)	Underwood, C.F.	80-120	
Underwood, P.	When Christmas Comes Around (1st, 4to, ipcb, 26p, 6cp, pep)	Duffield	1915	Smith, Jessie W.	700-900	
Ungerer, Tomi	Adelaide (1st, 4to, ibds, 40p, 2-color, DJ/2.75)	Harper	(1959)	Ungerer, Tomi	70-120	
Ungerer, Tomi	Ask Me a Question (1st, 8vo, 32p, ibds, 2-color, DJ/2.50)	Harper	(1968)	Ungerer, Tomi	50-85	
Ungerer, Tomi	Christmas Eve at the Mellops (1st, ob8vo, [32]p, fp 2-color, DJ/2.50)	Harper	(1960)	Ungerer, Tomi	60-90	
Ungerer, Tomi	Crictor (1st, 4to, green ibds, 32p, 2-color, DJ/2.50)	Harper	(1958)	Ungerer, Tomi	65-100	R
Ungerer, Tomi	Emile (1st, 4to, 32p, ibds, 2-color, DJ/2.50)	Harper	(1960)	Ungerer, Tomi	70-120	
Ungerer, Tomi	Horrible (1st, lg4to, tan cl, [102]p, fp color, DJ/10.00)	Atheneum	1960	Ungerer, Tomi	80-130	
Ungerer, Tomi	Mellops Go Diving for Treasure (1st, lg8vo, ibds, unpag, 2-color, DJ/2.00)	Harper	(1957)	Ungerer, Tomi	50-90	
Ungerer, Tomi	Mellops Go Flying (1st, lg ob8vo, ibds, [32]p, 2-color, DJ/2.00)	Harper	(1957)	Ungerer, Tomi	60-100	R
Ungerer, Tomi	Mellops Go Spelunking (1st, ob8vo, ibds, [32]p, color, DJ/2.50)	Harper	(1963)	Ungerer, Tomi	50-85	
Ungerer, Tomi	Mellops Strike Oil (1st, ob8vo, 32p, fp 2-color, DJ/2.00)	Harper	(1958)	Ungerer, Tomi	50-85	
Ungerer, Tomi	Moon Man (1st, folio, 40p, color, DJ/4.50)	Harper	(1967)	Ungerer, Tomi	70-120	
Ungerer, Tomi	Orlando the Brave Vulture (1st, 4to, 32p, 2-color, ibds, DJ/3.50)	Harper	(1966)	Ungerer, Tomi	40-60	
Ungerer, Tomi	Rufus (1st, lg4to, 32p, ibds, color, DJ/2.95)	Harper	1961	Ungerer, Tomi	60-100	
Ungerer, Tomi	Snail, Where are You? (1st, 8vo, [32]p, fp color, DJ/2.25)	Harper	(1962)	Ungerer, Tomi	50-80	R
Ungerer, Tomi	The Hat (1st, 4to, [32]p, ipcb, p-o, fp color, cep, DJ/3.50)	Parents Mag. Pr.	(1970)	Ungerer, Tomi	45-70	
Ungerer, Tomi	Three Robbers (1st {std}, 4to, 39p, color, cep, DJ/3.50, NYTBI)	Atheneum	(1962)	Ungerer, Tomi	100-165	
Ungerer, Tomi	Underground Sketchbook (1st {std}, ob8vo, ibds, [148]p, b/w, DJ/3.95)	Viking	(1964)	Ungerer, Tomi	45-70	
Ungerer, Tomi	Zeralda's Ogre (1st, 4to, ibds, [32]p, color, DJ/3.95)	Harper	(1967)	Ungerer, Tomi	50-80	
Unknown	Christmas Letter (1st, 12mo, 85p, 13pl)	Cupples/Leon	1902	Smith, Wuanita	50-80	
Unknown	Leather Bottel (1st, 16mo, pcb, p-o, 14p, uncut)	(Concord)	(1903)	Bradley, Will	90-120	
Unknown	Rule Britannia (4to, ibds, [66]p, 8 fp color)	L: Hodder	[1916]	Robinson, Charles	225-350	
Unknown	Soldiers of the King (4to, [66]p, ibds, 8cp)	L: Hodder	[1916]	Robinson, Charles	225-350	
Unknown	Wonders of Wilmington (lg4to, [12]p, ibds, 5 fp b/w)	Hull	[1925]	Robinson, W. Heath	220-320	
Unnerstad, Edith	Little O (1st {std}, 8vo, 150p, b/w, DJ/2.50)	Macmillan	(1957)	Slobodkin, Louis	40-65	*
Unnerstad, Edith	Pysen (1st {std}, 8vo, 172p, b/w, DJ/2.50)	Macmillan	(1955)	Slobodkin, Louis	30-45	*
Unnerstad, Edith	Saucepan Journey (1st {std}, 8vo, 180p, b/w, DJ/2.50)	Macmillan	1951	Slobodkin, Louis	25-45	
Unterecker, John	Dreaming Zoo (1st, sm4to, [30]p, 3-color, DJ/3.50)	H.Z. Walck	1965	Weinheimer, George	30-50	*
Untermeyer, Louis	Book of Noble Thoughts (1st, 8vo, 121p, ibds, 1-color, dep, DJ/3.00)	A.A. Group	(1946)	Kent, Rockwell	60-95	
Untermeyer, Louis	Chip: My Life and Times (1st, ob8vo, 102p, fp b/w, pep)	Harcourt	(1933)	Neville, Vera	60-90	R*
Untermeyer, Louis	Kitten Who Barked (1st, ob4to, ibds, [32]p, color)	Golden Press	(1962)	Obligado, Lilian	40-65	R
Untermeyer, Louis	Love Lyrics (1st, ob12mo, ibds, 44p, color, DJ/0.95)	NY: Odyssey Pr.	(1965)	Frasconi, Antonio	25-45	*
Untermeyer, Louis	Magic Circle (1st, 8vo, 288p, fp b/w, DJ/3.00)	Harcourt	(1952)	Krush, Beth & Joe	35-60	*
Untermeyer, Louis	New Songs for New Voices (1st, lg4to, 258p, b/w, pep)	Harcourt	(1928)	Bacon, Peggy	30-50	*
Untermeyer, Louis	One and One and One (1st {std}, 4to, [63]p, fp b/w, cep)	Crowell-Collier	(1962)	Jones, Robert	65-100	
Untermeyer, Louis	Tales from the Ballet (1st, lg4to, ibds, 91p, fp color, DJ/5.95)	Golden Press	(1968)	Provensen, A.& M.	60-90	
Untermeyer, Louis (ed)	Golden Treasury of Poetry (1st, 4to, 324p, ibds, color, DJ/4.95)	Golden Press	(1959)	Anglund, Joan W.	80-120	R
Unwin, Nora S.	Doughnuts for Lin (1st {std}, ob8vo, ibds, [46]p, color, DJ/1.75)	Aladdin	(1950)	Unwin, Nora S.	30-50	*
Unwin, Nora S.	Lucy & Little Red Horse (1st, 4to, 36p, p-o, gilt, 8 fp color, DJ)	L: A. Moring	(1943)	Unwin, Nora S.	55-80	
Unwin, Nora S.	Poquito, Little Mexican Duck (1st, sm ob4to, [32]p, 1-color, DJ/2.75)	McKay	1959	Unwin, Nora S.	30-50	
Unwin, Nora S.	Sinbad the Cygnet (1st, ob8vo, [48]p, 2-color, DJ/4.50)	John Day	1970	Unwin, Nora S.	35-50	
Unwin, Nora S.	Way of the Shepherd (1st, sm4to, 32p, fp 2-color, pep, DJ/2.50)	McGraw-Hill	(1963)	Unwin, Nora S.	25-45	
Updike, John	Bottom's Dream (1st, ob4to, 34p, fp color, pep, DJ/3.95)	Knopf	(1969)	Chappell, Warren	100-150	
Updike, John	Child's Calendar (1st, lg8vo, [30]p, fp 2-color, DJ/3.25)	Knopf	(1965)	Burkert, Nancy	60-90	R
Upham, Elizabeth	Little Brown Bear (1st, sm4to, [58]p, 8 fp color, DJ/1.00)	Platt/Munk	(1942)	Hartwell, Marjorie	50-80	
Upham, Elizabeth	Little Brown Bear & His Friends (1st, sm4to, [56]p, color, pep, DJ)	Platt/Munk	(1952)	Hartwell, Marjorie	50-80	
Upham, Elizabeth	Little Brown Bear Goes to School (1st, sm4to, [52]p, fp col, pep, DJ/1.25)	Platt/Munk	(1955)	Hartwell, Marjorie	50-80	
Upham, Elizabeth	Little Brown Monkey (1st, sm4to, ibds, [56]p, color, pep, DJ/1.00)	Platt/Munk	(1949)	Hartwell, Marjorie	50-80	
Upington, Marion	Beautiful Culpeppers (1st {std}, 8vo, 113p, 2-color, DJ/2.95)	F. Watts	(1963)	Slobodkin, Louis	45-70	
Upjohn, Anna M.	Friends in Strange Garments (1st, 8vo, 148p, 4cp)	Houghton	1927	Upjohn, Anna M.	25-40	
Upton, Bertha	Adventures of Two Dutch Dolls & Golliwogg (1st, ob4to, 64p, ibds, 29cp, pep)	Longmans	(1895)	Upton, Florence	500-700	
Upton, Bertha	Golliwogg at Sea-Side (1st, ob4to, ibds, 63p, color, pep)	L: Longmans	1898	Upton, Florence	450-600	R
Upton, Bertha	Golliwogg in Holland (1st, ob4to, 64p, ibds, 31 fp color, dep)	L: Longmans	1904	Upton, Florence	450-650	R
Upton, Bertha	Golliwogg in War! (1st, ob4to, 65p, ibds, color)	L: Longmans	1899	Upton, Florence	400-600	R
Upton, Bertha	Golliwogg's Auto Go Cart (1st, ob4to, ibds, 66p, color)	L: Longmans	1901	Upton, Florence	400-650	R
Upton, Bertha	Golliwogg's Bicycle Club (1st, ob4to, 62p, ibds, fp color)	L: Longmans	1896	Upton, Florence	500-700	
Upton, Bertha	Golliwogg's Christmas (1st, ob4to, 62p, ipcb, 31 fp color)	L: Longmans	1907	Upton, Florence	450-700	R
Upton, Bertha	Golliwogg's Circus (1st, ob4to, ibds, 31 fp color)	L: Longmans	1903	Upton, Florence	500-700	R
Upton, Bertha	Golliwogg's Desert Island (1st, ob4to, ibds, 64p, color)	L: Longmans	1906	Upton, Florence	450-650	
Upton, Bertha	Golliwogg's Fox Hunt (1st, ob4to, 66p, ipcb, 32 fp color)	L: Longmans	1905	Upton, Florence	300-500	
Upton, Bertha	Golliwogg's Polar Adventures (1st, ob4to, 63p, ibds, color)	L: Longmans	1900	Upton, Florence	450-650	R
Upton, Bertha	Little Hearts (4to, ibds, 62p, color)	L: Routledge	1897	Upton, Florence	500-750	
Upton, Bertha	Vege-Men's Revenge (1st, ob4to, ibds, 63p, color)	L: Longmans	1897	Upton, Florence	500-700	R
Upton, Florence	Adventures of Borbee & the Wisp (1st, lg sq8vo, ibds, [67]p, 31 color)	L: Longmans	1908	Upton, Florence	300-500	R
Upton, Florence	Golliwogg's Air-Ship (1st, ob4to, ipcb, 65p, color)	L: Longmans	1902	Upton, Florence	400-600	R
Urmston, Mary	New Boy (1st {std}, 8vo, 207p, b/w, DJ/2.25)	Doubleday	(1950)	Turkle, Brinton	30-45	
Urmston, Mary	Seven and Sam (1st, 8vo, 188p, fp b/w, DJ/2.50)	Doubleday	1955	Paull, Grace	25-40	*

AUTHOR: 216

AUTHOR	TITLE	PUBLISHER	DATE	ARTIST	PRICE	LC
Urquhart, Elizabeth	Horace (1st {std}, 8vo, 115p, b/w, DJ/2.00)	Dutton	1951	Pastor, Rosita	40-65	*
Uttley, Alison	Adventures of No Ordinary Rabbit (1st, 8vo, 208p, b/w, DJ)	L: Faber	(1937)	Buckels, Alec	50-80	*
Uttley, Alison	Adventures of Peter & Judy in Bunnyland (4to, ibds, 39p, 8cp)	L: Collins	(1935)	Young, Lennie	130-200	
Uttley, Alison	Flower Show (1st, 12mo, ibds, 65p, fp color)	L: Heinemann	(1955)	Wigglesworth, Kath.	30-50	
Uttley, Alison	Fuzzypeg Goes to School (1st, 8vo, blue cl, 100p, p-o, color, pep)	L: Collins	(1938)	Tempest, Margaret	130-175	
Uttley, Alison	Going to the Fair (1st, 12mo, ibds, 72p, color)	L: Heinemann	(1951)	Wigglesworth, Kath.	35-50	
Uttley, Alison	Gray Rabbit Finds a Shoe (1st, 12mo, 63p, ipcb, color, pep)	L: Collins	(1960)	Tempest, Margaret	30-50	
Uttley, Alison	Great Adventure of Hare (1st, 8vo, 107p, ipcb, p-o, color, pep)	L: Heinemann	1931	Tempest, Margaret	50-80	
Uttley, Alison	Grey Rabbit & the Circus (1st, 12mo, ibds, 61p, color)	L: Collins	1961	Tempest, Margaret	35-50	
Uttley, Alison	Grey Rabbit's May Day (1st, 12mo, 63p, ipcb, color)	L: Collins	1963	Tempest, Margaret	30-50	
Uttley, Alison	Hare & the Easter Egg (1st, sq12mo, 80p, green bds, 16 fp color)	L: Collins	(1952)	Tempest, Margaret	40-60	
Uttley, Alison	Hare and the Easter Eggs (1st, 12mo, ibds, 80p, fp color, DJ)	L: Collins	1952	Tempest, Margaret	40-65	
Uttley, Alison	Hare Goes Shopping (1st, 12mo, ibds, 63p, color)	L: Collins	(1965)	Tempest, Margaret	35-50	
Uttley, Alison	How Little Grey Rabbit Got Back her Tail (1st, 8vo, 109p, ipcb, p-o, color)	L: Heinemann	1930	Tempest, Margaret	50-80	
Uttley, Alison	Knot Squirrel Tied (1st, 8vo, 101p, grey pcb, p-o, 23 fp color, pep)	L: Collins	1937	Tempest, Margaret	60-90	
Uttley, Alison	Little Grey Rabbit & Weasels (1st, 80p, pcb, p-o, color, pep)	L: Collins	1947	Tempest, Margaret	50-85	
Uttley, Alison	Little Grey Rabbit Goes to Sea (1st, 12mo, ibds, 80p, fp color)	L: Collins	(1954)	Tempest, Margaret	35-50	
Uttley, Alison	Little Grey Rabbit's Christmas (1st, sq8vo, 104p, ibds, color)	L: Collins	1939	Tempest, Margaret	50-85	
Uttley, Alison	Little Grey Rabbit's Pancake Day (1st, 12mo, 63p, ipcb, color, DJ)	L: Collins	1967	Tempest, Margaret	30-50	
Uttley, Alison	Little Grey Rabbit's Party (1st, 12mo, ibds, 112p, fp color, pep)	L: Collins	(1936)	Tempest, Margaret	60-90	
Uttley, Alison	Little Grey Rabbit's Valentine (1st, 8vo, 92p, ibds, color)	L: Collins	(1953)	Tempest, Margaret	40-65	
Uttley, Alison	Moldy Warp the Mole (1st, 12mo, ibds, 88p, color)	L: Collins	(1940)	Tempest, Margaret	50-70	
Uttley, Alison	Moonshine & Magic (1st, 8vo, 208p, cloth, 8cp)	L: Faber	1932	Townsend, William	60-90	
Uttley, Alison	Mouse Telegrams (1st, 12mo, ibds, 65p, fp color)	L: Heinemann	(1955)	Wigglesworth, Kath.	30-50	
Uttley, Alison	Mrs. Mouse Spring-Cleans (1st, 12mo, 70p, bds, p-o, color)	L: Heinemann	(1952)	Wigglesworth, Kath.	40-65	
Uttley, Alison	Mustard, Pepper and Salt (1st, 8vo, 230p, b/w, DJ)	L: Faber	1938	Raverat, Gwen	30-50	*
Uttley, Alison	Snug & the Chimney-Sweeper (1st, 12mo, ibds, 69p, fp color)	L: Heinemann	(1953)	Wigglesworth, Kath.	30-50	
Uttley, Alison	Snug and Serena Pick Cowslips (1st, 12mo, bds, p-o, 72p, fp color)	L: Heinemann	1950	Wigglesworth, Kath.	40-65	
Uttley, Alison	Squirrel Goes Skating (1st, sq8vo, 112p, p-o, color, pep)	L: Collins	1934	Tempest, Margaret	50-80	
Uttley, Alison	Story of Fuzzypeg the Hedgehog (1st, 8vo, 98p, ipcb, p-o, color, pep)	L: Heinemann	1932	Tempest, Margaret	60-90	
Uttley, Alison	Toad's Castle (1st, 12mo, 70p, bds, p-o, fp color)	L: Heinemann	(1951)	Wigglesworth, Kath.	40-65	
Uttley, Alison	Traveller in Time (1st AM, 8vo, 306p, b/w, DJ/2.50)	Putnam	(1940)	Bray, Phyllis	120-200	
Uttley, Alison	Wise Owl's Story (1st, 12mo, 108p, ipcb, p-o, pep)	L: Collins	1935	Tempest, Margaret	55-80	
Vacheron, Edith	Here is Henri! (1st, 8vo, 60p, fp color, DJ/2.50)	Scribner	(1959)	Kahl, Virginia	30-50	*
Vacheron, Edith	More About Henri! (1st, 8vo, 64p, fp 3-color, DJ/2.75)	Scribner	(1961)	Kahl, Virginia	25-45	
Vaile, Charlotte	Orcutt Girls (1st, sm8vo, 316p, green/gilt, 5pl)	W.A. Wilde	(1896)	Merrill, Frank T.	30-50	
Valen, Herb	Boy Who Could Enter Paintings (1st {std}, 8vo, 60p, color, DJ/3.50)	Little/Brown	(1968)	Perl, Susan	20-30	
Valens, Evan G.	Wild Fire (1st {std}, 4to, [32]p, color, DJ/3.75)	World	1963	Hurd, Clement	30-50	
Valens, Evan G.	Wingfin & Topple (1st {std}, sm4to, [32]p, b/w, DJ/3.50)	World	(1962)	Hurd, Clement	45-70	R
Van Anrooy, Frans	Sea Horse (1st AM {std}, 4to, [32]p, color, DJ/3.75)	Harcourt	1968	Tol, Jaap	30-50	*
Van Der Veer, Judy	To the Rescue (1st {std}, 8vo, 160p, b/w, DJ/4.50)	Harcourt	(1969)	Galdone, Paul	20-35	
Van Derveer, Helen	Little Slam Bang (1st, 8vo, ibds, 38p, color, pep)	Volland	(1928)	Ransom, Fletcher	60-90	
Van Doren, Mark	Dick & Tom in Town (1st, 8vo, 80p, col frn, b/w pl)	Macmillan	1932	Richards, George M.	50-80	R*
Van Doren, Mark	Somebody Came (1st {std}, 8vo, [48]p, fp color, cep, DJ/3.50)	Harlin Quist	(1966)	Fox, Lorraine	40-65	
Van Doren, Mark	Transparent Tree (1st, 4to, ipcb, 87p, 2-color, pep, DJ/1.50)	Henry Holt & Co.	(1940)	Van Doren, Margaret	70-100	R
Van Dresser, Jasmine	Gibby of Clamshell Alley (1st, sm8vo, 378p, p-o, 8pl, pep)	Dodd	1916	Van Dresser, Wm.	25-45	*
Van Dresser, Jasmine	How to Find Happyland (1st, lg8vo, 122p, p-o, AEG, 10cp)	Putnam	1907	Storer, Florence	45-70	
Van Dresser, Jasmine	Jimsey (1st, sm8vo, blue/gilt, 90p, p-o, 4cp)	Rand/McNally	(1925)	Gregory, Dorothy L.	100-150	
Van Dyke, Henry	Blue Flower (1st, sm8vo, 298p, blue/gilt, teg, 3cp by...)	Scribner	1902	Pyle, Howard	30-50	
Van Dyke, Henry	Broken Soldier & Maid of France (1st, 8vo, 66p, teg, blue/gilt, 2 ticp)	Harper	1919	Schoonover, Frank	35-60	
Van Dyke, Henry	Companionable Books (1st, sm8vo, blue/gilt, 391p, cvr by...)	Scribner	1922	Armstrong, Margaret	25-45	
Van Dyke, Henry	Days Off (1st, 12mo, teg, 322p, uncut)	Scribner	1907	Armstrong, Margaret	25-40	
Van Dyke, Henry	First Christmas Tree (1st, 8vo, olive/gilt, 76p, teg, 4pl)	Scribner	1897	Pyle, Howard	70-100	
Van Dyke, Henry	Fisherman's Luck (1st [new ed.], 12mo, 285p, cvr by...)	Scribner	1905	Armstrong, Margaret	25-40	
Van Dyke, Henry	Little Rivers (1st, 12mo, teg, 348p, uncut, blue/gilt)	Scribner	1903	Armstrong, Margaret	25-40	
Van Dyke, Henry	Lost Boy (1st, 12mo, 69p, green/gilt, 3pl by...)	Harper	1914	Wyeth, N.C.	30-50	
Van Dyke, Henry	Spirit of Christmas (1st, sm8vo, 59p, gilt, teg)	Scribner	1905	Armstrong, Margaret	55-80	
Van Dyke, Henry	Story of the Other Wise Man (8vo, gold cl, 87p, designs by...)	Harper	(1907)	Monetti, E.	80-120	
Van Dyke, Henry	Story of the Other Wise Man (1st, lg8vo, teg, 72p, uncut, 8 ticp, pep)	Harper	(1920)	Flanagan, J.R.	55-80	
Van Dyke, Henry	The Mansion (1st, 8vo, 45p, green/gilt, 2 ticp, pep)	Harper	1911	Green, Eliz. S.	35-60	
Van Dyke, Henry	Through South America (1st, 8vo, blue/gilt, 428p, cvr by...)	Crowell	(1912)	Armstrong, Margaret	60-90	
Van Dyke, Henry	Unknown Quantity (1st, 12mo, teg, 370p, uncut)	Scribner	1912	Armstrong, Margaret	25-40	
Van Dyke, John C.	Opal Sea (1st, 12mo, 262p, green/gilt, cvr by...)	Scribner	1906	Armstrong, Margaret	30-50	
Van Dyke, John C.	Studies in Pictures (1st, 12mo, 136p, maroon/gilt)	Scribner	1907	Armstrong, Margaret	25-40	
Van Dyne, Edith	Aunt Jane's Nieces (1st, 12mo, p-o, 325p, 6pl)	Reilly/Britton	(1906)	Nelson, Emile A.	225-325	
Van Dyne, Edith	Aunt Jane's Nieces Abroad (1st, 12mo, green cl, p-o, 5pl)	Reilly/Britton	(1906)	Nelson, Emile A.	180-250	
Van Dyne, Edith	Aunt Jane's Nieces on Vacation (1st, sm8vo, 305p, tan cl, p-o, frn by....)	Reilly/Britton	(1912)	Nelson, Emile A.	100-150	
Van Dyne, Edith	Flying Girl (1st [1], sm8vo, red cl, 232p, 4pl)	Reilly/Britton	(1911)	Nuyttens, Joseph P.	200-300	
Van Dyne, Edith	Flying Girl & her Chum (1st, 12mo, 313p, p-o, red/white, 4pl)	Reilly/Britton	(1912)	Nuyttens, Joseph P.	220-300	
Van Eyssen, Shirley	In the Beginning (1st, folio, gilt, 64p, fp color, cep, DJ)	Harlin Quist	1970	Claveloux, Nicole	70-120	*
Van Gorden, Scott	Pioneer's Hoard (1st, 8vo, 530p, b/w, pep)	Rhodes/McClure	1902	DeLay, H.S.	30-45	
Van Hichtum, Ninke	Afke's Ten (1st, 8vo, 255p, col frn, b/w, DJ/2.00)	Lippincott	(1936)	Van Stockum, Hilda	40-65	
Van Housen, Nita	Poogie & Sibella (1st, 8vo, green cl, 81p, 8 fp color)	Whitman	(1932)	Brock, Emma	30-50	*
Van Leeuwen, Jean	Great Cheese Conspiracy (1st, 8vo, 87p, fp b/w, cep, DJ/3.95)	Random	(1969)	Gobbato, Imero	30-50	
Van Leeuwen, Jean	Timothy's Flower (1st, ob4to, pcb, gilt, [44]p, fp color, cep, DJ/3.50)	Random	(1967)	Barnett, Moneta	30-50	
Van Loon, Hendrik	Adventures & Escapes/Gustavas Vasa (1st {std} lg8vo 136p, col, pep, DJ/2.50)	Dodd	1945	Van Loon, Hendrik	30-50	
Van Loon, Hendrik	Elephant Up a Tree (1st, 8vo, p-o, 206p, 3cp, pep)	Simon/Schuster	1933	Van Loon, Hendrik	50-80	
Van Loon, Hendrik	Folk Songs of Many Lands (1st, 4to, ibds, 96p, color)	Simon/Schuster	1938	Van Loon, Hendrik	30-60	

AUTHOR	TITLE	PUBLISHER	DATE	ARTIST	PRICE	LC
Van Loon, Hendrik	History with a Match (1st, sm4to, 126p, p-o, color)	McKay	1917	Van Loon, Hendrik	55-90	
Van Loon, Hendrik	Message of the Bells (1st {std}, 12mo, ibds, gilt, pep, 16p, color)	(Garden City)	(1942)	Van Loon, Hendrik	55-80	*
Van Loon, Hendrik	Story of Mankind (1st, lg8vo, 479p, gilt, p-o, NM, PPPa)	Boni/Liveright	(1921)	Van Loon, Hendrik	100-150	
Van Loon, Hendrik	Wilbur the Hat (1st, sm4to, ibds, 110p, p-o, fp color, pep)	H.B. Liveright	(1925)	Van Loon, Hendrik	80-120	R
Van Millingen	Constantinople (1st, 4to, 282p, teg, tan/gilt, 63cp)	L: A&C Black	1906	Goble, Warwick	150-250	
Van Rosen, Rosa	Baker's Dozen (1st, 4to, [31]p, 1-color, DJ/1.50)	Appleton-Century	(1946)	Latham, Barbara	40-65	*
Van Sickle, James H.	Magic Key (1st, 12mo, blue cl, 270p, 10 fp b/w)	Houghton	(1931)	Perkins, Lucy F.	30-50	*
Van Sinderen, Adrian	Peter Makebelieve (1st, lg8vo, 65p, 5 fp color)	Yale U. Press	1945	Bacon, Peggy	50-85	
Van Stockum, Hilda	Andries (1st, 8vo, 192p, grey cl, 1 dp color, fp b/w, DJ/2.00)	Viking	1942	Van Stockum, Hilda	30-50	
Van Stockum, Hilda	Angel's Alphabet (1st, lg8vo, [64]p, ipcb, fp b/w, DJ/1.50)	Viking	1948	Van Stockum, Hilda	50-80	
Van Stockum, Hilda	Canadian Summer (1st, 8vo, 190p, fp b/w, DJ/2.50)	Viking	1948	Van Stockum, Hilda	25-45	*
Van Stockum, Hilda	Cottage at Bantry Bay (1st, 8vo, 252p, fp b/w, pep, DJ/2.50)	Viking	1938	Van Stockum, Hilda	30-50	
Van Stockum, Hilda	Day on Skates (1st {std}, ob4to, 40p, 8cp, pep, DJ/2.50, NH)	Harper	1934	Van Stockum, Hilda	100-175	
Van Stockum, Hilda	Francie on the Run (1st, 8vo, 303p, pep, b/w, DJ/2.50)	Viking	1939	Van Stockum, Hilda	30-50	
Van Stockum, Hilda	Friendly Gables (1st, 8vo, 186p, b/w, DJ/2.75)	Viking	(1960)	Van Stockum, Hilda	25-40	
Van Stockum, Hilda	Gerrit & the Organ (1st, 8vo, 178p, col frn, fp b/w, DJ/2.50)	Viking	1943	Van Stockum, Hilda	30-50	
Van Stockum, Hilda	Kersti and St. Nicholas (1st, 4to, 70p, p-o, color, DJ/2.00)	Viking	1940	Van Stockum, Hilda	30-45	
Van Stockum, Hilda	King Oberon's Forest (1st, lg8vo, 151p, fp b/w, pep, DJ/2.75)	Viking	(1957)	Marlin, Brigid	30-45	
Van Stockum, Hilda	Little Old Bear (1st, lg8vo, 32p, b/w, DJ/1.75)	Viking	(1962)	Van Stockum, Hilda	25-45	*
Van Stockum, Hilda	Mogo's Flute (1st, 8vo, 88p, fp b/w, DJ/3.50)	Viking	(1966)	Van Stockum, Hilda	25-40	
Van Stockum, Hilda	Patsy & the Pup (1st, sm8vo, 82p, ipcb, fp b/w, DJ/1.50)	Viking	1950	Van Stockum, Hilda	30-45	
Van Stockum, Hilda	Pegeen (1st, 8vo, 268p, b/w, pep, DJ/2.00)	Viking	1941	Van Stockum, Hilda	30-50	
Van Stockum, Hilda	The Mitchells (1st, 8vo, 246p, b/w, DJ/2.50)	Viking	1945	Van Stockum, Hilda	25-45	
Van Stockum, Hilda	Winged Watchman (1st, 8vo, 204p, b/w, DJ/3.25)	Farrar, Straus	(1962)	Van Stockum, Hilda	25-45	
Van Sutphen, Wm. G.	Golfer's Alphabet (1st, sq8vo, ibds, [58]p, 28pl)	Harper	1898	Frost, A.B.	300-450	
Van Valkenburgh, H.	Myself & I (1st, 12mo, [36]p, color)	Volland	(1918)	Unknown	35-60	*
Van Vrooman, Maria	Ju-Ju and his Friends (1st, lg8vo, 126p, color, pep, DJ/2.00)	Whitman	1939	Wallower, Lucille	25-40	
Van Vrooman, Maria	Shine (1st {std}, 12mo, 50p, ibds, b/w, pep, DJ/1.00)	Dutton	(1939)	Hogan, Inez	50-80	
Vance, Eleanor G.	Tall Book of Fairy Tales (1st, lg4to, ibds, 124p, color, pep, DJ/1.00)	Harper	(1947)	Sharp, William	60-100	
Vance, Louis J.	Bronze Bell (1st, sm8vo, 361p, 4cp)	Dodd	1909	Fisher, Harrison	25-45	
Vance, Marguerite	Beloved Friend (1st, 8vo, 120p, fp b/w, gilt, DJ/3.50)	Holt, Rinehart	(1963)	Weisgard, Leonard	25-45	
Vance, Marguerite	Jeptha and the New People (1st {std}, 8vo, 113p, fp b/w, DJ/2.50)	Dutton	1960	MacLean, Robert	20-35	
Vance, Marguerite	Marta (1st, 16mo, ibds, 56p, 7 fp color, pep)	Harper	1937	Boyle, Mildred	30-45	
Vance, Marguerite	Martha, Daughter of Virginia (1st {std}, 8vo, 190p, col frn, b/w, DJ/2.50)	Dutton	1947	Walker, Nedda	20-30	
Vance, Marguerite	Paula (1st, 8vo, 223p, green cl, uncut, b/w, dep, DJ/2.00)	Dodd	1939	Angelo, Valenti	25-45	
Vance, Marguerite	Star for Hansi (1st {std}, 8vo, ibds, 30p, 2-color, DJ/1.00)	Harper	1936	Paull, Grace	70-100	
Varble, Rachel	Pepys' Boy (1st {std}, 8vo, 253p, b/w, DJ/2.75)	Doubleday	1955	Werth, Kurt	30-50	
Varga, Judy	Janko's Wish (1st, ob8vo, [32]p, fp 3-color, pep, DJ/3.50)	Wm. Morrow	(1969)	Varga, Judy	20-30	
Varga, Judy	Miss Lollipop's Lion (1st, 8vo, unpag, color, DJ/2.75)	Wm. Morrow	1963	Varga, Judy	20-30	
Varga, Judy	Pig in the Parlor (1st, sm4to, [32]p, fp 2-color, pep, DJ/2.75)	Wm. Morrow	1963	Varga, Judy	25-45	
Various	Adventures of Odysseus (1st, 8vo, 227p, green/gilt, teg, 13pl)	Dutton	(1900)	Robinson, Charles	165-220	
Various	Big Book of Train Stories (1st, folio, ibds, unpag, color)	Grosset/Dunlap	1955	Weisgard, Leonard	40-65	
Various	Book of Modern Ballads (sm4to, AEG, gilt, 6 chromos)	Hildesheimer	[1890]	Havers, Alice	80-135	*
Various	Brains & Bravery (1st, 8vo, 398p, green/gilt, 8pl)	L: Chambers	1903	Rackham, Arthur	300-450	
Various	Child's Stamp Book of Old Verses (1st, 8vo, bds, p-o, 12 color stamps)	Duffield	1915	Smith, Jessie W.	350-500	
Various	Golden Fairy Book (1st AM, 8vo, 312p, gilt, b/w)	Appleton	1894	Millar, H.R.	70-100	
Various	Good Dog Book (1st, 8vo, blue cl, 264p, p-o, 5cp)	Houghton	1924	Tenggren, Gustaf	50-80	
Various	Merry Times (sm folio, [48]p, ibds, color & b/w)	L: R. Tuck	[1900]	Wain, Louis	450-600	
Various	Old Old Tales Retold (1st, ob4to, [108]p, blue/gilt, color, pep)	Volland	(1923)	Richardson, F.	120-185	
Various	Peep into Cat-Land (sq8vo, 32p, ibds)	L: Warne	1890	Howell, C.E.	80-120	
Various	Ruby Fairy Book (1st, 8vo, 281p, AEG, gilt, b/w)	L: Hutchinson	(1900)	Millar, H.R.	80-120	
Various	Sleepy-Song Book (1st, 4to, ibds, p-o, 12cp, pep)	L: Harrap	(1915)	Anderson, Anne	100-165	
Various	Sleepy-Song Book (1st AM, 4to, 77p, blue cl, p-o, 12cp, pep)	McBride	1915	Anderson, Anne	120-200	
Various	Sung Under the Silver Umbrella (1st, lg8vo, 211p, red cl, fp b/w)	Macmillan	1935	Lathrop, Dorothy	30-50	
Various	Told Under the Blue Umbrella (1st, lg8vo, 161p, b/w)	Macmillan	1933	Davis, Marguerite	30-50	*
Various	Told Under the Christmas Tree (1st {std}, 8vo, 304p, b/w, DJ/3.00)	Macmillan	1948	Petershams	35-50	
Various	Told Under the Magic Umbrella (1st, lg8vo, 248p, b/w, DJ/2.00)	Macmillan	1939	Jones, Eliz. O.	30-50	
Various	Wayfarer's Love (1st, 8vo, 78p, green/gilt, uncut, cvr by...)	L: Constable	1904	Crane, Walter	70-100	
Various	Whole Family (1st, sm8vo, 314p, blue/gilt, 12pl)	Harper	1908	Stephens, Alice B.	60-90	
Various	Wimp & the Woodle (1st, 4to, blue/gilt bds, 180p, 7cp, pep)	Suttonhouse	1935	Pogany, Willy	250-350	R
Varley, Dimitry	Whirly Bird (1st, 4to, [32]p, color, pep, DJ/3.00)	Knopf	(1961)	Rojankovsky, Feodor	60-90	
Varner, Velma	Animal Frolic (1st, ob8vo, [48]p, b/w, DJ/2.75, NYTBI)	Putnam	(1954)	Sojo, Toba	40-65	*
Varney, Joyce	Half-Time Gypsy (1st {std}, 8vo, gilt, 239p, fp b/w, DJ/4.50)	Bobbs-Merrill	(1968)	Hyman, Trina S.	50-85	
Varney, Joyce	Magic Maker (1st {std}, 8vo, 176p, b/w, DJ/3.95)	Bobbs-Merrill	(1967)	Hyman, Trina S.	40-65	
Vassos, Ruth	Contempo (1st, lg4to, [50]p, woodcuts)	Dutton	1929	Vassos, John	120-180	
Vassos, Ruth	Humanities (1st, lg4to, 140p, 24 fp b/w)	Dutton	1935	Vassos, John	80-120	
Vassos, Ruth	Ultimo (1st, lg8vo, [52]p, ibds, 22pl)	Dutton	1930	Vassos, John	100-165	
Vaughan, Samuel	Who Ever Heard of Kangaroo Eggs? (1st {std}, 4to, unpag, color, DJ/2.75)	Doubleday	(1957)	Weisgard, Leonard	50-80	
Vaughn, Robert	Then & Now (1st, 8vo, 461p, black/gilt, 8pl)	(Minneap)	1900	Russell, Charles M.	250-400	
Vavra, Robert	Tiger Flower (1st AM {std}, 4to, ibds, [45]p, color, DJ/5.95)	Reynal	(1969)	Cowles, Fleur	30-50	
Vaygouny, Margarite	Peter the Stork (1st {std}, 8vo, 109p, fp b/w, DJ/2.25)	Macmillan	1951	Hauman, G.& D.	25-40	*
Veale, E.	Bonny Birds (8vo, wraps, 16p, b/w)	Hubbard	(1896)	Cox, Palmer	70-100	
Veale, E.	Busy Brownies (8vo, [16]p, wraps, b/w)	Hubbard	(1896)	Cox, Palmer	100-160	
Veale, E.	Captivating Stories/Animals (1st, 4to, yellow cl, [96]p, 2-color)	Juvenile Pub.	(1908)	Cox, Palmer	180-280	
Veale, E.	Christmas Pudding (sm8vo, blue cl, p-o, 320p, b/w)	Caldwell	(1900)	Cox, Palmer	65-100	
Veale, E.	First Trousers (8vo, wraps, 32p, b/w)	Hubbard	1897	Cox, Palmer	70-120	
Veale, E.	Fox's Story (8vo, wraps, 32p, b/w)	Hubbard	1897	Cox, Palmer	70-120	
Veale, E.	Funny Foxes (8vo, 32p, wraps, unpag, b/w)	Hubbard	(1896)	Cox, Palmer	140-200	

AUTHOR	TITLE	PUBLISHER	DATE	ARTIST	PRICE	LC
Veale, E.	Jolly Chinee (8vo, wraps, 32p, b/w)	Hubbard	1897	Cox, Palmer	70-120	
Veale, E.	Merry Mice (8vo, wraps, 32p, b/w)	Hubbard	1896	Cox, Palmer	70-120	
Velvin, Ellen	Rataplan, a Rogue Elephant (1st, 12mo, red/gilt, 328p, p-o, 12cp)	Altemus	(1902)	Verbeek, Gustave	50-85	
VerBeck, Frank	Acrobatic Animals (1st, lg ob4to, ibds, [58]p, b/w)	R.H. Russell	1899	VerBeck, Frank	250-400	
VerBeck, Frank	Book of Bears (1st, lg4to, ibds, [85]p, color)	Lippincott	1906	VerBeck, Frank	250-400	
VerBeck, Frank	Hand-Book of Golf for Bears (1st, lg8vo, ipcb, [59]p, 1-color)	R.H. Russell	1900	VerBeck, Frank	425-600	*
VerBeck, Frank	Little Black Sambo & Monkey People (1st, 24mo, 62p, ibds, fp color, pep)	Altemus	(1928)	VerBeck, Frank	120-200	
VerBeck, Frank	Little Black Sambo & the Tiger Kitten (1st, 24mo, 62p, ibds, fp color, pep)	Altemus	(1926)	VerBeck, Frank	120-200	
VerBeck, Frank	The Dumpies (1st, ob12mo, 119p, b/w)	R.H. Russell	1897	VerBeck, Frank	160-225	
VerBeck, Frank	Three Bears (1st, lg4to, [60]p)	R.H. Russell	(1899)	VerBeck, Frank	400-650	
VerBeck, Frank	VerBeck's Bears in Mother Goose-Land (4to, gilt, bds, 3cp)	L: H. Milford	[1900]	VerBeck, Frank	225-300	
Vercel, Roger	In Sight of Eden (1st {std}, 8vo, 254p, DJ/2.50, frn by...)	Harcourt	(1934)	Kent, Rockwell	45-70	
Verdy, Violette	Giselle, or the Willis (1st, 4to, 50p, gilt, b/w, pep, DJ/4.95)	McGraw-Hill	(1970)	Brown, Marcia	50-80	
Verne, Jules	20 Thousand Leagues under the Sea (1st, lg8vo, 495p, p-o, color, WS)	Rand/McNally	(1922)	Winter, Milo	30-50	*
Verne, Jules	20 Thousand Leagues under the Sea (1st, lg8vo, 407p, p-o, 4cp, pep, SC)	Scribner	1925	Aylward, W.J.	70-125	
Verne, Jules	Antarctic Mystery (1st AM, 8vo, 336p, red/silver, 17 fp b/w)	Lippincott	1899	Roux, G.	800-1200	R
Verne, Jules	Dr. Ox's Experiment (1st {std}, 8vo, 100p, b/w, pep, DJ/3.95)	Macmillan	1963	DuBois, W.P.	30-50	
Verne, Jules	Michael Strogoff (1st, lg8vo, p-o, 397p, 9cp, pep, SC)	Scribner	1927	Wyeth, N.C.	200-300	
Verne, Jules	Mysterious Island (1st, lg8vo, 493p, gilt, p-o, 14cp, pep, SC)	Scribner	1918	Wyeth, N.C.	250-350	
Vernede, R.E.	Fair Dominion (1st AM, 8vo, blue cl, teg, 293p, uncut, 12cp)	J. Pott	1911	Cuneo, Cyrus	30-60	
Vetter, Marjorie	Cargo for Jennifer (1st {std}, 8vo, 240p, DJ/3.00, decor by...)	Longmans	1954	Spier, Peter E.	100-165	
Vickers, Vincent C.	Google Book (1st, lg4to, 53p, ibds, p-o, 24cp)	L: Medici	(1931)	Vickers, Vincent C.	350-500	
Viele, Herman K.	Heartbreak Hill (1st, 12mo, 330p, grey cl, p-o, 6cp, pep)	Duffield	1908	Rae, John	30-50	*
Viertel, Violette	Xingu (1st {std}, 8vo, 73p, green cl, 1-color, DJ/2.75)	Macmillan	(1959)	Kuskin, Karla	30-50	
Vildrac, Charles	Rose Island (1st, ob8vo, 100p, 1-color, DJ/3.75)	Lothrop, Lee	(1957)	Legrand, Edy	25-40	
Vimar, Auguste	Curly-Haired Hen (1st, sm4to, 95p, p-o, b/w)	D. Fitzgerald	(1914)	Vimar, Auguste	30-45	
Vincent, Kitty	Gin & Ginger (1st, 8vo, 145p, col frn, 19 fp b/w)	L: Bodley Head	1927	Fish, Anne H.	40-65	
Vinson, Pauline	Willie Goes to the Seashore (1st {std}, 4to, [32]p, color, cep, DJ/2.25)	Macmillan	1954	Vinson, Pauline	50-80	
Vinton, Iris	Flying Ebony (1st, sm8vo, 289p, olive cl, b/w, DJ/2.50)	Dodd	1947	Simont, Marc	30-50	
Vinton, Iris	Look Out for Pirates! (1st, lg8vo, ibds, 63p, fp color, pep, DJ/1.95)	Beginner Books	1961	Vestal, Herman B.	50-85	
Viorst, Judith	I'll Fix Anthony (1st, ob8vo, [32]p, color, DJ/3.50)	Harper	(1969)	Lobel, Arnold	30-40	
Viorst, Judith	Sunday Morning (1st, ob8vo, [32]p, color, DJ/2.95)	Harper	(1968)	Knight, Hilary	30-50	
Viorst, Judith	Try It Again, Sam (1st, lg8vo, [39]p, 2-color, DJ/3.75)	Lothrop, Lee	(1970)	Galdone, Paul	20-35	
Vipont, Elfrida	Bless this Day (1st AM {std}, lg8vo, 95p, color, DJ/3.25)	Harcourt	(1958)	Jones, Harold	40-65	
Vipont, Elfrida	Elephant and the Bad Baby (1st, ob4to, [32]p, color, DJ)	L: Hamilton	1969	Briggs, Raymond	70-100	
Vipont, Elfrida	Family at Dowbiggins (1st {std}, 8vo, 253p, b/w, DJ/2.75)	Bobbs-Merrill	(1955)	Freeman, Terry	25-40	
Vipont, Elfrida	Lark in the Morn (1st AM, 8vo, 234p, b/w, DJ/2.50)	Bobbs-Merrill	(1951)	James, Sandra	30-50	
Vipont, Elfrida	Lark on the Wing (1st AM, 8vo, 255p, b/w, DJ/2.50, CgM)	Bobbs-Merrill	1951	Freeman, Terry	45-70	
Vivienne	Hop, Skippy & Jump (1st, 12mo, ipcb, [32]p, color, pep)	Whitman	1947	Unknown	20-25	
Vogel, Amos	How Little Lori Visited Times Square (1st {std}, ob8vo [32]p col, DJ/2.95)	Harper	(1963)	Sendak, Maurice	350-500	
Vogel, Ilse-Margret	Don't Be Scared Book (1st {std}, ob8vo, [48]p, fp b/w, cep, DJ/2.95)	Atheneum	1964	Vogel, Ilse-Margret	20-35	*
Vogel, Ilse-Margret	Willy, Willy, Don't Be Silly (1st {std}, sq4to, [38]p, 1-color, DJ/3.50)	Atheneum	1965	Vogel, Ilse-Margret	30-50	
Voight, Virginia F.	Apple Tree Cottage (1st, sm8vo, 157p, green cl, b/w, cep, DJ/2.25)	Holiday House	(1949)	Wilkin, Eloise B.	50-80	
Voight, Virginia F.	Cuff, a Baby Bear (1st, 8vo, 64p, 1-color, DJ)	Putnam	(1969)	Tamer, Salem	30-50	
Voight, Virginia F.	House in Robin Lane (1st, sm8vo, 220p, yellow, cl, b/w, DJ/2.50)	Holiday House	(1951)	Martinez, Jean	25-45	
Voight, Virginia F.	Lions in the Barn (1st, sm8vo, 95p, yellow cl, b/w, pep, DJ/2.25)	Holiday House	1955	Wiese, Kurt	25-45	
Voight, Virginia F.	Rolling Show (1st, 8vo, 188p, red cl, b/w, cep, DJ/2.50)	Holiday House	1956	Wiese, Kurt	30-50	
Voight, Virginia F.	Zeke & the Fisher-Cat (1st, sm8vo, 201p, red cl, b/w, pep, DJ/2.50)	Holiday House	(1953)	McChesney, Harry	25-40	
Voltaire, J.F.	Candide (1st, 8vo, 111p, maroon/gilt, b/w, pep)	Random	1930	Kent, Rockwell	50-80	
Von Gottschalck, O.	Innocent Industries (1st, 4to, 100p, ibds, [50]p, b/w)	R.H. Russell	1903	Von Gottschalck	170-240	*
Von Hutten, Bettina	One Way Out (1st, 8vo, 99p, p-o, teg, lavender cl, 5cp)	Dodd	1906	Fisher, Harrison	50-80	
Von Juchen, Aurel	Holy Night (1st AM {std}, narrow ob4to, [29]p, ibds, color, DJ/4.95)	Atheneum	1968	Piatti, Celestino	30-50	*
Von Volkmann, Richard	Rusted Knight and other Stories (1st, lg8vo, 135p, silhouettes)	Humphries	1933	Landsberger, Marte	50-80	*
Voorhoeve, Rudolf	Tilio, Boy of Papua (1st, 8vo, 219p, col frn, DJ/1.75)	Lippincott	(1937)	Van Stockum, Hilda	30-50	
Vorse, Mary E.	Grubby Gets Clean (1st, 8vo, ipcb, [41]p, 1-color, cep, DJ/1.00)	W.R. Scott	1943	Blaisdell, Elinore	30-50	
Vorse, Mary E.	Skinny Gets Fat (1st, 8vo, ipcb, [41]p, 1-color, pep, DJ/1.00)	W.R. Scott	1940	Hogan, Inez	40-65	
Vorse, Mary E.	Wakey Goes to Bed (1st, 8vo, ipcb, [41]p, brown illus, cep, DJ/1.00)	W.R. Scott	1941	Hogan, Inez	40-65	
Vorse, Mary Heaton	Ninth Man (1st, sm8vo, 80p, 2cp, 2pl)	Harper	1920	Craig, Frank	40-65	*
Vorse, Mary Heaton	Very Little Person (1st, 12mo, 163p, green/gilt, 8pl)	Houghton	1911	O'Neill, Rose	40-65	
Voss, Richard	Sigurd Eckdal's Bride (1st, 12mo, 235p, 4pl)	Little/Brown	1900	Schoonover, Frank	30-50	
Vredenburg, Edric	Curly Heads & Long Legs (1st, 4to, 140p, ibds, color)	L: R. Tuck	[1914]	Cowham, Hilda	200-300	
Vredenburg, Edric	Golden Locks & Pretty Frocks (1st, 8vo, 136p, ibds, p-o, 12cp)	L: R. Tuck	[1914]	Richardson, Agnes	250-350	
Vredenburg, Edric	My Book of Favorite Fairy Tales (1st, 4to, 133p, ibds, 12cp)	Tuck/McKay	[1920]	Harbour, Jennie	120-170	*
Vredenburg, Edric	Old Fairy Tales (lg8vo, ibds, 104p, 8cp)	L: R. Tuck	[1912]	Brundage/Bowley	150-240	
Vredenburg, Edric	Tinker Tailor (4to, 136p, p-o, 12cp)	L: R. Tuck	[1914]	Aldin, Cecil	900-1500	
Vredenburg, Edric	Tinker, Tailor (1st, sm4to, 136p, bds, p-o, 12cp)	L: R. Tuck	[1914]	Wain, Louis	900-1200	
Waber, Bernard	Anteater Named Arthur (1st {std}, 4to, 46p, fp 2-color, DJ/3.25)	Houghton	1967	Waber, Bernard	40-65	R
Waber, Bernard	Cheese (1st, 24mo, ipcb, [32]p, fp 1-color, DJ/1.50)	Houghton	1967	Waber, Bernard	30-50	
Waber, Bernard	Firefly Named Torchy (1st {std}, 4to, [29]p, color, DJ/4.95)	Houghton	1970	Waber, Bernard	30-50	
Waber, Bernard	House on E. 88th Street (1st, 4to, 48p, fp 3-color, DJ/3.00)	Houghton	1962	Waber, Bernard	40-65	R
Waber, Bernard	How to Go about Laying an Egg (1st, 12mo, 32p, color, DJ/2.50)	Houghton	1963	Waber, Bernard	25-40	
Waber, Bernard	Just Like Abraham Lincoln (1st, 4to, 40p, fp color, pep, DJ/3.25)	Houghton	1964	Waber, Bernard	30-50	R
Waber, Bernard	Lorenzo (1st, 12mo, [47]p, fp 1-color, DJ/1.95)	Houghton	1961	Waber, Bernard	30-45	
Waber, Bernard	Lovable Lyle (1st {std}, 4to, 48p, color, DJ/3.95)	Houghton	1969	Waber, Bernard	40-65	*
Waber, Bernard	Lyle & the Birthday Party (1st, 4to, 48p, fp color, DJ/3.25)	Houghton	1966	Waber, Bernard	40-65	
Waber, Bernard	Lyle, Lyle, Crocodile (1st, 4to, 48p, color, DJ/3.25)	Houghton	1965	Waber, Bernard	40-65	
Waber, Bernard	Rich Cat, Poor Cat (1st, 4to, 48p, fp color, DJ/3.25)	Houghton	1963	Waber, Bernard	40-65	
Waber, Bernard	Rose for Mr. Bloom (1st {std}, lg8vo, 31p, color, DJ/3.25)	Houghton	1968	Waber, Bernard	30-50	

AUTHOR	TITLE	PUBLISHER	DATE	ARTIST	PRICE	LC
Waber, Bernard	You Look Ridiculous (1st, 8vo, 32p, color, DJ/3.25)	Houghton	1966	Waber, Bernard	30-50	
Waddell, Helen (tr)	Beasts and Saints (1st AM {std}, sm8vo, 151p, gilt, fp b/w, DJ/2.50)	Henry Holt & Co.	(1934)	Gibbings, Robert	45-65	
Waddell, Helen (tr)	Beasts and Saints (1st, 8vo, 151p, red/gilt, 6pl, DJ)	L: Constable	1934	Gibbings, Robert	80-125	
Wade, Blanche E.	Ant Ventures (1st, sm8vo, green cl, p-o, 246p, 5cp, pep)	Rand/McNally	(1924)	Cady, Harrison	80-130	
Wade, Blanche E.	Garden in Pink (1st, 8vo, 201p, p-o, blue cl, 12pl)	McClurg	1905	Perkins, Lucy F.	50-80	
Wade, Blanche E.	Magic Stone (1st, lg8vo, 254p, p-o, gilt, 7cp)	NY: Sully	1917	Carlson, George	50-85	
Wadsworth, Wallace	Modern Story Book (1st, lg4to, 124p, p-o, color)	Rand/McNally	(1931)	Eger, Ruth C.	100-150	
Wagenknecht, Ed	Fireside Book/Yuletide Tales (1st {std}, 8vo, 593p, gilt, color, DJ/3.75)	Bobbs-Merrill	(1948)	Chappell, Warren	25-45	
Wagner, Richard	Parsifal (1st, 4to, [192]p, grey/gilt, 16 ticp, pep)	L: Harrap	(1912)	Pogany, Willy	300-500	
Wagner, Richard	Parsifal (1st AM, 4to, maroon/gilt, teg, 16 ticp, pep)	Crowell	(1912)	Pogany, Willy	275-450	
Wagner, Richard	Rhinegold & the Valkyrie (1st, 4to, 160p, gilt, 34 ticp, pep)	L: Heinemann	1910	Rackham, Arthur	400-600	
Wagner, Richard	Rhinegold & the Valkyrie (1st AM, lg8vo, 160p, 34 ticp, pep)	Doubleday/Page	1910	Rackham, Arthur	350-500	
Wagner, Richard	Siegfried... (1st, sm4to, 182p, tan/gilt, 30 ticp, pep)	L: Heinemann	1911	Rackham, Arthur	300-500	
Wagner, Richard	Siegfried... (1st AM, sm4to, 182p, blue/gilt bds, 30 ticp)	Doubleday/Page	1911	Rackham, Arthur	250-400	
Wagner, Richard	Tale of Lohengrin (1st AM, 4to, grey/gilt, teg, 8 ticp)	Crowell	(1913)	Pogany, Willy	250-350	
Wagner, Richard	Tale of Lohengrin (1st, 4to, brown/gilt, 8 ticp, pep)	L: Harrap	[1913]	Pogany, Willy	250-400	
Wagner, Richard	Tannhauser (1st AM, lg8vo, black/gilt, unpag, 16 ticp)	Brentano's	[1911]	Pogany, Willy	250-400	
Wagner, Richard	Tannhauser (1st, 4to, [128]p, grey/gilt, 16 ticp)	L: Harrap	(1911)	Pogany, Willy	300-500	
Wagstaff, Hester	Doings of Dicky Daw (1st, sm4to, [45]p, ibds, fp 2-color, DJ/1.50)	Coward	(1940)	Wagstaff, Hester	30-45	
Wahl, Jan	Beast Book (1st, 16mo, [32]p, b/w, DJ/1.95)	Harper	(1964)	Eichel, E.W.	25-45	
Wahl, Jan	Cabbage Moon (1st {std}, sm ob8vo, [32]p, color, DJ/3.50)	Holt, Rinehart	(1965)	Adams, Adrienne	40-65	
Wahl, Jan	Christmas in the Forest (1st {std}, ob4to, [32]p, 1-color, DJ/3.50)	Macmillan	(1967)	Schick, Eleanor	30-50	
Wahl, Jan	Cobweb Castle (1st {std}, 8vo, [30]p, color, DJ/3.95)	Holt, Rinehart	(1968)	Gorey, Edward	60-90	
Wahl, Jan	Doctor Rabbit (1st {std}, ob8vo, [48]p, color, DJ/4.95)	Delacorte Pr.	(1970)	Parnall, Peter	40-65	
Wahl, Jan	Furious Flycycle (1st {std}, 8vo, 114p, blue cl, b/w, DJ/3.50)	Delacorte Pr.	(1968)	Krahn, Fernando	25-40	
Wahl, Jan	Hello, Elephant (1st {std}, ob12mo, ipcb, [32]p, fp 2-color, cep, DJ/2.50)	Holt, Rinehart	(1964)	Ardizzone, Edward	60-90	
Wahl, Jan	Howards Go Sledding (1st {std}, ob8vo, [28]p, 1-color, DJ/2.95)	Holt, Rinehart	(1964)	Johnson, John	25-40	
Wahl, Jan	May Horses (1st {std}, sq8vo, [41]p, fp color, pep, DJ/4.95)	Delacorte Pr.	(1969)	Lent, Blair	30-50	
Wahl, Jan	Pleasant Fieldmouse (1st, 8vo, 65p, ibds, b/w, cep, DJ/2.95)	Harper	(1964)	Sendak, Maurice	150-200	
Wahl, Jan	Pocahontas in London (1st {std}, 4to, [40]p, color, DJ/4.50)	Delacorte Pr.	(1967)	Alcorn, John	30-50	
Wahl, Jan	Prince Who was a Fish (1st {std}, 4to, 62p, color, DJ/4.95)	Simon/Schuster	(1970)	Jacques, Robin	25-45	
Wahl, Jan	Push Kitty (1st, 4to, [32]p, ibds, color, DJ/3.50)	Harper	(1968)	Williams, Garth	40-60	
Wahl, Jan	Rickety Rackety Rooster (1st {std}, sq8vo, [39]p, color, DJ/3.95)	Simon/Schuster	(1968)	Johnson, John	20-35	
Wahl, Jan	Runaway Jonah... (1st {std}, 8vo, 42p, ibds, 2-color, DJ/3.95)	Macmillan	1968	Shulevitz, Uri	30-50	
Wahl, Jan	The Fishermen (1st {std}, 8vo, [47]p, color, DJ/4.25)	Norton	(1969)	McCully, Emily	40-65	
Wahl, Jan	The Muffletumps (1st {std}, ob8vo, [46]p, fp 1-color, dep, DJ/3.50)	Holt, Rinehart	(1966)	Ardizzone, Edward	45-70	
Wahl, Jan	Wolf of My Own (1st {std}, ob4to, [32]p, fp color, DJ/4.95)	Macmillan	(1969)	Hoban, Lillian	30-45	
Wahl, Jan	Wonderful Kite (1st {std}, 4to, 92p, color, DJ/4.95)	Delacorte Pr.	(1970)	Shulevitz, Uri	30-45	
Wahlenberg, Anna	Old Swedish Fairy Tales (1st, lg8vo, p-o, 296p, pep, 8cp)	Penn	1925	Berkowitz, Jeannette	60-90	
Wahlenberg, Anna	Swedish Fairy Tales (1st, sm8vo, 158p, 14pl)	McClurg	1901	Armstrong, Helen	60-90	*
Wahn, J. & G.	Edgar, Runaway Elephant (1st, 4to, ipcb, [38]p, color, DJ/2.00)	W.R. Scott	(1941)	Wahn, J. & G.	60-100	
Wain, Louis	Big Dogs Little Dogs Cats & Kittens (1st, folio, ibds, [36]p, gilt, color)	L/NY: R. Tuck	[1900]	Wain, Louis	700-1000	
Wain, Louis	Cats at Play (folio, [12]p, color)	L: Blackie	[1918]	Wain, Louis	250-450	
Wain, Louis	Daddy Cat (1st AM, sm4to, 36p, ibds, color)	Dodge	(1915)	Wain, Louis	500-750	
Wain, Louis	Flossy & Fluffy (narrow 4to, wraps, shape book, [14]p, fp 2-color)	L: Valentine	(1919)	Wain, Louis	500-700	
Wain, Louis	Happy Hours with Louis Wain (4to, bds, p-o, 6 ticp)	L: J.F. Shaw	(1913)	Wain, Louis	600-900	
Wain, Louis	In Cat & Dog Land (lg4to, 36p, ibds, 12pl)	L: R. Tuck	[1900]	Wain, Louis	500-800	
Wain, Louis	Kits and Cats (folio, wraps, 4 fp color)	L: R. Tuck	(1919)	Wain, Louis	600-850	
Wain, Louis	Louis Wain Kitten Book (sq16mo, 87p, tan cl, fp color)	L: A. Treherne	1904	Wain, Louis	700-900	
Wain, Louis	Louis Wain's Baby Picture Book (1st, 4to, ibds, unpag, b/w)	L: Clarke	1903	Wain, Louis	250-450	
Wain, Louis	Louis Wain's Cats & Dogs (1st, folio, [28]p, ibds, color)	L: R. Tuck	(1903)	Wain, Louis	700-900	
Wain, Louis	Louis Wain's Children's Book (1st, 4to, 95p, ibds, 17pl)	L: Hutchinson	[1923]	Wain, Louis	400-650	
Wain, Louis	Louis Wain's Father Christmas (8vo, ibds, p-o, 5 ticp)	L: J.F. Shaw	(1912)	Wain, Louis	450-650	
Wain, Louis	Louis Wain's Painting Book (4to, bds, p-o, 4 ticp)	L: J. Shaw	[1910]	Wain, Louis	800-1200	
Wain, Louis	Music in Pussytown (ob4to, wraps, [12]p, color)	L: R. Tuck	[1915]	Wain, Louis	900-1300	
Wain, Louis	Nursery Cats (4to, ibds, 6 fp color)	L: R. Tuck	[1908]	Wain, Louis	700-1000	
Wain, Louis	Pussies & Puppies (1st, 4to, ibds, 96p, color & b/w)	L: Partridge	[1899]	Wain, Louis	800-1200	
Wain, Louis	Somebody's Pussies (4to, ibds, 13cp)	L: R. Tuck	[1920]	Wain, Louis	1000-1500	
Walcott, Earle A.	Blindfolded (1st, sm8vo, tan cl, 400p, 8pl)	Bobbs-Merrill	(1906)	Stephens, Alice B.	30-50	
Wald, Lilian D.	Windows on Henry Street (1st, 8vo, 348p, b/w)	Little/Brown	1934	Daugherty, James	60-100	
Waldeck, JoBesse	Exploring the Jungle (1st, 8vo, 56p, p-o, color, pep)	D.C. Heath	1941	Yap, Weda	25-40	*
Waldeck, JoBesse	Jungle Journey (1st, 8vo, 255p, b/w, pep, DJ/2.50)	Viking	1946	Wiese, Kurt	30-45	
Waldeck, Theodore	Jamba the Elephant (1st, 8vo, 224p, b/w, DJ/2.00)	Viking	1942	Wiese, Kurt	25-45	
Waldeck, Theodore	Lions on the Hunt (1st, 8vo, 251p, b/w, DJ/2.00)	Viking	1942	Wiese, Kurt	30-45	*
Waldeck, Theodore	On Safari (1st, 8vo, 208p, b/w, DJ/2.50)	Viking	1940	Wiese, Kurt	30-45	
Waldeck, Theodore	White Panther (1st, 8vo, 193p, b/w, pep, DJ/2.00)	Viking	1941	Wiese, Kurt	80-125	
Walden, Jane B.	Igloo (1st, 8vo, 211p, col frn, b/w)	Putnam	1931	Thorne, Diana	30-50	
Waldman, Dorothy	Goomer (1st {std}, 8vo, [64]p, b/w, DJ/1.75)	Ariel	(1952)	Nichols, Marie C.	40-65	
Waldstein, Henry F.	We Three Kings (1st {std}, ob4to, ibds, [23]p, color)	Harper	(1944)	Rey, Hans A.	80-120	
Walford, Lucy B.	Little Legacy (1st, 12mo, blue cl, 344p, teg, frn by...)	Herbert Stone	1899	Oakley, Violet	80-120	
Walker, Augusta	Back-Fence Story (1st {std}, 8vo, 145p, bds, gilt, b/w, DJ/4.95)	Knopf	1967	Martin, David S.	30-50	
Walker, Barbara	Dancing Palm Tree (1st, 8vo, 112p, fp b/w, pep, DJ/3.95)	Parents Mag. Pr.	(1968)	Siegl, Helen	25-40	*
Walker, Barbara	Hilili and Dilili (1st, 4to, 32p, color, DJ/2.95)	Follett	(1965)	Barss, William	30-45	
Walker, Barbara	Mouse and the Elephant (1st, 4to, [36]p, color, pep, DJ/3.50)	Parents Mag. Pr.	(1969)	McCully, Emily	40-65	*
Walker, Barbara	Pigs and Pirates (1st, ob4to, [46]p, fp color, DJ/4.95)	NY: David White	1969	Berson, Harold	30-45	
Walker, Barbara	Round Sultan & the Straight Answer (1st, 4to, ibds, [38]p, color, DJ/3.95)	Parents Mag. Pr.	(1970)	Henstra, Friso	30-45	
Walker, Barbara	Stargazer to the Sultan (1st, sm4to, [41]p, ipcb, color, pep, DJ/3.50)	Parents Mag. Pr.	1967	Low, Joseph	30-50	
Walker, Dugald S.	Dream Boats (1st, lg8vo, 219p, 4cp, 16pl, pep)	Doubleday/Page	1918	Walker, Dugald S.	125-200	

AUTHOR: 220

AUTHOR	TITLE	PUBLISHER	DATE	ARTIST	PRICE	LC
Walker, Dugald S.	Sally's ABC (1st, 4to, [58]p, buckram, 2-color, pep)	Harcourt	1929	Walker, Dugald S.	120-160	R
Walker, Joseph	How they Carried the Mail (1st, lg8vo, 305p, 3cp, 8pl)	Sears	(1930)	Dobias, Frank	40-65	
Walker, Margaret C.	Lady Hollyhock & her Friends (1st, 8vo, 153p, color)	Baker/Taylor	(1906)	Hunt, Mary I.	80-120	*
Walker, Margaret C.	Tales Come True & Tales Made New (1st, 8vo, 149p, p-o, color)	Baker/Taylor	1910	Orwig, Louise	35-50	
Walker, Paul E.	Peter Panda (1st, 8vo, 47p, 1-color, pep, DJ/1.50)	Nelson	(1940)	Kalab, Theresa	25-40	
Wallace, Dillon	Fur Trail Adventurers (1st, sm8vo, green cl, 320p, 7pl)	McClurg	1915	Deming, Edwin W.	45-70	
Wallace, Edna K.	Quest of the Dream (1st, 12mo, teg, 292p, blue/gilt)	Putnam	1913	Armstrong, Margaret	30-50	
Wallace, Lew	Chariot Race of Ben-Hur (1st, lg8vo, gilt, 133p, uncut, teg, 4cp)	Harper	1908	Ivanowski, Sigismond	40-60	
Wallace, Lew	First Christmas (1st, 8vo, 108p, teg, lavender/gilt, 4 tipl)	Harper	1902	(Photos)	40-65	
Wallace, Lew	Wooing of Malkatoon (1st, lg8vo, green/gilt, 168p, teg)	Harper	1898	DuMond	50-80	
Wallace, Susan A.	Along the Bosphorus (1st, sm8vo, teg, uncut, 383p, cvr by...)	Rand/McNally	1898	Denslow, W.W.	35-60	*
Waller, Mary Ella	Daughter of the Rich (1st, sm8vo, p-o, 296p, 5cp, pep)	Little/Brown	1924	Green, Eliz. S.	35-60	*
Wallis, I. Henry	Cloud Kingdom (1st, 12mo, green/gilt, 174p, teg, 18pl, pep)	L: John Lane	(1905)	Robinson, Charles	200-300	
Wallower, Lucille	Roll of Drums (1st, 8vo, 111p, col frn, pep, DJ/2.00)	Whitman	1945	Wallower, Lucille	50-75	
Walpole, Hugh	Jeremy (1st AM, 8vo, 304p, col frn, b/w, pep)	Doran	(1919)	Shepard, Ernest H.	30-50	
Walsh, Chad	Nellie & her Flying Crocodile (1st {std}, 8vo, 179p, b/w, DJ/2.50)	Harper	(1956)	Simont, Marc	30-50	
Walsh, John	The Truants (1st AM, 8vo, 80p, b/w, DJ/2.95)	Rand/McNally	(1968)	Ardizzone, Edward	50-75	
Walsh, Mary R.	Mullingar Heifer (1st {std}, 8vo, [61]p, b/w, pep, DJ/1.75)	Knopf	1946	Pitz, Henry C.	40-65	
Walsh, Mary R.	Widow Woman and her Goat (1st {std}, lg8vo, [64]p, b/w, DJ/1.75)	Knopf	(1949)	Pitz, Henry C.	20-35	
Walter, Eleanor D.	Bugs (1st, lg4to, wraps, [16]p, color)	Whitman	1931	Roberts, Helen M.	40-60	
Walters, George	Steam Shovel that Wouldn't Eat Dirt (1st, sm4to, ibds, [31]p, col, DJ/1.50)	Aladdin	(1948)	Duvoisin, Roger	50-80	*
Walters, L.	Year's at the Spring (1st, sm4to, 128p, green/gilt, 12cp, 12pl, cep)	L: Harrap	1920	Clarke, Harry	280-400	
Walters, L.	Year's at the Spring (1st AM, 4to, 128p, 12cp, 12pl)	Brentano's	(1920)	Clarke, Harry	200-300	
Walters, Marguerite	City-Country ABC (1st {std}, sm8vo, unpag, color, DJ/2.95)	Doubleday	(1966)	Ohlsson, Ib	30-45	
Walters, Marguerite	Real Santa Claus (1st, 4to, 31p, ibds, color, DJ/1.00)	Lothrop, Lee	1950	Wohlberg, Meg	25-40	
Walters, Marguerite	Up & Down and All Around (1st {std}, lg4to, unpag, 2-color, DJ/2.95)	F. Watts	1960	Suba, Susanne	40-60	
Walton, Isaac	Compleat Angler (1st, 4to, green/gilt, teg, 12cp, pep)	L: Harrap	(1931)	Rackham, Arthur	250-350	
Walton, Isaac	Compleat Angler (1st AM, sm4to, 224p, gilt, teg, 12cp, pep)	McKay	[1931]	Rackham, Arthur	200-300	
Warburg, Sandol	Curl up Small (1st, sq8vo, 32p, fp 3-color, DJ/3.00)	Houghton	1964	Hyman, Trina S.	40-70	
Warburg, Sandol	Hooray for Us (1st {std}, 24mo, ipcb, 48p, fp b/w, DJ/1.95)	Houghton	1970	Chwast, Jacqueline	25-40	*
Warburg, Sandol	Keep it Like a Secret (1st {std}, ob4to, 32p, color, DJ/3.00)	Little/Brown	(1961)	Chermayeff, Ivan	30-50	
Warburg, Sandol	My Very Own Special Particular & Personal Cat (1st, 8vo, 40p, DJ/3.25)	Houghton	1963	Charlip, Remy	70-125	
Warburg, Sandol (adap)	St. George and the Dragon (1st, lg8vo, 132p, fp 1-color, cep, DJ/4.50)	Houghton	1963	Baynes, Pauline	60-100	R*
Ward, Grace	In the Miz (1st, lg8vo, blue cl, p-o, 159p, 8cp)	Little/Brown	1904	Atwood, Clara E.	90-160	
Ward, Harry F.	In Place of Profit (1st, 8vo, green cl, 460p, gilt, woodcuts)	Scribner	1933	Ward, Lynd	40-60	
Ward, Lynd	Biggest Bear (1st, 4to, 84p, beige cl, b/w, DJ/2.75, CM)	Houghton	1952	Ward, Lynd	200-300	R
Ward, Lynd	God's Man (1st, 8vo, woodcuts, ipcb, 293p, cep)	Cape/Smith	(1929)	Ward, Lynd	200-320	
Ward, Lynd	Mad-Man's Drum (1st, 8vo, ipcb, [257]p, woodcuts, cep)	Cape/Smith	(1930)	Ward, Lynd	200-300	
Ward, Lynd	Nic of the Woods (1st {std}, 4to, 95p, fp 1-color, cep, DJ/3.75)	Houghton	1965	Ward, Lynd	40-65	R
Ward, Lynd	Vertigo (1st, 8vo, 231p, woodcuts)	Random	1937	Ward, Lynd	200-300	
Ward, Lynd	Wild Pilgrimage (1st, lg8vo, [190]p, p-o, woodcuts)	Smith/Haas	1932	Ward, Lynd	180-250	
Ward, Marion	Boat Children of Canton (1st {std}, sm4to, 92p, color, pep, DJ/2.00)	McKay	(1944)	Sewell, Helen	40-65	
Ward, Mrs. H.	Coryston Family (1st, sm8vo, red/gilt, 328p, 8pl)	Harper	1913	Green, Eliz. S.	50-80	
Ward, Mrs. H.	Milly & Olly (1st, 8vo, 302p, p-o, 8pl, pep)	Doubleday/Page	1907	Hallock, Ruth M.	30-50	
Ward, Mrs. H.	Milly and Olly (2nd ed., 8vo, 352p, b/w)	L: T.F. Unwin	1907	Pogany, Willy	70-120	*
Ward, Nanda	Black Sombrero (1st {std}, 12mo, grey cl, unpag, color, pep, DJ/1.75)	Ariel	(1952)	Ward, Lynd	45-60	
Ward, Nanda	Hi, Tom (1st, sm4to, 48p, tan cl, 3-color, DJ/3.00)	Hastings House	(1962)	Ward, Lynd	25-45	
Ward, Nanda	High Flying Hat (1st, 8vo, [56]p, color, pep, DJ/2.50)	Ariel	(1956)	Ward, Lynd	40-70	
Warde, Margaret	Holiday Book (1st, 8vo, 208p, 5pl)	Little/Brown	1925	Peck, Anne M.	25-40	
Ware, Leon	Crazy Dog (1st, lg8vo, 67p, b/w, DJ/1.50)	Whittlesey	(1944)	Dennis, Morgan	30-50	
Ware, Richard D.	In the Woods and on the Shore (1st, 8vo, 279p, photos, frn by...)	L.C. Page	1908	Bull, Charles L.	40-60	*
Waring, P. Alston	Peacock Country (1st, lg8vo, 100p, bds, 2-color, DJ/3.00)	John Day	(1948)	Bock, Vera	20-30	
Warner, Anne	Susan Clegg & the Man in the House (1st, 12mo, 279p, grey cl, 4pl)	Little/Brown	1907	Stephens, Alice B.	25-40	
Warner, Anne	Taming of Amorette (1st, sm8vo, 210p, green/gilt, 6pl)	Little/Brown	1915	Underwood, C.F.	20-25	
Warner, Anne	The Panther (1st, 8vo, teg, uncut, 91p, col frn, 3pl)	Small/Maynard	1908	Thomas, Paul K.	30-50	
Warner, Anne	When Woman Proposes (1st, sm8vo, 158p, teg, purple cl, 4cp)	Little/Brown	1911	Ditzler, C. Weber	25-40	
Warner, Charles D.	Backlog Studies (1st, 12mo, 257p, title page by...)	Houghton	1899	Rogers, Bruce	30-50	
Warner, Gertrude	Boxcar Children (1st, 8vo, blue/gilt, 146p, p-o, 4cp)	Rand/McNally	(1924)	Gregory, Dorothy L.	60-95	
Warner, Gertrude	World on a Farm (1st {std}, 12mo, 83p, wraps, b/w)	Friendship Pr.	1931	Adams, Adrienne	60-90	
Warner, Harriette	Story Song Book (1st, 4to, ibds, 38p, p-o, 10 fp color)	Chi: Cook	(1912)	Ross, M.T.	120-170	
Warner, J. (ed.)	Golden Book of Poetry (1st, lg4to, 67p, ibds, color)	Simon/Schuster	(1949)	Elliott, Gertrude	100-175	
Warner, Sunny B.	Tobias & his Big Red Satchel (1st 4to ibds [32]p fp 1-color, dep, DJ/3.00)	Knopf	(1961)	Warner, Sunny	30-45	*
Warner, Susan	Wide, Wide World (1st, 8vo, 592p, 6pl)	Fenno	(1904)	Dunton, W. Herbert	30-45	
Warren, Carro F.	Girl of the Governor (1st, 8vo, 407p, 9pl, cvr by...)	Scribner	1900	Armstrong, Margaret	35-60	
Warren, Carro F.	Little Betty Marigold... (1st, 12mo, 107p, 14 color)	C.M. Clark	1907	Goldsmith, Wallace	25-40	*
Warren, Geoffrey	Elixir of Life (1st, 12mo, 17p, green bds, p-o, 1-color)	Dublin: Jameson	1925	Clarke, Harry	500-800	
Warren, Ina R.	In Cupid's Court (1st, 12mo, 79p, white/gilt, fp b/w)	R.H. Russell	1900	Unknown	75-100	*
Warren, Ina R.	Mother Love (1st, 8vo, 166p, gilt, teg, p-o, col frn, pep)	Jacobs	(1911)	Boyer, Jane A.	30-50	
Warren, Maude R.	Little Pioneers (1st, 12mo, 253p, b/w, pep)	Rand/McNally	(1916)	Perkins, Lucy F.	30-50	
Warren, Maude R.	Manabozho the Great White Rabbit (1st, sm8vo, 133p, 8cp)	Rand/McNally	(1918)	Carr, Warner	40-65	
Warren, Maude R.	Mother Goose & her Friends (1st, lg8vo, 309p, p-o, pep, 12 ticp)	Doran	(1923)	Federer, Charles A.	65-100	
Warren, Maude R.	Robin Hood & his Merry Men (1st, 12mo, 290p, fp b/w)	Rand/McNally	(1914)	Winter, Milo	70-100	
Warren, Maude R.	Tales Told by Gander (8vo, green/gilt, 305p, p-o, 12 ticp, pep)	Doran	(1922)	Federer, Charles A.	70-100	
Warren, Robert P.	Gods of Mount Olympus (1st {std}, 8vo, 52p, fp 1-color, pep, DJ/1.50)	Random	(1959)	Moyers, William	80-130	R
Warwick, Charles	Mirabeau & the French Revolution (1st, 8vo, 483p, 15pl)	Lippincott	1905	Neill, John R.	50-90	
Washburn, Claude C.	Pages from the Book of Paris (1st, 8vo, pcb, p-o, 276p, b/w)	Houghton	1910	Hornby, Lester G.	30-50	
Washburne, Heluiz	Children of the Blizzard (1st, 8vo, 192p, b/w, DJ/2.50)	John Day	(1952)	Wiese, Kurt	25-40	
Washburne, Heluiz	Little Elephant's Christmas (1st, lg8vo, 30p, p-o, 2-color, DJ/1.00)	Whitman	1938	McConnell, Jean	30-50	

AUTHOR	TITLE	PUBLISHER	DATE	ARTIST	PRICE	LC
Washburne, Heluiz	Little Elephant's Picnic (1st, lg8vo, 30p, p-o, fp 2-color, pep, DJ/1.00)	Whitman	1939	McConnell, Jean	30-50	
Washburne, Heluiz	Rhamon: Boy of Kashmir (1st, lg8vo, 127p, red cl, color, pep, DJ/2.00)	Whitman	1939	Duvoisin, Roger	50-80	
Washburne, Marion	Every Day Essays (1st, 8vo, 156p, 15pl)	Rand/McNally	(1904)	Hallock, Ruth M.	30-50	
Washburne, Marion	Old Fashioned Fairy Tales (1st, lg8vo, brown/gilt, 102p, 3cp, pep)	Rand/McNally	(1909)	Webb, Margaret E.	70-100	*
Wasson, Mildred	Bill and Nancy (1st {std}, 8vo, 323p, 1-color, DJ/2.00)	Liveright	(1940)	Howe, Gertrude	30-50	
Wasson, Mildred	Nancy Sails (1st, 8vo, 295p, b/w, DJ/2.00)	Harper	1936	Berry, Erick	20-30	
Wasson, Valentina P.	Chosen Baby (1st {A}, ob8vo, blue cl, [48]p, color, pep)	Carrick/Evans	(1939)	Woodward, Hildegarde	55-80	*
Wasson, Valentina P.	Chosen Baby (1st {revised ed}, 8vo, 46p, color, DJ/2.00)	Lippincott	(1950)	Woodward, Hildegarde	30-50	
Watanna, Onoto	Japanese Blossom (1st, 8vo, 263p, gilt, uncut, teg, 4cp, dep)	Harper	1906	Zeigler, Lee W.	40-65	
Watanna, Onoto	Tama (1st, 8vo, 244p, uncut, gilt, teg, 4cp, dep)	Harper	1910	Kataoka, Genjiro	30-50	
Waterloo, Stanley	A Man & a Woman (1st {this pub}, 8vo, 250p, red cl, teg, cvr by...)	Way & Williams	1897	Bradley, Will	70-100	R
Waterloo, Stanley	Story of AB (1st, 8vo, black cl, 351p, PPPa, cvr by...)	Way & Williams	1897	Bradley, Will	130-200	
Waterloo, Stanley	The Seekers (1st, sm8vo, 257p, teg, red cl, cvr by...)	Herbert Stone	1900	Bradley, Will	75-120	
Waterloo, Stanley	Wolf's Long Howl (1st, 12mo, 288p, red cl, teg, cvr by...)	Herbert Stone	1899	Bradley, Will	60-100	
Waterman, Nixon (ed)	Ben King's Verse (1st, 12mo, 276p, gilt, 1 illus by...)	Chi: Forbes	1894	Denslow, W.W.	80-125	
Waters, Russell J.	El Estranjero (1st, 8vo, gilt, 298p, fp b/w)	Rand/McNally	1910	Chapin, Will E.	45-70	
Waterstone, Satella	Short Stories of Musical Melodies (1st, 4to, ibds, unpag, gilt, b/w, pep)	Volland	(1915)	Dodge, Katharine S.	140-200	
Watkin, Lawrence	Thomas Jones & his Nine Lives (1st, 8vo, 102p, b/w, pep, DJ/1.50)	Harcourt	1941	Holland, Janice	25-40	
Watkins, Hope	Cunning Fox (1st {std}, lg8vo, uncut, 118p, fp b/w, DJ/2.00)	Knopf	1943	Pitz, Henry C.	30-50	*
Watkins, Richard	Mystery of Willet (1st, 8vo, 167p, b/w, DJ/2.95)	Nelson	(1959)	Spier, Peter E.	30-50	
Watson, Elizabeth	Story of Bread (1st {std}, 12mo, ipcb, 48p, 4cp, pep)	Harper	1927	Daugherty, James	30-50	
Watson, Elizabeth	Story of Milk & How it Came About (1st {std}, 12mo, ipcb, 37p, 4cp, pep)	Harper	1927	Daugherty, James	30-50	
Watson, Emily R.	Lament of Billy Villy (1st, lg sq8vo, wraps, 8cp)	L: R. Tuck	[1894]	Wain, Louis	500-700	
Watson, H.B.M.	Chloris of the Island (1st, sm8vo, 281p, 32pl)	Harper	1900	Brock, C.& H.	50-80	*
Watson, H.B.M.	The Adventurers (1st, sm8vo, 298p, 20pl)	Harper	1899	Keller, Arthur I.	35-60	*
Watson, Helen O.	Fools over Horses (1st, 8vo, 237p, b/w, pep, DJ/2.75)	Houghton	1952	Dennis, Wesley	40-65	*
Watson, Jane W.	True Story of Smokey the Bear (1st, folio, ibds, [24]p, pep, BGB/#429)	Golden Press	1955	Rojankovsky, Feodor	50-80	
Watson, Nancy D.	Annie's Spending Spree (1st, sm4to, 45p, color, pep, DJ/2.50)	Viking	1957	Watson, Aldren A.	25-40	
Watson, Nancy D.	Fairy Tale Picture Book (1st {std}, lg4to, 91p, color, DJ/2.95)	Garden City	1957	Watson, Aldren A.	60-90	
Watson, Nancy D.	Sugar on Snow (1st, ob8vo, 43p, fp 1-color, DJ/3.00)	Viking	(1964)	Watson, Aldren A.	25-40	
Watson, Nancy D.	Toby and Doll (1st {std}, 8vo, 125p, 4cp, b/w, pep, DJ/2.75)	Bobbs-Merrill	1955	Watson, Aldren A.	20-30	
Watson, Nancy D.	When is Tomorrow? (1st, sm ob4to, [32]p, ibds, color, pep, DJ/2.00)	Knopf	(1955)	Watson, Aldren A.	20-35	
Watson, Sally	Magic at Wychwood (1st, 8vo, 128p, fp b/w, cep, DJ/4.50)	Knopf	(1970)	Bozzo, Frank	80-140	
Watson, Virginia	Princess Pocahontas (1st, lg8vo, 306p, blue/gilt, p-o, 9cp, pep)	Penn	1916	Edwards, George W.	100-165	
Watson, Virginia	Trail of Courage (1st, 8vo, grey cl, 181p, fp b/w, DJ/2.50)	Crowell	(1948)	Brown, Marcia	45-70	
Watson, Virginia	With Cortes the Conqueror (1st, lg8vo, p-o, 332p, 8cp, pep)	Penn	1917	Schoonover, Frank	60-100	
Watson, Virginia	With LaSalle the Explorer (1st, 8vo, 366p, p-o, col frn, 4pl, pep)	Henry Holt & Co.	1922	Pitz, Henry C.	25-45	
Wattles, Wallace D.	Hell-Fire Harrison (1st, sm8vo, 100p, green/gilt, 6cp, pep)	L.C. Page	1910	Merrill, Frank T.	25-40	
Watts, Isaac	Childhood Songs of Long Ago (1st, 8vo, 87p, 20pl, pep)	Herrick	(1897)	McManus, Blanche	70-100	
Watts, Isaac	Divine & Moral Songs for Children (16mo, bds, 62p, teg, 12 fp color)	L: E. Mathews	[1897]	Gaskin, Mrs. A.	100-175	
Watts, Mabel	Dozens of Cousins (1st, 4to, 46p, 2-color, DJ/2.00)	Whittlesey	(1950)	Duvoisin, Roger	50-85	
Watts, Mabel	Henrietta & the Hat (1st, 4to, [40]p, ibds, 2-color, DJ/2.75)	Parents Mag. Pr.	(1962)	Miller, Jane	20-35	
Watts, Mabel	I'm for You and You're for Me (1st, ob8vo, [32]p, color, DJ/2.75)	Abelard-Schuman	(1967)	Foreman, Michael	25-40	
Watts, Mabel	Light Across Piney Valley (1st, sm4to, [42]p, fp color, DJ/2.95)	Abelard-Schuman	1965	Barker, Carol	25-40	*
Watts, Mabel	Story of Zachary Zween (1st, 4to, [43]p, ipcb, dp color, pep, DJ/3.50)	Parents Mag. Pr.	(1967)	Hafner, Marylin	25-45	*
Waugh, Alec	Hot Countries (1st, 8vo, 304p, gilt, b/w)	Farrar/Rinehart	(1930)	Ward, Lynd	45-70	
Waugh, Alec	Most Women (1st, 8vo, gilt, 323p, 6 fp woodcuts)	Farrar/Rinehart	(1931)	Ward, Lynd	80-125	
Waugh, Alec	Square Book of Animals (1st, sq4to, [14]p, ibds, 12cp)	L: Heinemann	1900	Nicholson, Wm.	425-600	
Waugh, Alec	Square Book of Animals (1st AM, sq4to, [14]p, ibds, 12cp)	R.H. Russell	1900	Nicholson, Wm.	350-500	R
Waugh, Alec	Thirteen Such Years (1st, 8vo, 277p, green/gilt, b/w, frn by...)	Farrar/Rinehart	(1932)	Ward, Lynd	25-45	
Waugh, Dorothy	Among the Leaves & Grasses (1st, sm4to, orange cl, 93p, color)	Henry Holt & Co.	1931	Waugh, Dorothy	100-170	
Waugh, Frederick	Clan of Munes (1st, ob folio, blue cl, 58p, 8 fp color)	Scribner	1916	Waugh, Frederick	400-650	R
Waugh, Ida	Becky Longnose... (4to, wraps, 8cp)	McLoughlin	(1882)	Waugh, Ida	80-140	
Waugh, Ida	Holly Berries (1st, lg8vo, 48p, ibds, fp color, cep)	Dutton	(1881)	Waugh, Ida	150-220	
Waugh, Ida	Ideal Heads (1st, folio, brown/gilt, [51]p, AEG, 20 chromos)	Sunshine Co.	1890	Waugh, Ida	700-1000	
Waugh, Ida	Little Chicks and Baby Tricks (1st, 4to, ibds, 44p)	Dutton	1885	Waugh, Ida	100-170	
Waugh, Ida	Over the Hills (1st, 4to, ibds, [48]p, chromos)	McLoughlin	(1882)	Waugh, Ida	160-250	
Wavle, Ardra	Here they Are (1st, 8vo, cloth, 56p, color, pep)	D.C. Heath	(1940)	Disney Studios	40-65	
Waylett, Richard	Jock and Some Others (1st, 4to, ibds, [30]p, 16cp)	L: Lawrence/Jel.	[1916]	Aldin, Cecil	300-500	
Waylett, Richard	Mixed Pickles (1st, 12mo, ibds, 48p, p-o, 10cp)	L: Gale/Polden	[1916]	Various	35-60	
Waylett, Richard	Puppy Tales (1st, 4to, ibds, 16cp)	L: Lawrence	[1912]	Aldin, Cecil	180-240	
Wayne, Elaine	Bucky Bear Who Would not take his Nap (1st, sq12mo, [41]p, col, DJ/1.00)	Lothrop, Lee	(1944)	Weisgard, Leonard	45-70	
Weatherly, Fred E.	Among the Daisies (sm4to, ibds, [60]p, 16 fp color)	L: Hildesheimer	[1890]	Edwards, M. Ellen	100-165	
Weatherly, Fred E.	Book of Gnomes (1st, sm ob4to, [25]p, ibds, 8 chromos, pep)	L: Nister	[1900]	Hardy, E. Stuart	500-700	
Weatherly, Fred E.	Happy Childhood (12mo, ibds, fp color)	L: Hildesheimer	[1892]	Simmons/West	50-85	
Weatherly, Fred E.	Little Pickle (1st, sm8vo, [24]p, ibds, 7 chromos, pep)	L: Hildesheimer	(1885)	Dealy, Jane	80-145	
Weatherly, Fred E.	Out of Town (1st, 8vo, 64p, ibds, 12 chromos, dep)	Dutton	[1884]	Watt, Linnie	100-175	
Weatherly, Fred E.	Rhymes and Roses (4to, ibds, 32p, 8 chromos)	L: Hildesheimer	[1888]	Simmons/Wilson	80-140	
Weatherly, Fred E.	Told in the Twilight (1st, 8vo, 64p, ibds)	Dutton	[1883]	27 Chromos	120-200	
Weaver, Annie V.	Boochy's Wings (1st, ob12mo, 122p, color)	Stokes	1931	Weaver, Annie V.	50-85	*
Weaver, Annie V.	Frawg (1st, ob12mo, p-o, 128p, color, pep)	Stokes	1930	Weaver, Annie V.	160-240	
Webb, Clifford	Jungle Picnic (1st, lg8vo, 75p, 24 fp color, pep)	Warne	(1934)	Webb, Clifford	40-65	
Webb, E. & D.	Littlest Fairy (1st, sm4to, ibds, 158p, p-o, 8cp, pep)	Dodge	(1910)	Clements, Ruth S.	200-300	
Webb, M. St. John	Forest Fairies (1st, 16mo, 41p, ibds, 6 ticp)	L: Mod.Art.Soc	(1932)	Tarrant, Margaret	70-125	
Webb, M. St. John	Insect Fairies (1st, 12mo, beige bds, p-o, 42p, 6 ticp)	L: Mod.Art.Soc	(1925)	Tarrant, Margaret	100-160	
Webb, M. St. John	Little One in Between (1st, 12mo, 59p, blue/gilt, 4cp)	L: Harrap	1929	Tarrant, Margaret	45-60	
Webb, M. St. John	Littlest One Again (1st, 4to, p-o, bds, 4cp)	L: Harrap	1926	Tarrant, Margaret	70-100	
Webb, M. St. John	Magic Lamplighter (1st, 8vo, 167p, 7cp, pep)	L: Medici	1926	Tarrant, Margaret	60-90	

AUTHOR	TITLE	PUBLISHER	DATE	ARTIST	PRICE	LC
Webb, M. St. John	Pond Fairies (1st, 16mo, 41p, grey bds, p-o, 6 ticp)	L: Mod.Art.Soc	(1932)	Tarrant, Margaret	80-125	
Webb, M. St. John	Sea-Shore Fairies (1st, 16mo, 48p, tan bds, p-o, 6 fp color)	L: Mod.Art.Soc	(1925)	Tarrant, Margaret	200-300	
Webb, M. St. John	Seed Fairies (1st, 12mo, 39p, bds, p-o, 6 ticp, pep)	L: Mod.Art.Soc	[1923]	Tarrant, Margaret	180-260	
Webb, M. St. John	Wild Fruit Fairies (1st, 12mo, 41p, ibds, 6 ticp)	L: Medici	[1932]	Tarrant, Margaret	100-165	
Webb, Richard	Me & Lawson (1st, 12mo, 78p, 4pl, cvr by...)	Dillingham	(1905)	Denslow, W.W.	80-130	
Webb, Wheaton P.	Twelve Labors of Wimpole Stout (1st, 8vo, 176p, b/w, DJ/3.95)	Abingdon Press	(1970)	Savage, Steele	20-30	
Webb, Wheaton P.	Uncle Swithin's Inventions (1st, lg8vo, 114p, fp b/w, pep, DJ/2.00)	Holiday House	(1947)	Rounds, Glen	30-50	
Webber, Frank M.	Peter Painter & the Holidays (1st, lg8vo, [32]p, ibds, 2-color, DJ/1.00)	McKay	(1942)	Neville, Vera	40-60	
Webber, Frank M.	Peter Painter's Merry-Go-Round (1st {std} lg8vo, ibds, [32]p, col, DJ/1.00)	McKay	(1946)	Neville, Vera	45-70	
Webber, Irma E.	Anywhere in the World (1st, 8vo, ipcb, 64p, color, DJ/1.50)	W.R. Scott	(1947)	Webber, Irma	60-90	
Webber, Irma E.	Bits that Grow Big (1st, sm8vo, ipcb, 64p, 2-color, DJ/1.65)	W.R. Scott	(1949)	Webber, Irma	60-90	
Webber, Irma E.	It Looks Like This (1st, sm8vo, ibds, [40]p, b/w, DJ/1.00)	W.R. Scott	1949	Webber, Irma	50-80	
Webber, Irma E.	Thanks to Trees (1st, sm8vo, grey cl, 60p, 3-color, pep, DJ/2.00)	W.R. Scott	(1952)	Webber, Irma	50-80	
Webber, Irma E.	Travelers All (1st, sm8vo, ibds, [32]p, color, DJ/1.35)	W.R. Scott	1944	Webber, Irma	50-80	
Webber, Irma E.	Up Above & Down Below (1st, sm8vo, ibds, [31]p, color, DJ/1.00)	W.R. Scott	(1943)	Webber, Irma	70-100	
Weber, Henriette	Prize Song (1st, lg8vo, 272p, 2-color, pep, DJ/3.00)	Oxford U. Pr.	1935	Lawson, Marie A.	30-50	
Weber, Lenora M.	Gypsy Bridle (1st, 8vo, 275p, col frn, fp b/w, pep)	Little/Brown	1930	Wiese, Kurt	250-400	
Weber, Lenora M.	Meet the Malones (1st, 8vo, 218p, uncut, fp b/w, DJ/3.00)	Crowell	1943	Howe, Gertrude	60-100	
Weber, Lenora M.	Rocking Chair Ranch (1st, 8vo, 210p, uncut, 4pl, DJ/2.00)	Houghton	1936	Stahley, Joseph	60-90	
Weber, Lenora M.	Wind on the Prairie (1st, 8vo, 276p, pep, col frn, b/w)	Little/Brown	1929	Wiese, Kurt	100-160	
Webling, Peggy	Saints & their Stories (1st, 8vo, grey cl, 312p, 8cp, pep)	L: J. Nisbet	[1919]	Robinson, F. Cayley	80-120	
Webster, George	Santa Claus & his Works (4to, wraps, 6 chromos)	McLoughlin	1897	Nast, Thomas	220-350	
Webster, Jean	Daddy Long Legs (1st, 12mo, blue cl, 304p, b/w, PPP)	Century	1912	Webster, Jean	55-80	
Webster, Jean	Daddy Long Legs (1st, 8vo, 183p, blue/gilt, b/w, DJ/3.95)	NY: Meredith Pr.	(1967)	Ardizzone, Edward	50-80	
Webster, Jean	Dear Enemy (1st, sm8vo, 350p, blue cl, b/w)	Century	1915	Webster, Jean	50-80	
Webster, Jean	Jerry Junior (1st, sm8vo, green cl, p-o, 282p, 15pl)	Century	1907	Lowell, Orson	25-40	
Wedgwood, Henry A.	Bird Talisman (1st, lg8vo, 70p, gilt, 8cp)	L: Faber	1939	Raverat, Gwen	50-85	
Weeden, Howard	Bandanna Ballads (1st, 8vo, green/gilt, uncut, 90p, 24pl)	Doub./McClure	1899	Weeden, Howard	90-160	
Weedon, Lucy L.	Child Characters from Dickens (1st, 8vo, gilt, 320p, AEG, 6cp)	L: Nister	(1905)	Dixon, Arthur A.	75-125	
Weelen, Guy	Little Red Train (1st, sm4to, [24]p, fp 1-color, pep, DJ/2.95)	Lothrop, Lee	(1966)	Funai, Mamoru	30-50	
Weigle, Oscar	Story of Noah's Ark (1st, lg4to, [26]p, ipcb, color, pep, DJ/1.95)	Grosset/Dunlap	1957	Seiden, Art	60-90	R*
Weik, Mary H.	House at Cherry Hill (1st {std}, 8vo, 135p, b/w, DJ/2.00)	Knopf	1938	Bobri, Vladimir	30-50	*
Weik, Mary H.	Jazz Man (1st {std}, 8vo, 42p, b/w, cep, DJ/3.50, NH, NYTBI)	Atheneum	1966	Grifalconi, Ann	70-100	*
Weik, Mary H.	Scarlet Thread (1st {std}, lg8vo, 109p, red cl, b/w, DJ/4.50)	Atheneum	1968	Remington, Barbara	25-40	
Weil, Ann Y.	Animal Families (1st, ob4to, [31]p, color, pep, DJ/1.50)	Greenberg	(1946)	Vernam, Roger	30-50	
Weil, Ann Y.	Betsy Ross: Girl of Old Philadelphia (1st {std}, sm8vo, 192p, b/w, DJ/1.75)	Bobbs-Merrill	(1954)	James, Sandra	30-45	
Weil, Ann Y.	Eleanor Roosevelt: Courageous Girl (1st, sm8vo, 200p, fp b/w, DJ/2.25)	Bobbs-Merrill	(1965)	Morrow, Gray	25-35	
Weil, Ann Y.	John Phillip Sousa: Marching Boy (1st {std}, sm8vo, 192p, b/w, DJ/1.95)	Bobbs-Merrill	(1959)	Sampson, Kath.	25-35	
Weil, Ann Y.	John Quincy Adams: Boy Patriot (1st {std}, sm8vo, 192p, b/w, DJ/1.75)	Bobbs-Merrill	(1945)	Laune, Paul	25-40	
Weil, Ann Y.	My Dear Patsy (1st {std}, 8vo, 315p, b/w, DJ/2.00)	Bobbs-Merrill	(1941)	Robinson, Jessie	25-45	*
Weil, Ann Y.	Pussycat's Breakfast (1st, ob8vo, ibds, [47]p, color, DJ/1.25)	Greenberg	(1944)	Barton, Mary	20-35	*
Weil, Ann Y.	Red Sails to Capri (1st, 8vo, 156p, pep, DJ/2.50, NH)	Viking	1952	Falls, Charles B.	30-50	
Weil, Ann Y.	Silver Fawn (1st {std}, 8vo, 228p, 1-color, pep, DJ/2.00)	Bobbs-Merrill	(1939)	Leon, E.	25-45	
Weil, Ann Y.	Very First Day (1st, sm8vo, red cl, [32]p, 1-color, DJ/1.50)	Appleton-Century	(1946)	Robinson, Jessie	25-45	
Weil, Lisl	Alphabet of Puppy Care (1st, 4to, [41]p, fp 2-color, cep, DJ/3.75)	Abelard-Schuman	1968	Weil, Lisl	30-50	
Weil, Lisl	Bill the Brave (1st {std}, 8vo, ibds, 32p, color, DJ/1.50)	Houghton	(1948)	Weil, Lisl	30-50	
Weil, Lisl	Bitzli and the Big Bad Wolf (1st, sm4to, 47p, fp color, DJ/3.00)	Houghton	1960	Weil, Lisl	30-50	*
Weil, Lisl	Busiest Boy in Holland (1st, sm4to, 38p, 1-color, DJ/2.75)	Houghton	1959	Weil, Lisl	30-45	
Weil, Lisl	Eyes So-O Big (1st, sm sq4to, 48p, fp 1-color, DJ/3.25)	Houghton	1964	Weil, Lisl	30-50	*
Weil, Lisl	Fantastic Toy Shop (1st, 4to, 47p, color, DJ/3.50)	Abelard-Schuman	(1966)	Weil, Lisl	30-50	
Weil, Lisl	Golden Spinning Wheel (1st {std}, 4to, [40]p, color, DJ/4.95)	Macmillan	(1969)	Weil, Lisl	30-45	
Weil, Lisl	Happy Birthday in Barcelona (1st, sm sq4to, 48p, 1-color, cep, DJ/3.25)	Houghton	1965	Weil, Lisl	30-45	*
Weil, Lisl	Happy Ski ABC (1st, ob4to, 64p, fp 2-color, DJ/3.50)	Putnam	(1964)	Weil, Lisl	30-50	
Weil, Lisl	Hopping Knapsack (1st {std}, sm4to, [32]p, color, DJ/4.50)	Macmillan	1970	Weil, Lisl	30-45	
Weil, Lisl	I Wish, I Wish (1st, sm4to, 38p, 1-color, DJ/2.50)	Houghton	1957	Weil, Lisl	30-50	*
Weil, Lisl	Jacoble Tells the Truth (1st, 8vo, [20]p, color, DJ/1.00)	Houghton	1946	Weil, Lisl	40-65	*
Weil, Lisl	Lionhearted One (1st, sm4to, 47p, fp 1-color, DJ/3.00)	Houghton	1962	Weil, Lisl	30-45	
Weil, Lisl	Melissa (1st {std}, sm4to, [32]p, 2-color, DJ/3.25)	Macmillan	1966	Weil, Lisl	30-50	
Weil, Lisl	Melissa's Friend Fabrizzio (1st {std}, 4to, [32]p, color, DJ/3.95)	Macmillan	(1967)	Weil, Lisl	25-40	
Weil, Lisl	Mimi (1st, 4to, 48p, 3-color, DJ/3.00)	Houghton	1961	Weil, Lisl	30-50	
Weil, Lisl	Pudding's Wonderful Bone (1st, sm ob4to, [30]p, fp 1-color, cep, DJ/2.50)	Crowell	(1956)	Weil, Lisl	40-65	
Weil, Lisl	Shivers... (1st, 4to, 40p, fp 2-color, cep, DJ/3.25)	Houghton	1967	Weil, Lisl	30-50	
Weil, Lisl	Things that Go Bang (1st, 4to, 40p, color, DJ/4.50)	McGraw-Hill	(1969)	Weil, Lisl	30-50	*
Weilerstein, Sadie	Ten and a Kid (1st {std}, 8vo, 185p, b/w, DJ/2.95)	Doubleday	1961	Domanska, Janina	25-45	
Weisgard, Leonard	Athenians in the Classical Period (1st, 4to, 61p, 1-color, DJ/3.95)	Coward	(1963)	Weisgard, Leonard	40-65	
Weisgard, Leonard	Beginnings of Cities (1st {std}, 4to, 61p, brown illus, DJ)	Coward	(1968)	Weisgard, Leonard	30-50	*
Weisgard, Leonard	Clean Pig (1st, ob4to, [34]p, fp brown illus, pep, DJ/2.00)	Scribner	1952	Weisgard, Leonard	50-85	
Weisgard, Leonard	Down Huckleberry Hill (1st, ob4to, ibds, [31]p, fp 1-color, pep, DJ/2.00)	Scribner	1947	Weisgard, Leonard	50-80	
Weisgard, Leonard	First Farmers in the New Stone Age (1st, 4to, 63p, fp color, DJ)	Coward	(1966)	Weisgard, Leonard	30-50	*
Weisgard, Leonard	Just Like Me (1st, 8vo, [28]p, ibds, color, pep)	Treasure Books	(1954)	Weisgard, Leonard	30-50	*
Weisgard, Leonard	Mr. Peaceable Paints (1st, ob4to, [32]p, dp color, DJ/2.75)	Scribner	1956	Weisgard, Leonard	60-100	
Weisgard, Leonard	My First Picture Book (1st, folio, [24]p, ibds, color, pep, DJ/1.00)	Grosset/Dunlap	(1953)	Weisgard, Leonard	50-85	
Weisgard, Leonard	Pelican Here, Pelican There (1st, sm4to, [30]p, 6 dp color, pep, DJ/2.00)	Scribner	1948	Weisgard, Leonard	60-90	R
Weisgard, Leonard	Plymouth Thanksgiving (1st {std}, 4to, [64]p, dp color, DJ/3.95)	Doubleday	1967	Weisgard, Leonard	45-70	R
Weisgard, Leonard	Silly Willy Nilly (1st, sm4to, [32]p, 8 fp color, DJ/2.50)	Scribner	1953	Weisgard, Leonard	60-90	R
Weisgard, Leonard	Suki the Siamese Pussy (1st, 4to, [32]p, fp 2-color, DJ/2.00)	NY: Nelson	1937	Weisgard, Leonard	70-125	
Weisgard, Leonard	Treasures to See (1st {std}, sm4to, [32]p, rust cl, color, DJ/3.00)	Harcourt	(1956)	Weisgard, Leonard	50-80	R
Weisgard, Leonard	Who Dreams of Cheese? (1st, 4to, black cl, [32]p, color, DJ)	Scribner	1950	Weisgard, Leonard	60-100	R

AUTHOR	TITLE	PUBLISHER	DATE	ARTIST	PRICE	LC
Weisgard, Leonard	Whose Little Bird Am I? (1st, 24mo, ibds, [39]p, fp 1-color, pep, DJ/1.00)	Crowell	(1944)	Weisgard, Leonard	30-50	
Weisgard, Leonard	Would You Like to be a Monkey? (1st, sm8vo, ibds, [32]p, color, DJ/1.00)	Crowell	(1945)	Weisgard, Leonard	30-50	*
Weiss, Edna S.	Sally Saucer (1st, 8vo, 179p, yellow cl, b/w, DJ/2.75)	Houghton	1956	Stone, Helen	25-45	
Weiss, Edna S.	Truly Elizabeth (1st, 8vo, 178p, b/w, DJ/2.50)	Houghton	1957	Krush, Beth	30-50	*
Weiss, Renee K.	Bird from the Sea (1st, ob4to, [31]p, gilt, color, cep, DJ/4.50)	Crowell	(1970)	Young, Ed	30-50	
Weiss, Renee K.	Paper Zoo (1st {std}, sm4to, 38p, fp 2-color, DJ/4.50)	Macmillan	(1968)	Raskin, Ellen	60-90	R
Welch, Deshler	Story of Louise (1st, 12mo, tan cl, uncut, 194p, cvr by...)	Royal Colum. Pr.	1901	Denslow, W.W.	55-80	
Welch, Jean L.	Animals Came First (1st, sm8vo, ibds, [30]p, b/w, pep, DJ/1.50)	NY: Oxford U.Pr.	1948	Carroll, Ruth	30-50	
Welch, Ronald	Knight Crusader (1st, 8vo, 272p, fp b/w, pep, DJ, CgM)	L: Oxford U.Pr.	1954	Stobbs, William	40-65	
Welles, Winifred	Skipping Along (1st, 8vo, green cl, 52p, b/w, pep)	Macmillan	1931	Davis, Marguerite	25-40	*
Wellesley, Howard	All Kinds of Neighbors (1st, ob8vo, [26]p, fp color, pep, DJ)	Holt, Rinehart	1963	Aliki	30-50	
Wellman, Manly W.	Rebel Mail Runner (1st, sm8vo, 221p, red cl, b/w, pep, DJ/2.75)	Holiday House	(1954)	Van Veen, Stuyvesant	30-50	
Wellman, Manly W.	To Unknown Lands (1st, 8vo, 202p, black cl, b/w, pep, DJ/2.75)	Holiday House	(1956)	Fisher, Leonard	25-40	*
Wells, Amos R.	Rollicking Rhymes for Youngsters (1st, 8vo, 157p, 26 fp 2-color)	Revell	(1902)	Bridgman, L.J.	55-80	
Wells, Amos R.	Witchery Ways (1st, 12mo, 189p, 8pl)	Altemus	(1904)	Bridgman, L.J.	30-50	
Wells, Carolyn	Beauties (1st, folio, [63]p, gilt, ibds, p-o, 16 ticp)	Dodd	1913	Fisher, Harrison	600-900	
Wells, Carolyn	Bumblepuppy Book (1st, sq8vo, ibds, 82p, fp 1-color)	L: Isbiter	1903	Herford, Oliver	50-80	
Wells, Carolyn	Children of Our Town (1st, ob folio, ibds, [56]p, color, pep)	R.H. Russell	(1902)	Mars/Squire	750-1000	R
Wells, Carolyn	Emily Emmins Papers (1st, sm8vo, 273p, p-o, b/w)	Putnam	1907	Meyer, Josephine	60-90	*
Wells, Carolyn	Folly for the Wise (1st, 8vo, 170p, blue/gilt, cvr by...)	Bobbs-Merrill	(1904)	Armstrong, Margaret	55-90	
Wells, Carolyn	Folly in Fairyland (1st, 12mo, 261p, 12pl)	Altemus	(1901)	Morgan, Wallace	60-90	
Wells, Carolyn	Folly in the Forest (1st, 8vo, 282p, olive cl, 12pl)	Altemus	(1902)	Birch, Reginald	45-70	
Wells, Carolyn	Happychaps (1st, lg8vo, 135p, brown cl, fp b/w)	Century	1908	Cady, Harrison	120-180	
Wells, Carolyn	Idle Idyls (1st, sm8vo, green/gilt, teg, 155p, b/w pl)	Dodd	1900	Herford, Oliver	40-65	
Wells, Carolyn	In the Reign of Queen Dick (1st, 8vo, tan cl, 229p, 8pl)	Appleton	1904	Strothmann, F.	30-50	
Wells, Carolyn	Jingle Book (1st, sm8vo, 124p, blue cl, teg, b/w)	Macmillan	1899	Herford, Oliver	80-120	R
Wells, Carolyn	Jingle Book (8vo {new ed.}, green cl, p-o, 124p, b/w)	Donohue	(1906)	Herford, Oliver	40-60	*
Wells, Carolyn	Lover's Baedeker & Guide to Arcady (1st, 12mo, 115p, b/w, pep)	Stokes	(1912)	Blashfield, A.D.	50-80	
Wells, Carolyn	Merry-Go-Round (1st, sm8vo, gilt, 152p, 11pl)	R.H. Russell	1901	Newell, Peter	180-250	
Wells, Carolyn	Mother Goose's Menagerie (1st, lg8vo, tan cl, 111p, 12cp)	Noyes/Platt	1901	Newell, Peter	200-300	
Wells, Carolyn	Pete & Polly Stories (1st, lg8vo, green cl, 229p, 6pl)	McClurg	1902	Cory, Fanny	70-100	
Wells, Carolyn	Phenomenal Fauna (1st, sq8vo, [90]p, ibds, 21cp)	R.H. Russell	1902	Herford, Oliver	100-160	
Wells, Carolyn	Rubaiyat of a Motor Car (1st, 12mo, [60]p, ibds, 14cp)	Dodd	1906	Strothmann, F.	55-80	*
Wells, Carolyn	Rubaiyat of Bridge (1st, 12mo, p-o, [42]p, 1-color)	Harper	1909	Preston, May W.	30-50	
Wells, Carolyn	Seven Ages of Childhood (1st, sm4to, gilt, 56p, p-o, 7cp, pep)	Moffat	1909	Smith, Jessie W.	350-500	
Wells, Carolyn	Story of Betty (1st {1st bk.}, sm8vo, red cl, 260p, 32pl)	Century	1899	Birch, Reginald	50-80	
Wells, Carveth	Jungle Man & his Animals (1st, lg4to, ibds, 68p, 12cp)	Duffield	1925	Sarg, Tony	180-240	*
Wells, Carveth	Jungle Man & his Animals (1st {this pub}, 4to, 68p, ibds, 7cp)	McBride	(1925)	Sarg, Tony	170-240	
Wells, David D.	Her Ladyship's Elephant (1st, sm8vo, 234p, tan cl, cvr by...)	Henry Holt & Co.	1898	Nicholson, Wm.	25-40	
Wells, H.G.	Adventures of Tommy (1st, lg4to, 45p, bds, color)	L: Harrap	(1929)	Wells, H.G.	200-285	
Wells, H.G.	Adventures of Tommy (1st AM, 4to, red cl, [46]p, p-o, color)	Stokes	1929	Wells, H.G.	120-180	
Wells, H.G.	Adventures of Tommy (1st [this fmt.], 4to, 26p, wraps, color)	A.& W. Guild	1935	Wells, H.G.	30-50	
Wells, H.G.	First Men in the Moon (1st, 8vo, 312p, blue/gilt, 12pl)	Bowen-Merrill	(1901)	Hering, E.	600-800	
Wells, H.G.	First Men in the Moon (1st UK, 8vo, 342p, blue/gilt, 12pl, cep)	L: G. Newnes	1901	Shepperson, Claude	600-800	
Wells, H.G.	Little Wars (1st AM, 8vo, 180p, p-o, blue cl, 16pl)	Small/Maynard	(1913)	(Photos)	160-240	*
Wells, H.G.	Modern Utopia (1st, 8vo, red/gilt, uncut, teg, 393p, 7pl)	L: Chapman	1905	Sullivan, Edmund J.	200-300	
Wells, H.G.	War in the Air (1st, 8vo, blue/gilt, 389p, uncut, 16pl)	L: G. Bell	1908	Michael, A.C.	500-700	
Wells, H.G.	War in the Air (1st AM, 8vo, 395p, grey/gilt, uncut, 20pl)	Macmillan	1908	Pape, Eric	350-500	
Wells, H.G.	War of the Worlds (1st AM, 12mo, green cl, 291p, 16pl)	Harper	1898	Goble, Warwick	500-700	
Wells, H.G.	When the Sleeper Wakes (1st AM, 8vo, red/gilt, 328p, 3pl)	Harper	1899	Lanos, H.	300-500	
Wells, Peter	Mr. Tootwhistle's Invention (1st, 8vo, [32]p, orange cl, color, DJ/1.25)	Winston	(1942)	Wells, Peter	30-50	
Wells, Peter	Pirate's Apprentice (1st {std}, lg8vo, bds, [48]p, color, pep, DJ/0.75)	Winston	(1943)	Wells, Peter	25-40	
Wells, Rhea	Ali the Camel (1st {std}, sm8vo, 136p, fp color, pep)	Doubleday/Doran	1931	Wells, Rhea	30-55	
Wells, Rhea	Andy and Polly (1st {std}, lg ob8vo, [32]p, color)	Doubleday/Doran	1931	Wells, Rhea	60-90	R*
Wells, Rhea	Beppo the Donkey (1st {std}, 12mo, 135p, 15cp, pep)	Doubleday/Doran	1930	Wells, Rhea	30-50	
Wells, Rhea	Coco the Goat (1st {std}, sm8vo, 135p, dp color, pep)	Doubleday/Doran	1929	Wells, Rhea	30-50	
Wells, Rhea	Peppi the Duck (1st {std}, sm8vo, 118p, cp, pep)	Doubleday/Doran	1927	Wells, Rhea	30-50	
Wells, Rhea	Zeke the Raccoon (1st, sm8vo, green cl, 159p, 8cp, pep)	Viking	1933	Wells, Rhea	30-50	*
Wells, Rosemary	First Child (1st {std}, lg8vo, [32]p, color, DJ/4.25)	Hawthorn Books	(1970)	Wells, Rosemary	25-40	
Wells, Rosemary	John and the Rarey (1st {1}, 4to, bds, 42p, 2-color, cep, DJ/3.50)	Funk/Wagnalls	(1969)	Wells, Rosemary	30-50	
Wells, Rosemary	Martha's Birthday (1st {std}, lg8vo, [31]p, color, DJ/4.25)	Bradbury Press	(1970)	Wells, Rosemary	35-50	
Wells, Rosemary	Michael and the Mitten Test (1st {std}, 12mo, [35]p, color, DJ/3.50)	Bradbury Press	(1969)	Wells, Rosemary	25-40	
Wells, Rosemary	Miranda's Pilgrims (1st {std}, lg ob8vo, [32]p, color, DJ/4.50)	Bradbury Press	(1970)	Wells, Rosemary	30-50	*
Welsh, Charles	Stories Children Love (1st, sm8vo, 439p, 7cp)	Dodge	(1909)	Grimball, Meta	50-80	
Welsh, Richard	Kiddie-Kar Book (lg ob4to, ibds, p-o, 9cp)	Lippincott	(1920)	Stilwell, Sarah	170-265	*
Welty, Eudora	Ponder Heart (1st {std}, 8vo, ibds, 158p, b/w, DJ/3.00)	Harcourt	(1954)	Krush, Joe	150-225	
Welty, Eudora	Shoe Bird (1st {std}, lg8vo, 88p, b/w, DJ/3.50)	Harcourt	(1964)	Krush, Beth	150-225	
Wenning, Elizabeth	Christmas Mouse (1st, sm4to, [48]p, fp 2-color, DJ/2.95)	Holt	(1959)	Remington, Barbara	30-55	
Werner, Elsa	Golden Bible (1st {std}, folio, 124p, ibds, color, GGB)	Simon/Schuster	(1946)	Rojankovsky, Feodor	30-50	
Werner, Jadwiga	Squirrel Redcoat (1st AM {std}, lg8vo, 43p, color, DJ/2.95)	F. Watts	(1961)	Grabianski, Janusz	25-40	
Werner, Jane	Child's Book of Bible Stories (1st, lg4to, ibds, 53p, color, DJ/2.00)	Random	1944	Masha	30-50	
Werner, Jane	Christmas Story (1st, sm8vo, [28]p, ibds, color, LGB/#158)	Simon/Schuster	(1952)	Wilkin, Eloise B.	30-50	
Werner, Jane	Elves & Fairies (1st, sm folio, ibds, 76p, color, pep, GGB)	Simon/Schuster	(1951)	Williams, Garth	180-240	
Werner, Jane	Tall Book of Make-Believe (1st, narrow 4to, ibds, 92p, color, pep, DJ/1.00)	Harper	(1950)	Williams, Garth	100-160	
Wersba, Barbara	Boy Who Loved the Sea (1st, lg8vo, unpag, 1-color, DJ/2.50)	Coward	(1961)	Tomes, Margot	30-45	
Wersba, Barbara	Brave Balloon of Benjamin Buckley (1st {std}, 8vo, 66p, b/w, DJ/2.95)	Atheneum	1963	Tomes, Margot	30-45	
Wersba, Barbara	Do Tigers Ever Bite Kings? (1st {std}, lg8vo, [30]p, fp color, DJ/3.50)	Atheneum	1966	Rivoli, Mario	30-45	
Wersba, Barbara	Land of Forgotten Beasts (1st {std}, lg8vo, 88p, b/w, DJ/3.50)	Atheneum	1964	Tomes, Margot	30-45	*

AUTHOR	TITLE	PUBLISHER	DATE	ARTIST	PRICE	LC
Wersba, Barbara	Song for Clowns (1st {std}, lg8vo, 101p, b/w, DJ/3.75)	Atheneum	1965	Rivoli, Mario	25-40	
Werth, Kurt	King Thrushbeard (1st, sm4to, [32]p, fp color, DJ/3.95)	Viking	(1968)	Werth, Kurt	30-50	*
Werth, Kurt	Lazy Jack (1st {std}, lg8vo, [32]p, color, DJ/3.75)	Viking	(1970)	Werth, Kurt	30-45	*
Werth, Kurt	Monkey, the Lion & the Snake (1st, 8vo, ipcb, 31p, fp color, DJ/3.50)	Viking	(1967)	Werth, Kurt	30-45	*
Wesselhoeft, Lily	Diamond King.... (1st, 12mo, tan cl, 255p, 4pl)	Little/Brown	1907	Atwood, Clara E.	25-45	*
Wesselhoeft, Lily	Fairy-Folk of Blue Hill (1st, 8vo, 240p, blue/gilt, b/w)	J. Knight	1895	Eastman, A.L.	35-60	
Wesselhoeft, Lily	Madam Mary of the Zoo (1st, 12mo, 248p, blue/silver, 3pl by...)	Little/Brown	1899	Bridgman, L.J.	30-50	
Wesselhoeft, Lily	Ready the Reliable (1st, sm8vo, 265p, 4pl)	Little/Brown	1906	Emerson, Chase	30-50	
West, Jassamyn	Cress Delahanty (1st {std}, 8vo, 311p, b/w, DJ/3.75)	Harcourt	(1953)	Krush, Joe	25-40	
West, Michael P.	Clair De Lune (1st, lg4to, 137p, teg, brown/gilt, 8 ticp, pep)	L: Harrap	[1913]	Paul, Evelyn	160-220	
West, Paul	Pearl & Pumpkin (1st [1], lg8vo, green cl, 239p, p-o, 16cp, pep)	Dillingham	(1904)	Denslow, W.W.	350-500	
West, Paul	Pearl & Pumpkin (lg8vo, 239p, p-o, 16cp, later)	Donohue	[1911]	Denslow, W.W.	200-300	
Westcott, M.K.	Child Thoughts in Picture and Verse (1st, 16mo, 64p, ibds, 8cp)	L: Blackie	(1925)	Barker, Cicely M.	60-90	
Westerman, J.M.E.	Fairy Tales/Wonderland (1st, 4to, 160p, orange cl, 4cp, fp b/w)	L: Blackie	[1932]	Hassall, John	100-170	
Weston, Christine	Bhimsa the Dancing Bear (1st, sm8vo, 120p, 2-color, cep, DJ/2.00, NH)	Scribner	1945	Duvoisin, Roger	120-200	
Weston, Christine	There & Then (1st, sm8vo, 176p, green/gilt, fp b/w, DJ/2.50)	Scribner	1947	DeGoutiere, George	35-60	*
Weston, Harold	Patchwork Madonna (1st, sm8vo, 252p, fp pl, DJ/2.50)	Wm. Morrow	(1929)	Gay, Zhenya	25-35	
Weston, Jessie L.	Sir Gawain & the Green Knight (1st, 16mo, 96p, beige/gilt, b/w)	New Amsterdam	1899	Crawford, M.M.	60-100	
Weston, Jessie L.	Sir Gleges/Sir Libeaus Desconus (1st AM, 16mo, 77p, gilt, b/w)	New Amsterdam	1902	Watts, Caroline	60-100	
Wetmore, Claude H.	Bedtime Stories (1st, 4to, p-o, 120p, color)	Macaulay	1914	Bailey, Mildred L.	75-100	*
Wetmore, Claude H.	Queen Tiny's Little People (1st, 4to, 105p, p-o, color)	Macaulay	1914	Bailey, Mildred L.	75-100	*
Wetmore, Claude H.	Sweepers of the Sea (1st, sm8vo, green/gilt, 349p, 9pl)	Bowen-Merrill	(1900)	Coffin, G.A.	40-65	
Weyman, Stanley J.	Castle Inn (1st, 8vo, blue/gilt, 371p, frn by...)	L: Smith Elder	1898	Rackham, Arthur	140-200	
Wharton, Anne H.	Heirlooms in Miniatures (1st, 8vo, 259p, uncut, teg, col frn)	Lippincott	1898	Unknown	25-40	
Wharton, Edith	Book of the Homeless (1st, 4to, gilt, 155p, bds, 8cp, 13pl)	Scribner	1916	Various	200-300	
Wharton, Edith	Fruit of the Tree (1st, 12mo, 633p, red/gilt, 3pl)	Scribner	1907	Kimball, Alonzo	140-200	
Wharton, Edith	House of Mirth (1st, 8vo, 533p, gilt, teg, uncut, 8pl)	Scribner	1905	Wenzell, A.B.	140-200	
Wharton, Edith	Italian Backgrounds (1st, lg8vo, green/gilt, 214p, cvr by...)	Scribner	1905	Armstrong, Margaret	400-600	
Wharton, Edith	Italian Backgrounds (1st, lg8vo, gilt, 214p, teg, 12pl by...)	Scribner	1905	Peixotto, E.C.	400-600	
Wharton, Edith	Italian Villas and their Gardens (1st, 4to, teg, 270p, gilt, 15cp)	Century	1904	Parrish, Maxfield	700-1000	
Wharton, Edith	Motor-Flight through France (1st, 8vo, gilt, teg, 201p, 48pl)	Scribner	1908	(Photos)	140-200	
Wharton, Edith	Sanctuary (1st, 8vo, 184p, green/gilt, uncut, col frn, 10pl)	Scribner	1903	Clark, Walter A.	180-250	
Wharton, Thomas I.	Bobbo and other Fancies (1st, 12mo, gilt, 182p, uncut, 11pl)	Harper	1897	Various	40-70	
Wheeler, Candace	Doubledarling & Dreamspinner (1st, 8vo, 167p, blue cl, p-o, 11cp)	Fox Duffield	1905	Keith, Dora W.	80-120	
Wheeler, Eleanor	Jemmie, Kitten from Maine (1st {std}, sq8vo, p-o, 96p, fp 1-color, pep)	Smith/Haas	(1932)	Flack, Marjorie	70-120	
Wheeler, F.G.	Billy Whiskers at the Circus (1st, lg8vo, 147p, 6cp)	Saalfield	1908	DeBebian, Arthur	70-100	
Wheeler, Opal	Giotto Tended the Sheep (1st {std}, 4to, 96p, red cl, 2-color, DJ)	Dutton	(1938)	Bayley, Dorothy	50-80	
Wheeler, Opal	H.M.S. Pinafore (1st {std}, 4to, ibds, 96p, color, pep, DJ/3.00)	Dutton	1946	Kredel, Fritz	40-65	
Wheeler, Opal	Millet Tilled the Soil (1st {std}, 4to, 96p, red cl, 2-color, DJ/2.50)	Dutton	(1939)	Bayley, Dorothy	25-40	
Wheeler, Opal	Sebastian Bach (1st {std}, lg8vo, ibds, 126p, fp b/w, cep)	Dutton	(1937)	Greenwalt, Mary	30-50	
Wheeler, Opal	Sing for America (1st {std}, 4to, 127p, ibds, fp color, pep, DJ/3.75)	Dutton	(1944)	Tenggren, Gustaf	60-90	
Wheeler, Opal	Sing for Christmas (1st {std}, 4to, ibds, 127p, 12cp, pep, DJ/3.75)	Dutton	1943	Tenggren, Gustaf	80-120	
Wheeler, Opal	Sing in Praise (1st {std}, 4to, 94p, ibds, color, pep, DJ/3.75, CH)	Dutton	1946	Torrey, Marjorie	60-90	
Wheeler, Opal	Sing Mother Goose (1st {std}, 4to, 102p, ibds, color, DJ/3.75, CH)	Dutton	1945	Torrey, Marjorie	65-90	
Wheeler, Post	Albanian Wonder Tales (1st {std}, 8vo, 282p, col frn, b/w, pep, DJ/2.00)	Doubleday/Doran	1936	Petershams	65-100	
Wheeler, Post	Hathoo of the Elephants (1st, sm8vo, orange cl, 333p, pep by...)	Viking	1943	Falls, Charles B.	35-60	*
Wheelock, Sarah	Three Little Warrens (1st, 8vo, 227p, b/w, DJ/1.75)	Stokes	1935	Lawson, Marie A.	30-45	
Wheelwright, John T.	Bad Penny (1st, sm8vo, gilt, teg, 162p, b/w)	Lamson/Wolffe	1896	Attwood, F.G.	60-90	*
Whishaw, Frederick	Emperor's Englishman (1st, 8vo, 342p)	L: Hutchinson	1896	Goble, Warwick	90-120	*
White, Anne H.	Junket (1st, lg8vo, 184p, b/w, DJ/2.75)	Viking	1955	McCloskey, Robert	70-100	
White, Anne H.	Story of Serapina (1st, 4to, 128p, orange cl, b/w, DJ/2.50)	Viking	1951	Palazzo, Tony	35-60	*
White, Anne H.	Uninvited Donkey (1st, 8vo, 223p, blue cl, b/w, DJ/2.75)	Viking	(1957)	Freeman, Don	30-50	
White, Anne T.	All About the Stars (1st, 8vo, 144p, 1-color, pep, DJ/1.95)	Random	(1954)	Bileck, Marvin	50-80	R*
White, Anne T.	David the Giant Killer (1st, 8vo, 131p, fp b/w, DJ/4.50)	Crowell	(1970)	Thomas, Phero	40-65	*
White, Bessie	Bear Named Grumms (1st, lg8vo, 81p, b/w, DJ/2.50)	Houghton	1953	Sari	20-35	
White, Constance	Flip Flop Show (folio, bds, fp color)	Donohue	(1909)	White, Constance	70-120	
White, Eliza O.	Ann Frances (1st, 8vo, 126p, blue cl, 7cp, cep, DJ/1.75)	Houghton	1935	Sewell, Helen	35-60	
White, Eliza O.	Blue Aunt (1st, sm8vo, 144p, col frn & cvr by...)	Houghton	1918	Pyle, Katharine	35-60	
White, Eliza O.	Borrowed Sister (1st, sm8vo, 150p, green cl, p-o, 4pl)	Houghton	1906	Pyle, Katharine	60-90	
White, Eliza O.	Ednah and her Brothers (1st, sm8vo, 143p, gilt, 4pl)	Houghton	1900	Bush-Brown, Margaret	40-65	
White, Eliza O.	Farm Beyond the Town (1st, 8vo, 147p, 1-color, cep, DJ/1.75)	Houghton	1937	Boyle, Mildred	30-45	
White, Eliza O.	Green Door (1st, sm8vo, 212p, silhouettes, DJ/2.00)	Houghton	1930	Hummel, Lisl	40-65	
White, Eliza O.	I, Autobiography of a Cat (1st, lg8vo, 114p, b/w, pep, DJ/2.00)	Houghton	1941	Hutton, Clarke	50-85	
White, Eliza O.	Lending Mary (1st, 8vo, 114p, 7 fp 1-color)	Houghton	1934	Paull, Grace	20-30	
White, Eliza O.	Nancy Alden (1st, 8vo, 139p, 1-color, DJ/1.75)	Houghton	1936	Boyle, Mildred	25-45	
White, Eliza O.	Only Child (1st, sm8vo, 167p, grey cl, p-o, 4pl)	Houghton	1905	Pyle, Katharine	40-70	
White, Eliza O.	When Molly was Six (1st, 8vo, 133p, 3pl)	Houghton	1894	Pyle, Katharine	50-80	
White, Eliza O.	Where is Adelaide? (1st, 8vo, 155p, orange cl, b/w, dep)	Houghton	1933	Sewell, Helen	30-50	
White, Elwyn B.	Charlotte's Web (1st {std}, 8vo, 184p, b/w, pep, DJ/2.50, NH)	Harper	(1952)	Williams, Garth	500-800	R
White, Elwyn B.	Stuart Little (1st {std}, 8vo, tan cl, b/w, 131p, pep, DJ/2.00)	Harper	(1945)	Williams, Garth	500-800	R
White, Elwyn B.	Trumpet of the Swan (1st, 8vo, 210p, blue/gilt, fp b/w, cep, DJ/4.50)	Harper	(1970)	Frascino, Edward	50-80	R
White, Hervey	Snake Gold (1st, 12mo, 220p, decor by...)	Macmillan	1926	MacKinstry, Eliz.	25-45	
White, Richardson	Aesop's Fables in Rhyme (1st, lg4to, ibds, [100]p, 50pl, pep)	Saalfield	1903	Bull, Charles L.	140-240	*
White, Robb	Secret Sea (1st {std}, 8vo, 243p, fp b/w, pep, DJ/2.00)	Doubleday	1947	Barnum, Jay H.	30-50	*
White, Robb	Smuggler's Sloop (1st {std}, 8vo, 249p, 4 fp b/w, DJ/1.75)	Little/Brown	1937	Wyeth, Andrew	80-130	*
White, Robb	Smuggler's Sloop (1st [this pub.], 8vo, 249p, 4 fp b/w, DJ/1.00)	Doubleday	1947	Wyeth, Andrew	45-70	*
White, Roma	Brownies & Rose-Leaves (1st, 12mo, 200p, tan/gilt, 9pl, dep)	L: A.D. Innes	1892	Brooke, L. Leslie	75-100	
White, Roma	Moonbeams & Brownies (1st, sq12mo, 160p, 5pl)	L: A.D. Innes	1894	Brooke, L. Leslie	90-120	

AUTHOR	TITLE	PUBLISHER	DATE	ARTIST	PRICE	LC
White, Stewart E.	Arizona Nights (1st, 8vo, gilt, p-o, 351p, 7cp)	McClure	1907	Wyeth, N.C.	80-130	
White, Stewart E.	Camp and Trail (1st, 8vo, 236p, col frn, 11pl)	Outing	1907	(Photos)	40-65	
White, Stewart E.	Conjuror's House (1st, sm8vo, uncut, 260p, 6pl)	McClure	1903	Chapman, Charles S.	40-65	
White, Stewart E.	Daniel Boone (1st {std}, sm8vo, 308p, blue cl, p-o, 5pl, PPP)	Doubleday/Page	1922	Schuyler, Remington	90-120	R
White, Stewart E.	Daniel Boone (1st, lg8vo, 274p, p-o, 4cp, 10pl, pep)	Doubleday/Page	1926	Daugherty, James	60-90	
White, Stewart E.	Gold (1st, 12mo, green/gilt, 437p, pep, 4cp)	Doubleday/Page	1913	Fogarty, Thomas	50-80	
White, Stewart E.	Gray Dawn (1st, sm8vo, blue cl, 395p, 4cp, pep)	Doubleday/Page	1915	Fogarty, Thomas	20-35	
White, Stewart E.	Magic Forest (1st, sm8vo, 146p, gilt, teg, 6cp, pep)	Macmillan	1903	Bleeson	30-50	
White, Stewart E.	Rules of the Game (1st, sm8vo, 644p, 4cp)	Doubleday/Page	1910	Hiller, Lejaren A.	30-50	
White, Stewart E.	Sign at Six (1st, sm8vo, 264p, green/gilt, 6pl)	Bobbs-Merrill	(1912)	Bracker, M. Leone	40-65	
White, Stewart E.	The Forest (1st, 8vo, green cl, teg, 276p, 17pl)	Outlook	1903	Fogarty, Thomas	30-50	
White, Stewart E.	The Mountains (1st, 8vo, 282p, teg, col frn, 15pl)	McClure	1904	Lungren, Fernand	30-50	
White, Stewart E.	The Pass (1st, 8vo, 198p, blue cl, col frn, 14pl)	Outing	1906	Lungren, Fernand	30-50	
White, Stewart E.	The Riverman (1st, sm8vo, p-o, 368p, 12pl)	McClure	1908	Wyeth, N.C.	70-100	
White, Terence H.	Godstone and the Blackymor (1st AM {std}, 8vo, 224p, b/w, DJ)	L: J. Cape	(1959)	Ardizzone, Edward	60-100	
White, Terence H.	Ill-Made Knight (1st, 8vo, 291p, DJ/2.50, decor by...)	Putnam	1940	White, Terence H.	400-600	
White, Terence H.	Ill-Made Knight (1st UK, 8vo, 296p, red/gilt, b/w, DJ)	L: Collins	1941	White, Terence H.	350-500	
White, Terence H.	Mistress Masham's Repose (1st, 8vo, 255p, gilt, fp b/w, pep, DJ/3.00)	Putnam	(1946)	Eichenberg, Fritz	60-100	
White, Terence H.	Sword in the Stone (1st, 8vo, 339p, black cl, b/w, DJ)	L: Collins	1938	White, Terence H.	250-450	
White, Terence H.	Sword in the Stone (1st AM, 8vo, 311p, gilt, DJ/2.50, pep by....)	Putnam	1939	Lawson, Robert	250-400	
White, Terence H.	Sword in the Stone (1st AM, 8vo, 311p, gilt, b/w, DJ/2.50)	Putnam	1939	White, Terence H.	250-400	
White, Terence H.	Witch in the Wood (1st, 8vo, blue/gilt bds, 270p, b/w, DJ/2.50)	Putnam	1939	White, Terence H.	350-500	
White, William A.	Court of Boyville (1st, sm8vo, 358p, buckram, b/w pl, PPP)	Doub./McClure	1899	Lowell, Orson	140-200	
White, William A.	Martial Adventures of Henry and Me (1st, 8vo, 340p, red cl, 25 b/w)	Macmillan	1918	Sarg, Tony	30-50	
White, William C.	Mouseknees (1st, sm8vo, 144p, fp b/w, pep, DJ/1.75)	Random	(1939)	Johnson, Avery	60-100	
Whitehead, Roberta	Five & Ten (1st, 8vo, red cl, [41]p, color, pep, DJ/1.00)	Houghton	1943	Lenski, Lois	80-130	
Whitehead, Roberta	Peter Opens the Door (1st, 8vo, [20]p, color, DJ/1.00)	Houghton	1946	Bronson, Mildred	30-45	*
Whitehorn, Alan L.	Wonder Tales of Old Japan (1st, 8vo, gilt, 173p, p-o, 12cp)	L: Jack	1911	Obata, Shozan	70-100	*
Whitehorn, Alan L.	Wonder Tales of Old Japan (1st AM, 8vo, 173p, teg, p-o, 12cp)	Stokes	(1912)	Obata, Shozan	70-100	*
Whiteing, Richard	Paris of Today (1st, 4to, 249p, gilt, teg, b/w)	Century	1900	Castaigne, Andre	70-100	
Whitfield, Raoul	Silver Wings (1st, sm8vo, 234p, col frn, pep)	Knopf	1930	Dobias, Frank	60-100	*
Whitlock, Brand	Happy Average (1st, sm8vo, 347p, green/gilt, cvr by...)	Bobbs-Merrill	(1904)	Armstrong, Margaret	30-50	*
Whitman, Walt	Overhead the Sun (1st {std}, 4to, [37]p, color, DJ/4.95)	Farrar, Straus	(1969)	Frasconi, Antonio	40-65	R
Whitman, Walt	Poems of Leaves & Grass (1st, 4to, 260p, teg, gilt, 24 ticp)	L: J.M. Dent	1913	Cook, Margaret C.	120-170	
Whitman, Walt	There was a Child Went Forth (1st {std}, 4to, ipcb, [32]p, color, DJ/1.75)	Harper	(1943)	Gay, Zhenya	45-70	
Whitman, William	Navaho Tales (1st, sm8vo, 217p, b/w, pep)	Houghton	1925	Heins, John P.	40-65	
Whitney, A.D.T.	Mother Goose for Grown Folks (1st {new ed}, 12mo, 204p)	Houghton	1898	Hoppin, Augustus	30-50	*
Whitney, Caspar	On Snow-Shoes/Barren Grounds (1st, lg4to, gilt, teg, 324p, blue cl, b/w)	Harper	1896	Remington, Frederic	200-300	
Whitney, Caspar	Sporting Pilgrimage (1st, 8vo, 397p, red/gilt, b/w)	Harper	1895	Remington, Frederic	80-125	
Whitney, Elinor	Mystery Club (1st, sm8vo, 252p, b/w pl)	Stokes	1933	Siegel, William	25-40	*
Whitney, Elinor	Timothy & the Blue Cart (1st, sm8vo, 168p, p-o, col frn, fp b/w, pep)	Stokes	1930	Hader, B.& E.	40-65	
Whitney, Elinor	Tod of the Fens (1st, 8vo, 239p, red cl, col frn, b/w, pep, NH)	Macmillan	1928	Goble, Warwick	50-80	
Whitney, Elinor	Tyke-Y: His Book & his Mark (1st, 8vo, 78p, silhouettes)	Macmillan	1925	Whitney, Elinor	25-40	
Whitney, Helen H.	Bed-Time Book (1st, lg4to, ipcb, 31p, 6cp, pep)	Duffield	1907	Smith, Jessie W.	350-500	
Whitney, Helen H.	Punch and Judy Book (1st, lg sq8vo, ibds, 32p, color)	Duffield	1906	Harding, Charlotte	200-300	
Whitney, Phyllis	Mystery of the Gulls (1st, 8vo, 202p, b/w, DJ/2.50)	Westminster Pr.	(1949)	Smalley, Janet	30-50	
Whitney, Phyllis	Mystery on the Isle of Skye (1st, 8vo, 224p, b/w, DJ/2.75)	Westminster Pr.	(1955)	Keats, Ezra J.	30-45	*
Whitney, Phyllis	Place for Ann (1st, 8vo, 211p, col frn, DJ/2.00)	Houghton	1941	Blair, Helen	20-35	*
Whitney, Thomas	Prince Ivan, Firebird & Gray Wolf (1st, ob4to, [32]p, color, cep, DJ)	Scribner	1968	Hogrogian, Nonny	40-65	
Whitney, Thomas	Vasilisa the Beautiful (1st {std}, 8vo, [32]p, color, dep, DJ/4.95)	Macmillan	(1970)	Hogrogian, Nonny	40-70	R
Whitson, John H.	Barbara, Woman of the West (1st, sm8vo, green cl, 314p, 5pl)	Little/Brown	1903	Emerson, Chase	25-45	
Whittemore, Maria	Flower Fairies (1st, lg8vo, ibds, 80p)	L: Cassell	(1886)	(Chromos)	150-220	
Whittier, John G.	Jack in the Pulpit (1st, sq8vo, [38]p, color)	NY: S. Tilton	1883	Unknown	70-120	*
Whittier, John G.	Snowbound (lg8vo, gilt, teg, 96p, color)	Houghton	1906	Various	45-70	
Whittier, John G.	Snowbound (1st, 8vo, p-o, 123p, green cl, 12pl, pep)	Reilly/Britton	(1909)	Neill, John R.	60-90	
Whittier, John G.	Tent on the Beach (1st, sm8vo, green/gilt, 110p, teg)	Houghton	1899	Armstrong, Margaret	60-100	
Whitworth, Geoffrey	Book of Whimsies (1st, 8vo, 62p, gilt, teg, uncut, 12cp)	L: J.M. Dent	1909	Henderson, Keith	80-135	
Whyte, Adam G.	Christabel's Fairyland (1st, sm4to, ibds, p-o, 183p, color)	L: Chapman/Hall	1926	Gautier, Pauline	80-135	
Whyte, Christina	Adventures of Merry Wink (1st, 8vo, 199p, 12 fp b/w)	L: Hodder	[1906]	Wheelhouse, Mary V.	200-300	
Wibberley, Leonard	Beware of the Mouse (1st, 8vo, 189p, uncut, fp b/w, DJ/3.50)	Putnam	(1958)	Wing, Ronald	70-100	
Wibberley, Leonard	King's Beard (1st {std}, 8vo, 198p, pep, DJ/2.75)	Ariel	(1952)	Price, Christine	30-50	
Wibberley, Leonard	Secret of the Hawk (1st {std}, 8vo, 214p, b/w, pep, DJ/2.95)	Ariel	(1953)	Price, Christine	40-65	
Wibberley, Leonard	Time of the Lamb (1st, 16mo, 47p, fp b/w, cep, DJ/2.50)	NY: Washburn	(1961)	Kredel, Fritz	25-45	*
Wiberg, Harald	Christmas at Totem's Farm (1st AM, 4to, [30]p, fp 3-color, pep, DJ/4.50)	Coward	(1968)	Wiberg, Harald	70-120	*
Widdemer, Margaret	Binkie and Bell Dolls (1st, 8vo, tan cl, 146p, p-o, 8cp, pep)	Penn	1923	Price, Hattie L.	55-90	*
Wiederseim, Grace	Baby's Day (1st, 4to, ibds, 11 fp color)	Stokes	1910	Wiederseim, Grace	200-300	R
Wiederseim, Grace	Dolly Drake (1st, 4to, ibds, [16]p, shape book, color)	Stokes	(1909)	Wiederseim, Grace	200-300	*
Wiederseim, Grace	Ducky Daddles (folio, shape bk, 16p, ibds, color)	Stokes	(1911)	Wiederseim, Grace	150-225	
Wiederseim, Grace	Fido (shape book, folio, ibds, 16p, color)	Stokes	(1910)	Wiederseim, Grace	150-225	R
Wiederseim, Grace	Tiny Tots: their Adventures (1st, 4to, ibds, 12 fp color)	Stokes	(1909)	Wiederseim, Grace	250-350	
Wier, Ester A.	Easy Does It (1st, 8vo, 126p, b/w, DJ/3.50)	Vanguard Press	1965	Mars, Witold T.	30-50	
Wier, Ester A.	Gift of the Mountains (1st, 8vo, 116p, b/w, DJ/3.25)	McKay	1963	Lewis, Richard	20-30	
Wier, Ester A.	Long Year (1st, 8vo, 150p, b/w, DJ/3.95)	McKay	(1969)	Koering, Ursula	20-30	
Wier, Ester A.	Space Hut (1st, 8vo, 94p, b/w, DJ/3.95)	Stackpole Bks.	(1967)	Summers, Leo	20-30	
Wier, Ester A.	Straggler: Adventures of a Sea Bird (1st, 8vo, 85p, b/w, DJ/3.75)	McKay	(1970)	Vosburgh, Leonard	20-35	
Wier, Ester A.	The Loner (1st, 8vo, 153p, b/w, DJ/3.75, NH)	McKay	1963	Price, Christine	45-70	
Wier, Ester A.	The Rumptydoolers (1st, 8vo, 159p, b/w, DJ/3.50)	Vanguard Press	(1964)	Mars, Witold T.	30-50	*
Wier, Ester A.	The Winners (1st, 8vo, 179p, b/w, DJ/3.95)	McKay	(1968)	Koering, Ursula	20-30	*

AUTHOR	TITLE	PUBLISHER	DATE	ARTIST	PRICE	LC
Wier, Ester A.	Wind Chasers (1st, 8vo, 154p, b/w, DJ/3.50)	McKay	1967	Werth, Kurt	20-35	*
Wiese, Kurt	Buddy the Bear (1st, lg8vo, ibds, color, [32]p, pep, DJ/1.50)	Coward	1936	Wiese, Kurt	60-100	
Wiese, Kurt	Chinese Ink Stick (1st {std}, 8vo, 199p, 4cp, pep, DJ/2.00)	Doubleday/Doran	1929	Wiese, Kurt	80-125	
Wiese, Kurt	Cunning Turtle (1st, ob4to, 32p, fp 1-color, pep, DJ/2.00)	Viking	1956	Wiese, Kurt	40-65	*
Wiese, Kurt	Dog, the Fox and the Fleas (1st, sm ob4to, [32]p, fp 2-color, DJ/2.25)	McKay	(1953)	Wiese, Kurt	30-50	*
Wiese, Kurt	Ella the Elephant (1st, lg8vo, p-o, [31]p, 2-color, pep)	Coward	1931	Wiese, Kurt	40-65	
Wiese, Kurt	Fish in the Air (1st, ob4to, ipcb, [32]p, color, pep, DJ/2.00, CH)	Viking	1948	Wiese, Kurt	90-150	R*
Wiese, Kurt	Groundhog and his Shadow (1st, ob4to, 32p, color, pep, DJ/2.25)	Viking	(1959)	Wiese, Kurt	30-50	
Wiese, Kurt	Happy Easter (1st, ob8vo, ibds, 32p, color, DJ/1.50)	Viking	1952	Wiese, Kurt	40-70	
Wiese, Kurt	Joe Buys Nails (1st {std}, lg ob8vo, ibds, [54]p, color, pep)	Doubleday/Doran	1931	Wiese, Kurt	60-90	
Wiese, Kurt	Karoo the Kangaroo (1st {1st bk.}, sm4to, [35]p, color, pep)	Coward	1929	Wiese, Kurt	55-80	
Wiese, Kurt	Kurt Wiese's Picture Book of Animals (1st, lg8vo, [99]p, color, pep)	Coward	(1937)	Wiese, Kurt	50-70	
Wiese, Kurt	Liang & Lo (1st {std}, sm ob4to, ibds, [56]p, color, pep)	Doubleday/Doran	1930	Wiese, Kurt	45-70	
Wiese, Kurt	Little Boy Lost in Brazil (1st, ob8vo, [56]p, fp color, pep, DJ/2.00)	Dodd	1942	Wiese, Kurt	40-65	
Wiese, Kurt	Parrot Dealer (1st {std}, 8vo, 239p, b/w, pep)	Coward	(1932)	Wiese, Kurt	35-60	*
Wiese, Kurt	Rabbit Bros. Circus: One Night Only (1st, ob4to, 38p, fp 3-color, DJ/3.00)	Viking	1963	Wiese, Kurt	50-80	
Wiese, Kurt	Rabbit's Revenge (1st, lg ob8vo, ibds, [48]p, fp 1-color, pep, DJ/1.50)	Coward	(1940)	Wiese, Kurt	50-80	
Wiese, Kurt	Thief in the Attic (1st, 8vo, 43p, blue cl, color, DJ/3.00)	Viking	(1965)	Wiese, Kurt	25-40	
Wiese, Kurt	Wallie the Walrus (1st, lg8vo, [31]p, p-o, 3-color)	Coward	1930	Wiese, Kurt	40-65	
Wiese, Kurt	You Can Write Chinese (1st, ob4to, ibds, [64]p, color, pep, DJ/2.00, CH)	Viking	1945	Wiese, Kurt	120-180	
Wiesner, William	Grabbit, the Rascal (1st, lg8vo, 46p, 3-color, DJ/3.75)	Viking	(1969)	Wiesner, William	25-40	
Wiesner, William	Green Noses (1st, sm ob4to, [37]p, fp color, cep, DJ/3.95)	Four Winds Pr.	(1969)	Wiesner, William	40-65	
Wiesner, William	Happy-Go-Lucky (1st, ob4to, [28]p, color, DJ/4.50)	Seabury Press	(1970)	Wiesner, William	30-45	*
Wiesner, William	Three Good Friends (1st, sm4to, [31]p, ibds, fp color, DJ/1.50)	Harper	(1946)	Wiesner, William	30-45	
Wiesner, William	Tower of Babel (1st {std}, 4to, [32]p, color, DJ/3.95)	Viking	(1968)	Wiesner, William	25-40	
Wiggin & Smith	Talking Beasts (1st, sm8vo, 391p, teg, p-o, col frn, pl)	Doubleday/Page	1911	Nelson, Harold	30-50	
Wiggin, Kate D.	Affair at the Inn (1st, 12mo, tan cl, 220p, 6pl)	Houghton	1904	Justice, B. Martin	40-65	
Wiggin, Kate D.	Birds' Christmas Carol (1st, 8vo, 91p, green/gilt, color)	Houghton	1912	Wireman, Katharine	50-85	R
Wiggin, Kate D.	Cathedral Courtship (1st, 8vo, gilt, 104p, teg, 6pl)	Houghton	1901	Brock, Charles E.	35-60	*
Wiggin, Kate D.	Diary of a Goose Girl (1st, 12mo, 117p, tan cl, b/w)	Houghton	1902	Shepperson, Claude	30-50	
Wiggin, Kate D.	Fairy Ring (1st, 8vo, 445p, col frn, 25pl)	Doubleday/Page	1910	MacKinstry, Eliz.	100-180	
Wiggin, Kate D.	Mother Carey's Chickens (1st, sm8vo, green cl, 356p, 10pl)	Houghton	1911	Stephens, Alice B.	50-80	
Wiggin, Kate D.	Mother Carey's Chickens (1st, 8vo, 289p, p-o, 4cp, 10 b/w)	Houghton	1930	Green, Eliz. S.	40-60	
Wiggin, Kate D.	New Chronicles of Rebecca (1st, 12mo, p-o, 278p, 8pl)	Houghton	1907	Yohn, F.C.	30-50	
Wiggin, Kate D.	Old Peabody Pew (1st, 8vo, p-o, grey/gilt, teg, 143p, col frn, 5pl, pep)	Houghton	1907	Stephens, Alice B.	35-60	
Wiggin, Kate D.	Penelope's Irish Experiences (1st, 8vo, gilt, AEG, 335p, b/w)	L: Gay & Bird	1902	Brock, Charles E.	50-80	
Wiggin, Kate D.	Romance of a Christmas Card (1st, 8vo, 123p, teg, p-o, pep, 5cp)	Houghton	1916	Hunt, Alice E.	45-80	
Wiggin, Kate D.	Scottish Chiefs (1st, lg8vo, p-o, gilt, 503p, 17cp, pep, SC)	Scribner	1921	Wyeth, N.C.	200-300	
Wiggin, Kate D.	Susanna & Sue (1st, 8vo, 225p, teg, p-o, dep, b/w designs by...)	Houghton	1909	Wyeth, N.C.	80-145	
Wiggin, Kate D.	Tales of Laughter (1st, lg8vo, 331p, black cl, 8cp)	Doubleday/Page	1926	MacKinstry, Eliz.	70-100	
Wightman, Francis P.	Jingle Jangle Jumbly Lays... (1st, lg4to, [26]p, color)	NY: Blanchard	1899	Wightman, Francis P.	300-500	*
Wightman, Francis P.	Little Leather Breeches (1st, 4to, ibds, [48]p, color)	J.F. Taylor	1899	Wightman, Francis P.	250-350	
Wiig, Hanna	Tale of Tiny Tutak (1st AM, 16mo, [55]p, 2-color, pep, DJ/1.25)	Lippincott	[1957]	Skauge, Sven	30-50	
Wilbur, Richard	Digging for China: A Poem (1st {std}, 12mo, ibds, [32]p, fp color, DJ)	Doubleday	(1956)	DuBois, W.P.	50-85	
Wilbur, Richard	Loudmouse (1st {std}, 4to, [32]p, 1-color)	Crowell-Collier	(1963)	Almquist, Don	50-80	R*
Wilcox, Ella W.	Poems of Passion & Pleasure (4to, 267p, white/gilt, teg, 20 ticp, pep)	L: Gay/Hancock	(1912)	Tennant, Dudley	200-300	
Wilde, Oscar	Birthday of the Infanta (1st, lg8vo, 58p, blue cl, 3 dp color)	Macmillan	1929	Bianco, Pamela	40-60	
Wilde, Oscar	Canterville Ghost (1st AM, 16mo, 123p, blue/gilt, pl)	Bos: J.W. Luce	1906	Goldsmith, Wallace	150-250	
Wilde, Oscar	Fisherman & his Soul (1st, lg8vo, 212p, gilt, 15 ticp, pep)	Farrar/Rinehart	(1929)	Nadejen, Theodore	120-185	
Wilde, Oscar	Happy Prince (1st AM, 8vo, grey cl, 116p, 3pl)	Roberts Bros.	1888	Crane, Walter	350-500	
Wilde, Oscar	Happy Prince (1st, 8vo, p-o, 204p, gilt, 8cp)	Stokes	(1913)	Nichols, Spencer B.	80-125	
Wilde, Oscar	Happy Prince (1st, 4to, teg, gilt, 134p, 12 ticp, dep)	L: Duckworth	(1913)	Robinson, Charles	675-900	
Wilde, Oscar	Happy Prince (1st AM, 4to, 134p, gilt, teg, 12 ticp, pep)	Putnam	(1913)	Robinson, Charles	500-700	
Wilde, Oscar	Happy Prince (1st, lg8vo, blue/gilt, teg, 148p, pep, 12cp, DJ/3.50)	Winston	(1940)	Shinn, Everett	50-80	
Wilde, Oscar	Harlot's House (1st, sm4to, ibds, 105p, 16pl, DJ)	Dutton	1929	Vassos, John	120-180	
Wilde, Oscar	House of Pomegranates (1st, 8vo, 158p, gilt, uncut, dep, 4pl)	L: McIlvanie	1891	Shannon/Ricketts	700-1000	
Wilde, Oscar	House of Pomegranates (1st, 4to, teg, 162p, gilt, 16 ticp, pep)	L: Methuen	(1915)	King, Jessie	700-900	
Wilde, Oscar	House of Pomegranates (1st AM, 4to, teg, 162p, gilt 16ticp, pep)	Brentano's	[1915]	King, Jessie	600-850	
Wilde, Oscar	House of Pomegranates (1st, 8vo, black/gilt, 180p, 16pl, pep)	Dodd	1925	Kutcher, Ben	55-80	
Wilde, Oscar	Little Hans (1st, 4to, gilt, 48p, fp 1-color, cep, DJ/4.50)	Bobbs-Merrill	(1969)	Quackenbush, Rbt.	25-40	*
Wilde, Oscar	Salome... (1st, 8vo, blue/gilt, 10pl)	L: E. Mathews	1894	Beardsley, Aubrey	900-1300	
Wilde, Oscar	Salome... (sm8vo, 36p, black/gilt, 16pl)	Bos: J.W. Luce	1907	Beardsley, Aubrey	120-200	
Wilde, Oscar	Salome... (2nd, sm4to, gilt, 66p, teg, 16pl)	L: John Lane	1907	Beardsley, Aubrey	350-500	
Wilde, Oscar	Salome... (1st, 8vo, bds, 57p, 13pl)	Dutton	(1927)	Vassos, John	120-180	
Wilde, Oscar	Selfish Giant (1st, 8vo, [40]p, fp color, pep, DJ)	Holt, Rinehart	(1965)	Quackenbush, Rbt.	25-40	*
Wilde, Oscar	Selfish Giant (1st, 4to, [64]p, color, DJ/3.25)	Harlin Quist	1966	Danska, Herbert	25-45	
Wilde, Oscar	The Sphinx (4to, teg, 36p, gilt, uncut, 10pl)	J. Lane	1920	Alastair	500-750	
Wilde, Oscar	Woman of No Importance (1st, 12mo, 102p, pink/gilt, cvr by...)	L: John Lane	1894	Ricketts, Charles	500-700	
Wilder, Laura I.	By the Shores of Silver Lake (1st {std}, 8vo, 260p, col frn, DJ/2.00, NH)	Harper	1939	Sewell/Boyle	600-800	R
Wilder, Laura I.	Farmer Boy (1st {std}, 8vo, 230p, col frn, b/w, dep)	Harper	1933	Sewell, Helen	200-300	R*
Wilder, Laura I.	Farmer Boy (1st [new ed.], 8vo, 372p, b/w, uncut, cep, DJ/2.75)	Harper	(1953)	Williams, Garth	80-120	R
Wilder, Laura I.	Little House in Big Woods (1st {1st bk} {std}, 8vo, 176p, col frn, dep, NH)	Harper	1932	Sewell/Boyle	250-400	R
Wilder, Laura I.	Little House in the Big Woods (1st [new ed.], 8vo, 237p, b/w, DJ/2.75)	Harper	1953	Williams, Garth	140-200	R
Wilder, Laura I.	Little House on the Prairie (1st {std}, sq8vo, 200p, col frn, dep, DJ/2.00)	Harper	1935	Sewell/Boyle	300-500	R
Wilder, Laura I.	Little House on the Prairie (1st [new ed.], 8vo, 334p, b/w, DJ/2.75)	Harper	(1953)	Williams, Garth	100-175	R
Wilder, Laura I.	Little Town on the Prairie (1st {std} 8vo, 288p, col frn, dep, DJ/2.00, NH)	Harper	(1941)	Sewell/Boyle	600-800	R
Wilder, Laura I.	Long Winter (1st {std}, 8vo, 325p, col frn, dep, DJ/2.00, NH)	Harper	1940	Sewell/Boyle	600-800	R
Wilder, Laura I.	On the Banks of Plum Creek (1st {std}, 8vo, 239p, col frn, DJ/2.00, NH)	Harper	1937	Sewell/Boyle	600-800	

AUTHOR	TITLE	PUBLISHER	DATE	ARTIST	PRICE	LC
Wilder, Laura I.	On the Banks of Plum Creek (1st [new ed.], 8vo, 338p, color, DJ/2.75)	Harper	1953	Williams, Garth	80-130	
Wilder, Laura I.	These Happy Golden Years (1st {std}, 8vo, 299p, col frn, DJ/2.00)	Harper	(1943)	Sewell/Boyle	200-300	R
Wilder, Thornton	Bridge of San Luis Rey (1st AM, 8vo, 235p, 10pl, pep, DJ)	A. & C. Boni	1927	Drevenstedt, Amy	300-500	R
Wilder, Thornton	Bridge of San Luis Rey (1st, 8vo, 139p, red/gilt, 16 tip-in woodcuts)	L: Longmans	1929	Leighton, Clare	100-150	
Wilding, Suzanne	Book of Ponies (1st, sq8vo, pcb, 60p, 12 fp color, DJ/4.95)	St. Martin's	(1965)	Dennis, Wesley	30-50	
Wildsmith, Brian	Brian Wildsmith's ABC (1st, lg ob8vo, [57]p, color, DJ, KGM)	L: Oxford U.Pr.	1962	Wildsmith, Brian	60-100	
Wildsmith, Brian	Brian Wildsmith's ABC (1st AM {std}, lg ob8vo, color, pep, DJ/2.95, KGM)	F. Watts	1963	Wildsmith, Brian	50-75	
Wildsmith, Brian	Brian Wildsmith's Birds (1st AM, lg ob8vo, [34]p, color, DJ/4.95. NYTBI)	F. Watts	(1967)	Wildsmith, Brian	60-100	
Wildsmith, Brian	Brian Wildsmith's Circus (1st AM, sm4to, [34]p, color, DJ/4.95)	F. Watts	(1970)	Wildsmith, Brian	50-85	
Wildsmith, Brian	Brian Wildsmith's Fishes (1st AM, ob4to, [34]p, color, DJ/4.95)	F. Watts	(1968)	Wildsmith, Brian	50-80	
Wilhelmson, Carl	Midsummer Night (1st, 8vo, uncut, 305p, 10pl)	Farrar/Rinehart	1930	Ward, Lynd	70-120	
Wilhelmson, Carl	Speed of the Reindeer (1st, 8vo, 220p, b/w, pep, DJ/2.50)	Viking	1954	Busoni, Rafaello	25-40	
Wilkin, Esther B.	Linda & her Little Sisters (1st {A}, sm8vo, unpag, ibds, color, LGB/#214)	Simon/Schuster	(1954)	Wilkin, Eloise B.	60-90	
Wilkin, Esther B.	Play with Me (1st {A}, sm8vo, ibds, [24]p, color, pep, LGB/#567)	Golden Press	1967	Wilkin, Eloise B.	40-65	
Wilkin, Esther B.	So Big (1st {A}, sm8vo, ibds, [24]p, color, LGB/#574)	Golden Press	1968	Wilkin, Eloise B.	30-50	
Wilkins, Mary E.	Decorative Plaques (1st, sq12mo, [32]p, ibds, designs by…)	D. Lothrop Co.	(1883)	Barnes, George F.	425-600	
Wilkins, Mary E.	Heart's Highway (1st [1], sm8vo, green cl, 308p, 8pl)	Doubleday/Page	1900	DuMond	35-60	
Wilkins, Mary E.	Jerome, A Poor Man (1st, 12mo, 506p, gilt, 26pl)	Harper	1897	Keller, Arthur I.	35-60	
Wilkins, Mary E.	Six Trees (1st, 12mo, green/gilt, 206p, 16pl)	Harper	1903	Broughton, C.	35-60	
Wilkins, Mary E.	Wind in the Rose Bush (1st, sm8vo, green/gilt, 237p, 8pl)	Doubleday/Page	1903	Newell, Peter	80-140	
Wilkinson, Florence	Kings & Queens (1st, sm8vo, 138p, tan cl, uncut, 6pl)	McClure	1903	Betts, Ethel F.	35-60	
Wilkinson, Florence	Lady of the Flag-Flowers (1st, 12mo, 364p, cvr by…)	Herbert Stone	1899	Hazenplug, Frank	55-90	
Willard, Charles D.	Fall of Ulysses (1st, 8vo, grey pcb, gilt, [80]p, 4cp, dep)	Doran	1912	VerBeck, Frank	70-100	*
Willard, Frances E.	Wheel Within a Wheel (1st, 12mo, 75p, tan buckram, 7pl)	Revell	1895	(Photos)	90-120	
Willcox, Louise C.	Torch: Book of Poems for Boys (1st {std}, lg8vo, 514p, gilt, 7cp)	Harper	1924	Various	60-90	
Willett, Edward	Cat's Cradle Rhymes for Children (1st, lg8vo, ibds, 60p, fp color)	Worthington	1881	Kendrick, Charles	100-170	*
Williams, C.A.	ABC of Animals (1st, 4to, 17p, color, cep)	Stokes	(1911)	Williams, George A.	120-180	
Williams, C.A.	Bettijak Book (1st, 4to, p-o, color)	Stokes	(1914)	Williams, George A.	250-400	
Williams, C.A.	Magic Book (1st, 4to, 64p, color)	Stokes	(1912)	Williams, George A.	120-200	
Williams, C.A.	Mammy's Lil'l Chillums (1st, lg8vo, [63]p, ibds, fp color)	Stokes	(1904)	Williams, George A.	180-240	R
Williams, C.A.	Stories that Glue Told (1st, ob folio, [36]p, ibds, color)	Stokes	1907	Williams, George A.	130-200	*
Williams, C.A.	Story Book of Silhouettes (ob folio, ibds, b/w)	Stokes	(1914)	Williams, George A.	150-240	
Williams, Egerton	Ridolfo (1st, 8vo, p-o, 406p, 4cp)	McClurg	1906	Leyendecker, J.C.	40-70	
Williams, Eleanor	And a Good Fat Hen (1st, lg8vo, red cl, [47]p, DJ/1.50, lettering by…)	Putnam	(1939)	Gag, Flavia	30-50	
Williams, Emery	Alphabet of Indians (1st, folio, ipcb, [57]p, fp 1-color)	R.H. Russell	1900	Williams, Emery	275-450	*
Williams, Garth	Adventures of Benjamin Pink (1st, 8vo, 151p, green cl, b/w, DJ/2.00)	Harper	(1951)	Williams, Garth	60-90	
Williams, Garth	Baby Animals (1st {A}, 8vo, [24]p, ibds, color, LGB/#274)	Simon/Schuster	1952	Williams, Garth	25-40	R
Williams, Garth	Chicken Book (1st, lg ob8vo, ibds, [31]p, color, DJ/1.50)	Howell/Soskin	(1946)	Williams, Garth	100-150	
Williams, Garth	Chicken Book (1st {std}, lg ob8vo, [31]p, color, DJ/4.50)	Delacorte Pr.	(1970)	Williams, Garth	50-80	*
Williams, Garth	Rabbit's Wedding (1st, lg4to, ibds, unpag, 2-color, DJ/2.50)	Harper	(1958)	Williams, Garth	120-200	
Williams, George A.	Boy's Book of Indians & Wild West (1st, lg ob4to, p-o, 47p, 11cp)	Stokes	1911	Williams, George A.	80-120	
Williams, George A.	Boy's Book of Pirates & Great Sea Rovers (1st, ob4to, ibds, 47p, 11cp)	Stokes	1913	Williams, George A.	120-185	
Williams, Gwen M.	Timid Timothy (1st, sm ob8vo, ibds, [68]p, fp 1-color, pep, DJ/1.25)	W.R. Scott	1944	Weisgard, Leonard	40-70	
Williams, Harcourt	Tales from Ebony (1st, 8vo, 258p, 32cp)	L: Putnam	(1934)	Tunnicliffe, C.F.	140-200	
Williams, Herschel	Children of the Clouds (1st, 8vo, 224p, col frn, 10 b/w, pep)	NY: Nelson	1929	Wiese, Kurt	40-65	
Williams, Herschel	Jolly Old Whistle (1st, 8vo, 187p, purple cl, col frn, fp b/w, pep)	Nelson	1927	Wiese, Kurt	40-65	
Williams, Iolo A.	Where the Bee Sucks (1st, 4to, blue/gilt, 87p, teg, 12 ticp)	L: Medici	(1929)	Cameron, Katharine	70-125	
Williams, Jay	Change of Climate (1st {std}, 8vo, 241p, b/w, DJ/3.50)	Random	(1956)	Keats, Ezra J.	30-45	*
Williams, Jay	Cookie Tree (1st, lg8vo, [40]p, fp color, DJ/2.95)	Parents Mag. Pr.	1967	Hampton, Blake	25-40	
Williams, Jay	Danny Dunn & the Anti-Gravity Paint (1st, 8vo, 154p, b/w, DJ/2.50)	Whittlesey	(1956)	Keats, Ezra J.	25-40	
Williams, Jay	Danny Dunn & the Homework Machine (1st {std}, 8vo, 141p, b/w, DJ/2.95)	Whittlesey	(1958)	Keats, Ezra J.	20-35	
Williams, Jay	Danny Dunn and the Fossil Cave (1st {std}, 8vo, 146p, b/w, DJ/2.95)	Whittlesey	1961	Turkle, Brinton	20-35	
Williams, Jay	Danny Dunn and the Weather Machine (1st {std}, 8vo, 144p, b/w, DJ/2.95)	Whittlesey	(1959)	Keats, Ezra J.	25-40	*
Williams, Jay	Danny Dunn on a Desert Island (1st {std}, 8vo, 159p, b/w, DJ/2.75)	Whittlesey	1957	Keats, Ezra J.	20-35	
Williams, Jay	Danny Dunn on the Ocean Floor (1st {std}, 8vo, 156p, b/w, DJ/2.95)	Whittlesey	(1960)	Turkle, Brinton	20-35	
Williams, Jay	Eagle Jake and Indian Pete (1st, sm8vo, 38p, ibds, color, DJ/1.25)	NY: Rinehart	(1947)	Brimer, John B.	25-40	
Williams, Jay	Good-for-Nothing Prince (1st {std}, lg8vo, [48]p, 1-color, DJ/4.25)	Norton	(1969)	Gobbato, Imero	40-65	
Williams, Jay	King with Six Friends (1st, 8vo, [40]p, color, pep, DJ/3.50)	Parents Mag. Pr.	(1968)	Gobbato, Imero	40-65	
Williams, Jay	Philbert the Fearful (1st {std}, 8vo, 48p, color, DJ/3.25)	Norton	(1966)	Ohlsson, Ib	25-45	*
Williams, Jay	Practical Princess (1st, sm ob4to, [42]p, fp color, DJ/3.95)	Parents Mag. Pr.	(1969)	Henstra, Friso	30-45	*
Williams, Jay	Puppy Pie (1st {std}, 4to, [62]p, fp b/w, cep)	Crowell-Collier	(1962)	Blickenstaff, Wayne	50-80	*
Williams, Jay	Question Box (1st {std}, lg8vo, beige cl, 46p, fp 3-color, DJ/2.95)	Norton	1965	Zemach, Margot	40-65	*
Williams, Jay	Stolen Oracle (1st, 8vo, 222p, b/w, DJ/2.00)	NY: Oxford U.Pr.	(1943)	Chapman, Fred T.	25-40	*
Williams, Jay	Sword of King Arthur (1st, 8vo, 188p, b/w, DJ/3.95)	Crowell	(1968)	Glanzman, Louis	30-45	*
Williams, Jay	Tournament of the Lions (1st, lg8vo, black/gilt, 120p, 5 fp b/w, DJ/2.75)	H.Z. Walck	1960	Keats, Ezra J.	35-50	
Williams, Margery	Velveteen Rabbit (1st AM, 8vo, ibds, 33p, 7cp, pep)	Doran	(1922)	Nicholson, Wm.	450-600	
Williams, Margery	Velveteen Rabbit (1st, lg8vo, 19p, ipcb, 7cp, pep)	L: Heinemann	1922	Nicholson, Wm.	500-700	
Williams, Michael	Little Brother Francis of Assisi (1st, sm8vo, 188p, 4pl, dep)	Macmillan	1926	Artzybasheff, Boris	35-60	*
Williams, Orlando	Three Naughty Children (1st, lg8vo, 110p, fp 2-color)	L: Duckworth	1922	Monsell, J.R.	60-90	*
Williams, Ursula	Island Mackenzie (1st AM, 8vo, 128p, b/w, pep, DJ/2.95)	Wm. Morrow	1960	Ardizzone, Edward	70-100	
Williams, Ursula	The Moonball (1st AM {std}, 8vo, pcb, 138p, fp b/w, DJ/3.95)	Meredith Press	(1967)	Paton, Jane	40-65	
Williams, Wilbur H.	Fairy Tales from Folk Lore (1st, sm8vo, 288p, b/w)	Moffat	1908	Squire, Maud H.	40-60	
Williamson, C.& N.	Princess Passes (1st, 12mo, green cl, 369p, 12 pl by…)	Henry Holt & Co.	1905	Penfield, Edward	30-50	
Williamson, Hamilton	Baby Bear (1st {std}, 8vo, [55]p, green ibds, color)	Doubleday/Doran	(1930)	Hader, B.& E.	60-90	
Williamson, Hamilton	Humpy, Son of the Sands (1st {std}, 8vo, [47]p, color, pep)	Doubleday/Doran	1937	Hader, B.& E.	70-100	*
Williamson, Hamilton	Lion Cub: Jungle Tale (1st {std}, 8vo, ipcb, [51]p, color, pep)	Doubleday/Doran	(1931)	Hader, B.& E.	60-100	
Williamson, Hamilton	Little Elephant (1st {std}, sq8vo, ibds, [55]p, 4cp)	Doubleday/Doran	(1930)	Hader, B.& E.	40-65	
Williamson, Hamilton	Monkey Tale (1st {std}, 8vo, [49]p, pep, color)	Doubleday/Doran	(1929)	Hader, B.& E.	45-70	

AUTHOR	TITLE	PUBLISHER	DATE	ARTIST	PRICE	LC
Williamson, Hamilton	Stripey (1st {std}, 8vo, ibds, [47]p, color, pep, DJ/1.00)	Doubleday/Doran	1939	Hader, B.& E.	60-90	
Williamson, Hugh R.	Gods & Mortals in Love (1st, 4to, cloth, 82p, t.e. blue, 9 fp color)	L: Country Life	(1935)	Dulac, Edmund	180-250	
Williamson, Joanne	Iron Charm (1st {std}, 8vo, 201p, b/w, DJ/3.50)	Knopf	(1964)	Wildsmith, Brian	25-40	
Williston, Teresa P.	Hindu Stories (1st, 8vo, 111p, p-o, brown cl, 9cp, pep)	Rand/McNally	(1925)	Squire, Maud H.	50-85	
Williston, Teresa P.	Japanese Fairy Tales (1st, sm8vo, blue cl, 88p, 8 fp color, pep)	Rand/McNally	(1904)	Ogawa, Sanchi	55-80	
Willoughby, Rachel	Tunes for Tiny Troubadours (1st, lg4to, ibds, 31p, color, DJ/2.50)	Putnam	(1936)	Willoughby, Walter	60-90	
Willson, Dixie	Circus ABC (1st, 8vo, 97p, brown cl, 1-color, pep)	Stokes	1924	Berry, Erick	50-80	
Willson, Dixie	Clown Town (1st {std}, lg8vo, ibds, [62]p, color)	Doubleday/Page	1924	Berry, Erick	70-130	
Willson, Dixie	Empty Elephant (1st, 4to, ibds, [39]p, color)	Volland	(1923)	Berry, Erick	100-170	
Willson, Dixie	Honey Bear (1st, sm8vo, ibds, [36]p, pep, color)	Volland	(1923)	Barney, Maginel W.	70-100	
Willson, Dixie	Once Upon a Monday (1st, 8vo, ibds, 40p, color, pep)	Volland	(1931)	Berry, Erick	65-100	
Willson, Dixie	Pinky-Pup & Empty Elephant (1st, lg4to, ibds, 60p, color)	Volland	(1922)	Berry, Erick	200-300	
Willson, Dixie	Pinky-Pup & Empty Elephant (1st [new ed], sm4to, [62]p, ibds, color, pep)	Volland	(1928)	Berry, Erick	120-200	
Willson, Dixie	Tuffy Good Luck (1st, sq12mo, ipcb, pep, 39p, color)	Volland	(1927)	DeKarekjarto, I.	80-120	
Willson, John B.	Lucian's Wonderland... (1st, 8vo, brown/gilt, 163p, 15pl)	L: Blackwood	1899	Garnett, A. Payne	100-170	
Wilman, Stanley	Games for Playtime & Parties (1st, 4to, 82p, ibds, color)	L: Jack	[1914]	Tarrant, Margaret	100-180	
Wilson, Augusta	Devota (1st, 8vo, teg, p-o, 122p, red/gilt, 4cp, dep)	Dillingham	(1907)	Travis, Stuart	25-40	
Wilson, Barbara K.	Wonderful Cornet (1st, 8vo, 96p, b/w, DJ)	L: H. Hamilton	1958	Briggs, Raymond	50-85	
Wilson, Edmund	Undertaker's Garland (1st, 12mo, 192p, uncut, p-o, 5pl)	Knopf	1922	Artzybasheff, Boris	120-200	R
Wilson, Edward A.	Pirate's Treasure (1st, 8vo, ibds, [96]p, color, pep)	Volland	(1926)	Wilson, Edward A.	50-85	
Wilson, Eleanore H.	About Ricco (1st, 4to, pep, 123p, p-o, color, pep, DJ/2.00)	Whitman	1937	Wilson, Eleanore H.	60-100	
Wilson, Eleanore H.	Flyaway Flippety (1st {std}, lg8vo, 104p, pep, 14cp)	Harper	1932	Wilson, Eleanore H.	30-50	*
Wilson, Harry L.	Boss of the Little Arcady (1st, 8vo, green cl, 371p, 4pl)	Lothrop Pub.	1905	O'Neill, Rose	35-60	
Wilson, Harry L.	Lions of the Lord (1st, 8vo, p-o, 520p, 6pl)	Lothrop Pub.	(1903)	O'Neill, Rose	35-60	
Wilson, Harry L.	The Seeker (1st, 8vo, green cl, 341p, b/w)	Doubleday/Page	1904	O'Neill, Rose	30-50	
Wilson, Hazel	His Indian Brother (1st, 8vo, 188p, b/w, DJ/2.50)	Abingdon-Cokes.	(1955)	Henneberger, Rbt.	50-80	
Wilson, John F.	Tad Sheldon, Boy Scout (1st, sm8vo, 231p, b/w pl)	Sturgis/Walton	1913	Daugherty, James	120-200	
Wilson, Julia	Becky (1st, 4to, [40]p, fp 2-color, DJ/3.75)	Crowell	(1967)	Wilson, John	40-65	
Wilson, Richard	Indian Story Book (1st, 8vo, 272p, blue/gilt, 16cp)	L: Macmillan	1914	Pape, Frank	80-125	
Wilson, Richard	Russian Story Book (1st, 8vo, 307p, gilt, 16cp)	L: Methuen	1916	Pape, Frank	80-130	
Wilson, Romer	Green Magic (1st, 8vo, green cl, 448p, 8cp)	L: J. Cape	(1928)	Brunton, Violet	100-150	
Wilson, Romer	Red Magic... (1st, sm8vo, red/gilt, 368p, 8cp)	L: J. Cape	(1930)	Nielsen, Kay	500-700	
Wilson, Romer	Red Magic... (1st AM, 8vo, 368p, black cl, uncut, 8cp)	Harcourt	(1931)	Nielsen, Kay	400-650	
Wilson, Romer	Silver Magic (1st, 8vo, 432p, silver cl, 8cp)	L: J. Cape	(1929)	Brunton, Violet	130-180	
Wilson, Woodrow	George Washington (1st, 8vo, 333p, teg, 20pl)	Harper	1897	Pyle, Howard	80-120	
Wimberley, L. (comp)	Famous Cats of Fairyland (1st {std}, 8vo, 246p, DJ/2.50)	Dutton	1938	Wheeler, Nina B.	45-70	
Winder, Blanche	King Arthur & his Knights (8vo, 340p, p-o, 48cp, pep)	L: Ward Lock	[1925]	Theaker, Harry G.	100-165	
Windsor, Mary	About Things (1st, lg4to, ibds, 51p, color, pep, DJ/1.00)	Grosset/Dunlap	(1935)	Stone, Charlotte	65-100	
Windsor, Mary	Mr. Gallagher's Donkey (1st, 4to, [28]p, ipcb, color)	Garden City	(1950)	Darien, Elsie	25-40	
Winfrey, Guy	Bunny Bearskin (1st, 8vo, ibds, color, pep)	Milton Bradley	(1926)	Tessin, Louise D.	80-120	
Winfrey, Guy	Pussy Purr-Mew (1st, 8vo, [126]p, ibds, color, pep)	Milton Bradley	(1927)	Tessin, Louise D.	100-160	
Wing, Paul	Unsuccessful Elf (1st, ob4to, ibds, [44]p, 6 fp color, pep, DJ/1.50)	Rinehart	(1947)	Irvin, Rea	80-120	
Winlow, Clara V.	Kitten that Grew Too Fat (1st, lg ob8vo, gilt, 93p, 24 fp color)	Macrae Smith	(1929)	Hogan, Inez	80-125	
Winn, Marie	What Shall We Do & Allee Galloo! (1st, 4to, ibds, 87p, 2-color, DJ/5.95)	Harper	(1970)	Kuskin, Karla	30-50	
Winslow, Marjorie	Mud Pies & other Recipes (1st {std}, 8vo, [24]p, b/w, DJ/2.50)	Macmillan	1961	Blegvad, Erik	25-40	
Winsor, Frederick	Space Child's Mother Goose (1st {std}, 8vo, [88]p, b/w, pep, DJ/3.50)	Simon/Schuster	1958	Parry, Marian	140-225	
Winter, Alice A.	Jewel Weed (1st, 12mo, p-o, 434p, 5pl)	Bobbs-Merrill	(1910)	Fisher, Harrison	30-50	*
Winter, Milo	Billy Popgun (1st, 4to, ibds, p-o, 61p, 8cp, pep)	Houghton	1912	Winter, Milo	170-240	R
Winterfeld, Henry	Castaways in Lilliput (1st AM {std}, 8vo, 188p, b/w, DJ/3.00)	Harcourt	(1960)	Hutchinson, Wm.	50-80	*
Winterfeld, Henry	Star Girl (1st {std}, 8vo, 191p, b/w, DJ/2.75)	Harcourt	(1957)	Wegner, Fritz	200-300	
Wise, William	Lazy Young Duke of Dundee (1st {std}, 8vo, 47p, color, DJ/3.95)	Rand/McNally	(1970)	Cooney, Barbara	30-50	
Wise, Winifred	Revolt of the Darumas (1st, ob8vo, [38]p, fp color, DJ/3.95)	Parents Mag. Pr.	(1970)	Komoda, Beverly	25-40	
Wister, Annis L.	Happy-Go-Lucky (1st, 8vo, green/gilt, 115p, teg, 4cp)	Lippincott	1906	Johann, P.G.	35-60	*
Wister, Owen	Dragon of Wantley (1st, sm4to, teg, blue/gilt, 149p, b/w, pep)	Lippincott	1892	Stewardson, John	100-160	R
Wister, Owen	Jimmyjohn Boss (1st, 12mo, 333p, gilt, p-o, 5pl by...)	Harper	1900	Remington, Frederic	70-100	
Wister, Owen	Journey in Search of Christmas (1st, 8vo, teg, gilt, 93p, 3pl, pep)	Harper	1904	Remington, Frederic	70-100	
Wister, Owen	Members of the Family (1st, sm8vo, 317p, 12pl)	Macmillan	1911	Dunn, Harvey T.	30-50	
Wister, Owen	Mother (1st, 8vo, 95p, p-o, uncut, 3cp, 4pl, dep)	Dodd	1907	Rae, John	30-50	
Wister, Owen	New Swiss Family Robinson (1st, 4to, 25p, ipcb, b/w)	Duffield	1922	Nichols, F.	65-100	
Wister, Owen	Padre Ignacio (1st, 8vo, ibds, 65p, col frn)	Harper	1925	Hogg, Zack	30-45	
Wister, Owen	Red Men & White (1st, 12mo, 280p, gilt, 16pl)	Harper	1896	Remington, Frederic	80-130	
Wister, Owen	The Virginian (1st, 8vo, 504p, tan cloth, 8pl)	Macmillan	1902	Keller, Arthur I.	170-240	
Wister, Owen	The Virginian (1st, 8vo, red cl, p-o, 506p, teg, 10pl by...)	Macmillan	1911	Remington, Frederic	280-350	*
Wister, Owen	The Virginian (1st, 8vo, red cl, p-o, 506p, teg, 42 illus by...)	Macmillan	1911	Russell, Charles M.	280-350	*
Wither, George	Love Song (1st, 24mo, blue pcb, p-o, 14p, uncut)	(Concord)	(1903)	Bradley, Will	80-120	
Withers, Carl	American Riddle Book (1st, 8vo, 157p, b/w, DJ/2.75)	Abelard-Schuman	(1954)	Simont, Marc	25-45	*
Withers, Carl	Grindstone of God (1st {std}, 4to, [32]p, ibds, color, DJ/3.95)	Holt, Rinehart	(1970)	Bryson, Bernarda	40-65	
Withers, Carl	Painting the Moon (1st {std}, 4to, 29p, fp color, cep, DJ/4.95)	Dutton	(1970)	Adams, Adrienne	60-100	R
Withers, Carl	Tale of a Black Cat (1st {std}, ob8vo, [32]p, ibds, b/w, DJ/2.75)	Holt, Rinehart	(1966)	Cober, Alan E.	30-50	
Withers, Carl	World of Nonsense (1st {std}, 8vo, 117p, ibds, b/w, DJ/4.50)	Holt, Rinehart	(1968)	Johnson, John	40-65	*
Withers, Carl (comp)	Rocket in My Pocket (1st {std}, lg8vo, 248p, ipcb, b/w, DJ/3.50)	Henry Holt & Co.	1948	Suba, Susanne	30-50	R*
Withington, Eliz.	Lullabies of Many Lands (1st, 8vo, [32]p, ibds, 24 color, pep)	Caldwell	(1908)	Withington, Eliz.	80-120	
Wodehouse, P.G.	Gold Bat (1st, 8vo, 277p, red/gilt, 8pl)	L: A&C Black	1904	Whitwell, T.M.R.	700-1000	
Wodehouse, P.G.	Intrusion of Jimmy (1st, sm8vo, 314p, black/gilt, p-o, col frn)	NY: Watt	(1910)	Unknown	700-1000	
Wodehouse, P.G.	Little Nugget (1st AM, sm8vo, 300p, gilt, 3pl)	NY: W.J. Watt	(1914)	Grefe, Will	250-400	
Wodehouse, P.G.	Mike (1st, 8vo, 339p, olive cl, 12pl)	L: A&C Black	1909	Whitwell, T.M.R.	900-1500	
Wodehouse, P.G.	Piccadilly Jim (1st, sm8vo, 363p, orange cl, 8cp)	Dodd	1917	Preston, May W.	400-650	
Wodehouse, P.G.	Prince & Betty (1st AM, 12mo, 300p, black/gilt, p-o, 5pl)	NY: Watt	(1912)	Grefe, Will	600-900	

AUTHOR	TITLE	PUBLISHER	DATE	ARTIST	PRICE	LC
Wodehouse, P.G.	Psmith in the City (1st, 8vo, 266p, blue cl, 12pl)	L: A&C Black	1910	Whitwell, T.M.R.	800-1200	
Wodehouse, P.G.	William Tell Told Again (1st, 8vo, tan cl, teg, 105p, 16cp)	L: A&C Black	1904	Dadd, Philip	800-1200	
Wojciechowska, Maia	Hey, What's Wrong with This One? (1st, 8vo, 72p, fp b/w, DJ/3.95)	Harper	(1969)	Sandin, Joan	30-50	
Wojciechowska, Maia	Odyssey of Courage (1st {std}, 8vo, 182p, b/w, DJ/3.75)	Atheneum	1965	Smith, Alvin	30-45	
Wojciechowska, Maia	Shadow of a Bull (1st {std}, 8vo, 165p, red cl, fp b/w, DJ/3.50, NM)	Atheneum	1964	Smith, Alvin	70-100	R
Wolf, Alice S.	House of Cards (1st, 12mo, 281p, black/gilt, cvr by...)	Stone/Kimball	1896	Hazenplug, Frank	60-100	
Wolf, Ingrid	Pajaro-Cu-Cu (1st AM {std}, ob4to, [24]p, ibds, color, DJ/4.95)	Atheneum	(1967)	Wolf, Ingrid	25-40	*
Wolff, Carl F.	Pale Mountains (1st, 8vo, 204p, 8pl)	Minton Balch	1927	Peck, Anne M.	30-45	
Wolff, Carolyn	Three People (1st {std}, sq8vo, [46]p, 3-color, cep, DJ/3.95)	Harlin Quist	1968	Mack, Stanley	30-50	
Wolff, Robert	Feeling Blue (1st, 8vo, [32]p, fp color, cep, DJ)	Scribner	(1968)	Wolff, Robert	45-70	
Wolo	Amanda (1st, 4to, 37p, color, pep, DJ/2.00)	Wm. Morrow	1941	Wolo	80-125	
Wolo	Secret of the Ancient Oak (1st, 4to, 40p, color, pep, DJ/2.00)	Wm. Morrow	1942	Wolo	100-165	
Wolo	Tweedles, Be Brave! (1st, 4to, 31p, ibds, color, DJ/2.50)	Wm. Morrow	1943	Wolo	90-140	
Wondriska, William	123 - A Book to See (1st, 12mo, [26]p, fp 1-color, dep, DJ/2.50)	Pantheon	(1959)	Wondriska, William	60-90	R
Wondriska, William	All the Animals Were Angry (1st {std}, 8vo, ipcb, [36]p, b/w, dep, DJ/2.95)	Holt, Rinehart	(1970)	Wondriska, William	30-45	*
Wondriska, William	John John Twilliger (1st {std}, sm ob4to, unpag, ibds, 1-color, DJ/3.50)	Holt, Rinehart	(1966)	Wondriska, William	20-35	
Wondriska, William	Long Piece of String (1st {std}, ob8vo, [44]p, color, DJ/2.75)	Holt, Rinehart	1963	Wondriska, William	25-40	
Wondriska, William	Mr. Brown and Mr. Grey (1st {std}, sq8vo, 39p, color, cep, DJ/3.95)	Holt, Rinehart	(1968)	Wondriska, William	30-45	
Wondriska, William	Puff (1st sm4to, unpag, 1-color, pep, DJ/2.75)	Pantheon	(1960)	Wondriska, William	30-50	
Wondriska, William	Tomato Patch (1st {std}, 4to, [35]p, color, pep, DJ/3.50)	Holt, Rinehart	(1964)	Wondriska, William	60-90	R
Wood, Esther	Belinda Blue (1st {std}, 4to, [31]p, yellow cl, 1-color, DJ/2.00)	Longmans	(1940)	Kalab, Theresa	25-40	
Wood, Esther	Great Sweeping Day (1st {std}, 12mo, 158p, b/w, pep, DJ/1.75)	Longmans	1936	Wood, Esther	30-50	
Wood, Esther	House in the Hoo (1st {std}, lg8vo, [32]p, fp b/w, pep, DJ/1.50)	Longmans	(1941)	Kalab, Theresa	25-40	*
Wood, Esther	Pedro's Coconut Skates (1st {std}, sm8vo, 191p, pep, DJ/1.50)	Longmans	1938	Wood, Esther	25-40	
Wood, Esther	Pepper Moon (1st {std}, 4to, 32p, 2-color, DJ/2.00)	Longmans	(1940)	Bannon, Laura	40-65	*
Wood, Esther	Silk and Satin Lane (1st {std}, sm8vo, 255p, b/w, DJ/1.75)	Longmans	1939	Wiese, Kurt	25-40	
Wood, Eugene	Back Home (1st, sm8vo, grey cl, 286p, 8pl)	McClure	1905	Frost, A.B.	50-85	R
Wood, Helen J.	Funny Friends (8vo, ibds, color)	L: Nister	[1889]	Thompson, G.H.	100-165	
Wood, James P.	Elephant in the Barn (1st, 8vo, 115p, b/w, DJ/2.50)	Harper	(1961)	Kessler, Leonard	20-35	
Wood, James P.	Golden Swan (1st, 8vo, 170p, b/w, DJ/3.50)	Seabury Press	1965	Elgin, Kathleen	20-35	
Wood, James P.	People of Concord (1st, 8vo, 152p, b/w, DJ/4.95)	Seabury Press	(1970)	Cuffari, Richard	50-80	R*
Wood, John S.	Yale Yarns (1st, 12mo, 307p, buckram, gilt, cvr by...)	Putnam	1895	Armstrong, Margaret	55-80	
Wood, Lawson	Lawson Wood's Animal Book (4to, stiff wraps, unpag, color)	Whitman	1936	Wood, Lawson	80-130	
Wood, Lawson	Prehistoric Proverbs (sm folio, ibds, p-o, 12 ticp)	L: Collier	[1905]	Wood, Lawson	300-450	
Wood, Marni & Harrie	Something Perfectly Silly (1st, sm sq4to, ibds, [66]p, color, pep)	Knopf	1930	Wood, M.& H.	100-160	*
Wood, Nancy	Little Wrangler (1st {std}, 4to, 49p, DJ/3.25, b/w photos by...)	Doubleday	(1966)	Wood, Myron	25-40	
Woodcock, Louise	Smart Little Boy & his Smart Little Kitty (1st, ob8vo, ipcb, [20]p, color)	W.R. Scott	1947	Bloch, Lucienne	30-45	*
Woodcock, Louise	This is the Way the Animals Walk (1st, ob8vo, [20]p, spiral bds, color)	W.R. Scott	1946	Binney, Ida	40-60	*
Woodcock, Louise	Wiggles (1st {A}, sm8vo, [24]p, ibds, color, LGB/#166)	Simon/Schuster	1953	Wilkin, Eloise B.	50-75	*
Woodhouse, S.C.	Cats at School (1st, 4to, french fold, 21p)	L: Routledge	[1911]	Wain, Louis	1000-1500	*
Woodhouse, S.C.	Crude Ditties (1st, 16mo, 103p, tan cl, 24 fp color)	Swan/Dutton	1903	Macgregor, Angusine	80-125	*
Woodhouse, S.C.	Miss Bounce (1st, 16mo, 111p, color)	S. Sonnenschein	1903	Sichel, Gerald	100-160	
Woodhouse, S.C.	Two Cats at Large (1st, 4to, ibds, 24 fp color)	L: Routledge	[1910]	Wain, Louis	800-1200	
Woodruff, Elizabeth	Dickey Bird (1st, lg4to, black cl, 146p, 6 ticp, pep)	Milton Bradley	(1928)	Tenggren, Gustaf	280-400	
Woodruff, Elizabeth	Stories from the Magic World (1st, lg4to, 130p, p-o, 5cp, DJ/1.25)	McLoughlin	(1938)	Tenggren, Gustaf	250-350	
Woodruff, Helen S.	Mis' Beauty (1st, 12mo, 163p, p-o, 5cp)	A. Harriman	1911	Woodruff, Helen S.	80-120	*
Woods, Margaret L.	Come Unto these Yellow Sands (1st, 4to, ibds, 234p, 16cp, pep)	L: John Lane	1915	Hancock, John	100-175	
Woodward, Clifford	Dreams & Fables (1st, 8vo, 110p, green cl, b/w)	L: Longmans	1929	Everett, Ethel	30-50	*
Woodward, Hildegard	Everyday Children (1st, sq12mo, ipcb, [48]p, 1-color, pep, DJ/1.00)	NY: Oxford U.Pr.	(1935)	Woodward, Hildegarde	30-60	*
Woodward, Hildegard	Time Was (1st, 4to, [48]p, color, DJ/1.50)	Scribner	(1941)	Gag, Flavia	50-80	
Woody, Regina	Almena's Dogs (1st {std}, 8vo, 240p, fp b/w, DJ/2.75)	Ariel	(1954)	Fax, Elton C.	25-40	
Woole, Rose	Animal Legends of Many Lands (4to, gilt, 144p, 12cp)	Tuck/McKay	[1915]	Noble, Edwin	90-150	
Woolf, Rose	Children's Stories from Arabian Nights (1st, lg8vo, 144p, 10cp)	L: R. Tuck	[1914]	Theaker, Harry G.	70-100	*
Woolley, Catherine	David's Railroad (1st, 8vo, 159p, b/w, DJ/2.00)	Wm. Morrow	1949	Johnson, Iris B.	25-40	*
Woolley, Catherine	Ginnie and Geneva (1st, 8vo, 191p, fp b/w, DJ/2.00)	Wm. Morrow	1948	Johnson, Iris B.	50-85	*
Woolley, Catherine	Ginnie and the New Girl (1st, 8vo, 159p, fp b/w, DJ/2.50)	Wm. Morrow	1954	Johnson, Iris B.	50-85	
Woolley, Catherine	I Like Trains (1st {std}, 12mo, ipcb, [32]p, color)	Harper	(1944)	Spiegel, Doris	30-45	
Woolley, Catherine	Libby's Uninvited Guest (1st, 8vo, 191p, rust cl, b/w, DJ/4.25)	Wm. Morrow	(1970)	Frame, Paul	25-40	
Woolley, Catherine	Lunch for Lennie (1st, 8vo, 48p, b/w, DJ/2.00)	Wm. Morrow	1952	Wohlberg, Meg	25-40	*
Woolley, Catherine	Two Hundred Pennies (1st, 8vo, 128p, b/w, DJ/2.00)	Wm. Morrow	1947	Neville, Vera	25-40	
Worcester, Donald	Lone Hunter's Gray Pony (1st, 8vo, 94p, 1-color, DJ/2.50)	NY: Oxford U.Pr.	1956	Johnson, Harper	40-65	*
Wordsworth, William	Intimations of Immortality... (1st, lg8vo, gilt, unpag, 12cp)	L: J.M. Dent	[1913]	Neilson-Gray	125-180	
Worm, Piet	3 Little Horses (1st, narrow 4to, red bds, 62p, pep, DJ/2.95)	Random	(1954)	Worm, Piet	100-165	
Worth, Kathryn	Middle Button (1st {std}, 8vo, 275p, pep, DJ/2.00)	Doubleday/Doran	1941	Bayley, Dorothy	75-120	
Worth, Kathryn	They Loved to Laugh (1st {std}, sm8vo, grey cl, 269p, b/w, pep, DJ/2.00)	Doubleday/Doran	1942	DeAngeli, Marguerite	30-50	
Wotton, Mabel E.	Little Browns (1st, lg8vo, 216p, AEG, col frn, 7pl, pep)	L: Blackie	1900	Brock, Henry M.	40-70	*
Wright, Alan	Bingo and Babs (1st, 4to, bds, p-o, 12cp)	L: Blackie	(1919)	Wright, Alan	150-200	
Wright, Anna R.	Children of the Nineties (1st, lg8vo, ibds, 124p, 3-color, DJ/1.00)	Grosset/Dunlap	1936	Jones, Richard	40-70	
Wright, Dare	Doll and the Kitten (1st {std}, folio, 55p, b/w, DJ/2.50)	Doubleday	(1960)	(Photos)	50-80	
Wright, Dare	Edith and Mr. Bear (1st, folio, ibds, unpag, b/w, DJ/2.95)	Random	(1964)	(Photos)	120-160	
Wright, Dare	Gift from the Lonely Doll (1st, folio, unpag, ibds, b/w, DJ/2.95)	Random	(1966)	(Photos)	200-300	
Wright, Dare	Holiday for Edith & the Bears (1st {std}, lg4to ibds, unpag, b/w, DJ/2.50)	Doubleday	(1958)	(Photos)	100-160	
Wright, Dare	Little One (1st {std}, folio, ibds, b/w, DJ)	Doubleday	1959	(Photos)	120-200	
Wright, Dare	Lona, a Fairy Tale (1st, folio, unpag, b/w, DJ/4.95)	Random	(1963)	(Photos)	100-150	
Wright, Dare	Lonely Doll Learns a Lesson (1st, folio, ibds, [56]p, b/w)	Random	(1961)	(Photos)	70-100	
Wright, Ethel B.	Saturday Flight (1st, lg ob8vo, [20]p, spiral bds, color)	W.R. Scott	1944	Rose, Richard	50-80	
Wright, Ethel B.	Saturday Walk (1st, lg ob8vo, [20]p, spiral-bound, color)	W.R. Scott	1941	Rose, Richard	50-80	
Wright, Harold Bell	Uncrowned King (1st, 12mo, green/gilt, 118p, 5pl)	Book Supply Co.	1910	Neill, John R.	70-125	

AUTHOR	TITLE	PUBLISHER	DATE	ARTIST	PRICE	LC
Wright, Henrietta	Princess Liliwinkins (1st, 12mo, 220p, 9pl)	Harper	1889	Unknown	70-120	
Wright, Isa L.	Having Fun (1st, 12mo, 124p, color)	Houghton	(1929)	Woodward, Hildegarde	35-60	*
Wright, Isa L.	Remarkable Tale of a Whale (1st, 8vo, ibds, color, pep)	Volland	(1920)	Held, John	65-90	
Wright, Mabel O.	Four-Footed Americans... (1st, sm8vo, 432p, b/w)	Macmillan	1898	Seton, Ernest T.	75-100	
Wright, Mabel O.	Wabeno the Magician (1st, sm8vo, 344p, green/gilt, b/w)	Macmillan	1899	Gleeson, J.M.	35-60	
Wriston, Hildreth T.	Downstreet with Edith (1st {std}, 8vo, 198p, col frn, pep, DJ/1.50)	Doubleday/Doran	1935	Paull, Grace	40-65	
Wriston, Hildreth T.	Susan's Secret (1st {std}, 8vo, uncut, 126p, fp b/w, DJ/2.75)	Ariel	(1957)	Mars, Witold T.	25-45	
Wuorio, Eva-Lis	Happiness Flower (1st {std}, 8vo, 78p, gilt, dp b/w, pep, DJ/3.95)	World	(1969)	Bolognese, Don	25-40	
Wuorio, Eva-Lis	Island of Fish in the Trees (1st {std}, 8vo, 59p, 6 dp color, DJ/3.50, NYT)	World	(1962)	Ardizzone, Edward	60-100	R
Wuorio, Eva-Lis	Kali and the Golden Mirror (1st, 8vo, 64p, 3 dp color, DJ/3.75)	World	(1967)	Ardizzone, Edward	30-50	
Wuorio, Eva-Lis	Land of Right Up and Down (1st AM {std}, 8vo, 60p, dp color, DJ/3.50)	World	(1964)	Ardizzone, Edward	35-50	
Wuorio, Eva-Lis	Tal & the Magic Barruget (1st {std}, 8vo, 76p, 2-color, DJ/3.50)	World	(1965)	Bettina	30-45	
Wurth, Anne	Rag Doll Susie (1st, lg sq8vo, [16]p, ibds, 6 color, pep)	Saalfield	1939	Peat, Fern B.	75-100	
Wyants, Miche	Giraffe of King Charles X (1st, 12mo, 54p, color, DJ/2.50, NYTBI)	McGraw-Hill	(1964)	Wyants, Miche	30-50	*
Wyatt, Horace	Malice in Kulturland (1st AM, 12mo, 84p, ipcb, p-o, b/w)	Dutton	(1917)	Tell, W.	60-100	
Wyckoff, Charlotte C.	Jothy: Story of South Indian Jungle (1st {std}, 8vo, 305p, b/w, pep)	Longmans	1933	Wiese, Kurt	30-50	*
Wyckoff, Marjorie	Child's Book of Hymns (1st, lg4to, ibds, 44p, color, pep, DJ/1.50)	Random	(1945)	Masha	30-50	
Wyler, Rose	Oil Comes to Us (1st, ob8vo, ibds, [28]p, color, DJ/0.50)	Grosset/Dunlap	1937	Luykx, Th. D.	30-50	
Wyllarde, Dolf	Things (1st, lg8vo, blue/gilt, 137p, 4pl)	L: T.F. Unwin	(1915)	Peirse/Vane	80-120	*
Wyndham, Lee	Dance for Susie (1st, 8vo, 55p, fp b/w, DJ/2.00)	Dodd	1953	Miller, Jane	20-30	
Wyndham, Lee	Mourka: Mighty Cat (1st, sq8vo, [48]p, fp color, cep, DJ)	Parents Mag. Pr.	(1969)	Mikolaycak, Charles	30-45	
Wyse, Lois	P.S. Happy Anniversary (1st {std}, 24mo, 24p, color, DJ/1.95)	World	(1966)	Haley, Gail E.	20-35	*
Wyss, Johann D.	Swiss Family Robinson (8vo, green bds, 291p, gilt, 6cp, 8pl)	Nister/Dutton	[1900]	Kley, H.	75-100	
Wyss, Johann D.	Swiss Family Robinson (1st, 8vo, 307p, teg, grey/gilt, 12cp)	L: A&C Black	(1907)	Rountree, Harry	120-200	
Wyss, Johann D.	Swiss Family Robinson (1st, 8vo, 602p, red cl, b/w)	Harper	1909	Rhead, Louis	50-80	*
Wyss, Johann D.	Swiss Family Robinson (1st, 8vo, 454p, beige cl, 12cp, pep)	L: J.M. Dent	1910	Folkard, Charles	80-120	
Wyss, Johann D.	Swiss Family Robinson (1st AM, 4to, red cl, 25 ticp)	Hodder	[1913]	Robinson, Thomas H.	100-160	
Wyss, Johann D.	Swiss Family Robinson (1st, sm4to, 431p, teg, red/gilt, 25 ticp)	L: H. Milford	[1913]	Robinson, Thomas H.	120-180	
Wyss, Johann D.	Swiss Family Robinson (1st, lg8vo, 441p, 14cp, pep, WS)	Rand/McNally	(1916)	Winter, Milo	70-100	
Wyss, Johann D.	Swiss Family Robinson (8vo, 436p, color, pep)	Garden City	(1931)	Robinson, Thomas H.	35-60	*
Wyss, Johann D.	Swiss Family Robinson (1st, 8vo, 237p, fp b/w)	Whitman	(1935)	Bennett, Juanita C.	25-45	*
Wyss, Johann D.	Swiss Family Robinson (lg4to, 96p, ibds, col frn, b/w)	Saalfield	(1940)	Muheim, Henry	30-60	*
Wyss, Johann D.	Swiss Family Robinson (1st [deluxe ed.], 8vo, 388p, 9cp, DJ/3.00)	Grosset/Dunlap	(1949)	Ward, Lynd	40-65	
Yamaguchi, Tohr	Golden Crane (1st {std}, 4to, [37]p, fp b/w, DJ/3.00)	Holt, Rinehart	(1963)	Yamaguchi, Marianne	30-50	*
Yamaguchi, Tohr	Two Crabs and the Moonlight (1st {std}, 8vo, [32]p, b/w, pep, DJ/3.00)	Holt, Rinehart	(1965)	Yamaguchi, Marianne	25-45	
Yap, Weda	Abigail's Private Reason (1st, 12mo, 70p, col frn, b/w, pep, DJ/1.00)	Macmillan	1932	Yap, Weda	30-45	
Yashima, M. & T.	Plenty to Watch (1st, sm4to, 39p, color, DJ/2.50)	Viking	1954	Yashima, Taro	80-140	R
Yashima, Taro	Crow Boy (1st, lg4to, 37p, brown cl, color, DJ/2.75, CH)	Viking	1955	Yashima, Taro	100-175	
Yashima, Taro	Horizon is Calling (1st, 8vo, 276p, b/w, DJ/3.50)	Henry Holt & Co.	(1947)	Yashima, Taro	45-70	
Yashima, Taro	Momo's Kitten (1st, lg ob8vo, 33p, color, pep, DJ/2.50)	Viking	(1961)	Yashima, Taro	50-80	
Yashima, Taro	New Sun (1st, 8vo, 310p, b/w, DJ/2.75)	Henry Holt & Co.	(1943)	Yashima, Taro	50-70	
Yashima, Taro	Seashore Story (1st, ob4to, [42]p, color, dep, DJ/4.95, CH, NYTBI)	Viking	(1967)	Yashima, Taro	60-100	
Yashima, Taro	Umbrella (1st, sm ob4to, 32p, pep, fp color, DJ/2.50, CH)	Viking	(1958)	Yashima, Taro	100-165	R
Yashima, Taro	Village Tree (1st, 4to, grey cl, 34p, fp color, dep, DJ/2.50)	Viking	1953	Yashima, Taro	80-125	R
Yashima, Taro	Youngest One (1st, lg ob8vo, 33p, color, pep, DJ/2.75)	Viking	1962	Yashima, Taro	50-80	*
Yates, Elizabeth	Amos Fortune, Free Man (1st {std}, 8vo, 181p, b/w, DJ/2.50, NM)	Aladdin	1950	Unwin, Nora S.	100-165	R
Yates, Elizabeth	Around the Year in Iceland (1st, 8vo, 64p, color, pep)	D.C. Heath	1942	Nielsen, Jon	20-35	*
Yates, Elizabeth	Carey Girl (1st, sm8vo, 185p, DJ/2.75, decor by...)	Coward	(1956)	Hartmann, George	20-35	*
Yates, Elizabeth	Carolina's Courage (1st, 8vo, 94p, b/w, DJ/2.95)	Dutton	(1964)	Unwin, Nora S.	30-45	
Yates, Elizabeth	Children of the Bible (1st {std}, sm8vo, 92p, b/w, DJ/2.00)	Aladdin	1950	Unwin, Nora S.	40-65	
Yates, Elizabeth	Christmas Story (1st {std}, lg8vo, gilt, 54p, b/w, DJ/2.00)	Aladdin	1949	Unwin, Nora S.	40-65	
Yates, Elizabeth	Easter Story (1st {std}, 8vo, 127p, DJ/3.50)	Dutton	(1967)	Unwin, Nora S.	30-50	
Yates, Elizabeth	Is There a Doctor in the Barn? (1st {std}, 8vo, 207p, b/w, DJ/4.95)	Dutton	1966	Fleming, Guy	20-30	
Yates, Elizabeth	Lighted Heart (1st {std}, 8vo, 251p, b/w, DJ/4.50)	Dutton	1960	Unwin, Nora S.	25-45	
Yates, Elizabeth	Mountain Born (1st, 8vo, 118p, brown cl, b/w, pep, DJ/2.50, NH)	Coward	(1943)	Unwin, Nora S.	50-80	
Yates, Elizabeth	Next Fine Day: A Novel (1st, 8vo, 191p, b/w, DJ/3.75)	John Day	(1962)	Unwin, Nora S.	20-35	
Yates, Elizabeth	On That Night (1st {std}, 12mo, 95p, ibds, gilt, b/w, DJ/3.95)	Dutton	1969	Barkley, James	20-30	
Yates, Elizabeth	Once in the Year (1st, 8vo, red cl, p-o, [64]p, 1-color, DJ/2.00)	Coward	(1947)	Unwin, Nora S.	30-50	
Yates, Elizabeth	Patterns on the Wall (1st {std}, 8vo, 241p, DJ/2.00, b/w decor by...)	Knopf	1943	Chappell, Warren	20-30	
Yates, Elizabeth	Pebble in a Pool (1st {std}, 8vo, 284p, b/w, DJ/3.50)	Dutton	1958	(Photos)	20-30	
Yates, Elizabeth	Place for Peter (1st, 8vo, 184p, b/w, DJ/2.50)	Coward	(1952)	Unwin, Nora S.	25-35	
Yates, Elizabeth	Prudence Crandall, Woman of Courage (1st {std}, 8vo, 246p, b/w, DJ/3.00)	Aladdin	1955	Unwin, Nora S.	30-45	
Yates, Elizabeth	Rainbow 'Round the World (1st {std}, 8vo, 174p, b/w, pep, DJ/2.50, JABA)	Bobbs-Merrill	(1954)	Alden, Betty	45-70	R
Yates, Elizabeth	Sam's Secret Journal (1st, sm8vo, 142p, fp b/w, cep, DJ/3.50)	Friendship Pr.	(1964)	Eitzen, Allan	30-50	*
Yates, Elizabeth	Under the Little Fir (1st, 8vo, 96p, 2-color, pep, DJ/2.00)	Coward	(1942)	Unwin, Nora S.	25-40	
Yates, Elizabeth	With Pipe, Paddle and Song (1st {std}, 8vo, 256p, b/w, DJ/4.95)	Dutton	(1968)	Unwin, Nora S.	20-30	
Yates, Elizabeth	Your Prayers and Mine (1st, sm8vo, 64p, 1-color, DJ/2.00)	Houghton	1954	Unwin, Nora S.	20-30	
Yeats, Wm. Butler	Four Plays for Dancers (1st AM, 8vo, bds, 138p, 7pl)	L: Macmillan	1921	Dulac, Edmund	200-300	
Yeats, Wm. Butler	Irish Fairy and Folk Tales (1st AM, 8vo, 326p, AEG, 12pl, pep)	Scott/Scribner	1895	Torrance, James	140-200	
Yeats, Wm. Butler	Land of Hearts Desire (1st AM, 16mo, 43p, pcb, frn by...)	Herbert Stone	1894	Beardsley, Aubrey	600-900	
Yeats, Wm. Butler	Plays for an Irish Theatre (1st, 8vo, 224p, brown bds, uncut, 4cp)	L: A.H. Bullen	1911	Craig, Edward G.	120-200	
Yeats, Wm. Butler	Poems (1st, 8vo, 286p, beige/gilt, uncut, ti page by....)	L: T.F. Unwin	1895	Fell, H. Granville	800-1200	
Yeats, Wm. Butler	Poems of Spenser (1st, 16mo, purple/gilt, uncut, 290p, teg, 8cp)	L: Jack	(1906)	King, Jessie	150-225	
Yeo, Wilma	Mrs. Neverbody's Recipes (1st {std}, 24mo, [34]p, color, DJ/2.95)	Lippincott	(1968)	Aliki	30-50	*
Yeoman, John	Bear's Water Picnic (1st {std}, sm4to, [28]p, fp color, DJ/4.95)	Macmillan	1970	Blake, Quentin	20-35	
Yershov, P.	Humpy (1st {std}, sm4to, 72p, fp b/w, DJ/3.25)	Harcourt	(1966)	Ayer, Jacqueline	25-40	
Yezback, Steven	Pumpkinseeds (1st {std}, 4to, [30]p, 1-color, DJ/4.50)	Bobbs-Merrill	(1969)	Thompson, Mozelle	40-65	
Yoda, Junichi	Rolling Rice Ball (1st AM, 4to, [32]p, color, cep, DJ/3.50)	Parents Mag. Pr.	1969	Watanabe, Saburo	30-50	*

AUTHOR	TITLE	PUBLISHER	DATE	ARTIST	PRICE	LC
Yolen, Jane	Emperor and the Kite (1st, ob8vo, [31]p, color, cep, DJ/3.95, CH)	World	(1967)	Young, Ed	60-90	
Yolen, Jane	Gwinellen, Princess Who Could Not Sleep (1st {std} 4to, unpag, col DJ/2.95)	Macmillan	(1965)	Renfro, Ed	25-40	
Yolen, Jane	Inway Investigators (1st, 8vo, 80p, b/w, DJ/3.75)	Seabury Press	(1969)	Eitzen, Allan	20-30	
Yolen, Jane	Isabel's Noel (1st, sm4to, [30]p, fp 3-color, pep, DJ/2.95)	Funk/Wagnalls	(1967)	Roth, Arnold	30-50	*
Yolen, Jane	Minstrel & the Mountain (1st, 12mo, [60]p, gilt, color, cep, DJ/3.50)	World	(1967)	Rockwell, Anne	25-40	
Yolen, Jane	Pirates in Petticoats (1st [1st bk.], 8vo, 118p, DJ/3.25)	McKay	(1963)	Vosburgh, Leonard	60-95	
Yolen, Jane	Seventh Mandarin (1st, 4to, gilt, [34]p, color, cep, DJ/4.95)	Seabury Press	(1970)	Young, Ed	30-50	
Yolen, Jane	Witch Who Wasn't (1st {std}, 4to, ibds, [36]p, color, DJ/2.95)	Macmillan	1964	Roth, Arnold	20-35	
Yonge, Charlotte	Dove in the Eagle's Nest (1st, sm8vo, 294p, 3cp, 8pl, pep, DJ)	Macmillan	1926	DeAngeli, Marguerite	60-90	
Yonge, Charlotte	Heir of Redclyffe (1st, 8vo, blue/gilt, 524p, 4 illus by...)	L: Macmillan	1881	Greenaway, Kate	60-100	
Yonge, Charlotte	Lances of Lynwood (1st, 12mo, green cl, 217p, col frn, 6pl, pep)	Macmillan	1929	DeAngeli, Marguerite	30-60	
Yonge, Charlotte	Little Duke (1st, 8vo, 240p, red/gilt, 4cp)	Duffield	1923	Stevens, Beatrice	35-60	
Yonge, Charlotte	Little Duke (1st, sm8vo, 188p, blue cl, 3cp, 7pl, pep)	Macmillan	1927	DeAngeli, Marguerite	40-60	
Yonge, Charlotte	Little Lucy's Wonderful Globe (1st, 12mo, 103p, col frn, b/w, pep)	Harper	1927	Peck, Anne M.	20-30	
Yonge, Charlotte	Prince & the Page (1st, sm8vo, 246p, blue/gilt, 3cp, 8pl, pep)	Macmillan	1925	DeAngeli, Marguerite	40-70	
Yonge, Charlotte	Unknown to History (1st, 8vo, 470p, black cl, p-o, col frn, 8pl)	Harper	(1927)	Burd, Clara M.	30-45	
York, Carol B.	Doll in the Bakeshop (1st {std}, 8vo, 98p, fp b/w, DJ/3.50)	F. Watts	(1965)	Turkle, Brinton	30-45	
Yorke, S.P.	When Mother was Little (1st, 8vo, 176p, 13 fp b/w, pep)	L: Fisher/Unwin	1890	Ford, H.J.	150-220	*
Young, Charles	Night-Caps for the Babies (1st, 8vo, 126p, 8cp)	L: John Lane	(1907)	Walker, W.H.	60-90	
Young, Christie (ed)	Black Princess (1st, 8vo, 159p, ivory/gilt, 12cp)	L: Simpkin	(1916)	Anderson, Florence	100-160	
Young, Ella	Tangle-Coated Horse (1st {std}, 8vo, black cl, 186p, b/w, pep, NH)	Longmans	1929	Bock, Vera	65-100	
Young, Ella	Unicorn with Silver Shoes (1st {std}, sm8vo, gilt, 214p, 9pl, pep)	Longmans	1932	Lawson, Robert	70-120	R
Young, Ella	Wonder Smith & His Son (1st, 8vo, green/gilt, 191p, b/w, dep, NH)	Longmans	1927	Artzybasheff, Boris	70-100	R
Young, Evelyn	Wu & Lu & Li (1st, sq12mo, [31]p, green cl, color, DJ/0.75)	NY: Oxford U.Pr.	(1939)	Young, Evelyn	40-60	
Young, Gerald	Witch's Kitchen (1st, 8vo, p-o, 223p, gilt, 8cp)	L: Harrap	(1910)	Pogany, Willy	200-300	
Young, Gerald	Witch's Kitchen (1st AM, 8vo, 223p, teg, p-o, 8cp, pep)	Crowell	(1911)	Pogany, Willy	200-300	
Young, Lillian E.	Adventures of Tommy Cat the Sailor (1st, lg8vo, 165p, 20 fp color)	Sears	(1928)	Young, Lillian E.	70-100	
Young, Lillian E.	Pussy Willow's Naughty Kittens (1st, 4to, p-o, 54p, color)	Funk/Wagnalls	(1924)	Young, Lillian E.	80-150	
Young, Louise	Best Foot Forward (1st, lg ob8vo, 32p, fp 3-color, DJ/3.50)	Van Nostrand	(1968)	Rivoli, Mario	40-65	*
Young, Martha	Behind the Dark Pines (1st, sm8vo, 287p, tan cl, 27pl)	Appleton	1912	Conde, J.M.	35-60	
Young, Martha	Plantation Bird Legends (1st, 8vo, 249p, 28pl)	Appleton	1916	Conde, J.M.	90-120	*
Young, Miriam	Beware the Polar Bear (1st, 8vo, 35p, color, DJ/3.75)	Lothrop, Lee	(1970)	Quackenbush, Rbt.	20-25	*
Young, Miriam	Billy & Milly (1st, 4to, [32]p, color, DJ/3.50)	Lothrop, Lee	(1968)	Quackenbush, Rbt.	20-35	
Young, Miriam	Can't You Pretend? (1st, lg sq8vo, [31]p, color, DJ)	Putnam	(1970)	Kellogg, Steven	70-120	*
Young, Miriam	Dollar Horse (1st {std}, 8vo, 128p, b/w, DJ/2.75)	Harcourt	(1961)	Hutchinson, Wm.	50-80	
Young, Miriam	Georgie Finds Grandpa (1st {A}, 8vo, ibds, color, LGB/#196)	Simon/Schuster	(1954)	Wilkin, Eloise B.	50-85	
Young, Miriam	If I Drove a Truck (1st, ob4to, [31]p, color, DJ/3.50)	Lothrop, Lee	(1967)	Quackenbush, Rbt.	20-35	*
Young, Miriam	If I Flew a Plane (1st, ob4to, [32]p, color, DJ/3.95)	Lothrop, Lee	(1967)	Quackenbush, Rbt.	25-40	*
Young, Miriam	Jellybeans for Breakfast (1st, ob8vo, gilt, [40]p, fp color, cep, DJ/3.50)	Parents Mag. Pr.	(1968)	Komoda, Beverly	120-200	*
Young, Miriam	Marco's Chance (1st {std}, 8vo, 190p, b/w, DJ/3.00)	Harcourt	(1959)	Sibley, Don	30-50	*
Young, Miriam	Miss Suzy (1st, 4to, ipcb, [42]p, color, pep, DJ/2.75)	Parents Mag. Pr.	(1964)	Lobel, Arnold	60-100	
Young, Miriam	Mother Wore Tights (1st, 8vo, 255p, b/w, DJ/2.50)	Whittlesey	(1944)	Williamson, Howard	50-85	
Young, Miriam	Prance, a Carousel Horse (1st {std}, 8vo, uncut, 116p, b/w, pep, DJ/2.50)	Crowell	(1950)	Jones, Amy	60-100	
Young, Miriam	Up and Away (1st {std}, 8vo, 191p, fp b/w, DJ/3.25)	Harcourt	(1960)	Savitt, Sam	30-50	
Young, Percy	Ding Dong Bell (1st, 4to, ibds, 141p, b/w, DJ)	L: Dobson	(1957)	Ardizzone, Edward	50-80	
Young, Stark	Street of the Islands (1st, 8vo, 218p, fp b/w, pep, DJ/2.50)	Scribner	1930	Bischoff, Ilse	30-50	
Yulya	Bears are Sleeping (1st, ob12mo, [30]p, blue cl, color, DJ)	Scribner	(1967)	Hogrogian, Nonny	25-40	
Yurdin, Betty	Tiger in the Teapot (1st {std}, 12mo, ipcb, 29p, color, DJ/2.95)	Holt, Rinehart	(1968)	DuBois, W.P.	50-90	
Zacharias, Thomas	But Where is the Green Parrot? (1st AM {std}, 8vo, [20]p, color, DJ/3.50)	Delacorte Pr.	1968	Zacharias, Wanda	30-45	*
Zeitlin, Ida	Gessar-Khan (1st, sm4to, 203p, gilt, 18 fp color, pep)	Doran	(1927)	Nadejen, Theodore	50-85	
Zeitlin, Ida	King's Pleasure (1st {std}, lg8vo, 230p, blue/gilt, 17cp, cep)	Harper	1929	Nadejen, Theodore	60-90	
Zeitlin, Ida	Skazki (1st, 4to, 335p, black/gilt, teg, pep, 24 ticp)	Doran	(1926)	Nadejen, Theodore	70-100	
Zemach, Harve	Awake and Dreaming (1st {std}, ob4to, [46]p, color, DJ/4.95)	Farrar, Straus	(1970)	Zemach, Margot	40-65	R
Zemach, Harve	Hat with a Rose (1st, ob8vo, [32]p, 1-color, cep, DJ/1.95)	Dutton	1961	Zemach, Margot	40-65	*
Zemach, Harve	Mommy, Buy Me a China Doll (1st {std}, ob4to, 32p, color, cep, DJ/3.95)	Follett	(1966)	Zemach, Margot	30-50	R
Zemach, Harve	Nail Soup: Swedish Folktale (1st, 4to, 32p, color, DJ/2.50)	Follett	(1964)	Zemach, Margot	30-50	
Zemach, Harve	Salt, a Russian Tale (1st, ob4to, 32p, color, DJ/3.50)	Follett	(1965)	Zemach, Margot	30-50	
Zemach, Harve	Small Boy is Listening (1st [1st bk.], 8vo, 30p, 1-color, DJ/2.75)	Houghton	1959	Zemach, Margot	50-80	
Zemach, Harve	Speckled Hen (1st {std}, ob8vo, [36]p, color, DJ/3.50)	Holt, Rinehart	(1966)	Zemach, Margot	40-65	*
Zemach, Harve	The Judge: An Untrue Tale (1st {std}, ob4to, [46]p, color, DJ/4.50, CH)	Farrar, Straus	(1969)	Zemach, Margot	50-80	
Zemach, Harve	Too Much Nose... (1st {std}, 8vo, [44]p, ibds, 2-color, DJ/3.95)	Holt, Rinehart	(1967)	Zemach, Margot	30-45	
Zemach, Harve	Tricks of Master Dabble (1st {std}, 8vo, [32]p, ibds, color, DJ/3.50)	Holt, Rinehart	(1965)	Zemach, Margot	30-50	
Zemach, Margot	Little Tiny Woman (1st, sq24mo, [30]p, fp 2-color, DJ/1.95)	Bobbs-Merrill	1965	Zemach, Margot	25-45	
Zemach, Margot	Three Sillies: A Folk Tale (1st {std}, ob8vo, [32]p, color, DJ/3.25)	Holt, Rinehart	(1963)	Zemach, Margot	30-50	
Ziegler, Ursina	Squaps the Moonling (1st AM {std}, ob folio, [27]p, 2-color, DJ/4.95)	Atheneum	(1969)	Jucker, Sita	30-50	
Zimelman, Nathan	Beneath the Oak Tree (1st, lg ob8vo, 31p, b/w, DJ/2.95)	Steck-Vaughn	(1966)	Rogers, Carol	30-50	
Zimelman, Nathan	Once When I was Five (1st, 4to, 31p, fp 1-color, DJ/2.95)	Steck-Vaughn	(1967)	Rogers, Carol	25-40	*
Zimelman, Nathan	To Sing a Song as Big as Ireland (1st {std}, 4to, 32p, color, cep, DJ/3.95)	Follett	(1967)	Low, Joseph	30-45	*
Zimmern, Helen	Tales from the Edda (1st, 12mo, 146p, 3pl by...)	L: Sonnenschein	(1883)	Greenaway, Kate	80-140	*
Zimnik, Reiner	Bear on the Motorcycle (1st AM {std}, 4to, [38]p, fp color, cep, DJ/3.25)	Atheneum	1963	Zimnik, Reiner	40-65	
Zimnik, Reiner	Jonah, the Fisherman (1st AM, lg4to, [62]p, fp b/w, pep, DJ/3.00, NYTBI)	Pantheon	(1956)	Zimnik, Reiner	50-85	R
Zimnik, Reiner	Little Owl (1st AM {std}, 4to, [32]p, color, DJ/3.50, NYTBI)	Atheneum	1962	Zimnik, Reiner	30-50	
Zimnik, Reiner	Little Roaring Tiger (1st AM {std}, 8vo, 57p, fp b/w, DJ/3.00)	Pantheon	(1961)	Zimnik, Reiner	40-65	
Zimnik, Reiner	Proud Circus Horse (1st AM, lg4to, [32]p, fp b/w, cep, DJ/2.75)	Pantheon	(1957)	Zimnik, Reiner	30-50	*
Zimnik, Reiner	The Crane (1st AM, lg8vo, 94p, ibds, b/w, DJ/3.50)	Harper	(1970)	Zimnik, Reiner	30-50	
Ziner, Feenie	Counting Carnival (1st, 8vo, [32]p, 1-color, DJ/2.50)	Coward	(1962)	Galdone, Paul	25-45	*
Ziner, Feenie	Little Sailor's Big Pet (1st, lg8vo, [40]p, 1-color, pep, DJ/2.75)	Parnassus Press	(1958)	Steven, Leslie	30-50	
Zion, Gene	All Falling Down (1st, 4to, ipcb, [31]p, color, DJ/1.75, CH)	Harper	(1951)	Graham, Margaret B.	130-180	R

AUTHOR: 232

AUTHOR	TITLE	PUBLISHER	DATE	ARTIST	PRICE	LC
Zion, Gene	Dear Garbage Man (1st, 4to, ibds, [32]p, 2-color, DJ/2.00, NYTBI)	Harper	(1957)	Graham, Margaret B.	100-160	
Zion, Gene	Harry and the Lady Next Door (1st, 8vo, 62p, 2-color, DJ/1.95)	Harper	(1960)	Graham, Margaret B.	30-50	*
Zion, Gene	Harry by the Sea (1st, 4to, [32]p, color, DJ/3.25)	Harper	(1965)	Graham, Margaret B.	30-50	*
Zion, Gene	Harry the Dirty Dog (1st, 4to, ibds, [30]p, color, DJ/2.00)	Harper	(1956)	Graham, Margaret B.	100-150	R
Zion, Gene	Hide and Seek Day (1st, 4to, [29]p, ibds, fp color, DJ/2.00)	Harper	(1954)	Graham, Margaret B.	30-50	*
Zion, Gene	Jeffie's Party (1st, lg4to, [30]p, 2-color, DJ/2.50)	Harper	1957	Graham, Margaret B.	40-65	
Zion, Gene	Meanest Squirrel I Ever Met (1st, 4to, [40]p, ibds, color, DJ/3.00)	Scribner	(1962)	Graham, Margaret B.	30-50	
Zion, Gene	No Roses for Harry! (1st, 4to, [32]p, color, DJ/2.50)	Harper	(1958)	Graham, Margaret B.	40-65	
Zion, Gene	Plant Sitter (1st, 4to, [30]p, 2-color, DJ/2.50)	Harper	(1959)	Graham, Margaret B.	70-100	R
Zion, Gene	Really Spring (1st, lg4to, ipcb, [30]p, 2-color, DJ/2.50, NYTBI)	Harper	(1956)	Graham, Margaret B.	100-150	
Zion, Gene	Sugar Mouse Cake (1st, 4to, [48]p, ibds, 3-color, pep, DJ/3.50)	Scribner	(1964)	Graham, Margaret B.	40-65	
Zion, Gene	Summer Snowman (1st, narrow 4to, unpag, yellow, cl, color, cep, DJ/2.00)	Harper	(1955)	Graham, Margaret B.	100-160	
Zirbes, Laura	How Many Bears? (1st, 8vo, ibds, 64p, fp 2-color, DJ/2.50)	Putnam	(1960)	Johnson, Harper	25-40	
Zistel, Era (comp)	Treasury of Cat Stories (1st, sm8vo, grey cl, 278p, 12pl, DJ/2.75)	Greenberg	(1944)	Bacon, Peggy	50-80	
Zoff, Otto (ed)	Riddles Around the World (1st, 4to, ibds, [48]p, color, DJ/2.00)	Pantheon	(1946)	Kredel, Fritz	30-50	
Zogbaum, Rufus F.	Horse, Foot & Dragoons (1st, lg8vo, 176p, teg, b/w pl)	Harper	1888	Zogbaum, Rufus F.	200-300	
Zogbaum, Rufus F.	Junior Officer of the Watch (1st, sm8vo, 311p, 4pl)	Appleton	1908	Zogbaum, Rufus F.	30-50	
Zolotow, Charlotte	All that Sunlight (1st, 8vo, [31]p, ibds, color, DJ)	Harper	1967	Stein, Walter	20-35	
Zolotow, Charlotte	Big Sister, and Little Sister (1st, 4to, ibds, 24p, 2-color, pep, DJ/2.95)	Harper, Row	(1965)	Alexander, Martha	30-40	
Zolotow, Charlotte	Bunny Who Found Easter (1st, 12mo, [32]p, 2-color, pep, DJ/2.25)	Parnassus Press	(1959)	Peterson, Betty	30-50	
Zolotow, Charlotte	But Not Billy (1st, ob4to, [30]p, ibds, color, DJ/1.75)	Harper	1947	Cassal, Lys	70-100	
Zolotow, Charlotte	Do You Know What I'll Do? (1st, 4to, ibds, [27]p, fp 2-color, DJ/2.50)	Harper	(1958)	Williams, Garth	50-80	R
Zolotow, Charlotte	Flocks of Birds (1st, 8vo, [30]p, fp2-color, cep, DJ/2.75)	Abelard-Schuman	(1965)	Berg, Joan	30-50	
Zolotow, Charlotte	Hating Book (1st, ob sm8vo, 32p, ibds, color, DJ/2.95)	Harper	(1969)	Shecter, Ben	30-50	
Zolotow, Charlotte	I Have a Horse of My Own (1st, ob8vo, [31]p, 2-color, cep, DJ/2.75)	Abelard-Schuman	1964	Mitsuhashi, Yoko	30-50	
Zolotow, Charlotte	In My Garden (1st, sm4to, unpag, blue cl, fp color, DJ/2.75)	Lothrop, Lee	1960	Duvoisin, Roger	50-80	
Zolotow, Charlotte	Indian, Indian (1st, sm8vo, ibds, [28]p, color, LGB/#149)	Simon/Schuster	(1952)	Weisgard, Leonard	25-40	
Zolotow, Charlotte	Man with the Purple Eyes (1st, 8vo, 60p, 2-color, DJ/2.50)	Abelard-Schuman	(1961)	Lasker, Joe	30-50	*
Zolotow, Charlotte	Mr. Rabbit & the Lovely Present (1st, ob8vo, [32]p, ibds, dep, DJ/2.95, CH)	Harper	(1962)	Sendak, Maurice	100-160	
Zolotow, Charlotte	My Friend John (1st, ob 12mo, ipcb, 32p, fp 2-color, DJ/2.50)	Harper, Row	(1968)	Shecter, Ben	25-45	*
Zolotow, Charlotte	New Friend (1st, ob8vo, [31]p, fp color, cep, DJ/3.50)	Abelard-Schuman	1968	Stewart, Arvis	30-50	*
Zolotow, Charlotte	Not a Little Monkey (1st, sm4to, green cl, unpag, pep, color, DJ/2.50)	Lothrop, Lee	1957	Duvoisin, Roger	50-80	*
Zolotow, Charlotte	One Step, Two (1st, sm4to, [28]p, color, DJ/2.00)	Lothrop, Lee	1954	Duvoisin, Roger	70-100	
Zolotow, Charlotte	Over and Over (1st, 4to, ibds, unpag, fp color, DJ/2.75)	Harper	(1957)	Williams, Garth	60-100	
Zolotow, Charlotte	Park Book (1st {std}, ob sm4to, [32]p, color, pep, DJ/1.75)	Harper	(1944)	Rey, Hans A.	100-150	R
Zolotow, Charlotte	Poodle Who Barked at the Wind (1st, 4to, [30]p, 2-color, cep, DJ/2.95)	Lothrop, Lee	1964	Duvoisin, Roger	45-70	
Zolotow, Charlotte	Quarreling Book (1st {std}, sq16mo, unpag, b/w, DJ/1.95)	Harper	(1963)	Lobel, Arnold	25-40	
Zolotow, Charlotte	River Winding (1st, 8vo, 32p, 2-color)	Abelard-Schuman	(1970)	Shekerjian, Regina	25-45	*
Zolotow, Charlotte	Rose, a Bridge & Wild Black Horse (1st {std}, ob8vo, [33]p, color, DJ/2.95)	Harper	(1964)	Shulevitz, Uri	30-50	
Zolotow, Charlotte	Sky Was Blue (1st {std}, 4to, ibds, [31]p, color, DJ/2.95)	Harper	(1963)	Williams, Garth	70-100	
Zolotow, Charlotte	Sleepy Book (1st, sm4to, blue cl, [36]p, color, dep, DJ/2.75)	Lothrop, Lee	1958	Bobri, Vladimir	60-100	
Zolotow, Charlotte	Someday (1st, ob8vo, ipcb, [32]p, fp 2-color, DJ/2.50)	Harper	(1965)	Lobel, Arnold	70-100	
Zolotow, Charlotte	Storm Book (1st, sm4to, ipcb, [32]p, 7 fp color, cep, DJ/2.00, CH)	Harper	(1952)	Graham, Margaret B.	100-160	
Zolotow, Charlotte	Three Funny Friends (1st, 12mo, ipcb, 32p, 1-color, DJ/1.75)	Harper	(1961)	Chalmers, Mary	30-45	*
Zolotow, Charlotte	Tiger Called Thomas (1st, sm4to, [32]p, fp 2-color, pep, DJ/2.95)	Lothrop, Lee	1963	Werth, Kurt	25-45	
Zolotow, Charlotte	When I Have a Little Girl (1st, 12mo, ibds, 32p, 1-color, pep, DJ/1.95)	Harper	(1965)	Knight, Hilary	25-40	
Zolotow, Charlotte	When I Have a Son (1st, sq24mo, [40]p, 2-color, DJ/1.95)	Harper	(1967)	Knight, Hilary	25-40	
Zolotow, Charlotte	When the Wind Stops (1st, sm4to, [42]p, fp color, pep, DJ/2.75)	Abelard-Schuman	1962	Lasker, Joe	30-50	
Zolotow, Charlotte	White Marble (1st, 4to, unpag, fp 2-color, pep, DJ/2.75)	Abelard-Schuman	1963	Obligado, Lilian	40-65	
Zwilgmeyer, Dikken	Four Cousins (1st, sm8vo, 286p, 6cp)	Lothrop, Lee	(1923)	Heiberg, Astri W.	20-35	
Zwilgmeyer, Dikken	Inger Johanne's Lively Doings (1st, sm8vo, green cl, 261p, 8cp)	Lothrop, Lee	(1926)	Young, Florence L.	50-80	
Zwilgmeyer, Dikken	Johnny Blossom (1st, 8vo, 163p, p-o, gilt, 4cp, pep)	Pilgrim Press	(1912)	Young, Florence L.	30-50	
Zwilgmeyer, Dikken	Johnny Blossom (1st, 8vo, yellow cl, 157p, pep, 10 fp b/w, DJ/2.50)	Pilgrim Press	(1948)	D'Aulaire, I.& E.	45-70	
Zwilgmeyer, Dikken	What Happened to Inger Johanne (1st, sm8vo, grey cl, 283p, color)	Lothrop, Lee	(1919)	Young, Florence L.	30-45	

Section 2

Illustrator-Sorted

Index

AUTHOR	TITLE	PUBLISHER	DATE	ARTIST	PRICE	LC
Barr, Amelia E.	Knight of the Nets (1st, 8vo, 314p, cvr by...)	Dodd	1896	'AM'	25-40	*
Smith, Gertrude	Little Mother and Georgie (1st, sq8vo, beige cl, 150p, 12cp)	Harper	1905	'DD'	60-90	*
Smith, Gertrude	Little Precious (1st, 8vo, 146p, 15cp)	Harper	1904	'DD'	55-80	
Sidney, Margaret (cmp)	Lullabies and Jingles (1st, sm4to, ibds, 32p)	D. Lothrop Co.	1893	(5 Chromos)	100-160	
Crane, Thomas	Abroad (sq8vo, ipcb, 56p, pep)	L: Marcus Ward	(1882)	(Chromos)	120-180	
Crane, Thomas	At Home (sq8vo, 56p, ipcb)	L: Marcus Ward	(1880)	(Chromos)	120-180	
N/A	Daisy Days (4to, ipcb)	Fiske Co.	1890	(Chromos)	120-180	
Whittemore, Maria	Flower Fairies (1st, lg8vo, ibds, 80p)	L: Cassell	(1886)	(Chromos)	150-220	
Lecky, E.	Here, There, Everywhere (1st, 4to, unpag)	L: R. Tuck	(1890)	(Chromos)	100-165	
N/A	Isn't it Funny (4to, ibds)	L: Nister	1895	(Chromos)	250-350	
N/A	Kriss Kringle (4to, stiff wraps, [16]p, color)	McLoughlin	1897	(Chromos)	200-300	
N/A	Little Dutch Book (1st, 4to, ibds, [48]p)	McLoughlin	1909	(Chromos)	200-300	
N/A	Little People's Book of Airships (ob4to, ibds, [32]p)	L: Nister	[1905]	(Chromos)	250-400	
Sutton, Adah L.	Mushroom Fairies (1st, ob4to, ibds, 159p, 12cp)	Saalfield	(1910)	(Chromos)	225-300	R
Riley, James W.	Old Sweetheart of Mine (1st, sm ob4to, ibds, [26]p, AEG, color)	Bowen-Merrill	1891	(Chromos)	150-225	
Bates, Clara D.	On the Way to Wonderland (1st, 4to, [38]p, ibds, color, pep)	D. Lothrop Co.	(1885)	(Chromos)	120-200	
N/A	Santa Claus Picture Book (4to, ibds, 12cp)	McLoughlin	1901	(Chromos)	250-400	
N/A	Santa Claus Up-to-Date (4to, stiff wraps, fp color)	McLoughlin	1906	(Chromos)	250-350	
Brigham, S.J.	Under Blue Skies (4to, bds, unpag)	Worthington	1886	(Chromos)	100-170	
Moore, Clement C.	Night Before Christmas (4to, wraps, [14]p, color)	McLoughlin	1896	(Color Lithos)	300-500	
Parrish, Randall	Great Plains (1st, 8vo, 399p, 32pl)	McClurg	1907	(Engravings)	50-85	
N/A	Funny Little Darkies (1st, sq4to, wraps, 6cp)	McLoughlin	[1890]	(Lithos)	280-400	
Hope, Anthony	Adventure of Lady Ursula (1st, 8vo, grey/gilt, 125p, teg, uncut)	R.H. Russell	1898	(Photos)	50-80	
Bradley, Mary H.	Alice in Jungleland (1st, 8vo, 170p, green cl, b/w, pep)	Appleton	1927	(Photos)	90-120	*
Carroll, Lewis	Alice in Wonderland (lg ob8vo, unpag, [movie ed.], b/w)	Whitman	(1934)	(Photos)	100-160	*
Carroll, Lewis	Alice... & Through... (lg8vo, 297p, grey cl, col frn)	Grosset/Dunlap	[1919]	(Photos)	80-120	*
Mother Goose	Animal Mother Goose... (1st, 8vo, 168p, grey cl, b/w, pep)	Lothrop, Lee	(1921)	(Photos)	120-170	*
Seton, Ernest T.	Arctic Prairies (1st, lg8vo, 415p, green/gilt, uncut, b/w)	Scribner	1911	(Photos)	170-250	R
Burgess, Thornton	Aunt Sally's Friends in Fur (1st {std}, 8vo, 146p, b/w, DJ/2.75)	Little/Brown	(1955)	(Photos)	60-90	
Darling, Esther B.	Baldy of Nome (1st, 8vo, blue cl, 301p, 15pl)	Penn	1916	(Photos)	50-80	
Culbertson, Anne V.	Banjo Talks (1st, sm8vo, green/gilt, 171p, 23pl)	Bobbs-Merrill	(1905)	(Photos)	70-120	
King, Ben	Ben King's Southland Melodies (1st, 8vo, green cl, 128p, b/w)	Chi: Forbes	1911	(Photos)	150-220	
Chittenden, Wm. L.	Bermuda Verse (1st, 8vo, 68p, green cl, 29pl)	Putnam	1909	(Photos)	50-80	
Stratton-Porter, Gene	Birds of the Bible (1st, lg8vo, 469p, gilt, pep)	Jennings	(1909)	(Photos)	450-650	
McGovern, Ann	Black is Beautiful (1st, ob8vo, [40]p, fp b/w, cep, DJ/3.50)	Four Winds Pr.	(1969)	(Photos)	80-120	
English, Doug	Book of Nimble Beasts (1st, sm8vo, green/gilt, 318p)	L: E. Nash	1910	(Photos)	40-60	*
Lippincott, J.W.	Bun, a Wild Rabbit (1st, 12mo, 124p, p-o, 12pl)	Penn	1918	(Photos)	30-50	
White, Stewart E.	Camp and Trail (1st, 8vo, 236p, col frn, 11pl)	Outing	1907	(Photos)	40-65	
Johnson, Mary	Cat's Fairy Land... (1st, 12mo, 184p, gilt, b/w)	H. Carter	1900	(Photos)	120-200	
Doubleday, Russell	Cattle-Ranch To College (1st, 8vo, 347p, blue/gilt, 24pl)	Doub./McClure	1899	(Photos)	100-165	
Earle, Alice M.	Child Life in Colonial Days (1st, sm8vo, 418p, gilt, teg)	Macmillan	1899	(Photos)	50-80	
De La Mare, Walter	Child's Day (1st, lg8vo, 56p, 24 ti-pl)	L: Constable	1912	(Photos)	150-225	
Peary, Josephine	Children of the Arctic (1st, sm4to, cloth, 120p, p-o)	Stokes	(1903)	(Photos)	120-200	
Headland, I.T.	Chinese Boy and Girl (1st, 8vo, ibds, 176p, fp b/w)	Revell	(1901)	(Photos)	100-165	
Headland, I.T.	Chinese Mother Goose Rhymes (1st, 8vo, 157p, ibds)	Revell	(1900)	(Photos)	100-165	
Tileston, Mary W.	Chiquita (1st, 12mo, orange cl, 306p, col frn, 7pl)	Merrill	1902	(Photos)	30-50	
Davis, Richard H.	Congo and Coasts of Africa (1st, 8vo, teg, 220p, 32pl)	Scribner	1907	(Photos)	60-100	*
London, Jack	Cruise of the Snark (1st, 8vo, 340p, teg, p-o, blue/gilt, col frn)	Macmillan	1911	(Photos)	300-450	
Eaton, Jeanette	Daughter of the Seine (1st {std}, lg8vo, blue cl, 324p, pep, NH)	Harper	1929	(Photos)	60-100	
Singer, Isaac B.	Day of Pleasure (1st {std}, 8vo, 227p, fp b/w, DJ/4.50)	Farrar, Straus	(1969)	(Photos)	50-80	R*
Newman, Gertrude	Delicia and Adolphus (1st, 8vo, [33]p, ipcb, b/w, pep, DJ/0.50)	Rand/McNally	(1938)	(Photos)	40-70	
Nusbaum, Deric	Deric in Mesa Verde (1st, 8vo, 166p, 22pl, pep)	Putnam	1926	(Photos)	30-50	
Wright, Dare	Doll and the Kitten (1st {std}, folio, 55p, b/w, DJ/2.50)	Doubleday	(1960)	(Photos)	50-80	
Eickemeyer, Rudolf	Down South (1st, folio, ibds, [47]p, p-o, b/w)	R.H. Russell	1900	(Photos)	400-600	
Stevenson, Rbt. L.	Dr. Jekyll & Mr. Hyde (1st [Movie ed.], 8vo, 234p)	Grosset/Dunlap	[1941]	(Photos)	80-145	*
Brownell, Elizabeth	Dream Children (1st, sm8vo, 217p, b/w)	Bowen-Merrill	(1901)	(Photos)	60-90	
Howlett, Edwin	Driving Lessons (1st, lg8vo, 159p, 20pl)	R.H. Russell	1894	(Photos)	300-500	
Hall, Bertha P.	Ducky Daddles and the Three Bears (1st, ob4to, ibds, 57p)	Dutton	(1921)	(Photos)	100-165	
Robbins, Louis	Dutch Doll Ditties (1st, 4to, 23p, grey bds, p-o, b/w)	L: Longmans	1904	(Photos)	90-120	
Wright, Dare	Edith and Mr. Bear (1st, folio, ibds, unpag, b/w, DJ/2.95)	Random	(1964)	(Photos)	120-160	
Adamson, Joy	Elsa: Story of a Lioness (1st, 4to, [50]p, b/w, DJ/3.50)	Pantheon	1961	(Photos)	30-45	
Wallace, Lew	First Christmas (1st, 8vo, 108p, teg, lavender/gilt, 4 tipl)	Harper	1902	(Photos)	40-65	
Credle, Ellis	Flop-Eared Hound (1st, 8vo, [61]p, fp b/w, DJ/2.00)	NY: Oxford U.Pr.	(1938)	(Photos)	50-80	
Munroe, Kirk	Forward March (1st, 12mo, 254p, 20pl)	Harper	1899	(Photos)	50-80	*
Stratton-Porter, Gene	Friends In Feathers (1st, lg8vo, 335p, gilt, p-o, teg, b/w)	Doubleday/Page	1917	(Photos)	250-400	
Wright, Dare	Gift from the Lonely Doll (1st, folio, unpag, ibds, b/w, DJ/2.95)	Random	(1966)	(Photos)	200-300	
Lippincott, J.W.	Gray Squirrel (1st, 12mo, 144p, p-o, 7pl)	Penn	1921	(Photos)	30-50	
Breakenridge, Wm.	Helldorado (1st, lg8vo, brown cl, 256p, b/w)	Houghton	1928	(Photos)	65-80	
Longfellow, H.W.	Hiawatha (1st, lg8vo, 245p, p-o, buckram)	Rand/McNally	(1911)	(Photos)	100-165	
Wright, Dare	Holiday for Edith & the Bears (1st {std}, lg4to ibds, unpag, b/w, DJ/2.50)	Doubleday	(1958)	(Photos)	100-160	
Patch, Edith M.	Holiday Hill (1st, sq8vo, 135p, pep, b/w)	Macmillan	1931	(Photos)	30-50	
Earle, Alice M.	Home Life in Colonial Days (1st, sm8vo, teg, 470p)	Macmillan	1898	(Photos)	50-80	
Stratton-Porter, Gene	Homing With Birds (1st, 8vo, 381p, brown cl)	Doubleday/Page	1919	(Photos)	150-225	
Gaines, Mary L.	I Heah de Voices Callin' (1st, 12mo, p-o, 88p, 11pl)	(Atlanta)	1916	(Photos)	100-165	
Palmer, Helen	I Was Kissed by a Seal at the Zoo (1st, lg8vo, ibds, 62p, DJ/1.95)	Beginner Books	1962	(Photos)	50-80	*
Mills, Enos A.	In Beaver World (1st, 8vo, 228p, olive cl, 19pl, pep)	Houghton	1913	(Photos)	70-100	
Adams, W.I.L.	In Nature's Image (1st, sm4to, gilt, 114p, AEG)	Baker/Taylor	1898	(Photos)	80-125	
Armer, Laura A.	In Navajo Land (1st, 8vo, 107p, gilt, fp b/w, DJ/3.95)	McKay	1962	(Photos)	30-50	*

AUTHOR	TITLE	PUBLISHER	DATE	ARTIST	PRICE	LC
Day, Leigh G.	In Shadow Town (1st, 4to, p-o, [110]p, b/w)	Saalfield	(1907)	(Photos)	120-180	*
Meigs, Cornelia L.	Invincible Louisa (1st, sm8vo, 260p, red cl, 16pl, NM)	Little/Brown	1933	(Photos)	60-100	R
Laughlin, Elmer O.	Johnnie (1st, 12mo, 227p, teg, uncut)	Bowen-Merrill	1898	(Photos)	30-50	
Credle, Ellis	Johnny and his Mule (1st, sq12mo, [44]p, b/w, DJ/1.50)	NY: Oxford U.Pr.	1946	(Photos)	45-70	
Farjeon, Eleanor	Katy Kruse at the Seaside (1st, 4to, blue cl, 32p, p-o, 12 fp color)	McKay	(1932)	(Photos)	180-240	
Fyleman, Rose	Katy Kruse Dolly Book (1st AM, ob4to, ibds, 32p, 12cp)	Doran	(1927)	(Photos)	140-200	
Grover, Eulalie O.	Kittens and Cats (1st, 8vo, yellow cl, 78p, 39pl, dep)	Houghton	1911	(Photos)	100-180	
Gates, Josephine S.	Land of Delight (1st, lg8vo, green cl, 115p, 16pl)	Houghton	1915	(Photos)	35-60	*
Grey, Zane	Last of the Plainsmen (1st, 8vo, 314p, b/w, pl)	McClurg	1908	(Photos)	400-650	
Furlong, Charles W.	Let 'er Buck (1st, 8vo, 242p, gilt, p-o, 19pl)	Putnam	1921	(Photos)	80-130	
Dixon, Thomas	Life Worth Living (1st, 8vo, 140p, b/w, teg)	Doubleday/Page	1905	(Photos)	30-50	
Frees, Harry W.	Little Folks of Animal Land (1st, 8vo, 252p, blue/gilt, p-o, pep)	Lothrop, Lee	(1915)	(Photos)	100-150	*
Wright, Dare	Little One (1st {std}, folio, ibds, b/w, DJ)	Doubleday	1959	(Photos)	120-200	
Wells, H.G.	Little Wars (1st AM, 8vo, 180p, p-o, blue cl, 16pl)	Small/Maynard	(1913)	(Photos)	160-240	*
Wright, Dare	Lona, a Fairy Tale (1st, folio, unpag, b/w, DJ/4.95)	Random	(1963)	(Photos)	100-150	
Wright, Dare	Lonely Doll Learns a Lesson (1st, folio, ibds, [56]p, b/w)	Random	(1961)	(Photos)	70-100	
Commins, Dorothy	Lullabies of the World (1st {std}, lg4to, 266p, b/w, pep, DJ/12.95)	Random	1967	(Photos)	40-65	
Tarkington, Booth	Man from Home (1st, 8vo, 175p, tan cl, 7pl)	Harper	1908	(Photos)	60-90	
Mendoza, George	Marcel Marceau Alphabet Book (1st {std}, 4to, [63]p, color, pep, DJ/5.95)	Doubleday	(1970)	(Photos)	40-70	
Beard, Patten	Marjorie's Literary Dolls (1st, 4to, 114p, b/w)	Stokes	(1916)	(Photos)	100-165	
Beard, Patten	Marjorie's Little Doll School (1st, lg8vo, 208p, p-o, b/w)	Doran	(1917)	(Photos)	100-165	
Hine, Lewis W.	Men at Work (1st, sm4to, [48]p, b/w)	Macmillan	1932	(Photos)	30-50	*
Berry, Erick	Men, Moss and Reindeer: Challenge of Lapland (1st, 8vo, 96p, b/w, DJ/2.50)	Coward	(1959)	(Photos)	25-40	*
Stratton-Porter, Gene	Morning Face (1st, sm4to, 127p, blue/gilt, color & b/w)	Doubleday/Page	1916	(Photos)	250-350	
Dorr, Nell	Mother and Child (1st, 8vo, [89]p, grey bds, DJ/4.50)	Harper	(1954)	(Photos)	250-400	
Stratton-Porter, Gene	Moths of the Limberlost (1st, 4to, tan/gilt, 370p, color, pep)	Doubleday/Page	1912	(Photos)	220-300	
Wharton, Edith	Motor-Flight through France (1st, 8vo, gilt, teg, 201p, 48pl)	Scribner	1908	(Photos)	140-200	
Berry, Erick	Mr. Arctic: Account of Villajalmur Stefansson (1st, 8vo, 185p, DJ/4.50)	McKay	1966	(Photos)	20-35	
Stratton-Porter, Gene	Music of the Wild (1st, lg8vo, 430p, green/gilt, b/w)	Jennings/Graham	(1910)	(Photos)	180-260	
Caudill, Rebecca	My Appalachia: A Reminiscence (1st {std}, 4to, black cl, 90p, b/w, DJ/4.95)	Holt, Rinehart	(1966)	(Photos)	25-40	
Credle, Ellis	My Pet Peepelo (1st, lg8vo, green cl, 62p, b/w, DJ/2.00)	NY: Oxford U.Pr.	1948	(Photos)	30-50	
Gates, Josephine S.	Nanette Goes to Visit Grandmother (1st, 16mo, ibds, 53p, 6cp)	Houghton	1915	(Photos)	60-80	*
Gielow, Martha S.	Old Plantation Days (1st, sm8vo, 183p, tan cl, 13pl)	R.H. Russell	1902	(Photos)	100-150	
Borton, Elizabeth	Our Little Ethiopian Cousin (1st, sm8vo, 134p, DJ/1.00)	L.C. Page	1935	(Photos)	25-40	*
Butler, Edward C.	Our Little Mexican Cousin (1st, 12mo, 100p, 10pl)	L.C. Page	1905	(Photos)	30-60	*
Yates, Elizabeth	Pebble in a Pool (1st {std}, 8vo, 284p, b/w, DJ/3.50)	Dutton	1958	(Photos)	20-30	
London, Jack	People of the Abyss (1st, lg8vo, 319p, gilt, teg, uncut, 19pl)	Macmillan	1903	(Photos)	350-500	
Collodi, Carlo	Pinocchio (1st [Movie ed.], sm ob4to, ibds, [50]p)	Grosset/Dunlap	1939	(Photos)	70-100	
Shepperd, Eli	Plantation Songs for My Lady's Banjo (1st, lg8vo, 150p, 25pl)	R.H. Russell	1901	(Photos)	250-400	
Judson, Clara I.	Play Days (1st, 8vo, [39]p, ipcb, dep, b/w)	Grosset/Dunlap	(1937)	(Photos)	30-50	*
Ray, Anna C.	Playground Toni (1st, 8vo, ipcb, 136p, 4pl)	Crowell	(1900)	(Photos)	25-40	
Allen, Marie L.	Pocketful of Rhymes (1st {std}, 8vo, 47p, ibds, 16 fp color, DJ/1.25)	Harper	1939	(Photos)	45-70	
Dunbar, Paul L.	Poems of Cabin and Field (1st, 8vo, teg, 125p, uncut, green/gilt)	Dodd	1899	(Photos)	300-500	
Anthony, Edward	Pussycat Princess (1st, sm4to, red cl, 157p, b/w)	Century	1922	(Photos)	120-185	
Chittenden, Wm. L.	Ranch Verses (1st, sm8vo, 189p, gilt, 14pl)	Putnam	1893	(Photos)	125-200	
Brownell, Elizabeth	Really Babies (1st, 4to, p-o, gilt, 63p)	Rand/McNally	(1908)	(Photos)	150-220	
Omar Khayyam	Rubaiyat of Omar Khayyam (1st AM, 4to, teg, unpag, blue/gilt, 28 ticp)	Dodge	(1905)	(Photos)	120-200	
Hazelton, Elizabeth	Sammy, the Crow Who Remembered (1st, sm ob4to, [40]p, b/w, DJ)	Scribner	(1969)	(Photos)	25-40	
Frees, Harry W.	Sandman: His Animal Stories (1st, sm8vo, 273p, b/w)	L.C. Page	1916	(Photos)	80-120	
June, Larry	Shadow's Holiday (1st {std}, lg8vo, gilt, [43]p, b/w, cep, DJ)	Farrar/Rinehart	(1931)	(Photos)	40-65	*
Spyri, Johanna	Shirley Temple in Heidi (1st, 8vo, 404p, b/w)	Saalfield	(1937)	(Photos)	75-100	*
Peary, Josephine	Snow Baby (1st, sm4to, p-o, 84p, b/w, PPP)	Stokes	(1901)	(Photos)	150-225	R
Montgomery, R.	Snowman (1st {std}, 8vo, 130p, b/w, DJ/3.50)	Duell, Sloan	(1962)	(Photos)	30-45	
Stratton-Porter, Gene	Song of the Cardinal (1st {1st bk.}, 8vo, red/gilt, 163p, 17pl)	Bobbs-Merrill	(1903)	(Photos)	200-300	
Earle, Alice M.	Stage Coach and Tavern Days (1st, sm8vo, uncut, 449p, teg, b/w)	Macmillan	1900	(Photos)	60-100	
Terhune, Albert P.	Story of Damon and Pythias (1st, 12mo, 307p, 30pl)	Grosset/Dunlap	(1915)	(Photos)	40-65	
Newman, Gertrude	Story of Delicia (1st, 8vo, [61]p, ipcb, b/w)	Rand/McNally	(1935)	(Photos)	40-70	
Miller, Diane D.	Story of Walt Disney (1st {std}, 8vo, ibds, 247p, DJ/3.95)	Holt	(1957)	(Photos)	300-500	
Lloyd, John U.	Stringtown on the Pike (1st, sm8vo, 414p, tan cl, p-o, b/w)	Dodd	1900	(Photos)	40-70	
Huxley, Elspeth	Suki: A Little Tiger (1st, 4to, ibds, 46p, b/w, DJ/3.75)	Wm. Morrow	1964	(Photos)	30-50	
Adams, W.I.L.	Sunlight and Shadow (1st, 8vo, 141p, AEG)	Baker/Taylor	1897	(Photos)	90-160	
Krementz, Jill	Sweet Pea (1st {std}, 4to, 94p, b/w, DJ/4.50)	Harcourt	(1969)	(Photos)	50-85	
Kane, Henry B.	Tale of a Wood (1st, lg8vo, 112p, fp b/w, pep, DJ/3.00, NYTBI)	Knopf	(1962)	(Photos)	20-35	*
Kane, Henry B.	Tale of the Whitefoot Mouse (1st, 8vo, [48]p, fp b/w, DJ/1.50)	Knopf	(1940)	(Photos)	30-50	*
Stratton-Porter, Gene	Tales You Won't Believe (1st {std}, 8vo, 327p, grey cl, 23pl)	Doubleday/Page	1925	(Photos)	200-300	
London, Jack	The Road (1st, 8vo, grey/gilt, teg, 224p)	Macmillan	1907	(Photos)	400-600	
Mother Goose	Toni Frissell's Mother Goose (1st, sm4to, ibds, 94p, fp b/w, pep)	Harper	(1948)	(Photos)	80-130	
Reid, Carol M.	Toys at Play (1st, sq4to, wraps, 14p, color)	Whitman	1937	(Photos)	80-130	
Brininstool, E.A.	Trail Dust of a Maverick (1st, sm8vo, p-o, 249p)	Dodd	1914	(Photos)	35-60	
Lattimore, Eleanor	Turkistan Reunion (1st, 8vo, 296p, orange cl, 14pl, pep, DJ/2.75)	Hurst/Blackett	(1935)	(Photos)	120-200	*
Berry, Erick	Underwater Warriors (1st, 8vo, 152p, pep, DJ/3.95)	McKay	1967	(Photos)	25-45	
Disney, Walt	Walt Disney's Sleeping Beauty (1st, folio, ibds, 57p, color, GGB/#757)	Simon/Schuster	(1957)	(Photos)	100-165	
Stratton-Porter, Gene	What I Have Done with Birds (1st, lg8vo, 258p, green cl, p-o, 16 color)	Bobbs-Merrill	(1907)	(Photos)	250-400	
Humphrey, Henry	What is it For? (1st {std}, lg4to, 48p, b/w, DJ/4.50, NYTBI)	Simon/Schuster	(1969)	(Photos)	30-50	*
Garelick, May	What's Inside? (1st, ob8vo, unpag, beige cl, b/w, DJ/2.00)	W.R. Scott	(1955)	(Photos)	30-50	
Willard, Frances E.	Wheel Within a Wheel (1st, 12mo, 75p, tan buckram, 7pl)	Revell	1895	(Photos)	90-120	
Haggard, H. Rider	Winter Pilgrimage (1st, 8vo, blue/gilt, 335p, 31pl)	L: Longmans	1901	(Photos)	250-350	
Schloat, G. Warren	Wonderful Egg (1st, 4to, [48]p, b/w, DJ/2.25)	Scribner	(1952)	(Photos)	30-50	

ARTIST: 2

AUTHOR	TITLE	PUBLISHER	DATE	ARTIST	PRICE	LC
Skelding, Susie B.	Flowers from Dell and Bower (1st, 8vo, 128p, brown/gilt, AEG)	White/Stokes	1886	12 Chromos	120-180	
Skelding, Susie B.	Flowers from Glade and Garden (1st, lg8vo, [128]p, AEG, gilt)	White/Stokes	1884	12 Chromos	120-170	
Bennet, H.	Round the Hearth (4to, ibds)	Dutton	(1880)	13 Chromos	100-165	
Perrault, Charles	Ideal Fairy Tales (1st, 4to, [62]p, ibds)	McLoughlin	(1897)	16 Chromos	160-225	
Moore, Clement C.	Night Before Christmas (4to, ibds)	McLoughlin	[1888]	16 Chromos	300-500	
N/A	Simple Addition (lg8vo, p-o, blue cl, [16]p)	McLoughlin	[1880]	21 Chromos	200-300	
N/A	Aunt Louisa's Choice Present (sq4to, AEG)	Warne	(1880)	24 Chromos	100-165	
Weatherly, Fred E.	Told in the Twilight (1st, 8vo, 64p, ibds)	Dutton	(1883)	27 Chromos	120-200	
N/A	Father Tuck's Dog Show (lg ob4to, wraps)	L: R. Tuck	[1895]	4 Chromos	120-165	
N/A	Silly Hare (sm4to, ipcb)	McLoughlin	[1893]	4 Chromos	75-100	
N/A	Story of the American Firemen (folio, ibds)	McLoughlin	1909	4 Chromos	250-400	
Sidney, Margaret	Child's Day Book (1st, 4to, ibds, [32]p)	D. Lothrop Co.	1893	5 Chromos	100-170	
N/A	Cinderella (sm4to, ipcb)	Dutton	(1890)	5 Chromos	120-180	
Montefiore	Friend and Foe (8vo, ipcb, 107p)	Dutton	(1898)	5 Chromos	100-170	
N/A	Three Little Kittens (lg4to, ibds)	L: Nister	[1890]	5 Chromos	60-90	
Tucker, Elizabeth S.	Baby and Me! (4to, [13]p, ibds)	Worthington	[1890]	6 Chromos	100-170	*
N/A	Children All (4to, ibds)	D. Lothrop Co.	(1898)	6 Chromos	120-180	
N/A	Goody Two Shoes (folio, wraps, shape book)	McLoughlin	1897	6 Chromos	150-250	
N/A	No Place Like Home (ob4to, ibds, [22]p)	Nims & Knight	1891	6 Chromos	100-180	
Defoe, Daniel	Robinson Crusoe (lg8vo, A.E. red, 328p, red/gilt, 6 chromos)	L: Nister	[1890]	6 Chromos	100-170	
Daley, C.F.	Skating Party (1st, 4to, ibds)	Worthington	(1891)	6 Chromos	100-160	
N/A	Stories Merry and Wise (4to, ibds)	McLoughlin	(1898)	6 Chromos	150-250	
N/A	Three Little Kittens (4to, wraps)	McLoughlin	[1880]	6 Chromos	130-200	
N/A	Four Feet by Two (lg8vo, ibds, 72p)	L: Nister	[1890]	8 Chromos	125-200	
N/A	Merry Times (4to, ipcb, AEG)	Fiske Co.	1890	8 Chromos	100-160	
Sidney, Margaret	Ballad of the Lost Hare (1st, ob4to, ibds, [44]p, color)	D. Lothrop Co.	1882	9 Chromos	150-225	R
Sommerfelt, Aimee	Road to Agra (1st AM {std}, 8vo, 191p, b/w, DJ/3.50, JABA)	Criterion Bks.	(1961)	Aas, Ulf	30-45	
Sommerfelt, Aimee	White Bungalow (1st AM {std}, 8vo, 126p, b/w, DJ/3.00)	Criterion Bks.	(1964)	Aas, Ulf	25-45	
Goldsmith, Oliver	Deserted Village (1st, lg8vo, 59p, red/gilt, AEG, 119p, 33pl)	Harper	1902	Abbey, Edwin A.	60-90	
Lucas, E.V.	Edwin A. Abbey (1st AM, 8vo, 2 vols, pcb)	Scribner	1921	Abbey, Edwin A.	120-200	
Herrick, Robert	Herrick's Poems (lg4to, 188p, green cl)	Harper	1899	Abbey, Edwin A.	120-180	
Herrick, Robert	Poetry of... (1st, 4to, 188p, gilt, uncut, AEG, fp b/w)	Harper	1882	Abbey, Edwin A.	250-350	
Greenslet, Ferris	Quest of the Holy Grail (1st, 4to, 78p, gilt, teg, uncut, 26pl)	Curtis/Cameron	1902	Abbey, Edwin A.	160-240	
Goldsmith, Oliver	She Stoops to Conquer (1st, folio, 176p, AEG, fp b/w)	Harper	1887	Abbey, Edwin A.	120-200	
Long, John L.	Madame Butterfly (1st, 8vo, teg, gilt, 152p, uncut, 16pl)	Century	1903	Abbott, C.Y.	45-70	
Carroll, Lewis	Alice... & Through... (8vo, brown cl, p-o, 335p, 7cp)	Jacobs	[1912]	Abbott, Elenore P.	140-200	
Carroll, Lewis	Alice... & Through... (8vo, blue/gilt, 335p, 7cp)	Macrae Smith	[1925]	Abbott, Elenore P.	70-100	*
Andersen, Hans C.	Fairy Tales (1st, sm8vo, 489p, p-o, 7cp)	Jacobs	[1917]	Abbott, Elenore P.	70-120	
Grimm Bros.	Fairy Tales (1st, lg8vo, 308p, p-o, 12cp, pep, SC)	Scribner	1920	Abbott, Elenore P.	120-200	
Grimm Bros.	Fairy Tales (1st UK, 8vo, 308p, gilt, 12cp, pep)	L: Hodder	1921	Abbott, Elenore P.	160-240	
Andersen, Hans C.	Flower Maiden (1st, sm8vo, 118p, p-o, pep, 3cp by...)	Jacobs	(1922)	Abbott, Elenore P.	30-60	*
Stevenson, Rbt. L.	Kidnapped (1st, sm8vo, p-o, 332p, 7cp, pep)	Jacobs	(1915)	Abbott, Elenore P.	50-80	
Defoe, Daniel	Robinson Crusoe (1st, 8vo, blue cl, 320p, 6cp)	L: Harrap	1933	Abbott, Elenore P.	75-100	
Stevenson, Rbt. L.	Treasure Island (1st, sm8vo, 292p, cp, pep)	Jacobs	(1911)	Abbott, Elenore P.	45-80	*
Andersen, Hans C.	Wild Swans (1st, sm8vo, 117p, color, pep)	Jacobs	(1922)	Abbott, Elenore P.	50-80	*
Hawthorne, Nathaniel	Wonder Book (1st sm8vo, 201p, color, by...)	Macrae Smith	(1925)	Abbott, Elenore P.	30-50	
Montgomery, R.	Gray Wolf (1st, 8vo, 185p, col frn, DJ/2.25)	Houghton	1938	Abbott, Jacob	25-40	*
Montgomery, R.	Midnight (1st, sm8vo, 275p, b/w, DJ/2.00)	Henry Holt & Co.	(1940)	Abbott, Jacob	25-45	*
Montgomery, R.	Stan Ball of the Rangers (1st, 8vo, 250p, col frn, DJ/1.00)	McKay	1941	Abbott, Jacob	20-35	
Montgomery, R.	Timberline Tales (1st, 8vo, 264p, col frn, b/w, DJ/1.00)	McKay	1939	Abbott, Jacob	20-30	
Omar Khayyam	Rubaiyat of Omar Khayyam (sm4to, unpag, black/gilt, 7cp)	World	(1938)	Abdullah Kar, Hemzeh	60-90	
Palmer, C. Everard	Cloud with the Silver Lining (1st AM {std}, 8vo, gilt, 164p, b/w, DJ/3.95)	Pantheon	(1967)	Acs, Laszlo	20-35	
Farmer, Penelope	Emma in Winter (1st, 8vo, ibds, 160p, DJ)	L: Chatto	1966	Acs, Laszlo	30-45	
Taylor, Elizabeth	Mossy Trotter (1st AM {std}, 8vo, blue cl, 160p, DJ/3.25)	Harcourt	(1967)	Acs, Laszlo	20-35	
Adam, Helen D.	Charms and Dreams from Pedlar's Pack (1st, 8vo, 118p, red cl, col frn)	L: Hodder	1924	Adam, Helen D.	35-50	
Howard, Joan	13th Is Magic (1st, 8vo, 169p, fp b/w, pep, DJ/2.50)	Lothrop, Lee	(1950)	Adams, Adrienne	40-65	*
Rogers, Elizabeth	Angela of Angel Court (1st {std}, 8vo, 116p, green cl, b/w, pep, DJ/2.00)	Crowell	(1954)	Adams, Adrienne	30-50	*
Simon, Norma	Baby House (1st, lg8vo, mauve cl, [25]p, 1-color, dep, DJ/2.00)	Lippincott	1955	Adams, Adrienne	40-65	
Anderson, Lonzo	Bag of Smoke: Story of First Balloon (1st, 8vo, 179p, fp b/w, pep, DJ/2.00)	Viking	1942	Adams, Adrienne	30-50	*
Lewis, Beth H.	Blue Mountain (1st {std}, lg8vo, blue cl, 59p, fp b/w, dep, DJ/2.25)	Knopf	1956	Adams, Adrienne	35-50	
Gordon, Patricia	Boy Jones (1st, 8vo, red cl, 158p, 10pl, pep, DJ/2.00)	Viking	1943	Adams, Adrienne	45-60	
Goudey, Alice	Butterfly Time (1st, sm4to, unpag, color, DJ/3.25)	Scribner	(1964)	Adams, Adrienne	40-65	
Wahl, Jan	Cabbage Moon (1st {std}, sm ob8vo, [32]p, color, DJ/3.50)	Holt, Rinehart	(1965)	Adams, Adrienne	40-65	
Godden, Rumer	Candy Floss (1st, 8vo, pink cl, 63p, color, dep, DJ/2.50)	Viking	(1960)	Adams, Adrienne	50-80	R
Torjesen, Elizabeth	Captain Ramsay's Daughter (1st, 8vo, 223p, blue cl, fp b/w, pep, DJ/2.50)	Lothrop, Lee	(1953)	Adams, Adrienne	30-50	
Goudey, Alice	Day We Saw the Sun Come Up (1st, 4to, [32]p, fp color, DJ/2.95, CH)	Scribner	(1961)	Adams, Adrienne	60-90	
Friedrich, Priscilla	Easter Bunny that Overslept (1st, sm4to, yellow cl, [33]p, color, DJ/2.50)	Lothrop, Lee	1957	Adams, Adrienne	45-65	
Godden, Rumer	Fairy Doll (1st, 8vo, grey cl, 67p, 2-color, pep, DJ/2.50)	Viking	1956	Adams, Adrienne	60-100	R
Haviland, Virginia	Favorite Fairy Tales Told/Scotland (1st {std}, lg8vo, 92p, color, DJ/2.95)	Little/Brown	(1963)	Adams, Adrienne	50-85	R
Anderson, John (ed)	Fifteenth Century Cook'ry Boke (1st, 8vo, blue/gilt, 92p, color, DJ/4.50)	Scribner	(1962)	Adams, Adrienne	25-40	
Fisher, Aileen	Going Barefoot (1st, 4to, [34]p, dep, color, DJ/3.00)	Crowell	(1960)	Adams, Adrienne	30-45	*
Otto, Margaret G.	Great Aunt Victoria's House (1st {std}, 8vo, yellow cl, 120p, b/w, DJ/2.50)	Holt	(1957)	Adams, Adrienne	30-45	
Goudey, Alice	Houses from the Sea (1st, sm4to, [32]p, fp color, DJ/2.95, CH)	Scribner	(1959)	Adams, Adrienne	70-100	
Godden, Rumer	Impunity Jane (1st, 8vo, 48p, color, pep, DJ/2.50)	Viking	1954	Adams, Adrienne	65-100	R
Fisher, Aileen	In the Middle of the Night (1st {std}, 4to, [44]p, fp color, DJ/3.75)	Crowell	(1965)	Adams, Adrienne	40-65	R
Kennedy, Mary	Jenny (1st, 8vo, 153p, green cl, 11 fp b/w, DJ/2.50)	Lothrop, Lee	(1954)	Adams, Adrienne	30-55	
Grimm Bros.	Jorinda and Joringel (1st, 4to, [42]p, color, DJ)	Scribner	(1968)	Adams, Adrienne	30-50	
Leodhas, Sorche	Laird of Cockpen (1st {std}, 8vo, [32]p, ibds, color, DJ/3.95)	Holt, Rinehart	(1969)	Adams, Adrienne	30-50	

AUTHOR	TITLE	PUBLISHER	DATE	ARTIST	PRICE	LC
Howard, Joan	Light in the Tower (1st, sm4to, unpag, blue/gilt, dp color, DJ/2.50)	Lothrop, Lee	(1957)	Adams, Adrienne	30-50	
Massey, Jeanne	Littlest Witch (1st, sm ob4to, [33]p, orange cl, 2-color, DJ)	Knopf	(1959)	Adams, Adrienne	50-85	
Shura, Mary F.	Mary's Marvelous Mouse (1st, 8vo, [30]p, 2-color, pep, DJ/2.75)	Knopf	(1962)	Adams, Adrienne	30-50	
Godden, Rumer	Mouse House (1st, lg8vo, tan cl, 63p, color, pep, DJ/2.75)	Viking	1957	Adams, Adrienne	65-100	R
Carpenter, Frances	Mouse Palace (1st, 8vo, 60p, 3-color, DJ/2.95)	McGraw-Hill	(1964)	Adams, Adrienne	25-40	
Shura, Mary F.	Nearsighted Knight (1st {std}, 8vo, 111p, fp b/w, DJ/3.25)	Knopf	(1964)	Adams, Adrienne	25-45	
Withers, Carl	Painting the Moon (1st {std}, 4to, 29p, fp color, cep, DJ/4.95)	Dutton	(1970)	Adams, Adrienne	60-100	R
Anderson, Lonzo	Ponies of Mykillengi (1st, 8vo, [48]p, fp color, DJ)	Scribner	(1966)	Adams, Adrienne	40-65	
Myers, Madeleine	Pulling Strings (1st {std}, 8vo, 228p, DJ/2.50)	Holt	(1954)	Adams, Adrienne	25-40	
Field, Rachel	Rachel Field Story Book (1st {std}, 8vo, 124p, 2-color, dep, DJ/2.50)	Doubleday	(1958)	Adams, Adrienne	40-70	
Grimm Bros.	Shoemaker and the Elves (1st, sm4to, [32]p, fp color, DJ/2.95)	Scribner	(1960)	Adams, Adrienne	40-65	
Grimm Bros.	Snow White & Rose Red (1st, sm4to, [40]p, fp color, DJ/3.50)	Scribner	(1964)	Adams, Adrienne	30-50	
Godden, Rumer	Story of Holly and Ivy (1st, lg8vo, 64p, ibds, 2-color, pep, DJ/2.50)	Viking	(1958)	Adams, Adrienne	50-80	
Howard, Joan	Summer is Magic (1st, 8vo, 182p, fp b/w, pep, DJ/2.50)	Lothrop, Lee	(1952)	Adams, Adrienne	40-65	
Belting, Natalia	Summer's Coming In (1st {std}, ob4to, ibds, [48]p, color, DJ/5.50)	Holt, Rinehart	(1970)	Adams, Adrienne	30-45	
Udry, Janice M.	Theodore's Parents (1st, sm4to, [30]p, green cl, color, DJ/2.75)	Lothrop, Lee	(1958)	Adams, Adrienne	55-80	*
Andersen, Hans C.	Thumbelina (1st, sm4to, 64p, color, DJ/3.50)	Scribner	(1961)	Adams, Adrienne	45-70	
Gleaves, Suzanne	Tip and Dip (1st, lg8vo, rust cl, [62]p, 1-color, DJ/2.95)	Lippincott	(1960)	Adams, Adrienne	45-65	
Hendrich, Paula	Trudy's First Day at Camp (1st, sm4to, yellow cl, [29]p, color, DJ/2.75)	Lothrop, Lee	(1959)	Adams, Adrienne	40-65	
N/A	Twelve Dancing Princesses (1st, 8vo, ipcb, gilt, unpag, color, DJ/3.95)	Holt, Rinehart	(1966)	Adams, Adrienne	25-45	
Anderson, Lonzo	Two Hundred Rabbits (1st, ob4to, [32]p, ibds, fp color, DJ/3.95)	Viking	(1968)	Adams, Adrienne	30-50	
Andersen, Hans C.	Ugly Duckling (1st, 4to, [48]p, color, DJ/3.50)	Scribner	1965	Adams, Adrienne	30-45	
Bulla, Clyde R.	What Makes a Shadow (1st, ob8vo, [38]p, fp 3-color, DJ/2.50)	Crowell	(1962)	Adams, Adrienne	40-70	
Fisher, Aileen	Where Does Everyone Go? (1st, sm4to, [36]p, color, pep, DJ/3.50)	Crowell	(1961)	Adams, Adrienne	30-45	
Schiller, Barbara	White Rat's Tale (1st {std}, 8vo, [32]p, color, DJ/3.50)	Holt, Rinehart	(1967)	Adams, Adrienne	30-50	
Warner, Gertrude	World on a Farm (1st {std}, 12mo, 83p, wraps, b/w)	Friendship Pr.	1931	Adams, Adrienne	60-90	
Hood, Thomas	Tom Tucker and Little Bo Peep (4to, ibds, 44p, 13cp)	L: Cassell	1891	Adams, Alice W.	70-120	
Carroll, Lewis	Alice in Wonderland (sm8vo, tan cl, 126p, 4cp, pep)	L: Blackie	[1920]	Adams, Frank	80-120	
N/A	Babes in the Wood (4to, ibds, p-o, 12cp)	L: Blackie	[1910]	Adams, Frank	150-220	
Gray, Thomas	Elegy in a Country Church Yard (4to, gilt, unpag, teg, uncut, 8 ticp)	L: Medici	(1931)	Adams, Frank	70-120	
Grimm Bros.	Hansel and Gretel (4to, ibds, 12cp, pep)	Dodge	[1920]	Adams, Frank	100-150	
N/A	Jolly Old Sports (folio, ibds, p-o, 36cp)	L: Blackie	[1912]	Adams, Frank	170-240	
N/A	Mother Hubbard's Book of Rhymes (4to, ibds, p-o, 16cp)	L: Blackie	[1915]	Adams, Frank	180-250	
N/A	Old Mother Hubbard (4to, ibds, 12cp)	L: Blackie	[1900]	Adams, Frank	120-180	
N/A	Old Time Rhymes (1st, lg4to, gilt, 36 ticp, pep)	L: Blackie	1913	Adams, Frank	350-500	
Arnold, Matthew	Scholar-Gypsy (1st, 4to, gilt, unpag, 10 ticp, 10 tipl)	L: Nicholson	1933	Adams, Frank	70-100	
N/A	Sing a Song of Sixpence (4to, ibds, 12cp)	L: Blackie	[1912]	Adams, Frank	150-220	
N/A	Some Old Nursery Tales (lg8vo, ibds, 98p, 12cp)	L: Blackie	[1920]	Adams, Frank	120-200	
N/A	Story of Old Dame Trot and her Pig (4to, ibds, 12 color)	L: Blackie	[1908]	Adams, Frank	100-145	
N/A	Story of Simple Simon (1st AM, 4to, ibds, p-o, 12cp)	Dodge	[1920]	Adams, Frank	140-185	
N/A	Story of Simple Simon (1st, 4to, ibds, 12cp)	L: Blackie	[1920]	Adams, Frank	150-240	
Pope, Jessie	Three Jolly Huntsmen (4to, ibds, 12 color)	L: Blackie	(1912)	Adams, Frank	100-145	
N/A	Three Little Pigs (tall 4to, ibds, color)	L: Blackie	[1925]	Adams, Frank	90-120	
N/A	Tom the Piper's Son (4to, ibds, [32]p, 12cp, pep)	L: Blackie	[1920]	Adams, Frank	90-120	
Smith, Gertrude	When Roggie and Reggie were Five (1st, sq8vo, 169p, 8cp)	Harper	1909	Adams, Henrietta	60-90	
Sinclair, May	Judgment of Eve (1st, sm8vo, 122p, uncut, 8pl)	Harper	1908	Adams, J.W.	25-40	*
Stewart, Grace B.	Good Fairy (1st, 8vo, 128p, gilt, 4cp)	Reilly/Lee	(1930)	Adams, P.B.	75-125	
Bangs, John K.	R. Holmes and Co. (1st, 12mo, 230p, blue cl, 6pl)	Harper	1906	Adamson, Sydney	100-165	
Kobler, John	Afternoon in the Attic (1st, 4to, 135p, black cl, b/w, DJ/3.75)	Dodd	1950	Addams, Charles	50-85	
Addams, Charles	Black Maria (1st {std}, 4to, ibds, 96p, b/w, pep, DJ/3.95)	Simon/Schuster	1960	Addams, Charles	50-80	
Mother Goose	Charles Addams Mother Goose (1st, 4to, [54]p, color, cep, DJ/4.95)	Windmill Books	(1967)	Addams, Charles	80-125	
Addams, Charles	Groaning Board (1st, 4to, green bds, 88p, fp color, DJ/3.95)	Simon/Schuster	1964	Addams, Charles	60-85	
Addams, Charles	Homebodies (1st {std}, 4to, 90p, fp b/w, DJ/2.95)	Simon/Schuster	1954	Addams, Charles	40-65	
Addams, Charles	Nightcrawlers (1st, 4to, 96p, ipcb, color, DJ/3.95)	Simon/Schuster	1957	Addams, Charles	50-80	
Norton, Mary	Bonfires and Broomsticks (1st, 8vo, 119p, pep, b/w, DJ)	L: Dent	(1947)	Adshead, Mary	150-225	
Bone, Stephen	Little Boy and his House (1st AM, lg8vo, [90]p, p-o, color, DJ/2.00)	Winston	(1937)	Adshead, Mary	25-40	
Coatsworth, Eliz.	The Place (1st {std}, 8vo, 72p, color, DJ/3.50)	Holt, Rinehart	(1966)	Aeurbach, Marjorie	25-45	*
Lewis, Emily W.	Next-Door Morelands (1st, sm8vo, 342p, 4pl)	Little/Brown	1907	Aherns, E.W.	25-40	*
Alcott, Louisa M.	Jo's Boys... (sm8vo, teg, 358p, 10pl)	Little/Brown	1903	Ahrens, E.W.	50-80	*
Aichinger, Helga	Elephant, Mouse & the Flea (1st AM {std}, 12mo, [32]p, col, pep, DJ/3.25)	Atheneum	1967	Aichinger, Helga	30-45	
Aichinger, Helga	Rain Mouse (1st AM, lg sq8vo, [25]p, dp color, DJ/4.95)	F. Watts	(1970)	Aichinger, Helga	20-30	
Aichinger, Helga	The Shepherd (1st AM, ob4to, ibds, [20]p, fp color, pep, DJ/3.75)	Crowell	1967	Aichinger, Helga	40-65	*
Ainslie, Kathleen	At Great Aunt Martha's (ob8vo, ibds, [32]p, 16 color, p-o)	L: Castell	[1905]	Ainslie, Kathleen	100-160	
Ainslie, Kathleen	Catharine Susan and Me Goes Abroad (16mo, wraps, [24]p, color)	L: Castell	[1900]	Ainslie, Kathleen	120-170	
Ainslie, Kathleen	Catharine Susan and Me's Coming Out (16mo, wraps, [32]p, color)	L: Castell	[1910]	Ainslie, Kathleen	100-160	
Ainslie, Kathleen	Catharine Susan in Hot Water (sq16mo, wraps, color)	L: Castell	[1905]	Ainslie, Kathleen	100-160	
Ainslie, Kathleen	Catharine Susan's Little Holiday (12mo, wraps, color)	L: Castell	[1905]	Ainslie, Kathleen	90-120	*
Ainslie, Kathleen	Lady Tabitha and Us (ob12mo, wraps, [24]p, 14 color, pep)	L: Castell	[1900]	Ainslie, Kathleen	100-150	
Ainslie, Kathleen	Me and Catharine Susan (16mo, wraps, [40]p, 20 fp color)	L: Castell	[1903]	Ainslie, Kathleen	120-180	
Ainslie, Kathleen	Me and Catharine Susan Earns an Honest Penny (sq16mo, wraps, color)	L: Castell	[1905]	Ainslie, Kathleen	120-180	
Ainslie, Kathleen	Mops Versus Tails (ob8vo, [24]p, ibds, color, pep)	L: Castell	[1905]	Ainslie, Kathleen	120-200	
Ainslie, Kathleen	Oh! Poor Amelia Jane! (12mo, [28]p, wraps, color)	L: Castell	[1900]	Ainslie, Kathleen	120-170	
Ainslie, Kathleen	Sammy Goes a Hunting (8vo, ibds, [24]p, 12 fp color, pep)	L: Castell	[1900]	Ainslie, Kathleen	100-165	
Ainslie, Kathleen	Why Was He Late? (ob12mo, [22]p, 12cp, wraps)	L: Castell	[1905]	Ainslie, Kathleen	100-165	
Otsuka, Yuzo	Suho and the White Horse (1st AM {std}, ob4to, [48]p, color, DJ/5.00)	Bobbs-Merrill	(1969)	Akaba, Suekichi	30-50	
Ratzesberger, Anna	Ali Hassan of Hamadan (1st, 8vo, 95p, p-o, 12cp, pep)	Whitman	(1933)	Akbar, Ali	50-85	
Lifton, Betty	Cock and the Ghost Cat (1st {std}, lg8vo, 34p, 1-color, DJ/3.50)	Atheneum	1965	Akino, Fuku	30-45	
Lifton, Betty	Dwarf Pine Tree (1st {std}, lg8vo, 37p, color, DJ/3.50)	Atheneum	1963	Akino, Fuku	50-80	R

AUTHOR	TITLE	PUBLISHER	DATE	ARTIST	PRICE	LC
Ishii, Momoko	Issun Boshi, the Inchling (1st AM, ob8vo, gilt, [40]p, col, pep, DJ/3.50)	NY: Walker	(1967)	Akino, Fuku	30-50	
Morse, Samuel	Sea Sums (1st {std}, lg ob8vo, 32p, color, DJ/4.50)	Little/Brown	(1970)	Akino, Fuku	25-40	
Benet, William R.	Timothy's Angels (1st, sm4to, ipcb, [24]p, fp color, pep, DJ/2.00)	Crowell	(1947)	Alajalov, Constantin	55-80	
Wilde, Oscar	The Sphinx (4to, teg, 36p, gilt, uncut, 10pl)	J. Lane	1920	Alastair	500-750	
Field, Louis A.	Peter Rabbit and his Ma (12mo, ibds, fp color)	Saalfield	(1917)	Albert, Virginia	60-90	
Field, Louis A.	Peter Rabbit and his Pa (8vo, [24]p, ibds, color, pep)	Saalfield	(1908)	Albert, Virginia	60-100	R
Field, Louis A.	Peter Rabbit Goes to School (12mo, ibds, fp color)	Saalfield	(1917)	Albert, Virginia	40-65	
Potter, Beatrix	Tale of Peter Rabbit (12mo, grey bds, [56]p, fp color, pep)	Saalfield	(1916)	Albert, Virginia	50-80	
Ferguson, Charles	Abecedarian Book (1st {std}, 8vo, 131p, yellow cl, 2-color, DJ/3.95)	Little/Brown	(1964)	Alcorn, John	25-40	
Nash, Ogden	Everyone but Thee and Me (1st {std}, 8vo, 171p, b/w, DJ/3.95)	Little/Brown	(1962)	Alcorn, John	40-65	
Wahl, Jan	Pocahontas in London (1st {std}, 4to, [40]p, color, DJ/4.50)	Delacorte Pr.	(1967)	Alcorn, John	30-50	
McGinley, Phyllis	Wonderful Time (1st {std}, 4to, 47p, b/w, DJ/3.50, NYTBI)	Lippincott	(1966)	Alcorn, John	30-45	
LeSueur, Meridel	Little Brother of the Wilderness (1st {std}, 8vo, 68p, fp color, DJ/2.50)	Knopf	1947	Alden, Betty	50-75	
LeSueur, Meridel	Nancy Hanks of Wilderness Road (1st {std}, 8vo, 88p, color, DJ/2.50)	Knopf	(1949)	Alden, Betty	40-65	*
Yates, Elizabeth	Rainbow 'Round the World (1st {std}, 8vo, 174p, b/w, pep, DJ/2.50, JABA)	Bobbs-Merrill	(1954)	Alden, Betty	45-70	R
Byron, May	Animal Frolics (1st, 4to, unpag)	L: Hodder	[1916]	Aldin, Cecil	90-120	*
Aldin, Cecil	Artist's Models (1st AM, 4to, blue cl, 80p, 20 fp b/w)	Scribner	1930	Aldin, Cecil	180-240	
Aldin, Cecil	Artist's Models (1st, 4to, 80p, grey cl, 20 1-color)	L: Witherby	(1930)	Aldin, Cecil	200-300	
Howe-Nurse, Wilfred	Berkshire Vale (1st, folio, 45p, p-o, 22pl, pep)	L: Blackwell	1927	Aldin, Cecil	140-200	
Sewell, Anna	Black Beauty (1st, 4to, blue/gilt, 291p, 18 ticp, pep)	L: Jarrold	[1912]	Aldin, Cecil	250-350	
Sewell, Anna	Black Beauty (1st AM, 8vo, 291p, 18 ticp, pep)	Stokes	[1913]	Aldin, Cecil	200-300	
Aldin, Cecil	Bobtail Puppy Book (1st AM, lg8vo, 37p, ibds, 12 fp color)	NY: Hodder	[1915]	Aldin, Cecil	200-300	
Douglas, James	Bunch Book (1st AM, 8vo, green/gilt, 173p, col frn, b/w)	Appleton	1932	Aldin, Cecil	40-65	
Aldin, Cecil	Bunnyborough (1st, 4to, ibds, unpag, 16 fp color, pep)	L: H. Milford	(1919)	Aldin, Cecil	600-900	
Aldin, Cecil	Bunnyborough (1st [new ed.], lg8vo, [48]p, color, DJ)	L: Eyre/Spotts.	(1946)	Aldin, Cecil	150-220	
Aldin, Cecil	Cathedrals & Abbey Churches of England (1st, 4to, 111p, teg, 16cp, pep)	L: Eyre/Spotts.	(1924)	Aldin, Cecil	200-300	
Aldin, Cecil	Cecil Aldin Book (1st, lg8vo, cloth, p-o, 192p, 15cp)	L: Eyre/Spotts.	1932	Aldin, Cecil	130-200	
Byron, May	Cecil Aldin's Happy Family (1st, 4to, bds, teg, p-o, 36cp)	L: H. Frowde	[1912]	Aldin, Cecil	225-325	
Byron, May	Cecil Aldin's Merry Party (1st, 4to, ibds, p-o, gilt, teg, 36cp)	L: H. Frowde	1913	Aldin, Cecil	500-700	
Emanuel, Walter	Conceited Puppy... (1st AM, 12mo, ibds, p-o, color)	Dutton	(1905)	Aldin, Cecil	100-160	
Emanuel, Walter	Dog Day (1st, lg4to, ibds, [59]p, 28cp)	L: Heinemann	1902	Aldin, Cecil	250-400	
Emanuel, Walter	Dog Day (1st AM, lg4to, [59]p, ibds, 28cp)	R.H. Russell	1902	Aldin, Cecil	250-400	
Emanuel, Walter	Dog Day (24mo, 55p, ibds, 28cp)	Dutton	[1907]	Aldin, Cecil	100-160	
Aldin, Cecil	Dogs of Character (1st, sm4to, p-o, gilt, 118p, teg, 2cp)	L: Eyre/Spotts.	1927	Aldin, Cecil	160-225	
Emanuel, Walter	Dogs of War (1st, 8vo, tan/gilt, 243p, 12cp)	L: Bradbury/Ag	(1906)	Aldin, Cecil	200-300	
Chalmers, Patrick	Dozen Dogs or So (1st, 4to, 47p, brown cl, 13cp)	L: Eyre/Spotts.	1928	Aldin, Cecil	200-300	
Praed, Winthrop M.	Every-Day Characters (1st, 4to, white cl, 74p, b/w)	L: Kegan Paul	1898	Aldin, Cecil	300-500	
Aldin, Cecil	Farm Babies (4to, ipcb, 24cp, pep)	L/NY: Hodder	[1910]	Aldin, Cecil	350-500	
Aldin, Cecil	Farmyard Puppies (1st, lg sq8vo, ibds, 12cp)	L: H. Frowde	[1911]	Aldin, Cecil	250-350	
Aldin, Cecil	Field Babies (4to, ipcb, 24cp, pep)	L: H. Frowde	[1910]	Aldin, Cecil	250-400	
Aldin, Cecil	Gay Dog (1st, 4to, ibds, [50]p, 24cp)	L: Heinemann	1905	Aldin, Cecil	200-300	
Aldin, Cecil	Great Adventure (1st, folio, ibds, 16cp, pep)	L: H. Milford	[1920]	Aldin, Cecil	300-500	
Aldin, Cecil	Gyp's Hour of Bliss (1st, lg4to, ibds, 48p, 15cp, pep)	L: Collins	(1919)	Aldin, Cecil	300-450	
Surtees, Robert S.	Handley Cross (1st, lg8vo, 2 vols, gilt, 24cp)	L: E. Arnold	[1910]	Aldin, Cecil	250-400	
Kipling, Rudyard	His Apologies (1st {std}, 8vo, ibds, p-o, 17p, b/w)	Doubleday/Doran	1932	Aldin, Cecil	90-130	
Byron, May	Humpty & Dumpty Give a Fancy Dress Ball (sq8vo, ibds, 6 fp color)	L: Milford/OUP	(1913)	Aldin, Cecil	200-350	
Byron, May	Hungry Peter (1st AM, lg8vo, tan bds, 5cp, pep)	NY: Hodder	1914	Aldin, Cecil	100-165	*
Aldin, Cecil	Jack and Jill (1st, 4to, 24p, ibds, fp color, pep)	L: Frowde/Hodder	[1921]	Aldin, Cecil	400-650	
Waylett, Richard	Jock and Some Others (1st, 4to, ibds, [30]p, 16cp)	L: Lawrence/Jel.	[1916]	Aldin, Cecil	300-500	
Surtees, Robert S.	Jorrock's on 'Unting (1st, 16mo, teg, bds, 32p, p-o, 3 ticp)	L: Heinemann	1909	Aldin, Cecil	140-220	
Aldin, Cecil	Just Among Friends (1st AM, lg4to, 28p, color)	Scribner	1934	Aldin, Cecil	160-220	
Chalmers, Patrick	Last Muster (1st, 8vo, 127p, 24 b/w illus, DJ)	L: Eyre/Spotts.	1939	Aldin, Cecil	70-120	
Ashmore, Marion	Lost, Stolen and Strayed (1st AM, 8vo, 96p, col frn, b/w)	Scribner	1931	Aldin, Cecil	80-130	
Aldin, Cecil	Mac (1st AM, 4to, ibds, 24 fp color)	NY: Hodder	(1912)	Aldin, Cecil	350-500	
Aldin, Cecil	Merry and Bright (1st, lg4to, bds, p-o, 24cp, pep)	L: H. Frowde	(1911)	Aldin, Cecil	300-500	
Aldin, Cecil	Merry Puppy Book (1st, 4to, ibds, 36cp)	L: Frowde/Hodder	(1913)	Aldin, Cecil	350-500	
Aldin, Cecil	Mongrel Puppy Book (1st, sq4to, ibds, 12cp)	L: H. Milford	[1909]	Aldin, Cecil	250-400	
Aldin, Cecil	Mrs. Tickler's Caravan (1st AM, lg8vo, p-o, 91p, color, pep)	Scribner	1931	Aldin, Cecil	120-200	
Aldin, Cecil	Mrs. Tickler's Caravan (1st, sm4to, ibds, 91p, color, pep)	L: Eyre/Spotts.	1931	Aldin, Cecil	160-220	
Maeterlinck, Maurice	My Dog (1st, 8vo, 64p, teg, gilt, p-o, 6cp)	L: G. Allen	1913	Aldin, Cecil	150-220	
Irving, Washington	Old Christmas (1st AM, 8vo, [176]p, p-o, red/gilt, 27cp)	NY: Sully	1908	Aldin, Cecil	200-300	
Irving, Washington	Old Christmas (1st AM, 8vo, 176p, fp color)	Dodd	(1908)	Aldin, Cecil	100-160	
Irving, Washington	Old Fashioned Christmas Day (1st, 12mo, unpag, ibds, p-o, 6 ticp)	L: Hodder	[1910]	Aldin, Cecil	200-300	
Aldin, Cecil	Old Inns (1st AM, sm4to, teg, 149p, 16cp, fp b/w)	Doubleday/Page	1921	Aldin, Cecil	100-165	
Aldin, Cecil	Old Manor Houses (1st, sm4to, 108p, grey/gilt, 12cp, pep)	L: Heinemann	(1923)	Aldin, Cecil	140-200	
Maeterlinck, Maurice	Our Friend the Dog (1st AM, 8vo, 67p, gilt, 6cp)	Dodd	1913	Aldin, Cecil	180-250	
Steele, Richard	Perverse Widow (1st AM, 12mo, teg, ibds, p-o, 3 ticp)	Dent/Dutton	1909	Aldin, Cecil	85-130	
Steele, Richard	Perverse Widow (1st, 16mo, 31p, bds, p-o, teg, 3 ticp)	L: Heinemann	1909	Aldin, Cecil	100-160	
Aldin, Cecil	Pickles (1st, lg4to, ibds, [50]p, 24cp)	L: Frowde/Hodder	[1909]	Aldin, Cecil	250-400	
Dickens, Charles	Posthumous Papers of the Pickwick Club (1st, 2 vols, 4to, bds, color)	L: Chapman	1910	Aldin, Cecil	200-300	
Hutchinson, Henry N.	Prehistoric Man & Beast (1st, 8vo, gilt, 298p, 10pl)	L: Smith/Elder	1896	Aldin, Cecil	70-100	
Waylett, Richard	Puppy Tales (1st, 4to, ibds, 16cp)	L: Lawrence	[1912]	Aldin, Cecil	180-240	
Aldin, Cecil	Ratcatcher to Scarlet (1st, sq8vo, 123p, black cl, 15 fp b/w)	L: Eyre/Spotts.	[1926]	Aldin, Cecil	140-200	
Aldin, Cecil	Red Puppy Book (1st, lg sq8vo, blue cl, 48p, 12cp)	L: H. Frowde	[1910]	Aldin, Cecil	250-400	
Masefield, John	Right Royal (1st AM, 8vo, black/gilt, 116p, 4cp)	Macmillan	1922	Aldin, Cecil	150-225	
Hare, Kenneth	Roads and Vagabonds (1st, lg4to, 189p, red/gilt, 2cp)	L: Eyre/Spotts.	(1930)	Aldin, Cecil	250-350	
Aldin, Cecil	Romance of the Road (1st, folio, 123p, teg, buckram, 11 ticp)	L: Eyre/Spotts.	1928	Aldin, Cecil	200-300	
Aldin, Cecil	Rough and Tumble (4to, ibds, p-o, 24cp, pep)	L: H. Frowde	[1912]	Aldin, Cecil	350-500	

AUTHOR	TITLE	PUBLISHER	DATE	ARTIST	PRICE	LC
Fife, Duncan	Scarlet Blue and Green (1st, sm4to, 64p, gilt, 4 fp color)	L: Macmillan	1932	Aldin, Cecil	80-135	
Aldin, Cecil	Scarlet to M.F.H. (1st AM, 4to, 151p, red/gilt, color)	Scribner	(1933)	Aldin, Cecil	180-250	
Aldin, Cecil	Sleeping Partners (1st, 4to, blue bds, unpag, 20 ticp)	L: Eyre/Spotts.	1929	Aldin, Cecil	250-400	
Hope, Stanton	Smugglers' Gallows (1st, 8vo, 209p, red cl, col frn, 5pl)	L: Eyre/Spotts.	1936	Aldin, Cecil	45-70	
Hope, Stanton	Smugglers' Gallows (1st AM, 8vo, 209p, col frn, b/w, DJ/2.50)	Scribner	1937	Aldin, Cecil	30-50	
Robinson, Charles	Ten Little Puppy Dogs (1st, ob4to, green cl, fp b/w)	L: Sands	1902	Aldin, Cecil	600-800	
Emanuel, Walter	The Snob (1st, 4to, 35p, ibds, 19pl)	L: Lawrence/Bul.	1904	Aldin, Cecil	250-350	
Aldin, Cecil	The Twins (1st, lg4to, ibds, p-o, 24cp, pep)	L: Hodder	[1910]	Aldin, Cecil	200-300	
Aldin, Cecil	The Widow (1st AM, 12mo, 31p, ibds, p-o, 3 ticp)	Dutton	1909	Aldin, Cecil	80-125	*
Aldin, Cecil	Time I Was Dead (1st, lg8vo, 389p, gilt, 9cp)	L: Eyre/Spotts.	1934	Aldin, Cecil	140-200	
Vredenburg, Edric	Tinker Tailor (4to, 136p, p-o, 12cp)	L: R. Tuck	[1914]	Aldin, Cecil	900-1500	
Buckland, James	Two Little Runaways (1st, 8vo, 358p, teg, tan/gilt, fp b/w)	L: Longmans	1898	Aldin, Cecil	150-225	
Aldin, Cecil	Us (1st AM, 4to, [36]p, color, wraps)	A.& W. Guild	(1935)	Aldin, Cecil	80-120	
Aldin, Cecil	White Kitten Book (1st, lg sq8vo, ibds, [48]p, 12cp)	L: Frowde/Hodder	[1909]	Aldin, Cecil	200-300	
Aldin, Cecil	White Puppy Book (1st, lg sq8vo, ibds, [48]p, 12cp)	L: Frowde/Hodder	[1909]	Aldin, Cecil	200-300	
Heiberg, Neils	White-Ear and Peter (1st, 8vo, 222p, red/gilt, 16cp)	L: Macmillan	1912	Aldin, Cecil	200-300	
Morton, John B.	Who's Who in the Zoo (1st, 4to, 173p, 4cp)	L: Eyre/Spotts.	1933	Aldin, Cecil	90-120	
Fleuron, Svend	Wild Horses of Iceland (1st, 8vo, 234p, red cl, 15 fp b/w)	L: Eyre/Spotts.	[1933]	Aldin, Cecil	50-80	
N/A	Young Folks Birthday Book (sq12mo, 188p, fp color)	L: Hills & Co.	[1905]	Aldin, Cecil	120-170	*
Farrow, George E.	Zoo Babies (4to, green bds, 24 color)	L: H. Frowde	[1905]	Aldin, Cecil	300-425	*
Aldin, Cecil	Happy Annual (1st AM, sm folio, ibds, 48p, color)	Dutton	(1907)	Aldin/Hassall	250-350	
N/A	Two Well-Worn Shoe Stories (1st, ob folio, ibds, color)	L: Sands	1899	Aldin/Hassall	300-500	
Robinson, Philip S.	Bubble and Squeak (1st, 8vo, 230p, green cl, teg, 15pl)	L: Ibister	1902	Aldin/Shepherd	70-125	*
Malory, Thomas	Women of Morte Darthur (1st, 8vo, 251p, gilt, 4cp)	L: Methuen	1927	Alexander, A.D.	50-80	
Freschet, Berniece	Young Eagle (1st, lg8vo, unpag, color, DJ/3.25)	Scribner	(1965)	Alexander, James	20-35	
Zolotow, Charlotte	Big Sister, and Little Sister (1st, 4to, ibds, 24p, 2-color, pep, DJ/2.95)	Harper, Row	(1965)	Alexander, Martha	30-40	
Alexander, Martha G.	Blackboard Bear (1st {std}, ob12mo, [32]p, ipcb, 2-color, cep, DJ/2.95)	Dial Press	(1969)	Alexander, Martha	20-35	
Alexander, Martha G.	Bobo's Dream (1st {std}, sm8vo, [32]p, color, DJ/2.95)	Dial Press	(1970)	Alexander, Martha	25-40	
Udry, Janice M.	Mary Ann's Mud Day (1st, 16mo, 29p, color, DJ/2.50)	Harper	(1967)	Alexander, Martha	20-30	
Alexander, Martha G.	Story Grandmother Told (1st {std}, 8vo, [31]p, ipcb, 1-color, cep, DJ/2.95)	Dial Press	(1969)	Alexander, Martha	20-35	*
Orgel, Doris	Whose Turtle? (1st, 4to, [46]p, gilt, fp b/w, DJ/3.95)	World	(1968)	Alexander, Martha	30-45	*
Wellesley, Howard	All Kinds of Neighbors (1st, ob8vo, [26]p, fp color, pep, DJ)	Holt, Rinehart	1963	Aliki	30-50	
Hautzig, Esther	At Home, a Visit in Four Languages (1st {std}, 4to, [32]p, color, DJ/4.95)	Macmillan	(1968)	Aliki	30-50	*
Hawes, Judy	Bees and Beelines (1st, ob8vo, [40]p, color, DJ/2.75)	Crowell	(1964)	Aliki	30-45	*
Gans, Roma	Birds at Night (1st, sq8vo, 33p, color, DJ/3.25)	Crowell	(1968)	Aliki	30-45	
Lexau, Joan M.	Cathy is Company (1st, 8vo, [34]p, 2-color, pep, DJ/2.50)	Dial Press	(1961)	Aliki	25-40	*
Blomquist, David	Daddy is Home! (1st, lg8vo, [26]p, fp color, cep, DJ)	Holt, Rinehart	1963	Aliki	25-45	*
Aliki	Diogenes: Story of Greek Philosopher (1st, sq8vo, [32]p, color, DJ/4.25)	Prentice-Hall	(1968)	Aliki	25-45	
Clare, Helen	Five Dolls and the Duke (1st {std}, 8vo, 99p, b/w, DJ/3.95)	Prentice-Hall	(1968)	Aliki	25-40	
Ford, Henry W.	Fun with the Calendar (1st, 4to, [26]p, color, dep, DJ)	Holt, Rinehart	1964	Aliki	30-45	
Aliki	George and the Cherry Tree (1st, 8vo, 32p, fp color, DJ/3.75)	Dial Press	1964	Aliki	20-30	*
Thompson, Vivian L.	Horse that Liked Sandwiches (1st, 8vo, [48]p, fp 2-color, DJ/2.00)	Putnam	(1962)	Aliki	30-45	
Aliki	Hush Little Baby (1st, lg8vo, [32]p, color, cep, DJ/4.25)	Prentice-Hall	(1968)	Aliki	30-50	
Brandenberg, Franz	I Once Knew a Man (1st {std}, 8vo, [40]p, 1-color, DJ/3.95)	Macmillan	(1970)	Aliki	25-40	
Kalusky, Rebecca	Is it Blue as a Butterfly? (1st, 8vo, [30]p, color, cep, DJ/3.50)	Prentice-Hall	(1965)	Aliki	25-40	
Morrison, Sean	Is That a Happy Hippopotamus? (1st, 8vo, [46]p, fp 2-color, DJ/3.75)	Crowell	(1966)	Aliki	25-40	
Aliki	Keep Your Mouth Closed, Dear (1st, 8vo, [48]p, fp 1-color, cep, DJ/3.50)	Dial Press	(1966)	Aliki	20-30	*
Holding, James	Lazy Little Zulu (1st, 4to, [32]p, fp 3-color, dep, DJ/3.25)	Wm. Morrow	1962	Aliki	30-45	
Showers, Paul	Listening Walk (1st, ob8vo, [38]p, fp 2-color, DJ/2.50)	Crowell	(1961)	Aliki	20-30	*
Phelan, Mary K.	Mother's Day (1st, 8vo, [40]p, color, DJ/2.95)	Crowell	(1965)	Aliki	30-50	
Holding, James	Mr. Moonlight and Omar (1st, 4to, [32]p, fp 3-color, pep, DJ/3.25)	Wm. Morrow	1963	Aliki	30-45	
Yeo, Wilma	Mrs. Neverbody's Recipes (1st {std}, 24mo, [34]p, color, DJ/2.95)	Lippincott	(1968)	Aliki	30-50	*
Aliki	My Five Senses (1st, sq8vo, [40]p, 2-color, DJ/2.50)	Crowell	(1962)	Aliki	20-30	*
Aliki	My Visit to the Dinosaurs (1st, ob8vo, 33p, color, DJ/3.50)	Crowell	(1969)	Aliki	25-40	
Greenberg, Polly	Oh Lord, I Wish I was a Buzzard (1st, 4to, [31]p, color, DJ/4.50)	Macmillan	(1968)	Aliki	30-50	*
Kohn, Bernice	One Day it Rained Cats and Dogs (1st, 8vo, [32]p, fp 1-color, DJ/2.50)	Coward	(1965)	Aliki	30-50	
Holding, James	Sherlock on the Trail (1st, ob8vo, [32]p, fp color, pep, DJ/2.95)	Wm. Morrow	1964	Aliki	30-45	
Aliki	Story of Johnny Appleseed (1st, 8vo, [32]p, color, DJ/3.50)	Prentice-Hall	(1963)	Aliki	20-30	*
Aliki	Story of William Tell (1st, lg8vo, [32]p, fp color, DJ/3.25)	A.S. Barnes	(1961)	Aliki	20-30	*
Lexau, Joan M.	That's Good, That's Bad (1st, sm ob4to, [40]p, fp color, DJ/3.25)	Dial Press	1963	Aliki	30-50	
Aliki	The Eggs (1st, 4to, [32]p, fp color, DJ/3.95)	Pantheon	(1969)	Aliki	20-30	*
Fehr, Howard F.	This is My Family (1st, lg ob8vo, [27]p, color, cep, DJ)	Holt, Rinehart	1963	Aliki	25-40	
Heilbroner, Joan	This is the House Where Jack Lives (1st, 8vo, 62p, color, DJ/1.95)	Harper	(1962)	Aliki	30-50	*
Aliki	Three Gold Pieces (1st, 4to, [31]p, fp color, DJ/3.50)	Pantheon	1967	Aliki	20-30	*
Srivastava, Jane	Weighing and Balancing (1st, ob8vo, ibds, 32p, 2-color, DJ/3.75)	Crowell	(1970)	Aliki	30-50	
Marks, Mickey	What Can I Buy? (1st, 8vo, [33]p, 1-color, pep, DJ/2.50)	Dial Press	1962	Aliki	30-45	
Hodges, Margaret	What's for Lunch, Charlie? (1st, 8vo, 72p, fp b/w, DJ/2.75)	Dial Press	1961	Aliki	25-45	
Aliki	Wish Workers (1st, ob4to, unpag, color, DJ/3.50)	Dial Press	(1962)	Aliki	30-45	*
Allan, Marguerite B.	Rhyme Garden (1st, lg8vo, 64p, ipcb, 8cp)	L: Bodley Head	1917	Allan, Marguerite B.	40-65	
Tarry, Ellen	My Dog Rinty (1st, lg8vo, [48]p, ibds, DJ/1.50, b/w photos by...)	Viking	1946	Alland, A.& A.	200-300	R
Allen, Daphne	Birth of the Opal (1st, 4to, p-o, bds, 95p, 12 ticp)	L: Allen	1913	Allen, Daphne	80-130	
Mukerji, Dhan G.	Jungle Beasts and Men (1st, 8vo, 160p, col frn, b/w)	Dutton	(1923)	Allen, J.E.	25-40	
Mukerji, Dhan G.	Kari: The Elephant (1st, 8vo, 135p, b/w)	Dutton	(1922)	Allen, J.E.	20-30	
MacDonald, George	Princess and Curdie (1st AM, 8vo, 255p, gilt, 11 b/w)	Lippincott	1883	Allen, James	160-225	
Housman, Laurence	Cotton Woolleena (1st, 8vo, 36p, wraps, p-o)	L: Blackwell	[1933]	Allen, Marian	75-100	*
Allen, Marian	Wind in the Chimney (1st, 8vo, 89p, grey cl, 6 ticp)	L: Blackwell	[1931]	Allen, Marian	30-50	*
Blake, William	Songs of Innocence (1st, 8vo, 31p, p-o, 4cp)	L: Jack	[1905]	Allen, Olive	55-90	*
Hawthorne, Nathaniel	Tanglewood Tales (16mo, 107p, gilt, p-o, uncut, 8cp)	Jack/Dutton	[1908]	Allen, Olive	40-60	*

AUTHOR	TITLE	PUBLISHER	DATE	ARTIST	PRICE	LC
DeJong, Meindert	Nobody Plays with a Cabbage (1st, lg8vo, 52p, fp b/w, DJ/2.75)	Harper	(1962)	Allen, Tom	25-40	
Almond, Linda S.	When Peter Rabbit Went to School (1st, 16mo, p-o, 58p, 27 color)	Platt/Munk	(1935)	Almond, Linda	40-60	
Quiller-Couch, A.	Roll Call of Honor (1st, lg8vo, p-o, 348p, 9cp)	Nelson	[1911]	Almond, William D.	55-80	
Martin, Patricia	Dolls from Cheyenne (1st, 8vo, 38p, color, DJ)	Putnam	(1967)	Almquist, Don	25-40	
Heide, Florence P.	It Never is Dark (1st {std}, 8vo, 32p, color, DJ/1.95)	Follett	(1968)	Almquist, Don	20-35	
Wilbur, Richard	Loudmouse (1st {std}, 4to, [32]p, 1-color)	Crowell-Collier	(1963)	Almquist, Don	50-80	R*
Craig, M. Jean	Spring is Like the Morning (1st, lg8vo, 61p, 2-color, DJ/3.00)	Putnam	(1965)	Almquist, Don	20-35	*
Smith, William J.	What Did I See? (1st {std}, 4to, [61]p, ibds, fp b/w, cep)	Crowell-Collier	(1962)	Almquist, Don	60-100	R
Lynch, Patricia	Donkey Goes Visiting (1st {std}, 8vo, 229p, 4cp, b/w, pep, DJ/2.00)	Dutton	(1936)	Altendorf, George	45-70	
Eckert, Allan W.	King Snake (1st {std}, 8vo, 143p, b/w, DJ/4.75)	Little/Brown	(1968)	Altschuler, Franz	50-80	
Clark, Denis	Boomer (1st AM, 8vo, 144p, b/w, DJ/2.50)	Viking	1955	Ambler, C. Gifford	20-30	*
Burton, Hester	Beyond the Wier Bridge (1st AM, 8vo, 221p, b/w, DJ/4.50)	Crowell	(1970)	Ambrus, Victor	20-30	
Ambrus, Victor G.	Brave Soldier Janosh (1st AM {std}, 4to, [24]p, gilt, color, DJ/3.50)	Harcourt	(1967)	Ambrus, Victor	30-50	
Stevenson, William	Bushbabies (1st {std}, 8vo, 278p, b/w, cep, DJ/3.50)	Houghton	1965	Ambrus, Victor	25-45	
Farjeon, Eleanor	Calvacade of Queens (1st AM, sm4to, gilt, 243p, b/w, DJ/5.95)	H.Z. Walck	1965	Ambrus, Victor	25-40	
Burton, Hester	Castors Away! (1st AM {std}, 8vo, 254p, b/w, DJ/3.00, CgM)	World	(1963)	Ambrus, Victor	30-50	*
Robinson, Veronica	David in Silence (1st, 8vo, 126p, fp b/w, DJ/3.25)	Lippincott	1966	Ambrus, Victor	25-45	
Peyton, Kathleen M.	Edge of the Cloud (1st, 8vo, 166p, b/w, DJ, CgM)	L: Oxford U.Pr.	1969	Ambrus, Victor	40-65	
Peyton, Kathleen M.	Flambards (1st AM {std}, 8vo, 206p, b/w, DJ/3.95)	World	(1968)	Ambrus, Victor	30-45	
Guillot, Rene	Fofana (1st AM {std}, 8vo, 145p, b/w, DJ/3.00)	Criterion Bks.	(1962)	Ambrus, Victor	30-50	
Treadgold, Mary	Heron Ride (1st {std}, 8vo, 192p, b/w, DJ)	L: J. Cape	1962	Ambrus, Victor	25-45	
Sutcliff, Rosemary	Hound of Ulster (1st AM {std}, 8vo, 192p, b/w, DJ/3.50)	Dutton	(1963)	Ambrus, Victor	30-50	*
Manning-Sanders, Ruth	Jonnikin and the Flying Basket (1st, 8vo, 152p, 8cp, DJ)	L: Oxford U.Pr.	1969	Ambrus, Victor	20-35	
Chauncy, Nan	Lighthouse Keeper's Son (1st, 8vo, 133p, b/w, DJ)	L: Oxford U.Pr.	1969	Ambrus, Victor	30-45	
Ambrus, Victor G.	Little Cockerel (1st AM {std}, 4to, [24]p, ibds, color, DJ/3.50)	Harcourt	1968	Ambrus, Victor	30-50	
Burton, Hester	No Beat of Drum (1st {std}, 8vo, red cl, 190p, b/w, DJ)	L: Oxford U.Pr.	(1967)	Ambrus, Victor	30-45	
Sleigh, Barbara	North of Nowhere (1st AM {std}, 8vo, 223p, b/w, DJ)	Coward	(1966)	Ambrus, Victor	70-100	
Miles, Miska	Pieces of Home (1st {std}, 8vo, 60p, b/w, DJ/3.25)	Little/Brown	(1967)	Ambrus, Victor	25-40	
Peyton, Kathleen M.	Plan for Birdsmarsh (1st AM {std}, 8vo, 240p, green cl, b/w, DJ/3.75)	World	(1966)	Ambrus, Victor	25-40	
Serraillier, Ian	Robin and his Merry Men (1st, 4to, 64p, fp color, DJ/4.50)	H.Z. Walck	(1970)	Ambrus, Victor	35-50	
Peyton, Kathleen M.	Sea Fever (1st AM {std}, 8vo, 240p, b/w, DJ/3.50)	World	(1963)	Ambrus, Victor	25-40	
Ambrus, Victor G.	Seven Skinny Goats (1st AM {std}, sm4to, ibds, [24]p, color, DJ/3.95)	Harcourt	1970	Ambrus, Victor	30-45	
Mayne, William	The Changeling (1st AM {std}, 8vo, 153p, b/w, DJ/3.00)	Dutton	(1963)	Ambrus, Victor	45-70	
Bartos-Hoppner, B.	The Cossacks (1st AM {std}, 8vo, 295p, b/w, DJ/4.00)	H.Z. Walck	1963	Ambrus, Victor	30-45	
Griffiths, Helen	The Greyhound (1st AM, {std}, 8vo, 180p, b/w, DJ/3.25)	Doubleday	(1966)	Ambrus, Victor	25-40	
Ambrus, Victor G.	Three Poor Tailors (1st AM {std}, 4to, [24]p, bds, color, DJ/3.50, KGM)	Harcourt	(1966)	Ambrus, Victor	45-70	
Peyton, Kathleen M.	Thunder in the Sky (1st AM {std}, 8vo, 158p, b/w, DJ/3.75)	World	(1967)	Ambrus, Victor	25-40	
Burton, Hester	Time of Trial (1st AM {std}, 8vo, 216p, b/w, DJ/3.75, CgM)	World	(1964)	Ambrus, Victor	30-50	*
Balderson, Margaret	When Jays Fly to Barbmo (1st AM {std}, 8vo, 239p, b/w, DJ/4.25)	World	(1969)	Ambrus, Victor	20-35	
Almedingen, Edith M.	Young Mark (1st AM {std}, 8vo, 177p, b/w, DJ/3.75)	Farrar, Straus	(1968)	Ambrus, Victor	30-45	
North, Sterling	Abe Lincoln: Log Cabin to White House (1st {std}, 8vo, 184p, pep, DJ/1.50)	Random	(1956)	Ames, Lee	25-40	
Fenner, Phyllis R.	Circus Parade (1st {std}, lg8vo, beige cl, 174p, uncut, fp b/w, DJ/3.00)	Knopf	1954	Ames, Lee	30-50	
Balch, Glenn	Horse in Danger (1st, 8vo, 181p, b/w, DJ/2.75)	Crowell	(1960)	Ames, Lee	30-50	
Selden, George	Sir Arthur Evans... (1st {std}, 8vo, 35p, color, DJ/2.95)	Macmillan	(1964)	Ames, Lee	20-35	
McCracken, Harold	Winning of the West (1st {std}, lg4to, ibds, 64p, color, DJ/2.00)	Garden City	1955	Ames, Lee	30-50	
Ames, Mrs. E.	Really and Truly (1st, ob4to, ibds, [44]p, color)	L: E. Arnold	[1899]	Ames, Mrs. E.	250-400	
Ames, Mrs. E.	Tim and the Dusty Man (ob4to, 51p, ibds, 24cp)	L: Richards	[1903]	Ames, Mrs. E.	250-400	
Ames, Mrs. E.	Tremendous Twins (lg ob8vo, 95p, ibds, color)	L: Richards	1900	Ames, Mrs. E.	250-400	
Orcutt, William D.	Princess Kallisto (1st, 4to, 138p, ibds, 6 fp color)	Little/Brown	1902	Amsden, Harriette	150-220	
Orcutt, William D.	Princess Kallisto (1st UK, 4to, 139p, 6 fp color, pep)	L: Jack	1905	Amsden, Harriette	140-220	
Orcutt, William D.	Princess Kallisto (1st [this pub.], 8vo, 139p, p-o, 6 fp color)	Harper	(1911)	Amsden, Harriette	70-120	
N/A	100 Best Fairy Tales (folio, ibds, 123p, 8cp, DJ)	Whitman	(1937)	Anderson, Anne	120-180	
N/A	Aladdin and his Wonderful Lamp (12mo, 38p, color, pep)	NY: Nelson	1928	Anderson, Anne	55-80	
N/A	Ali Baba and the Forty Thieves (12mo, ibds, 4cp)	Nelson	[1920]	Anderson, Anne	65-90	
Anderson, Anne	Ann Anderson's Fairy Tale Book (1st AM, 4to, 190p, p-o, 12cp, pep)	Nelson	[1923]	Anderson, Anne	180-300	
N/A	Aucassin & Nicolette (1st, lg8vo, 131p, teg, 6cp)	L: A&C Black	1911	Anderson, Anne	90-160	
Anderson, Anne	Betty Book (1st, 4to, ibds, 32p, 13cp, pep)	L: Nelson	[1912]	Anderson, Anne	120-200	
Cost, March	Bitter Green of the Willow (1st {std}, sm4to, 76p, gilt, color, DJ/4.95)	Chilton	(1967)	Anderson, Anne	30-50	
N/A	Briar Rose Book of Old Fairy Tales (4to, p-o, 159p, 11cp, pep)	L: Jack	[1915]	Anderson, Anne	150-225	
Joan, Natalie	Cosy-Time Tales (1st, 4to, 47p, ibds, 9cp, pep)	L: T. Nelson	[1922]	Anderson, Anne	150-240	
N/A	Dandy-Andy Book (lg8vo, 24p, p-o, 12cp)	Nelson	[1907]	Anderson, Anne	120-170	
Anderson, Anne	Dickie-Burdie Book (8vo, tan cl, p-o, 12cp)	L: Nelson	[1916]	Anderson, Anne	160-225	
Andersen, Hans C.	Fairy Stories (lg4to, 160p, gilt, ibds, 8cp, pep)	L: Collins	[1915]	Anderson, Anne	170-250	
N/A	Fairy Tale Omnibus (1st, 4to, 182p, red cl, col frn, 4cp)	L: Collins	[1915]	Anderson, Anne	75-100	*
Grimm Bros.	Fairy Tales (lg4to, 128p, gilt, 8cp)	L: Collins	[1931]	Anderson, Anne	90-120	*
N/A	Favourite Fairy Tales (lg4to, ibds, 16 color)	L: Nelson	[1929]	Anderson, Anne	80-120	
N/A	Funny Bunny ABC (1st AM, folio, p-o, color)	NY: Sully	[1912]	Anderson, Anne	160-250	
Chaucer, Geoffrey	Gateway to Chaucer (1st, sm8vo, blue/gilt, 269p, teg, 16cp)	L: Nelson	(1912)	Anderson, Anne	130-200	
N/A	Gillyflower Garden Book (1st, lg8vo, [48]p, p-o, 12cp)	L: Nelson	[1915]	Anderson, Anne	150-220	
Spyri, Johanna	Heidi (1st, 8vo, green/gilt, 356p, p-o, 8cp, pep)	McKay	(1923)	Anderson, Anne	80-130	
Spyri, Johanna	Heidi (1st UK, 8vo, 328p, 8cp)	L: Harrap	1924	Anderson, Anne	75-100	*
Eliot, Ethel C.	House Above the Trees (1st, 4to, 143p, blue cl, p-o, 5cp)	L: Butterworth	(1921)	Anderson, Anne	140-220	
Joan, Natalie	Lie-Down Stories (1st, lg8vo, p-o, 77p, grey bds, 8cp)	L: Blackie	(1919)	Anderson, Anne	160-240	
Anderson, Anne	Maisie-Daisie Book (lg8vo, 24p, p-o, 12cp)	Nelson	[1918]	Anderson, Anne	120-165	
Heward, Constance	Mr. Pickles and the Party (1st, 12mo, 53p, bds, p-o, fp color, pep)	L: Warne	(1926)	Anderson, Anne	100-165	
Howes, Edith	Mrs. Kindbush (1st, 8vo, 160p, 4cp)	L: Cassell	1933	Anderson, Anne	100-150	
Anderson, Anne	Nursery Zoo (4to, p-o, red cl, unpag, color)	L: Nelson	[1925]	Anderson, Anne	80-125	
Mansion, Horace	Old English Nursery Songs (1st, 4to, ibds, p-o, 6cp)	L: Harrap	[1921]	Anderson, Anne	125-200	

AUTHOR	TITLE	PUBLISHER	DATE	ARTIST	PRICE	LC
Mansion, Horace	Old English Nursery Songs (1st AM, 4to, 87p, ibds, p-o, 6cp)	Brentano's	[1921]	Anderson, Anne	150-220	
Anderson, Anne	Old French Nursery Songs (1st, sm4to, 64p, ibds, p-o, 8cp)	L: Harrap	[1915]	Anderson, Anne	120-200	
Mother Goose	Old Mother Goose Nursery Rhyme Book (16mo, 96p, 24 color, ibds)	T. Nelson	[1920]	Anderson, Anne	80-120	
Mother Goose	Old Mother Goose... (lg4to, p-o, 144p, red cl, 24cp, pep)	T. Nelson	[1926]	Anderson, Anne	170-240	
N/A	Orange Tree (12mo, [16]p, bds, fp 1-color)	L: Hodder	[1909]	Anderson, Anne	60-100	
Anderson, Anne	Patsy Book (1st, lg4to, ibds, unpag, 12cp, pep)	L: Nelson	[1919]	Anderson, Anne	150-225	
Anderson, Anne	Purple Book (1st, 12mo, [16]p, purple cl, p-o, 12 fp color)	L: Frowde/Hodder	[1910]	Anderson, Anne	80-130	
Anderson, Anne	Rosie-Posie Book (4to, p-o, blue cl, 12cp)	T. Nelson	[1917]	Anderson, Anne	140-200	
N/A	Sleeping Beauty (1st, 12mo, ibds, 40p, color, pep)	NY: Nelson	1928	Anderson, Anne	60-90	
Various	Sleepy-Song Book (1st, 4to, ibds, p-o, 12cp, pep)	L: Harrap	(1915)	Anderson, Anne	100-165	
Various	Sleepy-Song Book (1st AM, 4to, 77p, blue cl, p-o, 12cp, pep)	McBride	1915	Anderson, Anne	120-200	
Barnes, Madeline	Stirabout Stories (1st, 4to, ibds, 80p, 8cp)	L: Blackie	[1929]	Anderson, Anne	120-170	
Underdown, E.	Stories from Chaucer (1st, 12mo, p-o, 157p, 8cp)	T. Nelson	1913	Anderson, Anne	55-80	
Southwold, Stephen	Three by Candlelight (sm8vo, 128p, blue/gilt, 2cp)	L: Collins	[1920]	Anderson, Anne	50-80	
Barnes, Madeline	Tub-Time Tales (1st, 4to, 79p, ibds, 8cp)	L: Blackie	1920	Anderson, Anne	180-250	
Kingsley, Charles	Water Babies (1st, lg8vo, yellow cl, p-o, 12cp)	L: Jack	(1924)	Anderson, Anne	200-300	
Kingsley, Charles	Water Babies (1st AM, lg8vo, blue/gilt, p-o, 180p, 12cp, pep)	Nelson	[1924]	Anderson, Anne	150-220	
Anderson, C.W.	Big Red (1st, ob4to, tan cl, pep, 64p, b/w, DJ/2.00)	Macmillan	1943	Anderson, C.W.	60-90	
Anderson, C.W.	Billy and Blaze (1st, sm4to, orange cl, [56]p, fp b/w)	Macmillan	1936	Anderson, C.W.	80-120	
Anderson, C.W.	Black Bay and Chestnut (1st, ob folio, [52]p, b/w, pep, DJ/2.50)	Macmillan	1939	Anderson, C.W.	70-100	*
Anderson, C.W.	Blaze and the Forest Fire (1st, sm4to, [55]p, fp b/w, DJ/1.25)	Macmillan	1938	Anderson, C.W.	60-90	*
Anderson, C.W.	Blaze and the Gray Spotted Pony (1st {std}, lg8vo, 46p, b/w, DJ/3.50)	Macmillan	1968	Anderson, C.W.	40-65	
Anderson, C.W.	Blaze and the Gypsies (1st, sm4to, green cl, [56]p, fp b/w, DJ/1.50)	Macmillan	1937	Anderson, C.W.	70-120	
Anderson, C.W.	Blaze and the Indian Cave (1st {std}, lg8vo, [47]p, b/w, DJ/2.95)	Macmillan	(1964)	Anderson, C.W.	40-65	
Anderson, C.W.	Blaze and the Lost Quarry (1st {std}, lg8vo, 46p, b/w, DJ/2.95)	Macmillan	1966	Anderson, C.W.	40-65	*
Anderson, C.W.	Blaze Finds the Trail (1st {std}, sm4to, [48]p, b/w, cep)	Macmillan	1950	Anderson, C.W.	45-60	
Anderson, C.W.	Bobcat (1st {std}, 8vo, 97p, b/w, DJ/2.50)	Macmillan	1949	Anderson, C.W.	50-80	
Anderson, C.W.	Crooked Colt (1st {std}, sq8vo, [48]p, fp b/w, cep, DJ/2.00)	Macmillan	1954	Anderson, C.W.	65-90	
Anderson, C.W.	Deep Through the Heart (1st, lg ob4to, [52]p, pep, b/w, DJ/3.00)	Macmillan	1940	Anderson, C.W.	70-100	
Anderson, C.W.	Filly for Joan (1st {std}, 8vo, 104p, b/w, DJ/3.00)	Macmillan	1960	Anderson, C.W.	45-70	
Anderson, C.W.	Heads Up and Heels Down (1st {std}, lg8vo, 144p, fp b/w, DJ/2.50)	Macmillan	1944	Anderson, C.W.	50-80	
Anderson, C.W.	High Courage (1st, 8vo, red cl, 124p, fp b/w, pep, DJ/1.75)	Macmillan	1941	Anderson, C.W.	45-70	
Paltenghi, Madalena	Honey on a Raft (1st, sm4to, ibds, [36]p, 15 fp b/w, pep, DJ/0.50)	Garden City	(1941)	Anderson, C.W.	50-80	
Paltenghi, Madalena	Honey the City Bear (1st, sm4to, 31p, ipcb, 14 fp b/w, DJ/0.50)	Grosset/Dunlap	1937	Anderson, C.W.	50-80	
Gard, Robert	Horse Named Joe (1st {std}, 8vo, 237p, 6 fp b/w, DJ/2.75)	Duell, Sloan	(1956)	Anderson, C.W.	30-45	
Anderson, C.W.	Horse of Hurricane Hill (1st {std}, 8vo, 107p, fp b/w, DJ/2.75)	Macmillan	1956	Anderson, C.W.	70-100	
Anderson, C.W.	Horse Show (1st, 4to, ibds, [94]p, b/w, DJ/2.50)	Harper	(1951)	Anderson, C.W.	50-80	
Anderson, C.W.	Horses are Folks (1st, ob4to, ibds, 89p, b/w, pep, DJ/3.50)	Harper	(1950)	Anderson, C.W.	60-100	
Anderson, C.W.	Linda and the Indians (1st {std}, 8vo, [50]p, b/w, DJ/2.00)	Macmillan	1952	Anderson, C.W.	45-70	*
Anderson, C.W.	Lonesome Little Colt (1st {std}, 4to, 46p, fp b/w, DJ/2.75)	Macmillan	1961	Anderson, C.W.	40-65	
Anderson, C.W.	Outlaw (1st {std}, 8vo, 99p, fp b/w, DJ/3.50)	Macmillan	(1967)	Anderson, C.W.	40-65	
Mason, Miriam E.	Pony Called Lightning (1st {std}, 8vo, 142p, b/w, DJ/1.75)	Macmillan	1948	Anderson, C.W.	50-80	*
Lippincott, J.W.	Red Roan Pony (1st {new ed}, sm8vo, 218p, red cl, 1 dp col, 6pl, DJ/2.50)	Lippincott	(1951)	Anderson, C.W.	30-50	
Paltenghi, Madalena	Remus Goes to Town (1st, sm4to, 29p, ipcb, 15 fp b/w, DJ/0.50)	Grosset/Dunlap	1938	Anderson, C.W.	60-90	
Paltenghi, Madalena	Rumpus Rabbit (1st {std}, narrow 4to, 25p, green cl, b/w, DJ/1.50)	Harper	1939	Anderson, C.W.	80-135	
Anderson, C.W.	Salute (1st, sm4to, tan cl, p-o, 63p, b/w, pep, DJ/2.00)	Macmillan	1940	Anderson, C.W.	70-100	*
Anderson, C.W.	The Smashers (1st, ob folio, 100p, b/w, DJ/5.00)	Harper	(1954)	Anderson, C.W.	70-100	
Anderson, C.W.	Thoroughbreds (1st, ob4to, 72p, b/w, pep, DJ/2.00)	Macmillan	1942	Anderson, C.W.	70-100	
Anderson, C.W.	Tomorrow's Champion (1st, ob4to, [84]p, green/gilt, fp b/w, DJ/3.00)	Macmillan	1946	Anderson, C.W.	70-100	
Anderson, C.W.	Touch of Greatness (1st, ob4to, blue cl, 96p, b/w, DJ/3.00)	Macmillan	1945	Anderson, C.W.	60-90	
Burgess, Thornton	Boy Scouts in a Trappers' Camp (1st, sm8vo, 362p, 5pl)	Penn	1915	Anderson, F.A.	120-200	*
Young, Christie (ed)	Black Princess (1st, 8vo, 159p, ivory/gilt, 12cp)	L: Simpkin	(1916)	Anderson, Florence	100-160	
Howes, Edith	Cradle Ship (1st, 8vo, 219p, blue cl, 4cp)	L: Cassell	1916	Anderson, Florence	80-120	
Sackville, Margaret	Dream Pedlar (1st, sm4to, 184p, blue/gilt, 16 ticp)	L: Simpkin	(1914)	Anderson, Florence	200-300	
Browne, Edgar G.	Magic Whistle (1st, lg8vo, 221p, ibds, p-o, 8cp)	Dodd	1920	Anderson, Florence	125-200	
Malcolm, Fiona	My Fairyland: Child's Own Visions (1st, 4to, 85p, grey ibds, 4 ticp)	L: Harrap	1916	Anderson, Florence	120-200	
Browne, Edgar G.	Nutcracker and Mouse King (1st, lg8vo, pink bds, 92p, p-o, 4cp)	Dodd	1916	Anderson, Florence	70-100	
Southwart, Elizabeth	Password to Fairyland (1st, 4to, 186p, tan cl, 8cp, pep)	L: Simpkin	[1920]	Anderson, Florence	250-400	
Anderson, Florence	Rainbow Twins (4to, ibds, 12cp, pep)	L: J. Johnson	(1919)	Anderson, Florence	250-400	
Sackville, Margaret	Travelling Companions... (1st, lg8vo, 132p, blue/gilt, 12cp)	L: Simpkin	(1915)	Anderson, Florence	250-400	
Littlewood, Samuel R.	Valentine and Orson (1st, 4to, 143p, p-o, 8cp, pep)	L: Simpkin	1919	Anderson, Florence	100-170	
Stang, Wendy	Hubert (1st {std}, 24mo, [31]p, color, pep, DJ/1.95, NYTBI)	Harlin Quist	(1967)	Anderson, Robert	50-85	
Hallin, Emily	Moya and the Flamingoes (1st, 8vo, 86p, fp b/w, DJ/3.50)	McKay	1969	Anderson, Rus	25-40	
Potter, Beatrix	Tale of Peter Rabbit (12mo, yellow cl, p-o, color)	Hurst	(1908)	Anderson, S.W.	80-120	*
Page, Thomas N.	Tommy Trot's Visit to Santa Claus (1st, 8vo, 98p, uncut, 6cp)	Scribner	1908	Anderson, Victor C.	45-70	
N/A	Cuddly-Kitty Book (1st, 8vo, tan cl, p-o, 12cp)	Nelson	[1915]	Anderson/Wright	150-220	
Joan, Natalie	Tales for Teeny Wee (1st AM, 4to, ibds, 248p, 8cp)	Whitman	(1935)	Anderson/Wright	140-200	
N/A	Around the World with Santa Claus (lg4to, ibds, 14 chromos)	McLoughlin	1896	Andre, R.	300-500	
Ewing, Juliana H.	Blue and Red.... (4to, ibds, 32p, chromos)	L: SPCK	[1881]	Andre, R.	170-240	
Ewing, Juliana H.	Blue Bells on the Lea (1st, ob8vo, ibds, 32p, chromos)	L: SPCK	[1884]	Andre, R.	100-180	
Andre, R.	Little Blossoms (sm4to, [32]p, ibds, 10 chromos)	L: G. Allen	1885	Andre, R.	400-600	
Ewing, Juliana H.	Master Fritz (1st, ob8vo, 32p, ibds, color)	L: SPCK	[1883]	Andre, R.	140-200	*
Ewing, Juliana H.	Our Garden (1st, ob8vo, ibds, 32p, color)	L: SPCK	[1883]	Andre, R.	120-180	*
Mrs. Valentine	Shakespearian Tales in Verse for Children (4to, gilt, AEG, 109p, chromos)	Armstrong/Warne	[1882]	Andre, R.	450-600	
Ewing, Juliana H.	Soldier's Children (ob12mo, 32p, 172p, ibds, chromos)	L: SPCK	[1883]	Andre, R.	200-300	
N/A	Three Bears (12mo, [16]p, linen, color)	McLoughlin	1888	Andre, R.	100-160	*
Ewing, Juliana H.	Week Spent in a Glass Pond (4to, ibds, 32p, chromos)	L: Wells/Gard.	[1883]	Andre, R.	250-450	
Adoff, Arnold (ed)	I am the Darker Brother (1st {std} [1st bk.], 8vo, 128p, b/w, DJ/4.95)	Macmillan	(1968)	Andrews, Benny	40-65	

AUTHOR	TITLE	PUBLISHER	DATE	ARTIST	PRICE	LC
Potter, Beatrix	Tale of the Faithful Dove (1st, 24mo, ibds, [47]p, fp color)	L: Warne	(1970)	Angel, Marie	60-90	
Bible	Twenty-Third Psalm (1st AM, 8vo, 20p, brown/gilt, color, DJ)	Crowell	1970	Angel, Marie	30-50	
Fisher, Aileen	We Went Looking (1st, lg ob8vo, blue cl, 25p, color, DJ/3.95)	Crowell	(1968)	Angel, Marie	25-40	
Cunningham, Julia	Vision of Francois the Fox (1st, 8vo, 31p, 3-color, DJ/2.75)	Houghton	1960	Angelo, Nicholas	20-30	
Angelo, Valenti	Acorn Tree (1st, sm4to, 39p, 1-color, DJ/2.50)	Viking	(1958)	Angelo, Valenti	30-50	
Tooze, Ruth	America (1st, lg8vo, 31p, color, DJ/2.00)	Viking	1956	Angelo, Valenti	40-60	
Angelo, Valenti	Angelino and Barefoot Saint (1st, sm4to, 62p, 1-color, DJ/2.75)	Viking	(1961)	Angelo, Valenti	30-45	*
Eaton, Anne T.	Animal's Christmas (1st, sm8vo, grey cl, 124p, 1-color, dep, DJ/2.00)	Viking	1944	Angelo, Valenti	45-75	R
Angelo, Valenti	Bells of Bleecker Street (1st, 8vo, 185p, pep, b/w, DJ/2.50)	Viking	1949	Angelo, Valenti	70-100	R
Angelo, Valenti	Big Little Island (1st, 8vo, 190p, b/w, pep, DJ/2.75)	Viking	1955	Angelo, Valenti	25-40	
North, Sterling	Birthday of Little Jesus (1st {std}, 4to, ipcb, 1-color, pep, DJ/2.50)	Grosset/Dunlap	(1952)	Angelo, Valenti	65-90	
Angelo, Valenti	Candy Basket (1st, sm4to, 38p, color, cep, DJ/2.50)	Viking	(1960)	Angelo, Valenti	30-45	*
Price, Olive M.	Donkey for the King (1st, sm8vo, 73p, fp 1-color, DJ/2.00)	Whittlesey	(1945)	Angelo, Valenti	30-50	*
Angelo, Valenti	Golden Gate (1st, 8vo, aqua/gilt, 273p, 1-color, dep, DJ/2.00)	Viking	1939	Angelo, Valenti	40-60	
Angelo, Valenti	Hill of Little Miracles (1st, 8vo, 200p, b/w, DJ/2.00)	Viking	1942	Angelo, Valenti	40-60	
Angelo, Valenti	Honey Boat (1st, 8vo, 160p, b/w, DJ/3.00)	Viking	(1959)	Angelo, Valenti	25-45	*
Gagliardo, Ruth	Let's Read Aloud (1st {std}, 8vo, 256p, b/w, DJ/4.95)	Lippincott	(1962)	Angelo, Valenti	40-65	
Sawyer, Ruth	Long Christmas (1st, 4to, 200p, buckram, 1-color, dep, DJ/2.50)	Viking	1941	Angelo, Valenti	40-60	
Angelo, Valenti	Look Out Yonder (1st, 8vo, 197p, b/w, DJ/2.00)	Viking	1943	Angelo, Valenti	30-45	
Angelo, Valenti	Marble Fountain (1st, 8vo, 223p, tan cl, b/w, pep, DJ/2.50)	Viking	1951	Angelo, Valenti	30-50	
Angelo, Valenti	Merry Marcos (1st, 8vo, 141p, red cl, b/w, DJ/3.25)	Viking	(1963)	Angelo, Valenti	30-50	
Angelo, Valenti	Nino (1st, lg8vo, beige cl, 244p, 1-color, pep, DJ/2.00, NH)	Viking	1938	Angelo, Valenti	50-80	
Angelo, Valenti	Paradise Valley (1st, 8vo, 230p, 1-color, DJ/2.00)	Viking	1940	Angelo, Valenti	40-65	*
Vance, Marguerite	Paula (1st, 8vo, 223p, green cl, uncut, b/w, dep, DJ/2.00)	Dodd	1939	Angelo, Valenti	25-45	
Sawyer, Ruth	Roller Skates (1st, lg8vo, 186p, 1-color, pep, DJ/2.00, NM)	Viking	1936	Angelo, Valenti	85-140	R
Angelo, Valenti	Rooster Club (1st, 8vo, 150p, rust/gilt, b/w, dep, DJ/2.00)	Viking	1944	Angelo, Valenti	40-65	
Hawthorne, Nathaniel	Scarlet Letter (1st, 8vo, 362p, uncut, color)	Random	1928	Angelo, Valenti	70-120	R*
Sterne, Laurence	Sentimental Journey/France & Italy (1st, lg8vo, 253p, black/gilt, 12 b/w)	Dodd	1929	Angelo, Valenti	50-80	
Bulla, Clyde R.	Song of Saint Francis (1st {std}, 8vo, 71p, b/w, pep, DJ/2.50)	Crowell	(1952)	Angelo, Valenti	35-50	
Bulla, Clyde R.	St. Valentine's Day (1st, 8vo, [38]p, fp 1-color, DJ/2.95)	Crowell	(1965)	Angelo, Valenti	25-45	
Angelo, Valenti	Tale of a Donkey (1st, 8vo, 110p, b/w, DJ/3.00)	Viking	(1966)	Angelo, Valenti	25-45	
Bible	This He Believed (1st, lg8vo, 80p, DJ/3.00, 1-color decor by...)	Viking	(1959)	Angelo, Valenti	30-45	
Moore, Clement C.	Visit from St. Nicholas (1st, ob8vo, ibds, [18]p, color)	Hawthorn House	(1937)	Angelo, Valenti	70-100	R
Eaton, Anne T.	Welcome Christmas (1st, 8vo, 128p, b/w, pep, DJ/2.50)	Viking	1955	Angelo, Valenti	30-45	
Anglund, Joan W.	A is for Always (1st {std}, 32mo, [32]p, color, DJ/1.95)	Harcourt	(1968)	Anglund, Joan W.	25-40	
Anglund, Joan W.	Book of Good Tidings (1st {std}, 32mo, [30]p, color, DJ/1.95)	Harcourt	(1965)	Anglund, Joan W.	25-40	
Anglund, Joan W.	Brave Cowboy (1st {std}, 12mo, unpag, 2-color, pep, DJ/1.95)	Harcourt	(1959)	Anglund, Joan W.	50-80	
Anglund, Joan W.	Childhood is a Time of Innocence (1st {std}, 12mo, [32]p, 2-color, DJ/1.95)	Harcourt	(1964)	Anglund, Joan W.	20-35	
Anglund, Joan W.	Christmas is a Time of Giving (1st {std}, 12mo, [32]p, 2-color, DJ/1.75)	Harcourt	(1961)	Anglund, Joan W.	30-45	
Anglund, Joan W.	Cowboy and his Friend (1st {std}, 12mo, [32]p, fp 1-color, pep, DJ/1.95)	Harcourt	(1961)	Anglund, Joan W.	25-40	
Anglund, Joan W.	Cup of Sun (1st {std}, 12mo, 63p, b/w, DJ/2.75)	Harcourt	(1967)	Anglund, Joan W.	25-40	
Anglund, Joan W.	Friend is Someone who Likes You (1st {std}, 12mo, [27]p, col, DJ/1.75, NYT)	Harcourt	(1958)	Anglund, Joan W.	35-50	
Untermeyer, Louis (ed)	Golden Treasury of Poetry (1st, 4to, 324p, ibds, color, DJ/4.95)	Golden Press	(1959)	Anglund, Joan W.	80-120	R
Anglund, Joan W.	In a Pumpkin Shell (1st {std}, lg8vo, yellow cl, [30]p, color, DJ/2.95)	Harcourt	(1960)	Anglund, Joan W.	40-65	
Anglund, Joan W.	Look Out the Window (1st {std}, 8vo, yellow cl, [36]p, 2-color, DJ/1.95)	Harcourt	(1959)	Anglund, Joan W.	45-70	
Anglund, Joan W.	Love is a Special Way of Feeling (1st {std}, 12mo, [30]p, 2-color, DJ/1.75)	Harcourt	(1960)	Anglund, Joan W.	35-50	
Anglund, Joan W.	Morning is a Little Child (1st {std}, lg8vo, [32]p, color, DJ/3.50)	Harcourt	(1969)	Anglund, Joan W.	40-65	
Anglund, Joan W.	Nibble Nibble Mousekin (1st {std}, lg8vo, [30]p, color, DJ/3.25)	Harcourt	(1962)	Anglund, Joan W.	50-80	
Anglund, Joan W.	Pocketful of Proverbs (1st, 24mo, [32]p, ibds, color, DJ/1.95)	Harcourt	(1964)	Anglund, Joan W.	30-45	
Anglund, Joan W.	Slice of Snow (1st {std}, 12mo, 63p, b/w, DJ/2.95)	Harcourt	(1970)	Anglund, Joan W.	25-45	
Anglund, Joan W.	Spring is a New Beginning (1st {std}, 12mo, [32]p, ipcb, color, DJ/1.95)	Harcourt	(1963)	Anglund, Joan W.	25-45	
Trent, Robbie	To Church We Go (1st, sm4to, ibds, [28]p, color, DJ/1.25)	Wilcox/Follett	1948	Anglund, Joan W.	70-100	
Anglund, Joan W.	What Color is Love? (1st {std}, 12mo, unpag, color, DJ/1.95)	Harcourt	(1966)	Anglund, Joan W.	25-45	
Anglund, Joan W.	Year is Round (1st {std}, 16mo, unpag, color, DJ/1.95)	Harcourt	(1966)	Anglund, Joan W.	20-35	
Anno, Mitsumasa	Topsy Turvies (1st {std}, 4to, 27p, color, DJ/3.50, NYTBI)	Walker/Weatherh.	(1970)	Anno, Mitsumasa	50-80	
Appleton, Honor	Bad Mrs. Ginger (1st, 32mo, 96p, stripe cl, color)	L: G. Richards	1902	Appleton, Honor C.	85-130	
Cradock, H.C.	Best Teddy Bear in the World (1st, 12mo, 96p, b/w)	L: Nelson	(1926)	Appleton, Honor C.	30-50	
Russell, Dorothy	Betty's Diary (1st, 8vo, 261p, gilt, p-o, 5cp)	L: Blackie	[1914]	Appleton, Honor C.	60-90	
Southwold, Stephen	Book of Animal Tales (1st, lg8vo, 286p, ibds, 8cp)	L: Harrap	1929	Appleton, Honor C.	70-100	*
Southwold, Stephen	Book of Animal Tales (1st AM, lg8vo, ibds, 286p, 8cp)	Crowell	(1929)	Appleton, Honor C.	65-100	
Bruce, Marjory	Book of Tales for Little Folks (1st, 8vo, 284p, ibds, 8cp by...)	L: Harrap	(1932)	Appleton, Honor C.	60-100	
Littlewood, Letty	Bower Book of Simple Poems.... (1st, 8vo, 267p, red cl, 10cp, pep)	L: O'Connor	(1922)	Appleton, Honor C.	100-165	
Littlewood, Samuel R.	Child of the Sea (1st, 8vo, gilt, 196p, 8cp, pep)	L: Simpkin	1915	Appleton, Honor C.	40-60	*
Burke, Thos. (ed.)	Children in Verse (1st, 8vo, 135p, blue cl, 8cp)	L: Duckworth	1913	Appleton, Honor C.	60-90	
Burke, Thos. (ed.)	Children in Verse (1st AM, 8vo, 135p, teg, 8 ticp)	(Boston)	1914	Appleton, Honor C.	60-90	
Lee, Frank H.	Children's King Arthur (1st, 8vo, 77p)	L: Harrap	1935	Appleton, Honor C.	55-80	*
Dickens, Charles	Christmas Carol (1st, 8vo, p-o, 153p, 8cp)	L: Simpkin	1914	Appleton, Honor C.	60-90	
Perrault, Charles	Fairy Tales (1st, sm4to, p-o, 107p, 12cp)	L: Simpkin	(1911)	Appleton, Honor C.	140-200	
Andersen, Hans C.	Fairy Tales (1st AM, 4to, blue/gilt, 179p, 12cp, pep)	NY: Nelson	[1922]	Appleton, Honor C.	150-250	
Cradock, H.C.	House of Fancy (1st, 4to, 32p)	L: O'Connor	1922	Appleton, Honor C.	60-90	*
Tyrell, Eleanor	How I Tamed the Wild Squirrels (1st, sq8vo, 111p, pep, p-o, 6cp)	L: Nelson	[1918]	Appleton, Honor C.	70-100	
Cradock, H.C.	Josephine and Her Dolls (1st, 4to, ibds, 47p, 12cp)	L: Blackie	1916	Appleton, Honor C.	250-350	
Cradock, H.C.	Josephine Dolly Book (lg8vo, ibds, p-o, 8cp)	L: Blackie	[1920]	Appleton, Honor C.	150-250	
Cradock, H.C.	Josephine is Busy (1st, lg8vo, ibds, 63p, p-o, 8cp)	L: Blackie	1918	Appleton, Honor C.	120-180	
Cradock, H.C.	Josephine Keeps House (1st, lg8vo, bds, p-o, 64p, 8cp)	L: Blackie	(1931)	Appleton, Honor C.	120-180	
Cradock, H.C.	Josephine Keeps School (1st, lg8vo, bds, p-o, 64p, 8cp)	L: Blackie	[1925]	Appleton, Honor C.	120-200	
Cradock, H.C.	Josephine's Birthday (1st, lg8vo, 64p, p-o, ibds, 8cp)	L: Blackie	(1920)	Appleton, Honor C.	200-300	
Cradock, H.C.	Josephine's Christmas Party (lg8vo, 64p, ipcb, p-o, 8cp)	L: Blackie	[1927]	Appleton, Honor C.	70-120	

AUTHOR	TITLE	PUBLISHER	DATE	ARTIST	PRICE	LC
Cradock, H.C.	Josephine's Happy Family (1st, sm4to, 63p, ipcb, p-o, 8cp)	L: Blackie	1917	Appleton, Honor C.	150-250	
Cradock, H.C.	Josephine's Happy Family (1st AM, 4to, bds, 63p, p-o, 8cp)	Stokes	[1920]	Appleton, Honor C.	150-225	
Cradock, H.C.	Josephine's Pantomime (1st, lg8vo, bds, p-o, 64p, 8cp)	L: Blackie	(1939)	Appleton, Honor C.	120-220	
Cradock, H.C.	Josephine, John and the Puppy (4to, bds, p-o, 8cp)	L: Blackie	[1920]	Appleton, Honor C.	65-90	
Tyrell, Eleanor	More About the Squirrels (1st, sq8vo, 111p, pep, p-o, 6cp)	L: Nelson	[1918]	Appleton, Honor C.	60-100	
Cradock, H.C.	Peggy and Joan (1st, 4to, 96p, p-o, 8cp, pep)	L: Blackie	[1922]	Appleton, Honor C.	70-120	
Andersen, Hans C.	Snow Queen (4to, ibds, 31p, 8cp)	L: Nelson	[1919]	Appleton, Honor C.	100-165	
Blake, William	Songs of Innocence (1st, 8vo, green/gilt, p-o, 49p, 12cp, pep)	L: H. Daniel	[1911]	Appleton, Honor C.	100-165	*
Chaundler, Christine	Thirteenth Orphan (1st, 8vo, 255p, col frn, 6pl)	L: J. Nisbet	[1920]	Appleton, Honor C.	40-60	*
Edgar, M.G.	Treasury of Verse for School and Home (1st, 8vo, 523p, color, pep)	Crowell	(1926)	Appleton, Honor C.	40-60	*
Kelly, Eric P.	Three Sides of Agiochook (1st, 8vo, 211p, b/w, pep, DJ/2.00)	Macmillan	1935	Appleton, LeRoy	25-45	
Bryant, Sara Cone	Brother Rabbit (1st, 16mo, p-o, 59p, 4cp, pep)	L: Harrap	1926	Appleton/Wilson	70-120	
McGowen, Tom	Biggest Toot in Toozelburg (1st, 8vo, [30]p, fp 3-color, DJ/4.95)	Reilly/Lee	(1970)	Appleyard, Dev	50-80	
Archer, Jean C.	Rosalina (1st, 16mo, 95p, 24cp)	L: Richards	1904	Archer, Jean C.	60-90	
Reeves, James	Angel and the Donkey (1st, lg ob8vo, [32]p, color, DJ)	L: Hamilton	1969	Ardizzone, Edward	40-65	
Reeves, James	Angel and the Donkey (1st AM, lg ob8vo, [32]p, color, DJ/4.50)	McGraw-Hill	(1970)	Ardizzone, Edward	30-50	
Graves, Robert	Ann at Highwood Hall (1st AM {std}, lg8vo, 48p, color, DJ/2.95)	Doubleday	(1966)	Ardizzone, Edward	45-70	
Gorham, Maurice	Back to the Local (1st, 8vo, 126p, red/gilt, 21 b/w, DJ)	L: P. Marshall	1949	Ardizzone, Edward	80-120	
Ardizzone, Edward	Baggage to the Enemy (1st, 12mo, blue cl, 121p, b/w, DJ)	L: J. Murray	1941	Ardizzone, Edward	100-150	
Maurois, Andre	Battle of France (1st {std}, 8vo, 210p, 8 fp b/w, DJ)	L: John Lane	1940	Ardizzone, Edward	45-70	
Reeves, James	Blackbird in the Lilac (1st, 8vo, blue/silver, 95p, b/w, DJ)	L: Oxford U.Pr.	1952	Ardizzone, Edward	50-80	
Hawksley, E.D.	Charles Dickens Birthday Book (1st, 8vo, [285]p, 12 fp b/w, DJ)	L: Faber	(1948)	Ardizzone, Edward	60-90	
Day-Lewis, Cecil	Christmas Eve (1st, sm8vo, unpag, wraps, col frn)	L: Faber	1954	Ardizzone, Edward	80-125	
Webster, Jean	Daddy Long Legs (1st, 8vo, 183p, blue/gilt, b/w, DJ/3.95)	NY: Meredith Pr.	(1967)	Ardizzone, Edward	50-80	
Ardizzone, Edward	Diana and her Rhinoceros (1st AM, ob4to, 32p, color, DJ/3.50)	H.Z. Walck	1964	Ardizzone, Edward	50-80	
Lines, Kathleen	Dick Whittington (1st, 8vo, 42p, color, DJ)	L: Bodley Head	(1970)	Ardizzone, Edward	50-85	
Lines, Kathleen	Dick Whittington (1st AM, 8vo, 42p, color, DJ/4.75)	H.Z. Walck	(1970)	Ardizzone, Edward	60-90	
Young, Percy	Ding Dong Bell (1st, 4to, ibds, 141p, b/w, DJ)	L: Dobson	(1957)	Ardizzone, Edward	50-80	
Chapman, Jean	Do You Remember What Happened? (1st, 8vo, gilt, [42]p, 2-color, DJ)	L: Angus/Rbrtsn.	1969	Ardizzone, Edward	50-85	
Gray, Nicholas S.	Down in the Cellar (1st, sm8vo, 203p, cloth, b/w, DJ)	L: Dobson	(1961)	Ardizzone, Edward	40-65	
Symonds, John	Elfrida and the Pig (1st, 4to, green cl, 48p, b/w, DJ)	L: Harrap	(1959)	Ardizzone, Edward	60-95	
Symonds, John	Elfrida and the Pig (1st AM, sm4to, 48p, b/w, DJ/2.95)	F. Watts	(1960)	Ardizzone, Edward	50-85	
Reeves, James	Exploits of Don Quixote (1st AM, 8vo, 219p, fp color, DJ)	H.Z. Walck	1960	Ardizzone, Edward	30-50	
Clewes, Dorothy	Fire-Brigade Willie (1st, 12mo, 48p, color, DJ)	L: Hamilton	(1970)	Ardizzone, Edward	30-50	
Cole, William	Folk Songs of England/Ireland/Scotland (1st AM {std}, 4to, 243p, 1-col, DJ)	Doubleday	1961	Ardizzone, Edward	65-90	
White, Terence H.	Godstone and the Blackymor (1st AM {std}, 8vo, 224p, b/w, DJ)	L: J. Cape	(1959)	Ardizzone, Edward	60-100	
Dickens, Charles	Great Expectations (1st, lg8vo, 457p, 8cp)	Heritage Press	(1939)	Ardizzone, Edward	90-120	*
Streatfeild, Noel	Growing Summer (1st, 8vo, blue cl, b/w, 223p, DJ)	L: Collins	1966	Ardizzone, Edward	30-50	
Wahl, Jan	Hello, Elephant (1st {std}, ob12mo, ipcb, [32]p, fp 2-color, cep, DJ/2.50)	Holt, Rinehart	(1964)	Ardizzone, Edward	60-90	
Ballantyne, Joan	Holiday Trench (1st, 8vo, blue/gilt, 120p, b/w, DJ)	L: T. Nelson	(1959)	Ardizzone, Edward	60-90	
Surtees, Robert S.	Hunting with Mr. Jorrocks (1st, 8vo, 186p, tan/gilt, color, DJ)	L: Oxford U.Pr.	1956	Ardizzone, Edward	60-100	
LeFanu, J. Sheridan	In a Glass Darkly (1st {1st illus bk.}, 8vo, black/gilt, 382p, b/w)	L: P. Davies	1929	Ardizzone, Edward	150-250	
Williams, Ursula	Island Mackenzie (1st AM, 8vo, 128p, b/w, pep, DJ/2.95)	Wm. Morrow	1960	Ardizzone, Edward	70-100	
Wuorio, Eva-Lis	Island of Fish in the Trees (1st {std}, 8vo, 59p, 6 dp color, DJ/3.50, NYT)	World	(1962)	Ardizzone, Edward	60-100	R
Farjeon, Eleanor	Jim at the Corner (1st AM, 8vo, 101p, b/w, cep, DJ/2.75)	H.Z. Walck	1958	Ardizzone, Edward	30-50	
Ardizzone, Edward	Johnny the Clockmaker (1st AM, 4to, [48]p, color, DJ/3.00)	H.Z. Walck	1960	Ardizzone, Edward	50-85	
Farjeon, Eleanor	Kaleidoscope (1st AM, 8vo, 157p, b/w, DJ/3.75)	H.Z. Walck	1963	Ardizzone, Edward	30-50	
Farjeon, Eleanor	Kaleidoscope (1st, 8vo, 157p, b/w, DJ)	L: Oxford U.Pr.	1963	Ardizzone, Edward	40-65	
Wuorio, Eva-Lis	Kali and the Golden Mirror (1st, 8vo, 64p, 3 dp color, DJ/3.75)	World	(1967)	Ardizzone, Edward	30-50	
Ballantyne, Joan	Kidnappers at Coombe (1st, 8vo, 203p, green/gilt, b/w, DJ)	L: T. Nelson	1960	Ardizzone, Edward	35-60	
Wuorio, Eva-Lis	Land of Right Up and Down (1st AM {std}, 8vo, 60p, dp color, DJ/3.50)	World	(1964)	Ardizzone, Edward	35-50	
Fox, Paula	Likely Place (1st {std}, 8vo, 57p, yellow cl, b/w, DJ/2.95)	Macmillan	(1967)	Ardizzone, Edward	30-50	
Farjeon, Eleanor	Little Bookroom (1st, 8vo, 302p, b/w, DJ, CgM)	L: Oxford U.Pr.	1955	Ardizzone, Edward	70-100	*
Farjeon, Eleanor	Little Bookroom (1st AM, 8vo, 302p, red cl, b/w, DJ/3.00)	NY: Oxford U.Pr.	1956	Ardizzone, Edward	70-100	R
Ardizzone, Edward	Little Girl & the Tiny Doll (1st, 8vo, 48p, color, DJ)	L: Constable	(1966)	Ardizzone, Edward	45-70	*
Ardizzone, Edward	Little Girl & the Tiny Doll (1st AM {std}, lg8vo, [48]p, color, DJ/2.75)	Delacorte Pr.	(1967)	Ardizzone, Edward	60-100	
Ardizzone, Edward	Little Tim & the Brave Sea Captain (1st AM, folio, [64]p, ibds, color)	Oxford U. Pr.	1936	Ardizzone, Edward	300-500	
Gorham, Maurice	Londoners (1st, 8vo, 158p, brown bds, 24 b/w, DJ)	L: P. Marshall	1951	Ardizzone, Edward	70-100	
Nesbit, Edith	Long Ago When I was Young (1st, 8vo, 127p, b/w, DJ)	L: Whiting	1966	Ardizzone, Edward	60-90	
Nesbit, Edith	Long Ago When I was Young (1st AM, 8vo, 127p, b/w, DJ/5.95)	F. Watts	(1966)	Ardizzone, Edward	50-85	
Ardizzone, Edward	Lucy Brown and Mr. Grimes (1st AM, sm folio, ibds, 32p, color)	Oxford U. Pr.	[1937]	Ardizzone, Edward	300-450	R
Streatfeild, Noel	Magic Summer (1st AM {std}, 8vo, 270p, b/w, cep, DJ/3.95)	Random	(1967)	Ardizzone, Edward	30-50	
Kaeser, Hildegarde	Mimff-Robinson (1st, 8vo, grey/silver, 184p, b/w, DJ)	L: Oxford U.Pr.	1958	Ardizzone, Edward	70-120	
Pearce, Philippa	Minnow on the Say (1st, 8vo, 241p, blue cl, b/w, DJ)	L: Oxford U.Pr.	(1955)	Ardizzone, Edward	70-100	
Estes, Eleanor	Miranda the Great (1st {std}, 8vo, 79p, b/w, DJ/3.25)	Harcourt	(1967)	Ardizzone, Edward	60-80	
Farjeon, Eleanor	Mrs. Malone (1st AM, 16mo, [24]p, b/w, DJ/1.75)	H.Z. Walck	1962	Ardizzone, Edward	50-80	
Bates, Herbert E.	My Uncle Silas (1st, 4to, 190p, fp b/w, DJ)	L: J. Cape	(1939)	Ardizzone, Edward	100-180	
Brand, Christianna	Naughty Children (1st AM {std}, 8vo, 314p, b/w, DJ/4.50)	Dutton	(1963)	Ardizzone, Edward	50-85	
Ardizzone, Edward	Nicholas and Fast Moving Diesel (1st, lg4to, yellow bds, 35p, color)	L: Eyre/Spotts.	[1947]	Ardizzone, Edward	250-400	R
Brand, Christianna	Nurse Matilda (1st AM {std}, 12mo, 128p, b/w, DJ/2.95)	Dutton	(1964)	Ardizzone, Edward	50-80	
Brand, Christianna	Nurse Matilda Goes to Town (1st AM {std}, 12mo, 128p, b/w, cep, DJ/3.25)	Dutton	(1968)	Ardizzone, Edward	40-65	
Farjeon, Eleanor	Old Nurse's Stocking-Basket (1st AM {std}, 8vo, 102p, b/w, DJ/3.50)	H.Z. Walck	1965	Ardizzone, Edward	50-85	
Ross, Diana	Old Perisher (1st, sm4to, [32]p, ibds, color, DJ)	L: Faber	(1965)	Ardizzone, Edward	70-100	
Day-Lewis, Cecil	Otterbury Incident (1st, 8vo, 148p, gilt, b/w, DJ)	L: Putnam	1948	Ardizzone, Edward	80-120	
Day-Lewis, Cecil	Otterbury Incident (1st AM, 8vo, cloth, 160p, b/w, DJ/2.00)	Viking	1949	Ardizzone, Edward	80-130	
Day-Lewis, Cecil	Otterbury Incident (1st [this pub], 8vo, 176p, yellow cl, fp b/w, DJ/3.75)	World	(1969)	Ardizzone, Edward	40-70	
Cook, Hartley K.	Over the Hills and Far Away (1st, 8vo, 263p, DJ, b/w pep by...)	L: Allen/Unwin	1947	Ardizzone, Edward	40-65	
Ardizzone, Edward	Paul, Hero of the Fire (1st AM, 8vo, ibds, [40]p, color, pep, DJ/1.00)	Houghton	(1948)	Ardizzone, Edward	120-200	

AUTHOR	TITLE	PUBLISHER	DATE	ARTIST	PRICE	LC
Ardizzone, Edward	Paul, Hero of the Fire (1st AM {revised, std}, sm4to, unpag, color, DJ/3.00)	H.Z. Walck	(1963)	Ardizzone, Edward	40-65	
De La Mare, Walter	Peacock Pie (1st, 8vo, 107p, yellow cl, b/w, DJ)	L: Faber	(1946)	Ardizzone, Edward	80-130	R
Graves, Robert	Penny Fiddle (1st {std}, lg8vo, gilt, 64p, 2-color, DJ)	L: Cassell	(1960)	Ardizzone, Edward	80-125	
Graves, Robert	Penny Fiddle (1st AM {std}, lg8vo, 62p, green cl, fp 2-color, DJ/2.50)	Doubleday	(1960)	Ardizzone, Edward	60-90	
Barrie, James M.	Peter Pan (1st AM, 8vo, 175p, 6 fp color, DJ/5.00)	Scribner	(1962)	Ardizzone, Edward	60-95	
Ardizzone, Edward	Peter the Wanderer (1st AM {std}, sm4to, [48]p, color, DJ/3.50)	H.Z. Walck	(1964)	Ardizzone, Edward	50-80	
Stonier, George W.	Pictures on the Pavement (1st, 8vo, 214p, brown cl, b/w, pep, DJ)	L: M. Joseph	1955	Ardizzone, Edward	60-100	
Reeves, James	Pigeons and Princesses (1st, 8vo, 113p, b/w, DJ)	L: Heinemann	(1956)	Ardizzone, Edward	50-85	*
Estes, Eleanor	Pinky Pye (1st {std}, sm8vo, 192p, pink cl, b/w, DJ/3.00)	Harcourt	(1958)	Ardizzone, Edward	60-90	R
Corrin, Stephen	Plucky Sailor and Postage Stamp (1st, 8vo, ibds, unpag, color)	L: Faber	1954	Ardizzone, Edward	60-90	*
Reeves, James	Prefabulous Animiles (1st, 8vo, 56p, blue/gilt, b/w, DJ)	L: Heinemann	(1957)	Ardizzone, Edward	60-85	
Reeves, James	Rhyming Will (1st AM, sm ob4to, [32]p, color, DJ/3.50)	McGraw-Hill	(1968)	Ardizzone, Edward	30-45	
Mitchison, Naomi	Rib of the Green Umbrella (1st, 8vo, 160p, b/w, DJ)	L: Collins	1960	Ardizzone, Edward	45-70	
Slade, Irene (comp)	Ring of Bells (1st, 8vo, 129p, b/w, DJ)	L: J. Murray	(1962)	Ardizzone, Edward	30-50	
Sicotte, Virginia	Riot of Quiet (1st {std}, 12mo, [32]p, color, DJ/2.95)	Holt, Rinehart	(1969)	Ardizzone, Edward	40-65	
Defoe, Daniel	Robinson Crusoe (1st AM {std}, lg8vo, 281p, blue/silver, pep, DJ)	F. Watts	1968	Ardizzone, Edward	30-50	
Reeves, James	Sailor Rumbelow (1st AM {std}, 8vo, 221p, b/w, DJ/3.75)	Dutton	1962	Ardizzone, Edward	30-50	*
Ardizzone, Edward	Sarah & Simon & No Red Paint (1st AM {std}, lg8vo, 48p, 2-color, DJ/2.75)	Delacorte Pr.	(1966)	Ardizzone, Edward	50-80	
Goldman, Joan M.	School in Our Village (1st, 8vo, 136p, b/w, cep, DJ)	L: Batsford	1957	Ardizzone, Edward	45-70	
Reeves, James	Secret Shoemakers (1st AM, 8vo, 96p, b/w, DJ/3.25)	Abelard-Schuman	1966	Ardizzone, Edward	30-50	
Gorham, Maurice	Showmen and Suckers (1st, 8vo, 262p, red bds, 35 b/w, DJ)	L: P. Marshall	(1951)	Ardizzone, Edward	80-120	
Faralla, Dana	Singing Cupboard (1st AM {std}, 8vo, 93p, b/w, DJ/3.25)	Lippincott	(1963)	Ardizzone, Edward	30-50	
Clewes, Dorothy	Special Branch Willie (1st, sm8vo, 48p, color, DJ)	L: Hamilton	1969	Ardizzone, Edward	40-65	
De La Mare, Walter	Stories from the Bible (1st AM {std}, 8vo, 420p, b/w, DJ/4.95)	Knopf	1961	Ardizzone, Edward	50-80	
Reeves, James	Story of Jackie Thimble (1st {std}, 12mo, 31p, b/w, DJ/1.95)	Dutton	(1964)	Ardizzone, Edward	30-50	
De La Mare, Walter	Story of Moses (1st, 8vo, 110p, b/w, DJ)	L: Faber	(1959)	Ardizzone, Edward	50-80	
Kenward, James	Suburban Child (1st, 8vo, 140p, white ipcb, 11 b/w, DJ)	L: Cambridge	1955	Ardizzone, Edward	50-80	
Bates, Herbert E.	Sugar for the Horse (1st, 12mo, 120p, b/w, DJ)	L: Joseph	1957	Ardizzone, Edward	50-85	
Trevor, Meriol	Sun Slower, Sun Faster (1st, 8vo, blue cl, 217p, b/w, DJ)	NY: Sheed Ward	(1957)	Ardizzone, Edward	40-65	
Faralla, Dana	Swanhilda-of-the-Swans (1st, 8vo, 92p, blue cl, b/w, DJ)	L: Blackie	(1964)	Ardizzone, Edward	40-65	
Estes, Eleanor	The Alley (1st {std}, 8vo, 283p, b/w, DJ/3.50)	Harcourt	(1964)	Ardizzone, Edward	50-80	R
Marshall, Archibald	The Dragon (1st AM {std}, lgob8vo, [32]p, color, DJ/3.25)	Dutton	(1967)	Ardizzone, Edward	30-50	
Gorham, Maurice	The Local (1st, 8vo, 51p, ipcb, 15 fp color)	L: Cassell	1939	Ardizzone, Edward	200-300	
Bloomfield, Paul	The Mediterranean (1st, 12mo, 247p, col frn, b/w)	L: Cassell	(1935)	Ardizzone, Edward	60-90	*
Wahl, Jan	The Muffletumps (1st {std}, ob8vo, [46]p, fp 1-color, dep, DJ/3.50)	Holt, Rinehart	(1966)	Ardizzone, Edward	45-70	
Walsh, John	The Truants (1st AM, 8vo, 80p, b/w, DJ/2.95)	Rand/McNally	(1968)	Ardizzone, Edward	50-75	
Buchan, John	Thirty-Nine Steps (1st AM, 8vo, 145p, col frn, b/w, DJ/3.25)	Dent/Dutton	(1964)	Ardizzone, Edward	40-70	*
Black, Margaret	Three Brothers and a Lady (1st, 4to, ibds, 62p, color, DJ)	L: Acorn Press	1947	Ardizzone, Edward	100-170	
Ardizzone, Edward	Tim All Alone (1st, 4to, red cl, unpag, color, DJ, KGM)	L: Oxford U.Pr.	(1957)	Ardizzone, Edward	200-300	
Ardizzone, Edward	Tim and Charlotte (1st, sm4to, ibds, [48]p, color, DJ/2.00)	Oxford U. Pr.	(1951)	Ardizzone, Edward	150-220	
Ardizzone, Edward	Tim and Ginger (1st AM, 4to, [48]p, color, DJ/3.50)	H.Z. Walck	(1965)	Ardizzone, Edward	50-80	*
Ardizzone, Edward	Tim and Lucy Go to Sea (1st AM, folio, ibds, [64]p, color, DJ/2.00)	Oxford U. Pr.	(1938)	Ardizzone, Edward	300-500	
Ardizzone, Edward	Tim in Danger (1st, 4to, ipcb, [48]p, color, DJ/2.50)	Oxford U. Pr.	(1953)	Ardizzone, Edward	140-220	
Ardizzone, Edward	Tim to the Lighthouse (1st, sm4to, ibds, [48]p, color, DJ)	L: Oxford U.Pr.	1968	Ardizzone, Edward	80-125	
Ardizzone, Edward	Tim to the Rescue (1st, sm4to, [48]p, ibds, color, DJ/2.50)	Oxford U. Pr.	(1949)	Ardizzone, Edward	150-250	
Ardizzone, Edward	Tim's Friend Towser (1st AM, sm4to, [48]p, color, DJ/3.50)	H.Z. Walck	(1962)	Ardizzone, Edward	50-85	
Lederer, William J.	Timothy's Song (1st {std}, sm8vo, gilt, 41p, b/w, DJ/2.95)	Norton	(1965)	Ardizzone, Edward	50-85	
Reeves, James	Titus in Trouble (1st, 4to, ibds, unpag, 46 color, DJ)	L: Bodley Head	(1959)	Ardizzone, Edward	120-180	R
Lyons, A. Neil	Tom, Dick and Harriet (1st, 8vo, 254p, green cl, b/w)	L: Cresset Pr.	(1937)	Ardizzone, Edward	150-225	
Reeves, James	Wandering Moon (1st AM {std}, 8vo, 73p, b/w, DJ/2.50)	Dutton	1960	Ardizzone, Edward	45-70	
Estes, Eleanor	Witch Family (1st {std}, 8vo, green cl, 186p, b/w, DJ/3.25)	Harcourt	(1960)	Ardizzone, Edward	40-65	
Ardizzone, Edward	Wrong Side of the Bed (1st AM {std}, 8vo, [32]p, color DJ/3.50)	Doubleday	(1970)	Ardizzone, Edward	50-80	R*
Clark, Leonard	Year Round (1st, 12mo, [32]p, color, DJ)	L: Hart-Davis	1966	Ardizzone, Edward	40-65	*
Ardley, Patricia B.	Adventures of Mr. Horace Hedgehog (1st, ob4to, ibds, 56p, 6 fp color)	L: Collins	(1935)	Ardley, E.C.	90-120	*
Aris, Ernest A.	Famous Animal Tales (1st, lg8vo, 158p, 8cp, pep)	L: Harrap	(1935)	Aris, Ernest A.	80-120	
Byron, May	Hole in the Wall (1st, 8vo, p-o, ipcb, 6 fp color, pep)	L: H. Milford	[1915]	Aris, Ernest A.	70-100	
Aris, Ernest A.	Three Bad Ducklings (1st, 24mo, ibds, [32]p, p-o, 8cp)	L: Partridge	[1917]	Aris, Ernest A.	70-120	
Armer, Laura A.	Forest Pool (1st {std}, 4to, 40p, pep, 8cp, DJ/2.50, CH)	Longmans	(1938)	Armer, Laura A.	125-200	R
Armer, Laura A.	Waterless Mountain (1st {std}, lg8vo, 212p, cloth, 16pl, DJ/2.50, NM)	Longmans	1931	Armer, Laura A.	120-200	R
Armer, Laura A.	Cactus (1st, 8vo, 102p, col frn, b/w)	Stokes	1934	Armer, Sidney	30-50	*
Armer, Laura A.	Dark Circle of Branches (1st {std}, lg8vo, 212p, 8pl, pep, DJ/2.50)	Longmans	1933	Armer, Sidney	30-45	
Armer, Laura A.	Farthest West (1st {std}, lg8vo, 190p, 8pl, pep, DJ/2.50)	Longmans	1939	Armer, Sidney	35-50	
Armer, Laura A.	Trader's Children (1st {std}, 8vo, 241p, b/w, DJ/2.50)	Longmans	1937	Armer, Sidney	50-85	*
Armfield, Constance	Armfield's Animal Book (1st, 8vo, 96p, orange cl, 8 ticp)	L: Duckworth	(1922)	Armfield, Maxwell	75-100	
N/A	Aucassin & Nicolette (1st, 8vo, 72p, color)	Dent/Dutton	1910	Armfield, Maxwell	60-80	*
Lee, Vernon	Ballet of the Nations (1st AM, 4to, ibds, 24p, uncut, 1-color)	Putnam	1915	Armfield, Maxwell	100-165	R*
Andersen, Hans C.	Fairy Tales (1st, sm4to, 392p, gilt, 24cp, pep)	Dent/Dutton	1910	Armfield, Maxwell	140-200	
Armfield, Constance	Flower Book (1st, lg8vo, 153p, teg, bds, uncut, 18cp)	L: Chatto	1910	Armfield, Maxwell	100-175	
Armfield, Maxwell	Hanging Garden... (1st, 4to, 75p, 8cp)	L: Simpkin	1914	Armfield, Maxwell	60-100	*
Mackenzie, Donald A.	Indian Fairy Stories (1st, 8vo, 200p, 8pl)	L: Blackie	1915	Armfield, Maxwell	50-80	
Morris, William	Life and Death of Jason (1st, lg8vo, 332p, blue cl, 6cp)	Swarthmore Pr.	(1915)	Armfield, Maxwell	80-130	
Andersen, Hans C.	Mermaid and other Tales (1st, sm8vo, 127p, p-o, gilt, 8cp)	Dent/Dutton	(1914)	Armfield, Maxwell	70-120	
Armfield, Constance	Sylvia's Travels (1st, sm4to, 256p, gilt, 16cp, pep)	L: Dent	1911	Armfield, Maxwell	120-180	
Armfield, Constance	Tales from Timbuktu (1st, lg8vo, 179p, gilt, col frn, 11 fp b/w)	L: Chatto	(1923)	Armfield, Maxwell	50-80	
Armfield, Constance	Tales from Timbuktu (1st AM, 8vo, 179p, col frn, 11 fp b/w)	Harcourt	[1924]	Armfield, Maxwell	45-70	
Andersen, Hans C.	Ugly Duckling (1st, sm8vo, gilt, 127p, p-o, 8cp)	L: Dent	(1913)	Armfield, Maxwell	70-100	
Shakespeare, Wm.	Winter's Tale (1st, sm4to, 98p, gilt, 12cp, pep, DJ)	L: Dent	(1922)	Armfield, Maxwell	90-140	
Armfield, Constance	Wonder Tales of the World (1st AM, 8vo, 271p, color)	Harcourt	1920	Armfield, Maxwell	70-100	*

AUTHOR	TITLE	PUBLISHER	DATE	ARTIST	PRICE	LC
Masefield, John	Reynard the Fox (1st, 4to, gilt, 116p, uncut, 4cp, 12pl)	L: Heinemann	1921	Armour, George D.	90-120	
Masefield, John	Reynard the Fox (1st AM, 4to, green/gilt, 339p, 4cp)	Macmillan	1921	Armour, George D.	70-100	
Snyder, Zilpha K.	Today is Saturday (1st {std}, ob8vo, 56p, DJ/3.75, b/w photos by...)	Atheneum	1969	Arms, John	30-50	
Gale, Agnes C.	Achilles and Hector (1st, 12mo, 176p, red/gilt, fp b/w)	Rand/McNally	(1904)	Armstrong, Helen	30-50	
Bouvet, Marguerite	Bernardo and Laurette (1st, sm8vo, 217p, green cl, b/w, pl)	McClurg	1901	Armstrong, Helen	30-50	
Magruder, Julia	Child Amy (1st, 8vo, 302p, red/gilt, 7pl)	Lothrop Pub.	(1894)	Armstrong, Helen	35-60	
Abbott, Jacob	Franconia Stories (1st, 8vo, 321p, p-o, blue/gilt, col frn, 12pl, pep)	Putnam	1923	Armstrong, Helen	40-70	
Bouvet, Marguerite	Little Marjorie's Love Story (1st, 12mo, 124p, 16pl)	McClurg	1891	Armstrong, Helen	30-60	
Bouvet, Marguerite	My Lady (1st, 12mo, beige/silver, 284p, 12pl)	McClurg	1894	Armstrong, Helen	40-60	
Bouvet, Marguerite	Prince Tip-Top (1st, 12mo, 134p, olive/white, b/w)	McClurg	1892	Armstrong, Helen	55-80	*
Wahlenberg, Anna	Swedish Fairy Tales (1st, sm8vo, 158p, 14pl)	McClurg	1901	Armstrong, Helen	60-90	*
Parsons, Frances T.	According to Season... (1st, sm8vo, 197p, green/gilt, cvr by...)	Scribner	1902	Armstrong, Margaret	35-60	*
Dante	Ad Astra (1st, lg4to, ipcb, unpag, b/w)	R.H. Russell	1902	Armstrong, Margaret	170-240	
Thanet, Octave	Adventure in Photography (1st, 12mo, 179p, photos, cvr by...)	Scribner	1893	Armstrong, Margaret	200-300	
Stockton, Frank	Adventures of Captain Horn (1st, sm8vo, green/gilt, 404p, cvr by...)	Scribner	1895	Armstrong, Margaret	30-50	
Arnold, Edwin	Adzuma (1st, 12mo, 170p, green/gilt)	Scribner	1893	Armstrong, Margaret	35-60	*
Meriwether, Lee	Afloat and Ashore on the Mediterranean (1st, sm8vo, brown/gilt, 363p)	Scribner	1892	Armstrong, Margaret	35-60	
Ely, Helena R.	Another Hardy Garden Book (1st, 8vo, teg, uncut, 243p, cvr by)	Macmillan	1905	Armstrong, Margaret	35-60	
Bourget, Paul	Antigone (1st, 8vo, red/gilt, uncut, 297p)	Scribner	1898	Armstrong, Margaret	35-60	*
Grant, Robert	Art of Living (1st, 8vo, 353p, green/gilt, teg, cvr by...)	Scribner	1895	Armstrong, Margaret	30-50	
Holland, Josiah G.	Arthur Bonnicastle (12mo, green/gilt, 422p, cvr by...)	Scribner	1896	Armstrong, Margaret	35-60	*
Grant, Robert	Bachelor's Christmas (1st, 12mo, olive/gilt, teg, 309p, cvr by...)	Scribner	1895	Armstrong, Margaret	35-60	
Andrews, Mary S.	Better Treasure (1st, 8vo, gilt, 72p, cvr by...)	Bobbs-Merrill	(1908)	Armstrong, Margaret	30-50	
Fox, John Jr.	Blue Grass and Rhododendron (1st, 8vo, teg, 294p, uncut)	Scribner	1901	Armstrong, Margaret	70-120	
Andrews, Mary S.	Bob and the Guides (1st, 8vo, green/gilt, 351p, teg)	Scribner	1906	Armstrong, Margaret	25-40	
Cable, George W.	Bonaventure (1st, 8vo, 314p, olive/gilt, teg)	Scribner	1902	Armstrong, Margaret	40-60	
Cable, George W.	Bylow Hill (1st, 8vo, teg, uncut, red/gilt, 209p, cvr by...)	Scribner	1902	Armstrong, Margaret	50-80	
Miller, Alice D.	Calderon's Prisoner (1st, 8vo, olive/gilt, 294p, cvr by...)	Scribner	1903	Armstrong, Margaret	40-65	
Dunbar, Paul L.	Candle-Lightin' Time (1st, 8vo, teg, 127p, green cl, uncut, cvr b7...)	Dodd	1901	Armstrong, Margaret	250-400	
Thoreau, Henry D.	Cape Cod (1st, 8vo, gilt, teg, 319p, cvr by...)	Crowell	(1908)	Armstrong, Margaret	80-125	
Merington, Marguerite	Captain Lettarblair (1st, 8vo, aqua/gilt, 212p, cvr by...)	Bobbs-Merrill	(1906)	Armstrong, Margaret	35-60	
Seawell, Molly E.	Chateau of Montplaisir (1st, 8vo, uncut, 245p, blue cl, cvr by...)	Appleton	1906	Armstrong, Margaret	30-50	
Abbott, Lyman	Christ's Secret of Happiness (1st, 8vo, bds, gilt, cvr by...)	Crowell	(1907)	Armstrong, Margaret	55-80	*
Earle, Alice M.	Colonial Days in Old New York (1st, sm8vo, 312p, gilt)	Scribner	1896	Armstrong, Margaret	60-100	
Hope, Anthony	Comedies of Courtship (1st, sm8vo, 377p, buckram/gilt)	Scribner	1896	Armstrong, Margaret	35-60	*
Van Dyke, Henry	Companionable Books (1st, sm8vo, blue/gilt, 391p, cvr by...)	Scribner	1922	Armstrong, Margaret	25-45	
Crawford, F. Marion	Constantinople (1st, 8vo, 79p, teg, cvr by...)	Scribner	1895	Armstrong, Margaret	40-65	
Earle, Alice M.	Costumes of Colonial Times (1st, 8vo, blue/gilt, 264p)	Scribner	1894	Armstrong, Margaret	70-100	
Martin, Edward S.	Cousin Anthony and I (1st, 12mo, 255p, green cl, cvr by...)	Scribner	1895	Armstrong, Margaret	30-60	
Dickens, Charles	Cricket on the Hearth (1st, sm8vo, teg, uncut, 174p, dep, cvr by..)	Putnam	1900	Armstrong, Margaret	30-50	
Sheldon, Charles	Crucifixion of Philip Strong (1st, 12mo, 267p, gray/gilt, cvr by...)	McClurg	1894	Armstrong, Margaret	30-50	*
Van Dyke, Henry	Days Off (1st, 12mo, teg, 322p, uncut)	Scribner	1907	Armstrong, Margaret	25-40	
Riley, James W.	Defective Santa Claus (1st, 12mo, green/gilt, 77p, cvr by...)	Bobbs-Merrill	(1904)	Armstrong, Margaret	70-120	R
Cable, George W.	Doctor Sevier (8vo, 473p, teg, olive/gilt)	Scribner	1898	Armstrong, Margaret	30-50	
Sedgwick, Anne D.	Dull Miss Archinard (1st, 12mo, 287p, beige/gilt, cvr by...)	Scribner	1898	Armstrong, Margaret	35-60	*
Horton, George	Edge of Hazard (1st, sm8vo, 429p, aqua cl, cvr by...)	Bobbs-Merrill	(1906)	Armstrong, Margaret	35-60	*
Cary, Elisabeth L.	Emerson, Poet and Thinker (1st, lg8vo, blue/gilt, teg, 284p, cvr by...)	Putnam	1904	Armstrong, Margaret	60-90	
Andrews, Mary S.	Eternal Masculine (1st, 8vo, 430p, green/gilt)	Scribner	1913	Armstrong, Margaret	40-60	
N/A	Fair Women from Vogue (4to, 28p, tan buckram, b/w)	Fashion Co.	1894	Armstrong, Margaret	140-220	
Stockton, Frank	Fanciful Tales (1st, 12mo, maroon cl, 135p, cvr by...)	Scribner	1894	Armstrong, Margaret	75-100	*
Armstrong, Margaret	Fieldbook of Western Wilderness (1st, 12mo, 596p, color)	Putnam	1915	Armstrong, Margaret	120-200	
Van Dyke, Henry	Fisherman's Luck (1st [new ed.], 12mo, 285p, cvr by...)	Scribner	1905	Armstrong, Margaret	25-40	
Barclay, Florence	Following of the Star (1st, sm8vo, 426p, teg, cvr by...)	Putnam	1911	Armstrong, Margaret	40-65	*
Wells, Carolyn	Folly for the Wise (1st, 8vo, 170p, blue/gilt, cvr by...)	Bobbs-Merrill	(1904)	Armstrong, Margaret	55-90	
Seawell, Molly E.	Fortunes of Fifi (1st, 8vo, 239p, cvr by...)	Bobbs-Merrill	(1903)	Armstrong, Margaret	30-50	
Seawell, Molly E.	Francezka (1st, sm8vo, 466p, green/gilt, cvr by...)	Bobbs-Merrill	(1902)	Armstrong, Margaret	35-60	
Harris, Joel C.	Free Joe... (1st, 8vo, brown cl, uncut, 236p, 1st cvr by...)	Scribner	1887	Armstrong, Margaret	170-240	
Stockton, Frank	Girl at Cobhurst (1st, 12mo, green/gilt, teg, 408p, cvr by...)	Scribner	1898	Armstrong, Margaret	45-70	
Warren, Carro F.	Girl of the Governor (1st, 8vo, 407p, 9pl, cvr by...)	Scribner	1900	Armstrong, Margaret	35-60	
Miller, James R.	Glimpses of Heavenly Life (1st, sm8vo, 32p, cvr by...)	Crowell	(1908)	Armstrong, Margaret	35-60	
Page, Thomas N.	Gordon Keith (1st, sm8vo, blue/gilt, 548p, b/w)	Scribner	1903	Armstrong, Margaret	40-70	
Gray, Maxwell	Great Refusal (1st, sm8vo, brown/gilt, 438p, cvr by...)	Appleton	1906	Armstrong, Margaret	50-80	
Hardy, Thomas	Group of Noble Dames (1st, 8vo, 292p, brown/gilt, cvr by....)	Harper	1891	Armstrong, Margaret	50-80	
Dodge, Mary Mapes	Hans Brinker (1st, 8vo, 393p, blue cl, cvr by...)	Scribner	1896	Armstrong, Margaret	35-60	
Whitlock, Brand	Happy Average (1st, sm8vo, 347p, green/gilt, cvr by...)	Bobbs-Merrill	(1904)	Armstrong, Margaret	30-50	*
Thanet, Octave	Heart of Toil (1st, sm8vo, teg, 255p, cvr by...)	Scribner	1898	Armstrong, Margaret	40-60	*
Burnett, Frances H.	His Grace of Osmonde (1st, 12mo, 465p, buckram, cvr by...)	Scribner	1897	Armstrong, Margaret	35-50	
Herrick, Francis H.	Home Life of Wild Birds (1st, 4to, teg, uncut, 148p, brown/gilt)	Putnam	1901	Armstrong, Margaret	55-90	
Peake, Elmore E.	House of Hawley (1st, 8vo, 341p, cvr by...)	Appleton	1905	Armstrong, Margaret	35-60	*
Parsons, Frances T.	How to Know the Ferns (1st, 8vo, brown/gilt, 215p)	Scribner	1899	Armstrong, Margaret	55-80	
Krehbiel, Henry E.	How to Listen to Music (1st, 12mo, 361p, gilt)	Scribner	1897	Armstrong, Margaret	55-80	
Cooke, Grace M.	Huldah (1st, sm8vo, 316p, cvr by...)	Bobbs-Merrill	(1904)	Armstrong, Margaret	35-60	
Storm, Theodor	Immensee (1st, 8vo, 130p, olive cl, 9cp)	McClurg	1907	Armstrong, Margaret	100-160	
Janvier, Thomas A.	In Old New York (1st, 12mo, 285p, rust/gilt, cvr by...)	Harper	1894	Armstrong, Margaret	60-100	
Erskine, Payne	Iona (1st, 8vo, blue cl)	Dibble	1891	Armstrong, Margaret	55-90	
Wharton, Edith	Italian Backgrounds (1st, lg8vo, green/gilt, 214p, cvr by...)	Scribner	1905	Armstrong, Margaret	400-600	
Bunner, H.C.	Jersey Street and Jersey Lane (1st, 8vo, blue/gilt, teg, 201p)	Scribner	1896	Armstrong, Margaret	70-100	R
Sacher-Masoch, L.	Jewish Tales (1st, 12mo, 317p, beige/gilt, cvr by...)	McClurg	1894	Armstrong, Margaret	60-100	*

AUTHOR	TITLE	PUBLISHER	DATE	ARTIST	PRICE	LC
Stockton, Frank	John Gayther's Garden... (1st, sm8vo, green/gilt, uncut, teg, 365p)	Scribner	1902	Armstrong, Margaret	50-85	R
Cable, George W.	John March, Southerner (1st, 12mo, green/gilt, teg, 513p)	Scribner	1894	Armstrong, Margaret	70-120	R
Cable, George W.	Kincaid's Battery (1st, 8vo, 396p, gilt, col frn, 6pl, cvr by...)	Scribner	1908	Armstrong, Margaret	40-65	
Lummis, Charles F.	King of the Broncos (1st, 12mo, 254p, red/gilt, photos, cvr by)	Scribner	1897	Armstrong, Margaret	80-130	
Burnett, Frances H.	Lady of Quality (1st, 12mo, 363p, buckram/gilt, b/w)	Scribner	1896	Armstrong, Margaret	60-90	
Lummis, Charles F.	Land of Poco Tiempo (1st, 8vo, 310p, orange/gilt, cvr by...)	Scribner	1893	Armstrong, Margaret	100-160	
Browning, Robert	Last Ride Together (1st, 8vo, [48]p, gilt, AEG, pep, cvr by...)	Putnam	1906	Armstrong, Margaret	100-170	
Irving, Washington	Legend of Sleepy Hollow (1st, sm8vo, teg, 191p, red/gilt, cvr by...)	Putnam	1899	Armstrong, Margaret	90-120	
Dunbar, Paul L.	Li'L' Gal (1st, 8vo, 124p, teg, green cl, cvr by...)	Dodd	1904	Armstrong, Margaret	300-450	
Bouvet, Marguerite	Little House in Pimlico (1st, 8vo, blue cl, 245p, b/w, cep)	McClurg	1897	Armstrong, Margaret	25-40	
Van Dyke, Henry	Little Rivers (1st, 12mo, teg, 348p, uncut, blue/gilt)	Scribner	1903	Armstrong, Margaret	25-40	
Ford, Paul L.	Love Finds the Way (1st, 8vo, teg, 108p, uncut, cvr by...)	Dodd	1904	Armstrong, Margaret	35-60	
Potter, Mary K.	Love in Art (1st, 12mo, 260p, gilt, teg, cvr by...)	L.C. Page	1898	Armstrong, Margaret	40-65	
Bunner, H.C.	Love in Old Cloathes (1st, sm8vo, 217p, gilt, teg, uncut)	Scribner	1896	Armstrong, Margaret	30-50	
Crockett, Samuel R.	Loves of Miss Ann (1st AM, 12mo, blue cl, 421p, cvr by...)	Dodd	1904	Armstrong, Margaret	40-60	*
Tarbell, Ida M.	Madame Roland (1st, sm8vo, 328p, blue/gilt, cvr by...)	Scribner	1896	Armstrong, Margaret	30-50	
Thoreau, Henry D.	Maine Woods (1st, 8vo, teg, 423p, green/gilt, b/w, cvr by...)	Crowell	(1909)	Armstrong, Margaret	70-120	
Thanet, Octave	Man of the Hour (1st, 12mo, green/gilt, 477p, cvr by...)	Bobbs-Merrill	(1905)	Armstrong, Margaret	30-50	
MacGrath, Harold	Man on the Box (1st, sm8vo, 361p, aqua cloth, cvr by...)	Bobbs-Merrill	(1904)	Armstrong, Margaret	25-40	
Tennyson, Alfred	Maud (1st, 8vo, teg, uncut, 107p, green/gilt, dep, 10cp)	Dodd	1905	Armstrong, Margaret	50-85	
Muller, F. Max	Memories... (2nd, lg8vo, 135p, blue/gilt, teg, cvr by...)	McClurg	1906	Armstrong, Margaret	100-170	
Blichfeldt, E.H.	Mexican Journey (1st, 8vo, 280p, orange cl, map, cvr by...)	Crowell	(1912)	Armstrong, Margaret	35-60	*
Barclay, Florence	Mistress of Shenstone (1st, lg8vo, 340p, teg, uncut, gilt, 8cp)	Putnam	1910	Armstrong, Margaret	50-80	
Miller, Alice D.	Modern Obstacle (1st, sm8vo, 273p, blue/gilt, cvr by...)	Scribner	1903	Armstrong, Margaret	100-165	
Bourget, Paul	Monica (1st, 12mo, 289p, red cl, cvr by...)	Scribner	1902	Armstrong, Margaret	30-50	*
Stockton, Frank	Mrs. Cliff's Yacht (1st, 12mo, 341p, 8pl, cvr by...)	Scribner	1896	Armstrong, Margaret	30-60	
Stimson, Frederic J.	Mrs. Knollys (1st, sm8vo, 207p, green/gilt, teg)	Scribner	1897	Armstrong, Margaret	30-60	*
Harland, Marion	National Cook Book (1st, sm8vo, 550p, yellow cl, cvr by...)	Scribner	1896	Armstrong, Margaret	50-80	
Bancroft, Hubert H.	New Pacific (1st, 8vo, 738p, map, cvr by...)	Bancroft Co.	1900	Armstrong, Margaret	80-130	
Burt, Mary E.	Odysseus, Hero of Ithaca (1st, 12mo, 223p, red cl, cvr by...)	Scribner	1898	Armstrong, Margaret	35-60	*
Reed, Myrtle	Old Rose and Silver (1st, 8vo, 364p, teg, lavender/gilt, cvr by...)	Putnam	1909	Armstrong, Margaret	35-60	
Van Dyke, John C.	Opal Sea (1st, 12mo, 262p, green/gilt, cvr by...)	Scribner	1906	Armstrong, Margaret	30-50	
Field, Henry M.	Our Western Archipelago (1st, 8vo, 250p, beige cl, cvr by...)	Scribner	1895	Armstrong, Margaret	100-150	
Sousa, John P.	Pipetown Sandy (1st, 8vo, brown/gilt, 383p, cvr by...)	Bobbs-Merrill	(1905)	Armstrong, Margaret	30-50	
Browning, Robert	Pippa Passes (1st, 8vo, teg, uncut, green/gilt, [133]p, pep)	Dodd	1900	Armstrong, Margaret	70-125	
Perry, Bliss	Plated City (1st, 12mo, brown cl, 397p)	Scribner	1895	Armstrong, Margaret	30-50	*
Cable, George W.	Posson Jane & Pere Raphael (1st, 12mo, teg, blue/gilt, 162p, uncut)	Scribner	1909	Armstrong, Margaret	40-60	
Arnold, Edwin	Potiphar's Wife (1st, 12mo, 127p, green/gilt)	Scribner	1892	Armstrong, Margaret	30-50	*
Ackerman, A.W.	Price of Peace (1st, sm8vo, 390p, rust/gilt, cvr by...)	McClurg	1894	Armstrong, Margaret	35-60	*
Johnson, Edward (ed)	Private Memoirs of Madame Roland (1st, 12mo, 381p, teg, cvr by...)	McClurg	1900	Armstrong, Margaret	35-60	
Wallace, Edna K.	Quest of the Dream (1st, 12mo, teg, 292p, blue/gilt)	Putnam	1913	Armstrong, Margaret	30-50	
Irving, Washington	Rip Van Winkle (1st, sm8vo, teg, uncut, red/gilt, 115p, cvr by)	Putnam	1899	Armstrong, Margaret	60-90	
Davies, Maria T.	Rose of Old Harpeth (1st, sm8vo, 312p, blue cl, cvr by...)	Bobbs-Merrill	(1911)	Armstrong, Margaret	35-50	
Perry, Bliss	Salem Kittredge (1st, 12mo, 291p, yellow/gilt, cvr by...)	Scribner	1894	Armstrong, Margaret	25-45	
Barrie, James M.	Sentimental Tommy (1st AM, sm8vo, 478p, brown/gilt, cvr by...)	Scribner	1896	Armstrong, Margaret	30-60	
Page, Thomas N.	Social Life in Old Virginia (1st, 8vo, teg, 109p, green/gilt)	Scribner	1897	Armstrong, Margaret	55-80	
Aldrich, Anne R.	Songs about Life, Love and Death (1st, 12mo, 133p, gilt, teg)	Scribner	1892	Armstrong, Margaret	55-80	
Field, Eugene	Songs by Eugene Field (1st, 4to, ipcb, 112p)	Scribner	1914	Armstrong, Margaret	90-120	
Browning, Eliz. B.	Sonnets from the Portuguese (1st, 12mo, AEG, gilt, [98]p, color)	Putnam	(1902)	Armstrong, Margaret	50-80	
Van Dyke, Henry	Spirit of Christmas (1st, sm8vo, 59p, gilt, teg)	Scribner	1905	Armstrong, Margaret	55-80	
Stevenson, Rbt. L.	St. Ives (1st, 8vo, 438p, brown/gilt, cvr by...)	Scribner	1897	Armstrong, Margaret	100-160	
Stevenson, Rbt. L.	Stevenson Song Book (1st, 4to, ibds, 119p, cvr by...)	Scribner	1897	Armstrong, Margaret	80-120	
McSpadden, J.W.	Stories From Wagner (8vo, [new ed.], 282p, cvr by...)	Crowell	(1914)	Armstrong, Margaret	35-60	
Stuart, Ruth M.	Story of Babette (1st, 12mo, 209p, beige/gilt, cvr by...)	Harper	1894	Armstrong, Margaret	40-60	*
Stockton, Frank	Storyteller's Pack (1st, sm8vo, 380p, gilt, 16pl, teg, cvr by...)	Scribner	1897	Armstrong, Margaret	60-100	
Cable, George W.	Strong Hearts (1st, 12mo, 214p, olive/gilt, teg)	Scribner	1899	Armstrong, Margaret	35-50	
Van Dyke, John C.	Studies in Pictures (1st, 12mo, 136p, maroon/gilt)	Scribner	1907	Armstrong, Margaret	25-40	
Bouvet, Marguerite	Sweet William (1st, 8vo, 209p, blue cl, 16 b/w, cep)	McClurg	1890	Armstrong, Margaret	35-60	
Kuhns, Oscar	Switzerland (2nd, 8vo, blue/gilt, 294p)	Crowell	(1910)	Armstrong, Margaret	40-60	
Swinburne, A.C.	Tale of Balen (1st AM, 8vo, 132p, olive/gilt, cvr by...)	Scribner	1896	Armstrong, Margaret	80-120	*
Bouvet, Marguerite	Tales of an Old Chateau (1st, 12mo, 235p, gilt)	McClurg	1899	Armstrong, Margaret	50-80	
Cary, Elisabeth L.	Tennyson (1st, lg8vo, blue/gilt, 312p, teg, cvr by...)	Putnam	1898	Armstrong, Margaret	50-85	
Whittier, John G.	Tent on the Beach (1st, sm8vo, green/gilt, 110p, teg)	Houghton	1899	Armstrong, Margaret	60-100	
Bingham, D.	The Bastille (1st AM, 8vo, 2 volumes, blue/gilt)	J. Pott	1901	Armstrong, Margaret	100-160	
Harrison, Mrs. Burton	The Carlyles (1st AM, 8vo, 283p, brown cl, cvr by...)	Appleton	1905	Armstrong, Margaret	30-50	*
Cable, George W.	The Grandissimes (8vo, 448p, teg, olive/gilt)	Scribner	1898	Armstrong, Margaret	30-50	
Bonney, Thomas G.	The Mediterranean (1st, 8vo, blue/gilt, 367p, gilt)	J. Pott	1902	Armstrong, Margaret	50-80	
Andrews, Mary S.	The Militants (1st, 12mo, teg, 378p, green/gilt, cvr by...)	Scribner	1907	Armstrong, Margaret	55-80	
Bonner, Geraldine	The Pioneer (1st, 12mo, 392p, blue/gilt, cvr by...)	Bobbs-Merrill	(1905)	Armstrong, Margaret	40-60	*
Sheridan, Richard B.	The Rivals (1st, 8vo, 131p, 17pl, cvr by...)	Crowell	(1907)	Armstrong, Margaret	40-60	
Barclay, Florence	The Rosary (1st, lg8vo, 389p, teg, blue/gilt)	Putnam	1910	Armstrong, Margaret	35-60	
Cary, Elisabeth L.	The Rossettis (1st, lg8vo, 310p, teg, uncut, gilt, cvr by...)	Putnam	1900	Armstrong, Margaret	100-165	
McCutcheon, George B.	The Sherrods (1st, sm8vo, 343p, cvr by...)	Dodd	1903	Armstrong, Margaret	30-50	
Grant, Robert	The Undercurrent (1st, 12mo, blue cl, 480p, cvr by...)	Scribner	1904	Armstrong, Margaret	30-60	
Miller, Elizabeth	The Yoke (1st, 12mo, 616p, blue/gilt, cvr by...)	Bobbs-Merrill	(1904)	Armstrong, Margaret	35-60	
Van Dyke, Henry	Through South America (1st, 8vo, blue/gilt, 428p, cvr by...)	Crowell	(1912)	Armstrong, Margaret	60-90	
Sullivan, Thomas R.	Tom Sylvester (1st, 12mo, 428p, green/silver, cvr by...)	Scribner	1893	Armstrong, Margaret	30-45	
Bourget, Paul	Tragic Idyl (1st, sm8vo, red/gilt, 452p, uncut)	Scribner	1896	Armstrong, Margaret	35-60	*

AUTHOR	TITLE	PUBLISHER	DATE	ARTIST	PRICE	LC
Kingsley, Florence M.	Transfiguration of Miss Philura (1st, 16mo, 81p, beige cl, cvr by....)	Funk/Wagnalls	(1901)	Armstrong, Margaret	40-60	
DuMaurier, George	Trilby (1st, sm8vo, 464p, beige/gilt, b/w, cvr by...)	Harper	1894	Armstrong, Margaret	35-60	
Morris, Clara	Trouble Woman (1st, 12mo, 58p, cvr by...)	Funk/Wagnalls	1904	Armstrong, Margaret	40-60	*
Smith, Mabell S.	Twenty Centuries of Paris (1st, 8vo, blue/gilt, 400p, cvr by...)	Crowell	(1913)	Armstrong, Margaret	50-80	
Page, Thomas N.	Under the Crust (1st, 8vo, 307p, green/gilt, cvr by...)	Scribner	1907	Armstrong, Margaret	40-65	
Isham, Frederic S.	Under the Rose (1st, 8vo, 427p, green cl, cvr by...)	Bobbs-Merrill	(1903)	Armstrong, Margaret	25-40	
Van Dyke, Henry	Unknown Quantity (1st, 12mo, teg, 370p, uncut)	Scribner	1912	Armstrong, Margaret	25-40	
Grant, Robert	Unleavened Bread (1st, 8vo, green/gilt, 431p, cvr by...)	Scribner	1900	Armstrong, Margaret	30-50	
Rives, Hallie E.	Valiants of Virginia (1st, 8vo, red/gilt, 432p)	Bobbs-Merrill	(1912)	Armstrong, Margaret	25-45	
Ford, Paul L.	Wanted a Chaperone (1st, 8vo, 109p, teg, uncut, cvr by...)	Dodd	1902	Armstrong, Margaret	40-65	
Ford, Paul L.	Wanted a Matchmaker (1st, 8vo, teg, 112p, cvr by...)	Dodd	1900	Armstrong, Margaret	40-65	
Reed, Myrtle	Weaver of Dreams (1st, 8vo, teg, 374p, blue/gilt)	Putnam	1911	Armstrong, Margaret	35-60	
Thoreau, Henry D.	Week Along the Concord and Merrimack Rivers (1st, 8vo, gilt)	Crowell	(1911)	Armstrong, Margaret	40-60	
Stevenson, Rbt. L.	Weir of Hermiston (1st AM, 8vo, teg, gilt, 266p, cvr by...)	Scribner	1896	Armstrong, Margaret	55-80	
Dunbar, Paul L.	When Malindy Sings (1st, 8vo, 144p, teg, cvr by...)	Dodd	1903	Armstrong, Margaret	300-450	
Harland, Marion	Where Ghosts Walk (1st, 8vo, green cl, teg, 305p, cvr by...)	Putnam	1898	Armstrong, Margaret	45-70	
Reed, Myrtle	White Shield (1st, 8vo, 343p, lavender/gilt, teg)	Putnam	1912	Armstrong, Margaret	35-60	
Daskam, Josephine	Whom the Gods Destroyed (1st, sm8vo, 236p, red/gilt, cvr by...)	Scribner	1902	Armstrong, Margaret	40-60	
Cary, Elisabeth L.	William Morris (1st, lg8vo, teg, blue/gilt, 296p, uncut)	Putnam	1902	Armstrong, Margaret	70-120	
Bradley, Mary H.	Wine of Astonishment (1st, 12mo, pcb, 313p, cvr by...)	Appleton	1919	Armstrong, Margaret	30-50	
Brown, Anna R.	Wine-Press (1st, 8vo, 390p, rust cl, cvr by...)	Appleton	1905	Armstrong, Margaret	35-60	*
Thomas, Edith M.	Winter Swallow... (1st, 12mo, 120p, teg, p-o, green/gilt, cvr by...)	Scribner	1896	Armstrong, Margaret	70-125	
Field, Eugene	With Trumpet and Drum (1st, 8vo, 126p, teg, blue/white, cvr by...)	Scribner	1892	Armstrong, Margaret	45-70	
Beerbohm, Max	Works of... (1st, 8vo, brown/gilt, 165p, uncut)	Scribner	1896	Armstrong, Margaret	180-270	
Jefferson, Charles E.	World's Christmas Tree (1st, sm8vo, 44p, green/gilt, cvr by...)	Crowell	(1906)	Armstrong, Margaret	40-60	*
Wood, John S.	Yale Yarns (1st, 12mo, 307p, buckram, gilt, cvr by...)	Putnam	1895	Armstrong, Margaret	55-80	
Nicholson, Meredith	Zelda Dameron (1st, 12mo, 411p, cvr by...)	Bobbs-Merrill	(1904)	Armstrong, Margaret	35-60	
Kearns, Frank	Rin Tin Tin (1st, [Cozy Corner Bk.], sq8vo, ipcb, [24]p, color, pep)	Whitman	1953	Armstrong, Samuel	30-50	
Coatsworth, Eliz.	Troll Weather (1st {std}, 8vo, 41p, fp b/w, DJ/2.95)	Macmillan	(1967)	Arndt, Ursula	20-30	
Butterfield, Marguerite	Adventures of Esteban (1st, 8vo, 121p, 3-color, DJ/2.50)	Scribner	(1956)	Arno, Enrico	20-30	
Benary-Isbert, Margot	Blue Mystery (1st {std}, 8vo, 190p, b/w, DJ/2.95, JABA)	Harcourt	(1957)	Arno, Enrico	35-50	
Ross, Eulalie (ed)	Blue Rose (1st {std}, 8vo, 186p, DJ/3.50)	Harcourt	(1966)	Arno, Enrico	20-30	
Curry, Jane L.	Down from the Lonely Mountain (1st {std}, 8vo, 128p, b/w, DJ/3.00)	Harcourt	(1965)	Arno, Enrico	20-30	
Coolidge, Olivia	Golden Days of Greece (1st, 8vo, 211p, b/w, DJ/3.95)	Crowell	(1968)	Arno, Enrico	20-30	*
Courlander, Harold	Hat-Shaking Dance (1st {std}, 8vo, 115p, b/w, DJ/2.95)	Harcourt	(1957)	Arno, Enrico	40-65	*
Courlander, Harold	King's Drum and other African Stories (1st {std}, 8vo, 125p, b/w, DJ/3.00)	Harcourt	(1962)	Arno, Enrico	30-50	
O'Clery, Helen (comp)	Mermaid Reader (1st {std}, 8vo, 193p, b/w, DJ/4.95)	F. Watts	(1964)	Arno, Enrico	60-90	
DeTrevino, Elizabeth	Nacar, the White Deer (1st, 8vo, 149p, b/w, DJ/3.25)	Farrar, Straus	(1963)	Arno, Enrico	20-30	
Joslin, Sesyle	Night They Stole the Alphabet (1st {std}, 8vo, 190p, DJ/3.95)	Harcourt	(1968)	Arno, Enrico	60-100	
Livingston, Myra C.	Old Mrs. Twindlytart (1st {std}, 8vo, 48p, b/w, DJ/2.75)	Harcourt	(1967)	Arno, Enrico	20-35	
Courlander, Harold	Olode the Hunter (1st {std}, sm8vo, 153p, b/w, DJ/3.75)	Harcourt	(1968)	Arno, Enrico	20-30	
Courlander, Harold	People of the Short Blue Corn (1st {std}, 8vo, 189p, b/w, DJ/4.95)	Harcourt	(1970)	Arno, Enrico	25-40	
Courlander, Harold	Tiger's Whisker (1st {std}, sm8vo, blue cl, 152p, fp b/w, DJ/3.25)	Harcourt	(1959)	Arno, Enrico	30-50	
DeTrevino, Elizabeth	Turi's Poppa (1st {std}, 8vo, green cl, 186p, b/w, DJ/3.75)	Farrar, Straus	(1968)	Arno, Enrico	25-40	
Bell-Zano, Gina	Wee Moose (1st, sm4to, unpag, ibds, color, pep, DJ/2.95)	Parents Mag. Pr.	1964	Arno, Enrico	20-35	
Benary-Isbert, Margot	Wicked Enchantment (1st {std}, 8vo, 181p, b/w, DJ/2.50)	Harcourt	(1955)	Arno, Enrico	25-40	
Hunter, Norman	Larky Legends (1st, 8vo, 220p, col frn, b/w, pep, DJ)	L: John Lane	1938	Arnold, James	80-145	
Hughes, Langston	Black Misery (1st {std}, ob12mo, black cl, [60]p, b/w, DJ/2.50)	NY: P. Ericksson	(1969)	Arouni	100-165	R
Janvier, Thomas A.	Santa Fe's Partner (1st, sm8vo, 237p, teg, green/gilt, 8pl)	Harper	1907	Arthurs, S.	30-50	
Aesopus	Aesop's Fables (1st AM, lg8vo, p-o, 86p, b/w wood engravings, pep)	Viking	1933	Artzybasheff, Boris	60-90	
Bianco, Margery W.	Apple Tree (1st, 8vo, bds, p-o, 47p, b/w, dep)	Doran	(1926)	Artzybasheff, Boris	40-65	
N/A	Arabian Nights (1st, 12mo, grey cl, 402p, 11 fp b/w)	Appleton-Century	(1936)	Artzybasheff, Boris	50-80	*
Artzybasheff, Boris	As I See (1st, 4to, unpag, col frn, fp b/w, DJ/7.50)	Dodd	1954	Artzybasheff, Boris	250-400	
Morris, Constance	Behind Moroccan Walls (1st, lg4to, 239p, 20pl, cep)	Macmillan	1931	Artzybasheff, Boris	75-100	
Artzybasheff, Boris	Busiest Man in Town (1st, sm8vo, 45p, gilt)	Time Inc.	1933	Artzybasheff, Boris	75-100	
Finney, Charles G.	Circus of Dr. Lao (1st, lg8vo, red cl, 154p, p-o, 8pl, pep, DJ/2.00)	Viking	1935	Artzybasheff, Boris	250-400	
Colum, Padraic	Creatures (1st, lg8vo, bds, 56p, 10 illus, pep)	Macmillan	1927	Artzybasheff, Boris	60-90	
Artzybasheff, Boris	Fairy Shoemaker (1st, sq8vo, bds, 114p, b/w)	Macmillan	1928	Artzybasheff, Boris	90-120	
Martineau, Harriet	Feats on the Fiord (1st, 8vo, 301p, blue/gilt, col frn, pep)	Macmillan	1924	Artzybasheff, Boris	40-65	
Colum, Padraic	Forge in the Forest (1st, sm8vo, 149p, black/gilt, pep, 9cp)	Macmillan	1925	Artzybasheff, Boris	60-100	
Kreymborg, Alfred	Funnybone Alley (1st, 4to, teg, 269p, gilt, 7 ticp, pep)	Macaulay	(1927)	Artzybasheff, Boris	100-160	
Mukerji, Dhan G.	Gay Neck (1st, 8vo, 197p, t.e. blue, gilt, b/w, pep, DJ, NM)	Dutton	(1927)	Artzybasheff, Boris	100-165	R
Mukerji, Dhan G.	Ghond the Hunter (1st {std}, 8vo, gilt, 204p, 3 dp pl, pep, DJ/2.50)	Dutton	(1928)	Artzybasheff, Boris	80-125	
Lynch, Maude B.	Henry the Navigator (1st, sm8vo, yellow cl, 72p, 4 fp b/w, pep, DJ/0.60)	NY: Nelson	1935	Artzybasheff, Boris	45-70	
King, Gordon (ed)	Herodotus (1st {std}, 8vo, buckram, 274p, 14pl, map, pep, DJ/2.50)	Doubleday/Doran	1929	Artzybasheff, Boris	75-100	
Nathan, Robert	Jonah (1st, sm8vo, 212p, 5 engravings)	Knopf	1934	Artzybasheff, Boris	40-65	
Lamb, Harold	Kirdy (1st {std}, sm8vo, red cl, uncut, 276p, frn & pep by...)	Doubleday/Doran	1933	Artzybasheff, Boris	40-65	
Williams, Michael	Little Brother Francis of Assisi (1st, sm8vo, 188p, 4pl, dep)	Macmillan	1926	Artzybasheff, Boris	35-60	*
Charskaya, L.A.	Little Princess Nina (1st, sm8vo, 288p, col frn by...)	Henry Holt & Co.	1924	Artzybasheff, Boris	40-60	*
Bufano, Remo	Magic Strings... (1st, 8vo, 182p, 11 b/w, DJ/1.50)	Macmillan	1939	Artzybasheff, Boris	45-70	*
Haskell, Helen E.	Nadya Makes her Bow (1st, sm8vo, green cl, uncut, 349p, b/w, DJ/2.00)	Dutton	1938	Artzybasheff, Boris	60-100	
Hall, Anna G.	Nansen (1st, lg8vo, 165p, 10pl, pep, DJ/2.50, NH)	Viking	1940	Artzybasheff, Boris	65-100	R
Colum, Padraic	Orpheus: Myths of the World (1st, 4to, 327p, grey cl, 20pl)	Macmillan	1930	Artzybasheff, Boris	40-70	
Artzybasheff, Boris	Poor Shaydullah (1st, sq8vo, [59]p, grey cl, 10 fp b/w)	Macmillan	1931	Artzybasheff, Boris	60-90	
Lustig, Sonia	Roses of the Winds (1st {std}, sm8vo, 275p, col frn, pep, b/w)	Doubleday/Page	1926	Artzybasheff, Boris	40-70	
Mirza, Youel B.	Rug that Went to Mecca (1st, 8vo, red/gilt, 60p, 5 fp b/w, DJ/1.00)	Stokes	1939	Artzybasheff, Boris	50-80	
Artzybasheff, Boris	Seven Simeons (1st, 4to, [32]p, green cl, color, dep, DJ/2.00, CH)	Viking	1937	Artzybasheff, Boris	125-200	
Harper, Theodore A.	Siberian Gold (1st {std}, 8vo, brown cl, 335p, col frn, pep)	Doubleday/Page	1927	Artzybasheff, Boris	30-50	

AUTHOR	TITLE	PUBLISHER	DATE	ARTIST	PRICE	LC
Mirza, Youel B.	Son of the Sword (1st, 8vo, black cl, 211p, pep, designs by...)	Viking	1934	Artzybasheff, Boris	45-70	
Dorey, Jacques	Three & the Moon (1st, sm4to, blue/silver, 103p, 8cp)	Knopf	1929	Artzybasheff, Boris	60-90	
Smith, Ruth (ed)	Tree of Life (1st, lg8vo, 496p, blue cl, fp b/w, DJ/5.00)	Viking	1942	Artzybasheff, Boris	60-100	R*
Wilson, Edmund	Undertaker's Garland (1st, 12mo, 192p, uncut, p-o, 5pl)	Knopf	1922	Artzybasheff, Boris	120-200	R
Mamin-Siberiak, D.N.	Verotchka's Tales (1st, 8vo, pink/gilt, uncut, 190p, 10pl, dep)	Dutton	(1922)	Artzybasheff, Boris	60-95	
Bock, George E.	What Makes the Wheels Go 'Round (1st, 4to, 76p, pep, dp color)	Macmillan	1931	Artzybasheff, Boris	120-200	*
Young, Ella	Wonder Smith & His Son (1st, 8vo, green/gilt, 191p, b/w, dep, NH)	Longmans	1927	Artzybasheff, Boris	70-100	R
Aruego, Jose	Juan and the Asuangs (1st, 4to, ibds, [32]p, fp color, cep, DJ)	Scribner	1970	Aruego, Jose	30-50	
Aruego, Jose	King and his Friends (1st [1st bk.], ob4to, [40]p, 2-color, DJ/3.50)	Scribner	(1969)	Aruego, Jose	30-50	
Prelutsky, Jack	Toucans Two (1st {std}, 8vo, [32]p, color, DJ/4.95)	Macmillan	(1970)	Aruego, Jose	25-40	
Kraus, Robert	Whose Mouse are You? (1st {std}, 4to, [36]p, color, pep, DJ/4.95)	Macmillan	(1970)	Aruego, Jose	40-65	*
Asch, Frank	Elvira Everything (1st, ob8vo, [48]p, ibds, b/w, DJ/2.95)	Harper	(1970)	Asch, Frank	50-80	
Asch, Frank	George's Store (1st, ob4to, [46]p, b/w, DJ/2.95)	McGraw-Hill	(1969)	Asch, Frank	30-45	
Asch, Frank	Linda (1st, ob4to, [46]p, b/w, DJ/3.95)	McGraw-Hill	(1969)	Asch, Frank	30-45	
Davis, Richard H.	Bar Sinister (1st, sm8vo, teg, uncut, 108p, 7cp)	Scribner	1903	Ashe, E.M.	45-70	
Bangs, John K.	In Camp with a Tin Soldier (1st, 12mo, grey cl, 194p, b/w)	R.H. Russell	1892	Ashe, E.M.	60-90	
Marvel, Ik.	Reveries of a Bachelor (1st, 8vo, 338p, blue cl, 17cp)	Bobbs-Merrill	(1906)	Ashe, E.M.	25-40	
Jaufre	Jaufry the Knight & Fair Brunissende (1st, 12mo, 124p, decor by...)	Holiday House	1935	Atherton, John	30-50	*
Barrie, James M.	Little One's Peter Pan and Wendy (1st, 24mo, 44p, cp, pep)	Scribner	(1930)	Atkins, Kathleen	60-90	R*
Barrie, James M.	Nursery Peter Pan (1st, 16mo, 48p, ibds, color)	L: Hodder	[1938]	Atkins, Kathleen	60-100	
Gaskell, C.M.	Lady Anne's Fairy Tales (1st, 4to, teg, 258p, white/gilt, 12cp)	L: Richards	1914	Atkinson, Maud T.	160-240	
Carroll, Lewis	Alice in Wonderland (1st, lg8vo, ibds, gilt, 148p, AEG, 12cp, pep)	L: R. Tuck	(1910)	Attwell, Mabel L.	350-500	
N/A	All About the Fairies (16mo, wraps, 5 fp color, b/w)	L: Swain	[1920]	Attwell, Mabel L.	180-220	
N/A	Baby's Book (4to, ibds, 16 fp color)	L: R. Tuck	[1915]	Attwell, Mabel L.	250-350	
Meade, L.T.	Band of Mirth (8vo, 320p, 4cp)	L: Chambers	(1917)	Attwell, Mabel L.	60-90	
Attwell, Mabel L.	Boo-Boos at the Seaside (8vo, unpag, ipcb, p-o, 13cp, pep)	Valentine	[1915]	Attwell, Mabel L.	100-160	*
Jacberns, Raymond	Boy and a Secret (1st, sm8vo, gilt, 304p, 10pl)	L: Chambers	1908	Attwell, Mabel L.	100-165	
Ashley, Doris	Children's Stories from French Fairy Tales (1st, lg8vo, 136p, ibds, 12cp)	L: R. Tuck	[1917]	Attwell, Mabel L.	200-300	
Baldwin, May	Dora: High School Girl (1st, 12mo, 319p, 6 fp b/w)	L: Chambers	1906	Attwell, Mabel L.	70-100	
Ashley, Doris	Fairy Stories from France (lg8vo, ibds, 108p, 6cp)	L: R. Tuck	[1915]	Attwell, Mabel L.	160-250	
Andersen, Hans C.	Fairy Tales (1st, sm4to, 141p, AEG, blue/gilt, 12cp)	L: R. Tuck	(1914)	Attwell, Mabel L.	250-400	
Grimm Bros.	Fairy Tales (1st AM, 4to, 136p, blue/gilt, 12cp)	McKay	[1914]	Attwell, Mabel L.	180-250	
Andersen, Hans C.	Fairy Tales, Stories and Legends (1st, 8vo, 541p, 4pl)	L: Cassell	(1910)	Attwell, Mabel L.	60-90	*
Attwell, Mabel L.	Fairy-Land (1st, 4to, 32p, bds, 8cp)	Nelson	(1918)	Attwell, Mabel L.	150-225	
Molesworth, Mrs.	February Boys (1st, 8vo, 266p, gilt, 8cp)	L: Chambers	1909	Attwell, Mabel L.	60-100	*
Queen Marie	Lost Princess (sm4to, red cl, 159p, 6 ticp, pep)	L: Warne	[1915]	Attwell, Mabel L.	80-120	
Attwell, Mabel L.	Lucie Attwell's Book of Verses (1st, 4to, ibds, color)	L: Dean	1960	Attwell, Mabel L.	60-100	
Attwell, Mabel L.	Lucie Attwell's Fairy Book (1st, 4to, 255p, red cl, 12cp)	L: Partridge	(1932)	Attwell, Mabel L.	220-300	
Attwell, Mabel L.	Lucie Attwell's Jolly Book (1st, 4to, ibds, 45p, color, pep)	L: Dean	(1950)	Attwell, Mabel L.	60-100	
Attwell, Mabel L.	Lucie Attwell's Painting Book (1st, 4to, ibds, color)	L: Dean	1961	Attwell, Mabel L.	60-100	
Mother Goose	Mother Goose Nursery Rhymes (4to, ibds, 16 fp color)	L: R. Tuck	[1910]	Attwell, Mabel L.	220-300	
Molesworth, Mrs.	Old Pincushion (1st AM, 8vo, 271p, brown cl, 8cp)	Dutton	[1910]	Attwell, Mabel L.	50-80	
Molesworth, Mrs.	Old Pincushion (1st, 8vo, 271p, 8cp)	L: Chambers	1910	Attwell, Mabel L.	75-100	*
Sylva, Carmen	Peeping Pansy (1st, 4to, red/gilt, 312p, 8 ticp)	L: Hodder	(1918)	Attwell, Mabel L.	400-600	
Barrie, James M.	Peter Pan and Wendy (1st AM, lg8vo, gilt, p-o, 185p, 12cp, pep, SC)	Scribner	1921	Attwell, Mabel L.	180-250	
Barrie, James M.	Peter Pan and Wendy (1st, lg8vo, 185p, blue/gilt, 12 ticp)	L: Hodder	(1921)	Attwell, Mabel L.	250-350	
N/A	Sister Susie and the Twins (4to, shape book, wraps, 1-color)	L: Valentine	[1914]	Attwell, Mabel L.	150-225	
N/A	Story Book (4to, ibds, 248p, 6cp)	Whitman	[1930]	Attwell, Mabel L.	150-220	
Jacberns, Raymond	Tabitha Smallways, Schoolgirl (1st, 8vo, 304p, 6cp)	L: Chambers	(1912)	Attwell, Mabel L.	100-150	
Baldwin, May	That Little Limb (1st, 8vo, 199p, ibds, 4pl)	L: Chambers	1905	Attwell, Mabel L.	180-240	
Jacberns, Raymond	Troublesome Dog (1st, 8vo, 297p, 6cp)	L: Chambers	(1911)	Attwell, Mabel L.	100-150	
Quiller-Couch, Mabel	Troublesome Ursula (1st, 8vo, blue/gilt, p-o, 311p, 8pl)	L: Chambers	1907	Attwell, Mabel L.	80-125	
Kingsley, Charles	Water Babies (1st, sm4to, 115p, red cl, 12cp, pep)	L: R. Tuck	[1916]	Attwell, Mabel L.	300-450	
Wheelwright, John T.	Bad Penny (1st, sm8vo, gilt, teg, 162p, b/w)	Lamson/Wolffe	1896	Attwood, F.G.	60-90	*
Grant, Robert	Jack Hall (1st, sm8vo, blue/gilt, 394p, b/w, PPP)	Jordan Marsh	1888	Attwood, F.G.	100-185	R
Bigham, Madge A.	Blackie, His Friends and Enemies (1st, sm8vo, 200p, 5pl)	Little/Brown	1906	Atwood, Clara E.	30-50	*
Wesselhoeft, Lily	Diamond King.... (1st, 12mo, tan cl, 255p, 4pl)	Little/Brown	1907	Atwood, Clara E.	25-45	*
Alcott, Louisa M.	Garland for Girls (1st, 8vo, 286p, 8pl)	Little/Brown	1908	Atwood, Clara E.	30-50	
Ward, Grace	In the Miz (1st, lg8vo, blue cl, p-o, 159p, 8cp)	Little/Brown	1904	Atwood, Clara E.	90-160	
Auerbach, Marjorie	King Lavra & the Barber (1st, ob4to, [40]p, fp 3-color, cep, DJ/3.50)	Knopf	(1964)	Auerbach, Marjorie	30-50	*
Hauff, Wilhelm	Caravan Tales (1st AM, 8vo, 338p, 15 ticp, pep)	Stokes	(1912)	Ault, Norman	80-125	
Ault, Norman	Dreamland Shores (1st AM, sm4to, 83p, 6 ticp, pep)	Dodd	(1920)	Ault, Norman	130-200	
Ault, L.& N.	Podgy Book of Tales (1st, 12mo, 223p, pict cl, 16cp)	L: Richards	(1907)	Ault, Norman	150-220	*
Ault, L.& N.	Sammy and the Snarlywink (1st, 16mo, 95p, green cl, 24cp)	L: Richards	1904	Ault, Norman	120-180	
Darton, F.J.H.	Seven Champions of Christendom (1st, 8vo, blue/gilt, teg, 416p, col frn)	L: Wells/Gard.	[1913]	Ault, Norman	65-100	R
Connolly, John	Story of an Old Fashioned Doll (1st, 8vo, 107p)	L: D. Nutt	1905	Ault, Norman	60-90	
Bickley, Francis L.	Adventures of Harlequin (1st, 8vo, 119p, bds, p-o, 20 color, pep)	L: Selwyn	1923	Austen, John	55-80	
Shakespeare, Wm.	As You Like It (1st, 4to, 111p, red cl, p-o, 6 ticp)	L: Jackson	1930	Austen, John	80-120	
Thornley, G. (tr.)	Daphnis & Chloe (1st, 4to, 200p, gilt, buckram, 12cp)	L: G. Bles	1925	Austen, John	100-150	
Lord Byron	Don Juan (1st, lg8vo, 17 woodcuts, 408p, buckram)	L: John Lane	(1926)	Austen, John	60-90	
N/A	Everyman & other Plays (1st, 4to, black cl, 201p, 18cp, pep)	L: Chapman	1925	Austen, John	100-165	
Perrault, Charles	Fairy Tales (1st, sm4to, blue bds, p-o, color)	L: Selwyn/Blount	1922	Austen, John	55-80	*
Allison, James M.	Five Black Cousins... (1st, sm8vo, 63p, white/gilt, uncut, designs)	L: J. Cape	(1924)	Austen, John	45-75	
France, Anatole	Gods are Athirst (1st, lg8vo, 285p, black/gilt, 12cp)	L: John Lane	(1927)	Austen, John	55-80	
Shakespeare, Wm.	Hamlet (1st, 4to, 175p, black bds, gilt, 35 b/w)	L: Selwyn/Blount	(1922)	Austen, John	220-300	
Shakespeare, Wm.	Hamlet (1st AM, 4to, black bds, b/w)	Dutton	(1922)	Austen, John	140-200	
Keen, Ralph H.	Little Ape (1st [1st bk.], 8vo, yellow cl, 68p, 4pl & cvr by...)	L: Hendersons	(1921)	Austen, John	145-200	
Flaubert, Gustave	Madame Bovary (1st, lg8vo, 416p, black/gilt, 13pl, pep)	L: John Lane	(1928)	Austen, John	70-125	

AUTHOR	TITLE	PUBLISHER	DATE	ARTIST	PRICE	LC
Defoe, Daniel	Moll Flanders (1st, 4to, 333p, black/gilt, 16pl, pep)	L: John Lane	(1929)	Austen, John	70-125	
Austen, Jane	Rogues in Porcelain (1st AM, lg8vo, 258p, bds, 15cp, pep)	Greenberg	1924	Austen, John	70-100	
Austen, Jane	Rogues in Porcelain (1st, sm4to, 258p, pink bds, p-o, 15cp, pep)	L: Chapman/Hall	1924	Austen, John	60-90	
Farjeon, Eleanor	Songs for Music.... (1st, sm8vo, 61p, frn by...)	L: Selwyn	(1922)	Austen, John	55-80	
Douglas, Norman	South Wind (1st, lg8vo, 2 volumes, 15cp)	Argus Books	1929	Austen, John	90-120	
Perrault, Charles	Tales of Past Times... (1st, sq8vo, blue bds, 63p, p-o, color)	L: Selwyn	(1922)	Austen, John	90-120	
Nesbit, Edith	Book of Dogs (1st, obsm4to, 55p, b/w)	Dutton	1898	Austen, Winifred	200-300	*
Austin, Cyril F.	Adventures of Benjamin and Christabel (1st, ob4to, unpag, color)	Nister/Dutton	(1911)	Austin, Hilda	60-90	*
Austin, Cyril F.	Edward Buttoneye and his Adventures (sq24mo, ibds, chromos)	L: Nister	[1910]	Austin, Hilda	75-100	*
Austin, Cyril F.	Little Blue Rabbit (sq24mo, ibds, [54]p, fp color)	L: Nister	[1905]	Austin, Hilda	80-125	
Austin, Margot	Archie Angel (1st {std}, sm4to, yellow cl, 45p, b/w, pep, DJ/2.50)	Dutton	1957	Austin, Margot	45-65	
Austin, Margot	Barney's Adventure (1st {std}, sm4to, ibds, [42]p, b/w, pep, DJ/1.00)	Dutton	(1941)	Austin, Margot	30-50	
Austin, Margot	Brave John Henry (1st {std}, sm4to, 43p, b/w, DJ/1.75)	Dutton	(1955)	Austin, Margot	30-45	
Austin, Margot	Churchmouse Stories (1st, 8vo, 171p, 5 fp color, pep, DJ/3.50)	Dutton	(1956)	Austin, Margot	30-45	
Austin, Margot	Effelli (1st {std}, 4to, ibds, [56]p, fp b/w, pep, DJ/1.50)	Dutton	1942	Austin, Margot	45-70	
Austin, Margot	First Prize for Danny (1st {std}, sm4to, ibds, 43p, b/w, pep, DJ/1.50)	Dutton	(1952)	Austin, Margot	40-65	
Austin, Margot	Gabriel Churchkitten (1st, sm4to, ipcb, [36]p, pep, b/w, DJ/1.00)	Dutton	1942	Austin, Margot	70-100	
Austin, Margot	Gabriel Churchkitten & Moths (1st {std}, sm4to, ipcb, [41]p, b/w, DJ/1.25)	Dutton	1948	Austin, Margot	65-90	
Austin, Margot	Growl Bear (1st {std}, sm4to, ipcb, 42p, pep, b/w, DJ/1.50)	Dutton	(1951)	Austin, Margot	45-70	
Austin, Margot	Lutie (1st {std}, sm4to, ibds, [42]p, b/w, DJ/1.25)	Dutton	1944	Austin, Margot	40-65	
Austin, Margot	Manuel's Kite String (1st, sm8vo, 112p, color, DJ/1.50)	Scribner	1943	Austin, Margot	40-65	
Mother Goose	Mother Goose Rhymes (1st, 4to, red cl, [83]p, color, pep, DJ/1.25)	Platt/Munk	(1940)	Austin, Margot	80-120	*
Austin, Margot	Moxie and Hanty and Bunty (1st, lg8vo, ipcb, [44]p, 1-color, DJ/1.00)	Scribner	1939	Austin, Margot	45-70	
Austin, Margot	Once Upon a Springtime (1st, lg8vo, [43]p, ipcb, fp 1-color, DJ/1.00)	Scribner	1940	Austin, Margot	30-50	
Austin, Margot	Peter Churchmouse (1st {std}, sm4to, ipcb, [41]p, b/w, pep, DJ/1.00)	Dutton	1941	Austin, Margot	70-100	
Austin, Margot	Poppet (1st {std}, sm4to, ibds, [38]p, b/w, DJ/1.50)	Dutton	(1949)	Austin, Margot	40-65	
Austin, Margot	Three Silly Kittens (1st {std}, 8vo, ibds, 44p, b/w, DJ/1.50)	Dutton	(1950)	Austin, Margot	35-60	
Austin, Margot	Trumpet (1st {std}, sq4to, ipcb, [40]p, b/w, pep, DJ/1.25)	Dutton	1943	Austin, Margot	40-65	
Austin, Margot	Tumble Bear (1st, sm4to, [44]p, olive cl, fp b/w, cep, DJ/1.50)	Scribner	(1940)	Austin, Margot	40-65	
Austin, Margot	Willamette Way (1st, sm4to, [44]p, tan cl, fp color, DJ/1.75)	Scribner	1941	Austin, Margot	45-70	
Austin, Margot	William's Shadow (1st {std}, sm4to, ibds, 43p, b/w, DJ/1.75)	Dutton	(1954)	Austin, Margot	30-50	
Harrison, Ada	Lucy's Village (1st, 16mo, unpag, 8cp, DJ)	L: Oxford U.Pr.	(1945)	Austin, Robert	45-70	
Sewell, Anna	Black Beauty (1st, sm8vo, 262p, 19pl)	L.C. Page	1902	Austin/Toaspern	80-125	
Averill, Esther	Adventures of Jack Ninepins (1st {std}, sm4to, 63p, color, DJ/1.75)	Harper	(1944)	Averill, Esther	80-120	
Averill, Esther	Cat Club (1st, sm8vo, 32p, 1-color, DJ/1.50)	Harper	1944	Averill, Esther	160-250	
Averill, Esther	Fire Cat (1st, 8vo, 63p, ibds, fp 3-color, DJ/1.95)	Harper	(1960)	Averill, Esther	100-165	
Averill, Esther	How the Brothers Joined Cat Club (1st {std}, sm8vo, 32p, 1-color, DJ/1.50)	Harper	(1953)	Averill, Esther	80-120	
Averill, Esther	Jenny's Adopted Brothers (1st, sm8vo, 32p, color, DJ/1.50)	Harper	(1952)	Averill, Esther	65-90	
Averill, Esther	Jenny's Bedside Book (1st, ob4to, ipcb, [36]p, color, DJ/2.50)	Harper	1959	Averill, Esther	100-140	
Averill, Esther	Jenny's Birthday Book (1st, ob4to, [32]p, ibds, color, DJ/2.00, NYTBI)	Harper	1954	Averill, Esther	100-165	
Averill, Esther	Jenny's First Party (1st, 12mo, 31p, color, DJ/1.50)	Harper	(1948)	Averill, Esther	70-100	
Averill, Esther	School for Cats (1st, 12mo, 31p, color, DJ/1.50)	Harper	(1947)	Averill, Esther	70-130	
Averill, Esther	When Jenny Lost her Scarf (1st, sm8vo, 30p, color, DJ/1.50)	Harper	(1951)	Averill, Esther	80-125	
Peattie, Donald C.	Child's Story of the World (1st, sq8vo, [148]p, color, pep, DJ/2.00)	Simon/Schuster	1937	Averill, Naomi	70-100	
Averill, Naomi	Choochee: Story of an Eskimo Boy (1st, lg sq8vo, [40]p, ibds, pep, color)	Grosset/Dunlap	1937	Averill, Naomi	70-100	
Peattie, Donald C.	Story of America (1st, sq8vo, [24]p, ibds, color, pep, DJ/0.50)	Grosset/Dunlap	1937	Averill, Naomi	35-50	
Peattie, Donald C.	Story of Ancient Civilization (1st, sq8vo, [24]p, ibds, color, pep, DJ/0.50)	Grosset/Dunlap	1937	Averill, Naomi	35-50	
Peattie, Donald C.	Story of the First Men (1st, sq8vo, ibds, [24]p, color, pep, DJ/0.50)	Grosset/Dunlap	1937	Averill, Naomi	30-50	
Averill, Naomi	Whistling-Two-Teeth (1st, lg sq8vo, [24]p, color, pep, DJ/0.50)	Grosset/Dunlap	1939	Averill, Naomi	60-100	
Dix, Beulah M.	Betty-Bide-at-Home (1st, sm8vo, 236p, b/w pl)	Henry Holt & Co.	1912	Avery, Faith	30-50	*
Malkus, Alida S.	Raquel of the Ranch Country (1st, sm8vo, 314p, b/w pl)	Harcourt	(1927)	Avison, George	30-45	*
Blume, Judy	One in the Middle is Green Kangaroo (1st, lg8vo, [32]p, 3-color, DJ/3.95)	Reilly/Lee	(1969)	Axeman, Lois	50-80	*
Yershov, P.	Humpy (1st {std}, sm4to, 72p, fp b/w, DJ/3.25)	Harcourt	(1966)	Ayer, Jacqueline	25-40	
Ayer, Jacqueline	Little Silk (1st {std}, sm ob4to, [32]p, color, DJ/4.50)	Harcourt	(1970)	Ayer, Jacqueline	25-45	
Ayer, Jacqueline	Nu Dang and his Kite (1st {std}, ob4to, [32]p, 3-color, pep, DJ/2.75)	Harcourt	(1959)	Ayer, Jacqueline	40-65	R*
Ayer, Jacqueline	Paper-Flower Tree (1st {std}, sm ob4to, [32]p, color, pep, DJ/2.95)	Harcourt	(1962)	Ayer, Jacqueline	25-40	
Maugham, W. Somerset	Princess September (1st {std}, 8vo, [38]p, 2-color, DJ)	Harcourt	(1969)	Ayer, Jacqueline	30-50	
Grimm Bros.	Rumpelstilskin (1st {std}, 4to, [32]p, color, DJ/3.50)	Harcourt	(1967)	Ayer, Jacqueline	30-50	
Ayer, Jacqueline	Wish for Little Sister (1st {std}, ob4to, [32]p, color, pep, DJ/2.95)	Harcourt	(1960)	Ayer, Jacqueline	25-40	
Landon, Margaret	Anna and the King of Siam (1st, 8vo, 391p, gilt, b/w, DJ/3.75)	John Day	1944	Ayer, Margaret	50-80	
Sowers, Phyllis A.	Dhan of the Pearl Country (1st, lg8vo, p-o, 125p, color, pep, DJ/2.00)	Whitman	1939	Ayer, Margaret	45-70	
Sowers, Phyllis A.	Elephant Boy of the Teak Forest (1st, 8vo, 169p, DJ/2.50)	J. Messner	(1949)	Ayer, Margaret	30-45	
Bothwell, Jean	Little Flute Player (1st, 8vo, 159p, b/w, DJ/2.00)	Wm. Morrow	1949	Ayer, Margaret	20-35	
Bothwell, Jean	Paddy and Sam (1st, 4to, [38]p, fp 3-color, pep, DJ/2.00)	Abelard Press	(1952)	Ayer, Margaret	25-40	*
Bothwell, Jean	River Boy of Kashmir (1st, 8vo, 246p, pep, DJ/2.00)	Wm. Morrow	1946	Ayer, Margaret	25-40	
Sowers, Phyllis A.	Sons of the Dragon (1st, 8vo, 285p, yellow cl, 4cp, pep, DJ/2.00)	Whitman	1942	Ayer, Margaret	25-45	
Verne, Jules	20 Thousand Leagues under the Sea (1st, lg8vo, 407p, p-o, 4cp, pep, SC)	Scribner	1925	Aylward, W.J.	70-125	
London, Jack	Sea Wolf (1st, 8vo, blue/gilt, teg, 366p, 6pl)	Macmillan	1904	Aylward, W.J.	400-600	
Babbitt, Natalie	Dick Foote & Shark (1st {std} [1st bk.], 4to, 25p, pep, 1-color, DJ/3.50)	Farrar, Straus	(1967)	Babbitt, Natalie	25-45	
Babbitt, Samuel F.	Forty-Ninth Magician (1st, 4to, [48]p, fp b/w, dep, DJ/2.95)	Pantheon	(1966)	Babbitt, Natalie	25-40	
Babbitt, Natalie	Knee-Knock Rise (1st {std}, sm8vo, 117p, b/w, pep, DJ/3.95, NH)	Farrar, Straus	(1970)	Babbitt, Natalie	60-90	
Babbitt, Natalie	Phoebe's Revolt (1st, ob4to, [36]p, 1-color, pep, DJ/3.50)	Farrar, Straus	1968	Babbitt, Natalie	25-40	
Babbitt, Natalie	Search for Delicious (1st {std}, 8vo, 167p, b/w, pep, DJ/3.95)	Farrar, Straus	(1969)	Babbitt, Natalie	30-50	R*
Babbitt, Natalie	The Something (1st {std}, 12mo, [39]p, b/w, pep, DJ/2.95)	Farrar, Straus	(1970)	Babbitt, Natalie	30-55	
Kingsley, Charles	Water Babies (1st, 12mo, 208p, b/w)	D.C. Heath	(1914)	Babbitt/Blossom	35-60	*
Ormondroyd, Edward	Time at the Top (1st, 8vo, 176p, b/w, DJ/2.95)	Parnassus Press	(1963)	Bach, Peggie	80-120	
Cervantes	Adventures of Don Quixote (1st, sm4to, 287p, color)	Houghton	1928	Bacharach, Herman I.	35-60	*
Swift, Jonathan	Gulliver's Travels (1st, lg8vo, green cl, 309p, 4cp)	Houghton	1931	Bacharach, Herman I.	30-50	*

AUTHOR	TITLE	PUBLISHER	DATE	ARTIST	PRICE	LC
Collodi, Carlo	Pinocchio (1st, 8vo, p-o, 213p, 5cp, pep)	Houghton	1927	Bacharach, Herman I.	80-120	
Mendoza, George	Mist Men (1st {std}, lg8vo, 45p, cep, DJ/3.95, b/w decor by...)	Doubleday	(1970)	Bacon, Paul	25-45	*
Bacon, Peggy	Animosities (1st {std}, 8vo, 106p, ibds, b/w)	Harcourt	(1931)	Bacon, Peggy	50-80	
Smith, Linell	Auction Pony (1st {std}, 8vo, 117p, yellow cl, fp b/w, DJ/3.75)	Little/Brown	(1965)	Bacon, Peggy	30-50	
Bacon, Peggy	Ballad of Tangle Street (1st, ob4to, ibds, 24p, b/w)	Macmillan	1929	Bacon, Peggy	120-180	
Robinson, Tom P.	Buttons (1st, lg4to, [63]p, red cl, p-o, b/w, DJ/2.00)	Viking	1938	Bacon, Peggy	50-80	
Gates, Doris	Cat and Mrs. Cary (1st, 8vo, 216p, b/w, DJ/3.50)	Viking	(1962)	Bacon, Peggy	25-40	
Bacon, Peggy	Cat Calls (1st {std}, lg8vo, 87p, b/w, DJ/2.50)	McBride	(1935)	Bacon, Peggy	55-80	
Lockridge, Frances	Cat Who Rode Cows (1st {std}, 8vo, yellow cl, 36p, b/w, DJ/2.25)	Lippincott	(1955)	Bacon, Peggy	45-70	
Hecht, Ben	Cat/Jumped Out of the Story (1st {std}, 8vo, bds, p-o, pep, color, DJ/1.25)	Winston	(1947)	Bacon, Peggy	65-100	
Bacon, Peggy	Ghost of Opalina (1st {std}, 8vo, 243p, b/w, DJ/4.95)	Little/Brown	(1967)	Bacon, Peggy	250-400	*
Coyle, Kathleen	Josephine (1st {std}, sm8vo, blue cl, 174p, b/w, DJ/2.00)	Harper	(1942)	Bacon, Peggy	35-50	
Quigg, Jane	Judy and her Turtle Osmond (1st {std}, 8vo, 35p, fp 1-color, DJ/2.75)	Macmillan	1960	Bacon, Peggy	30-50	R*
Stolz, Mary S.	Leftover Elf (1st, 8vo, 57p, green cl, fp b/w, DJ/2.00)	Harper	(1952)	Bacon, Peggy	30-50	
Bacon, Peggy	Lion-Hearted Kitten (1st, 8vo, 102p, 10pl)	Macmillan	1927	Bacon, Peggy	40-65	
Bacon, Peggy	Magic Touch (1st {std}, 8vo, 112p, b/w, DJ/3.95)	Little/Brown	(1968)	Bacon, Peggy	45-70	
Bacon, Peggy	Mercy and the Mouse (1st, 8vo, pink cl, 85p, 7pl, cep)	Macmillan	1928	Bacon, Peggy	50-80	*
Smith, Linell	Miranda & the Cat (1st {std}, 8vo, ipcb, 43p, b/w, DJ/2.75)	Little/Brown	(1963)	Bacon, Peggy	30-50	
Bacon, Peggy	Mischief in Mayfield (1st {std}, lg8vo, 177p, 15pl)	Harcourt	(1933)	Bacon, Peggy	60-100	
Lowrey, Janette S.	Mr. Heff & Mr. Ho (1st, 8vo, 148p, fp b/w, DJ/2.50)	Harper	(1952)	Bacon, Peggy	25-40	
Alexander, Lloyd C.	My Five Tigers (1st, 8vo, 118p, green cl, fp b/w, DJ/3.00)	Crowell	(1956)	Bacon, Peggy	30-50	
Bacon, Peggy	Mystery at East Hatchett (1st, 8vo, 170p, b/w, DJ/2.00)	Viking	1939	Bacon, Peggy	60-90	
Lockridge, Frances	Nameless Cat (1st {std}, 8vo, 78p, green cl, b/w, DJ/2.25)	Lippincott	(1954)	Bacon, Peggy	30-50	*
Untermeyer, Louis	New Songs for New Voices (1st, lg4to, 258p, b/w, pep)	Harcourt	(1928)	Bacon, Peggy	30-50	*
Govan, Christine	Number 5 Hackberry Street (1st {std}, 8vo, 187p, b/w, DJ/3.50)	World	(1964)	Bacon, Peggy	30-50	
Bacon, Peggy	Off With Their Heads! (1st {std}, lg4to, ibds, [89]p, b/w)	McBride	(1934)	Bacon, Peggy	60-100	
Runbeck, Margaret	Our Miss Boo (1st, 8vo, 226p, b/w, DJ/2.00)	Appleton-Century	1942	Bacon, Peggy	30-50	
Van Sinderen, Adrian	Peter Makebelieve (1st, lg8vo, 65p, 5 fp color)	Yale U. Press	1945	Bacon, Peggy	50-85	
Byars, Betsy C.	Rama, the Gypsy Cat (1st, 8vo, 109p, fp b/w, DJ/3.50)	Viking	1966	Bacon, Peggy	30-45	
Govan, Christine	Return to Hackberry Street (1st {std}, 8vo, 159p, b/w, DJ/3.95)	World	(1967)	Bacon, Peggy	25-40	
Sandburg, Carl	Rootabaga Country (1st, 4to, 259p, col frn, 16 b/w, pep)	Harcourt	(1929)	Bacon, Peggy	80-125	
Koenig, Richard	Seven Special Cats (1st {std}, 8vo, 57p, orange cl, b/w, DJ/2.75)	World	(1961)	Bacon, Peggy	30-50	
Bacon, Peggy	Starting from Scratch (1st {spiral}, [48]p, ibds, b/w, DJ/3.00)	J. Messner	1945	Bacon, Peggy	60-90	
Bacon, Peggy	Terrible Nuisance (1st {std}, 8vo, 142p, blue cl, 8pl, DJ/2.50)	Harcourt	(1931)	Bacon, Peggy	70-120	R
Bacon, Peggy	The Oddity (1st, 8vo, 71p, b/w, DJ/3.00)	Pantheon	(1962)	Bacon, Peggy	30-50	
Zistel, Era (comp)	Treasury of Cat Stories (1st, sm8vo, grey cl, 278p, 12pl, DJ/2.75)	Greenberg	(1944)	Bacon, Peggy	50-80	
Quigg, Jane	Trolling with Susie Bennett (1st {std}, 8vo, ibds, 28p, b/w, DJ/2.25)	Macmillan	1961	Bacon, Peggy	30-45	
Bacon, Peggy	True Philosopher (1st, 12mo, blue cl, 55p, 13pl)	Bos: Four Seas	1919	Bacon, Peggy	80-130	
McNulty, Faith	Wholly Cats (1st {std}, 8vo, 208p, b/w, DJ/3.50)	Bobbs-Merrill	(1962)	Bacon, Peggy	25-40	
Lefferts, Sara T.	Mr. Cinnamon Bear (1st, sq16mo, ibds, [47]p, color)	Bassette Co.	(1907)	Bacquet, Louise	120-200	
Baer, Howard	Now This, Now That (1st, ob4to, [30]p, tan cl, b/w, cep, DJ/2.25)	Holiday House	1957	Baer, Howard	30-50	
Baylor, Byrd	Before You Came this Way (1st {std}, 4to, [32]p, 1-color, DJ/4.75)	Dutton	(1969)	Bahti, Tom	40-65	
Wetmore, Claude H.	Bedtime Stories (1st, 4to, p-o, 120p, color)	Macaulay	1914	Bailey, Mildred L.	75-100	*
Wetmore, Claude H.	Queen Tiny's Little People (1st, 4to, 105p, p-o, color)	Macaulay	1914	Bailey, Mildred L.	75-100	*
Hewson, Isabel	Land of the Lost (1st, 4to, ibds, 60p, color, DJ/2.00)	Whittlesey	(1945)	Bailey, Olive	70-120	*
Eager, Edward	Mouse Manor (1st {std} 8vo, [57]p, 10 fp color, pep, DJ/2.00)	Ariel	(1952)	Bailey-Jones, Beryl	120-200	
Baker, Charlotte	Green Poodles (1st, 8vo, 218p, b/w, DJ/3.00)	McKay	(1956)	Baker, Charlotte	45-70	*
Baker, Charlotte	Nellie and the Mayor's Hat (1st, 8vo, 96p, color, pep, DJ/2.50)	Coward	(1947)	Baker, Charlotte	40-65	
Baker, Margaret	Black Cats and the Tinker's Wife (1st, 8vo, 112p, fp silhouettes)	L: Richards	1923	Baker, Mary	50-80	*
Baker, Margaret	Dunderpate (1st, 8vo, [96]p, fp silhouettes, DJ/2.00)	Dodd	1938	Baker, Mary	40-65	
Baker, Margaret	Fifteen Tales for Lively Children (1st AM, 8vo, 144p, b/w, DJ/2.00)	Dodd	1939	Baker, Mary	60-90	*
Baker, Margaret	Lady Arabella's Birthday Party (1st, 8vo, [95]p, silhouettes, pep, DJ/2.00)	Dodd	1940	Baker, Mary	40-65	
Baker, Margaret	Patsy and the Leprechaun (1st, 8vo, [109]p, silhouettes)	Duffield/Green	(1933)	Baker, Mary	40-65	
Baker, Margaret	Puppy Called Spinach (1st, 8vo, [96]p, silhouettes, DJ/2.00)	Dodd	1939	Baker, Mary	40-65	
Baker, Margaret	Three for an Acorn (1st AM, 8vo, [96]p, silhouettes, pep)	Dodd	(1935)	Baker, Mary	25-45	
Potter, Miriam C.	Captain Sandman (1st, 8vo, 233p, uncut, b/w, pep)	Dutton	(1926)	Balcom, Sophia T.	40-70	
Robinson, Mabel L.	Little Lucia's School (1st, 12mo, 138p, fp b/w, pep)	Dutton	(1926)	Balcom, Sophia T.	25-40	*
Singer, Caroline	Ali Lives in Iran (1st, 4to, 71p, color, pep)	Holiday House	1937	Baldridge, Cyrus L.	25-45	*
Singer, Caroline	Boomba Lives in Africa (1st, sm4to, ibds, [64]p, color, pep, DJ/1.75)	Holiday House	1935	Baldridge, Cyrus L.	35-60	
Bontemps, Arna	Chariot in the Sky (1st {std}, 8vo, 234p, b/w, DJ/2.50)	Winston	(1951)	Baldridge, Cyrus L.	80-120	
Seeger, Elizabeth	Five Brothers (1st, 8vo, 300p, b/w, DJ/3.75)	John Day	(1948)	Baldridge, Cyrus L.	25-40	
Allee, Marjorie H.	Great Tradition (1st, 8vo, 205p, uncut, 5cp, DJ/2.00)	Houghton	1937	Baldridge, Cyrus L.	25-40	
Morier, James	Hajji Baba of Ispahan (1st, 4to, 403p, gilt, color, DJ/3.50)	Random	1937	Baldridge, Cyrus L.	40-60	
Singer, Caroline	Half the World is Isfahan (1st, lg4to, ibds, 153p, 6 fp color, pep)	NY: Oxford U.Pr.	1936	Baldridge, Cyrus L.	90-160	R
Dodge, Mary Mapes	Hans Brinker (1st, 8vo, 289p, 10cp, dep)	Grosset/Dunlap	(1945)	Baldridge, Cyrus L.	30-50	
Skariatina, Irina	Little Era in Old Russia (1st {std}, 8vo, 392p, b/w, pep)	Bobbs-Merrill	(1934)	Baldridge, Cyrus L.	30-50	*
Davis, Robert	Pepperfoot of Thursday Market (1st, sm8vo, 187p, b/w, pep, DJ/2.00)	Holiday House	(1941)	Baldridge, Cyrus L.	35-60	R
Singer, Caroline	Santa Claus Comes to America (1st {std}, 4to, [32]p, ibds, color, DJ/1.00)	Knopf	1942	Baldridge, Cyrus L.	40-70	
Burglon, Nora	Shark Hole (1st, sm8vo, 244p, fp b/w, DJ/2.25)	Holiday House	(1943)	Baldridge, Cyrus L.	25-45	
Cooper, James F.	The Spy (1st, lg8vo, blue cl, 389p, p-o, 8cp, pep)	Minton Balch	1924	Baldridge, Cyrus L.	35-60	
Singer, Caroline	Turn to the East (1st, folio, 71p, ipcb, color)	Minton Balch	1926	Baldridge, Cyrus L.	70-120	
James, Neill	White Reindeer (1st, 8vo, 157p, b/w, pep, DJ/1.75)	Scribner	1940	Baldridge, Cyrus L.	25-45	
Balet, Jan B.	Amos and the Moon (1st, 4to, [26]p, ibds, dp color, pep, DJ/2.50)	NY: Oxford U.Pr.	1948	Balet, Jan B.	50-80	R*
Balet, Jan B.	Five Rollatinis (1st {std}, 4to, [24]p, fp color, pep, DJ/3.50)	Lippincott	(1959)	Balet, Jan B.	60-90	R*
Balet, Jan B.	Joanjo (1st, lg ob4to, [31]p, color, DJ/4.50)	Delacorte Pr.	(1967)	Balet, Jan B.	45-70	
Balet, Jan B.	King and the Broom Maker (1st, 4to, [23]p, fp color, DJ/4.50)	Delacorte Pr.	(1968)	Balet, Jan B.	30-50	
Selden, George	Mice, the Monks & the Christmas Tree (1st {std}, 8vo, 31p, color, DJ/2.95)	Macmillan	1963	Balet, Jan B.	40-65	
Balet, Jan B.	Ned and Ed and the Lion (1st, 4to, [28]p, ibds, color, pep, DJ/2.50)	Oxford U. Pr.	1949	Balet, Jan B.	40-70	

AUTHOR	TITLE	PUBLISHER	DATE	ARTIST	PRICE	LC
Balet, Jan B.	The Fence (1st {std}, 4to, [26]p, color, DJ/4.50)	Delacorte Pr.	(1969)	Balet, Jan B.	30-45	*
Omar Khayyam	Rubaiyat of Omar Khayyam (1st, 4to, bds, p-o, 6 ticp, 32 tipl)	L: Constable	1920	Balfour, Ronald E.	350-500	
Omar Khayyam	Rubaiyat of Omar Khayyam (1st AM, 4to, p-o, gilt, 6 ticp, 32 tipl)	Dodd	[1920]	Balfour, Ronald E.	320-425	
Raymond, Walter	Rebels of the New South (1st, sm8vo, 294p, 5pl)	C.H. Kerr	1905	Ball, Percy B.	60-95	
Brink, Carol R.	Lad with a Whistle (1st, 8vo, 235p, fp b/w, pep, DJ/2.00)	Macmillan	1941	Ball, Robert	30-50	
Schneider, Herman	Let's Look Under the City (1st, sm8vo, grey cl, 70p, 1-color, DJ/2.00)	W.R. Scott	(1954)	Ballantine, Bill	25-45	
Sage, Juniper	Man in the Manhole & Fix-It-Men (1st, lg8vo, ipcb, [40]p, color, DJ/1.50)	W.R. Scott	1946	Ballantine, Bill	30-50	
Schneider, Herman	Now Try This (1st, sm4to, ibds, 40p, 1-color, DJ/1.50)	W.R. Scott	(1947)	Ballantine, Bill	30-50	
Ballantyne, R.M.	Kitten Pilgrims (1st, lg8vo, ibds, 70p, color)	L: J. Nesbit	1882	Ballantyne, R.M.	80-140	
Meader, Stephen W.	Away to Sea (1st, 8vo, 233p, 9pl, DJ/2.50)	Harcourt	(1931)	Balmer, Clinton	70-120	
Sawyer, Ruth	Leerie (1st, 12mo, 309p, 4pl)	Harper	(1920)	Balmer, Clinton	30-50	
Bannerman, Helen	Little Black Bobtail (1st AM, 16mo, bds, 115p, p-o, 27cp)	Stokes	(1909)	Bannerman, Helen	200-300	
Bannerman, Helen	Little Black Mingo (1st, 16mo, 143p, green cl, color)	L: J. Nisbet	(1901)	Bannerman, Helen	300-500	
Bannerman, Helen	Little Black Mingo (1st AM, 16mo, ibds, 144p, color)	Stokes	(1902)	Bannerman, Helen	280-400	
Bannerman, Helen	Little Black Quasha (1st AM, 16mo, 110p, cp)	Stokes	(1908)	Bannerman, Helen	300-500	
Bannerman, Helen	Little Black Quibba (1st, 16mo, 143p, color)	L: J. Nisbet	(1902)	Bannerman, Helen	500-700	
Bannerman, Helen	Little Black Quibba (1st AM, 16mo, 143p, ibds, p-o, color)	Stokes	1903	Bannerman, Helen	350-500	
Bannerman, Helen	Little Black Sambo (1st, 16mo, green cl, 57p, 25 fp color)	L: Richards	1899	Bannerman, Helen	5000-8000	
Bannerman, Helen	Little Black Sambo (1st AM, 16mo, tan bds, 56p, fp color)	Stokes	[1901]	Bannerman, Helen	1500-2500	
Bannerman, Helen	Little Black Sambo (1st {large fmt}, sq8vo, AEG, 109p)	L: Richards	1903	Bannerman, Helen	1200-2000	
Bannerman, Helen	Little Black Sambo (1st, 24mo, ibds, 56p, color)	Reilly/Britton	1905	Bannerman, Helen	300-450	
Bannerman, Helen	Little Black Sambo (1st, 16mo, bds, p-o, 64p, color)	Altemus	[1920]	Bannerman, Helen	140-200	
Bannerman, Helen	Little Black Sambo (8vo, 59p, ibds, color)	McKay	(1931)	Bannerman, Helen	90-120	*
Bannerman, Helen	Little Black Sambo (1st {this fmt}, 4to, 59p, blue cl, DJ)	L: Chatto	(1932)	Bannerman, Helen	350-500	
Bannerman, Helen	Little Black Sambo (12mo, 113p, p-o, bds)	L: Chatto	1941	Bannerman, Helen	130-200	
Bannerman, Helen	Little Degchie Head (1st, 16mo, 143p, green cl, p-o, fp color)	L: J. Nisbet	1903	Bannerman, Helen	400-600	
Bannerman, Helen	Little Kettle-Head (1st AM, 16mo, 144p, ibds, col frn, cp)	Stokes	1904	Bannerman, Helen	350-500	
Bannerman, Helen	Pat and the Spider (1st, 16mo, 143p, fp color)	L: J. Nisbet	(1904)	Bannerman, Helen	350-500	
Bannerman, Helen	Pat and the Spider (1st AM, 16mo, ipcb, 143p, color)	Stokes	(1905)	Bannerman, Helen	250-400	
Bannerman, Helen	Sambo and the Twins (1st, 16mo, 92p, red cl, color, DJ/1.00)	Stokes	1936	Bannerman, Helen	200-300	
Bannerman, Helen	Sambo and the Twins (16mo, green bds, 90p, color, pep)	L: Nisbet	[1937]	Bannerman, Helen	120-200	
Bannerman, Helen	Story of the Teasing Monkey (1st AM, 16mo, 142p, cp)	Stokes	(1907)	Bannerman, Helen	300-425	*
Bannon, Laura	Baby Roo (1st, 8vo, 28p, b/w, pep, DJ/1.50)	Houghton	1947	Bannon, Laura	30-50	*
Bannon, Laura	Big Brother (1st, 4to, 48p, color, pep, DJ/2.50)	Whitman	1950	Bannon, Laura	35-50	*
Bannon, Laura	Billy and the Bear (1st, 4to, 47p, fp color, pep, DJ/2.50)	Houghton	1949	Bannon, Laura	30-50	
Bannon, Laura	Burro Boy and his Big Trouble (1st {A}, 8vo, 48p, b/w, pep, DJ/1.50)	Abingdon Press	(1955)	Bannon, Laura	20-35	
Lee, Melicent	Chang Chee (1st {std}, 8vo, 137p, b/w, pep, DJ/1.50)	Harper	1939	Bannon, Laura	40-65	*
Bannon, Laura	Famous Baby-Sitter (1st, 8vo, 47p, p-o, color, DJ/2.75)	Whitman	(1960)	Bannon, Laura	30-45	
Bannon, Laura	Gregorio & the White Llama (1st, lg8vo, 44p, pep, p-o, color, DJ/2.00)	Whitman	1944	Bannon, Laura	30-50	
Bannon, Laura	Hawaiian Coffee Picker (1st {std}, lg8vo, 48p, color, DJ/3.00)	Houghton	1962	Bannon, Laura	30-50	
Bannon, Laura	Hop-High, the Goat (1st {std}, 8vo, 64p, color, DJ/3.25)	Bobbs-Merrill	(1960)	Bannon, Laura	20-30	
Bannon, Laura	Horse on a Houseboat (1st, 8vo, 94p, pep, b/w, DJ/2.50)	Whitman	(1951)	Bannon, Laura	25-40	
Bannon, Laura	Katy Comes Next (1st, sq8vo, 47p, color, DJ/2.75)	Whitman	(1959)	Bannon, Laura	30-45	
Bannon, Laura	Little People of the Night (1st, 8vo, 31p, DJ/2.75)	Houghton	1963	Bannon, Laura	25-40	
Bannon, Laura	Little Sister Doll (1st, lg8vo, p-o, 30p, fp color, cep, DJ/2.00)	Whitman	(1955)	Bannon, Laura	30-45	*
Bannon, Laura	Manuela's Birthday in Old Mexico (1st, sq4to, 46p, p-o color, pep, DJ/2.00)	Whitman	1939	Bannon, Laura	40-60	
Bannon, Laura	Patty Paints a Picture (1st, lg sq8vo, [48]p, p-o, color, pep, DJ/2.00)	Whitman	1946	Bannon, Laura	40-65	
Bowman, James C.	Pecos Bill (1st, lg8vo, 296p, 6cp, 15pl, pep, DJ/2.50, NH)	Whitman	1937	Bannon, Laura	100-165	
Wood, Esther	Pepper Moon (1st {std}, 4to, 32p, 2-color, DJ/2.00)	Longmans	(1940)	Bannon, Laura	40-65	*
Norton, Alice	Rogue Reynard (1st, lg8vo, 96p, b/w, pep, DJ/2.50)	Houghton	1947	Bannon, Laura	150-220	
Bannon, Laura	Scary Thing (1st, sm8vo, 28p, b/w, DJ/2.00)	Houghton	1956	Bannon, Laura	30-50	
Bowman, James C.	Tales from a Finnish Tupa (1st, 8vo, grey cl, 273p, pep, 6cp, DJ)	Whitman	1936	Bannon, Laura	100-165	
McElravy, May F.	Tortilla Girl (1st, sm4to, 26p, p-o, 46p, pep, color, DJ/1.25)	Whitman	1946	Bannon, Laura	40-65	
Bannon, Laura	Watchdog (1st, 4to, [48]p, p-o, fp color, pep, DJ/2.50)	Whitman	1948	Bannon, Laura	40-65	
Bannon, Laura	When the Moon is New (1st, sq8vo, [48]p, color, pep, DJ/2.75)	Whitman	(1953)	Bannon, Laura	30-50	
Bannon, Laura	Whistle for a Pilot (1st, 8vo, 48p, fp, color, pep, DJ/3.00)	Houghton	1959	Bannon, Laura	20-30	
Bannon, Laura	Wonderful Fashion Doll (1st, 8vo, 86p, color, pep, DJ/2.25)	Houghton	1953	Bannon, Laura	200-300	
Morgenstern, Eliz.	Little Gardeners (1st AM, sm sq4to, 14p, p-o, color)	Whitman	1933	Bantzer, Marigard	60-90	*
Barnes, Nancy	Carlota (1st, 8vo, spiral-bound, 214p, uncut, b/w pl, DJ/2.75)	J. Messner	(1943)	Barber, John	25-40	
O'Neill, Mary	Ali (1st {std}, lg8vo, 122p, b/w, DJ/3.95)	Atheneum	1968	Barberis, Juan	20-30	*
DeSeyn, Donna E.	Termite Works for his Colony (1st, 8vo, 47p, fp 3-color, cep, DJ/2.95)	Holiday House	(1967)	Barberis, Juan	25-40	*
LeGallienne, R.	Romance of Perfume (1st, sm4to, 46p, ipcb, 8cp)	R. Hadnut	1928	Barbier, George	75-120	
Perez-Guerra, A.	Poppy, Adventures of a Fairy (12mo, [62]p, ibds, 16 color)	Rand/McNally	(1942)	Barclay, Betsy	40-60	*
Grimm Bros.	Golden Goose (1st, sm8vo, 23p, tan cl, 2-color, pep, DJ/1.00)	Houghton	1947	Bare, Arnold E.	60-100	
Kingman, Lee	Ilenka (1st, 4to, red cl, [48]p, color, pep, DJ/2.00)	Houghton/JLG	1945	Bare, Arnold E.	45-70	
Bare, Arnold E.	Maui's Summer (1st, 4to, yellow cl, [48]p, color, pep, DJ/2.50)	Houghton	1952	Bare, Arnold E.	45-70	
Kingman, Lee	Mikko's Fortune (1st {std}, sm ob4to, blue cl, 46p, color, pep, DJ/2.75)	Ariel	(1955)	Bare, Arnold E.	50-80	
Heath, Janet F.	Mooky & Tooky (1st, lg8vo, ipcb, [45]p, 1-color, pep, DJ/1.50)	Howell/Soskin	(1946)	Bare, Arnold E.	30-50	
Colby, Jean P.	Peter Paints the U.S.A. (1st, 4to, 47p, red cl, color, pep, DJ/2.50)	Houghton	1948	Bare, Arnold E.	40-65	
Kingman, Lee	Pierre Pidgeon (1st, 4to, [48]p, color, DJ/2.00, CH)	Houghton	1943	Bare, Arnold E.	70-120	
Mitchell, Edmund	Chickabiddy Stories (1st, 8vo, 150p, p-o, 4 ticp)	L: Wells/Gard.	(1899)	Barham, Sybil	100-165	
Baring, Maurice	Glass Mender (1st, 8vo, blue cl, 260p, teg, 12cp)	L: J. Nisbet	1910	Baring, Maurice	60-95	
Bates, Herbert E.	Achilles the Donkey (1st AM, 4to, [41]p, color, pep, DJ/3.95)	F. Watts	(1963)	Barker, Carol	30-50	
Godden, Rumer	Kitchen Madonna (1st AM, 8vo, 89p, ibds, 6 fp color, cep, DJ/3.75)	Viking	(1967)	Barker, Carol	25-45	
Watts, Mabel	Light Across Piney Valley (1st, sm4to, [42]p, fp color, DJ/2.95)	Abelard-Schuman	1965	Barker, Carol	25-40	*
Linnell, Olive	Autumn Songs with Music (4to, bds, p-o, 12 ticp)	L: Blackie	[1920]	Barker, Cicely M.	130-200	
Barker, Cicely M.	Book of Flower Fairies (1st, 8vo, green/gilt, 92p, color)	L: Blackie	(1927)	Barker, Cicely M.	220-300	
Westcott, M.K.	Child Thoughts in Picture and Verse (1st, 16mo, 64p, ibds, 8cp)	L: Blackie	(1925)	Barker, Cicely M.	60-90	

AUTHOR	TITLE	PUBLISHER	DATE	ARTIST	PRICE	LC
Barker, Cicely M.	Children's Book of Hymns (1st, lg8vo, blue/gilt, 84p, 12 ticp)	L: Blackie	[1929]	Barker, Cicely M.	80-120	
Barker, Cicely M.	Fairies of the Trees (16mo, ibds, p-o, unpag, fp color, pep)	L: Blackie	(1940)	Barker, Cicely M.	150-250	
Barker, Cicely M.	Flower Fairies of Autumn (12mo, ibds, p-o, 24cp)	L: Blackie	[1927]	Barker, Cicely M.	120-200	
Barker, Cicely M.	Flower Fairies of Spring (12mo, bds, p-o, 24cp)	L: Blackie	[1925]	Barker, Cicely M.	120-200	
Barker, Cicely M.	Flower Fairies of Summer (1st, 12mo, 25p, 24cp)	L: Blackie	[1923]	Barker, Cicely M.	120-200	
Barker, Cicely M.	Flower Fairy Alphabet (1st, 12mo, 24p, brown bds, p-o, 24cp)	L: Blackie	(1934)	Barker, Cicely M.	120-200	
Barker, Cicely M.	Flower Songs of the Seasons (1st, lg8vo, ibds, p-o, 12 ticp)	L: Blackie	[1928]	Barker, Cicely M.	100-165	
Barker, Cecily M.	Groundsel and Necklaces (1st, 16mo, p-o, 48p, 12cp, pep)	L: Blackie	[1946]	Barker, Cicely M.	50-85	
Barker, Dorothy O.	He Leadeth Me (1st AM, 8vo, 256p, gilt, 16cp, DJ/2.00)	NY: M.S. Mill	[1938]	Barker, Cicely M.	60-90	
Barker, Cicely M.	Spring Songs with Music (4to, ibds, p-o, 12 ticp)	L: Blackie	[1918]	Barker, Cicely M.	200-300	
Linnell, Olive	Spring Songs with Music (4to, bds, p-o, 12 ticp)	L: Blackie	[1920]	Barker, Cicely M.	120-200	
Barker, Cicely M.	Summer Songs with Music (4to, bds, p-o, 12 ticp)	L: Blackie	[1920]	Barker, Cicely M.	200-300	
Stern, Gladys B.	Ugly Dachshund (1st, 8vo, 132p, b/w, DJ/1.75)	Macmillan	1938	Barker, Kathleen F.	30-50	
Yates, Elizabeth	On That Night (1st {std}, 12mo, 95p, ibds, gilt, b/w, DJ/3.95)	Dutton	1969	Barkley, James	20-30	
Armstrong, William	Sounder (1st, 8vo, 116p, grey cl, fp b/w, cep, DJ/3.95, NM)	Harper, Row	(1969)	Barkley, James	120-200	R
O'Neill, Mary	Winds (1st {std}, ob8vo, [64]p, fp color, DJ/5.95)	Doubleday	1970	Barkley, James	30-45	
Lauber, Patricia	Runaway Flea Circus (1st {std}, 8vo, 72p, 1-color, DJ/1.95)	Random	(1958)	Barnes, Catherine	20-35	
Jewett, John H.	Bunny Stories (1st, sq8vo, 210p, b/w)	Stokes	1892	Barnes, Culmer	70-100	
Babcock, William H.	Cian of the Chariots (1st, sm8vo, 406p, b/w pl, gilt)	Lothrop Pub.	1898	Barnes, George F.	70-100	
Wilkins, Mary E.	Decorative Plaques (1st, sq12mo, [32]p, ibds, designs by...)	D. Lothrop Co.	(1883)	Barnes, George F.	425-600	
Molesworth, Mrs.	Bewitched Lamp (1st, 12mo, 128p, frn by...)	L: Chambers	1891	Barnes, Robert	40-70	*
Molesworth, Mrs.	Olivia (1st, 12mo, 456p, 8pl)	L: Chambers	1895	Barnes, Robert	35-60	
Grey, Sydney	Story-Land (sq8vo, 111p, ibds, 32 color)	L: R.T.S.	(1884)	Barnes, Robert	100-145	
Nelson, Mary J.	Fun with Music (1st, sm4to, 47p, color, DJ/1.50)	Whitman	1941	Barnett, G.& O.	30-45	
Hopkins, Lee B. (comp)	City Spreads its Wings (1st, 4to, 46p, fp 2-color, DJ/4.95)	F. Watts	(1970)	Barnett, Moneta	30-50	
Elting, Mary	Mongo Homecoming (1st {std}, lg8vo, 54p, fp 1-color, DJ/3.95)	M. Evans	(1969)	Barnett, Moneta	30-45	*
Van Leeuwen, Jean	Timothy's Flower (1st, ob4to, pcb, gilt, [44]p, fp color, cep, DJ/3.50)	Random	(1967)	Barnett, Moneta	30-50	
Phillips, Ethel C.	Calico (1st, 8vo, 139p, col frn, b/w, DJ/2.00)	Houghton	1937	Barney, Maginel W.	40-65	
Snedeker, Caroline D.	Downright Dencey (1st {std}, 8vo, 314p, col frn, pep, NH)	Doubleday/Doran	1927	Barney, Maginel W.	60-90	
Lefevre, Felicite	Fiddle Diddle Dee (1st, sm8vo, orange cl, [63]p, fp color, pep)	Greenberg	(1928)	Barney, Maginel W.	70-130	
Willson, Dixie	Honey Bear (1st, sm8vo, ibds, [36]p, color)	Volland	(1923)	Barney, Maginel W.	70-100	
Porter, Laura S.	Little Long Ago (1st, 8vo, 470p, b/w, pep)	Dutton	1927	Barney, Maginel W.	30-50	*
Bancroft, Alberta	Lost Village (1st, 8vo, 130p, green cl, 4 fp color)	Doran	(1927)	Barney, Maginel W.	55-80	
Muter, Gladys N.	Mother Let Me Do It (1st {std}, 12mo, ibds, [36]p, color)	Volland	(1925)	Barney, Maginel W.	55-80	*
Broughton, Philip	Pandy (1st, 12mo, ibds, 40p, 5 fp color, pep)	Volland	(1930)	Barney, Maginel W.	60-90	
Kyle, Anne D.	Prince of the Pale Mountains (1st, sm8vo, 250p, col frn, pep)	Houghton	1929	Barney, Maginel W.	30-50	*
Phillips, Ethel C.	Pyxie, Little Boy of the Pines (1st, 8vo, 164p, fp color, pep)	Houghton	1932	Barney, Maginel W.	30-50	
DeSegur, Sophie	Sophie, Story of a Bad Little Girl (1st, sm8vo, 157p, b/w, dep)	Knopf	1929	Barney, Maginel W.	25-45	*
Sawyer, Ruth	This Way to Christmas (1st, lg8vo, ibds, 175p, 10cp, pep)	Harper	1924	Barney, Maginel W.	90-145	
Barney, Maginel W.	Weather Signs & Rhymes (1st {std}, sq8vo, yellow cl, [103]p, 1-color, pep)	Knopf	1931	Barney, Maginel W.	80-125	
Thacher, Lucy W.	Listening Child (1st, sm8vo, 405p, blue cl, col frn, 11pl, pep)	Macmillan	1924	Barnhart, Nancy	40-65	
Bible	Lord is My Shepherd (1st, 4to, 263p, gilt, b/w, DJ/4.50)	Scribner	1949	Barnhart, Nancy	40-65	
Grahame, Kenneth	Wind in the Willows (1st, 8vo, gilt, 302p, p-o, 12cp, pep)	Scribner	1922	Barnhart, Nancy	120-180	
Brier, Howard M.	Backboard Magic (1st {std}, 8vo, 275p, fp b/w, DJ/2.50)	Random	(1949)	Barnum, Jay H.	40-65	
Flack, Marjorie	Boats on the River (1st, lg ob4to, ibds, color, DJ/2.50, CH)	Viking	1946	Barnum, Jay H.	130-200	R
Tunis, John R.	Buddy and the Old Pro (1st, 8vo, 189p, b/w, DJ/2.50)	Wm. Morrow	1955	Barnum, Jay H.	50-85	*
Tunis, John R.	Champion's Choice (1st, 8vo, 300p, fp b/w, DJ/2.00)	Harcourt	(1940)	Barnum, Jay H.	20-35	
Thayer, Jane	Charley and the New Car (1st, 8vo, 48p, 2-color, pep, DJ/2.25)	Wm. Morrow	1957	Barnum, Jay H.	25-45	
Thayer, Jane	Horse with the Easter Bonnet (1st, 8vo, 48p, 2-color, DJ/2.00)	Wm. Morrow	1953	Barnum, Jay H.	25-45	
Tunis, John R.	Kid from Tomkinsville (1st, 8vo, 355p, fp b/w, DJ/2.00)	Harcourt	(1940)	Barnum, Jay H.	20-35	
Schneider, E.B. (adap)	King Arthur & Knights of Roundtable (1st, 4to ibds unpag, col, pep DJ/1.00)	Random	1954	Barnum, Jay H.	30-50	
Malkus, Alida S.	Little Giant of the North (1st {std}, 8vo, 178p, b/w, pep, DJ/1.50)	Winston	(1952)	Barnum, Jay H.	25-40	
Barnum, Jay H.	Little Old Truck (1st, 8vo, 46p, blue cl, color, pep, DJ/2.00)	Wm. Morrow	1953	Barnum, Jay H.	40-65	
Sawyer, Ruth	Little Red Horse (1st, 8vo, 108p, brown cl, pep, color, DJ/2.50)	Viking	1950	Barnum, Jay H.	50-80	
Barnum, Jay H.	Motorcycle Dog (1st, 8vo, blue cl, 48p, 2-color, DJ/2.50)	Wm. Morrow	1958	Barnum, Jay H.	40-65	
Jewett, Eleanore	Mystery at Boulder Point (1st, 8vo, 281p, grey cl, fp b/w, DJ/2.50)	Viking	1949	Barnum, Jay H.	30-55	
Barnum, Jay H.	New Fire Engine (1st, 8vo, red cl, 47p, 2-color, pep, DJ/2.00)	Wm. Morrow	1952	Barnum, Jay H.	40-65	
Martin, Charles M.	Orphans of the Range (1st, 8vo, 192p, blue cl, fp b/w, DJ/2.00)	Viking	1950	Barnum, Jay H.	30-50	
Thayer, Jane	Popcorn Dragon (1st, 8vo, 48p, 3-color, DJ/2.00)	Wm. Morrow	1953	Barnum, Jay H.	30-50	
White, Robb	Secret Sea (1st {std}, 8vo, 243p, fp b/w, pep, DJ/2.00)	Doubleday	1947	Barnum, Jay H.	30-50	*
Carmer, Carl	Too Many Cherries (1st, 4to, 62p, ipcb, 2-color, pep, DJ/2.00)	Viking	1949	Barnum, Jay H.	45-70	
Brown, Gladys	Two-Bow Bill (1st, 8vo, 46p, blue cl, color, pep, DJ/2.00)	Wm. Morrow	1955	Barnum, Jay H.	40-65	
Carden, Priscilla	Vanilla Village (1st {std}, lg8vo, 58p, tan cl, pep, color, DJ/2.00)	Ariel	(1952)	Barnum, Jay H.	30-50	
Tunis, John R.	World Series (1st, sm8vo, 318p, blue cl, 24pl, pep, DJ/2.00)	Harcourt	(1941)	Barnum, Jay H.	30-50	
Barr, Catherine	Raffie (1st, 8vo, 32p, rust cl, 1-color, DJ/3.00)	H.Z. Walck	1968	Barr, Catherine	25-45	
Fox, Frances M.	Betty of Mackinaw (1st, 12mo, 109p, b/w)	L.C. Page	1901	Barry, Etheldred B.	25-40	*
Raymond, Evelyn	Boys & Girls of Brantham (1st, sm8vo, 283p, grey/gilt, 6pl)	Little/Brown	1899	Barry, Etheldred B.	30-50	*
Stevenson, Rbt. L.	Child's Garden of Verses (1st, 12mo, 107p, b/w)	L.C. Page	1900	Barry, Etheldred B.	30-50	*
Fox, Frances M.	County Christmas (1st, 12mo, 111p, 10pl)	L.C. Page	1907	Barry, Etheldred B.	25-45	*
Ewing, Juliana H.	Daddy Darwin's Dovecot (1st, 12mo, 78p, grey cl, 6pl)	Dana Estes	1898	Barry, Etheldred B.	35-60	*
Ewing, Juliana H.	Great Emergency (1st, 12mo, 166p, b/w pl)	L.C. Page	1897	Barry, Etheldred B.	30-50	*
Johnston, Annie F.	Little Colonel (1st, 12mo, 102p, green/gilt, b/w, PPP)	J. Knight	1896	Barry, Etheldred B.	180-260	R
Johnston, Annie F.	Little Colonel's Knight Comes Riding (1st, 8vo, 307p, 8pl)	L.C. Page	1907	Barry, Etheldred B.	40-65	
Cheever, Harriet A.	Little Mr. Van Vere of China (1st, sm8vo, 243p, col frn, b/w)	Estes & Lauriat	(1898)	Barry, Etheldred B.	40-60	*
Johnston, Annie F.	May Ware, Little Colonel's Chum (1st, sm8vo, 305p, tan cl, 8pl)	L.C. Page	1908	Barry, Etheldred B.	30-50	
Brainerd, Edna S.	Millicent in Dreamland (1st, 12mo, 94p, p-o, b/w)	L.C. Page	1902	Barry, Etheldred B.	25-40	
Fox, Frances M.	Mother Nature's Little Ones (1st, 12mo, 92p, fp b/w)	L.C. Page	1904	Barry, Etheldred B.	25-40	*
Saunders, Marshall	Nita (1st, 12mo, 77p, b/w)	L.C. Page	1904	Barry, Etheldred B.	25-40	*

AUTHOR	TITLE	PUBLISHER	DATE	ARTIST	PRICE	LC
Richards, Laura E.	Peggy (1st, 12mo, 308p, 8pl)	Dana Estes	(1899)	Barry, Etheldred B.	25-40	
Potter, Mary K.	Peggy's Trial (1st, 12mo, 97p, b/w)	L.C. Page	1901	Barry, Etheldred B.	25-45	
Fox, Frances M.	Seven Christmas Candles (1st, sm8vo, 192p, green cl, 6cp, pep)	L.C. Page	1909	Barry, Etheldred B.	45-70	
Johnston, Annie F.	Story of Dago (1st, 12mo, 101p, 10pl)	L.C. Page	1900	Barry, Etheldred B.	40-65	
Harland, Marion	When Grandmamma Was 14 (1st, sm8vo, 399p, 4pl)	Lothrop Pub.	1905	Barry, Etheldred B.	25-40	*
Barry, Katharina	'A' is for Anything (1st {std}, ob12mo, [55]p, fp 2-color, DJ/2.50)	World	(1961)	Barry, Katharina	40-70	R*
Barry, Robert E.	Faint George Who Wanted to be a Knight (1st, ob4to, 32p, 1-color, DJ/2.50)	Houghton	1957	Barry, Robert E.	40-65	
Means, Florence C.	Alicia (1st, 8vo, 266p, b/w, DJ/2.75)	Houghton	1953	Barss, William	20-30	
Walker, Barbara	Hilili and Dilili (1st, 4to, 32p, fp color, DJ/2.95)	Follett	(1965)	Barss, William	30-45	
Amend, Ottillie	Jolly Jungle Jingles (1st, ob4to, ibds, 30p, color)	Volland	(1929)	Barte, Eleanor	100-170	
Shippen, Kath. B.	Andrew Carnegie & the Age of Steel (1st {std}, 8vo, 183p, b/w, DJ/1.95)	Random	(1958)	Barth, Ernest	20-35	
Frisbie, William A.	ABC Mother Goose (1st, 4to, [52]p, beige cl, color)	Rand/McNally	(1905)	Bartholomew, F.	200-300	
Frisbie, William A.	Pirate Frog (1st, 4to, [94]p, ibds, color)	Rand/McNally	(1901)	Bartholomew, F.	150-220	
Salten, Felix	Bambi's Children (1st, 8vo, [41]p, ipcb, color)	Wonder Books	(1951)	Bartlett, William	20-30	
Barto, Emily N.	Chubby Bear (1st {std}, 16mo, [36]p, b/w, pep, DJ/0.85)	Longmans	(1941)	Barto, Emily N.	40-65	*
Mother Goose	Crooked Man (1st {std}, 12mo, [56]p, fp 1-color, pep)	Longmans	(1940)	Barto, Emily N.	30-45	
Mother Goose	Piper's Son (1st {std}, 16mo, blue cl, [56]p, fp b/w, pep, DJ/0.85)	Longmans	(1942)	Barto, Emily N.	40-65	
Greene, Constance	Girl Called Al (1st, 8vo, 127p, fp b/w, DJ/3.95)	Viking	(1969)	Barton, Byron	20-35	*
Marshall, Archibald	Peggy in Toyland (1st, 8vo, ipcb, 277p, b/w, pep)	Dodd	1920	Barton, Helen M.	40-60	*
Gray, Eliz. J.	Beppy Marlowe of Charles Town (1st, 8vo, 281p, color, pep, DJ/2.00)	Viking	1936	Barton, Loren	30-50	*
Weil, Ann Y.	Pussycat's Breakfast (1st, ob8vo, ibds, [47]p, color, DJ/1.25)	Greenberg	(1944)	Barton, Mary	20-35	*
Bascom, Louise R.	Bugaboo Men (1st, sq4to, green cl, [72]p, pep, color)	Sully/Kleinteich	(1914)	Bascom, Louise R.	100-165	*
Reit, Seymour	Round Things Everywhere (1st, 4to, [32]p, DJ, color photos by...)	McGraw-Hill	(1969)	Basen, Carol	30-50	
Baskin, Esther	Creatures of Darkness (1st {std}, 4to, [48]p, b/w, DJ/4.75)	Little/Brown	(1962)	Baskin, Leonard	40-65	
Baskin, Esther	Poppy and other Deadly Plants (1st {std}, 4to, 74p, fp color, DJ/12.50)	Delacorte Pr.	(1967)	Baskin, Leonard	70-100	
Klein, Leonore	Henri's Walk to Paris (1st, 4to, unpag, color, DJ/3.75)	W.R. Scott	(1962)	Bass, Saul	65-100	
Richards, Laura E.	Fairy Operettas (1st, 12mo, 119p, col frn, b/w)	Little/Brown	1916	Bassett, Mary R.	80-135	
Croll, Pauline	Just for You (1st, 12mo, ipcb, 37p, color, pep)	Volland	(1918)	Bassett, Mary R.	50-80	
Baum, L. Frank	Daring Twins (1st [1], sm8vo, blue cl, 317p, 4pl)	Reilly/Britton	(1911)	Batchelder, P.M.	250-350	
N/A	Little Golden Hair & the Three Bears (1st, 16mo, 111p, bds, p-o, fp color)	L: Nisbet	1904	Batchelor, Anne	160-240	
Bate, Norman	Who Built the Bridge? (1st, 4to, [32]p, fp 1-color, DJ/2.50)	Scribner	1954	Bate, Norman	80-130	R
Reed, Langford	Book of Nonsense Verse (1st AM, lg8vo, 159p, 26 b/w, DJ)	Putnam	1926	Bateman, Henry M.	30-50	
Carroll, Lewis	Further Nonsense Verse & Prose (1st, sm4to, 127p, yellow bds, b/w)	L: T.F. Unwin	1926	Bateman, Henry M.	70-100	
Carroll, Lewis	Further Nonsense Verse & Prose (1st AM, 4to, 118p, ipcb, p-o, b/w)	Appleton	1926	Bateman, Henry M.	70-100	
Garten, Jan	Alphabet Tale (1st, ob4to, ipcb, [55]p, fp color, pep, DJ/2.50)	Random	(1964)	Batherman, Muriel	30-50	
Jacobs, Joseph (ed)	Book of Wonder Voyages (1st, 8vo, 224p, uncut, 7pl)	L: D. Nutt	1896	Batten, John D.	180-240	
Jacobs, Joseph (ed)	Celtic Fairy Tales (1st, lg8vo, AEG, 267p, green cl, 8pl)	L: D. Nutt	1892	Batten, John D.	150-225	
Jacobs, Joseph (ed)	English Fairy Tales (1st, 8vo, 253p, AEG, 8pl)	L: D. Nutt	1890	Batten, John D.	120-170	
Jacobs, Joseph (ed)	English Fairy Tales (1st AM, 8vo, 253p, 8pl)	Putnam	1891	Batten, John D.	75-100	
Dixon, E. (ed)	Fairy Tales from Arabian Nights (1st AM, 8vo, 477p, gilt, p-o, col frn)	Putnam	(1893)	Batten, John D.	100-165	
Dixon, E. (ed)	Fairy Tales from Arabian Nights (1st, sm4to, 267p, gilt, teg, 5pl)	L: J.M. Dent	1893	Batten, John D.	120-180	
Dixon, E. (ed)	Fairy Tales from Arabian Nights (1st, 8vo, 477p, col frn, 16pl)	L: J.M. Dent	1907	Batten, John D.	100-175	
Jacobs, Joseph (ed)	Indian Fairy Tales (1st AM, 8vo, 255p, 8pl)	Putnam	1892	Batten, John D.	120-180	
Jacobs, Joseph (ed)	Indian Fairy Tales (1st, 8vo, 255p, uncut, 8pl)	L: D. Nutt	1892	Batten, John D.	120-200	
Hewlett, Maurice	Masque of Dead Florentines (1st, ob8vo, uncut, teg, 51p, 4pl)	L: J.M. Dent	1895	Batten, John D.	90-120	
Jacobs, Joseph (ed)	More Celtic Fairy Tales (1st, 8vo, 234p, 8pl)	L: D. Nutt	1894	Batten, John D.	120-170	
Jacobs, Joseph (ed)	More English Fairy Tales (1st, 8vo, blue cl, 243p, 8pl)	L: D. Nutt	1894	Batten, John D.	80-120	
Dickson, Maidie	Saga of the Sea-Swallow (1st, 8vo, 159p, gilt, teg, 4pl, cep)	A.D. Innes	1896	Batten/Fairbairn	80-140	
Ingold, John	Glimpses from Wonderland (1st, 8vo, 287p, blue/gilt, 5pl)	L: J. Long	1900	Bauerle, Amelia	35-60	*
Riley, James W.	All the Year Round (1st, 4to, gilt, ibds, [30]p, p-o, 12cp)	Bobbs-Merrill	(1912)	Baumann, Gustave	300-450	R
Banning, Kendall	Pirates! (1st {this pub}, 12mo, [31]p, wraps, 13 fp woodcuts)	Chi: Woodworth	1918	Baumann, Gustave	125-200	
Dalgliesh, Alice	Little Wooden Farmer (1st, ob4to, green cl, [43]p, color, pep)	Macmillan	1930	Baumeister, Margaret	40-60	*
Graham, Harry	Deportmental Ditties (1st, 4to, 127p, b/w)	L: Mills & Boon	(1909)	Baumer, Lewis	35-60	
Molesworth, Mrs.	Hermy, Story of a Little Girl (1st, sm8vo, 248p, gilt, 17pl)	L: Chambers	1898	Baumer, Lewis	40-65	
Hay, Ian	Lighter Side of School Life (1st, 8vo, 226p, gilt, uncut, teg, 12cp)	L: Foulis	(1914)	Baumer, Lewis	45-70	
Irving, Washington	Old Christmas (1st, 8vo, gilt, 284p, 8cp)	L: Constable	1918	Baumer, Lewis	55-80	*
Irving, Washington	Old Christmas (1st AM, 8vo, gilt, 284p, 8cp)	Houghton	1919	Baumer, Lewis	35-50	
Irving, Washington	Old Christmas & Bracebridge Hall (8vo, red cl, 285p, 8 color)	L: Constable	1918	Baumer, Lewis	35-60	
Molesworth, Mrs.	Three Witches (1st, 8vo, 278p, blue cl, 14pl)	L: Chambers	1900	Baumer, Lewis	40-60	*
Thackeray, Wm. M.	Vanity Fair (1st, 4to, 483p, p-o, teg, gilt, 20 ticp)	L: Hodder	[1913]	Baumer, Lewis	200-300	
Steele, William O.	Story of Daniel Boone (1st, 8vo, 175p, b/w, DJ/1.50)	Grosset/Dunlap	(1953)	Baumgartner, Warren	20-35	
Lagerlof, Selma	Wonderful Adventures of Nils (1st, lg8vo, 539p, b/w, pep, DJ/5.00)	Pantheon	(1947)	Baumhauer, Hans	30-50	
Paltock, Robert	Life & Adventures of Peter Wilkins (1st, lg8vo, 342p, gilt, 17cp, pep)	Dent/Dutton	1928	Bawden, Edward	100-165	
Andersen, Hans C.	Fairy Tales and Stories (1st, 8vo, blue/gilt, 512p, 4cp)	L: Routledge	1903	Bayes, Alfred W.	90-120	
Larken, Edmund P.	Sea-Prince (1st, 12mo, blue/gilt, teg, 340p, b/w, dep)	L: Jarrold	1899	Bayes, Jessie M.	100-150	
Brink, Carol R.	All Over Town (1st, 8vo, 291p, b/w, pep, DJ/2.00)	Macmillan	1939	Bayley, Dorothy	30-45	
Wheeler, Opal	Giotto Tended the Sheep (1st {std}, 4to, 96p, red cl, 2-color, DJ)	Dutton	(1938)	Bayley, Dorothy	50-80	
Deutsch, Babette	It's a Secret! (1st {std}, sq12mo, 47p, 2-color, pep, DJ/1.00)	Harper	(1941)	Bayley, Dorothy	70-120	R
Worth, Kathryn	Middle Button (1st {std}, 8vo, 275p, pep, DJ/2.00)	Doubleday/Doran	1941	Bayley, Dorothy	75-120	
Wheeler, Opal	Millet Tilled the Soil (1st {std}, 4to, 96p, red cl, 2-color, DJ/2.50)	Dutton	(1939)	Bayley, Dorothy	25-40	
Meigs, Cornelia L.	Vanished Island (1st {std}, 8vo, 258p, b/w, DJ/2.00)	Macmillan	1941	Bayley, Dorothy	25-40	
Ensor, Dorothy	Adventures of Hatim Tai (1st AM {std}, 8vo, 89p, 6cp, DJ/2.75)	H.Z. Walck	1962	Baynes, Pauline	30-45	
Tolkien, J.R.R.	Adventures of Tom Bombadil (1st, 8vo, ibds, 64p, 3-color, DJ)	L: Allen/Unwin	(1962)	Baynes, Pauline	200-300	
N/A	Arabian Nights (1st, 8vo, 348p, 16cp, DJ)	L: Blackie	1957	Baynes, Pauline	40-65	
Uden, Grant	Dictionary of Chivalry (1st, 8vo, 352p, color, DJ, KGM)	L: Longmans	1968	Baynes, Pauline	50-80	*
Tolkien, J.R.R.	Farmer Giles of Ham (1st, 8vo, 78p, orange cl, 2 fp color, pep, DJ)	L: Allen/Unwin	1949	Baynes, Pauline	350-500	
Tolkien, J.R.R.	Farmer Giles of Ham (1st AM {std}, 8vo, blue cl, 79p, color, DJ/2.00)	Houghton	1950	Baynes, Pauline	250-400	
Lewis, C.S.	Horse & his Boy (1st, sm8vo, grey/silver, 199p, b/w, pep, DJ)	L: G. Bles	(1954)	Baynes, Pauline	500-700	

AUTHOR	TITLE	PUBLISHER	DATE	ARTIST	PRICE	LC
Lewis, C.S.	Last Battle (1st, 8vo, blue cl, 184p, b/w, DJ, CgM)	L: G. Bles	1956	Baynes, Pauline	500-700	
Lewis, C.S.	Last Battle (1st AM {std}, sm8vo, 174p, blue cl, b/w, DJ/2.75)	Macmillan	(1956)	Baynes, Pauline	350-500	R
Lewis, C.S.	Lion, the Witch & the Wardrobe (1st AM {std}, 8vo, 154p, b/w, DJ/2.50)	Macmillan	1950	Baynes, Pauline	700-1000	
Lewis, C.S.	Lion, the Witch & the Wardrobe (1st, 8vo, green/silver, col frn, b/w, DJ)	L: G. Bles	(1950)	Baynes, Pauline	900-1300	
Lewis, C.S.	Magician's Nephew (1st, 8vo, 183p, green cl, b/w, DJ)	L: Bodley Head	1955	Baynes, Pauline	800-1000	
Lewis, C.S.	Magician's Nephew (1st AM {std}, sm8vo, 167p, green cl, b/w, DJ/2.75)	Macmillan	(1955)	Baynes, Pauline	700-1000	
Krutch, Joseph W.	Most Wonderful Animals that Never Were (1st {std}, 8vo, 187p, gilt, DJ/3.75)	Houghton	1969	Baynes, Pauline	80-140	
Lewis, C.S.	Prince Caspian (1st, 8vo, 194p, b/w, DJ)	L: G. Bles	(1951)	Baynes, Pauline	600-850	
Lewis, C.S.	Prince Caspian (1st AM {std}, sm8vo, 186p, green cl, 4 fp b/w, DJ/2.50)	Macmillan	1951	Baynes, Pauline	500-700	
Lewis, C.S.	Silver Chair (1st AM {std}, sm8vo, 208p, blue cl, 4 fp b/w, DJ/2.75)	Macmillan	1953	Baynes, Pauline	300-500	
Tolkien, J.R.R.	Smith of Wootton Major (1st AM {std}, 12mo, 62p, b/w, DJ/1.95)	Houghton	1967	Baynes, Pauline	80-125	
Warburg, Sandol (adap)	St. George and the Dragon (1st, lg8vo, 132p, fp 1-color, cep, DJ/4.50)	Houghton	1963	Baynes, Pauline	60-100	R*
Pourrat, Henri	Treasury of French Tales (1st, 8vo, 239p, ibds, fp b/w, DJ/3.00)	Houghton	1954	Baynes, Pauline	30-50	
Morris, James	Upstairs Donkey (1st, 8vo, 126p, b/w, DJ/3.00)	Pantheon	(1961)	Baynes, Pauline	50-80	
Baynes, Pauline	Victoria and the Golden Bird (1st, 8vo, [32]p, ibds, color)	L: Blackie	(1947)	Baynes, Pauline	40-65	
Lewis, C.S.	Voyage of the Dawn Treader (1st, 8vo, 223p, fp b/w, DJ)	L: G. Bles	(1952)	Baynes, Pauline	700-900	
Lewis, C.S.	Voyage of the Dawn Treader (1st AM {std}, sm8vo, 210p, b/w, DJ/2.75)	Macmillan	1952	Baynes, Pauline	500-700	
Steedman, Amy	Apple Pie... (8vo, 111p, AEG, gilt, p-o, 8cp)	L: Jack	[1908]	Beale, Evelyn	30-50	
Sherwood, Mary M.	Fairchild Family (sq8vo, 111p, gilt, p-o, 8cp)	Dutton	(1908)	Beale, Evelyn	55-80	
Bealer, Alex W.	Picture-Skin Story (1st, sq8vo, [27]p, pink cl, color, cep, DJ/2.75)	Holiday House	1957	Bealer, Alex W.	40-65	
N/A	Aladdin (1st, lg8vo, red cl, 39p, 8cp)	L: John Lane	1924	Beaman, S.G.H.	100-165	
N/A	Aladdin (1st AM, sm4to, 39p, 8cp)	McBride	1925	Beaman, S.G.H.	100-150	
Stevenson, Rbt. L.	Dr. Jekyll & Mr. Hyde (1st AM, lg8vo, 136p, gilt, 8pl, pep)	Dodd	1930	Beaman, S.G.H.	100-165	
N/A	Seven Voyages of Sinbad the Sailor (1st AM, sm4to, 71p, 8cp)	McBride	1926	Beaman, S.G.H.	100-170	R
Beaman, S.G.H.	Tales of Toytown (1st, 12mo, 158p, 6cp)	L: H. Milford	(1928)	Beaman, S.G.H.	60-100	
Twain, Mark	American Claimant (1st, 8vo, 277p, green/gilt, b/w)	Webster	1892	Beard, Dan	350-500	
Beard, Dan C.	Animal Book and Campfire Stories (1st, 8vo, 538p, col frn)	Moffat	1907	Beard, Dan	40-60	
Crosby, Ernest	Captain Jinks, Hero (1st, sm8vo, tan cl, 393p, 9pl)	Funk/Wagnalls	1902	Beard, Dan	40-65	
Barton, William E.	Hero in Homespun (1st, sm8vo, 393p, 10pl)	Lamson/Wolffe	1897	Beard, Dan	50-80	
Astor, John J.	Journey in Other Worlds (1st, sm8vo, blue/silver, 476p, 10pl)	Appleton	1894	Beard, Dan	200-300	
Beard, Dan C.	Moonblight ([revised ed.], sm8vo, 238p, green/gilt, uncut, b/w)	A. Brandt	1904	Beard, Dan	60-100	*
Twain, Mark	Tom Sawyer Abroad (1st, 8vo, 219p, white/gilt, b/w)	NY: Webster	1894	Beard, Dan	350-500	
Brown, Elijah P.	Ciderville Folks (1st, lg8vo, tan/gilt, 496p, b/w)	Date Pub. Co.	(1898)	Beard, Frank	50-80	*
Bryant, Sara Cone	Best Stories to Tell Children (1st, 8vo, blue/gilt, 181p, 16cp)	Houghton	1912	Beard, Patten	50-80	
Holloway, Jane	At Flower Farm (1st, 4to, 71p, ibds, p-o, 4cp)	Stern	1909	Beard/Kay	80-130	
Beardsley, Alice	Turn-Around Book (1st, 8vo, p-o, unpag)	Bobbs-Merrill	(1914)	Beardsley, Alice	120-200	
Sharp, Evelyn	At the Relton Arms (1st, 12mo, 182p, gilt, uncut, design by..)	L: John Lane	1895	Beardsley, Aubrey	80-130	
Symons, Arthur	Aubrey Beardsley (1st, lg8vo, 32p, bds, gilt, 6 b/w)	L: Unicorn Press	1898	Beardsley, Aubrey	170-240	
Ross, Robert B.	Aubrey Beardsley (1st, 12mo, 112p, teg, gilt, 16pl)	L: John Lane	1909	Beardsley, Aubrey	60-100	
Quilp, Jocelyn	Baron Verdigris (1st, 8vo, 214p, cvr & frn by...)	L: Henry Co.	1894	Beardsley, Aubrey	70-120	
Jerrold, Walter	Bon-Mots of C. Lamb & D. Jerrold (1st, 24mo, 192p, gilt, teg, cvr by...)	L: J.M. Dent	1893	Beardsley, Aubrey	90-120	
Beardsley, Aubrey	Book of 50 Drawings (1st, 4to, 212p)	L: Smithers	1897	Beardsley, Aubrey	250-400	
O'Sullivan, Vincent	Book of Bargains (1st, 8vo, 185p, frn by...)	L: Smithers	1896	Beardsley, Aubrey	80-125	
Allen, Grant	British Barbarians (1st, 8vo, olive/gilt, 202p, cvr by...)	L: John Lane	1895	Beardsley, Aubrey	100-175	
Adams, Francis	Child of the Age (1st, 8vo, 244p, green/gilt, cvr by...)	L: John Lane	1894	Beardsley, Aubrey	45-70	
Farr, Florence	Dancing Faun (1st, 8vo, 149p, ti-page & cvr by...)	L: E. Mathews	1894	Beardsley, Aubrey	200-300	
Green, Anna K.	Doctor, his Wife and the Clock (1st, 8vo, 131p, wraps, cvr by...)	L: T.F. Unwin	1895	Beardsley, Aubrey	250-400	
Hobbes, John O.	Dream & the Business (1st, 8vo, 444p, blue cl, teg, cvr by...)	L: T.F. Unwin	1906	Beardsley, Aubrey	100-150	
N/A	Early Work of Aubrey Beardsley (1st, lg4to, 157p, teg, uncut)	L: John Lane	1899	Beardsley, Aubrey	250-400	
Burney, Fanny	Evelina... (3rd ed., sm8vo, teg, 2 vols, uncut, gilt)	L: J.M. Dent	1893	Beardsley, Aubrey	350-450	
Ruding, Walter	Evil Motherhood (1st, 8vo, blue/gilt, 99p, uncut, frn by...)	L: E. Mathews	1896	Beardsley, Aubrey	120-200	
Machen, Arthur	Great God Pan & Inmost Light (1st AM, 12mo, 234p, gilt, cvr by...)	Roberts Bros.	1894	Beardsley, Aubrey	170-240	
Johnson, Ben	His Volpone (1st, 4to, 193p, blue/gilt, 7pl)	L: Smithers	1898	Beardsley, Aubrey	250-400	
Yeats, Wm. Butler	Land of Hearts Desire (1st AM, 16mo, 43p, pcb, frn by...)	Herbert Stone	1894	Beardsley, Aubrey	600-900	
Douglas, Robert B.	Life & Times of Madame Du Barry (1st, lg8vo, 386p, cvr by...)	L: Smithers	1896	Beardsley, Aubrey	140-200	
Makower, Stanley	Mirror of Music (1st, 8vo, 179p, uncut, cvr by...)	L: John Lane	1895	Beardsley, Aubrey	80-120	
D'Arcy, Ella	Monochromes (1st, 8vo, 260p, green cl, cvr & ti page by...)	L: John Lane	1895	Beardsley, Aubrey	75-100	*
MacLeod, Fiona	Mountain Lovers (1st, 8vo, 241p, blue/white, uncut, cvr by...)	L: John Lane	1895	Beardsley, Aubrey	60-100	
Brown, Vincent	My Brother (1st, 12mo, 176p, beige cl, frn by...)	L: John Lane	1896	Beardsley, Aubrey	100-165	
Grahame, Kenneth	Pagan Papers (1st, 12mo, bds, 165p, teg, title page by...)	Herbert Stone	1894	Beardsley, Aubrey	120-180	R
Bjornstjerne, Bjorn	Pastor Sang (1st, 8vo, 109p, teg, uncut, frn by...)	L: Longmans	1893	Beardsley, Aubrey	80-130	
Stacpoole, H.D.	Pierrot! (1st, 8vo, red cl, 163p, uncut, pep, cvr & title page by...)	L: John Lane	1896	Beardsley, Aubrey	75-100	*
Davidson, John	Plays by... (1st, 8vo, gilt, 294p, uncut, cvr by...)	L: E. Mathews	1894	Beardsley, Aubrey	100-160	
Dowson, Ernest	Poems of E. Dowson (1st, 12mo, 166p, green/gilt, teg, 4pl, cvr by...)	L: John Lane	1905	Beardsley, Aubrey	120-170	
Dostoievsky, Fedor	Poor Folk (1st, 8vo, 192p, title pg & cvr by...)	L: E. Mathews	1894	Beardsley, Aubrey	175-250	
Pope, Alexander	Rape of the Lock (1st, lg8vo, 47p, blue/gilt, AEG, 7pl)	L: Smithers	1896	Beardsley, Aubrey	350-500	
Wilde, Oscar	Salome... (1st, 8vo, blue/gilt, 10pl)	L: E. Mathews	1894	Beardsley, Aubrey	900-1300	
Wilde, Oscar	Salome... (sm8vo, 36p, black/gilt, 16pl)	Bos: J.W. Luce	1907	Beardsley, Aubrey	120-200	
Wilde, Oscar	Salome... (2nd, sm4to, gilt, 66p, teg, 16pl)	L: John Lane	1907	Beardsley, Aubrey	350-500	
Beardsley, Aubrey	Second Book of 50 Drawings (1st, 4to, red/gilt, 213p, 50pl)	L: Smithers	1899	Beardsley, Aubrey	250-400	
Shiel, Matthew P.	Shapes in the Fire (1st AM, 12mo, 324p, blue cl, cvr & ti page by..)	Roberts Bros.	1896	Beardsley, Aubrey	180-240	
Brooks, Edward	Story of King Arthur (1st AM, 12mo, 383p, 13pl)	Penn	1900	Beardsley, Aubrey	90-160	*
Beardsley, Aubrey	Under The Hill (1st, 4to, teg, blue/gilt, uncut, 15pl)	L: John Lane	1904	Beardsley, Aubrey	400-600	
Allen, Grant	Woman Who Did (1st, 8vo, 241p, green cl, uncut, cvr by...)	L: John Lane	1895	Beardsley, Aubrey	100-175	
Davidson, John	Wonderful Mission of Earl Lavender (1st, 8vo, gilt, uncut, cvr by..)	L: Ward/Down.	1895	Beardsley, Aubrey	70-120	*
Dawe, William C.	Yellow & White (1st, 12mo, 172p, yellow cl, cvr & ti page by...)	L: John Lane	1895	Beardsley, Aubrey	90-120	
Beatty, Hetty B.	Bronto (1st {std}, 8vo, 136p, b/w, DJ/2.00)	Doubleday	(1952)	Beatty, Hetty	25-40	
Beatty, Hetty B.	Droopy (1st, sm4to, 26p, color, DJ/2.50)	Houghton	1954	Beatty, Hetty	25-40	

AUTHOR	TITLE	PUBLISHER	DATE	ARTIST	PRICE	LC
Beatty, Hetty B.	Little Owl Indian (1st, sm4to, 32p, color, dep, DJ/2.25)	Houghton	1951	Beatty, Hetty	30-45	*
Beatty, Hetty B.	Little Wild Horse (1st, lg sq8vo, ibds, 31p, color, DJ/2.00)	Houghton	1949	Beatty, Hetty	40-65	*
Beatty, Hetty B.	Moorland Pony (1st, sm4to, 40p, color, cep, DJ/3.00)	Houghton	1961	Beatty, Hetty	50-75	
Beatty, Hetty B.	Thumps (1st, sm4to, 29p, fp color, dep, DJ/2.75)	Houghton	1955	Beatty, Hetty	25-40	
Meader, Stephen W.	Clear for Action! (1st, 8vo, 323p, fp b/w, pep, DJ/2.00)	Harcourt	(1940)	Beaudouin, Frank	120-165	
Richards, Laura E.	Golden Windows (1st, 8vo, 123p, green/gilt, teg, 5pl)	Little/Brown	1903	Becher, Arthur E.	50-80	
Bangs, John K.	Little Book of Christmas (1st, 12mo, 173p, 4cp)	Little/Brown	1912	Becher, Arthur E.	50-85	
Knipe, E.& A.	Lucky Sixpence (1st, sm8vo, 408p, 4pl, PPPa)	Century	1912	Becher, Arthur E.	200-300	
Buchan, John	Magic Walking Stick (1st, 8vo, red/gilt, 176p, b/w, pep)	Houghton	1932	Becher, Arthur E.	40-60	
Singmaster, Elsie	When Sarah Saved the Day (1st, 12mo, 135p, pink cl, 4pl)	Houghton	1909	Becher, Arthur E.	25-40	
Meader, Stephen W.	Buffalo and Beaver (1st {std}, 8vo, 189p, b/w, DJ/2.95)	Harcourt	(1960)	Beck, Charles	100-160	
Meader, Stephen W.	Everglades Adventure (1st {std}, 8vo, 192p, b/w, DJ/2.75)	Harcourt	(1957)	Beck, Charles	100-170	
Steele, William O.	Trail through Danger (1st {std}, 8vo, 184p, b/w, DJ/3.25)	Harcourt	(1965)	Beck, Charles	20-35	
Meader, Stephen W.	Wild Pony Island (1st {std}, 8vo, 192p, b/w, DJ/2.95)	Harcourt	(1959)	Beck, Charles	100-170	
Steele, William O.	Year of the Bloody Sevens (1st {std}, 8vo, 187p, fp b/w, DJ/3.25)	Harcourt	(1963)	Beck, Charles	20-30	
Beckenbaugh, G.	Cotton Tails (1st, ob4to, [99]p, ipcb, fp b/w)	R.H. Russell	1900	Beckenbaugh, G.	200-300	
N/A	Arabian Nights (1st, lg8vo, 242p, gilt, p-o, col frn, pep)	Sears	(1928)	Becker, Charlotte	30-50	
Catrevas, Christine	Fairy Tales for Little People (1st, lg8vo, 246p, p-o, col frn, pep)	Sears	(1927)	Becker, Charlotte	35-60	
Alger, Leclaire	Jan & Wonderful Mouth-Organ (1st {std}, 8vo, 177p, col frn, pep, DJ/2.00)	Harper	1939	Becker, Charlotte	40-65	
Blumenthal, Gertrude	Louise's Adventure (1st {std}, ob4to, ibds, [32]p, color, pep, DJ/1.00)	Doubleday/Doran	1941	Becker, Charlotte	30-50	*
Thomas, Eleanor	Mr. Pearly of Pepper Pot Lane (1st, 8vo, 84p, fp color, DJ/1.50)	Scribner	(1939)	Becker, Charlotte	25-45	
Becker, Charlotte	Surprise for Three Little Steps (1st, 12mo, ibds, [32]p, fp color)	Scribner	1947	Becker, Charlotte	25-45	
Dalgliesh, Alice	Young Aunts (1st, 8vo, 116p, red cl, fp color, DJ/1.75)	Scribner	1939	Becker, Charlotte	30-45	
Grimm Bros.	Fairy Tales (1st, 8vo, 382p, color, DJ/1.25, RC)	World	(1947)	Becker, May L.	30-60	*
Beckman, Per	Looking for Lucas (1st AM [1st bk.], 4to, [24]p, color)	NY: David White	(1967)	Beckman, Per	25-40	
Lucas, E.V.	Another Book of Verses for Children (1st AM, 8vo, 431p, 18pl)	Macmillan	1907	Bedford, Francis D.	60-90	
MacDonald, George	Back of the North Wind (1st AM, 8vo, 376p, 12pl, col frn, pep)	NY: Macmillan	(1924)	Bedford, Francis D.	70-125	
Barlow, Jane	Battle of the Frogs and Mice (1st, 8vo, green cl, unpag, 4pl)	L: Methuen	1894	Bedford, Francis D.	100-165	
MacDonald, Greville	Billy Barnicoat (1st AM, 8vo, 230p, col frn, fp b/w)	Dutton	1923	Bedford, Francis D.	50-80	
Barlow, Jane (tran)	Book of Nursery Rhymes (1st, 4to, ibds, 91p, 21cp)	L: Methuen	1897	Bedford, Francis D.	180-250	
Barlow, Jane (tran)	Book of Nursery Rhymes (1st AM, lg8vo, 91p, 21cp)	Doub./McClure	1897	Bedford, Francis D.	150-225	
Lucas, E.V.	Book of Shops (1st, ob4to, ipcb, 24cp)	L: Richards	1899	Bedford, Francis D.	200-270	
Dickens, Charles	Christmas Carol (1st, sm8vo, 166p, gilt, 4cp, 15pl, pep)	Macmillan	1923	Bedford, Francis D.	60-90	
MacDonald, Greville	Count Billy (1st {std}, 8vo, 246p, gilt, uncut, col frn, 6pl)	Dutton	1928	Bedford, Francis D.	50-80	
Dickens, Charles	Cricket on the Hearth (1st AM, 8vo, 182p, red/gilt, 8cp)	Harper	(1927)	Bedford, Francis D.	80-120	
Baring-Gould, Sabine	Crock of Gold (1st AM, 8vo, gilt, teg, 8pl)	L.C. Page	1899	Bedford, Francis D.	70-100	
Lucas, E.V.	Forgotten Tales of Long Ago (1st AM, 8vo, 424p, teg, gilt, fp b/w)	Stokes	(1906)	Bedford, Francis D.	70-125	
Lucas, E.V.	Forgotten Tales of Long Ago (1st, 8vo, gilt, 424p, teg, col frn, 22pl)	L: Wells/Gard.	1906	Bedford, Francis D.	100-165	
Lucas, E.V.	Four & Twenty Toilers (1st AM, ob4to, 103p, blue cl, p-o, 24cp)	McDevitt/Wilson	[1900]	Bedford, Francis D.	200-300	
Thackeray, Wm. M.	History of Henry Esmond (1st, 8vo, 476p, gilt, teg, 12cp)	L: Dent	1898	Bedford, Francis D.	50-80	
Coatsworth, Eliz.	Knock at the Door (1st, ob8vo, 73p, gilt, col frn, b/w)	Macmillan	1931	Bedford, Francis D.	40-60	
Dickens, Charles	Magic Fishbone (1st, ob8vo, [40]p, ibds, 7cp, pep)	L: Warne	(1922)	Bedford, Francis D.	70-100	
Bedford, Francis D.	Night of Wonders (1st, ob8vo, ibds, 124p, teg, 24cp, pep)	L: Richards	[1906]	Bedford, Francis D.	200-300	
Baring-Gould, Sabine	Old English Fairy Tales (1st AM, 8vo, teg, 400p, gilt, b/w)	Way & Williams	1895	Bedford, Francis D.	120-180	
Lucas, E.V.	Old Fashioned Tales (1st, 8vo, teg, 389p, gilt, col frn, b/w)	L: Wells/Gard.	[1905]	Bedford, Francis D.	80-120	
Taylor, Anne & Jane	Original Poems (2nd AM, 8vo, 415p, gilt, teg, tan cl, col frn)	Stokes	(1905)	Bedford, Francis D.	60-100	
Taylor, Anne & Jane	Original Poems (2nd, 8vo, 415p, teg, uncut, col frn)	L: Wells/Gard.	1905	Bedford, Francis D.	100-175	
Barrie, James M.	Peter and Wendy (1st, 8vo, 267p, green/gilt, 13pl)	L: Hodder	(1911)	Bedford, Francis D.	300-500	
Barrie, James M.	Peter and Wendy (1st AM, lg8vo, 267p, gilt, 13pl)	Scribner	(1911)	Bedford, Francis D.	250-350	
MacDonald, George	Princess & the Goblin (1st, 12mo, 267p, blue/gilt, col frn)	Macmillan	1926	Bedford, Francis D.	80-120	
Stevens, Frank L.	Through Merrie England (1st, 8vo, green/gilt, teg, 214p, 12cp, pep)	L: Warne	(1928)	Bedford, Francis D.	80-120	
Roberts, Elizabeth M.	Under the Tree (1st, lg8vo, p-o, 85p, col frn, b/w)	Viking	1930	Bedford, Francis D.	30-50	
Goldsmith, Oliver	Vicar of Wakefield (1st, 8vo, 222p, green/gilt, uncut, 12cp)	L: Dent	1898	Bedford, Francis D.	80-130	
Lucas, E.V.	Visit to London (1st, 4to, ipcb, 118p, 24cp)	L: Methuen	1902	Bedford, Francis D.	120-200	
Lucas, E.V.	Visit to London (1st AM, 4to, ibds, 118p, 24cp)	Brentano's	[1902]	Bedford, Francis D.	100-165	
Troutbeck, G.E.	Westminster Abbey (1st, 16mo, 278p, 13pl)	L: Methuen	1900	Bedford, Francis D.	40-65	
Herr, Charlotte	Bear Who Never was Cross (1st, 16mo, ibds, unpag, color)	Volland	(1913)	Beem, Frances	50-80	
Herr, Charlotte	Bee Who Would Not Work (1st, 16mo, ibds, unpag, color)	Volland	(1913)	Beem, Frances	60-90	
Gordon, Elizabeth	Dolly & Molly at Seashore (1st, 16mo, 32p, color)	Rand/McNally	(1914)	Beem, Frances	40-65	
Gordon, Elizabeth	Dolly & Molly at the Circus (1st, 16mo, 32p, color)	Rand/McNally	(1914)	Beem, Frances	40-65	
Judson, Clara I.	Garden Adventures of Tommy Tittlemouse (1st, sm8vo, 64p, color)	Rand/McNally	(1922)	Beem, Frances	30-50	
Herr, Charlotte	How Punky Dunk Helped Old Prince (1st, 16mo, ibds, unpag, color)	Volland	(1913)	Beem, Frances	50-80	
Fox, Frances M.	Little Bear's Adventures (1st, 8vo, 64p, blue cl, p-o, 8 fp color)	Rand/McNally	(1923)	Beem, Frances	45-70	
Sabin, Elbridge H.	Prince Trixie (1st, lg8vo, 142p, p-o, 8cp)	Rand/McNally	(1914)	Beem, Frances	100-165	
Herr, Charlotte	Unselfish Pig (1st, 12mo, wraps, [22]p, fp color)	Volland	(1913)	Beem, Frances	50-80	*
Herr, Charlotte	Wise Mamma Goose (1st, 12mo, wrap, [21]p, color)	Volland	(1913)	Beem, Frances	50-80	*
Sewell, Anna	Black Beauty (1st UK, sm4to, gilt, 229p, b/w)	L: Jarrold	1894	Beer, John	100-145	
Beerbohm, Max	50 Caricatures (1st, 8vo, green/gilt, 50 tipl)	L: Heinemann	1913	Beerbohm, Max	140-220	
Beerbohm, Max	A Survey (1st, 4to, gilt, col frn, 51 tipl)	L: Heinemann	1921	Beerbohm, Max	120-200	
Beerbohm, Max	Caricatures of 25 Gentlemen (1st, 4to, blue/gilt)	L: Smithers	1896	Beerbohm, Max	250-400	
Beerbohm, Max	Cartoons: Second Childhood of John Bull (1st, folio, [34]p, bds, 15cp)	L: Stephen Swift	(1911)	Beerbohm, Max	250-400	
Beerbohm, Max	Dreadful Dragon of Hay Hill (1st, lg8vo, 113p, ibds, gilt, col frn)	L: Heinemann	1928	Beerbohm, Max	60-90	
Beerbohm, Max	Observations (1st, 4to, 52pl, DJ)	L: Heinemann	1925	Beerbohm, Max	300-450	
Beerbohm, Max	Poet's Corner (1st, folio, ibds, 20cp)	L: Heinemann	1904	Beerbohm, Max	250-400	
Beerbohm, Max	Rossetti and his Circle (1st, 4to, blue/gilt, 23 ticp)	L: Heinemann	1922	Beerbohm, Max	140-220	
Lewis, D.B.W.	Stuffed Owl (1st AM, sm8vo, bds, p-o, 236p, 6pl, pep)	Coward	(1930)	Beerbohm, Max	30-50	
Beerbohm, Max	Things New and Old (1st, 4to, col frn, 49pl)	L: Heinemann	1923	Beerbohm, Max	120-200	
Beerbohm, Max	Zuleika Dobson (1st, 8vo, brown cl, 350p, gilt)	L: Heinemann	1911	Beerbohm, Max	170-240	

AUTHOR	TITLE	PUBLISHER	DATE	ARTIST	PRICE	LC
Clark, Ann N.	Little Indian Basket Maker (1st, sm ob8vo, 31p, fp color)	Melmont Pub.	(1957)	Begay, Harrison	30-50	*
Behn, Harry	All Kinds of Time (1st {std}, 12mo, ibds, [61]p, color, cep, DJ/2.00)	Harcourt	(1950)	Behn, Harry	65-100	R
Behn, Harry	Faraway Lurs (1st {std}, 8vo, 190p, b/w, DJ/3.00)	World	(1963)	Behn, Harry	40-65	R*
Behn, Harry	Golden Hive (1st {std}, 8vo, 61p, b/w, DJ/3.25)	Harcourt	(1966)	Behn, Harry	25-45	
Behn, Harry	House Beyond the Meadow (1st, 8vo, [46]p, ibds, 2-color, pep, DJ/2.50)	Pantheon	(1955)	Behn, Harry	30-45	
Behn, Harry	Little Hill (1st {std}, 12mo, 58p, ipcb, 1-color, cep, DJ/2.00)	Harcourt	(1949)	Behn, Harry	65-100	R
Behn, Harry	Omen of the Birds (1st {std}, 8vo, 157p, fp b/w, DJ/3.50)	World	(1964)	Behn, Harry	25-45	
Behn, Harry	Painted Cave (1st {std}, 8vo, ipcb, 63p, 1-color, cep, DJ/3.00)	Harcourt	(1957)	Behn, Harry	65-100	R
Behn, Harry	Windy Morning (1st {std}, 12mo, ipcb, 61p, 1-color, cep, DJ/2.00)	Harcourt	(1953)	Behn, Harry	65-100	R
Behn, Harry	Wizard in the Well (1st {std}, 12mo, ipcb, 62p, 1-color, cep, DJ/2.25)	Harcourt	(1956)	Behn, Harry	65-100	R
Beim, Jerrold	Swimming Hole (1st, 8vo, [45]p, color, DJ/2.00)	Wm. Morrow	1950	Beim, Jerrold	30-50	
Beistle, Aldarilla	I Spy (1st, 8vo, spiral-bound ibds, [17]p, color)	McKay	(1944)	Beistle, Mary A.	35-50	
Beistle, Aldarilla	Just Peggy (1st, sm8vo, ibds, 63p, silhouettes, DJ/0.50)	McKay	(1939)	Beistle, Mary A.	50-80	
Beistle, Aldarilla	Mr. Heinie (1st {std}, ob8vo, [32]p, ipcb, color, pep, DJ/1.00)	McKay	(1938)	Beistle, Mary A.	50-80	
Beistle, Aldarilla	Mr. Heinie & Scroot (1st {std}, ob8vo, [36]p, ibds, color, pep, DJ/1.00)	McKay	(1939)	Beistle, Mary A.	50-80	
Beistle, Aldarilla	Open Daily (1st {std}, lg8vo, ibds, 90p, color, DJ/2.00)	McKay	(1942)	Beistle, Mary A.	30-50	
Henderson, Lima L.	Resolute (1st, 8vo, 64p, ipcb, fp b/w, DJ/0.50)	McKay	(1940)	Beistle, Mary A.	50-80	
Bell, Thelma H.	Black Face (1st {std}, lg8vo, ibds, [48]p, color, pep)	Doubleday/Doran	1931	Bell, Corydon	40-65	
Bell, Thelma H.	Dash of Pepper (1st, 8vo, 159p, b/w, DJ/3.50)	Viking	(1965)	Bell, Corydon	25-40	
Gray, Eliz. J.	I Will Adventure (1st, 8vo, 208p, fp b/w, pep, DJ/4.00)	Viking	(1962)	Bell, Corydon	25-40	
Bell, Corydon	John Rattling-Gourd of Big Cove (1st {std}, lg8vo, 103p, b/w, DJ/2.50)	Macmillan	1955	Bell, Corydon	25-35	
Forbus, Ina B.	Magic Pin (1st, 8vo, 138p, b/w, DJ/2.50)	Viking	1956	Bell, Corydon	40-65	
Mills, Winifred H.	Marionettes, Masks & Shadows (1st {std}, lg8vo, 270p, col frn, b/w)	Doubleday/Page	1927	Bell, Corydon	40-60	*
Bell, Thelma H.	Pawnee (1st, 4to, 63p, ibds, b/w, pep, DJ/2.00)	Viking	1950	Bell, Corydon	40-65	
Bell, Thelma H.	Riddle of Time (1st, 8vo, 160p, b/w, DJ/3.50)	Viking	(1963)	Bell, Corydon	20-35	
Forbus, Ina B.	Secret Circle (1st, 8vo, 160p, b/w, DJ/2.50)	Viking	1958	Bell, Corydon	60-90	
Bell, Thelma H.	Snow (1st, sm4to, 55p, 1-color, DJ/2.50)	Viking	1954	Bell, Corydon	30-50	
Bell, Thelma H.	Yaller-Eye (1st, sm4to, 88p, ibds, b/w, pep, DJ/2.00)	Viking	1951	Bell, Corydon	25-45	
MacDonald, George	Phantastes (1st, sm8vo, 280p, aqua cloth, 14pl)	L: Chatto	1894	Bell, John	300-425	
N/A	Cinderella (16mo, ibds, color)	Reilly/Britton	1907	Bell, Robert A.	75-100	
Palgrave, Francis T.	Golden Treasury of Songs & Lyrics (1st, 8vo, 366p, teg, uncut, 25 ticp)	L: Dent	1907	Bell, Robert A.	200-300	
Grimm Bros.	Household Tales (1st, sm8vo, 400p, b/w, pep)	L: Dent	1901	Bell, Robert A.	150-250	*
N/A	Jack the Giant Killer (1st, 24mo, 82p, teg, uncut, 12pl, pep)	L: J.M. Dent	1894	Bell, Robert A.	70-120	
Shakespeare, Wm.	MidSummer Night's Dream (1st, sq8vo, green/gilt, teg, 128p, pep)	L: Dent	1895	Bell, Robert A.	100-160	
Omar Khayyam	Rubaiyat of Omar Khayyam (1st, 8vo, 33p)	L: G. Bell	1902	Bell, Robert A.	75-100	*
Lamb, Charles	Tales from Shakespeare (1st, 8vo, 362p, blue/gilt, teg, 15pl)	L: Freemantle	1899	Bell, Robert A.	70-100	
Shakespeare, Wm.	The Tempest (4to, teg, 106p, uncut, b/w, pep)	L: Freemantle	1901	Bell, Robert A.	80-120	
Bellew, Frank P.	Chip's Dogs (1st, ob4to, ibds, [64]p, b/w)	R.H. Russell	1895	Bellew, F.P.W.	125-200	*
Averill, Esther	King Philip: Indian Chief (1st {std}, 8vo, 147p, b/w, DJ/2.50)	Harper	(1950)	Belsky, Vera	45-60	
Bemelmans, Ludwig	Are You Hungry, Are You Cold? (1st {std}, 8vo, 245p, yellow, cl, DJ/3.95)	World	(1960)	Bemelmans, Ludwig	30-50	
Bemelmans, Ludwig	Best of Times (1st, folio, 188p, 50 color, pep, DJ/3.95)	Simon/Schuster	1948	Bemelmans, Ludwig	130-200	
Bemelmans, Ludwig	Blue Danube (1st, 8vo, blue cl, 153p, 14cp, pep, DJ/3.00)	Viking	1945	Bemelmans, Ludwig	70-100	
Bemelmans, Ludwig	Castle Number Nine (1st, 4to, [48]p, green/gilt, color, pep, DJ/2.00)	Viking	1937	Bemelmans, Ludwig	140-200	R
Bemelmans, Ludwig	Dirty Eddie (1st, 8vo, 240p, blue cl, b/w, DJ/2.75)	Viking	1947	Bemelmans, Ludwig	30-45	
Bemelmans, Ludwig	Donkey Inside (1st, 8vo, 224p, 4 dp color, DJ/3.00)	Viking	1941	Bemelmans, Ludwig	80-120	
Bemelmans, Ludwig	Father, Dear Father (1st, 8vo, 247p, b/w, DJ/3.50)	Viking	1953	Bemelmans, Ludwig	30-50	
Bemelmans, Ludwig	Fifi (1st, lg4to, ibds, [46]p, color, DJ/1.00)	Simon/Schuster	1940	Bemelmans, Ludwig	100-165	R
Bemelmans, Ludwig	Golden Basket (1st, sm4to, 96p, pink cl, color, dep, DJ/2.00, NH)	Viking	1936	Bemelmans, Ludwig	200-300	R
Bemelmans, Ludwig	Hansi (1st {1st book}, 4to, ibds, [64]p, color, pep, DJ/2.00)	Viking	1934	Bemelmans, Ludwig	200-320	
Bemelmans, Ludwig	Happy Place (1st {std}, 8vo, 59p, 3 dp color, DJ/2.50, NYTBI)	Little/Brown	(1952)	Bemelmans, Ludwig	70-120	
Bemelmans, Ludwig	High World (1st, 8vo, 113p, fp color, pep, DJ/2.75)	Harper	(1954)	Bemelmans, Ludwig	50-80	
Bemelmans, Ludwig	Holiday in France (1st, 8vo, 335p, ipcb, b/w, DJ/5.00)	Houghton	(1957)	Bemelmans, Ludwig	30-50	
Bemelmans, Ludwig	Hotel Bemelmans (1st, 8vo, 380p, yellow cl, b/w, pep, DJ/3.00)	Viking	1946	Bemelmans, Ludwig	40-65	*
Bemelmans, Ludwig	Italian Holiday (1st {std}, 4to, bds, 102p, b/w, pep, DJ/5.00)	Houghton	1961	Bemelmans, Ludwig	30-50	
Bemelmans, Ludwig	Life Class (1st, 8vo, 260p, red cl, p-o, b/w, DJ/2.50)	Viking	1938	Bemelmans, Ludwig	100-160	
Burnett, Whit	Literary Life & the Hell with It (1st, 8vo, 276p, b/w, dep, DJ/2.50)	Harper	1939	Bemelmans, Ludwig	35-50	
Bemelmans, Ludwig	Madeline (1st, lg4to, [48]p, ibds, color, pep, DJ/2.00, CH)	Simon/Schuster	1939	Bemelmans, Ludwig	400-650	R
Bemelmans, Ludwig	Madeline & the Bad Hat (1st, lg4to, red cl, 54p, pep, color, DJ/3.50)	Viking	(1956)	Bemelmans, Ludwig	200-300	
Bemelmans, Ludwig	Madeline and the Gypsies (1st, 4to, 56p, ibds, pep, color, DJ/3.50)	Viking	(1958)	Bemelmans, Ludwig	200-300	R
Bemelmans, Ludwig	Madeline in London (1st, lg4to, 56p, red cl, color, pep, DJ/3.50)	Viking	(1961)	Bemelmans, Ludwig	200-300	R*
Bemelmans, Ludwig	Madeline's Christmas (1st, 12mo, [24]p, wraps, color)	NY: McCall	1956	Bemelmans, Ludwig	150-250	
Bemelmans, Ludwig	Madeline's Rescue (1st, lg4to, 56p, red cl, color, pep, DJ/3.00, CM, NYTBI)	Viking	1953	Bemelmans, Ludwig	250-350	R
Bemelmans, Ludwig	Marina (1st, ob folio, [32]p, color, pep, DJ/3.95)	Harper	(1962)	Bemelmans, Ludwig	150-225	*
Bemelmans, Ludwig	My Life in Art (1st, folio, ibds, 63p, color, pep, DJ/5.95)	Harper	(1958)	Bemelmans, Ludwig	45-70	
Leaf, Munro	Noodle (1st, sm ob4to, brown cl, [48]p, fp 1-color, pep, DJ/1.50)	Stokes	1937	Bemelmans, Ludwig	250-350	
Bemelmans, Ludwig	Now I Lay Me Down to Sleep (1st, 8vo, 299p, DJ/2.50)	Viking	1943	Bemelmans, Ludwig	30-45	
Bemelmans, Ludwig	On Board Noah's Ark (1st, 8vo, pcb, 186p, color, pep, DJ/5.00)	Viking	(1962)	Bemelmans, Ludwig	30-50	*
Bemelmans, Ludwig	Parsley (1st, ob folio, 46p, green cl, fp color, DJ/3.50, NYTBI)	Harper	(1955)	Bemelmans, Ludwig	140-200	R
Bemelmans, Ludwig	Quito Express (1st, lg ob8vo, 47p, ibds, 1-color, DJ/1.00)	Viking	1938	Bemelmans, Ludwig	225-325	
Bemelmans, Ludwig	Rosebud (1st, sm4to, ibds, 32p, color, pep, DJ/1.00)	Random	1942	Bemelmans, Ludwig	160-220	
Bemelmans, Ludwig	Small Bear (1st, 8vo, 186p, col frn, b/w, pep, DJ/2.50)	Viking	1939	Bemelmans, Ludwig	80-120	*
Bemelmans, Ludwig	Street Where the Heart Lies (1st {std}, 8vo, 236p, b/w, DJ/3.95)	World	(1963)	Bemelmans, Ludwig	30-50	*
Bemelmans, Ludwig	Sunshine (1st, lg4to, [44]p, ibds, color, pep, DJ/2.50)	Simon/Schuster	(1950)	Bemelmans, Ludwig	180-260	
Bemelmans, Ludwig	Tale of Two Glimps (1st, ob8vo, [48]p, ibds, color)	NY: CBS	(1947)	Bemelmans, Ludwig	140-220	
Bemelmans, Ludwig	To the One I Love Best (1st, 8vo, 255p, b/w, pep, DJ/3.75)	Viking	1955	Bemelmans, Ludwig	70-120	
Bemelmans, Ludwig	Welcome Home! (1st, lg ob4to, [26]p, fp color, DJ/3.95)	Harper	(1960)	Bemelmans, Ludwig	150-220	R
Bemelmans, Ludwig	Woman of My Life (1st, 8vo, 218p, DJ/3.50, title pg & DJ by...)	Viking	1957	Bemelmans, Ludwig	30-50	*
Bemelmans, Ludwig	World of Bemelmans (1st, 8vo, 503p, b/w, pep, DJ/4.95)	Viking	1955	Bemelmans, Ludwig	60-95	

AUTHOR	TITLE	PUBLISHER	DATE	ARTIST	PRICE	LC
Meigs, Cornelia L.	Railroad West (1st {std}, sm8vo, 326p, 1-color, pep, DJ/2.00)	Little/Brown	1937	Bencker, Helen	25-45	
Stratton-Porter, Gene	Girl of the Limberlost (1st, 8vo, 485p, 4pl, pep)	Doubleday/Page	1909	Benda, W.T.	250-400	
Crawford, F. Marion	Little City of Hope (1st AM, sm8vo, 209p, grey cl, 8pl)	Macmillan	1907	Benda, W.T.	40-65	
Burnett, Frances H.	Little Hunchback Zia (1st, 12mo, p-o, 55p, 5pl, pep)	Stokes	(1916)	Benda, W.T.	40-65	
Cather, Willa	My Antonia (1st, 12mo, 418p, brown cl, 6pl)	Houghton	1918	Benda, W.T.	250-425	
Bendick, Jeanne	Blonk from Beneath the Sea (1st {std}, ob8vo, 55p, 1-color, pep, DJ/2.50)	F. Watts	1958	Bendick, Jeanne	40-65	
Clymer, Eleanor	Country Kittens (1st, lg8vo, 108p, fp 2-color, pep, DJ/2.25)	McBride	(1947)	Bendick, Jeanne	30-50	*
Green, Mary M.	Everybody has a House (1st, lg8vo, spiral-bound, [20]p, color)	W.R. Scott	1944	Bendick, Jeanne	60-90	
Bendick, Jeanne	First Book of Time (1st, 8vo, 70p, 1-color, DJ/2.50)	F. Watts	1963	Bendick, Jeanne	30-45	
Bendick, Jeanne	Fresh Look at Night (1st, 8vo, [40]p, fp 2-color, DJ/2.50)	F. Watts	1963	Bendick, Jeanne	30-45	
Clymer, Eleanor	Grocery Mouse (1st, lg8vo, 94p, color, pep, DJ/2.25)	McBride	1945	Bendick, Jeanne	40-65	
Schneider, Nina	Let's Find Out (1st, lg8vo, ibds, 38p, color, DJ/1.50)	W.R. Scott	(1946)	Bendick, Jeanne	50-80	
Bendick, Jeanne	Shape of the Earth (1st, 4to, 72p, ibds, 2-color, DJ/2.95)	Rand/McNally	1965	Bendick, Jeanne	25-40	
Mother Goose	Mother Goose (1st, 8vo, [64]p, color)	McLoughlin	(1909)	Bennett, C.H.	100-150	R
DeMusset, Paul	Mr. Wind & Madam Rain (lg8vo, 150p, red/gilt, AEG, 25pl)	Putnam	1904	Bennett, Charles	80-120	*
Brown, Caroline V.	Bold Robin (1st, sm8vo, gilt, 200p, uncut, teg, p-o, 7cp)	Dutton	(1905)	Bennett, F.I.	35-60	*
Mack, Robert E.	All Around the Clock (8vo, ibds, 64p, AEG, 23 chromos)	Dutton	[1895]	Bennett, Harriet	200-300	
Molesworth, Mrs.	Cozy Corner Stories (1st, sm4to, ibds, 12 chromos)	L: Nister	(1895)	Bennett, Harriet	120-200	
Mack, Robert E.	Old Father Time & his 12 Children (1st, 4to, ibds, unpag, chromos)	L: Nister	[1890]	Bennett, Harriet	120-200	
Molesworth, Mrs.	Palace in the Garden (1st, 8vo, 298p, white/gilt, b/w)	L: Hatchard	1887	Bennett, Harriet	75-100	*
Mack, Robert E.	Queen of the Meadow (lg8vo, ipcb, 16 chromos)	Dutton	[1885]	Bennett, Harriet	150-225	
Molesworth, Olive	Sunny Land Stories (1st, lg8vo, [72]p, ibds, 6cp)	L: Nister	[1907]	Bennett, Harriet	100-150	
Mack, Robert E.	When All is Young (1st, 4to, unpag, ibds, chromos)	Nister/Dutton	(1888)	Bennett, Harriet	120-200	
Bennett, John	Pigtail of Ah Lee Ben Loo (1st, lg8vo, 298p, orange cl, b/w, pep, NH)	Longmans	1928	Bennett, John	120-200	
Stevenson, Rbt. L.	Child's Garden of Verses (folio, ibds, 60p, color, pep)	Whitman	1932	Bennett, Juanita C.	50-80	
Stevenson, Rbt. L.	Child's Garden of Verses (1st {this fmt} ob8vo, [24]p, color, pep)	Grosset/Dunlap	1938	Bennett, Juanita C.	40-60	*
N/A	Cinderella (folio, [22]p, color)	Whitman	1935	Bennett, Juanita C.	40-60	*
Bannerman, Helen	New Story of Little Black Sambo (folio, wraps, [12]p, color)	Whitman	1932	Bennett, Juanita C.	200-300	
Wyss, Johann D.	Swiss Family Robinson (1st, 8vo, 237p, fp b/w)	Whitman	(1935)	Bennett, Juanita C.	25-45	*
Bennett, Rainey	Secret Hiding Place (1st {std}, ob4to, [30]p, color, DJ/3.00)	World	(1960)	Bennett, Rainey	30-50	
Leamy, Edmund	Fairy Minstrel of Glenmalure ([school ed.], sm8vo, 92p, b/w)	Longmans	1937	Bennett, Richard	30-50	*
Bennett, Richard	Hannah Marie (1st {std}, sm4to, 70p, ibds, 1-color, pep, DJ/1.50)	Doubleday/Doran	1939	Bennett, Richard	30-50	
Andersen, Hans C.	It's Perfectly True... (1st, 8vo, 305p, 29pl, pep, DJ/2.50)	Harcourt	(1938)	Bennett, Richard	70-100	R
Bennett, Richard	Mister Ole (1st {std}, 4to, 60p, color, DJ/2.00)	Doubleday/Doran	1940	Bennett, Richard	40-65	*
MacDonald, Betty	Mrs. Piggle-Wiggle (1st {std}, sm8vo, 119p, blue cl, b/w, DJ/2.00)	Lippincott	(1947)	Bennett, Richard	150-220	
Bennett, Richard	Skookum and Sandy (1st {std}, lg8vo, ipcb, [71]p, b/w, pep)	Doubleday/Doran	1935	Bennett, Richard	40-65	
Frost, Frances	Then Came Timothy (1st, 8vo, 155p, b/w, DJ/2.00)	Whittlesey	(1950)	Bennett, Richard	20-30	*
Lampman, Evelyn	Treasure Mountain (1st {std}, 8vo, 207p, b/w, DJ/2.50)	Doubleday	1949	Bennett, Richard	20-35	*
MacManus, Seumas	Well O'the World's End (1st, 8vo, 189p, b/w, DJ/2.00)	Macmillan	1939	Bennett, Richard	65-100	
Running, Corinne	When Coyote Walked the Earth (1st {std}, 8vo, 71p, b/w, DJ/2.00)	Henry Holt & Co.	(1949)	Bennett, Richard	45-70	*
Colum, Padraic	Where the Winds Never Blew... (1st, 8vo, 96p, 1-color, DJ/1.50)	Macmillan	1940	Bennett, Richard	30-50	
Davis, Mary G.	With Cap & Bells (1st, sm8vo, 246p, b/w, pep, DJ/2.00)	Harcourt	(1937)	Bennett, Richard	30-50	*
McKenna, Dolores	Adventures of a Wee Mouse (1st, 8vo, ipcb, [30]p, p-o, 6cp, pep)	Stokes/Saalfield	(1921)	Bennett, Ruth H.	30-50	
McKenna, Dolores	Adventures of the Bunny-Boys (16mo, green bds, 42p, p-o, 6cp, pep)	Stokes/Saalfield	(1921)	Bennett, Ruth H.	40-65	
Uchida, Yoshiko	In-Between Miya (1st, 8vo, 128p, fp b/w, cep, DJ/3.25)	Scribner	(1967)	Bennett, Susan	25-45	
Meadowcroft, Enid	Adventures of Peter Whiffen (1st, 8vo, 148p, b/w, pep, DJ/1.50)	Crowell	(1936)	Bennetts, Beatrice	20-35	
Banta, Nathaniel M.	Brownie Primer (1st, sm8vo, 98p, color)	Chi: Flanagan	(1905)	Benson, Alpha B.	70-120	
Coybee, Eden	Flower Book (1st, 24mo, 94p, green cl, fp color)	L: Richards	1901	Benson, Nellie	100-170	
Mockler, Geraldine	Spring Fairies & Sea Fairies (1st, sm8vo, 192p, red/gilt, b/w)	L: G. Allen	1897	Benson, Nellie	100-150	
Belloc, Hilaire	New Cautionary Tales (1st AM, 8vo, ibds, 79p, b/w)	Harper	1931	Bentley, Nicolas	50-80	
Belloc, Hilaire	New Cautionary Tales for Children (1st {std}, sm4to, ibds, 78p)	L: Duckworth	(1930)	Bentley, Nicolas	70-100	
Eliot, T.S.	Old Possum's Book of Practical Cats (1st, 8vo, 51p, 14 fp color, DJ)	L: Faber	(1940)	Bentley, Nicolas	600-900	
Lovell, Dorothy A.	Silvanus Goes to Sea (1st, lg ob8vo, blue ibds, [26]p, 12 color)	L: Faber	(1943)	Bentley, Nicolas	60-95	
Linklater, Eric	Wind on the Moon (1st, 12mo, 363p, fp b/w, DJ, CgM)	L: Macmillan	1944	Bentley, Nicolas	50-80	
Raphael, Arthur	Great Jug (1st, 8vo, 136p, col frn, b/w, DJ/1.00)	Reilly/Lee	(1936)	Benton, Clifford	70-125	
Mencken, H.L.	Europe After 8:15 (1st, sm8vo, gilt, 222p, 8pl)	J. Lane	1914	Benton, Thomas H.	100-150	
Parkman, Francis	Oregon Trail (1st, 8vo, 328p, 13cp, DJ/5.00)	Doubleday	1946	Benton, Thomas H.	25-40	
May, Julian	First Living Things (1st, 4to, [40]p, color, DJ/4.50)	Holiday House	(1970)	Berelson, Howard	25-40	
Berenstain, Stan	Bear Scouts (1st, 8vo, 63p, color, DJ/1.95)	Beginner Books	(1967)	Berenstain, Stan	20-35	
Berenstain, Stan	Bear's Vacation (1st, 8vo, 63p, color, DJ/1.95)	Beginner Books	(1968)	Berenstain, Stan	20-30	
Lindgren, Astrid	Emil in the Soup Tureen (1st AM {std}, 8vo, 126p, b/w, DJ/3.95)	Follett	(1970)	Berg, Bjorn	50-85	
Proysen, Alf	Pepperpot in the Magic Wood (1st AM {std}, 8vo, 86p, bds, b/w, DJ/3.50)	Pantheon	1968	Berg, Bjorn	25-40	
Zolotow, Charlotte	Flocks of Birds (1st, 8vo, [30]p, fp2-color, cep, DJ/2.75)	Abelard-Schuman	(1965)	Berg, Joan	30-50	
Martin, Patricia	Little Two and the Peach Tree (1st {std}, 8vo, 39p, 1-color, DJ/2.75)	Atheneum	1963	Berg, Joan	25-40	
Hodges, Elizabeth	Three Princes of Serendip (1st {std}, 8vo, 158p, b/w, DJ/3.95)	Atheneum	1964	Berg, Joan	25-40	
Minarik, Else H.	Winds that Come from Far Away (1st, 8vo, 32p, b/w, DJ/2.50)	Harper	(1964)	Berg, Joan	25-40	
Brink, Carol R.	Anything Can Happen on a River (1st, sm8vo, 224p, blue cl, b/w, DJ/1.75)	Macmillan	1934	Berger, William M.	25-40	
Rice, Rebecca	Giles of the Star (1st, 8vo, 350p, 6cp, pep, DJ/2.00)	Lothrop, Lee	(1928)	Berger, William M.	40-65	
Lindsay, Maud	Joyous Guests (1st, lg8vo, 208p, 13cp, pep)	Lothrop, Lee	(1921)	Berger, William M.	60-90	
Lindsay, Maud	Joyous Travelers (1st, 8vo, 157p, blue/gilt, col frn, pep)	Lothrop, Lee	(1919)	Berger, William M.	60-90	
Hawthorne, Hildegarde	Romantic Rebel (1st {std}, 8vo, 231p, fp b/w, NH)	Century	(1932)	Berger, William M.	30-50	
Benchley, Peter	Jonathan Visits the White House (1st, 4to, [32]p, 3-color, DJ/2.50)	McGraw-Hill	(1964)	Bergere, Richard	60-100	
Schatz, Letta	When Will my Birthday Be? (1st, lg8vo, 31p, 2-color, pep, DJ/2.50)	McGraw-Hill	1962	Bergere, Richard	25-45	
Donaldson, Lois	Karl's Wooden Horse (1st, ob8vo, [32]p, color)	NY: Laidlaw	1931	Bergman, Annie	30-50	*
Mutt, Eugenie	Fairy Tales from Baltic Shores (1st, lg8vo, p-o, 382p, pep, 8cp)	Penn	(1930)	Berkowitz, Jeannette	60-90	
Osbourne, M. (ed.)	Favorite Fairy Tales (1st, lg8vo, 365p, p-o, b/w & pep by...)	Penn	(1930)	Berkowitz, Jeannette	100-175	
Wahlenberg, Anna	Old Swedish Fairy Tales (1st, lg8vo, p-o, 296p, pep, 8cp)	Penn	1925	Berkowitz, Jeannette	60-90	
Schlein, Miriam	Shapes (1st, sq8vo, ibds, [33]p, color, DJ/1.75)	W.R. Scott	1952	Berman, Sam	40-65	

ARTIST: 24

AUTHOR	TITLE	PUBLISHER	DATE	ARTIST	PRICE	LC
Ehrhardt, Reinhold	Kikeri (1st AM {std}, ob4to, [32]p, color, DJ/4.95)	World	(1969)	Bernadette	40-65	*
Crawford, Phyllis	Second Shift (1st, sm8vo, blue cl, 211p, 1-color, DJ/2.00)	Henry Holt & Co.	(1943)	Bernbach, Graham	25-40	
Coatsworth, Eliz.	Down Half the World (1st {std}, 8vo, 98p, b/w, DJ/4.50)	Macmillan	(1968)	Bernstein, Zena	30-45	
Kyle, Anne D.	Apprentice of Florence (1st, 8vo, 276p, b/w, pep, NH)	Houghton	1933	Berry, Erick	40-65	
Evans, Eva K.	Araminta (1st, 8vo, 84p, b/w, pep, DJ/2.00)	Minton Balch	(1935)	Berry, Erick	50-80	
Evans, Eva K.	Araminta's Goat (1st, 8vo, 92p, b/w, DJ/2.00)	Putnam	(1938)	Berry, Erick	50-80	
Berry, Erick	Black Folk Tales (1st {std}, 8vo, 80p, 1-color)	Harper	1928	Berry, Erick	50-80	
Thompson, Mary W.	Blueberry Muffin (1st {std}, 8vo, 248p, b/w, DJ/2.00)	Longmans	(1942)	Berry, Erick	25-45	
Best, Herbert	Border Iron (1st, 8vo, 219p, b/w, pep, DJ/2.00)	Viking	1945	Berry, Erick	20-35	
Hillyer, William	Box of Daylight (1st {std}, 8vo, 179p, b/w, pep)	Knopf	1931	Berry, Erick	25-40	
Allee, Marjorie H.	Camp at Westlands (1st, 8vo, 241p, b/w, pep, DJ/2.00)	Houghton	1941	Berry, Erick	20-30	
Abdullah, Achmed	Cat Had Nine Lives (1st, lg8vo, 312p, gilt, b/w)	Farrar/Rinehart	(1933)	Berry, Erick	30-50	*
Morse, Elizabeth	Chang of the Siamese Jungle (1st {std}, sm8vo, 195p, b/w, pep)	Dutton	(1930)	Berry, Erick	25-45	*
Willson, Dixie	Circus ABC (1st, 8vo, 97p, brown cl, 1-color, pep)	Stokes	1924	Berry, Erick	50-80	
Hutchinson, Veronica	Circus Comes to Town (1st, 4to, ipcb, [66]p, color, pep)	Minton Balch	(1932)	Berry, Erick	40-60	
Willson, Dixie	Clown Town (1st {std}, lg8vo, [62]p, color)	Doubleday/Page	1924	Berry, Erick	70-130	
Seabrook, Katie	Colette & Baba in Timbuctoo (1st {std}, 8vo, 168p, frn by...)	Coward	(1933)	Berry, Erick	25-40	*
DuChaillu, Paul	Country of the Dwarfs (1st, 12mo, 261p, b/w, pep)	Harper	1928	Berry, Erick	25-45	*
Fyleman, Rose	Doll's House (1st {std}, 8vo, 99p, color, pep)	Doubleday/Doran	1931	Berry, Erick	50-80	
Malkus, Alida S.	Dragon Fly of Zuni (1st, 8vo, 213p, uncut, fp b/w, pep)	Harcourt	(1928)	Berry, Erick	30-60	*
Willson, Dixie	Empty Elephant (1st, 4to, ibds, [39]p, color)	Volland	(1923)	Berry, Erick	100-170	
Gardiner, Alice C.	Father's Gone A-Whaling (1st {std}, 8vo, 198p, col frn, DJ)	Doubleday/Page	1926	Berry, Erick	35-60	
Justus, May	Fiddle Away (1st, sq8vo, [28]p, ipcb, col frn, DJ/0.50)	Grosset/Dunlap	(1942)	Berry, Erick	30-45	
Malkus, Alida S.	Fifth for the King (1st {std}, sm8vo, 250p, col frn, b/w)	Harper	1931	Berry, Erick	20-30	
Best, Herbert	Flag of the Desert (1st, 8vo, 242p, b/w, DJ/2.00)	Viking	1936	Berry, Erick	25-40	*
Best, Herbert	Garram the Chief (1st {std}, 8vo, 261p, b/w, pep)	Doubleday/Doran	1932	Berry, Erick	25-45	
Best, Herbert	Garram the Hunter (1st {std}, 8vo, 332p, 6pl, pep, NH)	Doubleday/Doran	1930	Berry, Erick	30-50	
Berry, Erick	Girls in Africa (1st, 8vo, 128p, col frn, fp b/w, pep, DJ/2.00)	Macmillan	1928	Berry, Erick	40-65	
Berry, Erick	Go and Find Wind (1st, 8vo, 251p, 6pl, DJ/2.00)	Oxford U. Pr.	(1939)	Berry, Erick	20-30	
Berry, Erick	Green Door to the Sea (1st, 8vo, 192p, b/w, DJ/2.75)	Viking	1955	Berry, Erick	20-35	
Best, Herbert	Gunsmith's Boy (1st, 8vo, 220p, col frn, b/w, pep, DJ/2.00)	Winston	1942	Berry, Erick	20-35	
Berry, Erick	Hay-Foot, Straw-Foot (1st, 8vo, 95p, pep, DJ/2.50)	Viking	1954	Berry, Erick	20-30	
Berry, Erick	Honey of the Nile (1st, 8vo, 224p, b/w, DJ/2.00)	Oxford U. Pr.	(1938)	Berry, Erick	20-30	
Justus, May	House in No-End Hollow (1st {std}, 8vo, 286p, col frn, pep, DJ/2.00)	Doubleday/Doran	1938	Berry, Erick	30-50	
Berry, Erick	Humbo the Hippo (1st {std}, sm8vo, ipcb, [41]p, color, pep)	Harper	1932	Berry, Erick	60-90	
Berry, Erick	Humbo the Hippo (8vo, ibds, [18]p, 1-color, pep, DJ/0.50)	Grosset/Dunlap	1938	Berry, Erick	50-80	
Evans, Eva K.	Jerome Anthony (1st, 8vo, blue cl, 88p, b/w, DJ/2.00)	Putnam	(1936)	Berry, Erick	40-60	*
Berry, Erick	Juma of the Hills (1st, 8vo, 260p, b/w, pep)	Harcourt	(1932)	Berry, Erick	30-50	*
Evans, Eva K.	Key Corner (1st, 8vo, 206p, tan cl, pep, fp b/w, DJ/2.00)	Putnam	(1938)	Berry, Erick	30-60	
Kyser, Halsa A.	Little Cumsee in Dixie (1st {std}, sm8vo, 158p, b/w, pep, DJ/1.50)	Longmans	1938	Berry, Erick	50-80	*
Berry, Erick	Little Farm in the Big City (1st, sm4to, ibds, [47]p, 3-color, DJ/1.50)	Viking	1947	Berry, Erick	30-45	
Lefevre, Felicite	Little Henry and the Tiger (1st {std}, 8vo, ipcb, [41]p, color, pep)	Harper	1931	Berry, Erick	40-65	
Berry, Erick	Lock her Through (1st, 8vo, 246p, 8pl, DJ/2.00)	Oxford U. Pr.	1940	Berry, Erick	20-30	
DuChaillu, Paul	Lost in the Jungle (1st, 12mo, 269p, fp b/w, pep)	Harper	1928	Berry, Erick	30-60	*
Berry, Erick	Mom Du Jos... (1st {std}, 8vo, 116p, col frn, cep, DJ/1.75)	Doubleday/Doran	1931	Berry, Erick	80-120	
Evans, Eva K.	Mr. Jones & Mr. Finnigan (1st, 8vo, [32]p, tan cl, 2-color, dep, DJ/1.00)	NY: Oxford U.Pr.	(1941)	Berry, Erick	30-50	
DuChaillu, Paul	My Apingi Kingdom (1st, 12mo, 263p, b/w, pep)	Harper	1928	Berry, Erick	30-50	*
Snyder, Madeline	My Book of Parties (1st {std}, 8vo, 191p, col frn)	Doubleday/Doran	1928	Berry, Erick	20-30	
Best, Herbert	Mystery of the Flaming Hut (1st {std}, sm8vo, 307p, b/w)	Harper	1932	Berry, Erick	25-40	
Wasson, Mildred	Nancy Sails (1st, 8vo, 295p, b/w pl, DJ/2.00)	Harper	1936	Berry, Erick	20-30	
Best, Herbert	Not Without Danger (1st, 8vo, 286p, pep, DJ/2.50)	Viking	1951	Berry, Erick	20-35	
Willson, Dixie	Once Upon a Monday (1st, 8vo, ibds, 40p, color, pep)	Volland	(1931)	Berry, Erick	65-100	
Berry, Erick	One-String Fiddle (1st, lg8vo, [64]p, peach cl, pep, color, DJ/1.50)	Winston	(1939)	Berry, Erick	30-50	
Berry, Erick	Penny-Whistle (1st, 8vo, [40]p, yellow cl, color)	Macmillan	1930	Berry, Erick	40-65	
Robertson, Keith	Pilgrim Goose (1st, lg8vo, 80p, b/w, pep, DJ/2.00)	Viking	1956	Berry, Erick	25-40	
Willson, Dixie	Pinky-Pup & Empty Elephant (1st, lg4to, ibds, 60p, color)	Volland	(1922)	Berry, Erick	200-300	
Willson, Dixie	Pinky-Pup & Empty Elephant (1st [new ed], sm4to, [62]p, ibds, color, pep)	Volland	(1928)	Berry, Erick	120-200	
Berry, Erick	Pretty Little Doll (1st, sm sq8vo, [30]p, color, DJ/1.00)	Oxford U. Pr.	1946	Berry, Erick	30-50	
Fyleman, Rose	Princess Comes to Our Town (1st {std}, sm8vo, 158p, col frn, pep)	Doubleday/Doran	1928	Berry, Erick	35-60	*
Best, Herbert	Ranger's Ransom (1st {std}, sm8vo, 192p, b/w, DJ/1.75)	Aladdin	1953	Berry, Erick	25-40	
Miller, Janet	Sammy & Silverband (1st, 8vo, 236p, col frn, 9pl)	Houghton	1931	Berry, Erick	20-35	
Berry, Erick	Seven Beaver Skins (1st {std}, 8vo, 275p, b/w, dep, DJ/2.50)	Winston	(1948)	Berry, Erick	20-30	
Nolen, Eleanor W.	Shipment for Susannah (1st, 8vo, 82p, b/w, DJ/1.25)	Nelson	1938	Berry, Erick	50-80	
Berry, Erick	Sojo: Story of Little Lazy Bones (1st, 8vo, ibds, [40]p, b/w, pep)	Harter	(1934)	Berry, Erick	45-70	
Best, Herbert	Son of the White Man (1st, 8vo, orange cl, 315p, b/w, pep)	Doubleday/Doran	1931	Berry, Erick	30-60	
Malkus, Alida S.	Spindle Imp (1st, sm8vo, pink cl, 176p, uncut, fp b/w, pep)	Harcourt	(1931)	Berry, Erick	35-60	
Berry, Erick	Strings to Adventure (1st, 8vo, 221p, 7pl, pep, DJ/2.00)	Lothrop, Lee	1935	Berry, Erick	30-50	
Berry, Erick	Sunhelmet Sue (1st, 8vo, 239p, yellow cl, fp b/w, DJ/2.00)	Lothrop, Lee	1936	Berry, Erick	25-40	
Berry, Erick	Sybil Lidington's Ride (1st, lg8vo, 128p, blue cl, b/w, pep, DJ/2.50)	Viking	1952	Berry, Erick	25-40	
Best, Herbert	Tal of the Four Tribes (1st {std}, sm8vo, 295p, b/w, pep, DJ/1.00)	Doubleday/Doran	1938	Berry, Erick	20-35	
Berry, Erick	There is the Land (1st, 8vo, 240p, b/w, DJ)	Oxford U. Pr.	(1943)	Berry, Erick	20-35	
Berry, Erick	Whistle Round the Bend (1st, 8vo, 266p, b/w pl, DJ/2.00)	Oxford U. Pr.	(1941)	Berry, Erick	20-35	
Robinson, Gertrude	White Heron Feather (1st {std}, 12mo, orange cl, 299p, b/w, pep)	Harper	(1930)	Berry, Erick	30-60	*
Berry, Erick	Winged Girl of Knossos (1st, 8vo, 253p, b/w, pep, DJ/2.00, NH)	Appleton-Century	1933	Berry, Erick	80-140	
Byars, Betsy C.	Dancing Camel (1st, 8vo, 30p, b/w, DJ/2.75)	Viking	(1965)	Berson, Harold	30-50	*
Hildick, E.W.	Dragon that Lived Under Manhattan (1st, lg8vo, 62p, fp b/w, DJ/3.95)	Crown	(1970)	Berson, Harold	20-35	
Montgomery, R.	In Happy Hollow (1st {std}, lg8vo, 128p, fp b/w, DJ/2.50)	Doubleday	1958	Berson, Harold	20-35	
Hunt, Mabel L.	Johnny-Up and Johnny-Down (1st {std}, 8vo, 93p, 1-color, DJ/3.95)	Lippincott	(1962)	Berson, Harold	20-30	

AUTHOR	TITLE	PUBLISHER	DATE	ARTIST	PRICE	LC
Perkins, Al	King Midas and the Golden Touch (1st, 8vo, ibds, 62p, fp color, pep, DJ)	Beginner Books	(1969)	Berson, Harold	30-45	*
Chase, Mary	Loretta Mason Potts (1st {std}, 8vo, 221p, b/w, DJ/3.50)	Lippincott	(1958)	Berson, Harold	30-50	
McGinley, Phyllis	Mince Pie and Mistletoe (1st, 8vo, [32]p, fp 2-color, DJ/2.95)	Lippincott	(1961)	Berson, Harold	25-45	
Lear, Edward	Pelican Chorus (1st, 8vo, [41]p, gilt, color, pep, DJ/2.95)	Parents Mag. Pr.	(1967)	Berson, Harold	25-40	
Walker, Barbara	Pigs and Pirates (1st, ob4to, [46]p, fp color, DJ/4.95)	NY: David White	1969	Berson, Harold	30-45	
Berson, Harold	Raminagrobis and the Mice (1st, sm8vo, [32]p, b/w, DJ/2.50)	Seabury Press	(1965)	Berson, Harold	25-40	
Burchardt, Nellie	Reggie's No-Good Bird (1st {std}, 8vo, uncut, 140p, b/w, DJ/3.50)	F. Watts	(1967)	Berson, Harold	50-80	*
Littlefield, Wm. J.	Seventh Son of a Seventh Son (1st, 8vo, 190p, fp b/w, DJ/3.50)	Lothrop, Lee	(1959)	Berson, Harold	50-80	
Andersen, Hans C.	The Nightingale (1st, lg8vo, 31p, fp 3-color, DJ/2.95)	Lippincott	(1962)	Berson, Harold	30-50	R
Faralla, Dana	Wonderful Flying-Go-Round (1st {std}, 94p, b/w, DJ/3.50)	World	(1965)	Berson, Harold	25-40	
Beskow, Elsa	Adventures of Peter and Lotta (1st AM {std}, lg ob8vo, ibds, 15 color)	Harper	(1931)	Beskow, Elsa	120-180	
Beskow, Elsa	Aunt Brown's Birthday (1st AM, ob folio, [23]p, ibds, 16cp)	Harper	1930	Beskow, Elsa	120-180	
Beskow, Elsa	Aunt Green, Aunt Brown & Aunt Lavender (1st AM, ob folio, 30p, bds, 15cp)	Harper	1928	Beskow, Elsa	150-225	
Beskow, Elsa	Buddy's Adventures in Blueberry Patch (1st, lg ob4to, [34]p, ibds, color)	Harper	[1931]	Beskow, Elsa	120-180	
Beskow, Elsa	Elf Children of the Woods (1st, lg ob4to, [32]p, color)	Harper	1932	Beskow, Elsa	120-180	
Beskow, Elsa	Hat House (1st, ob4to, ibds, [34]p, fp color)	Harper	1931	Beskow, Elsa	120-180	
Beskow, Elsa	Olle's Ski Trip (1st AM, lg4to, [29]p, ibds, 14 fp color)	Harper	[1928]	Beskow, Elsa	120-180	
Beskow, Elsa	Peter's Voyage (1st AM, sq4to, ibds, [14]p, color)	Knopf	1931	Beskow, Elsa	80-140	
Beskow, Elsa	Sun-Egg (1st AM, ob4to, [26]p, ibds, 12cp)	Harper	1933	Beskow, Elsa	120-180	R
Beskow, Elsa	Tale of Wee Little Old Woman (1st AM, sq4to, ibds, [22]p, color)	Harper	1930	Beskow, Elsa	120-170	
Barrows, Marjorie	My Rhyme & Picture Book (1st, 4to, ibds, [24]p, fp color)	Whitman	(1930)	Best, Roy	60-90	
Barrie, James M.	Peter Pan Picture Book (1st, folio, ibds, [89]p, 24cp, pep)	Whitman	(1931)	Best, Roy	80-120	
Brooks, Walter	To and Again (1st, sm8vo, 196p, 10 fp b/w, pep)	Knopf	1927	Best-Maugard, A.	160-240	
Durant, Nancy M.	Oliver & the Crying Chip (1st, 8vo, 79p, blue cl, 10 b/w)	Sherman French	1915	Betacourt, A.B.	30-50	*
Bettina	Angelo and Rosaline (1st, lg4to, ibds, 48p, color, DJ)	L: Collins	1957	Bettina	50-80	
Bettina	Castle in the Sand (1st, sm4to, 47p, b/w, DJ/1.75)	Harper	(1951)	Bettina	40-65	
Bettina	Cocolo Comes to America (1st, folio, ibds, [32]p, color, DJ/2.50)	Harper	1949	Bettina	60-100	
Bettina	Cocolo's Home (1st, folio, ibds, [32]p, color, DJ/2.50)	Harper	1950	Bettina	60-100	
Bettina	Dolls (1st {std}, 12mo, [24]p, color, DJ/1.95)	Ariel	(1963)	Bettina	30-50	
Haviland, Virginia	Favorite Fairy Tales Told in England (1st {std}, lg8vo, 88p, color, DJ/2.75)	Little/Brown	(1959)	Bettina	50-85	
Bettina	For the Leg of a Chicken (1st AM {std}, folio, color, DJ/4.95)	F. Watts	(1960)	Bettina	35-50	
Bettina	Goat Boy (1st AM {std}, lg8vo, [24]p, color, DJ/3.25)	Norton	(1966)	Bettina	40-60	
Bettina	Horse for the Island (1st {std}, 8vo, 213p, b/w, DJ/2.75)	Harper	(1952)	Bettina	25-40	
Kingman, Lee	Magic Christmas Tree (1st {std}, lg8vo, 48p, color, pep, DJ/2.75)	Ariel	(1956)	Bettina	30-45	
Bettina	Of Uncles and Aunts (1st AM {std}, 8vo, [24]p, color, DJ/2.75)	Norton	(1964)	Bettina	30-45	
Bettina	Pantaloni (1st, folio, unpag, ibds, color, DJ/2.50)	Harper	1957	Bettina	50-80	
Bettina	Paolo and Panetto (1st AM, folio, unpag, color, DJ/4.95)	F. Watts	(1960)	Bettina	65-100	
Bettina	Piccolo (1st, 32mo, 64p, fp color, DJ/1.25)	Harper	(1954)	Bettina	40-65	R
Saint-Cecere, Gilles	Piruwayu and the Rainbow (1st {std}, 4to, 47p, color, DJ)	L: Oxford U.Pr.	1958	Bettina	30-50	
Bettina	Poo-Tsee the Water Tortoise (1st, 4to, [32]p, color, DJ)	L: Chatto	(1943)	Bettina	50-80	
Bettina	Sardines and the Angel (1st, sm4to, ibds, [24]p, color, DJ)	L: Oxford U.Pr.	1967	Bettina	30-50	
Hackett, Walter	Swans of Ballycastle (1st {std}, 8vo, 64p, blue cl, color, DJ/2.75)	Ariel	(1954)	Bettina	30-50	
Wuorio, Eva-Lis	Tal & the Magic Barruget (1st {std}, lg8vo, 76p, 2-color, DJ/3.50)	World	(1965)	Bettina	30-45	
Bettina	Trovato (1st {std}, 4to, 47p, color, DJ/3.50)	Ariel	1959	Bettina	30-50	
Jewett, Sarah O.	Betty Leicester's Christmas (1st, 12mo, 68p, ibds, 8cp)	Houghton	1899	Betts, Anna W.	55-80	*
Mills, Weymer J.	Caroline of Courtlandt Street (1st, 8vo, 291p, gilt, teg, 6cp)	Harper	1905	Betts, Anna W.	60-80	
Lippmann, Julie M.	Dreamland (1st, sm8vo, green/gilt, 211p, 5pl, dep)	Penn	1901	Betts, Anna W.	30-45	
Hawthorne, Hildegarde	Lure of the Garden (1st, 4to, uncut, 259p, teg, dep, 6cp by...)	Century	1911	Betts, Anna W.	150-225	
Hoyt, Eleanor	Nancy's Country Christmas (1st, 8vo, teg, 224p, uncut, col frn)	Doubleday/Page	1904	Betts, Anna W.	35-60	
Barr, Amelia E.	Song of a Single Note (1st, sm8vo, 330p, 4pl)	Dodd	1902	Betts, Anna W.	25-40	
Marks, Jeannette	Through Welsh Doorways (1st, 8vo, 244p, rust/gilt, 4pl)	Houghton	1909	Betts, Anna W.	30-50	
Silberrad, Una L.	Good Comrade (1st, 12mo, 365p, blue/gilt, col frn, 3pl)	Doubleday/Page	1907	Betts, Anna Whelan	25-40	*
Ingpen, Roger	1000 Poems for Children (1st, lg8vo, 563p, 8cp, pep)	Jacobs	(1923)	Betts, Ethel F.	200-300	
MacDonough, Glen	Babes in Toyland (1st, lg8vo, 180p, tan cloth, 7cp, pep)	Fox Duffield	1904	Betts, Ethel F.	180-270	
MacDonough, Glen	Babes in Toyland (2nd, 8vo, aqua cl, 180p, p-o, 7cp)	Macaulay	(1924)	Betts, Ethel F.	100-160	
Riley, James W.	Boy Lives on our Farm (1st, sq4to, p-o, [18]p, 5cp)	Bobbs-Merrill	(1908)	Betts, Ethel F.	120-170	
Mother Goose	Complete Mother Goose (1st, lg8vo, 227p, 11cp)	Stokes	(1909)	Betts, Ethel F.	200-280	
Grimm Bros.	Fairy Tales (1st, 4to, 117p, p-o, brown cl, 6cp)	Stern	1909	Betts, Ethel F.	200-300	
Mother Goose	Favorite Nursery Rhymes (1st, 4to, 47p, 6cp)	Stokes	(1906)	Betts, Ethel F.	130-200	*
Castle, Agnes	Heart of Lady Ann (1st, 12mo, 263p, lavender/gilt, 4cp, pep)	Harper	1905	Betts, Ethel F.	35-60	
Riley, James W.	Host of Children (1st, lg8vo, p-o, 189p, brown/gilt, 16cp, pep)	Bobbs-Merrill	(1920)	Betts, Ethel F.	200-300	R
Wilkinson, Florence	Kings & Queens (1st, sm8vo, 138p, tan cl, uncut, 6pl)	McClure	1903	Betts, Ethel F.	35-60	
Burnett, Frances H.	Little Princess (1st, sm4to, 266p, blue/gilt, teg, p-o, 12cp)	Scribner	1905	Betts, Ethel F.	120-180	
Riley, James W.	Orphant Annie Book (1st, sq folio, [30]p, ibds, 8cp)	Bobbs-Merrill	(1908)	Betts, Ethel F.	170-240	
Riley, James W.	Raggedy Man (1st, sq4to, [30]p, p-o, 8cp)	Bobbs-Merrill	(1907)	Betts, Ethel F.	180-240	R
Riley, James W.	Riley Child Verse (1st, lg8vo, p-o, 58p, 8cp)	Bobbs-Merrill	(1906)	Betts, Ethel F.	120-200	R
Riley, James W.	Runaway Boy (1st, lg8vo, p-o, red cl, [40]p, pep, 8cp)	Bobbs-Merrill	(1906)	Betts, Ethel F.	120-180	
Chapin, Anna A.	True Story of Humpty Dumpty (1st, lg8vo, 205p, p-o, pep, 6cp)	Dodd	1905	Betts, Ethel F.	200-280	
Riley, James W.	While the Heart Beats Young (1st, lg8vo, 110p, p-o, 16cp, dep)	Bobbs-Merrill	(1906)	Betts, Ethel F.	120-200	
Kelly, James P.	Prince Izon (1st, 8vo, 399p, brown cl, p-o, 5cp, pep)	McClurg	1910	Betts, H.& E.	50-80	
Banks, Charles E.	Child of the Sun (1st, 8vo, tan cl, teg, 166p, 16cp)	Herbert Stone	1900	Betts, Louis	60-90	
Bevans, Tom	Where, O Where? (1st, 8vo, [48]p, ibds, color, dep, DJ/1.00)	Viking	1939	Bevans, Tom	25-45	
Andersen, Hans C.	Snow Queen (1st, lg8vo, red cl, 209p, col frn, 1-color, pep)	Dutton	(1929)	Beverly/Ellender	70-120	
Travers, Pamela L.	Fox at the Manger (1st {std}, sm8vo, 75p, brown cl, b/w, DJ/3.00)	Norton	(1962)	Bewick, Thomas	80-120	
Travers, Pamela L.	Fox at the Manger (1st UK, 12mo, 75p, b/w, pep, DJ)	L: Collins	1963	Bewick, Thomas	70-100	
Symonds, John	Away to the Moon (1st, 8vo, 64p, b/w, pep, DJ/2.25)	Lippincott	(1956)	Bianco, Pamela	30-50	
Bianco, Pamela	Beginning with A (1st, 4to, [58]p, blue/silver, b/w, DJ/2.50)	NY: Oxford U.Pr.	1947	Bianco, Pamela	75-100	
Wilde, Oscar	Birthday of the Infanta (1st, lg8vo, 58p, blue cl, 3 dp color)	Macmillan	1929	Bianco, Pamela	40-60	

AUTHOR	TITLE	PUBLISHER	DATE	ARTIST	PRICE	LC
Bianco, Pamela	Doll in the Window (1st, sq8vo, 32p, blue cl, color, pep, DJ/2.00)	NY: Oxford U.Pr.	1953	Bianco, Pamela	60-90	
Hazeltine, Alice	Easter Book of Legends and Stories (1st, 8vo, 392p, b/w, DJ/2.75)	Lothrop, Lee	(1947)	Bianco, Pamela	30-50	
De La Mare, Walter	Flora: A Book of Drawings (1st AM, 4to, ibds, 45p, uncut, 8cp)	Lippincott	(1919)	Bianco, Pamela	80-120	
De La Mare, Walter	Flora: A Book of Drawings (1st, 4to, 45p, ibds, 8cp)	L: Heinemann	(1919)	Bianco, Pamela	90-120	
Bianco, Pamela	Joy & the Christmas Angel (1st, 8vo, bds, 40p, 3-color, pep, DJ/1.75)	NY: Oxford U.Pr.	1949	Bianco, Pamela	45-70	
Blake, William	Land of Dreams (1st, lg8vo, 42p, gilt, b/w, pep, DJ/2.00)	Macmillan	1928	Bianco, Pamela	55-80	
Bianco, Pamela	Little Houses far Away (1st, 8vo, green/gilt, 87p, b/w, DJ/2.25)	NY: Oxford U.Pr.	(1951)	Bianco, Pamela	50-85	
Andersen, Hans C.	Little Mermaid (1st, 12mo, 56p, green/gilt, 1-color, pep, DJ/1.25)	Holiday House	1935	Bianco, Pamela	60-90	
Bianco, Margery W.	Little Wooden Doll (1st, 12mo, 65p, blue cl, pep, 6cp)	Macmillan	1925	Bianco, Pamela	70-130	
Bianco, Pamela	Look-Inside Easter Egg (1st, sq12mo, 38p, bds, dep, 8 fp color, DJ/1.75)	NY: Oxford U.Pr.	1952	Bianco, Pamela	50-80	R
Bianco, Pamela	Paradise Square (1st, sm8vo, 94p, yellow cl, 12 fp 1-color, dep, DJ/2.00)	NY: Oxford U.Pr.	1950	Bianco, Pamela	40-65	
Bianco, Pamela	Playtime in Cherry Street (1st, 8vo, 96p, ibds, fp b/w, pep, DJ/2.00)	NY: Oxford U.Pr.	1948	Bianco, Pamela	50-80	
Bianco, Margery W.	Skin Horse (1st, 8vo, ibds, 42p, pep, 5cp, DJ)	Doran	(1927)	Bianco, Pamela	160-240	
Bianco, Pamela	Starlit Journey (1st, 12mo, 47p, blue cl, col frn, b/w, pep, DJ/1.25)	Macmillan	1933	Bianco, Pamela	70-100	
Ewing, Juliana H.	Three Christmas Trees (1st, 12mo, green/gilt, 88p, col frn, dep)	Macmillan	1930	Bianco, Pamela	35-60	
Mathis, Sharon B.	Brooklyn Story (1st [1st bk.] {std}, sm8vo, 56p, b/w)	NY: Hill & Wang	1970	Bible, Charles	60-90	
Bice, Clare	Jory's Cove (1st {std}, 8vo, 104p, color, pep, DJ/2.00)	Macmillan	1941	Bice, Clare	25-40	
Moore, Clement C.	Night Before Christmas (16mo, ibds, 62p, color)	Rand/McNally	(1938)	Biers, C.	25-40	
Rodman, Maia	Market Day for 'Ti Andre (1st, 4to, 48p, b/w, DJ/2.00)	Viking	1952	Bigaud, Wilson	50-80	
Graham, Lorenz	I, Momolu (1st, 8vo, 226p, b/w, DJ/4.00)	Crowell	(1966)	Biggers, John	70-100	
Meigs, Cornelia L.	Helga and the White Peacock (1st, sm8vo, gilt, 81p, frn by...)	Macmillan	1922	Bigham, Ruth	30-50	
White, Anne T.	All About the Stars (1st, 8vo, 144p, 1-color, pep, DJ/1.95)	Random	(1954)	Bileck, Marvin	50-80	R*
Fisher, M.F.K.	Alphabet for Gourmets (1st, 8vo, 255p, 2-color, DJ/3.00)	Viking	1949	Bileck, Marvin	80-125	
Lawrence, Mildred	Crissy at the Wheel (1st {std}, 8vo, 200p, DJ/2.50)	Harcourt	(1952)	Bileck, Marvin	25-45	*
Rosenquist, Fingal	Nipper Shiffer's Donkey (1st, 8vo, 141p, uncut, b/w, DJ/2.50)	Harper	(1955)	Bileck, Marvin	40-65	
Colver, Anne	Nobody's Birthday (1st, 8vo, [42]p, color, cep, DJ/2.75)	Knopf	(1961)	Bileck, Marvin	40-65	
DeRegniers, Beatrice	Penny (1st, 16mo, 62p, ipcb, fp color, pep, DJ/3.95)	Viking	(1966)	Bileck, Marvin	45-70	
MacNeice, Louis	Penny that Rolled Away (1st, sq12mo, 37p, ipcb, b/w, cep, DJ/2.25)	Putnam	(1954)	Bileck, Marvin	40-65	R
Scheer, Julian	Rain Makes Applesauce (1st, 4to, [30]p, fp color, DJ/4.95, CH, NYTBI)	Holiday House	1964	Bileck, Marvin	70-100	
Johnston, Johanna	Sugarplum (1st, ob4to, [40]p, fp 2-color, dep, DJ/2.00)	Knopf	(1955)	Bileck, Marvin	50-80	R*
Freeman, Barbara	Timi: Tale of a Griffin (1st, 8vo, 48p, b/w, DJ/4.50)	Grosset/Dunlap	(1970)	Bileck, Marvin	30-45	
Kazin, Alfred	Walker in the City (1st {std}, 8vo, 176p, b/w, DJ/4.50)	Harcourt	(1951)	Bileck, Marvin	30-50	
Dole, Nathan H.	Russian Fairy Book (1st UK, 8vo, 126p, pep, 16cp)	L: Richards	1908	Bilibin, Ivan	450-600	
Bilibin, Ivan	Russian Wonder Tales (1st AM, 8vo, 323p, tan cl, 12cp)	Century	1912	Bilibin, Ivan	250-400	
Carpenter, Frances	Tales of a Russian Grandmother (1st AM {std}, lg8vo, 292p, 8cp, dep)	Doubleday/Doran	1933	Bilibin, Ivan	90-120	
Towers, Alton	Child's Aesop (1st AM, 16mo, red cl, 117p, color)	Stokes	[1902]	Billinghurst, Percy	80-120	*
Howard, Henry	Doings of the Dollymites (1st, 24mo, red cl, 94p, 23cp)	L: Sands	(1905)	Billinghurst, Percy	100-160	
Aesopus	Hundred Fables of Aesop (1st, 4to, 201p, yellow cl, fp b/w)	L: John Lane	1899	Billinghurst, Percy	125-180	
La Fontaine, J.	Hundred Fables of La Fontaine (1st, 8vo, green cl, 202p, fp b/w)	L: John Lane	1900	Billinghurst, Percy	120-180	
Aesopus	Never-Grow-Old Stories (1st, 8vo, 144p, color)	Lyons/Carnahan	(1925)	Billinghurst, Percy	35-60	*
Desmond, G.G.	The Other Side (1st, lg8vo, green cl, 196p, 4cp)	L: G. Richards	1903	Billinghurst, Percy	60-95	
Billings, Augusta	Gilbert the Gay Poodle (1st, sm4to, ibds, 32p, 2-color, DJ/1.00)	Viking	1949	Billings, A.& H.	45-70	
Billings, Henry	Diesel-Electric 4030 (1st, 4to, 69p, pep, DJ/2.50)	Viking	1950	Billings, Henry	30-50	R*
Marquand, Josephine	Chi Ming & the Writing Lesson (1st AM, 4to, [32]p, fp color, DJ/4.95)	F. Watts	1970	Binder, Pearl	30-45	
Marquand, Josephine	Chi Ming and the Tiger Kitten (1st AM, 4to, [32]p, fp color, DJ/3.95)	F. Watts	(1965)	Binder, Pearl	30-45	
Binney, Ida	Boppet, Please Stop It (1st, 8vo, ipcb, 48p, 1-color, DJ/1.50)	W.R. Scott	1946	Binney, Ida	40-60	
Woodcock, Louise	This is the Way the Animals Walk (1st, ob8vo, [20]p, spiral bds, color)	W.R. Scott	1946	Binney, Ida	40-60	*
Carryl, Charles E.	Admiral's Caravan (1st, sq8vo, 140p, gilt, b/w, PPP)	Century	1892	Birch, Reginald	100-170	R
Nash, Ogden	Bad Parents' Garden of Verse (1st, 8vo, 132p, b/w, DJ/2.00)	Simon/Schuster	1936	Birch, Reginald	40-65	
Brown, Abbie F.	Christmas Angel (1st, sm8vo, ibds, 82p, 6pl)	Houghton	1910	Birch, Reginald	25-45	
Cloud, Virginia W.	Down Durley Lane (1st, lg8vo, 99p, teg, green/gilt, 1-color)	Century	1898	Birch, Reginald	60-90	
Braley, Berton	Enchanted Flivver (1st, 8vo, blue/gilt, 255p, b/w)	Century	(1926)	Birch, Reginald	70-100	*
Shute, Henry A.	Farming It (1st, 12mo, 248p, gilt, 16pl)	Houghton	1909	Birch, Reginald	30-50	
Wells, Carolyn	Folly in the Forest (1st, 8vo, 282p, olive cl, 12pl)	Altemus	(1902)	Birch, Reginald	45-70	
Burnett, Frances H.	Giovanni & the Other (1st, 8vo, 193p, olive/gilt, 9pl, cep)	Scribner	1892	Birch, Reginald	100-160	
Jepson, Edgar	Happy Pollyooly (1st, sm8vo, 314p, 5pl)	Bobbs-Merrill	(1915)	Birch, Reginald	40-65	
Jamison, C.V.	Lady Jane (1st, 8vo, gilt, 233p, b/w)	Century	1891	Birch, Reginald	50-80	
Burnett, Frances H.	Little Lord Fauntleroy (1st [1], 8vo, 209p, gilt, 26 b/w, PPP)	Scribner	1886	Birch, Reginald	600-900	
Burnett, Frances H.	Little Lord Fauntleroy (1st [new ed.], 8vo, 246p, teg, p-o, 10cp)	Scribner	1911	Birch, Reginald	100-160	
Alcott, Louisa M.	Little Men (sm8vo, 381p, teg, green/gilt, 15pl)	Little/Brown	1901	Birch, Reginald	35-60	
Burnett, Frances H.	Little St. Elizabeth (1st AM, 8vo, 146p, 12 b/w)	Scribner	1890	Birch, Reginald	75-125	
Malory, Thomas	Malory's King Arthur (1st, 8vo, 421p, cp, pep)	Baker/Taylor	(1911)	Birch, Reginald	70-100	*
Bennett, John	Master Skylark (1st, 12mo, brown cl, 380p, b/w, PPP)	Century	1897	Birch, Reginald	85-140	
Johnston, Annie F.	Miss Santa Claus of the Pullman (1st, 8vo, 172p, gilt, col frn, 8pl)	Century	1913	Birch, Reginald	40-65	
Savery, Constance	Moonshine in Candle Light (1st {std}, sm8vo, 149p, fp b/w, pep, DJ/1.75)	Longmans	1937	Birch, Reginald	40-65	*
Moore, Clement C.	Night Before Christmas (1st {std}, lg8vo, ibds, [43]p, color, DJ/1.50)	Harcourt	(1937)	Birch, Reginald	90-160	R
Burnett, Frances H.	One I Knew Best of All (1st, 12mo, 325p, gilt, teg, b/w)	Scribner	1893	Birch, Reginald	70-100	
Chambers, Robert	Orchard-Land (1st, sm4to, 112p, 7cp)	Harper	1903	Birch, Reginald	150-225	
Chambers, Robert	Outdoorland (1st, lg8vo, 105p, 7cp)	Harper	1902	Birch, Reginald	100-165	
Burnett, Frances H.	Piccino (1st, sq8vo, olive/gilt, 203p, 15pl)	Scribner	1894	Birch, Reginald	80-130	
Lloyd, John U.	Red-Head (1st, 8vo, teg, gilt, 208p, 10 fp b/w)	Dodd	1903	Birch, Reginald	40-65	
Burnett, Frances H.	Sara Crew (1st [1], 8vo, 83p, gilt, 6pl)	Scribner	1888	Birch, Reginald	180-250	
Lloyd, John U.	Scroggins (1st, sm8vo, 119p, gilt, teg, 4pl)	Dodd	1904	Birch, Reginald	40-65	
Wells, Carolyn	Story of Betty (1st {1st bk.}, sm8vo, red cl, 260p, 32pl)	Century	1899	Birch, Reginald	50-80	
Nesbit, Edith	The Wouldbegoods (1st AM, sm8vo, gilt, 313p, 16pl)	Harper	1901	Birch, Reginald	180-250	
Burnett, Frances H.	Two Little Pilgrims' Progress (1st, sq8vo, 191p, gilt, 12pl)	Scribner	1895	Birch, Reginald	120-200	R
Perry, Nora	Another Flock of Girls (1st, sq8vo, 194p, green/gilt, b/w)	Little/Brown	1890	Birch/Copeland	50-80	
Buck, Pearl S.	Dragon Fish (1st, 8vo, 63p, b/w, DJ/2.00)	John Day	(1944)	Bird, Esther B.	80-120	*

AUTHOR	TITLE	PUBLISHER	DATE	ARTIST	PRICE	LC
Rand, Ann	Did a Bear Just Walk There? (1st {std}, 4to, [27]p, color, DJ/3.75)	Harcourt	(1966)	Birnbaum, Abe	60-90	
Birnbaum, Abe	Green Eyes (1st, sq4to, [40]p, pep, color, DJ/3.50, CH, NYTBI)	Capitol Pub. Co.	(1953)	Birnbaum, Abe	70-100	R
Reid, Alastair	Supposing (1st {std}, lg8vo, 48p, 2-color, DJ/3.00)	Little/Brown	(1960)	Birnbaum, Abe	20-35	
Field, Rachel	Bird Began to Sing (1st, 8vo, 64p, p-o, 4cp, pep)	Wm. Morrow	(1932)	Bischoff, Ilse	30-60	
Phillips, Ethel C.	Gay Madelon (1st, 8vo, 142p, 4cp)	Houghton	1931	Bischoff, Ilse	30-45	
Foster, Elizabeth	Gigi (1st, lg8vo, 118p, col frn, b/w, pep, DJ/2.00)	Houghton	1943	Bischoff, Ilse	30-45	
Kuebler, Katharine	Hansel the Gander (1st, 8vo, 45p, green cl, 8 fp color, pep)	Wm. Morrow	(1930)	Bischoff, Ilse	25-45	
Hunt, Mabel L.	Little Grey Gown (1st, 8vo, 168p, b/w, DJ/1.75)	Stokes	1939	Bischoff, Ilse	25-40	
Moore, Clement C.	Night Before Christmas (1st, 24mo, ibds, [37]p, color)	Holiday House	(1937)	Bischoff, Ilse	80-130	R
Phillips, Ethel C.	Peter Peppercorn (1st, sm4to, 148p, pep, color, DJ/2.00)	Houghton	1939	Bischoff, Ilse	30-50	
Dalgliesh, Alice	Reuben & his Red Wheelbarrow (1st, 4to, ibds, [28]p, pep, color, DJ/0.50)	Grosset/Dunlap	1946	Bischoff, Ilse	30-50	
Young, Stark	Street of the Islands (1st, 8vo, 218p, fp b/w, pep, DJ/2.50)	Scribner	1930	Bischoff, Ilse	30-50	
Bischoff, Ilse	Wonderful Poodle (1st, lg8vo, 79p, pep, b/w, DJ/2.25)	Crowell	(1949)	Bischoff, Ilse	30-50	
Bontemps, Arna	You Can't Pet a Possum (1st, 8vo, 120p, red cl, 4cp)	Wm. Morrow	1934	Bischoff, Ilse	60-100	*
Haskell, Helen E.	Katrinka Grows Up (1st {std}, sm8vo, 310p, gilt, uncut, 6 fp b/w)	Dutton	1932	Bishcoff, Ilse	30-50	
Derleth, August	Country of the Hawk (1st {std}, 8vo, 192p, b/w, pep, DJ/1.75)	Aladdin	1952	Bjorklund, Lorence	50-85	
Montgomery, R.	Crazy Kill Range (1st {std}, 8vo, 192p, b/w, DJ/2.95)	World	(1963)	Bjorklund, Lorence	20-30	
Steele, William O.	DeSoto, Child of the Sun: Search for Gold (1st {std}, 8vo, 190p, DJ/1.75)	Aladdin	1956	Bjorklund, Lorence	20-30	
May, Julian	First Men (1st, sq8vo, [48]p, b/w, DJ/3.95)	Holiday House	(1968)	Bjorklund, Lorence	20-35	
Selden, George	Heinrich Schliemann (1st {std}, lg8vo, unpag, 2-color, DJ/2.95)	Macmillan	(1964)	Bjorklund, Lorence	25-40	
May, Julian	Horses, how They Came to Be (1st, sq8vo, [36]p, color, DJ/3.75)	Holiday House	(1968)	Bjorklund, Lorence	20-35	
Montgomery, R.	Kinkajou on the Town (1st, 8vo, 159p, b/w, DJ/3.75)	World	(1967)	Bjorklund, Lorence	20-30	
George, Jean C.	Moon of the Gray Wolves (1st, 8vo, 37p, b/w, DJ/3.75)	Crowell	(1969)	Bjorklund, Lorence	25-35	
Taylor, Don A.	Old Sam & the Horse Thieves (1st {std}, 8vo, 160p, fp b/w, DJ/3.50)	Follett	(1967)	Bjorklund, Lorence	25-40	
Norton, Andre	Scarface (1st, 8vo, 263p, black cl, p-o, b/w, DJ/2.75)	Harcourt	(1948)	Bjorklund, Lorence	200-300	
Means, Florence C.	Shadow Over Wide Ruin (1st, 8vo, 227p, 6 fp 1-color, pep, DJ/2.00)	Houghton	1942	Bjorklund, Lorence	25-45	
Judson, Clara I.	St. Lawrence Seaway (1st, 8vo, 160p, b/w, DJ/3.95)	Follett	(1959)	Bjorklund, Lorence	20-30	
Schaefer, Jack W.	Stubby Pringle's Christmas (1st, 8vo, 43p, 2-color, cep, DJ/2.75)	Houghton	1964	Bjorklund, Lorence	120-180	
Norton, Andre	Sword in Sheath (1st {std}, 8vo, 246p, b/w, DJ/2.50)	Harcourt	(1949)	Bjorklund, Lorence	250-400	
Schaefer, Jack W.	The Mavericks (1st, 8vo, 184p, b/w, DJ/3.25)	Houghton	1967	Bjorklund, Lorence	120-180	
Schaefer, Jack W.	The Plainsmen (1st, 8vo, uncut, 252p, b/w, cep, DJ/3.25)	Houghton	1963	Bjorklund, Lorence	120-180	
Montgomery, R.	Thornbush Jungle (1st {std}, 8vo, 159p, b/w, DJ/3.50)	World	(1966)	Bjorklund, Lorence	20-30	
Garthwaite, Marion	Tomas & the Red-Headed Angel (1st, 8vo, 190p, b/w, DJ/2.50)	J. Messner	(1950)	Bjorklund, Lorence	25-40	
Belloc, Hilaire	Bad Child's Book of Beasts (1st, sm4to, 47p, grey bds, b/w)	L: Duckworth	(1896)	Blackwood, B.T.	225-350	
Belloc, Hilaire	Cautionary Tales for Children (1st, sq8vo, ibds, 79p, b/w)	L: E. Nash	(1907)	Blackwood, B.T.	130-180	
Belloc, Hilaire	Modern Traveller (1st, 8vo, ibds, 80p, b/w)	L: E. Arnold	1898	Blackwood, B.T.	140-200	
Belloc, Hilaire	Moral Alphabet (1st, lg8vo, 63p, ibds, b/w)	L: E. Arnold	1899	Blackwood, B.T.	120-170	
Belloc, Hilaire	More Beasts for Worse Children (1st, ob4to, ibds, 48p)	L: Duckworth	1897	Blackwood, B.T.	160-240	
Belloc, Hilaire	Songs from Bad Child's Book of Beasts (1st, 4to, 35p, ibds, b/w)	L: Duckworth	1932	Blackwood, B.T.	60-100	
Henry, Marguerite	Auno and Tauno (1st, 4to, [27]p, ibds, p-o, color, pep, DJ/1.00)	Whitman	1940	Blackwood, Gladys	60-100	
Rue, Flora	Cocoa Dancer (1st, 4to, 27p, p-o, fp color, pep, DJ/1.25)	Whitman	1945	Blackwood, Gladys	60-90	
Henry, Marguerite	Dilly-Dally Sally (1st, sq4to, [16]p, pep, color)	Saalfield	1940	Blackwood, Gladys	70-100	
Henry, Marguerite	Geraldine Belinda (1st, sm8vo, [60]p, p-o, color, pep, DJ/0.60)	Platt/Munk	(1942)	Blackwood, Gladys	100-165	
True, Barbara	Their First Igloo on Baffin Island (1st, 4to, [28]p, p-o, col, pep, DJ/1.00)	Whitman	1943	Blackwood, Gladys	25-45	
Nelson, Rhoda	Wagon Train West (1st, 8vo, 224p, 4cp, fp b/w, pep, DJ/2.00)	Crowell	1939	Blaisdell, Elinore	30-45	
Mukerji, Dhan G.	Chief of the Herd (1st {std}, 8vo, 168p, 6pl, pep)	Dutton	(1929)	Blaine, Mahlon	30-45	
Pease, Howard	Jinx Ship (1st {std}, 8vo, uncut, 324p, col frn, pep)	Doubleday/Page	1927	Blaine, Mahlon	80-125	
Lang, Andrew	Tartan Tales (1st {std}, sm8vo, 301p, black cl, 8pl, pep, DJ/1.50)	Longmans	1928	Blaine, Mahlon	50-85	
Pease, Howard	Tattooed Man (1st {std}, sm8vo, 332p, col frn, b/w)	Doubleday/Page	1926	Blaine, Mahlon	70-100	
Means, Florence C.	Assorted Sisters (1st, 8vo, 250p, 4 fp 2-color, DJ/2.50)	Houghton	1947	Blair, Helen	30-50	
Govan, Christine	Carolina Caravan (1st, 8vo, 224p, uncut, 5 fp 1-color, DJ/2.00)	Houghton	1942	Blair, Helen	120-180	
Means, Florence C.	Great Day in the Morning (1st, 8vo, red cl, 182p, 6cp, pep, DJ/2.00)	Houghton	1946	Blair, Helen	30-50	
Means, Florence C.	Hetty of the Grande Deluxe (1st, 8vo, grey cl, 188p, 8cp, pep, DJ/2.50)	Houghton	1951	Blair, Helen	30-50	
Means, Florence C.	House Under the Hill (1st, 8vo, 184p, 8 fp 1-color, pep, DJ/2.50)	Houghton	1949	Blair, Helen	30-50	
Phillips, Ethel C.	Jeanne-Marie and her Golden Bird (1st, 8vo, 112p, 7pl)	Houghton	1934	Blair, Helen	100-160	
Means, Florence C.	Moved-Outers (1st, 12mo, 154p, orange cl, 5cp, pep, DJ/2.00, NH)	Houghton	1945	Blair, Helen	80-140	
Whitney, Phyllis	Place for Ann (1st, 8vo, 211p, col frn, DJ/2.00)	Houghton	1941	Blair, Helen	20-35	*
Allee, Marjorie H.	The House (1st, 8vo, 181p, b/w pl, DJ/2.00)	Houghton	1944	Blair, Helen	30-50	
Blaisdell, E. Ward	Animals at the Fair (1st, ob4to, [47]p, color)	R.H. Russell	(1902)	Blaisdell, E. Ward	250-350	
Culbertson, Anne V.	At the Big House (1st, sm8vo, blue cl, p-o, 348p, b/w)	Bobbs-Merrill	(1904)	Blaisdell, E. Ward	55-80	
Calhoun, Mary Eliz.	Dorothy's Rabbit Stories (1st, sm8vo, 115p, grey cl, 10pl)	Crowell	(1907)	Blaisdell, E. Ward	55-80	*
Hunt, Mabel L.	69th Grandchild (1st {std}, 8vo, 68p, fp b/w, DJ/1.75)	Lippincott	(1951)	Blaisdell, Elinore	25-40	
Hunt, Mabel L.	Double Birthday Present (1st {std}, sm8vo, 52p, red cl, col frn, DJ/1.50)	Lippincott	(1947)	Blaisdell, Elinore	45-70	
Blaisdell, Elinore	Falcon, Fly Back (1st, 8vo, red/gilt, 177p, fp 3-color, pep, DJ/2.50)	J. Messner	(1939)	Blaisdell, Elinore	50-75	
Vorse, Mary E.	Grubby Gets Clean (1st, 8vo, ipcb, [41]p, 1-color, cep, DJ/1.00)	W.R. Scott	1943	Blaisdell, Elinore	30-50	
Hunt, Mabel L.	Matilda's Buttons (1st {std}, 8vo, 132p, b/w, DJ/1.75)	Lippincott	(1948)	Blaisdell, Elinore	30-50	
Lockridge, Frances	Proud Cat (1st {std}, 8vo, 95p, b/w, DJ/2.25)	Lippincott	(1951)	Blaisdell, Elinore	30-45	
De La Mare, Walter	Rhymes & Verses (1st {std}, lg8vo, 344p, pl, DJ/3.00)	Henry Holt & Co.	(1947)	Blaisdell, Elinore	30-55	
Cutler, U. Waldo	Stories of King Arthur (1st, 8vo, 308p, fp 1-color, pep, DJ/2.00)	Crowell	(1941)	Blaisdell, Elinore	40-65	
Tibber, Robert	Aristide (1st, 4to, ipcb, 61p, 1-color, DJ/3.50)	Dial Press	(1966)	Blake, Quentin	30-50	
Yeoman, John	Bear's Water Picnic (1st {std}, sm4to, [28]p, fp color, DJ/4.95)	Macmillan	1970	Blake, Quentin	20-35	
Schickel, Richard	Gentle Knight (1st AM, 8vo, 58p, 1-color, pep, DJ/2.75)	Abelard-Schuman	1964	Blake, Quentin	25-40	
Corddry, Thomas	Kibby's Big Feet (1st, lg8vo, 112p, b/w, DJ/3.50)	Follett	(1970)	Blake, Quentin	25-45	
Blake, William	Art of William Blake (1st, 4to, green/gilt, 56p, 51pl)	Moffat	1907	Blake, William	75-100	
Barrie, James M.	Blampied Edition of Peter Pan (1st, 4to, 216p, white cl, 12 ticp, pep)	L: Hodder	1939	Blampied, Edmund	300-500	
Barrie, James M.	Peter Pan and Wendy (1st AM, sm4to, 216p, gilt, 12cp, pep, DJ/3.50)	Scribner	1940	Blampied, Edmund	120-200	
Stevenson, Rbt. L.	Travels with a Donkey in the Cevennes (1st, 8vo, 189p, gilt, 8pl, pep)	L: John Lane	1931	Blampied, Edmund	90-120	
Wells, Carolyn	Lover's Baedeker & Guide to Arcady (1st, 12mo, 115p, b/w, pep)	Stokes	(1912)	Blashfield, A.D.	50-80	

AUTHOR	TITLE	PUBLISHER	DATE	ARTIST	PRICE	LC
Blatter, Dorothy	Uncle Ali's Secret (1st, lg8vo, 32p, p-o, color, pep, DJ/1.00)	Whitman	1939	Blatter, Dorothy	30-50	
White, Stewart E.	Magic Forest (1st, sm8vo, 146p, gilt, teg, 6cp, pep)	Macmillan	1903	Bleeson	30-50	
Holt, Isabella	Adventures of Rinaldo (1st {std}, 8vo, 142p, b/w, DJ/3.00)	Little/Brown	(1959)	Blegvad, Erik	25-45	
Norton, Mary	Bed-Knob & Broomstick (1st AM {std}, sm8vo, blue cl, 189p, b/w, DJ/3.00)	Harcourt	(1957)	Blegvad, Erik	80-140	
Langton, Jane	Diamond in the Window (1st, 8vo, ibds, 242p, b/w, DJ/2.95)	Harper	1962	Blegvad, Erik	50-80	
Miles, Miska	Dusty and the Fiddlers (1st {std}, 8vo, 52p, b/w, DJ/2.95)	Little/Brown	(1962)	Blegvad, Erik	25-40	
Stafford, Jean	Elephi (1st {std}, sm8vo, 76p, b/w, DJ/3.50)	Ariel	1962	Blegvad, Erik	40-65	
Brenner, Barbara	Five Pennies (1st, 8vo, [30]p, color, dep, DJ/3.25)	Knopf	(1964)	Blegvad, Erik	30-50	*
Kingman, Lee	Flivver, the Heroic Horse (1st {std}, lg8vo, 75p, b/w, pep, DJ/2.50)	Doubleday	1958	Blegvad, Erik	30-45	
Kendall, Carol S.	Gammage Cup (1st {std}, 8vo, 221p, blue cl, b/w, DJ/3.25, NH)	Harcourt	(1959)	Blegvad, Erik	40-65	
Orgel, Doris	Good-Byes of Magnus Marmalade (1st, 8vo, 32p, b/w, DJ/2.75)	Putnam	(1966)	Blegvad, Erik	20-35	
Blegvad, Lenore	Great Hamster Hunt (1st {std}, 8vo, 32p, b/w, DJ/2.95)	Harcourt	(1969)	Blegvad, Erik	30-50	*
Smith, Robert P.	Jack Mack (1st, 8vo, ipcb, [29]p, color, DJ/2.50)	Coward	(1960)	Blegvad, Erik	30-50	
Fritz, Jean	Late Spring (1st, 8vo, [31]p, fp 1-color, cep, DJ/2.50)	Coward	1957	Blegvad, Erik	60-90	
Sharp, Margery	Miss Bianca in the Orient (1st AM {std}, 8vo, 144p, gilt, b/w, DJ/4.95)	Little/Brown	(1970)	Blegvad, Erik	40-65	
Blegvad, Lenore	Mr. Jensen and Cat (1st {std}, 12mo, 32p, color, DJ/2.95)	Harcourt	(1965)	Blegvad, Erik	40-60	
Winslow, Marjorie	Mud Pies & other Recipes (1st {std}, 8vo, [24]p, b/w, DJ/2.50)	Macmillan	1961	Blegvad, Erik	25-40	
Pohlmann, Lilton	Myrtle Albertine's Song (1st {std}, 8vo, 218p, b/w, DJ/3.00)	Coward	(1958)	Blegvad, Erik	25-45	
Anthony, Edward	Oddity Land (1st AM {std}, 8vo, 64p, b/w, DJ/2.50)	Doubleday	(1957)	Blegvad, Erik	25-40	
Blegvad, Lenore	One is for the Sun (1st {std}, ob8vo, [32]p, color, DJ/3.50)	Harcourt	(1968)	Blegvad, Erik	30-50	
Orgel, Doris	Phoebe and the Prince (1st, ob 12mo, 31p, b/w, DJ)	Putnam	(1969)	Blegvad, Erik	20-35	
Miles, Miska	Pony in the Schoolhouse (1st {std}, 8vo, 60p, b/w, DJ/2.95)	Little/Brown	(1964)	Blegvad, Erik	20-30	
Livingston, Myra C.	See What I Found (1st {std}, 12mo, [32]p, b/w, DJ/1.95)	Harcourt	(1962)	Blegvad, Erik	20-35	
Langton, Jane	Swing in the Summerhouse (1st, 8vo, ipcb, 185p, b/w, DJ/3.95)	Harper	(1967)	Blegvad, Erik	60-95	
Andersen, Hans C.	The Swineherd (1st {std}, sq8vo, 32p, color, DJ/2.75)	Harcourt	(1958)	Blegvad, Erik	50-85	R
Jackson, Richard	Year is a Window (1st {std}, 12mo, [28]p, color, DJ/1.95)	Doubleday	1963	Blegvad, Erik	25-40	
Williams, Jay	Puppy Pie (1st {std}, 4to, [62]p, fp b/w, cep)	Crowell-Collier	(1962)	Blickenstaff, Wayne	50-80	*
Green, Mary M.	Everybody Eats (1st [rev. ed.], 8vo, ibds, [20]p, fp color, DJ/1.00)	Young Scott	1950	Bloch, Lucienne	100-165	
Monrad, Jean	How Many Kisses Good Night? (1st, lg ob8vo, ibds, [20]p, color, DJ/1.00)	W.R. Scott	1949	Bloch, Lucienne	30-50	
Brenner, Anita	I Want to Fly (1st, lg8vo, [34]p, ipcb, color, pep, DJ/1.50)	W.R. Scott	1943	Bloch, Lucienne	40-60	*
Green, Mary M.	Is it Hard? Is it Easy? (1st, sq8vo, ibds, [20]p, 3-color, DJ/1.00)	W.R. Scott	1948	Bloch, Lucienne	60-100	
Bradford, Margaret	Keep Singing, Keep Humming (1st, lg ob8vo, ibds, 66p, color, DJ/2.00)	Young Scott	(1946)	Bloch, Lucienne	35-50	
Hurd, Edith T.	Sandpipers (1st, sq8vo, [40]p, ipcb, 2-color, DJ/1.95, NYTBI)	Crowell	(1961)	Bloch, Lucienne	30-50	*
Woodcock, Louise	Smart Little Boy & his Smart Little Kitty (1st, ob8vo, ipcb, [20]p, color)	W.R. Scott	1947	Bloch, Lucienne	30-45	*
Hurd, Edith T.	Starfish (1st, ob8vo, [40]p, fp 3-color, DJ/2.50)	Crowell	(1962)	Bloch, Lucienne	30-50	*
Hewes, Agnes D.	Swords on the Sea (1st, sm8vo, 272p, col frn, 7pl, pep)	Knopf	1928	Bloch, Lucienne	25-40	
Brown, Margaret W.	Willie's Walk to Grandmama (1st, sm8vo, ipcb, [26]p, color)	W.R. Scott	1944	Bloch, Lucienne	70-100	
Blodgett, Mabel F.	Magic Slippers (1st, 12mo, 90p, 4cp)	Little/Brown	1917	Blodgett, Mabel F.	70-100	
Blodgett, Mabel F.	Peasblossom (1st, 8vo, 177p, p-o, 5cp)	Doran	(1917)	Blodgett, Mabel F.	35-60	*
Dearden, Harold	Wonderful Adventure (1st, sm8vo, 115p, p-o, b/w)	Cosmopolitan	1928	Blood, W.C.	25-40	*
Garis, Howard	Uncle Wiggily & Alice in Wonderland (1st, 4to, gilt, 361p, 8cp, pep, p-o)	Fenno	(1918)	Bloomfield, Edward	100-175	
Garis, Howard	Uncle Wiggily & Mother Goose (1st, lg8vo, 175p, p-o, gilt, color)	Fenno	(1916)	Bloomfield, Edward	150-225	
Garis, Howard	Uncle Wiggily's Arabian Nights (1st, 4to, gilt, 8cp, pep)	Fenno	(1917)	Bloomfield, Edward	200-300	
Arnold, Edwin	Japonica (1st, sm4to, teg, uncut, gilt, 128p, b/w pl)	Scribner	1891	Blum, Robert	100-160	
Eastman, Charles A.	Indian Boyhood (1st, 8vo, gilt, teg, 289p, 4pl)	McClure	1902	Blumenschein, E.L.	100-180	
Bennet, Robert A.	Thyra: Romance of the Polar Pit (1st, 12mo, 258p, gilt, 5pl)	Henry Holt & Co.	1901	Blumenschein, E.L.	30-50	*
Cooke, Marjorie B.	Dual Alliance (1st, sm8vo, 165p, blue cl, col frn, 4pl, dep)	Doubleday/Page	1915	Blumenschein, Mary	25-40	
Schwatka, Fred	Children of the Cold (1st, 12mo, 212p, gilt, b/w)	NY: Cassell	(1886)	Bobbett, Walter	100-165	
Ayers, Ray F.	King of Kinkiddie... (1st, sm8vo, 262p, 15pl)	Dutton	1904	Bobbett, Walter	100-165	
Neidlinger, Wm. H.	Owl and the Woodchuck (1st, lg8vo, [56]p, ibds, 4cp)	Rand/McNally	(1901)	Bobbett, Walter	50-85	
Neidlinger, Wm. H.	Small Songs for Small Singers (1st, lg4to, 57p, ibds, color)	NY: Schirmer	1896	Bobbett, Walter	50-90	
Beale, Will	Binky (1st, lg8vo, 125p, fp b/w, DJ/2.50)	Lothrop, Lee	(1954)	Bobri, Vladimir	20-35	
Slobodkina, Esphyr	Boris and his Balalaika (1st, sm4to, [42]p, color, DJ/2.95)	Abelard-Schuman	1964	Bobri, Vladimir	25-40	
Weik, Mary H.	House at Cherry Hill (1st {std}, 8vo, 135p, b/w, DJ/2.00)	Knopf	1938	Bobri, Vladimir	30-50	*
Budney, Blossom	Kiss is Round: Verses (1st, 4to, [34]p, fp color, dep, DJ/2.50, NYTBI)	Lothrop, Lee	1954	Bobri, Vladimir	100-165	R*
Rice, Inez	March Wind (1st, 4to, [30]p, fp color, pep, DJ/2.75)	Lothrop, Lee	(1957)	Bobri, Vladimir	50-80	R
Budney, Blossom	N is for Nursery School (1st, 4to, [27]p, color, pep, DJ/2.50)	Lothrop, Lee	1956	Bobri, Vladimir	40-65	
Zolotow, Charlotte	Sleepy Book (1st, sm4to, blue cl, [36]p, color, dep, DJ/2.75)	Lothrop, Lee	1958	Bobri, Vladimir	60-100	
Gottlieb, Suzanne	What is Red? (1st, sm4to, [19]p, fp color, DJ/2.95)	Lothrop, Lee	1961	Bobri, Vladimir	30-50	
Branley, Franklyn	What the Moon is Like (1st, ob8vo, ipcb, [40]p, fp 2-color, DJ/2.50)	Crowell	(1963)	Bobri, Vladimir	25-40	
Littlefield, Wm. J.	Whiskers of Ho Ho (1st, lg sq8vo, [32]p, fp color, pep, DJ/2.75)	Lothrop, Lee	1958	Bobri, Vladimir	30-50	
Bonsels, Waldemar	Adventures of Maya the Bee (1st, 4to, 224p, p-o, 6 dp 3-color)	Boni	1929	Bock, Vera	25-40	
N/A	Arabian Nights (1st, 8vo, 308p)	Longmans	1946	Bock, Vera	35-60	*
Gibson, Katharine	Bow Bells (1st {std}, 8vo, 124p, fp b/w, pep, DJ/2.00)	Longmans	1943	Bock, Vera	30-50	
Brewton, Sara W.	Bridled with Rainbows (1st {std}, lg8vo, 191p, DJ/2.75, b/w decor by...)	Macmillan	1949	Bock, Vera	25-45	
Leodhas, Sorche	By Loch and Lin (1st {std}, 8vo, 130p, fp b/w, DJ/4.95)	Holt, Rinehart	(1969)	Bock, Vera	30-50	
Gibson, Katharine	Cinders (1st {std}, sm8vo, 132p, fp b/w, pep, DJ/1.75)	Longmans	1939	Bock, Vera	25-40	
Sawyer, Ruth	Cottage for Betsy (1st {std}, 8vo, 120p, yellow cl, b/w, DJ/2.50)	Harper	(1954)	Bock, Vera	25-35	
Karazin, N.N.	Cranes Flying South (1st {std}, 8vo, 235p, blue cl, b/w, pep, DJ/2.50)	Doubleday/Doran	1931	Bock, Vera	30-50	
Kelly, Eric P.	Girl Who Would Be Queen (1st, lg8vo, 201p, DJ/2.00, decor by...)	McClurg	1939	Bock, Vera	50-80	
Gibson, Katharine	Jock's Castle (1st {std}, lg8vo, 139p, pep, b/w, DJ/2.00)	Longmans	1940	Bock, Vera	25-40	
Ershov, Peter P.	Little Magic Horse (1st, sm4to, [128]p, fp 2-color, pep, DJ/2.50)	Macmillan	1942	Bock, Vera	60-90	R
Softly, Barbara	Magic People Around the World (1st AM {std} sq8vo, [48]p, 1-color, DJ/3.50)	Holt, Rinehart	(1970)	Bock, Vera	30-50	*
Carus, Helena	Metten of Tyre (1st {std}, 8vo, 171p, col frn, fp b/w, pep)	Doubleday/Doran	1930	Bock, Vera	25-40	
Waring, P. Alston	Peacock Country (1st, lg8vo, 100p, bds, 2-color, DJ/3.00)	John Day	(1948)	Bock, Vera	20-30	
Segal, E.A.	Ring and a Riddle (1st {std}, sm4to, 65p, col frn, 1-color, DJ/2.00)	Lippincott	(1944)	Bock, Vera	30-50	
Lang, Andrew	Rose Fairy Book (1st {std}, 8vo, 212p, pink/gilt, 9cp, DJ/2.50)	Longmans	(1948)	Bock, Vera	40-65	
Leodhas, Sorche	Sea-Spell and Moor-Magic (1st {std}, 8vo, ibds, 207p, 10 fp b/w, DJ/4.95)	Holt, Rinehart	(1968)	Bock, Vera	30-45	

AUTHOR	TITLE	PUBLISHER	DATE	ARTIST	PRICE	LC
Turngren, Ellen	Shadows into Mist (1st {std}, 8vo, 207p, b/w, DJ/2.75)	Longmans	1958	Bock, Vera	20-35	
Brewton, Sara W.	Sing a Song of Seasons (1st {std}, lg8vo, 200p, DJ/3.50, b/w decor by...)	Macmillan	(1955)	Bock, Vera	25-45	
Young, Ella	Tangle-Coated Horse (1st {std}, 8vo, black cl, 186p, b/w, pep, NH)	Longmans	1929	Bock, Vera	65-100	
Kingsley, Charles	The Heroes (1st, 8vo, 196p, fp 1-color, pep, DJ/2.00)	Macmillan	(1954)	Bock, Vera	30-50	R
Edmonds, Walter D.	Wolf Hunt (1st {std}, 8vo, 112p, b/w, cep, DJ/4.50)	Little/Brown	(1970)	Bock, William	50-80	R*
Eager, Edward	Half Magic (1st {std}, 8vo, 217p, b/w, DJ/2.75)	Harcourt	(1954)	Bodecker, N.M.	120-200	
Gibson, Josephine	Is There a Mouse in the House? (1st {std}, 12mo, [32]p, pep, b/w, DJ/1.95)	Macmillan	(1965)	Bodecker, N.M.	20-30	
Eager, Edward	Magic by the Lake (1st {std}, 8vo, 183p, b/w, DJ/2.95)	Harcourt	(1957)	Bodecker, N.M.	70-120	
Shura, Mary F.	Shoe Full of Shamrock (1st {std}, sm4to, 64p, b/w, DJ/3.75)	Atheneum	1965	Bodecker, N.M.	20-30	
Eager, Edward	Time Garden (1st {std}, 8vo, 188p, b/w, DJ/3.00)	Harcourt	1958	Bodecker, N.M.	120-200	
Eager, Edward	Well-Wishers (1st {std}, 8vo, 191p, b/w, DJ/3.25)	Harcourt	(1960)	Bodecker, N.M.	80-140	
Mehdevi, Alexander	Bungling Pedro & other Majorcan Tales (1st {std}, 8vo, 117p, b/w, DJ/4.50)	Knopf	(1970)	Bodor, Isabel	20-35	
Jepson, Edgar	Garden at 19 (1st AM, 12mo, 299p, green/white, 4pl)	Wessels/Bissell	1910	Boehm, H.R.	120-200	
Coatsworth, Eliz.	Grandmother Cat & the Hermit (1st {std}, 8vo, 87p, fp b/w, DJ/4.50)	Macmillan	(1970)	Boker, Irving	20-35	
Trease, Geoffrey	Bows Against the Barons (1st, 12mo, 152p, b/w, DJ)	L: M. Lawrence	1934	Boland, Michael	60-100	
De La Mare, Walter	Broomsticks & other Fairy Tales (1st, 8vo, 378p, fp woodcuts)	L: Constable	1925	Bold	70-100	*
De La Mare, Walter	Stuff & Nonsense (1st, 12mo, green/gilt, 110p, teg, woodcuts)	L: Constable	1927	Bold	70-100	
Lexau, Joan M.	Benjie (1st, sm ob4to, [38]p, fp b/w, DJ/3.00)	Dial Press	(1964)	Bolognese, Don	30-50	
Lexau, Joan M.	Benjie on His Own (1st {std}, sm ob4to, ipcb, [38]p, fp b/w, DJ/3.95)	Dial Press	(1970)	Bolognese, Don	30-50	*
Roscoe, William	Butterfly's Ball & Grasshopper's Feast (1st, ob4to, [32]p, color, DJ/3.50)	McGraw-Hill	(1967)	Bolognese, Don	30-50	
Loken, Anna B.	Colt from the Dark Forest (1st, 8vo, 127p, b/w, DJ/3.00)	Lothrop, Lee	(1959)	Bolognese, Don	20-30	
O'Neill, Mary	Fingers are Always Bringing Me News (1st {std}, 8vo, 40p, 2-color, DJ/3.50)	Doubleday	(1969)	Bolognese, Don	25-45	
Wuorio, Eva-Lis	Happiness Flower (1st {std}, 8vo, 78p, gilt, dp b/w, pep, DJ/3.95)	World	(1969)	Bolognese, Don	25-40	
Rinkoff, Barbara	Headed for Trouble (1st {std}, lg8vo, 119p, b/w, DJ/4.50)	Knopf	(1970)	Bolognese, Don	20-30	
Smith, William J.	If I Had a Boat (1st {std}, ob8vo, [32]p, fp color, cep, DJ/2.95)	Macmillan	(1966)	Bolognese, Don	40-65	R*
Brooks, Walter	Jimmy Takes Vanishing Lessons (1st, lg8vo, [28]p, 1-color, cep, DJ/2.95)	Knopf	(1965)	Bolognese, Don	50-80	
Lexau, Joan M.	Jose's Christmas Secret (1st, lg8vo, 54p, fp b/w, pep, DJ/2.95)	Dial Press	(1963)	Bolognese, Don	25-40	
Lexau, Joan M.	More Beautiful than Flowers (1st, 8vo, [26]p, fp color, DJ/2.95)	Lippincott	(1966)	Bolognese, Don	25-40	*
Bolognese, Don	Once Upon a Mountain (1st, 8vo, [34]p, fp 2-color, DJ/2.95)	Lippincott	(1967)	Bolognese, Don	20-35	*
Mohan, Beverly	Punia and the King of the Sharks (1st, 4to, [32]p, color, DJ/2.50)	Follett	(1964)	Bolognese, Don	25-40	
Bolognese, Elaine	Sleepy Watchdog (1st, lg sq8vo, [33]p, fp 1-color, DJ/2.95)	Lothrop, Lee	(1964)	Bolognese, Don	25-45	
Coatsworth, Eliz.	The Secret (1st {std}, 4to, [31]p, 1-color, DJ/2.75)	Macmillan	(1965)	Bolognese, Don	25-40	
Hunt, Irene	Trail of Apple Blossoms (1st {std}, 8vo, 64p, color, DJ/3.95)	Follett	(1968)	Bolognese, Don	30-50	
Chase, Mary	Wicked Pigeon Ladies in the Garden (1st, lg8vo, 115p, b/w, cep, DJ/3.95)	Knopf	(1968)	Bolognese, Don	80-140	
Faulkner, William	Wishing Tree (1st {std}, 8vo, 82p, b/w, gilt, DJ/3.95)	Random	(1967)	Bolognese, Don	100-165	
Bishop, Claire H.	Yeshu, Called Jesus (1st {std}, 8vo, 97p, fp b/w, cep, DJ/3.50)	Farrar, Straus	(1966)	Bolognese, Don	30-50	
N/A	Arabian Nights (1st, 8vo, 257p, 4cp, b/w)	Winston	(1924)	Bolton, Adelaide H.	25-40	*
Molesworth, Mrs.	Imogen (1st, 12mo, 272p, gilt, 4pl)	L: Chambers	1892	Bone, Herbert A.	30-50	
Bone, Gertrude	This Old Man (1st, lg8vo, 131p, blue bds, gilt, frn by...)	L: Macmillan	1925	Bone, Muirhead	35-60	
Ressner, Phil	August Explains (1st, 4to, [32]p, ibds, fp 2-color DJ/2.50)	Harper	(1963)	Bonsall, Crosby	40-65	*
Bonsall, Crosby	Case of the Cat's Meow (1st, 8vo, 64p, 2-color, DJ/1.95)	Harper	(1965)	Bonsall, Crosby	25-40	
Bonsall, Crosby	Case of the Dumb Bells (1st, 8vo, 64p, fp 2-color, DJ/1.95)	Harper	(1966)	Bonsall, Crosby	25-40	
Bonsall, Crosby	Case of the Hungry Stranger (1st, 8vo, 64p, 2-color, DJ/1.95)	Harper	(1963)	Bonsall, Crosby	25-40	
Bonsall, Crosby	It's Mine! (1st, 16mo, ipcb, [32]p, 1-color, DJ/1.95)	Harper	(1964)	Bonsall, Crosby	25-40	
Kahn, Joan	Seesaw (1st, 16mo, [24]p, b/w, DJ/1.95)	Harper	(1964)	Bonsall, Crosby	25-40	
Bonsall, Crosby	What Spot? (1st {std}, 8vo, 64p, 2-color, DJ/1.95)	Harper	(1963)	Bonsall, Crosby	20-35	
Humphrey, Mabel	Book of the Cat (1st, folio, ibds, [40]p, 6cp)	Stokes	1903	Bonsall, Eliz. F.	500-800	R
Repplier, Agnes	Fireside Sphinx (1st, 12mo, teg, 305p, gilt, 4pl)	Houghton	1901	Bonsall, Eliz. F.	30-50	
Bonte, George W.	Fun & Nonsense (1st, 4to, p-o, [40]p, color)	Caldwell	(1904)	Bonte, Willard	80-120	*
Johnson, Clifton (ed)	Oaktree Fairy Book (1st, 8vo, p-o, 365p)	Little/Brown	1905	Bonte, Willard	60-90	
Dickens, Charles	Christmas Carol (1st, 12mo, 113p, b/w)	L.C. Page	1913	Boog, Carle M.	30-50	
Linderman, Frank B.	How It Came About Stories (1st, 8vo, 221p, p-o, 6cp)	Scribner	1921	Boog, Carle M.	160-250	
Garst, Shannon	Story of Buffalo Bill (1st {std}, 8vo, 237p, uncut, fp b/w, pep, DJ/1.75)	Bobbs-Merrill	(1938)	Boog, Carle M.	50-80	*
Cooper, James F.	The Pathfinder (1st, 8vo, 540p, blue/gilt, p-o, 8cp, pep)	NY: Nelson	(1928)	Boog, Carle M.	30-50	*
Thompson, William	Wigwam Wonder Tales (1st, sm8vo, 156p, b/w)	Scribner	1919	Boog, Carle M.	30-45	
Riley, James W.	Flying Islands of the Night (1st, sm4to, bds, 124p, gilt, 16 ticp pep)	Bobbs-Merrill	(1913)	Booth, Franklin	125-200	R
Pickett, George E.	Heart of a Soldier (1st, 8vo, 215p, pcb, uncut, b/w)	NY: Moyle	(1913)	Booth, Franklin	60-90	
Dreiser, Theodore	Hoosier Holiday (1st [1], lg8vo, teg, olive bds, gilt, 513p, 32pl, pep)	NY: J. Lane	1916	Booth, Franklin	80-130	
Twain, Mark	Prince & the Pauper (1st, 8vo, teg, 284p, gilt, uncut, p-o, 7cp)	Harper	(1917)	Booth, Franklin	60-90	
Owen, Caroline D.	Seth Way (1st, sm8vo, 413p, col frn)	Houghton	1917	Booth, Franklin	40-65	
Nicholson, Meredith	The Poet (1st, 8vo, teg, 189p, blue/gilt, cep, 4cp)	Houghton	1914	Booth, Franklin	45-70	
Baker, Cornelia	Young People in Old Places (1st, 8vo, green cl, 322p, fp b/w)	Bobbs-Merrill	(1906)	Booth, Franklin	35-60	*
Martin, Patricia	Sing, Sailor, Sing (1st, sm ob4to, [30]p, fp 2-color, cep, DJ/3.50)	Golden Gate	(1966)	Booth, Graham	20-35	
Ryan, Marah E.	House of the Dawn (1st, 8vo, 407p, 4pl, pep)	McClurg	1914	Booth, Hanson	45-70	
Havighurst, Marion	First Book of Oregon Trail (1st {std}, 8vo, 60p, fp 1-color, pep, DJ/1.95)	F. Watts	(1960)	Borten, Helen	30-45	
Borten, Helen	Halloween (1st, 8vo, [34]p, fp 2-color, DJ/2.95)	Crowell	(1965)	Borten, Helen	25-40	
Longstreth, Joseph	Little Big Feather (1st, 4to, [40]p, color, pep, DJ/2.50, NYTBI)	Abelard-Schuman	1956	Borten, Helen	40-65	
Branley, Franklyn	Moon Seems to Change (1st, sq8vo, [40]p, color, DJ/1.95)	Crowell	(1960)	Borten, Helen	30-50	
Branley, Franklyn	Rain and Hail (1st, sq8vo, [40]p, color, DJ/2.50)	Crowell	(1963)	Borten, Helen	30-50	*
Borten, Helen	The Jungle (1st {std}, 4to, [32]p, ipcb, 13 dp color, pep, DJ/3.75)	Harcourt	1968	Borten, Helen	25-40	
Eberle, Irmengarde	Family to Raise (1st, 8vo, 92p, color, DJ/2.00)	Holiday House	1939	Bostelmann, Else	25-40	
Eberle, Irmengarde	Hop, Skip & Fly (1st, 8vo, 70p, grey cl, 2-color, DJ/2.00)	Holiday House	(1937)	Bostelmann, Else	30-50	*
Eberle, Irmengarde	Sea-Horse Adventure (1st, 8vo, [55]p, blue cl, 2-color, DJ/2.00)	Holiday House	(1937)	Bostelmann, Else	30-50	*
Gall, Alice C.	Splasher (1st, 8vo, 136p, fp 1-color, cep, DJ/2.00)	Oxford U. Pr.	(1945)	Bostelmann, Else	20-30	
Tucker, Elizabeth S.	Cats & Kittens (1st, lg4to, ibds, [26]p, 6 chromos)	Stokes	1895	Boston, Frederick	140-220	*
Boston, Lucy M.	Children of the Green Knowe (1st, sm8vo, 157p, cloth, 6pl, DJ)	L: Faber	(1954)	Boston, Peter	100-170	
Boston, Lucy M.	Children of the Green Knowe (1st AM {std}, 8vo, 157p, pcb, b/w, DJ/2.75)	Harcourt	(1955)	Boston, Peter	80-140	R
Boston, Lucy M.	Enemy at Green Knowe (1st AM {std}, 8vo, 156p, b/w, DJ/3.25)	Harcourt	(1964)	Boston, Peter	70-100	

AUTHOR	TITLE	PUBLISHER	DATE	ARTIST	PRICE	LC
Boston, Lucy M.	River at Green Knowe (1st AM {std}, 8vo, 153p, green cl, b/w, DJ/3.00)	Harcourt	(1959)	Boston, Peter	80-130	
Boston, Lucy M.	Sea Egg (1st {std}, 8vo, green cl, 94p, fp b/w, DJ/2.50)	Harcourt	(1967)	Boston, Peter	30-50	
Boston, Lucy M.	Stranger at Green Knowe (1st AM {std}, 8vo, 158p, b/w, DJ/3.00)	Harcourt	(1961)	Boston, Peter	70-125	
Boston, Lucy M.	Stranger at Green Knowe (1st, 8vo, 158p, b/w, DJ, CgM)	L: Faber	(1961)	Boston, Peter	70-125	
Boston, Lucy M.	Treasure of Green Knowe (1st AM {std}, 8vo, 185p, b/w, DJ/3.00)	Harcourt	(1958)	Boston, Peter	80-130	
Boswell, Hazel	French Canada (1st, ob8vo, 82p, 25cp, DJ/2.00)	Viking	1938	Boswell, Hazel	40-60	
Irving, Washington	Rip Van Winkle (1st, 12mo, 218p, red/gilt, b/w pl)	L: Macmillan	1908	Boughton, George	55-80	*
Bourgeois, Florence	Beachcomber Bobbie (1st {std}, ob12mo, ipcb, [32]p, color, pep)	Doubleday/Doran	1935	Bourgeois, Florence	30-50	
Bourgeois, Florence	Trailer Dog Trix & Nancy (1st {std}, lg 8vo, [32]p, ibds, DJ/0.75)	Doubleday/Doran	1938	Bourgeois, Florence	40-65	
Burnett, Frances H.	Lost Prince (1st, sm8vo, 415p, blue/gilt, 16pl)	Century	1915	Bower, Maurice L.	50-80	
Farrow, George E.	King's Gardens (1st, 8vo, 43p)	L: Hutchinson	1896	Bowley, Ada L.	75-100	*
Nesbit, Edith	Nine Unlikely Tales for Children (1st, 8vo, gilt, 279p, b/w)	L: T.F. Unwin	1901	Bowley/Millar	160-250	
Savery, Constance	Pippin's House (1st {std}, sm8vo, 207p, 6 fp b/w, pep)	Longmans	1931	Bowman, Charlot	60-90	*
Thomas, Dylan	Me and My Bike (1st AM, 4to, red cl, 53p, b/w, DJ/5.00)	McGraw-Hill	(1965)	Box, Leonora	65-90	
Boxer, Devorah	26 Ways to be Somebody Else (1st, ob8vo, [56]p, color, pep, DJ/3.25, NYTBI)	Pantheon	(1960)	Boxer, Devorah	40-65	*
Boyajian, Zabelle C.	Armenian Legends & Poems (folio, cloth, 196p, ticp)	Dent/Dutton	[1915]	Boyajian, Zabelle C.	200-300	
Boyajian, Zabelle C.	Gilgamesh: Dream of Eternal Quest (1st, lg4to, teg, 110p, gilt 15ticp)	L: G.W. Jones	1924	Boyajian, Zabelle C.	250-400	
Boyde, Richard	Last Dodo (1st {std}, 8vo, 131p, fp b/w, dep, DJ/3.75)	Farrar, Straus	(1967)	Boyde, Richard	40-65	
Fryer, Jane E.	Mary Frances First Aid Book (1st, lg8vo, p-o, 144p, gilt, color)	Winston	(1916)	Boyer, Jane A.	200-300	
Fryer, Jane E.	Mary Frances Knitting & Crocheting Book (1st, lg8vo, 270p, gilt, p-o, 7cp)	Winston	(1918)	Boyer, Jane A.	200-300	
Fryer, Jane E.	Mary Frances Sewing Book (1st, lg8vo, p-o, 280p, blue cl, pep)	Winston	(1913)	Boyer, Jane A.	200-300	
Warren, Ina R.	Mother Love (1st, 8vo, 166p, gilt, teg, p-o, col frn, pep)	Jacobs	(1911)	Boyer, Jane A.	30-50	
Earl, John P.	Captain of the School Team (1st, 12mo, 324p, 7pl, pep)	Penn	1910	Boyer, Ralph L.	80-125	
McIntyre, John T.	In the Rockies with Kit Carson (1st, sm8vo, p-o, 220p, b/w)	Penn	1913	Boyer, Ralph L.	30-50	
White, Eliza O.	Farm Beyond the Town (1st, 8vo, 147p, 1-color, cep, DJ/1.75)	Houghton	1937	Boyle, Mildred	30-45	
Clymer, Eleanor	Here Comes Pete (1st, lg8vo, 96p, color, DJ/2.00)	McBride	1944	Boyle, Mildred	40-65	*
Nelson, Rhoda	High Timber (1st, sm8vo, 280p, b/w, DJ/2.00)	Crowell	(1941)	Boyle, Mildred	30-50	*
Vance, Marguerite	Marta (1st, 16mo, ibds, 56p, 7 fp color, pep)	Harper	1937	Boyle, Mildred	30-45	
White, Eliza O.	Nancy Alden (1st, 8vo, 139p, 1-color, DJ/1.75)	Houghton	1936	Boyle, Mildred	25-45	
Aikins, Ruth	Smiling Princess (1st, sq8vo, [31]p, p-o, color, pep)	Norcross	(1922)	Boyle, Mildred	100-165	
Hunt, Mabel L.	Susan Beware! (1st, 8vo, 243p, green cl, b/w, pep, DJ/1.75)	Stokes	1937	Boyle, Mildred	30-50	
Clymer, Eleanor	Yard for John (1st, 8vo, 94p, fp 2-color, pep, DJ/2.00)	McBride	1943	Boyle, Mildred	40-65	*
Mendoza, George	Are You my Friend? (1st, 8vo, [31]p, color, DJ/4.95)	Prentice-Hall	(1970)	Bozzo, Frank	25-40	
Watson, Sally	Magic at Wychwood (1st, 8vo, 128p, fp b/w, cep, DJ/4.50)	Knopf	(1970)	Bozzo, Frank	80-140	
Chaconas, Doris	Way the Tiger Walked (1st {std}, ob8vo, [32]p, ipcb, fp color, DJ/4.95)	Simon/Schuster	(1970)	Bozzo, Frank	35-50	
Aiken, Joan	Whispering Mountain (1st AM, 8vo, 237p, b/w, pep, DJ/3.95)	Doubleday	(1969)	Bozzo, Frank	70-90	R*
Streatfeild, Noel	Fearless Treasure (1st, 8vo, 272p, b/w, DJ)	L: Joseph	1953	Braby, Dorothea	25-45	
Bracker, Charles	Chester (1st, sm4to, [48]p, p-o, color, DJ/2.00)	J. Messner	1939	Bracker, Charles	50-75	
Beach, Rex	Iron Trail (1st, sm8vo, red/gilt, 390p, 8pl)	Harper	1913	Bracker, M. Leone	30-50	
Hough, Emerson	John Rawn, Prominent Citizen (1st, sm8vo, 385p, 6pl)	Bobbs-Merrill	(1912)	Bracker, M. Leone	30-50	*
White, Stewart E.	Sign at Six (1st, sm8vo, 264p, green/gilt, 6pl)	Bobbs-Merrill	(1912)	Bracker, M. Leone	40-65	
Becker, Edna	900 Buckets of Paint (1st, ob8vo, ibds, [22]p, 2-color, DJ/1.50)	Abingdon-Cokes.	1949	Bradfield, Margaret	30-50	*
Judson, Clara I.	Lost Violin: They Came from Bohemia (1st, 8vo, 204p, b/w, pep, DJ/2.25)	Houghton	1947	Bradfield, Margaret	25-40	
MacLellan, Esther	Suzy and the Dog School (1st {std}, 8vo, 46p, b/w, pep, DJ/1.75)	Ariel	1953	Bradfield, Margaret	30-45	*
Heward, Constance	Pillow Stories (1st, sm8vo, 150p, b/w)	L: Richards	1901	Bradley, Gertrude	80-130	
Radford, Dollie	Songs for Somebody (1st, 8vo, ibds, 28p, 6cp)	L: D. Nutt	1893	Bradley, Gertrude	200-300	
Bradley, Mary H.	Alice in Elephantland (1st, sm8vo, 187p, b/w, pep)	Appleton	1929	Bradley, Mary H.	55-80	*
Waterloo, Stanley	A Man & a Woman (1st {this pub}, 8vo, 250p, red cl, teg, cvr by...)	Way & Williams	1897	Bradley, Will	70-100	R
Hope, Anthony	Adventure of Lady Ursula (1st, 8vo, 125p, grey/silver, teg, cvr by...)	R.H. Russell	1898	Bradley, Will	50-80	
N/A	American Stage of Today (1st, folio, [86]p, ipcb, b/w designs by...)	Collier	(1910)	Bradley, Will	120-200	
Chambers, Robert	Ashes of Empire (1st, 12mo, 342p, cvr by...)	Stokes	(1898)	Bradley, Will	80-125	
Monroe, Harriet	Columbian Ode (1st, 12mo, 23p, wraps, cvr by...)	Chi: W.I. Way	1893	Bradley, Will	220-350	
Monroe, Harriet	Dance of the Seasons (1st, 8vo, 20p, wraps, cvr & ti page by..)	R.F. Seymour	1911	Bradley, Will	100-170	R
Raine, William M.	Daughter of Raasay (1st [1st bk.], 12mo, 311p, cvr by...)	Stokes	(1902)	Bradley, Will	120-180	*
Lamb, Charles	Dissertation Upon a Roast Pig (1st, 16mo, 19p, pcb, p-o, 1-color)	(Concord)	(1903)	Bradley, Will	100-165	
A.E.	Earth Breath (1st, 12mo, 94p, ipcb, uncut, cover & title page by...)	J. Lane	(1897)	Bradley, Will	180-260	R
Gosse, Edmund	In Russet & Silver (1st, 12mo, 159p, tan cl, cvr by...)	Stone/Kimball	1894	Bradley, Will	120-170	*
Unknown	Leather Bottel (1st, 16mo, pcb, p-o, 14p, uncut)	(Concord)	(1903)	Bradley, Will	90-120	
Irving, Washington	Legend of Sleepy Hollow (1st, 12mo, 61p, ibds, p-o, cvr by...)	R.H. Russell	(1897)	Bradley, Will	120-180	
Wither, George	Love Song (1st, 24mo, blue pcb, p-o, 14p, uncut)	(Concord)	(1903)	Bradley, Will	80-120	
Herrick, Robert	Love's Dilemmas (1st, sm8vo, 193p, teg, cvr by...)	Herbert Stone	1898	Bradley, Will	100-165	
Meredith, Owen	Lucille (1st, 8vo, 382p, red/gilt, teg, cvr by...)	Stokes	(1897)	Bradley, Will	70-100	
Bradley, Will	Peter Poodle... (1st, sq4to, 166p, ibds, 26 fp color, pep)	Dodd	1906	Bradley, Will	700-1000	
LeGallienne, R.	Quest of the Golden Girl (1st, sm8vo, green/gilt, 308p, teg, cvr by...)	J. Lane	1896	Bradley, Will	90-120	
Browning, Robert	Rabbi Ben Ezra (1st, 16mo, 16p, pcb, p-o)	(Concord)	(1902)	Bradley, Will	75-100	
Irving, Washington	Rip Van Winkle (1st, sm8vo, bds, 35p, frn & cvr by...)	R.H. Russell	(1897)	Bradley, Will	200-300	
Hobbes, John O.	Robert Orange (1st, 12mo, 341p, blue/gilt, teg, title page by...)	Stokes	1900	Bradley, Will	40-65	
LeGallienne, R.	Romance of Zion Chapel (1st {std}, sm8vo, 297p, teg, cvr by...)	J. Lane	1898	Bradley, Will	100-165	
Omar Khayyam	Rubaiyat of Omar Khayyam (1st, 16mo, green ipcb, 61p, b/w)	R.H. Russell	(1897)	Bradley, Will	100-170	
Hobbes, John O.	School for Saints (1st, sm8vo, 405p, grey/gilt, cvr by...)	Stokes	(1897)	Bradley, Will	65-90	
Hough, Emerson	Singing Mouse Stories (1st [1st bk], 12mo, gilt, [182]p, teg, cvr by...)	Forest/Stream	1895	Bradley, Will	120-180	
Waterloo, Stanley	Story of AB (1st, 8vo, black cl, 351p, PPPa, cvr by...)	Way & Williams	1897	Bradley, Will	130-200	
Waterloo, Stanley	The Seekers (1st, sm8vo, 257p, teg, red cl, cvr by...)	Herbert Stone	1900	Bradley, Will	75-120	
Gissing, George	The Whirlpool (1st AM, 8vo, 424p, green cl, cvr by...)	Stokes	(1897)	Bradley, Will	60-90	
Mason, Walt	Uncle Walt (1st, 8vo, brown cl, teg, 189p, cvr by...)	Chi: Adams	1910	Bradley, Will	80-120	
Crane, Stephen	War is Kind (1st, tall 8vo, ipcb, woodcuts, 96p, uncut)	Stokes	1899	Bradley, Will	800-1200	
Hall, Tom	When Hearts are Trumps (1st, 12mo, gilt, 128p, teg, title page by...)	Stone/Kimball	1894	Bradley, Will	55-80	*
Waterloo, Stanley	Wolf's Long Howl (1st, 12mo, 288p, red cl, teg, cvr by...)	Herbert Stone	1899	Bradley, Will	60-100	

AUTHOR	TITLE	PUBLISHER	DATE	ARTIST	PRICE	LC
Bradley, Will	Wonderbox Stories (1st, 8vo, 154p, gold cl, fp b/w)	Century	1916	Bradley, Will	400-600	
LeGallienne, R.	Young Lives (1st, sm8vo, teg, 386p, cvr by...)	J. Lane	1899	Bradley, Will	100-145	
Dalgliesh, Alice	Happy School Year (1st, sm8vo, 141p, color)	Rand/McNally	(1924)	Brand, Mary S.	25-40	*
Brande, Marlie	Sleepy Nicholas (1st {std}, ob8vo, [29]p, 2-color, DJ/3.50)	Follett	(1970)	Brande, Marlie	20-30	
Stokes, Hugh	Belgium (1st, lg4to, black/gilt, 143p, 52 fp b/w)	L: Kegan Paul	1916	Brangwyn, Frank	120-180	
Sparrow, Walter S.	Book of Bridges (1st, 4to, gilt, 415p, teg, uncut, 36cp)	L: John Lane	1915	Brangwyn, Frank	100-170	
Hyne, Charles J.	Captured Cruiser (1st, 8vo, brown/gilt, 288p, 6 fp b/w)	L: Blackie	1893	Brangwyn, Frank	60-95	
Kinglake, A.W.	Eothen (1st AM, sm4to, 30p, teg, 12cp)	Lippincott	[1913]	Brangwyn, Frank	100-170	
Sparrow, Walter S.	Frank Brangwyn: His Work (1st, sm4to, gilt, 258p, teg, 20cp)	L: Kegan Paul	1910	Brangwyn, Frank	100-175	
Phillpotts, Eden	Girl & The Faun (1st, sm4to, 78p, 4cp)	L: Cecil Palmer	1916	Brangwyn, Frank	120-170	
Phillpotts, Eden	Girl & The Faun (1st AM, sm4to, pict cl, 78p, 4cp)	Lippincott	1917	Brangwyn, Frank	100-160	
Sparrow, Walter S.	Prints & Drawings of Frank Brangwyn (1st, 4to, 287p, gilt, 50pl)	L: John Lane	1919	Brangwyn, Frank	150-250	
Omar Khayyam	Rubaiyat of Omar Khayyam (1st, sm4to, 135p, grey cl, 5cp)	L: Gibbings	1906	Brangwyn, Frank	120-180	
Omar Khayyam	Rubaiyat of Omar Khayyam (1st, 12mo, beige/gilt, teg, 69p, 8 ticp, pep)	L: Foulis	(1910)	Brangwyn, Frank	100-160	
Omar Khayyam	Rubaiyat of Omar Khayyam (8vo, blue/gilt, 110p, 8cp)	L: Foulis	1913	Brangwyn, Frank	80-130	
Omar Khayyam	Rubaiyat of Omar Khayyam (4to, gilt, uncut, buckram, 15 ticp)	L: Foulis	(1919)	Brangwyn, Frank	130-200	
Omar Khayyam	Rubaiyat of Omar Khayyam (lg8vo, green/gilt, 4 color, pep)	L: Sampson Low	[1920]	Brangwyn, Frank	60-100	
Cupples, George	Spliced Yarn (1st, sm8vo, 300p, gilt, 5 fp b/w)	L: Gibbings	1899	Brangwyn, Frank	40-70	
Crockett, Samuel R.	Tales of Our Coasts (1st AM, 8vo, 203p, red buckram, teg, uncut)	Dodd	1896	Brangwyn, Frank	70-100	*
Barman, Christian	The Bridge (1st, sm4to, green/gilt, 249p, uncut, 24cp)	J. Lane	1926	Brangwyn, Frank	120-180	
Preston, Hayter	Windmills (1st, 4to, yellow cl, 125p, uncut, 16cp, dep)	Lane/Dodd	(1923)	Brangwyn, Frank	150-220	
Leighton, Robert	Wreck of the Golden Fleece (1st, 8vo, 352p, green cl, 6pl)	L: Blackie	(1893)	Brangwyn, Frank	80-130	
Baruch, Dorothy W.	Bobby Goes Riding (1st, 8vo, [35]p, red cl, color, pep)	Lothrop, Lee	1934	Brann, Esther	30-50	*
Carr, Mary J.	Children of the Covered Wagon (1st, 8vo, 318p, b/w, pep, DJ/2.00)	Crowell	(1934)	Brann, Esther	30-50	
Cooper, Frederic T.	Argosy of Fables (1st, 4to, 485p, blue cl, 24 ticp, pep)	Stokes	(1921)	Bransom, Paul	150-250	
McCracken, Harold	Biggest Bear on Earth (1st, sm4to, 114p, col frn, 6pl, cep, DJ/2.00)	Stokes	(1943)	Bransom, Paul	40-65	
Chaffee, Allen	Brownie: Engineer of Beaver Brook (1st, lg8vo, 99p, 4cp, pep)	Milton Bradley	(1925)	Bransom, Paul	40-70	
London, Jack	Call of the Wild (1st, 8vo, 254p, p-o, blue cl, 16cp, pep)	Macmillan	1912	Bransom, Paul	200-300	
Baker, Olaf	Dusty Star (1st, 8vo, 302p, aqua/gilt, uncut, 4pl, pep)	Dodd	1922	Bransom, Paul	40-65	
Alexander, Charles	Fang in the Forest (1st, sm8vo, 244p, 4pl)	Dodd	1923	Bransom, Paul	20-30	
McCracken, Harold	Flaming Bear (1st {std}, 8vo, 222p, b/w, DJ/2.50)	Lippincott	(1951)	Bransom, Paul	40-65	*
Roberts, Chas. G.D.	Fleet of the Furtive (1st, sm8vo, 384p, gilt, pep, frn by...)	Macmillan	1913	Bransom, Paul	20-30	
Miller, Leo E.	Hidden People (1st, 8vo, 321p, 8pl)	Scribner	1920	Bransom, Paul	30-50	*
Roberts, Chas. G.D.	Hoof and Claw (1st AM, 8vo, 291p, 8pl)	NY: Macmillan	1914	Bransom, Paul	40-65	
Miller, Leo E.	In the Tiger's Lair (1st, 8vo, 252p, 4pl)	Scribner	1921	Bransom, Paul	30-50	
McCracken, Harold	Last of the Sea Otters (1st, sm4to, 99p, col frn, fp b/w, pep, DJ/2.00)	Stokes	1942	Bransom, Paul	40-65	
Thompson, Jeannette	Over Indian and Animal Trails (1st, 8vo, gilt, p-o, 263p, 8cp, pep)	Stokes	(1918)	Bransom, Paul	40-60	*
Lippincott, J.W.	Phantom Deer (1st {std}, sm8vo, blue cl, 192p, 1 dp cp, 4pl, DJ/3.00)	Lippincott	(1954)	Bransom, Paul	30-50	
Dodge, Louis	Sandman's Forest (1st, 8vo, 293p, p-o, green/gilt, pep, 6cp)	Scribner	1918	Bransom, Paul	80-120	
Dodge, Louis	Sandman's Mountain (1st, 8vo, 278p, green/gilt, pep, 6cp)	Scribner	1920	Bransom, Paul	80-120	
Roberts, Chas. G.D.	Secret Trails (1st, 12mo, 212p, green/gilt, 8pl)	Macmillan	1916	Bransom, Paul	30-50	
Chaffee, Allen	Tawny Goes Hunting (1st, sm4to, 76p, 2-color, DJ/2.00)	Random	1937	Bransom, Paul	30-50	
Baker, Olaf	Thunder Boy (1st, 8vo, red cl, 288p, 4pl, pep)	Dodd	1924	Bransom, Paul	30-50	*
Lippincott, J.W.	Wahoo Bobcat (1st {std}, 8vo, 207p, 1 dp color, 4 dp b/w, DJ/2.50)	Lippincott	(1950)	Bransom, Paul	60-90	
Squier, Emma-Lindsay	Wild Heart (1st, sm8vo, green cl, 220p, b/w)	Cosmopolitan	1922	Bransom, Paul	30-60	
Lippincott, J.W.	Wilderness Champion (1st {std}, lg8vo, 195p, 6 dp b/w, 5pl, cep, DJ/2.50)	Lippincott	(1944)	Bransom, Paul	45-70	
Grahame, Kenneth	Wind in the Willows (1st, 8vo, blue/gilt, teg, 351p, 10cp, pep)	Scribner	1913	Bransom, Paul	160-240	
Lippincott, J.W.	Wolf King (1st, 8vo, 316p, col frn, 4pl, pep)	Penn	(1933)	Bransom, Paul	30-50	
Gatti, Attilio	Wrath of Moto (1st, lg8vo, 160p, b/w, DJ/2.50)	Scribner	1941	Bransom, Paul	40-65	
Perkins, Marlin	Zooparade (1st {A}, 4to, beige cl, 94p, 16 fp color, pep, DJ/2.95)	Rand/McNally	(1954)	Bransom, Paul	55-80	
Chapman, William G.	Green Timber Trails (1st, 8vo, green cl, 283p, 8pl)	Century	1919	Bransom/Bull	30-50	
Kaigh-Eustace, E.	Jungle Babies (1st, 8vo, 256p, black cl, p-o, color, pep)	Rand/McNally	(1930)	Bransom/Nelson	25-45	
Heimeran, Ernst	Story of the Coal-Black Horse (1st AM, 4to, [32]p, color, DJ/2.95)	NY: Hart	(1968)	Braun, Beatrice	30-45	
Braune, Anna	Honey Chile (1st {std}, 4to, 153p, color, pep, DJ/2.00)	Doubleday/Doran	1937	Braune, Anna	100-165	
Nye, Edgar W.	Guest at the Ludlow (1st, sm8vo, red/gilt, 272p, teg, 21pl)	Bowen-Merrill	1897	Braunhold, L.	30-50	
Towne, Robert D.	Teddy Bears at the Circus (1st, 12mo, ibds, [12]p, color)	Reilly/Britton	(1907)	Bray, J.R.	80-120	
Towne, Robert D.	Teddy Bears Come to Life (1st, 12mo, ibds, unpag, color)	Reilly/Britton	(1907)	Bray, J.R.	100-160	
Towne, Robert D.	Teddy Bears on a Tobaggon (1st, 12mo, ibds, [12]p, color)	Reilly/Britton	(1907)	Bray, J.R.	100-150	
Uttley, Alison	Traveller in Time (1st AM, 8vo, 306p, b/w, DJ/2.50)	Putnam	(1940)	Bray, Phyllis	120-200	
Bailey, Carolyn S.	For the Children's Hour (1st, 8vo, 336p, 8pl)	Milton Bradley	1906	Breck, G. William	25-40	*
Twain, Mark	Huckleberry Finn (1st, lg8vo, p-o, 421p, col frn, b/w)	Harper	(1923)	Brehm, Worth	30-50	
Tarkington, Booth	Penrod & Sam (1st, sm8vo, 356p, green/gilt, 8pl, PPP)	Doubleday/Page	1916	Brehm, Worth	100-165	
Burnett, Frances H.	My Robin (1st, 12mo, green/gilt, 42p, col frn)	Stokes	(1912)	Brennan, Alfred	80-120	
Monjo, Ferdinand N.	Drinking Gourd (1st, 8vo, 62p, color, DJ/2.50)	Harper	(1970)	Brenner, Fred	30-45	
Blackmore, R.D.	Lorna Doone (1st, lg8vo, p-o, 351p, black cl, color, pep)	Milton Bradley	(1921)	Brett, Harold M.	60-90	
Hale, Lucretia	Peterkin Papers (1st, 8vo, 219p, p-o, 4cp)	Houghton	1924	Brett, Harold M.	30-45	
Cooper, James F.	The Spy (1st, 8vo, 415p, p-o, 8cp)	Houghton	1924	Brett, Harold M.	30-50	
Johnston, Annie F.	Two Little Knights of Kentucky (1st, 8vo, 203p, blue/gilt, 8cp)	L.C. Page	1907	Brett, Harold M.	30-50	
Schultz, James W.	With the Indians in the Rockies (1st, lg8vo, 252p, p-o, 4cp)	Houghton	1925	Brett, Harold M.	30-50	
Brett, Molly	Story of a Toy Car (1st, 4to, 63p)	L: Warne	(1938)	Brett, Molly	60-90	*
Bishop, Claire H.	Lafayette: French-American Hero (1st, 8vo, 80p, fp 2-color, DJ/2.25)	Garrard Pub.	(1960)	Brevannes, Maurice	20-30	
Peart, Hendry	Red Falcons of Tremoine (1st {std}, 8vo, 244p, fp b/w, cep, DJ/3.00)	Knopf	(1956)	Brevannes, Maurice	20-35	*
Stevenson, Rbt. L.	Child's Garden of Verses (1st, 12mo, 68p, color)	Rand/McNally	(1942)	Brice, Tony	30-50	*
N/A	Three Little Kittens (1st, 12mo, ipcb, [32]p, fp 1-color)	Rand/McNally	1938	Brice, Tony	25-40	*
N/A	Three Little Pigs (1st, 12mo, ipcb, [47]p, fp color)	Rand/McNally	1941	Brice, Tony	25-45	*
Potter, Miriam C.	Timmy Mouse (1st, 16mo, [32]p, ibds, color, pep)	Rand/McNally	1951	Brice, Tony	50-80	
Dearmer, Mabel	Child's Life of Christ (1st, 8vo, 290p, 8cp)	L: Methuen	1906	Brickdale, E.F.	60-100	*
Browning, Robert	Dramatis Personae... (1st, sm4to, 246p, teg, green/gilt, 10cp)	L: Chatto	1909	Brickdale, E.F.	60-90	

AUTHOR	TITLE	PUBLISHER	DATE	ARTIST	PRICE	LC
Leighton (ed.)	Fleur & Blanchefleur (1st, sm4to, 61p, 37 color)	L: O'Connor	(1922)	Brickdale, E.F.	60-100	
Fairless, Michael	Gathering of Brother Hilarius (1st, 8vo, 142p, teg, gilt, 8 ticp)	L: Duckworth	1913	Brickdale, E.F.	45-70	
Brickdale, E.F.	Golden Book of Famous Women (1st, 4to, blue/gilt, 200p, 16 ticp)	L: Hodder	[1916]	Brickdale, E.F.	140-200	
Brickdale, E.F.	Golden Book of Songs & Ballads (1st, 198p, green/gilt, 24 ticp)	L: Hodder	[1915]	Brickdale, E.F.	150-225	
Palgrave, Francis T.	Golden Treasury of Songs & Lyrics (8vo, yellow cl, 459p, 12 ticp)	Hodder	[1915]	Brickdale, E.F.	90-120	
Tennyson, Alfred	Idylls of the King (1st, 4to, 174p, gilt, 21 ticp)	L: Hodder	(1911)	Brickdale, E.F.	200-300	
N/A	Old English Songs & Ballads (1st, lg4to, 198p, 24 ticp)	L: Hodder	[1915]	Brickdale, E.F.	200-300	
Browning, Robert	Pippa Passes (1st, 8vo, 254p, gilt, teg, uncut, 10cp)	L: Chatto	1908	Brickdale, E.F.	80-125	
Browning, Robert	Pippa Passes (1st AM, 8vo, 254p, grey/gilt, 10cp)	Lippincott	1909	Brickdale, E.F.	70-100	
Dyer, Ruth O.	Adventures of the Ink Spots (1st, 8vo, orange cl, 158p, col frn, pep)	Lothrop, Lee	(1923)	Bridgman, L.J.	80-120	
Bridgman, L.J.	Bridgman's Kewts (1st, sm4to, [94]p, color, pep)	Caldwell	(1902)	Bridgman, L.J.	100-165	
N/A	Bumps & Thumps (sq4to, pict tan cloth, color)	Caldwell	(1903)	Bridgman, L.J.	100-170	
Bridgman, L.J.	Bunny's House (1st, 4to, [40]p, color)	Caldwell	(1904)	Bridgman, L.J.	60-100	
Pratt, Charles S.	Buz-Buz (1st, sm8vo, 102p, fp b/w)	Lothrop Pub.	1898	Bridgman, L.J.	60-90	
Bonte, George W.	Christmas Stocking Rhymes (4to, tan cl, p-o, 38p, 17 color)	Caldwell	(1904)	Bridgman, L.J.	180-250	
Pool, Maria L.	Chums (1st, 8vo, 241p, 4pl)	L.C. Page	1900	Bridgman, L.J.	30-50	
Horwitz, Carolyn N.	Fairy-Lure (1st, 12mo, 345p, 1-color decor by...)	D. Lothrop Co.	(1891)	Bridgman, L.J.	55-80	*
Bridgman, L.J.	Farmer Fox (1st, 4to, [36]p, ibds, p-o, color)	Caldwell	(1900)	Bridgman, L.J.	80-125	
Poulsson, Emilie	Finger Plays for Nursery & Kindergarten (1st, lg8vo, 80p, gilt, b/w)	D. Lothrop Co.	1893	Bridgman, L.J.	60-100	
Bridgman, L.J.	Guess (1st, 4to, ibds, [104]p, color, pep)	Caldwell	(1901)	Bridgman, L.J.	100-150	
Bridgman, L.J.	Guess Again (1st, 4to, ibds, [104]p, color)	Caldwell	(1902)	Bridgman, L.J.	100-150	
Gulliver, Lemeul	Gulliver's Bird Book (1st, lg4to, 103p, color, pep)	L.C. Page	1902	Bridgman, L.J.	120-180	
Poulsson, Emilie	In the Child's World (1st, sq8vo, 443p, b/w, pep)	Milton Bradley	1893	Bridgman, L.J.	70-100	
Blanchard, Amy E.	Journey of Joy (1st, 8vo, 305p, 7pl)	Dana Estes	(1908)	Bridgman, L.J.	30-50	
Fitzhugh, Percy K.	King Time (1st, 8vo, green/gilt, 233p, 8cp, pep)	Caldwell	(1908)	Bridgman, L.J.	200-300	R
Crowninshield, Mrs.	Light-House Children Abroad (1st, 8vo, 446p, 38 b/w, gilt)	D. Lothrop Co.	1889	Bridgman, L.J.	40-65	
Pool, Maria L.	Little Bermuda (1st, 8vo, 163p, 4pl)	L.C. Page	1899	Bridgman, L.J.	25-45	
MacDonald, Eliz. R.	Little Canadian Cousin (1st, sm8vo, 129p, 6pl)	L.C. Page	1904	Bridgman, L.J.	30-50	
Badger, Joseph E.	Lost City (1st, 8vo, 326p, blue/gilt, 8pl)	Dana Estes	(1898)	Bridgman, L.J.	60-90	
Wesselhoeft, Lily	Madam Mary of the Zoo (1st, 12mo, 248p, blue/silver, 3pl by...)	Little/Brown	1899	Bridgman, L.J.	30-50	
Bridgman, L.J.	Mother Wild Goose & her Wild Beast Show (1st, lg4to, ibds, [104]p, color)	Caldwell	(1900)	Bridgman, L.J.	225-350	
N/A	My High School Days (1st, 8vo, teg, green/gilt, color)	Caldwell	(1908)	Bridgman, L.J.	70-90	
Hamlin, Myra	Nan in the City (1st, 12mo, 251p, red cl, 3pl)	Roberts Bros.	1897	Bridgman, L.J.	35-60	
Hamlin, Myra	Nan's Chicopee Children (1st, 12mo, 223p, 5pl)	Little/Brown	1900	Bridgman, L.J.	30-50	
Messer, Clarence J.	Next-Night Stories (1st, 12mo, 261p, 8pl)	Lothrop, Lee	1912	Bridgman, L.J.	30-50	
Hazelton, Mary	Our Little African Cousin (1st, 12mo, 98p, b/w)	L.C. Page	1902	Bridgman, L.J.	30-50	
Allen, Willis B.	Play Away (1st, 12mo, 171p, tan cl, 6pl)	D. Estes	(1902)	Bridgman, L.J.	25-45	
Wells, Amos R.	Rollicking Rhymes for Youngsters (1st, 8vo, 157p, 26 fp 2-color)	Revell	(1902)	Bridgman, L.J.	55-80	
Bridgman, L.J.	Santa Claus Club (1st, sm8vo, [80]p, color, pep)	Caldwell	(1907)	Bridgman, L.J.	80-130	
Bridgman, L.J.	Seem-So's (1st, 8vo, p-o, [80]p, silhouettes, col frn)	Caldwell	(1906)	Bridgman, L.J.	75-100	*
Morrison, Mary J.	Stories True & Fancies New (1st, 8vo, 208p, 11pl)	Estes & Lauriat	(1898)	Bridgman, L.J.	70-100	*
Steward, Ray M.	Surprising Adventures of Man in the Moon (1st, sm4to, 142p, 12cp)	Lee & Shepard	(1903)	Bridgman, L.J.	150-225	
Riley, Alice C.	Voyage of the Wishbone Boat (1st, lg8vo, ipcb, 205p, fp color, pep)	Caldwell	(1907)	Bridgman, L.J.	100-165	
Wells, Amos R.	Witchery Ways (1st, 12mo, 189p, 8pl)	Altemus	(1904)	Bridgman, L.J.	30-50	
Smith, Mary P.W.	Young Puritans of Old Hadley (1st, 12mo, 345p, gilt, 5pl, dep)	Roberts Bros.	1897	Bridgman, L.J.	45-70	
Briggs, Barbara	Licorice (1st, 4to, [24]p, ibds, 2-color, pep, DJ/2.00)	Aladdin	(1949)	Briggs, Barbara	50-80	
Nesbit, Wilbur D.	Oh Skin-nay! (1st, ob folio, [125]p, illus)	Volland	(1913)	Briggs, C.A.	80-125	
Nesbit, Wilbur D.	When a Feller Needs a Friend (1st, 4to, ibds, [96]p, 2-color)	Volland	(1914)	Briggs, C.A.	90-145	*
Vipont, Elfrida	Elephant and the Bad Baby (1st, ob4to, [32]p, color, DJ)	L: Hamilton	1969	Briggs, Raymond	70-100	
Briggs, Raymond	Fee-Fi-Fo-Fum (1st AM, lg ob8vo, 40p, 2-color, DJ/3.00)	Coward	1964	Briggs, Raymond	60-85	
Briggs, Raymond	Jim & the Beanstalk (1st, 4to, [40]p, color, DJ)	L: Hamilton	1970	Briggs, Raymond	50-80	*
Briggs, Raymond	Mother Goose Treasury (1st AM, 4to, gilt, 217p, color, DJ/8.95, KGM)	Coward	(1966)	Briggs, Raymond	60-90	
Manning-Sanders, Ruth	Peter & the Piskies (1st AM, 8vo, 215p, b/w, DJ)	NY: Roy	(1958)	Briggs, Raymond	30-50	
Briggs, Raymond	Ring-a-Ring O'Roses (1st AM, sm4to, 48p, fp color, DJ/3.00)	Coward	(1962)	Briggs, Raymond	60-90	
Mayne, William	Whistling Rufus (1st AM {std}, 8vo, 120p, b/w, DJ/3.00)	Dutton	(1965)	Briggs, Raymond	25-40	
Briggs, Raymond	White Land (1st AM {std}, sm ob4to, 48p, 2-color, DJ/3.00)	Coward	1963	Briggs, Raymond	30-50	*
Mayne, William	William Mayne's Book of Giants (1st AM {std}, 8vo, 215p, b/w, DJ/4.95)	Dutton	(1969)	Briggs, Raymond	30-50	*
Wilson, Barbara K.	Wonderful Cornet (1st, 8vo, 96p, b/w, DJ)	L: H. Hamilton	1958	Briggs, Raymond	50-85	
Bright, Robert	Georgie and the Magician (1st {std}, ob4to, ibds, 46p, 1-color, DJ/3.25)	Doubleday	(1966)	Bright, Robert	45-70	
Bright, Robert	Georgie to the Rescue (1st {std}, ob4to, [32]p, 2-color, DJ/1.75)	Doubleday	1956	Bright, Robert	45-70	
Bright, Robert	Georgie's Halloween (1st {std}, ob4to, ibds, [32]p, color, DJ/2.00)	Doubleday	1958	Bright, Robert	45-70	
Bright, Robert	Hurrah for Freddie! (1st {std}, ob8vo, [39]p, 1-color, cep, DJ/2.00)	Doubleday	1953	Bright, Robert	30-50	
Bright, Robert	I Like Red (1st {std}, sq8vo, ipcb, [30]p, 2-color, pep, DJ/1.50)	Doubleday	1955	Bright, Robert	30-50	
Bright, Robert	Me & the Bears (1st {std}, ob8vo, ibds, [34]p, fp 1-color, cep, DJ/1.25)	Doubleday	1951	Bright, Robert	30-50	
Bright, Robert	Miss Pattie (1st {std}, sm4to, ipcb, unpag, 2-color, pep, DJ/2.00)	Doubleday	1954	Bright, Robert	30-50	
Bright, Robert	My Red Umbrella (1st, 12mo, [32]p, 1-color, DJ/2.00)	Wm. Morrow	1959	Bright, Robert	25-40	
Bright, Robert	Richard Brown & Dragon (1st {std}, 8vo, 81p, ipcb, 1-color, cep, DJ/2.00)	Doubleday	(1952)	Bright, Robert	25-40	
Bright, Robert	Travels of Ching (1st, ob8vo, ipcb, [65]p, 1-color, pep, DJ/1.25)	W.R. Scott	1943	Bright, Robert	40-65	
Evans, C.S.	Reynard the Fox (1st, 4to, 127p, p-o, 6cp)	Dodd	(1923)	Brightwell, L.R.	40-65	
Brill, George R.	Rhymes of the Golden Age (1st, lg8vo, 121p, gilt, p-o, pep, 12 color)	Stern	1908	Brill, George R.	70-125	*
Williams, Jay	Eagle Jake and Indian Pete (1st, sm8vo, 38p, ibds, color, DJ/1.25)	NY: Rinehart	(1947)	Brimer, John B.	25-40	
Brisley, Joyce L.	Further Doings of Milly-Molly-Mandy (1st AM, 12mo, 95p, color)	L: Harrap	1932	Brisley, Joyce L.	30-50	
Brisley, Joyce L.	Milly-Molly-Mandy Stories (1st, 12mo, 95p, col frn)	L: Harrap	1928	Brisley, Joyce L.	50-85	*
Bigham, Madge A.	Stories of Mother Goose Village (1st, sq8vo, 196p, gilt, color, pep)	Rand/McNally	(1903)	Brison, Ella S.	80-130	
Eaton, Jeanette	Betsy's Napoleon (1st, 8vo, 274p, bds, color, pep, DJ/2.50)	Wm. Morrow	1936	Brissaud, Pierre	30-50	
O'Neill, Moira	Elf-Errant (1st, 8vo, teg, 109p, pink/gilt, 7pl)	L: Lawrence/Bul.	1895	Britten, William E.	80-120	
Watson, H.B.M.	Chloris of the Island (1st, sm8vo, 281p, 32pl)	Harper	1900	Brock, C.& H.	50-80	*
Farnol, Jeffery	Amateur Gentleman (1st UK, 8vo, blue/gilt, 599p, teg, 21cp)	L: Sampson Low	(1916)	Brock, Charles E.	75-100	*

AUTHOR	TITLE	PUBLISHER	DATE	ARTIST	PRICE	LC
Galt, John	Annals of the Parish (1st, 12mo, gilt, 334p, AEG, 40pl, pep)	L: Macmillan	1896	Brock, Charles E.	60-80	
Dickens, Charles	Battle of Life (1st, 12mo, gilt, 165p, teg, 8cp)	L: J.M. Dent	1907	Brock, Charles E.	50-85	
Hohler, Mrs. Edwin	Bravest of them All (1st, sm8vo, 214p, blue/gilt, 8pl)	L: Macmillan	1899	Brock, Charles E.	45-70	
Farnol, Jeffery	Broad Highway (1st, lg8vo, 493p, blue/gilt, p-o, 24cp)	L: Sampson Low	1910	Brock, Charles E.	60-90	
Farnol, Jeffery	Broad Highway (1st AM, lg8vo, 518p, p-o, teg, 24cp)	Little/Brown	1912	Brock, Charles E.	55-80	
Wiggin, Kate D.	Cathedral Courtship (1st, 8vo, gilt, 104p, teg, 6pl)	Houghton	1901	Brock, Charles E.	35-60	*
Irving, Washington	Christmas at Bracebridge Hall (1st, 8vo, 267p, teg, 24cp, dep)	L: Dent	1906	Brock, Charles E.	50-80	
Dickens, Charles	Christmas Carol (1st, 12mo, 158p, teg, 8cp)	Dent/Dutton	(1905)	Brock, Charles E.	40-65	
Gaskell, Mrs.	Cranford (1st AM, sm8vo, teg, green/gilt, 255p, 24cp)	Dent/Dutton	1904	Brock, Charles E.	40-60	
Molesworth, Mrs.	Cuckoo Clock (1st, 8vo, 196p, 16cp, pep)	L: Macmillan	1931	Brock, Charles E.	50-80	
Cowper, William	Diverting History of John Gilpin (1st, 8vo, 50p, teg, blue/gilt, 12pl)	L: Aldine House	1898	Brock, Charles E.	60-90	*
Hartland, Edwin	English Fairy & Folk Tales (1st, sm8vo, 282p, AEG, 13pl)	L: W. Scott	1893	Brock, Charles E.	75-100	*
Malet, Lucas	Golden Galleon (1st, 12mo, grey/gilt, 158p, 6cp)	L: Hodder	(1910)	Brock, Charles E.	35-50	
Swift, Jonathan	Gulliver's Travels (1st, 12mo, 381p, green/gilt, AEG, b/w)	Macmillan	1894	Brock, Charles E.	70-125	*
Dickens, Charles	Haunted Man (1st, 8vo, 184p, teg, vellum, 8cp)	Dent/Dutton	1907	Brock, Charles E.	70-120	
Farnol, Jeffery	Honorable Mr. Tawnish (1st, 8vo, 118p, gilt, teg, 8cp)	L: Sampson Low	1913	Brock, Charles E.	55-80	
Farnol, Jeffery	Honorable Mr. Tawnish (1st AM, sm8vo, 165p, lavender/gilt, 4cp)	Little/Brown	1913	Brock, Charles E.	45-70	
Manning, Anne	Household of Sir Thomas More (1st, 12mo, 185p, teg, 24cp, dep)	L: J.M. Dent	1906	Brock, Charles E.	45-75	
Hood, Thomas	Humerous Poems (1st, sm8vo, AEG, 236p, gilt, b/w, cep)	L: Macmillan	1893	Brock, Charles E.	60-90	
Scott, Walter	Ivanhoe (1st, 8vo, blue/gilt, 523p, teg, uncut, 12cp, dep)	L: Dent	1899	Brock, Charles E.	70-100	
Irving, Washington	Keeping of Christmas... (1st, 12mo, 267p, teg, gilt, 24cp, pep)	Dutton	1906	Brock, Charles E.	55-80	
Stevenson, Rbt. L.	Kidnapped (1st, 8vo, 251p)	L: Macmillan	1928	Brock, Charles E.	55-80	*
Scott, Walter	Lady of the Lake (1st, 12mo, 236p, gilt, b/w)	L: Service/Paton	1898	Brock, Charles E.	30-50	
Lamb, Charles	Last Essays of Elia (1st, 12mo, 254p, teg, uncut)	L: Dent	1900	Brock, Charles E.	50-80	
Dickens, Charles	Life of Nicholas Nickleby (lg8vo, 711p, gilt, 16cp)	Dodd	1931	Brock, Charles E.	60-100	
Malet, Lucas	Little Peter (1st {new ed.}, sm4to, 175p, teg, white cl, uncut, 8 ticp)	L: H. Frowde	1909	Brock, Charles E.	60-90	
Corkey, Ethel	Magic Circle (1st, lg8vo, gilt, 256p, col frn, b/w)	L: Blackie	[1924]	Brock, Charles E.	50-80	
Farjeon, Eleanor	Martin Pippin in the Apple Orchard (1st, 8vo, brown cl, 369p, 5 ticp)	L: Collins	(1921)	Brock, Charles E.	60-90	
Lamb, Charles	Mrs. Leicester's School (1st, 8vo, 125p, blue cl, 5pl)	L: Wells/Gard.	(1904)	Brock, Charles E.	30-50	
Ewing, Juliana H.	Mrs. Overtheway's Rememberances (12mo, red/gilt, p-o, 209p, color)	L: H. Frowde	(1911)	Brock, Charles E.	30-50	
Phillpotts, Eden	Nancy Owlett (1st AM, 8vo, 262p, gilt, 8cp)	NY: Macmillan	1933	Brock, Charles E.	25-40	
Austen, Jane	Northanger Abbey (1st, 8vo, 206p, gilt, 24cp)	L: J.M. Dent	1907	Brock, Charles E.	60-90	
Wiggin, Kate D.	Penelope's Irish Experiences (1st, 8vo, gilt, AEG, 335p, b/w)	L: Gay & Bird	1902	Brock, Charles E.	50-80	
Dickens, Charles	Posthumous Papers of the Pickwick Club (1st AM, lg8vo, 687p, 16cp, pep)	Dodd	1930	Brock, Charles E.	55-80	
Austen, Jane	Pride and Prejudice (1st, 8vo, 336p, teg, gilt, uncut, 24 color)	L: J.M. Dent	1907	Brock, Charles E.	55-80	
Nesbit, Edith	Railway Children (1st, 8vo, 309p, uncut, teg, gilt, 20pl)	L: Wells/Gard.	(1906)	Brock, Charles E.	250-450	
Gaster, Moses	Rumanian Legends & Fairy Tales (1st, 4to, 133p, ibds, 12cp)	L: R. Tuck	(1923)	Brock, Charles E.	100-180	
Atkinson, John C.	Scenes in Fairyland (1st, 8vo, 246p, green/gilt, 4pl)	L: Macmillan	1892	Brock, Charles E.	80-140	
Eliot, George	Silas Marner (1st, sm8vo, green/gilt, 262p, teg, 24cp, dep)	L: Dent	1905	Brock, Charles E.	50-85	
Dickens, Charles	The Chimes (1st, 12mo, teg, gilt, uncut, 167p, 8cp)	L: J.M. Dent	1906	Brock, Charles E.	40-60	*
Cooper, James F.	The Pathfinder (1st, 12mo, 463p, red/gilt, b/w)	L: Macmillan	1900	Brock, Charles E.	30-50	
Raymond, Walter	Tryphena In Love... (1st, 12mo, gilt, teg, 295p, col frn, 12pl)	L: Dent	1912	Brock, Charles E.	50-80	
Goldsmith, Oliver	Vicar of Wakefield (1st, 8vo, 242p, gilt, teg, uncut, 25cp, dep)	L: Dent	1904	Brock, Charles E.	45-70	
Kingsley, Charles	Westward Ho! (16mo, blue/gilt, 2 volumes, teg, uncut, b/w)	L: Macmillan	1896	Brock, Charles E.	60-90	
Sharp, Evelyn	Youngest Girl in the School (1st, 8vo, 326p)	L: Macmillan	1901	Brock, Charles E.	40-60	*
Marchioness/London	Magic Ink Spot (1st, 8vo, 208p, 16cp)	L: Macmillan	1928	Brock, E./Stewart	90-120	*
Brock, Emma	At Midsummer Time (1st {std}, 8vo, 80p, color, pep, DJ/1.50)	Knopf	1940	Brock, Emma	25-40	*
Davis, Mary G.	Baker's Dozen (1st {std}, 8vo, 207p, orange cl, dep, decor by...)	Harcourt	(1930)	Brock, Emma	25-40	
Brock, Emma	Ballet for Mary (1st {std}, sm8vo, 79p, color, pep, DJ/2.50)	Knopf	1954	Brock, Emma	25-40	
Brock, Emma	Beppo (1st, sm4to, 79p, p-o, color, DJ/2.00)	Whitman	1936	Brock, Emma	50-80	*
Brock, Emma	Bird's Christmas Tree (1st {std}, ob12mo, [64]p, color, DJ/1.50)	Knopf	1946	Brock, Emma	45-70	*
Browne, Frances	Granny's Wonderful Chair (1st, sm8vo, 184p, 3cp, fp b/w, pep)	Macmillan	1924	Brock, Emma	30-50	*
Brock, Emma	Greedy Goat (1st, sq8vo, [45]p, 1-color, pep)	Knopf	1931	Brock, Emma	50-80	
Davis, Mary G.	Handsome Donkey (1st, lg8vo, yellow cl, 67p, uncut, fp 3-color, pep)	Harcourt	(1933)	Brock, Emma	30-50	
Ludmann, Oscar	Hansi the Stork (1st, ob8vo, p-o, 62p, fp color)	Whitman	(1932)	Brock, Emma	40-70	
Brock, Emma	Heedless Susan (1st {std}, lg8vo, blue cl, 169p, b/w, DJ/1.75)	Knopf	1939	Brock, Emma	40-65	
Brock, Emma	Hen that Kept House (1st {std}, ob4to, [40]p, color, dep)	Knopf	1933	Brock, Emma	60-90	
Brock, Emma	Here Comes Kristie (1st {std}, 8vo, 81p, color, pep, DJ/1.75)	Knopf	1942	Brock, Emma	30-50	
Brock, Emma	High in the Mountains (1st, 4to, 78p, p-o, color, pep, DJ/2.00)	Whitman	1938	Brock, Emma	50-80	
Brock, Emma	Kristie and the Colt (1st {std}, 8vo, [88]p, color, DJ/2.00)	Knopf	1949	Brock, Emma	30-50	
Brock, Emma	Little Duchess Anne of Britany (1st {std}, 8vo, 197p, b/w, DJ/2.50)	Knopf	1948	Brock, Emma	40-65	
Brock, Emma	Little Fat Gretchen (1st {std}, ob8vo, [41]p, 1-color)	Knopf	1934	Brock, Emma	30-50	
Hunt, Clara W.	Little House in Green Valley (1st, 12mo, 95p, green cl, fp 1-color)	Houghton	1932	Brock, Emma	30-50	
Horne, Richard H.	Memoirs of a London Doll (1st UK, 8vo, 175p, blue cl, 2cp)	L: Harrap	1923	Brock, Emma	60-90	*
Bowen, William	Merrimeg (1st, 12mo, 166p, green/gilt, 7cp, pep)	Macmillan	1923	Brock, Emma	30-50	*
Bigham, Madge A.	More Mother Goose Village Stories (1st, 8vo, 274p, color)	Rand/McNally	(1922)	Brock, Emma	50-80	
Brock, Emma	Nobody's Mouse (1st {std}, sq8vo, [40]p, color, pep, DJ/1.75)	Knopf	1938	Brock, Emma	45-70	
Hoffmann, Ernst T.	Nutcracker & Mouse King (1st, lg8vo, 123p, orange cl, p-o, color)	Whitman	(1930)	Brock, Emma	80-130	
Brock, Emma	One Little Indian Boy (1st, sq8vo, [44]p, fp color, pep)	Knopf	1932	Brock, Emma	40-65	
Brock, Emma	Pancakes and the Merry-Go-Round (1st {std}, 8vo, 77p, b/w, DJ/2.50)	Knopf	1960	Brock, Emma	25-40	
Brock, Emma	Patty on Horseback (1st {std}, 8vo, 79p, b/w, DJ/2.50)	Knopf	1959	Brock, Emma	30-50	
Brock, Emma	Pet for Barbi (1st {std}, sm8vo, 50p, b/w, uncut, DJ/1.50)	Knopf	1947	Brock, Emma	25-40	*
Brock, Emma	Pig with a Front Porch... (1st {std}, sq8vo, [43]p, color, pep, DJ/1.75)	Knopf	1937	Brock, Emma	45-70	*
Brock, Emma	Plaid Cow (1st {std}, 8vo, 80p, b/w, DJ/2.50)	Knopf	1961	Brock, Emma	30-50	
Van Housen, Nita	Poogie & Sibella (1st, 8vo, green cl, 81p, 8 fp color)	Whitman	(1932)	Brock, Emma	30-50	*
Brock, Emma	Present for Auntie (1st {std}, sm8vo, [96]p, b/w, DJ/1.00)	Knopf	1939	Brock, Emma	30-45	
Brock, Emma	Runaway Sardine (1st, 8vo, ibds, [42]p, color, pep)	Knopf	1929	Brock, Emma	30-45	
Davis, Mary G.	Sandy's Kingdom (1st, lg8vo, green cl, 79p, b/w, pep, DJ/1.75)	Harcourt	(1935)	Brock, Emma	30-50	*

AUTHOR	TITLE	PUBLISHER	DATE	ARTIST	PRICE	LC
King, Marian	Sean & Sheela (1st, lg8vo, p-o, 135p, dp color, pep, DJ/2.00)	Whitman	1937	Brock, Emma	30-50	
Brock, Emma	Skipping Island (1st, sm4to, [33]p, color, pep, DJ/2.95)	Knopf	1958	Brock, Emma	30-50	
Boggs, Ralph S.	Three Golden Oranges (1st {std}, 8vo, 137p, 6pl, pep, DJ/2.00)	Longmans	1936	Brock, Emma	35-50	
Brock, Emma	Three Ring Circus (1st {std}, 8vo, 110p, color, pep, DJ/2.50)	Knopf	1950	Brock, Emma	25-40	*
Brock, Emma	To Market! To Market! (1st, ob8vo, ibds, [41]p, color, pep)	Knopf	1930	Brock, Emma	50-80	
Brock, Emma	Topsy-Turvy Family (1st {std}, 8vo, 86p, 8 fp color, pep, DJ/2.00)	Knopf	1943	Brock, Emma	40-65	
Brock, Emma	Uncle Bennie Goes Visiting (1st {std}, 8vo, ibds, 57p, 8cp, pep, DJ/2.00)	Knopf	1944	Brock, Emma	25-40	
DeSegur, Sophie	Wise Little Donkey (1st, 8vo, p-o, 191p, pep, 4cp)	Whitman	(1931)	Brock, Emma	25-40	
Drinkwater, John	All About Me (1st, 8vo, 103p, teg, gilt, 9pl, pep)	L: Collins	1928	Brock, Henry M.	50-80	
Frazer, Mrs. J.G.	Asinette (1st, 8vo, 212p, green cl, 8cp)	L: J.M. Dent	1900	Brock, Henry M.	40-70	
Thackeray, Wm. M.	Ballads & Songs (1st, 12mo, AEG, 276p, red/gilt, b/w)	L: Cassell	1896	Brock, Henry M.	60-100	
N/A	Beauty & the Beast (4to, wraps, 6cp)	L: Warne	[1895]	Brock, Henry M.	100-160	
N/A	Book of Fairy Tales (1st, 4to, gilt, unpag, pep, 24cp)	L: Warne	[1914]	Brock, Henry M.	250-400	
Nichols, Beverly	Book of Old Ballads (1st, 4to, 279p, brown/gilt, 16cp, pep)	L: Hutchinson	1934	Brock, Henry M.	100-175	
Dickens, Charles	Christmas Carol (1st AM, 8vo, red/gilt, 77p, 4cp)	Dodd	(1935)	Brock, Henry M.	60-90	*
Gaskell, Mrs.	Cranford (1st, 8vo, 313p, red/gilt, teg, b/w)	L: J. Nisbet	1900	Brock, Henry M.	60-80	
Mowbray, John	Dismal Jimmy of the Fourth (1st, 8vo, 215p, p-o, col frn, 3pl)	L: Cassell	1928	Brock, Henry M.	30-50	*
Fortescue, J.W.	Drummer's Coat (1st, 8vo, 184p, uncut, red/gilt, 4pl)	L: Macmillan	1899	Brock, Henry M.	70-100	
Andersen, Hans C.	Fairy Tales (1st, 8vo, 408p, b/w)	L: Seeley	(1909)	Brock, Henry M.	75-100	*
Andersen, Hans C.	Fairy Tales and Stories (1st AM, sm8vo, 408p, 8pl)	C.L. Bowman	1909	Brock, Henry M.	75-100	*
Lover, Samuel	Handy Andy (1st, 12mo, 523p, blue/gilt, AEG, pep, 40pl)	L: Macmillan	1896	Brock, Henry M.	70-100	
N/A	Hop O' My Thumb (4to, wraps, 8cp)	L: Warne	[1910]	Brock, Henry M.	70-100	
Ewing, Juliana H.	Jacanapes (1st, 8vo, 196p, 8cp)	L: Bell	1913	Brock, Henry M.	50-80	
Marryat, Frederick	Jacob Faithful (1st, 8vo, blue/gilt, 416p, AEG, b/w, dep)	L: Macmillan	1895	Brock, Henry M.	60-90	
Marryat, Frederick	Japhet in Search of a Father (1st, 12mo, blue/gilt, 401p, AEG, 14pl, pep)	L: Macmillan	1895	Brock, Henry M.	80-120	
Cooper, James F.	Last of the Mohicans (1st, 8vo, green/gilt, 398p, AEG, 25pl)	L: Macmillan	1900	Brock, Henry M.	40-70	
Frazer, Lilly	Leaves from The Golden Bough (1st, 8vo, 248p, gilt, teg, b/w)	L: Macmillan	1924	Brock, Henry M.	40-60	
Wotton, Mabel E.	Little Browns (1st, lg8vo, 216p, AEG, col frn, 7pl, pep)	L: Blackie	1900	Brock, Henry M.	40-70	*
Stevenson, Rbt. L.	Master of Ballantrae (1st, 8vo, 259p)	L: Macmillan	1928	Brock, Henry M.	40-60	*
Sharp, Evelyn	Micky... (1st, 8vo, 240p)	L: Macmillan	1905	Brock, Henry M.	40-60	*
Drinkwater, John	More About Me (1st AM, 8vo, 109p, orange cl, b/w)	Houghton	1930	Brock, Henry M.	30-50	
Irving, Washington	Old Christmas Day (12mo, 34p, p-o, 5cp)	L: Foulis	[1912]	Brock, Henry M.	50-80	
Irving, Washington	Old English Christmas (1st AM, 12mo, 123p, ibds, p-o, 17 ticp)	Jacobs	(1910)	Brock, Henry M.	55-80	
Irving, Washington	Old English Christmas (1st, 12mo, 124p, blue/gilt, 17 ticp)	L: Foulis	[1910]	Brock, Henry M.	70-100	
N/A	Old Fairy Tales (1st, 4to, [32]p, gilt, 11cp)	L: Warne	(1914)	Brock, Henry M.	150-225	R
Milne, A.A.	Once On a Time (1st, 8vo, 316p, blue cl, p-o, col frn, 4pl)	L: Hodder	(1917)	Brock, Henry M.	200-300	
Frazer, Sir James	Pasha the Pom (1st, 12mo, 117p, 4 fp b/w)	L: Blackie	1937	Brock, Henry M.	30-50	
N/A	Puss in Boots (4to, cloth, p-o, 8cp)	Warne	[1900]	Brock, Henry M.	70-100	
Bird, Richard	Ryecroft Rivals (1st, 8vo, beige cl, 256p, 6pl)	L: Blackie	(1923)	Brock, Henry M.	30-50	*
Lady Frazer	Singing Wood (1st, 8vo, 144p, col frn, b/w)	L: A&C Black	1931	Brock, Henry M.	40-60	
Cooper, James F.	The Deerslayer (1st, 12mo, 522p, gilt, b/w, uncut)	L: Macmillan	1900	Brock, Henry M.	30-50	
Kingsley, Charles	The Heroes (1st, 8vo, 212p, 16cp)	L: Macmillan	1928	Brock, Henry M.	60-90	*
Dawson, Alec J.	The Message (1st, 8vo, 386p, black/gilt, 4ticp)	L: Richards	1907	Brock, Henry M.	45-70	
Cooper, James F.	The Pioneers (1st, 8vo, 455p, red/gilt, AEG, 25pl)	L: Macmillan	1901	Brock, Henry M.	40-70	
Goldsmith, Oliver	Vicar of Wakefield (1st AM, 8vo, blue/gilt, teg, 7cp)	Lippincott	1912	Brock, Henry M.	60-90	
Coke, Desmond	Youth Youth! (1st, 8vo, 304p, blue/gilt, teg, 8pl)	L: Chapman/Hall	1919	Brock, Henry M.	30-50	*
Savery, Constance	Reb and the Redcoats (1st {std}, 8vo, 241p, b/w, DJ/3.75)	Longmans	1961	Brock, Vera	30-50	
Blackmore, R.D.	Lorna Doone (1st, lg4to, 520p, teg, gilt, 16 ticp)	L: Boots	[1931]	Brock/Brittan	80-140	
Haggard, H. Rider	Mahatma & the Hare (1st, 8vo, 165p, red/gilt, 12pl)	L: Longmans	1911	Brock/Horton	250-350	
Nesbit, Edith	Oswald Bastable & Others (1st, 12mo, teg, 369p, gilt, 22pl)	L: Wells/Gard.	(1905)	Brock/Millar	250-400	
Bedford, Ruth	Fairies and Fancies (1st, 8vo, ibds, p-o, 8cp, 9pl)	L: A&C Black	1929	Broman, Mela K.	180-240	
Bromhall, Winifred	Chipmunk that Went to Church (1st {std}, sm4to, [40]p, color, DJ/2.00)	Knopf	(1952)	Bromhall, Winifred	40-65	*
Perry, Catherine	Island of Enchantment (1st, 4to, 157p, 10 tipl, pep)	L: Hutchinson	[1926]	Bromhall, Winifred	60-90	*
Bromhall, Winifred	Mary Ann's First Picture (1st {std}, 4to, ibds, [32]p, color, DJ/1.50)	Knopf	(1948)	Bromhall, Winifred	40-65	
Bromhall, Winifred	Middle Matilda (1st, ob4to, [34]p, fp 2-color, pep, DJ/2.95)	Knopf	(1962)	Bromhall, Winifred	30-45	
Bromhall, Winifred	Mrs. Polly's Party (1st {std}, 4to, ibds, [32]p, 3-color, DJ/1.50)	Knopf	(1949)	Bromhall, Winifred	30-40	
Bromhall, Winifred	Princess & Woodcutter's Daughter (1st, ob4to, [33]p, 3-color, pep, DJ/2.00)	Knopf	(1955)	Bromhall, Winifred	30-50	
Johnston, Annie F.	Road of the Loving Heart (1st, sm8vo, gilt, 77p, pep, b/w)	L.C. Page	1922	Bromhall, Winifred	45-70	
Avery, Kay	Wee Willow Whistle (1st {std}, sm4to, ipcb, [32]p, color, DJ/1.50)	Knopf	(1947)	Bromhall, Winifred	50-80	
Eliot, Ethel C.	Wind Boy (1st {std}, 8vo, 238p, col frn, b/w)	Doubleday/Page	1923	Bromhall, Winifred	40-70	
Turner, Nancy B.	Zodiac Town (1st, 8vo, 131p, gilt, 13 b/w, pep)	Atl. Monthly Pr.	(1921)	Bromhall, Winifred	35-60	
Whitehead, Roberta	Peter Opens the Door (1st, 8vo, [20]p, color, DJ/1.00)	Houghton	1946	Bronson, Mildred	30-45	*
Coatsworth, Eliz.	Boy with the Parrot (1st, 8vo, green cl, 101p, dp color, cep)	Macmillan	1930	Bronson, Wilfrid	30-60	*
Bronson, Wilfrid S.	Cats (1st {std}, 8vo, [78]p, color, pep, DJ/2.00)	Harcourt	(1950)	Bronson, Wilfrid	40-65	
Bronson, Wilfrid S.	Children of the Sea (1st, lg8vo, 264p, col frn, pep, b/w, DJ/2.00)	Harcourt	(1940)	Bronson, Wilfrid	60-100	
Bronson, Wilfrid S.	Chisel-Tooth Tribe (1st, 8vo, 200p, 4cp, b/w, pep, DJ/2.50)	Harcourt	(1939)	Bronson, Wilfrid	30-45	
Bronson, Wilfrid S.	Coyotes (1st, 8vo, [63]p, yellow cl, b/w, DJ/1.75)	Harcourt	(1946)	Bronson, Wilfrid	25-45	
Bronson, Wilfrid S.	Fingerfins (1st, 8vo, blue cl, 54p, 2-color)	Macmillan	1930	Bronson, Wilfrid	25-45	
Bronson, Wilfrid S.	Freedom and Plenty (1st {std}, 8vo, 123p, b/w, DJ/2.95)	Harcourt	1953	Bronson, Wilfrid	25-40	
Lent, Henry B.	Grindstone Farm (1st, 8vo, 127p, b/w, DJ/1.75)	Macmillan	1935	Bronson, Wilfrid	30-45	
Desmond, Alice C.	Lucky Llama (1st {std}, 8vo, 62p, b/w, DJ/1.50)	Macmillan	1939	Bronson, Wilfrid	40-65	
Bronson, Wilfrid S.	Paddlewings (1st, 8vo, 106p, 4 fp color, b/w, cep)	Macmillan	1931	Bronson, Wilfrid	30-50	
Bronson, Wilfrid S.	Pinto's Journey (1st, 8vo, 55p, 4 fp 2-color, pep, DJ/2.50)	J. Messner	1948	Bronson, Wilfrid	30-50	
Bronson, Wilfrid S.	Pollwiggle's Progress (1st, sq8vo, 122p, frn by...)	Macmillan	1932	Bronson, Wilfrid	30-50	
Bronson, Wilfrid S.	Starlings (1st, sq8vo, [78]p, b/w, pep, DJ/2.00)	Harcourt	(1948)	Bronson, Wilfrid	25-40	
Coatsworth, Eliz.	Tonio & the Stranger (1st, 8vo, 69p, b/w, DJ/0.50)	Grosset/Dunlap	(1941)	Bronson, Wilfrid	25-40	
Bronson, Wilfrid S.	Water People (1st, lg8vo, 119p, color, pep, DJ/1.00)	Wise-Parlow	(1935)	Bronson, Wilfrid	30-50	
Bronson, Wilfrid S.	Wonder World of Ants (1st, 8vo, 87p, color, pep, DJ/1.50)	Harcourt	(1937)	Bronson, Wilfrid	30-50	

AUTHOR	TITLE	PUBLISHER	DATE	ARTIST	PRICE	LC
Sharp, Margery	Rescuers: a Fantasy (1st, 8vo, green/gilt, 158p, b/w, DJ)	L: Collins	1959	Brook, Judith	170-250	
Lawless, Emily	Book of Gilly (1st, 8vo, 298p, blue/gilt, teg, uncut, 4pl)	L: Smith Elder	1906	Brooke, L. Leslie	80-125	
White, Roma	Brownies & Rose-Leaves (1st, 12mo, 200p, tan/gilt, 9pl, dep)	L: A.D. Innes	1892	Brooke, L. Leslie	75-100	
Molesworth, Mrs.	Carved Lions (1st, 8vo, 195p, blue cl, 7pl)	Macmillan	1895	Brooke, L. Leslie	80-130	
MacDonald, George	Dealings with Fairies (1st AM, 8vo, 284p, gilt)	NY: Routledge	1891	Brooke, L. Leslie	700-1000	
Molesworth, Mrs.	Girls & I (1st, 12mo, orange cl, 192p, 7pl, cep)	L: Macmillan	1892	Brooke, L. Leslie	80-120	
N/A	Golden Goose Book (1st, sq4to, green cl, unpag, 8cp)	L: Warne	(1905)	Brooke, L. Leslie	125-200	
Grimm Bros.	House in the Wood (1st, lg8vo, 89p, ibds, 7cp, pep)	L: F. Warne	(1909)	Brooke, L. Leslie	140-220	
Brooke, L. Leslie	Johnny Crow's Garden (1st, 8vo, ibds, 48p, p-o, 8cp)	L: Warne	1903	Brooke, L. Leslie	125-200	R
Brooke, L. Leslie	Johnny Crow's New Garden (1st, 8vo, [48]p, blue bds, p-o, 8cp, pep)	L: Warne	1935	Brooke, L. Leslie	80-130	
Brooke, L. Leslie	Johnny Crow's Party (1st, sq8vo, green bds, p-o, [48]p, 8cp)	L: Warne	1907	Brooke, L. Leslie	130-200	
MacDonald, George	Light Princess (1st, sm8vo, 192p, gilt, 3pl, cep)	L: Blackie	(1890)	Brooke, L. Leslie	200-325	
N/A	Little Bo Peep (4to, ipcb, [12]p, color)	L: Warne	[1906]	Brooke, L. Leslie	70-125	
Mockler, Geraldine	Little Girl from Next Door (1st, 8vo, 160p, 2pl by...)	L: Blackie	1896	Brooke, L. Leslie	60-90	*
Scripps, Harriet J.	Little Handful (1st, 8vo, 224p, ibds, 4pl)	L: Blackie	(1894)	Brooke, L. Leslie	80-125	
Armstrong, Annie	Marian (1st, 8vo, 224p, 4pl)	L: Blackie	1892	Brooke, L. Leslie	60-90	*
Molesworth, Mrs.	Mary (1st, 8vo, 180p, gilt, 7pl)	L: Macmillan	1893	Brooke, L. Leslie	75-100	*
Molesworth, Mrs.	Miss Mouse & her Boys (1st, 8vo, green/gilt, 198p, 7pl)	L: Macmillan	1897	Brooke, L. Leslie	40-60	
White, Roma	Moonbeams & Brownies (1st, sq12mo, 160p, 5pl)	L: A.D. Innes	1894	Brooke, L. Leslie	90-120	
Molesworth, Mrs.	My New Home (1st, 8vo, red cl, 207p, 7 fp b/w & cvr by...)	L: Macmillan	1894	Brooke, L. Leslie	50-80	
Lear, Edward	Nonsense Songs (1st, 8vo, AEG, [148]p, gilt, 14cp, pep)	L: Warne	[1900]	Brooke, L. Leslie	170-240	
Molesworth, Mrs.	Nurse Heatherdale's Story (1st, 12mo, 202p, red/gilt, cep, 7pl)	L: Macmillan	1891	Brooke, L. Leslie	70-120	
Lang, Andrew	Nursery Rhyme Book (1st, 8vo, AEG, 288p, green/gilt, fp b/w, pep)	L: Warne	1897	Brooke, L. Leslie	150-225	
N/A	Nursery Rhyme Picture Book (1st, 4to, ipcb, [32]p, p-o, 16cp, pep)	L: Warne	(1905)	Brooke, L. Leslie	150-220	
N/A	Nursery Rhymes (1st, 16mo, grey bds, 48p, p-o, 8cp, pep)	L: Warne	[1917]	Brooke, L. Leslie	70-100	
N/A	Oranges & Lemons (1st, 4to, [26]p, wraps, 8cp)	L: Warne	[1913]	Brooke, L. Leslie	120-180	
Molesworth, Mrs.	Oriel Window (1st, 8vo, 182p, 7pl)	Macmillan	1896	Brooke, L. Leslie	70-100	
Lear, Edward	Pelican Chorus (1st, sq8vo, [63]p, ibds, p-o, 7cp)	L: Warne	(1899)	Brooke, L. Leslie	100-175	
Browning, Robert	Pippa Passes (1st, 8vo, green cl, 72p, 7pl)	L: Duckworth	1898	Brooke, L. Leslie	75-125	
Brooke, L. Leslie	Ring O' Roses (lg8vo, [59]p, blue/gilt, pep, 32cp)	L: Warne	[1901]	Brooke, L. Leslie	60-100	
Charles, Robert H.	Roundabout Turn (1st, sq8vo, [54]p, orange/gilt, pep, 4cp)	L: Warne	1930	Brooke, L. Leslie	100-160	
Strain, E.H.	School in Fairyland (1st, 8vo, green cl, 186p, 7pl)	L: T.F. Unwin	1896	Brooke, L. Leslie	120-200	
Molesworth, Mrs.	Sheila's Mystery (1st, sm8vo, 198p, 7pl)	L: Macmillan	1895	Brooke, L. Leslie	50-85	*
Somervell, Arthur	Singing Time (1st, 4to, ibds, p-o, 48p, b/w)	L: Constable	1899	Brooke, L. Leslie	120-200	
Nash, Thomas	Spring Song (1st, 8vo, unpag, wraps, teg, 16 color)	L: J.M. Dent	1898	Brooke, L. Leslie	80-125	
Brooke, L. Leslie	Tailor & the Crow (1st, sq8vo, gilt, p-o, 40p, 6cp, pep)	L: Warne	(1911)	Brooke, L. Leslie	100-175	
Lear, Edward	The Jumblies (1st, sq8vo, [64]p, ibds, p-o, 14cp, pep)	L: Warne	(1900)	Brooke, L. Leslie	120-170	
N/A	Three Bears (4to, wraps, 8cp)	L: Warne	(1900)	Brooke, L. Leslie	100-180	
Mayne, William	Rolling Season (1st, 8vo, 175p, bds, b/w, DJ)	L: Oxford U.Pr.	1960	Brooker, Christopher	30-45	
Wilkins, Mary E.	Six Trees (1st, 12mo, green/gilt, 206p, 16pl)	Harper	1903	Broughton, C.	35-60	
Tarkington, Booth	Seventeen (1st, 12mo, 328p, orange/gilt, 12pl)	Harper	(1916)	Brown, Arthur W.	60-100	
Brown, Beatrice B.	Paris Pair (1st, ob8vo, 59p, color)	Dutton	(1923)	Brown, Beatrice B.	40-65	
Marks, Jeannette	Cheerful Cricket... (1st, 4to, [124]p, green cl, dep, color)	Small/Maynard	1907	Brown, Edith	120-200	R
Sabin, Elbridge H.	Stella's Adventures in Starland (1st, 8vo, 210p, 9pl)	Small/Maynard	1907	Brown, Edith	80-130	
Brown, Abbie F.	Star Jewels... (1st, 8vo, green/gilt, 133p, 5pl)	Houghton	1905	Brown, Ethel C.	25-40	*
Sachs, Marilyn	Amy Moves In (1st {std}, 8vo, 191p, b/w, DJ/2.95)	Doubleday	(1964)	Brown, Judith	20-25	
Lobe, Mira	Grandma in the Apple Tree (1st, lg8vo, 94p, fp b/w, DJ/4.95)	McGraw-Hill	(1970)	Brown, Judith	20-35	*
Brown, Judith	Max & the Truffle Pig (1st, 8vo, 46p, 2-color, pep, DJ/2.50)	Abingdon Press	(1963)	Brown, Judith	20-35	
Colum, Padraic	Stone of Victory (1st, 8vo, 119p, red cl, b/w, DJ/3.75)	McGraw-Hill	(1966)	Brown, Judith	20-35	
Robinson, Mabel L.	Sarah's Daikin (1st, sm8vo, 271p, green/gilt, uncut, b/w)	Dutton	(1927)	Brown, Julie	25-40	*
Meader, Stephen W.	Topsail Island Treasure (1st {std}, 8vo, 189p, b/w, DJ/3.50)	Harcourt	(1966)	Brown, Marbury	120-185	
Sherlock, Philip	Anansi the Spider Man (1st {std}, 8vo, green cl, 112p, b/w, DJ/2.50)	Crowell	(1954)	Brown, Marcia	80-140	R
Brown, Marcia	Backbone of the King (1st, 8vo, yellow cl, 180p, 1-color, DJ/4.50)	Scribner	(1966)	Brown, Marcia	40-65	
Perrault, Charles	Cinderella (1st, sm4to, [32]p, gilt, color, DJ/2.00, CM)	Scribner	(1954)	Brown, Marcia	150-220	
N/A	Dick Whittington & his Cat (1st, 4to, ibds, [32]p, 1-color, DJ/1.75, CH)	Scribner	1950	Brown, Marcia	100-165	R
Brown, Marcia	Felice (1st, sm4to, [32]p, color, pep, DJ/2.95)	Scribner	(1958)	Brown, Marcia	80-125	R
Prince Ahmed	Flying Carpet (1st, 4to, [48]p, color, DJ/3.00)	Scribner	(1956)	Brown, Marcia	50-80	R
Verdy, Violette	Giselle, or the Willis (1st, 4to, 50p, gilt, b/w, pep, DJ/4.95)	McGraw-Hill	(1970)	Brown, Marcia	50-80	
Brown, Marcia	Henry Fisherman (1st, sm ob4to, [32]p, color, pep, DJ/2.00, CH)	Scribner	1949	Brown, Marcia	100-165	
Brown, Marcia	How, Hippo (1st, sq8vo, [32]p, fp color, pep, DJ/3.50)	Scribner	(1969)	Brown, Marcia	60-100	R
Brown, Marcia	Little Carousel (1st {1st Bk}, sm4to, [32]p, ipcb, color, DJ/2.00)	Scribner	1946	Brown, Marcia	100-185	
Brown, Marcia	Once a Mouse (1st, lg8vo, [32]p, 3-color, DJ/2.95, CM, NYTBI)	Scribner	(1961)	Brown, Marcia	220-300	R
Brown, Marcia	Peter Piper's Alphabet (1st, ob4to, ibds, [32]p, color, pep, DJ/2.95)	Scribner	(1959)	Brown, Marcia	100-165	
Perrault, Charles	Puss in Boots (1st, 4to, [30]p, color, pep, DJ/2.00, CH)	Scribner	(1952)	Brown, Marcia	120-170	R
Brown, Marcia	Skipper John's Cook (1st, sm4to, unpag, color, pep, DJ/2.00, CH)	Scribner	1951	Brown, Marcia	100-165	
Andersen, Hans C.	Steadfast Tin Soldier (1st, 4to, [30]p, color, DJ/2.25, CH)	Scribner	(1953)	Brown, Marcia	80-130	R*
Brown, Marcia	Stone Soup (1st, sm4to, [48]p, 2-color, pep, DJ/2.00, CH)	Scribner	1947	Brown, Marcia	100-165	
Brown, Marcia	Tamarindo! (1st, sm4to, tan cl, [32]p, color, DJ/2.95)	Scribner	(1960)	Brown, Marcia	60-90	
Brown, Marcia	The Neighbors (1st, 4to, [32]p, fp 3-color, pep, DJ)	Scribner	(1967)	Brown, Marcia	50-85	
Asbjornsen, P.C.	Three Billy Goats Gruff (1st {std}, sm4to, green cl, unpag, color, DJ/3.00)	Harcourt	(1957)	Brown, Marcia	60-90	
Watson, Virginia	Trail of Courage (1st, 8vo, grey cl, 181p, fp b/w, DJ/2.50)	Crowell	(1948)	Brown, Marcia	45-70	
Andersen, Hans C.	Wild Swans (1st, sm4to, 80p, 1-color, DJ/3.50)	Scribner	(1963)	Brown, Marcia	50-80	R*
Brown, Margery	Animals Made by Me (1st, 4to, [32]p, color, DJ)	Putnam	(1970)	Brown, Margery	40-65	*
Allred, Gordon	Old Crackfoot (1st {std}, 8vo, 116p, fp b/w, dep, DJ/2.95)	NY: I. Obolensky	(1965)	Brown, Margery	25-45	
Brown, Margery	That Ruby (1st, 8vo, 154p, b/w, DJ/3.95)	Reilly/Lee	(1969)	Brown, Margery	30-50	*
Henty, G.A.	By Pike and Dike (1st, 12mo, 384p, 10pl)	L: Blackie	1890	Brown, Maynard	70-100	
Shannon, Monica	Goose Grass Rhymes (1st {std}, sm8vo, 155p, col frn, b/w, pep)	Doubleday/Doran	1930	Brown, Neva K.	40-60	*
Hess, Fjeril	Magic Switch (1st, 8vo, 74p, 4 fp color, pep)	Macmillan	1929	Brown, Neva K.	30-50	

AUTHOR	TITLE	PUBLISHER	DATE	ARTIST	PRICE	LC
Brown, Neva K.	Uncle Amos Puppet Show (1st {std}, 8vo, 56p, col frn, b/w, pep)	Doubleday/Doran	1930	Brown, Neva K.	25-45	
Brown, Palmer	Beyond the Pawpaw Trees (1st {1st bk}, 12mo, grey cl, 121p, b/w, DJ/2.50)	Harper	(1954)	Brown, Palmer	150-250	R
Brown, Palmer	Cheerful (1st, 16mo, beige cl, 58p, fp color, DJ/1.50)	Harper	(1957)	Brown, Palmer	150-250	R
Brown, Palmer	Silver Nutmeg (1st, 12mo, green cl, 137p, b/w, DJ/2.50)	Harper	(1956)	Brown, Palmer	150-250	
Brown, Palmer	Something for Christmas (1st, 16mo, white cl, 32p, color, DJ/1.95)	Harper	(1958)	Brown, Palmer	150-250	R
Sherman, Fanny J.	Admiral Wags of USS Lexington (1st {std}, sm4to, 84p, 1-color, DJ/2.25)	Dodd	1943	Brown, Paul	70-120	
Downey, Fairfax	Army Mule (1st, sm8vo, 192p, b/w, DJ/2.50)	Dodd	1945	Brown, Paul	50-80	
Brown, Paul	Black & White (1st, ob4to, ibds, [62]p, b/w, pep, DJ/1.50)	Scribner	1939	Brown, Paul	150-220	
Sewell, Anna	Black Beauty (1st, lg ob8vo, [128]p, fp b/w, DJ/3.00)	Scribner	(1952)	Brown, Paul	120-200	*
Tempski, Armine	Bright Spurs (1st, 12mo, 283p, peach cl, uncut, b/w, DJ/2.50)	Dodd	1946	Brown, Paul	60-90	
Davis, Lavinia R.	Buttonwood Island (1st {std}, sm8vo, 299p, b/w, pep, DJ/2.00)	Doubleday/Doran	1940	Brown, Paul	70-120	
Downey, Fairfax	Cats of Destiny (1st, 8vo, blue cl, 170p, 39 fp b/w, DJ/2.50)	Scribner	1950	Brown, Paul	50-80	
Downey, Fairfax	Cavalry Mount (1st, 8vo, 227p, b/w, DJ/2.50)	Dodd	1946	Brown, Paul	80-120	
Brown, Paul	Circus School (1st, 4to, [64]p, color, DJ/2.00)	Scribner	1946	Brown, Paul	125-200	
Hall, Esther G.	College on Horseback (1st, 12mo, 319p, pep)	Random	1933	Brown, Paul	50-80	*
Brown, Paul	Crazy Quilt (1st, ob4to, ipcb, [120]p, fp b/w, pep)	Scribner	1934	Brown, Paul	200-300	
Brown, Paul	Daffy Taffy (1st, 4to, [32]p, color, cep, DJ/2.50)	Scribner	1955	Brown, Paul	100-145	
Downey, Fairfax	Dogs of Destiny (1st, 8vo, 186p, b/w, DJ/2.50)	Scribner	1949	Brown, Paul	100-165	
Brown, Paul	Draw Horses: It's Fun & Easy (1st, 8vo, ibds, 60p, b/w, DJ/2.00)	Scribner	1949	Brown, Paul	100-165	
Brown, Paul	Fire! The Mascot (1st, 4to, red cl, [96]p, b/w, DJ/2.00)	Scribner	1939	Brown, Paul	100-160	
Harper, Wilhelmina	Flying Hoofs (1st, 8vo, 292p, red cl, 3 dp cp, b/w, DJ/2.00)	Houghton	1939	Brown, Paul	200-300	
Pace, Mildred M.	Friend of Animals (1st, 8vo, 125p, pink cl, fp b/w, DJ/1.60)	Scribner	1942	Brown, Paul	80-140	
Smith, Lawrence B.	Fur or Feather (1st, 4to, 144p, fp b/w, DJ/4.00)	Scribner	1946	Brown, Paul	80-140	
Alsop, Reese F.	George and his Horse Bill (1st, 8vo, 164p, red cl, b/w, DJ/2.50)	Dodd	1948	Brown, Paul	60-100	
Eames, Genevieve T.	Ghost Town Cowboy (1st, 8vo, 176p, beige cl, uncut, b/w, pep, DJ/2.50)	J. Messner	(1951)	Brown, Paul	50-80	
Knott, M.O.	Gone Away with O'Malley (1st {std}, 8vo, red cl, 280p, b/w, pep, DJ/3.00)	Doubleday/Doran	1944	Brown, Paul	70-100	
Eames, Genevieve T.	Good Luck Colt (1st, 8vo, 191p, red cl, fp b/w, DJ/2.50)	J. Messner	(1953)	Brown, Paul	60-100	
Palmer, Elizabeth	Good Old Clipsy (1st, 8vo, 194p, tan cl, fp 1-color, DJ/1.75)	Scribner	1941	Brown, Paul	60-100	
Cooper, Page	Great Horse Stories (1st {std}, 8vo, 366p, maroon cl, fp b/w, DJ/3.50)	Doubleday	1946	Brown, Paul	50-85	
Judson, Clara I.	Green Ginger Jar (1st, 8vo, green cl, 210p, fp b/w, pep, DJ/2.50)	Houghton	1949	Brown, Paul	50-85	
Brown, Paul	Hi Guy the Cinderella Horse (1st, lg8vo, [62]p, b/w, DJ/2.00)	Scribner	(1944)	Brown, Paul	100-165	
Davis, Lavinia R.	Hobby Horse Hill (1st {std}, 8vo, 270p, uncut, b/w, DJ/2.00)	Doubleday/Doran	1939	Brown, Paul	120-200	
Caffrey, Nancy	Horse Haven (1st {std}, 8vo, 96p, b/w, DJ/2.50)	Dutton	1955	Brown, Paul	70-100	
Eames, Genevieve T.	Horse to Remember (1st, 8vo, 146p, b/w, pep, DJ/2.50)	J. Messner	(1947)	Brown, Paul	50-80	
Downey, Fairfax	Horses of Destiny (1st, 8vo, 186p, rust cl, b/w, DJ/2.50)	Scribner	1949	Brown, Paul	80-140	
Lamb, Dean I.	Incurable Filibuster (1st, 8vo, 298p, uncut, b/w, pep)	Farrar/Rinehart	(1934)	Brown, Paul	50-80	*
Downey, Fairfax	Jezebel the Jeep (1st, 8vo, 150p, grey cl, uncut, b/w, DJ/2.00)	Dodd	1944	Brown, Paul	50-80	
Aunt Jo	Jo and Uncle George Kritters (1st, lg8vo, ibds, color)	Little/Brown	1922	Brown, Paul	80-140	
Johns, Rowland	Jock the King's Pony (1st {std}, 8vo, ibds, 60p, b/w, pep, DJ/1.00)	Dutton	(1936)	Brown, Paul	120-200	
Strickland, Harold	Juggernaut of the Rangers (1st, 8vo, 130p, b/w, DJ/2.50)	Dodd	1946	Brown, Paul	80-120	
Houston, Joan	Jump-Shy (1st, 8vo, 261p, b/w, DJ/2.75)	Crowell	(1956)	Brown, Paul	100-170	
Tracy, Edward B.	King of the Stallions (1st, 8vo, orange cl, 241p, b/w, DJ/2.50)	Dodd	1947	Brown, Paul	60-100	
Aunt Jo	Kritters of Kitchen Kingdom (1st, sm4to, 39p, ibds, 16 fp color)	Little/Brown	1922	Brown, Paul	80-125	R
Davis, Lavinia R.	Melody, Mutton, Bone & Sam (1st {std}, 8vo, 245p, b/w, DJ/2.25)	Doubleday	1947	Brown, Paul	80-125	
Brown, Paul	Merrylegs (1st, sm8vo, [64]p, grey cl, 1-color, pep, DJ/2.00)	Scribner	1946	Brown, Paul	80-120	
Brown, Paul	Mick & Mac (1st, 4to, ibds, [96]p, b/w, pep)	Scribner	1937	Brown, Paul	120-185	
Aspden, Don	Mike of Company D. (1st, 8vo, 261p, green cl, b/w, DJ/2.00)	Scribner	1939	Brown, Paul	60-95	*
Bagnold, Enid	National Velvet (1st [new. ed.], 8vo, 306p, b/w, DJ/3.00)	Wm. Morrow	1949	Brown, Paul	60-100	*
Brown, Paul	No Trouble at All (1st, 8vo, 126p, b/w, DJ/1.50)	Scribner	1940	Brown, Paul	70-100	
Tempski, Armine	Pam's Paradise Ranch (1st, 8vo, 333p, orange cl, uncut, pep, DJ/2.00)	Dodd	1940	Brown, Paul	50-85	
Brown, Paul	Piper's Pony (1st, ob4to, ipcb, [120]p, fp b/w, pep)	Scribner	1935	Brown, Paul	150-250	
Davis, Lavinia R.	Plow Penny Mystery (1st {std}, 8vo, 275p, b/w, pep, DJ/2.00)	Doubleday/Doran	1942	Brown, Paul	60-90	
Brown, Paul	Polo (1st, lg8vo, ibds, 88p, b/w, DJ/2.00)	Scribner	1949	Brown, Paul	80-130	
Brown, Paul	Pony Farm (1st, 8vo, [92]p, ibds, pep, DJ/2.00)	Scribner	(1948)	Brown, Paul	100-180	
Brown, Paul	Pony School (1st, 8vo, [93]p, ibds, pep, DJ/2.00)	Scribner	(1950)	Brown, Paul	80-125	
Brown, Paul	Puff Ball (1st, 12mo, blue cl, [32]p, color, cep, DJ/1.00)	Scribner	1942	Brown, Paul	80-120	
Judson, Clara I.	Reaper Man (1st, 8vo, 156p, b/w, DJ/2.50)	Houghton	1948	Brown, Paul	80-130	
Bialk, Elisa	Ride 'Em Peggy! (1st, 8vo, red cl, 196p, dp b/w, DJ/2.25)	Houghton	1950	Brown, Paul	70-120	
Disston, Harry	Riding Rhymes for Young Readers (1st, 4to, ibds, 67p, b/w, DJ/2.75)	B. Wheelright	1951	Brown, Paul	70-125	
Bontemps, Arna	Sam Patch... (1st, sq8vo, yellow cl, 39p, color, pep, DJ/2.00)	Houghton	1951	Brown, Paul	100-180	
Downey, Fairfax	Seventh's Staghound (1st, 8vo, 230p, b/w, DJ/2.50)	Dodd	1948	Brown, Paul	80-135	
Brown, Paul	Silver Heels (1st, 8vo, [125]p, b/w, DJ/2.50)	Scribner	(1951)	Brown, Paul	60-100	
Brown, Paul	Sparkie & Puff Ball (1st, 4to, [32]p, red cl, color, DJ/2.50)	Scribner	1954	Brown, Paul	70-100	
McKenney, John	Tackroom Tattles (1st, 8vo, 230p, beige cl, fp b/w, cep)	Scribner	1934	Brown, Paul	60-100	
Brown, Paul	Three Rings: A Circus Book (1st, 4to, ibds, [76]p, color, pep, DJ/2.00)	Scribner	1938	Brown, Paul	160-250	
Brown, Paul	War Paint: An Indian Pony (1st, 4to, [96]p, b/w, DJ/2.00)	Scribner	1936	Brown, Paul	70-120	
Bialk, Elisa	Wild Horse Island (1st, 8vo, green cl, 201p, fp b/w, pep, DJ/2.00)	Houghton	1951	Brown, Paul	50-80	
Burke, Trude	Wild Stranger (1st {std}, 8vo, 129p, b/w, DJ/2.50)	Holt	(1953)	Brown, Paul	80-140	
Moore, Elaine T.	Winning Your Spurs (1st {std}, 4to, 123p, b/w, DJ/4.75)	Little/Brown	(1954)	Brown, Paul	100-165	*
Miller, Olive B.	Come Play with Me (1st, sm8vo, ibds, [38]p, color, pep)	Volland	(1918)	Browne, Carmen L.	100-160	*
Haynes, Louise M.	Over the Rainbow Bridge (1st, sq8vo, [42]p, ibds, color)	Volland	(1920)	Browne, Carmen L.	80-120	
Miller, Olive B.	Sunny Rhymes/Happy Children (1st, 8vo, ibds, [40]p, pep, color)	Volland	(1917)	Browne, Carmen L.	60-90	*
Eliot, George	Adam Bede (1st, 4to, 523p, p-o, teg, gilt, 16cp)	L: Chambers	[1900]	Browne, Gordon	80-120	
Haggard, H. Rider	Benita, an African Romance (1st, 8vo, 344p, red/gilt, 16pl)	L: Cassell	1906	Browne, Gordon	120-185	
Masefield, John	Book of Discoveries (1st, 8vo, 354p, teg, 53 b/w, pep)	L: Wells/Gard.	1910	Browne, Gordon	60-100	R
Hoffman, Alice S.	Book of the Sagas (1st, 8vo, AEG, 320p, gilt, 6cp)	L: Nister	[1913]	Browne, Gordon	90-135	
Meade, L.T.	Daddy's Girl (1st, 8vo, 340p, blue cl, teg, b/w)	L: G. Newnes	1901	Browne, Gordon	30-50	*
Corkran, Alice	Down the Snow Stairs (1st, 8vo, gilt, 257p, 5 fp b/w)	L: Blackie	1887	Browne, Gordon	50-90	

AUTHOR	TITLE	PUBLISHER	DATE	ARTIST	PRICE	LC
Farrow, George E.	Dwindleberry Zoo (1st, lg8vo, gilt, AEG, 208p, b/w)	L: Blackie	1909	Browne, Gordon	125-200	*
Farrow, George E.	Escape of the Mullingong (1st, 12mo, AEG, 148p, gilt)	L: Blackie	1907	Browne, Gordon	120-180	
Henty, G.A.	Held Fast for England (1st UK, 12mo, 352p, b/w)	L: Blackie	1892	Browne, Gordon	150-250	
Sharp, Evelyn	Hill that Fell Down (1st, 8vo, green/gilt, 275p)	L: Blackie	1909	Browne, Gordon	80-120	
Henty, G.A.	Lion of St. Mark (1st, 12mo, 384p, blue/gilt, 10pl)	L: Blackie	1889	Browne, Gordon	100-185	
Allen, Grant	Miss Cayley's Adventures (1st AM, 8vo, 344p, tan cl, b/w)	Putnam	1899	Browne, Gordon	50-80	*
Stevenson, Rbt. L.	Pavilion on the Links (1st, 8vo, 96p, gilt, col frn, fp b/w, pep)	L: Chatto	1913	Browne, Gordon	50-85	
Jones, Harry	Prince Boo Hoo & Little Smuts (1st, sq8vo, 319p, teg, uncut, b/w)	L: Wells/Gard.	(1896)	Browne, Gordon	120-200	
Lang, Andrew	Prince Prigio (1st, sm8vo, 144p, gilt, 9 fp b/w, pep)	L: Arrowsmith	1889	Browne, Gordon	120-180	
Lang, Andrew	Prince Ricardo of Pantouflia (1st, 12mo, 204p, gilt, 12pl)	L: Arrowsmith	(1893)	Browne, Gordon	130-200	
Thackeray, Wm. M.	Rose & the Ring (lg8vo, 159p, green cl, col frn, 12pl, pep)	Stokes	[1910]	Browne, Gordon	60-95	
Crockett, Samuel R.	Sir Toady Crusoe (1st AM, 8vo, 356p, b/w)	Stokes	(1905)	Browne, Gordon	40-70	
Crockett, Samuel R.	Sir Toady Crusoe (1st, 8vo, 406p, blue cl, 19pl)	L: Wells/Gard.	1905	Browne, Gordon	60-90	
Haggard, H. Rider	Spirit of Bambatse (1st AM, 8vo, 329p, green/gilt, 8pl)	NY: Longmans	1906	Browne, Gordon	80-140	
Crockett, Samuel R.	Surprising Adventures of Sir Toady Lion (1st AM, 8vo, 314p, b/w)	Stokes	(1897)	Browne, Gordon	55-80	
McKay (ed.)	Tale of the Cauldron (1st, ob8vo, 64p, ibds, 16cp)	MacLeod	1927	Browne, Gordon	70-100	
Brereton, Frederick	Tom Stapleton the Boy Scout (1st, 12mo, 287p, gilt, col frn, 6pl)	L: Blackie	1911	Browne, Gordon	50-85	
Lever, Charles	Templelogue Lever (1st, 4to, AEG, green cl, 631p, 32cp)	NY: Pollard	1880	Browne, H.K.	160-200	
Machray, Robert	Night Side of London (1st, 8vo, yellow cl, 300p, b/w)	Lippincott	1902	Browne, Tom	35-60	
Nesbit, Edith	New Treasure Seekers (1st, 8vo, red/gilt, 328p, teg, 33 fp b/w)	L: T.F. Unwin	1904	Browne/Baumer	180-240	
Nesbit, Edith	Story of the Treasure Seekers (1st, 8vo, 296p, AEG, 17pl)	L: T.F. Unwin	1899	Browne/Baumer	280-350	
Nesbit, Edith	Bastable Children (1st {this fmt}, 8vo, 293p, col frn, DJ)	Coward	(1929)	Browne/Blam	50-80	
Crockett, Samuel R.	Sweetheart Travellers (1st AM, lg8vo, 310p, ibds, teg, b/w)	Stokes	(1895)	Browne/Groome	60-90	*
Mackie, Pauline B.	Flight of Rosy Dawn (1st, 12mo, 98p, b/w)	L.C. Page	1903	Bruce, Josephine	30-50	*
Ewing, Juliana H.	Jacanapes (1st {this pub}, 12mo, 71p, rust cl, 6pl)	Dana Estes	(1902)	Bruce, Josephine	25-40	*
Bruce, Josephine	School Days (1st, 4to, 165p, ipcb, 11cp, pep)	Brentano's	1907	Bruce, Josephine	70-120	
Tolboom, Wanda	Shining Bird (1st {std}, 8vo, ibds, [48]p, color, DJ/2.25)	Aladdin	(1955)	Bruce, Robert	25-45	
Tolboom, Wanda	Tosie of the Far North (1st {std}, 4to, [64]p, 2-color, DJ/2.75)	Aladdin	1954	Bruce, Robert	30-50	
Maurois, Andre	Fatapoufs & Thinifers (1st, 4to, pep, blue cl, 92p, color, DJ/2.00)	Henry Holt & Co.	(1940)	Bruller, Jean	60-100	
Bruna, Dick	Dick Bruna's Cinderella (1st {std}, sq12mo, ibds, 28p, fp color, DJ/1.00)	Follett	(1966)	Bruna, Dick	30-45	*
N/A	Adventures of Jack (narrow folio, wraps, [16]p, color)	Stecher	1921	Brundage, Frances	50-80	
Kaplan, A.O.	Baby's Biography (1st, sm4to, AEG, 67p, gilt, color)	Brentano's	1891	Brundage, Frances	125-200	
Taylor, Ida Scott	Baby's Book (sm4to, AEG, gilt, 4 chromos)	L: R. Tuck	[1898]	Brundage, Frances	100-180	
Brundage, Frances	Cat's Pajamas (sq4to, ipcb, shape book, [16]p, color)	NY: Stecher	1932	Brundage, Frances	80-120	
Stevenson, Rbt. L.	Child's Garden of Verses (1st, 8vo, [306]p, col frn, b/w)	Saalfield	(1924)	Brundage, Frances	35-60	*
Nesbit, Edith	Children's Shakespeare (1st AM, 8vo, gilt, 76p, ibds, 11 fp b/w)	Altemus	(1900)	Brundage, Frances	75-100	
Dickens, Charles	Christmas Stories from Dickens (4to, AEG, gilt, 12cp)	L: R. Tuck	[1898]	Brundage, Frances	180-240	
Asbjornsen, P.C.	East of the Sun, West o/t Moon (1st, lg8vo, 248p, col frn)	Saalfield	(1924)	Brundage, Frances	35-60	*
Andersen, Hans C.	Fairy Tales (1st, lg8vo, [310]p, ibds, col frn, b/w)	Saalfield	(1925)	Brundage, Frances	30-50	*
N/A	Goldilocks (folio, wraps, color)	Saalfield	1919	Brundage, Frances	55-80	
Spyri, Johanna	Heidi (1st, 8vo, 307p, p-o, col frn, b/w)	Saalfield	(1924)	Brundage, Frances	25-40	
Gilbert, Henry	King Arthur (1st, lg8vo, 242p, p-o, color, b/w)	Saalfield	1929	Brundage, Frances	50-80	
Tucker, Elizabeth S.	Little Belles & Beaux (1st, lg4to, [26]p, ibds, 6cp)	Stokes	1896	Brundage, Frances	200-300	
Tucker, Elizabeth S.	Little Men & Maids (1st, 4to, ibds, [26]p, 6cp)	Stokes	1896	Brundage, Frances	200-300	*
Mother Goose	Mother Goose ABC (4to, 14p, wraps, color)	Donohue	(1913)	Brundage, Frances	75-100	*
Moore, Clement C.	Night Before Christmas (folio, wraps, color)	Saalfield	[1915]	Brundage, Frances	80-120	
Potter, Beatrix	Peter Rabbit (folio, wraps, [12]p, fp color)	C.E. Graham	[1914]	Brundage, Frances	100-165	
Collodi, Carlo	Pinocchio (1st, lg8vo, 247p, p-o, col frn, b/w)	Saalfield	(1924)	Brundage, Frances	60-100	
MacDonald, George	Princess & the Goblin (1st, 12mo, 251p, blue cl, p-o, col frn)	Saalfield	(1927)	Brundage, Frances	30-50	
Irving, Washington	Rip Van Winkle (1st, sm8vo, 92p, col frn, fp b/w)	Saalfield	(1927)	Brundage, Frances	30-50	*
N/A	Snow White & Rose Red (sq4to, wraps, [16]p, color)	Stecher	1929	Brundage, Frances	40-60	
N/A	Tale of the Little Bunnies (1st, 4to, wraps, shape book, color)	S. Gabriel	1914	Brundage, Frances	70-125	
Stevenson, Rbt. L.	Treasure Island (1st, lg8vo, 230p, col frn, b/w, pep)	Saalfield	(1924)	Brundage, Frances	25-45	
N/A	Wedding Bells (4to, blue/silver, AE silver, 4 chromos)	L: R. Tuck	[1900]	Brundage, Frances	150-225	
N/A	Whose Little Kitty are You? (folio, ibds, color)	NY: S. Gabriel	1913	Brundage, Frances	130-200	
Vredenburg, Edric	Old Fairy Tales (lg8vo, ibds, 104p, 8cp)	L: R. Tuck	[1912]	Brundage/Bowley	150-240	
Nesbit, Edith	Royal Children of English History (1st, 4to, 94p, AEG, 10cp)	L: R. Tuck	[1896]	Brundage/Bowley	180-260	
Chesson, Nora	Tales from Tennyson (4to, 96p, ibds, 6 chromos)	L: R. Tuck	[1890]	Brundage/Bowley	140-200	
Bible	Ecclesiasticus... (1st, 4to, black/gilt, 165p, teg, 16cp)	L: John Lane	1927	Brunton, Violet	90-160	
Wilson, Romer	Green Magic (1st, 8vo, green cl, 448p, 8cp)	L: J. Cape	(1928)	Brunton, Violet	100-150	
Wilson, Romer	Silver Magic (1st, 8vo, 432p, silver cl, 8cp)	L: J. Cape	(1929)	Brunton, Violet	130-180	
Tagore, Rabindranath	Moon, for What Do You Wait? (1st {std}, sm ob8vo, [32]p, color, DJ)	Atheneum	1967	Bryan, Ashley	25-40	*
Knight, Mary	Fox that Wanted 9 Golden Tales (1st {std}, 12mo, 94p, b/w, cep, DJ/3.95)	Macmillan	(1969)	Bryan, Brigitte	30-50	
Godden, Rumer	Operation Sippacik (1st AM, 8vo, 109p, fp b/w, DJ/3.50)	Viking	(1969)	Bryan, James	25-40	
Bryan, Dorothy	Bobby Wanted a Pony (1st {std}, 8vo, [32]p, ibds, color, DJ/1.00)	Dodd	1937	Bryan, Marguerite	30-50	
Bryan, Dorothy	Friendly Little Jonathan (1st, lg ob8vo, ibds, [32]p, b/w, cep, DJ/1.25)	Dodd	1939	Bryan, Marguerite	30-50	*
O'Dell, Scott	King's Fifth (1st {std}, 8vo, 264p, b/w, DJ/3.95, NH)	Houghton	1966	Bryant, Samuel	40-65	
Edmonds, Walter D.	Musket and the Cross (1st {std}, 8vo, 514p, b/w, pep, DJ/10.00)	Little/Brown	(1968)	Bryant, Samuel	30-50	
Gregory, Horace	Alphabet for Joanna (1st {std}, 24mo, [24]p, color, DJ/2.50)	Holt, Rinehart	(1963)	Bryson, Bernarda	30-50	
Best, Herbert	Bright Hunter of the Skies (1st {std}, 8vo, 164p, b/w, pep, DJ/3.50)	Macmillan	1961	Bryson, Bernarda	20-35	
Belting, Natalia	Calendar Moon (1st {std}, 8vo, [62]p, ibds, color, DJ/3.50)	Holt, Rinehart	(1964)	Bryson, Bernarda	30-50	
Bryson, Bernarda	Gilgamesh: Man's First Story (1st {std}, 4to, ipcb, 112p, color, DJ/4.95)	Holt, Rinehart	(1967)	Bryson, Bernarda	60-95	R
Withers, Carl	Grindstone of God (1st {std}, 4to, [32]p, ibds, color, DJ/3.95)	Holt, Rinehart	(1970)	Bryson, Bernarda	40-65	
Keating, Norma	Mr. Chu (1st {std}, sm8vo, 34p, 3-color, DJ/3.75)	Macmillan	(1965)	Bryson, Bernarda	25-40	
Austen, Jane	Pride and Prejudice (1st, lg8vo, 374p, b/w, DJ/3.95)	Macmillan	1962	Bryson, Bernarda	25-40	*
Clarke, Pauline	Return of the Twelves (1st AM {std}, 8vo, 253p, fp b/w, DJ/3.75)	Coward	(1964)	Bryson, Bernarda	40-65	
Platt, Rutherford	River of Life (1st, 8vo, 309p, b/w, DJ/5.00)	Simon/Schuster	1956	Bryson, Bernarda	25-40	
Appel, Benjamin	Shepherd of the Sun (1st {std}, 8vo, 87p, fp b/w, DJ/2.95)	Obolensky	(1961)	Bryson, Bernarda	25-40	

ARTIST: 38

AUTHOR	TITLE	PUBLISHER	DATE	ARTIST	PRICE	LC
Stockton, Frank	Storyteller's Pack (1st, 8vo, 358p, fp b/w, cep, DJ/5.95)	Scribner	(1968)	Bryson, Bernarda	30-50	R*
Belting, Natalia	Sun is a Golden Earring (1st {std}, ob8vo, [48]p, 3-color, DJ/3.50, CH)	Holt, Rinehart	(1962)	Bryson, Bernarda	45-70	R
Bryson, Bernarda	Twenty Miracles of St. Nicolas (1st {std}, 4to, 88p, 1-color, DJ/4.75)	Little/Brown	(1960)	Bryson, Bernarda	30-50	
Ogburn, Charlton	White Falcon (1st, 8vo, tan/silver, 51p, b/w, pep, DJ/2.25)	Houghton	1955	Bryson, Bernarda	65-90	R
Bryson, Bernarda	Zoo of Zeus (1st, 4to, [56]p, fp color, DJ/6.00)	NY: Grossman	1964	Bryson, Bernarda	40-60	*
Boden, Hilda	Marlows Wins a Prize (1st AM {std}, 8vo, 120p, b/w, DJ/2.50)	McKay	(1957)	Buchanan, Lilian	25-40	
Kendall, Carol S.	Other Side of the Tunnel (1st, 8vo, 192p, b/w, DJ/2.75)	Abelard-Schuman	(1957)	Buchanan, Lilian	30-50	
Damjan, Mischa	Mau: King of the Cats (1st AM {std}, 4to, [30]p, 2-color, DJ/2.00)	Putnam	(1963)	Buchi, Werner	30-50	
Jackson, Linda	Petey (1st, sq8vo, 56p, fp 1-color, DJ/1.50)	Harcourt	(1942)	Buck, Dorothy	30-50	
Uttley, Alison	Adventures of No Ordinary Rabbit (1st, 8vo, 208p, b/w, DJ)	L: Faber	(1937)	Buckels, Alec	50-80	*
De La Mare, Walter	Come Hither (1st, lg8vo, 696p, green cl, b/w)	L: Constable	1923	Buckels, Alec	60-80	*
De La Mare, Walter	Come Hither (1st AM, lg8vo, gilt, 696p, b/w)	Knopf	(1923)	Buckels, Alec	50-80	
De La Mare, Walter	Miss Jemima (1st, sm8vo, ipcb, p-o, 36p, col frn, 3 fp b/w)	L: Blackwell	[1925]	Buckels, Alec	90-160	R*
Housman, Laurence	Turn Again Tales (1st, 4to, 280p, p-o, 6 ticp)	L: B. Blackwell	[1930]	Buckels, Alec	80-125	
Glendon, George	Emperor of the Air (1st, 8vo, 311p, red/gilt, 8pl)	L: Methuen	1910	Buckland, Arthur H.	55-80	*
Nesbit, Edith	The Wouldbegoods (1st, sm8vo, red/gilt, 331p, teg, 18pl)	L: T.F. Unwin	(1901)	Buckland, Arthur H.	200-300	
Townend, Jack	Railroad ABC (1st, ob24mo, ibds, [57]p, color, DJ/0.50)	F. Watts	1944	Budd, Denison	50-80	*
Lampman, Evelyn	Shy Stegosaurus of Cricket Creek (1st {std}, 8vo, 220p, b/w, DJ/2.75)	Doubleday	1955	Buel, Robert	70-120	
Buff, Mary	Dancing Cloud (1st, ob4to, ipcb, 80p, fp color, cep, DJ/2.00)	Viking	1937	Buff, Conrad	80-120	R
Buff, M.& C.	Kobi, a Boy of Switzerland (1st, sm4to, 128p, dp color, dep, DJ/2.00)	Viking	1939	Buff, Conrad	35-60	
Buff, M.& C.	Apple and the Arrow (1st, sm4to, 75p, gilt, color, pep, DJ/3.00, NH)	Houghton	1951	Buff, M.& C.	70-100	
Buff, Mary	Big Tree (1st, 4to, 79p, grey cl, b/w, DJ/3.00, NH)	Viking	1946	Buff, M.& C.	60-90	
Buff, M.& C.	Colorado: River of Mystery (1st, 4to, 86p, fp 1-color, cep, DJ/4.95)	CA: Ritchie Pr.	(1968)	Buff, M.& C.	30-50	
Buff, Mary	Dash and Dart (1st, sm4to, 73p, 4 dp cp, dep, DJ/2.00, CH)	Viking	1942	Buff, M.& C.	80-125	
Buff, M.& C.	Elf Owl (1st, 4to, 74p, 1-color, pep, DJ/2.75)	Viking	(1958)	Buff, M.& C.	65-100	R
Buff, M.& C.	Forest Folk (1st, 4to, 64p, 1-color, pep, DJ/3.00)	Viking	(1962)	Buff, M.& C.	30-50	
Buff, M.& C.	Hah-Nee of the Cliff Dwellers (1st, 4to, 68p, color, DJ/3.00)	Houghton	1956	Buff, M.& C.	60-100	R
Buff, M.& C.	Hurry, Skurry & Flurry (1st, sm4to, 73p, pep, 1-color, DJ/2.75)	Viking	1954	Buff, M.& C.	65-100	R
Buff, M.& C.	Kemi: An Indian Boy Before White Man Came (1st, 8vo, 90p, b/w, DJ/3.50)	CA: Ritchie Pr.	(1966)	Buff, M.& C.	40-65	
Buff, Mary	Magic Maize (1st, 4to, 76p, pep, 9 fp color, DJ/3.00, NH)	Houghton	1953	Buff, M.& C.	70-100	
Buff, M.& C.	Peter's Pinto (1st, 4to, 95p, b/w, DJ/2.00)	Viking	1949	Buff, M.& C.	25-45	
Buff, M.& C.	Trix and Vix (1st, 4to, 24p, b/w, DJ/2.75)	Houghton	1960	Buff, M.& C.	25-45	
Mother Goose	Mother Goose in Silhouettes (1st, sq16mo, 78p, b/w)	Houghton	1907	Buffam, Katharine G.	80-125	
Gate, Ethel M.	Tales from the Secret Kingdom (1st, sm4to, 93p, ibds, silhouettes)	Yale U. Press	1919	Buffam, Katharine G.	45-70	
Deihl, Edna G.	Magic Lake (1st, 12mo, p-o, 125p, 1-color)	Whitman	(1930)	Builta, Marie V.	30-45	
White, Richardson	Aesop's Fables in Rhyme (1st, lg4to, ibds, [100]p, 50pl, pep)	Saalfield	1903	Bull, Charles L.	140-240	*
Dyer, Walter A.	All Around Robin Hood's Barn (1st {std}, lg8vo, 204p, p-o, 24cp)	Doubleday/Page	1926	Bull, Charles L.	70-120	
Evarts, Hal G.	Bald Face & other Animal Stories (1st, 8vo, 317p, 8pl, pep)	Knopf	1921	Bull, Charles L.	50-80	
Saunders, Marshall	Beautiful Joe's Paradise (1st, sm8vo, red/gilt, p-o, 365p, 15pl, pep)	L.C. Page	1902	Bull, Charles L.	120-200	
London, Jack	Before Adam (1st, 8vo, brown cl, 242p, uncut, 8cp)	Macmillan	1907	Bull, Charles L.	150-250	
Dyer, Walter A.	Country Cousins (1st {std}, lg8vo, 164p, col frn, 11pl, pep)	Doubleday/Doran	1927	Bull, Charles L.	60-90	
Roberts, Chas. G.D.	Earth's Enigmas (1st, 12mo, 285p, red/gilt, 10pl)	L.C. Page	1903	Bull, Charles L.	70-120	
Roberts, Theodore G.	Flying Plover (1st, sm8vo, 125p, tan cl, 6pl, cvr by...)	L.C. Page	1909	Bull, Charles L.	40-60	
Pardee, Lucius C.	Folk of the Woods (1st, lg8vo, gilt, p-o, 129p, teg, 10cp, pep)	Doubleday/Page	1913	Bull, Charles L.	40-70	
Terhune, Albert P.	Further Adventures of Lad (1st, sm8vo, 341p, col frn)	Doran	(1922)	Bull, Charles L.	80-120	
Roberts, Chas. G.D.	Haunters of the Silences (1st, 8vo, 316p, gilt, b/w, pep)	L.C. Page	1907	Bull, Charles L.	50-75	
Ware, Richard D.	In the Woods and on the Shore (1st, 8vo, 279p, photos, frn by...)	L.C. Page	1908	Bull, Charles L.	40-60	*
Roberts, Chas. G.D.	Kindred of the Wild (1st, 8vo, 374p, green/gilt, teg, 50pl)	L.C. Page	1902	Bull, Charles L.	50-80	
Linderman, Frank B.	Kootenai Why Stories (1st, sm8vo, 166p, blue cl, 4cp)	Scribner	1926	Bull, Charles L.	100-165	
Scoville, Samuel	Lords of the Wild (1st, sm8vo, green cl, 246p, 4pl, pep)	Wm. Morrow	1928	Bull, Charles L.	25-45	
Long, William J.	Mother Nature (1st {std}, lg8vo, green/gilt, 330p, 8cp)	Harper	(1923)	Bull, Charles L.	40-60	
Darling, Esther B.	Navarre of the North (1st {std}, 8vo, 268p, pep, frn by...)	Doubleday/Doran	1930	Bull, Charles L.	55-80	
Crump, Irving	Og - Son of Fire (1st, 8vo, 198p, b/w, pep)	Dodd	1922	Bull, Charles L.	25-45	
Judson, Katherine	Old Crow Stories (1st, 8vo, 163p, blue cl, 6pl)	Little/Brown	1917	Bull, Charles L.	30-50	
Evarts, Hal G.	Passing of the Old West (1st, 8vo, 234p, 8pl)	Little/Brown	1921	Bull, Charles L.	50-80	
Litsey, E. Carl	Race of the Swift (1st, sm8vo, gilt, uncut, 151p, 4pl)	Little/Brown	1905	Bull, Charles L.	25-40	*
Roberts, Theodore G.	Red Feathers (1st, sm8vo, p-o, 325p, col frn, 10pl, pep)	L.C. Page	1907	Bull, Charles L.	40-65	
Roberts, Chas. G.D.	Red Fox (1st, 8vo, uncut, 340p, teg, 48pl)	L.C. Page	1905	Bull, Charles L.	50-80	
Baker, Olaf	Shasta of the Wolves (1st, 8vo, 276p, 4cp)	Dodd	1919	Bull, Charles L.	30-45	
Hoyt, Vance J.	Silver Boy (1st, 8vo, blue/silver, 265p, pep, 6pl)	Lothrop, Lee	(1929)	Bull, Charles L.	30-50	
Hawkes, Clarence	Silversheene: King of Sled Dogs (1st, 12mo, 234p, 4pl)	Milton Bradley	(1924)	Bull, Charles L.	25-40	*
Bryson, Charles L.	Tan & Teckle (1st, 8vo, grey cl, 238p, 8pl)	Revell	(1908)	Bull, Charles L.	35-60	
Bull, Charles L.	Under the Roof of the Jungle (1st, 8vo, green/gilt, 271p, 4cp)	L.C. Page	1911	Bull, Charles L.	50-80	
Roberts, Chas. G.D.	Watchers of the Trails (1st, 8vo, uncut, 361p, 48pl, pep)	L.C. Page	1904	Bull, Charles L.	50-85	
Hawkes, Clarence	White Czar... (1st, 12mo, 202p, b/w pl)	Milton Bradley	1923	Bull, Charles L.	25-40	*
London, Jack	White Fang (1st, 8vo, blue cl, 328p, 8cp, PPP)	Macmillan	1906	Bull, Charles L.	300-450	
Chaffee, Allen	Wild Folk (1st, 8vo, 323p, pep, col frn by...)	Milton Bradley	(1930)	Bull, Charles L.	25-45	
Annixter, Paul	Wilderness Ways (1st, lg8vo, p-o, 313p, col frn, 13pl)	Penn	(1930)	Bull, Charles L.	60-80	*
Long, William J.	Wood-Folk Comedies (1st, lg8vo, green/gilt, 307p, 8pl)	Harper	(1920)	Bull, Charles L.	45-70	
Tunis, John R.	Iron Duke (1st, 8vo, 276p, b/w, pep, DJ/2.00)	Harcourt	(1938)	Bull, Johan	20-35	
N/A	Arabian Nights (1st, sm4to, 299p, p-o, gilt, 20 ticp)	L: Constable	1912	Bull, Rene	300-500	
N/A	Arabian Nights (1st AM, sm4to, p-o, 299p, teg, 20 ticp)	Dodd	1912	Bull, Rene	250-400	
N/A	Arabian Nights (8vo, 299p, green cl, p-o, 7 ticp, later)	L: Constable	[1917]	Bull, Rene	150-220	
Davidson, Gladys	Arabian Nights Retold for Children (8vo, 352p, red cl, 16cp)	L: Blackie	[1925]	Bull, Rene	75-100	*
Merimee, Prosper	Carmen (1st AM, 4to, 204p, teg, red/gilt, 16cp, pep)	Hearst	[1916]	Bull, Rene	200-300	
Merimee, Prosper	Carmen (1st, 4to, 204p, red/gilt, teg, pep, 16cp)	L: Hutchinson	[1916]	Bull, Rene	250-350	
Fyleman, Rose	Garland of Roses (1st, 8vo, blue/gilt, 129p, col frn, 16pl)	L: Methuen	1928	Bull, Rene	120-180	
Swift, Jonathan	Gulliver's Travels (1st, 8vo, 346p, brown/gilt, b/w)	L: Wells/Gard.	[1918]	Bull, Rene	160-220	

AUTHOR	TITLE	PUBLISHER	DATE	ARTIST	PRICE	LC
Strang, Herbert	Old Man of the Mountain (1st, 8vo, 322p, green/gilt, fp b/w by...)	L: H. Frowde	(1916)	Bull, Rene	75-100	
Omar Khayyam	Rubaiyat of Omar Khayyam (1st, 4to, blue/gilt, [88]p, 10 ticp)	L: Hodder	[1913]	Bull, Rene	425-600	
Johnson, A.E.	Russian Ballet (1st AM, 4to, gilt, 240p, teg, 12cp)	Houghton	1913	Bull, Rene	250-350	
Johnson, A.E.	Russian Ballet (1st, lg4to, 240p, teg, gilt, uncut, 12cp)	L: Constable	1913	Bull, Rene	300-500	
Raleigh, Francis	Ralph Somerby at Panama (1st, sm8vo, 305p, p-o, 10pl, pep)	L.C. Page	1913	Bull/Edwards	25-40	
London, Jack	Call of the Wild (1st, 8vo, teg, 231p, green/gilt, 10cp, pep, PPP)	Macmillan	1903	Bull/Goodwin	500-700	
La Fontaine, J.	La Fontaine's Fables (1st, sm ob4to, ibds, [64]p, color)	L: T. Nelson	1905	Bull/Park	160-240	
Bullard, Marion	Somersaulting Rabbit (1st, ob4to, 45p, ibds, 12pl)	Dutton	(1927)	Bullard, Marion	100-170	*
Hough, Emerson	Singing Mouse Stories (1st, 12mo, 235p, green/gilt, decor by...)	Bobbs-Merrill	(1910)	Bunker, Mayo	30-50	
Alden, Raymond M.	Why the Chimes Rang (sm8vo, olive cl, p-o, [40]p)	Bobbs-Merrill	(1909)	Bunker, Mayo	30-50	
MacDonald, Ray	Mad Scientist (1st, 8vo, blue cl, 242p, 8pl)	NY: Cochrane	1908	Bunnell, Charles B.	75-100	*
Burbank, Addison	Cedar Deer (1st, 8vo, 157p, dp color, DJ/2.00)	Coward	1940	Burbank, Addison	20-30	
Burchard, Peter	Bimby (1st, 8vo, 91p, b/w, DJ/3.50)	Coward	(1968)	Burchard, Peter	25-45	*
Rowand, Phyllis	Cats Who Stayed for Dinner (1st, 8vo, ipcb, [41]p, color, pep)	Wonder Books	(1951)	Burchard, Peter	35-50	
Hays, Wilma P.	Highland Halloween (1st, 8vo, 64p, fp 1-color, DJ/2.50)	Coward	(1962)	Burchard, Peter	20-30	
Bradford, Roark	How Come Christmas (1st, 8vo, ibds, 22p, b/w, DJ/1.00)	Harper	(1948)	Burchard, Peter	20-35	
Fritz, Jean	I, Adam (1st, 8vo, 255p, b/w, DJ/3.75)	Coward	(1963)	Burchard, Peter	50-80	R
Burchard, Peter	Jed (1st, 8vo, 94p, DJ/3.00)	Coward	(1960)	Burchard, Peter	20-35	
Bulla, Clyde R.	John Billington, Friend of Squanto (1st, 8vo, 88p, b/w, DJ/2.50)	Crowell	(1956)	Burchard, Peter	20-35	
Burchard, Peter	River Queen (1st {std} [1st bk.], sm4to, 40p, ipcb, color, pep, DJ/3.00)	Macmillan	(1957)	Burchard, Peter	40-65	
Shotwell, Louisa	Roosevelt Grady (1st {std}, 8vo, 151p, b/w, DJ/2.95)	World	(1963)	Burchard, Peter	25-40	
Toon, Gladys E.	Animal Story Book (1st, folio, 63p, ibds, 12cp)	Saalfield	(1928)	Burd, Clara M.	35-60	
N/A	Animals on the Farm (1st, 4to, linen, [20]p, 8cp)	Saalfield	1936	Burd, Clara M.	30-50	
Stevenson, Rbt. L.	Child's Garden of Verses (1st, 4to, ibds, [36]p, 8 fp color)	Saalfield	(1930)	Burd, Clara M.	30-60	
Marks, Jeannette	Children in the Wood Stories (1st, sm8vo, 141p, p-o, 6cp)	Milton Bradley	1919	Burd, Clara M.	25-40	
Toon, Gladys E.	Ducky Dee (1st, 4to, ibds, unpag, 8cp)	Saalfield	1928	Burd, Clara M.	35-60	*
Alcott, Louisa M.	Eight Cousins (1st, 8vo, 253p, p-o, 4cp, pep)	Winston	(1931)	Burd, Clara M.	30-50	
Grimm Bros.	Fairy Tales (1st, 8vo, ibds, 6cp)	Donohue	(1920)	Burd, Clara M.	35-60	
Smith, Laura R.	Good-Night Stories (1st, lg8vo, 120p, ipcb, 8cp by...)	Chi: Stanton	(1921)	Burd, Clara M.	50-80	
Spyri, Johanna	Heidi (1st, 8vo, gilt, p-o, 290p, 4cp, pep)	Winston	(1924)	Burd, Clara M.	30-50	
Alcott, Louisa M.	Little Men (1st, 8vo, 349p, p-o, 4cp, pep)	Winston	(1928)	Burd, Clara M.	30-50	
Mother Goose	Mother Goose in Song & Rhyme (1st, 4to, 87p, 2-color, pep)	C.E. Graham	(1930)	Burd, Clara M.	40-60	*
Alcott, Louisa M.	Old-Fashioned Girl (1st, 8vo, 342p, p-o, 4cp)	Winston	(1928)	Burd, Clara M.	25-40	
Alcott, Louisa M.	Rose in Bloom (1st, 8vo, p-o, 320p, 4cp)	Winston	(1933)	Burd, Clara M.	25-40	
Edgeworth, Maria	Simple Susan and other Tales (1st, sm8vo, 216p, 4cp, fp b/w)	Macmillan	1929	Burd, Clara M.	25-40	
Yonge, Charlotte	Unknown to History (1st, 8vo, 470p, black cl, p-o, col frn, 8pl)	Harper	(1927)	Burd, Clara M.	30-45	
Bailey, Carolyn S.	Wonder Stories (1st, 8vo, p-o, 344p, 6cp, pep)	Milton Bradley	1920	Burd, Clara M.	30-50	*
Hosie, Margaret	Mother Goose Nursery Rhymes (1st, 8vo, 125p, ibds, 8cp 16pl)	Chi: Stanton	(1919)	Burd/Higgins	80-130	
Bartusek, Libushka	Happy Times in Czechoslovakia (1st {std}, 4to, 61p, color, pep, DJ/2.00)	Knopf	(1940)	Bures, Yarka	50-80	
North, Sterling	Hurry, Spring! (1st {std}, 8vo, 58p, b/w, DJ/3.75)	Dutton	(1966)	Burger, Carl	20-30	
Burnford, Sheila	Incredible Journey (1st {std}, 8vo, 145p, fp b/w, DJ/3.75)	Little/Brown	1961	Burger, Carl	75-120	
North, Sterling	Little Rascal (1st {std}, 8vo, 78p, b/w, DJ/3.50)	Dutton	(1965)	Burger, Carl	20-30	
Gipson, Fred B.	Old Yeller (1st, 8vo, ibds, 158p, 6 fp b/w, DJ/2.75, NH)	Harper	(1956)	Burger, Carl	45-70	*
Gipson, Fred B.	Recollection Creek (1st, 8vo, 248p, b/w, DJ/2.95)	Harper	(1959)	Burger, Carl	20-25	
Gipson, Fred B.	Savage Sam (1st {std}, 8vo, 214p, bds, b/w, DJ/3.00)	Harper	(1962)	Burger, Carl	20-30	
Ackerman, Francis	Tonk and Tonka (1st {std}, 8vo, 47p, b/w, DJ/2.95)	Dutton	(1962)	Burger, Carl	20-30	
Burgess, Gelett	Blue Goops & Red (1st, sm4to, green cl, 81p, 2-color, pep)	Stokes	(1909)	Burgess, Gelett	250-400	
Burgess, Gelett	Burgess Nonsense Book (1st, 8vo, teg, 239p, gilt, b/w)	Stokes	(1901)	Burgess, Gelett	170-240	
Burgess, Gelett	Cat's Elegy (1st, 12mo, tan ipcb, [43]p, 1-color)	McClurg	1913	Burgess, Gelett	90-160	R*
Burgess, Gelett	Goop Directory of Juvenile Offenders (1st, 12mo, 78p, ibds)	Stokes	(1913)	Burgess, Gelett	100-160	
Burgess, Gelett	Goop Tales Alphabetically Told (1st, sq4to, blue cl, 106p, b/w)	Stokes	(1904)	Burgess, Gelett	140-200	
Burgess, Gelett	Goops & How to be Them (1st, sq4to, [96]p, ibds, fp b/w, PPP)	Stokes	(1900)	Burgess, Gelett	350-500	
Burgess, Gelett	Lady Mechante (1st, 8vo, 393p, lavender cl, 8pl)	Stokes	(1909)	Burgess, Gelett	50-80	
Burgess, Gelett	Lively City O'Ligg (1st, 8vo, 219p, ibds, 8cp)	Stokes	(1899)	Burgess, Gelett	130-200	
Burgess, Gelett	Why Be a Goop? (1st, sq8vo, p-o, red cl, 159p)	Stokes	1924	Burgess, Gelett	120-180	
Barton, William E.	Prairie Schooner (1st, sm8vo, 382p, 5pl)	W.A. Wilde	(1900)	Burgess, H.	25-40	*
Sewell, Anna	Black Beauty (8vo, p-o, 357p, 20 fp color)	Platt/Peck	(1911)	Burke, J.M.	60-90	
DeJong, Meindert	Big Goose & Little White Duck (1st, 8vo, 169p, b/w, DJ/3.50)	Harper	(1963)	Burkert, Nancy	25-45	
Updike, John	Child's Calendar (1st, lg8vo, [30]p, fp 2-color, DJ/3.25)	Knopf	(1965)	Burkert, Nancy	60-90	R
Andersen, Hans C.	Fir Tree (1st, 8vo, 34p, p-o, color, DJ/3.95)	Harper	(1970)	Burkert, Nancy	40-65	
Dahl, Roald	James & the Giant Peach (1st [2], sm4to, 118p, gilt, color, cep, DJ/3.95)	Knopf	(1961)	Burkert, Nancy	400-600	
Dahl, Roald	James & the Giant Peach (1st [1], sm4to, 118p, gilt, color, cep, DJ/3.95)	Knopf	(1961)	Burkert, Nancy	2000-3000	
Carlson, Natalie S.	Jean-Claude's Island (1st, 8vo, 147p, fp b/w, DJ/3.50)	Harper	(1963)	Burkert, Nancy	30-50	R
Lear, Edward	Scroobius Pip (1st, lg4to, [28]p, fp color, pep, DJ/3.95)	Harper	(1968)	Burkert, Nancy	40-65	
Andersen, Hans C.	The Nightingale (1st, 4to, 32p, ibds, color, DJ/3.95)	Harper	(1965)	Burkert, Nancy	40-60	R
Frost, William H.	Court of King Arthur (1st, 12mo, red/gilt, 302p, 6pl)	Scribner	1896	Burleigh, Sydney R.	75-100	
Burne-Jones, Edward	Beginning of the World (1st, lg4to, 23p, ibds, fp b/w)	L: Longmans	1902	Burne-Jones, Edward	250-350	
Morris, William	Doom of King Acrisius (1st, 8vo, teg, uncut, 82p, 11pl)	R.H. Russell	1902	Burne-Jones, Edward	100-160	
Morris, William	Pygmalion & the Image (1st, 8vo, white/gilt, teg, 34p, 5pl)	R.H. Russell	1903	Burne-Jones, Edward	80-120	
Ford, Ford Madox	Queen Who Flew (1st, 12mo, 118p, frn by...)	L: Bliss Sands	1894	Burne-Jones, Edward	80-125	*
Bible	Song of Songs... (1st AM, narrow 4to, [21]p, 6pl)	R.H. Russell	1902	Burne-Jones, Edward	100-160	*
Burningham, John	Borka (1st, 4to, ibds, [32]p, fp color, pep, KGM)	L: J. Cape	1963	Burningham, John	50-80	
Burningham, John	Cannonball Simp (1st AM {std}, 4to, [32]p, color, DJ/3.95)	Bobbs-Merrill	(1967)	Burningham, John	50-80	*
Fleming, Ian	Chitty Chitty Bang Bang! (1st AM, lg8vo, 114p, b/w, pep, DJ/3.50)	Random	(1964)	Burningham, John	80-130	
Schatz, Letta	Extraordinary Tug-of-War (1st AM {std}, ob4to, 48p, fp color, DJ/3.95)	Follett	(1968)	Burningham, John	30-50	
Burningham, John	Harquin (1st AM {std}, 4to, [32]p, color, DJ/3.50)	Bobbs-Merrill	(1968)	Burningham, John	50-85	*
Burningham, John	John Burningham's ABC (1st, 4to, ibds, dep)	L: J. Cape	(1964)	Burningham, John	45-70	
Burningham, John	Mr. Gumpy's Outing (1st {std}, 4to, [32]p, ibds, fp color, KGM, NYTBI)	L: J. Cape	1970	Burningham, John	80-125	

AUTHOR	TITLE	PUBLISHER	DATE	ARTIST	PRICE	LC
Burningham, John	The Seasons (1st, 4to, [32]p, bds, dp color, DJ)	L: J. Cape	1969	Burningham, John	50-85	
Burningham, John	Trubloff (1st AM {std}, 4to, [41]p, ibds, color, DJ/3.95)	Random	(1965)	Burningham, John	45-70	
Robinson, Mabel L.	Robin & Tito (1st, 8vo, 192p, col frn, b/w)	Macmillan	1930	Burns, Eloise	25-40	*
McNeely, Marian H.	Rusty Ruston (1st {std}, 12mo, green cl, 293p, col frn, 5pl, dep)	Longmans	1928	Burns, Eloise	50-85	*
Graham, Shirley	Story of Phillis Wheatley (1st, 8vo, 176p, b/w, pep, DJ/2.75)	J. Messner	(1949)	Burns, Robert	30-50	*
Farjeon, Eleanor	Perfect Zoo (1st {this pub.}, 4to, 47p, color)	L: Harrap	1947	Burrell, Kathleen	50-80	*
Carlson, Bernice	Listen! And Help Tell the Story (1st, lg8vo, 176p, 2-color, cep, DJ/3.95)	Abingdon Press	(1965)	Burris, Burmah	30-50	
Fyleman, Rose	51 New Nursery Rhymes (1st {std}, ob4to, ibds, 98p, color)	Doubleday/Doran	1932	Burroughs, Dorothy	80-130	R
Burton, Virginia L.	Calico the Wonder Horse (1st, narrow ob8vo, color, [58]p, DJ/1.00)	Houghton	1941	Burton, Virginia L.	170-250	
Burton, Virginia L.	Choo-Choo (1st, lg4to, red cl, [48]p, b/w, pep, DJ/1.50)	Houghton	(1937)	Burton, Virginia L.	100-160	R*
Peck, Leigh	Don Coyote (1st, sm4to, 78p, color, cep, DJ/2.00)	Houghton	1942	Burton, Virginia L.	60-90	
Andersen, Hans C.	Emperor's New Clothes (1st, 8vo, 43p, ibds, color, pep, DJ/2.00)	Houghton	1949	Burton, Virginia L.	80-120	
Bontemps, Arna	Fast Sooner Hound (1st, lg8vo, beige cl, 28p, color, pep, DJ/1.75)	Houghton	(1942)	Burton, Virginia L.	70-130	
Burton, Virginia L.	Katy & the Big Snow (1st, sm ob4to, 32p, blue cl, color, pep, DJ/2.50)	Houghton	1943	Burton, Virginia L.	100-150	
Burton, Virginia L.	Life Story: Play in Five Acts (1st, sm ob4to, 67p, gilt, fp color, DJ/5.00)	Houghton	1962	Burton, Virginia L.	60-90	R
Burton, Virginia L.	Little House (1st, lg sq8vo, 40p, green cl, color, pep, DJ/2.00, CM)	Houghton	1942	Burton, Virginia L.	180-250	R
Burton, Virginia L.	Maybelle the Cable Car (1st, sq lg8vo, 42p, pep, color, DJ/2.75)	Houghton	1952	Burton, Virginia L.	125-200	R
Burton, Virginia L.	Mike Mulligan & his Steam Shovel (1st, sq8vo, [48]p, color, pep, DJ/1.50)	Houghton	1939	Burton, Virginia L.	140-200	R
Bontemps, Arna	Sad-Faced Boy (1st, 8vo, 118p, col frn, 7pl, pep, DJ/2.00)	Houghton	1937	Burton, Virginia L.	80-130	
Malcolmson, Anne	Song of Robin Hood (1st, 4to, 123p, color, DJ/5.00, CH)	Houghton	1947	Burton, Virginia L.	120-180	
Belting, Natalia	Pierre of Kaskaskia (1st {std}, 8vo, 162p, b/w, DJ/2.00)	Bobbs-Merrill	(1951)	Busch, Paul	20-30	*
Eggleston, Edward	Hoosier Schoolboy (1st [1], 12mo, 181p, 5pl, PPP)	Scribner	1883	Bush, G.D.	150-220	
White, Eliza O.	Ednah and her Brothers (1st, sm8vo, 143p, gilt, 4pl)	Houghton	1900	Bush-Brown, Margaret	40-65	
Muhlenweg, Fritz	Big Tiger and Christian (1st, 8vo, yellow cl, 592p, b/w, pep, DJ/4.95)	Pantheon	(1952)	Busoni, Rafaello	120-200	
Faulkner, John	Chooky (1st {std}, 8vo, 250p, beige cl, b/w, DJ/3.00)	Norton	(1950)	Busoni, Rafaello	30-50	
Alden, Raymond M.	Christmas Tree Forest (1st, sm4to, [32]p, fp color, pep, DJ/2.25)	Bobbs-Merrill	1958	Busoni, Rafaello	30-45	
Rosen, Sidney	Doctor Paracelsus (1st {std}, 8vo, 214p, b/w, DJ/3.50)	Little/Brown	(1959)	Busoni, Rafaello	20-35	*
Resnick, William S.	Dragon Ship (1st, 8vo, 214p, col frn, DJ/2.75)	Coward	1942	Busoni, Rafaello	30-50	
DeLeeuw, Cateau	Dutch West Indies & Philippines (1st, 8vo, ibds, 25p, 2-color, DJ/1.25)	Holiday House	(1943)	Busoni, Rafaello	40-65	
Bianco, Margery W.	Forward, Commandos! (1st, 8vo, 184p, color, DJ/2.00)	Viking	1944	Busoni, Rafaello	20-30	
Beim, Lorraine	Gregori's Lamb (1st, 8vo, 92p, ipcb, color, pep)	Saalfield	1948	Busoni, Rafaello	30-50	
Bunn, Harriet	Johann Sebastian Bach (1st, 4to, 56p, ipcb, color, DJ/1.00)	Random	(1942)	Busoni, Rafaello	20-30	
Lowrey, Janette S.	Lavender Cat (1st {std}, 8vo, 180p, b/w, DJ/2.00)	Harper	(1944)	Busoni, Rafaello	25-40	
Hawkins, Quail	Mark, Mark, Shut the Door! (1st, 8vo, [31]p, ipcb, 2-color, DJ/1.50)	Holiday House	(1947)	Busoni, Rafaello	35-60	*
Robertson, Keith	Missing Brother (1st, 8vo, 220p, orange cl, b/w, DJ/2.50)	Viking	1950	Busoni, Rafaello	30-50	
Fish, Helen D.	Pegs of History (1st, 4to, 44p, b/w, DJ/2.00)	Stokes	1943	Busoni, Rafaello	30-45	
Stone, Eugenia	Robin Hood's Arrow (1st, lg8vo, 162p, b/w, DJ/2.50)	Wilcox/Follett	(1948)	Busoni, Rafaello	40-65	
Beim, Lorraine	Sasha and the Samovar (1st, 8vo, [68]p, fp b/w, pep, DJ/1.75)	Harcourt	(1944)	Busoni, Rafaello	120-200	
Schmidt, Sarah L.	Shadow over Winding Ranch (1st, 8vo, 298p, beige cl, b/w, DJ/2.00)	Random	(1940)	Busoni, Rafaello	35-60	*
Collins, Dale	Shipmates Down Under (1st, sm8vo, green cl, 188p, b/w, cep, DJ/2.25)	Holiday House	(1950)	Busoni, Rafaello	25-40	
Busoni, Rafaello	Somi Builds a Church (1st, lg8vo, 109p, b/w, pep, DJ/2.00)	Viking	1943	Busoni, Rafaello	20-35	
Alessios, Alison B.	Spear of Ulysses (1st {std}, 8vo, 213p, b/w, pep, DJ/1.75)	Longmans	1941	Busoni, Rafaello	30-50	
Wilhelmson, Carl	Speed of the Reindeer (1st, 8vo, 220p, b/w, pep, DJ/2.50)	Viking	1954	Busoni, Rafaello	25-40	
Stone, Eugenia	Squire for King Arthur (1st, lg8vo, 158p, fp b/w, DJ/2.95)	Follett	(1955)	Busoni, Rafaello	50-85	
Prud'Hommeaux, Rene	Sunken Forest (1st, 8vo, 248p, b/w, pep, DJ/2.50)	Viking	1949	Busoni, Rafaello	25-40	
Alden, Raymond M.	Why the Chimes Rang (1st, 4to, red cl, [28]p, color, pep, DJ/1.75)	Bobbs-Merrill	1954	Busoni, Rafaello	30-45	
MacHarg, Wm. B.	Let's Pretend... (1st, 8vo, 80p, ibds, fp color)	Volland	1914	Butler, Bonnibel	80-140	
Phillips, Ethel C.	Little Sally Waters (1st, 8vo, 143p, color, pep)	Houghton	1926	Butler, Edith F.	40-65	
Phillips, Ethel C.	Wee Ann (1st, 12mo, 134p, 4cp, pep)	Houghton	1919	Butler, Edith F.	30-50	
Gardiner, Linda	Sylvia in Flowerland (1st, 8vo, grey bds, 198p, gilt, 16 b/w)	L: Seeley	1899	Butler, H.E.	70-125	
Browning, Robert	Pied Piper of Hamelin (1st AM, sm ob4to, [26]p, ibds, fp color)	Nister/Dutton	(1906)	Butler-Stoney, T.	100-165	*
Meader, Stephen W.	Lonesome End (1st {std}, 8vo, 190p, b/w, DJ/3.50)	Harcourt	(1968)	Butterfield, Ned	80-120	
Buzzati, Dino	Bear's Famous Invasion of Sicily (1st, 4to, 146p, 16 fp color, DJ/2.75)	Pantheon	1947	Buzzati, Dino	80-150	
Byars, Betsy C.	The Groober (1st, ob8vo, ibds, 32p, b/w, DJ/2.50)	Harper	(1967)	Byars, Betsy	30-50	
Girvin, Brenda	Round Fairyland with Alice (1st, 8vo, brown/gilt, 186p, b/w, pep, DJ)	L: Wells/Gard.	(1948)	Cable, W. Lindsay	30-50	*
Dalgliesh, Alice	Enchanted Book (1st, lg8vo, 246p, blue/gilt, pep, fp color, DJ/3.00)	Scribner	(1947)	Cacciola, Concetta	55-80	
Govan, Christine	Judy and Chris (1st, 8vo, 210p, b/w, pep, DJ/2.00)	Houghton	1936	Caddy, Alice	150-220	
Govan, Christine	Narcissus an' De Chillun (1st, 8vo, 226p, b/w, DJ/2.00)	Houghton	1938	Caddy, Alice	150-220	
Govan, Christine	Those Plummer Children (1st, 8vo, 196p, b/w, pep)	Houghton	1934	Caddy, Alice	140-200	
Merryman, Mildred P.	Bonbon & Bonbonette (1st, 8vo, 96p, p-o, color, pep)	Rand/McNally	1924	Cadie, V. Eliz.	80-130	
Campbell, Ruth	Cat Whose Whiskers Slipped (1st, 8vo, ibds, color, pep)	Volland	(1925)	Cadie, V. Eliz.	60-100	
Hankins, Maude M.	Daddy Gander (1st, 12mo, ibds, [40]p, color, pep)	Volland	(1928)	Cadie, V. Eliz.	80-140	
Merryman, Mildred P.	Mr. Wubbles Bubbles (1st, 12mo, spiral bds, [44]p, color)	Saalfield	1936	Cadie, V. Eliz.	60-90	
Campbell, Ruth	Turtle Whose Snap Unfastened (1st, lg8vo, 93p, ibds, color, pep)	Volland	(1927)	Cadie, V. Eliz.	70-120	
Hardy, Mary E.	Girl of the Forest (1st, lg8vo, p-o, 222p, color, pep)	Whitman	1927	Cady, Cora J.	30-50	*
Burgess, Thornton	Adventures of Bob White (1st, 16mo, grey cl, 6pl)	Little/Brown	1919	Cady, Harrison	120-180	
Burgess, Thornton	Adventures of Bobby Coon (1st, 16mo, 117p, 6pl)	Little/Brown	1918	Cady, Harrison	120-180	
Burgess, Thornton	Adventures of Buster Bear (1st, 16mo, 120p, tan cl, 6pl)	Little/Brown	1916	Cady, Harrison	120-180	
Burgess, Thornton	Adventures of Chatterer the Red Squirrel (1st, 16mo, 120p, 6pl)	Little/Brown	1915	Cady, Harrison	120-185	
Burgess, Thornton	Adventures of Grandfather Frog (1st, 12mo, 120p, 6pl)	Little/Brown	1915	Cady, Harrison	120-180	
Burgess, Thornton	Adventures of Jerry Muskrat (1st, 12mo, 120p, 6pl)	Little/Brown	1914	Cady, Harrison	120-180	
Burgess, Thornton	Adventures of Jimmy Skunk (1st, 12mo, 118p, grey cl, 6pl)	Little/Brown	1918	Cady, Harrison	120-185	
Burgess, Thornton	Adventures of Johnny Chuck (1st, 12mo, 120p, 6pl)	Little/Brown	1913	Cady, Harrison	120-185	
Burgess, Thornton	Adventures of Mr. Mocker (1st, 8vo, tan cloth, 120p, 6pl)	Little/Brown	1914	Cady, Harrison	120-185	
Burgess, Thornton	Adventures of Ol' Mistah Buzzard (1st, 12mo, 119p, 6pl)	Little/Brown	1919	Cady, Harrison	120-180	
Burgess, Thornton	Adventures of Old Mr. Toad (1st, 12mo, 120p, 6pl)	Little/Brown	1916	Cady, Harrison	120-185	
Burgess, Thornton	Adventures of Peter Cottontail (1st, 12mo, 120p, 6pl)	Little/Brown	1914	Cady, Harrison	120-180	
Burgess, Thornton	Adventures of Poor Mrs. Quack (1st, 12mo, 119p, cloth, 6pl)	Little/Brown	1917	Cady, Harrison	120-185	

AUTHOR	TITLE	PUBLISHER	DATE	ARTIST	PRICE	LC
Burgess, Thornton	Adventures of Prickly Porky (1st, 12mo, grey cl, 116p, 6pl)	Little/Brown	1916	Cady, Harrison	120-180	
Burgess, Thornton	Adventures of Reddy Fox (1st, 16mo, grey cl, 120p, 6pl)	Little/Brown	1913	Cady, Harrison	120-170	
Burgess, Thornton	Adventures of Sammy Jay (1st, 12mo, 119p, 6pl)	Little/Brown	1915	Cady, Harrison	120-200	
Burgess, Thornton	Adventures of Uncle Billy Possum (1st, 12mo, 117p, grey cl, 6pl)	Little/Brown	1914	Cady, Harrison	120-180	
Murray, Gilbert	Airplane Spider (1st, 12mo, grey cl, 86p, p-o, 7cp)	Little/Brown	1920	Cady, Harrison	120-180	*
Murray, Gilbert	Airplane Spider (1st UK, 8vo, 86p, tan bds, p-o, 7cp)	L: A&C Black	1921	Cady, Harrison	120-180	
Palmer, Winthrop	American Songs for Children (1st, ob4to, 64p, b/w)	Macmillan	1931	Cady, Harrison	70-125	
N/A	Animal Alphabet (4to, 24p, color, wraps, pep)	Whitman	[1930]	Cady, Harrison	120-200	*
Wade, Blanche E.	Ant Ventures (1st, sm8vo, green cl, p-o, 246p, 5cp, pep)	Rand/McNally	(1924)	Cady, Harrison	80-130	
Burgess, Thornton	At Paddy the Beaver's Pond (1st {std}, 8vo, 146p, col frn, DJ/2.00)	Little/Brown	1950	Cady, Harrison	65-80	
Burgess, Thornton	At the Smiling Pool (1st {std}, sq8vo, 185p, red cl, color, pep, DJ/2.00)	Little/Brown	1945	Cady, Harrison	80-140	
Burgess, Thornton	Billy Mink (1st, 8vo, p-o, 196p, 8cp)	Little/Brown	1924	Cady, Harrison	80-140	
Burgess, Thornton	Blacky the Crow (1st, sm8vo, 206p, p-o, 8cp)	Little/Brown	1922	Cady, Harrison	80-140	
Burgess, Thornton	Bowser the Hound (1st, 8vo, p-o, 206p, 8cp)	Little/Brown	1920	Cady, Harrison	100-160	
Burgess, Thornton	Burgess Animal Paint Book (ob folio, [24]p, wraps, 7 fp color)	Saalfield	1925	Cady, Harrison	120-200	
Burgess, Thornton	Burgess Animal Stories (1st, sq8vo, [96]p, cloth, color, DJ/0.75)	Platt/Munk	(1942)	Cady, Harrison	80-125	
Burgess, Thornton	Buster Bear's Twins (1st, 8vo, p-o, 207p, 8cp)	Little/Brown	1923	Cady, Harrison	90-150	
Cady, Harrison	Caleb Cottontail (1st, 8vo, 127p, 2-color, pep)	Houghton	1921	Cady, Harrison	120-180	
Burnett, Frances H.	Cozy Lion (1st, 12mo, 104p, blue cl, 20cp)	Century	1907	Cady, Harrison	70-100	R
Burgess, Thornton	Crooked Little Path (1st {std}, 8vo, red cl, 185p, fp 2-color, DJ/2.00)	Little/Brown	1946	Cady, Harrison	45-70	
Chambers, Robert	Garden-Land (1st, lg8vo, 129p, ipcb, 8cp, pep)	Appleton	1907	Cady, Harrison	160-225	
Burgess, Thornton	Grandfather Frog Gets a Ride (1st, 12mo, ibds, 29p, color)	Stoll/Edwards	(1928)	Cady, Harrison	75-100	
Burgess, Thornton	Great Joke on Jimmy Skunk (1st, 12mo, ibds, 29p, color)	Stoll/Edwards	(1928)	Cady, Harrison	75-100	
Burgess, Thornton	Happy Jack (1st, 8vo, 204p, p-o, 8cp)	Little/Brown	1918	Cady, Harrison	100-160	
Wells, Carolyn	Happychaps (1st, lg8vo, 135p, brown cl, fp b/w)	Century	1908	Cady, Harrison	120-180	
Cady, Harrison	Holiday Time on Butternut Hill (1st, 24mo, ibds, unpag, 12 color)	Whitman	(1929)	Cady, Harrison	60-90	
N/A	Jack Frost Arrives on Butternut Hill (1st, 12mo, ibds, color, pep)	Whitman	(1929)	Cady, Harrison	80-125	
Burgess, Thornton	Jerry Muskrat at Home (1st, 8vo, 206p, p-o, 8cp)	Little/Brown	1926	Cady, Harrison	80-140	
Burgess, Thornton	Jerry Muskrat Wins Respect (4to, wraps, color)	NY: J. Eggers	(1928)	Cady, Harrison	70-120	*
Burgess, Thornton	Lightfoot the Deer (1st, 8vo, p-o, blue cl, 205p, 8cp)	Little/Brown	1921	Cady, Harrison	70-125	
Burgess, Thornton	Little Joe Otter (1st, 8vo, olive cl, p-o, 198p, 8cp)	Little/Brown	1925	Cady, Harrison	80-140	
Burgess, Thornton	Little Pete's Adventure (1st, 12mo, ibds, [59]p, fp color)	McLoughlin	(1941)	Cady, Harrison	40-65	
Burgess, Thornton	Little Red's Adventure (1st, 12mo, ibds, [59]p, fp color)	McLoughlin	(1942)	Cady, Harrison	45-65	
Burgess, Thornton	Longlegs the Heron (1st, 8vo, olive cl, p-o, 207p, 8cp)	Little/Brown	1927	Cady, Harrison	80-140	
Burgess, Thornton	Mother West Wind How Stories (1st, 12mo, 228p, 8cp)	Little/Brown	1916	Cady, Harrison	100-160	
Burgess, Thornton	Mother West Wind When Stories (1st, 12mo, tan cl, 227p, 8cp)	Little/Brown	1917	Cady, Harrison	130-185	
Burgess, Thornton	Mother West Wind Why Stories (1st, 12mo, 230p, 8cp)	Little/Brown	1915	Cady, Harrison	120-185	
Burgess, Thornton	Mrs. Peter Rabbit (1st, 8vo, 205p, p-o, 8cp)	Little/Brown	1919	Cady, Harrison	90-140	
Burgess, Thornton	Neatness of Bobby Coon (1st, 12mo, ibds, 29p, color)	Stoll/Edwards	(1927)	Cady, Harrison	70-100	
Burgess, Thornton	Old Granny Fox (1st, 8vo, p-o, green cl, 202p, 8cp)	Little/Brown	1920	Cady, Harrison	80-130	
Burgess, Thornton	On the Green Meadows (1st {std}, 8vo, 182p, red cl, color, DJ/2.00)	Little/Brown	1944	Cady, Harrison	50-80	
Burnett, Frances H.	Queen Silver-Bell (1st, 16mo, p-o, 132p, 20cp)	Century	1906	Cady, Harrison	140-200	R
Burnett, Frances H.	Racketty-Packetty House (1st, 12mo, 130p, p-o, 24cp)	Century	1906	Cady, Harrison	150-225	
Ripley, Sherman	Raggedies in Fairy Land (1st, 4to, 96p, p-o, 3cp, pep)	Rand/McNally	(1930)	Cady, Harrison	150-220	
Ripley, Sherman	Raggedy Animal Book (1st, 4to, p-o, 96p, fp color, pep)	Rand/McNally	(1928)	Cady, Harrison	150-250	
Burnett, Frances H.	Spring Cleaning (1st, 12mo, p-o, 100p, 20cp)	Century	1908	Cady, Harrison	100-150	
Cady, Harrison	Time to Get Up (4to, ibds)	Stoll/Edwards	1928	Cady, Harrison	80-120	*
Burgess, Thornton	Tommy & the Wishing-Stone (1st, 12mo, 290p, gilt, b/w pl)	Century	1915	Cady, Harrison	100-165	*
Burgess, Thornton	Whitefoot the Wood Mouse (1st, 8vo, p-o, blue cl, 181p, 8cp)	Little/Brown	1922	Cady, Harrison	90-120	
Franchot, Annie W.	Bugs, Wings & other Things (1st, 8vo, 99p, green/gilt, pep, 7cp)	Dutton	(1918)	Cady/Smith	170-220	
Graham, Lorenz	How God Fix Jonah (1st, 8vo, 171p, fp b/w, pep, DJ/2.50)	Reynal/Hitchcock	(1946)	Calapai, Letterio	50-80	
Blackburn, Henry G.	Breton Folk (1st, lg8vo, gilt, 200p, AEG, cep)	L: Sampson Low	1880	Caldecott, Randolph	140-200	
Ewing, Juliana H.	Daddy Darwin's Dovecot (1st, sm8vo, 52p, ibds, gilt, teg, col frn)	L: SPCK	[1884]	Caldecott, Randolph	80-120	
Ewing, Juliana H.	Daddy Darwin's Dovecot (1st AM, 12mo, 62p, ibds)	Roberts Bros.	1886	Caldecott, Randolph	70-100	
Goldsmith, Oliver	Elegy on the Glory of Her Sex... (1st, ob8vo, wraps, [24]p, 6cp)	L: Routledge	(1885)	Caldecott, Randolph	70-100	
Caldecott, R.	Fox Jumps Over the Parson's Gate (ob8vo, wraps, 24p, 6cp)	L: Routledge	1883	Caldecott, Randolph	120-200	*
Caldecott, R.	Gleanings from the Graphic (1st, ob folio, ibds, gilt, 84p, 32 color)	L: Routledge	1889	Caldecott, Randolph	200-300	
Caldecott, R.	Graphic Pictures (1st, ob folio, 93p, color)	L: Routledge	1883	Caldecott, Randolph	180-270	
Ewing, Juliana H.	Jacanapes (1st, lg8vo, ibds, 184p, teg, col frn)	L: SPCK	1884	Caldecott, Randolph	140-200	
Tennyson, H.	Jack & the Bean Stalk (1st, sq8vo, 70p, green cl, b/w)	L: Macmillan	1886	Caldecott, Randolph	170-240	
Caldecott, R.	Last Graphic Pictures (1st, ob folio, ipcb, [71]p, color)	L: Routledge	1888	Caldecott, Randolph	150-225	
Ewing, Juliana H.	Lob Lie-by-the-Fire (1st, 8vo, 72p, ibds)	L: SPCK	(1885)	Caldecott, Randolph	80-130	
Caldecott, R.	More Graphic Pictures (1st, ob folio, ibds, 32cp)	L: Routledge	1887	Caldecott, Randolph	125-200	
Irving, Washington	Old Christmas (8vo, gilt, 165p, b/w, AEG)	L: Macmillan	1894	Caldecott, Randolph	80-120	
Caldecott, R.	Panjandrum Picture Book (ob. sm4to, [98]p, color)	L: Warne	[1890]	Caldecott, Randolph	120-200	
Caldecott, R.	Queen of Hearts (1st, 8vo, wraps, 32p, 9cp)	L: Routledge	(1881)	Caldecott, Randolph	100-165	
Caldecott, R.	Sketch Book (1st, ob4to, 48p, color)	L: Routledge	1883	Caldecott, Randolph	165-220	
Caldecott, R.	Three Jovial Huntsmen (1st, ob8vo, p-o, 7 ticp)	L: Warne	[1908]	Caldecott, Randolph	90-120	*
Locker, Mrs. F.	What the Blackbird Said (1st, sq8vo, 87p, gilt, fp b/w)	L: Routledge	1881	Caldecott, Randolph	100-170	
Sweeney, James J.	Three Young Rats (1st {std}, lg4to, 130p, fp b/w, DJ/6.00)	NY: Valentin	(1944)	Calder, Alexander	60-90	R*
Fitzpatrick, Percy	Jock of the Bushveld (1st, 8vo, 474p, gilt, col frn, 22pl)	L: Longmans	1907	Caldwell, Edmund G.	120-200	
Page, Valerie K.	Pi Gal (1st, lg8vo, 127p, fp b/w, DJ/3.95)	Dodd	(1970)	Callaert, Jacques	20-30	
Stevenson, Rbt. L.	Treasure Island (1st, 8vo, 339p, 12cp)	L: Cassell	1911	Cameron, John	75-100	*
Chisholm, Louey	Enchanted Land (1st AM, lg8vo, 211p, AEG, green/gilt, 30cp)	Putnam	[1906]	Cameron, Katharine	150-225	
Chisholm, Louey	Enchanted Land (1st, lg8vo, 211p, p-o, white/gilt, teg, 30cp, cep)	L: Jack	(1906)	Cameron, Katharine	160-250	
Thomas, Philip	Flowers I Love (1st, 4to, 81p, 24cp)	L: Jack	(1916)	Cameron, Katharine	70-120	*
Aitken, James R.	In a City Garden (1st, 8vo, 106p, tan bds, gilt, 7 ticp)	L: Foulis	1913	Cameron, Katharine	80-125	
Chisholm, Louey	In Fairyland (1st, lg8vo, 211p, p-o, AEG, 30cp, pep)	Putnam/Jack	(1904)	Cameron, Katharine	130-200	

AUTHOR	TITLE	PUBLISHER	DATE	ARTIST	PRICE	LC
Steedman, Amy	Legends & Stories of Italy... (1st, lg8vo, 188p, teg ibds, gilt, 12 ticp)	L: Jack	[1909]	Cameron, Katharine	120-200	
Browning, Eliz. B.	Rhyme of the Duchess May (1st, 12mo, p-o, wraps, uncut, 5cp)	L: Foulis	[1907]	Cameron, Katharine	70-100	
MacGregor, Mary	Stories of King Arthur's Knights (12mo, 155p, ipcb, 8 ticp)	L: Jack	(1909)	Cameron, Katharine	80-120	
Kingsley, Charles	Water Babies (1st, 24mo, 117p, green cl, uncut, 8 ticp)	Jack/Dutton	[1906]	Cameron, Katharine	40-60	*
Kingsley, Charles	Water Babies (1st AM, 4to, gilt, uncut, p-o, teg, 246p, 8 ticp)	Stokes	[1911]	Cameron, Katharine	100-170	
Williams, Iolo A.	Where the Bee Sucks (1st, 4to, blue/gilt, 87p, teg, 12 ticp)	L: Medici	(1929)	Cameron, Katharine	70-125	
Brown, Margaret W.	Baby Animals (1st, lg8vo, ipcb, [48]p, color, pep, DJ/0.50)	Random	(1941)	Cameron, Mary	50-80	
Benstead, V. (adap)	Three Little Pigs (1st, lg8vo, ibds, [28]p, color, pep, DJ/0.50)	Random	1942	Cameron, Mary	30-50	*
Cameron, Polly	Cat Who Couldn't Purr (1st, 8vo, [32]p, 1-color, cep, DJ/2.25)	Coward	(1957)	Cameron, Polly	70-100	
Cameron, Polly	Child's Book of Nonsense (1st, sq8vo, ipcb, [30]p, color, DJ/2.50)	Coward	(1960)	Cameron, Polly	80-125	R
Cameron, Polly	I Can't, Said the Ant (1st, lg8vo, [42]p, fp 1-color, DJ/2.50)	Coward	(1961)	Cameron, Polly	80-125	R
Gask, Lilian	True Stories of Big Game & Jungles (1st, 8vo, 235p, 16cp)	L: Harrap	1933	Cameron, W.F.	40-70	
Rawlings, Marjorie K.	Cross Creek Cookery (1st, 8vo, 230p, color, pep, DJ/2.50)	Scribner	1942	Camp, Robert	120-200	
Locke, William J.	Christmas Mystery (1st, 8vo, 54p, green/gilt, 4pl, dep)	NY: John Lane	1910	Campbell, Blendon	75-100	*
Bontemps, Arna	Popo & Fifina (1st, 8vo, 100p, orange cl, 6pl)	Macmillan	1932	Campbell, E. Simms	150-220	R
Raymond, Margaret T.	Roberta Goes Adventuring (1st, 8vo, ibds, 96p, color, pep)	Volland	(1931)	Campbell, Eleanor	60-90	
Campbell, Lang	Dinky Ducklings (1st, 12mo, ibds, 39p, color, pep)	Volland	(1928)	Campbell, Lang	80-125	
Campbell, Lang	Funnyfeathers (1st, 4to, 86p, tan cl, 6cp, pep)	Dutton	(1917)	Campbell, Lang	65-100	
Campbell, Lang	Merry Murphy (1st, 12mo, [44]p, color, pep)	Algonquin	1929	Campbell, Lang	40-65	
Garis, Howard	Uncle Wiggily & his Flying Rug (1st {this pub}, 12mo, 33p, bds, color, pep)	Whitman	(1940)	Campbell, Lang	50-85	
Garis, Howard	Uncle Wiggily & the Beaver Boys (1st, 8vo, olive cl, p-o, color)	C.E. Graham	(1929)	Campbell, Lang	50-80	
Garis, Howard	Uncle Wiggily & the Pirates (1st, 8vo, [31]p, red cl, p-o, color)	C.E. Graham	(1931)	Campbell, Lang	50-80	
Garis, Howard	Uncle Wiggily & the Pirates (sq12mo, 33p, ibds, color)	Whitman	(1940)	Campbell, Lang	35-60	*
Garis, Howard	Uncle Wiggily Goes Camping (sq12mo, ibds, 33p, color)	Whitman	(1940)	Campbell, Lang	35-60	
Garis, Howard	Uncle Wiggily on Roller Skates (1st {this pub}, 12mo, 33p, color)	Whitman	(1940)	Campbell, Lang	35-60	*
Garis, Howard	Uncle Wiggily Plays Indian Hunter (1st, 12mo, bds, 33p, color)	Whitman	(1940)	Campbell, Lang	35-60	*
Garis, Howard	Uncle Wiggily's Apple Roast (1st, 8vo, red cloth, p-o, color)	C.E. Graham	(1924)	Campbell, Lang	35-60	
Garis, Howard	Uncle Wiggily's June Bug Friends (1st, 8vo, red cl, p-o, color)	C.E. Graham	(1931)	Campbell, Lang	50-80	
Garis, Howard	Uncle Wiggily's Picture Book (1st, 8vo, 217p, orange cl, 12cp, pep)	Platt/Munk	(1940)	Campbell, Lang	45-70	
Garis, Howard	Uncle Wiggily's Visit to the Farm (1st, sq12mo, 33p, p-o, color)	C.E. Graham	(1927)	Campbell, Lang	35-60	
Garis, Howard	Uncle Wiggily's Woodland Games (1st, sq12mo, [32]p, p-o, color)	C.E. Graham	(1922)	Campbell, Lang	35-60	
Fessenden, Laura D.	2002: Childlife One Hundred Years from Now (1st, 8vo, 184p, b/w)	Jamieson-Higgins	(1902)	Campbell, S.P.	400-600	*
Eaton, Seymour	Adventures of the Traveling Bears (4to, ibds, 63p, col frn, b/w)	Barse/Hopkins	(1915)	Campbell, V. Floyd	250-400	
Eaton, Seymour	Roosevelt Bears (1st, 4to, 180p, bds, p-o, 16cp)	Stern	1906	Campbell, V. Floyd	400-600	R
Eaton, Seymour	Travelling Bears Across the Sea (lg8vo, ibds, col frn, b/w)	Barse/Hopkins	(1916)	Campbell, V. Floyd	250-400	
Eaton, Seymour	Travelling Bears at Play (1st, 4to, 62p, color)	Barse/Hopkins	(1916)	Campbell, V. Floyd	250-400	
Eaton, Seymour	Travelling Bears in New York (1st, 4to, 60p, color)	Barse/Hopkins	(1915)	Campbell, V. Floyd	250-400	
Eaton, Seymour	Travelling Bears in Outdoor Sports (1st, 4to, 60p, col frn)	Barse/Hopkins	(1915)	Campbell, V. Floyd	250-400	
Eaton, Seymour	Travelling Bears in the East & West (1st, 4to, bds, 63p, p-o, cp)	Barse/Hopkins	(1915)	Campbell, V. Floyd	250-400	
Becker, John L.	New Feathers for the Old Goose (1st, lg8vo, 60p, color, cep, DJ/3.00)	Pantheon	(1956)	Campbell, Virginia	50-80	R*
Olcott, F.J.	Wonder Tales from Baltic Wizards (1st {std}, sm8vo, 234p col frn, pep)	Longmans	1928	Candell, Victor G.	40-65	
Cannon, Wilma	Peter is Sweeter (1st, sq12mo, [40]p, bds, 2-color, DJ/1.00)	Lothrop, Lee	(1942)	Cannon, Marian	35-50	
De La Mare, Walter	Songs of Childhood (1st, sm8vo, 173p, gilt, teg, 8cp)	L: Longmans	1923	Canziani, Estella	70-100	
Carroll, Lewis	Alice... & Through... (1st, sm8vo, ibds, 234p, b/w, pep)	Whitman	(1945)	Card, Linda	30-50	*
Carigiet, Alois	Anton and Anne (1st AM, ob folio, [44]p, color, DJ/7.00)	H.Z. Walck	(1969)	Carigiet, Alois	40-65	
Chonz, Selina	Bell for Ursli (1st AM, ob4to, bds, [44]p, fp color, DJ/2.50)	NY: Oxford U.Pr.	(1950)	Carigiet, Alois	70-100	
Chonz, Selina	Florina & the Wild Bird (1st AM, ob fol, ibds, [28]p, color, DJ/3.00, NYTBI)	NY: Oxford U.Pr.	(1953)	Carigiet, Alois	70-100	
Carigiet, Alois	Pear Tree, Birch Tree/Barberry Bush (1st AM {std}, obfol, [33]p, DJ/5.00)	H.Z. Walck	1967	Carigiet, Alois	30-50	*
Chonz, Selina	The Snowstorm (1st AM {std}, ob folio, [28]p, 12 fp color)	H.Z. Walck	1958	Carigiet, Alois	70-100	
Carle, Eric	Pancakes, Pancakes (1st AM {std}, 4to, [30]p, color, DJ)	Knopf	(1970)	Carle, Eric	30-50	*
Carle, Eric	Tiny Seed (1st, 4to, [34]p, fp color, dep, DJ/4.50)	Crowell	1970	Carle, Eric	30-50	*
Pool, Maria L.	Red-Bridge Neighborhood (1st, 12mo, gilt, 369p, 13pl)	Harper	1898	Carleton, Clifford	25-45	
Carruth, Hayden	Track's End (1st, 12mo, blue cl, 230p, 9pl, pep)	Harper	1911	Carleton, Clifford	40-60	
Bailey, Carolyn S.	Li'l Hannibal (1st, 8vo, [24]p, p-o, color, pep)	Platt/Munk	(1938)	Carlson, George	60-90	
Wade, Blanche E.	Magic Stone (1st, lg8vo, 254p, p-o, gilt, 7cp)	NY: Sully	1917	Carlson, George	50-85	
Donahey, Mary D.	Prince Without a Country (1st, sm4to, p-o, 125p, 6cp)	Barse/Hopkins	(1916)	Carlson, George	50-80	
Spyri, Johanna	Tiss - A Little Alpine Waif (1st, lg8vo, 78p, col frn, pep)	Crowell	(1921)	Carlson, George	30-50	
Carmer, Carl	Wildcat Furs to China (1st {std}, 8vo, 76p, fp color, DJ/2.00)	Knopf	(1945)	Carmer, Elizabeth	30-50	
Hough, Emerson	Young Alaskans (1st, sm8vo, orange cl, 291p, 4pl, PPP)	Harper	1908	Carpenter, D.	160-220	R*
Garland, Hamlin	Prairie Songs (1st, green/gilt, 164p, teg, uncut)	Stone/Kimball	1893	Carpenter, H.T.	70-120	R
Carpenter, John	Improving Songs for Anxious Children (lg ob4to, 50p, ibds, 19 color)	Schirmer	(1913)	Carpenter, J.& R.	120-180	*
Carpenter, John	When Little Boys Sing (1st, ob folio, [39]p, ibds, color)	McClurg	(1904)	Carpenter, J.& R.	120-200	
Ostrander, Fannie	Goose Family Tales (1st, sq8vo, 87p, gilt, color)	Conkey	(1905)	Carqueville, Will	100-160	
Phillips, J.	Trip to Fairyland (1st, sq8vo, [53]p, gilt)	Conkey	(1905)	Carqueville, Will	100-160	
Fox, Frances M.	Adventures of Sonny Bear (1st, sm8vo, 80p, 15cp)	Rand/McNally	(1916)	Carr, Warner	55-80	
Judson, Clara I.	Billy Robin (1st, 12mo, ipcb, 76p, 10cp)	Rand/McNally	(1917)	Carr, Warner	30-50	
Warren, Maude R.	Manabozho the Great White Rabbit (1st, sm8vo, 133p, 8cp)	Rand/McNally	(1918)	Carr, Warner	40-65	
Latham, Jean L.	Nutcracker (1st, 8vo, [32]p, p-o, color, DJ/1.95)	Bobbs-Merrill	1961	Carreas, Jose	30-50	
Adoff, Arnold	City in All Directions (1st {std}, 8vo, 128p, fp b/w, DJ/5.95)	Macmillan	(1969)	Carrick, Donald	25-40	
Carrick, Carol	Clearing in the Forest (1st {std}, ob8vo, [30]p, fp 2-color, DJ/4.50)	Dial Press	(1970)	Carrick, Donald	30-50	*
Carrick, Carol	Swamp Spring (1st {std}, sm4to, [32]p, color, DJ/4.50)	Macmillan	(1969)	Carrick, Donald	30-50	
Carrick, Carol	The Brook (1st {std}, sm4to, [30]p, fp 3-color, DJ/3.95)	Macmillan	(1967)	Carrick, Donald	30-45	*
Carrick, Carol	The Pond (1st {std}, sm4to, [30]p, fp color, DJ/4.95)	Macmillan	(1970)	Carrick, Donald	30-50	*
Fyleman, Rose	Picture Rhymes from Foreign Lands (1st, 8vo, 70p, b/w, DJ/1.00)	Stokes	1935	Carrick, Valery	40-65	
Carrick, Valery	Valery Carrick's Picture Folk-Tales (1st, 4to, 94p, p-o, b/w, DJ)	Stokes	1926	Carrick, Valery	70-100	
Fyleman, Rose	Widdy-Widdy-Wurkey (1st, 8vo, 70p, beige cl, b/w)	L: Blackwell	1934	Carrick, Valery	40-60	*
Coatsworth, Eliz.	Silky: An Incredible Tale (1st, 8vo, 143p, ibds, fp b/w, DJ/2.75)	Pantheon	(1953)	Carroll, John	20-35	
Welch, Jean L.	Animals Came First (1st, sm8vo, ibds, [30]p, b/w, pep, DJ/1.50)	NY: Oxford U.Pr.	1948	Carroll, Ruth	30-50	

AUTHOR	TITLE	PUBLISHER	DATE	ARTIST	PRICE	LC
Carroll, Ruth	Beanie (1st, 4to, [48]p, blue cl, fp 1-color, DJ/2.50)	NY: Oxford U.Pr.	1953	Carroll, Ruth	30-45	
Carroll, Ruth	Bounce and the Bunnies (1st, 4to, [48]p, p-o, color, pep. DJ/1.25)	Reynal/Hitchcock	(1934)	Carroll, Ruth	30-50	
Carroll, Ruth	Bumble Pup (1st, 4to, 31p, b/w, DJ/3.50)	H.Z. Walck	1968	Carroll, Ruth	30-50	
Carroll, Ruth	Chessie (1st, 4to, ibds, [48]p, color, pep, DJ/2.00)	J. Messner	(1936)	Carroll, Ruth	40-65	
Carroll, Ruth	Chessie and her Kittens (1st, 4to, [48]p, color, pep, DJ/2.00)	J. Messner	(1937)	Carroll, Ruth	40-65	
Carroll, Ruth	Chimp and the Clown (1st, ob8vo, [31]p, color, DJ/3.50)	H.Z. Walck	1968	Carroll, Ruth	25-40	
Carroll, Ruth	Christmas Kitten (1st, 8vo, [30]p, fp 2-color, DJ/3.50)	H.Z. Walck	1970	Carroll, Ruth	25-40	
Carroll, Ruth	Danny and the Poi Pup (1st, 4to, 47p, fp color, DJ/3.75)	H.Z. Walck	1965	Carroll, Ruth	25-40	
Carroll, Ruth	Digby, the Only Dog (1st, 4to, 47p, 1-color, cep, DJ/2.75)	NY: Oxford U.Pr.	1955	Carroll, Ruth	30-50	
Carroll, Ruth	Flying House (1st {std}, ob8vo, 127p, color, pep, DJ/2.00)	Macmillan	1946	Carroll, Ruth	50-80	
Carroll, Ruth	Luck of the Roll and Go (1st, 12mo, 132p, b/w, pep, DJ/1.50)	Macmillan	1935	Carroll, Ruth	25-40	
Coleman, Satis	New Singing Time (1st, 4to, 32p, color, DJ/2.50)	John Day	(1950)	Carroll, Ruth	30-45	
Carroll, Ruth	Old Mrs. Billups and the Black Cats (1st, 8vo, 48p, color, DJ/3.50)	H.Z. Walck	1961	Carroll, Ruth	30-45	
Carroll, Ruth	Peanut (1st, 8vo, 45p, fp 1-color, DJ/1.75)	H.Z. Walck	1951	Carroll, Ruth	25-45	
Carroll, Ruth	Pet Tale (1st, sq8vo, [47]p, ibds, b/w, pep, DJ/1.50)	NY: Oxford U.Pr.	1949	Carroll, Ruth	30-50	
Carroll, Ruth	Runaway Pony, Runaway Dog (1st, lg8vo, 80p, fp color, cep, DJ/3.50)	H.Z. Walck	1963	Carroll, Ruth	30-45	
Carroll, Ruth	Salt & Pepper (1st, 8vo, 30p. 2-color, cep, DJ/2.00)	NY: Oxford U.Pr.	1952	Carroll, Ruth	25-40	
Carroll, Ruth	School in the Sky (1st, ob8vo, 136p, b/w, pep, DJ/1.75)	Macmillan	1945	Carroll, Ruth	25-35	
Carroll, Ruth	Tough Enough (1st, 4to, [64]p, 1-color, DJ/2.75)	NY: Oxford U.Pr.	1954	Carroll, Ruth	50-85	R
Carroll, Ruth	Tough Enough & Sassy (1st, 4to, 63p, fp 1-color, cep, DJ/2.75)	H.Z. Walck	1958	Carroll, Ruth	50-85	
Carroll, Ruth	Tough Enough's Indians (1st, 4to, 64p, fp 1-color, cep, DJ/2.75)	H.Z. Walck	1960	Carroll, Ruth	50-85	
Carroll, Ruth	Tough Enough's Pony (1st, 4to, 64p, b/w, DJ/2.75)	NY: Oxford U.Pr.	1957	Carroll, Ruth	50-85	
Carroll, Ruth	Tough Enough's Trip (1st, 4to, 64p, 1-color, DJ/2.75)	NY: Oxford U.Pr.	1956	Carroll, Ruth	50-85	
Hall, William N.	Watch the Kitten Grow (1st, sm4to, spiral bds, unpag, color)	Crowell	1946	Carroll, Ruth	30-50	
Carroll, Ruth	What Whiskers Did (1st, lg8vo, [39]p, fp b/w, pep)	Macmillan	1932	Carroll, Ruth	40-70	*
Carroll, Ruth	Where's the Bunny? (1st, ob8vo, [30]p, color, DJ/2.00)	Oxford U. Pr.	1950	Carroll, Ruth	40-65	
Carroll, Ruth	Where's the Kitty? (1st, ob8vo, [32]p, color, DJ/2.75)	H.Z. Walck	(1962)	Carroll, Ruth	40-65	
Scott, Lucy M.	Dewdrops from Fairyland (1st, 8vo, 91p, 9cp, pep)	L: Warne	(1912)	Carse, A. Duncan	85-130	
Andersen, Hans C.	Fairy Tales (1st, 8vo, 373p, 12cp, pep)	L: A&C Black	(1912)	Carse, A. Duncan	70-100	
Craik, Dinah	Adventures of a Brownie (sm4to, grey cl, p-o, 12cp)	Whitman	(1920)	Carsey, Alice	35-60	*
Dodge, Mary Mapes	Hans Brinker (1st, 8vo, 239p, p-o, color, pep)	Whitman	(1917)	Carsey, Alice	40-65	
DeAmicis, Edmondo	Heart of Boyhood (1st, 8vo, 198p, 8cp, 24 fp b/w)	Whitman	(1918)	Carsey, Alice	35-50	
Collodi, Carlo	Pinocchio (1st, lg8vo, 205p, p-o, 8cp)	Whitman	(1917)	Carsey, Alice	60-90	
Spyri, Johanna	Heidi (4to, p-o, 240p, 8cp)	Whitman	(1916)	Carsey, Ann	80-120	
Beaty, John Y.	Baby Whale, Sharp Ears (1st, sq8vo, 106p, fp color, pep, DJ/2.00)	Lippincott	(1938)	Carter, Helene	100-175	*
Bouton, Elizabeth	Grandmother's Doll (1st, lg8vo, 106p, gilt, 7cp, pep)	Duffield/Green	(1931)	Carter, Helene	55-80	*
Ransome, Arthur	Peter Duck (1st AM, 8vo, 427p, b/w, pep)	Lippincott	1933	Carter, Helene	40-70	
Carter, Helene	Smoky and Pinocchio (1st, lg8vo, [36]p, 2-color, DJ/1.00)	Lippincott	1940	Carter, Helene	30-50	*
Ransome, Arthur	Swallowdale (1st AM, 8vo, 393p, b/w, pep)	Lippincott	1932	Carter, Helene	60-90	
Ransome, Arthur	Swallows & Amazons (1st AM, 8vo, green cl, 343p, b/w, pep, DJ/2.00)	Lippincott	1931	Carter, Helene	70-120	R
Snyder, Anne	50000 Names for Jeff (1st {std}, 8vo, 70p, fp b/w, cep, DJ)	Holt, Rinehart	(1969)	Carty, Leo	40-65	
Myers, Walter	Where Does the Day Go? (1st, sm ob4to, [40]p, fp color, DJ/3.50)	Parents Mag. Pr.	(1969)	Carty, Leo	50-80	*
Latham, Jean L.	Eli Whitney (1st, 8vo, 80p, fp 3-color, DJ/2.50)	Garrard Pub.	(1963)	Cary	30-50	
Belting, Natalia	Long-Tailed Bear (1st, 8vo, 96p, b/w, DJ/2.95)	Bobbs-Merrill	1961	Cary, Louis F.	20-30	
McNeil, Everett	Lost Treasure Cave (1st, 8vo, tan cl, 352p, 8pl)	Dutton	1905	Cary, William M.	35-60	
Brooks, Elbridge S.	Master of Strong Hearts (1st, 8vo, 314p, 10pl)	Dutton	1898	Cary, William M.	35-60	
Zolotow, Charlotte	But Not Billy (1st, ob4to, [30]p, ibds, color, DJ/1.75)	Harper	1947	Cassal, Lys	70-100	
Leamy, Edmund	Fairy Minstrel of Glenmalure (1st, sm8vo, 92p, p-o, 4cp)	D. Fitzgerald	(1913)	Casseau, Vera	50-85	*
Sorensen, Virginia	House Next Door: Utah, 1896 (1st, 8vo, 223p, b/w, pep, DJ/3.00)	Scribner	(1954)	Cassel, Lili	20-30	*
Shippen, Kath. B.	Moses (1st, 8vo, blue cl, 132p, DJ/2.00, frn by...)	Harper	(1949)	Cassel, Lili	35-60	
Mother Goose	Rainbow Mother Goose (1st, 8vo, 160p, 8cp, pep, DJ/1.00, RC)	World	(1947)	Cassel, Lili	50-80	R
Casserley, Anne	Roseen (1st {std}, sm8vo, green cl, 152p, b/w, cep)	Harper	1929	Casserley, Anne	30-45	
Casserley, Anne	Whins of Knockattan (1st {std}, sm8vo, 178p, silhouettes)	Harper	1928	Casserley, Anne	30-50	*
Austin, Mary	Children Sing in the Far West (1st, sm8vo, 187p, b/w)	Houghton	1928	Cassidy, Gerald	40-65	
Mitchell, S. Weir	Adventures of Francois (1st, 8vo, 321p, orange cl, 15pl)	Century	1898	Castaigne, Andre	40-60	
MacGrath, Harold	Carpet from Bagdad (1st, 12mo, 390p, olive cl, 5cp)	Bobbs-Merrill	(1911)	Castaigne, Andre	30-50	
Catherwood, Mary	Lazarre (1st, sm8vo, 436p, gilt, 5pl)	Bowen-Merrill	1901	Castaigne, Andre	30-50	
Parker, Gilbert	Money Master (1st, 12mo, green/gilt, 360p, 6pl)	Harper	1915	Castaigne, Andre	30-50	
Whiteing, Richard	Paris of Today (1st, 4to, 249p, gilt, teg, b/w)	Century	1900	Castaigne, Andre	70-100	
Parker, Gilbert	The Weavers (1st, sm8vo, 530p, olive/gilt, 8pl)	Harper	1907	Castaigne, Andre	25-40	
Kingsley, Charles	Theseus (1st {std}, folio, ibds, 46p, color, DJ/2.95)	Macmillan	1964	Castellon, Federico	40-70	
Holberg, Ruth	At the Sign of the Golden Anchor (1st {std}, 8vo, 209p, pep, b/w, DJ/2.25)	Doubleday	(1947)	Castle, Jane	20-35	
May, Charles P.	Box Turtle Lives in Armor (1st, sm8vo, 42p, 2-color, cep, DJ/2.50)	Holiday House	(1960)	Castle, Jane	25-40	*
Pace, Mildred M.	Juliette Low (1st, 8vo, 186p, b/w, DJ/2.00)	Scribner	1947	Castle, Jane	20-30	
Castle, Jane	Peep-Lo (1st, 8vo, [34]p, blue cl, b/w, pep, DJ/2.50)	Holiday House	1959	Castle, Jane	25-40	
Hekking, Johanna	Pigtails (1st, 8vo, 112p, 10cp, DJ/2.00)	Stokes	1937	Castle, Molly	35-50	
Meader, Stephen W.	Longshanks (1st, 12mo, 243p, b/w pl)	Harcourt	(1928)	Caswell, Edward	70-100	
Judson, Clara I.	They Came from Sweden (1st, 8vo, 213p, b/w, pep, DJ/2.00)	Houghton	1942	Caswell, Edward	25-45	
Cavally, Fred. L.	Mother Goose's Teddy Bears (1st, 4to, red cl, [64]p, p-o, 32cp)	Bobbs-Merrill	1907	Cavally, Frederick	300-500	
Deutsch, Babette	I Often Wish (1st, lg8vo, [60]p, fp 1-color, cep, DJ/4.00)	Funk/Wagnalls	(1966)	Cellini, Eva	30-50	R
Johnson, Ryerson	Let's Walk up the Wall (1st, ob8vo, [48]p, fp 3-color, DJ/3.75)	Holiday House	(1967)	Cellini, Eva	30-45	
Fall, Thomas	Canalboat to Freedom (1st, 8vo, 215p, fp b/w, pep, DJ/3.50)	Dial Press	1966	Cellini, Joseph	25-45	
Eckert, Allan W.	In Search of a Whale (1st {std}, 4to, 158p, color, DJ/5.95)	Doubleday	(1970)	Cellini, Joseph	25-40	
Hunter, Mollie	Kelpie's Pearls (1st AM, 8vo, 112p, b/w, DJ/3.25)	Funk/Wagnalls	(1966)	Cellini, Joseph	25-40	
Conklin, Gladys	Little Apes (1st, 8vo, [40]p, 3-color, DJ/4.50)	Holiday House	(1970)	Cellini, Joseph	25-40	
Hall, Lynn	Secret of Stonehouse (1st {std}, 8vo, 155p, b/w, DJ/3.50)	Follett	(1968)	Cellini, Joseph	40-65	
Hough, Emerson	King of Gee Whiz (1st, lg8vo, 210p, green cl, 8cp)	Bobbs-Merrill	(1906)	Cesare, Oscar E.	150-240	R
Mother Goose	Mother Goose (1st AM, 12mo, 125p, color)	Dent/Dutton	[1927]	Chadburn, Mabel	50-80	*

AUTHOR	TITLE	PUBLISHER	DATE	ARTIST	PRICE	LC
Dahl, Roald	Fantastic Mr. Fox (1st {std}, 8vo, 62p, gilt, fp b/w, cep, DJ/3.95)	Knopf	(1970)	Chaffin, Donald	300-500	R
Hutchison, Collister	Toward Daybreak (1st {std}, lg8vo, 88p, fp b/w, DJ/3.00)	Harper	(1950)	Chagall, Marc	50-85	
Chalmers, Audrey	Birthday of Obash (1st, 12mo, ibds, 79p, fp b/w, DJ/1.00)	Oxford U. Pr.	(1937)	Chalmers, Audrey	30-50	
Chalmers, Audrey	Fancy Be Good (1st, 8vo, [46]p, ibds, b/w, DJ/1.00)	Viking	1941	Chalmers, Audrey	30-50	*
Chalmers, Audrey	Hundreds and Hundreds of Pancakes (1st, ob4to, ibds, 39p, color, DJ/1.00)	Viking	1942	Chalmers, Audrey	40-70	
Chalmers, Audrey	Kitten's Tale (1st, 8vo, [46]p, ibds, b/w, DJ/1.50)	Viking	1946	Chalmers, Audrey	30-50	
Chalmers, Audrey	Mr. Topple's Wish (1st, ob8vo, [36]p, ibds, fp b/w, pep, DJ/1.50)	Viking	1948	Chalmers, Audrey	30-50	*
Chalmers, Audrey	Poppadilly (1st, 12mo, ibds, 40p, 1-color, pep, DJ/1.00)	Viking	1945	Chalmers, Audrey	30-50	
Howes, Edith	Sandals of Pearl (1st, 8vo, 246p, t-i col frn, 8 pl)	Wm. Morrow	1928	Chalmers, Audrey	50-85	
Chalmers, Mary	Be Good, Harry (1st, 24mo, 32p, 1-color, DJ/1.95)	Harper	(1967)	Chalmers, Mary	40-65	
Chalmers, Mary	Boats Finds a House (1st, 24mo, 32p, ibds, color, DJ/1.50)	Harper	(1958)	Chalmers, Mary	50-80	
Chalmers, Mary	Cat Who Liked to Pretend (1st, 24mo, 32p, ibds, 2-color, DJ/1.95)	Harper	(1959)	Chalmers, Mary	50-80	
Chalmers, Mary	Christmas Story (1st, sq32mo, [24]p, color, DJ/1.00)	Harper	(1956)	Chalmers, Mary	50-80	
Chalmers, Mary	Come for a Walk with Me (1st, 16mo, [30]p, ipcb, 3-color, DJ/1.50)	Harper	(1955)	Chalmers, Mary	50-85	
Lindquist, Jennie	Crystal Tree (1st, 8vo, 297p, ibds, fp b/w, cep, DJ/3.95)	Harper	(1966)	Chalmers, Mary	30-50	
Bechtle, Raymond	Every Day is a World (1st, 8vo, 63p, b/w, DJ)	Harper	(1957)	Chalmers, Mary	30-50	
Chalmers, Mary	George Appleton (1st, 24mo, 32p, color, DJ/1.50)	Harper	(1957)	Chalmers, Mary	40-65	
Sharmat, Marjorie	Goodnight Andrew, Goodnight Craig (1st, 12mo, 32p, color, DJ/2.95)	Harper	(1969)	Chalmers, Mary	25-40	
Heilbroner, Joan	Happy Birthday Present (1st, 8vo, 63p, color, DJ/1.95)	Harper	(1962)	Chalmers, Mary	25-45	
Chalmers, Mary	Hat for Amy Jean (1st, 24mo, [32]p, 1-color, pep, DJ/1.50)	Harper	(1956)	Chalmers, Mary	50-80	
Chalmers, Mary	Here Comes the Trolley Car (1st, ob4to, [34]p, 2-color, pep, DJ/2.00)	Harper	(1955)	Chalmers, Mary	50-80	
Calhoun, Mary	House of Thirty Cats (1st, 8vo, 218p, b/w, DJ/3.50)	Harper	(1965)	Chalmers, Mary	20-30	
Baruch, Dorothy W.	I Would Like to be a Pony (1st, 8vo, 32p, b/w, DJ/2.00)	Harper	(1959)	Chalmers, Mary	20-30	
Krauss, Ruth	I Write It (1st, 12mo, [32]p, ibds, color, DJ/2.50)	Harper	(1970)	Chalmers, Mary	40-65	
Chalmers, Mary	Kevin (1st, 24mo, [32]p, ibds, 3-color, DJ/1.50)	Harper	(1957)	Chalmers, Mary	40-65	
Chalmers, Mary	Mr. Cat's Wonderful Surprise (1st, 8vo, 32p, ipcb, 3-color, DJ/2.50)	Harper	(1961)	Chalmers, Mary	40-65	
Nordstrom, Ursula	Secret Language (1st, 8vo, 167p, b/w, DJ/2.75)	Harper	1960	Chalmers, Mary	80-120	
Chalmers, Mary	Take a Nap, Harry (1st, 24mo, 32p, color, DJ/1.95)	Harper	1964	Chalmers, Mary	40-65	
Zolotow, Charlotte	Three Funny Friends (1st, 12mo, ipcb, 32p, 1-color, DJ/1.75)	Harper	(1961)	Chalmers, Mary	30-45	*
Boegehold, Betty	Three to Get Ready (1st, 8vo, 64p, color, DJ/1.95)	Harper	(1965)	Chalmers, Mary	30-45	
Chalmers, Mary	Throw a Kiss, Harry (1st, 24mo, ibds, 32p, 1-color, DJ/1.25)	Harper	(1958)	Chalmers, Mary	60-90	
Collodi, Carlo	Adventures Every Child Should Know (1st, 12mo, 241p, 8cp)	Doubleday/Page	1909	Chamberlin, E.H.	50-80	*
Paquin, Samuel S.	Garden Fairies (1st, 8vo, 179p, p-o, 4cp)	Moffat	1908	Chamberlin, E.H.	100-165	
Tappan, Eva M.	House with the Silver Door (1st, sm8vo, green cl, 184p, p-o, 4cp)	Houghton	1913	Chamberlin, E.H.	30-50	*
Boylan, Grace D.	Pipes of Clovis (1st, sm8vo, 258p, green cl, 4cp)	Little/Brown	1913	Chamberlin, E.H.	25-40	*
Kingsley, Florence M.	Those Brewster Children (1st, 12mo, tan cl, 214p, 3pl)	Dodd	1910	Chamberlin, E.H.	25-40	*
Knevels, Gertrude	Wonderful Bed (1st, 8vo, 229p, 4cp)	Bobbs-Merrill	(1912)	Chamberlin, Emily H.	40-60	*
Scott, Walter	Quentin Durward (1st, lg8vo, 422p, gilt, p-o, 13cp, pep, SC)	Scribner	1923	Chambers, C.B.	80-120	
Champney, Elizabeth	Romance of Old Japan (1st, 8vo, 444p, gilt, teg, 96pl)	Putnam	1917	Champney, Frere	70-120	
Chan, Chih-Yi	Good-Luck Horse (1st, ob8vo, [47]p, pep, 10 fp color, DJ/1.50, CH)	Whittlesey	(1943)	Chan, Plato	70-120	
Channing, Blanche	Zodiac Stories (1st, sm8vo, 311p, gilt, b/w)	Dutton	1899	Channing Blanche	35-60	*
Waters, Russell J.	El Estranjero (1st, 8vo, gilt, 298p, fp b/w)	Rand/McNally	1910	Chapin, Will E.	45-70	
Barnes, James	Drake and his Yeomen (1st, 8vo, 415p, teg, gilt, col frn, 7pl)	Macmillan	1899	Chapman, Carlton	30-50	
White, Stewart E.	Conjuror's House (1st, sm8vo, uncut, 260p, 6pl)	McClure	1903	Chapman, Charles S.	40-65	
Jewett, Eleanore	Big John's Secret (1st, 8vo, blue cl, 236p, b/w, DJ/3.25)	Viking	(1962)	Chapman, Fred T.	25-40	
Coatsworth, Eliz.	Door to the North (1st {std}, 8vo, 246p, b/w, DJ/2.50)	Winston	(1950)	Chapman, Fred T.	25-40	
Latham, Jean L.	Drake: The Man they Called a Pirate (1st, 8vo, 278p, b/w, DJ/2.95)	Harper	(1960)	Chapman, Fred T.	30-50	
Jewett, Eleanore	Hidden Treasure of Glaston (1st, 8vo, 307p, b/w, pep, DJ/2.50, NH)	Viking	1946	Chapman, Fred T.	100-175	
Coatsworth, Eliz.	Indian Encounters (1st {std}, 8vo, 264p, b/w, DJ/3.50)	Macmillan	1960	Chapman, Fred T.	30-45	
Berry, Erick	King's Jewel (1st, 8vo, 189p, b/w, DJ/2.75)	Viking	1957	Chapman, Fred T.	25-40	
Govan, Christine	Mystery at Deserted Mill (1st, 8vo, 152p, b/w, DJ/2.50)	Sterling	1958	Chapman, Fred T.	120-180	
Govan, Christine	Mystery at Moccasin Bend (1st, 8vo, 191p, b/w, DJ/2.50)	Sterling	(1957)	Chapman, Fred T.	60-100	
Williams, Jay	Stolen Oracle (1st, 8vo, 222p, b/w, DJ/2.00)	NY: Oxford U.Pr.	(1943)	Chapman, Fred T.	25-40	*
Hurd, Edith T.	Wreck of the Wild Wave (1st, 8vo, 247p, b/w, pep, DJ/2.50)	Oxford U. Pr.	(1942)	Chapman, Fred T.	30-50	*
Skipper, Mervyn	Fooling of King Alexander (1st AM {std}, 4to, 30p, 2-color, DJ/4.50)	Atheneum	1967	Chapman, Gaynor	25-45	
Chapman, Gaynor	Luck Child (1st AM {std}, 4to, [32]p, color, DJ/4.50)	Atheneum	1968	Chapman, Gaynor	25-40	
Malory, Thomas	Story of Sir Galahad (1st, 8vo, 223p, tan cl, 7cp, pep)	Dutton	(1908)	Chapman, William E.	45-70	
Grey, Zane	Tappan's Burro (1st {std}, lg8vo, gilt, 253p, p-o, 7cp)	Harper	(1923)	Chapman/Street	250-450	
Updike, John	Bottom's Dream (1st, ob4to, 34p, fp color, pep, DJ/3.95)	Knopf	(1969)	Chappell, Warren	100-150	
Wagenknecht, Ed	Fireside Book/Yuletide Tales (1st {std}, 8vo, 593p, gilt, color, DJ/3.75)	Bobbs-Merrill	(1948)	Chappell, Warren	25-45	
Fleischman, Sid	Ghost in the Noonday Sun (1st {std}, 8vo, 173p, b/w, DJ/3.95)	Little/Brown	(1965)	Chappell, Warren	30-50	
Grimm Bros.	Hansel & Gretel (1st {std}, sm4to, [32]p, color, pep, DJ/2.00)	Knopf	1944	Chappell, Warren	40-60	
Richter, Conrad	Light in the Forest (1st {std}, lg8vo, 176p, fp b/w, cep, DJ/4.95)	Knopf	1966	Chappell, Warren	30-50	*
Yates, Elizabeth	Patterns on the Wall (1st {std}, 8vo, 241p, DJ/2.00, b/w decor by...)	Knopf	1943	Chappell, Warren	20-30	
Prokofieff, Serge	Peter & the Wolf (1st {std}, sm ob4to, [32]p, p-o, color, DJ/2.00)	Knopf	(1940)	Chappell, Warren	80-125	
Goodwin, John B.	Pleasant Pirate (1st {std}, sm4to, ibds, [32]p, color, DJ/2.00)	Knopf	1940	Chappell, Warren	40-70	
Chappell, Warren	They Say Stories (1st, 8vo, 79p, color, pep, DJ/3.00)	Knopf	(1960)	Chappell, Warren	40-65	R
David, Julian	Three Hanses (1st {std}, 8vo, 283p, 6cp, 12pl, DJ/2.00)	Little/Brown	1942	Chappell, Warren	30-50	
McCleery, William	Wolf Story (1st {std}, 12mo, 82p, red cl, p-o, col frn, DJ/2.00)	Knopf	1947	Chappell, Warren	60-100	R
Charlip, Remy	Arm in Arm (1st, 4to, [39]p, white cl, color, pep, DJ/3.50, NYTBI)	Parents Mag. Pr.	(1969)	Charlip, Remy	50-85	
Cook, Bernadine	Curious Little Kitten (1st, sm ob4to, [48]p, green cl, 1-color, DJ/2.25)	W.R. Scott	1956	Charlip, Remy	60-100	*
Brown, Margaret W.	David's Little Indian (1st, 16mo, blue cl, [48]p, fp color, DJ/2.50)	W.R. Scott	(1956)	Charlip, Remy	100-170	R
Miles, Betty	Day of Summer (1st, 8vo, [31]p, fp color, cep, DJ)	Knopf	1960	Charlip, Remy	50-80	
Miles, Betty	Day of Winter (1st, 8vo, [32]p, color, cep, DJ/2.75)	Knopf	1961	Charlip, Remy	50-80	
Brown, Margaret W.	Dead Bird (1st, ob8vo, blue cl, [48]p, color, DJ/2.75)	W.R. Scott	(1958)	Charlip, Remy	120-200	R
Charlip, Remy	Dress Up & Let's Have a Party (1st, ob8vo, ipcb [25]p, 3-col, pep, DJ/1.50)	W.R. Scott	1956	Charlip, Remy	60-90	R
Charlip, Remy	Fortunately (1st, 4to, [41]p, dp color, DJ/2.95)	Parents Mag. Pr.	(1964)	Charlip, Remy	40-65	
Brown, Margaret W.	Four Fur Feet (1st, 4to, [48]p, ibds, DJ/3.00)	W.R. Scott	1961	Charlip, Remy	50-70	

AUTHOR	TITLE	PUBLISHER	DATE	ARTIST	PRICE	LC
Krauss, Ruth	Moon or a Button (1st, 12mo, [48]p, ipcb, b/w, DJ/1.50)	Harper	(1959)	Charlip, Remy	60-100	
Charlip, Remy	Mother, Mother, I Feel Sick... (1st, ob4to, unpag, color, pep, DJ/2.95)	Parents Mag. Pr.	(1966)	Charlip, Remy	45-70	
Warburg, Sandol	My Very Own Special Particular & Personal Cat (1st, 8vo, 40p, DJ/3.25)	Houghton	1963	Charlip, Remy	70-125	
Martin, Judith	Tree Angel (1st, sq12mo, [49]p, 3-color, cep, DJ/1.95)	Knopf	(1962)	Charlip, Remy	50-80	
Krauss, Ruth	What a Fine Day for.... (1st, ob8vo, [40]p, black/gilt, color, DJ/3.50)	Parents Mag. Pr.	(1967)	Charlip, Remy	40-65	
Miles, Betty	What is the World? (1st, 4to, [40]p, fp color, dep, DJ/3.00)	Knopf	(1958)	Charlip, Remy	50-80	
Charlip, Remy	Where is Everybody? (1st, lg ob8vo, yellow cl, [50]p, 1-color, DJ/2.25)	W.R. Scott	1957	Charlip, Remy	60-100	R
Krumgold, Joseph	And Now Miguel (1st {std}, 8vo, 245p, b/w, pep, DJ/2.75, NM)	Crowell	(1953)	Charlot, Jean	100-165	
Claudel, Paul	Book of Christopher Columbus (1st, 4to, 57p, blue/silver, 2-color, dep)	Yale U. Press	1930	Charlot, Jean	80-130	
Brenner, Anita	Boy Who Could Do Anything (1st, lg8vo, 136p, fp color, cep, DJ/2.75)	W.R. Scott	(1942)	Charlot, Jean	70-120	
Brown, Margaret W.	Child's Good Morning (1st, sq4to, ibds, [32]p, fp color, DJ/2.00)	W.R. Scott	1952	Charlot, Jean	170-250	
Brown, Margaret W.	Child's Good Night Book (1st, 12mo, ibds, [24]p, color, DJ/1.00, CH)	W.R. Scott	1943	Charlot, Jean	120-200	
Rhoads, Dorothy	Corn Grows Ripe (1st, sm4to, 88p, pep, 1-color, DJ/2.75, NH)	Viking	1956	Charlot, Jean	70-100	
Charlot, Jean	Dance of Death (1st, lg ob8vo, black/silver, [102]p, fp b/w, DJ/2.50)	Sheed/Ward	(1951)	Charlot, Jean	80-130	
Morris, Ann A.	Digging in Yucatan (1st {std}, lg8vo, 279p, pep, b/w)	Doubleday/Doran	1931	Charlot, Jean	55-80	*
Brenner, Anita	Dumb Juan & the Bandits (1st, 8vo, green cl, [47]p, 1-color, DJ/2.50)	W.R. Scott	(1957)	Charlot, Jean	50-80	
Brown, Margaret W.	Fox Eyes (1st, 8vo, [32]p, ibds, color, DJ/1.50)	Pantheon	1951	Charlot, Jean	80-130	
Brenner, Anita	Hero by Mistake (1st, 8vo, 43p, ipcb, pep, 1-color, DJ/2.00, NYTBI)	W.R. Scott	(1953)	Charlot, Jean	100-175	
Hunt, Marigold	Hester & the Gnomes (1st, 8vo, 124p, blue cl, fp b/w, pep, DJ/2.50)	Whittlesey	(1955)	Charlot, Jean	50-80	
Tyman, Loretta	Julio (1st, 8vo, beige cl, 176p, fp b/w, DJ/2.50)	Abelard-Schuman	(1955)	Charlot, Jean	45-70	
Schlein, Miriam	Kittens, Cubs & Babies (1st, sm4to, green cl, [48]p, color, DJ)	W.R. Scott	1959	Charlot, Jean	120-200	
Bishop, Claire H.	Martin DePorres, Hero (1st, lg8vo, 120p, beige cl, fp b/w, pep, DJ/2.50)	Houghton	1954	Charlot, Jean	70-120	
Parish, Helen R.	Our Lady of Guadalupe (1st, sm4to, 48p, 6 dp color, DJ/3.00)	Viking	1955	Charlot, Jean	70-100	
Bulla, Clyde R.	Poppy Seeds (1st, lg8vo, [38]p, color, pep, DJ/2.75)	Crowell	(1955)	Charlot, Jean	125-200	
Clark, Ann N.	Secret of the Andes (1st, lg8vo, 131p, grey cl, col frn, pep, DJ/2.50, NM)	Viking	1952	Charlot, Jean	100-160	R
Brown, Margaret W.	Seven Stories about a Cat Named Sneakers (1st, sm8vo, 144p, b/w, DJ/2.50)	W.R. Scott	(1955)	Charlot, Jean	65-90	
Rhoads, Dorothy	Story of Chan Yuc (1st {std}, sq8vo, [45]p, ibds, color, DJ/1.50)	Doubleday/Doran	1941	Charlot, Jean	80-125	
Del Rio, A.M.	Sun, Moon & a Rabbit (1st, sm ob4to, gilt, 191p, color, DJ/3.00)	Sheed/Ward	1935	Charlot, Jean	120-200	R
Shannon, Monica	Tawnymore (1st {std}, sm8vo, 254p, col frn, fp b/w, pep)	Doubleday/Doran	1931	Charlot, Jean	80-130	
Brenner, Anita	Timid Ghost (1st, 4to, [48]p, cloth, 1-color, DJ/3.95)	W.R. Scott	(1966)	Charlot, Jean	50-80	
Ferrer, Melchor	Tito's Hats (1st, lg sq8vo, [28]p, ibds, 1-color, dep, DJ/0.50)	Garden City	(1940)	Charlot, Jean	80-120	
Brown, Margaret W.	Two Little Trains (1st, lg sq8vo, ipcb, [32]p, pep, color, DJ/1.75)	W.R. Scott	1949	Charlot, Jean	120-185	R
Schlein, Miriam	When Will the World be Mine? (1st, 4to, unpag, pep, color, DJ/2.25, CH)	W.R. Scott	(1953)	Charlot, Jean	100-170	
Hughes, Richard A.	Spider's Palace (1st AM {std}, 8vo, 163p, color, DJ/1.50)	Harper	1932	Charlton, George	140-200	
Sutcliff, Rosemary	High Deeds of Finn MacCool (1st AM {std}, 8vo, 189p, b/w, DJ/3.95)	Dutton	(1967)	Charlton, Michael	30-50	
Lovelace, Maud H.	Golden Wedge (1st {std}, 8vo, 189p, color, DJ/2.00)	Crowell	(1942)	Chase, Charlotte	100-165	
Gratacap, L.P.	Mayor of New York (1st, sm8vo, red/gilt, 471p, 4pl)	Dillingham	(1910)	Chase, Joseph C.	70-100	
Burgess, Thornton	Christmas Reindeer (1st, 12mo, 139p, red/gilt, 7pl, pep)	Macmillan	1926	Chase, Rhoda	120-200	
Hughes, Rupert	Fairy Detective (1st, 12mo, 72p, tan cl, p-o, 5pl)	Harper	(1919)	Chase, Rhoda	30-60	*
Lyman, Betty K.	Peter-Pan Twins are Glad to Help (sm4to, ibds, 12p, color)	Whitman	1928	Chase, Rhoda	35-60	
Lyman, Betty K.	Playtime for the Peter-Pan Twins (1st, 4to, ibds, fp color, pep)	Whitman	1928	Chase, Rhoda	30-50	
Taggart, Marion A.	Pussy-Cat Town (1st, sm8vo, 245p, green/gilt, color, pep)	L.C. Page	1906	Chase, Rhoda	45-70	
Courlander, Harold	Cow-Tail Switch (1st, lg8vo, brown cl, 143p, b/w, DJ/2.50, NH)	Henry Holt & Co.	(1947)	Chastain, Madye L.	50-80	*
Scott, Sally	Sue Ann's Busy Day (1st, 8vo, [57]p, b/w, DJ/1.75)	Harcourt	(1948)	Chastain, Madye L.	20-35	*
Hurd, Edith T.	White Horse (1st {std}, lg8vo, [31]p, color, DJ/3.50)	Harper	(1970)	Chen, Tony	25-40	*
Denton, Clara J.	Daisy Dells (1st, lg8vo, 222p, p-o, color)	Whitman	(1927)	Cheney, Garnett	60-90	
Lide, Alice A.	Pearls of Fortune (1st, sm8vo, 276p, col frn, 11 fp b/w, dep)	Little/Brown	1931	Cheney, Philip	25-40	*
Chermayeff, Ivan	Blind Mice & other Numbers (1st, 4to, 40p, ibds, 2-color, dep)	NY: Colorcraft	(1961)	Chermayeff, Ivan	30-50	
Smith, William J.	Ho for a Hat! (1st {std}, lg narrow 4to, 47p, color, cep, DJ/3.25)	Little/Brown	(1964)	Chermayeff, Ivan	30-50	*
Warburg, Sandol	Keep it Like a Secret (1st {std}, ob4to, 32p, color, DJ/3.00)	Little/Brown	(1961)	Chermayeff, Ivan	30-50	
Nash, Ogden	New Nutcracker Suite (1st {std}, sm4to, 48p, color, cep, DJ/3.50)	Little/Brown	(1962)	Chermayeff, Ivan	60-90	R
Ott, John	Peter Pumpkin (1st {std}, ob4to, [43]p, fp 3-color, dep, DJ/3.25)	Doubleday	1963	Chermayeff, Ivan	50-80	
Chess, Victoria	Fletcher & Zenobia (1st {std}, 12mo, [68]p, ibds, color, DJ/3.95)	Meredith Press	(1967)	Chess, Victoria	30-50	
Lystad, Mary	Millicent the Monster (1st, sq8vo, [32]p, fp color, dep, DJ/3.25)	Harlin Quist	(1968)	Chess, Victoria	20-30	
Belloc, Hilaire	But Soft - We are Observed (1st, 8vo, 312p, gilt, b/w, DJ)	L: Arrowsmith	(1928)	Chesterton, G.K.	70-100	
Chesterton, G.K.	Coloured Lands (1st, lg8vo, 238p, yellow cl, color, DJ)	L: Sheed/Ward	1938	Chesterton, G.K.	80-120	
Belloc, Hilaire	Haunted House (1st, 8vo, 269p, 37 illus, DJ)	L: Arrowsmith	(1927)	Chesterton, G.K.	80-125	
Belloc, Hilaire	Missing Masterpiece (1st, 8vo, 319p, b/w, DJ)	L: Arrowsmith	(1929)	Chesterton, G.K.	120-200	
Belloc, Hilaire	Postmaster-General (1st, 8vo, 286p, 30 illus, DJ)	L: Arrowsmith	(1932)	Chesterton, G.K.	120-200	
Belloc, Hilaire	Shadowed! (1st AM {std}, sm8vo, 312p, 37 illus, DJ/2.50)	Harper	1929	Chesterton, G.K.	100-160	
Justus, May	Banjo Billy and Mr. Bones (1st, 8vo, 63p, p-o, fp color, pep, DJ/1.50)	Whitman	1944	Chisholm, Christine	20-30	
Bryant, Bernice M.	Pedie and the Twins (1st, 8vo, 32p, p-o, color, pep, DJ/1.00)	Whitman	1942	Chisholm, Christine	30-45	
Justus, May	Sammy (1st, lg8vo, p-o, 47p, color, pep, DJ/2.00)	Whitman	1946	Chisholm, Christine	25-40	
Justus, May	Susie (1st, 8vo, 46p, p-o, color, pep, DJ/1.50)	Whitman	1947	Chisholm, Christine	20-30	
Bonner, Mary G.	365 Bedtime Stories (1st, lg8vo, 302p, p-o, 20cp)	Stokes	1923	Choate/Curtis	40-70	
Choate, Florence	Abby in the Gobi (1st, ob4to, ibds, 63p, color, pep)	McBride	(1929)	Choate/Curtis	60-90	*
Andersen, Hans C.	Andersen Fairy Book (1st, lg8vo, 416p, 8cp, pep)	Stokes	(1921)	Choate/Curtis	60-90	*
Bonner, Mary G.	Daddy's Bedtime Fairy Stories (1st, 12mo, p-o, 120p, color)	Stokes	(1916)	Choate/Curtis	40-70	
Choate, Florence	Dance of the Hours (1st, 8vo, 242p, pep, fp b/w)	Harcourt	(1934)	Choate/Curtis	25-40	*
Cervantes	Don Quixote (1st, lg8vo, 341p, p-o, 4cp, pep)	Stokes	1922	Choate/Curtis	30-50	
N/A	Indian Fairy Book (1st, 8vo, 303p, 8cp, pep)	Stokes	(1916)	Choate/Curtis	80-120	
Banks, Helen W.	Life of Jesus Retold for Children (1st AM, 4to, 93p, p-o, 5cp, 9pl)	Stokes	(1922)	Choate/Curtis	35-60	*
Choate, Florence	Little People of the Hills (1st, 8vo, 234p, fp b/w)	Harcourt	(1928)	Choate/Curtis	30-50	*
Eells, Elsie S.	Magic Tooth (1st, 8vo, orange cl, 243p, col frn, 10 fp b/w)	Little/Brown	1927	Choate/Curtis	40-60	*
Choate, Florence	Pinafores & Pantalets (1st, 8vo, 207p, uncut, pep, 8 fp 2-color)	Harcourt	(1931)	Choate/Curtis	30-50	*
Mother Goose	Stokes Wonder Book of Mother Goose (1st, 4to, 240p, 24cp, pep)	Stokes	(1919)	Choate/Curtis	60-90	
Chrestien, F.H.	Evelyn and the Fish (1st, 4to, 48p, ibds, color, DJ/2.00)	Hyperion Press	(1945)	Chrestien, F.H.	40-65	
Rush, William M.	Duff, Story of a Bear (1st {std}, 8vo, 149p, b/w, DJ/2.25)	Longmans	1950	Christensen, G.D.	25-45	

AUTHOR	TITLE	PUBLISHER	DATE	ARTIST	PRICE	LC
Montgomery, R.	Wapiti the Elk (1st {std}, 8vo, 186p, b/w, DJ/2.50)	Little/Brown	(1952)	Christensen, G.D.	25-45	
Montgomery, R.	White Mountaineer (1st {std}, 8vo, 177p, b/w, DJ/2.75)	Little/Brown	1953	Christensen, G.D.	20-35	
Christensen, Haaken	Little Bruin and Per (1st {A}, ob8vo, [24]p, 1-color, DJ/1.25)	Abingdon-Cokes.	1951	Christensen, Haaken	30-45	
Christie, G.F.	Round De Ole Plantation (1st, 4to, ibds, unpag, 24 fp color)	L: Blackie	[1906]	Christie, G.F.	425-600	*
Rinehart, Mary R.	Amazing Adventures of Letitia Carberry (1st, sm8vo, 344p, green cl, 10pl)	Bobbs-Merrill	(1911)	Christy, Howard C.	50-80	
Christy, Howard C.	American Girl (1st, lg8vo, 157p, p-o, 16cp)	Moffat	1906	Christy, Howard C.	80-120	
Christy, Howard C.	Christy Girl (1st, lg8vo, [48]p, p-o, 16cp)	Bobbs-Merrill	(1906)	Christy, Howard C.	140-200	
Longfellow, H.W.	Courtship of Miles Standish (1st, lg8vo, 152p, grey/gilt, 8cp, pep)	Bobbs-Merrill	(1903)	Christy, Howard C.	60-100	
Riley, James W.	Discouraging Model (1st, lg8vo, ipcb, [12]p, color)	Bobbs-Merrill	(1914)	Christy, Howard C.	90-120	R*
Hope, Anthony	Dolly Dialogues (1st, 8vo, 202p, p-o, teg, 18pl)	R.H. Russell	1901	Christy, Howard C.	55-80	R
Major, Charles	Dorothy Vernon of Haddon Hall (1st, 8vo, 369p, blue/gilt, col frn)	Macmillan	1902	Christy, Howard C.	30-50	
Christy, Howard C.	Drawings (1st lg ob folio, [58]p, ibds, gilt, 28pl)	Moffat	1905	Christy, Howard C.	250-350	
Longfellow, H.W.	Evangeline (1st, lg8vo, red/gilt, 132p, 6cp)	Bobbs-Merrill	(1905)	Christy, Howard C.	50-85	
Sousa, John P.	Fifth String (1st, 8vo, green cl, 124p, teg, b/w pl)	Bowen-Merrill	(1902)	Christy, Howard C.	30-50	
Riley, James W.	Good-Bye Jim (1st, sq8vo, gilt, [33]p, 11cp, pep)	Bobbs-Merrill	(1913)	Christy, Howard C.	60-90	
Nicholson, Meredith	House of a Thousand Candles (1st, 8vo, 382p, 7cp)	Bobbs-Merrill	(1905)	Christy, Howard C.	25-40	
Scott, Walter	Lady of the Lake (1st, 4to, [79]p, green/gilt, 13cp)	Bobbs-Merrill	(1910)	Christy, Howard C.	100-175	
N/A	Liberty Belles (1st, folio, [56]p, brown/gilt, 8cp)	Bobbs-Merrill	(1912)	Christy, Howard C.	250-400	
Davis, Richard H.	Lion & the Unicorn (1st [1], 12mo, 204p, green/gilt, 6pl)	Scribner	1899	Christy, Howard C.	35-60	
Chambers, Robert	Maid-at-Arms (1st, 12mo, green/gilt, 343p, 8pl)	Harper	1902	Christy, Howard C.	30-50	
Rinehart, Mary R.	Man in the Lower Ten (1st, 8vo, green cl, 372p, 5cp)	Bobbs-Merrill	(1909)	Christy, Howard C.	100-165	
Beach, Rex	Ne'er-Do-Well (1st, 12mo, 402p, p-o, 8pl)	Harper	1911	Christy, Howard C.	30-50	
Page, Thomas N.	Old Gentleman of the Black Stock (1st, 12mo, 170p, teg, 7cp)	Scribner	1900	Christy, Howard C.	40-65	
Riley, James W.	Old Sweetheart of Mine (1st, 8vo, gilt, [94]p, p-o, 19pl, pep)	Bobbs-Merrill	(1902)	Christy, Howard C.	80-135	
Christy, Howard C.	Our Girls (1st, lg8vo, 159p, p-o, 16cp)	Moffat	1907	Christy, Howard C.	140-200	
Riley, James W.	Riley Roses (1st, lg8vo, [30]p, green/gilt, 8cp)	Bobbs-Merrill	(1909)	Christy, Howard C.	70-120	
Christy, Howard C.	Songs of Sentiment (1st, 8vo, 128p, grey/gilt, p-o, 12cp, dep)	Moffat	1910	Christy, Howard C.	90-160	
Cable, George W.	The Cavalier (1st [1], 8vo, red/gilt, 311p, 8pl)	Scribner	1901	Christy, Howard C.	60-90	
Tennyson, Alfred	The Princess (1st, 4to, [95]p, brown/gilt, 14cp)	Bobbs-Merrill	(1911)	Christy, Howard C.	100-180	
Riley, James W.	The Rose (1st, sm4to, ibds, [16]p, color)	Bobbs-Merrill	(1914)	Christy, Howard C.	60-90	
Isham, Frederic S.	Under the Rose (1st, 8vo, 427p, green cl, 4cp by…)	Bobbs-Merrill	(1903)	Christy, Howard C.	25-40	
Ford, Paul L.	Wanted a Chaperone (1st, 8vo, 109p, teg, uncut, 6cp)	Dodd	1902	Christy, Howard C.	40-65	
Ford, Paul L.	Wanted a Matchmaker (1st, 8vo, 112p, teg, green/gilt, 5pl by…)	Dodd	1900	Christy, Howard C.	40-65	
Pitman, Norman	Chinese Wonder Book (1st, ob8vo, 219p, ibds, 12cp)	L: J.M. Dent	1919	Chu-T'ang, Li	60-100	
Chubb, Ida M.	Little Pickaninnies (1st, lg4to, [20]p, wraps, fp color)	Whitman	1929	Chubb, Ida M.	150-225	
Deutsch, Babette (tr)	Crocodile (1st AM, ob4to, 31p, b/w)	Lippincott	(1931)	Chukovsky, Korney	130-200	
Gates, Josephine S.	Tommy Sweet Tooth (1st, sq16mo, ibds, 64p, color, pep)	Houghton	(1911)	Churbuck, Esther V.	60-90	
Harris, Joel C.	Nights with Uncle Remus (1st, 8vo, 416p, blue/gilt, 20pl, cep)	Bos: Osgood	1883	Church/Beard	400-650	
Harris, Joel C.	Uncle Remus (1st [1], lg8vo, 231p, gilt, 8pl, dep, PPP)	Appleton	1881	Church/Moser	900-1500	
Hawthorne, Nathaniel	Wonder Book (1st, lg8vo, p-o, 232p, col frn)	Sears	(1928)	Chuse, Anne	30-50	*
Chute, Marchette	Around and About (1st {std}, 8vo, red cl, 124p, 1-color, pep, DJ/2.95)	Dutton	1957	Chute, Marchette	30-50	
Chute, Marchette	Rhymes About the City (1st, 8vo, 57p, silhouettes, DJ/1.25)	Macmillan	1946	Chute, Marchette	45-60	
Chute, Marchette	Rhymes About the Country (1st, sm4to, tan cl, 74p, b/w, pep, DJ/1.50)	Macmillan	1941	Chute, Marchette	50-70	
Cole, William	Aunt Bella's Umbrella (1st {std}, sm8vo, [45]p, color, DJ/3.50)	Doubleday	(1970)	Chwast, Jacqueline	30-45	
Latham, Jean L.	Cuckoo that Couldn't Count (1st {std}, 8vo, ibds, [32]p, fp color, DJ/2.50)	Macmillan	1961	Chwast, Jacqueline	30-50	
Neville, Mary	First and Last Annual Pet Parade (1st, lg ob8vo, [46]p, b/w, cep, DJ/3.50)	Pantheon	(1968)	Chwast, Jacqueline	30-50	*
Warburg, Sandol	Hooray for Us (1st {std}, 24mo, ipcb, 48p, fp b/w, DJ/1.95)	Houghton	1970	Chwast, Jacqueline	25-40	*
Livingston, Myra C.	Whispers (1st {std}, 12mo, 48p, b/w, DJ/2.25)	Harcourt	(1958)	Chwast, Jacqueline	30-45	
Livingston, Myra C.	Wide Awake (1st {std}, 12mo, 48p, b/w, DJ/2.25)	Harcourt	(1959)	Chwast, Jacqueline	20-30	*
Merriam, Eve	Finding a Poem (1st {std}, 8vo, 68p, fp b/w, cep, DJ, NYTBI)	Atheneum	1970	Chwast, Seymour	30-45	*
Gill, Joan	Sara's Granny & the Groodle (1st {std}, 4to, [32]p, color, DJ/3.95, NYTBI)	Doubleday	(1969)	Chwast, Seymour	30-50	
Coatsworth, Eliz.	Atlas & Beyond (1st {std}, 12mo, 61p, p-o, dep, woodcuts by…)	Harper	1924	Cimino, Harry	40-60	*
Hancock, H. Irving	Chuggins (1st, 12mo, 95p, col frn, 4pl)	Altemus	(1904)	Claghorn, Joseph C.	120-200	
Bird, Mary H.	Snow Man's Christmas (1st, 16mo, p-o, green cl, 87p, 24 color, pep)	Stern	1908	Claghorn, Joseph C.	60-100	
Habberton, John	With the Dream Maker (1st, sm8vo, 112p, 5pl)	Jacobs	1898	Claghorn, Joseph C.	40-65	
Ewing, Frank	I-A-Goo & his Forest Friends (1st, 4to, ibds, 110p, b/w, pep, DJ/1.50)	Foster & Stewart	(1947)	Clare, Ernie	30-50	
Harper, Theodore A.	Mushroom Boy (1st, 8vo, 215p, 4cp, pep)	Penn	1924	Clark, Florenz	30-50	
Baum, L. Frank	Life and Adventures of Santa Claus (1st [1], lg8vo, 206p, 20cp, pep)	Bowen-Merrill	1902	Clark, Mary C.	600-800	
Deland, Margaret	Awakening of Helena Richie (1st, sm8vo, 357p, col frn, 7pl)	Harper	1906	Clark, Walter A.	25-40	
Chaucer, Geoffrey	Canterbury Tales (1st, lg8vo, 235p, teg, gilt, 6cp)	Fox Duffield	1904	Clark, Walter A.	55-80	
Davis, Richard H.	Captain Macklin (1st, sm8vo, teg, uncut, 328p, 7pl)	Scribner	1902	Clark, Walter A.	40-65	
Smith, Francis H.	Fortunes of Oliver Horn (1st, smo, green/gilt, uncut, 552p, b/w)	Scribner	1902	Clark, Walter A.	25-40	
Janvier, Thomas A.	Legends of the City of Mexico (1st, 8vo, gilt, 164p, 6pl by…)	Harper	1910	Clark, Walter A.	60-90	
Wharton, Edith	Sanctuary (1st, 8vo, 184p, green/gilt, uncut, col frn, 10pl)	Scribner	1903	Clark, Walter A.	180-250	
Warren, Geoffrey	Elixir of Life (1st, 12mo, 17p, green bds, p-o, 1-color)	Dublin: Jameson	1925	Clarke, Harry	500-800	
Andersen, Hans C.	Fairy Tales (1st AM, 4to, 319p, grey cl, p-o, teg, 16 ticp)	Brentano's	(1916)	Clarke, Harry	600-900	
Andersen, Hans C.	Fairy Tales (1st, 4to, 319p, teg, 16 ticp, 24pl)	L: Harrap	1916	Clarke, Harry	800-1100	
Perrault, Charles	Fairy Tales (1st AM, 4to, blue/gilt, 160p, 12cp, 12pl)	Dodge	[1922]	Clarke, Harry	400-600	
Perrault, Charles	Fairy Tales (1st, 4to, blue/gilt, 160p, 12cp, 12pl)	L: Harrap	(1922)	Clarke, Harry	500-700	
Andersen, Hans C.	Fairy Tales (2nd, 4to, 320p, green cl, 16cp, 24pl)	L: Harrap	(1930)	Clarke, Harry	225-325	
Andersen, Hans C.	Fairy Tales (2nd AM, 4to, 16cp)	Brentano's	(1930)	Clarke, Harry	160-240	
Swinburne, A.C.	Selected Poems… (1st, 4to, black/gilt, 217p, 10pl, pep)	Lane/Dodd	(1928)	Clarke, Harry	300-500	
Perrault, Charles	Sleeping Beauty (1st, 4to, teg, blue/gilt, 12cp)	Dodge	[1922]	Clarke, Harry	300-450	
Poe, Edgar A.	Tales of Mystery… (1st AM, 4to, p-o, 8 ticp, 24pl)	Brentano's	[1919]	Clarke, Harry	425-600	
Poe, Edgar A.	Tales of Mystery… (1st, 4to, 383p, p-o, teg, 8 ticp, 24pl)	L: Harrap	1919	Clarke, Harry	500-700	
Poe, Edgar A.	Tales of Mystery… (1st {this pub}, 4to, p-o, 412p, 8 ticp)	Tudor	1933	Clarke, Harry	180-250	
Walters, L.	Year's at the Spring (1st, sm4to, 128p, green/gilt, 12cp, 12pl, cep)	L: Harrap	1920	Clarke, Harry	280-400	
Walters, L.	Year's at the Spring (1st AM, 4to, 128p, 12cp, 12pl)	Brentano's	(1920)	Clarke, Harry	200-300	

AUTHOR	TITLE	PUBLISHER	DATE	ARTIST	PRICE	LC
Brown, Alice	Merrylinks (1st, ob4to, ipcb, p-o, [91]p, fp b/w)	McClure	1903	Clarke, Louise	80-120	R
Lide, Alice A.	Inemak: Little Greenlander (1st, sm8vo, 148p, blue cl, fp b/w)	Rand/McNally	(1927)	Clarke, William W.	25-45	*
Hinkle, Thomas C.	Split-Ear (1st, sm8vo, 269p, p-o, 1 ticp, fp b/w)	Rand/McNally	1925	Clarke, William W.	40-65	
Clarkson, L.	Buttercup's Visit... (folio, cloth, chromos)	Dutton	1881	Clarkson, L.	90-120	
Clarkson, L.	Fly-Away Fairies (1st, 4to, ibds, unpag, 16cp)	Dutton	1882	Clarkson, L.	120-200	
Clarkson, L.	Heartsease & Happy Days (folio, AEG, gilt, 12 chromos)	Dutton	1883	Clarkson, L.	120-200	
Clarkson, L.	Indian Summer (1st, folio, 52p, AEG, gilt, 12cp, cep)	Dutton	1881	Clarkson, L.	120-200	
Clarkson, L.	Violet Among the Lilies (4to, silver/gilt, AEG, 8cp)	Dutton	1885	Clarkson, L.	150-250	
Montgomery, Lucy M.	Anne of Green Gables (1st, sm8vo, 429p, p-o, gilt, 8pl, PPP)	L.C. Page	1908	Claus, M.A.	2000-3000	
Bryce, Marion	Nancy in the Wood (1st, 8vo, 200p, 8cp, pep)	L: John Lane	1914	Clausen, Katharine	45-60	
Van Eyssen, Shirley	In the Beginning (1st, folio, gilt, 64p, fp color, cep, DJ)	Harlin Quist	1970	Claveloux, Nicole	70-120	*
Ruy-Vidal, Francois	Secret Journey of Hugo the Brat (1st AM sq8vo, [32]p, color, DJ/3.75, NYT)	Harlin Quist	(1969)	Claveloux, Nicole	50-85	
Monreal, Guy	Teletrips of Alala (1st, sq4to, [36]p, fp color, DJ, NYTBI)	Harlin Quist	1970	Claveloux, Nicole	50-80	
Michelson, Miriam	Anthony Overman (1st, 8vo, 330p, 5pl)	Doubleday/Page	1906	Clay, John Cecil	25-40	*
Donahey, Mary D.	Castle of Grumpy Grouch (1st, sm4to, 150p, color)	Stern	1908	Clay, John Cecil	100-165	
Clay, John Cecil	Lovers' Mother Goose (1st, 4to, 92p, p-o, gilt, color, pep)	Bobbs-Merrill	(1905)	Clay, John Cecil	100-165	
Aldrich, Thomas B.	Marjorie Daw (1st, lg8vo, teg, 123p, gilt, col frn)	Houghton	1908	Clay, John Cecil	35-60	
Nicholson, Meredith	Zelda Dameron (1st, 12mo, 411p, 8cp by...)	Bobbs-Merrill	(1904)	Clay, John Cecil	35-60	
Clay/Herford	Cupid's Cyclopedia (1st, 12mo, ibds, [104]p, color, gilt)	Scribner	1910	Clay/Herford	70-100	
Clayton, Margaret	Amabel and Crispin (1st, 8vo, 133p, blue cl, fp b/w, pep)	L: Chatto	1911	Clayton, Margaret	35-60	
Clayton, John	Bunny Brothers (8vo, pcb, 96p)	L: Sully	(1911)	Clayton, Margaret	80-130	
Clayton, John	Dot in Dreamland (1st, 8vo, 88p, green cl, p-o, 10cp)	Whitman	(1916)	Clayton, Margaret	60-90	
Clayton, Jacqueline	Georgie-Porgie Book (8vo, p-o, unpag, 12cp)	L: Nelson	[1913]	Clayton, Margaret	80-130	
Clayton, Jacqueline	Twirly-Whirly Book (8vo, p-o, unpag, 12cp)	L: Nelson	[1913]	Clayton, Margaret	80-130	
Darton, F.J.H.	Wonder Book of Beasts (1st, 8vo, 403p, gilt, teg, 22pl)	L: Wells/Gard.	(1909)	Clayton, Margaret	100-165	
Hopkins, Henry C.	Moon-Boat (1st, 4to, tan/gilt, [27]p, p-o, 11cp)	McKay	(1918)	Clayton, W. Philip	150-200	
Toye, William	How Summer Came to Canada (1st AM, 4to, 32p, color, DJ/3.95)	H.Z. Walck	1969	Cleaver, Elizabeth	30-50	
Toye, William	Mountain Goats of Temlaham (1st AM, 4to, 32p, color, DJ/3.95)	H.Z. Walck	1969	Cleaver, Elizabeth	30-50	
Downie, Mary (ed)	Wind Has Wings (1st AM, sm4to, 95p, fp color, cep, DJ/5.95)	H.Z. Walck	(1968)	Cleaver, Elizabeth	25-40	*
Stuart, Ruth M.	Daddy'Do-Funny's Wisdom Jingles (1st, sm8vo, 95p, b/w, pep)	Century	1913	Clements, G.H.	120-200	R
Carroll, Lewis	Alice... & Through... (4to, ibds, 5 fp color)	L: Hutchinson	(1934)	Clements, M.L.	200-300	
Tarkington, Booth	Beasley's Christmas Party (1st, 8vo, 100p, gilt, color)	Harper	1909	Clements, Ruth S.	50-80	
Webb, E. & D.	Littlest Fairy (1st, sm4to, ibds, 158p, p-o, 8cp, pep)	Dodge	(1910)	Clements, Ruth S.	200-300	
Bigham, Madge A.	Overheard in Fairyland (1st, sm8vo, 237p, col frn, cp)	Little/Brown	(1909)	Clements, Ruth S.	40-65	
Barbour, Ralph H.	Half-Back (1st, 8vo, orange cl, 267p, b/w, PPP)	Appleton	1899	Clinedinst, B. West	120-200	
Dixon, Thomas	The One Woman (1st, 8vo, 350p, teg, red/gilt, 8pl)	Doubleday/Page	1903	Clinedinst, B. West	50-80	
Gaggin, Eva R.	All Those Buckles (1st, 8vo, 250p, b/w, DJ/2.00)	Viking	1945	Cloete, Mildred	25-40	
Hunter, Richard	Little Pickles (sm4to, ibds, 44p, color)	L: Blackie	[1900]	Cobb, Ruth	170-240	
Hunter, Richard	Silver Bubbles... (1st, 4to, [40]p, color)	L: Nelson	[1903]	Cobb, Ruth	170-240	
Hunter, Richard	Dollies (1st, 24mo, olive cl, 95p)	L: Richards	1902	Cobb/Hunter	120-200	*
Garfield, Leon	Mr. Corbett's Ghost (1st AM, 8vo, 87p, b/w, DJ/3.50, NYTBI)	Pantheon	(1968)	Cober, Alan E.	25-45	
Withers, Carl	Tale of a Black Cat (1st {std}, ob8vo, [32]p, ibds, b/w, DJ/2.75)	Holt, Rinehart	(1966)	Cober, Alan E.	30-50	
Cunningham, Julia	Viollet (1st, 8vo, 82p, fp b/w, cep, DJ/3.25)	Pantheon	(1966)	Cober, Alan E.	20-30	*
Belting, Natalia	Winter's Eve (1st {std}, 8vo, [48]p, pcb, cep, color, DJ/4.95, NYTBI)	Holt, Rinehart	(1969)	Cober, Alan E.	30-50	
Norton, Andre	Sword is Drawn (1st, 8vo, 180p, col frn, 4 fp b/w, pep, DJ/2.00)	Houghton	1944	Coburn, Duncan	250-400	
Taylor, Bayard	Boys of Other Countries (1st, 8vo, gilt, 260p, col frn, b/w)	Putnam	1912	Coburn, Frederick S.	25-40	
Dickens, Charles	Christmas Carol (1st, sm4to, 157p, teg, b/w pl)	Putnam	1900	Coburn, Frederick S.	30-50	*
Dickens, Charles	The Chimes (1st, 12mo, 189p, AEG, grey/gilt, 4cp, 11pl)	Putnam	1911	Coburn, Frederick S.	55-80	
Potter, Beatrix	Story of Peter Rabbit (1st, 8vo, green cl, p-o, color)	Whitman	(1924)	Cochran, J.T.	70-125	
DeMorgan, Mary	Windfairies and other Tales (1st, sm8vo, 236p, gilt, AEG, 6 fp color)	L: Seeley	1900	Cockerell, Olive	90-120	
Knatchbull-Hugessen	Princess with Pea-Green Nose (1st, 12mo, 114p, col frn, pep)	Harper	1927	Cocks, Myra	30-50	
Byars, Betsy C.	Summer of the Swans (1st {std}, 8vo, 142p, fp b/w, DJ/3.95, NM)	Viking	(1970)	Coconis, Ted	100-160	
Holberg, Ruth	Restless Johnny (1st, 8vo, 210p, b/w, pep, DJ/2.50)	Crowell	(1950)	Coe, Lloyd	20-35	
Wetmore, Claude H.	Sweepers of the Sea (1st, sm8vo, green/gilt, 349p, 9pl)	Bowen-Merrill	(1900)	Coffin, G.A.	40-65	
Coffin, Julia H.	Vendor of Dreams (1st, lg8vo, 108p, blue/gilt, teg, 3cp)	Dodd	1917	Coffin, Haskell	55-80	*
Hoffmann, Eleanor	Lion of Barbary (1st, 8vo, 217p, blue cl, b/w, DJ/2.00)	Holiday House	(1946)	Coggins, Jack	25-45	
Clark, Ann N.	Along Sandy Trails (1st {std}, lg8vo, 31p, color, DJ/4.95)	Viking	(1969)	Cohn, Alfred	30-45	*
Steele, William O.	Spooky Thing (1st {std}, 8vo, 80p, fp b/w, DJ/2.75)	Harcourt	(1960)	Coker, Paul	20-30	
Scott, Walter	Ivanhoe (1st, 12mo, 336p, 10cp, pep)	Row, Peterson	(1914)	Cole, Clarence L.	30-50	*
Canton, William	Child's Book of Warriors (1st, sm8vo, green/gilt, teg, uncut, 319p, 3cp)	L: J.M. Dent	(1912)	Cole, Herbert	80-120	
Rhys, Ernest (ed.)	English Fairy Tales (12mo, p-o, 474p, gilt, 8cp)	Dutton	1906	Cole, Herbert	60-90	
Rhys, Ernest (ed.)	Fairy-Gold (1st, 8vo, 474p, 12cp)	L: J.M. Dent	1906	Cole, Herbert	70-120	
Swift, Jonathan	Gulliver's Travels (1st, sm8vo, green cl, 355p, 27pl)	J. Lane	1900	Cole, Herbert	50-80	*
Ingoldsby, Thomas	Ingoldsby Legends (1st, 8vo, 640p, teg, gilt, b/w)	L/NY: J. Lane	1903	Cole, Herbert	50-80	
Omar Khayyam	Rubaiyat of Omar Khayyam (1st, 8vo, 65p)	L: John Lane	1901	Cole, Herbert	80-120	*
Hare, Christopher	Story of Bayard (1st, 8vo, 256p, color)	L: Dent	1911	Cole, Herbert	60-90	
Hutchinson, W.M.L.	Sunset of the Heroes (8vo, 281p, green/gilt, pep, teg, 8cp)	L: J.M. Dent	[1910]	Cole, Herbert	70-100	*
Hopkins, Marjorie	And the Jackal Played the Masinko (1st, ob4to, [41]p, 3-color, pep, DJ/3.50)	Parents Mag. Pr.	(1969)	Cole, Olivia, H.	25-40	
Cole, Walter	ABC Book of People (1st, lg4to, [59]p, color, dep)	Minton Balch	(1932)	Cole, Walter	100-165	
Coolidge, Susan	What Katy Did (1st, 8vo, p-o, 271p, 5cp, pep)	Little/Brown	1924	Coleman, Ralph P.	30-50	
Dickens, Charles	Boys and Girls from Dickens (1st, lg8vo, 277p, 7pl, pep)	Macaulay	1910	Coll, Joseph C.	80-125	
Mundy, Talbot	Hira Singh (1st, sm8vo, green cl, 308p, 6pl)	Bobbs-Merrill	(1918)	Coll, Joseph C.	70-100	
Murphy, Nettie S.	Isn't It So? (1st, sm8vo, 92p, b/w)	Lippincott	1902	Coll, Joseph C.	70-120	
Mundy, Talbot	Ivory Trail (1st, sm8vo, 411p, 6pl)	Bobbs-Merrill	(1919)	Coll, Joseph C.	70-100	
Mundy, Talbot	King of the Khyber Rifles (1st, 8vo, 395p, 7 dp b/w, gilt)	Bobbs-Merrill	(1916)	Coll, Joseph C.	100-175	
Doyle, Arthur Conan	Lost World (1st AM, 8vo, 309p, gilt, 11pl by...)	Hodder/Doran	[1912]	Coll, Joseph C.	400-600	
Rousseau, Victor	Messiah of the Cylinder (1st, sm8vo, green/gilt, 319p, 11pl)	McClurg	1917	Coll, Joseph C.	100-175	
Merritt, Abraham	Moon Pool (1st, sm8vo, 433p, gilt, frn by...)	Putnam	1919	Coll, Joseph C.	100-175	

AUTHOR	TITLE	PUBLISHER	DATE	ARTIST	PRICE	LC
Asbjornsen, P.C.	East of the Sun, West o/t Moon (1st, 12mo, 198p, cp, pep)	Macmillan	1928	Collin, Hedvig	50-80	
Kristoffersen, Eva	Hans Christian of Elsinore (1st, sq4to, 80p, pep, color, DJ/2.00)	Whitman	1937	Collin, Hedvig	55-80	
Kristoffersen, Eva	Merry Matchmakers (1st, 8vo, 95p, ibds, color, pep, DJ/2.00)	Whitman	1940	Collin, Hedvig	30-50	
Andersen, Hans C.	Real Princess (1st, 4to, green cl, p-o, [18]p, color)	Whitman	1932	Collin, Hedvig	40-60	
Treffinger, Carolyn	Jimmy's Shoes (1st, 12mo, red cl, 219p, pep, 3pl)	Penn	(1934)	Collings, R.C.	35-60	*
Stevens, Thomas	Children of the World from A to Z (1st, 4to, [58]p, 26cp)	R.H. Russell	1903	Collins, A.H.	250-350	
Collins, Charles	All Round the Farm (4to, ibds, [66]p, 12 chromos)	L: Nister	[1880]	Collins, Charles	200-300	
Fisher, Aileen	Trapped by the Mountain Storm (1st {std}, sm8vo, 124p, b/w, DJ/2.00)	Aladdin	1950	Collins, Fred	20-30	*
DeJong, Meindert	Bible Days (1st, ob4to, 80p, fp b/w, pep)	Fideler Co.	(1949)	Collins, Kreigh	30-50	
Miller, Warren H.	Lone Woodsman (1st {std}, 8vo, 230p, col frn, pep, DJ/2.00)	Winston	(1943)	Collins, Kreigh	50-80	*
Herford, Oliver	Smoker's Yearbook (1st, lg8vo, [28]p, p-o, 12cp)	Moffat	1908	Collins, Sewell	80-125	
Francis, Sally R.	Scat, Scat (1st, 12mo, [32]p, p-o, color, pep)	Platt/Munk	1940	Collison, Elizabeth	30-50	
Bianco, Margery W.	Penny and the White Horse (1st, lg4to, ibds, [24]p, fp color, DJ/2.00)	J. Messner	(1942)	Collison, Marjory	45-70	
Hunt, Mabel L.	Sibby Botherbox (1st {std}, lg8vo, 174p, blue cl, pep, b/w, DJ/2.00)	Lippincott	(1945)	Collison, Marjory	30-50	
Carroll, Lewis	Through the Looking Glass (1st, sm4to, [30]p, ipcb, color, pep)	NY: Maxton	1947	Collison, Marjory	50-80	*
Kingsley, Charles	Water Babies (1st, 4to, 56p, color, pep, DJ/2.50)	Duell, Sloan	(1946)	Collison, Marjory	30-50	
Colman, Margery	Bramble (1st AM {std}, 4to, ibds, 32p, color, DJ/2.00)	Coward	(1945)	Colman, Margery	35-50	
Colver, Alice M.	Wish Fairy of Sunshine & Shadow Forest (1st, 24mo, ibds, p-o, 63p, color)	Altemus	(1919)	Colver, Alice	60-90	R
Murphy, Ruby B.	Who's Who in Mother Goose Land (1st, 12mo, [31]p, ibds, 1-color)	Rand/McNally	1935	Combet, Fernande	35-60	
Grimm Bros.	Fairy Tales (1st, lg8vo, 244p, p-o, col frn, 1-color, pep)	Sears	(1926)	Combs, Lorraine	80-125	
DeJong, Meindert	Tower by the Sea (1st {std}, 8vo, 113p, DJ/2.00)	Harper	(1950)	Comfort, Barbara	25-40	
Stevenson, Rbt. L.	Child's Garden of Verses (1st, sm4to, 91p, color)	McLoughlin	(1909)	Comstock, Enos B.	60-100	
Comstock, Enos B.	Fairy Frolics (1st, 4to, [64]p, p-o, 6cp)	Rand/McNally	(1913)	Comstock, Enos B.	160-220	
Comstock, Enos B.	Tuck-Me-In Stories (1st, lg8vo, 76p, color)	Moffat	1917	Comstock, Enos B.	80-125	
Dewey, Katharine F.	Star People (1st, 8vo, 232p, blue cl, fp b/w)	L: Longmans	1910	Comstock, Frances B.	50-85	
Aesopus	Aesop's Fables (1st, 8vo, 275p, 16cp)	Moffat	1905	Conde, J.M.	120-180	
Aesopus	Aesop's Fables (1st, 8vo, 259p, gilt, p-o, cp)	Platt/Peck	(1913)	Conde, J.M.	40-60	*
Young, Martha	Behind the Dark Pines (1st, sm8vo, 287p, tan cl, 27pl)	Appleton	1912	Conde, J.M.	35-60	
Bourke, S.T.E.	Fables in Feathers (1st, sq8vo, 114p, 9pl)	Crowell	(1907)	Conde, J.M.	40-60	
Paine, Albert B.	Hollow Tree (1st, lg8vo, 128p, ibds, b/w, PPP)	R.H. Russell	1898	Conde, J.M.	200-300	
Paine, Albert B.	Hollow Tree Nights & Days (1st, 8vo, 290p, green cl, b/w)	Harper	(1916)	Conde, J.M.	40-65	
Paine, Albert B.	Hollow Tree Snowed-In Book (1st, 8vo, cloth, 285p, b/w)	Harper	1910	Conde, J.M.	200-300	
Paine, Albert B.	In the Deep Woods (1st, lg8vo, 134p, ipcb, 52pl)	R.H. Russell	1899	Conde, J.M.	220-300	
Harrington, John W.	Jumping Kangaroo & Apple-Butter Cat (1st, lg8vo, 130p, b/w)	McClure	1900	Conde, J.M.	80-125	
Carter, Charles F.	Katooticut (1st, lg8vo, ipcb, 153p, fp b/w)	R.H. Russell	1899	Conde, J.M.	160-240	*
Paine, Albert B.	Mr. Crow & the Whitewash (1st, 12mo, 120p, p-o, gilt, b/w)	Harper	(1917)	Conde, J.M.	60-100	
Paine, Albert B.	Mr. Rabbit's Wedding (1st, sm8vo, gilt, p-o, 123p, fp b/w)	Harper	(1917)	Conde, J.M.	60-100	
Young, Martha	Plantation Bird Legends (1st, 8vo, 249p, 28pl)	Appleton	1916	Conde, J.M.	90-120	*
Harris, Joel C.	Uncle Remus & Brer Rabbit (1st, ob4to, [63]p, green cl, p-o, color)	Stokes	1907	Conde, J.M.	300-450	
Harris, Joel C.	Uncle Remus & the Little Boy (1st, 8vo, 173p, brown cl, uncut, p-o, 8cp)	Small/Maynard	(1910)	Conde, J.M.	150-220	R
Dowson, Ernest	Beauty & the Beast (1st, 4to, 118p, green/gilt, teg, uncut, 4cp)	L: John Lane	1908	Condor, Charles	180-240	
Sage, Agnes C.	Two Girls of Old New Jersey (1st, 8vo, 195p, 16pl)	Stokes	(1912)	Connah, D.J.	30-50	
Farmer, Penelope	Charlotte Sometimes (1st AM {std}, 8vo, 192p, b/w, DJ/4.95)	Harcourt	1969	Conner, Chris	80-135	
Thomson, Clara L.	Celtic Wonder World (1st, 8vo, 155p, b/w)	L: H. Marshall	1902	Conner, E.	70-100	
Norton, Andre	Octagon Magic (1st, 8vo, 189p, fp b/w, DJ/3.95)	World	(1967)	Conner, Mac	150-250	
Mayakovsky, Vladimir	Timothy's Horse (1st, ob4to, [29]p, fp color, cep, DJ, NYTBI)	Pantheon	(1970)	Constantini, Flavio	60-90	*
Heal, Edith	Robin Hood (1st, lg8vo, 626p, p-o, 8 fp color, pep, WS)	Rand/McNally	(1928)	Content, Dan	40-65	
Molloy, Anne	The Pigeoneers (1st, lg8vo, 180p, grey cl, woodcuts, dep, DJ/2.50)	Houghton	1947	Converse, Elizabeth	30-50	
Cook, Walter	Peggy's Travels (1st, 4to, 98p, brown bds, 15cp)	L: Blackie	(1908)	Cook, Alice M.	125-200	
Whitman, Walt	Poems of Leaves & Grass (1st, 4to, 260p, teg, gilt, 24 ticp)	L: J.M. Dent	1913	Cook, Margaret C.	120-170	
Carlson, Natalie S.	Tomahawk Family (1st, sm8vo, 170p, fp b/w, DJ/2.75)	Harper	(1960)	Cook, Stephen	20-30	
Campbell, A.M.	Fairy Flights in Cloudland (4to, ibds, 16cp)	L: A. Cooke	[1915]	Cook/Christie	160-240	
Cooke, Donald E.	Nutcracker of Nuremberg (1st, 8vo, 148p, gilt, fp 2-color, pep, DJ/2.00)	Winston	(1938)	Cooke, Donald E.	50-80	
Cooke, Donald E.	The Firebird (1st AM, 8vo, 144p, 4cp, fp b/w, gilt, pep, DJ/2.00)	Winston	(1939)	Cooke, Donald E.	35-45	
Asbjornsen, P.C.	East of the Sun, West o/t Moon (1st, 8vo, p-o, 289p, green cl, 8cp, pep)	McKay	(1921)	Cooke, Edna	75-100	
Mother Goose	Mother Goose Nursery Rhymes (1st, 8vo, red/gilt, 385p, 11cp, pep)	Cupples/Leon	(1930)	Cooke, Edna	60-100	
Montgomery, Lucy M.	Pat of Silver Bush (1st, sm8vo, 329p, col frn)	Stokes	1933	Cooke, Edna	140-200	
Irving, Washington	Rip Van Winkle (1st, 12mo, 69p, beige cl, 4cp)	Lippincott	(1923)	Cooke, Edna	40-60	*
Irving, Washington	Rip Van Winkle & Sleepy Hollow (1st, 8vo, 148p, red/gilt, 8cp, pep)	Lippincott	(1924)	Cooke, Edna	30-50	
Ewing, Juliana H.	Stories by J.H. Ewing (1st, lg8vo, blue cl, p-o, 426p, 8cp)	Duffield	1920	Cooke, Edna	60-90	
Molesworth, Mrs.	Stories by Mrs. Molesworth (1st, 4to, p-o, green cl, 353p, 8cp)	Duffield	1922	Cooke, Edna	70-100	
Cunningham, Julia	Onion Journey (1st, 8vo, 36p, color, DJ/3.50)	Pantheon	(1967)	Cooley, Lydia	20-25	
Montgomery, F.T.	Wonderful Electric Elephant (1st, 8vo, 253p, 50pl)	Saalfield	1903	Coolidge, C.M.	70-100	*
Malmberg, Bertil	Ake & his World (1st, 8vo, 176p, red/gilt, uncut, fp b/w, DJ/2.00)	Farrar/Rinehart	(1940)	Cooney, Barbara	100-165	
Morse, Samuel	All in a Suitcase (1st {std}, lg ob8vo, 48p, color, DJ/3.75)	Little/Brown	(1966)	Cooney, Barbara	50-80	
Seeger, Ruth C.	Animal Folk Songs for Children (1st {std}, 4to, gilt, 80p, b/w, DJ/2.50)	Doubleday	1950	Cooney, Barbara	60-90	
McEwen, Catherine	Away We Go! (1st {std}, 8vo, 111p, color, pep, DJ/2.50)	Crowell	(1956)	Cooney, Barbara	60-100	*
Salten, Felix	Bambi: Life in the Woods (1st {std}, 8vo, 190p, fp 1-color, cep, DJ/4.95)	Simon/Schuster	(1970)	Cooney, Barbara	30-50	
Kingman, Lee	Best Christmas (1st {std}, sm8vo, 95p, b/w, cep, DJ/1.50)	Doubleday	(1949)	Cooney, Barbara	60-90	
Crawford, Phyllis	Blot: Little City Cat (1st {this pub}, sq8vo, 56p, dep, b/w, DJ/1.50)	Henry Holt & Co.	(1946)	Cooney, Barbara	50-80	
Kent, Louise A.	Brookline Trunk (1st, 8vo, 306p, b/w, pep, DJ/3.00)	Houghton	1955	Cooney, Barbara	60-100	
Cooney, Barbara	Captain Pottle's House (1st, 12mo, 172p, green cl, b/w, DJ/1.50)	Farrar/Rinehart	(1943)	Cooney, Barbara	50-80	
Chaucer, Geoffrey	Chanticleer & the Fox (1st, 4to, [36]p, red cl, color, dep, DJ/3.00, CM)	Crowell	(1958)	Cooney, Barbara	100-165	R
Belting, Natalia	Christmas Folk (1st {std}, ob4to, [40]p, ipcb, color, DJ/4.95)	Holt, Rinehart	(1969)	Cooney, Barbara	40-65	
Brown, Margaret W.	Christmas in the Barn (1st, ob8vo, red cl, [32]p, color, pep, DJ/1.75)	Crowell	(1952)	Cooney, Barbara	120-180	
Kay, Helen	City Springtime (1st, 4to, 48p, fp color, DJ/2.75)	Hastings House	(1957)	Cooney, Barbara	60-90	*
N/A	Cock Robin (1st, ob8vo, [30]p, color, DJ/3.25)	Scribner	(1965)	Cooney, Barbara	45-70	*
Huxley, Aldous	Crows of Pearblossom (1st, 8vo, [40]p, 1-color, pep, DJ/3.50)	Random	(1967)	Cooney, Barbara	60-90	

AUTHOR	TITLE	PUBLISHER	DATE	ARTIST	PRICE	LC
Proddow, Penelope	Dionysos & the Pirates (1st {std}, 4to, ibds, [40]p, color, DJ/4.95)	Doubleday	(1970)	Cooney, Barbara	50-80	R
Haviland, Virginia	Favorite Fairy Tales Told in Spain (1st {std}, 8vo, 87p, color, DJ/2.95)	Little/Brown	(1963)	Cooney, Barbara	50-85	R
Anderson, Neil	Freckle Face (1st, 8vo, 32p, fp 1-color, dep, DJ/2.50)	Crowell	(1957)	Cooney, Barbara	45-70	*
Marshall, Catherine	Friends with God (1st, 4to, 48p, 2-color, DJ/2.00)	Whittlesey	1956	Cooney, Barbara	30-50	
Quigg, Jane	Fun for Freddy (1st, 8vo, 106p, green cl, b/w, DJ/2.75)	NY: Oxford U.Pr.	(1953)	Cooney, Barbara	60-90	
Leonard, Nellie	Grandfather Whiskers, M.D. (1st {std}, sm8vo, 216p, b/w, DJ/2.00)	Crowell	1953	Cooney, Barbara	100-165	
Leonard, Nellie	Graymouse Family (1st, sm8vo, 209p, b/w, DJ/2.00)	Crowell	(1950)	Cooney, Barbara	50-80	R
Seidlin, Oskar	Green Wagons (1st, 8vo, 130p, b/w, DJ/2.00)	Houghton	1943	Cooney, Barbara	40-65	*
Montgomery, R.	Hill Ranch (1st {std}, 8vo, green cl, 200p, uncut, b/w, DJ/2.50)	Doubleday	(1951)	Cooney, Barbara	30-50	
Beim, Lorraine	Just Plain Maggie (1st {std}, 8vo, 185p, green cl, fp b/w, DJ/2.25)	Harcourt	(1950)	Cooney, Barbara	40-65	
Goodsell, Jane	Katie's Magic Glasses (1st, lg8vo, 43p, color, cep, DJ/3.50)	Houghton	1965	Cooney, Barbara	30-50	
Montgomery, R.	Kildee House (1st {std}, 8vo, 209p, gilt, b/w, DJ/2.50, NH)	Doubleday	(1949)	Cooney, Barbara	70-100	R
Cooney, Barbara	King of Wreck Island (1st {1st bk}, lg8vo, blue cl, 91p, fp b/w, DJ/1.50)	Farrar/Rinehart	(1941)	Cooney, Barbara	70-100	
Wise, William	Lazy Young Duke of Dundee (1st {std}, 8vo, 47p, color, DJ/3.95)	Rand/McNally	(1970)	Cooney, Barbara	30-50	
Marshall, Peter	Let's Keep Christmas (1st, 12mo, ibds, [32]p, 2-color, pep, DJ/1.50)	McGraw-Hill	1953	Cooney, Barbara	40-65	
Otto, Margaret G.	Little Brown Horse (1st, 8vo, [30]p, fp 1-color, dep, DJ/2.50)	Knopf	(1959)	Cooney, Barbara	60-90	
Brown, Margaret W.	Little Fir Tree (1st, ob8vo, [32]p, orange cl, color, dep, DJ/2.00)	Crowell	1954	Cooney, Barbara	70-120	
Cooney, Barbara	Little Juggler (1st, 8vo, 46p, color, pep, DJ/3.00)	Hastings House	(1961)	Cooney, Barbara	40-65	
Cooney, Barbara	Little Prayer (1st, ob16mo, [34]p, ibds, color, DJ/1.25)	Hastings House	(1967)	Cooney, Barbara	40-65	
Alcott, Louisa M.	Little Women (1st {std}, lg8vo, 554p, b/w, DJ/3.50)	Crowell	(1955)	Cooney, Barbara	70-100	
Buckmaster, Henrietta	Lucy and Loki (1st, sq8vo, [32]p, yellow cl, fp 2-color, DJ/2.50)	Scribner	(1958)	Cooney, Barbara	50-80	*
Krasilovsky, Phyllis	Man Who Didn't Wash his Dishes (1st {std}, sm4to, [33]p, ibds, col, DJ/1.50)	Doubleday	(1950)	Cooney, Barbara	45-70	
Lear, Edward	Owl & the Pussycat (1st {std}, 8vo, 26p, color, DJ/2.95)	Little/Brown	(1961)	Cooney, Barbara	40-65	*
Field, Eugene	Papillot, Clignot et Dodo (1st, 8vo, [25]p, 1-color, DJ/3.25)	Ariel	(1964)	Cooney, Barbara	30-50	
De La Mare, Walter	Peacock Pie (1st, lg8vo, 117p, fp b/w, cep, DJ/3.00)	Knopf	(1961)	Cooney, Barbara	30-50	
Reynolds, Barbara	Pepper (1st, 8vo, grey cl, 169p, fp b/w, DJ/2.00)	Scribner	(1952)	Cooney, Barbara	45-70	
Kingman, Lee	Peter's Long Walk (1st {std}, sm ob4to, 47p, ibds, color, DJ/2.50)	Doubleday	1953	Cooney, Barbara	65-100	R
Lansing, Elisabeth H.	Pony that Kept a Secret (1st {std}, 8vo, 117p, b/w, pep, DJ/2.00)	Crowell	(1952)	Cooney, Barbara	40-65	
Lansing, Elisabeth H.	Pony that Ran Away (1st {std}, sm8vo, 149p, red cl, b/w, dep, DJ/2.00)	Crowell	(1951)	Cooney, Barbara	60-100	R
Lansing, Elisabeth H.	Pony Worth his Salt (1st {std}, 8vo, 168p, b/w, pep, DJ/2.00)	Crowell	1953	Cooney, Barbara	45-70	
Otto, Margaret G.	Pumpkin, Ginger & Spice (1st {std}, sm8vo, 116p, yellow cl, b/w, DJ/2.00)	Holt	(1954)	Cooney, Barbara	60-90	
Kingman, Lee	Quarry Adventure (1st {std}, 8vo, 209p, b/w, DJ/2.50)	Doubleday	1951	Cooney, Barbara	50-80	
Kingman, Lee	Rocky Summer (1st, 8vo, 209p, blue cl, b/w, DJ/2.50)	Houghton	1948	Cooney, Barbara	50-80	
Molloy, Anne	Shaun and the Boat (1st, lg8vo, 43p, green bds, 3-color, pep, DJ/3.50)	Hastings House	(1965)	Cooney, Barbara	45-70	
Molloy, Anne	Shooting Star Farm (1st, 8vo, 231p, b/w, dep, DJ/2.50)	Houghton	1946	Cooney, Barbara	60-100	
Kay, Helen	Snow Birthday (1st {std}, ob4to, 46p, fp color, DJ/2.50)	Ariel	(1955)	Cooney, Barbara	60-90	*
Grimm Bros.	Snow White & Rose Red (1st AM {std}, lg8vo, 47p, color, DJ/2.75)	Delacorte Pr.	(1966)	Cooney, Barbara	45-70	
Cooney, Barbara	The Kellyhorns (1st, 8vo, red cl, 259p, b/w, DJ/2.00)	Farrar/Rinehart	(1942)	Cooney, Barbara	70-100	
Otto, Margaret G.	Three Little Dachshunds (1st {std}, lg ob8vo, [25]p, color, DJ)	Holt, Rinehart	1963	Cooney, Barbara	50-85	*
Behn, Harry	Timmy's Search (1st, 8vo, 93p, wraps, fp color)	Seabury Press	(1958)	Cooney, Barbara	50-80	*
Aldrich, Mary M.	Too Many Pets (1st {std}, 8vo, 66p, fp b/w, DJ/2.00)	Macmillan	1952	Cooney, Barbara	70-100	*
Brown, Margaret W.	Where Have You Been? (1st, ob16mo, [29]p, 1-color, dep, DJ/1.25)	Crowell	1952	Cooney, Barbara	100-165	R
Jewett, Sarah O.	White Heron (1st, 8vo, 34p, fp 3-color, DJ/3.50)	Crowell	(1963)	Cooney, Barbara	70-120	R
Mason, Miriam E.	Yours with Love, Kate (1st, 8vo, 277p, b/w, DJ/3.00)	Houghton	1952	Cooney, Barbara	40-70	
N/A	Arabian Nights (1st, 8vo, 501p, 4cp by...)	L: Routledge	1904	Cooper, Alfred W.	140-200	
Bangs, John K.	Autobiography of Methuselah (1st, sm8vo, 185p, grey cl, 12cp)	Dodge	1909	Cooper, F.G.	45-70	
Jones, Mary A.	Tell Me About Heaven (1st {A}, 4to, 70p, color, pep, DJ/2.50)	Rand/McNally	(1956)	Cooper, Marjorie	20-35	
Nesbit, Edith	Daphne of Fitzroy Street (1st AM, 12mo, 417p, col frn by..)	Doubleday/Page	1909	Cootes, F. Graham	80-145	
Sabin, Edwin L.	Beaufort Chums (1st, sm8vo, 281p, 4pl)	Crowell	1905	Copeland, Charles	30-55	
Sewell, Anna	Black Beauty (1st, 12mo, 319p, b/w)	Rand/McNally	(1904)	Copeland, Charles	45-70	
Long, William J.	Brier-Patch Philosophy (1st, 12mo, 296p, teg, col frn, 4pl)	Ginn & Co.	1906	Copeland, Charles	35-60	
Hawkes, Clarence	Field & Forest Friends (1st, 12mo, 207p, pep, 4pl)	F.G. Browne	1913	Copeland, Charles	30-50	
Dudley, Albertus T.	Great Year (1st, sm8vo, 302p, 6pl)	Lothrop, Lee	(1907)	Copeland, Charles	40-65	
Long, William J.	How Animals Talk (1st, lg8vo, green/gilt, teg, 301p, 8cp)	Harper	(1919)	Copeland, Charles	40-65	
Hurd, Marian K.	Miss Billy: Neighborhood Story (1st, sm8vo, gilt, 349p, 6pl)	Lothrop Pub.	1905	Copeland, Charles	35-60	*
Long, William J.	Northern Trails (1st, 8vo, teg, 390p, gilt, col frn, b/w)	Ginn & Co.	1905	Copeland, Charles	30-50	
Collodi, Carlo	Pinocchio (1st, 12mo, 212p, gilt, 12cp, pep)	Ginn & Co.	(1904)	Copeland, Charles	80-140	
Collodi, Carlo	Pinocchio in Africa (1st AM, 12mo, green cl, 152p, b/w)	Ginn & Co.	(1911)	Copeland, Charles	100-170	
Fox, Frances M.	What Gladys Saw (1st, 12mo, green cl, 318p, 5pl)	W.A. Wilde	(1902)	Copeland, Charles	30-50	
Spyri, Johanna	What Sami Sings with the Birds (1st, 8vo, 90p, blue cl, 3cp, pep)	Crowell	(1917)	Copeland, Charles	25-40	
Rich, Edwin G.	Why-So Stories (1st, sm8vo, gilt, 207p, col frn, b/w)	Small/Maynard	(1918)	Copeland, Charles	30-50	*
Baum, L. Frank	New Wizard of Oz (1st, lg8vo, 209p, gilt, 8 fp color, DJ/1.75)	Bobbs-Merrill	(1944)	Copelman, Evelyn	80-130	
Alden, Raymond M.	Once there Was a King (1st, lg8vo, 176p, 9cp, DJ/2.00)	Bobbs-Merrill	1946	Copelman, Evelyn	30-50	*
Kingsley, Charles	Westward Ho! (1st, 12mo, 589p, 15pl)	L: J. Long	1904	Copping, Harold	55-80	*
Corbet, K.& S.	Animal Land Where there are No People (1st AM, ob8vo, 48p, b/w)	Dutton	1897	Corbet, Katherine	120-170	
Corbett, Bertha	Baby Days (1st, 4to, grey cloth, color)	Rand/McNally	(1910)	Corbett, Bertha L.	120-200	
Grover, Eulalie O.	Overall Boys (1st, sq8vo, 123p, pict cl, color pep)	Rand/McNally	(1905)	Corbett, Bertha L.	100-165	
Corbett, Bertha	Sun-Bonnet Babies (1st, sq8vo, green bds, b/w)	(Minneapolis)	1900	Corbett, Bertha L.	180-220	
Grover, Eulalie O.	Sunbonnet Babies' Book (1st [this pub], sq8vo, 106p, color, pep)	Rand/McNally	(1902)	Corbett, Bertha L.	120-200	
Hogate, Etta C.	Sunbonnets & Overalls... (1st, 8vo, 83p, color, pep)	Rand/McNally	(1914)	Corbett, Bertha L.	80-125	
Procter, E.H.	Rabbit's Day in Town (1st, 4to, ibds, [48]p, 20 fp color)	L: Blackie	[1908]	Corbould, Walton	140-220	*
Schneider, Herman	Follow the Sunset (1st {std}, 4to, ibds, 43p, color, cep, DJ/2.75)	Doubleday	(1952)	Corcos, Lucille	70-125	R
Martin, Patricia	Grandma's Gun (1st, 8vo, [47]p, color, DJ/3.50)	Golden Gate	(1968)	Corey, Robert	25-40	
Kyne, Peter B.	Kindred of the Dust (1st, sm8vo, 376p, 4pl)	Cosmopolitan	1920	Cornwell, Dean	30-50	
Kyne, Peter B.	Valley of the Giants (1st, sm8vo, 388p, col frn, b/w)	Doubleday	1918	Cornwell, Dean	30-50	*
Nash, Ogden	Parents Keep Out (1st {std}, 8vo, 187p, b/w, DJ/2.75)	Little/Brown	1951	Corrigan, Barbara	50-85	R*
Burgess, Thornton	Boy Scouts of Woodcraft Camp (1st, sm8vo, p-o, 345p, 5pl)	Penn	1912	Corson, C.S.	120-170	*
Lummis, Charles F.	Enchanted Burro (1st, sm8vo, 277p, teg, 15pl)	Way & Williams	1897	Corwin, C.A.	60-100	

AUTHOR	TITLE	PUBLISHER	DATE	ARTIST	PRICE	LC
Hodges, Elizabeth	Serendipity Tales (1st {std}, lg8vo, 179p, fp b/w, DJ/3.95)	Atheneum	1966	Corwin, June	25-40	*
Carroll, Lewis	Alice in Wonderland (1st, 12mo, brown cl, 192p, 12pl)	Rand/McNally	(1902)	Cory, Fanny	50-90	
Brown, Abbie F.	Book of Saints & Friendly Beasts (1st, 12mo, tan cl, 225p, 8pl)	Houghton	1900	Cory, Fanny	75-100	
Butler, Ellis P.	Confessions of a Daddy (1st, 8vo, red cl, 107p, 9pl)	Century	1907	Cory, Fanny	40-65	
Baum, L. Frank	Enchanted Island of Yew (1st [1], lg8vo, 242p, tan cl, 8cp, pep)	Bobbs-Merrill	(1903)	Cory, Fanny	600-850	
Spofford, Harriet	Fairy Changeling (1st, 8vo, 75p, 20pl)	Badger	1911	Cory, Fanny	80-140	
Mother Goose	Fanny Cory Mother Goose (1st, 4to, gilt, p-o, 74p, 12cp, pep)	Bobbs-Merrill	(1913)	Cory, Fanny	170-260	R
Bowman, Rowland	Freckles & Tan (1st, 16mo, 68p, gilt, b/w)	Rand/McNally	1904	Cory, Fanny	35-50	
Cooke, Grace M.	Huldah (1st, sm8vo, 316p, 8pl by…)	Bobbs-Merrill	(1904)	Cory, Fanny	35-60	
Hill, William	Jackie Boy in Rainbowland (1st, 8vo, p-o, 84p, color)	Rand/McNally	(1911)	Cory, Fanny	90-145	
Reid, Sydney	Josey & the Chipmunk (1st, sm8vo, 301p, 17pl)	Century	1900	Cory, Fanny	40-65	
Loomis, Charles B.	Just Rhymes (1st, sm8vo, ibds, 70p, b/w)	R.H. Russell	1899	Cory, Fanny	75-100	
Cory, Fanny	Little Me (1st {std}, sm8vo, ipcb, [56]p, fp b/w)	Dutton	(1936)	Cory, Fanny	35-60	*
Musson, Bennet	Maisie & her Dog Snip in Fairyland (1st, 8vo, 165p, 8cp)	Harper	1903	Cory, Fanny	70-120	
Baum, L. Frank	Master Key (1st [1], 8vo, 245p, olive/gilt, p-o, 12cp)	Bowen-Merrill	(1901)	Cory, Fanny	350-500	
Daskam, Josephine	Memoirs of a Baby (1st, sm8vo, 272p, blue cl, b/w)	Harper	1904	Cory, Fanny	30-50	
Tappan, Eva M.	Old Ballads in Prose (1st, 12mo, 228p, 4 b/w pl)	Houghton	1901	Cory, Fanny	35-50	
Cory, Fanny	Our Baby Book (4to, pink cl, [89]p, p-o, color)	Bobbs-Merrill	(1907)	Cory, Fanny	90-120	
Wells, Carolyn	Pete & Polly Stories (1st, lg8vo, green cl, 229p, 6pl)	McClurg	1902	Cory, Fanny	70-100	
Johnson, Burges	Pleasant Tragedies of Childhood (1st, lg8vo, gilt, 119p, 30pl, pep)	Harper	1905	Cory, Fanny	100-160	
Brown, Abbie F.	Pocket Full of Posies (1st, 8vo, 169p, tan cl, 5pl)	Houghton	1902	Cory, Fanny	35-60	
Baker, Cornelia	Queen's Page (1st, sm8vo, 319p, 12pl)	Bobbs-Merrill	(1905)	Cory, Fanny	50-85	
Aspinwall, Alicia	Short Poems for Short People (1st {std}, 8vo, pink/gilt, 129p, b/w, cep)	Dutton	(1929)	Cory, Fanny	30-45	*
Cory, Fanny	Sonny Sayings (1st, ob4to, ibds, 112p, b/w)	Dutton	(1929)	Cory, Fanny	60-90	
Stuart, Ruth M.	Sonny, A Christmas Guest (1st, sm8vo, 135p, teg, gilt, 13pl)	Century	1904	Cory, Fanny	40-65	
Gates, Josephine S.	Sunshine Annie (1st, 8vo, 148p, red cl, p-o, 15cp, pep)	Bobbs-Merrill	(1910)	Cory, Fanny	80-125	
Carroll, Lewis	Through the Looking Glass (1st, 12mo, 218p, tan cl, b/w)	Rand/McNally	(1917)	Cory, Fanny	40-65	
Taylor, Bert L.	Well in the Wood (1st, 8vo, 191p, blue/gilt, 8pl)	Bobbs-Merrill	(1904)	Cory, Fanny	50-80	
Bigham, Madge A.	Wishing Fairies (1st, 8vo, blue cl, 37p, 8cp)	Dodd	1915	Cory, Fanny	70-125	
Loomis, Charles B.	Yankee Enchantments (1st, 8vo, 328p, gilt, 20 fp b/w, pep)	McClure	1900	Cory, Fanny	70-100	
Flower, Esther	Nurse Nora's Up-to-Date Fairy Tales (1st, 12mo, 163p, 9pl)	J. Pott	1903	Cory/Graef	60-90	
Farjeon, B.L.	Lucy & their Majesties (1st, sm8vo, 332p, tan cl, 20pl)	Century	1904	Cory/Varian	35-60	
Latham, Jean L.	Carry On, Mr. Bowditch (1st, 8vo, green cl, 251p, fp b/w, DJ/2.75, NM)	Houghton	1955	Cosgrave, John O.	70-120	
Judson, Clara I.	Donald McKay: Designer of Clipper Ships (1st, 8vo, 134p, DJ/1.75)	Scribner	1943	Cosgrave, John O.	30-45	
Meader, Stephen W.	Guns for the Saratoga (1st {std}, 8vo, 207p, b/w, DJ/2.75)	Harcourt	(1955)	Cosgrave, John O.	100-170	
Havighurst, Walter	Long Ships Passing (1st, 8vo, 291p, b/w, DJ/3.00)	Macmillan	1942	Cosgrave, John O.	30-50	
Molloy, Anne	Lucy's Christmas (1st, lg8vo, 46p, red cl, color, DJ/2.00)	Houghton	1950	Cosgrave, John O.	25-45	
Gilman, Eliz. L.	Picnic Adventures (1st, 8vo, green cl, 192p, 12 dp 1-color, DJ/2.00)	Farrar/Rinehart	(1940)	Cosgrave, John O.	80-120	
Sinclair, Upton	The Gnomobile (1st, 8vo, tan cl, 181p, b/w, DJ/1.50)	Farrar/Rinehart	(1936)	Cosgrave, John O.	140-200	
Meader, Stephen W.	Voyage of the Javelin (1st {std}, 8vo, 189p, b/w, DJ/2.95)	Harcourt	(1959)	Cosgrave, John O.	100-165	
Saint-Exupery, A.	Wind, Sand & Stars (1st AM, 8vo, 306p, pep, 1-color designs, DJ/2.75)	Reynal/Hitchcock	(1939)	Cosgrave, John O.	150-250	*
Cosgrove, Margaret	Bone for Bone (1st, lg8vo, 128p, color, DJ/3.95)	Dodd	(1968)	Cosgrove, Margaret	30-45	*
Malkus, Alida S.	Meadows in the Sea (1st {std}, 8vo, 71p, dp color, DJ/2.75)	World	(1960)	Cosgrove, Mildred	40-65	
Montgomery, Lucy M.	Jane of Lantern Hill (1st, sm8vo, 297p, gilt, col frn, DJ/2.00)	Stokes	1937	Costello, Louise	100-170	
Boesel, Ann S.	Sing & Sing Again (1st, 4to, 72p, ibds, color, DJ/2.50)	Oxford U. Pr.	(1938)	Costello, Louise	40-65	
Hawkins, Quail	Don't Run, Apple! (1st, 8vo, ipcb, [36]p, b/w, pep)	Holiday House	(1944)	Cote, Phyllis	30-50	
Foster, Elizabeth	Gigi in America (1st, 8vo, 123p, b/w, pep, DJ/2.00)	Houghton	1946	Cote, Phyllis	25-40	
Holberg, Ruth	Tibby's Venture (1st {std}, 8vo, 122p, b/w, pep, DJ/1.75)	Doubleday/Doran	(1943)	Cote, Phyllis	25-40	
Holberg, Ruth	Wonderful Voyage (1st {std}, 8vo, 208p, pep, b/w, DJ/2.00)	Doubleday/Doran	(1945)	Cote, Phyllis	30-45	
Riley, James W.	Riley Baby Book (1st, 8vo, [35]p, red/gilt, t-i col frn)	Bobbs-Merrill	(1913)	Cotton, William	120-180	R
Coatsworth, Eliz.	Maine Ways (1st {std}, 8vo, 213p, b/w, DJ/2.75)	Macmillan	1947	Coughlin, Mildred	20-30	
Morris, Phyllis	Adventures of Willy & Nilly (1st, sm8vo, tan cl, 8cp, 7pl)	L: John Lane	1921	Cowham, Hilda	200-300	
Cowham, Hilda	Blacklegs and Others (1st, 4to, 76p, teg, gilt, color)	L: Kegan Paul	1911	Cowham, Hilda	200-300	
Meade, L.T.	Bunch of Cousins (1st, 8vo, 220p, 4pl, cep)	L: Chambers	1911	Cowham, Hilda	50-80	*
Vredenburg, Edric	Curly Heads & Long Legs (1st, 4to, 140p, ibds, color)	L: R. Tuck	[1914]	Cowham, Hilda	200-300	
Cowham, Hilda	Curly Heads and Long Legs (8vo, 140p, ipcb, p-o, 12cp)	L: R. Tuck	[1910]	Cowham, Hilda	250-350	
Cowham, Hilda	Daddy Long Legs (4to, [30]p, ibds, 6cp, pep)	L: Gale/Polden	[1915]	Cowham, Hilda	250-400	
Kent, Kathleen	Daddy Long-Legs (1st, 4to, [30]p, ibds, 6cp, pep)	L: Gale/Polden	[1917]	Cowham, Hilda	90-140	
Cowham, Hilda	Fiddlesticks (1st AM, 4to, unpag, ipcb, color)	NY: Young & Co.	1901	Cowham, Hilda	250-350	
Cowham, Hilda	Good Old Nursery Rhymes (8vo, ibds, 10 fp color)	L: Gale/Polden	[1916]	Cowham, Hilda	220-300	
Lea, John	Magic Knocker (1st, sm4to, ibds, color)	Stokes	[1914]	Cowham, Hilda	100-150	
Quiller-Couch, Mabel	Pair of Red Polls (1st, 8vo, 190p, 6pl)	L: Jack	(1905)	Cowham, Hilda	50-80	*
N/A	Peter Pickle and his Dog Fido (1st, ob4to, ibds, [20]p, color)	L: D. Nutt	(1906)	Cowham, Hilda	150-225	
Jacberns, Raymond	Poor Uncle Harry (1st, 8vo, 275p, red cl, 6cp)	L: Chambers	1910	Cowham, Hilda	55-80	*
Cowham, Hilda	Somebody's Baby (4to, ibds, 16 fp color)	L: R. Tuck	[1915]	Cowham, Hilda	160-250	
Grierson, Eliz. W.	Vivian's Lesson (1st, 12mo, 292p, gilt, 10pl)	L: Chambers	1907	Cowham, Hilda	40-65	
Lea, John	Willie Wimple's Adventures (1st, 4to, ibds, 16cp)	L: T.F. Unwin	(1908)	Cowham, Hilda	225-350	
Cowham, Hilda	Winnie Wimple & Ragged Robin (ibds, 9cp)	L: T.F. Unwin	[1910]	Cowham, Hilda	250-350	
Vavra, Robert	Tiger Flower (1st AM {std}, 4to, ibds, [45]p, color, DJ/5.95)	Reynal	(1969)	Cowles, Fleur	30-50	
Macaulay, Thomas B.	Lays of Ancient Rome (1st AM, black/gilt, teg, 180p, 13 ticp)	Longmans	1929	Cox, Elijah A.	60-90	
Cox, Palmer	Another Brownie Book (1st, 4to, 144p, ibds, b/w)	Century	(1890)	Cox, Palmer	200-300	
Veale, E.	Bonny Birds (8vo, wraps, 16p, b/w)	Hubbard	(1896)	Cox, Palmer	70-100	
Cox, Palmer	Brownie Clown of Brownie Town (ob8vo, 103p, ibds, color)	Century	[1908]	Cox, Palmer	300-450	
Cox, Palmer	Brownie Year Book (lg4to, [26]p, ibds, 12cp)	McLoughlin	1895	Cox, Palmer	300-450	
Cox, Palmer	Brownies & Prince Florimel (1st, lg8vo, tan cl, 246p, p-o)	Century	1918	Cox, Palmer	160-225	
Cox, Palmer	Brownies Abroad (1st, 4to, 144p, ibds, b/w)	Century	(1899)	Cox, Palmer	250-400	
Cox, Palmer	Brownies Around the World (1st, 4to, ibds, 144p, b/w)	Century	(1894)	Cox, Palmer	250-400	
Cox, Palmer	Brownies at Home (1st, 4to, ibds, 144p)	Century	(1893)	Cox, Palmer	250-400	

AUTHOR	TITLE	PUBLISHER	DATE	ARTIST	PRICE	LC
Cox, Palmer	Brownies in Fairyland (1st, sm8vo, 118p, cloth, b/w)	Century	(1925)	Cox, Palmer	250-400	
Cox, Palmer	Brownies in the Philippines (1st, 4to, ibds, 144p)	Century	(1904)	Cox, Palmer	250-400	R
Cox, Palmer	Brownies Through the Union (1st, 4to, ibds, 144p)	Century	(1895)	Cox, Palmer	250-400	R
Cox, Palmer	Brownies: Their Book (1st, 4to, green ipcb, 144p, b/w, cep, PPP)	Century	(1887)	Cox, Palmer	300-500	R
Veale, E.	Busy Brownies (8vo, [16]p, wraps, b/w)	Hubbard	(1896)	Cox, Palmer	100-160	
Veale, E.	Captivating Stories/Animals (1st, 4to, yellow cl, [96]p, 2-color)	Juvenile Pub.	(1908)	Cox, Palmer	180-280	
Veale, E.	Christmas Pudding (sm8vo, blue cl, p-o, 320p, b/w)	Caldwell	(1900)	Cox, Palmer	65-100	
Cox, Palmer	Comic Yarns (1st, 8vo, 517p, blue/gilt, b/w, dep)	Hubbard	1889	Cox, Palmer	120-180	
Veale, E.	First Trousers (8vo, wraps, 32p, b/w)	Hubbard	1897	Cox, Palmer	70-120	
Veale, E.	Fox's Story (8vo, wraps, 32p, b/w)	Hubbard	1897	Cox, Palmer	70-120	
Cox, Palmer	Frontier Humor (1st, 24mo, 343p, b/w)	Hubbard	(1895)	Cox, Palmer	80-130	R
Veale, E.	Funny Foxes (8vo, 32p, wraps, unpag, b/w)	Hubbard	(1896)	Cox, Palmer	140-200	
Veale, E.	Jolly Chinee (8vo, wraps, 32p, b/w)	Hubbard	1897	Cox, Palmer	70-120	
Veale, E.	Merry Mice (8vo, wraps, 32p, b/w)	Hubbard	1896	Cox, Palmer	70-120	
Cox, Palmer	Palmer Cox Brownie Primer (1st, 12mo, 108p, yellow bds)	Century	1906	Cox, Palmer	140-240	
Cox, Palmer	Palmer Cox's Fairy Book (sm4to, green cloth, 6 fp color)	Hurst	(1902)	Cox, Palmer	200-300	
Cox, Palmer	Queer People with Paws & Claws (1st, lg8vo, ibds, [109]p, b/w)	Hubbard	(1888)	Cox, Palmer	160-220	
Cox, Palmer	Queerie Queers with Hands, Wings & Claws (lg8vo, ibds, b/w)	Larkin	(1887)	Cox, Palmer	600-900	
Yeats, Wm. Butler	Plays for an Irish Theatre (1st, 8vo, 224p, brown bds, uncut, 4cp)	L: A.H. Bullen	1911	Craig, Edward G.	120-200	
Craig, Edward G.	Woodcuts & Some Words (1st, 4to, 122p, blue cl, 59pl)	L: Dent	1924	Craig, Edward G.	100-180	
Vorse, Mary Heaton	Ninth Man (1st, sm8vo, 80p, 2cp, 2pl)	Harper	1920	Craig, Frank	40-65	*
Kipling, Rudyard	Rewards & Fairies (1st, 8vo, red/gilt, tcg, 338p, 4pl)	L: Macmillan	1910	Craig, Frank	100-160	
Gimmage, Peter	Picture Book of Ships (1st, 4to, 64p, fp color, pep)	Macmillan	1930	Craig, Helen	45-80	*
Greene, Graham	Little Horse Bus (1st, sq8vo, 35p, gilt, color, DJ)	L: Parrish	1952	Craigie, Dorothy	300-450	
Greene, Graham	Little Steamroller (1st, sq8vo, 33p, color, DJ)	L: Parrish	1953	Craigie, Dorothy	300-450	
Greene, Graham	Little Steamroller (1st AM, 8vo, 33p, blue cl, color, DJ/2.00)	Lothrop, Lee	1955	Craigie, Dorothy	200-300	
Greene, Graham	Little Train (1st, ob8vo, 42p, color, DJ)	L: Eyre/Spotts.	1946	Craigie, Dorothy	300-450	
Greene, Grahame	Little Train (1st AM, 8vo, 36p, color, DJ/2.00)	Lothrop, Lee	1958	Craigie, Dorothy	200-300	
Montgomery, R.	Yellow Eyes (1st, 8vo, 243p, b/w, pep, DJ/2.00)	Caxton Press	1937	Cram, L.D.	50-80	*
Cramer, Rie	Diamond Princess (1st, ob8vo, [56]p, 4 fp color)	L: Warne	(1931)	Cramer, Rie	200-300	
Andersen, Hans C.	Fairy Tales (1st, lg8vo, 349p, grey/gilt, 17 ticp)	L: H. Milford	(1921)	Cramer, Rie	250-350	
Grimm Bros.	Fairy Tales (1st, 4to, p-o, 367p, 23cp)	Penn	1922	Cramer, Rie	120-180	
Osbourne, M. (ed.)	Favorite Fairy Tales (1st, lg8vo, 365p, p-o, 20cp by...)	Penn	(1930)	Cramer, Rie	100-175	
Douglas, Barbara	Favorite French Fairy Tales (1st AM, 8vo, 255p, 7cp)	Dodd	(1921)	Cramer, Rie	90-120	
Ransom, Will	Little Dutchy... (1st, 4to, 79p, ibds, 12 ticp)	L: Harrap	(1925)	Cramer, Rie	130-180	
Joan, Natalie	Little Mothers (1st, ob8vo, ibds, p-o, 12 fp color)	L: H. Milford	[1923]	Cramer, Rie	120-180	
N/A	Old Songs in French & English (1st, 4to, p-o, 63p, 24cp)	Penn	1923	Cramer, Rie	120-180	
N/A	Oriental Fairy Tales (1st, 8vo, p-o, 627p, gilt, 16 ticp)	Duffield	1923	Cramer, Rie	120-200	
DeVries, P.J.C.	Princess Who Grew (1st, 8vo, 112p, p-o, col frn, 5pl)	Stokes	1927	Cramer, Rie	80-130	
Andersen, Hans C.	Snow Queen (sq8vo, 32p, ibds, 15 fp color)	L: Blackie	[1910]	Cramer, Rie	70-100	
Marion, Francis	Truant Tricycle (1st, 4to, ipcb, [25]p, color, pep, DJ/1.00)	Hollow Tree Hse.	1948	Crandall, C. Leslie	60-90	
DeTrevino, Elizabeth	Carpet of Flowers (1st, 8vo, 88p, b/w, pep, DJ/2.50)	Crowell	(1955)	Crane, Alan H.	25-45	
Crane, Donn	Flippy and Skippy (1st, sq8vo, [48]p, color, pep, DJ/1.50)	Winston	(1940)	Crane, Donn	30-50	*
Molesworth, Mrs.	Adventures of Herr Baby (1st, lg8vo, red/gilt, 171p, 13pl, dep)	L: Macmillan	1881	Crane, Walter	100-160	
Crane, Walter	Aladdin's Picture Book (4to, unpag, ipcb, 24 color)	L: Routledge	[1880]	Crane, Walter	400-600	
Crane, Walter	An Artist's Reminiscences (1st, 8vo, 520p, brown cl, teg)	Macmillan	1907	Crane, Walter	70-100	
Konody, Paul G.	Art of Walter Crane (1st, folio, teg, 147p, 16cp)	L: G. Bell	1902	Crane, Walter	300-500	
Crane, Walter	Baby's Bouquet (1st, ob8vo, ipcb, 56p, 11cp)	L: Routledge	[1878]	Crane, Walter	225-350	
Aesopus	Baby's Own Aesop (1st, sq12mo, ipcb, 56p, color, pep)	L: Routledge	1887	Crane, Walter	250-350	
Crane, Walter	Bases of Design (1st, lg8vo, teg, blue/gilt, 365p, b/w, pep)	L: G. Bell	1898	Crane, Walter	150-220	
N/A	Beauty & the Beast Picture Book (4to, yellow cl, 24cp)	Dodd	[1915]	Crane, Walter	120-180	*
Beeching (ed.)	Book of Christmas Verse (1st, sm8vo, 174p, teg, gilt, designs by..)	L: Methuen	1895	Crane, Walter	120-180	
Reid, K.E.J.	Book of Wedding Days (1st, 4to, red/silver, t.e. silver, [108]p)	L: Longmans	1889	Crane, Walter	280-350	
Harrison, Mrs. Burton	Bric-a-Brac Stories (1st, 12mo, 299p, 24 illus, pep)	Scribner	1885	Crane, Walter	125-200	
Molesworth, Mrs.	Children of the Castle (1st, 12mo, 196p, gilt, cep, b/w & cvr by...)	L: Macmillan	1890	Crane, Walter	80-120	
Gould, Frederick J.	Children's Plutarch (1st, 8vo, 171p, 3pl)	Harper	1910	Crane, Walter	120-200	
Molesworth, Mrs.	Christmas Child (1st, 12mo, 223p, gilt, 7pl, cep)	L: Macmillan	1880	Crane, Walter	120-200	
Molesworth, Mrs.	Christmas Posy (1st, 12mo, 215p, gilt, cep, b/w, cvr by...)	Macmillan	1888	Crane, Walter	80-120	
Molesworth, Mrs.	Christmas-Tree Land (1st, 12mo, 223p, red/gilt, 8pl)	L: Macmillan	1884	Crane, Walter	120-170	
N/A	Cinderella's Picture Book (1st, 4to, 8cp)	J. Lane	(1897)	Crane, Walter	140-200	
Crane, Walter	Columbia's Courtship (1st, 4to, [12]p, blue/gilt, 12cp)	Prang Co.	[1893]	Crane, Walter	300-500	
Molesworth, Mrs.	Cuckoo Clock (12mo, 242p, blue cl, 8pl)	L: Macmillan	1905	Crane, Walter	40-70	
Cervantes	Don Quixote (1st AM, lg8vo, 246p, 11cp)	J. Lane	1900	Crane, Walter	120-185	
Cervantes	Don Quixote (1st, lg8vo, 245p, uncut, 11cp)	L: Blackie	1900	Crane, Walter	200-270	
N/A	Fairy Ship (lg sq4to, wraps, 12p)	J. Lane	(1890)	Crane, Walter	100-160	
Grimm Bros.	Fairy Tales (1st, 4to, ibds)	Worthington	(1888)	Crane, Walter	160-240	
D'Aulnoy	Fairy Tales (1st, 8vo, 535p, teg, cvr by...)	L: Lawrence	1892	Crane, Walter	150-225	
Crane, Walter	Flora's Feast (1st, lg8vo, ibds, 40cp, dep)	L: Cassell	1889	Crane, Walter	225-325	
Crane, Walter	Floral Fantasy (1st, 4to, 48p, 44cp, pep)	L: Harper	1899	Crane, Walter	400-600	
Crane, Walter	Flower Wedding (1st, lg8vo, ipcb, 40cp, pep)	L: Cassell	1905	Crane, Walter	250-400	
Crane, Walter	Flowers from Shakespeare's Garden (1st, 4to, ibds, uncut, 40cp, pep)	L: Cassell	1906	Crane, Walter	250-400	
Molesworth, Mrs.	Four Winds Farm (1st, 8vo, blue cl, 180p, 6pl)	L: Macmillan	1886	Crane, Walter	100-170	
Crane, Walter	Goody Two Shoes... ([new ed.], 4to, red cl, 18cp, pep)	J. Lane	(1901)	Crane, Walter	200-300	
Wilde, Oscar	Happy Prince (1st AM, 8vo, grey cl, 116p, 3pl)	Roberts Bros.	1888	Crane, Walter	350-500	
Ellis, Frederick S.	History of Reynard the Fox (1st, sm8vo, 289p, uncut, designs by...)	L: D. Nutt	1897	Crane, Walter	170-250	
Grimm Bros.	Household Stories (1st, 12mo, 269p, AEG, 11pl, pep)	L: Macmillan	1882	Crane, Walter	250-350	
Crane, Walter	Ideals in Art (1st, 8vo, teg, 287p, gilt, b/w, cvr by...)	L: G. Bell	1905	Crane, Walter	125-200	
Crane, Walter	India Impressions (1st, lg8vo, green/gilt, 325p, 16pl)	Macnillan	1907	Crane, Walter	125-200	

AUTHOR	TITLE	PUBLISHER	DATE	ARTIST	PRICE	LC
Gilbert, Henry	King Arthur's Knights (1st, 8vo, gilt, teg, 367p, 16cp)	L: Jack	1911	Crane, Walter	250-350	R
Gilbert, Henry	King Arthur's Knights (1st AM, lg8vo, 367p, gilt, teg, 16cp, dep)	Stokes	1911	Crane, Walter	200-300	
Crane, Walter	Legends for Lionel (1st, lg8vo, ibds, 40p, color, pep)	L: Cassell	1887	Crane, Walter	200-300	
Crane, Walter	Line & Form (1st, 8vo, 282p, teg, blue/gilt, pep)	L: G. Bell	1900	Crane, Walter	180-250	
Molesworth, Mrs.	Little Miss Peggy (1st, 12mo, red cl, 195p, 12pl)	L: Macmillan	1887	Crane, Walter	85-130	
Crane, Walter	Masque of Days (1st, 4to, [40]p, ipcb, color, pep)	L: Cassell	1901	Crane, Walter	250-325	
DeMorgan, Mary	Necklace of Princess Fiorimonde (1st, 12mo, gilt, 184p, AEG, dep)	L: Macmillan	1880	Crane, Walter	200-280	
Deland, Margaret	Old Garden (1st, 8vo, 114p, color, pep, cvr by...)	L: McIlvaine	1893	Crane, Walter	200-300	
Deland, Margaret	Old Garden (1st AM, 8vo, 114p, uncut, color, dep)	Houghton	1894	Crane, Walter	150-250	
Marzials, Theo	Pan Pipes (1st, lg ob4to, tan ibds, 51p, dep, color)	L: Routledge	1883	Crane, Walter	200-300	
Crane, Walter	Pothooks & Perseverance (1st, sq8vo, ibds, [24]p, color, pep)	L: Marcus Ward	1886	Crane, Walter	250-350	
Crane, Walter	Queen Summer (1st, folio, ibds, teg, 40p, color, pep)	L: Cassell	1891	Crane, Walter	280-350	
Molesworth, Mrs.	Rectory Children (1st, 8vo, gilt, 212p, 7pl)	L: Macmillan	1889	Crane, Walter	70-100	
Gilbert, Henry	Robin Hood (1st AM, 8vo, teg, gilt, 16cp, pep)	Stokes	(1912)	Crane, Walter	120-185	
Crane, Walter	Romance of the Three R's (1st, sq4to, ibds, [80]p, color, pep)	L: Marcus Ward	1886	Crane, Walter	300-450	
Kelly, Arthur	Rosebud and Other Tales (1st, sm4to, 78p, 20 ticp)	L: T.F. Unwin	1909	Crane, Walter	200-300	
Molesworth, Mrs.	Rosy (1st, sm8vo, red/gilt, 204p, 8pl)	L: Macmillan	1882	Crane, Walter	90-120	
Calmour, Alfred C.	Rumbo Rhymes (1st, lg8vo, green ibds, 99p, 23cp, pep)	L: Harper	1911	Crane, Walter	250-400	
Spenser, Edmund	Shepheard's Calendar (1st, 8vo, ibds, gilt, 118p, 12pl, pep)	L: Harper	1898	Crane, Walter	400-600	
Crane, Walter	Sirens Three (1st, 4to, 25p, grey bds, pep)	L: Macmillan	1886	Crane, Walter	300-450	
Crane, Walter	Slateandpencilvania (1st, sq8vo, ibds, 24p, color)	L: Marcus Ward	1885	Crane, Walter	200-300	
Crane, Walter	Sleeping Beauty and Blue Beard (1st, 24mo, [24]p, color, pep)	L: John Lane	1914	Crane, Walter	150-200	R
Molesworth, Mrs.	Studies & Stories (1st, 8vo, 256p, gilt, uncut, pep, frn by...)	L: A.D. Innes	1893	Crane, Walter	150-200	
Rhead, George W.	Treatment of Drapery in Art (1st, 8vo, 119p, 32pl, cvr by...)	L: G. Bell	1904	Crane, Walter	120-170	
Crane, Walter	Triplets (1st, lg4to, ibds, color, 1/500 signed)	L: Routledge	1899	Crane, Walter	450-600	
Molesworth, Mrs.	Two Little Waifs (1st, 8vo, gilt, 216p, 7pl)	L: Macmillan	(1883)	Crane, Walter	120-180	
Molesworth, Mrs.	US: An Old Fashioned Story (1st, 8vo, red/gilt, 240p, 7pl)	L: Macmillan	1885	Crane, Walter	80-120	
Crane, Walter	Walter Crane's Picture Book (4to, ibds, [145]p, color)	Cupples/Leon	(1903)	Crane, Walter	120-200	
Various	Wayfarer's Love (1st, 8vo, 78p, green/gilt, uncut, cvr by...)	L: Constable	1904	Crane, Walter	70-100	
Crane, Walter	William Morris to Whistler (1st, 12mo, 277p, blue cl)	L: G. Bell	1911	Crane, Walter	100-175	
Hawthorne, Nathaniel	Wonder Book (1st, lg8vo, 210p, cloth, 19cp)	L: McIlvaine	1892	Crane, Walter	250-350	
Hawthorne, Nathaniel	Wonder Book (1st AM, lg8vo, 210p, 19cp)	Houghton	1893	Crane, Walter	200-300	
Hawthorne, Nathaniel	Wonder Book & Tanglewood Tales (1st, 8vo, gilt, teg, 421p)	Houghton	1898	Crane/Edwards	220-300	
Sawyer, Ruth	Silver Sixpence (1st, sm8vo, blue cl, 331p, 4pl)	Harper	1921	Crank, James H.	20-30	*
Mencken, H.L.	Christmas Story (1st {std}, sq12mo, [31]p, p-o, pep, color, DJ/1.00)	Knopf	1946	Crawford, Bill	60-90	
Stratton-Porter, Gene	Freckles (1st, 8vo, teg, 433p, uncut, 6pl, PPPa)	Doubleday/Page	1904	Crawford, E. Stetson	450-700	
Weston, Jessie L.	Sir Gawain & the Green Knight (1st, 16mo, 96p, beige/gilt, b/w)	New Amsterdam	1899	Crawford, M.M.	60-100	
Butler, Charles	Pigs is Pigs (1st [this publ.], 12mo, 37p, 5pl)	McClure	1906	Crawford, Will	30-50	
Parker, Arthur C.	Skunny Wundy (1st, lg8vo, p-o, 262p, 7 ticp, pep)	Doran	(1926)	Crawford, Will	70-130	
Credle, Ellis	Across the Cotton Patch (1st, ob4to, green cl, [59]p, b/w, DJ/1.50)	Nelson	1935	Credle, Ellis	60-100	
Credle, Ellis	Adventures of Tittletom (1st {std}, 8vo, 79p, red cl, b/w, DJ/1.75)	NY: Oxford U.Pr.	1949	Credle, Ellis	30-50	*
Credle, Ellis	Big Doin's on Razorback Ridge (1st, 8vo, orange cl, 125p, b/w, DJ/2.75)	Nelson	(1956)	Credle, Ellis	30-50	
Credle, Ellis	Big Fraid, Little Fraid (1st, 4to, [48]p, 1-color, DJ/2.50)	Nelson	(1964)	Credle, Ellis	35-50	
Benet, Laura	Caleb's Luck (1st, lg8vo, [28]p, ibds, pep, color, DJ/0.50)	Grosset/Dunlap	1942	Credle, Ellis	65-80	R
Credle, Ellis	Down, Down the Mountain (1st, 4to, [47]p, 2-color, DJ/2.00)	Nelson	1934	Credle, Ellis	70-100	
Credle, Ellis	Goat that Went to School (1st, lg8vo, [28]p, ipcb, color, pep, DJ/0.50)	Grosset/Dunlap	(1940)	Credle, Ellis	35-50	
Credle, Ellis	Here Comes the Showboat (1st, lg8vo, 95p, b/w, DJ/2.50)	Nelson	(1949)	Credle, Ellis	25-40	
Credle, Ellis	Little Jeemes Henry (1st, sq8vo, 44p, b/w, DJ/1.50)	Nelson	1936	Credle, Ellis	70-100	
Credle, Ellis	Monkey See, Monkey Do (1st, 4to, [46]p, bds, 2-color, DJ/3.25)	Nelson	(1968)	Credle, Ellis	25-45	
Credle, Ellis	Pig-O-Wee (1st, sm4to, ibds, [44]p, color, DJ/1.00)	Rand/McNally	(1936)	Credle, Ellis	30-50	
Lindsay, Maud	Posey & the Pedlar (1st, sm8vo, tan cl, 186p, fp b/w, DJ/1.50)	Lothrop, Lee	1938	Credle, Ellis	70-120	
Creekmore, Raymond	Ali's Elephant (1st {std}, 4to, ibds, [40]p, b/w, DJ/2.00)	Macmillan	1949	Creekmore, Raymond	30-50	
Creekmore, Raymond	Fujio (1st {std}, 8vo, unpag, b/w, pep, DJ/2.00)	Macmillan	1951	Creekmore, Raymond	25-45	
Creekmore, Raymond	Little Fu (1st {std}, 4to, ibds, [49]p, b/w, DJ/2.00)	Macmillan	1947	Creekmore, Raymond	25-45	
Creekmore, Raymond	Little Skipper (1st {std}, 4to, [40]p, b/w, DJ/2.00)	Macmillan	1950	Creekmore, Raymond	35-50	
Creekmore, Raymond	Lokoshi Learns to Hunt Seals (1st {std}, 4to, [48]p, b/w, DJ/1.75)	Macmillan	1946	Creekmore, Raymond	30-50	
Garst, Shannon	Rusty at Ram's Horn Ranch (1st {std}{A}, 8vo, 191p, b/w, DJ/2.50)	Abingdon-Cokes.	(1951)	Creekmore, Raymond	30-45	
Crespi, Pachita	Gift of the Earth (1st, sm8vo, ibds, [32]p, color, DJ/1.25)	Scribner	1946	Crespi, Pachita	30-50	
Crews, Donald	Ten Black Dots (1st, 12mo, [26]p, color, DJ/3.50)	Scribner	(1968)	Crews, Donald	30-50	*
Crews, Donald	We Read: A and Z (1st, sq8vo, ipcb, [52]p, color, cep, DJ/3.50)	Harper	(1967)	Crews, Donald	35-50	
Levy, Mimi C.	Corrie and the Yankee (1st, 8vo, 189p, blue cl, b/w, DJ/3.00)	Viking	(1958)	Crichlow, Ernest	30-50	
Sterling, Dorothy	Forever Free (1st {std}, 8vo, 208p, b/w, DJ/2.95)	Doubleday	(1963)	Crichlow, Ernest	25-45	*
Lansdown, Brenda	Galumph (1st, sq8vo, 48p, yellow cl, fp 2-color, DJ/3.00)	Houghton	1963	Crichlow, Ernest	25-45	*
Lexau, Joan M.	Maria (1st {std}, 4to, [32]p, color, DJ/2.95)	Dial Press	(1964)	Crichlow, Ernest	40-65	*
Sterling, Dorothy	Mary Jane (1st {std}, 8vo, 214p, fp b/w, DJ/2.75)	Doubleday	1959	Crichlow, Ernest	30-50	
Drdek, Richard E.	Street Dog (1st, lg ob8vo, 48p, fp 1-color, cep)	L.W. Singer	(1967)	Crichlow, Ernest	45-65	*
Beim, Lorraine	Two is a Team (1st, 8vo, [61]p, red cl, fp 2-color, pep, DJ/1.75)	Harcourt	(1945)	Crichlow, Ernest	40-65	
Guy, Anne W.	William (1st, 8vo, 124p, fp b/w, DJ/2.95)	Dial Press	1961	Crichlow, Ernest	25-45	*
Crockett, Lucy H.	Lucio and his Nuong (1st, 4to, [56]p, p-o, fp 3-color, pep, DJ/2.00)	Henry Holt & Co.	(1939)	Crockett, Lucy	50-80	R
Crockett, Lucy H.	That Mario (1st, 8vo, 181p, green cl, fp b/w, pep, DJ/1.50)	Henry Holt & Co.	(1940)	Crockett, Lucy	30-45	
Courlander, Harold	Uncle Bouqui of Haiti (1st, 8vo, 126p, 1-color, pep, DJ/2.00)	Wm. Morrow	1942	Crockett, Lucy	40-65	
Sherratt, J.H.L.	Goblin Gobblers (1st, ob8vo, 64p, bds, p-o, 10cp)	L: Warne	(1910)	Crombie, Charles E.	140-225	
Crosby, Percy L.	Dear Sooky (1st, 8vo, ipcb, 124p, 7 ticp, dep)	Putnam	1929	Crosby, Percy L.	60-90	
Bacon, Josephine D.	Idyll of All Fool's Day (1st, sm8vo, 120p, p-o, 10pl)	Dodd	1908	Crosby, Raymond M.	25-40	*
Cross, Genevieve	Pop-Corn Lamb & Peppermint Sticks (1st, ob4to, ipcb, [32]p, 1-color, pep)	Cross Pub.	1949	Cross, Genevieve	40-65	*
Croswell, Volney	How to Hide a Hippopotamus (1st, ob12mo, [30]p, color, DJ/2.00, NYTBI)	Dodd	(1958)	Croswell, Volney	40-65	*
De La Mare, Walter	Peacock Pie (1st AM [new ed.], 8vo, 111p, blue/gilt, 2-color, DJ/2.00)	Henry Holt & Co.	1936	Crowe, Jocelyn	40-65	*
Fenner, Phyllis R.	Horses, Horses, Horses (1st, 8vo, 285p, b/w, pep, DJ/2.50)	F. Watts	(1949)	Crowell, Pers	20-30	

AUTHOR	TITLE	PUBLISHER	DATE	ARTIST	PRICE	LC
Balch, Glenn	Midnight Colt (1st, 8vo, 194p, b/w, DJ/2.50)	Crowell	(1952)	Crowell, Pers	30-50	
McGraw, Eloise J.	Sawdust in his Shoes (1st, 8vo, 264p, col frn, b/w, pep, DJ/2.50)	Coward	(1950)	Crowell, Pers	200-300	
Fisher, Aileen	Timber! Logging in Michigan (1st {std} 8vo, 191p, color, DJ/1.75)	Aladdin	1955	Crowell, Pers	30-50	
Cruikshank, George	Cruikshank Fairy Book (1st, 8vo, 216p, gilt, b/w)	Putnam	1897	Cruikshank, George	250-350	
Layard, George S.	Cruikshank's Portraits of Himself (1st, 8vo, 98p, 17pl)	L: Spencer	1897	Cruikshank, George	120-180	
Grego, Joseph	Cruikshank's Water Colours (1st, 4to, gilt, teg, 326p, 67cp)	L: A&C Black	1903	Cruikshank, George	200-300	
Munroe, Kirk	Golden Days of '49 (1st, sm8vo, 351p, col frn, pep)	Dodd	1924	Crump, Leslie	40-65	R
Cruse, Laurence	Village in Normandy (1st {std}, ob4to, ibds, [32]p, color, DJ/3.75)	Bobbs-Merrill	(1968)	Cruse, Laurence	30-50	
Lampman, Evelyn	Tilted Sombrero (1st {std}, 8vo, 264p, gilt, b/w, DJ/3.50)	Doubleday	1966	Cruz, Ray	30-45	
Schultz, James W.	In the Great Apache Forest (1st, 8vo, 225p, green cl, 4pl)	Houghton	1920	Cue, Harold	30-50	*
Davies, Mary C.	Little Freckled Person (1st, 8vo, 104p, col, frn, 8pl)	Houghton	1919	Cue, Harold	25-40	
Borton, Elizabeth	Our Little Aztec Cousin of Long Ago (1st, sm8vo, blue cl, 83p, 6pl)	L.C. Page	(1934)	Cue, Harold	25-40	*
Borton, Elizabeth	Pollyanna & the Secret Mission (1st, sm8vo, 263p, gilt, DJ/2.50, frn by…)	L.C. Page	(1951)	Cue, Harold	30-45	
Borton, Elizabeth	Pollyanna's Castle in Mexico (1st, sm8vo, 322p, gilt, col frn)	L.C. Page	(1934)	Cue, Harold	25-40	*
Borton, Elizabeth	Pollyanna's Door to Happiness (1st, sm8vo, gilt, 359p, col frn, DJ/2.00)	L.C. Page	(1936)	Cue, Harold	30-45	
Morey, Walter	Angry Waters (1st {std}, 8vo, 224p, b/w, DJ/4.95)	Dutton	(1969)	Cuffari, Richard	20-35	
Martin, Patricia	James Madison (1st, 8vo, 63p, color, DJ)	Putnam	(1970)	Cuffari, Richard	25-35	
Stuart, Jesse	Old Ben (1st, 8vo, ipcb, 92p, fp b/w, DJ/3.95)	McGraw-Hill	(1970)	Cuffari, Richard	50-80	R*
Wood, James P.	People of Concord (1st, 8vo, 152p, b/w, DJ/4.95)	Seabury Press	(1970)	Cuffari, Richard	50-80	R*
Cullen, Countee	Copper Sun (1st {std}, sm8vo, bds, 89p, b/w)	Harper	1927	Cullen, Charles	120-200	
Eaton, Seymour	More about Teddy B. & Teddy G. (1st, 4to, 186p, ibds, p-o, 15cp)	Stern	1907	Culver, R.K.	400-600	
Eaton, Seymour	Roosevelt Bears Abroad (1st, 4to, ibds, p-o, 178p, 12cp)	Stern	1908	Culver, R.K.	400-600	
Cummings, Walter	Girl in the White Hat (1st, 4to, 32p, fp 2-color, pep, DJ/2.25, NYTBI)	Whittlesey	1959	Cummings, Walter	50-80	*
DeRegniers, Beatrice	Giant Book (1st {std}, 8vo, 188p, b/w, DJ/4.75)	Atheneum	1966	Cummings, Wm. L.	30-50	*
Vernede, R.E.	Fair Dominion (1st AM, 8vo, blue cl, teg, 293p, uncut, 12cp)	J. Pott	1911	Cuneo, Cyrus	30-60	
Brereton, Frederick	Indian & Scout (1st, 8vo, 368p, gilt, 6pl)	L: Blackie	1911	Cuneo, Cyrus	35-60	
Bindloss, Harold	Masters of the Wheat-Lands (1st, 8vo, 354p, 7pl)	Stokes	(1910)	Cuneo, Cyrus	30-50	*
Harris-Burland, J.	Princess Thora (1st, 8vo, 360p, blue/gilt, 4pl)	Little/Brown	1904	Cuneo, Cyrus	100-170	
O'Hara, Mary	My Friend Flicka (1st, 8vo, 349p, col frn, 14pl, DJ/2.50)	Lippincott	1941	Curry, John S.	55-80	
Clay, Beatrice	Stories of King Arthur (1st, 8vo, 322p, gilt, p-o, 8cp)	L: Dent	1905	Curtis, Dora	60-90	
Ryan, Marah E.	Flute of the Gods (1st, 8vo, 338p, uncut, p-o, pep, 24 photo plates by…)	Stokes	(1909)	Curtis, Edward	250-400	
Cooke, Edmund V.	Story Club (1st, 8vo, p-o, 210p, 8cp)	Dodge	(1912)	Curtis, Eliza	30-50	*
Gray, Eliz. J.	Meredith's Ann (1st {std}, sm8vo, yellow cl, 267p, col frn, pep)	Doubleday/Page	1927	Cutts, G.B.	30-50	
Gray, Eliz. J.	Tangle Garden (1st {std}, sm8vo, 327p, pep, col frn by…)	Doubleday/Doran	1928	Cutts, G.B.	25-40	*
Czaja, Helen	Bountiful Cow (1st, sm ob4to, ibds, [55]p, b/w, DJ/1.50)	Henry Holt & Co.	(1944)	Czaja, Michael	25-45	
Stephens, William	Octopus Lives in the Ocean (1st, 8vo, 44p, color, DJ/3.50)	Holiday House	(1968)	D'Attilio, Anthony	30-45	*
Stephens, William	Sea Horse: Fish in Armor (1st, 8vo, 48p, color, DJ/3.50)	Holiday House	(1969)	D'Attilio, Anthony	25-45	
Burglon, Nora	Children of the Soil (1st {std}, 8vo, 272p, pep, col frn, NH)	Doubleday/Doran	1932	D'Aulaire, E. Parin	75-100	*
Everson, Howard	Coming of the Dragon Ships (1st {std}, 8vo, gilt, 128p, 4cp, 6pl, pep)	Dutton	1931	D'Aulaire, E. Parin	60-90	*
Seabrook, Katie	Gao of the Ivory Coast (1st, 8vo, 121p, col frn, 4pl)	Coward	(1931)	D'Aulaire, E. Parin	50-80	
Scott, Gabriel	Kari (1st {std}, 8vo, 242p, blue cl, uncut, col frn, 7pl, pep)	Doubleday/Doran	1931	D'Aulaire, E. Parin	30-50	
Matheson, John	Needle in the Haystack (1st, sq8vo, 189p, ibds, 8cp, pep)	Wm. Morrow	1930	D'Aulaire, E. Parin	70-100	
Mukerji, Dhan G.	Rama, Hero of India (1st {std}, 8vo, red/gilt, 219p, dep)	Dutton	(1930)	D'Aulaire, E. Parin	70-100	
D'Aulaire, I.& E.	Abraham Lincoln (1st {std}, folio, 55p, ibds, 5 fp color, DJ/2.00, CM)	Doubleday/Doran	1939	D'Aulaire, I.& E.	200-300	R
D'Aulaire, I.& E.	Animals Everywhere (1st {std}, 4to, folding panels, color, pep)	Doubleday/Doran	1940	D'Aulaire, I.& E.	280-400	
D'Aulaire, I.& E.	Animals Everywhere (1st {this fmt}, 4to, ibds, [29]p, color, pep, DJ/2.00)	Doubleday	1954	D'Aulaire, I.& E.	80-130	
D'Aulaire, I.& E.	Benjamin Franklin (1st {std}, 4to, ibds, [48]p, color, DJ/2.50)	Doubleday	(1950)	D'Aulaire, I.& E.	90-140	
D'Aulaire, I.& E.	Buffalo Bill (1st {std}, 4to, ibds, [40]p, color, DJ/2.75)	Doubleday	1952	D'Aulaire, I.& E.	80-125	
D'Aulaire, I.& E.	Children of the North Lights (1st, lg4to, ibds, [40]p, color, pep, DJ/2.00)	Viking	1935	D'Aulaire, I.& E.	170-250	
D'Aulaire, I.& E.	Columbus (1st {std}, lg4to, ibds, 57p, pep, color, DJ/3.00)	Doubleday	1955	D'Aulaire, I.& E.	100-170	R
D'Aulaire, I.& E.	Conquest of the Atlantic (1st, lg4to, ibds, 55p, color)	Viking	1933	D'Aulaire, I.& E.	120-185	
Burglon, Nora	Cuckoo Calls (1st, 8vo, 280p, col frn, pep, DJ/2.00)	Winston	(1940)	D'Aulaire, I.& E.	50-80	
D'Aulaire, I.& E.	D'Aulaire's Book of Greek Myths (1st {std}, lg4to, 192p, color, DJ/4.95)	Doubleday	1962	D'Aulaire, I.& E.	60-100	
D'Aulaire, I.& E.	Don't Count Your Chicks (1st {std}, folio, [40]p, ibds, col, pep, DJ/2.50)	Doubleday/Doran	1943	D'Aulaire, I.& E.	150-250	R
Asbjornsen, P.C.	East of the Sun, West o/t Moon (1st, 4to, 188p, 22 fp b/w, pep, DJ/3.50)	Viking	1938	D'Aulaire, I.& E.	50-80	
D'Aulaire, I.& E.	Foxie (1st {std}, ob4to, red cl, [40]p, b/w, pep, DJ/2.00)	Doubleday	1949	D'Aulaire, I.& E.	100-165	
D'Aulaire, I.& E.	George Washington (1st {std}, lg4to, ibds, [55]p, 13 fp color)	Doubleday/Doran	(1936)	D'Aulaire, I.& E.	70-100	
Zwilgmeyer, Dikken	Johnny Blossom (1st, 8vo, yellow cl, 157p, pep, 10 fp b/w, DJ/2.50)	Pilgrim Press	(1948)	D'Aulaire, I.& E.	45-70	
D'Aulaire, I.& E.	Leif the Lucky (1st {std}, lg4to, ibds, [56]p, color, pep, DJ/2.50)	Doubleday/Doran	1941	D'Aulaire, I.& E.	100-160	
D'Aulaire, I.& E.	Lord's Prayer (1st {std}, lg4to, [32]p, ibds, color, pep)	Doubleday/Doran	1934	D'Aulaire, I.& E.	70-100	
D'Aulaire, I.& E.	Magic Meadow (1st {std}, lg4to, ibds, 55p, pep, 25 color, DJ/3.00)	Doubleday	1958	D'Aulaire, I.& E.	100-150	
D'Aulaire, I.& E.	Magic Rug (1st {std}, ob4to, [63]p, ibds, pep, color)	Doubleday/Doran	1931	D'Aulaire, I.& E.	250-350	
D'Aulaire, I.& E.	Nils (1st {std}, 4to, ibds, [40]p, color, pep, DJ/2.50)	Doubleday	(1948)	D'Aulaire, I.& E.	120-185	
D'Aulaire, I.& E.	Norse Gods and Giants (1st {std}, lg4to, 154p, fp color, pep, DJ/5.95)	Doubleday	(1967)	D'Aulaire, I.& E.	80-120	R
D'Aulaire, I.& E.	Ola (1st {std}, lg4to, ibds, [55]p, color, pep, DJ/2.00)	Doubleday/Doran	1932	D'Aulaire, I.& E.	130-180	R
D'Aulaire, I.& E.	Ola & Blakken & Line Sine & Trine (1st {std}, folio, [39]p, ibds, color)	Doubleday/Doran	1933	D'Aulaire, I.& E.	120-185	
D'Aulaire, I.& E.	Pocahantas (1st {std}, 4to, ibds, [40]p, color, DJ/2.50)	Doubleday	1946	D'Aulaire, I.& E.	120-200	
Aanrud, Hans.	Sidsel Longskirt & Solve Suntrap (1st, 8vo, 257p, gilt, 4cp, pep, DJ/2.00)	Winston	(1935)	D'Aulaire, I.& E.	70-100	
D'Aulaire, I.& E.	Star Spangled Banner (1st {std}, lg4to, ibds, [38]p, color, pep)	Doubleday/Doran	1942	D'Aulaire, I.& E.	75-125	
D'Aulaire, I.& E.	Too Big (1st {std}, sm sq8vo, ibds, [32]p, color, pep, DJ/1.00)	Doubleday/Doran	1945	D'Aulaire, I.& E.	60-90	
D'Aulaire, I.& E.	Two Cars (1st {std}, sq8vo, [30]p, color, DJ/1.50)	Doubleday	1955	D'Aulaire, I.& E.	45-70	
D'Aulaire, I.& E.	Wings for Per (1st {std}, lg4to, ibds, [40]p, color, pep, DJ/2.50)	Doubleday/Doran	(1944)	D'Aulaire, I.& E.	80-125	
Morrow, Elizabeth	Beast, Bird & Fish (1st {std}, 4to, [59]p, color, pep)	Knopf	1933	D'Harnoncourt, R.	100-165	
D'Harnoncourt, R.	Mexicana (1st {std}, 4to, [104]p, ipcb, fp b/w, dep)	Knopf	1931	D'Harnoncourt, R.	65-90	
Morrow, Elizabeth	Painted Pig (1st, 4to, ipcb, 32p, fp color, pep)	Knopf	1930	D'Harnoncourt, R.	100-170	R
Baring-Gould, Sabine	Broom-Squire (1st, 8vo, 384p, uncut, gilt, 12pl)	L: Methuen	1896	Dadd, Frank	100-160	*
Irving, Washington	Old Christmas (1st, 8vo, 115p, gilt, p-o, teg, 2cp, 16pl, pep)	Putnam	(1916)	Dadd, Frank	40-60	*
Wodehouse, P.G.	William Tell Told Again (1st, 8vo, tan cl, teg, 105p, 16cp)	L: A&C Black	1904	Dadd, Philip	800-1200	

AUTHOR	TITLE	PUBLISHER	DATE	ARTIST	PRICE	LC
Stevens, D.K.	Ballads of the Be-Ba-Boes (1st, 4to, yellow cl, 100p)	Houghton	1913	Daland, Katharine	160-240	
Dalgliesh, Alice	Sailor Sam (1st, sq12mo, ipcb, [38]p, cep, color)	Scribner	1935	Dalgliesh, Alice	35-60	
Dali, Salvador	50 Secrets of Magic Craftmanship (1st, 4to, 192p, color, DJ/7.50)	Dial	1948	Dali, Salvador	200-300	
Cellini, Benvenuto	Autobiography of Benvenuto Cellini (1st, sm4to, 442p, 15cp)	Doubleday	1946	Dali, Salvador	140-200	
DeMontaigne, Michel	Essays (1st, 8vo, 472p, bds, gilt, 15 fp color)	Doubleday	1947	Dali, Salvador	200-350	
Dali, Salvador	Hidden Faces (1st, 8vo, black cl, 413p, b/w frn, DJ/3.00)	Dial	1944	Dali, Salvador	200-300	
Sandoz, Maurice	House Without Windows (1st, sm4to, 101p, gilt, 7cp, DJ)	L: W. Campion	1950	Dali, Salvador	200-300	
Shakespeare, Wm.	Macbeth (1st {std}, lg8vo, black bds, 125p, 12 fp b/w, pep)	Garden City	1946	Dali, Salvador	200-300	
Sandoz, Maurice	On the Verge (1st {std}, 4to, 127p, col frn, cep, DJ/4.50)	Doubleday	1950	Dali, Salvador	170-240	
Dali, Salvador	Secret Life of Salvador Dali (1st AM, sm4to, p-o, 400p, buckram, 3cp)	Dial	1942	Dali, Salvador	150-225	
Sandoz, Maurice	The Maze (1st {std}, 8vo, 110p, gilt, uncut, 13pl, DJ/2.50)	Doubleday/Doran	1945	Dali, Salvador	160-245	
Starbird, Kaye	Don't Ever Cross a Crocodile (1st, 8vo, 62p, b/w, DJ/2.95)	Lippincott	(1963)	Dalton, Kit	20-30	*
Sandburg, Helga	Joel & the Wild Goose (1st, ob4to, [34]p, ibds, fp color, pep, DJ/3.50)	Dial Press	1963	Daly, Thomas	50-75	R
Dana, Mary P.	Jingle Book (1st, sm4to, [32]p, 3-color)	W.R. Scott	1940	Dana, Mary P.	50-80	
Ashley, Fred	Temple of Fire (1st, 8vo, green/gilt, 332p, 8pl)	L: I. Pitman	1905	Daniel, Vincent S.	80-130	
Lyman, Edward B.	Me'ow Jones (1st, sm8vo, p-o, 91p, 5cp, pep)	Doran	(1917)	Daniels, Julia	40-65	
Haviland, Virginia	Favorite Fairy Tales Told in Russia (1st {std}, sm8vo, 86p, color, DJ/2.95)	Little/Brown	1961	Danska, Herbert	50-85	
Richter, Conrad	Over the Blue Mountain (1st, 8vo, 81p, b/w, cep, DJ/3.75)	Knopf	(1967)	Danska, Herbert	20-30	*
Wilde, Oscar	Selfish Giant (1st, 4to, [64]p, color, DJ/3.25)	Harlin Quist	1966	Danska, Herbert	25-45	
Danska, Herbert	Street Kids (1st, lg8vo, 160p, fp b/w, cep, DJ)	Knopf	(1970)	Danska, Herbert	30-45	
Windsor, Mary	Mr. Gallagher's Donkey (1st, 4to, [28]p, ipcb, color)	Garden City	(1950)	Darien, Elsie	25-40	
Cleary, Beverly	Beezus and Ramona (1st, 8vo, 159p, b/w, DJ/2.50)	Wm. Morrow	(1955)	Darling, Louis	50-80	*
Beim, Jerrold	Country Garage (1st, 8vo, 48p, color, DJ/2.00)	Wm. Morrow	1952	Darling, Louis	30-50	
Beim, Jerrold	Country School (1st, 8vo, 48p, color, DJ/2.00)	Wm. Morrow	1955	Darling, Louis	30-50	
Cleary, Beverly	Ellen Tebbits (1st, 8vo, 160p, b/w, DJ/2.00)	Wm. Morrow	1951	Darling, Louis	50-80	*
Butterworth, Oliver	Enormous Egg (1st {std}, 8vo, 187p, b/w, DJ/2.95)	Little/Brown	1956	Darling, Louis	45-70	
Cleary, Beverly	Henry and Beezus (1st, 8vo, 192p, b/w, DJ/2.50)	Wm. Morrow	1952	Darling, Louis	60-100	
Cleary, Beverly	Henry and Ribsy (1st, 8vo, 192p, b/w, DJ/2.50)	Wm. Morrow	1954	Darling, Louis	60-90	
Cleary, Beverly	Henry Huggins (1st [1st bk.], 8vo, 155p, b/w, DJ/2.00)	Wm. Morrow	1950	Darling, Louis	70-100	
Cleary, Beverly	Mouse & the Motorcycle (1st, 8vo, 158p, b/w, DJ/2.95)	Wm. Morrow	1965	Darling, Louis	25-40	
Cameron, Eleanor	Mr. Bass's Planetoid (1st {std}, sm8vo, 227p, b/w, DJ/3.00)	Little/Brown	(1958)	Darling, Louis	200-300	
Cleary, Beverly	Otis Spofford (1st, 8vo, 191p, b/w, DJ/2.50)	Wm. Morrow	1953	Darling, Louis	20-35	
Cleary, Beverly	Ramona the Pest (1st, 8vo, 192p, fp b/w, DJ/3.75)	Wm. Morrow	(1968)	Darling, Louis	20-30	
Cleary, Beverly	Ribsy (1st, 8vo, 192p, fp b/w, DJ/2.95)	Wm. Morrow	1964	Darling, Louis	20-35	
Cleary, Beverly	Runaway Ralph (1st, 8vo, 175p, b/w, DJ/3.95)	Wm. Morrow	(1970)	Darling, Louis	30-50	R
Kjelgaard, Jim	Stormy (1st, sm8vo, 190p, grey cl, pep, DJ/2.95)	Holiday House	(1959)	Darling, Louis	25-45	
Beim, Jerrold	Thin Ice (1st, 8vo, 46p, color, DJ/2.00)	Wm. Morrow	1956	Darling, Louis	30-50	
Kraus, Robert	Unidentified Flying Elephant (1st {std}, lg4to, [30]p, fp color, DJ/4.95)	Windmill Books	(1968)	Darrow, Whitney	30-50	
Schweitzer, Byrd B.	Chinese Bug (1st, 4to, 48p, gilt, dp color, DJ/3.50)	Houghton	1968	Darwin, Beatrice	30-50	
Udry, Janice M.	Sunflower Garden (1st, ob4to, 37p, fp 3-color, pep, DJ/3.95)	Harvey House	(1969)	Darwin, Beatrice	50-80	
Darwin, Bernard	Ishybushy & Topknot (1st, 4to, tan cl, 64p, 7cp)	L: Country Life	(1946)	Darwin, Elinor	100-165	
Darwin, Bernard	Mr. Tootleoo & Co. (1st AM, ob 4to, [45]p, ibds, 22 fp color)	Harper	(1936)	Darwin, Elinor	350-500	*
Darwin, Bernard	Oboli Boboli & Little Joboli (1st, 4to, 79p, tan cl, 5 fp color)	L: Country Life	(1938)	Darwin, Elinor	100-165	
Darwin, Bernard	Tootleoo Two (1st AM, ob4to, ipcb, [42]p, fp color)	Harper	(1928)	Darwin, Elinor	160-220	
Pain, Eva	Stories Barry Told Me (1st, 8vo, ibds, 94p, color)	L: Longmans	1927	Darwin, Mrs. Bernard	90-150	
Aesopus	Fables of Aesop (1st, 8vo, 254p, p-o, gilt, color, pep)	Whitman	(1925)	Dash, Joseph E.	30-50	
Schlein, Miriam	Big Green Thing (1st, 8vo, 60p, color)	Grosset/Dunlap	(1963)	Dauber, Elizabeth	20-35	
Eaton, Jeanette	Lee: Gallant General (1st, 8vo, 72p, b/w, DJ/2.00)	Wm. Morrow	1953	Daugherty, Harry	25-40	
Sandburg, Carl	Abe Lincoln Grows Up (1st, lg8vo, 222p, b/w, pep)	Harcourt	1928	Daugherty, James	30-50	
Daugherty, James	Abraham Lincoln (1st, 4to, 216p, fp 1-color, DJ/3.50)	Viking	1943	Daugherty, James	55-80	
Chapin, Harry	Adventures of Johnny Appleseed (1st, 8vo, 244p, b/w, DJ/2.50)	Coward	1930	Daugherty, James	40-70	
McElroy, Margaret	Adventures of Johnny T. Bear (1st, 12mo, 105p, color, pep)	Dutton	(1926)	Daugherty, James	40-65	
Daugherty, Sonia	All Things New (1st, sm8vo, 296p, orange cl, b/w, DJ/1.75)	Nelson	1936	Daugherty, James	30-50	*
Daugherty, James	Andy & the Lion (1st, 4to, ipcb, [79]p, color, pep, DJ/2.00, CH)	Viking	1938	Daugherty, James	140-220	R
Dickens, Charles	Barnaby Rudge (1st, 8vo, 637p, col frn, b/w)	Heritage Press	(1941)	Daugherty, James	25-45	*
Hunt, Mabel L.	Better Known as Johnny Appleseed (1st {std}, 8vo, 212p, cep, DJ/2.50, NH)	Lippincott	(1950)	Daugherty, James	60-90	R
Rickert, Edith	Blacksmith & the Birds (1st {std}, 12mo, 46p, orange cl, pep, b/w)	Doubleday/Doran	1928	Daugherty, James	30-50	
Irving, Washington	Bold Dragoon (1st, lg8vo, 240p, blue cl, b/w, pep, DJ/2.50)	Knopf	1930	Daugherty, James	40-60	
Meigs, Cornelia L.	Call of the Mountain (1st {std}, 8vo, 258p, 9 fp 1-color, DJ/2.00)	Little/Brown	1940	Daugherty, James	30-55	
Chapman, Maristan	Clue of the Faded Dress (1st, sm8vo, 237p, b/w, uncut, DJ/2.00)	Appleton-Century	1938	Daugherty, James	30-45	*
Appel, David	Comanche... (1st {std}, 8vo, 224p, dp b/w, DJ/2.50)	World	(1951)	Daugherty, James	30-50	*
Lang, Andrew	Conquest of Montezuma's Empire (1st {std}, sm8vo, 235p, 8pl, pep, DJ/1.50)	Longmans	1928	Daugherty, James	30-50	
Finger, Charles J.	Courageous Companions (1st {std}, lg8vo, 304p, gilt, pep, 10pl)	Longmans	(1929)	Daugherty, James	35-60	
White, Stewart E.	Daniel Boone (1st, lg8vo, 274p, p-o, 4cp, 10pl, pep)	Doubleday/Page	1926	Daugherty, James	60-90	
Daugherty, James	Daniel Boone (1st {this pub}, 4to, 95p, color, pep, DJ/2.50, NM)	Viking	1939	Daugherty, James	120-180	R
Rogers, Cameron	Drake's Quest (1st, sm8vo, 284p, col frn)	Doubleday/Page	1927	Daugherty, James	25-45	
Sandburg, Carl	Early Moon (1st {std}, lg8vo, 136p, b/w)	Harcourt	(1930)	Daugherty, James	70-120	*
Elkin, Benjamin	Gillespie & the Guards (1st, 4to, 62p, fp 1-color, DJ/2.50, CH)	Viking	1956	Daugherty, James	80-125	
Chapman, Maristan	Girls of Glen Hazard (1st, sm8vo, 264p, b/w, DJ/2.00)	Appleton-Century	1937	Daugherty, James	30-45	*
Aydelotte, Dora	Green Gravel (1st, 12mo, green cl, uncut, 249p, b/w, DJ/2.00)	Appleton-Century	1937	Daugherty, James	25-40	
Daugherty, James	Henry David Thoreau (1st, sm4to, 111p, gilt, 2-color, DJ)	Viking	(1967)	Daugherty, James	25-40	
Irving, Washington	History of New York (1st {std}, lg8vo, 427p, uncut, pep, DJ/2.50)	Doubleday/Doran	1928	Daugherty, James	80-130	R
Dix, Beulah M.	Hugh Gwyeth: Roundhead Cavalier (1st, 12mo, pep, b/w)	Macmillan	1928	Daugherty, James	35-60	*
Bible	In the Beginning... (1st, 4to, cloth, color, DJ/2.00)	NY: Oxford U.Pr.	(1941)	Daugherty, James	55-80	
Burrows, Elizabeth	Irene of Tundra Towers (1st {std}, 8vo, 311p, col frn, pep)	Doubleday/Doran	1928	Daugherty, James	35-60	*
Benet, Stephen	John Brown's Body (1st {std}, 8vo, 376p, dp pl)	Doubleday/Doran	1928	Daugherty, James	25-40	
Shapiro, Irwin	John Henry & Double-Jointed Steam Drill (1st, lg8vo, [55]p, b/w, DJ/1.50)	J. Messner	(1945)	Daugherty, James	30-50	
Burrows, Elizabeth	Judy of the Whale Gates (1st {std}, 8vo, 296p, col frn)	Doubleday/Doran	1930	Daugherty, James	25-40	

AUTHOR	TITLE	PUBLISHER	DATE	ARTIST	PRICE	LC
Horne, Richard H.	King Penguin (1st, 12mo, tan cl, 95p, 4cp, pep)	Macmillan	1925	Daugherty, James	30-50	
Bible	Kingdom & Power & Glory (1st, 4to, 170p, brown cl, fp b/w, DJ/2.50)	Knopf	1929	Daugherty, James	60-100	
Bruce, Marie	Kris & Kristina (1st {std}, 8vo, ibds, 60p, color, pep)	Doubleday/Doran	(1927)	Daugherty, James	40-65	
Daugherty, James	Landing of the Pilgrims (1st, 8vo, 186p, color, pep, DJ/1.50)	Random	(1950)	Daugherty, James	25-40	
Cooper, James F.	Last of the Mohicans (1st, 8vo, 440p, color, RC)	World	1957	Daugherty, James	25-40	
Daugherty, James	Lincoln's Gettysburg Address (1st {std}, lg4to, ibds, [40]p, color, DJ/5.00)	Whitman	(1947)	Daugherty, James	60-90	
Powers, Alfred	Long Way to Frisco (1st {std}, 8vo, 181p, b/w, DJ/2.50)	Little/Brown	1951	Daugherty, James	30-50	
Train, Arthur	Lost Gospel (1st, sm8vo, 77p, col frn)	Scribner	1925	Daugherty, James	20-35	
Elkin, Benjamin	Loudest Noise in the World (1st, 4to, 64p, fp 1-color, DJ/2.50)	Viking	1954	Daugherty, James	40-70	R
Daugherty, James	Magna Charta (1st, 8vo, 181p, 1-color, DJ/1.50)	Random	(1956)	Daugherty, James	25-45	
Daugherty, James	Marcus and Narcissa Whitman (1st, 8vo, 158p, b/w, pep, DJ/2.50)	Viking	1953	Daugherty, James	40-70	R
Daugherty, Sonia	Mashinka's Secret (1st, 12mo, 276p, 28 b/w)	Stokes	1932	Daugherty, James	30-50	
Ross, Margaret I.	Morgan's Fourth Son (1st {std}, 8vo, 252p, uncut, 6pl, DJ/2.00)	Harper	(1940)	Daugherty, James	30-50	
Irwin, Violet	Mountain of Jade (1st, sm8vo, 236p, green cl, fp b/w)	Macmillan	1926	Daugherty, James	30-50	
Daugherty, James	Of Courage Undaunted (1st, sm4to, 168p, b/w, DJ/3.50)	Viking	1951	Daugherty, James	40-65	
Parkman, Francis	Oregon Trail (1st, 8vo, 385p, color, pep, DJ/3.00)	Farrar/Rinehart	(1931)	Daugherty, James	45-70	
Daugherty, James	Picnic: Frolic in 2 Colors & 3 Parts (1st, 4to, 79p, 2-color, DJ/3.50)	Viking	(1958)	Daugherty, James	30-50	
Pierson, Clara D.	Plucky Allens (1st, sm8vo, green/gilt, 327p, 5 fp b/w)	Dutton	(1925)	Daugherty, James	30-50	
Daugherty, James	Poor Richard (1st, sm4to, brown cl, 158p, 2-color, pep, DJ/2.50)	Viking	1941	Daugherty, James	100-165	
Swift, Hildegarde H.	Railroad to Freedom (1st, 8vo, 364p, b/w, pep, NH)	Harcourt	(1932)	Daugherty, James	50-80	
Miers, Earl S.	Rainbow Book of American History (1st {std}, 4to, 319p, color, DJ/4.95)	World	(1955)	Daugherty, James	60-90	R
Daugherty, Charles	Robert Goddard: Trail Blazer to Stars (1st {std}, 8vo, [48]p, col, DJ/2.95)	Macmillan	(1964)	Daugherty, James	25-40	
Lamb, Peter O.	Sign of the Buffalo Skull (1st, 12mo, 288p, 14 b/w)	Stokes	1932	Daugherty, James	25-45	
Quiller-Couch, A.	Splendid Spur (1st, lg8vo, orange cl, 274p, p-o, 15cp)	Doran	(1927)	Daugherty, James	35-50	
Quiller-Couch, A.	Splendid Spur (1st {this pub.}, lg8vo, p-o, 274p, 4cp, pep)	Garden City	1937	Daugherty, James	35-60	*
Watson, Elizabeth	Story of Bread (1st {std}, 12mo, ipcb, 48p, 4cp, pep)	Harper	1927	Daugherty, James	30-50	
Watson, Elizabeth	Story of Milk & How it Came About (1st {std}, 12mo, ipcb, 37p, 4cp, pep)	Harper	1927	Daugherty, James	30-50	
Parsons, Geoffrey	Stream of History (1st, lg8vo, 590p, gilt, b/w, pep)	Scribner	1928	Daugherty, James	35-60	
Wilson, John F.	Tad Sheldon, Boy Scout (1st, sm8vo, 231p, b/w pl)	Sturgis/Walton	1913	Daugherty, James	120-200	
Daugherty, Sonia	Ten Brave Women (1st {std}, 8vo, 147p, b/w, DJ/2.75)	Lippincott	(1953)	Daugherty, James	30-45	
Daugherty, James	Trappers and Traders of the Far West (1st, 8vo, 181p, 1-color, DJ/1.50)	Random	(1952)	Daugherty, James	30-50	
Garis, Howard	Tuftoo the Clown (1st, sm8vo, 283p, 10 b/w, pep)	Appleton	1928	Daugherty, James	40-65	*
Stowe, Harriet B.	Uncle Tom's Cabin (1st, lg8vo, 446p, fp b/w, pep)	E. McCann	(1929)	Daugherty, James	60-90	
Daugherty, Sonia	Vanka's Donkey (1st, 8vo, ivory cl, 62p, 1-color, pep, DJ/1.50)	Stokes	1940	Daugherty, James	50-80	
Daugherty, James	Walt Whitman's America (1st {std}, sm4to, 110p, 3-color, DJ/3.95)	World	(1964)	Daugherty, James	35-50	
Daugherty, Sonia	Way of an Eagle (1st, 8vo, 352p, fp b/w, DJ/2.50)	NY: Oxford U.Pr.	(1941)	Daugherty, James	30-50	
Daugherty, James	West of Boston (1st, 4to, 94p, yellow cl, 1-color, DJ/3.00)	Viking	1956	Daugherty, James	40-70	
Doyle, Arthur Conan	White Company (1st, 8vo, 403p, col frn, 2 dp pl, 7pl, pep)	Harper	1928	Daugherty, James	35-50	
Daugherty, James	Wild Wild West (1st, 4to, ibds, [34]p, color, pep, DJ/2.50)	McKay	(1948)	Daugherty, James	60-90	
Wald, Lilian D.	Windows on Henry Street (1st, 8vo, 348p, b/w)	Little/Brown	1934	Daugherty, James	60-100	
Daugherty, Sonia	Wings of Glory (1st, 8vo, 236p, gilt, color, DJ/2.50)	NY: Oxford U.Pr.	(1940)	Daugherty, James	40-65	
Daugherty, Charles	Wisher (1st, ob4to, 40p, fp 2-color, pep, DJ/2.50)	Viking	(1960)	Daugherty, James	30-50	
Escott-Inman, H.	Wulnoth the Wanderer ([new ed.] {std}, sm8vo, 316p, 8pl, pep)	Longmans	1928	Daugherty, James	30-50	
Shapiro, Irwin	Yankee Thunder (1st, 8vo, 205p, gilt, b/w, DJ/2.50)	J. Messner	(1944)	Daugherty, James	35-60	
Robinson, William H.	Golden Palace of Neverland (1st, sm8vo, green cl, 307p, 6cp)	Dutton	1907	Davidson, Clara D.	60-90	
Ironmonger, Ira	Alligator Smiling in the Sawgrass (1st, lg8vo, [44]p, fp color, DJ/3.75)	Young Scott	(1965)	Davidson, Sandra	30-50	
Cumberland, Charles	Seven Glass Gooseberries (1st, 8vo, p-o, 192p, 4cp)	L: G. Richards	1921	Daviel, M.	60-90	
Fenton, Edward	Aleko's Island (1st {std}, 8vo, 246p, b/w, pep, DJ/2.50)	Doubleday	1948	Davis, Dimitris	20-35	*
Graves, Robert	Greek Gods and their Heroes (1st {std}, lg8vo, 160p, b/w, DJ/2.95)	Doubleday	1960	Davis, Dimitris	30-50	
Bishop, Claire H.	Present from Petros (1st, 8vo, blue cl, 85p, b/w, pep, DJ/2.50)	Viking	(1961)	Davis, Dimitris	20-30	*
Ruskin, John	King of the Golden River (ob8vo, 43p, cloth, chromo frn)	McLoughlin	(1905)	Davis, G.A.	60-90	
Grey, Zane	Spirit of the Border (1st, 12mo, 266p, blue cl, 4 b/w)	A.L. Burt	(1906)	Davis, J. Watson	250-400	
Steele, William O.	No-Name Man of the Mountain (1st {std}, 8vo, 79p, b/w, DJ/2.95)	Harcourt	(1964)	Davis, Jack	20-35	
Coatsworth, Eliz.	Up Hill and Down (1st {std}, 8vo, 188p, b/w, DJ/2.50)	Knopf	1947	Davis, James	25-40	
Bowen, Vernon	Lazy Beaver (1st, 4to, [36]p, ibds, color, DJ/2.00)	McKay	1948	Davis, Jim	30-50	*
Madison, Lucy F.	Captain Kitty Colonial (1st, 8vo, blue cl, 309p, p-o, col frn)	Penn	1923	Davis, Marguerite	25-45	*
Stevenson, Rbt. L.	Child's Garden of Verses (1st, 16mo, 121p, col frn, b/w)	Macmillan	1927	Davis, Marguerite	25-45	*
Coatsworth, Eliz.	House-Boat Summer (1st, 8vo, 191p, p-o, 1-color, pep, DJ/2.00)	Macmillan	1942	Davis, Marguerite	70-100	
Coatsworth, Eliz.	Littlest House (1st, 8vo, p-o, 150p, 1-color, pep, DJ/1.50)	Macmillan	1940	Davis, Marguerite	30-50	
Brink, Carol R.	Magical Melons (1st, 8vo, 193p, fp b/w, cep, DJ/2.00)	Macmillan	1944	Davis, Marguerite	70-100	
Coatsworth, Eliz.	Plum Daffy Adventure (1st {std}, 8vo, 161p, blue cl, b/w, pep, DJ/2.50)	Macmillan	1947	Davis, Marguerite	30-50	
Rossetti, Christina	Sing-Song (1st, 16mo, green cl, 122p, b/w, pep)	Macmillan	1924	Davis, Marguerite	30-50	
Welles, Winifred	Skipping Along (1st, 8vo, green cl, 52p, b/w)	Macmillan	1931	Davis, Marguerite	25-40	*
Tileston, Mary W.	Sugar & Spice & all that's Nice (1st [revised], 8vo, red/gilt, 220p, 4cp)	Little/Brown	1928	Davis, Marguerite	35-60	
Richards, Laura E.	Tirra Lirra (1st, 8vo, 194p, col frn, pep, DJ/2.50, NH)	Little/Brown	1932	Davis, Marguerite	45-70	
Various	Told Under the Blue Umbrella (1st, lg8vo, 161p, b/w)	Macmillan	1933	Davis, Marguerite	30-50	*
Coatsworth, Eliz.	Trudy and the Tree House (1st, 8vo, 114p, fp b/w, DJ/1.75)	Macmillan	1944	Davis, Marguerite	30-50	*
Coatsworth, Eliz.	Twelve Months Make a Year (1st, 8vo, 198p, 1-color, pep, DJ/2.00)	Macmillan	1943	Davis, Marguerite	25-40	
Alcott, Louisa M.	Under the Lilacs (1st, 8vo, 284p, p-o, 6cp, pep)	Little/Brown	1928	Davis, Marguerite	30-50	
Davis, Robert	Partners of Powder Hole (1st, 8vo, wraps, 167p, b/w)	Holiday House	(1947)	Davis, Marshall	25-40	
Ovington, Mary W.	Zeke (1st, sm8vo, blue cl, 205p, uncut, b/w)	Harcourt	(1931)	Davis, Natalie H.	80-130	
Dawson, Lucy	Dogs as I See Them (1st AM, lg4to, [89]p, fp color, pep, DJ/1.00)	Grosset/Dunlap	(1937)	Dawson, Lucy	70-125	
Lewis, Lorna	Puppy & the Cat (1st, sq8vo, 44p, fp b/w, DJ/0.50)	Grosset/Dunlap	(1940)	Dawson, Lucy	25-40	
Bayne, Marie	Fairy Tales from Erin's Isle (1st, 8vo, green cl, 132p, teg, b/w)	L: Sands	1908	Dawson/Petts	70-120	
Smith, Gertrude	Boys of Marmiton Prairie (1st, sm8vo, gilt, 262p, 5pl)	Little/Brown	1899	Day, Bertha C.	30-50	*
Pyle, Katharine	Where the Wind Blows (1st, 4to, 120p, p-o, 11cp)	R.H. Russell	1902	Day, Bertha C.	200-300	
Pyle, Katharine	Where the Wind Blows (1st {this pub.}, 8vo, 295p, 10pl)	Dutton	(1910)	Day, Bertha C.	50-85	
Garis, Howard	White Crystals (1st, sm8vo, tan cl, 243p, 6pl)	Little/Brown	1904	Day, Bertha C.	40-60	

AUTHOR	TITLE	PUBLISHER	DATE	ARTIST	PRICE	LC
Baker, George A.	Point Lace and Diamonds (1st, 4to, 82p, gilt, 12cp)	Stokes	1892	Day, Francis	100-165	
Beston, Henry	Chimney Farm Bedtime Stories (1st {std}, 8vo, 79p, DJ/3.75)	Holt, Rinehart	(1966)	Day, Maurice	25-45	
Totheroh, Dan	David Hotfoot (1st, 8vo, p-o, 246p, col frn, 4pl)	Doran	(1926)	Day, Maurice	30-50	
Jewett, Eleanore	Egyptian Tales of Magic (1st, 8vo, 257p, 8cp)	Little/Brown	1924	Day, Maurice	50-85	
Beston, Henry	Firelight Fairy Book (1st, 8vo, 257p, color, pep)	Atl. Monthly Pr.	(1919)	Day, Maurice	65-100	
Bergengren, Ralph	Jane, Joseph and John (1st, 4to, ibds, 62p, 6cp)	Atl. Monthly Pr.	(1918)	Day, Maurice	50-85	*
Chase, Mary Ellen	Mary Christmas (1st, sm8vo, ibds, 142p, b/w frn by...)	Little/Brown	1926	Day, Maurice	50-80	
Dunbar, Aldis	Once There was a Prince (1st, 8vo, 302p, blue cl, pep, col frn)	Little/Brown	1928	Day, Maurice	40-60	*
King, Beulah	Ruffs & Pompons (1st, 8vo, 256p, col frn, 6pl, pep)	Little/Brown	1924	Day, Maurice	30-50	
Beston, Henry	Starlight Wonder Book (1st, 8vo, 262p, gilt, col frn, fp b/w, pep)	Atl. Monthly Pr.	(1923)	Day, Maurice	50-80	*
Eaton, Jeanette	Story of Transportation (1st {std}, sm8vo, 52p, cp, pep)	Harper	1927	Day, Maurice	25-40	
Eaton, Jeanette	That Lively Man: Ben Franklin (1st, 8vo, 253p, b/w, DJ/2.50)	Wm. Morrow	1948	Day, Maurice	20-25	
Brown, Abbie F.	Under the Rowan Tree (1st, 8vo, p-o, 189p, col frn, pep)	Houghton	1926	Day, Maurice	25-45	*
Jewett, Eleanore	Wonder Tales from Tibet (1st, sm8vo, 183p, green cl, 8cp)	Little/Brown	1922	Day, Maurice	50-80	
Steele, Robert (ed)	Russian Garland (1st, 8vo, 243p, 6cp)	McBride	1916	De Rosciszewski, R.	200-300	*
Coatsworth, Eliz.	Alice-All-by-Herself (1st, lg8vo, 181p, col frn, 7pl, pep, DJ/2.00)	Macmillan	1937	DeAngeli, Marguerite	60-90	
DeAngeli, Marguerite	Black Fox of Lorne (1st {std}, 4to, 191p, 11 fp b/w, DJ/2.95, NH)	Doubleday	1956	DeAngeli, Marguerite	45-70	
DeAngeli, Marguerite	Bright April (1st {std}, sq8vo, 86p, color, pep, DJ/2.50)	Doubleday	(1946)	DeAngeli, Marguerite	55-80	
Means, Florence C.	Candle in the Mist (1st, sm8vo, 252p, blue cl, pep, 4pl)	Houghton	1931	DeAngeli, Marguerite	40-65	
Ferris, Helen	Challenge Stories/Courage & Love for Girls (1st {std}, 8vo, 328p, col frn)	Doubleday/Doran	1936	DeAngeli, Marguerite	30-45	*
Kelly, Eric P.	Christmas Nightingale (1st, 8vo, red cl, 73p, 4 b/w)	Macmillan	1932	DeAngeli, Marguerite	30-50	
DeAngeli, Marguerite	Copper-Toed Boots (1st {std}, sm4to, ibds, [92]p, color, pep, DJ/2.00)	Doubleday/Doran	1938	DeAngeli, Marguerite	65-90	
Sackett, Rose M.	Cousin from Clare (1st, sm8vo, 270p, green cl, 4pl)	Macmillan	1932	DeAngeli, Marguerite	30-50	
Meigs, Cornelia L.	Covered Bridge (1st, sq8vo, 145p, blue cl, col frn, b/w, DJ/2.00)	Macmillan	1936	DeAngeli, Marguerite	40-60	
DeAngeli, Marguerite	Door in the Wall (1st {std}, 8vo, 112p, color, pep, DJ/2.50, NM)	Doubleday	(1949)	DeAngeli, Marguerite	80-125	R
Yonge, Charlotte	Dove in the Eagle's Nest (1st, sm8vo, 294p, 3cp, 8pl, pep, DJ)	Macmillan	1926	DeAngeli, Marguerite	60-90	
DeAngeli, Marguerite	Elin's Amerika (1st {std}, sq8vo, tan cl, [96], color, pep, DJ/2.00)	Doubleday/Doran	1941	DeAngeli, Marguerite	70-100	
DeAngeli, Marguerite	Empty Barn (1st, 8vo, 60p, color, DJ/3.25)	Westminster Pr.	(1966)	DeAngeli, Marguerite	30-55	
Grimm Bros.	Goose Girl (1st {std}, 4to, 31p, fp color, dep, DJ/2.75)	Doubleday	(1964)	DeAngeli, Marguerite	30-50	
DeAngeli, Marguerite	Henner's Lydia (1st {std}, sq8vo, ibds, [70]p, color, DJ/2.00)	Doubleday/Doran	1936	DeAngeli, Marguerite	70-100	
Robinson, Tom P.	In & Out (1st, lg8vo, 140p, color, pep, DJ/2.50)	Viking	1943	DeAngeli, Marguerite	50-85	
DeAngeli, Marguerite	Jared's Island (1st {std}, lg8vo, blue/gilt, 95p, col frn, DJ/2.50)	Doubleday	1947	DeAngeli, Marguerite	40-70	
Gemmill, Jane B.	Joan Wanted a Kitty (1st, 8vo, blue cl, 150p, color, pep, DJ/2.00)	Winston	(1937)	DeAngeli, Marguerite	60-90	
DeAngeli, Marguerite	Just Like David (1st {std}, 8vo, green cl, 122p, color, pep, DJ/2.50)	Doubleday	(1951)	DeAngeli, Marguerite	50-80	
Gale, Elizabeth	Katrina Van Ost & Silver Rose (1st, sm8vo, 294p, fp b/w)	Putnam	(1934)	DeAngeli, Marguerite	45-70	
Yonge, Charlotte	Lances of Lynwood (1st, 12mo, green cl, 217p, col frn, 6pl, pep)	Macmillan	1929	DeAngeli, Marguerite	30-60	
Hawkins, Quail	Little Book of Prayers and Graces (1st, sq12mo, [32]p, ibds, pep, DJ/1.00)	Doubleday	(1952)	DeAngeli, Marguerite	25-45	
Yonge, Charlotte	Little Duke (1st, sm8vo, 188p, blue cl, 3cp, 7pl, pep)	Macmillan	1927	DeAngeli, Marguerite	40-60	
Forbes, Helen	Mario's Castle (1st, 12mo, 198p, col frn, pep, 3pl)	Macmillan	1928	DeAngeli, Marguerite	40-60	*
Gray, Eliz. J.	Meggy McIntosh (1st {std}, 8vo, 274p, col frn, pep, NH)	Doubleday/Doran	1930	DeAngeli, Marguerite	60-90	
Meigs, Cornelia L.	New Moon (1st, sm8vo, blue/gilt, 251p, col frn by...)	Macmillan	1924	DeAngeli, Marguerite	35-50	
DeAngeli, Marguerite	Nursery & Mother Goose Rhymes (1st {std}, folio, 192p, color, DJ, CH)	Doubleday	1954	DeAngeli, Marguerite	120-180	R
Bible	Old Testament (1st {std}, lg4to, 256p, color, pep, DJ)	Doubleday	(1960)	DeAngeli, Marguerite	60-85	
DeAngeli, Marguerite	Petite Suzanne (1st {std}, sq8vo, ibds, [88]p, color, pep, DJ/2.00)	Doubleday/Doran	1937	DeAngeli, Marguerite	120-160	
Hawkins, Quail	Prayers & Graces for Small Children (1st, sq8vo [32]p, ibds, color, DJ/0.50)	Grosset/Dunlap	(1941)	DeAngeli, Marguerite	60-90	
Yonge, Charlotte	Prince & the Page (1st, sm8vo, 246p, blue/gilt, 3cp, 8pl, pep)	Macmillan	1925	DeAngeli, Marguerite	40-70	
Kyle, Anne D.	Red Sky over Rome (1st, 8vo, 260p, 8pl, DJ/2.00)	Houghton	1938	DeAngeli, Marguerite	40-60	*
Faulkner, Nancy	Side Saddle for Dandy (1st {std}, 8vo, 214p, b/w, DJ/2.75)	Doubleday	(1954)	DeAngeli, Marguerite	25-40	
DeAngeli, Marguerite	Skippack School (1st {std}, sq8vo, [88]p, color, pep, DJ/2.00)	Doubleday/Doran	1939	DeAngeli, Marguerite	80-120	
DeAngeli, Marguerite	Summer Day with Ted & Nina (1st {std}, 8vo, ibds, [32]p, color, DJ/0.75)	Doubleday/Doran	1940	DeAngeli, Marguerite	80-130	
DeAngeli, Marguerite	Ted & Nina Go to Grocery Store (1st {std}, ob12mo, [32]p, ibds, color, pep)	Doubleday/Doran	1935	DeAngeli, Marguerite	60-90	
DeAngeli, Marguerite	Ted & Nina Have a Happy Rainy Day (1st {std}, ob12mo, ibds, color)	Doubleday/Doran	1936	DeAngeli, Marguerite	60-90	
DeAngeli, Marguerite	Thee, Hannah! (1st {std}, sq8vo, [94]p, color, DJ/2.00)	Doubleday/Doran	1940	DeAngeli, Marguerite	70-100	R
Worth, Kathryn	They Loved to Laugh (1st {std}, sm8vo, grey cl, 269p, b/w, pep, DJ/2.00)	Doubleday/Doran	1942	DeAngeli, Marguerite	30-50	
DeAngeli, Marguerite	Turkey for Christmas (1st, 12mo, [49]p, ibds, 1-color, pep, DJ/0.75)	Westminster Pr.	(1944)	DeAngeli, Marguerite	35-50	
DeAngeli, Marguerite	Turkey for Christmas (1st {this fmt}, lg8vo, 48p, 4 fp color, DJ/2.95)	Westminster Pr.	(1965)	DeAngeli, Marguerite	25-45	
DeAngeli, Marguerite	Up the Hill (1st {std}, sq8vo, tan cl, 88p, color, pep, DJ/2.00)	Doubleday/Doran	1942	DeAngeli, Marguerite	70-125	
DeAngeli, Marguerite	Yonie Wondernose (1st {std}, sq4to, [39]p, ibds, fp col, pep, DJ/2.00, CH)	Doubleday/Doran	1944	DeAngeli, Marguerite	80-140	
Wheeler, F.G.	Billy Whiskers at the Circus (1st, lg8vo, 147p, 6cp)	Saalfield	1908	DeBebian, Arthur	70-100	
Montgomery, F.T.	Billy Whiskers at the Fair (1st, lg8vo, ibds, 163p, cp)	Saalfield	(1909)	DeBebian, Arthur	70-120	
Pickard, William B.	Adventures of Alcassim (1st, 8vo, 352p, red/gilt, fp b/w)	L: J. Cape	1936	DeBosschere, Jean	40-65	
DeBosschere, Jean	Beasts & Men (4to, 179p, green cl, 12cp, pep)	L: Heinemann	(1918)	DeBosschere, Jean	200-300	
DeBosschere, Jean	Christmas Tales of Flanders (1st AM, 4to, 144p, gilt, 12cp, pep)	Dodd	1917	DeBosschere, Jean	180-240	
DeBosschere, Jean	City Curious (1st, 8vo, 178p, 8cp, pep)	L: Heinemann	(1920)	DeBosschere, Jean	180-240	
DeBosschere, Jean	City Curious (1st AM, sq8vo, yellow cl, 178p, 8cp, pep)	Dodd/Heinemann	1920	DeBosschere, Jean	180-240	
DeBosschere, Jean	Closed Door (1st, 8vo, 131p, 16pl)	L: John Lane	1917	DeBosschere, Jean	100-165	
Cervantes	Don Quixote (1st, 4to, 311p, black/gilt, 25 color)	L: Constable	1922	DeBosschere, Jean	120-200	
Aristophanes	Eleven Comedies (1st, 8vo, 2 vols, black/gilt, 16cp)	H. Liveright	1928	DeBosschere, Jean	100-160	
Anthony, E. & J.	Fairies Up-to-Date (1st, 8vo, red cl, p-o, [207]p, color)	Little/Brown	1923	DeBosschere, Jean	180-250	
DeBosschere, Jean	Folk Tales of Flanders (1st AM, 4to, 179p, teg, gilt, 12cp, pep)	Dodd	1918	DeBosschere, Jean	160-240	
Swift, Jonathan	Gulliver's Travels (1st AM, 4to, 135p, blue/gilt, 4cp)	Dodd/Heinemann	[1920]	DeBosschere, Jean	160-240	
DeBosschere, Jean	Gulliver's Travels into Lilliput (1st, 4to, 135p, pink cl, 4cp)	L: Heinemann	(1920)	DeBosschere, Jean	160-235	
Cervantes	History of Don Quixote... (1st, 4to, 311p, gilt, 25cp)	L: Constable	1922	DeBosschere, Jean	200-300	
DeBosschere, Jean	Love Books of Ovid (1st, lg8vo, 216p, blue/gilt, 16cp)	L: John Lane	1925	DeBosschere, Jean	100-175	
Aldington (tr.)	The Decameron... (1st, lg8vo, black cl, p-o, 576p, 16cp)	Garden City	(1930)	DeBosschere, Jean	55-80	
Sinclair, May	Uncanny Stories (1st AM, sm8vo, red/gilt, 362p, 21pl)	NY: Macmillan	1923	DeBosschere, Jean	100-160	
DeBosschere, Jean	Weird Islands (1st, lg8vo, 210p, blue cl, col frn, b/w)	L: Chapman/Hall	1921	DeBosschere, Jean	120-180	*
DeBrunhoff, Jean	ABC of Babar (1st AM, sq8vo, ibds, [60]p, color, pep)	Random	(1936)	DeBrunhoff, Jean	200-325	

AUTHOR	TITLE	PUBLISHER	DATE	ARTIST	PRICE	LC
DeBrunhoff, Jean	Babar & Father Christmas (1st {this pub.}, sq8vo, ibds, [30]p)	Wonder Books	(1940)	DeBrunhoff, Jean	70-100	
DeBrunhoff, Jean	Babar & Father Christmas (1st AM, folio, ibds, [40]p, color, pep, DJ/3.00)	Random	(1940)	DeBrunhoff, Jean	500-700	
DeBrunhoff, Jean	Babar & His Children (1st AM, folio, ibds, [40]p, color, pep, DJ/3.00)	Random	(1938)	DeBrunhoff, Jean	500-700	R
DeBrunhoff, Jean	Babar & Zephir (1st, 4to, ibds, 39p, color, DJ/1.00)	Random	(1942)	DeBrunhoff, Jean	200-300	
DeBrunhoff, Jean	Babar the King (1st {this format}, sq8vo, ibds, 48p, color, pep)	Random	(1935)	DeBrunhoff, Jean	120-200	*
DeBrunhoff, Jean	Babar the King (1st AM, lg folio, 48p, ibds, color, pep)	Smith/Haas	1935	DeBrunhoff, Jean	500-700	R
DeBrunhoff, Jean	Babar the King (1st UK, folio, 48p, ibds, color)	L: Methuen	1936	DeBrunhoff, Jean	400-600	
DeBrunhoff, Jean	Babar's Friend Zephir (1st UK, folio, 42p, ibds, color)	L: Methuen	1937	DeBrunhoff, Jean	400-600	
DeBrunhoff, Jean	Story of Babar (1st AM, folio, 47p, ibds, color, pep)	Smith/Haas	1933	DeBrunhoff, Jean	500-700	
DeBrunhoff, Jean	Story of Babar (1st {this format}, sq8vo, ibds, 48p, color)	Random	(1933)	DeBrunhoff, Jean	150-225	
DeBrunhoff, Jean	Story of Babar (1st UK, folio, ibds, 48p, color)	L: Methuen	1934	DeBrunhoff, Jean	400-650	
DeBrunhoff, Jean	Travels of Babar (1st AM, folio, ibds, 47p, color, pep)	Smith/Haas	1934	DeBrunhoff, Jean	450-650	R
DeBrunhoff, Jean	Travels of Babar (1st {this format}, sq8vo, 48p, ibds, color)	Random	(1934)	DeBrunhoff, Jean	150-220	
DeBrunhoff, Jean	Zephir's Holidays (1st AM, folio, ibds, color, pep, DJ/3.00)	Random	(1937)	DeBrunhoff, Jean	400-600	R
DeBrunhoff, Laurent	Anatole & his Donkey (1st AM {std}, ob4to, [38]p, 1-color, cep, DJ/2.95)	Macmillan	1963	DeBrunhoff, Laurent	60-90	
DeBrunhoff, Laurent	Babar & the Professor (1st, lg4to, ibds, 40p, color, pep, DJ/3.95)	Random	(1957)	DeBrunhoff, Laurent	80-125	R
DeBrunhoff, Laurent	Babar at the Seashore (1st, sq32mo, [28]p, ibds, color, DJ)	Random	(1969)	DeBrunhoff, Laurent	50-85	
DeBrunhoff, Laurent	Babar Comes to America (1st, lg4to, [64]p, color, pep, DJ/3.95)	Random	(1965)	DeBrunhoff, Laurent	70-100	
DeBrunhoff, Laurent	Babar Goes on a Picnic (1st, sq32mo, ibds, [28]p, color, DJ)	Random	(1969)	DeBrunhoff, Laurent	60-100	
DeBrunhoff, Laurent	Babar Goes Skiing (1st, sq32mo, [28]p, ibds, color, DJ)	Random	(1969)	DeBrunhoff, Laurent	60-100	
DeBrunhoff, Laurent	Babar Loses his Crown (1st, 8vo, 63p, color, pep, DJ/1.95)	Beginner Books	(1967)	DeBrunhoff, Laurent	50-85	
DeBrunhoff, Laurent	Babar the Gardner (1st, sq32mo, ibds, [28]p, color, DJ)	Random	(1969)	DeBrunhoff, Laurent	50-85	
DeBrunhoff, Laurent	Babar's Birthday Surprise (1st AM, lg4to, [28]p, ibds, color, DJ/3.95)	Random	(1970)	DeBrunhoff, Laurent	50-80	
DeBrunhoff, Laurent	Babar's Castle (1st, lg4to, 30p, ibds, color, pep, DJ/3.95)	Random	(1962)	DeBrunhoff, Laurent	60-100	
DeBrunhoff, Laurent	Babar's Cousin that Rascal Arthur (1st AM, folio, 47p, ibds, col, DJ/3.50)	Random	(1948)	DeBrunhoff, Laurent	400-600	
DeBrunhoff, Laurent	Babar's French Lessons (1st AM, lg4to, [28]p, color, DJ/3.95)	Random	(1963)	DeBrunhoff, Laurent	80-120	
DeBrunhoff, Laurent	Babar's Picnic (1st AM, folio, 39p, ibds, color, DJ/3.50)	Random	(1949)	DeBrunhoff, Laurent	450-600	
DeBrunhoff, Laurent	Babar's Visit to Bird Island (1st UK, sm folio, 39p, ibds, color)	L: Methuen	(1952)	DeBrunhoff, Laurent	350-500	
DeBrunhoff, Laurent	Bonhomme (1st AM, 8vo, [48]p, fp 1-color, cep, DJ/2.95)	Pantheon	1965	DeBrunhoff, Laurent	90-140	
DeBrunhoff, Laurent	Captain Serafina (1st {std}, 4to, [30]p, color, DJ/3.00)	World	(1963)	DeBrunhoff, Laurent	70-120	
Roselli, Auro	Cats of the Eiffel Tower (1st {std}, 8vo, 44p, color, DJ/3.25)	Delacorte Pr.	(1967)	DeBrunhoff, Laurent	45-70	
DeBrunhoff, Laurent	Picnic at Babar's (1st UK, folio, 40p, ibds, color, pep)	L: Methuen	(1950)	DeBrunhoff, Laurent	300-450	
DeBrunhoff, Laurent	Serafina the Giraffe (1st {std}, 4to, [30]p, color, DJ/3.00)	World	(1961)	DeBrunhoff, Laurent	70-120	
DeBrunhoff, Laurent	Serafina's Lucky Find (1st {std}, 4to, [30]p, color, DJ/3.00)	World	(1962)	DeBrunhoff, Laurent	70-120	
Obligado, George	Warrior & the Princess (1st, 4to, ibds, [60]p, color, pep)	Golden Press	1961	DeGaspari, Giorgi	50-80	
Allee, Marjorie H.	Ann's Surprising Summer (1st, sm8vo, 198p, b/w, pep)	Houghton	1933	DeGogorza, Maitland	30-50	*
Allee, Marjorie H.	Jane's Island (1st, 8vo, 235p, green cl, fp b/w, pep, NH)	Houghton	1931	DeGogorza, Maitland	50-80	*
Weston, Christine	There & Then (1st, sm8vo, 176p, green/gilt, fp b/w, DJ/2.50)	Scribner	1947	DeGoutiere, George	35-60	*
Willson, Dixie	Tuffy Good Luck (1st, sq12mo, ipcb, pep, 39p, color)	Volland	(1927)	DeKarekjarto, I.	80-120	
Bennett, John	Barnaby Lee (1st, 12mo, 454p, blue/gilt, 34pl, PPP)	Century	1902	DeLand, Clyde O.	70-130	
Crowley, Mary C.	Daughter of New France (1st, sm8vo, 409p, blue/gilt, 6pl)	Little/Brown	1901	DeLand, Clyde O.	30-50	
Oxley, James M.	Fife & Drum at Louisburg (1st, 12mo, 307p, 4pl)	Little/Brown	1899	DeLand, Clyde O.	30-50	
Major, Charles	Forest Hearth (1st, sm8vo, teg, green/gilt, 354p, 8pl)	Macmillan	1903	DeLand, Clyde O.	30-50	
Mitchell, S. Weir	Mr. Kris Kringle (1st, sm8vo, teg, 105p, 5cp)	Jacobs	1893	DeLand, Clyde O.	120-200	R
Chesnutt, Charles	Wife of His Youth (1st, sm8vo, 323p, pink/gilt, b/w)	Houghton	1899	DeLand, Clyde O.	350-500	
Alger, Horatio	Young Musician (1st, sm8vo, 341p, 7pl)	Penn	1906	DeLand, Clyde O.	50-80	
Kaufmann, Alicia	No Room for Nicky (1st {std}, ob4to, [32]p, 2-color, DJ/3.95)	Hawthorn Books	(1969)	DeLarrea, Vicki	25-45	
Starbird, Kaye	Pheasant on a Route Seven (1st {std}, 8vo, 74p, fp b/w, cep, DJ/3.50)	Lippincott	(1968)	DeLarrea, Victoria	40-65	R*
Van Gorden, Scott	Pioneer's Hoard (1st, 8vo, 530p, b/w, pep)	Rhodes/McClure	1902	DeLay, H.S.	30-45	
DuBois, W.E.B.	Quest of the Silver Fleece (1st, 8vo, 434p, grey cl, 4pl)	McClurg	1911	DeLay, H.S.	250-400	
Grey, Zane	The Shortstop (1st, sm8vo, green cl, 310p, 6pl)	McClurg	1909	DeLay, H.S.	800-1200	
Edmonds, Walter D.	Wilderness Clearing (1st, 8vo, 156p, b/w, DJ/2.50)	Dodd	1944	DeMartelly, John	40-65	*
Kalnay, Francis	Chucaro, Wild Pony of Pampa (1st {std}, 8vo, 126p, b/w, DJ/2.75, NH)	Harcourt	(1958)	DeMiskey, Julian	40-65	
Montgomery, R.	Tim's Mountain (1st {std}, 8vo, 218p, b/w, DJ/2.95)	World	(1959)	DeMiskey, Julian	20-30	
Butterworth, Oliver	Trouble with Jenny's Ear (1st {std}, 8vo, 275p, fp b/w, DJ)	Little/Brown	(1960)	DeMiskey, Julian	80-125	
Green, Louisa M.	Brother of the Birds (1st AM, 4to, 123p, purple/gilt, 21 tipl)	McKay	(1929)	DeMonvel, M.B.	80-125	
Egan, Maurice F.	Everybody's Saint Francis (1st, 8vo, green/gilt, teg, 191p, 8cp)	Century	1912	DeMonvel, M.B.	60-90	
France, Anatole	Girls & Boys (1st AM, 4to, 25p, ipcb, 12cp)	Duffield	1913	DeMonvel, M.B.	120-180	
DeMonvel, M.B.	Good Children & Bad (1st AM, ob4to, 48p, gilt, color)	Cassell	(1890)	DeMonvel, M.B.	170-220	
DeMonvel, M.B.	Jeanne d' Arc (1st, ob4to, white cl, 47p, color)	(Paris)	[1896]	DeMonvel, M.B.	180-240	
DeMonvel, M.B.	Joan of Arc (1st AM, ob4to, 47p, purple cl, color)	Century	1907	DeMonvel, M.B.	120-180	
DeMonvel, M.B.	Joan of Arc (1st {this pub}, ob8vo, tan cl, p-o, [25]p, 10 color)	McKay	1918	DeMonvel, M.B.	60-90	*
France, Anatole	Our Children (1st AM, 4to, ibds, 25p, 12cp)	Duffield	1917	DeMonvel, M.B.	100-160	
DePaola, Tomie	Fight the Night (1st {std}, 4to, [33]p, color, DJ/3.50)	Lippincott	(1968)	DePaola, Tomie	30-45	
Lexau, Joan M.	Finders Keepers, Losers Weepers (1st, 8vo, [36]p, 3-color, pep, DJ/3.25)	Lippincott	(1967)	DePaola, Tomie	25-40	
Schneider, Nina	Hercules: Gentle Giant (1st {std}, ob4to, [48]p, fp 1-color, cep, DJ/3.95)	Hawthorn Books	(1969)	DePaola, Tomie	30-45	
Boylan, Eleanor	How to Be a Puppeteer (1st {std}, 8vo, 132p, b/w, DJ/4.95)	McCall Pub.	(1970)	DePaola, Tomie	20-35	
DePaola, Tomie	Joe and the Snow (1st {std}, 8vo, [32]p, color, DJ/4.25)	Hawthorn Books	(1968)	DePaola, Tomie	25-45	
DePaola, Tomie	Journey of the Kiss (1st {std}, ob8vo, [39]p, color, DJ/3.95)	Hawthorn Books	(1970)	DePaola, Tomie	25-45	
Shapp, Martha	Let's Find Out about Summer (1st, 8vo, 42p, color, DJ/2.50)	F. Watts	1963	DePaola, Tomie	25-40	
Alexenberg, Melvin	Light and Sight (1st, 4to, [46]p, 2-color, cep, DJ/4.50)	Prentice-Hall	(1969)	DePaola, Tomie	25-40	*
DePaola, Tomie	Monsters' Ball (1st {std}, 8vo, [31]p, color, DJ/4.25)	Hawthorn Books	(1970)	DePaola, Tomie	30-45	
DePaola, Tomie	Parker Pig, Esquire (1st {std}, 12mo, [32]p, color, DJ/3.95)	Hawthorn Books	(1969)	DePaola, Tomie	30-45	
Jacobs, Leland (ed)	Poetry for Chuckles and Grins (1st, lg8vo, 64p, 2-color, DJ)	Garrard Pub.	(1968)	DePaola, Tomie	50-80	
Jane, Mary C.	Rocking-Chair Ghost (1st {std}, 8vo, 58p, b/w, DJ/2.95)	Lippincott	(1969)	DePaola, Tomie	25-45	*
Rinkoff, Barbara	Rutherford T. Finds 21B (1st, 8vo, [47]p, fp 2-color, DJ)	Putnam	(1970)	DePaola, Tomie	30-50	
Miller, Lisa	Sound (1st, 8vo, [46]p, fp 2-color, DJ/2.95)	Coward	(1965)	DePaola, Tomie	30-45	
Alexenberg, Melvin	Sound Science (1st, 4to, [48]p, 2-color, cep, DJ/4.75)	Prentice-Hall	(1968)	DePaola, Tomie	25-40	*

AUTHOR	TITLE	PUBLISHER	DATE	ARTIST	PRICE	LC
Epstein, Samuel	Take this Hammer (1st {std}, 8vo, [32]p, color, DJ/3.95)	Hawthorn Books	(1969)	DePaola, Tomie	25-40	
Belpre, Pura	Tiger and the Rabbit (1st {std}, 8vo, 127p, ipcb, fp b/w, DJ/2.95)	Lippincott	(1965)	DePaola, Tomie	25-40	
Hardendorff, Jeanne	Tricky Peik & other Picture Tales (1st, 8vo, 122p, gilt, fp b/w, DJ/3.25)	Lippincott	(1967)	DePaola, Tomie	30-45	
DePaola, Tomie	Who Needs Holes? (1st {std}, 8vo, [30]p, color, DJ/3.95)	Hawthorn Books	(1970)	DePaola, Tomie	30-45	*
DePaola, Tomie	Wonderful Dragon of Timlin (1st {std}, lg8vo, unpag, color, DJ/3.50)	Bobbs-Merrill	(1966)	DePaola, Tomie	35-50	
Fisher, Aileen	Fisherman of Galilee (1st, 8vo, 223p, b/w, DJ/2.95)	Nelson	1959	DePol, John	20-35	*
DeRegniers, Beatrice	Little Book (1st, 32mo, [24]p, color, dep, DJ/2.50)	H.Z. Walck	1961	DeRegniers, Beatrice	25-40	
Brown, Margaret W.	House of a Hundred Windows (1st, 4to, 32p, ibds, color, DJ/1.75)	Harper	1945	DeVeyrac, Robert	80-130	
Brown, Margaret W.	SHHhhh... Bang! (1st {std}, sm4to, ipcb, [32]p, fp 2-color, cep, DJ/1.50)	Harper	(1943)	DeVeyrac, Robert	80-130	
Brereton, Frederick	On the Field of Waterloo (1st, sm8vo, 400p, gilt, 8pl)	L: Blackie	1915	DeWalton, John	70-100	
Lambert, Clara	Story of Alaska (1st {std}, sq4to, ibds, [40]p, color, pep, DJ/1.50)	Harper	(1940)	DeWitt, C.H.	60-100	
McNeer, May	Story of California (1st {std}, 4to, [32]p, ibds, color, pep, DJ/1.50)	Harper	1944	DeWitt, C.H.	60-90	
McClintock, Marshall	Story of New England (1st {std}, 4to, ibds, 39p, color, pep, DJ/1.50)	Harper	1941	DeWitt, C.H.	60-100	
Hark, Ann	Story of Pennsylvania Dutch (1st {std}, 4to, [32]p, ibds, col, pep, DJ/1.50)	Harper	1943	DeWitt, C.H.	40-65	
Gilchrist, Marie	Story of the Great Lakes (1st {std}, 4to, [32]p, ibds, color, DJ/1.50)	Harper	(1942)	DeWitt, C.H.	50-80	
McNeer, May	Story of the Great Plains (1st {std}, 4to, ibds, 32p, color, pep, DJ/1.50)	Harper	(1943)	DeWitt, C.H.	35-50	
McClintock, Marshall	Story of the Mississippi (1st {std}, 4to, ibds, 39p, color, pep, DJ/1.50)	Harper	1941	DeWitt, C.H.	50-80	
McNeer, May	Story of the South-West (1st, sq4to, ibds, [32]p, color, pep, DJ/1.75)	Harper	(1948)	DeWitt, C.H.	60-90	
Weatherly, Fred E.	Little Pickle (1st, sm8vo, [24]p, ibds, 7 chromos, pep)	L: Hildesheimer	(1885)	Dealy, Jane	80-145	
Mother Goose	Mother Goose Picture Book (1st, 12mo, 119p, color, pep)	S. Gabriel	(1939)	Deane, Elsie	55-80	*
Sharp, Evelyn	All the Way to Fairyland (1st, 8vo, 196p, 8cp & cvr by...)	L/NY: Longmans	1898	Dearmer, Mabel	200-300	
Dearmer, Mabel	Book of Penny Toys (1st, lg8vo, ibds, 94p, 14 color)	L: Macmillan	1899	Dearmer, Mabel	300-450	*
Dearmer, Mabel	Cockyolly Bird (1st, 4to, 221p, 10 ticp)	L: Hodder	(1914)	Dearmer, Mabel	170-240	*
Housman, Laurence	Story of the Seven Young Goslings (1st, 4to, ibds, [32]p, 6cp)	L: Blackie	1899	Dearmer, Mabel	300-450	
Sharp, Evelyn	Wymps & other Fairy Tales (1st, 8vo, 190p, 8cp)	NY: J. Lane	1897	Dearmer, Mabel	250-350	
Purnell, Idella	Talking Bird (1st, sq8vo, 95p, col frn, 9pl, pep)	Macmillan	1930	Dehlsen, Frances P.	25-45	
Lindgren, Astrid	Skrallan and the Pirates (1st {std}, lg4to, 48p, color, DJ/4.95)	Doubleday	(1969)	Deler/Hallgren	50-80	
Delessert, Etienne	Endless Party (1st AM {std}, 4to, [32]p, color, DJ/4.50)	Harlin Quist	(1967)	Delessert, Etienne	30-50	
Lifton, Betty	Secret Seller (1st {std}, 4to, [42]p, fp color, DJ/3.95)	Norton	(1967)	Delessert, Etienne	45-70	
Ionesco, Eugene	Story Number 1 (1st AM, 4to, [32]p, color, DJ/4.50, NYTBI)	Harlin Quist	(1968)	Delessert, Etienne	60-95	
Ionesco, Eugene	Story Number 2 (1st AM, 4to, [30]p, color, DJ/3.95)	Harlin Quist	(1970)	Delessert, Etienne	30-50	
Delessert, Etienne	The Tree (1st AM {std}, 8vo, [28]p, fp color, pep, DJ/3.95)	Harlin Quist	(1966)	Delessert, Etienne	30-50	
Mendoza, George	Wart Snake in a Fig Tree (1st {std}, 8vo, ibds, [32]p, color, cep, DJ/3.95)	Dial Press	(1968)	Delessert, Etienne	30-50	
La Fontaine, J.	Fables of La Fontaine (1st, 4to, 304p, teg, gilt, 24pl)	L: Nimmo	1884	Delierre, A.	250-400	
Stoddard, William O.	Little Smoke (1st, 8vo, blue/gilt, 295p, 14pl, PPP)	Appleton	1891	Dellenbaugh, Fred	160-250	
Deming, Therese O.	American Animal Life (1st, ob4to, [74]p, p-o, 24cp)	Stokes	1916	Deming, Edwin W.	150-220	
Deming, Therese O.	Animal Folk of Wood & Plain (1st, ob4to, [38]p, p-o, 12cp)	Stokes	(1916)	Deming, Edwin W.	120-180	
Garland, Hamlin	Boy Life on the Prairie (1st, 12mo, brown/gilt, 423p, teg, 8pl)	Macmillan	1899	Deming, Edwin W.	55-80	
Deming, Therese O.	Children of the Wild (1st, 4to, [26]p, 6cp)	Stokes	(1902)	Deming, Edwin W.	90-120	
Deming, Therese O.	Cosel: With Geronimo on His Last Raid (1st, lg8vo, 125p, 6cp, DJ/1.25)	Davis Co.	1938	Deming, Edwin W.	60-100	
Deming, Therese O.	Four-Footed Wilderness People (1st, ob4to, ibds, 38p, 12cp)	Stokes	1916	Deming, Edwin W.	120-200	*
Wallace, Dillon	Fur Trail Adventurers (1st, sm8vo, green cl, 320p, 7pl)	McClurg	1915	Deming, Edwin W.	45-70	
Quick, Herbert	In the Fairyland of America (1st, 8vo, green cl, 190p, p-o, b/w)	Stokes	(1901)	Deming, Edwin W.	120-200	
Deming, Therese O.	Indian Child Life (1st, ob4to, ibds, [74]p, 18cp)	Stokes	1899	Deming, Edwin W.	160-225	
Deming, Therese O.	Indians of the Wigwams (1st, 12mo, 239p, 31 fp color, DJ/1.50)	Whitman	1938	Deming, Edwin W.	60-90	
Grinnell, George B.	Jack Among the Indians (1st, 12mo, 301p, 8pl)	Stokes	(1900)	Deming, Edwin W.	50-80	
Grinnell, George B.	Jack in the Rockies (1st, 12mo, 272p, green cl, 8pl)	Stokes	(1904)	Deming, Edwin W.	40-70	
Grinnell, George B.	Jack, the Young Ranchman (1st, 12mo, 304p, 8pl)	Stokes	1899	Deming, Edwin W.	50-80	
Deming, Therese O.	Little Braves (1st, ob4to, [48]p, 9 fp color)	Stokes	1929	Deming, Edwin W.	80-120	*
Deming, Therese O.	Little Brothers of the West (1st, sm4to, p-o, [26]p, 6cp)	Stokes	(1902)	Deming, Edwin W.	100-160	
Deming, Therese O.	Little Indian Folk (1st, ob4to, [38]p, 9cp)	Stokes	1899	Deming, Edwin W.	170-220	*
Deming, Therese O.	Little Red People (1st, ob4to, [38]p, 9cp)	Stokes	1899	Deming, Edwin W.	160-220	*
Deming, Therese O.	Many Snows Ago (1st, ob4to, [96]p, 18 fp color)	Stokes	1929	Deming, Edwin W.	100-170	
King, Charles	Medal of Honor (1st, 12mo, p-o, teg, 348p, 3pl by...)	Hobart	1905	Deming, Edwin W.	35-60	*
Deming, Therese O.	Red Folk & Wild Folk (1st, 4to, [51]p, p-o, 12cp)	Stokes	(1902)	Deming, Edwin W.	120-200	
Deming, Therese O.	Red People of the Wooded Country (1st, 12mo, 191p, fp color)	Whitman	(1932)	Deming, Edwin W.	60-100	
McElrath, Frances	The Rustler (1st, 8vo, 425p, 7pl)	Funk/Wagnalls	1902	Deming, Edwin W.	60-90	
Deming, Therese O.	Wigwam Children (1st, ob4to, [48]p, 9 fp color)	Stokes	1929	Deming, Edwin W.	90-170	
Eastman, Charles A.	Wigwam Evenings (1st, 12mo, 253p, 18pl)	Little/Brown	1909	Deming, Edwin W.	80-125	
Mother Goose	Original Melodies from... (1st, lg8vo, green cl, 96p, color, cep, DJ/1.25)	Phi: Davis Co.	(1938)	Deming, Kathryn O.	100-170	
Haines, Alice C.	Indian Boys & Girls (1st, sm4to, p-o, 47p, 4cp, 6pl)	Stokes	(1906)	Deming/Mar	100-165	
King, Charles	Apache Princess (1st, 12mo, 328p, p-o, teg, 8pl)	Hobart	1903	Deming/Remington	80-140	
Graves, Alfred P.	Irish Fairy Book (1st, 8vo, 410p, col frn, 11pl, pep)	L: T.F. Unwin	(1909)	Denham, George	80-140	
Graves, Alfred P.	Irish Fairy Book (1st AM, gilt, 310p, col frn, 13pl, pep)	Stokes	[1910]	Denham, George	80-125	
Graves, Alfred P.	Irish Fairy Book (1st [this pub.], 8vo, 310p, col frn, b/w)	L: A&C Black	(1938)	Denham, George	35-50	
Reid, Lionel	Miss Carlotta (1st, ob4to, [48]p, color, pep, DJ/1.25)	Oxford U. Pr.	(1936)	Denison, Richard	40-65	*
King, Elizabeth	New House that Jack Built (1st, 4to, ibds, [31]p, color, pep)	McBride	1932	Dennis, Alice	45-70	
Barbour, Ralph H.	Boys' Book of Dogs (1st, sm8vo, 238p, b/w)	Dodd	1928	Dennis, Morgan	30-50	*
Dennis, Morgan	Burlap (1st, ob8vo, ibds, [41]p, b/w, DJ/1.00)	Viking	1945	Dennis, Morgan	40-65	
Frost, Frances	Cat that Went to College (1st, lg8vo, 64p, b/w, pep, DJ/2.00)	Whittlesey	(1951)	Dennis, Morgan	60-100	
Ware, Leon	Crazy Dog (1st, lg8vo, 67p, b/w, DJ/1.50)	Whittlesey	(1944)	Dennis, Morgan	30-50	
Robertson, Keith	Dog Next Door (1st, 8vo, 222p, pep, DJ/2.50)	Viking	1950	Dennis, Morgan	25-40	*
Selden, George	Dog that Could Swim Underwater (1st, 8vo, grey cl, 126p, b/w, DJ/2.50)	Viking	1956	Dennis, Morgan	30-50	
Anthony, Edward	Every Dog has his Say (1st, sm4to, 63p, fp b/w, DJ/3.00)	Watson-Guptill	(1947)	Dennis, Morgan	50-80	
Knight, Ruth A.	Friend in the Dark (1st, lg8vo, 64p, b/w pl, DJ/1.00)	Grosset/Dunlap	(1937)	Dennis, Morgan	40-65	*
Dennis, Morgan	Himself and Burlap on TV (1st, ob8vo, 41p, red cl, b/w, DJ/2.00)	Viking	1954	Dennis, Morgan	30-50	
Dennis, Morgan	Kitten on the Keys (1st, lg ob8vo, 43p, b/w, DJ/2.25)	Viking	(1961)	Dennis, Morgan	30-50	
Frost, Frances	Little Fox (1st, 8vo, 112p, b/w, pep, DJ/2.25)	Whittlesey	(1952)	Dennis, Morgan	25-40	*

AUTHOR	TITLE	PUBLISHER	DATE	ARTIST	PRICE	LC
Robinson, Tom P.	Lost Dog Jerry (1st, 8vo, 191p, brown cl, b/w, DJ/2.50)	Viking	1952	Dennis, Morgan	25-45	
Darling, Esther B.	Luck of the Trail (1st {std}, 8vo, uncut, 309p, col frn, pep)	Doubleday/Doran	1933	Dennis, Morgan	30-50	*
Robinson, Tom P.	Pete (1st, 8vo, 139p, b/w, DJ/2.00)	Viking	1941	Dennis, Morgan	30-50	*
Dennis, Morgan	Pup Himself (1st, ob8vo, ipcb, [42]p, fp 1-color, pep, DJ/1.00)	Viking	1943	Dennis, Morgan	30-50	*
Morton, Elizabeth	Rags the Firehouse Dog (1st {std}, 4to, 38p, 1-color, DJ/2.00)	Winston	(1952)	Dennis, Morgan	30-50	*
Tippett, James S.	Shadow and the Stocking (1st {std}, 24mo, 50p, ibds, fp b/w, pep, DJ/0.75)	Harper	1937	Dennis, Morgan	30-50	
Dennis, Morgan	Skit and Skat (1st, ob8vo, 42p, ibds, b/w, DJ/1.50)	Viking	1951	Dennis, Morgan	30-50	*
Bishop, Austin	Tom of the Raiders (1st, 8vo, 260p, blue cl, 4pl)	Harcourt	1921	Dennis, Morgan	25-40	*
Malcolmson, David	Yipe (1st {std}, 8vo, 112p, red cl, b/w, DJ/2.75)	Little/Brown	(1955)	Dennis, Morgan	25-45	*
Henry, Marguerite	Album of Horses (1st {A}, 4to, 112p, fp color, pep, DJ/2.95)	Rand/McNally	(1951)	Dennis, Wesley	50-80	R
Henry, Marguerite	All About Horses (1st, lg8vo, 144p, b/w, pep, DJ/1.95)	Random	(1962)	Dennis, Wesley	25-40	
Henry, Marguerite	Always Reddy (1st, 8vo, 79p, tan cloth, 1-color, DJ/1.75)	Whittlesey	(1947)	Dennis, Wesley	30-50	
Piper, Watty (ed)	Animal Story Book (1st, folio, [73]p, p-o, fp color, pep, DJ/2.50)	Platt/Munk	(1954)	Dennis, Wesley	30-50	
Henry, Marguerite	Benjamin West & his Cat Grimalkin (1st {std}, lg8vo, 147p, pep, DJ/2.50)	Bobbs-Merrill	(1947)	Dennis, Wesley	40-65	
Sewell, Anna	Black Beauty (1st, 8vo, 315p, color, pep, DJ/1.25, RC)	World	(1946)	Dennis, Wesley	25-45	
Henry, Marguerite	Black Gold (1st, lg8vo, 172p, b/w, pep, DJ/2.95)	Rand/McNally	(1957)	Dennis, Wesley	30-50	
Lyons, Dorothy	Blue Smoke (1st {std}, 8vo, 244p, b/w, DJ/2.75)	Harcourt	(1953)	Dennis, Wesley	50-85	
Wilding, Suzanne	Book of Ponies (1st, sq8vo, pcb, 60p, 12 fp color, DJ/4.95)	St. Martin's	(1965)	Dennis, Wesley	30-50	
Henry, Marguerite	Born to Trot (1st {A}, lg8vo, 219p, gilt, pep, color, DJ/2.75)	Rand/McNally	(1950)	Dennis, Wesley	50-85	
Henry, Marguerite	Brighty of the Grand Canyon (1st {A}, lg8vo, 224p, pep, 4 fp col, DJ/2.95)	Rand/McNally	(1953)	Dennis, Wesley	45-70	R
McIlvaine, Jane	Cammie's Challenge (1st {std}, 8vo, 244p, b/w, DJ/3.50)	Bobbs-Merrill	(1962)	Dennis, Wesley	25-40	
Henry, Marguerite	Cinnabar: One O'Clock Fox (1st {A}, lg8vo, 154p, b/w, pep, DJ/2.95)	Rand/McNally	(1956)	Dennis, Wesley	70-120	
Lyons, Dorothy	Copper Khan (1st {std}, 8vo, 232p, tan cl, b/w, DJ/2.50)	Harcourt	(1950)	Dennis, Wesley	100-150	
Henry, Marguerite	Dear Readers & Riders (1st, lg8vo, 223p, b/w, DJ/3.95)	Rand/McNally	(1969)	Dennis, Wesley	30-50	
Arundel, Jocelyn	Dugan and the Hobo (1st {std}, 8vo, 121p, b/w, DJ/2.95)	Whittlesey	(1960)	Dennis, Wesley	25-40	
Henry, Marguerite	Five O'Clock Charlie (1st {A}, 8vo, [42]p, bds, color, DJ/2.00)	Rand/McNally	1962	Dennis, Wesley	25-40	
Dennis, Wesley	Flip (1st, 8vo, [63]p, b/w, pep, b/w, DJ/1.50)	Viking	1941	Dennis, Wesley	30-50	
Dennis, Wesley	Flip and the Cows (1st, 8vo, [63]p, b/w, DJ/1.50)	Viking	1942	Dennis, Wesley	25-40	*
Watson, Helen O.	Fools over Horses (1st, 8vo, 237p, b/w, pep, DJ/2.75)	Houghton	1952	Dennis, Wesley	40-65	*
Daly, Maureen	Ginger Horse (1st, 8vo, 89p, color ti-page, fp b/w, DJ/3.50)	Dodd	1964	Dennis, Wesley	20-30	
Lyons, Dorothy	Golden Sovereign (1st, 8vo, 259p, fp b/w, DJ/2.00)	Harcourt	(1946)	Dennis, Wesley	90-145	*
Knight, Ruth A.	Halfway to Heaven (1st, 8vo, 184p, col frn, DJ/2.75)	Whittlesey	(1952)	Dennis, Wesley	25-40	
Lyons, Dorothy	Harlequin Hullabaloo (1st {std}, 8vo, 264p, b/w, DJ/2.50)	Harcourt	(1949)	Dennis, Wesley	70-100	
Dennis, Wesley	Holiday (1st, ob4to, [61]p, ibds, b/w, DJ/2.00)	Viking	1946	Dennis, Wesley	30-50	
Reynolds, Marjorie	Horse Called Mystery (1st, 8vo, 205p, fp b/w, DJ/2.95)	Harper	(1964)	Dennis, Wesley	30-45	*
Henry, Marguerite	Justin Morgan had a Horse (1st, 4to, [89]p, 1-color, pep, DJ/2.75, NH)	Wilcox/Follett	1945	Dennis, Wesley	60-100	
Miles, Miska	Kickapoo (1st {std}, 8vo, 54p, b/w, DJ/2.75)	Little/Brown	(1961)	Dennis, Wesley	30-45	
Henry, Marguerite	King of the Wind (1st {A}, lg8vo, red cl, 175p, color, pep, DJ/2.75, NM)	Rand/McNally	(1948)	Dennis, Wesley	100-175	R
Holt, Jack	Lance and his First Horse (1st, sm4to, 48p, fp b/w, DJ/2.00)	Whittlesey	(1949)	Dennis, Wesley	25-40	
Hays, Wilma P.	Little Hawaiian Horse (1st {std}, 8vo, 40p, b/w, DJ/2.50)	Little/Brown	(1963)	Dennis, Wesley	25-40	
Hays, Wilma P.	Little Horse that Raced a Train (1st {std}, 8vo, 32p, b/w, DJ/2.75)	Little/Brown	(1959)	Dennis, Wesley	25-40	
Hays, Wilma P.	Little Lone Coyote (1st {std}, 8vo, 34p, blue cl, b/w, DJ/2.75)	Little/Brown	(1961)	Dennis, Wesley	30-45	
Henry, Marguerite	Little-or-Nothing from Nottingham (1st, ob8vo, 64p, fp 2-color, DJ/2.00)	Whittlesey	(1949)	Dennis, Wesley	50-85	*
Arundel, Jocelyn	Mighty Mo (1st {std}, 8vo, 124p, green cl, col frn, b/w, pep, DJ/2.95)	Whittlesey	(1961)	Dennis, Wesley	30-50	
Henry, Marguerite	Misty of Chincoteague (1st {A}, lg8vo, 173p, color, pep, DJ/2.75, NH)	Rand/McNally	(1947)	Dennis, Wesley	60-100	
Henry, Marguerite	Muley-Ears, Nobody's Dog (1st, 4to, [62]p, tan cl, color, cep, DJ/2.75)	Rand/McNally	(1959)	Dennis, Wesley	30-50	
Gates, Doris	My Brother Mike (1st, 8vo, 191p, b/w, DJ/2.50)	Viking	1948	Dennis, Wesley	30-45	
Pace, Mildred M.	Old Bones, the Wonder Horse (1st, 8vo, 119p, fp b/w, pep, DJ/2.95)	Whittlesey	(1955)	Dennis, Wesley	25-40	
Hays, Wilma P.	Pup Who Became a Police Dog (1st {std}, 8vo, 44p, b/w, DJ/2.75)	Little/Brown	(1963)	Dennis, Wesley	20-35	
Dean, Graham M.	Riders of the Gabilans (1st, 8vo, 191p, b/w, pep, DJ/2.00)	Viking	1944	Dennis, Wesley	25-45	
Henry, Marguerite	Sea Star: Orphan of Chincoteague (1st, lg8vo, 172p, color, pep, DJ/2.75)	Rand/McNally	(1949)	Dennis, Wesley	40-65	
Miles, Miska	See a White Horse (1st {std}, 8vo, 38p, b/w, DJ/2.75)	Little/Brown	(1963)	Dennis, Wesley	25-40	
Arundel, Jocelyn	Simba of the White Mane (1st {std}, 8vo, 127p, b/w, DJ/2.95)	Whittlesey	(1958)	Dennis, Wesley	30-45	
Daly, Maureen	Small War of Sargeant Donkey (1st, 8vo, 85p, b/w, DJ/3.50)	Dodd	(1966)	Dennis, Wesley	20-30	
Lyons, Dorothy	Smoke Rings (1st {std}, 8vo, 222p, DJ/3.25, frn by...)	Harcourt	1960	Dennis, Wesley	100-165	
Henry, Marguerite	Stormy: Misty's Foal (1st {A}, lg8vo, 224p, fp color, pep, DJ/3.95)	Rand/McNally	(1963)	Dennis, Wesley	50-80	*
Black, Mary M.	Summerfield Farm (1st, sm4to, 143p, b/w, DJ/2.50)	Viking	1951	Dennis, Wesley	40-65	
Coates, Belle	That Colt, Fireplug (1st, 8vo, 55p, 1-color, DJ/2.50)	Scribner	(1958)	Dennis, Wesley	25-40	
Robertson, Keith	Ticktock and Jim (1st {std}, 8vo, 240p, b/w, DJ/2.50)	Winston	(1948)	Dennis, Wesley	25-45	*
Dennis, Wesley	Tumble, Story of a Mustang (1st {std}, lg8vo, 48p, b/w, DJ/3.50)	Hastings House	(1966)	Dennis, Wesley	25-40	
Henry, Marguerite	Wagging Tails (1st {A}, 4to, brown cl, 64p, 24 fp color, pep, DJ/2.95)	Rand/McNally	(1955)	Dennis, Wesley	40-65	
Henry, Marguerite	White Stallion of Lipizza (1st {std}, 4to, 116p, color, pep, DJ/3.95)	Rand/McNally	(1964)	Dennis, Wesley	60-90	
Gordon, Hampden C.	Rhymes of the Red Triangle (1st, 8vo, ibds, [60]p, chromos)	J. Lane	[1918]	Dennys, Joyce	120-200	
Johnson, J.P.	20 Years of Hus'ling (1st, 8vo, 664p, tan cl, 48 b/w)	Chi: Thompson	1900	Denslow, W.W.	100-165	
Wallace, Susan A.	Along the Bosphorus (1st, sm8vo, teg, uncut, 383p, cvr by...)	Rand/McNally	1898	Denslow, W.W.	35-60	*
Read, Opie	Arkansas Planter (1st, 8vo, teg, 315p, cvr by...)	Rand/McNally	(1896)	Denslow, W.W.	60-90	
Waterman, Nixon (ed)	Ben King's Verse (1st, 12mo, 276p, gilt, 1 illus by...)	Chi: Forbes	1894	Denslow, W.W.	80-125	
Denslow, W.W.	Billy Bounce (1st, 8vo, orange cl, 279p, p-o, 16cp)	Dillingham	(1906)	Denslow, W.W.	350-500	
Armstrong, Leroy	Byrd Flam in Town (1st, 8vo, 139p, cvr & illus by...)	Chi: Bearhope	(1894)	Denslow, W.W.	35-60	*
Fessenden, Laura D.	Colonial Dame (1st, 12mo, 116p, cvr by...)	Rand/McNally	1897	Denslow, W.W.	40-60	
Stoddard, Charles W.	Cruise Under the Crescent (1st, 8vo, 358p, cvr by...)	Rand/McNally	(1898)	Denslow, W.W.	50-80	*
Denslow, W.W.	Denslow's 5 Little Pigs (1st, 4to, wraps, [12]p, color, pep)	Dillingham	(1903)	Denslow, W.W.	170-250	
Denslow, W.W.	Denslow's Animal Fair (1st, 4to, wraps, unpag, color)	Dillingham	(1904)	Denslow, W.W.	170-250	
Denslow, W.W.	Denslow's Humpty Dumpty (1st, 4to, grey cl, p-o, 74p, fp color)	Dillingham	(1903)	Denslow, W.W.	300-450	R
Mother Goose	Denslow's Mother Goose (1st [1], 4to, ibds, [96]p, color, pep)	McClure	1901	Denslow, W.W.	500-750	R
Denslow, W.W.	Denslow's Night Before Christmas (1st, 4to, ibds, p-o, 64p, color)	Dillingham	(1902)	Denslow, W.W.	500-800	
Denslow, W.W.	Denslow's Night Before Christmas (lg8vo, p-o, [32]p, color, later)	Donohue	[1915]	Denslow, W.W.	250-350	
Denslow, W.W.	Denslow's One Ring Circus (1st, 4to, wraps, [74]p, color, pep)	Dillingham	(1903)	Denslow, W.W.	300-500	

AUTHOR	TITLE	PUBLISHER	DATE	ARTIST	PRICE	LC
Denslow, W.W.	Denslow's One Ring Circus (lg4to, [74]p, red cl, p-o, color)	Donohue	[1913]	Denslow, W.W.	300-500	
Denslow, W.W.	Denslow's Three Little Kittens (1st, 4to, wraps, [12]p, color)	Dillingham	(1904)	Denslow, W.W.	250-350	
Denslow, W.W.	Denslow's Tom Thumb (1st, 4to, wraps, [12]p, color, pep)	Dillingham	(1903)	Denslow, W.W.	170-250	
Denslow, W.W.	Denslow's Zoo (1st, 4to, [12]p, wraps, color, pep)	Dillingham	(1903)	Denslow, W.W.	180-250	
Baum, L. Frank	Dot and Tot of Merryland (1st [1], lg8vo, 225p, gilt, color, pep)	George Hill	1901	Denslow, W.W.	750-1000	R
Baum, L. Frank	Dot and Tot of Merryland (2nd, lg8vo, 225p, color)	Bobbs-Merrill	(1903)	Denslow, W.W.	300-500	
Eastman, Charlotte	Evolution of Dodd's Sister (1st, 12mo, gilt, 230p, cvr by...)	Rand/McNally	1897	Denslow, W.W.	30-50	*
Baum, L. Frank	Father Goose: His Book (1st [1], 4to, ibds, [106]p, color)	George Hill	(1899)	Denslow, W.W.	3000-4000	R
Baum, L. Frank	Father Goose: His Book (4to, unpag, ibds, color)	Donohue	[1913]	Denslow, W.W.	180-270	
Homer, A.N.	Hernani the Jew (1st, 8vo, 332p, cvr by...)	Rand/McNally	(1897)	Denslow, W.W.	30-50	
Denslow, W.W.	House that Jack Built (1st, 4to, [12]p, wraps, color, pep)	Dillingham	(1903)	Denslow, W.W.	200-280	
Denslow, W.W.	Jack & the Bean Stalk (1st, 4to, wraps, [12]p, color)	Dillingham	(1903)	Denslow, W.W.	180-280	
Johnston, Isabel M.	Jeweled Toad (1st, lg8vo, 211p, ibds, 11cp)	Bobbs-Merrill	(1907)	Denslow, W.W.	500-750	
About, Edmond	King of the Mountains (1st, sm8vo, 246p, cvr by...)	Rand/McNally	1897	Denslow, W.W.	30-50	*
Denslow, W.W.	Little Red Riding Hood (1st, 4to, [12]p, wraps, color)	Dillingham	(1903)	Denslow, W.W.	170-240	
Edwards, Harry S.	Marbeau Cousins (1st {this pub}, sm8vo, 294p, cvr by....)	Rand/McNally	(1898)	Denslow, W.W.	40-65	
Denslow, W.W.	Mary Had a Little Lamb (1st, 4to, wraps, [12]p, color)	Dillingham	(1903)	Denslow, W.W.	150-250	
Webb, Richard	Me & Lawson (1st, 12mo, 78p, 4pl, cvr by...)	Dillingham	(1905)	Denslow, W.W.	80-130	
Baum, L. Frank	New Wizard of Oz (2nd, lg8vo, green cl, [261]p, 16cp, pep)	Bobbs-Merrill	(1903)	Denslow, W.W.	1200-1800	
Boylan, Grace D.	Old House (1st, 12mo, 112p, cvr by...)	E.R. Herrick	(1897)	Denslow, W.W.	40-65	
Denslow, W.W.	Old Mother Hubbard (1st, 4to, wraps, [12]p, color)	Dillingham	(1903)	Denslow, W.W.	200-265	
West, Paul	Pearl & Pumpkin (1st [1], lg8vo, green cl, 239p, p-o, 16cp, pep)	Dillingham	(1904)	Denslow, W.W.	350-500	
West, Paul	Pearl & Pumpkin (lg8vo, 239p, p-o, 16cp, later)	Donohue	[1911]	Denslow, W.W.	200-300	
Loti, Pierre	Romance of a Child (1st, 8vo, 179p, teg, gilt, cvr by...)	Rand/McNally	1897	Denslow, W.W.	55-80	
Amber	Rosemary and Rue (1st, 12mo, 303p, cvr by...)	Rand/McNally	1896	Denslow, W.W.	40-60	*
Denslow, W.W.	Scarecrow & the Tin Man (1st, 4to, [74]p, p-o, color)	Dillingham	(1904)	Denslow, W.W.	600-800	
Denslow, W.W.	Scarecrow & the Tin Man (4to, red cl, p-o, [74]p, color)	Donohue	[1913]	Denslow, W.W.	220-325	
Denslow, W.W.	Simple Simon (1st, 4to, wraps, unpag, color)	Dillingham	(1904)	Denslow, W.W.	120-180	
Baum, L. Frank	Songs of Father Goose (1st, 4to, ibds, 84p, b/w)	George Hill	1900	Denslow, W.W.	425-600	
Baum, L. Frank	Songs of Father Goose (2nd, 4to, 83p, ibds, b/w)	Bobbs-Merrill	(1909)	Denslow, W.W.	200-300	
Welch, Deshler	Story of Louise (1st, 12mo, tan cl, uncut, 194p, cvr by...)	Royal Colum. Pr.	1901	Denslow, W.W.	55-80	
Halstead, Murat	Story of the Philippines (1st, lg8vo, 400p, gilt, cvr by...)	(Chicago)	(1898)	Denslow, W.W.	100-165	
Denslow, W.W.	Tom Thumb (1st, 4to, [12]p, wraps, color)	Dillingham	(1903)	Denslow, W.W.	250-350	
Read, Opie	Waters of Caney Fork (1st, 8vo, 287p, cvr by...)	Rand/McNally	1898	Denslow, W.W.	45-70	
Denslow, W.W.	When I Grow Up (1st, 4to, 104p, 24 color, tan cl)	Century	1909	Denslow, W.W.	170-240	
Baum, L. Frank	Wonderful Wizard of Oz (1st [1], 8vo, 261p, 24cp, pep, PPP)	George Hill	1900	Denslow, W.W.	6000-9000	R
Derrick, Freda	Ark Book (1st, ob sm4to, ibds, unpag, p-o, color)	L: Blackie	[1920]	Derrick, Freda	130-200	
Gulick, Peggy	Dear Uncle Looy (1st {std}, 4to, ibds, [30]p, 2-color, DJ/1.75)	Knopf	(1951)	Dersser, Elizabeth	70-100	
N/A	Arabian Nights (1st, 4to, 240p, teg, white/gilt, 12 ticp)	L: Hodder	(1924)	Detmold, Edward J.	500-700	
N/A	Arabian Nights (1st AM, lg8vo, blue/gilt, 297p, p-o, 12 ticp)	Dodd	(1925)	Detmold, Edward J.	400-650	
Lemonnier, Camille	Birds & Beasts (1st, 8vo, gilt, teg, 196p, 6cp)	L: G. Allen	(1911)	Detmold, Edward J.	170-240	
Hudson, Wm. Henry	Birds in Town & Village (1st, 8vo, 274p, green/gilt, 8cp)	L: Dent	1919	Detmold, Edward J.	160-225	
Hudson, Wm. Henry	Birds in Town & Village (1st AM, 8vo, blue/gilt, 323p, 8cp)	Dutton	(1920)	Detmold, Edward J.	140-200	
Dugdale, Florence E.	Book of Baby Beasts (4to, ibds, p-o, [120]p, 19ticp)	NY: Hodder	[1912]	Detmold, Edward J.	350-500	
Dugdale, Florence E.	Book of Baby Birds (1st, sm4to, 120p, pcb, p-o, 19 ticp)	L: Hodder	[1912]	Detmold, Edward J.	300-500	
Kaberry, Charles J.	Book of Baby Dogs (1st, 4to, bds, 120p, p-o, 19 ticp)	L: H. Frowde	(1914)	Detmold, Edward J.	300-400	
Dugdale, Florence E.	Book of Baby Pets (1st, lg4to, ibds, [120]p, p-o, 19 ticp)	L: Hodder	[1913]	Detmold, Edward J.	300-500	
Aesopus	Fables of Aesop (1st, lg4to, 152p, brown/gilt, pep, 23 ticp)	L: Hodder	[1909]	Detmold, Edward J.	500-750	
Stawell, R. (ed.)	Fabre's Book of Insects (1st AM, 4to, 271p, green/gilt, 12 ticp)	Dodd	1921	Detmold, Edward J.	200-300	
Fabre	Fabre's Book of Insects (1st, lg4to, 184p, white/gilt, 12 ticp)	L: Hodder	(1921)	Detmold, Edward J.	250-350	
Stawell, R. (ed.)	Fabre's Book of Insects (1st {this pub.}, 4to, 271p, 12 ticp)	Tudor	1935	Detmold, Edward J.	100-150	
Maeterlinck, Maurice	Hours of Gladness (1st, 4to, 181p, uncut, white/gilt, 20 ticp)	L: G. Allen	(1912)	Detmold, Edward J.	400-600	
Kipling, Rudyard	Jungle Book (1st, 8vo, 314p, red/gilt, teg, 16cp)	L: Macmillan	1908	Detmold, Edward J.	250-400	
Kipling, Rudyard	Jungle Book (1st AM, 8vo, green/gilt, teg, 351p, 16cp, pep)	Century	1913	Detmold, Edward J.	200-300	
Maeterlinck, Maurice	Life of the Bee (1st, 4to, 232p, uncut, white/gilt, teg, 13 ticp)	L: G. Allen	1911	Detmold, Edward J.	300-500	
Maeterlinck, Maurice	Life of the Bee (1st AM, 4to, 262p, teg, green/gilt, 13 ticp)	Dodd	1912	Detmold, Edward J.	250-400	
Maeterlinck, Maurice	News of Spring (1st AM, 4to, green/gilt, uncut, 213p, teg, 20 ticp)	Dodd	1913	Detmold, Edward J.	400-600	
Kaberry, Charles J.	Our Little Neighbors (4to, pcb, gilt, 105p, 12 ticp)	L: Oxford U.Pr.	(1921)	Detmold, Edward J.	250-400	
Shuldham, Edward B.	Pictures from Birdland (1st {1st bk.}, 4to, ibds, 24cp)	L: Dent	1899	Detmold, Edward J.	600-850	
Hall, Arthur V.	Poems of a South African (1st, 8vo, 313p, gilt, 6cp)	L: Longmans	1931	Detmold, Edward J.	120-185	
Hall, Arthur V.	Rainbow Houses for Boys & Girls (1st, 8vo, blue cl, 92p, 6cp)	L: J. Cape	1923	Detmold, Edward J.	140-225	
Ponsot, Georges	Romance of the River (1st AM, 8vo, green/gilt, 290p, col frn)	Dodd	(1924)	Detmold, Edward J.	35-60	*
Maeterlinck, Maurice	Visions of Spring... (1st, 4to, teg, 213p, gilt, 20 ticp)	Dodd	1913	Detmold, Edward J.	400-600	
Devlin, Wende	How Fletcher was Hatched (1st, sm4to, [39]p, ibds, color, pep, DJ/3.50)	Parents Mag. Pr.	(1969)	Devlin, W.& H.	30-50	
Devlin, Wende	Kiss for a Warthog (1st, 4to, 37p, color, DJ/4.95)	Van Nostrand	(1970)	Devlin, W.& H.	30-50	
Himes, Vera C.	Ola and the Runaway Bread (1st, 8vo, ipcb, [64]p, fp color, pep)	Crowell	(1932)	Dewey, Katharine	40-65	*
Kincaid, Charles A.	Deccan Nursery Tales (1st, 8vo, 135p, 8cp)	L: Macmillan	1914	Dhurandhar, M.V.	50-85	
Carlson, Natalie S.	Half-Sisters (1st, 8vo, 163p, fp b/w, DJ/3.95)	Harper	(1970)	DiGrazia, Thomas	20-35	*
Sewell, Anna	Black Beauty (1st, lg8vo, 278p, teg, p-o, 12cp)	Barse/Hopkins	(1911)	Dickey, Robert L.	40-60	*
Terhune, Albert P.	Book of Famous Dogs (1st {std}, 8vo, 300p, b/w pl, DJ/2.75)	Doubleday/Doran	1937	Dickey, Robert L.	50-80	
Baring-Gould, Sabine	Grettir and Outlaw (1st, sm8vo, 384p, gilt, 10pl)	L: Blackie	1890	Diemer, M. Zeno	60-90	
Batchelor, Julie	Cap for Mul Chand (1st {std}, 8vo, 56p, fp 1-color, DJ/2.00)	Harcourt	(1950)	Dillon, Corrine	25-40	*
Leodhas, Sorche	Claymore and Kilt (1st {std}, lg8vo, 157p, ibds, gilt, fp b/w, DJ/3.95)	Holt, Rinehart	(1967)	Dillon, L.& D.	30-50	
Beyer, Audrey W.	Dark Venture (1st {std}, 8vo, 205p, b/w, DJ)	Knopf	1968	Dillon, L.& D.	30-50	*
Haugaard, Erik	Hakon of Rogen's Saga (1st, 8vo, 132p, fp b/w, DJ/3.00)	Houghton	1963	Dillon, L.& D.	30-50	
Bierhorst, John	Ring in the Prairie (1st {std}, ob4to, 36p, fp color, cep, DJ/4.50)	Dial Press	(1970)	Dillon, L.& D.	45-70	*
Pilkington, Francis	Shamrock and Spear (1st {std}, 8vo, 177p, b/w, DJ/4.50)	Holt, Rinehart	(1968)	Dillon, L.& D.	35-50	
Haugaard, Erik	Slave's Tale (1st, 8vo, 217p, fp b/w, DJ/3.00)	Houghton	1965	Dillon, L.& D.	30-50	

AUTHOR	TITLE	PUBLISHER	DATE	ARTIST	PRICE	LC
Laing, Frederick	Why Heimdall Blew His Horn (1st, lg8vo, 96p, color)	Silver Burdette	(1969)	Dillon, L.& D.	40-65	
Dwight, Grace	Yellow Cat & Friends (1st, lg8vo, ipcb, 88p, 14cp)	Appleton	1905	Dimock, Edith	60-90	
McNeill, James	Double Knights (1st, 8vo, 128p, fp b/w, DJ/3.50)	H.Z. Walck	1964	Dimson, Theo	30-50	
Martin, Patricia	Bony Pony (1st, 4to, 44p, color, DJ/2.75)	Putnam	(1965)	Dines, Glen	20-35	*
Martin, Patricia	Daniel Boone (1st, 8vo, 62p, color, DJ/1.95)	Putnam	(1965)	Dines, Glen	25-40	
Dines, Glen	Mysterious Machine (1st {std}, 8vo, 140p, b/w, pep, DJ/2.75)	Macmillan	(1957)	Dines, Glen	20-30	
Dines, Glen	Tiger in the Cherry Tree (1st {std}, 4to, unpag, color, DJ/2.50)	Macmillan	(1958)	Dines, Glen	40-65	
Dines, Glen	Useful Dragon of Sam Ling Toy (1st {std}, 4to, ibds, unpag, col, DJ/2.75)	Macmillan	(1956)	Dines, Glen	60-100	
Holman, Felice	Silently, the Cat & Miss Theodosia (1st {std}, 8vo, 58p, b/w, DJ/2.95)	Macmillan	(1965)	Dinnerstein, Harvey	25-35	
Cosgrove, Rachel R.	Hidden Valley of Oz (1st, lg8vo, blue cl, p-o, 313p, b/w, pep, DJ/2.50)	Reilly/Lee	(1951)	Dirk	250-400	
Disney, Walt	40 Big Pages of Mickey Mouse (folio, wraps, color)	Whitman	(1936)	Disney Studios	125-200	*
Disney, Walt	ABC Mickey Mouse Alphabet Book (1st, lg8vo, [32]p, color, pep)	Whitman	(1936)	Disney Studios	170-240	*
Disney, Walt	Adventures of Mickey Mouse (1st UK [this fmt.], 12mo, ibds, [32]p, color)	L: Harrap	(1931)	Disney Studios	400-600	
Disney, Walt	Adventures of Mickey Mouse Book # 2 (1st, 8vo, [32]p, ibds, pep, color)	McKay	(1932)	Disney Studios	300-450	
Disney, Walt	Animals from Snow White & the Seven Dwarfs (4to, stiff wrps, 11 fp color)	Whitman	1938	Disney Studios	140-200	
Field, Robert	Art of Walt Disney (1st, 4to, tan cl, 290p, color)	Macmillan	1942	Disney Studios	250-400	
Disney, Walt	Ave Maria (1st, 4to, blue/gilt, [32]p, color, pep)	Random	(1940)	Disney Studios	140-200	
Grant, Joseph C.	Baby Weems (1st {std}, lg8vo, [64]p, blue cl, 2-color, pep, DJ/1.00)	Doubleday/Doran	1941	Disney Studios	80-140	
Disney, Walt	Bambi Picture Book (folio, [12]p, linen wraps, color)	Whitman	1942	Disney Studios	120-200	
Disney, Walt	Big Bad Wolf & Little Red Riding Hood (1st, 4to, ipcb, 60p, color)	Blue Ribbon	(1934)	Disney Studios	250-350	
Harris, Joel C.	Brer Rabbit Rides the Fox (1st, 8vo, ibds, [32]p, fp color, pep)	Grosset/Dunlap	(1946)	Disney Studios	100-165	
Disney, Walt	Cold-Blooded Penguin (1st {std}, sm8vo, ibds, [24]p, pep, color, LGB/#D2)	Simon/Schuster	1944	Disney Studios	40-65	
Disney, Walt	Come Play with Donald Duck (1st, 8vo, ibds, [32]p, fp color, pep)	Grosset/Dunlap	(1948)	Disney Studios	80-130	
Disney, Walt	Come Play with Mickey Mouse (1st, 8vo, ibds, [32]p, fp color, pep)	Grosset/Dunlap	(1948)	Disney Studios	80-130	
Disney, Walt	Country Cousin (1st, 4to, ibds, [20]p, color)	McKay	1937	Disney Studios	100-150	*
Disney, Walt	Dance of the Hours (1st {std}, lg8vo, ibds, [36]p, color, pep)	Harper	(1940)	Disney Studios	140-200	
Disney, Walt	Disney's Bambi (1st, 4to, [52]p, color)	Simon/Schuster	(1941)	Disney Studios	80-140	
Disney, Walt	Disney's Bambi (8vo, [32]p, color, pep)	Grosset/Dunlap	(1942)	Disney Studios	75-100	
Disney, Walt	Disney's Bambi (8vo, 101p, color)	D.C. Heath	(1944)	Disney Studios	50-80	*
Disney, Walt	Disney's Cinderella (8vo, [34]p, color, pep)	Whitman	1950	Disney Studios	80-120	*
Disney, Walt	Disney's Cinderella (1st, folio, ibds, [26]p, color, GGB)	Simon/Schuster	(1950)	Disney Studios	90-160	*
Disney, Walt	Disney's Davy Crockett (1st, 4to, ibds, 48p, color, pep, BGB/#435)	Simon/Schuster	(1955)	Disney Studios	60-90	*
Disney, Walt	Disney's Dumbo (1st, lg ob8vo, wraps, [12]p, color)	Disney Prod.	1941	Disney Studios	170-240	*
Disney, Walt	Disney's Dumbo (1st {this pub}, 8vo, ibds, [42]p, color, LGB/#D3)	Simon/Schuster	(1947)	Disney Studios	30-50	
Disney, Walt	Disney's Forest Friends (lg8vo, [28]p, ibds, color, pep)	Grosset/Dunlap	(1938)	Disney Studios	100-170	*
Disney, Walt	Disney's Lady & the Tramp (1st, folio, unpag, ipcb, color, BGB)	Simon/Schuster	(1955)	Disney Studios	100-165	*
Mother Goose	Disney's Mother Goose (1st, folio, ibds, [28]p, color, GGB)	Simon/Schuster	(1949)	Disney Studios	100-170	*
Disney, Walt	Disney's Pedro (1st, 8vo, [32]p, ipcb, color, pep)	A.& W. Guild	1943	Disney Studios	70-100	*
Disney, Walt	Disney's Peter Pan (1st, folio, ipcb, unpag, color, GGB)	Simon/Schuster	1952	Disney Studios	100-160	*
Disney, Walt	Disney's Pinocchio (1st, 4to, ibds, [76]p, color, pep)	Random	1939	Disney Studios	250-400	R
Disney, Walt	Disney's Pinocchio (folio, [12]p, color)	Whitman	(1940)	Disney Studios	80-120	*
Disney, Walt	Disney's Pinocchio (1st {this pub}, folio, ipcb, color, BGB)	Simon/Schuster	(1954)	Disney Studios	120-200	*
Disney, Walt	Disney's Surprise Package (1st, sm4to, ibds, 92p, color, pep, GGB)	Simon/Schuster	1944	Disney Studios	100-165	
Disney, Walt	Disney's Thumper (1st, 8vo, [32]p, ipcb, color, pep)	Grosset/Dunlap	(1942)	Disney Studios	100-170	*
Disney, Walt	Disney's Version of Pinocchio (ob8vo, [48]p, color, pep)	Grosset/Dunlap	1939	Disney Studios	100-145	*
Disney, Walt	Disney's Version of Pinocchio (sq12mo, [24]p, color)	Whitman	(1940)	Disney Studios	100-160	*
Disney, Walt	Donald Duck (1st, folio, wraps, [14]p, color)	Whitman	1935	Disney Studios	600-900	R
Disney, Walt	Donald Duck (4to, ibds, [33]p, color, pep)	Grosset/Dunlap	(1936)	Disney Studios	300-500	*
Disney, Walt	Donald Duck & his Friends (1st, 4to, ipcb, 45p, b/w, pep)	Whitman	1937	Disney Studios	170-240	*
Ayer, Jean	Donald Duck & his Friends (8vo, 102p, pep, color)	D.C. Heath	(1939)	Disney Studios	100-160	
Brumbaugh, Florence	Donald Duck & his Nephews (1st, 8vo, cloth, 66p, pep, color)	D.C. Heath	(1940)	Disney Studios	55-80	
Disney, Walt	Donald Duck Days (1st, 8vo, ibds, 2-color)	L: Birn Bros.	(1937)	Disney Studios	200-300	
Disney, Walt	Donald Duck has his Ups & Downs (lg8vo, wraps, 24p, color)	Whitman	(1937)	Disney Studios	170-240	*
Disney, Walt	Donald Duck his Story Book (1st, 4to, ipcb, 46p, pep, b/w)	Whitman	1937	Disney Studios	120-180	*
Disney, Walt	Donald Duck in High Andes (1st, 8vo, [32]p, color)	A.& W. Guild	1943	Disney Studios	120-200	*
Disney, Walt	Donald Duck Off the Beam (1st [Big-Little], 32mo, 425p, ibds)	Whitman	(1943)	Disney Studios	120-180	*
Disney, Walt	Donald Duck Sees South America (1st, 8vo, 138p, maps, color, pep)	D.C. Heath	(1945)	Disney Studios	60-100	
Disney, Walt	Donald Duck Treasury (1st, lg8vo, 116p)	Golden Press	1960	Disney Studios	80-120	*
Disney, Walt	Donald's Lucky Day (1st, ob4to, wraps, [20]p, fp color)	Whitman	(1939)	Disney Studios	200-300	
Disney, Walt	Donald's Penguin (1st, sm4to, ibds, [24]p, pep, color)	Garden City	1940	Disney Studios	100-170	*
Disney, Walt	Dopey: He Don't Talk None (1st, sm folio, wraps, [12]p, color)	Whitman	1938	Disney Studios	150-225	
Disney, Walt	Dumbo of the Circus (1st, sq4to, ibds, [52]p, color, pep)	Garden City	(1941)	Disney Studios	200-300	
Disney, Walt	Dumbo of the Circus (1st {this pub}, 8vo, 90p, color, pep)	D.C. Heath	(1948)	Disney Studios	75-100	*
Disney, Walt	Elmer Elephant (1st, 8vo, ibds, 46p, color)	McKay	(1936)	Disney Studios	200-300	
Disney, Walt	Elmer Elephant (folio, wraps, [10]p, fp color, linen)	Whitman	1938	Disney Studios	180-250	
Taylor, Deems	Fantasia (1st, folio, tan cloth, 158p, 15 ticp, pep, DJ/3.75)	Simon/Schuster	1940	Disney Studios	250-400	
Leaf, Munro	Ferdinand the Bull (4to, wraps, 31p, color)	Whitman	(1936)	Disney Studios	170-250	
Leaf, Munro	Ferdinand the Bull (1st {this pub}, ob8vo, [14]p, wraps, 6 color)	Dell	1938	Disney Studios	100-165	
Leaf, Munro	Ferdinand the Bull (1st, 4to, [8]p, stiff wraps, color)	Whitman	(1938)	Disney Studios	120-180	R
Disney, Walt	Figaro and Cleo (1st, 8vo, ibds, [27]p, color, pep)	Random	1940	Disney Studios	120-200	
Disney, Walt	Golden Touch (1st, 8vo, ibds, 212p, 6cp, pep)	Whitman	(1937)	Disney Studios	120-200	
Dahl, Roald	Gremlins (1st, 4to, ibds, [48]p, fp color, pep, DJ/1.00)	Random	(1943)	Disney Studios	2000-3000	
Wavle, Ardra	Here they Are (1st, 8vo, cloth, 56p, color, pep)	D.C. Heath	(1940)	Disney Studios	40-65	
Disney, Walt	Hiawatha (1st, 4to, ibds, [20]p, fp color, pep)	McKay	1937	Disney Studios	125-200	
Disney, Walt	Honest John & Giddy (1st, 8vo, [24]p, ibds, color, pep)	Random	1940	Disney Studios	80-120	
Disney, Walt	Jiminy Cricket (1st, 8vo, ibds, [24]p, color, pep)	Random	1940	Disney Studios	120-200	
Disney, Walt	Life of Donald Duck (1st, 4to, ibds, 72p, color, pep)	Random	(1941)	Disney Studios	200-300	
Brown, Margaret W.	Little Pig's Picnic... (1st, 8vo, 102p, cloth, color, dep)	D.C. Heath	(1939)	Disney Studios	60-90	

AUTHOR	TITLE	PUBLISHER	DATE	ARTIST	PRICE	LC
Disney, Walt	Little Red Riding Hood & Big Bad Wolf (1st, 8vo, 32p, wraps, fp b/w)	McKay	(1934)	Disney Studios	200-300	
Disney, Walt	Little Wise Hen (1st, ob4to, 48p, ibds, 9 fp color)	Whitman	(1934)	Disney Studios	170-240	
Carroll, Lewis	Mad-Hatter's Tea Party (1st, sm8vo, [28]p, ibds, color, LGB/#D23)	Simon/Schuster	(1951)	Disney Studios	20-30	
Disney, Walt	Magnificent Mr. Toad (1st, 4to, [32]p, color)	Grosset/Dunlap	(1949)	Disney Studios	150-220	
Disney, Walt	Mickey & the Beanstalk (1st, 8vo, ipcb, [32]p, color, pep)	Grosset/Dunlap	(1947)	Disney Studios	100-160	*
Disney, Walt	Mickey Mouse (1st {Big-Little}, 32mo, ibds, 316p, b/w)	Whitman	1933	Disney Studios	120-200	*
Disney, Walt	Mickey Mouse & his Friends (1st, lg4to, [10]p, wraps, 8cp)	Whitman	(1936)	Disney Studios	200-300	
Disney, Walt	Mickey Mouse & his Friends (1st {this pub}, 8vo, 102p, color)	NY: Nelson	1937	Disney Studios	80-120	*
Disney, Walt	Mickey Mouse & his Horse Tanglefoot (1st, 8vo, ibds, 60p, color)	McKay	(1936)	Disney Studios	300-450	
Disney, Walt	Mickey Mouse & Mail Pilot (1st {Big-Little}, 32mo, ibds, 296p, b/w)	Whitman	1933	Disney Studios	120-200	*
Mother Goose	Mickey Mouse & Mother Goose (1st, 8vo, ibds, 136p, pep)	Whitman	(1937)	Disney Studios	250-350	
Disney, Walt	Mickey Mouse & Pluto (1st, sm4to, ibds [66]p, 1-color, pep)	Whitman	1936	Disney Studios	250-400	
Disney, Walt	Mickey Mouse ABC Story (1st, 8vo, ipcb, [31]p, color, pep)	Whitman	(1937)	Disney Studios	250-400	
Disney, Walt	Mickey Mouse Air Pilot (1st, 8vo, ibds, 2-color)	L: Birn Bros.	(1937)	Disney Studios	220-320	
Disney, Walt	Mickey Mouse Alphabet ABC (folio, [16]p, linen wraps, color)	W. Disney Prod.	1938	Disney Studios	300-400	
Disney, Walt	Mickey Mouse Alphabet from A to Z (4to, ibds, [32]p, color)	Whitman	(1936)	Disney Studios	250-350	
Disney, Walt	Mickey Mouse Alphabet from A to Z (1st, ibds, [32]p, 1-color)	L: Collins	[1936]	Disney Studios	200-300	
Disney, Walt	Mickey Mouse at the Circus (1st UK, 4to, ibds, color)	L: Birn Bros.	(1937)	Disney Studios	200-300	
Disney, Walt	Mickey Mouse Birthday Book (1st, 4to, ibds, 64p, color, BGB/#482)	Simon/Schuster	(1953)	Disney Studios	60-100	*
Disney, Walt	Mickey Mouse Crusoe (1st, 8vo, stiff wraps, 71p, col frn, b/w)	Whitman	(1936)	Disney Studios	150-250	
Disney, Walt	Mickey Mouse Fire Brigade (1st, 4to, ibds, color)	Whitman	1936	Disney Studios	250-350	
Disney, Walt	Mickey Mouse Fire Brigade (1st UK, ibds, 77p, b/w)	L: Collins	1936	Disney Studios	180-270	
Disney, Walt	Mickey Mouse has a Busy Day (1st, sq4to, wraps, 16p, color)	Whitman	(1937)	Disney Studios	140-240	
Disney, Walt	Mickey Mouse has a Party (1st, lg8vo, wraps, 48p, 2-color)	Whitman	1938	Disney Studios	200-300	
Disney, Walt	Mickey Mouse in Giantland (1st UK, 8vo, 93p, ibds, color)	L: Collins	(1934)	Disney Studios	300-500	
Disney, Walt	Mickey Mouse in Giantland (1st, 8vo, 45p, p-o, fp color, pep)	McKay	(1934)	Disney Studios	350-550	
Disney, Walt	Mickey Mouse in King Arthur's Court (1st, lg8vo, 48p, color)	Blue Ribbon	(1933)	Disney Studios	100-150	R*
Disney, Walt	Mickey Mouse in Pigmy Land (1st, 4to, ipcb, 71p, col frn, b/w)	Whitman	1936	Disney Studios	200-300	*
Disney, Walt	Mickey Mouse Movie Stories (1st, 8vo, gilt, 190p, p-o, b/w)	McKay	(1931)	Disney Studios	450-600	R
Disney, Walt	Mickey Mouse on Tour (8vo, ibds, 1-color)	L: Birn Bros.	(1935)	Disney Studios	200-300	
Disney, Walt	Mickey Mouse Presents Father Noah's Ark (1st, lg8vo, ibds, color)	L: Birn Bros.	(1934)	Disney Studios	180-250	
Disney, Walt	Mickey Mouse Story Book (1st, 8vo, 62p, wraps, b/w)	McKay	(1931)	Disney Studios	350-500	
Disney, Walt	Mickey Mouse the Boat-Builder (1st, ob8vo, [28]p, ibds, color, pep)	Grosset/Dunlap	1938	Disney Studios	250-400	
Disney, Walt	Mickey Mouse Waddle Book (1st, sm4to, ibds, [33]p, color, pep)	Blue Ribbon	(1934)	Disney Studios	300-500	
Palmer, Robin	Mickey Never Fails (1st, 8vo, 102p, color, pep, DJ/1.00)	D.C. Heath	(1939)	Disney Studios	75-120	
Emerson, Caroline	Mickey Sees the U.S.A. (1st, 8vo, 138p, color, pep)	D.C. Heath	(1944)	Disney Studios	50-80	
Disney, Walt	Mickey's Clock (1st, 4to, ibds, 76p, 1-color)	L: Collins	1938	Disney Studios	250-400	
Moore, Clement C.	Night Before Christmas (1st, sm4to, ibds, fp color)	L: Collins	1934	Disney Studios	140-200	
Disney, Walt	Nursery Stories from Silly Symphony (1st, 8vo, 212p, ibds, 6cp, pep)	Whitman	(1937)	Disney Studios	160-240	
Disney, Walt	Nutcracker Suite (1st, lg sq4to, ibds, [72]p, color, pep)	Little/Brown	1940	Disney Studios	125-200	
Disney, Walt	Our Friend the Atom (1st, 4to, 166p, pep, color, GGB)	Simon/Schuster	(1956)	Disney Studios	100-165	
Disney, Walt	Pastoral (1st {std}, lg8vo, [36]p, color, pep)	Harper	(1940)	Disney Studios	120-180	
Disney, Walt	Peculiar Penguins (1st, 8vo, 45p, red cl, p-o, color, pep)	McKay	(1934)	Disney Studios	250-400	
Disney, Walt	Pinocchio Picture Book (lg4to, [14]p, wraps, color)	Grosset/Dunlap	(1940)	Disney Studios	140-220	R*
Disney, Walt	Pinocchio Picture Book (lg4to, wraps, color, shape bk.)	Whitman	1940	Disney Studios	170-240	*
Disney, Walt	Pluto & the Puppy (1st, 4to, ibds, [36]p, color, pep)	Grosset/Dunlap	(1937)	Disney Studios	160-240	
Disney, Walt	Practical Pig (1st, lg sq8vo, ibds, [24]p, color, pep)	Garden City	1940	Disney Studios	170-240	
Disney, Walt	Princess Elizabeth Gift Book (1st, lg8vo, white cl, 224p, color)	L: Hodder	[1933]	Disney Studios	80-130	
Grahame, Kenneth	Reluctant Dragon (1st, 4to, [72]p, ibds, color, pep)	Garden City	(1941)	Disney Studios	250-350	
Disney, Walt	Robber Kitten (1st, ob4to, ipcb, 46p, 9 fp color, pep)	McKay	(1935)	Disney Studios	200-300	
Disney, Walt	Runaway Lamb at County Fair (1st, sm4to, ipcb, [31]p, color)	Grosset/Dunlap	(1949)	Disney Studios	80-120	*
Disney, Walt	Santa's Workshop (1st UK, 8vo, 124p, 8cp)	L: Collins	1934	Disney Studios	180-250	
Emerson, Caroline	School Days in Disneyville (1st, 8vo, 102p, color, pep)	D.C. Heath	(1939)	Disney Studios	60-90	
Disney, Walt	Snow White & Seven Dwarfs (lg4to, ibds, 80p, color)	Grosset/Dunlap	(1937)	Disney Studios	250-400	
Disney, Walt	Snow White & Seven Dwarfs (1st {this pub}, sq4to, ibds, color)	McKay	1937	Disney Studios	300-500	
Disney, Walt	Snow White & Seven Dwarfs (1st, ob8vo, ipcb, [36]p, color)	Grosset/Dunlap	(1938)	Disney Studios	200-300	
Disney, Walt	Snow White & Seven Dwarfs (1st, 12mo, 63p, ibds, 14 color)	Whitman	(1938)	Disney Studios	200-300	
Disney, Walt	Snow White & Seven Dwarfs (folio, 12p, wraps, color)	Whitman	1938	Disney Studios	400-600	R
Disney, Walt	Snow White & the Seven Dwarfs (1st UK, lg4to, 80p, ibds, color)	L: Collins	(1938)	Disney Studios	185-265	
Disney, Walt	Sorcerer's Apprentice (1st, ob8vo, ibds, 34p, color, pep)	Grosset/Dunlap	(1940)	Disney Studios	200-300	
Disney, Walt	Stories from Fantasia (narrow 4to, [movie ed.], [72]p, ibds, color, pep)	Random	(1940)	Disney Studios	90-145	
Disney, Walt	Story of Casey Jr. (1st, lg8vo, ibds, [26]p, 4 fp color, pep)	Garden City	(1941)	Disney Studios	120-180	
Disney, Walt	Story of Timothy's House (1st, sm4to, ibds, [28]p, color, pep)	Garden City	(1941)	Disney Studios	140-200	
Palmer, H. Marion	Three Caballeros (1st, 4to, ibds, 56p, fp color, pep, DJ/1.25)	Random	(1944)	Disney Studios	350-500	
Disney, Walt	Three Little Pigs (1st, sm4to, ibds, 62p, 12 color, pep)	Blue Ribbon	(1933)	Disney Studios	200-350	R
Disney, Walt	Three Orphan Kittens (1st, ob4to, ibds, [46]p, 9 color)	McKay	(1935)	Disney Studios	160-240	
Disney, Walt	Through the Picture Frame (1st, sq8vo, [24]p, ibds, color, LGB/#D1)	Simon/Schuster	1944	Disney Studios	40-65	*
Disney, Walt	Thumper (1st, 8vo, [32]p, ibds, color)	Grosset/Dunlap	(1942)	Disney Studios	60-90	
Disney, Walt	Timid Elmer (1st, sq24mo, ipcb, 64p, b/w)	Whitman	1939	Disney Studios	100-165	
Disney, Walt	Tortoise & the Hare (1st, ob4to, ibds, 48p, 9 fp color)	McKay	(1935)	Disney Studios	200-300	*
Andersen, Hans C.	Ugly Duckling (1st, ob4to, [40]p, p-o, color, pep, DJ/1.00)	Lippincott	(1939)	Disney Studios	200-300	
Harris, Joel C.	Uncle Remus Stories (1st, sm folio, ibds, 92p, color, GGB)	Simon/Schuster	(1947)	Disney Studios	80-120	*
Disney, Walt	Walt Disney Parade (1st, 4to, 176p, color, pep)	Garden City	(1940)	Disney Studios	120-200	*
Carroll, Lewis	Walt Disney's Alice in Wonderland (1st UK, 4to, ibds, color, pep)	L: Dean	(1951)	Disney Studios	200-300	
Disney, Walt	Walt Disney's Circus (1st, 4to, [28]p, color, pep)	Simon/Schuster	1944	Disney Studios	160-225	
Disney, Walt	Walt Disney's Clock Cleaners (folio, wraps, [5]p, color)	Whitman	1938	Disney Studios	180-250	
Disney, Walt	Walt Disney's Pedro (1st, 8vo, ipcb, [32]p, color, pep)	A.& W. Guild	1943	Disney Studios	80-130	
Kingsley, Charles	Water Babies (1st, 4to, ibds, 125p, col frn, 1-color)	L: Collins	1936	Disney Studios	250-400	

AUTHOR	TITLE	PUBLISHER	DATE	ARTIST	PRICE	LC
Disney, Walt	Water Babies' Circus (8vo, 78p, color pep)	D.C. Heath	(1940)	Disney Studios	80-130	
Disney, Walt	Who's Afraid of the Big Bad Wolf (1st, 12mo, wraps, 31p, b/w)	McKay	(1933)	Disney Studios	125-200	
Disney, Walt	Wise Little Hen (1st, ob4to, 48p, fp color)	McKay	(1934)	Djsney Studios	200-300	*
Disney, Walt	Wise Little Hen (1st {this fmt}, folio, [8]p, wraps, color)	Disney Prod.	(1937)	Disney Studios	200-300	*
Disney, Walt	Wonderful Tar Baby (1st, 8vo, ipcb, [32]p, color, pep)	Grosset/Dunlap	(1946)	Disney Studios	90-160	*
Farnol, Jeffery	My Lady Caprice (1st, 8vo, teg, p-o, 289p, color)	Dodd	1907	Ditzler, C. Weber	25-40	
Brady, Cyrus T.	My Lady's Slipper (1st, sm8vo, gilt, teg, 245p, 4pl)	Dodd	1905	Ditzler, C. Weber	25-40	
Warner, Anne	When Woman Proposes (1st, sm8vo, 158p, teg, purple cl, 4cp)	Little/Brown	1911	Ditzler, C. Weber	25-40	
N/A	Book of New Fairy Tales (4to, grey bds, p-o, [72]p, 7cp by…)	Dodge	[1910]	Dixon, Arthur A.	80-120	
Weedon, Lucy L.	Child Characters from Dickens (1st, 8vo, gilt, 320p, AEG, 6cp)	L: Nister	(1905)	Dixon, Arthur A.	75-125	
Hauff, Wilhelm	Fairy Tales (1st, 8vo, 344p, gilt, pep, 6cp, 12pl)	Nister/Dutton	[1910]	Dixon, Arthur A.	120-200	
Everett-Green, Evelyn	King's Butterfly (1st, sm8vo, 72p, p-o, gilt, b/w)	Nister/Dutton	(1900)	Dixon, Arthur A.	30-50	
Hinkson, Henry A.	King's Liege (1st, 8vo, 224p, blue cl, col frn, 3pl)	L: Blackie	1910	Dixon, Arthur A.	55-80	*
Laboulaye, E.R.	Laboulaye's Fairy Tales (1st, 8vo, 335p, green/gilt, 6cp, pep)	L: Nister	[1908]	Dixon, Arthur A.	100-185	
Everett-Green, Evelyn	Princess's Token (1st, sm8vo, 48p, gilt, b/w)	Nister/Dutton	(1902)	Dixon, Arthur A.	30-50	
Lang, Andrew	Tales of a Fairy Court (1st, 8vo, 108p, gilt, AEG, 12cp)	L: Collins	(1907)	Dixon, Arthur A.	170-240	
Kingsley, Charles	The Heroes (12mo, grey cl, p-o, 157p, 4cp, dep)	L: Blackie	[1907]	Dixon, Arthur A.	55-80	
Kingsley, Charles	Water Babies (1st, 8vo, green/gilt, AEG, 336p, 6cp)	Nister/Dutton	[1908]	Dixon, Arthur A.	200-300	
Gordon, Hampden C.	Lost Princess (1st, 8vo, 159p, 4cp)	L: J. Murray	(1933)	Dixon, George S.	40-70	*
Mulford, Clarence	Bar-20 Days (1st, 8vo, 412p, 4cp)	McClurg	1911	Dixon, Maynard	200-300	
Balch, Frederic H.	Bridge of the Gods (1st, sm8vo, teg, 280p, 8pl)	McClurg	1902	Dixon, Maynard	35-60	
Mulford, Clarence	Buck Peters, Ranchman (1st, 8vo, 367p, 4cp)	McClurg	1912	Dixon, Maynard	200-300	
Mulford, Clarence	Coming of Cassidy (1st, 8vo, 438p, 5cp)	McClurg	1913	Dixon, Maynard	200-300	
Kelly, Florence	Delafield Affair (1st, sm8vo, ibds, 422p, 4cp)	McClurg	1909	Dixon, Maynard	40-60	
Hanson, Joseph M.	Frontier Ballads (1st, 8vo, ibds, 92p, 7cp, pep)	McClurg	1910	Dixon, Maynard	60-90	
Coolidge, Dane	Hidden Water (1st, 8vo, ibds, 483p, 4cp)	McClurg	1910	Dixon, Maynard	50-80	
Mulford, Clarence	Hopalong Cassidy (1st, 8vo, 392p, ipcb, 5cp)	McClurg	1910	Dixon, Maynard	250-350	
Dixon, Maynard	Injun Babies (1st, 8vo, 72p, p-o, 7cp, pep)	Putnam	(1923)	Dixon, Maynard	70-100	
Morrow, W.C.	Lentala of the South Seas (1st, 8vo, grey cl, 278p, p-o, 7cp)	Stokes	(1908)	Dixon, Maynard	70-100	
Bronson, E.B.	Red Blooded (1st, 8vo, 342p, 10pl)	McClurg	1910	Dixon, Maynard	80-120	
Bronson, E.B.	Reminiscences of a Ranchman (1st [revised ed], 8vo, p-o, 369p, 8cp)	McClurg	(1910)	Dixon, Maynard	100-165	
Boyles, Kate	Spirit Trail (1st, 8vo, 416p, ibds, 4cp)	McClurg	1910	Dixon, Maynard	40-60	
Lynde, Francis	Taming of Red Butte Western (1st, 12mo, 410p, 4pl)	Scribner	1910	Dixon, Maynard	30-50	
Coolidge, Dane	The Texican (1st, 8vo, beige cl, 369p, 5cp)	McClurg	1911	Dixon, Maynard	60-90	
Kyne, Peter B.	Three Godfathers (1st, 8vo, gilt, 95p, 4pl)	Doran	(1913)	Dixon, Maynard	50-80	
Service, Robert W.	Trail of Ninety-Eight (1st, sm8vo, 514p, 4pl)	Dodd	1911	Dixon, Maynard	45-70	
Brady, Cyrus T.	West Wind (1st, 8vo, gilt, 389p, 4cp)	McClurg	1910	Dixon, Maynard	30-60	
Teal, Valentine	Angel Child (1st, sm8vo, ipcb, [40]p, color, pep, DJ/1.00)	Rand/McNally	1946	Doane, Pelagie	30-50	
Doane, Pelagie	Animals Here and There (1st {std}, 4to, ipcb, [48]p, color, DJ/0.50)	Doubleday/Doran	1945	Doane, Pelagie	50-80	
Doane, Pelagie	Book of Nature (1st {std}, 4to, 110p, fp color, DJ/4.00)	Oxford U. Pr.	1952	Doane, Pelagie	30-45	
Shepard, Birse	Cat Next Door (1st, 8vo, 64p, fp b/w, pep, DJ/1.50)	Oxford U. Pr.	(1943)	Doane, Pelagie	20-30	
Stevenson, Rbt. L.	Child's Garden of Verses (1st, sq4to, ibds, [30]p, fp color, pep, DJ/1.00)	Garden City	1942	Doane, Pelagie	50-80	
Bertail, Inez	Favorite Nursery Songs (1st, 8vo, ipcb, 42p, color, pep, DJ/0.50)	Random	(1941)	Doane, Pelagie	35-50	
Honness, Elizabeth	Flight of Fancy (1st, 8vo, 44p, 3-color, pep, DJ/1.25)	Oxford U. Pr.	(1941)	Doane, Pelagie	30-50	*
Tritten, Charles	Heidi Grows Up (1st UK, 8vo, 256p, green cl, col frn, 19pl, pep)	L: Collins	(1939)	Doane, Pelagie	40-65	*
Brown, Beatrice C.	Jonathan Bing (1st, sq12mo, ipcb, [48]p, fp b/w, dep, DJ/0.75)	Oxford U. Pr.	(1936)	Doane, Pelagie	60-90	*
Nast, Elsa R.	Little Steps (1st, lg8vo, ibds, [36]p, color, pep, DJ/0.50)	Grosset/Dunlap	1947	Doane, Pelagie	30-45	
Doane, Pelagie (ed)	Littlest Ones (1st, 12mo, [32]p, color, DJ/1.75)	Oxford U. Pr.	1956	Doane, Pelagie	30-45	*
Sutton, Margaret	Magic Makers and Bramble Bush Man (1st, lg8vo, 114p, ipcb, b/w, pep)	Grosset/Dunlap	(1936)	Doane, Pelagie	50-85	
Paxon, Mary	Mary Paxon, her Book (1st {std}, 8vo, 98p, ipcb, b/w)	Doubleday/Doran	1931	Doane, Pelagie	25-40	
Jacobs, Joseph	Molly Whuppie (1st AM, 8vo, tan cl, [46]p, fp 3-color, DJ/1.50)	Oxford U. Pr.	[1939]	Doane, Pelagie	70-120	
Mother Goose	Mother Goose (1st, lg8vo, ibds, [52]p, color, pep)	Random	(1940)	Doane, Pelagie	45-80	*
Doane, Pelagie	One Rainy Night (1st, 16mo, [32]p, color, cep, DJ/2.00)	Oxford U. Pr.	1957	Doane, Pelagie	30-50	
Quigg, Jane	Polly Peters (1st, 8vo, 77p, 8 fp 1-color, DJ/1.25)	Oxford U. Pr.	(1942)	Doane, Pelagie	25-45	
Boesel, Ann S.	Singing with Peter and Patsy (1st, ob4to, 48p, yellow cl, color, DJ/2.00)	Oxford U. Pr.	(1944)	Doane, Pelagie	30-50	
Doane, Pelagie	Small Child's Bible (1st, 4to, 142p, fp color, DJ/3.00)	Oxford U. Pr.	1946	Doane, Pelagie	30-50	
Doane, Pelagie	Small Child's Book of Verse (1st, 4to, 142p, fp color, DJ/3.00)	Oxford U. Pr.	1948	Doane, Pelagie	25-45	
MacNeil, Marion	Soldier Sammy (1st AM, sq12mo, [48]p, 3-color, pep, DJ/1.00)	Oxford U. Pr.	(1942)	Doane, Pelagie	40-65	
McKelvey, Gertrude	Stories to Live By (1st, 12mo, 62p, b/w, cep, DJ/0.75)	Winston	(1943)	Doane, Pelagie	20-35	
Doane, Pelagie	The Boy Jesus (1st, sm4to, 54p, fp color, DJ/3.00)	NY: Oxford U.Pr.	1953	Doane, Pelagie	30-55	
Bible	Three Prayers for Children (1st, lg4to, [32]p, ibds, color, pep, DJ/1.00)	Grosset/Dunlap	(1941)	Doane, Pelagie	45-70	
Hathaway, Cynthia	Two Bridgets (1st {std}, sm4to, [32]p, ibds, color, pep, DJ/1.00)	Doubleday/Doran	1941	Doane, Pelagie	30-50	*
Dobias, Dorathea F.	Casey Joins the Circus (1st, sq8vo, ibds, [33]p, color, pep)	Grosset/Dunlap	(1936)	Dobias, Dorathea	55-80	*
Adams, Katharine	Blackthorn (1st, sm8vo, 218p, col frn)	Macmillan	1931	Dobias, Frank	20-35	
Desmond, Alice C.	Boys of the Andes (1st, 8vo, 56p, p-o, color, pep)	D.C. Heath	(1941)	Dobias, Frank	25-45	*
N/A	Breman Band (1st, 16mo, [42]p, ibds, color, pep)	Macmillan	1927	Dobias, Frank	50-85	
Stinetorf, Louise	Children of North Africa (1st {std}, 8vo, 189p, col frn, b/w, DJ/2.00)	Lippincott	(1943)	Dobias, Frank	25-45	*
Mirza, Youel B.	Children of the Housetops (1st {std}, 8vo, 248p, col frn, b/w)	Doubleday/Doran	1931	Dobias, Frank	30-50	
Meigs, Cornelia L.	Clearing Weather (1st, 8vo, blue cl, 312p, 3cp, pep, NH)	Little/Brown	1928	Dobias, Frank	60-90	
Borie, Lysbeth	David Has his Day (1st, lg8vo, ibds, 63p, 2-color, pep, DJ/1.75)	Lippincott	(1934)	Dobias, Frank	40-65	
Beston, Henry	Five Bears & Miranda (1st, lg8vo, [60]p, blue cl, fp color, DJ/2.00)	Macmillan	1939	Dobias, Frank	60-100	*
Morris, Cora	Gypsy Story-Teller (1st {std}, 8vo, 206p, col frn, 16 b/w, pep)	Macmillan	1931	Dobias, Frank	45-70	*
Walker, Joseph	How they Carried the Mail (1st, lg8vo, 305p, 3cp, 8pl)	Sears	(1930)	Dobias, Frank	40-65	
N/A	Jack & the Beanstalk (1st, sq16mo, ibds, color, pep)	Macmillan	1927	Dobias, Frank	50-85	
Siebe, Josephine	Kasperle's Adventures (1st lg sq8vo, pink cl, 199p, 6cp, pep)	Macmillan	1929	Dobias, Frank	30-50	
Bannerman, Helen	Little Black Sambo (1st, 16mo, ibds, [39]p, color)	Macmillan	1927	Dobias, Frank	160-225	
Farrow, Dorothy P.	Little Brown Hen (1st, sq12mo, [48]p, orange cl, color, cep, DJ/1.00)	Macmillan	1941	Dobias, Frank	40-65	
MacNeil, Marion	Monty Marine (1st, sq12mo, [48]p, 3-color, pep, DJ/1.00)	Oxford U. Pr.	(1943)	Dobias, Frank	40-70	*

AUTHOR	TITLE	PUBLISHER	DATE	ARTIST	PRICE	LC
Schmidt, Sarah L.	New Land (1st, sm8vo, 317p, brown cl, 9 fp b/w, pep, NH)	McBride	1933	Dobias, Frank	40-65	
Kelsey, Alice	Once the Hodja (1st {std}, 12mo, 170p, b/w, pep, DJ/2.00)	Longmans	1943	Dobias, Frank	30-50	
Neikirk, Mabel O.	Oscar the Trained Seal (1st, ob4to, ibds, [24]p, color, dep, DJ/0.50)	Grosset/Dunlap	(1940)	Dobias, Frank	60-90	
Dobias, Frank	Picture Book of Flying (1st, 4to, 64p, fp color, pep, DJ/2.00)	Macmillan	1928	Dobias, Frank	80-125	
N/A	Puss in Boots (1st, sq16mo, [41]p, color, pep)	Macmillan	1937	Dobias, Frank	70-100	*
Fleming, Waldo	Pygmy's Arrow (1st, 8vo, 310p, pep, DJ/2.00)	Lothrop, Lee	1938	Dobias, Frank	30-50	*
Whitfield, Raoul	Silver Wings (1st, sm8vo, 234p, col frn, pep)	Knopf	1930	Dobias, Frank	60-100	*
Hosford, Dorothy	Sons of the Volsungs (1st, 8vo, 168p, b/w, pep)	Macmillan	1932	Dobias, Frank	20-35	
Burtis, Thomson	Straight Shooting (1st {std}, 8vo, 279p, col frn)	Doubleday/Doran	1931	Dobias, Frank	25-45	*
Fleming, Waldo	Talking Drums (1st {std}, 8vo, 307p, col frn, b/w, pep, DJ/2.00)	Doubleday/Doran	1936	Dobias, Frank	30-50	
N/A	Three Billy Goats Gruff (1st, sq16mo, ibds, color)	Macmillan	1927	Dobias, Frank	40-65	
Bunn, Harriet	Trailer Tracks (1st, 8vo, 241p, b/w, pep, DJ/1.75)	Macmillan	1937	Dobias, Frank	30-50	
Kuh, Charlotte	Train, a Boat & an Island (1st, sq8vo, 89p, col frn, b/w)	Macmillan	1932	Dobias, Frank	30-50	
Burtis, Thomson	War of the Ghosts (1st {std}, 8vo, 262p, col frn, pep)	Doubleday/Doran	1932	Dobias, Frank	25-45	*
Abdullah, Achmed	Year of the Wood Dragon (1st, 12mo, 249p, fp b/w woodcuts)	Brentano's	(1926)	Dobias, Frank	30-50	
Marshall, Dean	Silver Robin (1st {std}, 8vo, 246p, b/w, pep, DJ/2.50)	Dutton	1947	Dobias/McGuckin	120-200	
Dobrin, Arnold	Gerbils (1st, lg8vo, 63p, DJ/3.75)	Lothrop, Lee	(1970)	Dobrin, Arnold	25-40	*
Dobrin, Arnold	Snow Fox (1st, ob4to, [32]p, fp 2-color, DJ/3.50)	Coward	1968	Dobrin, Arnold	30-45	*
Fox, Frances M.	Little Giant's Neighbours (1st, 12mo, 132p, b/w)	L.C. Page	1903	Dodge, F.E.	25-40	*
Putnam, Nina W.	Adventures in the Open (1st, sm8vo, ibds, color)	Volland	(1918)	Dodge, Katharine S.	55-80	*
Reid, Sydney	How Sing Found the World is Round (1st, 12mo, [40]p, ibds, color)	Volland	(1921)	Dodge, Katharine S.	80-120	*
Sylvester, Charles	Manny & Co. (1st, 8vo, ibds, [40]p, color)	Volland	1913	Dodge, Katharine S.	60-90	
Cox-McCormack, N.	Peeps: Really Truly Sunshine Fairy (1st, 8vo, [37]p, ibds, color)	Volland	(1918)	Dodge, Katharine S.	75-100	
Waterstone, Satella	Short Stories of Musical Melodies (1st, 4to, ibds, unpag, gilt, b/w, pep)	Volland	(1915)	Dodge, Katharine S.	140-200	
Jacobs-Bond, Carrie	Tales of Little Cats (1st, sq12mo, ibds, [38]p, color, pep)	Volland	(1918)	Dodge, Katharine S.	80-125	
Jacobs-Bond, Carrie	Tales of Little Dogs (1st, sq8vo, ibds, [35]p, color, pep)	Volland	(1921)	Dodge, Katharine S.	80-125	
Putnam, Nina W.	Winkle, Twinkle & Lollypop (1st, 8vo, ibds, [95]p, fp color, pep)	Volland	(1918)	Dodge, Katharine S.	70-120	
Dodworth, Dorothy	Dangerous Day for Mrs. Doodlepunk (1st, ob8vo, unpag, 1-color, DJ/1.50)	W.R. Scott	(1954)	Dodworth, Dorothy	30-45	
Dodworth, Dorothy	Mrs. Doodlepunk Trades Work (1st, ob8vo, red cl, [48]p, 1-color, DJ/2.25)	W.R. Scott	1957	Dodworth, Dorothy	30-50	
Hoge, Dorothy	Black Heart of Indri (1st, 4to, ibds, [44]p, color, DJ/3.50)	Scribner	1966	Domanska, Janina	30-50	
Reck, Alma	Clocks Tell the Time (1st, 8vo, 48p, 2-color, DJ/2.75)	Scribner	(1960)	Domanska, Janina	25-40	
Fournier, Catherine	Coconut Thieves (1st, 4to, [32]p, 3-color, DJ/3.25)	Scribner	(1964)	Domanska, Janina	30-50	*
Laskowski, Jerzy	Dragon Liked Smoked Fish (1st, 4to, [32]p, fp 3-color, DJ/3.95)	Seabury Press	(1967)	Domanska, Janina	30-50	
Kunhardt, Dorothy	Gas Station Gus (1st, 12mo, 65p, ipcb, 1-color, DJ/1.95)	Harper	(1962)	Domanska, Janina	30-50	
Konopnicka, Maria	Golden Seed (1st, 8vo, [48]p, color, DJ/3.50)	Scribner	(1962)	Domanska, Janina	25-45	
Johnson, Sally (ed)	Harper Book of Princes (1st, 8vo, 330p, b/w, DJ/4.95)	Harper	(1964)	Domanska, Janina	30-45	
Fisher, Aileen	I Like Weather (1st, sm4to, [35]p, color, pep, DJ/3.50)	Crowell	(1963)	Domanska, Janina	30-50	
Kay, Mara	In Place of Katia (1st, 8vo, 224p, DJ/3.25)	Scribner	(1963)	Domanska, Janina	30-50	
Domanska, Janina	Look: There is a Turtle Flying (1st {std}, 4to, [32]p, color, DJ/4.50)	Macmillan	(1968)	Domanska, Janina	25-40	
Beresford, Elisabeth	Magic World (1st AM, 8vo, 153p, b/w, DJ/3.50)	Bobbs-Merrill	(1965)	Domanska, Janina	40-65	
Domanska, Janina	Marilka (1st {std}, 8vo, [32]p, color, dep, DJ/4.95)	Macmillan	(1970)	Domanska, Janina	25-40	
Laskowski, Jerzy	Master of the Royal Cats (1st, 4to, [32]p, color, DJ/3.50)	Seabury Press	(1965)	Domanska, Janina	30-45	*
Lindgren, Astrid	Mischievous Meg (1st, sm8vo, 139p, fp b/w, DJ/2.75)	Viking	(1962)	Domanska, Janina	60-90	
Deutsch, Babette	More Tales of Faraway Folk (1st {std}, 8vo, 93p, b/w, DJ/2.75)	Harper	(1963)	Domanska, Janina	30-50	R*
Tooze, Ruth	Nikkos of the Pink Pelican (1st, lg8vo, 64p, 2-color, DJ/2.75)	Viking	(1964)	Domanska, Janina	25-45	
Domanska, Janina	Palmiero and the Ogre (1st {std}, ob4to, [32]p, 2-color, DJ/3.95)	Macmillan	(1967)	Domanska, Janina	30-45	
Carlson, Natalie S.	Song of the Lop-Eared Mule (1st, 8vo, 79p, b/w, DJ/2.75)	Harper	(1961)	Domanska, Janina	20-30	
Leskov, Nicholas	Steel Flea (1st [rev. ed.], 8vo, 56p, color, cep, DJ/2.95)	Harper	(1964)	Domanska, Janina	30-45	*
Weilerstein, Sadie	Ten and a Kid (1st {std}, 8vo, 185p, b/w, DJ/2.95)	Doubleday	1961	Domanska, Janina	25-45	
Domanska, Janina	The Turnip (1st {std}, ob4to, [32]p, color, DJ/4.95)	Macmillan	(1969)	Domanska, Janina	25-40	
Kelly, Eric P.	Trumpeter of Krakow (1st {new ed. std}, lg8vo, 208p, b/w, DJ/3.95)	Macmillan	(1966)	Domanska, Janina	20-35	
Domanska, Janina	Why So Much Noise? (1st, 8vo, ibds, [32]p, 2-color, DJ/2.50)	Harper	(1965)	Domanska, Janina	25-40	
Hardendorff, Jeanne	Little Cock (1st {std}, 4to, [32]p, color, DJ/4.95)	Lippincott	(1969)	Domjan, Joseph	30-50	
Donahey, William	Adventures of the Teenie Weenies (1st, 4to, 128p, p-o, 9cp)	Reilly/Lee	(1920)	Donahey, William	300-450	
Donahey, William	Alice & the Teenie Weenies (1st, lg8vo, 105p, p-o, color, pep)	Reilly/Lee	(1927)	Donahey, William	300-450	
Mother Goose	Children's Mother Goose (1st, 4to, 120p, p-o, 12cp, pep)	Reilly/Lee	(1921)	Donahey, William	300-450	
Donahey, William	Down the River with the Teenie Weenies (1st, 4to, p-o, 128p, 8cp)	Reilly/Lee	(1921)	Donahey, William	300-450	
Marino, Josef	Hi! Ho! Pinocchio (1st, 4to, 127p, col frn, p-o, b/w, cep, DJ/1.00)	Reilly/Lee	(1940)	Donahey, William	200-300	
Sampson, Emma S.	Miss Minerva's Scallywags (1st, 12mo, red cl, 321p, b/w)	Reilly/Lee	(1927)	Donahey, William	50-85	
Donahey, William	Teenie Weenie Days (1st, lg8vo, 65p, 4 fp color, pep, DJ/1.00)	Whittlesey	(1944)	Donahey, William	200-300	
Mother Goose	Teenie Weenie Man's Mother Goose (1st, 4to, 126p, 12cp, pep)	Reilly/Lee	(1921)	Donahey, William	200-300	
Donahey, William	Teenie Weenie Neighbors (1st {std}, 8vo, 68p, 5 color, pep, DJ/1.00)	Whittlesey	(1945)	Donahey, William	200-300	
Donahey, William	Teenie Weenie Town (1st, 8vo, 71p, red cl, p-o, color, pep, DJ/1.50)	Whittlesey	(1942)	Donahey, William	200-300	
Donahey, William	Teenie Weenies in Wonderland (1st, 4to, 120p, color)	Reilly/Lee	(1923)	Donahey, William	250-400	
Donahey, William	Teenie Weenies Under the Rose Bush (1st, 4to, p-o, 120p, 8cp)	Reilly/Lee	(1922)	Donahey, William	250-400	
Thompson, Ruth P.	Wonder Book (1st, sm4to, green cl, 217p, p-o, 7cp)	Reilly/Lee	(1929)	Donahey, William	200-300	
Schlein, Miriam	Laurie's New Brother (1st, 4to, unpag, color, pep, DJ/2.75)	Abelard-Schuman	1961	Donald, Elizabeth	20-30	
Moore, Clement C.	Night Before Christmas (1st, lg8vo, ibds, [22]p, color, pep)	Grosset/Dunlap	(1948)	Dorcas	50-85	
Hanson, Charles H.	Stories of the Days of King Arthur (1st, 12mo, 271p, gilt, fp b/w)	L: Nelson	1884	Dore, Gustave	80-140	
Poe, Edgar A.	The Raven (1st, folio, gilt, 23p, AEG, engravings by...)	Harper	1884	Dore, Gustave	200-300	
Montgomery, R.	Beaver Water (1st {std}, 8vo, 214p, b/w, DJ/2.75)	World	(1956)	Doremus, Robert	20-35	*
Judson, Clara I.	Soldier Doctor: Story of William Gorgas (1st, 8vo, 151p, b/w, DJ/1.60)	Scribner	1942	Doremus, Robert	30-45	
Dorian, Edith	When the Snow is Blue (1st, 4to, [20]p, 2-color, dep, DJ/2.75)	Lothrop, Lee	(1960)	Dorian, Edith	25-45	
Heath, Janet F.	Built-Upon House (1st, lg8vo, 126p, p-o, color, pep)	Whitman	(1929)	Dotterer, Lloyd J.	35-60	*
Johnson, James W.	God's Trombones (1st, 8vo, bds, gilt, 56p, 8pl, DJ)	Viking	1927	Douglas, Aaron	300-500	
Kennedy, Mary	Surprise to the Children (1st {std}, sm sq4to, 88p, ibds, 6cp)	Doubleday/Doran	1933	Dowd, James H.	50-85	
Broadbent, Helen	Sing-A-Song (1st, ob folio, ibds, unpag, 8cp)	L: M. Goshen	1912	Dowdall, N.	150-220	*
Butler, Elinor B.	Diamond Spider & other Stories (1st, sm8vo, 201p, b/w pl)	A. Harriman	1910	Dowling, C.M.	30-55	

AUTHOR	TITLE	PUBLISHER	DATE	ARTIST	PRICE	LC
Colfer, Enid	Cucumber: Story of a Siamese Cat (1st, 8vo, 98p, b/w, DJ/2.95)	Nelson	(1961)	Dowling, Victor	20-30	
Downer, Mary L.	The Flower (1st, ob8vo, brown cl, [32]p, 3-color, DJ/1.75)	W.R. Scott	1955	Downer, Mary L.	30-50	*
Coatsworth, Eliz.	Lucky Ones (1st {std}, 8vo, 84p, fp b/w, DJ/3.95)	Macmillan	(1968)	Doyle, Janet	20-35	
Montalba, Anthony R.	Doyle Fairy Book (1st, 12mo, 582p, red/gilt, AEG, 36pl)	L: Dean	1890	Doyle, Richard	250-350	
Lang, Andrew	Princess Nobody (1st, lg8vo, ibds, 56p, color, pep)	L: Longmans	(1884)	Doyle, Richard	400-600	
Ramal, Walter	Songs of Childhood (1st, 16mo, 106p, teg, gilt, frn by...)	L: Longmans	1902	Doyle, Richard	350-500	
Smith, Gertrude	Jolly Polly Stories (1st, lg sq8vo, 99p, b/w)	Small/Maynard	1918	Drake, Elise D.	30-50	
Farley, Walter	Man O'War (1st, 8vo, 326p, b/w, DJ/3.95)	Random	(1962)	Draper, Alice	50-80	
Farley, Walter	Black Stallion Challenged (1st {std}, 8vo, 246p, b/w, DJ/2.95)	Random	(1964)	Draper, Angie	50-80	
Henty, G.A.	St. Bartholomew's Eve (1st, 12mo, gilt, 384p, 12pl)	L: Blackie	1894	Draper, Herbert J.	120-185	
Drayton, Grace	Baby Bears & their Wishing Rings (1st, lg ob8vo, 167p, color)	Century	(1914)	Drayton, Grace	200-300	
N/A	Bettina's Bonnet (sq12mo, ibds, 10 fp color)	Hearst	1915	Drayton, Grace	120-180	*
Drayton, Grace	Dolly Dimples and Bobby Bounce (1st, 8vo, ibds, 86p, b/w)	Cupples/Leon	(1931)	Drayton, Grace	200-300	
Drayton, Grace	Let's Go to the Zoo (1st, ob4to, 44p, ibds, shape bk., 6cp)	Duffield	(1914)	Drayton, Grace	200-300	
Mother Goose	Nursery Rhymes from Mother Goose (sm8vo, 111p, color)	Scribner	1916	Drayton, Grace	160-240	*
Cammack, Key	Spartan Primer (1st, 4to, ipcb, fp color)	Duffield	1913	Drayton, Grace	160-240	
Gulick, Peggy	Sing Sang Sung & Willie (1st {std}, 4to, ibds, [31]p, color, DJ/1.50)	Knopf	(1947)	Dresser, Elizabeth	70-100	
Henry, Marguerite	Robert Fulton: Boy Craftsman (1st {std}, sm8vo, uncut, 187p, b/w, DJ/1.50)	Bobbs-Merrill	(1945)	Dresser, Lawrence	30-45	
Wilder, Thornton	Bridge of San Luis Rey (1st AM, 8vo, 235p, 10pl, pep, DJ)	A.& C. Boni	1927	Drevenstedt, Amy	300-500	R
Bible	In the Morning (1st, ob8vo, ipcb, [26]p, fp 1-color, pep)	Abingdon-Cokes.	1947	Drew, Louise	35-50	*
Sleigh, Barbara	Carbonel, King of Cats (1st AM {std}, 8vo, 253p, color, DJ/2.75)	Bobbs-Merrill	(1957)	Drummond, Violet	200-300	
Drummond, Violet H.	Flying Postman ([new ed.] {std}, 4to, unpag, color, DJ/3.25)	H.Z. Walck	(1964)	Drummond, Violet	25-45	
Drummond, Violet H.	Mrs. Easter and the Storks (1st, 4to, 31p, color, DJ, KGM)	L: Faber	(1957)	Drummond, Violet	80-125	
DuBois, W.P.	Alligator Case (1st, 8vo, 63p, ibds, fp color, cep, DJ/3.50)	Harper	(1965)	DuBois, W.P.	50-80	R*
DuBois, W.P.	Bear Party (1st, sm8vo, ibds, [48]p, color, DJ/2.00, CH)	Viking	1951	DuBois, W.P.	100-165	
Kunhardt, Dorothy	Billy the Barber (1st, 12mo, 47p, ibds, color, DJ/1.95)	Harper	1961	DuBois, W.P.	40-65	
DuBois, W.P.	Call Me Bandicoot (1st, 8vo, 63p, ibds, color, DJ/3.95)	Harper	(1970)	DuBois, W.P.	40-65	
Caudill, Rebecca	Certain Small Shepherd (1st {std}, sq8vo, 48p, ibds, fp color, DJ/3.50)	Holt, Rinehart	(1965)	DuBois, W.P.	45-70	R
Wilbur, Richard	Digging for China: A Poem (1st {std}, 12mo, ibds, [32]p, fp color, DJ)	Doubleday	(1956)	DuBois, W.P.	50-85	
Verne, Jules	Dr. Ox's Experiment (1st {std}, 8vo, 100p, b/w, pep, DJ/3.95)	Macmillan	1963	DuBois, W.P.	30-50	
DuBois, W.P.	Elisabeth the Cow Ghost (1st [1st bk.], sq16mo, [47]p, color)	NY: Nelson	1936	DuBois, W.P.	200-300	
Fenton, Edward	Fierce John (1st {std}, 8vo, 59p, fp 1-color, pep, DJ/2.00)	Doubleday	1959	DuBois, W.P.	30-50	
DuBois, W.P.	Flying Locomotive (1st, ob8vo, ibds, 47p, color, DJ/1.00)	Viking	1941	DuBois, W.P.	90-130	
DuBois, W.P.	Giant Otto (1st, sq16mo, [40]p, ibds, 17cp, pep)	Viking	1936	DuBois, W.P.	150-225	
DuBois, W.P.	Great Geppy (1st, sm4to, 92p, 22 fp color, dep, DJ/2.00)	Viking	1940	DuBois, W.P.	120-200	R
McKinley, Charles	Harriett (1st, sm4to, 44p, 1-color, pep, DJ/2.00)	Viking	1946	DuBois, W.P.	80-130	R
DuBois, W.P.	Horse in the Camel Suit (1st, sq8vo, 79p, ibds, color, DJ/3.95)	Harper	(1967)	DuBois, W.P.	60-100	
Clement, Marguerite	In France (1st, 8vo, blue cl, 151p, dp b/w, pep, DJ/3.00)	Viking	1956	DuBois, W.P.	30-50	
Grattan, Madeleine	Jexium Island (1st, 8vo, blue cl, 184p, b/w, pep, DJ/2.75)	Viking	(1957)	DuBois, W.P.	50-85	
DuBois, W.P.	Lazy Tommy Pumpkinhead (1st, 8vo, ipcb, 28p, fp color, DJ/2.50)	Harper	(1966)	DuBois, W.P.	120-170	
MacDonald, George	Light Princess (1st, 4to, ibds, 48p, color, pep, DJ/3.50)	Crowell	(1962)	DuBois, W.P.	45-70	
DuBois, W.P.	Lion (1st, sm4to, 36p, color, pep, DJ/3.00, CH)	Viking	1956	DuBois, W.P.	120-200	R
Dahl, Roald	Magic Finger (1st, 8vo, 40p, b/w, pep, DJ/2.50)	Harper	(1966)	DuBois, W.P.	200-300	
Greener, Leslie	Moon Ahead (1st, 8vo, green cl, 256p, fp b/w, pep, DJ/2.50)	Viking	1951	DuBois, W.P.	30-50	
Godden, Rumer	Mousewife (1st, 8vo, 46p, fp b/w, DJ/2.00)	Viking	1951	DuBois, W.P.	60-90	
Ames, Evelyn	My Brother Bird (1st, 8vo, 125p, red cl, fp b/w, pep, DJ/2.75)	Dodd	1954	DuBois, W.P.	40-65	
DuBois, W.P.	Otto and the Magic Potatoes (1st, sm4to, 48p, dp color, DJ/4.95)	Viking	(1970)	DuBois, W.P.	60-90	
DuBois, W.P.	Otto at Sea (1st, sq16mo, ibds, [40]p, color, pep)	Viking	1936	DuBois, W.P.	150-225	
DuBois, W.P.	Otto in Africa (1st, 4to, 35p, color, pep, DJ/2.50)	Viking	(1961)	DuBois, W.P.	60-100	R
DuBois, W.P.	Otto in Texas (1st, sm4to, 45p, color, pep, DJ/2.50)	Viking	(1959)	DuBois, W.P.	100-165	R
Lear, Edward	Owl & the Pussycat (1st {std}, 12mo, ibds, unpag, color, pep, DJ/1.75)	Doubleday	1961	DuBois, W.P.	30-50	*
DuBois, W.P.	Peter Graves (1st, lg8vo, ibds, 168p, dep, DJ/2.50)	Viking	1950	DuBois, W.P.	80-120	
Doyle, Arthur Conan	Poison Belt (1st {std}, 8vo, 158p, fp b/w, pep, DJ/4.50)	Macmillan	(1964)	DuBois, W.P.	35-50	
DuBois, W.P.	Porko Von Popbutton (1st, 8vo, ibds, 80p, fp color, DJ/3.95)	Harper	(1969)	DuBois, W.P.	70-100	R
DuBois, W.P.	Pretty Pretty Peggy Moffitt (1st, 8vo, 32p, ibds, color, DJ/2.95)	Harper	(1968)	DuBois, W.P.	70-120	
Plimpton, George	Rabbit's Umbrella (1st, 8vo, 159p, yellow cl, b/w, pep, DJ/2.75)	Viking	1955	DuBois, W.P.	80-140	
Plant, Richard	S.O.S. Geneva (1st, 8vo, 246p, b/w, DJ/2.00)	Viking	1939	DuBois, W.P.	120-170	
DuBois, W.P.	Squirrel Hotel (1st, sm4to, red cl, 48p, pep, b/w, DJ/2.00)	Viking	1952	DuBois, W.P.	70-120	
DuBois, W.P.	The Giant (1st, lg8vo, 124p, grey cl, fp b/w, DJ/2.75)	Viking	1954	DuBois, W.P.	100-165	R
N/A	Three Little Pigs in Verse (1st, 8vo, 32p, color, pep, DJ/2.50)	Viking	(1962)	DuBois, W.P.	50-80	R
DuBois, W.P.	Three Policemen (1st, sm4to, blue cl, 92p, 16 color, pep, DJ/2.00)	Viking	1938	DuBois, W.P.	120-200	
Yurdin, Betty	Tiger in the Teapot (1st {std}, 12mo, ipcb, 29p, color, DJ/2.95)	Holt, Rinehart	(1968)	DuBois, W.P.	50-90	
Bishop, Claire H.	Twenty & Ten (1st, lg8vo, 76p, pep, b/w, DJ/2.50)	Viking	1952	DuBois, W.P.	40-65	
DuBois, W.P.	Twenty-One Balloons (1st, lg8vo, ibds, 179p, b/w, DJ/2.50, NM)	Viking	1947	DuBois, W.P.	160-225	R
Gordon, Patricia	Witch of Scrapfaggot Green (1st, sm4to, ibds, 78p, 10 fp b/w, DJ/2.50)	Viking	1948	DuBois, W.P.	65-90	
Ashford, Daisy	Young Visitors (1st, 8vo, 91p, ibds, b/w, DJ/1.75)	Doubleday	1951	DuBois, W.P.	45-70	
DuMaurier, George	Legend of Camelot (1st, ob4to, ibds, 95p, b/w)	Harper	1898	DuMaurier, George	120-180	
DuMaurier, George	The Martian (1st, 8vo, orange/gilt, 471p, b/w)	Harper	1897	DuMaurier, George	55-90	
Wilkins, Mary E.	Heart's Highway (1st [1], sm8vo, green cl, 308p, 8pl)	Doubleday/Page	1900	DuMond	35-60	
Wallace, Lew	Wooing of Malkatoon (1st, lg8vo, green/gilt, 168p, teg)	Harper	1898	DuMond	50-80	
Mayne, William	Glass Ball (1st AM {std}, sm4to, 63p, fp 1-color, DJ/2.95)	Dutton	(1962)	Duchesne, Janet	20-35	
Mayne, William	Plot Night (1st AM {std}, 8vo, 126p, b/w, DJ)	Dutton	(1968)	Duchesne, Janet	25-40	*
Grimm Bros.	Fairy Tales (1st, 8vo, 408p)	L: J. Nisbet	1906	Dudley, Ambrose	80-125	*
Justus, May	At the Foot of Windy Low (1st, 8vo, green cl, 80p, 10cp, pep)	Volland	(1930)	Dudley, Carrie	50-80	
Justus, May	Gabby Gaffer (1st, 8vo, green/gilt, 80p, 10cp, pep)	Volland	(1929)	Dudley, Carrie	50-80	
Baxter, Betty	Supposin' (1st, 12mo, ibds, 40p, color, pep)	Volland	(1931)	Dudley, Carrie	60-100	
Grey, Zane	Desert Gold (1st, 12mo, 325p, gilt, p-o, 4pl)	Harper	1913	Duer, Douglas	150-225	
Grey, Zane	Riders of the Purple Sage (1st, 12mo, tan/gilt, 335p, p-o, 4pl)	Harper	1912	Duer, Douglas	500-700	

AUTHOR	TITLE	PUBLISHER	DATE	ARTIST	PRICE	LC
Campbell, John F.	Celtic Dragon Myth (1st, 8vo, 172p, gilt, p-o, 5cp)	J. Grant	1911	Duff, Rachel	120-170	
Masefield, John	Martin Hyde (1st, 8vo, 303p, teg, green cl, uncut, 16pl)	L: Wells/Gard.	1910	Dugdale, Thomas C.	60-90	
Dugo, Andre	Dogcatcher's Dog (1st {std}, 4to, ibds, [32]p, fp 2-color, DJ/2.00, NYTBI)	Holt	(1952)	Dugo, Andre	30-55	
Druon, Maurice	Tistou of the Green Thumbs (1st AM, 8vo, 178p, fp b/w, DJ/2.75)	Scribner	(1958)	Duheme, Jacqueline	30-45	
Crary, Mary	Daughter of the Stars (1st, 4to, 190p, 2cp by...)	L: Hatchard	1939	Dulac, Edmund	140-220	R
Queen Marie	Dreamer of Dreams (1st, lg8vo, 181p, grey/gilt, 6 ticp)	L: Hodder	[1915]	Dulac, Edmund	275-400	
Dulac, Edmund	Edmund Dulac's Fairy Book (1st AM, 4to, p-o, gilt 174p, 16 ticp)	Doran	(1916)	Dulac, Edmund	300-450	
Dulac, Edmund	Edmund Dulac's Fairy Book (1st, 4to, gilt, 174p, 16 ticp, pep)	L: Hodder	(1916)	Dulac, Edmund	350-500	
Stawell, Mrs. R.	Fairies I Have Met (1st, 8vo, green cl, 117p, 8cp)	L: John Lane	[1907]	Dulac, Edmund	250-400	
Stawell, Mrs. R.	Fairies I Have Met (8vo, 117p, blue/gilt, 8cp)	L: Hodder	[1910]	Dulac, Edmund	250-350	
Perrault, Charles	Fairy Garland (1st, lg8vo, 251p, 12 ticp)	L: Cassell	(1928)	Dulac, Edmund	170-240	
Perrault, Charles	Fairy Garland (1st AM, lg8vo, blue/gilt, 251p, p-o, 12 ticp)	Scribner	(1929)	Dulac, Edmund	150-220	
Yeats, Wm. Butler	Four Plays for Dancers (1st AM, 8vo, bds, 138p, 7pl)	L: Macmillan	1921	Dulac, Edmund	200-300	
Williamson, Hugh R.	Gods & Mortals in Love (1st, 4to, cloth, 82p, t.e. blue, 9 fp color)	L: Country Life	(1935)	Dulac, Edmund	180-250	
Beauclerk, Helen	Green Lacquer Pavillion (1st, 12mo, tan/gilt, 319p, 10pl)	L: Collins	1926	Dulac, Edmund	100-165	
Beauclerk, Helen	Green Lacquer Pavillion (1st AM, 12mo, 319p, gilt, b/w)	Doran	(1926)	Dulac, Edmund	70-100	
Rosenthal, Leonard	Kingdom of the Pearl (1st AM, 4to, 152p, teg, bds, p-o, 10 ticp)	Brentano's	[1920]	Dulac, Edmund	450-650	
Beauclerk, Helen	Love of the Foolish Angel (1st AM, 8vo, blue cl, 271p, b/w, dep)	Cosmopolitan	1929	Dulac, Edmund	100-145	
Beauclerk, Helen	Love of the Foolish Angel (1st, 8vo, blue/gilt, 251p, b/w)	L: Collins	1929	Dulac, Edmund	100-180	
Dulac, Edmund	Lyrics Pathetic & Humorous from A to Z (1st, 4to, ibds, [49]p, color, pep)	L: Warne	1908	Dulac, Edmund	400-600	
Housman, Laurence	Magic Horse (1st, sm sq8vo, [58]p, gilt, 12cp)	L: Hodder	(1911)	Dulac, Edmund	250-400	
Stawell, Mrs. R.	My Days with the Fairies (1st, 4to, 169p, red/gilt, 8 ticp)	L: Hodder	(1913)	Dulac, Edmund	350-500	
Dulac, Edmund	Picture Book for the French Red Cross (1st, 4to, gilt, 135p, 19 ticp)	L: Hodder	(1915)	Dulac, Edmund	300-500	R
Poe, Edgar A.	Poetical Works of Edgar A. Poe (1st AM, 4to, 192p, bds, 28cp)	Doran	[1921]	Dulac, Edmund	250-350	
Housman, Laurence	Princess Badoura (1st, 4to, teg, 113p, gilt, 10 ticp, pep)	L: Hodder	[1913]	Dulac, Edmund	500-700	
Smith, C.M. (tran)	Queen Bee (1st, 8vo, 125p, gilt, pep, 2cp by...)	L: Nelson	1907	Dulac, Edmund	160-225	
Omar Khayyam	Rubaiyat of Omar Khayyam (1st, lg4to, white/gilt, unpag, 20 ticp)	L: Hodder	[1909]	Dulac, Edmund	400-600	
Omar Khayyam	Rubaiyat of Omar Khayyam (1st {this pub.}, lg8vo, 197p, cp)	Doubleday/Doran	1930	Dulac, Edmund	50-80	
Bronte, Charlotte	Shirley (1st, 8vo, 2 volumes, teg)	L: Dent	1905	Dulac, Edmund	130-200	
N/A	Sinbad the Sailor (1st, lg4to, 223p, gilt, bds, p-o, 23 ticp)	L: Hodder	[1914]	Dulac, Edmund	500-700	
Quiller-Couch, A.	Sleeping Beauty... (1st, 4to, 129p, gilt, 30 ticp)	L: Hodder	(1910)	Dulac, Edmund	400-600	
Quiller-Couch, A.	Sleeping Beauty... (1st AM, lg4to, 129p, maroon/gilt, 30 ticp)	NY: Hodder	[1910]	Dulac, Edmund	300-500	
Quiller-Couch, A.	Sleeping Beauty... (8vo, 196p, black cl, p-o, 8cp, pep)	Garden City	[1932]	Dulac, Edmund	50-90	
Queen Marie	Stealers of Light (1st, 4to, blue/gilt, 190p, 2 ticp)	L: Hodder	1916	Dulac, Edmund	250-350	
Andersen, Hans C.	Stories from Andersen (4to, blue cl, 16cp)	Doubleday/Doran	(1930)	Dulac, Edmund	100-160	
Housman, Laurence (ed)	Stories from Arabian Nights (1st, 4to, 133p, 50 ticp)	L: Hodder	(1907)	Dulac, Edmund	325-450	
Housman, Laurence (ed)	Stories from Arabian Nights (1st AM, 4to, 133p, gilt, 50 ticp)	Scribner	(1907)	Dulac, Edmund	350-500	
Housman, Laurence (ed)	Stories from Arabian Nights (8vo, 24 ticp, later)	L: Hodder	[1911]	Dulac, Edmund	120-180	
N/A	Stories from Arabian Nights (lg8vo, 205p, 8cp, pep, later)	Garden City	[1932]	Dulac, Edmund	75-100	
Andersen, Hans C.	Stories... (1st, 4to, 250p, orange/gilt, 28 ticp, pep)	L: Hodder	[1911]	Dulac, Edmund	450-650	R
N/A	Tales from Arabian Nights (sm4to, 190p, gilt, 20 ticp, later)	L: Hodder	[1920]	Dulac, Edmund	170-220	
Hawthorne, Nathaniel	Tanglewood Tales (1st, 4to, 245p, gilt, 14 ticp, pep)	L: Hodder	(1919)	Dulac, Edmund	200-270	
Bronte, Anne	Tenant of Wildfell Hall... (1st AM, 12mo, 548p, green/gilt, 12 color)	Dutton	1922	Dulac, Edmund	60-90	
Poe, Edgar A.	The Bells... (1st, 4to, teg, green/gilt, pep, 28 ticp)	L: Hodder	(1912)	Dulac, Edmund	300-450	
Andersen, Hans C.	The Nightingale (1st, 4to, blue/gilt, 125p, 12 ticp)	L: Hodder	[1911]	Dulac, Edmund	350-500	
Shakespeare, Wm.	The Tempest (1st, 4to, blue/gilt, 144p, 40 ticp)	L: Hodder	[1908]	Dulac, Edmund	350-500	
Stevenson, Rbt. L.	Treasure Island (1st, 4to, 255p, brown/gilt, 12cp)	L: Benn	(1927)	Dulac, Edmund	200-300	
Stevenson, Rbt. L.	Treasure Island (1st AM, lg8vo, 287p, green/gilt, 12 ticp)	Doran	(1927)	Dulac, Edmund	180-220	
Stevenson, Rbt. L.	Treasure Island (1st {this pub}, 8vo, green cl, 287p, 8cp)	Garden City	[1930]	Dulac, Edmund	100-160	
Locke, William J.	Beloved Vagabond (1st, 8vo, 267p, 16cp)	L: John Lane	1922	Dulac, Jean	80-120	
Gallico, Paul	Day Jean-Pierre was Pignapped (1st AM {std}, 4to, 44p, color, pep, DJ/3.25)	Doubleday	(1965)	Dulac, Jean	25-45	
Gallico, Paul	Day the Guinea-Pig Talked (1st AM {std}, sm4to, 44p, color, DJ/3.25)	Doubleday	(1964)	Dulac, Jean	25-40	
Banta, Nathaniel M.	Four-and-Forty Fairies (1st, 12mo, grey cl, 128p, 1-color, pep)	Chi: Flanagan	1923	Dulin, Dorothy	60-90	
Smith, Laura R.	Runaway Bunny (1st, sm8vo, 128p, pep, color)	Chi: Flanagan	1923	Dulin, Dorothy	35-60	
Banta, Nathaniel M.	Brownies and the Goblins (1st, 8vo, 128p, color, pep)	Chi: Flanagan	1915	Dulin, J.H.	60-90	
Grimm Bros.	Fairy Tales (1st, sm sq4to, 275p, p-o, 11cp, 7pl, pep, WS)	Rand/McNally	(1913)	Dunlap, Hope	75-100	
Craik, Dinah	Little Lame Prince (1st, lg8vo, p-o, 121p, gilt, color)	Rand/McNally	(1909)	Dunlap, Hope	75-100	
Garnett, Louise A.	Muffin Shop (1st, folio, ibds, p-o, 79p, color)	Rand/McNally	(1908)	Dunlap, Hope	120-200	
Browning, Robert	Pied Piper of Hamelin (1st, sm4to, p-o, gilt, 56p, pep, color)	Rand/McNally	(1910)	Dunlap, Hope	100-145	
Garnett, Louise A.	Rhyming Ring (1st, 4to, ibds, 64p, 7cp, pep)	Rand/McNally	(1910)	Dunlap, Hope	100-165	
McCabe, Olivia	Rose Fairies (1st, lg8vo, 159p, p-o, green cl, 12cp, pep)	Rand/McNally	(1911)	Dunlap, Hope	120-170	
Brooks, Noah	Boy Emigrants (1st, lg8vo, brown cl, 381p, teg, 10cp, pep, SC)	Scribner	1914	Dunn, Harvey T.	80-130	
Rhodes, Eugene M.	Desire of the Moth (1st, 12mo, 149p, 2pl)	Henry Holt & Co.	1916	Dunn, Harvey T.	100-170	
London, Jack	John Barleycorn (1st, 8vo, 343p, gilt, 8pl)	Century	1913	Dunn, Harvey T.	250-400	
Wister, Owen	Members of the Family (1st, sm8vo, 317p, 12pl)	Macmillan	1911	Dunn, Harvey T.	30-50	
Hornung, E.W.	Shadow of the Rope (1st, sm8vo, gilt, teg, 377p, 3pl)	Scribner	1906	Dunn, Harvey T.	40-60	
Beach, Rex	Silver Horde (1st, 12mo, red cl, p-o, 389p, 8pl)	Harper	1909	Dunn, Harvey T.	30-50	
Dickens, Charles	Tale of Two Cities (1st, lg8vo, teg, p-o, 362p, 10cp, pep)	Cosmopolitan	1921	Dunn, Harvey T.	75-120	
Rhodes, Eugene M.	West is West (1st, 8vo, 304p, black cloth, frn by...)	H.K. Fly	(1917)	Dunn, Harvey T.	100-165	
Kyne, Peter B.	Cappy Ricks (1st, sm8vo, 349p, 4pl)	H.K. Fly	(1916)	Dunn/Fischer	60-90	*
Hains, T. Jenkins	Black Barque (1st, sm8vo, 322p, 5pl)	L.C. Page	1905	Dunton, W. Herbert	40-70	*
Chapman, Katharine H.	Fusing Force (1st, 8vo, 416p, col frn)	McClurg	1911	Dunton, W. Herbert	30-45	
Parrish, Randall	Keith of the Border (1st, 8vo, 362p, 4cp)	McClurg	1910	Dunton, W. Herbert	35-60	
Bateson, Carlen	Man in the Camlet Cloak (1st, sm8vo, 320p, gilt, teg, 4pl)	Saalfield	1903	Dunton, W. Herbert	35-60	*
Costello, F.H.	Nelson's Yankee Boy (1st, 12mo, 293p, 6pl)	Henry Holt & Co.	1904	Dunton, W. Herbert	35-60	*
Chipman, Charles P.	Two Boys and a Dog (1st, 12mo, 272p, 4pl)	Saalfield	1903	Dunton, W. Herbert	35-50	R
Grey, Zane	Wanderer of the Wasteland (1st {std}, sm8vo, red cl, 419p, 3pl)	Harper	(1923)	Dunton, W. Herbert	120-200	
Warner, Susan	Wide, Wide World (1st, 8vo, 592p, 6pl)	Fenno	(1904)	Dunton, W. Herbert	30-45	

AUTHOR	TITLE	PUBLISHER	DATE	ARTIST	PRICE	LC
Bindloss, Harold	Winston of the Prairie (1st, sm8vo, p-o, 340p, 3cp)	Stokes	(1907)	Dunton, W. Herbert	35-60	
Lewis, Alfred H.	Wolfville Folks (1st, 12mo, 321p, frn by...)	Appleton	1908	Dunton, W. Herbert	80-125	
Duplaix, Georges	Gaston & Josephine (1st, 4to, 47p, ibds, color)	NY: Oxford U.Pr.	1933	Duplaix, Georges	200-300	
Duplaix, Georges	Gaston & Josephine (1st {this pub.}, lg4to, 48p, color)	Harper	1936	Duplaix, Georges	120-200	
Duplaix, Georges	Pee-Gloo (1st, 4to, [40]p, ibds, pep, color, DJ/2.00)	Harper	1935	Duplaix, Georges	250-350	
Duplaix, Georges	Popo the Hippopotamus (1st, ob12mo, ibds, [28]p, fp color)	Whitman	(1935)	Duplaix, Georges	120-200	
Lindgren, Astrid	Kati in Italy (1st, 8vo, 152p, color, DJ/2.50)	Grosset/Dunlap	(1961)	Dupuy, Daniel	40-65	
Lindgren, Astrid	Kati in Paris (1st, 8vo, 152p, color, DJ/2.50)	Grosset/Dunlap	(1961)	Dupuy, Daniel	40-65	
Duvoisin, Roger	A for the Ark (1st, 4to, [46]p, ibds, color, DJ/2.00)	Lothrop, Lee	1952	Duvoisin, Roger	70-100	
Duvoisin, Roger	All Aboard! (1st, folio, 44p, ibds, color, DJ/1.00)	Grosset/Dunlap	(1935)	Duvoisin, Roger	130-180	
Menotti, Gian-Carlo	Amahl & Night Visitors (1st, lg8vo, 86p, bds, 17 color, pep, DJ/2.75)	Whittlesey	(1952)	Duvoisin, Roger	50-80	
Duvoisin, Roger	And There was America (1st {std}, 8vo, 75p, color, pep, DJ/2.00)	Knopf	1938	Duvoisin, Roger	30-50	
Janice	Angelique (1st, 4to, 32p, color, pep, DJ/2.25)	Whittlesey	1960	Duvoisin, Roger	50-80	
Fatio, Louise	Anna the Horse (1st {std}, 8vo, ipcb, [48]p, 3-color, pep, DJ/1.75)	Aladdin	(1951)	Duvoisin, Roger	50-80	
Friedrich, Priscilla	April Umbrella (1st, 4to, [34]p, fp color, DJ/2.95)	Lothrop, Lee	1963	Duvoisin, Roger	30-50	
Showalter, Jean B.	Around the Corner (1st {std}, 4to, [30]p, 3-color, pep, DJ/2.95)	Doubleday	(1965)	Duvoisin, Roger	35-50	
Misch, Robert J.	At Daddy's Office (1st {std}, sm4to, ibds, [32]p, color, DJ/1.50)	Knopf	(1946)	Duvoisin, Roger	60-95	
McCullough, John	At Our House (1st, sm4to, [41]p, ibds, 1-color, DJ/1.25)	W.R. Scott	1943	Duvoisin, Roger	30-50	
Tresselt, Alvin	Autumn Harvest (1st, sm4to, ipcb, [25]p, color, pep, DJ/2.00)	Lothrop, Lee	1951	Duvoisin, Roger	40-65	
Tresselt, Alvin	Beaver Pond (1st, 4to, [32]p, fp color, pep, DJ/4.50)	Lothrop, Lee	1970	Duvoisin, Roger	50-80	
Weston, Christine	Bhimsa the Dancing Bear (1st, sm8vo, 120p, 2-color, cep, DJ/2.00, NH)	Scribner	1945	Duvoisin, Roger	120-200	
Coggins, Herbert	Busby & Co. (1st, 8vo, 96p, rust cl, fp b/w, pep, DJ/2.25)	Whittlesey	(1952)	Duvoisin, Roger	30-50	
Tworkov, Jack	Camel Who Took a Walk (1st {std}, 4to, [32]p, ibds, 2-color, DJ/2.00)	Aladdin	(1951)	Duvoisin, Roger	60-90	
Jones, Idwal	Chef's Holiday (1st {std}, sm8vo, 210p, b/w, DJ/3.00)	Longmans	1952	Duvoisin, Roger	40-65	
Stevenson, Rbt. L.	Child's Garden of Verses (1st, 4to, 112p, ibds, color, DJ/2.50)	Heritage Press	1944	Duvoisin, Roger	40-60	*
Duvoisin, Roger	Christmas Cake (1st, ob12mo, [29]p, b/w, ibds, pep, DJ/0.50)	A.A. Group	(1941)	Duvoisin, Roger	60-100	
Fatio, Louise	Christmas Forest (1st, 8vo, ibds, [44]p, pep, fp 3-color, dep, DJ/1.25)	Aladdin	(1950)	Duvoisin, Roger	60-90	
Hays, Wilma P.	Christmas on the Mayflower (1st, 8vo, unpag, fp 1-color, pep, DJ/2.50)	Coward	(1956)	Duvoisin, Roger	30-45	
Hall, William N.	Christmas Pony (1st {std}, sm4to, ipcb, [32]p, color, DJ/1.50)	Knopf	(1948)	Duvoisin, Roger	60-90	
Duvoisin, Roger	Christmas Whale (1st {std}, ob8vo, [45]p, ibds, color, DJ/1.25)	Knopf	(1945)	Duvoisin, Roger	70-100	
Puner, Helen	Daddies: What They Do All Day (1st, 4to, [34]p, ibds, color, DJ/1.75)	Lothrop, Lee	1946	Duvoisin, Roger	50-85	
Duvoisin, Roger	Day and Night (1st, 4to, [36]p, fp color, pep, DJ/2.95)	Knopf	(1960)	Duvoisin, Roger	45-70	
Frye, Dean	Days of Sunshine, Days of Rain (1st, 4to, 32p, fp 3-color, pep, DJ/2.95)	McGraw-Hill	1965	Duvoisin, Roger	30-50	
Gregor, Arthur	Does Poppy Live Here? (1st, 4to, [34]p, fp color, pep, DJ/2.50)	Lothrop, Lee	1957	Duvoisin, Roger	30-50	
Fischer, Marjorie	Dog Cantbark (1st {std}, lg8vo, [32]p, gilt, color, cep, DJ/1.50)	Random	(1940)	Duvoisin, Roger	30-50	
Fatio, Louise	Doll for Marie (1st, sm4to, [24]p, 2-color, DJ/2.50)	Whittlesey	(1957)	Duvoisin, Roger	40-65	
Duvoisin, Roger	Donkey-Donkey (1st, 8vo, ibds, [46]p, color, pep)	Whitman	(1933)	Duvoisin, Roger	150-220	
Duvoisin, Roger	Donkey-Donkey (1st {this pub}, sm4to, ipcb, pep, 39p, color, DJ/0.50)	Grosset/Dunlap	(1940)	Duvoisin, Roger	70-120	
Watts, Mabel	Dozens of Cousins (1st, 4to, 46p, 2-color, DJ/2.00)	Whittlesey	(1950)	Duvoisin, Roger	50-85	
Dayton, Mona	Earth and Sky (1st, 4to, ibds, [25]p, fp color, pep, DJ/3.50)	Harper	(1969)	Duvoisin, Roger	45-70	
Duvoisin, Roger	Easter Treat (1st {std}, sm4to, [16]p, 1-color, DJ/2.00)	Knopf	(1954)	Duvoisin, Roger	70-100	
Ettinger, Harold	Fair, Fantastic Paris (1st {std}, 8vo, 250p, b/w, gilt, DJ/3.00)	Bobbs-Merrill	(1944)	Duvoisin, Roger	45-70	
Hilles, Helen	Farm Wanted (1st, 8vo, 236p, brown cl, uncut, 1-color, DJ/3.00)	J. Messner	(1951)	Duvoisin, Roger	30-50	
Haviland, Virginia	Favorite Fairy Tales Told in France (1st {std}, lg8vo, 91p, color, DJ/2.75)	Little/Brown	(1959)	Duvoisin, Roger	50-85	
Root, Charlet	Feast of Lamps (1st, lg8vo, 75p, p-o, pep, color, DJ/2.00)	Whitman	1938	Duvoisin, Roger	70-125	
Tabak, Mary N.	Fish is Not a Pet (1st, 4to, 32p, fp 2-color, pep, DJ/2.50)	Whittlesey	(1959)	Duvoisin, Roger	50-80	*
Pratt, Margaret	Flash of Washington Square (1st, 4to, green cl, [29]p, dp color, DJ/2.00)	Lothrop, Lee	1954	Duvoisin, Roger	50-80	
Tresselt, Alvin	Follow the Road (1st, sm4to, unpag, color, DJ/2.50)	Lothrop, Lee	1953	Duvoisin, Roger	35-60	
Tresselt, Alvin	Follow the Wind (1st, sm4to, ibds, [26]p, color, DJ/2.00)	Lothrop, Lee	(1950)	Duvoisin, Roger	50-80	
Duvoisin, Roger	Four Corners of the World (1st {std}, lg8vo, 128p, color, DJ/3.00)	Knopf	1948	Duvoisin, Roger	45-70	
Tresselt, Alvin	Frog in the Well (1st, sm4to, green cl, [32]p, color, pep, DJ/2.75)	Lothrop, Lee	1958	Duvoisin, Roger	50-80	
Duvoisin, Roger	Happy Hunter (1st, ob4to, [32]p, fp 3-color, dep, DJ/2.75, NYTBI)	Lothrop, Lee	1961	Duvoisin, Roger	60-90	*
Fatio, Louise	Happy Lion (1st, sm4to, [30]p, yellow cl, 2-color, DJ/1.95, NYTBI)	Whittlesey	(1954)	Duvoisin, Roger	100-165	R
Fatio, Louise	Happy Lion and the Bear (1st, 4to, 32p, gilt, fp 3-color, DJ/2.95)	Whittlesey	(1964)	Duvoisin, Roger	50-85	
Fatio, Louise	Happy Lion in Africa (1st, sm4to, green cl, 30p, 2-color, DJ/2.00, NYTBI)	Whittlesey	(1955)	Duvoisin, Roger	80-130	
Fatio, Louise	Happy Lion Roars (1st, 4to, 32p, 2-color, DJ/2.25)	Whittlesey	(1957)	Duvoisin, Roger	50-85	
Fatio, Louise	Happy Lion's Quest (1st, sm4to, 26p, fp color, DJ/2.75)	Whittlesey	(1961)	Duvoisin, Roger	40-65	
Fatio, Louise	Happy Lion's Vacation (1st, 4to, 32p, fp 3-color, DJ/2.95)	Whittlesey	(1967)	Duvoisin, Roger	40-65	
Fontaine, Robert	Happy Time (1st, 8vo, 269p, p-o, fp b/w, DJ/2.50)	Simon/Schuster	(1945)	Duvoisin, Roger	30-50	
Tresselt, Alvin	Hi, Mister Robin! (1st, 4to, ibds, [26]p, color, pep, DJ/2.00)	Lothrop, Lee	1950	Duvoisin, Roger	60-90	
Tresselt, Alvin	Hide and Seek Fog (1st, lg8vo, [32]p, color, DJ/3.50, CH, NYTBI)	Lothrop, Lee	(1965)	Duvoisin, Roger	60-90	
Calhoun, Mary	Houn' Dog (1st, 4to, [32]p, fp 3-color, DJ/2.75)	Wm. Morrow	1959	Duvoisin, Roger	60-90	R
Duvoisin, Roger	House of Four Seasons (1st, 4to, [34]p, color, pep, DJ/2.50)	Lothrop, Lee	1956	Duvoisin, Roger	40-65	
Calhoun, Mary	Hungry Leprechaun (1st, lg ob8vo, [30]p, fp 2-color, pep, DJ/2.75)	Wm. Morrow	1962	Duvoisin, Roger	50-80	
Tresselt, Alvin	I Saw the Sea Come In (1st, sm4to, [28]p, color, pep, DJ/2.50)	Lothrop, Lee	1954	Duvoisin, Roger	45-70	
Jordan, Mildred	I Won't, said the King (1st {std}, 8vo, 104p, color, DJ/2.00)	Knopf	1945	Duvoisin, Roger	45-70	
Zolotow, Charlotte	In My Garden (1st, sm4to, unpag, blue cl, fp color, DJ/2.75)	Lothrop, Lee	1960	Duvoisin, Roger	50-80	
Tresselt, Alvin	It's Time Now! (1st, 4to, [32]p, fp color, pep, DJ/3.95)	Lothrop, Lee	(1969)	Duvoisin, Roger	40-65	*
Elliot, Kathleen	Jo-Yo's Idea (1st {std}, lg8vo, 114p, fp color, cep, DJ/2.00)	Knopf	1939	Duvoisin, Roger	60-90	
Tresselt, Alvin	Johnny Maple-Leaf (1st, 4to, 28p, ibds, color, DJ/2.00)	Lothrop, Lee	1948	Duvoisin, Roger	45-70	*
Howard, Janet	Jumpy the Kangaroo (1st, sq12mo, [42]p, ibds, color, pep, DJ/1.00)	Lothrop, Lee	(1944)	Duvoisin, Roger	65-100	
Frye, Dean	Lamb and the Child (1st, 4to, 32p, color, DJ/2.75)	McGraw-Hill	1963	Duvoisin, Roger	30-50	
Holl, Adelaide	Lisette (1st, 4to, [32]p, fp 1-color, DJ/2.75)	Lothrop, Lee	1962	Duvoisin, Roger	45-70	
Duvoisin, Roger	Little Boy Who was Drawing (1st, lg8vo, [56]p, color)	Scribner	1932	Duvoisin, Roger	160-225	
Allen, Hazel	Little Church on the Big Rock (1st, 8vo, [48]p, fp 3-color, DJ/2.50)	Scribner	(1958)	Duvoisin, Roger	40-65	*
Schlein, Miriam	Little Red-Nose (1st, 4to, [42]p, fp 2-color, pep, DJ/2.50)	Abelard-Schuman	1955	Duvoisin, Roger	30-50	
Frost, Frances	Little Whistler (1st, lg8vo, green cl, 48p, fp color, DJ/2.00)	Whittlesey	(1949)	Duvoisin, Roger	50-80	
Duvoisin, Roger	Lonely Veronica (1st, 4to, [39]p, color, pep, DJ/3.00)	Knopf	(1963)	Duvoisin, Roger	40-60	

AUTHOR	TITLE	PUBLISHER	DATE	ARTIST	PRICE	LC
DeQuattrociocchi, N.	Love and Dishes (1st {std}, 8vo, 416p, b/w, DJ/4.00)	Bobbs-Merrill	(1950)	Duvoisin, Roger	30-50	*
Attwood, William	Man Who Could Grow Hair (1st {std}, sm8vo, 240p, ipcb, b/w, DJ/2.75)	Knopf	1949	Duvoisin, Roger	50-80	
Aesopus	Miller, His Son & their Donkey (1st, sm4to, 30p, fp 2-color, pep, DJ/2.50)	Whittlesey	(1962)	Duvoisin, Roger	30-50	
Duvoisin, Roger	Missing Milkman (1st, 4to, [32]p, color, pep, DJ/3.25)	Knopf	(1967)	Duvoisin, Roger	30-50	
Mother Goose	Mother Goose (1st, folio, 144p, yellow cl, color, pep)	Heritage Press	(1936)	Duvoisin, Roger	100-160	R
Mother Goose	Mother Goose (1st {new ed}, 4to, ipcb, 112p, color, pep, DJ/2.50)	Heritage Press	(1943)	Duvoisin, Roger	60-90	*
Rigby, Douglas	Moustachio (1st, 4to, [31]p, ibds, 1-color, DJ/1.50)	Harper	(1947)	Duvoisin, Roger	70-125	
Moore, Clement C.	Night Before Christmas (1st, folio, ibds, [32]p, color, pep, DJ/1.50)	Garden City	1954	Duvoisin, Roger	120-200	R
Calhoun, Mary	Nine Lives of Homer C. Cat (1st, sm4to, [32]p, fp 3-color, DJ/2.75)	Wm. Morrow	1961	Duvoisin, Roger	50-80	
Zolotow, Charlotte	Not a Little Monkey (1st, sm4to, green cl, unpag, pep, color, DJ/2.50)	Lothrop, Lee	1957	Duvoisin, Roger	50-80	*
Lipkind, Will	Nubber Bear (1st {std}, 4to, [36]p, ibds, color, DJ/3.25)	Harcourt	1966	Duvoisin, Roger	50-85	
Freschet, Berniece	Old Bullfrog (1st, 4to, [25]p, fp color, pep, DJ)	Scribner	(1968)	Duvoisin, Roger	50-80	
Zolotow, Charlotte	One Step, Two (1st, sm4to, [28]p, color, DJ/2.00)	Lothrop, Lee	1954	Duvoisin, Roger	70-100	
Duvoisin, Roger	One Thousand Christmas Beards (1st, sm4to, [32]p, ibds, 2-col, pep, DJ/1.95)	Knopf	(1955)	Duvoisin, Roger	80-120	
Duvoisin, Roger	Our Veronica Goes to Petunia's Farm (1st, 4to, [32]p, color, pep, DJ/2.95)	Knopf	(1962)	Duvoisin, Roger	30-45	
Duvoisin, Roger	Petunia (1st {std}, sm4to, ibds, [32]p, color, DJ/1.50)	Knopf	(1950)	Duvoisin, Roger	70-120	
Duvoisin, Roger	Petunia & the Song (1st {std}, sm4to, ibds, [32]p, color, DJ/1.75)	Knopf	(1951)	Duvoisin, Roger	70-100	
Duvoisin, Roger	Petunia Takes a Trip (1st {std}, sm4to, [32]p, color, pep, DJ/2.00)	Knopf	(1953)	Duvoisin, Roger	70-100	R
Duvoisin, Roger	Petunia's Christmas (1st {std}, sm4to, [34]p, color, pep, DJ/2.00)	Knopf	(1952)	Duvoisin, Roger	70-100	
Duvoisin, Roger	Petunia, Beware! (1st, 4to, [32]p, color, DJ/2.95)	Knopf	(1958)	Duvoisin, Roger	40-65	
Duvoisin, Roger	Petunia, I Love You (1st, 4to, [32]p, color, DJ/3.25)	Knopf	(1965)	Duvoisin, Roger	30-50	*
Browning, Robert	Pied Piper of Hamelin (1st, folio, ibds, [42]p, color, pep)	Grosset/Dunlap	(1936)	Duvoisin, Roger	80-120	R
Adelson, Leone	Please Pass the Grass! (1st, sm4to, [32]p, fp 3-color, pep, DJ/3.00)	McKay	1960	Duvoisin, Roger	30-50	
Smith, William J.	Poems from France (1st, 8vo, 226p, b/w, DJ/4.50)	Crowell	(1967)	Duvoisin, Roger	30-50	*
Martin, Patricia	Pointed Brush (1st, sm4to, red cl, [36]p, color, pep, DJ/2.75)	Lothrop, Lee	1959	Duvoisin, Roger	30-50	
Zolotow, Charlotte	Poodle Who Barked at the Wind (1st, 4to, [30]p, 2-color, cep, DJ/2.95)	Lothrop, Lee	1964	Duvoisin, Roger	45-70	
Holl, Adelaide	Rain Puddle (1st, ob4to, [33]p, color, DJ/2.95)	Lothrop, Lee	(1965)	Duvoisin, Roger	30-50	
Fatio, Louise	Red Bantam (1st, sm4to, 32p, fp 2-color, DJ/2.75)	Whittlesey	(1963)	Duvoisin, Roger	50-80	R
Holl, Adelaide	Remarkable Egg (1st, ob4to, [26]p, color, DJ/3.50)	Lothrop, Lee	(1968)	Duvoisin, Roger	40-65	*
Washburne, Heluiz	Rhamon: Boy of Kashmir (1st, lg8vo, 127p, red cl, color, pep, DJ/2.00)	Whitman	1939	Duvoisin, Roger	50-80	
Courlander, Harold	Ride with the Sun (1st, 8vo, 296p, green cl, b/w, DJ/3.50)	Whittlesey	(1955)	Duvoisin, Roger	30-50	*
Elliot, Kathleen	Riema... (1st {std}, 8vo, 54p, ibds, color, pep, DJ/2.00)	Knopf	1937	Duvoisin, Roger	70-100	R
Defoe, Daniel	Robinson Crusoe (1st, 8vo, 287p, pcb, pep, 4 fp color, DJ/1.25, RC)	World	(1946)	Duvoisin, Roger	45-70	
Puner, Helen	Sitter Who Didn't Sit (1st, sm4to, ibds, [26]p, color, pep, DJ/1.50)	Lothrop, Lee	1949	Duvoisin, Roger	50-80	
Elliot, Kathleen	Soomoon, Boy of Bali (1st {std}, 8vo, 88p, ibds, pep, color, DJ/2.00)	Knopf	1938	Duvoisin, Roger	80-120	R
Moran, Jim	Sophocles the Hyena (1st, sm4to, red cl, 48p, 2-color, DJ/2.25)	Whittlesey	(1954)	Duvoisin, Roger	60-100	
Duvoisin, Roger	Spring Snow (1st, 8vo, [32]p, color, fp 1-color, pep, DJ/2.95)	Knopf	(1963)	Duvoisin, Roger	50-85	R*
Walters, George	Steam Shovel that Wouldn't Eat Dirt (1st, sm4to, ibds, [31]p, col, DJ/1.50)	Aladdin	(1948)	Duvoisin, Roger	50-80	*
Pratt, Margaret	Successful Secretary (1st, sm8vo, 144p, p-o, 15 fp b/w, DJ/2.00)	Lothrop, Lee	(1946)	Duvoisin, Roger	50-80	
Tresselt, Alvin	Sun Up (1st, sm4to, ibds, pep, [25]p, color, DJ/2.00)	Lothrop, Lee	1949	Duvoisin, Roger	55-80	
Calhoun, Mary	Sweet Patootie Doll (1st, sm4to, yellow cl, [32]p, 3-color, DJ/2.75)	Wm. Morrow	1957	Duvoisin, Roger	80-135	
Hudson, Wm. Henry	Tales of the Pampas (1st, 8vo, beige cl, 245p, 6pl, DJ/2.00)	Knopf	1939	Duvoisin, Roger	40-65	
Carlson, Natalie S.	Talking Cat (1st, sq8vo, 87p, red cl, 15 fp b/w, DJ/2.50)	Harper	(1952)	Duvoisin, Roger	60-90	
Janus, Grete	Teddy (1st, 16mo, unpag, color, DJ/1.50)	Lothrop, Lee	(1964)	Duvoisin, Roger	30-45	
Foster, Doris	Tell Me, Little Boy (1st, 4to, [28]p, ibds, color, DJ/2.00)	Lothrop, Lee	1953	Duvoisin, Roger	50-85	*
Duvoisin, Roger	They Put Out to Sea (1st {std}, lg8vo, 171p, 8 dp color, pep, DJ/3.00)	Knopf	1943	Duvoisin, Roger	70-100	R
Fatio, Louise	Three Happy Lions (1st, sm4to, 32p, fp 2-color, DJ/2.25)	Whittlesey	(1959)	Duvoisin, Roger	45-70	
Duvoisin, Roger	Three Sneezes... (1st {std}, 8vo, 244p, color, pep, DJ/2.00)	Knopf	1941	Duvoisin, Roger	40-60	
Tworkov, Jack	Tigers Don't Bite (1st {std}, 4to, ibds, [32]p, fp 1-color, DJ/2.25)	Dutton	(1956)	Duvoisin, Roger	50-80	
Tresselt, Alvin	Timothy Robbins Climbs the Mountain (1st, 4to, [30]p, color, pep, DJ/2.75)	Lothrop, Lee	(1960)	Duvoisin, Roger	30-50	
Marsh, Edith	Trillium Hill (1st, 8vo, 159p, DJ/2.50, pep & DJ by...)	Lothrop, Lee	(1955)	Duvoisin, Roger	30-45	*
Duvoisin, Roger	Two Lonely Ducks (1st, ob8vo, [36]p, 2-color, pep, DJ/2.00)	Knopf	1955	Duvoisin, Roger	50-80	
Tresselt, Alvin	Under the Trees and Through the Grass (1st, 4to, [28]p, color, DJ/2.95)	Lothrop, Lee	1962	Duvoisin, Roger	30-50	
Attwood, Frederic	Vavache: Cow who Painted Pictures (1st {std}, sm8vo, 77p, color, DJ/2.25)	Aladdin	(1950)	Duvoisin, Roger	30-50	*
Duvoisin, Roger	Veronica (1st, 4to, [36]p, color, pep, DJ/2.95)	Knopf	(1961)	Duvoisin, Roger	45-70	
Duvoisin, Roger	Veronica's Smile (1st, lg8vo, [32]p, color, pep, DJ/3.00)	Knopf	(1964)	Duvoisin, Roger	45-70	
Powers, Tom	Virgin with Butterflies (1st {std}, 8vo, 188p, black cl, b/w, DJ/2.50)	Bobbs-Merrill	(1945)	Duvoisin, Roger	45-70	
Dorritt, Susan	Wait till Sunday (1st, 4to, [42]p, fp color, pep, DJ/2.50)	Abelard-Schuman	1957	Duvoisin, Roger	40-70	
Tresselt, Alvin	Wake Up, City! (1st, 8vo, unpag, color, DJ/2.50)	Lothrop, Lee	1957	Duvoisin, Roger	30-50	
Tresselt, Alvin	Wake Up, Farm! (1st, 8vo, [33]p, color, DJ/2.50)	Lothrop, Lee	1955	Duvoisin, Roger	30-50	
Duvoisin, Roger	What is Right for Tulip (1st, 4to, [30]p, color, cep, DJ/3.95)	Knopf	(1969)	Duvoisin, Roger	40-65	
Tresselt, Alvin	White Snow, Bright Snow (1st, 4to, ibds, 33p, color, DJ/2.00, CM)	Lothrop, Lee	(1947)	Duvoisin, Roger	100-165	R
Hall, William N.	Winkie's World (1st {std}, 8vo, [30]p, ibds, color, pep, DJ/2.00)	Doubleday	1958	Duvoisin, Roger	50-80	
Friedrich, Otto	Wishing Well in the Woods (1st, sm4to, unpag, ibds, color, DJ/2.75)	Lothrop, Lee	1961	Duvoisin, Roger	40-65	
Calhoun, Mary	Wobble the Witch Cat (1st, 4to, [30]p, color, DJ/2.75)	Wm. Morrow	1958	Duvoisin, Roger	50-85	
Tresselt, Alvin	World in the Candy Egg (1st, lg ob8vo, [32]p, fp color, dep, DJ/3.75)	Lothrop, Lee	1967	Duvoisin, Roger	45-70	
Ostrander, Fannie	Gift of the Magic Staff (1st, 8vo, 221p, green cl, 8pl)	Revell	(1902)	Dwiggens, Will	50-80	
Bangs, John K.	Andiron Tales (1st, lg8vo, green cl, p-o, 119p, 8cp)	Winston	(1906)	Dwiggens, C.V.	120-200	*
Coatsworth, Eliz.	Creaking Stair (1st, 8vo, 110p, black/silver, b/w, DJ/5.00)	Coward	1949	Dwiggins, W.A.	30-50	
Dwiggins, Wm. A.	Marionette in Motion (1st, 8vo, 25p, b/w, DJ/1.50)	(Detroit)	1939	Dwiggins, W.A.	140-200	
Nicholson, Meredith	The Poet (1st, 8vo, teg, 189p, 4cp & designs by...)	Houghton	1914	Dwiggins, W.A.	45-70	
Harris, Joel C.	Witch Wolf... (1st {std}, 12mo, 30p, tan pcb, b/w)	Bacon/Brown	1921	Dwiggins, W.A.	220-300	R
Ash, Fenton	Black Opal (1st, 8vo, 320p, blue cl, 3 color)	L: J.F. Shaw	(1915)	E.S.H.	180-250	
Totheroh, Dan	Last Dragon (1st, 8vo, 186p, 8cp, pep)	Doran	(1927)	Eadie, Eleanor	25-40	
Galsworthy, John	Memories (1st, 4to, green/gilt, 70p, teg, 4 ticp, 24pl)	Scribner	(1914)	Earl, Maud	90-150	
Coblentz, Catherine	Blue & Silver Necklace (1st {std}, 8vo, 242p, blue cl, 6pl, DJ/2.00)	Little/Brown	1937	Earle, Edwin	30-45	*
Coatsworth, Eliz.	Here I Stay (1st, 8vo, 246p, gilt, b/w, DJ/2.00)	Coward	1938	Earle, Edwin	25-40	
Schlein, Miriam	Henry's Ride (1st, 8vo, [24]p, color, DJ/1.50)	Abingdon Press	1956	Earle, Vana	20-25	

AUTHOR	TITLE	PUBLISHER	DATE	ARTIST	PRICE	LC
Evans, Eva K.	People are Important (1st, 8vo, 86p, b/w, DJ/2.50, JABA)	Capitol Pub. Co.	(1951)	Earle, Vana	30-45	
Jacberns, Raymond	Attic Boarders (1st, sm8vo, 298p, 6cp)	L: Chambers	1909	Earnshaw, Harold C.	40-60	*
Wesselhoeft, Lily	Fairy-Folk of Blue Hill (1st, 8vo, 240p, blue/gilt, b/w)	J. Knight	1895	Eastman, A.L.	35-60	
Cummings, E.E.	Fairy Tales (1st {std}, sm4to, 36p, ibds, color, DJ/4.50)	Harcourt	(1965)	Eaton, John	70-100	R
Asimov, Isaac	The Moon (1st {std}, 8vo, 29p, color, DJ/1.00)	Follett	1966	Ebel, Alex	25-45	
Bontemps, Arna	Mr. Kelso's Lion (1st {std}, 8vo, 48p, DJ/3.95)	Lippincott	(1970)	Ebert, Len	120-180	
Lowe, Edith	Cookie, the Rabbit (1st, narrow 4to, [24]p, ibds, color, pep)	Garden City	(1949)	Eckart, Frances	30-50	
Lowe, Edith	Little Bear Who Wanted Friends (1st, narrow 4to, ibds, [24]p, color, pep)	Garden City	(1949)	Eckart, Frances	30-50	
Fleming, W.M.M.	Hunted Piccaninnies (1st, 8vo, 185p, grey cl, 7cp)	L: J.M. Dent	1927	Edmunds, Kay	100-170	
Edwards, George W.	Alsace-Lorraine (1st AM, 4to, 344p, teg, blue/gilt, 18cp, 17pl)	Penn	(1918)	Edwards, George W.	90-120	
Mabie, Hamilton W.	Book of Christmas (1st, 12mo, 369p, gilt, 12pl)	Macmillan	1909	Edwards, George W.	50-75	
Edwards, George W.	Book of Old English Love Songs (1st, 8vo, 159p, gilt, b/w)	NY: Macmillan	1897	Edwards, George W.	100-180	
Edwards, George W.	Forest of Arden (1st, sm4to, red/gilt, 213p, teg, 6cp)	Stokes	(1914)	Edwards, George W.	35-60	
Dodge, Mary Mapes	Hans Brinker (1st, 8vo, 380p, gilt, p-o, teg, 8cp, pep)	Scribner	1915	Edwards, George W.	60-90	
Seawell, Molly E.	Midshipman Paulding (1st, sm8vo, 133p, gilt, b/w)	Appleton	1891	Edwards, George W.	40-60	
Watson, Virginia	Princess Pocahontas (1st, lg8vo, 306p, blue/gilt, p-o, 9cp, pep)	Penn	1916	Edwards, George W.	100-165	
Lummis, Charles F.	Pueblo Indian Folk Stories (new ed., 12mo, 257p, b/w)	Appleton	1920	Edwards, George W.	40-65	
Barr, Robert	Strong Arm (1st, 8vo, 336p, cvr by...)	Stokes	1899	Edwards, George W.	20-30	
Hawthorne, Nathaniel	Tanglewood Tales (1st sm4to, AEG, gilt, 190p, b/w pl)	Houghton	1887	Edwards, George W.	100-160	*
Hawthorne, Nathaniel	Tanglewood Tales (1st UK, 4to, 190p, b/w)	L: Chatto	1888	Edwards, George W.	80-130	
Farmer, James E.	The Grenadier (1st, sm8vo, 328p, red cl, cvr by...)	Dodd	1898	Edwards, George W.	25-40	
Edwards, George W.	Thus Think and Smoke Tobacco (1st, sm4to, red/gilt, AEG, b/w)	Stokes	1891	Edwards, George W.	250-400	
Curtis, George W.	Prue & I (8vo, teg, 234p)	Crowell	1899	Edwards, Harry C.	25-40	
Stuart, Ruth M.	River's Children (1st, 12mo, 179p, green/gilt, 5pl)	Century	1904	Edwards, Harry C.	45-70	
Hamblen, Herbert E.	Story of a Yankee Boy (1st, 12mo, 339p, 4pl)	Scribner	1898	Edwards, Harry C.	30-50	
Edwards, Lionel	Beasts of the Chase (1st, 4to, 49p, red/gilt, 8 fp color, DJ)	L: Putnam	1950	Edwards, Lionel	80-130	
Gorse, Golden	Moorland Mousie (1st AM, sm4to, 106p, 16pl)	Scribner	1929	Edwards, Lionel	45-70	
Edwards, Lionel	Sketches in Stable and Kennel (1st, 4to, brown cl, 59p, 12 ticp)	L: Putnam	1933	Edwards, Lionel	120-200	
Weatherly, Fred E.	Among the Daisies (sm4to, ibds, [60]p, 16 fp color)	L: Hildesheimer	[1890]	Edwards, M. Ellen	100-165	
Gillilan, Strickland	Danny & Fanny (1st, lg8vo, p-o, 96p, color, pep)	Rand/McNally	(1928)	Eger, Ruth C.	40-65	
Jackson, Leroy F.	Jolly Jingle Picture Book (1st, 4to, [96]p, p-o, fp color, pep)	Rand/McNally	(1937)	Eger, Ruth C.	70-90	
Wadsworth, Wallace	Modern Story Book (1st, lg4to, 124p, p-o, color)	Rand/McNally	(1931)	Eger, Ruth C.	100-150	
Fox, Frances M.	Nancy Davenport (1st, 12mo, 261p, p-o, 5cp)	Rand/McNally	(1928)	Eger, Ruth C.	25-40	*
Beard, Patten	Pillow-Time Tales (1st, lg8vo, p-o, 96p, color)	Rand/McNally	(1927)	Eger, Ruth C.	60-90	*
Jackson, Leroy F.	Rimskittle's Book (1st, lg4to, [110]p, p-o, color, pep)	Rand/McNally	(1926)	Eger, Ruth C.	100-160	
Beard, Patten	Twilight Tales (1st, lg8vo, p-o, 96p, 7cp)	Rand/McNally	(1929)	Eger, Ruth C.	55-80	
Ramsden, Evelyn (ed)	Singing Town (1st AM, 8vo, 97p, ibds, color, pep, DJ/2.75)	Macmillan	1959	Egner, Thorbjorn	20-35	
Lear, Edward	Limericks by Lear (1st {std}, 4to, unpag, fp color, DJ/3.95)	World	(1965)	Ehlert, Lois	25-40	
O'Neill, Mary	What is that Sound! (1st {std}, 8vo, 54p, b/w, DJ/3.50)	Atheneum	1966	Ehlert, Lois	20-30	*
Wahl, Jan	Beast Book (1st, 16mo, [32]p, b/w, DJ/1.95)	Harper	(1964)	Eichel, E.W.	25-45	
Fischer, Marjorie	All on a Summer's Day (1st {std}, 8vo, 157p, green cl, b/w, pep, DJ/2.00)	Random	(1941)	Eichenberg, Fritz	30-50	
Hall, Rosalys	Animals to Africa (1st, ob8vo, [27]p, fp color, dep, DJ/1.50)	Holiday House	(1939)	Eichenberg, Fritz	45-65	
Eichenberg, Fritz	Ape in a Cape (1st {std}, 4to, [32]p, color, pep, DJ/2.00, CH)	Harcourt	(1952)	Eichenberg, Fritz	100-160	R
Duncan, Eula G.	Big Road Walker (1st, lg8vo, 121p, cep, 17 fp b/w, DJ/1.75)	Stokes	1940	Eichenberg, Fritz	140-200	
Sewell, Anna	Black Beauty (Special Ed., sm8vo, 288p, 45p, pep, 10cp, DJ/2.00)	Grosset/Dunlap	(1945)	Eichenberg, Fritz	45-70	R
Eichenberg, Fritz	Dancing in the Moon (1st {std}, 4to, red cl, [21]p, color, pep, DJ/2.25)	Harcourt	(1955)	Eichenberg, Fritz	70-120	R
N/A	Dick Whittington & his Cat (1st, 24mo, ipcb, [38]p, 2-color)	Holiday House	1937	Eichenberg, Fritz	75-100	R*
Hughes, Richard A.	Don't Blame Me! (1st {std}, sm8vo, 159p, b/w, DJ/1.50)	Harper	(1940)	Eichenberg, Fritz	40-65	
Salten, Felix	Favorite Animal Stories (1st, 8vo, orange cl, 243p, b/w, DJ/3.00)	J. Messner	(1948)	Eichenberg, Fritz	30-50	
Swift, Jonathan	Gulliver's Travels (1st, lg8vo, 343p, b/w)	Heritage Press	1940	Eichenberg, Fritz	45-80	*
Hunt, Mabel L.	Have You Seen Tom Thumb? (1st, sm8vo, 259p, b/w, dep, DJ/2.00, NH)	Stokes	1942	Eichenberg, Fritz	100-175	
Deutsch, Babette	Heroes of the Kalevala (1st, lg8vo, 238p, blue cl, 12pl, cep, DJ/2.50)	J. Messner	(1940)	Eichenberg, Fritz	50-80	
Turpin, Edna	Littling of Gaywood (1st, 12mo, 265p, pep, b/w, DJ/2.00)	Random	(1939)	Eichenberg, Fritz	35-55	
Dolbier, Maurice	Magic Shop (1st, 8vo, 74p, ipcb, 1-color, DJ/1.75)	Random	(1946)	Eichenberg, Fritz	45-70	
Jagendorf, Mortiz	Merry Pranks (1st AM, 8vo, 188p, 2-color, DJ/2.50)	Vanguard Press	1938	Eichenberg, Fritz	40-65	*
Hoffmann, Eleanor	Mischief in Fez (1st, lg8vo, 109p, blue cl, 8 fp 1-color, dep, DJ/2.00)	Holiday House	(1943)	Eichenberg, Fritz	45-70	
White, Terence H.	Mistress Masham's Repose (1st, 8vo, 255p, gilt, fp b/w, pep, DJ/3.00)	Putnam	(1946)	Eichenberg, Fritz	60-100	
Lenotre, Therese	Mystery of Dog Flip (1st, sm8vo, 190p, b/w, dep, DJ/1.75)	Stokes	1939	Eichenberg, Fritz	30-50	
Dobbs, Rose	No Room (1st, sm8vo, [48]p, ibds, b/w, DJ/1.50)	Coward	(1944)	Eichenberg, Fritz	30-50	
Davis, Robert	Padre Porko (1st, sm8vo, 165p, grey cl, fp b/w, cep, DJ/2.00)	Holiday House	(1939)	Eichenberg, Fritz	50-80	R
Coatsworth, Eliz.	Peaceable Kingdom (1st, lg ob8vo, [39]p, 2-color, pep, DJ/2.75)	Pantheon	(1958)	Eichenberg, Fritz	30-50	
Eberle, Irmengarde	Phoebe-Belle (1st, 8vo, 63p, 1-color, pep, DJ/1.25)	Greystone Press	(1941)	Eichenberg, Fritz	35-50	
N/A	Puss in Boots (1st, 24mo, [38]p, ibds, color, pep)	Holiday House	1936	Eichenberg, Fritz	60-90	
Schackne, Stewart	Rowena the Skating Cow (1st, sm4to, [61]p, tan cl, 28 fp color, DJ/1.50)	Scribner	1940	Eichenberg, Fritz	65-100	
Keats, Mark	Sancho & Stubborn Mule (1st, ob12mo, ipcb, [41]p, 2-color, pep, DJ/1.00)	W.R. Scott	(1944)	Eichenberg, Fritz	40-65	
Burglon, Nora	Sticks Across the Chimney (1st, sm8vo, 256p, 1-color, DJ/2.00)	Holiday House	(1938)	Eichenberg, Fritz	60-90	
Beston, Henry	Tree that Ran Away (1st, sm8vo, 69p, green cl, cep, b/w, DJ/1.00)	Macmillan	1941	Eichenberg, Fritz	200-320	
Eberle, Irmengarde	Wide Fields (1st, lg8vo, 193p, green cl, 8pl, DJ/2.50)	Crowell	1943	Eichenberg, Fritz	30-50	
Gannett, Ruth S.	Wonderful House-Boat-Train (1st {std}, 8vo, 63p, pep, b/w, DJ/2.00)	Random	(1949)	Eichenberg, Fritz	45-65	
Bronte, Emily J.	Wuthering Heights (1st, sm4to, 213p, ibds, b/w, DJ/5.00)	Random	1943	Eichenberg, Fritz	30-50	
Rowland, Eva E.	In & Out of the Nursery (1st, ob folio, [62]p)	R.H. Russell	(1900)	Eickmeyer, Rudolf	350-500	
Pearce, Philippa	Tom's Midnight Garden (1st, 8vo, 229p, b/w, DJ, CgM)	L: Oxford U.Pr.	1958	Einzig, Susan	70-100	
Eisgruber, Elsa	Spin Top Spin (1st AM, 4to, ibds, [32]p, color)	Macmillan	1929	Eisgruber, Elsa	90-120	
Yolen, Jane	Inway Investigators (1st, 8vo, 80p, b/w, DJ/3.75)	Seabury Press	(1969)	Eitzen, Allan	20-30	
Yates, Elizabeth	Sam's Secret Journal (1st, sm8vo, 142p, fp b/w, cep, DJ/3.50)	Friendship Pr.	(1964)	Eitzen, Allan	30-50	*
Murray, Hilda	Flower Legends for Children (1st, ob4to, ibds, 63p, 14cp, pep)	L: Longmans	1901	Eland, John S.	120-200	
Farley, Walter	Black Stallion Revolts (1st {std}, 8vo, 305p, b/w, DJ/2.00)	Random	(1953)	Eldridge, Harold	50-85	
Farley, Walter	Black Stallion's Sulky Colt (1st {std}, 8vo, 248p, b/w, DJ/2.00)	Random	(1954)	Eldridge, Harold	45-70	*

AUTHOR	TITLE	PUBLISHER	DATE	ARTIST	PRICE	LC
Farley, Walter	Island Stallion's Fury (1st {std}, 8vo, 243p, b/w, DJ/2.00)	Random	(1951)	Eldridge, Harold	50-80	
De La Mare, Walter	Three Royal Monkeys (1st, 8vo, 272p, purple cl, 1-color, DJ)	L: Faber	(1946)	Eldridge, Mildred	45-70	
Hall, Lynn	Shy Ones (1st {std}, 8vo, 188p, b/w, DJ/3.25)	Follett	(1967)	Elgaard, Greta	25-45	
Havighurst, Marion	Climb a Lofty Ladder (1st {std}, 8vo, 242p, b/w, DJ/2.75)	Winston	1952	Elgin, Jill	20-35	*
Berkley, Ethel S.	Big and Little, Up & Down (1st, sm8vo, [48]p, b/w, DJ/2.50)	W.R. Scott	(1960)	Elgin, Kathleen	25-45	*
Wood, James P.	Golden Swan (1st, 8vo, 170p, b/w, DJ/3.50)	Seabury Press	1965	Elgin, Kathleen	20-35	
Selsam, Millicent	Underwater Zoos (1st, 8vo, 96p, b/w, DJ/2.75)	Wm. Morrow	1961	Elgin, Kathleen	25-40	
Shipman, Nell	Kurly Kew & Tree-Princess (1st, sm8vo, 200p, orange cl, 6cp, pep)	MacVeagh/Dial	1930	Ellender, Elizabeth	35-60	*
Warner, J. (ed.)	Golden Book of Poetry (1st, lg4to, 67p, ibds, color)	Simon/Schuster	(1949)	Elliott, Gertrude	100-175	
Anderson, Isabel	Great Sea Horse (1st, 4to, red/gilt, teg, 251p, 24cp, pep)	Little/Brown	1909	Elliott, John	180-250	
Stephan, A. Condie	Fairy Tales of a Parrot (1st, 8vo, ibds, [90]p, 6 ticp, dep)	Nister/Dutton	(1892)	Ellis, Tristam	120-200	
Mitchell, Muriel M.	Adventures of Nip & Tuck (1st, 8vo, 40p, pep, ipcb, color)	Volland	(1927)	Ellsworth, Mary	70-125	
Hofman, Caroline	All Around the Sun-Dial (1st, 4to, 79p, col frn)	Dutton	(1917)	Elmer, Rachel R.	30-50	*
Hofman, Caroline	Little Red Balloon (1st, 12mo, ibds, [39]p, color)	Volland	(1918)	Elmer, Rachel R.	60-90	
Hofman, Caroline	Princess Finds a Playmate (1st, 12mo, ibds, unpag, color)	Volland	(1918)	Elmer, Rachel R.	60-100	*
Leonard, Mary F.	Susan Grows Up (1st, 8vo, 307p, 8pl)	Crowell	(1914)	Elmer, Rachel R.	25-40	*
Hofman, Caroline	Wise Gray Cat (1st, 12mo, ipcb, unpag, color)	Volland	(1918)	Elmer, Rachel R.	80-120	*
Montgomery, F.T.	On a Lark to the Planets (1st, 12mo, blue/silver, 180p, 7cp)	Saalfield	1904	Elrod, Winifred D.	200-300	
Carr, Robert V.	Cowboy Lyrics (1st, sm8vo, 229p, teg)	Small/Maynard	(1912)	Elwell, Robert F.	60-100	
Lamb, Charles	Tales from Shakespeare (1st, 8vo, 346p, p-o, 6cp)	Houghton	1925	Elwell, Robert F.	30-50	
Chase, Mary	Virginia of Elk Creek Valley (1st, sm8vo, 297p, gilt, frn by...)	L.C. Page	1917	Elwell, Robert F.	30-50	
Schatz, Letta	A Rhinoceros? Preposterous! (1st, ob4to, 32p, color, DJ/2.50)	Steck-Vaughn	(1965)	Emberley, Ed	30-45	
Branley, Franklyn	Big Dipper (1st, ob8vo, [40]p, color, DJ/2.50)	Crowell	(1962)	Emberley, Ed	30-45	
Gans, Roma	Birds Eat and Eat and Eat (1st, ob8vo, ibds, [40]p, fp 2-color, DJ/2.50)	Crowell	(1963)	Emberley, Ed	30-50	
Goldin, Augusta	Bottom of the Sea (1st, sq8vo, [28]p, color, DJ/3.25)	Crowell	(1967)	Emberley, Ed	30-45	
Emberley, Edward	Cock-a-Doodle-Doo (1st {std}, 12mo, [32]p, ibds, color, DJ/2.50)	Little/Brown	(1964)	Emberley, Ed	30-50	
Showers, Paul	Columbus Day (1st, 8vo, [40]p, fp 2-color, DJ/2.95)	Crowell	(1965)	Emberley, Ed	25-40	
Emberley, Barbara	Drummer Hoff (1st, ob4to, [32]p, color, DJ/4.25, CM)	Prentice-Hall	(1967)	Emberley, Ed	80-135	
Broun, Heywood	Fifty-First Dragon (1st, 12mo, [48]p, fp 1-color, cep, DJ/3.95)	Prentice-Hall	(1968)	Emberley, Ed	30-45	
LesTina, Dorothy	Flag Day (1st, 8vo, [38]p, 2-color, DJ/2.95)	Crowell	(1965)	Emberley, Ed	35-60	
Branley, Franklyn	Flash, Crash, Rumble and Roll (1st, ob8vo, [40]p, color, DJ/2.75)	Crowell	(1964)	Emberley, Ed	30-50	
Emberley, Edward	Green Says Go (1st {std}, 4to, 32p, color, DJ/3.95)	Little/Brown	(1968)	Emberley, Ed	30-50	*
Hawes, Judy	Ladybug, Ladybug, Fly Away Home (1st, ob8vo, [39]p, 2-color, DJ/3.25)	Crowell	(1967)	Emberley, Ed	30-50	
Emberley, Edward	London Bridge is Falling Down (1st {std}, ob4to, 32p, color, DJ/3.50)	Little/Brown	(1967)	Emberley, Ed	30-50	
Penn, Ruth B.	Mommies are for Loving (1st, ob8vo, [32]p, 2-color, DJ/1.95)	Putnam	1962	Emberley, Ed	25-40	
Emberley, Barbara	Night's Nice (1st, 12mo, [26]p, color, pep, DJ/1.95)	Doubleday	1963	Emberley, Ed	40-65	
Emberley, Barbara	One Wide River to Cross (1st, ob4to, [32]p, color, DJ/3.95, CH)	Prentice-Hall	(1966)	Emberley, Ed	50-85	
Emberley, Edward	Parade Book (1st {std}, ob4to, 28p, color, DJ/2.95)	Little/Brown	(1962)	Emberley, Ed	30-50	
Emberley, Edward	Punch and Judy (1st {std}, 4to, 27p, color, DJ/2.95, NYTBI)	Little/Brown	(1965)	Emberley, Ed	40-65	
Emberley, Edward	Rosebud (1st {std}, ob4to, 32p, color, DJ/3.00)	Little/Brown	(1966)	Emberley, Ed	30-50	
Emberley, Barbara	Simon's Song (1st, 12mo, [32]p, 3-color, DJ/3.95)	Prentice-Hall	(1969)	Emberley, Ed	30-45	
Emberley, Barbara	Story of Paul Bunyan (1st, 4to, [32]p, color, DJ/3.25)	Prentice-Hall	(1963)	Emberley, Ed	30-50	
Goldin, Augusta	Straight Hair, Curly Hair (1st, ob4to, ipcb, [38]p, fp 2-color, DJ/3.25)	Crowell	(1966)	Emberley, Ed	20-35	*
Sitomer, Mindel	What is Symmetry? (1st, ob8vo, 33p, color, DJ/3.75)	Crowell	(1970)	Emberley, Ed	30-45	
Phelan, Mary K.	White House (1st {std}, 8vo, unpag, 3-color, DJ/2.50)	Holt, Rinehart	(1962)	Emberley, Ed	25-40	
Emberley, Edward	Wing on a Flea (1st {std} [1st bk.], 4to, 48p, color, DJ/2.95, NYTBI)	Little/Brown	(1961)	Emberley, Ed	50-80	
Schackburg, Richard	Yankee Doodle (1st, ob4to, [30]p, fp 3-color, pep, DJ/3.75)	Prentice-Hall	(1965)	Emberley, Ed	30-50	
Whitson, John H.	Barbara, Woman of the West (1st, sm8vo, green cl, 314p, 5pl)	Little/Brown	1903	Emerson, Chase	25-45	
Wesselhoeft, Lily	Ready the Reliable (1st, sm8vo, 265p, 4pl)	Little/Brown	1906	Emerson, Chase	30-50	
N/A	Arabian Nights (1st, 12mo, 318p, col frn, 7pl)	Baker/Taylor	1910	Emerson/D'Emo	30-50	*
Emett, Rowland	New World for Nellie (1st AM {std}, 4to, [40]p, ipcb, color, pep, DJ/2.00)	Harcourt	(1952)	Emett, Rowland	60-90	R
Emmet, Rosina	Pretty Peggy... (lg sq8vo, ibds, 64p, chromos)	Dodd	1880	Emmet, Rosina	90-120	
Heinlein, Robert	Have Space Suit-Will Travel (1st, 8vo, 276p, b/w, DJ/2.95)	Scribner	1958	Emshwiller, Ed	200-300	
France, Anatole	In ALL France (1st, 8vo, gilt, p-o, 110p, color, pep)	Whitman	(1930)	Enders, Lucille	30-50	*
Endres, Ernest	Day with The Gnomes (1st, 24mo, [54]p, ibds, pep, 19 color)	L: Nister	[1910]	Endres, Ernest	120-200	
Englefield, Cicely	Tail of a Guinea-Pig (1st AM, 24mo, ipcb, 43p, fp b/w, pep)	NY: Oxford U.Pr.	[1937]	Englefield, Cicely	30-45	
King, Marian	Amnon, Lad of Palestine (1st, sm8vo, 96p, color, pep)	Houghton	1931	Enright, Elizabeth	40-65	
Enright, Elizabeth	Borrowed Summer (1st, sm8vo, 275p, b/w, DJ/2.50)	Rinehart	(1946)	Enright, Elizabeth	50-80	
Enright, Elizabeth	Christmas Tree for Lydia (1st, 24mo, ipcb, 38p, 1-color, dep, DJ/1.00)	Rinehart	(1951)	Enright, Elizabeth	40-65	
Rowe, Nellie	Crystal Locket (1st, lg8vo, 143p, ipcb, 10cp, pep)	Whitman	1935	Enright, Elizabeth	35-50	
Enright, Elizabeth	Four-Story Mistake (1st, 8vo, 177p, 9 fp 1-color, pep, DJ/1.75)	Farrar/Rinehart	(1942)	Enright, Elizabeth	60-100	
King, Marian	Kees (1st {std}, 4to, 79p, ibds, color, pep)	Harper	1930	Enright, Elizabeth	60-85	
King, Marian	Kees & Kleintje (1st, 4to, 80p, p-o, color, pep)	Whitman	(1934)	Enright, Elizabeth	50-80	
Enright, Elizabeth	Kintu (1st, sm8vo, p-o, 54p, color, DJ/1.00)	Farrar/Rinehart	1935	Enright, Elizabeth	50-85	
Enright, Elizabeth	Sea is All Around (1st, 8vo, 124p, green cl, 6cp, pep, DJ/2.00)	Farrar/Rinehart	(1940)	Enright, Elizabeth	40-65	
Enright, Elizabeth	Spiderweb for Two: Melendy Maze (1st, 8vo, 209p, uncut, b/w, DJ/2.50)	Rinehart	(1951)	Enright, Elizabeth	50-80	*
Enright, Elizabeth	The Saturdays (1st, sm8vo, red cl, 175p, fp 1-color, pep, DJ/2.00)	Farrar/Rinehart	(1941)	Enright, Elizabeth	30-50	
Enright, Elizabeth	Then There were Five (1st, 8vo, blue cl, 241p, uncut, b/w, DJ/2.00)	Farrar/Rinehart	(1944)	Enright, Elizabeth	30-50	
Enright, Elizabeth	Thimble Summer (1st, 8vo, 124p, color, pep, DJ/2.00, NM)	Farrar/Rinehart	1938	Enright, Elizabeth	150-220	R
Tippett, James S.	Toys and Toy Makers (1st {std}, sm8vo, 144p, cp, pep)	Harper	1931	Enright, Elizabeth	25-35	
Hunt, Clara W.	About Harriet (1st, 8vo, 150p, p-o, fp color)	Houghton	1916	Enright, Maginel W.	35-60	
Bancroft, Laura	Babes in Birdland (1st, lg8vo, green cl, 116p, 8cp)	Reilly/Britton	(1911)	Enright, Maginel W.	400-650	R
Bancroft, Laura	Bandit Jim Crow (1st, 12mo, 62p, 15cp)	Reilly/Britton	(1906)	Enright, Maginel W.	350-500	R
Gordon, Elizabeth	Billy Bunny's Fortune (1st, 12mo, [40]p, ibds, color, pep)	Volland	(1919)	Enright, Maginel W.	60-90	
Stilwell, Alison	Chin Ling & Chinese Cricket (1st {std}, sm4to, ibds, [48]p, color, DJ/2.25)	Macmillan	1947	Enright, Maginel W.	70-120	
Judson, Clara I.	Flower Fairies (1st, lg8vo, p-o, pep, 93p, 6cp)	Rand/McNally	(1915)	Enright, Maginel W.	75-100	*
Huntington, Ida M.	Garden of Hearts' Delight (1st, lg8vo, p-o, gilt, 167p, 15cp)	Rand/McNally	(1911)	Enright, Maginel W.	100-160	
Dodge, Mary Mapes	Hans Brinker (1st, lg8vo, p-o, teg, 345p, 8cp, pep)	McKay	1918	Enright, Maginel W.	70-120	R

AUTHOR	TITLE	PUBLISHER	DATE	ARTIST	PRICE	LC
Spyri, Johanna	Heidi (1st, lg8vo, 368p, p-o, gilt, pep, 8cp, WS)	Rand/McNally	(1921)	Enright, Maginel W.	50-80	
Seegmiller, Wilhelmina	Journeys in Storyland (1st, sm8vo, [120]p, pep, color)	Houghton	1922	Enright, Maginel W.	55-80	*
Brown, Julia	Mermaid's Gift (1st, 8vo, blue/gilt, p-o, 168p, 8cp)	Rand/McNally	(1912)	Enright, Maginel W.	120-170	
Bancroft, Laura	Mr. Woodchuck (1st, 8vo, 62p, ibds, color, cep)	Reilly/Britton	(1906)	Enright, Maginel W.	350-550	R
Bancroft, Laura	Policeman Blue Jay (1st, 12mo, ibds, 115p, 8cp)	Reilly/Britton	(1907)	Enright, Maginel W.	400-600	
Bancroft, Laura	Prairie-Dog Town (1st, 8vo, 61p, 14 fp color)	Reilly/Britton	(1906)	Enright, Maginel W.	350-500	R
Bancroft, Laura	Prince Mud-Turtle (1st, 12mo, 61p, tan cl, cep, 14 fp color)	Reilly/Britton	(1906)	Enright, Maginel W.	300-450	R
Mother Goose	Songs from Mother Goose (1st, 4to, 83p, color)	Macmillan	1920	Enright, Maginel W.	120-180	*
Bancroft, Laura	Sugar-Loaf Mountain (1st, 12mo, 64p, 16cp, cep)	Reilly/Britton	(1906)	Enright, Maginel W.	300-450	R
Gordon, Elizabeth	Tale of Johnny Mouse (1st, 12mo, ibds, unpag, color, pep)	Volland	(1920)	Enright, Maginel W.	80-120	
Bancroft, Laura	Twinkle and Chubbins (1st, 12mo, 384p, yellow cl, color)	Reilly/Britton	(1911)	Enright, Maginel W.	400-600	
Bancroft, Laura	Twinkle's Enchantment (1st, 12mo, 64p, 15cp)	Reilly/Britton	(1906)	Enright, Maginel W.	350-500	R
Knobel, E.	When Little Thoughts Go Rhyming (1st, 8vo, p-o, 96p, 10cp)	Rand/McNally	(1916)	Enright, Maginel W.	70-120	
Miller, Olive B.	Whisk Away on a Sunbeam (1st, lg8vo, [93]p, pep, ibds, color)	Volland	(1919)	Enright, Maginel W.	90-150	
Baum, L. Frank	Father Goose's Yearbook (1st, 8vo, [128]p, p-o, buckram, color, pep)	Reilly/Britton	(1907)	Enright, Walter J.	300-450	
Joyce, James	Cat and the Devil (1st, 8vo, [48]p, color, pep, DJ/3.50)	Dodd	(1964)	Erdoes, Richard	100-175	R
LeSieg, Theo	Come Over to My House (1st, 8vo, 63p, ibds, color, pep, DJ/1.95)	Beginner Books	(1966)	Erdoes, Richard	40-65	*
King, Alexander	Memoirs of a Certain Mouse (1st, lg8vo, 92p, fp b/w, pep, DJ/2.95)	McGraw-Hill	(1966)	Erdoes, Richard	30-50	*
Dow, Katherine	My Time of Year (1st, 12mo, [32]p, fp 2-color, DJ/2.25, NYTBI)	H.Z. Walck	1961	Erhard, Walter	25-40	
Salten, Felix	Bambi's Children (1st, 4to, 63p, ibds, fp color, pep, DJ/1.00)	Random	(1950)	Erickson, Phoebe	25-45	
Sewell, Anna	Black Beauty (1st, 4to, 62p, ibds, color, pep, DJ)	Random	1949	Erickson, Phoebe	40-60	*
Erickson, Phoebe	Double or Nothing (1st, lg8vo, 127p, b/w, DJ/2.75)	Harper	(1958)	Erickson, Phoebe	25-40	
De Witt, Johanna	Littlest Reindeer (1st, lg8vo, [28]p, ipcb, color, DJ/1.00)	Children's Press	(1946)	Erickson, Phoebe	30-50	
Lasky, Muriel	Proud Little Kitten (1st, 4to, ibds, 32p, color)	Universal Books	1944	Erika	30-50	
Rahr, Ruth	Journey of the Toys (1st, 4to, 87p, p-o, blue cl, pep, color)	(Wisconsin)	(1934)	Ertz, Bruno	65-90	
Carpenter, Frances	African Wonder Tales (1st {std}, lg8vo, 215p, b/w, DJ/3.95)	Doubleday	(1963)	Escourido, Joseph	40-65	
Marcy, Mary E.	Rhymes of Early Jungle Folk (1st, lg8vo, 124p, woodcuts, pep)	Chi: Kerr	1922	Esherick, Wharton H.	80-125	
Evans, Eva K.	Surprise for Araminta (1st, sq8vo, [28]p, col frn, pep, DJ/0.50)	Grosset/Dunlap	1942	Eshner, Ann	65-90	
Rand, Ann	Edward and the Horse (1st {std}, 4to, [30]p, color, pep, DJ/3.00)	Harcourt	(1961)	Eskell, Olle	60-100	
Ducorron, C.A.F.	Boy King of the Cannibal Islands (1st {std}, 8vo, p-o, 257p, b/w pl)	Bobbs-Merrill	(1932)	Eskridge, Robert	40-65	
Crew, Helen	Alanna (1st {std}, 8vo, 233p, col frn, pep, DJ/2.00)	Harper	1929	Esley, Joan	30-50	
Rosman, Alice G.	Jock the Scot (1st, lg8vo, gilt, 204p, p-o, 7cp, DJ)	Minton Balch	(1930)	Esley, Joan	40-65	
Bacon, Josephine D.	Luck of Lowry (1st {std}, sm8vo, 303p, b/w, pep)	Longmans	1931	Esley, Joan	20-35	*
McNeely, Marian H.	Way to Glory (1st {std}, 8vo, 240p, b/w)	Longmans	1932	Esley, Joan	35-60	*
Estes, Eleanor	Echoing Green (1st {std}, 8vo, 263p, b/w, DJ/3.00)	Macmillan	1947	Estes, Eleanor	40-65	
Estes, Eleanor	Ginger Pye (1st {std}, 8vo, 250p, yellow cl, b/w, DJ/2.50, NM)	Harcourt	(1951)	Estes, Eleanor	120-200	R
Estes, Eleanor	Little Oven (1st {std}, ob8vo, [32]p, color, DJ/2.25)	Harcourt	1955	Estes, Eleanor	70-100	
Estes, Eleanor	Lollipop Princess (1st {std}, ob8vo, [32]p, 1-color, DJ/2.50)	Harcourt	(1967)	Estes, Eleanor	60-90	
Estes, Eleanor	Sleeping Giant (1st, 8vo, 101p, green cl, fp color, DJ/3.00)	Harcourt	(1948)	Estes, Eleanor	80-125	
Ets, Marie H.	Another Day (1st, lg ob8vo, 40p, pep, b/w, DJ/1.75)	Viking	1953	Ets, Marie H.	50-80	R
Ets, Marie H.	Automobiles for Mice (1st, ob4to, 31p, color, DJ/3.00)	Viking	(1964)	Ets, Marie H.	40-65	
Ets, Marie H.	Bad Boy, Good Boy (1st, sm4to, 49p, 1-color, pep, DJ/3.95)	Crowell	(1967)	Ets, Marie H.	30-50	
Ets, Marie H.	Beasts & Nonsense (1st, 8vo, 64p, b/w, pep, DJ/2.00, NYTBI)	Viking	1952	Ets, Marie H.	50-80	
Ets, Marie H.	Cow's Party (1st, 4to, 32p, color, pep, DJ/2.50)	Viking	(1958)	Ets, Marie H.	50-85	
Ets, Marie H.	Gilberto and the Wind (1st, 4to, 32p, 1-color, cep, DJ/3.00)	Viking	(1963)	Ets, Marie H.	60-90	R*
Ets, Marie H.	In the Forest (1st, lg ob8vo, ipcb, [45]p, b/w, DJ/1.00, CH)	Viking	1944	Ets, Marie H.	80-145	R
Ets, Marie H.	Just Me (1st, ob8vo, [32]p, b/w, DJ/2.50, CH)	Viking	(1965)	Ets, Marie H.	70-100	*
Ets, Marie H.	Little Old Automobile (1st, 4to, ipcb, [32]p, b/w, pep, DJ/1.50)	Viking	1948	Ets, Marie H.	60-90	
Ets, Marie H.	Mr. Penny (1st {1st book}, ob4to, ibds, 48p, b/w, pep, DJ/1.00)	Viking	1935	Ets, Marie H.	120-200	
Ets, Marie H.	Mr. Penny's Circus (1st, 4to, 64p, b/w, DJ/2.50)	Viking	(1961)	Ets, Marie H.	60-100	
Ets, Marie H.	Mr. Penny's Race Horse (1st, sm4to, 63p, b/w, pep, DJ/2.00, CH)	Viking	1956	Ets, Marie H.	100-165	R
Ets, Marie H.	Mr. T.W. Anthony Woo (1st, ob4to, ibds, 54p, pep, b/w, DJ/2.00, CH)	Viking	1951	Ets, Marie H.	100-160	
Ets, Marie H.	Nine Days to Christmas (1st, 4to, 48p, color, DJ/3.25, CM)	Viking	(1959)	Ets, Marie H.	150-225	
Ets, Marie H.	Oley, the Sea Monster (1st, 4to, ipcb, [32]p, b/w, pep, DJ/1.50)	Viking	1947	Ets, Marie H.	90-140	
Ets, Marie H.	Play with Me (1st, sm4to, 31p, color, DJ/2.50, CH)	Viking	(1955)	Ets, Marie H.	100-170	R
Ets, Marie H.	Story of a Baby (1st, lg4to, 63p, blue cl, pep, b/w, DJ/2.50)	Viking	1939	Ets, Marie H.	70-100	
Ets, Marie H.	Talking Without Words (1st, ob8vo, [32]p, b/w, cep, DJ/2.75, NYTBI)	Viking	1968	Ets, Marie H.	40-65	
Thompson, Kay	Miss Pooky Peckinpaugh (1st {std}, 4to, ibds, [30]p, b/w, DJ/4.95)	Harper	(1970)	Eula, Joe	150-225	
N/A	Baby's Animal Book (sm8vo, ibds, 10cp)	Platt/Munk	1929	Eulalie	55-80	
Piper, Watty	Brimful Book (1st, 4to, [74]p, p-o, color, pep)	Platt/Munk	(1929)	Eulalie	60-100	
Stevenson, Rbt. L.	Child's Garden of Verses (1st, sm4to, 85p, p-o, 11 fp color, pep)	Platt/Munk	(1929)	Eulalie	55-80	
Mother Goose	Favorite Mother Goose Rhymes (4to, ibds, color)	Platt/Munk	(1937)	Eulalie	50-80	
Piper, Watty	Ginger Bread Boy (1st, 4to, ibds, [40]p, p-o, color, pep)	Platt/Munk	(1927)	Eulalie	60-90	R
Bannerman, Helen	Little Black Sambo (4to, 40p, green bds, p-o, color)	Platt/Munk	(1927)	Eulalie	200-300	
Howland, Ethel	Scary-Ann/Cookie Man (1st, 8vo, ibds, 100p, color, pep)	Suttonhouse	1932	Eulalie	60-100	
Maeterlinck, Maurice	The Swarm (1st, 8vo, green cl, p-o, 113p, frn by...)	Dodd	1906	Euwer, Anthony	30-50	
N/A	Sleeping Beauty Picture Book (4to, 24cp)	Dodd	[1915]	Evans, E.	120-200	
March, Eleanor S.	Three Naughty Elves (1st, ob4to, 37p, ibds, color)	L: Liberty	[1903]	Evans, E.	200-300	*
Sayers, Frances C.	Ginny and Custard (1st, 8vo, 128p, b/w, pep, DJ/2.00)	Viking	1951	Evans, Eileen	30-45	
Sayers, Frances C.	Sally Tait (1st, 8vo, 126p, b/w, pep, DJ/2.00)	Viking	1948	Evans, Eileen	25-45	
Donahey, Mary D.	Adventure of a Happy Dolly (4to, p-o, 123p, 5cp)	Barse/Hopkins	(1914)	Evans, G.	80-120	
Gregory, L.F.	Mama Nelly & I (1st, 4to, p-o, 167p, green cl, 5cp)	Stern	1908	Evans, Grace	120-180	
Friskey, Margaret	Adventure for Beginners (1st, sm4to, color, pep, DJ/1.00)	Wilcox/Follett	(1944)	Evans, Katherine	35-50	
Elkin, Benjamin	Big Jump (1st {std}, lg8vo, ibds, [65]p, color, DJ/1.95)	Beginner Books	(1958)	Evans, Katherine	60-90	
Tazewell, Charles	Littlest Angel (1st, lg8vo, ibds, [28]p, color, pep, DJ/1.00)	Children's Press	(1946)	Evans, Katherine	60-100	
Evans, Katherine	Michael Angelo Mouse (1st, 8vo, [28]p, ibds, color, DJ/1.00)	Wilcox/Follett	(1945)	Evans, Katherine	25-40	
Bannon, Laura	Nemo Meets the Emperor (1st, lg8vo, p-o, 45p, color, pep, DJ/2.75)	Whitman	(1957)	Evans, Katherine	40-60	
Novinger, Virginia	Tommy on Time (1st, lg8vo, [28]p, p-o, fp color, pep, DJ/1.50)	Whitman	(1952)	Evans, Katherine	25-45	

AUTHOR	TITLE	PUBLISHER	DATE	ARTIST	PRICE	LC
Evatt, Harriet	Big Indian and Little Bear (1st, 8vo, [32]p, fp 2-color, pep, DJ/1.75)	Bobbs-Merrill	1954	Evatt, Harriet	30-45	
Dickens, Charles	Christmas Carol (8vo, bds, p-o, 168p, 13 ticp)	Crowell	[1915]	Everett, Ethel	70-100	
Woodward, Clifford	Dreams & Fables (1st, 8vo, 110p, green cl, b/w)	L: Longmans	1929	Everett, Ethel	30-50	*
Fyleman, Rose	Old Fashioned Girls (1st, 8vo, 33p, gilt, teg, 12cp)	L: Methuen	1928	Everett, Ethel	30-50	
Blyton, Enid	Silver & Gold (1st AM, sq8vo, uncut, gilt, p-o, 128p, 8cp, pep)	NY: Nelson	(1928)	Everett, Ethel	100-165	
N/A	Stories from Aunt Judy (1st, 8vo, teg, uncut, 268p, 8cp, pep)	L: Bell	1913	Everett, Ethel	50-85	
Kingsley, Charles	Water Babies (1st, 8vo, 282p, p-o, 8cp)	Winston	(1930)	Everett, Ethel	70-120	
Brady, Cyrus T.	And Thus He Came (1st, sm8vo, 103p, teg, 6 ticp)	Putnam	1916	Everett, Walter	45-70	
Pender, Lydia	Barnaby and the Horses (1st, sm4to, [40]p, color, pep, DJ/2.75)	Abelard-Schuman	1961	Evers, Alie	30-50	
Colmont, Marie	Along the Coast (1st, folio, ibds, [24]p, fp color, pep, DJ/1.50)	Harper	1939	Exeter, Alexandra	200-300	
Colmont, Marie	Down the River (1st {std}, lg4to, ibds, [24]p, pep, 5 dp color, DJ/1.50)	Harper	1940	Exeter, Alexandra	150-250	
Fabres, Oscar	Kwik and Kwak (1st, sm4to, [48]p, ibds, fp color, pep, DJ/1.50)	Crown Pub.	1942	Fabres, Oscar	40-70	*
Brown, Slater	Talking Skyscraper (1st, 4to, ibds, 48p, fp color, DJ/2.00)	Hyperion Press	(1945)	Fabres, Oscar	45-70	
Andersen, Hans C.	Thumbelina (1st, 4to, ibds, [48]p, fp color, pep, DJ/1.75)	Hyperion Press	(1943)	Fabres, Oscar	60-100	
Adelson, Leone	Who Blew that Whistle? (1st, lg8vo, ipcb, 45p, 1-color, pep, DJ/1.50)	W.R. Scott	(1946)	Fabres, Oscar	45-70	
Haskell, Helen E.	O-Heart-San (1st, 12mo, 128p, 6cp, pep)	L.C. Page	1908	Fairbanks, Frank	30-50	
Siddiqui, Ashraf	Toontoony Pie (1st {std}, 8vo, 158p, b/w, DJ/3.50)	World	(1961)	Fairservis, Jan	20-30	
Treadgold, Mary	Winter Princess (1st AM, 8vo, 112p, b/w, DJ/3.50)	Van Nostrand	(1964)	Falconer, Pearl	30-50	
Fallon, Sara W.	Animal-Alphabet Book (1st, ob4to, [54]p, color)	L: G. Allen	1899	Fallon, Sara W.	180-250	*
Falls, Charles B.	ABC Book (1st, lg4to, [30]p, ibds, 26cp, pep)	Doubleday/Page	1923	Falls, Charles B.	170-240	
Falls, Charles B.	ABC Book (lg4to, orange ibds, [30]p, fp color)	Doubleday/Doran	1939	Falls, Charles B.	120-185	R*
Baity, Eliz. C.	America Before Man (1st, lg8vo, 224p, pep, maps, b/w, DJ/4.50)	Viking	1953	Falls, Charles B.	45-60	R
Baity, Eliz. C.	Americans Before Columbus (1st, lg8vo, 256p, gilt, pep, b/w, DJ/4.00, NH)	Viking	1951	Falls, Charles B.	40-65	
Shippen, Kath. B.	Bridle for Pegasus (1st, lg8vo, 192p, b/w, DJ/3.50)	Viking	1951	Falls, Charles B.	25-40	
Falls, Charles B.	First 3000 Years (1st, sm4to, 220p, color, DJ/6.00)	Viking	(1960)	Falls, Charles B.	50-85	
Post, Emily	Flight of a Moth (1st, sm8vo, 253p, cvr by...)	Dodd	1904	Falls, Charles B.	40-65	
Singleton, Esther	Golden Rod Fairy Book (1st, 8vo, blue/gilt, 342p, pep, 16cp)	Dodd	1903	Falls, Charles B.	150-220	
Shippen, Kath. B.	Great Heritage (1st, lg8vo, 230p, yellow cl, b/w, pep, DJ/3.50)	Viking	1947	Falls, Charles B.	30-55	
Wheeler, Post	Hathoo of the Elephants (1st, sm8vo, orange cl, 333p, pep by...)	Viking	1943	Falls, Charles B.	35-60	*
Ford, Sewell	Horses Nine (1st, sm8vo, 270p, cvr by...)	Scribner	1903	Falls, Charles B.	40-65	
Leonard, Mary F.	How the Two Ends Met (1st, sm8vo, 97p, 4pl)	Crowell	(1903)	Falls, Charles B.	55-80	*
Crockett, Samuel R.	May Margaret (1st AM, sm8vo, 375p, blue cl, cvr by...)	Dodd	1905	Falls, Charles B.	25-45	*
Byrne, Donn	Messer Marco Polo (1st, 12mo, 147p, 4pl, DJ)	Century	1921	Falls, Charles B.	40-65	
Falls, Charles B.	Modern ABC Book (1st, lg4to, [32]p, 26 color)	NY: J. Day	1930	Falls, Charles B.	160-240	*
Mother Goose	Mother Goose (1st {std}, lg4to, 96p, black cl, color, pep)	Doubleday/Page	1924	Falls, Charles B.	120-200	
Shippen, Kath. B.	New Found World (1st, lg8vo, 262p, blue cl, b/w, pep, DJ/3.50, NH)	Viking	1945	Falls, Charles B.	45-70	
Maeterlinck, Maurice	Old Fashioned Flowers (1st, sm8vo, 105p, 6cp)	Dodd	1905	Falls, Charles B.	45-70	
MacLaren, Ian	Our Neighbors (1st, sm8vo, 341p, gilt, cvr by...)	Dodd	1903	Falls, Charles B.	25-45	
Weil, Ann Y.	Red Sails to Capri (1st, 8vo, 156p, pep, DJ/2.50, NH)	Viking	1952	Falls, Charles B.	30-50	
Grimm Bros.	Snow White & Seven Dwarfs (sm4to, 236p, green cl, p-o, 12cp, pep)	Dodd	1913	Falls, Charles B.	120-180	
Long, Laura	Square Sails & Spice Islands (1st {std}, 8vo, 249p, b/w, pep, DJ/2.50)	Longmans	1945	Falls, Charles B.	30-50	
Donahey, Mary D.	Talking Bird & Wonderful Wishes (1st, lg8vo, p-o, 146p, 6cp, pep)	Whitman	(1920)	Falls, Charles B.	200-300	
Jerome, Jerome K.	Tea-Table Talk (1st, 12mo, 153p, blue cl, cvr by...)	Dodd	1903	Falls, Charles B.	30-50	
Stevenson, Rbt. L.	Treasure Island (1st, 8vo, 287p, color, pep, DJ/1.25, RC)	World	(1946)	Falls, Charles B.	30-50	*
Hart, Lavinia	When a Maid Marries (1st, sm8vo, 210p, cvr by...)	Dodd	1904	Falls, Charles B.	25-40	
Bowie, Walter R.	When Jesus was Born (1st {std}, sq16mo, [20]p, ibds, color)	Harper	1928	Falls, Charles B.	55-80	
Cook, William W.	Wilby's Dan (1st, 12mo, 325p, 8cp)	Dodd	1904	Falls, Charles B.	50-80	
Singleton, Esther	Wild Flower Fairy Book (1st, 8vo, gilt, 354p, teg, pep, 16cp)	Dodd	1905	Falls, Charles B.	150-225	
Bailey, Carolyn S.	Wonderful Days (1st, lg8vo, 254p, col frn)	Whitman	(1929)	Falls, Charles B.	40-60	*
Dickerson, Mary A.	Wonderful Wishes of Jacky & Jean (1st, sm4to, 146p, 6cp)	Wessels	(1905)	Falls, Charles B.	100-165	*
Burgess, Gelett	Maxims of Methuselah (1st, 12mo, ibds, 108p, 4cp)	Stokes	(1907)	Fancher, Louis D.	40-65	
Burgess, Gelett	Maxims of Noah (1st, 12mo, ibds, 119p, color)	Stokes	(1913)	Fancher, Louis D.	40-65	
Moore, Clement C.	Night Before Christmas (1st, 8vo, [32]p, color, pep, DJ/0.50)	Grosset/Dunlap	(1935)	Fanchette	60-100	
Lucas, E.V.	All the World Over (1st, ob4to, gilt, 30ff, ibds, 30cp)	L: Richards	1898	Farmiloe, Edith	150-250	
Farmiloe, Edith	Mr. Biddle & the Dragon (1st, 4to, red cl, 47p, 20pl)	L: Skeffington	1904	Farmiloe, Edith	150-225	
De La Mare, Walter	Story of Miss Jemima (1st {this fmt}, 8vo, ibds, 55p, color, pep, DJ/0.50)	Grosset/Dunlap	(1940)	Farnam, Nellie	60-90	
Miller, Olive Thorne	Kristy's Rainy Day Picnic (1st, 12mo, 235p, p-o, 4cp, pep)	Houghton	1906	Farnsworth, Ethel	30-50	
Jewett, John H.	Little Governor in Fableland (1st, narrow 8vo, 104p, ibds, 5cp)	Stokes	(1907)	Farnsworth, Ethel	60-90	
Howells, William D.	Boy's Town (1st, sm8vo, aqua/gilt, 247p, 23pl, PPP)	Harper	1890	Farny, H.F.	170-250	
Gordon, Hampden C.	Flower Name Fancies (1st, 4to, 60p, green cl, 31 fp b/w)	L: John Lane	1918	Fauconnet, Guy P.	55-80	*
Bowman, James C.	Seven Silly Wise Men (1st, 8vo, p-o, [30]p, fp color, DJ/2.50)	Whitman	(1965)	Faulkner, John	25-40	*
Bowman, James C.	Who Was Tricked? (1st, 8vo, [32]p, fp color, DJ/2.50)	Whitman	(1966)	Faulkner, John	25-40	*
Priolo, Pauline	Piccolina and the Easter Bells (1st {std}, sm ob4to, 48p, color, DJ/3.00)	Little/Brown	(1962)	Fava, Rita	30-50	*
Carlson, Natalie S.	Sashes Red & Blue (1st, 8vo, 107p, b/w, DJ/2.50)	Harper	(1956)	Fava, Rita	20-30	
Starbird, Kaye	Speaking of Cows (1st, 8vo, 70p, b/w, DJ/2.95)	Lippincott	(1960)	Fava, Rita	25-45	
Woody, Regina	Almena's Dogs (1st {std}, 8vo, 240p, fp b/w, DJ/2.75)	Ariel	(1954)	Fax, Elton C.	25-40	
Garst, Shannon	Buffalo Bill (1st, 8vo, 214p, uncut, b/w, pep, DJ/2.75)	J. Messner	(1948)	Fax, Elton C.	30-50	
Faulkner, Georgene	Melindy's Medal (1st, 8vo, 172p, b/w, pep, DJ/2.25)	J. Messner	(1945)	Fax, Elton C.	50-80	*
Hayes, Florence	Skid (1st, 8vo, 216p, b/w, DJ/2.50)	Houghton	1948	Fax, Elton C.	40-65	
Schatz, Letta	Taiwo and her Twin (1st, lg8vo, 128p, b/w, DJ/2.95)	McGraw-Hill	1964	Fax, Elton C.	20-30	
Aardema, Verna	Tales from the Story Hat (1st, 4to, 72p, b/w, DJ/3.50)	Coward	(1960)	Fax, Elton C.	40-65	*
Courlander, Harold	Terrapin's Pot of Sense (1st {std}, lg8vo, 125p, b/w, DJ/3.00)	Holt	(1957)	Fax, Elton C.	30-50	
Eaton, Jeanette	Trumpeter's Tale.... (1st, 8vo, 191p, b/w, DJ/3.50)	Wm. Morrow	1955	Fax, Elton C.	40-65	
Warren, Maude R.	Mother Goose & her Friends (1st, lg8vo, 309p, p-o, pep, 12 ticp)	Doran	(1923)	Federer, Charles A.	65-100	
Warren, Maude R.	Tales Told by Gander (8vo, green/gilt, 305p, p-o, 12 ticp, pep)	Doran	(1922)	Federer, Charles A.	70-100	
Kerina, Jane	African Crafts (1st, 4to, 64p, 1-color)	Lion Press	(1970)	Feelings, Tom	45-70	*
Lester, Julius B.	Black Folktales (1st, 8vo, 159p, fp b/w, cep, DJ/4.50)	R.W. Baron	1969	Feelings, Tom	60-95	
Schatz, Letta	Bola and the Oba's Drummers (1st, 8vo, 156p, b/w, pep, DJ/4.50)	McGraw-Hill	(1967)	Feelings, Tom	30-50	*

AUTHOR	TITLE	PUBLISHER	DATE	ARTIST	PRICE	LC
Bond, Ruskin	Panther's Moon (1st, 8vo, 68p, fp b/w, DJ/3.50)	Random	(1969)	Feelings, Tom	30-55	*
Blue, Rose	Quiet Place (1st, 8vo, 57p, b/w, DJ/3.50)	F. Watts	(1969)	Feelings, Tom	40-65	*
Molarsky, Osmond	Song of the Empty Bottles (1st, lg8vo, [55]p, color, pep, DJ/3.75)	H.Z. Walck	1968	Feelings, Tom	40-65	
Arnott, Kathleen	Tales of Temba (1st, 8vo, 144p, fp b/w, cep, DJ/4.50)	H.Z. Walck	(1969)	Feelings, Tom	25-45	
Lester, Julius B.	To Be a Slave (1st {std}, 8vo, 160p, black/gilt, b/w, DJ/3.95, NH)	Dial Press	(1968)	Feelings, Tom	80-140	
Garfield, Nancy	Tuesday Elephant (1st, 4to, [44]p, fp 2-color, DJ/3.95)	Crowell	(1968)	Feelings, Tom	30-50	
Heady, Eleanor	When the Stones Were Soft (1st, 8vo, 94p, ibds, fp b/w, DJ/3.50)	Funk/Wagnalls	(1968)	Feelings, Tom	40-65	
Feelings, Muriel	Zamani Goes to Market (1st, 8vo, [44]p, 2-color, DJ/3.95)	Seabury Press	(1970)	Feelings, Tom	45-70	R*
Titcomb, Margaret	Voyage of the Flying Bird (1st, 8vo, 236p, b/w, DJ/3.50)	Dodd	(1963)	Feher, Joseph	20-30	
Juster, Norton	Phantom Tollbooth (1st, 8vo, 255p, blue cl, b/w, pep, DJ/3.95)	Epstein/Carroll	(1961)	Feiffer, Jules	400-600	
Juster, Norton	Phantom Tollbooth (1st UK, 8vo, 256p, bds, b/w, DJ)	L: Collins	1962	Feiffer, Jules	250-400	
Nesbit, Edith	Book of Dragons (1st, 8vo, 290p, gilt, teg, 8 fp color by...)	L: Harper	1901	Fell, H. Granville	450-600	
Bible	Book of Job (1st, sm4to, teg, gilt, 103p, uncut, fp b/w)	L: J.M. Dent	1896	Fell, H. Granville	120-200	
Rhys, Grace (ed.)	Fairy Gifts (1st, 12mo, 61p, uncut, teg, gilt, 16pl)	L: J.M. Dent	1895	Fell, H. Granville	70-100	
N/A	History of Ali Baba (1st, 24mo, 63p, b/w)	L: J.M. Dent	1895	Fell, H. Granville	75-100	*
N/A	History of Cinderella (1st, 24mo, 63p, gilt, teg, uncut, 14pl)	L: J.M. Dent	1894	Fell, H. Granville	100-160	
Yeats, Wm. Butler	Poems (1st, 8vo, 286p, beige/gilt, uncut, ti page by....)	L: T.F. Unwin	1895	Fell, H. Granville	800-1200	
Bible	Song of Songs... (1st, 4to, 16p, gilt, teg, buckram, 12pl)	L: Chapman	1897	Fell, H. Granville	130-200	
Hawthorne, Nathaniel	Tanglewood Tales (1st, sm8vo, 222p, uncut, 12cp)	Dent/Dutton	1903	Fell, H. Granville	100-160	
Maud, Constance E.	Wagner's Heroes (1st, 8vo, 284p, black/silver, 8pl)	L: E. Arnold	1895	Fell, H. Granville	55-80	
Hawthorne, Nathaniel	Wonder Book (1st, 8vo, teg, ibds, gilt, 24cp)	L: J.M. Dent	1910	Fell, H. Granville	100-160	
N/A	Wonder Stories from Herodotus (1st, 8vo, 163p, 12cp)	Harper	1900	Fell, H. Granville	100-150	
Fellows, Muriel	Land of Little Rain (1st, 8vo, 121p, fp color, pep, DJ/2.00)	Winston	1936	Fellows, Muriel	50-80	
Fellows, Muriel	Little Magic Painter (1st, 8vo, 111p, p-o, 13cp, DJ/2.00)	Winston	(1938)	Fellows, Muriel	40-65	
Felt, Sue	Contrary Woodrow (1st {std}, ob4to, unpag, color, DJ/2.50)	Doubleday	1958	Felt, Sue	50-85	
Forbus, Ina B.	Melissa (1st, 8vo, 190p, b/w, DJ/3.00)	Viking	(1962)	Felt, Sue	60-90	
Felt, Sue	Rosa-Too-Little (1st {std}, ob4to, [30]p, 1-color, DJ/2.00)	Doubleday	(1950)	Felt, Sue	60-90	
Boylston, Helen D.	Carol on Tour (1st {std}, sm8vo, 205p, red cl, 4pl, DJ/2.50)	Little/Brown	1946	Felten, Major	200-300	
Culbertson, Polly	Bear Facts (1st {std}, 8vo, [30]p, ibds, color, DJ/1.25)	Winston	(1948)	Fennell, Paul J.	30-45	
Fenner, Carol E.	Tigers in the Cellar (1st {std}, sm4to, [32]p, color, DJ/3.00)	Harcourt	(1963)	Fenner, Carol	70-125	*
Sears, Paul M.	Barn Swallow (1st, 8vo, 45p, fp 2-color, cep, DJ/2.00)	Holiday House	(1955)	Ferguson, Walter	20-35	
Adrian, Mary	Gray Squirrel (1st, 8vo, 46p, rust cl, 2-color, cep, DJ/2.00)	Holiday House	(1955)	Ferguson, Walter	25-40	
Fern, Eugene	Pepito's Story (1st, sm4to, [46]p, fp color, DJ/3.25)	Ariel	1960	Fern, Eugene	50-85	*
Memling, Carl	Little Bear's Mother (1st {std}, 4to, [41]p, 3-color, DJ/2.75)	Ariel	1959	Fern, Gene	30-45	
Harris, Christie	West with the White Chiefs (1st {std}, 8vo, 214p, b/w, DJ/3.95)	Atheneum	1965	Ferro, Walter	25-40	
Fox, Paula	Maurice's Room (1st {std}, 8vo, 63p, b/w, DJ/2.95)	Macmillan	(1966)	Fetz, Ingrid	20-30	
Clymer, Eleanor	Sociable Toby (1st, 8vo, 81p, fp b/w, pep, DJ/2.50)	F. Watts	(1956)	Fetz, Ingrid	30-50	*
Lovelace, Maud H.	Valentine Box (1st, 8vo, [45]p, fp b/w, DJ/3.50)	Crowell	(1966)	Fetz, Ingrid	40-65	
Molarsky, Osmond	Where the Good Luck Was (1st, lg8vo, 63p, fp b/w, DJ/4.25)	H.Z. Walck	(1970)	Fetz, Ingrid	30-45	*
Clymer, Eleanor	Belinda's New Spring Hat (1st, 8vo, 32p, 2-color, DJ/3.50)	F. Watts	(1969)	Fiammenghi, Gioia	20-35	
Fenton, Edward	Golden Doors (1st {std}, 8vo, 262p, b/w, DJ/2.95)	Doubleday	1957	Fiammenghi, Gioia	20-35	
Learnard, Rachel	Lucky Pete (1st, 8vo, 158p, fp b/w, DJ/2.50)	Abelard-Schuman	1954	Fiammenghi, Gioia	30-45	*
Gallico, Paul	Mrs. 'Arris Goes to Paris (1st AM {std}, 12mo, 157p, b/w, DJ/2.50)	Doubleday	1958	Fiammenghi, Gioia	25-40	
Gallico, Paul	Mrs. 'Arris Goes to Parliament (1st AM {std}, 12mo, 152p, b/w, DJ/2.95)	Doubleday	1965	Fiammenghi, Gioia	25-40	
Gaeddert, Lou Ann	Noisy Nancy Norris (1st {std}, sm8vo, 63p, color, DJ/3.25)	Doubleday	(1965)	Fiammenghi, Gioia	25-40	
Moore, Lilian	Once Upon a Season (1st, 8vo, 96p, 1-color, DJ/2.75)	Abingdon Press	(1962)	Fiammenghi, Gioia	30-45	
Moore, Lilian	Papa Albert (1st {std}, ob4to, [48]p, color, DJ/3.95)	Atheneum	1964	Fiammenghi, Gioia	25-40	*
Jagendorf, Moritz	Priceless Cats (1st, 8vo, 158p, b/w, DJ/3.00)	Vanguard Press	(1956)	Fiammenghi, Gioia	25-40	
Gallico, Paul	Thomasina (1st AM {std}, 8vo, 288p, DJ/3.95, frn by...)	Doubleday	1957	Fiammenghi, Gioia	20-30	
Fiedler, Jean	Big Brother Danny (1st, sm8vo, unpag, blue cl, fp b/w, DJ/1.75)	Holiday House	1953	Fiedler, Harold	20-35	
Fiedler, Maggi	Corky's Pet Parade (1st, sm4to, [32]p, ipcb, color)	Pied Piper Bks.	(1946)	Fiedler, Maggi	40-70	*
Field, Rachel	All Through the Night (1st, 24mo, ibds, [40]p, 1-color, DJ/0.50)	Macmillan	1940	Field, Rachel	35-60	
Field, Rachel	Alphabet for Boys & Girls (1st {std}, 16mo, red cl, [59]p, color, cep)	Doubleday/Page	1926	Field, Rachel	70-100	
Field, Rachel	Christmas Time (1st, 24mo, [32]p, white pcb, col frn, cep, DJ/0.50)	Macmillan	1941	Field, Rachel	30-50	
Farjeon, Eleanor	Come Christmas (1st AM, sm8vo, ipcb, 62p, color)	Stokes	1928	Field, Rachel	50-80	
Bianco, Margery W.	House that Grew Smaller (1st, 12mo, 40p, p-o, color, cep, DJ/1.50)	Macmillan	1931	Field, Rachel	50-80	
Field, Rachel	Just Across the Street (1st, sm8vo, 109p, b/w, DJ/1.50)	Macmillan	1933	Field, Rachel	40-65	
Field, Rachel	Little Book of Days (1st {std}, 16mo, green cl, [59]p, color, cep)	Doubleday/Page	1927	Field, Rachel	35-60	
Field, Rachel	Little Dog Toby (1st, 12mo, blue cl, 118p, 4cp, pep)	Macmillan	1928	Field, Rachel	30-50	
Field, Rachel	Patchwork Plays (1st {std}, sm8vo, 139p, blue cl, b/w, DJ/1.25)	Doubleday/Doran	1930	Field, Rachel	40-60	
Field, Rachel	Pocket-Handkerchief Park (1st {std}, 12mo, 61p, color, cep)	Doubleday/Doran	1929	Field, Rachel	35-60	
Field, Rachel	Poems (1st {std}, 8vo, 118p, DJ/2.50, decorations by...)	Macmillan	1957	Field, Rachel	25-40	*
Field, Rachel	Pointed People (1st, sm8vo, 98p, orange cl, b/w, DJ)	Yale U. Press	1924	Field, Rachel	50-80	
Field, Rachel	Polly Patchwork (1st {std}, 16mo, 56p, color)	Doubleday/Doran	1928	Field, Rachel	30-50	
Gate, Ethel M.	Punch & Robinetta (1st, sm8vo, 118p, brown cl, 8pl)	Yale U. Press	1923	Field, Rachel	35-60	*
Field, Rachel	Susanna B. & William C. (1st, 24mo, 62p, yellow cl, cep, color)	Wm. Morrow	1934	Field, Rachel	30-50	
Field, Rachel	Taxis & Toadstools (1st {std}, 8vo, 129p, green cl, color, cep)	Doubleday/Page	1926	Field, Rachel	50-85	R
Field, Rachel	Yellow Shop (1st {std}, 16mo, 62p, tan cl, color, dep, DJ/0.75)	Doubleday/Doran	1931	Field, Rachel	60-90	
Field, Eugene	Tribune Primer (1st, 8vo, ipcb, gilt, 63p, uncut, b/w)	Reilly/Britton	(1916)	Field, Roswell	30-50	
Filosa, Dorothea	Parsley the Horse (1st, ob4to, ibds, [32]p, fp color, pep, DJ/1.00)	Garden City	1940	Filosa, Dorothea	60-90	
Filosa, Dorothea	Susi (1st, 4to, 32p, ibds, color, pep, DJ/1.00)	Garden City	1939	Filosa, Dorothea	60-90	
Brown, Margaret W.	Hidden House (1st {std}, sq8vo, ibds, unpag, color, DJ/2.50)	Henry Holt & Co.	(1953)	Fine, Aaron	60-100	
Finger, Charles J.	Adventure Under Sapphire Skies (1st, 12mo, 293p, uncut, b/w)	Wm. Morrow	1931	Finger, Helen	30-50	
Shirk, Jeannette C.	Bela the Juggler (1st {std}, lg8vo, green cl, 66p, 2-color, pep, DJ/1.75)	Suttonhouse	(1936)	Finger, Helen	45-70	
Finger, Charles J.	Bobbie and Jock and the Mailman (1st, 8vo, 155p, b/w, pep, DJ/2.00)	Henry Holt & Co.	(1938)	Finger, Helen	30-50	
Finger, Charles J.	Golden Tales from Far Away (1st, 8vo, 233p, col frn, pep, DJ/2.00)	Winston	(1940)	Finger, Helen	30-50	
Justus, May	Here Comes Mary Ellen (1st, 8vo, 140p, col frn, b/w, DJ/1.50)	Lippincott	(1940)	Finger, Helen	30-45	
Finger, Charles J.	Magic Tower (1st, sm8vo, 118p, ipcb, p-o, fp b/w, cep)	Kings Arms Pr.	1933	Finger, Helen	50-80	*

AUTHOR	TITLE	PUBLISHER	DATE	ARTIST	PRICE	LC
Hall, William N.	Seven Little Elephants (1st, 4to, [32]p, ibds, color, DJ/1.50)	Crowell	1947	Fini	25-40	
Nusbaum, Aileen	Seven Cities of Cibola (1st, 8vo, 167p, 6 dp cp, pep)	Putnam	1926	Finnan, Margaret	50-90	
Nusbaum, Aileen	Zuni Indian Tales (1st, 8vo, 167p, gilt, dp color, pep)	Putnam	1926	Finnan, Margaret	50-80	*
Munroe, Kirk	At War with Pontiac (1st, 12mo, 320p, grey/gilt, 8pl)	Scribner	1895	Finnemore, J.	30-50	
Henty, G.A.	When London Burned (1st AM, 12mo, 403p, gilt, b/w)	Scribner	1894	Finnemore, J.	100-165	
Finta, Alexander	Herdboy of Hungary (1st {std}, 8vo, 166p, b/w, pep)	Harper	1932	Finta, Alexander	25-40	
Eaton, Jeanette	Jeanne d'Arc: Warrior Saint (1st {std}, 12mo, 102p, b/w)	Harper	1931	Finta, Alexander	20-35	
Finta, Alexander	My Brothers & I (1st, 8vo, tan cl, 185p, b/w, DJ/2.00)	Holiday House	(1940)	Finta, Alexander	25-45	
Postgate, Oliver	Ice Dragon (1st, 24mo, 48p, color, DJ/2.95)	Holiday House	(1968)	Firmin, Peter	30-45	
Postgate, Oliver	King of the Nogs (1st, 24mo, 48p, color, DJ/2.95)	Holiday House	(1968)	Firmin, Peter	30-45	
Postgate, Oliver	Nogbad and the Elephants (1st, 8vo, 47p, fp 2-color, pep, DJ/3.50)	NY: David White	(1967)	Firmin, Peter	40-65	
Postgate, Oliver	Noggin and the Moon Mouse (1st, 8vo, 47p, fp 2-color, pep, DJ/3.50)	NY: David White	(1967)	Firmin, Peter	40-65	
Pease, Howard	Foghorns (1st {std}, 8vo, uncut, 295p, col frn, pep, DJ/2.00)	Doubleday/Doran	1937	Fischer, Anton O.	80-130	
Melville, Herman	Moby Dick (1st, lg8vo, 414p, black/gilt, p-o, 15cp, pep)	Winston	(1931)	Fischer, Anton O.	35-60	
Sinclair, Bertrand	North of Fifty-Three (1st, sm8vo, 345p, 4pl)	Little/Brown	1914	Fischer, Anton O.	30-50	
Evans, Lawton	Once to Every Man (1st, sm8vo, 317p, 4pl)	H.K. Fly	(1914)	Fischer, Anton O.	35-60	
London, Jack	Son of the Sun (1st, 8vo, blue cl, 333p, 3pl)	Doubleday/Page	1912	Fischer, Anton O.	300-450	
Grimm Bros.	Good-for-Nothings (1st AM {std}, ob4to, unpag, color, DJ/2.75)	Harcourt	(1957)	Fischer, Hans	50-80	R*
Fischer, Hans	Pitschi (1st, ob folio, ibds, [32]p, color, pep, DJ/3.00, NYTBI)	Harcourt	1953	Fischer, Hans	100-160	R
Fischer, Hans	Puss in Boots (1st AM {std}, 4to, [32]p, color, DJ/3.00)	Harcourt	(1959)	Fischer, Hans	60-90	*
Fischer, Hans	The Birthday (1st {std}, ob4to, ipcb, 32p, color, pep, DJ/3.00)	Harcourt	1954	Fischer, Hans	80-130	R
Grimm Bros.	Traveling Musicians (1st AM {std}, lg4to, [28]p, color, DJ/3.00)	Harcourt	(1955)	Fischer, Hans	60-95	
Black, Irma S.	Dog Doctor (1st, lg ob8vo, ipcb, [40]p, 1-color, DJ/1.25)	W.R. Scott	(1947)	Fischetti, John R.	45-75	
Vincent, Kitty	Gin & Ginger (1st, 8vo, 145p, col frn, 19 fp b/w)	L: Bodley Head	1927	Fish, Anne H.	40-65	
Parker, Dorothy	High Society (1st, lg4to, ipcb, 65p, fp b/w, deg)	Putnam	(1920)	Fish, Anne H.	120-200	*
Fish, Anne H.	Noah's Ark Book (1st, lg8vo, ibds, 55p, fp 2-color)	L: Bodley Head	[1918]	Fish, Anne H.	120-200	
Omar Khayyam	Rubaiyat of Omar Khayyam (1st, 4to, gilt, uncut, 108p, ibds, 19pl, dep)	L: Bodley Head	(1922)	Fish, Anne H.	500-800	
Omar Khayyam	Rubaiyat of Omar Khayyam (1st AM, 4to, ibds, gilt, 20 fp color)	Dutton	(1922)	Fish, Anne H.	250-400	
Fisher, Aileen	Runny Days, Sunny Days (1st, 8vo, 126p, ibds, silhouettes, DJ/2.75)	Abelard-Schuman	(1958)	Fisher, Aileen	25-40	
Fisher, Harrison	American Beauties (1st, 4to, 93p, 21cp)	Bobbs-Merrill	(1909)	Fisher, Harrison	250-400	
Fisher, Harrison	American Belles (1st, folio, ibds, gilt, [64]p, p-o, teg, 16 ticp)	Dodd	1911	Fisher, Harrison	650-800	
Fisher, Harrison	American Girl (1st, folio, brown bds, p-o, 12 ticp)	Scribner	1909	Fisher, Harrison	600-850	
Fisher, Harrison	American Girls in Miniature (1st, 8vo, ibds, p-o, 32cp)	Scribner	1912	Fisher, Harrison	250-350	
Fisher, Harrison	Bachelor Belles (1st, 4to, [134]p, p-o, grey/gilt, 22cp)	Dodd	1908	Fisher, Harrison	250-400	
Wells, Carolyn	Beauties (1st, folio, [63]p, gilt, ibds, p-o, 16 ticp)	Dodd	1913	Fisher, Harrison	600-900	
McCutcheon, George B.	Beverly of Graustark (1st, 8vo, blue cl, 357p, 5cp)	Dodd	1904	Fisher, Harrison	25-40	
Isham, Frederic S.	Black Friday (1st, 8vo, 409p, 6pl)	Bobbs-Merrill	(1904)	Fisher, Harrison	30-50	
Page, Thomas N.	Bred in the Bone (1st, 8vo, 274p, teg, 8pl)	Scribner	1904	Fisher, Harrison	30-50	
Vance, Louis J.	Bronze Bell (1st, sm8vo, 361p, 4cp)	Dodd	1909	Fisher, Harrison	25-45	
McCutcheon, George B.	Butterfly Man (1st, sm8vo, teg, 121p, lavender cl, 4cp)	Dodd	1910	Fisher, Harrison	25-40	
Ford, Paul L.	Checked Love Affair (1st, 8vo, 112p, teg, gilt, 5pl)	Dodd	1903	Fisher, Harrison	35-60	
McCutcheon, George B.	Cowardice Court (1st, 12mo, 140p, p-o, 5cp)	Dodd	1906	Fisher, Harrison	40-65	
McCutcheon, George B.	Day of the Dog (1st, 8vo, red/gilt, 137p, 5cp, pep)	Dodd	1904	Fisher, Harrison	40-60	
Tennyson, Alfred	Dream of Fair Women (1st, lg8vo, [96]p, p-o, 22cp)	Bobbs-Merrill	(1907)	Fisher, Harrison	200-300	
Tennyson, Alfred	Dream of Fair Women (lg8vo, p-o, 148p, 21cp)	Grosset/Dunlap	(1907)	Fisher, Harrison	180-250	
Fisher, Harrison	Fair Americans (1st, 4to, gilt, [100]p, p-o, 22cp)	Scribner	1911	Fisher, Harrison	300-500	
Seawell, Molly E.	Francezka (1st, sm8vo, 466p, green/gilt, 7pl by...)	Bobbs-Merrill	(1902)	Fisher, Harrison	35-60	
Fisher, Harrison	Garden of Girls (1st, folio, gilt, [68]p, p-o, ibds, 16 ticp, dep)	Dodd	1910	Fisher, Harrison	600-800	
Fisher, Harrison	Girl's Life (1st, folio, pcb, p-o, 16cp)	Scribner	1913	Fisher, Harrison	700-1000	
Phillips, David G.	Golden Fleece (1st, sm8vo, 326p, b/w)	McClure	1903	Fisher, Harrison	20-35	*
MacGrath, Harold	Half a Rogue (1st, 12mo, red cl, 449p, p-o, 4pl)	Bobbs-Merrill	(1906)	Fisher, Harrison	25-40	
Fisher, Harrison	Harrison Fisher Book (1st, 4to, gilt, p-o, 9cp)	Scribner	1907	Fisher, Harrison	300-500	
Fisher, Harrison	Harrison Fisher Girls (1st, lg4to, [48]p, gilt, p-o, teg, 12 ticp, pep)	Dodd	1914	Fisher, Harrison	600-900	
Longfellow, H.W.	Hiawatha (1st, lg8vo, p-o, gilt, 189p, 16cp)	Bobbs-Merrill	(1906)	Fisher, Harrison	120-200	
McCutcheon, George B.	Husbands of Edith (1st, 12mo, 126p, 5cp)	Dodd	1908	Fisher, Harrison	30-50	
Michelson, Miriam	In The Bishop's Carriage (1st, 8vo, red cl, 280p, 6pl)	Bobbs-Merrill	(1904)	Fisher, Harrison	25-40	
McCutcheon, George B.	Jane Cable (1st, sm8vo, 336p, p-o, 5cp)	Dodd	1906	Fisher, Harrison	25-45	
Winter, Alice A.	Jewel Weed (1st, 12mo, p-o, 434p, 5pl)	Bobbs-Merrill	(1910)	Fisher, Harrison	30-50	*
Fisher, Harrison	Little Gift Book (1st, lg8vo, ibds, p-o, 32cp)	Scribner	1913	Fisher, Harrison	200-300	
Fisher, Harrison	Maidens Fair (1st, folio, [63]p, grey bds, gilt, p-o, 16 ticp)	Dodd	1912	Fisher, Harrison	600-800	
Nicholson, Meredith	Main Chance (1st, 12mo, 419p, 6pl)	Bobbs-Merrill	(1903)	Fisher, Harrison	20-30	
McCutcheon, George B.	Man from Brodneys (1st, 8vo, p-o, 355p, 4cp)	Dodd	1908	Fisher, Harrison	25-45	
Frederic, Harold	Market Place (1st, 12mo, 401p, 8pl)	Stokes	1899	Fisher, Harrison	40-65	
Mathews, Frances A.	My Lady Peggy Goes to Town (1st, 12mo, teg, 338p, 8pl)	Bowen-Merrill	1901	Fisher, Harrison	40-65	
McCutcheon, George B.	Nedra (1st, sm8vo, 343p, p-o, 5cp)	Dodd	1905	Fisher, Harrison	25-45	
Von Hutten, Bettina	One Way Out (1st, 8vo, 99p, p-o, teg, lavender cl, 5cp)	Dodd	1906	Fisher, Harrison	50-80	
Fisher, Harrison	Pictures in Color (1st, folio, gilt, p-o, bds, 16cp)	Scribner	1910	Fisher, Harrison	700-1000	
Brebner, Percy	Princess Maritza (1st, 8vo, 357p, frn by...)	McBride	1906	Fisher, Harrison	20-25	
McCutcheon, George B.	Purple Parasol (1st, 8vo, green/gilt, 108p, 5cp)	Dodd	1905	Fisher, Harrison	40-70	
Castle, A.& E.	Rose of the World (1st, 8vo, 414p, tan cl, 4pl by...)	Stokes	(1905)	Fisher, Harrison	20-35	
Harte, Bret	Salomy Jane (1st, 8vo, p-o, blue/gilt, 78p, col frn by...)	Houghton	1910	Fisher, Harrison	80-140	
Atherton, Gertrude	Splendid Idle Forties (1st, 8vo, 389p, gilt, 8pl)	Macmillan	1902	Fisher, Harrison	100-160	
McCutcheon, George B.	The Alternative (1st, 8vo, teg, p-o, 119p, 4cp, pep)	Dodd	1909	Fisher, Harrison	30-50	
Phillips, David G.	The Cost (1st, sm8vo, 402p, grey/gilt, 16pl)	Bobbs-Merrill	(1904)	Fisher, Harrison	30-50	
Bonner, Geraldine	The Pioneer (1st, 12mo, 392p, blue/gilt, 6pl)	Bobbs-Merrill	(1905)	Fisher, Harrison	40-60	*
Isham, Frederic S.	The Strollers (1st, sm8vo, 499p, gilt, 8pl)	Bowen-Merrill	(1902)	Fisher, Harrison	25-40	
Palmer, Frederick	The Vagabond (1st, sm8vo, 476p, 6pl)	Scribner	1903	Fisher, Harrison	25-40	
Perry, Francis F.	Their Hearts' Desire (1st, lg8vo, teg, 152p, 6cp, dep)	Dodd	1909	Fisher, Harrison	70-100	

AUTHOR	TITLE	PUBLISHER	DATE	ARTIST	PRICE	LC
Jerome, Jerome K.	Three Men on Wheels (1st AM, 12mo, 301p, green cl, b/w)	Dodd	1900	Fisher, Harrison	50-80	
McCutcheon, George B.	What's His Name? (1st, 12mo, 243p, 4cp)	Dodd	1911	Fisher, Harrison	30-50	
Rinehart, Mary R.	When a Man Marries (1st, 12mo, 353p, 5cp)	Bobbs-Merrill	(1909)	Fisher, Harrison	40-65	
Johnson, Gerald W.	America Grows Up (1st, 8vo, 223p, grey cl, fp b/w, DJ/3.75)	Wm. Morrow	1960	Fisher, Leonard	30-50	
Johnson, Gerald W.	America is Born (1st, lg8vo, 254p, red cl, b/w, DJ/3.95, NH)	Wm. Morrow	1959	Fisher, Leonard	50-85	R
Johnson, Gerald W.	America Moves Forward (1st, 8vo, 256p, blue cl, fp b/w, DJ/3.95, NH)	Wm. Morrow	1960	Fisher, Leonard	40-65	
Eaton, Jeanette	America's Own Mark Twain (1st, 8vo, 251p, b/w, DJ/3.00)	Wm. Morrow	1958	Fisher, Leonard	20-35	
Johnson, Gerald W.	British Empire (1st, 8vo, 158p, b/w, DJ/4.25)	Wm. Morrow	(1969)	Fisher, Leonard	20-35	
Taylor, Florance	Carrier Boy (1st, 8vo, 160p, b/w, DJ/2.50)	Abelard-Schuman	(1956)	Fisher, Leonard	25-40	
Thayer, Ernest	Casey at the Bat (1st, 8vo, 32p, fp b/w, DJ/2.65, NYTBI)	F. Watts	(1964)	Fisher, Leonard	30-50	*
Surany, Anico	Covered Bridge (1st, ob4to, [33]p, color, DJ/3.25)	Holiday House	(1967)	Fisher, Leonard	25-40	
Johnson, Gerald W.	Franklin D. Roosevelt Portrait of a Great Man (1st, lg8vo, 192p, DJ/3.75)	Wm. Morrow	1967	Fisher, Leonard	25-40	
Engle, Paul	Golden Child (1st {std}, 8vo, 127p, 1-color, DJ/3.50)	Dutton	(1962)	Fisher, Leonard	30-45	
Surany, Anico	Golden Frog (1st, ob4to, [39]p, fp color, cep, DJ/3.00)	Putnam	(1963)	Fisher, Leonard	50-80	
Belting, Natalia	Indy and Mr. Lincoln (1st, ob4to, [32]p, fp 2-color, DJ/2.95)	Holt	(1960)	Fisher, Leonard	30-45	
L'Engle, Madeleine	Journey with Jonah: One Act Play (1st {std}, 8vo, 63p, b/w, DJ/3.75)	Farrar, Straus	(1967)	Fisher, Leonard	60-90	
Surany, Anico	Jungle Jumble (1st, 4to, 45p, 1-color, DJ/3.00)	Putnam	(1966)	Fisher, Leonard	40-65	
Surany, Anico	Kati and Kormos (1st, ob8vo, [39]p, fp 2-color, DJ/2.95)	Holiday House	(1966)	Fisher, Leonard	25-40	
Scheffer, Victor	Little Calf (1st, 8vo, 140p, green cl, 1-color, DJ)	Scribner	(1970)	Fisher, Leonard	30-50	
Surany, Anico	Malachy's Gold (1st, 4to, [46]p, color, DJ/4.50)	Holiday House	(1968)	Fisher, Leonard	25-40	
Latham, Jean L.	Man of the Monitor: Story of John Ericsson (1st, 8vo, 231p, b/w, DJ/3.50)	Harper	(1962)	Fisher, Leonard	30-50	
Surany, Anico	Monsieur Jolicoeur's Umbrella (1st, 4to, [44]p, fp color, DJ/3.50)	Putnam	(1967)	Fisher, Leonard	40-65	*
Armour, Richard	Our Presidents (1st, sm4to, 80p, fp 3-color, cep, DJ/3.50)	Norton	(1964)	Fisher, Leonard	30-50	*
Surany, Anico	Ride the Cold Wind (1st, 4to, [45]p, fp color, DJ/3.50)	Putnam	(1964)	Fisher, Leonard	50-80	R
Felton, Harold	Sergeant O'Keefe and his Mule Balaam (1st, 8vo, 94p, b/w, DJ/3.25)	Dodd	1962	Fisher, Leonard	25-40	
Johnson, Gerald W.	Supreme Court (1st, 8vo, 127p, fp b/w, DJ/2.95)	Wm. Morrow	1962	Fisher, Leonard	50-75	R*
Johnson, Gerald W.	The Cabinet (1st, 8vo, 160p, fp b/w, DJ/3.50)	Wm. Morrow	1966	Fisher, Leonard	30-50	
Johnson, Gerald W.	The Congress (1st, 8vo, 128p, fp b/w, DJ/2.95)	Wm. Morrow	1963	Fisher, Leonard	30-50	
Johnson, Gerald W.	The Presidency (1st, 8vo, 128p, fp b/w, DJ/2.95)	Wm. Morrow	1962	Fisher, Leonard	30-50	
Wellman, Manly W.	To Unknown Lands (1st, 8vo, 202p, black cl, b/w, pep, DJ/2.75)	Holiday House	(1956)	Fisher, Leonard	25-40	*
Belting, Natalia	Verity Mullens and the Indian (1st, 4to, [32]p, fp 3-color, DJ/3.25)	Holt, Rinehart	(1960)	Fisher, Leonard	30-50	*
Bellairs, John	Face in the Frost (1st {std}, 8vo, 174p, b/w, DJ/4.95)	Macmillan	1969	Fitschen, Marilyn	50-80	
Bellairs, John	Pedant and the Shuffly (1st {std}, 8vo, 75p, b/w, DJ/2.95)	MacMillan	1968	Fitschen, Marilyn	50-85	
Fitzgerald, John T.	Bixby of Boston (1st, 12mo, uncut, 83p, 20pl)	Broadway	1906	Fitzgerald, John	25-40	*
Montgomery, F.T.	Billy Whiskers in the South (1st, lg8vo, green/gilt, 148p, 6cp)	Saalfield	(1917)	Fitzgerald, Will	70-130	
Fitzhugh, Louise	Bang Bang, You're Dead (1st, ob4to, ibds, 32p, b/w, DJ/3.95, NYTBI)	Harper	(1969)	Fitzhugh, Louise	100-165	
Fitzhugh, Louise	Harriet the Spy (1st, 8vo, 298p, b/w, DJ/3.95)	Harper	(1964)	Fitzhugh, Louise	140-225	
Scoppettone, Sandra	Suzuki Beane (1st {std}, 4to, 95p, ibds, b/w, DJ/2.50)	Doubleday	1961	Fitzhugh, Louise	150-220	
Sanders, Martha	Alexander & the Magic Mouse (1st, 4to, 44p, fp color, cep, DJ/3.95)	Amer. Heritage	1969	Fix, Phillipe	80-120	
Flack, Marjorie	All Around the Town (1st {std}, 8vo, 283p, col frn, b/w, pep)	Doubleday/Doran	1929	Flack, Marjorie	70-100	
Flack, Marjorie	Angus & the Cat (1st {std}, lg ob8vo, [32]p, ibds, color)	Doubleday/Doran	1931	Flack, Marjorie	100-145	
Flack, Marjorie	Angus & the Ducks (1st {std}, lg ob8vo, [32]p, ibds, color, pep)	Doubleday/Doran	1930	Flack, Marjorie	90-135	
Flack, Marjorie	Angus Lost (1st {std}, sm ob4to, [32]p, ibds, color, pep)	Doubleday/Doran	1932	Flack, Marjorie	80-125	
Flack, Marjorie	Ask Mr. Bear (1st, sq8vo, [32]p, color, pep, DJ/1.00)	Macmillan	1932	Flack, Marjorie	75-100	
Heyward, DuBose	Country Bunny & Little Gold Shoes (1st, sm4to, [48]p, color, DJ/2.00)	Houghton	1939	Flack, Marjorie	120-170	
Flack, Marjorie	Humphrey (1st {std}, 4to, ibds, [80]p, color, pep)	Doubleday/Doran	1934	Flack, Marjorie	50-80	
Wheeler, Eleanor	Jemmie, Kitten from Maine (1st {std}, sq8vo, p-o, 96p, fp 1-color, pep)	Smith/Haas	(1932)	Flack, Marjorie	70-120	
Colt, Terry S.	Knights, Goats & Battleships (1st {std}, 8vo, 316p, color, pep)	Doubleday/Doran	1930	Flack, Marjorie	50-85	*
Flack, Edith	Marionettes (1st, sm4to, 115p, b/w)	Stokes	1929	Flack, Marjorie	30-50	
Flack, Marjorie	New Pet (1st {std}, sm4to, ibds, [32]p, color, DJ/1.50)	Doubleday/Doran	(1943)	Flack, Marjorie	55-80	
Flack, Marjorie	Restless Robin (1st, sm ob4to, [48]p, green cl, color, pep, DJ/1.50)	Houghton	1937	Flack, Marjorie	80-130	
Dall, Anna R.	Scamper's Christmas (1st, sq8vo, 71p, dp color)	Macmillan	1934	Flack, Marjorie	50-80	R
Dall, Anna R.	Scamper: Bunny Who Went to the White House (1st, sq8vo, 72p, 5cp, fp b/w)	Macmillan	(1934)	Flack, Marjorie	70-100	
Flack, Marjorie	Taktuk, Arctic Boy (1st {std}, 8vo, 139p, uncut, col frn, pep, DJ)	Doubleday/Doran	1928	Flack, Marjorie	50-80	*
Flack, Marjorie	Tim Tadpole… (1st {std}, sm8vo, [32]p, ibds, p-o, color, pep)	Doubleday/Doran	1934	Flack, Marjorie	60-100	
Flack, Marjorie	Topsy (1st {std}, ob4to, ibds, [32]p, color, pep, DJ/1.00)	Doubleday/Doran	1935	Flack, Marjorie	100-165	
Orton, Helen F.	Twin Lambs (1st, ob12mo, 106p, 6cp)	Stokes	1931	Flack, Marjorie	30-50	*
Flack, Marjorie	Walter the Lazy Mouse (1st {std}, 4to, [80]p, color, cep, DJ/2.00)	Doubleday/Doran	1937	Flack, Marjorie	200-300	
Flack, Marjorie	William & his Kitten (1st, ob8vo, ibds, [32]p, color, pep, DJ/1.25)	Houghton	1938	Flack, Marjorie	60-100	
Flack, Marjorie	Willy Nilly (1st, 4to, ibds, [32]p, color, pep, DJ/1.00)	Macmillan	1936	Flack, Marjorie	100-165	
Flagg, James M.	Adventures of Kitty Cobb (1st, lg sq4to, ibds, [67]p, b/w, pep)	Doran	(1912)	Flagg, James M.	100-145	
Flagg, James M.	All in the Same Boat (1st, 12mo, 105p, b/w)	Life Pub. Co.	1908	Flagg, James M.	25-40	
Brennan, George H.	Bill Truetell (1st, 8vo, 282p, col frn & cvr by…)	McClurg	1909	Flagg, James M.	25-40	
Flagg, James M.	City People (1st, ob folio, ibds, [84]p, b/w)	Scribner	1909	Flagg, James M.	100-160	
Crawford, F. Marion	Diva's Ruby (1st, 8vo, 430p, gilt, 12pl)	Macmillan	1908	Flagg, James M.	30-50	*
Long, John L.	Felice (1st, sm8vo, 156p, frn by…)	Moffat	1908	Flagg, James M.	25-40	*
Brainerd, Eleanor H.	How Could You, Jean? (1st, sm8vo, 337p, 4pl)	Doubleday/Page	1917	Flagg, James M.	25-40	*
Flagg, James M.	I Should Say So (1st, sm8vo, gilt, ipcb, p-o, 202p, b/w, pep)	Doran	(1914)	Flagg, James M.	60-100	
Page, Thomas N.	John Marvel, Assistant (1st, 12mo, 573p, green cl, 8pl)	Scribner	1909	Flagg, James M.	25-40	
Nicholson, Meredith	Little Brown Jug at Kildare (1st, sm8vo, blue cl, 422p, 5pl)	Bobbs-Merrill	(1908)	Flagg, James M.	25-40	
Barbour, Ralph H.	Orchard Princess (1st, 8vo, p-o, 219p, 4cp)	Lippincott	1905	Flagg, James M.	25-40	
Spearman, Frank	Robert Kimberly (1st, sm8vo, 437p, gilt, 4cp)	Scribner	1911	Flagg, James M.	25-40	
Flagg, Elisha	Rookie (1st, 8vo, 63p, beige cl, b/w, DJ/1.00)	Whitman	1940	Flagg, James M.	20-35	
Brown, Katharine H.	White Roses (1st, sm8vo, 333p, b/w)	Duffield	1910	Flagg, James M.	30-50	
Flagg, James M.	Why they Married (1st, 12mo, 107p, ibds)	Life Pub. Co.	1906	Flagg, James M.	100-150	
Van Dyke, Henry	Story of the Other Wise Man (1st, lg8vo, teg, 72p, uncut, 8 ticp, pep)	Harper	(1920)	Flanagan, J.R.	55-80	
Thayer, Jane	Cat that Joined the Club (1st, lg8vo, [32]p, color, DJ/3.25)	Wm. Morrow	1967	Fleishman, Seymour	25-45	
Thayer, Jane	Curious, Furious Chipmunk (1st, lg8vo, [32]p, color, DJ/3.50)	Wm. Morrow	(1969)	Fleishman, Seymour	25-45	

ARTIST: 76

AUTHOR	TITLE	PUBLISHER	DATE	ARTIST	PRICE	LC
Thayer, Jane	Gus Was a Friendly Ghost (1st, lg8vo, [32]p, color, pep, DJ/2.75)	Wm. Morrow	1962	Fleishman, Seymour	25-45	*
Thayer, Jane	I'm Not a Cat, Said Emerald (1st, lg8vo, [32]p, color, DJ/3.75)	Wm. Morrow	(1970)	Fleishman, Seymour	25-45	
Thayer, Jane	Little Mr. Greenthumb (1st, lg8vo, [32]p, fp 3-color, DJ/3.50)	Wm. Morrow	(1968)	Fleishman, Seymour	25-45	
Yates, Elizabeth	Is There a Doctor in the Barn? (1st {std}, 8vo, 207p, b/w, DJ/4.95)	Dutton	1966	Fleming, Guy	20-30	
Flemwell, George	Alpine Flowers & Gardens (1st, 8vo, 167p, gilt, teg, 20cp)	L: A&C Black	1910	Flemwell, George	90-160	
Chaucer, Geoffrey	Canterbury Tales (1st, 4to, gilt, 637p, teg, 24cp)	L: Medici	1928	Flint, William R.	140-220	
Chaucer, Geoffrey	Canterbury Tales (1st AM, 8vo, 245p, 12cp)	Cape/Smith	1930	Flint, William R.	70-100	*
Kingsley, Charles	Heroes/Greek Fairy Tales (1st, 8vo, 166p, 9 ticp)	L: Medici	1928	Flint, William R.	100-165	
Kempis, Thomas	Imitation of Christ (1st, sm4to, 280p, teg, gilt, 274p, 8cp)	L: Chatto	1908	Flint, William R.	100-170	
Gilbert, W.S.	Iolanthe... (1st, 4to, green/gilt, teg, 224p, uncut, 32cp)	L: G. Bell	1910	Flint, William R.	200-300	
Malory, Thomas	Le Morte D'Arthur (1st, lg8vo, gilt, teg, 2 volumes, 36cp)	L: P.L. Warner	(1920)	Flint, William R.	200-300	
Malory, Thomas	Le Morte D'Arthur (lg8vo, 531p, red/gilt, teg, 24cp)	Hale-Cushman	(1927)	Flint, William R.	120-180	*
N/A	Odyssey of Homer (1st AM, 8vo, 332p, teg, gilt, 20cp)	Hale-Cushman	(1930)	Flint, William R.	100-160	*
Gilbert, W.S.	Princess Ida (1st, lg8vo, 150p, green/gilt, 8cp)	L: G. Bell	1912	Flint, William R.	90-160	
Gilbert, W.S.	Savoy Operas (1st, 4to, 208p, gilt, teg, uncut, 32cp)	L: G. Bell	1909	Flint, William R.	160-240	
Arnold, Matthew	Scholar-Gypsy and Thyrsis (1st, 4to, 67p, 10cp)	L: P.L. Warner	(1910)	Flint, William R.	100-170	
Bible	Song of Songs... (1st, lg8vo, 66p, teg, brown/gilt, 10 ticp)	L: P.L. Warner	1913	Flint, William R.	75-100	
Burns, Robert	Songs & Lyrics of Robert Burns (1st, 8vo, uncut, teg, 12ticp)	L: P.L. Warner	1911	Flint, William R.	250-400	
Farjeon, Eleanor	Tales from Chaucer (1st, 8vo, red/gilt, 244p, 12cp)	L: Medici	1930	Flint, William R.	60-90	
Kingsley, Charles	The Heroes (1st, 8vo, 166p, uncut, gilt, teg, 12 ticp)	L: P.L. Warner	1914	Flint, William R.	80-125	
Gilbert, W.S.	The Mikado (1st, 8vo, gilt, 96p, 8cp)	L: Macmillan	1928	Flint, William R.	80-130	
Flint, William R.	Watercolors of William Russell Flint (1st, ob. folio, 8 ticp)	L: Studio	(1920)	Flint, William R.	120-170	
Gilbert, W.S.	Yeoman of the Guard (1st, 8vo, 102p, gilt, 8cp)	L: Macmillan	1929	Flint, William R.	80-130	
Floethe, Louise	Fisherman and his Boat (1st, ob4to, [32]p, color, DJ/2.95)	Scribner	(1961)	Floethe, L.& R.	30-45	
Fisher, Cyrus	Avion My Uncle Flew (1st, sm8vo, 244p, fp b/w, DJ/2.50, NH)	Appleton-Century	(1946)	Floethe, Richard	60-90	
Streatfeild, Noel	Ballet Shoes (1st AM, 8vo, 294p, color, DJ/2.00)	Random	(1937)	Floethe, Richard	80-125	
Streatfeild, Noel	Circus Shoes (1st {std}, 8vo, 401p, color, DJ/2.00)	Random	(1939)	Floethe, Richard	50-65	
Streatfeild, Noel	Dancing Shoes (1st {std}, 8vo, 273p, b/w, DJ)	Random	1957	Floethe, Richard	80-140	
Brown, Margaret W.	Dream Book (1st, sm4to, ibds, [24]p, 2-color, pep, DJ/1.50)	Random	(1950)	Floethe, Richard	70-120	
Floethe, Louise	Fountain of the Friendly Lion (1st, 4to, [32]p, fp color, DJ)	Scribner	1966	Floethe, Richard	25-40	
Burglon, Nora	Gate Swings In (1st {std}, 8vo, 208p, pep, b/w, DJ/2.00)	Little/Brown	1937	Floethe, Richard	50-80	
Floethe, Richard	If I Were Captain (1st, sm4to, [32]p, fp 2-color, DJ)	Scribner	(1956)	Floethe, Richard	25-40	
Shippen, Kath. B.	Mr. Bell Invents the Telephone (1st, 8vo, 183p, 2-color, DJ/1.50)	Random	(1952)	Floethe, Richard	30-50	
Collodi, Carlo	Pinocchio (1st {std}, 8vo, 239p, pep, fp color, pep, DJ/1.00, RC)	World	(1946)	Floethe, Richard	30-50	
Streatfeild, Noel	Secret of the Lodge (1st {std}, 8vo, 233p, 7 fp 2-color, DJ/2.00)	Random	(1940)	Floethe, Richard	120-200	
Goudge, Elizabeth	Smoky House (1st AM, 8vo, 286p, 6pl, DJ/2.00)	Coward	(1940)	Floethe, Richard	60-90	
Havighurst, Walter	Song of the Pines (1st {std}, 8vo, 205p, maps, dep, b/w, DJ/2.50, NH)	Winston	(1949)	Floethe, Richard	50-85	
Streatfeild, Noel	Stranger in Primrose Lane (1st {std}, 8vo, 338p, p-o, 7cp, DJ/2.00)	Random	(1941)	Floethe, Richard	100-160	*
Fischer, Marjorie	Street Fair (1st, 8vo, blue/gilt, 216p, 18cp, pep, DJ/2.00)	Smith/Haas	(1935)	Floethe, Richard	40-65	*
Cunningham, Caroline	Talking Stone (1st {std}, 8vo, 116p, 2-color, DJ/1.75)	Knopf	1939	Floethe, Richard	30-45	
Streatfeild, Noel	Tennis Shoes (1st, 8vo, 290p, 8 fp 2-color, DJ/2.00)	Random	(1938)	Floethe, Richard	120-200	
Streatfeild, Noel	Theater Shoes (1st {std}, 8vo, 282p, color, DJ/2.00)	Random	(1945)	Floethe, Richard	30-50	*
Goudge, Elizabeth	Valley of Song (1st AM, 8vo, 281p, b/w, DJ/3.00)	Coward	(1952)	Floethe, Richard	50-85	
Flora, James	Day the Cow Sneezed (1st {std}, 4to, [41]p, 3-color, pep, DJ/2.95)	Harcourt	1957	Flora, James	50-80	R*
Flora, James	Fabulous Firework Family (1st {std}, 4to, [40]p, color, pep, DJ/2.75)	Harcourt	(1955)	Flora, James	50-85	R*
Flora, James	Joking Man (1st {std}, 8vo, [30]p, 2-color, DJ/3.25)	Harcourt	(1968)	Flora, James	30-50	
Flora, James	Kangaroo for Christmas (1st {std}, sm4to, [31]p, fp 3-color, pep, DJ/2.95)	Harcourt	(1962)	Flora, James	30-50	
Flora, James	Leopold, See-through Crumbpicker (1st {std}, 4to, unpag, b/w, pep, DJ/2.75)	Harcourt	(1961)	Flora, James	30-50	
Flora, James	Little Hatchy Hen (1st {std}, 4to, [32]p, color, DJ/3.50)	Harcourt	(1969)	Flora, James	25-40	*
Flora, James	My Friend Charlie (1st {std}, sm4to, [32]p, 2-color, DJ/2.75)	Harcourt	(1964)	Flora, James	30-50	
Flora, James	Sherwood Walks Home (1st {std}, sm ob4to, unpag, color, DJ/3.25)	Harcourt	(1966)	Flora, James	30-50	*
Krauss, Ruth	Bouquet of Littles (1st, 12mo, ipcb, [22]p, color, DJ/2.50)	Harper	(1963)	Flora, Jane	25-45	
Sargant, Alice	Crystal Ball (1st, 8vo, uncut, 119p, 10 fp b/w)	L: G. Bell	(1894)	Florence, Mary S.	150-225	
Harris, Laura	Away We Go (1st, 4to, ibds, [47]p, color, pep)	Garden City	1945	Flory, Jane	20-35	
Strong, Rowland	Yoyo's Animal Friends (1st, 4to, 170p, teg, 3cp)	Dent/Dutton	1913	Flower, Noel	50-80	
Curry, Jane L.	Change-Child (1st {std}, 8vo, 174p, b/w, DJ)	Harcourt	(1969)	Floyd, Gareth	30-50	
Ballard, Martin	Emir's Son (1st AM {std}, sm4to, 32p, color, DJ/3.75)	World	1967	Floyd, Gareth	25-45	
Curry, Jane L.	The Sleepers (1st {std}, 8vo, 255p, b/w, DJ/4.50)	Harcourt	(1968)	Floyd, Gareth	30-50	
Green, Anna K.	Dark Hollow (1st, sm8vo, 381p, green cl, 4pl)	Dodd	1914	Fogarty, Thomas	50-80	*
White, Stewart E.	Gold (1st, 12mo, green/gilt, 437p, pep, 4cp)	Doubleday/Page	1913	Fogarty, Thomas	50-80	
White, Stewart E.	Gray Dawn (1st, sm8vo, blue cl, 395p, 4cp, pep)	Doubleday/Page	1915	Fogarty, Thomas	20-35	
McFarlane, Arthur E.	Great Bear Island (1st, sm8vo, 290p, 8pl)	Houghton	1911	Fogarty, Thomas	30-50	
Becker, May L.	Louisa Alcott's People (1st, lg8vo, 211p, gilt, p-o, 4cp, pep, SC)	Scribner	1936	Fogarty, Thomas	120-165	
LeGallienne, R.	October Vagabonds (1st, 8vo, ipcb, teg, gilt, 201p, col frn, pep)	Kennerley	1910	Fogarty, Thomas	55-90	R
Field, Rachel	People from Dickens (1st, lg8vo, p-o, 208p, 8cp, pep, SC)	Scribner	1935	Fogarty, Thomas	70-100	
White, Stewart E.	The Forest (1st, 8vo, green cl, teg, 276p, 17pl)	Outlook	1903	Fogarty, Thomas	30-50	
Pearson, Edmund L.	Voyage of the Hoppergrass (1st, sm8vo, 348p, b/w, PPPa)	Macmillan	1913	Fogarty, Thomas	80-125	R
Foley, James W.	Christmas Prayer (1st, 16mo, ibds, [24]p, color)	Volland	(1915)	Foley, James W.	55-80	*
Aesopus	Aesop's Fables (1st, 8vo, 209p, gilt, 12cp)	L: A&C Black	(1912)	Folkard, Charles	100-165	
Carroll, Lewis	Alice in Wonderland (8vo, 174p, blue cl, 6cp)	L: A&C Black	(1929)	Folkard, Charles	130-200	
N/A	Arabian Nights (1st, 8vo, 412p, teg, gilt, 12cp)	L: A&C Black	(1913)	Folkard, Charles	150-220	
Pollock, Nellie	Belgian Playmates (sq12mo, 122p, red cl, col frn, 4pl)	L: Gay/Hancock	[1918]	Folkard, Charles	80-120	
Glover, William J.	British Fairy & Folk Tales (1st, sq8vo, 281p, 8cp)	L: A&C Black	1920	Folkard, Charles	90-140	
Hoffman, Alice S.	Children's Shakespeare (1st, sq8vo, 472p, 21cp)	L: Dent	1911	Folkard, Charles	100-160	
Grimm Bros.	Fairy Tales (1st, 8vo, 331p, cream cl, 12cp)	L: A&C Black	(1911)	Folkard, Charles	100-170	*
N/A	Fairy Tales in Other Lands (1st, 12mo, 96p, ibds, 4cp)	L: Cassell	[1925]	Folkard, Charles	80-120	
Phillpotts, Eden	Flint Heart (1st, 8vo, 310p, teg, gilt, 16cp)	L: Smith Elder	1910	Folkard, Charles	100-160	
Phillpotts, Eden	Flint Heart (1st AM, 8vo, 334p, 16cp)	Dutton	(1910)	Folkard, Charles	80-120	

AUTHOR	TITLE	PUBLISHER	DATE	ARTIST	PRICE	LC
Ingoldsby, Thomas	Jackdaw of Rheims (1st, folio, unpag, white/gilt, teg, 12 ticp)	L: Gay/Hancock	1913	Folkard, Charles	150-225	
Ingoldsby, Thomas	Jackdaw of Rheims (1st AM, lg4to, unpag, teg, purple/gilt, 12 ticp)	Winston	1914	Folkard, Charles	150-220	
Daglish, Alice (ed.)	Land of Nursery Rhyme (1st, 8vo, 240p, fp color, pep)	Dutton	(1932)	Folkard, Charles	70-100	*
Black, Dorothy	Magic Egg (1st, 4to, 111p, col frn, 11pl, pep)	L: A&C Black	1922	Folkard, Charles	100-150	
Mother Goose	Mother Goose (1st AM, 8vo, 340p, 8cp)	Dutton	(1932)	Folkard, Charles	120-180	
Mother Goose	Mother Goose Nursery Rhymes (1st, 8vo, 159p, ibds, color)	L: A&C Black	(1919)	Folkard, Charles	150-225	
Mother Goose	Mother Goose Nursery Tales (1st, 4to, 219p, 16cp, pep)	L: A&C Black	(1923)	Folkard, Charles	150-220	
Garnett, Louise A.	Ottoman Wonder Tales (1st, sq8vo, 266p, blue/gilt, teg, 12cp)	L: A&C Black	1915	Folkard, Charles	100-175	
Collodi, Carlo	Pinocchio (1st, sq8vo, p-o, ibds, 268p, 13cp)	Dent/Dutton	1911	Folkard, Charles	90-120	
Collodi, Carlo	Pinocchio (1st {this pub.}, 8vo, p-o, DJ)	McKay	(1925)	Folkard, Charles	75-100	
MacDonald, George	Princess & Curdie (1st, 8vo, 238p, tan cl, 8cp, DJ)	L: Dent	(1949)	Folkard, Charles	40-65	
Broadwood, Lucy	Songs from Alice in Wonderland (4to, blue/gilt, 48p, p-o, 12 ticp)	L: A&C Black	1921	Folkard, Charles	140-200	
Carroll, Lewis	Songs from Alice... & Through... (1st, 4to, 48p, gilt, p-o, 12 ticp)	L: A&C Black	(1921)	Folkard, Charles	250-400	
Wyss, Johann D.	Swiss Family Robinson (1st, 8vo, 454p, beige cl, 12cp, pep)	L: J.M. Dent	1910	Folkard, Charles	80-120	
Folkard, Charles	Teddy Tail of the Daily Mail (1st, 4to, ibds, 32p, 1-color)	L: A&C Black	[1915]	Folkard, Charles	100-165	
Folkard, Charles	Teddy Tail's Fairy Tale (4to, ibds, 32p, b/w)	L: A&C Black	[1920]	Folkard, Charles	80-120	
Kossak-Szczucka, Z.	Troubles of a Gnome (1st, 4to, ibds, p-o, 102p, 8cp)	L: A&C Black	1928	Folkard, Charles	160-240	
Brook, Arthur W.	Witch's Hollow (1st, 8vo, 211p, 8cp)	L: A&C Black	1920	Folkard, Charles	140-180	*
Brook, Arthur W.	Witch's Hollow (1st AM, 8vo, 211p, 8cp)	Stokes	1921	Folkard, Charles	90-140	
Obligado, George	Magic Butterfly (1st, folio, 62p, ibds, color, pep)	Golden Press	(1963)	Fontana, Ugo	50-90	
Bechstein, Ludwig	Rabbit Catcher (1st, folio, 32p, ibds, fp color)	Macmillan	1962	Fontana, Ugo	100-165	
Bishop, Claire H.	Big Loop (1st, 8vo, tan cl, 221p, fp b/w, pep, DJ/3.00)	Viking	1955	Fontsere, Carles	30-50	
Lund, Doris	Attic of the Wind (1st, 4to, [38]p, color, pep, DJ/2.95)	Parents Mag. Pr.	(1966)	Forberg, Ati	25-40	
O'Connor, Edwin	Benjy, a Ferocious Fairy Tale (1st {std}, 8vo, 143p, color, cep, DJ/4.00)	Little/Brown	(1957)	Forberg, Ati	30-45	
Orgel, Doris	Cindy's Sad and Happy Tree (1st, 8vo, [40]p, fp 1-color, cep, DJ/3.50)	Knopf	(1967)	Forberg, Ati	25-40	
Orgel, Doris	Cindy's Snowdrops (1st, 8vo, [38]p, 1-color, cep, DJ/3.25)	Knopf	(1966)	Forberg, Ati	25-40	
Fisher, Aileen	Easter (1st, 8vo, [40]p, color, DJ/2.95)	Crowell	(1968)	Forberg, Ati	25-45	
Schiller, Barbara	Erec and Enid (1st {std}, 8vo, 45p, 1-color, DJ/4.25)	Dutton	(1970)	Forberg, Ati	30-45	
McGinley, Phyllis	Girl and her Room (1st {std}, ob4to, [38]p, fp 1-color, dep, DJ/2.95)	F. Watts	1963	Forberg, Ati	30-50	*
Fisher, Aileen	Jeanne d'Arc (1st, 4to, 52p, fp color, pep, DJ/4.50)	Crowell	(1970)	Forberg, Ati	30-50	R
Peterson, Phyllis	Log Cabin in the Forest (1st, lg8vo, 24p, 2-color, dep, DJ/2.00)	Houghton	1954	Forberg, Ati	30-50	R*
Levenson, Dorothy	Magic Carousel (1st, sm ob4to, [36]p, color, dep, DJ/3.50)	Parents Mag. Pr.	(1967)	Forberg, Ati	25-40	
Sanford, Wendy	Puma & the Pearl (1st, lg ob8vo, [39]p, 1-color, DJ/3.50)	Walker	(1962)	Forberg, Ati	25-40	*
Mendoza, George	Starfish Trilogy (1st {1}, 8vo, bds, 44p, color, cep, DJ)	Funk/Wagnalls	(1969)	Forberg, Ati	25-45	
Forbes, Elizabeth S.	King Arthur's Wood (1st, ob folio, 120p, buckram, 14cp)	L: Simpkin	1904	Forbes, Eliz. S.	900-1200	
Napjus, Alice	Freddie Found a Frog (1st, 12mo, [27]p, color, DJ/4.95)	Van Nostrand	(1969)	Ford, George	25-40	*
Harman, Humphrey	Tales Told Near a Crocodile (1st AM {std}, 8vo, 185p, b/w, DJ/3.95)	Viking	(1967)	Ford, George	25-45	
Brookfield, Mrs. A.	Aesop's Fables for Little Readers (1st, 4to, red/gilt, 71p, b/w)	L: T.F. Unwin	[1888]	Ford, H.J.	200-300	
Lang, Leonora B.	All Sorts of Stories Book (1st, 12mo, AEG, 377p, gilt, 5cp)	L: Longmans	1911	Ford, H.J.	200-325	
Lang, Andrew	Animal Story Book (1st, 12mo, AEG, 400p, blue/gilt, cep)	L: Longmans	1896	Ford, H.J.	150-250	
N/A	Arabian Nights (1st, 12mo, 424p, AEG, blue/gilt, b/w, cep)	L: Longmans	1898	Ford, H.J.	400-600	
Lang, Andrew	Blue Poetry Book (1st, 12mo, blue/gilt, AEG, 243p, 12pl, cep)	L: Longmans	1891	Ford, H.J.	170-240	
Lang, Andrew	Book of Princes & Princesses (1st, 12mo, gilt, 361p, AEG, 8cp)	L: Longmans	1908	Ford, H.J.	180-240	
Lang, Andrew	Book of Romance (1st, 12mo, AEG, 384p, gilt, 8cp, pep)	L: Longmans	1902	Ford, H.J.	180-240	
Lang, Leonora B.	Book of Saints & Heroes (1st, 8vo, blue/gilt, teg, 351p, 12cp)	L: Longmans	1912	Ford, H.J.	120-170	
Newbolt, Henry J.	Book of the Happy Warrior (1st, sm8vo, blue/gilt, 284p, 8cp)	L: Longmans	1917	Ford, H.J.	65-90	
Lang, Andrew	Brown Fairy Book (1st, 8vo, AEG, 350p, 8cp, 22pl, cep)	L: Longmans	1904	Ford, H.J.	250-400	
Lang, Andrew	Crimson Fairy Book (1st, 12mo, gilt, AEG, 371p, 8cp, pep)	L: Longmans	1903	Ford, H.J.	250-400	
Benson, E.F.	David Blaize and the Blue Door (1st, sm8vo, 217p, b/w)	Doran	(1919)	Ford, H.J.	80-120	
Lang, Andrew	Disentanglers (1st, 12mo, 418p, AEG, 7pl, cep)	L: Longmans	1902	Ford, H.J.	120-180	
Taylor, Una	Early Italian Love Stories (1st, sm4to, 144p, 13 fp b/w)	L: Longmans	1899	Ford, H.J.	120-200	
Lang, Andrew (ed)	Fairy Nurse & other Stories (1st, 12mo, 192p, gilt, col frn, b/w)	L: Longmans	1923	Ford, H.J.	45-70	
Lang, Andrew	Green Fairy Book (1st, 12mo, AEG, 366p, gilt, b/w, cep)	L: Longmans	1892	Ford, H.J.	300-450	
Lang, Andrew	Grey Fairy Book (1st, 12mo, AEG, 387p, 32pl, cep)	L: Longmans	1900	Ford, H.J.	250-400	
Scott, Walter	Kenilworth (1st, 4to, teg, red/gilt, 551p, uncut, 12cp)	L: Jack	(1920)	Ford, H.J.	120-200	
Lang, Andrew	Lilac Fairy Book (1st, 12mo, 369p, gilt, AEG, 6cp)	L: Longmans	1910	Ford, H.J.	250-400	
Lang, Andrew	Little Wildrose (1st, 12mo, 258p, blue/gilt, col frn, 19 b/w, pep)	L: Longmans	1906	Ford, H.J.	100-170	
Lang, Andrew	Olive Fairy Book (1st, 12mo, AEG, 336p, 8cp, pep)	L: Longmans	1907	Ford, H.J.	250-400	
Lang, Andrew	Orange Fairy Book (1st, 12mo, orange/gilt, 358p, AEG, 8cp)	L: Longmans	1906	Ford, H.J.	250-400	
Greene, Harry P.	Pilot & Other Stories (1st, 8vo, 229p, 8cp)	Macmillan	1916	Ford, H.J.	120-200	
Lang, Andrew	Pink Fairy Book (1st, 12mo, gilt, AEG, 360p, b/w, cep)	L: Longmans	1897	Ford, H.J.	250-400	
Lang, Andrew	Red Book of Animal Stories (1st, 12mo, gilt, AEG, 379p, 33pl)	L: Longmans	1899	Ford, H.J.	160-240	
Lang, Andrew	Red Romance Book (1st, 12mo, 366p, AEG, 8cp, 28pl, pep)	L: Longmans	1905	Ford, H.J.	140-225	
Lang, Andrew	Red True Story Book (1st, 12mo, gilt, 419p, AEG, 19pl, cep)	L: Longmans	1895	Ford, H.J.	200-320	
Lang, Andrew	Strange Story Book (1st, lg8vo, teg, gilt, 312p, 12cp)	L: Longmans	1913	Ford, H.J.	250-350	
Lang, Andrew	Tales of Troy & Greece (1st, sm8vo, 302p, teg, uncut, 16pl)	L: Longmans	1907	Ford, H.J.	80-140	
Lang, Andrew	Trusty John... (1st, sm8vo, maroon/gilt, 258p, col frn, 14pl)	L: Longmans	1906	Ford, H.J.	150-225	
Lang, Andrew	Violet Fairy Book (1st, 12mo, 388p, AEG, 8cp, cep)	L: Longmans	1901	Ford, H.J.	250-400	
Yorke, S.P.	When Mother was Little (1st, 8vo, 176p, 13 fp b/w, pep)	L: Fisher/Unwin	1890	Ford, H.J.	150-220	*
Lang, Andrew	Yellow Fairy Book (1st, 12mo, AEG, 321p, 22pl, cep)	L: Longmans	1894	Ford, H.J.	220-320	
Bick, Christopher	Bells of Heaven: Story of Joan of Arc (1st, 8vo, 246p, DJ/3.00)	Dodd	1949	Ford, Lauren	30-45	*
Bible	Christmas Book: Gospel of St. Luke (1st, ob4to, [48]p, color, DJ/4.50)	Dodd	(1963)	Ford, Lauren	30-45	*
Ford, Lauren	Lauren Ford's Christmas Book (1st, lg ob8vo, [46]p, fp color, DJ/4.50)	Dodd	(1963)	Ford, Lauren	20-35	
Bible	Little Book about God (1st, 12mo, ibds, [96]p, color, pep)	Doubleday/Doran	1934	Ford, Lauren	40-65	
DeSegur, Sophie	Memoirs of a Donkey (1st, 16mo, blue cl, 238p, fp b/w, pep)	Macmillan	1924	Ford, Lauren	50-85	
Ford, Lauren	Our Lady's Book (1st, 8vo, 269p, gilt, color, DJ/4.50)	Dodd	(1962)	Ford, Lauren	20-30	
Killilea, Marie	Treasure on the Hill (1st, lg8vo, gilt, 155p, fp b/w, DJ/3.50)	Dodd	1960	Ford, Lauren	30-50	
Lang, Andrew	Blue Fairy Book (1st, 12mo, 390p, blue/gilt, AEG, fp b/w, cep)	L: Longmans	1889	Ford/Hood	850-1300	

AUTHOR	TITLE	PUBLISHER	DATE	ARTIST	PRICE	LC
Lang, Andrew (ed)	History of Whittington (new ed., 8vo, 160p, fp b/w)	L: Longmans	1898	Ford/Hood	70-100	
Lang, Andrew	Red Fairy Book (1st, 12mo, red/gilt, AEG, 367p, b/w)	L: Longmans	1890	Ford/Speed	500-800	
Martin, Bill	Adam's Balm (1st, 8vo, [32]p, color, cep)	CA: Bowmar	(1970)	Foreman, Michael	30-50	*
Foreman, Michael	Great Sleigh Robbery (1st AM {std}, 4to, [32]p, color, DJ/3.95)	Pantheon	(1969)	Foreman, Michael	30-50	*
Watts, Mabel	I'm for You and You're for Me (1st, ob8vo, [32]p, color, DJ/2.75)	Abelard-Schuman	(1967)	Foreman, Michael	25-40	
Mikhalkov, Sergei	Let's Fight (1st AM, lg8vo, [54]p, fp color, cep, DJ/3.50)	Pantheon	(1968)	Foreman, Michael	30-45	
Foreman, Michael	Perfect Present (1st AM, 4to, 32p, fp color, DJ)	Coward	1967	Foreman, Michael	30-50	
Charters, Janet	The General (1st AM {std}, 4to, unpag, ibds, color, pep, DJ/3.50)	Dutton	1961	Foreman, Michael	30-50	
Foreman, Michael	Travels of Horatio (1st AM {std}, 4to, [32]p, color, DJ/3.95)	Pantheon	(1970)	Foreman, Michael	30-50	
Foreman, Michael	Two Giants (1st AM {std}, 4to, [30]p, color, DJ/3.95)	Pantheon	(1967)	Foreman, Michael	30-50	*
Omond, George W.	Belgium (1st, sm4to, 390p, black/gilt, 77cp)	L: A&C Black	1908	Forestier, Amedee	100-175	
Pemberton, Max	House Under the Sea (1st AM, sm8vo, 346p, brown/gilt, 8pl)	Appleton	1902	Forestier, Amedee	35-60	
Pemberton, Max	Pro Patria (1st, 8vo, 316p, red/gilt, 16pl)	L: Ward Lock	1901	Forestier, Amedee	60-100	
Henderson, John	Jamaica (1st, sm8vo, 86p, blue/gilt, teg, 24cp)	L: A&C Black	1906	Forrest, A.S.	90-160	
Forrest, A.S.	Morocco (1st, lg8vo, gilt, 231p, teg, 74cp)	L: A&C Black	1904	Forrest, A.S.	100-165	
Norman	Ten Little Boer Boys (1sst, ob4to, unpag, ibds, 14cp)	L: Dean	[1900]	Forrest, A.S.	170-240	
Stowe, Harriet B.	Uncle Tom's Cabin (8vo, green cl, 531p, col frn, 16pl)	L: Nelson	[1900]	Forrest, A.S.	100-160	*
Stowe, Harriet B.	Uncle Tom's Cabin (16mo, p-o, gilt, 115p, 8cp)	Jack/Dutton	[1908]	Forrest, A.S.	55-80	*
Bond, Michael	Bear Called Paddington (1st, 8vo, red/silver, 128p, b/w, DJ)	L: Collins	1958	Fortnum, Peggy	130-200	
Bond, Michael	Bear Called Paddington (1st AM, 8vo, 128p, yellow cl, b/w, DJ/2.50)	Houghton	1960	Fortnum, Peggy	100-160	
Farjeon, Eleanor	Children's Bells (1st AM {std}, lg8vo, 212p, b/w, DJ/3.50)	H.Z. Walck	(1960)	Fortnum, Peggy ·	25-45	
Bond, Michael	More About Paddington (1st AM, 8vo, aqua cl, 128p, b/w, DJ/2.50)	Houghton	(1962)	Fortnum, Peggy	70-100	*
Nichols, Beverly	Mountain of Magic (1st, 8vo, 302p, col frn, b/w, DJ)	L: J. Cape	1950	Fortnum, Peggy	30-50	
Bond, Michael	Paddington at Work (1st AM, 8vo, 128p, b/w, DJ/3.25)	Houghton	1967	Fortnum, Peggy	50-80	
Bond, Michael	Paddington Goes to Town (1st AM, 8vo, 125p, b/w, DJ/3.25)	Houghton	1968	Fortnum, Peggy	50-80	
Foster, Genevieve	Abraham Lincoln (1st, sm8vo, 111p, color, DJ/2.00)	Scribner	(1950)	Foster, Genevieve	80-130	
Foster, Genevieve	Abraham Lincoln's World (1st, sm4to, 347p, b/w, cep, DJ/3.50, NH)	Scribner	1944	Foster, Genevieve	80-120	R
Foster, Genevieve	Augustus Ceasar's World (1st, 4to, 330p, col frn, b/w, DJ/3.50)	Scribner	1947	Foster, Genevieve	70-120	
Foster, Genevieve	Birthdays of Freedom (1st, 4to, [59]p, color, DJ/2.75, NH)	Scribner	(1952)	Foster, Genevieve	70-125	
Cavanah, Frances	Boyhood Adventures of Our Presidents (1st, 8vo, 256p, fp b/w, DJ/2.00)	Rand/McNally	(1938)	Foster, Genevieve	30-50	
Cavanah, Frances	Children of the White House (1st, 8vo, 35p, ipcb, b/w, DJ/0.50)	Rand/McNally	(1936)	Foster, Genevieve	20-35	
Foster, Genevieve	George Washington (1st, 4to, 93p, dp color, DJ/2.00, NH)	Scribner	(1949)	Foster, Genevieve	70-125	
Foster, Genevieve	George Washington's World (1st, 4to, 348p, 1-color, cep, DJ/3.00, NH)	Scribner	1941	Foster, Genevieve	70-125	R
Judson, Clara I.	Mary Jane's Friends in Holland (1st, sm8vo, 213p, b/w, pep, DJ/0.50)	Grosset/Dunlap	(1939)	Foster, Genevieve	20-30	
Judson, Clara I.	Pioneer Girl (1st {A}, 8vo, ipcb, 80p, fp 1-color, pep, DJ/0.50)	Rand/McNally	(1939)	Foster, Genevieve	45-70	
Foster, Genevieve	World of Captain John Smith, 1580-1631 (1st, 4to, 406p, bds, b/w, DJ/4.95)	Scribner	(1959)	Foster, Genevieve	70-125	
Foster, Genevieve	Year of Columbus, 1492 (1st, 8vo, 64p, color, DJ)	Scribner	(1969)	Foster, Genevieve	25-45	
Foster, Genevieve	Year of Independence, 1776 (1st, lg8vo, 64p, color, DJ/3.50)	Scribner	(1970)	Foster, Genevieve	25-45	
Foster, Joanna	Pete's Puddle (1st, 8vo, 21p, color, DJ/1.25)	Houghton	1950	Foster, Joanna	25-35	
Judson, Clara I.	Alice Ann (1st, sm8vo, gilt, 300p, b/w, DJ/1.50)	Barse/Hopkins	(1928)	Foster, John M.	25-40	
Macmillan, Cyrus	Canadian Fairy Tales (1st, sm4to, 203p 12cp, 14pl, pep)	Dodd	1922	Foster, Marcia L.	80-125	
Locke, William J.	Golden Journey of Mr. Paradyne (1st AM, 8vo, ibds, 53p, 8cp, pep)	Dodd	1924	Foster, Marcia L.	55-80	*
Gordon, Elizabeth	Happy Home Children (1st, 12mo, [34]p, ibds, color, pep)	Volland	(1924)	Foster, Marcia L.	60-90	
France, Anatole	Little Sea-Dogs (1st, 8vo, 149p, 8cp, pep)	L: Bodley Head	1925	Foster, Marcia L.	40-60	*
Grahame, Kenneth	The Headswoman (1st AM, 8vo, 53p, 8cp, DJ)	Dodd	1922	Foster, Marcia L.	70-100	
Syrett, Netta	Tinkelly Winkle (1st AM, 8vo, 157p, green cl, 8cp)	Dodd	1923	Foster, Marcia L.	30-50	
Muter, Gladys N.	Told in Our Neighborhood (1st, sm8vo, ibds, color)	Volland	(1925)	Foster, Marcia L.	40-60	*
Mayne, William	Underground Alley (1st {std}, 8vo, 168p, b/w, DJ)	L: Oxford U.Pr.	1958	Foster, Marcia L.	40-65	
Brink, Carol R.	Family Sabbatical (1st, 8vo, 256p, b/w, DJ/2.75)	Viking	1956	Foster, Susan	25-40	*
Bingham, Clifton	Pretty Pets (4to {enlarged ed.}, [20]p, 4 chromos)	L: Nister	[1910]	Foster, W.L.	90-120	
Chesterton, G.K.	Innocence of Father Brown (1st AM, sm8vo, red/gilt, 334p, 7pl)	NY: J. Lane	1911	Foster, Will F.	175-275	
Coatsworth, Eliz.	Night & the Cat (1st {std}, lg8vo, blue cl, 55p, 10pl, DJ/3.00)	Macmillan	1950	Foujita	45-70	
Stewart, Anna B.	Little Brother Goose (1st, 8vo, 107p, illus, pep)	McBride	1928	Fouse, Dorothea	40-65	
Newman, Isidora	Shades of Blue (8vo, blue/silver, 96p, 16cp)	NY: Harrison Co.	(1927)	Fouts, Herbert E.	70-100	
Gag, Flavia	A Wish for Mimi (1st {std}, 8vo, 156p, b/w, DJ/2.75)	Holt	(1958)	Fox, Dorothea	50-80	
Fox, Dorothea	Miss Twiggley's Tree (1st, sm4to, unpag, color, DJ/2.95)	Parents Mag. Pr.	(1966)	Fox, Dorothea	25-40	
Lardner, Ring	Bib Ballads (1st {1st bk.}, 8vo, teg, brown/gilt, [63]p, 2-color)	Volland	(1915)	Fox, Fontaine	200-280	R
Jackson, Shirley	9 Magic Wishes (1st {std}, lg4to, 45p, fp color, cep)	Crowell-Collier	(1963)	Fox, Lorraine	80-145	
Van Doren, Mark	Somebody Came (1st {std}, 8vo, [48]p, fp color, cep, DJ/3.50)	Harlin Quist	(1966)	Fox, Lorraine	40-65	
Clark, Ann N.	Bear Cub (1st, sm4to, 62p, 3 dp color, fp b/w, DJ/3.50)	Viking	(1965)	Frace, Charles	20-35	
Latham, Jean L.	David Glasgow Faragut: Our First Admiral (1st, 8vo, 80p, color, DJ)	Garrard Pub.	(1967)	Frame, Paul	30-50	
Martin, Patricia	Jacqueline Kennedy Onassis (1st, 8vo, 62p, color, DJ)	Putnam	(1969)	Frame, Paul	25-35	
Martin, Patricia	John Fitzgerald Kennedy (1st, 8vo, 64p, color, DJ/1.95)	Putnam	(1964)	Frame, Paul	25-40	*
Calhoun, Mary	Katie John (1st, 8vo, 134p, fp b/w, DJ/2.50)	Harper	(1960)	Frame, Paul	25-45	
Woolley, Catherine	Libby's Uninvited Guest (1st, 8vo, 191p, rust cl, b/w, DJ/4.25)	Wm. Morrow	(1970)	Frame, Paul	25-40	
Bishop, Claire H.	Mozart: Music Magician (1st, 8vo, 138p, DJ)	Garrard Pub.	(1968)	Frame, Paul	20-35	
Mason, Miriam E.	Sara and the Winter Gift (1st {std}, 8vo, 152p, fp b/w, DJ/4.50)	Macmillan	(1968)	Frame, Paul	30-50	
Heathers, Anne	Handful of Surprises (1st {std}, 4to, unpag, 2-color, DJ/2.95)	Harcourt	(1961)	Frances, Esteban	25-45	
Heathers, Anne	Thread Soldier (1st {std}, 12mo, unpag, 1-color, DJ/1.95)	Harcourt	1960	Frances, Esteban	20-35	*
Francis, Frank	Magic Wallpaper (1st, sm ob4to, [27]p, fp color, DJ/3.95)	Abelard-Schuman	(1970)	Francis, Frank	30-50	*
Francis, Frank	Timimoto's Great Adventure (1st, 4to, [28]p, color, DJ/4.50)	Holiday House	(1969)	Francis, Frank	25-40	
Francis, J.G.	Book of Cheerful Cats (1st, ob8vo, 37p, b/w, PPPa)	Century	1892	Francis, J.G.	120-200	
Francis, J.G.	Joyous Aztecs (1st {std}, ob8vo, 42p, b/w)	Century	(1929)	Francis, J.G.	50-80	
Le Marchand, Jacques	Adventures of Ulysses (1st, lg4to, 48p, fp color, pep, DJ/3.95)	Criterion Bks.	(1960)	Francois, Andre	40-65	*
Francois, Andre	Crocodile Tears (1st, narrow ob 4to, unpag, fp color, NYTBI)	Universe	(1956)	Francois, Andre	50-80	*
Symonds, John	Grodge-Cat & the Window Cleaner (1st, 4to, 61p, fp 1-color, DJ/3.50)	Pantheon	(1965)	Francois, Andre	30-50	*
Harris, Isobel	Little Boy Brown (1st, sm4to, 44p, tan cl, 1-color, cep, DJ/1.75)	Lippincott	1949	Francois, Andre	80-125	R
Symonds, John	Magic Currant Bun (1st AM {std}, 8vo, ibds, 38p, 1-color, DJ/2.00, NYTBI)	Lippincott	(1952)	Francois, Andre	40-65	

AUTHOR	TITLE	PUBLISHER	DATE	ARTIST	PRICE	LC
Stephane, Nelly	Roland (1st AM, lg4to, [32]p, ipcb, fp 2-color, DJ/3.25, NYTBI)	Harcourt	(1958)	Francois, Andre	50-80	
Symonds, John	Tom and Tabby (1st AM {std}, 4to, ibds, [80]p, 1-color, DJ/4.95)	NY: Universe	(1964)	Francois, Andre	50-85	
Symonds, John	Travelers Three (1st {std}, 8vo, 48p, 2-color, DJ/2.75)	Lippincott	1953	Francois, Andre	30-50	
Francois, Andre	You Are Ri-di-cu-lous (1st, ob4to, [32]p, color, DJ/3.95, NYTBI)	Pantheon	(1970)	Francois, Andre	40-65	*
Francoise	Big Rain (1st, 4to, [32]p, pink cl, color, DJ/2.95)	Scribner	1961	Francoise	50-80	
Francoise	Biquette, the White Goat (1st, sm4to, [32]p, fp color, DJ/2.00)	Scribner	1953	Francoise	30-45	*
McNeil, Marion	Blue Elephant and the Pink Pig (1st, 4to, [40]p, ibds, color, pep)	Saalfield	(1931)	Francoise	120-180	
Francoise	Chouchou (1st, 4to, [32]p, blue cl, fp color, DJ/2.95, NYTBI)	Scribner	1958	Francoise	70-100	
Francoise	Fanchette & Jeannot (1st AM, 4to, ibds, [24]p, color, DJ/0.50)	Grosset/Dunlap	1937	Francoise	80-120	
Francoise	Gay ABC (1st, lg8vo, grey cl, [55]p, fp color, DJ/1.75)	Scribner	(1939)	Francoise	80-120	R
Mother Goose	Gay Mother Goose (1st, 4to, beige cl, 63p, fp color, DJ/1.75)	Scribner	(1938)	Francoise	80-125	
Francoise	Jeanne-Marie Counts her Sheep (1st, sm4to, [32]p, fp color, DJ/2.00)	Scribner	1951	Francoise	70-100	R
Francoise	Jeanne-Marie In Gay Paris (1st, sm4to, unpag, fp color, DJ/2.75)	Scribner	1956	Francoise	100-160	
McNeil, Marion	Little Green Cart (1st, 4to, ibds, [38]p, color, pep)	Saalfield	(1931)	Francoise	45-60	
Francoise	Minou (1st, sm4to, [32]p, fp color, DJ/2.95)	Scribner	1962	Francoise	50-80	
Francoise	Mr. & Mrs. So and So (1st, 4to, [36]p, color, pep, DJ/1.50)	Oxford U. Pr.	(1939)	Francoise	70-100	
Francoise	Noel for Jeanne-Marie (1st {std}, sm4to, unpag, grey cl, color, DJ/2.25)	Scribner	1953	Francoise	60-95	R
Francoise	Small-Trot (1st {std}, sm4to, green cl, [32]p, color, DJ/2.00)	Scribner	1952	Francoise	70-100	
Francoise	Story of Colette (1st, 4to, [32]p, ibds, fp color, pep, DJ/1.50)	Scribner	(1940)	Francoise	70-125	
Francoise	Thank-You Book (1st, sm4to, [32]p, fp 3-color, cep, DJ/2.00)	Scribner	1947	Francoise	40-65	
Francoise	Things I Like (1st, sm4to, [32]p, fp color, DJ/3.25)	Scribner	1960	Francoise	40-65	
Francoise	What Do You Want to Be? (1st, 4to, green cl, [30]p, fp color, DJ/2.75)	Scribner	1957	Francoise	80-130	
Judson, Clara I.	Abraham Lincoln, Friend of People (1st, 8vo, 206p, fp color, dep, DJ/3.50)	Wilcox/Follett	(1950)	Frankenberg, Rbt.	30-50	
Annixter, Jane	Ahmeek (1st, 8vo, 63p, b/w, DJ/3.75)	Holiday House	(1970)	Frankenberg, Rbt.	20-35	
Judson, Clara I.	Benjamin Franklin (1st, lg8vo, 204p, b/w, DJ/3.50)	Follett	(1957)	Frankenberg, Rbt.	25-35	
Meader, Stephen W.	Cape May Packet (1st {std}, 8vo, 218p, tan cl, DJ/4.50)	Harcourt	(1969)	Frankenberg, Rbt.	70-125	
Scheer, George	Cherokee Animal Tales (1st, 8vo, 79p, fp b/w, DJ/3.50)	Holiday House	(1968)	Frankenberg, Rbt.	25-45	
Sawyer, Ruth	Daddles: Story of a Plain Hound-Dog (1st {std}, 8vo, 99p, b/w, DJ/3.50)	Little/Brown	(1964)	Frankenberg, Rbt.	20-35	
Martin, Patricia	Eskimos: People of Alaska (1st, 8vo, 64p, color, DJ)	Parents Mag. Pr.	(1970)	Frankenberg, Rbt.	25-40	
Judson, Clara I.	George Washington, Leader of the People (1st, lg8vo, 224p, b/w, DJ/3.50)	Wilcox/Follett	1951	Frankenberg, Rbt.	30-50	
Balch, Glenn	Indian Saddle-Up (1st, 8vo, 210p, b/w, DJ/2.50)	Crowell	(1953)	Frankenberg, Rbt.	30-50	
Martin, Patricia	Indians: The First Americans (1st, 8vo, 64p, color, DJ)	Parents Mag. Pr.	(1970)	Frankenberg, Rbt.	25-40	
Agle, Nan H.	Makon and the Dauphin (1st, 8vo, 126p, b/w, DJ/2.95)	Scribner	(1961)	Frankenberg, Rbt.	20-35	
Judson, Clara I.	Mighty Soo... (1st, lg8vo, 192p, b/w, DJ/3.50)	Follett	(1955)	Frankenberg, Rbt.	25-45	
Mowat, Farley	Owls in the Family (1st {std}, 8vo, 103p, b/w, DJ/2.95)	Little/Brown	(1961)	Frankenberg, Rbt.	25-45	
Montgomery, R.	Silver Hills (1st {std}, 8vo, 213p, b/w, DJ/3.00)	World	(1958)	Frankenberg, Rbt.	20-30	
Ormondroyd, Edward	Tale of Alain (1st, lg8vo, 94p, b/w, DJ/2.75)	Follett	(1960)	Frankenberg, Rbt.	50-80	*
Lampman, Evelyn	Tree Wagon (1st {std}, 8vo, 253p, b/w, DJ/2.75)	Doubleday	1953	Frankenberg, Rbt.	25-45	
Grant, Bruce	Zachary, the Governor's Pig (1st {std}, lg8vo, 139p, b/w, DJ/2.95)	World	(1960)	Frankenberg, Rbt.	30-45	
Byington, Eloise	Mother Goose Fun (1st, sm8vo, p-o, gilt, 128p, color, pep)	Whitman	(1931)	Frantz, Kathleen	45-60	
Byington, Eloise	Wishbone Children (1st, 8vo, blue cl, p-o, 64p, pep, color)	Whitman	(1934)	Frantz, Kathleen	30-50	
Stolz, Mary S.	Dragons of the Queen (1st, 8vo, 47p, ibds, fp b/w, DJ/3.50)	Harper	(1969)	Frascino, Edward	20-30	
Sharmat, Marjorie	Gladys told Me to Meet her Here (1st, 4to, ibds, 31p, color, pep, DJ/3.95)	Harper	(1970)	Frascino, Edward	30-50	*
Stolz, Mary S.	Say Something (1st, 4to, ibds, [32]p, fp color, DJ/3.50)	Harper	(1968)	Frascino, Edward	30-45	
Stolz, Mary S.	Singular Hen & her Peculiar Children (1st, ob8vo, 48p, color, DJ/3.50)	Harper	(1969)	Frascino, Edward	25-45	*
White, Elwyn B.	Trumpet of the Swan (1st, 8vo, 210p, blue/gilt, fp b/w, cep, DJ/4.50)	Harper	(1970)	Frascino, Edward	50-80	R
Krauss, Ruth	Cantilever Rainbow (1st, 8vo, [46]p, 1-color, pep, DJ/2.95)	Pantheon	(1965)	Frasconi, Antonio	40-65	
Singer, Isaac B.	Elijah the Slave (1st {std}, 4to, [31]p, color, purple cl, pep, DJ/4.95)	Farrar, Straus	(1970)	Frasconi, Antonio	60-100	
N/A	House that Jack Built (1st {std} 4to, [32]p, 3-color dep, DJ/3.00, CH, NYT)	Harcourt	(1958)	Frasconi, Antonio	100-170	R
Frasconi, Antonio	Kaleidoscope in Woodcuts (1st {std}, 16mo {accordian}, color)	Harcourt	1968	Frasconi, Antonio	60-80	
Untermeyer, Louis	Love Lyrics (1st, ob12mo, ibds, 44p, color, DJ/0.95)	NY: Odyssey Pr.	(1965)	Frasconi, Antonio	25-45	*
Whitman, Walt	Overhead the Sun (1st {std}, 4to, [37]p, color, DJ/4.95)	Farrar, Straus	(1969)	Frasconi, Antonio	40-65	R
Frasconi, Antonio	See & Say (1st {std}, 4to, yellow cl, [32]p, color, pep, DJ/3.00, NYTBI)	Harcourt	(1955)	Frasconi, Antonio	80-125	R
Frasconi, Antonio	See Again, Say Again (1st {std}, 4to, [32]p, ibds, color, DJ/3.25)	Harcourt	(1964)	Frasconi, Antonio	50-80	R
Frasconi, Antonio	Snow & the Sun (1st {std}, 4to, unpag, ibds, color, DJ/3.00)	Harcourt	(1961)	Frasconi, Antonio	30-50	
Frasconi, Antonio	Sunday in Monterey (1st {std}, narrow 24mo, unpag, color, DJ)	Harcourt	(1964)	Frasconi, Antonio	80-130	
Benedetti, Mario	Unstill Life (1st {std}, 8vo, 127p, fp b/w, cep, DJ/5.95)	Harcourt	(1969)	Frasconi, Antonio	25-45	*
Aiken, Joan	Armitage, Armitage, Fly Away Home (1st {std}, 8vo, 214p, b/w, DJ/3.95)	Doubleday	(1968)	Fraser, Betty	80-125	
Johnson, Crockett	Castles in the Sand (1st {std}, 8vo, [48]p, color, DJ/3.50)	Holt, Rinehart	(1965)	Fraser, Betty	25-40	
Bennett, Rowena B.	Songs from Around a Toadstool Table (1st {std}, sm8vo, 61p, b/w, DJ/3.50)	Follett	(1967)	Fraser, Betty	20-30	
Gay, John	Beggar's Opera (1st, 4to, 93p, bds, p-o, 8cp)	L: Heinemann	1921	Fraser, Claud L.	75-125	
MacFall, Haldane	Book of Lovat Claud Fraser (1st, 4to, ipcb, 183p, 8cp)	L: Dent	1923	Fraser, Claud L.	120-200	
Preston, Hayter	House of Vanities (1st, 12mo, 59p, bds, b/w)	L: John Lane	1922	Fraser, Claud L.	60-90	
Nodier, Charles	Luck of the Bean Rows (1st, lg8vo, 60p, ibds, 28 color)	L: O'Connor	(1921)	Fraser, Claud L.	120-185	
Fraser, Claud L.	Lute of Love (1st, 16mo, ipcb, 66p, p-o, b/w)	L: Selwyn	(1920)	Fraser, Claud L.	50-80	
N/A	Nursery Rhymes (1st, 4to, 46p, ibds, 23 color)	L: Jack	(1919)	Fraser, Claud L.	120-200	
Fraser, Claud L.	Nursery Rhymes (1st AM, 8vo, 46p, cp)	Knopf	[1920]	Fraser, Claud L.	100-185	
De La Mare, Walter	Peacock Pie (1st AM, lg8vo, 128p, blue/gilt, 16cp)	Henry Holt & Co.	(1924)	Fraser, Claud L.	70-100	
De La Mare, Walter	Peacock Pie (1st, lg8vo, teg, 127p, blue/gilt, 16cp)	L: Constable	(1924)	Fraser, Claud L.	100-165	
Fraser, Claud L.	Pirates (1st AM {std}, 4to, ibds, 159p, 8pl)	McBride	1922	Fraser, Claud L.	120-170	
Goldoni, Carlo	The Liar (1st AM, 8vo, 93p, bds, col frn, b/w, DJ)	Knopf	1922	Fraser, Claud L.	75-100	
Goldoni, Carlo	The Liar (1st, sm4to, ibds, 93p, p-o, col frn)	L: Selwyn	1922	Fraser, Claud L.	55-80	*
Nodier, Charles	Woodcutter's Dog (1st, lg8vo, 18p, p-o, bds, 12 color)	L: O'Connor	(1921)	Fraser, Claud L.	100-165	
Colum, Padraic	At the Gateways of the Day (1st, lg8vo, 217p, fp b/w)	Yale U. Press	1924	Fraser, Juliette M.	30-50	
Colum, Padraic	Bright Islands (1st, 8vo, 233p, gilt, pep, b/w)	Yale U. Press	1925	Fraser, Juliette M.	40-60	
Craddock, Charles E.	Young Mountaineers (1st, 12mo, 262p, green/gilt, 4pl)	Houghton	1897	Fraser, Malcolm	40-60	
Foyle, Kathleen	Little Good People (1st AM, 8vo, 163p, 8cp, pep, DJ/2.50)	NY: Warne	(1949)	Fraser, Peter	50-85	
Gordon, Elizabeth	King Gumdrop (1st, lg8vo, 112p, p-o, fp color, pep)	Whitman	(1916)	Frazee, Hazel	100-165	

AUTHOR	TITLE	PUBLISHER	DATE	ARTIST	PRICE	LC
Lyle, G.M.	Little Travelers in Wales (1st, 8vo, p-o, 127p, gilt, b/w, pep)	Whitman	1929	Frazee, Hazel	30-50	
North, Sterling	Five Little Bears (1st, 8vo, ipcb, [32]p, 1-color, pep, DJ/0.50)	Rand/McNally	(1935)	Frazee/Biers	50-85	
Seawell, Molly E.	Betty at Fort Blizzard (1st, 8vo, 224p, teg, p-o, 4cp)	Lippincott	1916	Frederick, Edmund	25-40	
Chambers, Robert	Gay Rebellion (1st, sm8vo, 299p, red/gilt, p-o, 4pl)	Appleton	1913	Frederick, Edmund	25-40	
Chambers, Robert	Green Mouse (1st, 8vo, 281p, p-o, 6cp, pep)	Appleton	1910	Frederick, Edmund	30-50	
Lanier, Sidney	Boy's Mabinogion (1st, 8vo, 361p, gilt, 12pl, cep, PPPa)	Scribner	1881	Fredericks, Alfred	150-250	
Lanier, Sidney	Knightly Legends of Wales (1st, 8vo, 361p, red/gilt, 12pl, cep)	Scribner	1901	Fredericks, Alfred	40-65	
De La Mare, Walter	Love (1st, 8vo, 592p, grey/gilt, col frn, 24 b/w)	L: Faber	1943	Freedman, Barnett	55-90	
Freeman, Don	Add-a-Line Alphabet (1st, 4to, [32]p, color, DJ/3.95)	Golden Gate	(1968)	Freeman, Don	60-90	
Freeman, Don	Beady Bear (1st, lg ob8vo, red cl, 48p, fp b/w, DJ/2.00)	Viking	1954	Freeman, Don	50-80	
Brown, Myra B.	Best Friends (1st, 12mo, [47]p, fp 2-color, DJ/2.95)	Golden Gate	(1967)	Freeman, Don	25-40	*
Brown, Myra B.	Best of Luck (1st, 12mo, [46]p, fp 2-color, DJ/3.25)	Golden Gate	(1969)	Freeman, Don	25-40	*
Lindgren, Astrid	Bill Bergson & White Rose Rescue (1st, 8vo, 215p, b/w, DJ/3.50)	Viking	(1965)	Freeman, Don	50-80	
Lindgren, Astrid	Bill Bergson Lives Dangerously (1st, sm8vo, 214p, b/w, pep, DJ/2.50)	Viking	1954	Freeman, Don	60-100	
Freeman, Don	Botts: The Naughty Otter (1st, ob4to, [46]p, b/w, cep, DJ/3.00)	Golden Gate	(1963)	Freeman, Don	50-80	
Cunningham, Julia	Burnish Me Bright (1st, 8vo, 78p, fp b/w, DJ/3.95)	Pantheon	(1970)	Freeman, Don	50-80	R*
Bauer, Helen	California Indian Days (1st {std}, 4to, 160p, b/w, DJ/3.50)	Doubleday	1963	Freeman, Don	25-45	
Freeman, Don	Chuggy & Blue Caboose (1st, ob4to, 48p, red cl, color, DJ/2.50)	Viking	1951	Freeman, Don	50-80	
Randolph, Jane	Circus in Peter's Closet (1st, 8vo, blue cl, 48p, 3-color, pep, DJ/2.50)	Crowell	(1955)	Freeman, Don	40-70	
Freeman, Don	Come Again, Pelican (1st, 8vo, 44p, color, pep, DJ/3.00)	Viking	(1961)	Freeman, Don	80-120	
Freeman, Don	Corduroy (1st, 8vo, 32p, ipcb, color, DJ/3.50)	Viking	(1968)	Freeman, Don	70-120	
Freeman, Don	Cyrano the Crow (1st, 4to, 47p, ibds, color, DJ/2.75)	Viking	(1960)	Freeman, Don	50-80	
Freeman, Don	Dandelion (1st, ob4to, 48p, 2-color, DJ/3.00)	Viking	(1964)	Freeman, Don	40-65	
Freeman, Don	Fly High, Fly Low (1st, 4to, blue cl, 56p, color, pep, DJ/3.00, CH)	Viking	(1957)	Freeman, Don	60-90	
Freeman, Don	Forever Laughter (1st, ob8vo, [64]p, 1-color, cep, DJ/4.50)	Golden Gate	(1970)	Freeman, Don	30-50	
Bulla, Clyde R.	Ghost Town Treasure (1st, 8vo, yellow cl, 86p, b/w, pep, DJ/2.50)	Crowell	(1957)	Freeman, Don	30-60	
Freeman, Don	Guard Mouse (1st, 4to, 47p, ibds, fp color, DJ/3.50)	Viking	(1967)	Freeman, Don	30-50	
Freeman, Don	Hattie the Backstage Bat (1st {std}, ob4to, [32]p, color, DJ/3.50)	Viking	(1970)	Freeman, Don	30-50	
Philbrook, Elizabeth	Hobo Hill (1st, lg8vo, 96p, fp b/w, DJ/2.50)	Viking	1954	Freeman, Don	25-40	
Freeman, Don	It Shouldn't Happen (1st {std}, 8vo, [212]p, b/w, DJ/2.00)	Harcourt	(1945)	Freeman, Don	30-50	
Burch, Robert	Joey's Cat (1st, 8vo, [40]p, color, DJ/3.50)	Viking	(1969)	Freeman, Don	30-50	
Embry, Margaret	Kid Sister (1st, sm8vo, 165p, yellow cl, fp b/w, pep, DJ/2.50)	Holiday House	(1958)	Freeman, Don	30-45	
Sauer, Julia L.	Mike's House (1st, sm4to, red cl, 31p, 2-color, pep, DJ/2.50)	Viking	1954	Freeman, Don	45-70	
Koch, Dorothy	Monkeys are Funny that Way (1st, narrow 4to, [25]p, fp 2-color, DJ/2.75)	Holiday House	1962	Freeman, Don	40-65	
Freeman, Don	Mop Top (1st, sm4to, beige cl, 48p, 1-color, pep, DJ/2.00)	Viking	1955	Freeman, Don	60-90	
Saroyan, William	My Name is Aram (1st {std}, 8vo, 220p, col frn, b/w, DJ/2.50)	Harcourt	(1940)	Freeman, Don	70-100	
Freeman, Don	Night the Lights Went Out (1st, lg8vo, 48p, blue cl, 1-color, DJ/2.00)	Viking	1958	Freeman, Don	60-90	
Freeman, Don	Norman the Doorman (1st, sm ob4to, yellow cl, 64p, color, pep, DJ/3.00)	Viking	(1959)	Freeman, Don	60-90	
Atkinson, Brooks	Once Around the Sun (1st {std}, 8vo, 376p, blue cl, fp b/w, DJ/4.00)	Harcourt	(1951)	Freeman, Don	40-65	
Freeman, Lydia	Pet of the Met (1st, sm ob4to, 63p, pep, color, DJ/2.50)	Viking	1953	Freeman, Don	90-150	R
Freeman, Don	Rainbow of My Own (1st, ob8vo, [32]p, fp color, DJ/3.00)	Viking	(1966)	Freeman, Don	30-50	
Corbett, Scott	Sauce for the Gander (1st AM, 8vo, yellow cl, 238p, fp b/w, DJ/3.00)	Crowell	(1951)	Freeman, Don	30-50	
Galt, Tom	Seven Days from Sunday (1st {std}, 8vo, rust cl, 215p, b/w, DJ/3.00)	Crowell	(1956)	Freeman, Don	40-65	
Sonneborn, Ruth	Seven in a Bed (1st, sq8vo, [31]p, fp color, DJ/2.95)	Viking	(1968)	Freeman, Don	30-45	
Freeman, Don	Ski Pup (1st, 4to, 56p, fp color, pep, DJ/3.50)	Viking	(1963)	Freeman, Don	40-65	
Freeman, Don	Space Witch (1st, sm4to, blue cl, 47p, 1-color, DJ/2.00)	Viking	(1959)	Freeman, Don	45-70	
Clark, Ann N.	Third Monkey (1st, sm4to, 44p, color, pep, DJ/2.50)	Viking	1956	Freeman, Don	40-65	
Clark, Ann N.	This for That (1st, 4to, 62p, fp 3-color, cep, DJ/3.50)	Golden Gate	(1965)	Freeman, Don	30-50	
Freeman, Don	Tilly Witch (1st, 4to, [32]p, color, DJ/3.95)	Viking	(1969)	Freeman, Don	30-50	
Freeman, Don	Turtle and the Dove (1st, 8vo, 43p, blue cl, 1-color, DJ/2.50)	Viking	1964	Freeman, Don	25-40	
White, Anne H.	Uninvited Donkey (1st, 8vo, 223p, blue cl, b/w, DJ/2.75)	Viking	(1957)	Freeman, Don	30-50	
Thurber, James	White Deer (1st, 8vo, green cl, 115p, color, DJ/2.50)	Harcourt	(1945)	Freeman, Don	150-225	
Freeman, Leila C.	Nip & Tuck (1st, 4to, orange cl, p-o, 156p, 8cp, pep)	Sears	(1926)	Freeman, Leila C.	120-200	
Freeman, Leila C.	Nip & Tuck in Toyland (1st, 4to, 160p, p-o, 8cp, pep)	Sears	(1927)	Freeman, Leila C.	120-200	
Field, Rachel	American Folk & Fairy Tales (1st, 8vo, 302p, green cl, 8cp, pep)	Scribner	1929	Freeman, Margaret	60-90	
Cohen, Octavus R.	Black to Nature (1st, 12mo, 308p, orange cl, b/w, DJ/2.00)	Appleton-Century	1935	Freeman, Margaret	200-300	
Capuana, Luigi	Golden-Feather (1st {std}, 8vo, 205p, col frn, b/w, pep)	Dutton	(1930)	Freeman, Margaret	35-60	*
Lardner, Ring	Story of a Wonder Man (1st, sm8vo, gilt, 151p, green cl, b/w)	Scribner	1927	Freeman, Margaret	70-120	
Lamprey, Louise	Treasure Valley (1st, 8vo, 337p, yellow cl, p-o, 4cp, pep)	Wm. Morrow	(1928)	Freeman, Margaret	30-50	*
Vipont, Elfrida	Family at Dowbiggins (1st {std}, 8vo, 253p, b/w, DJ/2.75)	Bobbs-Merrill	(1955)	Freeman, Terry	25-40	
Foulds, Elfrida V.	Lark on the Wing (1st, 8vo, 234p, b/w, DJ, CgM)	L: Oxford U.Pr.	1950	Freeman, Terry	60-90	*
Vipont, Elfrida	Lark on the Wing (1st AM, 8vo, 255p, b/w, DJ/2.50, CgM)	Bobbs-Merrill	1951	Freeman, Terry	45-70	
French, Fiona	Jack of Hearts (1st AM {std}, 4to, [24]p, color, DJ/4.50)	Harcourt	(1970)	French, Fiona	45-60	
Arthur, Lady Kate	Dream of Little Hazy Cream (1st, folio, 40p, ibds, p-o, 12cp)	L: Bickers	[1909]	Frere, Catherine	125-200	*
Bergengren, Ralph	David the Dreamer (1st, ob4to, green cl, 67p, p-o, gilt, 10 fp color)	Atl. Monthly Pr.	(1922)	Freud, Tom	500-800	
Tallant, Edith	Danny and Prue (1st, 8vo, 143p, blue cl, p-o, 2-color, pep, DJ/2.00)	Crowell	(1938)	Freund, Rudolf	30-50	
Montgomery, R.	Iceblink (1st, sm8vo, 288p, b/w, pep, DJ/2.00)	Holt	1941	Freund, Rudolf	20-35	
Hurd, Edith T.	Jerry the Jeep (1st, ob4to, [32]p, ipcb, 1-color, pep, DJ/1.00)	Lothrop, Lee	(1945)	Friday, Theodore	40-65	
Nesbit, Wilbur D.	As Children Do (1st, 12mo, ibds, 96p, pep, decor by...)	Volland	(1929)	Friend, Ellery	55-80	
Collodi, Carlo	Adventures of Pinocchio (1st {this fmt}, lg8vo, 254p, p-o, 5cp, pep, WS)	Rand/McNally	(1939)	Friend, Esther	60-100	
Moore, Clement C.	Night Before Christmas (1st, 4to, ibds, [25]p, color, pep, DJ/1.00)	Wilcox/Follett	1949	Friend, Esther	35-60	
Anderson, Bernice	Topsy Turvy's Pigtails (1st, lg8vo, 91p, p-o, fp 2-color, b/w, pep)	Rand/McNally	(1930)	Friend, Esther	60-100	
Adams, Ruth	Fidelia (1st, lg8vo, [32]p, 1-color, pep, DJ/3.95)	Lothrop, Lee	1970	Froberg, Ati	25-40	
Alcott, Louisa M.	Frost King (4to, ipcb, unpag, color, pep)	Whitman	(1929)	Frobisher, Marie S.	140-200	
Grimm Bros.	Golden Bird (1st AM {std}, sq4to, [32]p, fp color, DJ/4.50)	Doubleday	1970	Fromm, Lilo	30-50	
Stockton, Frank	Associate Hermits (1st, 12mo, green/gilt, 257p, 9pl)	Harper	1899	Frost, A.B.	80-120	R
Stuart, Ruth M.	Aunt Amity's Silver Wedding (1st, 12mo, green/gilt, 228p, b/w)	Century	1909	Frost, A.B.	35-60	
Wood, Eugene	Back Home (1st, sm8vo, grey cl, 286p, 8pl)	McClure	1905	Frost, A.B.	50-85	R

AUTHOR	TITLE	PUBLISHER	DATE	ARTIST	PRICE	LC
Frost, A.B.	Book of Drawings (1st, folio, [80]p, p-o, ibds, 39pl)	Collier	1904	Frost, A.B.	150-220	
Frost, A.B.	Bull Calf (1st, ob8vo, 112p, 105pl)	Scribner	1892	Frost, A.B.	160-225	
Frost, A.B.	Carlo (1st, lg ob8vo, 109p, b/w)	Doubleday/Page	1913	Frost, A.B.	120-200	
Harris, Joel C.	Chronicles of Aunt Minervy Ann (1st [1], 8vo, teg, uncut, 210p, 31pl)	Scribner	1899	Frost, A.B.	120-180	R
Boyle, Virginia F.	Devil Tales (1st, sm8vo, 211p, 28pl)	Harper	1900	Frost, A.B.	200-300	*
Munkittrick, R.K.	Farming (1st, 8vo, green pcb, [102]p, 1-color)	Harper	1891	Frost, A.B.	90-120	R
Stuart, Ruth M.	Golden Wedding (1st, 12mo, 366p, gilt, 8pl)	Harper	1893	Frost, A.B.	50-80	
Van Sutphen, Wm. G.	Golfer's Alphabet (1st, sq8vo, ibds, [58]p, 28pl)	Harper	1898	Frost, A.B.	300-450	
Thanet, Octave	Heart of Toil (1st, sm8vo, teg, 215p, 24pl by...)	Scribner	1898	Frost, A.B.	40-60	*
Adams, Frederick	John Henry Smith (1st, 8vo, 346p, gilt, p-o, b/w)	Doubleday/Page	1905	Frost, A.B.	80-140	
Carruth, Hayden	Mr. Milo Bush (1st, 12mo, green/gilt, 217p, 4pl)	Harper	1899	Frost, A.B.	70-120	
Page, Thomas N.	Pastime Stories (1st, 12mo, grey cl, 220p, fp b/w)	Harper	1894	Frost, A.B.	45-70	
Craddock, Charles E.	Phantoms of the Foot-Bridge (1st, 12mo, 353p, green/gilt, 14pl)	Harper	1895	Frost, A.B.	100-165	
Stockton, Frank	Pomona's Travels (1st [1], 12mo, 275p, teg, gilt, 10pl)	Scribner	(1894)	Frost, A.B.	70-100	
Lloyd, Nelson M.	Soldier of the Valley (1st, 12mo, red/gilt, 335p, 34 fp b/w)	Scribner	1904	Frost, A.B.	30-50	
Stuart, Ruth M.	Solomon Crow's Christmas Pockets (1st, 12mo, gilt, 201p, 14pl)	Harper	1897	Frost, A.B.	50-80	
Stockton, Frank	Squirrel Inn (1st, sm8vo, 222p, teg, b/w)	Century	1891	Frost, A.B.	55-80	
Frost, A.B.	Stuff & Nonsense (1st, 4to, ipcb, 92p, b/w)	Scribner	(1884)	Frost, A.B.	120-170	
Carroll, Lewis	Tangled Tale (1st, 8vo, 152p, AEG, red/gilt, 6pl)	L: Macmillan	1885	Frost, A.B.	400-600	
Phillips, Henry W.	The Pets (1st, 12mo, 47p, tan cl, 5pl)	McClure	1906	Frost, A.B.	30-50	
Harris, Joel C.	Uncle Remus & his Friends (1st, 8vo, 357p, green/gilt, 12pl)	Houghton	1892	Frost, A.B.	250-400	
Thanet, Octave	Missionary Sheriff (1st, 12mo, 248p, blue/gilt, 15pl)	Harper	1897	Frost/Carleton	35-60	
Harris, Joel C.	Uncle Remus Returns (1st, 12mo, 175p, col frn, 7pl)	Houghton	(1918)	Frost/Conde	130-200	R
Carroll, Lewis	Rhyme? And Reason? (1st, 8vo, 214p, green/gilt, b/w)	L: Macmillan	1883	Frost/Holiday	220-285	
Stuart, Ruth M.	Moriah's Mourning (1st, 12mo, gilt, 218p, 8pl)	Harper	1898	Frost/Kemble	60-90	
Stuart, Ruth M.	Second Wooing of Salina Sue (1st, 12mo, gilt, 236p, 12pl)	Harper	1905	Frost/Kemble	50-80	
Harris, Joel C.	Tar-Baby (1st, 8vo, 90p, gilt, teg, uncut, 9pl)	Appleton	1904	Frost/Kemble	200-300	
Harris, Joel C.	Uncle Remus (Gift ed., 4to, green/gilt, 265p, 12pl)	Appleton	1920	Frost/Kemble	200-300	
Knight, Marjorie	Land of Lost Handkerchiefs (1st {std}, 8vo, 92p, fp color, DJ/2.50)	Dutton	1954	Fry Rosalie	25-45	
N/A	Plain Jane (1st, 16mo, 95p, green stripe cl, color)	L: G. Richards	1903	Fry, G.M.C.	130-175	
Aesopus	Aesop's Fables (1st, lg8vo, gilt, p-o, 136p, 8cp)	McKay	(1929)	Fry, Nora	60-100	
Fry, Rosalie K.	Bandy Boy's Treasure Island (1st {std}, 16mo, [29]p, color, pep, DJ/0.75)	Dutton	(1941)	Fry, Rosalie K.	70-100	
Fry, Rosalie K.	Bumblebuzz (1st {std}, lg8vo, ibds, [25]p, color, DJ/1.50)	Dutton	1938	Fry, Rosalie K.	60-100	
Fry, Rosalie K.	Deep in the Forest (1st AM, 12mo, 95p, 5 fp color, DJ/2.50)	Dodd	1956	Fry, Rosalie K.	60-100	*
Fry, Rosalie K.	Ladybug! Ladybug! (1st {std}, 8vo, [33]p, ibds, fp 2-color, dep, DJ/1.00)	Dutton	1940	Fry, Rosalie K.	50-85	*
Fry, Rosalie K.	Matelot, Little Sailor of Brittany (1st {std}, 8vo, 128p, b/w, DJ/2.75)	Dutton	1958	Fry, Rosalie K.	25-35	
Fry, Rosalie K.	Mountain Door (1st AM {std}, 8vo, 128p, b/w, DJ/2.95)	Dutton	1961	Fry, Rosalie K.	50-85	
Fry, Rosalie K.	Pipkin Sees the World (1st {std}, 8vo, 96p, b/w, DJ/2.00)	Dutton	1951	Fry, Rosalie K.	20-30	
Fry, Rosalie K.	Secret of the Ron Mor Skerry (1st AM {std}, 8vo, 95p, b/w, DJ/2.50)	Dutton	1959	Fry, Rosalie K.	100-150	*
Fry, Rosalie K.	Wind Call (1st {std}, sm8vo, gilt, 115p, fp color, DJ/2.50)	Dutton	(1955)	Fry, Rosalie K.	60-90	
Sharp, Margery	Lost at the Fair (1st {std}, sm8vo, 57p, fp 2-color, DJ/2.95)	Little/Brown	(1965)	Fry, Rosalind	25-40	
Montgomery, F.T.	Billy Whiskers' Kids (1st, sq8vo, 134p, gilt, 6cp)	Saalfield	(1903)	Fry, W.H.	70-120	
Evans, Florence A.	Jewel Story Book (1st, 12mo, 102p, green cl, 4pl)	Saalfield	1903	Fry, W.H.	25-45	
Sutton, Adah L.	Mr. Bunny - His Book (4to, ipcb, 106p, color)	Saalfield	(1900)	Fry, W.H.	200-300	*
Denison, Mary	Yellow Violin (1st, 12mo, 311p, green/gilt, 4pl)	Saalfield	1902	Fry, W.H.	50-80	R*
Mabie, Hamilton W.	Fairy Tales Every Child Should Know (1st, 8vo, 266p, p-o, 8cp)	Doubleday/Page	1915	Frye, Mary H.	60-100	
Mabie, Hamilton W.	Myths Every Child Should Know (1st, lg8vo, p-o, 224p, 11cp)	Doubleday/Page	1914	Frye, Mary H.	60-90	
Gray, Eliz. J.	Tilly-Tod (1st {std}, sm8vo, 173p, blue cl, col frn, b/w, pep)	Doubleday/Doran	1929	Frye, Mary H.	35-60	*
Lagerlof, Selma	Wonderful Adventures of Nils (1st, lg8vo, 263p, 24cp, pep)	Doubleday/Page	1913	Frye, Mary H.	120-200	
Burgess, Thornton	Burgess Animal Book for Children (1st, 8vo, 363p, green cl, p-o, cp)	Little/Brown	1920	Fuertes, Louis A.	100-170	
Burgess, Thornton	Burgess Bird Book for Children (1st, 8vo, p-o, 351p, 32cp)	Little/Brown	1919	Fuertes, Louis A.	120-180	
Fujikawa, Gyo	Child's Book of Poems (1st, lg4to, 117p, ipcb, dp color, pep)	Grosset/Dunlap	(1969)	Fujikawa, Gyo	30-50	
Morel, Eve (comp)	Fairy Tales & Fables (1st, lg4to, 124p, color, pep)	Grosset/Dunlap	(1970)	Fujikawa, Gyo	50-80	
Baruch, Dorothy W.	I Like Automobiles (1st, 8vo, [55]p, color, pep)	NY: J. Day	(1931)	Fujikawa, Gyo	35-60	*
Moore, Clement C.	Night Before Christmas (1st, 4to, ibds, color, pep)	Grosset/Dunlap	(1961)	Fujikawa, Gyo	60-100	
Fullylove, John	Edinburgh (1st, 8vo, 176p, teg, blue/gilt, 21cp)	L: A&C Black	1904	Fullylove, John	80-125	
Buck, Pearl S.	Big Flight (1st, 8vo, 47p, fp b/w, DJ/2.95)	John Day	(1965)	Funai, Mamoru	70-100	R*
Howard, Coralie (comp)	First Book of Short Verse (1st, 8vo, 125p, b/w, DJ)	F. Watts	(1964)	Funai, Mamoru	45-75	
Benchley, Nathaniel	Flying Lesson of Gerald Pelican (1st, lg8vo, 31p, 2-color, DJ/3.50)	Harper	(1970)	Funai, Mamoru	30-45	*
Weelen, Guy	Little Red Train (1st, sm4to, [24]p, fp 1-color, pep, DJ/2.95)	Lothrop, Lee	(1966)	Funai, Mamoru	30-50	
Hood, Flora	Living in Navajoland (1st, 8vo, [64]p, fp 1-color, DJ)	Putnam	(1970)	Funai, Mamoru	30-50	*
Parish, Peggy	Ootah's Lucky Day (1st, 8vo, 63p, color, DJ/2.50)	Harper	(1970)	Funai, Mamoru	20-25	*
Holl, Adelaide	Runaway Giant (1st, 4to, [28]p, fp 2-color, pep, DJ/3.50)	Lothrop, Lee	1967	Funai, Mamoru	25-45	*
Benchley, Nathaniel	Several Tricks of Edgar Dolphin (1st, 8vo, 60p, color, DJ/2.50)	Harper	(1970)	Funai, Mamoru	20-30	
Hunt, Mabel L.	John of Pudding Lane (1st, 8vo, 161p, color, pep, DJ/1.75)	Stokes	(1941)	Funk, Clotilde	25-45	
Hunt, Mabel L.	Ladycake Farm (1st, 8vo, 126p, fp b/w, pep, DJ/2.25)	Lippincott	(1952)	Funk, Clotilde	20-30	
Seeger, Ruth C.	Let's Build a Railroad (1st {std}, 4to, ibds, [32]p, color, DJ/2.50)	Aladdin	(1954)	Funk, Tom	30-50	
Learnard, Rachel	Mrs. Roo and the Bunnies (1st, lg8vo, 29p, color, pep, DJ/2.25)	Houghton	1953	Funk, Tom	50-80	
Battles, Edith	Terrible Trick or Treat (1st, lg8vo, [48]p, fp color, DJ/3.95)	Young Scott	(1970)	Funk, Tom	25-45	
Girvin, Brenda	Round Fairyland with Alice & the White Rabbit (1st, 8vo, 312p, b/w)	L: Wells/Gard.	1916	Furniss, Dorothy	70-100	
Furniss, Dorothy	Sky High: Flight of Fancy for Children (1st, ob4to, 169p, 15cp, 31pl)	L: Routledge	[1905]	Furniss, Dorothy	150-220	*
Farrow, George E.	Missing Prince (1st, lg8vo, 197p, green/gilt, AEG, b/w, cep)	L: Hutchinson	1896	Furniss, H.& D.	100-165	
Farrow, George E.	Missing Prince (1st AM, 8vo, 198p, pict cl, b/w)	Dodd	1897	Furniss, H.& D.	80-120	*
Farrow, George E.	Wallypug of Why (1st, 8vo, green/gilt, 201p, AEG, 15pl)	L: Hutchinson	(1895)	Furniss, H.& D.	200-300	
Allen, F.M.	Brayhard (1st, 8vo, teg, 308p, green/gilt, b/w, pep)	L: Ward/Down.	1890	Furniss, Harry	60-90	
Parry, Edward A.	Gamble Gold (1st. sq8vo, ibds, 248p, AEG, gilt, 15pl)	L: Hutchinson	1907	Furniss, Harry	60-80	
Burnand, Francis (ed)	Incompleat Angler (1st, 8vo, 94p, b/w)	L: Bradbury	1887	Furniss, Harry	100-170	
Carroll, Lewis	Sylvie & Bruno (1st, 8vo, AEG, 400p, gilt, 46 b/w)	L: Macmillan	1889	Furniss, Harry	140-200	

AUTHOR	TITLE	PUBLISHER	DATE	ARTIST	PRICE	LC
Carroll, Lewis	Sylvie & Bruno Concluded (1st, 8vo, red/gilt, AEG, 423p, b/w)	L: Macmillan	1893	Furniss, Harry	170-270	
Farrow, George E.	Wallypug of Why (1st AM, 8vo, 201p, b/w illus)	Dodd	1896	Furniss, Harry	200-300	
Browne, Maggie	Wanted - A King (1st, 12mo, 193p, green/gilt, teg, pep)	L: Cassell	1890	Furniss, Harry	140-220	*
Fyleman, Rose	Fairy Queen (1st, 8vo, 64p, cloth, col frn, pep)	Doran	(1923)	Fyleman, Rose	65-90	
Szekely, Sari	Marika (1st, sm4to, 62p, p-o, fp color, pep, DJ/1.50)	Whitman	1939	Gabor, Barbara	60-100	
Williams, Eleanor	And a Good Fat Hen (1st, lg8vo, red cl, [47]p, DJ/1.50, lettering by...)	Putnam	(1939)	Gag, Flavia	30-50	
Tracy, Thomas H.	Book of the Poodle (1st, 4to, gilt, 136p, b/w, DJ/5.00)	Viking	1950	Gag, Flavia	35-50	
Turner, Thyra	Christmas House... (1st, 12mo, ibds, 25p, 14 color, DJ/1.00)	Scribner	1943	Gag, Flavia	80-120	
Gag, Flavia	Chubby's First Year (1st, 24mo, [31]p, fp color, DJ/1.95)	Henry Holt & Co.	1960	Gag, Flavia	30-45	
Dalgliesh, Alice	Davenports & Cherry Pie (1st, 8vo, 196p, grey cl, fp b/w, DJ/2.50)	Scribner	(1949)	Gag, Flavia	50-85	
Dalgliesh, Alice	Davenports are at Dinner (1st, 8vo, ivory cl, 182p, b/w, DJ/2.50)	Scribner	1948	Gag, Flavia	50-85	
Gag, Flavia	Four Legs and a Tail (1st {std}, 8vo, 150p, b/w, DJ/2.50)	Holt	(1952)	Gag, Flavia	25-40	
McDevitt, Jean	No, No, Taffy (1st {std}, 4to, ibds, 47p, 2-color, DJ/2.50)	Doubleday	1952	Gag, Flavia	45-70	*
Dobbs, Rose	Once Upon a Time (1st, 8vo, 117p, b/w, DJ/2.00)	Random	(1950)	Gag, Flavia	25-45	
Gag, Flavia	Sing a Song of Seasons (1st, 4to, ibds, 29p, b/w, DJ/1.50)	Coward	(1936)	Gag, Flavia	50-80	*
Gag, Asta	Sue & Sew-and-Sew (1st, 8vo, 63p, ibds, b/w, pep)	Coward	(1931)	Gag, Flavia	40-60	*
Palmer, Robin	The Barkingtons (1st, 8vo, 112p, grey cl, 2-color, pep, DJ/2.00)	Harper	(1948)	Gag, Flavia	30-50	*
Woodward, Hildegard	Time Was (1st, 4to, [48]p, color, DJ/1.50)	Scribner	(1941)	Gag, Flavia	50-80	
Gag, Flavia	Tweeter of Prairie Dog Town (1st {std}, 8vo, 61p, b/w, DJ/2.25)	Holt	(1957)	Gag, Flavia	40-65	*
Travers, Georgia	Wily Woodchucks (1st, sm ob4to, ibds, [32]p, color, DJ/1.50)	Coward	(1946)	Gag, Flavia	50-80	
Gag, Wanda	ABC Bunny (1st {std}, lg4to, ibds, [32]p, b/w, pep, NH)	Coward	1933	Gag, Wanda	400-600	R
Gag, Wanda	Funny Thing (1st, lg ob8vo, [32]p, yellow ipcb, b/w, pep)	Coward	1929	Gag, Wanda	200-350	
Gag, Wanda	Gone is Gone (1st, 12mo, yellow cl, [63]p, col frn, b/w, DJ/1.00)	Coward	(1935)	Gag, Wanda	300-450	
Gag, Wanda	Growing Pains (1st, lg8vo, 479p, blue ibds, b/w, DJ/3.75)	Coward	1940	Gag, Wanda	160-240	
Gag, Wanda	Millions of Cats (1st [1st bk.], lg ob8vo, ipcb, [32]p, b/w, pep, NH)	Coward	1928	Gag, Wanda	250-400	R
Grimm Bros.	More Tales from Grimm (1st, 8vo, 257p, blue cl, col frn, b/w, DJ/2.75)	Coward	(1947)	Gag, Wanda	180-250	R
Gag, Wanda	Nothing at All (1st, lg ob8vo, ibds, [32]p, color, pep, DJ/1.75, CH)	Coward	(1941)	Gag, Wanda	200-300	
Gag, Wanda	Snippy & Snappy (1st, lg ob8vo, yellow ibds, [48]p, b/w, pep)	Coward	1931	Gag, Wanda	160-240	
Grimm Bros.	Snow White & Seven Dwarfs (1st, 8vo, green ibds, 43p, b/w, DJ/1.00, CH)	Coward	(1938)	Gag, Wanda	180-260	
Grimm Bros.	Tales from Grimm (1st, 8vo, blue cl, 237p, col frn, 6pl, DJ/2.00)	Coward	(1936)	Gag, Wanda	280-400	R
Gag, Wanda	Three Gay Tales from Grimm (1st, 8vo, ipcb, 63p, b/w, DJ/1.50)	Coward	(1943)	Gag, Wanda	160-225	
Gag, Wanda	Wanda Gag's Story Book (1st, ob16mo, [112]p, yellow bds, p-o, pep)	Coward	(1932)	Gag, Wanda	170-240	
Armour, Richard	Adventures of Egbert the Easter Egg (1st, sm4to, 43p, color, cep, DJ/2.75)	McGraw-Hill	(1965)	Galdone, Paul	30-45	
Offit, Sidney	Adventures of Homer Fink (1st, 8vo, 181p, b/w, DJ/3.50)	St. Martin's	(1966)	Galdone, Paul	20-30	
Armour, Richard	All Sizes and Shapes of Monkeys and Apes (1st, 4to, 37p, color, DJ/4.50)	McGraw-Hill	(1970)	Galdone, Paul	30-45	*
Titus, Eve	Anatole (1st, sm4to, 32p, blue cl, color, DJ/2.00, CH)	Whittlesey	(1956)	Galdone, Paul	70-120	
Titus, Eve	Anatole & the Cat (1st, sm4to, 32p, red cl, color, DJ/2.25, CH)	Whittlesey	(1957)	Galdone, Paul	80-120	
Titus, Eve	Anatole and the Piano (1st, 4to, 32p, color, DJ/2.75)	McGraw-Hill	(1966)	Galdone, Paul	40-65	
Titus, Eve	Anatole and the Poodle (1st, 4to, 32p, fp 2-color, dep, DJ/2.75)	Whittlesey	(1965)	Galdone, Paul	40-65	
Titus, Eve	Anatole and the Robot (1st, 4to, 32p, fp 2-color, dep, DJ/2.50)	Whittlesey	(1960)	Galdone, Paul	40-65	
Titus, Eve	Anatole and the Thirty Thieves (1st, 4to, 32p, fp 2-color, DJ/4.50)	McGraw-Hill	(1969)	Galdone, Paul	40-65	
Titus, Eve	Anatole and the Toyshop (1st, 4to, 36p, color, DJ/4.50)	McGraw-Hill	(1970)	Galdone, Paul	30-50	
Titus, Eve	Anatole over Paris (1st, 4to, 32p, color, DJ/2.75)	Whittlesey	(1961)	Galdone, Paul	30-50	
Armour, Richard	Animals on the Ceiling (1st, 4to, 32p, fp 2-color, dep, DJ/2.95)	McGraw-Hill	(1966)	Galdone, Paul	30-50	
Miers, Earl S.	Ball of Fire (1st {std}, 8vo, 220p, b/w, DJ/2.50)	World	(1956)	Galdone, Paul	20-30	
Goodman, George	Bascombe, Fastest Hound Alive (1st, 4to, 31p, fp 2-color, pep, DJ/2.75)	Wm. Morrow	1958	Galdone, Paul	60-90	
Corbett, Scott	Baseball Trick (1st {std}, 8vo, 105p, b/w, DJ/3.25)	Little/Brown	(1965)	Galdone, Paul	20-30	*
Titus, Eve	Basil & the Lost Colony (1st, 8vo, 95p, b/w, DJ/2.95)	Whittlesey	(1964)	Galdone, Paul	30-50	
Titus, Eve	Basil of Baker Street (1st, 8vo, beige cl, 96p, b/w, DJ/2.75)	Whittlesey	(1958)	Galdone, Paul	40-70	
Hopkinson, Frances	Battle of the Kegs (1st {std}, 4to, [32]p, color, DJ/3.75)	Crowell	(1964)	Galdone, Paul	50-80	*
Martin, Patricia	Benjie Goes into Business (1st, 4to, [30]p, 2-color, DJ/2.75)	Putnam	(1961)	Galdone, Paul	30-45	*
Renick, Marion	Big Basketball Prize (1st, 4to, [32]p, color, DJ/3.25)	Scribner	1963	Galdone, Paul	25-40	
Saxe, John	Blind Men and the Elephants (1st, smob4to, [48]p, fp 2-color, DJ/2.50)	Whittlesey	(1963)	Galdone, Paul	20-35	
Renick, Marion	Boy at Bat (1st, 4to, [32]p, fp color, DJ/2.95)	Scribner	(1961)	Galdone, Paul	30-45	*
Mann, Peggy	Boy with a Billion Pets (1st, sq8vo, [44]p, 2-color, DJ)	Coward	(1968)	Galdone, Paul	25-40	
Grimm Bros.	Bremen Town Musicians (1st, sm ob4to, 32p, 2-color, DJ/3.75)	McGraw-Hill	(1968)	Galdone, Paul	30-50	
Peterson, Hans	Brownie (1st AM, 24mo, [32]p, color, DJ/1.50)	Lothrop, Lee	(1965)	Galdone, Paul	20-35	*
Shaw, Richard	Budd's Noisy Wagon (1st, ob8vo, [32]p, fp 3-color, DJ/2.95)	NY: Warne	(1968)	Galdone, Paul	45-70	
Steele, William O.	Buffalo Knife (1st {std}, 8vo, 177p, b/w, DJ/2.25)	Harcourt	(1952)	Galdone, Paul	25-40	*
Goetz, Lee G.	Camel in the Sea (1st, 8vo, 58p, 2-color, DJ/2.95)	McGraw-Hill	(1966)	Galdone, Paul	25-45	
Carryl, Charles E.	Capital Ship (1st, ob4to, [32]p, color, dep, DJ/2.75)	Whittlesey	1963	Galdone, Paul	35-50	R
Ziner, Feenie	Counting Carnival (1st, 8vo, [32]p, 1-color, DJ/2.50)	Coward	(1962)	Galdone, Paul	25-45	*
Everson, Dale	Different Dog (1st, 4to, blue cl, 31p, 2-color, pep, DJ/2.75)	Wm. Morrow	1960	Galdone, Paul	30-50	
Corbett, Scott	Disappearing Dog Trick (1st {std}, 8vo, 108p, b/w, DJ/3.25)	Little/Brown	(1963)	Galdone, Paul	20-35	
Mowat, Farley	Dog Who Wouldn't Be (1st {std}, 8vo, 238p, DJ/3.95)	Little/Brown	(1957)	Galdone, Paul	30-45	
Armour, Richard	Dozen Dinosaurs (1st, 4to, 32p, 2-color, DJ/3.95)	McGraw-Hill	(1967)	Galdone, Paul	30-45	
Johnston, Johanna	Edie Changes her Mind (1st, sm4to, 48p, fp 2-color, DJ/2.75)	Putnam	(1964)	Galdone, Paul	30-50	
Rinkoff, Barbara	Elbert the Mind Reader (1st, 8vo, 112p, b/w, DJ/3.25)	Lothrop, Lee	(1967)	Galdone, Paul	40-70	
Steele, William O.	Far Frontier (1st {std}, 8vo, 185p, fp b/w, DJ/2.95)	Harcourt	(1959)	Galdone, Paul	20-30	
Myers, Grace	Fishing Cat (1st, ob8vo, yellow cl, [24]p, 1-color, pep, DJ/1.25)	Abingdon Press	1953	Galdone, Paul	30-50	
Steele, William O.	Flaming Arrows (1st {std}, 8vo, 178p, b/w, DJ/2.75)	Harcourt	(1957)	Galdone, Paul	30-60	*
Showers, Paul	Follow Your Nose (1st, ob8vo, [40]p, fp 2-color, DJ/2.50)	Crowell	1963	Galdone, Paul	25-40	
Merriam, Eve	Gaggle of Geese (1st, sm4to, yellow cl, [31]p, fp 2-color, pep, DJ)	Knopf	(1960)	Galdone, Paul	50-80	*
Fritz, Jean	George Washington's Breakfast (1st, 8vo, [47]p, fp 2-color, DJ/3.75)	Coward	(1969)	Galdone, Paul	30-50	
Gage, Wilson	Ghost of Five Owl Farm (1st {std}, 8vo, 127p, b/w, DJ/3.50)	World	(1966)	Galdone, Paul	20-30	
Hawthorne, Nathaniel	Golden Touch (1st, 8vo, orange cl, 61p, fp 2-color, dep, DJ/2.50)	Whittlesey	(1959)	Galdone, Paul	40-65	
Buckley, Helen E.	Grandfather and I (1st, ob4to, [32]p, fp color, DJ/2.75)	Lothrop, Lee	(1959)	Galdone, Paul	30-45	
Buckley, Helen E.	Grandmother and I (1st, 4to, [30]p, fp color, DJ/2.75)	Lothrop, Lee	(1961)	Galdone, Paul	25-40	

AUTHOR	TITLE	PUBLISHER	DATE	ARTIST	PRICE	LC
Plenn, Doris T.	Green Song (1st {std}, 8vo, 126p, b/w, DJ/2.50)	McKay	(1954)	Galdone, Paul	25-45	
Corbett, Scott	Hairy Horror Trick (1st {std}, 8vo, 101p, b/w, DJ/3.50)	Little/Brown	(1969)	Galdone, Paul	20-35	
Dodge, Mary Mapes	Hans Brinker (1st [Jr. Deluxe], 8vo, 319p, col frn, b/w)	Doubleday	(1954)	Galdone, Paul	30-45	
Aesopus	Hare and the Tortoise (1st, ob4to, [31]p, fp 2-color, pep, DJ/2.50)	Whittlesey	(1962)	Galdone, Paul	25-45	
N/A	Henny Penny (1st, narrow ob4to, [32]p, 3-color, DJ/3.50)	Seabury Press	1968	Galdone, Paul	30-50	
Ross, Nancy W.	Heroines of the Early West (1st, 8vo, 182p, b/w, pep, DJ/1.95)	Random	(1960)	Galdone, Paul	20-30	
Branley, Franklyn	High Sounds, Low Sounds (1st, ob8vo, ibds, [40]p, fp 2-color, DJ/3.25)	Crowell	(1967)	Galdone, Paul	30-45	
N/A	History of Simple Simon (1st, smob4to, [32]p, fp 2-color, dep, DJ/2.75)	McGraw-Hill	(1966)	Galdone, Paul	30-50	
Nye, Harry	Home is If You Find It (1st {std}, 12mo, 251p, b/w, DJ/2.00)	Doubleday	1947	Galdone, Paul	30-50	
N/A	House that Jack Built (1st, sm ob4to, 32p, fp 2-color, pep, DJ/2.25)	Whittlesey	(1961)	Galdone, Paul	30-45	
Schlein, Miriam	How Do You Travel? (1st, 8vo, unpag, color, DJ/1.50)	Abingdon Press	1954	Galdone, Paul	25-40	
Musselman, M.M.	I Married a Redhead (1st, sm8vo, 244p, b/w, DJ/3.00)	Crowell	(1949)	Galdone, Paul	30-45	
Jackson, C. Paul	Jamesville Jets (1st, 8vo, 143p, b/w, DJ/2.75)	Follett	(1959)	Galdone, Paul	25-40	
Meeks, Esther	Jeff and Mr. James' Pond (1st, 8vo, [35]p, color, DJ/2.95)	Lothrop, Lee	(1962)	Galdone, Paul	30-45	*
Cheney, Cora	Key of Gold (1st {std}, 8vo, 127p, DJ/2.25)	Holt	(1955)	Galdone, Paul	25-40	*
Kusan, Ivan	Koko and the Ghosts (1st AM {std}, 8vo, 215p, b/w, DJ/3.75)	Harcourt	(1966)	Galdone, Paul	20-35	
Corbett, Scott	Lemonade Trick (1st {std}, 8vo, 103p, b/w, DJ/2.75)	Little/Brown	(1960)	Galdone, Paul	20-35	
Peterson, Hans	Liselott and the Goloff (1st AM {std}, 8vo, 157p, b/w, DJ/3.50)	Coward	(1964)	Galdone, Paul	20-35	
Buckley, Helen E.	Little Boy & the Birthdays (1st, 8vo, [36]p, color, DJ/3.00)	Lothrop, Lee	(1965)	Galdone, Paul	30-50	
Emerson, Caroline	Little Green Car (1st, 8vo, ipcb, [28]p, color, pep, DJ/0.50)	Grosset/Dunlap	(1946)	Galdone, Paul	60-100	*
N/A	Little Tom Tucker (1st, sm ob4to, [39]p, fp color, DJ/4.50)	McGraw-Hill	(1970)	Galdone, Paul	30-45	
Baldwin, Clara	Little Tuck (1st {std}, lg8vo, 95p, yellow cl, b/w, DJ/2.00)	Doubleday	(1959)	Galdone, Paul	30-50	
Steele, William O.	Lone Hunt (1st {std}, 8vo, 176p, b/w, DJ/2.75)	Harcourt	(1956)	Galdone, Paul	20-35	
Showers, Paul	Look at Your Eyes (1st, ob8vo, [30]p, color, DJ)	Crowell	(1962)	Galdone, Paul	25-40	
Corbett, Scott	Mailbox Trick (1st {std}, 8vo, 103p, fp b/w, DJ/2.95)	Little/Brown	(1961)	Galdone, Paul	25-45	
Calhoun, Mary	Making the Mississippi Shout (1st, 8vo, 96p, b/w, DJ/2.50)	Wm. Morrow	1957	Galdone, Paul	20-35	
Otto, Margaret G.	Man in the Moon (1st {std}, sm8vo, green cl, 128p, fp b/w, DJ/2.50)	Holt	(1957)	Galdone, Paul	40-65	
Gage, Wilson	Miss Osborne-the-Mop (1st {std}, 8vo, 156p, b/w, DJ/2.95)	World	(1963)	Galdone, Paul	20-35	
MacGregor, Ellen	Miss Pickerell and the Geiger Counter (1st, 8vo, 123p, b/w, DJ/2.25)	Whittlesey	(1953)	Galdone, Paul	40-65	
MacGregor, Ellen	Miss Pickerell Goes to Mars (1st, sm8vo, red cl, 128p, fp b/w, DJ/2.25)	Whittlesey	(1951)	Galdone, Paul	45-70	
MacGregor, Ellen	Miss Pickerell Goes to the Arctic (1st, 8vo, 126p, b/w, DJ/2.25)	Whittlesey	(1954)	Galdone, Paul	30-45	
MacGregor, Ellen	Miss Pickerell Goes Undersea (1st, 8vo, 128p, b/w, DJ/2.25)	Whittlesey	(1953)	Galdone, Paul	30-45	
Montgomery, R.	Mister Jim (1st {std}, 8vo, 219p, b/w, DJ/2.75)	World	(1957)	Galdone, Paul	30-50	
McGraw, Eloise J.	Moccasin Trail (1st, 8vo, 247p, DJ/2.75, NH, b/w frn by...)	Coward	1952	Galdone, Paul	30-50	
Galdone, Paul	Monkey and the Crocodile (1st, 4to, [32]p, color, DJ/4.50)	Seabury Press	(1969)	Galdone, Paul	30-50	*
Miers, Earl S.	Monkey Shines (1st {std}, 8vo, 207p, b/w, DJ/2.50)	World	(1952)	Galdone, Paul	20-30	
MacGregor, Ellen	Mr. Ferguson of the Fire Department (1st, 4to, 32p, 2-color, dpep, DJ/2.25)	Whittlesey	(1956)	Galdone, Paul	30-45	
MacGregor, Ellen	Mr. Pringle and Mister Buttonhouse (1st, 4to, 32p, fp color, dep, DJ/2.00)	Whittlesey	(1957)	Galdone, Paul	30-50	
Thayer, Jane	Mrs. Perrywinkle's Pets (1st, sm8vo, 45p, 2-color, dep, DJ/2.00)	Wm. Morrow	1955	Galdone, Paul	30-50	
Lord, Nancy	My Dog and I (1st, sm4to, 31p, fp 2-color, pep, DJ/2.25)	Whittlesey	1958	Galdone, Paul	40-65	
Buckley, Helen E.	My Sister and I (1st, 4to, [32]p, 3-color, cep, DJ/2.95)	Lothrop, Lee	(1963)	Galdone, Paul	30-50	
Black, Irma S.	Night Cat (1st, lg ob8vo, [32]p, black cl, cep, b/w, DJ/2.25)	Holiday House	1957	Galdone, Paul	40-65	
Fenton, Edward	Nine Lives (1st, 4to, ipcb, 62p, pep, b/w, DJ/2.50)	Pantheon	(1951)	Galdone, Paul	40-65	
Armour, Richard	Odd Old Mammals (1st, 4to, 36p, 2-color, DJ/3.95)	McGraw-Hill	(1968)	Galdone, Paul	30-45	
Bulla, Clyde R.	Old Charlie (1st, sm8vo, 80p, b/w, DJ/2.50)	Crowell	1957	Galdone, Paul	30-50	
Martin, Sarah C.	Old Mother Hubbard and Her Dog (1st, ob4to, 32p, color, DJ/2.25)	Whittlesey	(1960)	Galdone, Paul	30-50	
Hodges, Margaret	One Little Drum (1st, 8vo, 63p, b/w, DJ/2.25)	Follett	(1958)	Galdone, Paul	25-40	
Belpre, Pura	Ote, a Puerto Rican Folktale (1st, 4to, [32]p, color, DJ/3.95)	Pantheon	(1969)	Galdone, Paul	30-50	
Galdone, Paul	Paddy the Penguin (1st, sm4to, [30]p, 2-color, pep, DJ/3.00)	Crowell	(1959)	Galdone, Paul	40-65	*
Hawthorne, Nathaniel	Pandora's Box (1st, 8vo, 58p, fp 1-color, dep, DJ/2.95)	McGraw-Hill	(1967)	Galdone, Paul	30-45	
Bianki, Vitali	Peek the Piper (1st {std}, 8vo, 63p, b/w, DJ/2.95)	NY: Braziller	(1964)	Galdone, Paul	20-30	
O'Neill, Mary	People I'd Like to Keep (1st {std}, lg8vo, 64p, color, DJ/2.95)	Doubleday	1964	Galdone, Paul	20-30	
Steele, William O.	Perilous Road (1st {std}, 8vo, 191p, blue cl, b/w, DJ/2.95, NH, JABA)	Harcourt	(1958)	Galdone, Paul	40-65	
Eager, Edward	Playing Possum (1st, lg8vo, [32]p, green cl, 1-color, pep, DJ/2.50)	Putnam	1955	Galdone, Paul	80-125	
Frost, Frances	Rocket Away! (1st, 4to, 48p, b/w, DJ/2.00)	Whittlesey	(1953)	Galdone, Paul	30-50	
Cheney, Cora	Rocking Chair Buck (1st {std}, 8vo, 128p, b/w, DJ/2.25)	Holt	(1956)	Galdone, Paul	25-40	
Branley, Franklyn	Rusty Rings a Bell (1st, 8vo, [30]p, 2-color, DJ/2.50)	Crowell	(1957)	Galdone, Paul	25-45	
Saxon, Gladys	Sea Beach Adventure (1st {std}, 8vo, 190p, b/w, DJ/2.75)	Holt	(1956)	Galdone, Paul	25-40	
Lampman, Evelyn	Shy Stegosaurus of Indian Springs (1st {std} 8vo, 232p, gilt, b/w, DJ/2.75)	Doubleday	(1962)	Galdone, Paul	80-120	
Iden, Carol	Sidney's Ghost (1st, 8vo, 127p, fp b/w, DJ/2.95)	World	(1969)	Galdone, Paul	20-35	
Bialk, Elisa	Silver Purse (1st {std}, sm8vo, 169p, orange cl, b/w, DJ/2.50)	World	(1952)	Galdone, Paul	25-45	
Faulkner, Nancy	Small Clown (1st {std}, 8vo, 62p, fp 1-color, DJ/2.50)	Doubleday	(1960)	Galdone, Paul	25-45	
Dolson, Hildegarde	Sorry to Be So Cheerful (1st {std}, 8vo, 207p, b/w, DJ/3.50)	Random	(1955)	Galdone, Paul	30-50	*
Todd, Ruthven	Space Cat (1st, sm8vo, 69p, blue cl, fp b/w, DJ/2.00)	Scribner	(1952)	Galdone, Paul	80-125	
Todd, Ruthven	Space Cat and the Kittens (1st, 8vo, 94p, b/w, DJ/2.50)	Scribner	(1958)	Galdone, Paul	70-100	
Todd, Ruthven	Space Cat Meets Mars (1st, 8vo, 72p, b/w, DJ/2.25)	Scribner	(1957)	Galdone, Paul	70-120	
Todd, Ruthven	Space Cat Visits Venus (1st, 8vo, 87p, fp b/w, DJ/2.00)	Scribner	(1955)	Galdone, Paul	70-125	
Coles, Robert	Star of Wonder (1st, sm4to, 48p, fp b/w, pep, DJ/2.25)	Whittlesey	(1953)	Galdone, Paul	30-50	
Goldin, Augusta	Sunlit Sea (1st, ob8vo, 33p, color, DJ/3.50)	Crowell	(1968)	Galdone, Paul	20-35	*
Goudey, Alice	Sunnyvale Fair (1st, 8vo, [62]p, fp 1-color, DJ/2.95)	Scribner	(1962)	Galdone, Paul	30-45	
Bulla, Clyde R.	Sword in the Tree (1st {std}, 8vo, 113p, red cl, b/w, DJ/2.50)	Crowell	1956	Galdone, Paul	30-50	
Johnston, Johanna	That's Right, Edie (1st, 4to, 46p, fp 2-color, DJ/3.50)	Putnam	(1966)	Galdone, Paul	30-45	
MacGregor, Ellen	Theodore Turtle (1st, sm4to, green cl, 32p, color, pep, DJ/2.00)	Whittlesey	1955	Galdone, Paul	50-85	
Jacobs, Joseph (ed)	Three Wishes (1st, ob4to, 32p, fp 2-color, pep, DJ/2.50)	Whittlesey	(1961)	Galdone, Paul	25-45	*
Branley, Franklyn	Timmy and the Tin-Can Telephone (1st, 8vo, [42]p, 2-color, dep, DJ/2.50)	Crowell	(1959)	Galdone, Paul	30-45	
Van Der Veer, Judy	To the Rescue (1st {std}, 8vo, 160p, b/w, DJ/4.50)	Harcourt	(1969)	Galdone, Paul	20-35	
Mother Goose	Tom, Tom the Piper's Son (1st, ob4to, 32p, color, DJ/2.50)	Whittlesey	1964	Galdone, Paul	40-70	R*
Steele, William O.	Tomahawks and Trouble (1st {std}, 8vo, 213p, b/w, DJ/2.50)	Harcourt	1955	Galdone, Paul	20-30	

ARTIST: 84

AUTHOR	TITLE	PUBLISHER	DATE	ARTIST	PRICE	LC
Miers, Earl S.	Touchdown Trouble (1st {std}, 8vo, 221p, DJ/2.50)	World	(1953)	Galdone, Paul	20-30	
Viorst, Judith	Try It Again, Sam (1st, lg8vo, [39]p, 2-color, DJ/3.75)	Lothrop, Lee	(1970)	Galdone, Paul	20-35	
Daniels, Guy	Tsar's Riddles (1st, 4to, 32p, 2-color, DJ/3.75)	McGraw-Hill	(1967)	Galdone, Paul	25-40	
Corbett, Scott	Turnabout Trick (1st {std}, 8vo, 105p, b/w, DJ/3.50)	Little/Brown	(1967)	Galdone, Paul	20-35	
Greene, Roberta	Two and Me Makes Three (1st, 4to, unpag, color, DJ)	Crowell	(1970)	Galdone, Paul	30-50	*
Lear, Edward	Two Old Bachelors (1st, 4to, [32]p, fp 2-color, pep, DJ/2.50)	Whittlesey	(1962)	Galdone, Paul	40-60	R*
Hirshberg, Al	Varsity Double Play (1st {std}, sm8vo, 246p, DJ/2.75)	Little/Brown	(1956)	Galdone, Paul	20-35	
Moore, Clement C.	Visit from St. Nicholas (1st, ob8vo, [32]p, color, DJ/2.95)	McGraw-Hill	(1968)	Galdone, Paul	30-50	*
Phleger, Fred	Whales Go By (1st {std}, lg8vo, ipcb, 62p, p-o, pep, color, DJ/1.95)	Random	(1959)	Galdone, Paul	50-85	
Callahan, Lorna	Where the Trail Divides (1st, 8vo, 188p, b/w, DJ/3.00)	Whittlesey	(1957)	Galdone, Paul	45-70	
Schatz, Letta	Whiskers, My Cat (1st, sm4to, 32p, fp 1-color, DJ/3.50)	McGraw-Hill	(1967)	Galdone, Paul	50-80	
Steele, William O.	Wilderness Journey (1st {std}, sm8vo, aqua cl, 209p, b/w, DJ/2.50)	Harcourt	(1953)	Galdone, Paul	25-40	
Steele, William O.	Winter Danger (1st {std}, 8vo, 183p, grey cl, b/w, DJ/2.25)	Harcourt	(1954)	Galdone, Paul	25-40	
Rabelais	Wise Fool (1st {std}, 4to, ibds, [32]p, color, DJ/3.95)	Random	(1968)	Galdone, Paul	25-40	
Martin, Patricia	Woody's Big Trouble (1st, 4to, 46p, fp 2-color)	Putnam	(1967)	Galdone, Paul	20-30	
Armour, Richard	Year Santa Went Modern (1st, 4to, [32]p, 3-color, DJ/2.75)	McGraw-Hill	(1964)	Galdone, Paul	30-50	
Showers, Paul	Your Skin and Mine (1st, sq8vo, [36]p, 2-color, DJ/2.95)	Crowell	(1965)	Galdone, Paul	30-45	
Selden, George	I See What I See! (1st {std}, sm ob4to, [46]p, color, DJ/3.50)	Ariel	(1962)	Galster, Robert	20-30	
Franchot, Annie W.	White Giant & Black Giant (1st, lg8vo, ipcb, 72p, fp b/w)	Dutton	(1924)	Gamble, James	50-80	
Gannett, Lewis	Cream Hill (1st, 8vo, 191p, b/w, pep, DJ/3.50)	Viking	(1949)	Gannett, Ruth C.	25-40	
Gannett, Ruth S.	Dragons of Blueland (1st, 8vo, 87p, blue/gilt, pep, b/w, DJ/2.00)	Random	(1951)	Gannett, Ruth C.	40-65	
Gannett, Ruth S.	Elmer & the Dragon (1st, 8vo, 86p, red/gilt, pep, b/w, DJ/2.00)	Random	(1950)	Gannett, Ruth C.	40-65	
Thomas, Dorothy	Hi-Po the Hippo (1st {std}, folio, [48]p, ibds, color, DJ/3.00)	Random	(1942)	Gannett, Ruth C.	100-165	
Bailey, Carolyn S.	Miss Hickory (1st, lg8vo, tan cl, 123p, fp b/w, pep, DJ/2.50, NM)	Viking	1946	Gannett, Ruth C.	80-130	R
Gannett, Ruth S.	My Father's Dragon (1st, 8vo, 86p, gilt, b/w, pep, DJ/2.00, NH)	Random	(1948)	Gannett, Ruth C.	60-90	R
Reyher, Rebecca	My Mother/Most Beautiful Woman i/t World (1st, 8vo, [39]p, color, DJ, CH)	Howell/Soskin	(1945)	Gannett, Ruth C.	60-100	*
Gill, Richard	Paco Goes to the Fair (1st, 4to, [49]p, color, pep, DJ/2.00)	Henry Holt & Co.	(1940)	Gannett, Ruth C.	30-50	
Boutwell, Edna	Red Rooster (1st {std}, 8vo, [48]p, color, DJ/1.75)	Aladdin	(1950)	Garbutt, Bernard	25-45	*
Schwetzky, Otto	Peter Teeter Stories (1st, ob4to, [63]p, ipcb, color, pep)	Chi: Thompson	1905	Garman, R.H.	100-160	
Garner, Elvira	Ezekiel (1st [1st bk.], lg8vo, ibds, [44]p, color, DJ/1.50)	Henry Holt & Co.	1937	Garner, Elvira	120-200	
Garner, Elvira	Ezekiel Travels (1st, lg8vo, [46]p, ibds, color, DJ/1.50)	Henry Holt & Co.	(1938)	Garner, Elvira	160-225	
Garner, Elvira	Sarah Faith Anderson (1st, 8vo, [106]p, color, DJ/2.00)	J. Messner	(1939)	Garner, Elvira	100-175	
Garner, Elvira	Way Down in Tennessee (1st, lg8vo, [96]p, ibds, color, pep, DJ/2.00)	J. Messner	(1941)	Garner, Elvira	200-300	
Willson, John B.	Lucian's Wonderland... (1st, 8vo, brown/gilt, 163p, 15pl)	L: Blackwood	1899	Garnett, A. Payne	100-170	
Garnett, Eve	Family from One End Street (1st, 8vo, 212p, b/w, pep, DJ, CgM)	L: Muller	1937	Garnett, Eve	80-125	
Richards, Laura E.	Joyous Story of Toto (1st, 12mo, 226p, fp b/w)	Roberts Bros.	1885	Garrett, E.H.	30-50	
De La Rame, L.	Bimbi (1st AM, 8vo, 303p, 8pl)	Lippincott	1892	Garrett, Edmund H.	60-100	*
Garthwaite, Jimmy	Zoo Book (1st {std}, lg4to, ibds, [32]p, color)	Harper	1929	Garthwaite, Jimmy	80-120	
Baring-Gould, Sabine	Book of Fairy Tales (1st, 8vo, teg, 244p, gilt, uncut, 5pl)	L: Methuen	1894	Gaskin, Arthur J.	120-170	
Neale, Dr.	Good King Wenceslas (1st, sm4to, ipcb, [32]p, 6 woodcuts)	Cornish Bros.	1895	Gaskin, Arthur J.	150-250	
Andersen, Hans C.	Stories and Fairy Tales (1st, 2 vols, 8vo, teg, green/gilt, uncut)	L: G. Allen	1893	Gaskin, Arthur J.	250-350	
Andersen, Hans C.	Stories and Fairy Tales (1st AM, sm8vo, 826p, green cl, b/w)	Dodd	1897	Gaskin, Arthur J.	100-165	
Watts, Isaac	Divine & Moral Songs for Children (16mo, bds, 62p, teg, 12 fp color)	L: E. Mathews	[1897]	Gaskin, Mrs. A.	100-175	
Barrett, Leone	Buffin (1st, 8vo, 30p, green cl, p-o, color, pep, DJ/1.00)	Whitman	1935	Gaug, Margaret	40-65	
Dickens, Charles	Christmas Carol (1st, 4to, 121p, t-i frn, 23pl)	S.E. Cassino	1887	Gaugengigl, I.M.	100-160	*
Whyte, Adam G.	Christabel's Fairyland (1st, sm4to, ibds, p-o, 183p, color)	L: Chapman/Hall	1926	Gautier, Pauline	80-135	
Gay, Romney	Bonny's Wish (1st, sq12mo, [36]p, ibds, color, pep, DJ/0.50)	Grosset/Dunlap	1938	Gay, Romney	20-40	
Gay, Romney	Conny and Uncle Dick (1st, ob8vo, ipcb, [32]p, color, pep, DJ/0.50)	Grosset/Dunlap	1941	Gay, Romney	45-70	
Gay, Romney	Five Little Playmates (1st, 12mo, ibds, [61]p, color)	Grosset/Dunlap	(1941)	Gay, Romney	30-50	*
Gay, Romney	Funny Noise (1st, sq12mo, [34]p, ibds, color, pep, DJ/0.50)	Grosset/Dunlap	1935	Gay, Romney	25-40	
Quigg, Jane	Jean & Jon are Six (1st, 8vo, 54p, 1-color, DJ/1.50)	Nelson	1936	Gay, Romney	30-50	
Gay, Romney	Peter's Adventure (1st, sq12mo, ibds, [34]p, color)	Whitman	1936	Gay, Romney	30-50	
Gay, Romney	Picture Book of Poems (1st, sq8vo, 36p, ibds, color, pep, DJ/0.50)	Grosset/Dunlap	1940	Gay, Romney	30-50	
Gay, Romney	Romney Gay ABC (1st, 4to, ibds, [30]p, color, DJ/0.50)	Grosset/Dunlap	(1946)	Gay, Romney	60-90	
Mother Goose	Romney Gay Mother Goose (1st, sq4to, ipcb, 56p, color, pep)	Grosset/Dunlap	(1936)	Gay, Romney	65-90	
Gay, Romney	Toby & Sue (1st, sq12mo, ibds, [34]p, color, pep, DJ/0.50)	Grosset/Dunlap	1937	Gay, Romney	35-50	
Gay, Romney	Tommy Grows Wise (1st, sq12mo, ibds, [30]p, color, pep)	Grosset/Dunlap	1939	Gay, Romney	30-50	
Crespi, Pachita	170 Cats (1st {std}, ob4to, ibds, [27]p, 1-color, pep, DJ/1.00)	Random	(1939)	Gay, Zhenya	60-100	
McKown, Gretchen	All the Days Were Antonia's (1st, 8vo, 268p, fp b/w, pep, DJ/2.00)	Viking	1939	Gay, Zhenya	40-65	
Gay, Zhenya	Bits and Pieces (1st, lg8vo, 63p, b/w, DJ/2.50)	Viking	1958	Gay, Zhenya	20-30	
Cochran, Hamilton	Buccaneer Islands (1st, 8vo, 249p, blue cl, b/w, DJ/2.00)	NY: Nelson	1941	Gay, Zhenya	20-35	
Crespi, Pachita	Cabita's Rancho (1st, 8vo, 208p, b/w, DJ/2.00)	Messner	1942	Gay, Zhenya	25-45	*
Hoffmann, Eleanor	Cat of Paris (1st, 8vo, 145p, blue cl, b/w, pep, DJ/1.75)	Stokes	1940	Gay, Zhenya	30-50	
Swinnerton, Frank	Cats and Rosemary (1st {std}, 8vo, 182p, b/w, DJ/2.50)	Knopf	1948	Gay, Zhenya	25-45	
Gay, Zhenya	Dear Friends (1st, 4to, 47p, b/w, DJ/1.95)	Harper	(1959)	Gay, Zhenya	30-50	
Gay, Zhenya	Fish Story (1st, sq8vo, ipcb, [27]p, fp 2-color, pep, DJ/0.50)	Garden City	(1939)	Gay, Zhenya	25-45	
Crespi, Pachita	Happy Birthday (1st, ob8vo, ipcb, [35]p, 1-color, DJ/1.00)	Viking	1939	Gay, Zhenya	30-45	
Gay, Zhenya	I'm Tired of Lions (1st, 8vo, 30p, color, DJ/2.50)	Viking	1961	Gay, Zhenya	25-40	
Quigg, Jane	Jiggy Likes Nantucket (1st, 8vo, 96p, fp 1-color, DJ/2.75)	NY: Oxford U.Pr.	1954	Gay, Zhenya	30-50	*
Strong, L.A.G.	King Richard's Land (1st AM {std}, 12mo, 231p, col frn, b/w, pep, DJ/2.00)	Knopf	1934	Gay, Zhenya	40-65	
Gay, Zhenya	Look! (1st, sm4to, unpag, 2-color, pep, DJ/2.00)	Viking	1952	Gay, Zhenya	30-45	
Mason, Miriam E.	Major and his Camels (1st {std}, 8vo, 130p, b/w, DJ/2.00)	Macmillan	(1953)	Gay, Zhenya	25-40	
Crespi, Pachita	Manuelito of Costa Rica (1st, sm4to, [40]p, color, pep, DJ/1.50)	J. Messner	(1940)	Gay, Zhenya	40-65	
Sayers, Frances C.	Mr. Tidy Paws (1st, 8vo, ibds, 64p, b/w, pep, DJ/1.50)	Viking	1935	Gay, Zhenya	50-80	
Parton, Ethel	Mule of the Parthenon (1st {std}, 8vo, 243p, blue cl, col frn, b/w, DJ)	Doubleday/Doran	1932	Gay, Zhenya	30-50	
Gay, Zhenya	Pancho & His Burro (1st, sm4to, ibds, pep, [29]p, color)	Wm. Morrow	1930	Gay, Zhenya	55-80	
Weston, Harold	Patchwork Madonna (1st, sm8vo, 252p, b/w pl, DJ/2.50)	Wm. Morrow	(1929)	Gay, Zhenya	25-35	
Coatsworth, Eliz.	Peddler's Cart (1st {std}, 8vo, 151p, b/w, DJ/2.75)	Macmillan	(1956)	Gay, Zhenya	20-35	

AUTHOR	TITLE	PUBLISHER	DATE	ARTIST	PRICE	LC
Gay, Zhenya	Sakimura (1st, 8vo, ibds, [42]p, color, DJ/1.50)	Viking	1937	Gay, Zhenya	50-80	
Gay, Zhenya	Shire Colt (1st {std}, lg4to, ibds, [62]p, lithos, pep, DJ/2.00)	Doubleday/Doran	1931	Gay, Zhenya	80-140	R
Gay, Zhenya	Small One (1st, sm4to, 31p, b/w, DJ/2.00)	Viking	(1958)	Gay, Zhenya	25-45	
Mansfield, Katherine	Stories by Katherine Mansfield (1st, 4to, 215p, DJ/4.00, designs by...)	Knopf	1930	Gay, Zhenya	40-65	
Mason, Miriam E.	Sugarbush Family (1st {std}, 8vo, 137p, b/w, DJ/2.00)	Macmillan	1954	Gay, Zhenya	25-45	
Whitman, Walt	There was a Child Went Forth (1st {std}, 4to, ipcb, [32]p, color, DJ/1.75)	Harper	(1943)	Gay, Zhenya	45-70	
Gaidar, Arkady	Timur and his Gang (1st, 8vo, 125p, b/w, DJ/1.75)	Scribner	1943	Gay, Zhenya	30-50	
Gay, Zhenya	Town Cats (1st {std}, sm4to, ipcb, 110p, fp b/w)	Knopf	1932	Gay, Zhenya	60-90	
Hoffmann, Eleanor	Travels of a Snail (1st, 8vo, 140p, b/w, DJ/1.50)	Stokes	1939	Gay, Zhenya	30-45	
Montgomery, R.	Troopers Three (1st {std}, 8vo, 233p, col frn, pep)	Doubleday/Doran	1932	Gay, Zhenya	25-40	*
Gay, Zhenya	What's Your Name? (1st, lg8vo, 47p, 1-color, pep, DJ/2.00)	Viking	1955	Gay, Zhenya	30-45	
Jones, Idwal	Whistler's Van (1st, 8vo, 235p, b/w, pep, DJ/2.00, NH)	Viking	1936	Gay, Zhenya	50-80	
Gay, Zhenya	Wonderful Things! (1st, 4to, tan cl, 62p, fp b/w, DJ/2.50)	Viking	1954	Gay, Zhenya	40-65	
Gaze, Harold	Coppertop (1st AM, lg8vo, 338p, blue/gilt, 12cp)	Harper	(1924)	Gaze, Harold	150-200	
Underhill, Zoe (ed)	Dwarf's Tailor... (1st, lg8vo, 260p, p-o by...)	Harper	(1924)	Gaze, Harold	40-65	
Gaze, Harold	Goblin's Glen (1st, 8vo, 242p, red/gilt, 6cp, pep)	Little/Brown	1924	Gaze, Harold	300-500	
Hubbell, Rose S.	If I Could Fly (1st, 8vo, teg, 113p, 5cp, pep)	Putnam	1917	Gaze, Harold	120-200	
Gaze, Harold	Merry Piper (1st AM, 8vo, yellow cl, 247p, 8cp, 12pl, pep)	Little/Brown	1925	Gaze, Harold	200-300	
Gaze, Harold	Merry Piper (1st UK, lg8vo, 247p, 8cp, 12pl, pep)	L: Longmans	1925	Gaze, Harold	200-300	
Donahey, Mary D.	Peter & Prue... (1st, sm8vo, 258p, p-o, 5cp, pep)	Rand/McNally	(1924)	Gaze, Harold	140-200	
Bourne, Gwen	Wonder World Fairy Tale Book (1st, 4to, blue cl, 90p, 4pl)	L: Cecil Palmer	(1931)	Gaze, Harold	200-300	
Heinlein, Robert	Between Planets (1st, 8vo, 222p, b/w, DJ/2.50)	Scribner	1951	Geary, Clifford	200-300	
Heinlein, Robert	Farmer in the Sky (1st, 8vo, 216p, b/w, DJ/2.50)	Scribner	1950	Geary, Clifford	200-300	
Heinlein, Robert	Red Planet (1st, 8vo, 211p, b/w, DJ/2.50)	Scribner	1949	Geary, Clifford	200-300	
Heinlein, Robert	Space Cadet (1st, 8vo, 242p, b/w, DJ/2.50)	Scribner	1948	Geary, Clifford	350-500	
Heinlein, Robert	Starman Jones (1st, 8vo, 305p, b/w, DJ/2.50)	Scribner	1953	Geary, Clifford	200-300	
Gedo, Leopold	Who is Johnny? (1st AM, 8vo, 242p, b/w, pep, DJ/2.00)	Viking	1939	Gedo, Leopold	40-65	
Gee, John	Bunnie Bear (1st, 8vo, ibds, color)	Volland	(1928)	Gee, John	60-100	
McMahon, Jo	Deenie Folks and Friends of Theirs (1st, 8vo, ibds, unpag, color, pep)	Volland	(1925)	Gee, John	70-100	
Atwater, Richard	Doris and the Trolls (1st, 8vo, 124p, blue cl, 1-color, pep)	Rand/McNally	(1931)	Gee, John	60-100	
Nesbit, Wilbur D.	In Tumbledown Town (1st, sm8vo, unpag, ibds, color, pep)	Volland	(1926)	Gee, John	60-100	
Sherman, James W.	Quart of Moonlight (1st, sm8vo, 147p, blue cl, b/w)	Little/Brown	1928	Gee, John	25-45	
Aldredge, Edna	The Timbertoes (1st, 8vo, pep, p-o, red cl, 117p, color)	Harter	(1932)	Gee, John	75-100	*
Sandburg, Helga	Gingerbread (1st, 8vo, 192p, b/w, DJ/3.50)	Dial Press	1964	Geer, Charles	45-70	
Mowat, Farley	Lost in the Barrens (1st {std}, 8vo, 244p, b/w, DJ/3.00)	Little/Brown	(1956)	Geer, Charles	45-70	
Montgomery, R.	McNulty's Holiday (1st {std}, 8vo, 150p, b/w, DJ/3.50)	Duell, Sloan	(1963)	Geer, Charles	20-30	*
Sorensen, Virginia	Plain Girl (1st {std}, 8vo, 151p, b/w, DJ/2.50)	Harcourt	(1955)	Geer, Charles	25-45	
Meigs, Cornelia L.	Wild Geese Flying (1st {std}, 8vo, 194p, b/w, DJ/2.75)	Macmillan	1957	Geer, Charles	20-35	
Mother Goose	My First Mother Goose (1st, lg8vo, ipcb, [32]p, color, pep, DJ/1.00)	Wilcox/Follett	(1946)	Gehr, Mary	50-80	*
Grimm Bros.	Fisherman and his Wife (1st, sm4to, [32]p, b/w, DJ/2.50, NYTBI)	Pantheon	1957	Gekiere, Madeleine	80-120	
Gekiere, Madeleine	Frilly Lily and the Princess (1st, lg8vo, 25p, fp 2-color, DJ/2.75)	Lippincott	(1960)	Gekiere, Madeleine	50-80	*
Helm, Ruth	Gwendolyn (1st AM, 8vo, 43p, 1-color, dep, DJ/2.00)	NY: Oxford U.Pr.	1952	Gekiere, Madeleine	30-50	
Ciardi, John	John J. Plenty & Fiddler Dan (1st, 4to, [37]p, fp b/w, DJ/2.95, NYTBI)	Lippincott	(1963)	Gekiere, Madeleine	50-85	R
Helm, Ruth	Mr. Putterbee's Jungle (1st AM, 8vo, 47p, fp 1-color, pep, DJ/2.25)	NY: Oxford U.Pr.	(1953)	Gekiere, Madeleine	30-50	
Engelhard, Georgia	Peterli and the Mountain (1st, lg8vo, 39p, fp 1-color, pep, DJ/2.25)	Lippincott	(1954)	Gekiere, Madeleine	30-50	*
Ciardi, John	Reason for the Pelican (1st, lg8vo, 64p, blue cl, b/w, DJ/3.00, NYTBI)	Lippincott	(1959)	Gekiere, Madeleine	50-85	
Bradbury, Ray	Switch on the Night (1st, sq8vo, ibds, [48]p, color, cep, DJ/2.50, NYTBI)	Pantheon	1955	Gekiere, Madeleine	400-650	
Gekiere, Madeleine	Who Gave Us Peacocks.... (1st, 4to, unpag, color, cep, DJ/3.00, NYTBI)	Pantheon	(1953)	Gekiere, Madeleine	90-150	
Martin, Patricia	Friend of Miguel (1st, 8vo, 45p, color, DJ/2.95)	Rand/McNally	1967	Genia	25-40	
Caudill, Rebecca	House of the Fifers (1st {std}, 8vo, 184p, b/w, DJ/2.75)	Longmans	1954	Genia	20-30	
George, Jean C.	Bubo: Great-Horned Owl (1st {std}, sm8vo, 184p, b/w, DJ/3.00)	Dutton	(1954)	George, Jean C.	25-40	*
George, Jean C.	Dipper of Copper Creek (1st {std}, sm8vo, 183p, fp b/w, pep, DJ/3.50)	Dutton	(1956)	George, Jean C.	30-50	R*
George, Jean C.	Gull Number 737 (1st, 8vo, 198p, b/w, DJ/3.50)	Crowell	1964	George, Jean C.	20-35	*
George, Jean C.	Hole in the Tree (1st {std}, 8vo, [57]p, grey cl, pep, b/w, DJ/2.50)	Dutton	(1957)	George, Jean C.	25-45	
George, Jean C.	Masked Prowler... (1st {std}, 8vo, 183p, b/w, pep, DJ/2.75)	Dutton	1950	George, Jean C.	25-40	
George, Jean C.	Meph: Pet Skunk (1st {std}, 8vo, 180p, b/w, DJ/2.75)	Dutton	1952	George, Jean C.	25-40	
George, Jean C.	My Side of the Mountain (1st {std}, 8vo, 178p, pep, b/w, DJ/3.00, NH)	Dutton	1959	George, Jean C.	40-65	
George, Jean C.	Snow Tracks (1st {std}, 8vo, 61p, b/w, DJ/2.50)	Dutton	1958	George, Jean C.	25-40	
George, Jean C.	Summer of the Falcon (1st {std}, 8vo, 153p, b/w, DJ/2.95)	Crowell	(1962)	George, Jean C.	20-35	
George, Jean C.	Vison: The Mink (1st {std}, 8vo, 194p, b/w, pep, DJ/2.50)	Dutton	1949	George, Jean C.	25-45	*
George, Jean C.	Vulpes: The Red Fox (1st {std}, 8vo, 184p, pep, b/w, DJ/2.50)	Dutton	1948	George, Jean C.	30-50	R
Frey, Nina A.	River Horse (1st, 8vo, 150p, green cl, b/w, DJ/2.50)	W.R. Scott	(1953)	George, Rene	30-50	*
Bain, Robert N.	Russian Fairy Tales (1st, 8vo, 264p, gilt, b/w)	Way & Williams	1895	Gere, Charles M.	120-170	*
Gere, Frances K.	Once Upon a Time in Egypt (1st, ob4to, ibds, 71p, color, pep, DJ/2.00)	Longmans	1937	Gere, Frances K.	80-120	R
McConnell, Margaret	Bobo the Barrage Balloon (1st, lg8vo, 36p, ipcb, 1-color, pep, DJ/1.50)	Lothrop, Lee	1943	Gergely, Tibor	40-65	
Conger, Marion	Circus Time (1st {A}, sm8vo, [42]p, ibds, color, LGB/#31)	Simon/Schuster	(1948)	Gergely, Tibor	30-45	
Lowrey, Janette S.	Day in the Jungle (1st {A}, sm4to, ibds, [42]p, color, pep, LGB/#18)	Simon/Schuster	1943	Gergely, Tibor	40-60	*
Hauser, Heinrich	Folding Father (1st, lg ob8vo, ipcb, [24]p, 2-color, pep, DJ/1.00)	Lothrop, Lee	1942	Gergely, Tibor	40-65	
Greene, Jean	Forgetful Elephant (1st {std}, 4to, ipcb, [32]p, color, pep, DJ/1.00)	McKay	(1945)	Gergely, Tibor	60-90	
Lilly, Jean	Hundred Tuftys (1st {std}, sm4to, [32]p, ipcb, 2-color, pep, DJ/1.50)	Dutton	(1940)	Gergely, Tibor	70-100	
Dolbier, Maurice	Jenny: Bus that Nobody Loved (1st, 4to, 43p, ipcb, color, pep, DJ/1.25)	Random	1944	Gergely, Tibor	45-70	
Dolbier, Maurice	Magic Bus (1st, lg8vo, 43p, ibds, color)	Wonder Books	1948	Gergely, Tibor	25-45	
Duplaix, Georges	Merry Shipwreck (1st {std}, 4to, ibds, [34]p, color, dep, DJ/1.50)	Harper	(1942)	Gergely, Tibor	120-165	
DeLeeuw, Hendrik	Peewee the Mousedeer (1st {std}, lg8vo, ibds, 71p, 1-color, pep, DJ/2.00)	McKay	1943	Gergely, Tibor	60-90	
Mitchell, Lucy S.	Red, White & Blue Auto (1st, ob8vo, ibds, [33]p, color, DJ/1.00)	W.R. Scott	1943	Gergely, Tibor	60-100	
Brown, Margaret W.	Seven Little Postmen (1st {A}, 8vo, ibds, [28]p, color, LGB/#134)	Simon/Schuster	1952	Gergely, Tibor	30-50	
Tompkins, Jane	Storks Fly Home (1st {std}, 8vo, 58p, col frn, b/w, DJ/1.50)	Stokes	(1943)	Gergely, Tibor	30-50	
Krumgold, Joseph	Sweeny's Adventure (1st, 4to, [40]p, ibds, color, pep, DJ/1.00)	Random	(1942)	Gergely, Tibor	40-70	

AUTHOR	TITLE	PUBLISHER	DATE	ARTIST	PRICE	LC
Pratt, Margaret	Talking Typewriter (1st {std}, sm4to, ibds, 38p, color, pep, DJ/1.00)	Lothrop, Lee	(1940)	Gergely, Tibor	50-80	
Duplaix, Georges	Topsy Turvy Circus (1st {std}, lg8vo, [40]p, ibds, color, pep, DJ/1.50)	Harper	(1940)	Gergely, Tibor	80-125	
Fox, Frances M.	True Monkey Stories (1st, lg8vo, 55p, green cl, fp color, pep, DJ/1.75)	Lothrop, Lee	(1941)	Gergely, Tibor	35-50	
Edmonds, Walter D.	Two Logs Crossing (1st, 8vo, 82p, green/gilt, fp b/w, pep, DJ/2.50)	Dodd	1943	Gergely, Tibor	50-85	
Rosvall, Toivo D.	Very Stupid Folk (1st {std}, 12mo, cloth, 52p, b/w, DJ/1.00)	Dutton	1938	Gergely, Tibor	30-45	
Ferris, Helen	Watch Me, said the Jeep (1st {std}, ob4to, [28]p, ipcb, color, DJ/1.00)	Garden City	(1944)	Gergely, Tibor	40-70	
Brown, Margaret W.	Wheel on the Chimney (1st, 4to, [28]p, tan cl, color, DJ/3.00, CH)	Lippincott	(1954)	Gergely, Tibor	120-180	R
Turner, Nancy B.	When it Rained Cats & Dogs (1st {std}, 4to, ibds, [32]p, color, DJ/1.00)	Lippincott	(1946)	Gergely, Tibor	60-100	R
Gerson, Virginia	Happy Heart Family (1st, sm4to, 35p, p-o, color)	Fox Duffield	1904	Gerson, Virginia	100-165	
Fitch, William C.	Knighting of the Twins (1st {1st bk}, 8vo, tan cl, 275p, b/w)	Roberts Bros.	(1891)	Gerson, Virginia	90-120	*
Gerson, Virginia	Little Dignity (1st {1st bk.}, sm4to, 64p, chromos)	NY: Routledge	1881	Gerson, Virginia	120-200	
Gerson, Virginia	More Adventures of the Happy Heart Family (1st, sm4to, 47p, p-o, 4cp)	Fox Duffield	1905	Gerson, Virginia	100-165	
Moore, Clement C.	Visit from Santa Claus (4to, ibds, 12cp, 24p)	Stokes/Allen	1887	Gerson, Virginia	200-270	
Treadgold, Mary	No Ponies (1st, 8vo, 290p, fp b/w, DJ)	L: J. Cape	1946	Gervis, Ruth	25-45	
Barne, Kitty	She Shall Have Music (1st AM, 8vo, 261p, b/w, DJ)	Dodd	1939	Gervis, Ruth	30-50	
Barne, Kitty	Visitors from London (1st, 8vo, 262p, b/w, DJ, CgM)	L: J.M. Dent	1940	Gervis, Ruth	70-120	
Waddell, Helen (tr)	Beasts and Saints (1st AM {std}, sm8vo, 151p, gilt, fp b/w, DJ/2.50)	Henry Holt & Co.	(1934)	Gibbings, Robert	45-65	
Waddell, Helen (tr)	Beasts and Saints (1st, 8vo, 151p, red/gilt, 6pl, DJ)	L: Constable	1934	Gibbings, Robert	80-125	
Harrison, Godfrey	Bird Diary (1st, 12mo, 151p, p-o, 20pl, gilt)	L: Dent	1936	Gibbings, Robert	75-100	
Gibbings, Robert	Iorana! (1st AM, lg8vo, 157p, uncut, p-o, gilt, b/w, pep)	Houghton	1932	Gibbings, Robert	60-90	R
Gibbings, Robert	Lovely is The Lee (1st AM {std}, 8vo, 199p, green/gilt, b/w, DJ/3.00)	Dutton	1945	Gibbings, Robert	40-60	
Gibbings, Robert	Over the Reefs (1st, 8vo, 240p, gilt, b/w wood engravings, pep, DJ)	L: Dent	1948	Gibbings, Robert	40-70	
Doorly, Eleanor	Radium Woman (1st, 8vo, 184p, b/w woodcuts, CgM)	L: Heinemann	(1939)	Gibbings, Robert	50-80	
Gibbings, Robert	Trumpets from Montparnasse (1st AM {std}, 8vo, 200p, gilt, 8cp, DJ/5.00)	Dutton	(1955)	Gibbings, Robert	30-45	
Powys, Llewelyn	Twelve Months (1st UK, ob8vo, 88p, uncut, gilt, b/w, DJ)	L: John Lane	(1936)	Gibbings, Robert	70-100	
Gibbs, George	American Sea Fights (1st, elephant folio, 12 ticp)	R.H. Russell	1902	Gibbs, George	300-500	
Montgomery, Lucy M.	Anne of Avonlea (1st, sm8vo, 367p, p-o, green cl, col frn)	L.C. Page	1909	Gibbs, George	300-500	
Montgomery, Lucy M.	Chronicles of Avonlea (1st, sm8vo, 306p, p-o, gilt, col frn)	L.C. Page	1912	Gibbs, George	250-400	
Montgomery, Lucy M.	Golden Road (1st, sm8vo, 369p, p-o, gilt, col frn)	L.C. Page	1913	Gibbs, George	160-220	
Montgomery, Lucy M.	Kilmeny of the Orchard (1st, sm8vo, 256p, p-o, 4cp)	L.C. Page	1910	Gibbs, George	200-300	
Crowninshield, Mrs.	Lattitude 19 (1st, sm8vo, 418p, red cl, 7pl)	Appleton	1898	Gibbs, George	40-60	*
Harris, Joel C.	Little Union Scout (1st, 8vo, green/gilt, 181p, 8pl)	McClure	1904	Gibbs, George	150-225	
Montgomery, Lucy M.	Story Girl (1st, sm8vo, 365p, gilt, p-o, col frn)	L.C. Page	1911	Gibbs, George	150-225	
Thurston, Katherine	The Mystics (1st, sm8vo, black/gilt, 191p, 8pl)	Harper	1907	Gibbs, George	30-50	
Hurd, Marian K.	When She Came Home from College (1st, 12mo, 272p, 7pl)	Houghton	1909	Gibbs, George	25-45	*
Davis, Richard H.	About Paris (1st, 12mo, gilt, 219p, 30pl)	Harper	1895	Gibson, Charles D.	40-65	
Gibson, Charles D.	Americans (1st, ob folio, ipcb, [88]p, teg, fp b/w)	R.H. Russell	1900	Gibson, Charles D.	170-240	
Beach, Rex	Auction Block (1st, 8vo, 440p, red/gilt, 28pl)	Harper	1914	Gibson, Charles D.	20-40	
Bangs, John K.	Booming of Acre Hill (1st, 12mo, teg, uncut, 265p, b/w)	Harper	1900	Gibson, Charles D.	40-65	
Goodloe, Abbe C.	College Girls (1st, 12mo, gilt, 288p, 11pl)	Scribner	1895	Gibson, Charles D.	30-50	
Masson, Thomas L.	Corner in Women (1st, 8vo, teg, ipcb, gilt, 332p, cvr by...)	Moffat	1905	Gibson, Charles D.	35-60	
Gibson, Charles D.	Drawings (1st, ob folio, [88]p, ibds, teg, b/w)	R.H. Russell	1897	Gibson, Charles D.	160-240	
Gibson, Charles D.	Education of Mr. Pipp (1st, ob folio, ibds, [78]p, b/w)	R.H. Russell	1899	Gibson, Charles D.	170-240	
Gibson, Charles D.	Eighty Drawings including Weaker Sex (1st, ob folio, teg, unpag, ibds, b/w)	Scribner/Lane	1903	Gibson, Charles D.	150-240	
Gibson, Charles D.	Everyday People (1st, ob folio, ibds, teg, [80]p, b/w pl)	Scribner	1904	Gibson, Charles D.	160-250	
Gibson, Charles D.	Gibson Book (1st, ob folio, 2 volumes, red cl, teg, b/w)	Scribner	1906	Gibson, Charles D.	250-350	
Chambers, Robert	Japonette (1st, 8vo, 384p, p-o, 21 b/w)	Appleton	1912	Gibson, Charles D.	30-50	
Addison, Julia	Mrs. John Vernon (1st, 12mo, p-o, 205p, frn by...)	Badger	1909	Gibson, Charles D.	25-40	*
Gibson, Charles D.	Our Neighbors (1st, ob folio, [68]p, b/w)	Scribner	1905	Gibson, Charles D.	180-250	
Gibson, Charles D.	Pictures of People (1st, ob folio, teg, unpag, ibds, b/w)	R.H. Russell	1896	Gibson, Charles D.	200-300	
Downey, Fairfax	Portrait of an Era (1st, lg8vo, 391p, b/w, pep, DJ/3.50)	Scribner	(1936)	Gibson, Charles D.	50-80	
Magruder, Julia	Princess Sonia (1st, 12mo, teg, gilt, 225p, 19pl)	Century	1895	Gibson, Charles D.	60-100	
Gibson, Charles D.	Sketches in Egypt (1st, sm4to, tan buckram, 115p, b/w)	Doub./McClure	1899	Gibson, Charles D.	200-300	
Gibson, Charles D.	Social Ladder (1st, ob. folio, [79]p, teg, b/w)	R.H. Russell	1902	Gibson, Charles D.	180-240	
Davis, Richard H.	Soldiers of Fortune (1st, 12mo, 364p, 6pl, yellow/gilt)	Scribner	1897	Gibson, Charles D.	40-70	
Chambers, Robert	Streets of Ascalon (1st, sm8vo, 440p, gilt, 14 double pg pl)	Appleton	1912	Gibson, Charles D.	30-50	
Magruder, Julia	The Violet (1st, sm8vo, teg, 210p, 11pl)	Longmans	1896	Gibson, Charles D.	50-80	
Davis, Richard H.	Van Bibber & Others (1st, 12mo, 249p, gilt, 4pl)	Harper	1892	Gibson, Charles D.	30-50	
Gibson, Charles D.	Widow & Her Friends (1st, ob folio, [79]p, teg, bds, b/w)	R.H. Russell	1901	Gibson, Charles D.	140-200	
Gibson, Lydia	Teacup Whale (1st, ob8vo, ipcb, dep, 23p, b/w)	Farrar/Rinehart	(1934)	Gibson, Lydia	60-100	
Montgomery, R.	Golden Stallion's Revenge (1st {std}, sm8vo, 242p, b/w, DJ/2.75)	Little/Brown	(1953)	Giguere, George	25-40	
Caudill, Rebecca	Best-Loved Doll (1st {std}, 8vo, [64]p, fp 1-color, DJ/3.50)	Holt, Rinehart	(1962)	Gilbert, Elliott	30-45	
Colcock, Annie T.	Margaret Tudor (1st, 12mo, 169p, green cl)	Stokes	(1902)	Gilbert, W.B.	25-40	
Gilbert, W.S.	Bab Ballads (1st AM, 16mo, 184p, grey bds, uncut, b/w)	R.H. Russell	1901	Gilbert, W.S.	60-90	
Munroe, Kirk	Under the Great Bear (1st, 12mo, 313p, 12pl)	Doubleday/Page	1900	Giles, Howard	35-60	*
Bianco, Margery W.	All About Pets (1st, sm8vo, 134p, pep, decor by...)	Macmillan	1929	Gilkison, Grace	20-35	
Gilkison, Grace	Little Arthur (1st {std}, 8vo, 126p, col frn, fp b/w)	Doubleday/Doran	1931	Gilkison, Grace	20-35	
Farjeon, Eleanor	More Nursery Rhymes of London Town (1st, 8vo, unpag, red cl, col frn)	L: Duckworth	1917	Gill, MacDonald	60-90	
Farjeon, Eleanor	Nursery Rhymes of London Town (1st, 8vo, 63p, blue/gilt, col frn)	L: Duckworth	(1916)	Gill, MacDonald	80-125	
Boston, Lucy M.	Castle of Yew (1st AM {std}, 8vo, 58p, b/w, DJ/2.95)	Harcourt	(1965)	Gill, Margery	30-50	
Thomas, Edward	Complete Fairy Tales (1st AM, 8vo, 94p, ibds, b/w, pep, DJ/3.95)	F. Watts	(1966)	Gill, Margery	40-65	
Cooper, Susan	Dawn of Fear (1st AM {std}, 8vo, 157p, b/w, DJ/4.95)	Harcourt	(1970)	Gill, Margery	50-80	
Mayne, William	Day Without Wind (1st AM, sm4to, 59p, fp 1-color, DJ/3.50)	Dutton	(1964)	Gill, Margery	30-45	*
Mayne, William	Old Zion (1st AM {std}, sm4to, 64p, 1-color, DJ/3.95)	Dutton	(1967)	Gill, Margery	25-40	
Cooper, Susan	Over Sea, Under Stone (1st AM {std}, 8vo, 252p, b/w, DJ/3.50)	Harcourt	(1966)	Gill, Margery	800-1200	
Arthur, Ruth	Requiem for a Princess (1st {std}, 8vo, 182p, b/w, DJ)	Atheneum	1967	Gill, Margery	40-65	
De La Mare, Walter	Tom Tiddler's Ground (1st AM {std}, lg8vo, 253p, b/w, DJ/3.50)	Knopf	(1962)	Gill, Margery	30-45	
Craig, M. Jean	What Did You Dream? (1st, 4to, [42]p, color, DJ/2.95)	Abelard-Schuman	1964	Gill, Margery	20-35	

AUTHOR	TITLE	PUBLISHER	DATE	ARTIST	PRICE	LC
DeRegniers, Beatrice	Little Girl and her Mother (1st, ob4to, [30]p, 1-color, DJ/3.25)	Vanguard Press	(1963)	Gilman, Esther	25-45	
Chamisso, A.	Peter Schlemihl (1st, lg8vo, 104p, green/gilt, p-o, 35 woodcuts)	McKay	(1929)	Gincano, John	50-85	
Meader, Stephen W.	Will to Win and other Stories (1st, 8vo, 300p, b/w, DJ/2.00)	Harcourt	1936	Gincano, John	120-185	
Hodges, Elizabeth	Free as a Frog (1st {std}, 8vo, [32]p, b/w, DJ/3.25, NYTBI)	Addison-Wesley	(1969)	Giovanopoulos, P.	30-50	
Coatsworth, Eliz.	George and Red (1st {std}, 8vo, 55p, brown/gilt, dp b/w, DJ/3.95)	Macmillan	(1969)	Giovanopoulos, P.	25-40	
Fox, Paula	How Many Miles to Babylon? (1st, 12mo, 117p, b/w, DJ/3.95)	NY: David White	(1967)	Giovanopoulos, P.	50-80	
Dean, Leigh	Looking Down Game (1st, 8vo, 34p, b/w, DJ/2.95)	Funk/Wagnalls	(1968)	Giovanopoulos, P.	25-40	
Barnstone, Aliki	Real Tin Flower (1st {std}, 8vo, 54p, fp b/w, cep, DJ/3.95)	Crowell-Collier	(1968)	Giovanopoulos, P.	30-50	*
Krasilovsky, Phyllis	Susan Sometimes (1st {std}, 12mo, 31p, ibds, 3-color, DJ/1.95)	Macmillan	1962	Giventer, Abbi	25-40	
Day, Marguerite	Tell 'Em Again Tales (1st, sq4to, ibds, 48p, 3 fp color, pep)	Duffield	1924	Glackens, Louis M.	70-120	
Seawell, Molly E.	Papa Bouchard (1st, 12mo, 261p, uncut, teg, b/w)	Scribner	1901	Glackens, William	25-40	
Page, Thomas N.	Santa Claus's Partner (1st, 12mo, red/gilt, 177p, teg, 8cp)	Scribner	1899	Glackens, William	35-60	
Tietjens, Eunice H.	Romance of Antar (1st, 8vo, 219p, gilt, fp b/w)	Coward	1929	Glanckoff, Sam	30-50	
Green, Mary M.	Everybody Eats (1st, lg8vo, spiral bds, [20]p, color)	W.R. Scott	1946	Glannon, Edward J.	35-50	
Mitchell, Lucy S.	Guess What's in the Grass (1st, sm ob4to, ibds, [30]p, 2-col, pep, DJ/1.50)	W.R. Scott	1945	Glannon, Edward J.	60-90	
Stolz, Mary S.	Juan (1st, 8vo, 131p, fp b/w, DJ/3.95)	Harper	(1970)	Glanzman, Louis	30-50	R
Sachs, Marilyn	Marv (1st {std}, 8vo, 160p, b/w, DJ/3.95)	Doubleday	(1970)	Glanzman, Louis	20-35	
Stolz, Mary S.	Noonday Friends (1st, 8vo, 182p, b/w, DJ/3.50, NH)	Harper	(1965)	Glanzman, Louis	30-50	
Sachs, Marilyn	Peter and Veronica (1st {std}, 8vo, 174p, b/w, DJ/3.95)	Doubleday	(1969)	Glanzman, Louis	20-35	
Lindgren, Astrid	Pippi Goes on Board (1st, 8vo, 140p, b/w, DJ/2.00)	Viking	1957	Glanzman, Louis	60-100	
Lindgren, Astrid	Pippi in the South Seas (1st, 8vo, 126p, b/w, DJ/2.00)	Viking	(1959)	Glanzman, Louis	50-80	
Lindgren, Astrid	Pippi Longstocking (1st, 8vo, 158p, b/w, DJ/2.00)	Viking	1950	Glanzman, Louis	80-140	
Williams, Jay	Sword of King Arthur (1st, 8vo, 188p, b/w, DJ/3.95)	Crowell	(1968)	Glanzman, Louis	30-45	*
Sachs, Marilyn	Veronica Ganz (1st {std}, 8vo, 156p, b/w, DJ/3.50)	Doubleday	(1968)	Glanzman, Louis	20-35	
Ciardi, John	Wish-Tree (1st {std}, 4to, [96]p, b/w)	Crowell-Collier	(1962)	Glanzman, Louis	50-80	
Stolz, Mary S.	Wonderful Terrible Time (1st, 8vo, 182p, fp b/w, DJ/3.95)	Harper	(1967)	Glanzman, Louis	25-45	
Aiken, Conrad	Cats & Bats & Things with Wings (1st {std}, 4to, [38]p, color, pep, DJ/4.50)	Atheneum	1965	Glaser, Milton	50-80	R
Menotti, Gian-Carlo	Help, Help, the Golobolinks (1st, sm4to, ibds, [56]p, color, DJ/4.95, NYT)	McGraw-Hill	(1970)	Glaser, Milton	50-80	*
Tresselt, Alvin	Smallest Elephant in the World (1st, 4to, [32]p, 3-color, pep, DJ)	Knopf	(1959)	Glaser, Milton	25-45	*
Embry, Margaret	My Name is Lion (1st, 8vo, 46p, fp b/w, DJ/3.75)	Holiday House	(1970)	Glattauer, Ned	20-30	
Gleason, Jane	Young and Happy Rooster (1st, 8vo, p-o, 64p, gilt, fp color, pep)	Whitman	1934	Gleason, Jane	60-90	*
Wright, Mabel O.	Wabeno the Magician (1st, sm8vo, 344p, green/gilt, b/w)	Macmillan	1899	Gleeson, J.M.	35-60	
Juster, Norton	Alberic the Wise (1st, 4to, 67p, gilt, b/w, DJ/3.50, NYTBI)	Pantheon	(1965)	Gnoli, Domenico	45-75	
Curry, Jane L.	Beneath the Hill (1st {std}, 8vo, 255p, b/w, DJ/4.25)	Harcourt	(1967)	Gobbato, Imero	30-50	
Olsen, Aileen	Big Fish (1st, 8vo, 47p, orange cl, b/w, DJ/3.95)	Lothrop, Lee	(1970)	Gobbato, Imero	30-50	*
Rothberg, Abraham	Boy and the Dolphin (1st {std}, 8vo, 85p, fp b/w, DJ/4.25)	Norton	(1969)	Gobbato, Imero	40-65	
Merriam, Eve	Catch a Little Rhyme (1st {std}, lg8vo, 51p, b/w, DJ/3.50)	Atheneum	1966	Gobbato, Imero	20-30	
Daniels, Guy	Foma the Terrible (1st {std}, ob4to, [38]p, color, DJ/4.50)	Delacorte Pr.	(1970)	Gobbato, Imero	40-65	*
Williams, Jay	Good-for-Nothing Prince (1st {std}, lg8vo, [48]p, 1-color, DJ/4.25)	Norton	(1969)	Gobbato, Imero	40-65	
Van Leeuwen, Jean	Great Cheese Conspiracy (1st, 8vo, 87p, fp b/w, cep, DJ/3.95)	Random	(1969)	Gobbato, Imero	30-50	
Rudolph, Marguerita	I am Your Misfortune (1st, 4to, [32]p fp color, cep, DJ/3.50)	Seabury Press	(1968)	Gobbato, Imero	40-65	*
Williams, Jay	King with Six Friends (1st, 8vo, [40]p, color, pep, DJ/3.50)	Parents Mag. Pr.	(1968)	Gobbato, Imero	40-65	
Mendoza, George	Practical Man (1st, 12mo, [32]p, b/w, DJ/2.95)	Lothrop, Lee	(1968)	Gobbato, Imero	25-40	
Russell, Solveig	The Mushmen (1st, 8vo, 94p, b/w, DJ/3.50)	Dodd	1968	Gobbato, Imero	30-50	
Conger, Lesley	Tops and Bottoms (1st, ob4to, [40]p, fp color, DJ/3.95)	Four Winds Pr.	(1970)	Gobbato, Imero	50-80	*
Kendall, Carol S.	Whisper of Glocken (1st {std}, 8vo, 256p, yellow cl, b/w, DJ/3.50)	Harcourt	(1965)	Gobbato, Imero	40-65	R*
Linde, Gunnell	White Stone (1st AM, 8vo, 185p, b/w, DJ/3.25)	Harcourt	(1964)	Gobbato, Imero	30-50	
Owen, Dora	Book of Fairy Poetry (1st, 4to, 180p, grey cl, 16 ticp, pep)	L: Longmans	1920	Goble, Warwick	350-500	
Marchant, Bessie	Captives of the Kaid (1st, 8vo, 208p, 4cp, pep)	L: Collins	[1904]	Goble, Warwick	40-65	*
Chaucer, Geoffrey	Complete Poetical Works of... (1st, 4to, 607p, blue/gilt, teg, 32cp)	L: Macmillan	1912	Goble, Warwick	200-300	
Van Millingen	Constantinople (1st, 4to, 282p, teg, tan/gilt, 63cp)	L: A&C Black	1906	Goble, Warwick	150-250	
Whishaw, Frederick	Emperor's Englishman (1st, 8vo, 342p)	L: Hutchinson	1896	Goble, Warwick	90-120	*
Craik, Dinah	Fairy Book (1st, 4to, 379p, teg, green/gilt, 32cp)	L: Macmillan	1913	Goble, Warwick	350-500	
Craik, Dinah	Fairy Book (1st {this format}, 8vo, 232p, red/gilt, 16cp)	L: Macmillan	1923	Goble, Warwick	180-275	
Day, Lal Behari	Folk Tales of Bengal (1st, 4to, red/gilt, 274p, 32cp)	L: Macmillan	1912	Goble, Warwick	350-500	
Gasquet, Abbot	Greater Abbeys of England (1st, lg8vo, gilt, uncut, 378p, teg, 60cp)	L: Chatto	1908	Goble, Warwick	180-240	
Gasquet, Abbot	Greater Abbeys of England (1st AM, lg8vo, gilt, 378p, teg, 60cp)	Dodd	1908	Goble, Warwick	150-220	
James, Grace	Green Willow... (1st, sm4to, blue/gilt, 281p, 40 ticp)	L: Macmillan	1910	Goble, Warwick	400-600	
James, Grace	Green Willow... (1st {this format}, 8vo, gilt, 281p, 16cp)	L: Macmillan	1912	Goble, Warwick	150-220	
Molesworth, Mrs.	Grim House (1st, 8vo, 289p, teg, 6pl)	L: J. Nisbet	1899	Goble, Warwick	80-120	*
Mackenzie, Donald A.	Indian Myth & Legend (1st, lg8vo, 463p, teg, gilt, 8cp, 32pl)	L: Gresham	1913	Goble, Warwick	170-240	
Barlow, Jane	Irish Ways (1st, 8vo, 262p, teg, gilt, uncut, 16cp)	L: G. Allen	(1909)	Goble, Warwick	185-250	
Stevenson, Rbt. L.	Kidnapped (1st AM, sm8vo, 327p, blue cl, 16pl)	Macmillan	1925	Goble, Warwick	160-220	
Marryat, Frederick	King's Own (1st, 8vo, 451p, 6pl)	L: Oxford U.Pr.	1907	Goble, Warwick	100-165	
Basile, Giovanni B.	Stories from the Pentamerone (1st, 4to, red/gilt, 304p, 32cp)	L: Macmillan	1911	Goble, Warwick	250-400	
Irving, Washington	The Alhambra (1st, 8vo, blue cl, 3cp)	L: Macmillan	1926	Goble, Warwick	70-125	
Whitney, Elinor	Tod of the Fens (1st, 8vo, 239p, red cl, col frn, b/w, pep, NH)	Macmillan	1928	Goble, Warwick	50-80	
Stevenson, Rbt. L.	Treasure Island (1st, sm8vo, 312p, blue cl, 4cp)	L: Macmillan	1923	Goble, Warwick	100-165	
Wells, H.G.	War of the Worlds (1st AM, 12mo, green cl, 291p, 16pl)	Harper	1898	Goble, Warwick	500-700	
Kingsley, Charles	Water Babies (1st, 4to, AEG, green/gilt, 32 ticp)	L: Macmillan	1909	Goble, Warwick	300-500	
Kingsley, Charles	Water Babies (1st {this format}, 8vo, teg, 273p, gilt, 16cp)	L: Macmillan	1910	Goble, Warwick	180-250	
Stables, Gordon	Young Peggy McQueen (1st, 8vo, 152p, gilt, 4cp)	L: Collins	1903	Goble, Warwick	80-120	
Daringer, Helen F.	Keepsake Ring (1st {std}, 8vo, 174p, b/w, DJ/2.50)	Harcourt	(1953)	Godwin, E.& S.	50-80	
Lang, Andrew	Blue Fairy Book (1st, 8vo, teg, p-o, black/gilt, 16cp)	McKay	(1921)	Godwin, Frank	80-140	
Stevenson, Rbt. L.	Kidnapped (1st, 8vo, 348p, gilt, p-o, 4cp, 12pl, pep)	Winston	(1925)	Godwin, Frank	30-50	*
Malory, Thomas	King Arthur & his Knights (1st, lg8vo, p-o, 256p, pep, 4cp)	Winston	(1927)	Godwin, Frank	30-50	
Lamb, Charles	Tales from Shakespeare (1st, 8vo, p-o, 323p, 12pl)	Winston	(1924)	Godwin, Frank	35-60	
Stevenson, Rbt. L.	Treasure Island (1st, 8vo, 304p, p-o, 3cp)	Winston	(1924)	Godwin, Frank	30-50	*

AUTHOR	TITLE	PUBLISHER	DATE	ARTIST	PRICE	LC
Trachsel, Myrtle	Elizabeth of the Mayflower (1st {std}, 8vo, 207p, b/w, pep, DJ/2.50)	Macmillan	1950	Godwin, Stephani	25-45	*
Davis, Robert	That Girl of Pierre's (1st, 8vo, 230p, rust cl, b/w, pep, DJ/2.50)	Holiday House	(1948)	Goff, Lloyd L.	25-40	
Goffstein, M.B.	Across the Sea (1st {std}, 12mo, [38]p, color, DJ/2.50)	Farrar, Straus	(1968)	Goffstein, M.B.	30-50	
Goffstein, M.B.	Brookie and her Lamb (1st {std}, 24mo, [31]p, b/w, DJ/1.95)	Farrar, Straus	(1967)	Goffstein, M.B.	30-50	
Goffstein, M.B.	Goldie the Dollmaker (1st {std}, ob12mo, 55p, b/w, DJ/3.50)	Farrar, Straus	(1969)	Goffstein, M.B.	30-45	
Goffstein, M.B.	Sleepy People (1st {std}, 32mo, blue cl, [28]p, b/w, cep, DJ/1.95)	Farrar, Straus	(1966)	Goffstein, M.B.	25-45	
Goffstein, M.B.	The Gats! (1st, 32mo, [33]p, ipcb, 1-color, cep, DJ/1.95)	Pantheon	1966	Goffstein, M.B.	40-65	
Goffstein, M.B.	Two Piano Tuners (1st {std}, 8vo, 65p, b/w, DJ/3.50)	Farrar, Straus	(1970)	Goffstein, M.B.	30-50	
Chute, Marchette	Wonderful Winter (1st {std}, 8vo, 216p, pep, DJ/3.00)	Dutton	1954	Golden, Grace	40-65	*
Wilde, Oscar	Canterville Ghost (1st AM, 16mo, 123p, blue/gilt, pl)	Bos: J.W. Luce	1906	Goldsmith, Wallace	150-250	
Warren, Carro F.	Little Betty Marigold... (1st, 12mo, 107p, 14 color)	C.M. Clark	1907	Goldsmith, Wallace	25-40	*
Kneeland, Clarissa A.	Smuggler's Island (1st, 8vo, red cl, 355p, b/w, PPPa)	Houghton	1915	Goldsmith, Wallace	70-120	R*
Brent, Stuart	Strange Disappearance of Mr. Toast (1st, lg8vo, 62p, b/w, DJ/2.50)	Viking	(1964)	Goldstein, Leslie	20-30	
Sterne, Emma G.	All About Little Boy Blue (1st, 24mo, ibds, p-o, 48p, color)	Cupples/Leon	(1924)	Gooch, Thelma	50-80	
Sterne, Emma G.	All About Peter Pan (1st, 24mo, tan bds, 48p, p-o, 8cp)	Cupples/Leon	(1924)	Gooch, Thelma	50-80	
Moore, Clement C.	Night Before Christmas (1st, lg4to, [24]p, ipcb, color, pep, DJ/0.50)	Grosset/Dunlap	1937	Gooch, Thelma	100-150	R
Malot, Hector	Nobody's Boy (1st, lg8vo, p-o, 308p, 8cp, pep)	Cupples/Leon	(1930)	Gooch, Thelma	45-70	
Lawrence, Josephine	Rainbow Hill (1st, sm4to, 312p, blue bds, 4pl)	Cupples/Leon	1924	Gooch, Thelma	20-30	
Stevenson, Rbt. L.	Child's Garden of Verses (1st, 12mo, 91p, b/w, pep)	Whitman	(1931)	Good, Paula R.	25-45	*
Marryat, Frederick	Children of the New Forest (1st, lg8vo, black cl, p-o, 9cp, pep, SC)	Scribner	1927	Good, Stafford	80-120	
Lamprey, Louise	Tomahawk Trail (1st, 8vo, 313p, gilt, 4cp, pep)	Stokes	1934	Good, Stafford	30-45	
Kidd, Dudley	Bull of the Kraal (1st, 8vo, 302p, gilt, teg, uncut, 12cp)	L: A&C Black	1908	Goodall, Agnes M.	80-130	
Goodall, John S.	Adventures of Paddy Pork (1st AM {std}, ob12mo, [60]p, fp b/w, DJ/2.75)	Harcourt	(1968)	Goodall, John S.	40-65	
Read, Miss	Village School (1st [1st bk.] {std}, 8vo, ipcb, 238p, fp b/w, pep, DJ/3.00)	Houghton	1956	Goodall, John S.	40-70	
La Fontaine, J.	Fables of Jean De La Fontaine (1st, 8vo, 469p, 12pl)	L: Heinemann	1933	Gooden, Stephen	100-160	
Henry, O.	Gift of the Magi (1st, 8vo, 30p, ibds, 8 fp b/w, DJ)	L: Harrap	1939	Gooden, Stephen	80-130	
Omar Khayyam	Rubaiyat of Omar Khayyam (1st, 12mo, 64p, 4 ticp)	L: Harrap	1940	Gooden, Stephen	30-50	
N/A	Arabian Nights (1st, lg8vo, 327p, fp color)	Grosset/Dunlap	(1946)	Goodenow, Earle	30-50	*
Goodenow, Earle	Owl Who Hated the Dark (1st, sm4to, [31]p, 2-color, DJ/3.75)	H.Z. Walck	(1969)	Goodenow, Earle	40-65	
Conklin, Gladys	How Insects Grow (1st, 8vo, 127p, color, DJ/3.95)	Holiday House	(1969)	Goodenow, Girard	20-30	
DeJong, Meindert	Smoke Above the Lane (1st, 8vo, 58p, b/w, cep, DJ/1.75)	Harper	(1951)	Goodenow, Girard	25-40	
Lindsey, William	Apples of Istakhar (1st, sm8vo, 100p, brown/gilt, cvr by...)	Copeland & Day	1895	Goodhue, B.G.	70-120	
Clark, G.O	Nightmare Land (1st, lg4to, [105]p, color)	R.H. Russell	1901	Goodwin, C.L.	200-300	
Lyle, Eugene P.	Lone Star (1st, 8vo, p-o, 431p, 4pl)	Doubleday/Page	1907	Goodwin, Philip R.	35-60	
Pierson, Clara D.	Among the Farmyard People (1st, 12mo, teg, uncut, 245p, 11pl)	Dutton	1899	Gordon, Frederic C.	60-90	
Pierson, Clara D.	Among the Forest People (1st, 12mo, teg, 219p, gilt)	Dutton	(1898)	Gordon, Frederic C.	60-90	
Pierson, Clara D.	Among the Meadow People (1st, 12mo, 127p, gilt, teg, b/w, uncut)	Dutton	1897	Gordon, Frederic C.	60-90	
Pierson, Clara D.	Among the Night People (1st, 12mo, 221p, teg, 11pl)	Dutton	(1902)	Gordon, Frederic C.	60-90	
Pierson, Clara D.	Among the Pond People (1st, 12mo, 210p, teg, 12 b/w)	Dutton	1901	Gordon, Frederic C.	60-90	
MacLaren, Ian	Doctor of the Old School (1st {this fmt.}, 209p, bds, gilt, AEG, b/w)	L: Hodder	1895	Gordon, Frederic C.	60-100	
Ewing, Juliana H.	Jacanapes (1st, 8vo, 80p, gilt, AEG, 7pl)	Dutton	1893	Gordon, Frederic C.	40-60	*
Kingsley, Charles	Water Babies (1st, sm8vo, 308p, gilt, b/w)	Stokes	1891	Gordon, Frederic C.	100-165	
DeRegniers, Beatrice	Shadow Book (1st {std}, sm ob4to, [23]p, DJ/2.75, NYTBI, b/w photos by...)	Harcourt	(1960)	Gordon, Isabel	30-50	*
Beresford, Elisabeth	The Wombles (1st, 8vo, 189p, green cl, b/w, DJ)	L: Benn	1968	Gordon, Margaret	250-350	
Beresford, Elisabeth	The Wombles (1st AM {std}, 8vo, 183p, b/w, DJ/4.95)	Meredith Press	(1969)	Gordon, Margaret	100-165	
Gordon, Mary D.	Crystal Ball (1st, 8vo, 235p, 8cp, pep)	Little/Brown	1920	Gordon, Mary D.	25-40	
Jones, DuPre	Adventures of Gremlin (1st {std}, 12mo, ibds, 112p, b/w, DJ/3.95)	Lippincott	(1966)	Gorey, Edward	100-150	
Jacobs, Frank	Alvin Steadfast on Vernacular Island (1st, 8vo, 64p, fp b/w, DJ/3.50)	Dial Press	(1965)	Gorey, Edward	60-90	
Holman, Felice	At the Top of my Voice (1st {std}, 8vo, 55p, red/gilt, b/w, pep, DJ/3.75)	Norton	(1970)	Gorey, Edward	60-90	
Gorey, Edward	Blue Aspic (1st {std}, ob12mo, [64]p, ipcb, b/w, DJ/2.95)	NY: Meredith Pr.	(1968)	Gorey, Edward	120-200	
Rees, Ennis	Brer Rabbit and his Tricks (1st, lg ob8vo, [48]p, 2-color, DJ/3.95)	Young Scott	(1967)	Gorey, Edward	80-125	R
Gorey, Edward	Bug Book (1st {std}, 24mo, wraps, [32]p, color)	Looking Glass	(1959)	Gorey, Edward	500-800	R
Moore, Merrill	Case-Record from a Sonnetorium (1st, 8vo, grey/red, unpag, b/w, DJ/1.50)	NY: Twayne	(1951)	Gorey, Edward	120-200	
Redford, Polly	Christmas Bower (1st {std}, 8vo, 192p, b/w, DJ/3.95)	Dutton	1967	Gorey, Edward	30-50	
Wahl, Jan	Cobweb Castle (1st {std}, 8vo, [30]p, color, DJ/3.95)	Holt, Rinehart	(1968)	Gorey, Edward	60-90	
Lamport, Felicia	Cultural Slag (1st {std}, 8vo, 136p, b/w, DJ/3.95)	Houghton	1966	Gorey, Edward	50-80	
Lamport, Felicia	Cultural Slag (1st UK, 8vo, 136p, b/w, DJ)	L: Gollancz	1967	Gorey, Edward	65-90	
Lear, Edward	Dong with a Luminous Nose (1st, ob8vo, [46]p, b/w, DJ/2.95, NYTBI)	Young Scott	(1969)	Gorey, Edward	70-120	R
Gorey, Edward	Doubtful Guest (1st {std}, ob8vo, ibds, [30]p, b/w, DJ/2.00)	Doubleday	1957	Gorey, Edward	200-300	
McGregor, Dion	Dream World of Dion McGregor (1st, 8vo, ibds, 213p, fp b/w, DJ/3.95)	Bernard Geis	(1964)	Gorey, Edward	60-100	
Gorey, Edward	Epiplectic Bicycle (1st, ob8vo, ibds, [64]p, fp b/w, DJ/3.00)	Dodd	(1969)	Gorey, Edward	90-140	
Gorey, Edward	Gilded Bat (1st {std}, ob12mo, [62]p, ibds, b/w, DJ/3.00)	Simon/Schuster	(1966)	Gorey, Edward	100-165	
Levine, Rhoda	He Was There from Day We Moved In (1st, 12mo, [24]p, color, cep, DJ/2.95)	Harlin Quist	(1968)	Gorey, Edward	60-95	
Moore, Merrill	Illegitimate Sonnets (1st {1st illus}, 8vo, gilt, 125p, pep, DJ/2.75)	NY: Twayne	(1950)	Gorey, Edward	160-250	
Ciardi, John	King Who Saved Himself from being Saved (1st {std}, sq12mo, b/w, DJ/2.95)	Lippincott	1965	Gorey, Edward	80-120	
Gorey, Edward	Listing Attic (1st {std}, sm8vo, [62]p, ibds, b/w, DJ/2.00)	Duell, Sloan	(1954)	Gorey, Edward	150-225	
Ciardi, John	Man Who Sang the Sillies (1st {std}, lg8vo, 63p, b/w, DJ/3.00)	Lippincott	(1961)	Gorey, Edward	60-90	
Orgel, Doris	Merry, Rose & Christmas-Tree June (1st, 8vo, 77p, fp b/w, DJ/3.95)	Knopf	(1969)	Gorey, Edward	75-120	
Ciardi, John	Monster Den (1st, lg8vo, 62p, ibds, fp b/w, DJ/2.95, NYTBI)	Lippincott	(1966)	Gorey, Edward	60-100	
Rees, Ennis	More of Brer Rabbit's Tricks (1st, ob8vo, [48]p, ibds, 2-color, DJ/3.95)	Young Scott	(1968)	Gorey, Edward	60-90	
Gorey, Edward	Object Lesson (1st {std}, ob8vo, unpag, tan bds, b/w, DJ/2.00)	Doubleday	1958	Gorey, Edward	200-300	
Fenton, Edward	Penny Candy (1st {std}, 8vo, ibds, 46p, b/w, DJ/3.95)	Holt, Rinehart	(1970)	Gorey, Edward	65-90	
Dehn, Paul	Quake, Quake, Quake (1st AM, 8vo, 109p, b/w, DJ/3.50)	Simon/Schuster	1961	Gorey, Edward	50-75	
Mayne, William	Ravensgill (1st AM {std}, 8vo, 174p, DJ/4.25 by...)	Dutton	(1970)	Gorey, Edward	30-45	
Gorey, Edward	Remembered Visit (1st {std}, 8vo, ibds, [64]p, b/w, DJ/2.50)	Simon/Schuster	(1965)	Gorey, Edward	100-165	
Lamport, Felicia	Scrap Irony (1st {std}, 8vo, 126p, b/w, DJ/3.00)	Houghton	1961	Gorey, Edward	70-100	
Ciardi, John	Someone Could Win a Polar Bear (1st {std}, 8vo, 62p, b/w, DJ/3.95)	Lippincott	(1970)	Gorey, Edward	50-80	R
Lear, Edward	The Jumblies (1st, ob8vo, [48]p, tan cl, b/w, DJ/2.95)	Young Scott	(1968)	Gorey, Edward	60-90	

AUTHOR	TITLE	PUBLISHER	DATE	ARTIST	PRICE	LC
Levine, Rhoda	Three Ladies Beside the Sea (1st {std}, ob8vo, [32]p, color, cep, DJ)	Atheneum	1963	Gorey, Edward	60-90	
Gorey, Edward	Unstrung Harp (1st {std]-[1st bk.], 8vo, [62]p, ibds, b/w, DJ/2.00)	Duell, Sloan	(1953)	Gorey, Edward	200-300	
Gorey, Edward	Utter Zoo (1st {std}, sq12mo, unpag, ibds, b/w, DJ/3.95)	Meredith Press	(1967)	Gorey, Edward	120-200	
Spark, Muriel	Very Fine Clock (1st AM, ob8vo, [32]p, fp b/w, pep, DJ/3.95)	Knopf	(1968)	Gorey, Edward	60-90	
Neumeyer, Peter	Why We have Day and Night (1st, ob8vo, ibds, [38]p, color, DJ/3.50)	Young Scott	(1970)	Gorey, Edward	60-85	
Gorey, Edward	Willowdale Handcar (1st, sq24mo, wraps, unpag, b/w)	Bobbs-Merrill	(1962)	Gorey, Edward	150-220	
Ciardi, John	You Know Who (1st, lg8vo, 63p, fp b/w, DJ/3.50)	Lippincott	(1964)	Gorey, Edward	50-85	
Ciardi, John	You Read to Me, I'll Read to You (1st AM, lg8vo, 64p, fp 1-color, DJ/3.50)	Lippincott	(1962)	Gorey, Edward	60-90	R
Flaubert, Gustave	Temptation of St. Anthony (1st, sm8vo, 360p, teg, gilt, 8pl)	L: H.S. Nichols	1895	Gorski, S.	100-180	
Robinson, Mabel L.	King Arthur and His Knights (1st, 8vo, 174p, 1-color, DJ/1.50)	Random	(1953)	Gorsline, Douglas	30-50	*
Latham, Jean L.	Medals for Morse: Artist & Inventor (1st {std}, 8vo, 192p, 1-color, DJ/1.75)	Aladdin	1954	Gorsline, Douglas	30-50	
Malkus, Alida S.	Story of Good Queen Bess (1st, 8vo, 177p, b/w, DJ/1.50)	Grosset/Dunlap	(1953)	Gorsline, Douglas	20-30	*
Edmonds, Walter D.	They Had a Horse (1st, 8vo, 60p, fp b/w, DJ/3.50)	Dodd	(1962)	Gorsline, Douglas	50-80	R
Brooks, Eva C.	Francisco... (1st, sm8vo, 152p, 6pl)	L.C. Page	1910	Goss, John	30-50	
Montgomery, Lucy M.	Further Chronicles of Avonlea (1st, sm8vo, 301p, 6pl)	L.C. Page	1920	Goss, John	100-170	
Murphy, Marguerite	Necklace of Jewels (1st, sm8vo, 123p, blue/gilt, 8pl)	L.C. Page	1918	Goss, John	20-30	
Garis, Howard	Rick & Ruddy (1st, sm8vo, p-o, 282p, 6pl)	Milton Bradley	1920	Goss, John	30-60	
Gotch, Phyllis M.	Romance of a Boo-Bird Chick (1st, 8vo, ibds, 60p, 15 fp color)	L: R.B. Johnson	1903	Gotch, Phyllis M.	100-150	
Henty, G.A.	Out on the Pampas (1st, sm8vo, 301p, green cl, cp)	L: H. Frowde	1910	Gough, Arthur J.	120-200	
Picard, Barbara	Mermaid & the Simpleton (1st AM, 8vo, 254p, fp b/w, pep, DJ)	Criterion Bks.	(1970)	Gough, Philip	40-65	*
Farjeon, Eleanor	Old Nurse's Stocking Basket (1st, 8vo, 115p, col frn, b/w, DJ)	London U. Press	1949	Gough, Philip	40-65	
Brentano, Clemens	Fairy Tales from Brentano (1st, 8vo, 252p, gilt, b/w)	L: T.F. Unwin	1885	Gould, F. Carruthers	170-240	*
Brentano, Clemens	Fairy Tales from Brentano (sm8vo, 326p, col frn, 8pl)	Stokes	(1925)	Gould, F. Carruthers	35-60	*
Begbie, Harold	Great Men (1st, sm4to, 51p, ibds, 24cp)	L: Richards	1901	Gould, F. Carruthers	140-240	
Marzetti, Ada C.	In the Land of Nod (1st, 8vo, 81p, red/gilt, b/w)	L: Griffith	1887	Gould, F. Carruthers	70-120	*
Begbie, Harold	Political Struwwelpeter (4to, ipcb, [24]p, color)	L: Richards	1899	Gould, F. Carruthers	160-225	
Begbie, Harold	Struwwelpeter Alphabet (1st, 4to, ipcb, [26]p, color)	L: Richards	1900	Gould, F. Carruthers	180-220	
Gould, F.C.	Tales Told in the Zoo (1st, lg8vo, 136p, col frn, 5pl)	L: T.F. Unwin	1900	Gould, F. Carruthers	55-80	
Herbertson, Agnes	Be-Wee the Gnome... (1st AM, 8vo, p-o, ibds, 116p, pep, 20cp)	Cupples/Leon	(1921)	Govey, Lilian	100-170	
Herbertson, Agnes	Book of Happy Gnomes (1st, 8vo, 191p)	L: H. Milford	(1924)	Govey, Lilian	75-100	*
Herbertson, Agnes	Dolly Book (1st, 4to, 62p)	L: H. Milford	1920	Govey, Lilian	75-100	*
Heward, Constance	Grandpa & the Tiger (1st AM, 8vo, 121p, orange cl, p-o, color pep)	Jacobs	(1924)	Govey, Lilian	100-160	
Strang, Herbert	Rose Book of the Fairies (4to, ibds, 6cp)	L: H. Milford	(1922)	Govey, Lilian	200-300	
Strang, Herbert	Rose Fairy Book (1st, 4to, 303p, p-o, pep, 12 ticp)	L: Hodder	(1912)	Govey, Lilian	250-350	
Gilmour, Margaret	Seven Little Spillikins (1st AM, ob8vo, unpag, p-o, color)	McKay	[1930]	Govey, Lilian	70-90	
Marsh, Lewis	Tales of the Fairies (1st, 8vo, gilt, 5cp, 7 b/w)	L: Hodder	[1912]	Govey, Lilian	150-220	
Syrett, Netta	Toby & the Odd Beasts (1st, 8vo, 139p, blue cl, p-o, 5cp)	L: Butterworth	(1921)	Govey, Lilian	100-165	
Rives, Amelia	Athelwold (1st, 12mo, uncut, 118p, 8pl)	Harper	1893	Gow, M.	80-120	
Green, Margaret (ed)	Big Book of Animal Fables (1st AM {std}, lg8vo, 240p, color, DJ/4.95)	F. Watts	(1965)	Grabianski, Janusz	30-50	
Grabianski, Janus	Grabianski's Cats (1st AM, ob4to, [32]p, color, cep, DJ/3.95)	F. Watts	1966	Grabianski, Janusz	40-70	
Werner, Jadwiga	Squirrel Redcoat (1st AM {std}, lg8vo, 43p, color, DJ/2.95)	F. Watts	(1961)	Grabianski, Janusz	25-40	
Merrill, Margaret	Bears in My Kitchen (1st, 8vo, 249p, b/w, DJ/3.95)	McGraw-Hill	(1956)	Graboff, Abner	50-80	
Simon, Norma	Daddy Days (1st, 4to, [40]p, color, dep, DJ/2.50, NYTBI)	Abelard-Schuman	(1958)	Graboff, Abner	30-50	
Schwalje, Marjory	Mr. Angelo (1st, sm4to, unpag, ipcb, 20 dp color, DJ/2.75)	Abelard-Schuman	(1960)	Graboff, Abner	30-45	
Holl, Adelaide	Mrs. McGarrity's Peppermint Sweater (1st, ob4to, [40]p, 2-color, DJ/3.50)	Lothrop, Lee	1966	Graboff, Abner	30-50	
Alexander, Anne	Noise in the Night (1st {A}, 4to, [41]p, fp color, pep, DJ/2.75)	Rand/McNally	1960	Graboff, Abner	20-30	
Schlein, Miriam	Sun Looks Down (1st, 4to, [42]p, fp color, cep, DJ/2.50, NYTBI)	Abelard-Schuman	(1954)	Graboff, Abner	50-85	R*
Dickens, Charles	Christmas Carol (1st, 12mo, ibds, [60]p, color)	McLoughlin	(1940)	Graef, Robert A.	30-50	*
Irving, Washington	Rip Van Winkle (1st, 12mo, ibds, [60]p, fp color)	McLoughlin	(1941)	Graef, Robert A.	30-60	*
Zion, Gene	All Falling Down (1st, 4to, ipcb, [31]p, color, DJ/1.75, CH)	Harper	(1951)	Graham, Margaret B.	130-180	R
Graham, Margaret B.	Be Nice to Spiders (1st, lg8vo, [32]p, 3-color, cep, DJ/2.95)	Harper	(1967)	Graham, Margaret B.	30-45	
Shippen, Kath. B.	Big Mose (1st {std}, 8vo, grey cl, 90p, b/w, DJ/2.00)	Harper	(1953)	Graham, Margaret B.	40-65	
Norman, Charles	Crumb that Walked: More about Jane Jonquil (1st, 8vo, 52p, fp b/w, DJ/1.75)	Harper	(1951)	Graham, Margaret B.	30-45	
Zion, Gene	Dear Garbage Man (1st, 4to, ibds, [32]p, 2-color, DJ/2.00, NYTBI)	Harper	(1957)	Graham, Margaret B.	100-160	
Gordon, Shirley	Green Hornet Lunchbox (1st {std}, 8vo, [31]p, color, DJ/3.75)	Houghton	(1970)	Graham, Margaret B.	30-45	*
Owsley, Jennifer	Handy Guide to Grownups (1st {std}, 8vo, [40]p, ipcb, 1-col, pep, DJ/1.00)	Random	(1950)	Graham, Margaret B.	25-40	*
Zion, Gene	Harry and the Lady Next Door (1st, 8vo, 62p, 2-color, DJ/1.95)	Harper	(1960)	Graham, Margaret B.	30-50	*
Zion, Gene	Harry by the Sea (1st, 4to, [32]p, color, DJ/3.25)	Harper	(1965)	Graham, Margaret B.	30-50	*
Zion, Gene	Harry the Dirty Dog (1st, 4to, ibds, [30]p, color, DJ/2.00)	Harper	(1956)	Graham, Margaret B.	100-150	R
Zion, Gene	Hide and Seek Day (1st, 4to, [29]p, ibds, fp color, DJ/2.00)	Harper	(1954)	Graham, Margaret B.	30-50	*
Norman, Charles	Hunch, Munch and Crunch (1st, 8vo, 46p, fp b/w, DJ/2.00)	Harper	(1952)	Graham, Margaret B.	30-45	*
Zion, Gene	Jeffie's Party (1st, lg4to, [30]p, 2-color, DJ/2.50)	Harper	1957	Graham, Margaret B.	40-65	
Zion, Gene	Meanest Squirrel I Ever Met (1st, 4to, [40]p, ibds, color, DJ/3.00)	Scribner	(1962)	Graham, Margaret B.	30-50	
Norman, Charles	Mr. Upstairs and Mr. Downstairs (1st, 8vo, 52p, fp b/w, DJ/1.75)	Harper	(1950)	Graham, Margaret B.	30-45	*
Zion, Gene	No Roses for Harry! (1st, 4to, [32]p, color, DJ/2.50)	Harper	(1958)	Graham, Margaret B.	40-65	
Zion, Gene	Plant Sitter (1st, 4to, [30]p, 2-color, DJ/2.50)	Harper	(1959)	Graham, Margaret B.	70-100	R
Zion, Gene	Really Spring (1st, lg4to, ipcb, [30]p, 3-color, DJ/2.50, NYTBI)	Harper	(1956)	Graham, Margaret B.	100-150	
Zolotow, Charlotte	Storm Book (1st, sm4to, ipcb, [32]p, 7 fp color, cep, DJ/2.00, CH)	Harper	(1952)	Graham, Margaret B.	100-160	
Zion, Gene	Sugar Mouse Cake (1st, 4to, [48]p, ibds, 3-color, pep, DJ/3.50)	Scribner	(1964)	Graham, Margaret B.	40-65	
Zion, Gene	Summer Snowman (1st, narrow 4to, unpag, yellow, cl, color, cep, DJ/2.00)	Harper	(1955)	Graham, Margaret B.	100-200	
Smith, Dodie	Hundred and One Dalmations (1st AM, 8vo, 199p, b/w, DJ/2.75)	Viking	(1957)	Grahame-Johnstone	200-300	
Gallico, Paul	Manxmouse (1st AM {std}, 8vo, blue/gilt, 188p, b/w, DJ/4.95)	Coward	1968	Grahame-Johnstone	90-150	
Smith, Dodie	Starlight Barking (1st AM {std}, 8vo, 156p, b/w, DJ/3.95)	Simon/Schuster	(1967)	Grahame-Johnstone	100-165	
Gramatky, Hardie	Bolivar (1st, lg8vo, 62p, color, pep, DJ/2.95)	Putnam	(1961)	Gramatky, Hardie	30-50	
Gramatky, Hardie	Creeper's Jeep (1st, lg8vo, [64]p, color, DJ/2.25)	Putnam	(1948)	Gramatky, Hardie	80-140	
Gramatky, Hardie	Happy's Christmas (1st, 8vo, 58p, fp color, DJ/4.50)	Putnam	(1970)	Gramatky, Hardie	30-50	
Gramatky, Hardie	Hercules (1st, sm4to, [72]p, red cl, color, pep, DJ/2.00)	Putnam	(1940)	Gramatky, Hardie	100-160	
Gramatky, Hardie	Homer & the Circus Train (1st, lg8vo, [62]p, pep, color, DJ/2.75)	Putnam	(1957)	Gramatky, Hardie	50-80	

AUTHOR	TITLE	PUBLISHER	DATE	ARTIST	PRICE	LC
Gramatky, Hardie	Little Toot (1st, sq8vo, [93]p, pep, color, DJ/1.50)	Putnam	1939	Gramatky, Hardie	150-220	R
Gramatky, Hardie	Little Toot on the Grand Canal (1st, 8vo, 86p, fp color, DJ/3.95)	Putnam	(1968)	Gramatky, Hardie	30-50	
Gramatky, Hardie	Little Toot on the Thames (1st, sm8vo, 87p, fp color, DJ/3.50)	Putnam	(1964)	Gramatky, Hardie	60-90	
Gramatky, Hardie	Loopy (1st, 4to, [72]p, color, pep, DJ/2.25)	Putnam	(1941)	Gramatky, Hardie	70-120	
Gramatky, Hardie	Nikos and the Sea God (1st, lg8vo, [64]p, fp color, DJ/3.50)	Putnam	(1963)	Gramatky, Hardie	30-50	
Teilhet, Darwin	Skwee-Gee (1st {std}, 4to, ibds, [40]p, color, DJ/1.50)	Doubleday/Doran	1940	Gramatky, Hardie	60-100	
Gramatky, Hardie	Sparky: Story of a Little Trolley Car (1st, 8vo, 66p, color, pep, DJ/2.50)	Putnam	(1952)	Gramatky, Hardie	50-80	
Proudfit, Isabel	Treasure Hunter (1st, lg8vo, 206p, uncut, dp b/w, dep, DJ/2.50)	J. Messner	(1939)	Gramatky, Hardie	75-100	*
Hawkins, Quail	Who Wants an Apple (1st, 8vo, [39]p, ipcb, b/w, pep, DJ/1.00)	Holiday House	(1942)	Granahan, L.& D.	25-40	
Burroughs, Edgar R.	Tarzan Twins (1st, 8vo, 126p, ibds, 14 fp color)	Volland	(1927)	Grant, Doug	180-270	*
London, Jack	Abysmal Brute (1st, 12mo, 169p, frn by...)	Century	1913	Grant, Gordon	250-400	
Culver, Henry B.	Book of Old Ships (1st {this pub}, 4to, 306p, ibds, 5cp)	Garden City	(1935)	Grant, Gordon	45-70	
Graham, Harry	Deportmental Ditties (1st AM, 16mo, 134p, 3pl)	Duffield	1909	Grant, Gordon	30-60	*
Stratton-Porter, Gene	Fire Bird (1st {std}, 8vo, 71p, tan bds, pep, 3cp by...)	Doubleday/Page	1922	Grant, Gordon	280-400	
Culver, Henry B.	Forty Famous Ships (1st {std}, 4to, 320p, gilt, 5 fp color, pep, DJ/7.50)	Doubleday/Doran	1936	Grant, Gordon	50-80	
Grant, Gordon	Greasy Luck (1st, 4to, white cl, 128p, b/w, pep)	NY: W.F. Payson	(1932)	Grant, Gordon	40-60	
Stratton-Porter, Gene	Keeper of the Bees (1st {std}, sm8vo, 515p, 4cp, pep)	Doubleday/Page	1925	Grant, Gordon	100-165	
Tarkington, Booth	Penrod (1st [1], sm8vo, p-o, 345p, blue cl, b/w, PPP)	Doubleday/Page	1914	Grant, Gordon	250-350	
Tarkington, Booth	Penrod Jashber (1st {std}, sm8vo, blue cl, 321p, b/w)	Doubleday/Doran	1929	Grant, Gordon	45-70	
Grant, Gordon	Sail Ho! (1st, 4to, 126p, 1-color, pep)	NY: W.F. Payson	(1931)	Grant, Gordon	50-80	
London, Jack	Scarlet Plague (1st, 8vo, 181p, gilt, b/w, pep)	Macmillan	1915	Grant, Gordon	250-400	
Grant, Gordon	Secret Voyage (1st, 8vo, 60p, b/w, DJ/1.50)	Wm. Morrow	1942	Grant, Gordon	30-50	
Morrow, Honore	Ship's Monkey (1st, 8vo, 188p, fp color, pep, DJ/2.00)	Wm. Morrow	1933	Grant, Gordon	25-40	
Grant, Gordon	Ships Under Sail (1st, lg4to, ibds, 25p, color, pep, DJ/1.00)	Garden City	(1939)	Grant, Gordon	35-60	
Grant, Gordon	Story of the Ship (1st, folio, ipcb, [48]p, color, pep)	McLoughlin	1919	Grant, Gordon	55-90	
Grant, Vernon	Flibbity Jibbit & the Key Keeper (1st, 12mo, ipcb, [32]p, color)	Junket Folks	1943	Grant, Vernon	50-80	
Grant, Vernon	Tinker Tim the Toy Maker (1st, lg4to, ibds, 29p, color, pep)	Whitman	1934	Grant, Vernon	100-165	R
Quiller-Couch, A.	Treasure Book of Children's Verse (4to, 336p, teg, gilt, 20 ticp, pep)	L: Hodder	[1911]	Gray, Millicent E.	100-170	
Gilstrap, Robert	Sultan's Fool (1st {std}, lg8vo, 95p, fp b/w, DJ/2.75)	Holt	(1958)	Greco, Robert	25-40	
Read, Elfreida	Magical Egg (1st AM {std}, 12mo, 95p, aqua cl, pep, fp b/w, DJ/3.25)	Lippincott	(1965)	Green, Alison	30-45	*
Dickens, Charles	Old Curiosity Shop (1st, 12mo, 618p, col frn, 23 b/w)	Macrae Smith	(1925)	Green, C.	25-45	*
Elliot, Huger	Alliterative Alphabet... (1st, 4to, [55]p, blue bds, color, pep, DJ/2.50)	McKay	(1947)	Green, Eliz. S.	85-120	
Hardy, Arthur S.	Aurelie (1st, 8vo, 31p, blue pcb, p-o, 3cp)	Harper	1912	Green, Eliz. S.	70-100	
Humphrey, Mabel	Book of the Child (1st, folio, ibds, 4cp by...)	Stokes	(1903)	Green, Eliz. S.	750-1000	
Peabody, Josephine	Book of the Little Past (1st, sm4to, 50p, p-o, pcb, 6cp)	Houghton	1908	Green, Eliz. S.	80-120	
Singmaster, Elsie	Bred in the Bone (1st, 8vo, green/gilt, 300p, 6pl)	Houghton	1925	Green, Eliz. S.	35-60	
Morris, Margaretta	Bryn Mawr Stories (1st, 8vo, 296p, teg, green/gilt, illus by...)	Jacobs	(1901)	Green, Eliz. S.	60-100	
Buchanan, Thompson	Castle Comedy (1st, 8vo, lavender cl, teg, 235p, 4cp, pep)	Harper	1904	Green, Eliz. S.	50-80	
Ward, Mrs. H.	Coryston Family (1st, sm8vo, red/gilt, 328p, 8pl)	Harper	1913	Green, Eliz. S.	50-80	
Waller, Mary Ella	Daughter of the Rich (1st, sm8vo, p-o, 296p, 5cp, pep)	Little/Brown	1924	Green, Eliz. S.	35-60	*
Daskam, Josephine	Her Fiance (1st, 12mo, 164p, 5pl)	Altemus	(1904)	Green, Eliz. S.	50-80	
Malloch, Douglas	Little Hop Skipper (1st, 8vo, 99p, blue cl, col frn)	Doran	(1926)	Green, Eliz. S.	35-60	
LeGallienne, R.	Maker of Rainbows (1st, 8vo, 104p, gilt, teg, p-o, 2cp, 3pl)	Harper	1912	Green, Eliz. S.	120-200	R
N/A	May & November Correspondence (1st, lg8vo, 24p, bds, p-o & frn by...)	Houghton	1928	Green, Eliz. S.	40-60	
Wiggin, Kate D.	Mother Carey's Chickens (1st, 8vo, 289p, p-o, 4cp, 10 b/w)	Houghton	1930	Green, Eliz. S.	40-60	
LeGallienne, R.	Old Country House (1st, 4to, bds, teg, 144p, 6pl)	Harper	1902	Green, Eliz. S.	120-200	
Donnell, Annie H.	Rebecca Mary (1st, 12mo, blue/gilt, 194p, p-o, col frn, 8pl)	Harper	1905	Green, Eliz. S.	60-90	
Chambers, Robert	River-Land (1st, lg8vo, gilt, 92p, 8cp)	Harper	1904	Green, Eliz. S.	120-200	
N/A	Songs of Bryn Mawr College (1st, lg ob4to, 137p, p-o, ibds, b/w, dep)	C.W. Beck	1903	Green, Eliz. S.	125-180	
Duncan, Norman	Suitable Child (1st, 8vo, ipcb, teg, 96p, pep, 5 ticp)	Revell	1909	Green, Eliz. S.	60-90	
Lamb, Charles	Tales from Shakespeare (1st, lg8vo, gilt, teg, 377p, p-o, pep, 11cp)	McKay	1922	Green, Eliz. S.	125-200	
Gerry, Margarita S.	The Flowers (1st, 8vo, 40p, green cl, p-o, 3cp)	Harper	1910	Green, Eliz. S.	60-90	
Van Dyke, Henry	The Mansion (1st, 8vo, 45p, green/gilt, 2 ticp, pep)	Harper	1911	Green, Eliz. S.	35-60	
Donnell, Annie H.	Very Small Person (1st, sm8vo, p-o, 193p, 8cp)	Harper	1906	Green, Eliz. S.	60-90	
Burnett, Frances H.	White People (1st, 12mo, 112p, grey/gilt, 4pl)	Harper	(1917)	Green, Eliz. S.	40-65	
Lamb, Charles	Mrs. Leicester's School (1st, sq8vo, 128p, ibds, 20cp)	L: Dent	1899	Green, Winifred	90-120	
Chambers, Robert	Outdoorland (1st, lg8vo, green cl, 311p, 22cp)	Appleton	1931	Green/Birch	100-150	
Greenaway, Kate	A Apple Pie (1st, ob4to, green ibds, [44]p, A.E. Red, color, cep)	L: Routledge	[1886]	Greenaway, Kate	300-500	
Russell, Mary A.	April Baby's Book of Tunes (1st, sq8vo, tan cl, 75p, 16cp)	L: Macmillan	1900	Greenaway, Kate	250-350	
N/A	Around the House (1st, 4to, ibds, 96p, 63 illus)	Worthington	1888	Greenaway, Kate	100-160	
N/A	Baby's Birthday Book (sq16mo, ibds, A.E. pink, color)	L: Marcus Ward	[1885]	Greenaway, Kate	170-240	
Barker, Mrs. S.	Birthday Book for Children (1st, 32mo, 128p, green/gilt, p-o, 12cp)	L: Routledge	(1880)	Greenaway, Kate	200-300	
Jerrold, A.	Cruise in the Acorn (1st, 8vo, 140p, p-o, gilt, 6 ticp)	L: Marcus Ward	1875	Greenaway, Kate	280-400	
Ruskin, John (ed.)	Dame Wiggin of Lee (1st, 12mo, 20p, gilt)	L: G. Allen	1885	Greenaway, Kate	150-200	
Foster, Myles B.	Day in a Child's Life (1st, 4to, 29p, ibds, color)	L: Routledge	[1881]	Greenaway, Kate	450-600	
N/A	Diamonds & Toads (4to, linen wraps, 6cp)	McLoughlin	[1875]	Greenaway, Kate	200-270	
Mavor, William	English Spelling Book (1st, 12mo, grey bds, 108p, b/w)	L: Routledge	1885	Greenaway, Kate	180-260	
Butt, Geraldine	Esther, a Story for Children (1st, 8vo, 271p, green cl, 4 ticp)	L: Marcus Ward	1878	Greenaway, Kate	220-280	
Knox, Kathleen	Fairy Gifts (sm8vo, ibds, 128p, 4pl by...)	Dutton	[1882]	Greenaway, Kate	170-250	
Holt, Ardern	Fancy Dresses Described (2nd, 12mo, 105p, 48pl)	L: Debenham	[1881]	Greenaway, Kate	130-200	
Richards, Laura E.	Five Mice in a Mousetrap (8vo, 228p, cloth, b/w, dep)	Estes & Lauriat	(1880)	Greenaway, Kate	100-165	
Ranking, Boyd M.	Flowers & Fancies (1st, 24mo, 186p, 4 color)	L: Marcus Ward	1882	Greenaway, Kate	200-285	
Greenaway, Kate	Greenaway's Babies (12mo, linen, 12p, color)	Saalfield	1907	Greenaway, Kate	120-180	
Coolidge, Susan	Guernsey Lily (lg sq8vo, brown/gilt, 238p, pep, 9 b/w by...)	Roberts Bros.	1881	Greenaway, Kate	125-200	
Yonge, Charlotte	Heir of Redclyffe (1st, 8vo, blue/gilt, 524p, 4 illus by...)	L: Macmillan	1881	Greenaway, Kate	60-100	
Goddard, Julia	Kaspar & Seven Wonderful Pigeons of Wurzburg (12mo, 240p, col frn, 4pl)	L: Marcus Ward	[1880]	Greenaway, Kate	80-120	
Spielmann, M.H.	Kate Greenaway (1st, lg8vo, blue cl, 301p, 52cp)	L: A&C Black	1905	Greenaway, Kate	120-180	
Greenaway, Kate	Kate Greenaway's Alphabet (1st, 48mo, ibds, [32]p, color)	L: Routledge	[1885]	Greenaway, Kate	200-300	

AUTHOR	TITLE	PUBLISHER	DATE	ARTIST	PRICE	LC
Greenaway, Kate	Kate Greenaway's Birthday Book (1st, 24mo, beige cl, color)	L: Routledge	[1880]	Greenaway, Kate	200-300	
Greenaway, Kate	Kate Greenaway's Book of Games (1st, lg sq8vo, ipcb, 64p, 24cp, cep)	L: Routledge	[1889]	Greenaway, Kate	200-300	
Greenaway, Kate	Language of Flowers (1st, 16mo, green ibds, 80p, color)	L: Routledge	[1884]	Greenaway, Kate	250-400	
Taylor, Jane	Little Ann... (1st, lg8vo, ibds, 64p, color, cep)	L: Routledge	[1883]	Greenaway, Kate	300-450	
Greenaway, Kate	Marigold Garden (1st, 4to, green ibds, 60p, color)	L: Routledge	[1885]	Greenaway, Kate	250-350	
Mother Goose	Mother Goose (1st, 12mo, yellow ibds, 48p, fp color, cep)	L: Routledge	[1881]	Greenaway, Kate	400-600	
Mother Goose	Mother Goose (4to, ibds, [48]p, color)	McLoughlin	[1882]	Greenaway, Kate	200-300	
Greenaway, Kate	Painting Book (1st, lg8vo, 80p, wraps)	L: Routledge	[1884]	Greenaway, Kate	250-350	
Browning, Robert	Pied Piper of Hamelin (1st, 4to, orange ibds, 64p, a.e. blue, color)	L: Routledge	[1888]	Greenaway, Kate	220-300	
Harte, Bret	Queen of the Pirate Isle (1st, 8vo, tan cl, 58p, AEG, color)	L: Chatto	[1886]	Greenaway, Kate	350-500	
Harte, Bret	Queen of the Pirate Isle (1st AM, 8vo, 58p, AEG, color)	Houghton	1887	Greenaway, Kate	250-400	
Greenaway, Kate	Queen Victoria's Jubilee Garland (1st, ob8vo, 127p, wraps, AEG, color)	L: Routledge	1887	Greenaway, Kate	300-400	
Allingham, William	Rhymes for the Young Folks (1st, 8vo, 75p, 2 illus by...)	L: Cassell	(1887)	Greenaway, Kate	170-240	
Cresswell, Beatrice	Royal Progress of King Pepito (1st, 4to, tan ibds, 48p, 12cp)	L: SPCK	(1889)	Greenaway, Kate	250-350	
Zimmern, Helen	Tales from the Edda (1st, 12mo, 146p, 3pl by...)	L: Sonnenschein	(1883)	Greenaway, Kate	80-140	*
Greenaway, Kate	Trot's Journey (1st, p-o, 8vo, 79p)	Worthington	(1882)	Greenaway, Kate	100-160	
Clark, Mary S.	Turnaside Cottage (8vo, [new ed.], green/gilt, 191p, col frn)	L: Marcus Ward	[1880]	Greenaway, Kate	170-240	
Haile, Ellen	Two Grey Girls & their Opposite Neighbors (1st, 4to, ibds, 258p, b/w)	NY: Cassell	(1880)	Greenaway, Kate	65-100	
Greenaway, Kate	Under the Window (1st, lg8vo, green ibds, 64p, color, cep)	L: Routledge	[1878]	Greenaway, Kate	350-500	
Greenaway, Kate	Under the Window (sq8vo, green ibds, 63p, color)	McLoughlin	[1879]	Greenaway, Kate	250-350	
Disney, Walt	Disney's Tonka (1st, 8vo, ipcb, 60p, color, pep)	Golden Press	(1959)	Greene, Hamilton	90-160	*
Fryer, Jane E.	Mary Frances Housekeeper (1st, lg8vo, 253p, blue/gilt, p-o, color)	Winston	(1914)	Greene, Julia	250-400	
Mother Goose	Mother Goose Nursery Rhymes (1st, 8vo, 256p, color, pep)	Winston	(1928)	Greene, Julia	35-60	*
Spyri, Johanna	Story of Rico (1st, 8vo, 163p, blue cl, 3cp)	Beacon Press	(1921)	Greene, Julia	35-60	*
Lackey, Eunice	Lucky Blacky (1st {std}, 8vo, 118p, 2-color, pep, DJ/2.50, NYTBI)	F. Watts	(1953)	Greene, Winifred	30-50	
Durston, Georgia R.	Candle Light (1st, 4to, ibds, 116p, 12 fp 1-color, pep)	Saalfield	(1906)	Greenland, Katharine	80-120	*
Page, Margaret	In Childhood Land (1st, 4to, [116]p, ibds, color)	Saalfield	1903	Greenland, Katharine	130-200	
Alden, Raymond M.	Knights of the Silver Shield (1st, lg8vo, tan cl, 149p, 10cp)	Bobbs-Merrill	(1906)	Greenland, Katharine	100-150	*
Beebe, Katharine	Roger and Rose (1st, 12mo, 185p, p-o, 19pl)	Saalfield	1903	Greenland, Katharine	30-50	
Alden, Raymond M.	Why the Chimes Rang (1st, lg8vo, 148p, 10pl)	Bobbs-Merrill	(1908)	Greenland, Katharine	60-90	
Cowan, James	Daybreak (1st, sm8vo, gilt, 399p, teg, 4pl)	NY: Richmond	1896	Greenough, Walter C.	80-120	
Compton, Margaret	Snow Bird & Water Tiger... (1st UK, 8vo, 201p, teg, gilt, b/w)	L: Lawrence	1895	Greenough, Walter C.	80-125	
Holder, Charles F.	Treasure Divers (1st, 12mo, 207p, blue/silver, 13pl)	Dodd	1898	Greenough, Walter C.	30-50	
Atherton, Gertrude	Valiant Runaways (1st, sm8vo, 276p, 8pl)	Dodd	1898	Greenough, Walter C.	45-70	
Latham, Jean L.	Man Who Never Snoozed (1st {std}, 8vo, [32]p, 2-color, DJ/2.50)	Macmillan	1961	Greenwald, Sheila	40-65	
Brink, Carol R.	Pink Motel (1st {std}, 8vo, 182p, pink cl, b/w, DJ/2.75)	Macmillan	1959	Greenwald, Sheila	20-35	*
Wheeler, Opal	Sebastian Bach (1st {std}, lg8vo, ibds, 126p, fp b/w, cep)	Dutton	(1937)	Greenwalt, Mary	30-50	
N/A	Adventures of Mr. Mouse (lg4to, ibds, [48]p, 16 fp color)	L: Collins	[1918]	Greenwood, W.E.	90-165	
Spyri, Johanna	Eveli (1st, 8vo, red/gilt, 272p, 8cp, pep)	Lippincott	(1926)	Greer, Blanche	30-50	
Spyri, Johanna	Little Singer (1st, 8vo, 272p, red/gilt, col frn, 7pl, pep)	Lippincott	(1926)	Greer, Blanche	25-40	
Spyri, Johanna	Peppino (1st, 12mo, 114p, red cl, 4cp)	Lippincott	(1926)	Greer, Blanche	35-60	*
Abbott, Eleanor H.	Sick-a-Bed-Lady (1st, 8vo, 371p, 9pl)	Century	1911	Greer, Blanche	30-50	
Greer, Blanche	Thunder's Tail (1st, 4to, ipcb, [24]p, 1-color, DJ/1.00)	Coward	1944	Greer, Blanche	40-70	
Biggers, Earl D.	Agony Column (1st, 8vo, 193p, brown cl, 9pl)	Bobbs-Merrill	(1916)	Grefe, Will	70-100	
MacGrath, Harold	Best Man (1st, 8vo, 207p, green/gilt, p-o, 8pl)	Bobbs-Merrill	(1907)	Grefe, Will	25-40	
Futrelle, Jacques	Chase of the Golden Plate (1st, sm8vo, 220p, green cl, p-o, 11pl)	Dodd	1906	Grefe, Will	50-80	
Cabell, James B.	Eagle's Shadow (1st, 8vo, red/gilt, 256p, 8pl, pep)	Doubleday/Page	1904	Grefe, Will	100-160	
Dix, Beulah M.	Little Captive Lad (1st, sm8vo, 286p, b/w pl)	Macmillan	1902	Grefe, Will	25-40	
Wodehouse, P.G.	Little Nugget (1st AM, sm8vo, 300p, gilt, 3pl)	NY: W.J. Watt	(1914)	Grefe, Will	250-400	
Wodehouse, P.G.	Prince & Betty (1st AM, 12mo, 300p, black/gilt, p-o, 5pl)	NY: Watt	(1912)	Grefe, Will	600-900	
Fox, Frances M.	Angeline Goes Traveling (1st, 12mo, p-o, 256p, 5cp)	Rand/McNally	(1927)	Gregory, Dorothy L.	30-50	*
Warner, Gertrude	Boxcar Children (1st, 8vo, blue/gilt, 146p, p-o, 4cp)	Rand/McNally	(1924)	Gregory, Dorothy L.	60-95	
Fox, Frances M.	Ellen Jane (1st, 8vo, 104p, gilt, p-o, 4cp)	Rand/McNally	(1924)	Gregory, Dorothy L.	25-40	
Fox, Frances M.	Janey (1st, 12mo, 151p, blue cl, p-o, 4cp)	Rand/McNally	(1925)	Gregory, Dorothy L.	25-40	
Van Dresser, Jasmine	Jimsey (1st, sm8vo, blue/gilt, 90p, p-o, 4cp)	Rand/McNally	(1925)	Gregory, Dorothy L.	100-150	
Craine, Edith	Littlebits (1st, 8vo, 133p, p-o, gilt, 4cp)	Rand/McNally	(1926)	Gregory, Dorothy L.	60-100	
Boyle, E.	Scrap Basket Sam (1st, 12mo, 82p, p-o, gilt, 4cp)	Rand/McNally	(1923)	Gregory, Dorothy L.	30-50	
Fox, Frances M.	Sister Sally (1st, 8vo, 105p, gilt, p-o, 4cp)	Rand/McNally	(1925)	Gregory, Dorothy L.	25-40	
Shetter, Stella C.	When Grandma Was a Little Girl (1st, 12mo, 250p, p-o, 4cp)	Rand/McNally	(1926)	Gregory, Dorothy L.	25-40	
Gregory, Lady Isabella	Golden Apple (1st AM, 8vo, 117p, tan cl, 8cp)	Putnam	1916	Gregory, Margaret	120-180	*
Scott, Walter	Ivanhoe (1st AM, 8vo, 564p, 12cp)	Lippincott/Jack	[1915]	Greiffenhagen, M.	50-80	*
Scott, Walter	Ivanhoe (1st, lg8vo, gilt, teg, 12cp)	McKay	[1920]	Greiffenhagen, M.	30-45	
Haggard, H. Rider	Montezuma's Daughter (1st, 8vo, green/gilt, uncut, 24pl)	L: Longmans	1893	Greiffenhagen, M.	200-300	
Haggard, H. Rider	She ([new ed.], 8vo, 300p, buckram, b/w)	L: Longmans	1894	Greiffenhagen/Kerr	70-120	
Haggard, H. Rider	Cleopatra (1st, sm8vo, blue/gilt, 336p, 29pl, pep)	L: Longmans	1889	Greiffenhagen/Wood.	300-500	
Bicknell, Anne G.	Flower Folk (1st, 4to, 71p, gilt, fp color, DJ/2.50)	Putnam	(1936)	Grenwis, Martina	100-150	
Gretz, Susanna	Teddybears 1 to 10 (1st, sm ob4to, [23]p, color, DJ/2.95)	Follett	1969	Gretz, Susanna	30-50	*
Cone, Molly	Other Side of the Fence (1st, 8vo, 117p, fp b/w, DJ/3.25)	Houghton	1967	Gretzer, John	30-45	*
Baker, Elizabeth	Stronger than Hate (1st {std}, 8vo, 185p, b/w, DJ/3.50)	Houghton	1969	Gretzer, John	20-30	
Pope, Edith	Biggety Chameleon (1st, ob8vo, [32]p, fp 3-color, cep, DJ/1.50)	Scribner	1946	Grider, Dorothy	30-50	
Jones, Mary A.	Tell Me About Prayer (1st {A}, 4to, 72p, color, pep, DJ/2.00)	Rand/McNally	(1948)	Grider, Dorothy	20-35	
Pine, Tillie S.	Africans Knew (1st, sm4to, 28p, 3-color, DJ/3.50)	McGraw-Hill	(1967)	Grifalconi, Ann	40-65	
Bishop, Elizabeth	Ballad of Burglar of Babylon (1st {std}, ob8vo, [43]p, 3-col, cep, DJ/3.95)	Farrar, Straus	(1968)	Grifalconi, Ann	200-300	R*
Bouchard, Lois K.	Boy Who Wouldn't Talk (1st {std}, lg8vo, 74p, DJ/3.50)	Doubleday	(1969)	Grifalconi, Ann	25-45	
Reid, Barbara	Carlo's Cricket (1st, sm4to, 58p, color, DJ/3.50)	McGraw-Hill	1967	Grifalconi, Ann	25-45	
Grifalconi, Ann	City Rhythms (1st {std}, 4to, ibds, [32]p, color, DJ/4.95)	Bobbs-Merrill	(1965)	Grifalconi, Ann	50-80	
Hughes, Langston	Don't You Turn Back (1st, lg8vo, 78p, color, DJ/3.95)	Knopf	(1969)	Grifalconi, Ann	60-100	
Weik, Mary H.	Jazz Man (1st {std}, 8vo, 42p, b/w, cep, DJ/3.50, NH, NYTBI)	Atheneum	1966	Grifalconi, Ann	70-100	*

AUTHOR	TITLE	PUBLISHER	DATE	ARTIST	PRICE	LC
Byars, Betsy C.	Midnight Fox (1st, 8vo, 157p, fp b/w, DJ/4.50)	Viking	(1968)	Grifalconi, Ann	30-50	
Embry, Margaret	Peg-Leg Willy (1st, 8vo, [45]p, ibds, 1-color, DJ/2.95)	Holiday House	(1966)	Grifalconi, Ann	25-40	
Johnston, Johanna	Special Bravery (1st, 8vo, 94p, b/w, DJ/3.50)	Dodd	(1967)	Grifalconi, Ann	50-80	
Baldwin, Anne	Sunflowers for Tina (1st, sm4to, [45]p, fp 3-color, cep, DJ/4.50)	Four Winds Pr.	(1970)	Grifalconi, Ann	40-65	*
Forbus, Ina B.	Tawny's Trick (1st, 8vo, 187p, b/w, DJ/3.50)	Viking	1965	Grifalconi, Ann	40-65	
Hopkins, Lee B. (comp)	This Street's for Me! (1st, lg8vo, [38]p, color, DJ/3.50)	Crown	(1970)	Grifalconi, Ann	25-45	
Grifalconi, Ann	Toy Trumpet (1st {std}, 4to, [32]p, color, DJ/4.95)	Bobbs-Merrill	(1968)	Grifalconi, Ann	30-50	
Bacmeister, Rhoda	Voices in the Night (1st {std}, 8vo, 117p, b/w, DJ/3.25)	Bobbs-Merrill	(1965)	Grifalconi, Ann	30-45	
Welsh, Charles	Stories Children Love (1st, sm8vo, 439p, 7cp)	Dodge	(1909)	Grimball, Meta	50-80	
Steele, William O.	Francis Marion, Young Swamp Fox (1st {std}, sm8vo, 192p, b/w, DJ/1.75)	Bobbs-Merrill	(1954)	Gringhuis, Dirk	20-30	
Gripe, Maria	Hugo (1st {std}, 8vo, 153p, b/w, DJ/3.95)	Delacorte Pr.	(1970)	Gripe, Harald	40-65	
Gripe, Maria	Josephine (1st AM {std}, 8vo, 133p, pink cl, b/w, DJ/3.95)	Delacorte Pr.	(1970)	Gripe, Harald	40-65	
Aesopus	Aesop's Fables (4to, ibds, 390p, b/w)	NY: Cassell	1884	Griset, Ernest H.	200-300	*
Aesopus	Book of Fables (12mo, 249p, 32cp)	Am. Book Exch.	1880	Griset, Ernest H.	100-150	
Manning, William	Child's Dream of the Zoo (sq4to, 24p, wraps)	L: Routledge	1889	Griset, Ernest H.	90-120	
Knatchbull-Hugessen	Mountain-Sprite's Kingdom (1st, sm8vo, 372p, red/gilt, b/w, pep)	L: Routledge	1881	Griset, Ernest H.	80-125	
Grishina-Givago, N.	Gresha and his Clay Pig (1st, 8vo, 138p, p-o, color)	Stokes	1930	Grishina-Givago, N.	80-125	
Grishina-Givago, N.	Magic Squirrel (1st, 8vo, 142p, p-o, 3cp, 7pl)	Stokes	1934	Grishina-Givago, N.	80-125	
Grishina-Givago, N.	Peter-Pea (1st, 8vo, gilt, p-o, 95p, fp color)	Stokes	1926	Grishina-Givago, N.	100-165	
Grishina-Givago, N.	Shorty: Nursery Tale from Far Away (1st, ob12mo, 77p, blue cl, b/w)	Lippincott	1924	Grishina-Givago, N.	60-90	
Grishina-Givago, N.	Sparrow House (1st, 8vo, p-o, 175p, 5cp)	Stokes	1928	Grishina-Givago, N.	100-160	
O'Neill, Mary	Anna Amelia's Apteryx (1st {std}, sm8vo, unpag, color, DJ/2.95)	Doubleday	1966	Groedel, Burt	30-45	*
Smith, Nora A.	Adventures of a Doll (1st, 8vo, p-o, 64p, color)	McClure	1907	Groesbeck, Dan S.	35-60	
Prentiss, Lois (comp)	Dickens' Year Book (1st, 8vo, [147]p, tan bds, p-o, b/w)	McClurg	1913	Groesbeck, Dan S.	80-130	
Swift, Jonathan	Gulliver's Travels (1st, sm8vo, 304p, cp, pep)	Doubleday/Page	1912	Groesbeck, Dan S.	25-45	
Graham, Harry	Misrepresentative Women (1st, 12mo, ibds, 120p, 12pl)	Duffield	1906	Groesbeck, Dan S.	25-45	
Eastman, Charles A.	Old Indian Days (1st, sm8vo, p-o, 279p, 4cp)	McClure	1907	Groesbeck, Dan S.	70-100	
Morris, William	Wolf's Head & the Queen (1st, 8vo, 243p, gilt, p-o, col frn, 13pl, pep)	Scribner	1931	Grofe, Nelson	60-100	
Ash, Fenton	Trip to Mars (1st AM, 8vo, red/gilt, 318p, 6cp)	Chambers/Lipp.	1909	Groome, W.H.C.	250-350	
Gropper, William	Alay-Oop (1st, 8vo, [194]p, fp b/w)	Coward	1930	Gropper, William	100-165	
Parks, Gale T.	Here Comes Daddy (1st, ob8vo, ibds, unpag, color, DJ/1.00)	W.R. Scott	1951	Gropper, William	60-100	
Edmonds, Walter D.	Hound Dog Moses & the Promised Land (1st, 8vo, [84]p, b/w, pep, DJ/2.50)	Dodd	(1954)	Gropper, William	40-65	*
Gropper, William	Little Tailor (1st, 8vo, [96]p, fp 1-color, pep, DJ/2.75)	Dodd	1955	Gropper, William	65-100	
Edmonds, Walter D.	Uncle Ben's Whale (1st, 8vo, [82]p, fp b/w, DJ/2.75, NYTBI)	Dodd	(1955)	Gropper, William	40-65	
Meigs, Cornelia L.	Crooked Apple Tree (1st, 8vo, 300p, col frn, fp b/w)	Little/Brown	1929	Grose, Helen M.	20-30	
Kent, Louise A.	Douglas of Porcupine (1st, 8vo, 320p, col frn, pep)	Houghton	1931	Grose, Helen M.	25-45	*
Blumberg, Fannie B.	Rowena Teena Tot & Blackberries (1st, lg8vo, ibds, p-o, 32p, fp color, pep)	Whitman	(1934)	Grosjean, Mary	100-180	
Caudill, Rebecca	Did You Carry the Flag Today, Charlie? (1st {std}, 8vo, 94p, b/w, DJ/3.50)	Holt, Rinehart	(1966)	Grossman, Nancy	30-50	R*
Hill, Elizabeth S.	Evan's Corner (1st {std}, sq8vo, [47]p, fp 2-color, DJ/3.50)	Holt, Rinehart	(1967)	Grossman, Nancy	40-65	*
DeJong, Meindert	Far Out the Long Canal (1st, 8vo, 231p, fp b/w, DJ/3.50)	Harper	(1964)	Grossman, Nancy	20-35	
Levy, Harry	Not Over Ten Inches High (1st, 8vo, 48p, fp b/w, cep, DJ/3.95)	McGraw-Hill	(1968)	Grossman, Nancy	40-65	*
Baum, Betty	Patricia Crosses Town (1st, 8vo, 178p, b/w, DJ/3.50)	Knopf	(1965)	Grossman, Nancy	25-40	
Pomerantz, Charlotte	Ask the Windy Sea (1st, 4to, [32]p, color, DJ/3.95)	Young Scott	(1968)	Grossman/Siegel	20-35	*
Fyleman, Rose	40 Good-Night Tales (1st AM, 8vo, 131p, p-o, 4cp, pep)	Doran	(1924)	Grosvenor, Thelma C.	30-50	
Fyleman, Rose	Fairies & Chimneys (1st, sm8vo, 62p, col frn, silhouettes)	Doran	(1920)	Grosvenor, Thelma C.	40-65	
Hooker, Forrestine	Little House on the Desert (1st {std}, 8vo, 220p, col frn)	Doubleday/Page	1924	Grosvenor, Thelma C.	50-80	
Fyleman, Rose	Rainbow Cat (1st AM, 8vo, 117p, p-o, 4cp, pep)	Doran	(1923)	Grosvenor, Thelma C.	50-85	
Groth, Eleanor	Adventures in a Dishpan (1st, lg8vo, ibds, 31p, color, pep, DJ/0.50)	Grosset/Dunlap	(1936)	Groth, Milt	45-70	
Gruelle, Johnny	All About Cinderella (1st, 16mo, brown bds, p-o, color)	Cupples/Leon	(1916)	Gruelle, Johnny	80-120	
Gruelle, Johnny	All About Hansel & Gretel (1st, sq16mo, ibds, p-o, 48p, 8cp)	Cupples/Leon	(1917)	Gruelle, Johnny	120-180	R*
Bannerman, Helen	All About Little Black Sambo (1st, 16mo, 48p, bds, p-o, 8cp)	Cupples/Leon	(1917)	Gruelle, Johnny	250-400	
Gruelle, Johnny	All About Little Red Riding Hood (sq16mo, ibds, p-o, 48p, color)	Cupples/Leon	(1916)	Gruelle, Johnny	100-145	
Gruelle, Johnny	All About Mother Goose (sq16mo, 48p, color)	Cupples/Leon	(1916)	Gruelle, Johnny	120-180	*
Gruelle, Johnny	All About the Little Small Red Hen (1st, 16mo, 48p, grey bds, p-o, 8cp)	Cupples/Leon	(1917)	Gruelle, Johnny	100-165	
McEvoy, Joseph P.	Bam Bam Clock (1st, sq12mo, ibds, [38]p, color, pep)	Volland	(1920)	Gruelle, Johnny	100-165	
Gruelle, Johnny	Beloved Belindy (1st, lg8vo, ibds, [95]p, color, pep)	Volland	(1926)	Gruelle, Johnny	100-170	
Gruelle, Johnny	Cheery Scarcrow (1st, 12mo, ibds, [39]p, pep, 6cp)	Volland	(1929)	Gruelle, Johnny	100-160	
Gruelle, Johnny	Cruise of the Rickety-Robin (1st, folio, 13p, 3-color, wraps)	Manning Pub.	1931	Gruelle, Johnny	250-350	
Gruelle, Johnny	Eddie Elephant (1st, 12mo, ibds, [39]p, color, pep)	Volland	(1921)	Gruelle, Johnny	100-160	
Grimm Bros.	Fairy Tales (1st, lg8vo, 419p, p-o, gilt, 11pl)	Cupples/Leon	(1914)	Gruelle, Johnny	350-500	
Gruelle, Johnny	Friendly Fairies (1st, lg8vo, [86]p, ibds, color, pep)	Volland	(1919)	Gruelle, Johnny	140-225	
Gruelle, Johnny	Funny Little Book (1st, 12mo, ibds, [40]p, pep, color)	Volland	(1917)	Gruelle, Johnny	125-200	
Gruelle, Johnny	Johnny Gruelle's Golden Book (lg4to, 79p, ibds, color)	Donohue	(1929)	Gruelle, Johnny	80-140	
Gruelle, Johnny	Johnny Mouse & Wishing Stick (1st, lg8vo, ipcb, 89p, color, pep)	Bobbs-Merrill	(1922)	Gruelle, Johnny	100-160	R
Gruelle, Johnny	Little Brown Bear (1st, 12mo, ibds, [40]p, color, pep)	Volland	(1920)	Gruelle, Johnny	80-120	
Gruelle, Johnny	Little Sunny Stories (1st, 12mo, ibds, [40]p, color, pep)	Volland	(1919)	Gruelle, Johnny	100-170	
Gruelle, Johnny	Magical Land of Noom (1st, lg8vo, ibds, 157p, 12cp, pep)	Volland	(1922)	Gruelle, Johnny	350-500	
Lawrence, Josephine	Man in the Moon Stories... (1st, 4to, 121p, gilt, p-o, 8cp, pep)	Cupples/Leon	(1922)	Gruelle, Johnny	200-300	
Gruelle, Johnny	Marcella Stories (1st, 8vo, ibds, 94p, color, pep)	Volland	(1929)	Gruelle, Johnny	100-165	
Gruelle, Johnny	My Very Own Fairy Stories (1st, lg8vo, ibds, [95]p, color, pep)	Volland	(1917)	Gruelle, Johnny	150-220	
Malot, Hector	Nobody's Boy (1st AM, 8vo, 372p, green/gilt, p-o, 4cp)	Cupples/Leon	1916	Gruelle, Johnny	60-100	
Gruelle, Johnny	Orphant Annie Story Book (1st, lg8vo, 85p, p-o, color, pep)	Bobbs-Merrill	(1921)	Gruelle, Johnny	120-170	
Gruelle, Johnny	Paper Dragon (1st, 8vo, ibds, [96]p, color, pep)	Volland	(1926)	Gruelle, Johnny	100-160	
Hubbell, Rose S.	Quacky Doodles... (1st, 8vo, ibds, [88]p, color)	Volland	(1916)	Gruelle, Johnny	80-130	
Gruelle, Johnny	Raggedy Andy Goes Sailing (1st, 12mo, [59]p, ipcb, 10 fp color)	McLoughlin	(1941)	Gruelle, Johnny	55-80	*
Gruelle, Johnny	Raggedy Andy Stories (1st, lg8vo, ibds, unpag, color, pep)	Volland	(1920)	Gruelle, Johnny	140-200	
Gruelle, Johnny	Raggedy Ann & Golden Butterfly (1st, lg8vo, 95p, ibds, color, cep)	Gruelle Co.	(1940)	Gruelle, Johnny	50-80	
Gruelle, Johnny	Raggedy Ann & Happy Toad (1st, 12mo, ibds, [50]p, color)	McLoughlin	1940	Gruelle, Johnny	55-80	*

AUTHOR	TITLE	PUBLISHER	DATE	ARTIST	PRICE	LC
Gruelle, Johnny	Raggedy Ann & Laughing Brook (1st, 12mo, ibds, [59]p, color)	McLoughlin	1940	Gruelle, Johnny	55-80	*
Gruelle, Johnny	Raggedy Ann & Left-Handed Safety Pin (1st, 12mo, 45p, color, pep)	Whitman	(1935)	Gruelle, Johnny	40-60	*
Gruelle, Johnny	Raggedy Ann Helps Grandpa Hoppergrass (1st, 12mo, ibds, [50]p, color)	McLoughlin	1940	Gruelle, Johnny	40-60	*
Gruelle, Johnny	Raggedy Ann in Cookie Land (1st, lg8vo, ibds, 95p, color, pep)	Volland	(1931)	Gruelle, Johnny	120-200	
Gruelle, Johnny	Raggedy Ann in Deep Deep Woods (1st, lg8vo, ibds, [95]p, color, pep)	Volland	(1930)	Gruelle, Johnny	120-200	
Gruelle, Johnny	Raggedy Ann in the Garden (1st, 12mo, [61]p, ipcb, 10 fp color)	McLoughlin	1940	Gruelle, Johnny	55-80	*
Gruelle, Johnny	Raggedy Ann in the Golden Meadow (1st, folio, ibds, [58]p, 14 color, pep)	Whitman	1935	Gruelle, Johnny	100-175	R
Gruelle, Johnny	Raggedy Ann Stories (1st, lg8vo, ibds, [95]p, color, pep)	Volland	(1918)	Gruelle, Johnny	150-220	
Gruelle, Johnny	Raggedy Ann Stories (1st {this pub}, lg8vo, 95p, color)	Gruelle Co.	(1947)	Gruelle, Johnny	55-80	*
Gruelle, Johnny	Raggedy Ann's Alphabet Book (1st, 12mo, [38]p, ibds, pep, color)	Volland	(1925)	Gruelle, Johnny	140-200	
Gruelle, Johnny	Raggedy Ann's Lucky Pennies (1st, 8vo, ibds, 94p, color, pep)	Volland	(1932)	Gruelle, Johnny	120-180	
Gruelle, Johnny	Raggedy Ann's Magical Wishes (1st, lg8vo, 94p, ibds, color, pep)	Volland	(1928)	Gruelle, Johnny	140-200	
Gruelle, Johnny	Raggedy Ann's Wishing Pebble (1st, lg8vo, ibds, unpag, color, pep)	Volland	(1925)	Gruelle, Johnny	140-200	
Gruelle, Johnny	Raggedy Ann.../Camel/Wrinkled Knees (8vo, ibds, [95]p, pep, color)	Volland	(1924)	Gruelle, Johnny	150-220	
Snyder, Fairmont	Rhymes for Kindly Children (1st, lg8vo, ibds, [95]p, color, pep)	Volland	(1916)	Gruelle, Johnny	120-180	R
Fairmont, Ethel	Rhymes for Kindly Children (4to, [127]p, color, pep)	Wise-Parlow	(1937)	Gruelle, Johnny	50-80	
Putnam, Nina W.	Sunny Bunny (1st, 8vo, ibds, [42]p, color, pep)	Volland	(1918)	Gruelle, Johnny	120-185	
Gruelle, Johnny	Wooden Willie (1st, lg8vo, ibds, 95p, color, pep)	Volland	(1927)	Gruelle, Johnny	150-220	
Gruelle, Justin	Camel with Wrinkled Knees (1st {this pub}, 12mo, ibds, [59]p, color)	McLoughlin	(1941)	Gruelle, Justin	50-85	
Gruelle, Justin	Mother Goose Parade (1st, lg4to, ibds, [31]p, color, pep)	Volland	(1929)	Gruelle, Justin	80-120	
Fox, Frances M.	Nannette (1st, 8vo, 80p, red/gilt, color, pep)	Volland	(1929)	Gruelle, Justin	70-100	
Gruelle, Johnny	Raggedy Ann & Betsy Bonnet String (1st, lg8vo, 95p, ibds, color)	Gruelle Co.	(1943)	Gruelle, Justin	55-80	
Gruelle, Johnny	Raggedy Ann in Snow White Castle (1st, lg8vo, ibds, 95p, color)	Gruelle Co.	(1946)	Gruelle, Justin	70-100	
Gruelle, Johnny	Raggedy Ann in the Magic Book (1st, lg8vo, [91]p, ibds, color)	Gruelle Co.	(1939)	Gruelle, Worth	70-100	
Thompson, Charles M.	Calico Cat (1st, 12mo, green/gilt, 228p, 8pl)	Houghton	1908	Gruger, Frederic R.	40-60	
Johnson, Owen	Tennessee Shad (1st, 12mo, red cl, 307p, 8pl, PPP)	Baker/Taylor	1911	Gruger, Frederic R.	80-120	
Johnson, Owen	The Varmint (1st, 12mo, 396p, green cl, 6pl, PPP)	Baker/Taylor	1910	Gruger, Frederic R.	60-100	
Harris-Burland, J.	Gold Worshipers (1st, 12mo, 310p, brown cl, 6pl)	Dillingham	(1906)	Grunwald, Charles	50-80	
Godfrey, Hollis	Man Who Ended War (1st, 8vo, blue/gilt, 301p, p-o, 4pl)	Little/Brown	1908	Grunwald, Charles	60-100	
Lansdale, M.H.	Chateaux of Touraine (1st, 4to, 363p, uncut, teg, gilt, 16cp)	Century	1906	Guerin, Jules	75-100	
Hichens, Robert	Holy Land (1st, 4to, 302p, green/gilt, uncut, teg, 18cp)	Century	1910	Guerin, Jules	80-125	
Hichens, Robert	Near East (1st, 4to, teg, blue/gilt, 18cp, fp b/w)	Century	1913	Guerin, Jules	100-165	
Crawford, Phyllis	Let's Go! (1st, sm8vo, 73p, b/w, DJ/1.50)	Henry Holt & Co.	(1949)	Guerin, Theodore	30-50	*
Lida	Little French Farm (1st {std}, 4to, ibds, [26]p, color, pep, DJ/1.00)	Harper	1939	Guertik, Helene	120-180	
Carpenter, Frances	Elephant's Bathtub (1st {std}, lg8vo, 219p, b/w, DJ/3.50)	Doubleday	(1962)	Guggenheim, Hans	30-50	
Arora, Shirley L.	What Then, Raman? (1st, 8vo, 176p, fp, b/w, DJ/3.50, JABA)	Follett	(1960)	Guggenheim, Hans	40-65	
Frost, Frances	Pool in the Meadow (1st, 8vo, 73p, blue cl, b/w)	Houghton	1933	Guglielmi	50-80	*
Guirma, Frederic	Princess of the Full Moon (1st {std}, 4to, [32]p, color, DJ/4.95)	Macmillan	(1970)	Guirma, Frederic	30-45	
Moore, Hannah	Deeds of Daring done by Girls (1st, sm8vo, 300p, 6cp)	Stokes	(1906)	Gunn, Archie	25-40	*
Gurney, Nancy	King, the Mice and the Cheese (1st, 8vo, 63p, color, DJ/1.95)	Beginner Books	(1965)	Gurney, Nancy	50-80	
Dooley, Mrs.	Dem Good Ole Times (1st, sm4to, 151p, teg, 16 ticp)	Doubleday/Page	1906	Gutherz, Suzanne	100-170	
Low, Frances H.	Little Men in Scarlet (1st, 8vo, 237p, green/gilt, b/w)	L: Jarrold	1896	Guthrie, James J.	50-85	
Chenault, Nell	Parsifal the Poddley (1st {std}, 8vo, 83p, b/w, DJ/2.75)	Little/Brown	(1960)	Guthrie, Vee	45-70	
Gray, P.L.	In a Car of Gold (1st, 12mo, 156p, brown/gilt, 6pl)	Saalfield	1902	Gutman, Bernard	30-50	
Carroll, Lewis	Alice in Wonderland (1st, 4to, 165p, blue cl, 10cp, pep)	Dodge	1907	Gutmann, Bessie P.	200-300	
Dunham, Edith	Diary of a Mouse (1st, sm8vo, red cl, p-o, unpag, fp color, pep)	Dodge	(1907)	Gutmann, Bessie P.	200-300	
Dalton, Agnes M.	From Sioux to Susan (1st, 8vo, 342p, 22 b/w illus)	Century	1905	Gutmann, Bessie P.	75-100	*
Carroll, Lewis	Through the Looking Glass (1st, 8vo, blue cl, 185p, 10cp)	Dodge	(1909)	Gutmann, Bessie P.	150-225	
Kapp, Paul (adap)	Cat Came Fiddling (1st {std}, sm sq4to, ibds, 80p, b/w, DJ/3.00)	Harcourt	(1956)	Haas, Irene	60-100	R
DeRegniers, Beatrice	Little House of Your Own (1st {std}, 8vo, [38]p, b/w, DJ/1.75, NYTBI)	Harcourt	(1954)	Haas, Irene	45-70	R*
Banks, Richard	Mysterious Leaf (1st {std}, 8vo, 51p, fp b/w, DJ/2.50)	Harcourt	(1954)	Haas, Irene	150-225	R
DeRegniers, Beatrice	Something Special (1st {std}, 8vo, [46]p, fp b/w, DJ/2.25)	Harcourt	(1958)	Haas, Irene	30-50	
Enright, Elizabeth	Tatsinda (1st {std}, 8vo, 80p, fp color, DJ/3.50)	Harcourt	(1963)	Haas, Irene	70-120	R
Joslin, Sesyle	There is a Dragon in my Bed (1st {std}, sq8vo, [64]p, fp b/w, DJ/2.25)	Harcourt	(1961)	Haas, Irene	50-80	R*
DeRegniers, Beatrice	Was It a Good Trade? (1st {std}, ob8vo, [29]p, ibds, color, DJ/1.95, NYTBI)	Harcourt	1956	Haas, Irene	60-100	R*
Enright, Elizabeth	Zeee (1st {std}, sm8vo, 46p, fp color, DJ/3.50)	Harcourt	(1965)	Haas, Irene	45-70	
Hacker, Lilian P.	Susan (1st, 4to, [52]p, ibds, gilt, 10cp, pep)	L: Hodder	(1912)	Hacker, Lilian	150-250	
Williamson, Hamilton	Baby Bear (1st {std}, 8vo, [55]p, green ibds, color)	Doubleday/Doran	(1930)	Hader, B.& E.	60-90	
Garrard, Phillis	Banana Tree House (1st, lg8vo, 108p, color, pep, DJ/2.00)	Coward	(1938)	Hader, B.& E.	40-65	
Hader, B.& E.	Big City (1st, 4to, [60]p, fp color, cep, DJ/2.50)	Macmillan	1947	Hader, B.& E.	120-200	
Baruch, Dorothy W.	Big Fellow at Work (1st {std}, 12mo, 103p, b/w, pep)	Harper	1930	Hader, B.& E.	75-100	
Hader, B.& E.	Big Snow (1st, sm4to, blue cl, [48]p, color, dep, DJ/2.50, CM)	Macmillan	1948	Hader, B.& E.	180-250	R
Hader, B.& E.	Billy Butter (1st, ob8vo, 92p, color, pep, DJ/2.00)	Macmillan	1936	Hader, B.& E.	50-80	
Stoddard, Anne	Bingo is My Name (1st {std}, 8vo, [58]p, color)	Century	(1931)	Hader, B.& E.	50-80	
Hader, B.& E.	Cat & the Kitten (1st, 8vo, 98p, green cl, color, pep, DJ/2.00)	Macmillan	1940	Hader, B.& E.	40-65	
N/A	Chicken Little & Little Half Chick (1st, sq12mo, ibds, color)	Macmillan	1927	Hader, B.& E.	55-80	*
Hader, B.& E.	Chuck-a-Luck & his Reindeer (1st, lg ob8vo, ipcb, 28p, color)	Houghton	1933	Hader, B.& E.	70-120	*
Hader, B.& E.	Cock-a-Doodle-Doo (1st, sm4to, [56]p, fp color, DJ/2.00, CH)	Macmillan	(1939)	Hader, B.& E.	100-175	
Hader, B.& E.	Cricket (1st, 8vo, p-o, red cl, 160p, color, pep, DJ/2.00)	Macmillan	1938	Hader, B.& E.	50-80	
Hader, B.& E.	Ding Dong Bell (1st {std}, 4to, ipcb, 45p, fp color, DJ/2.50)	Macmillan	1957	Hader, B.& E.	40-65	
Peedie, Jean M.	Donald in Numberland (1st, 8vo, ipcb, [64]p, color, dep)	R.D. Henkle	(1927)	Hader, B.& E.	100-160	
Hahn, Julia L.	Everyday Fun (1st [reader ed.], 12mo, 154p, color, pep)	Houghton	(1935)	Hader, B.& E.	50-80	*
Hader, B.& E.	Farmer in the Dell (1st, sm4to, green cl, [90]p, color, pep)	Macmillan	1931	Hader, B.& E.	55-80	*
Hader, B.& E.	Friendly Phoebe (1st {std}, 8vo, 45p, color, DJ/2.25)	Macmillan	1953	Hader, B.& E.	40-65	
Stoddard, Anne	Good Little Dog (1st {std}, 8vo, ibds, [59]p, 16cp)	Century	(1930)	Hader, B.& E.	60-90	
Hader, B.& E.	Green & Gold (1st, 8vo, 48p, color, pep, DJ/1.00)	Macmillan	1936	Hader, B.& E.	70-125	
Grimm Bros.	Hansel and Gretel (1st, sq8vo, ibds, color)	Macmillan	1927	Hader, B.& E.	70-100	
Stoddard, Anne	Here Bingo! (1st {std}, sq8vo, ibds, [61]p, 16 fp color)	Century	(1932)	Hader, B.& E.	60-90	

AUTHOR	TITLE	PUBLISHER	DATE	ARTIST	PRICE	LC
Hader, B.& E.	Home on the Range... (1st {std}, 4to, [38]p, picb, fp color, DJ/2.50)	Macmillan	1955	Hader, B.& E.	45-70	*
Williamson, Hamilton	Humpy, Son of the Sands (1st {std}, 8vo, [47]p, color, pep)	Doubleday/Doran	1937	Hader, B.& E.	70-100	*
Hader, B.& E.	Jamaica Johnny (1st {std}, sq8vo, 90p, green cl, 6 fp color, pep, DJ/2.00)	Macmillan	1935	Hader, B.& E.	70-100	
Miller, Jane	Jimmy the Groceryman (1st, sm8vo, 88p, blue cl, color, pep)	Houghton	(1934)	Hader, B.& E.	70-120	
Williamson, Hamilton	Lion Cub: Jungle Tale (1st {std}, 8vo, ipcb, [51]p, color, pep)	Doubleday/Doran	(1931)	Hader, B.& E.	60-100	
Hader, B.& E.	Lions & Tigers & Elephants Too (1st {std}, lg ob8vo, ibds, [61]p, color)	Longmans	1930	Hader, B.& E.	65-100	
Hader, B.& E.	Little Antelope... (1st {std}, 4to, 41p, ibds, color, DJ/3.00)	Macmillan	1962	Hader, B.& E.	40-65	
Hader, B.& E.	Little Appaloosa (1st {std}, sm4to, [43]p, color, DJ/2.50)	Macmillan	(1949)	Hader, B.& E.	60-90	
Hader, B.& E.	Little Chip of Willow Hill (1st {std}, 8vo, 42p, fp color, cep, DJ/2.50)	Macmillan	1958	Hader, B.& E.	50-80	
Williamson, Hamilton	Little Elephant (1st {std}, sq8vo, ibds, [55]p, 4cp)	Doubleday/Doran	(1930)	Hader, B.& E.	40-65	
Hader, B.& E.	Little Red Hen (1st, 24mo, [42]p, color)	Macmillan	1928	Hader, B.& E.	50-85	
Hader, B.& E.	Little Stone House (1st, sm4to, green cl, [63]p, color, DJ/2.00)	Macmillan	(1944)	Hader, B.& E.	50-80	
Hader, B.& E.	Little Town (1st, 4to, [87]p, orange cl, pep, color, DJ/2.00)	Macmillan	1941	Hader, B.& E.	65-90	
Hader, B.& E.	Little White Foot (1st {std}, 8vo, blue cl, unpag, color, cep, DJ/2.25)	Macmillan	1952	Hader, B.& E.	50-85	
Hader, B.& E.	Lost in the Zoo (1st {std}, sm4to, unpag, color, DJ/2.50)	Macmillan	1951	Hader, B.& E.	50-80	*
Lee, Melicent	Marcos, Mountain Boy of Mexico (1st, sm4to, p-o, 79p, color, pep, DJ/2.00)	Whitman	1937	Hader, B.& E.	40-60	
Hader, B.& E.	Midget & Bridget (1st, lg ob8vo, 90p, orange cl, color, pep, DJ/2.00)	Macmillan	1934	Hader, B.& E.	60-100	
Hader, B.& E.	Mighty Hunter (1st, sm4to, [49]p, color, pep, DJ/2.00, CH)	Macmillan	(1943)	Hader, B.& E.	70-120	
Williamson, Hamilton	Monkey Tale (1st {std}, 8vo, [49]p, pep, color)	Doubleday/Doran	(1929)	Hader, B.& E.	45-70	
Hader, B.& E.	Mr. Billy's Gun (1st {std}, 4to, unpag, color, DJ/3.50)	Macmillan	1960	Hader, B.& E.	30-50	
Seaman, Louise	Mr. Peck's Pets (1st {std}, 8vo, ibds, 96p, b/w, pep, DJ/2.00)	Macmillan	1947	Hader, B.& E.	30-50	
Hader, B.& E.	Old Woman & Crooked Sixpence (1st, 16mo, [42]p, color)	Macmillan	1928	Hader, B.& E.	60-90	*
Mother Goose	Picture Book of Mother Goose (1st, lg sq8vo, [151]p, color, pep)	Coward	(1930)	Hader, B.& E.	200-300	
Hader, B.& E.	Picture Book of the States (1st {std}, ob folio, color, [60]p, pep)	Harper	1928	Hader, B.& E.	60-90	
Hader, B.& E.	Picture Book of Travel (1st, 4to, p-o, 63p, color, pep)	Macmillan	1928	Hader, B.& E.	70-100	
Lecky, Prescott	Play-Book of Words (1st, 4to, [72]p, fp 1-color)	Stokes	1933	Hader, B.& E.	50-85	
Hader, B.& E.	Quack-Quack... (1st {std}, 4to, 47p, ibds, color, DJ/3.00)	Macmillan	1961	Hader, B.& E.	30-50	
Hader, B.& E.	Rainbow's End (1st, sq8vo, 168p, 4 fp color, DJ/2.00)	Macmillan	1945	Hader, B.& E.	45-70	
Hader, B.& E.	Reindeer Trail (1st {std}, sm4to, blue cl, unpag, color, DJ/3.25)	Macmillan	(1959)	Hader, B.& E.	35-50	
Dalgliesh, Alice	Smiths & Rusty (1st, 8vo, 118p, b/w, DJ/1.75)	Scribner	1936	Hader, B.& E.	40-65	
Hader, B.& E.	Snow in the City: Winter's Tale (1st {std}, 4to, 41p, color, DJ/3.50)	Macmillan	1963	Hader, B.& E.	30-50	
Bigham, Madge A.	Sonny Elephant (1st, sm8vo, 201p, cloth, p-o, col frn, b/w)	Little/Brown	1930	Hader, B.& E.	60-100	
Hader, B.& E.	Spunky (1st, ob8vo, blue cl, 90p, color, pep)	Macmillan	1933	Hader, B.& E.	55-80	*
Hader, B.& E.	Squirrely of Willow Hill (1st {std}, 8vo, [47]p, color, cep, DJ/2.00)	Macmillan	1950	Hader, B.& E.	50-80	
Hader, B.& E.	Stop, Look & Listen (1st, sq12mo, ipcb, 48p, 2-color, pep, DJ/1.00)	Longmans	(1936)	Hader, B.& E.	60-90	*
Feuillet, Octave	Story of Mr. Punch (1st, 8vo, 139p, p-o, col frn, fp b/w, pep)	Dutton	(1929)	Hader, B.& E.	30-50	
Hader, B.& E.	Story of Pancho (1st, sm4to, tan cloth, [56]p, color, DJ/2.00)	Macmillan	1942	Hader, B.& E.	70-125	
Hader, B.& E.	Story of the Three Bears (1st, 16mo, [42]p, ibds, color, pep)	Macmillan	1928	Hader, B.& E.	60-90	
Williamson, Hamilton	Stripey (1st {std}, 8vo, ibds, [47]p, color, pep, DJ/1.00)	Doubleday/Doran	1939	Hader, B.& E.	60-90	
Lent, Henry B.	The Farmer (1st, sq16mo, ipcb, [42]p, color, pep)	Macmillan	1937	Hader, B.& E.	40-60	
Hader, B.& E.	The Runaways (1st {std}, sm4to, green cl, 38p, color, DJ/3.00)	Macmillan	1956	Hader, B.& E.	40-65	
Hader, B.& E.	The Skyrocket (1st, lg8vo, 148p, grey/red, 4 fp color, cep, DJ/2.50)	Macmillan	1946	Hader, B.& E.	30-55	
Whitney, Elinor	Timothy & the Blue Cart (1st, sm8vo, 168p, p-o, col frn, fp b/w, pep)	Stokes	1930	Hader, B.& E.	40-65	
Mason, Miriam E.	Timothy has Ideas (1st, 8vo, 127p, blue cl, fp b/w, DJ/1.50)	Macmillan	1943	Hader, B.& E.	40-65	
Hader, B.& E.	Tommy Thatcher Goes to Sea (1st, sq8vo, 95p, 6 fp color, pep, DJ/2.00)	Macmillan	1937	Hader, B.& E.	35-50	
Hader, B.& E.	Tooky... (1st {std}, lg ob8vo, ibds, [61]p, color, pep)	Longmans	1931	Hader, B.& E.	75-100	*
Hader, B.& E.	Two Funny Clowns (1st, ob8vo, [52]p, color)	Coward	(1929)	Hader, B.& E.	50-85	
Andersen, Hans C.	Ugly Duckling (1st, 24mo, [42]p, ibds, color, pep)	Macmillan	1927	Hader, B.& E.	35-60	
Hader, B.& E.	Under the Pig-Nut Tree (1st, sm8vo, 63p, ibds, color, DJ/1.25)	Knopf	1930	Hader, B.& E.	40-65	
Moore, Clement C.	Visit from St. Nicholas (1st, 24mo, [42]p, ibds, pep, color)	Macmillan	1937	Hader, B.& E.	50-85	R
Kipling, Rudyard	Wee Willie Winkie (1st, 12mo, ibds, color)	Macmillan	1927	Hader, B.& E.	60-100	
Hader, B.& E.	What'll You Do when You Grow Up? (1st {std}, 12mo, ipcb, [63]p, col, pep)	Longmans	1929	Hader, B.& E.	75-100	*
Hahn, Julia L.	Who Knows: A Little Primer (1st [reader ed.], 12mo, 46p, color)	Houghton	(1937)	Hader, B.& E.	50-80	*
Dalgliesh, Alice	Wings for the Smiths (1st, 8vo, blue cl, 89p, 3cp, cep, DJ/1.75)	Scribner	1937	Hader, B.& E.	40-65	
Hader, B.& E.	Wish on the Moon (1st {std}, sm sq4to, 40p, dep, color, DJ/2.75)	Macmillan	1954	Hader, B.& E.	45-70	
Meigs, Cornelia L.	Wonderful Locomotive (1st, ob8vo, gilt, 104p, 3cp, pep, DJ/2.00)	Macmillan	1928	Hader, B.& E.	80-130	
Hader, Berta	Whiffy McMann (1st, sq12mo, [56]p, ipcb, 1-color)	NY: Oxford U.Pr.	(1933)	Hader, Berta	80-140	
Emerson, Edwin	Adventures of Theodore Roosevelt (1st {std}, 8vo, 336p, gilt, b/w)	Dutton	(1928)	Hader, Elmer	30-50	*
Gaggin, Eva R.	Down Ryton Water (1st, 8vo, green/silver, 369p, b/w, pep, DJ/2.00, NH)	Viking	1941	Hader, Elmer	70-100	
Hooker, Forrestine	Garden of the Lost Key (1st {std}, 8vo, 288p, col frn, pep)	Doubleday/Doran	1929	Hader, Elmer	75-100	*
McBride, Mary M.	How Dear to My Heart (1st {std}, 8vo, 196p, b/w, DJ/2.00)	Macmillan	1940	Hader, Elmer	30-50	
Singmaster, Elsie	Isle of Que (1st {std}, 8vo, 152p, DJ/2.25, designs by...)	Longmans	(1948)	Hader, Elmer	45-65	
Holway, Hope K.	Story of Health (1st {std}, sm8vo, 150p, col frn, fp b/w, dep)	Harper	1931	Hader, Elmer	40-65	*
Camp, Ruth O.	Story of the Markets (1st {std}, 12mo, 128p, col frn, b/w)	Harper	1929	Hader, Elmer	55-80	*
Tresselt, Alvin	Bonnie Bess, Weathervane Horse (1st, 4to, ibds, [25]p, color, DJ/1.75)	Lothrop, Lee	1949	Hafner, Marylin	30-50	*
Watts, Mabel	Story of Zachary Zween (1st, 4to, [43]p, ipcb, dp color, pep, DJ/3.50)	Parents Mag. Pr.	(1967)	Hafner, Marylin	25-45	*
Hale, Kathleen	Orlando Buys a Farm (1st, ob folio, 32p, wraps, color)	L: Country Life	1942	Hale, Kathleen	200-300	
Hale, Kathleen	Orlando, Marmalade Cat-Camping Holiday (1st AM, folio, [32]p, col, DJ/2.50)	Scribner	[1938]	Hale, Kathleen	300-500	
Dickinson, Peter	Heartsease (1st AM {std}, 8vo, 223p, b/w, DJ/4.95)	Little/Brown	(1969)	Hales, Robert	30-50	
Lindgren, Astrid	Seacrow Island (1st AM {std}, 8vo, 287p, b/w, DJ/5.95)	Viking	1969	Hales, Robert	50-85	
Haley, Gail E.	My Kingdom for a Dragon (1st, 8vo, [34]p, wraps, fp 2-color)	VA: Crozet	(1962)	Haley, Gail E.	30-50	*
Haley, Gail E.	One Two, Buckle My Shoe (1st {std}, 4to, 63p, color, pep, DJ/3.25)	Doubleday	(1964)	Haley, Gail E.	60-90	*
Wyse, Lois	P.S. Happy Anniversary (1st {std}, 24mo, 24p, color, DJ/1.95)	World	(1966)	Haley, Gail E.	20-35	*
Butler, Francelia	Skip Rope Book (1st, 12mo, [40]p, ipcb, color, pep, DJ/1.95)	Dial Press	1963	Haley, Gail E.	20-30	
Haley, Gail E.	Story, a Story (1st {std}, sq4to, [36]p, color, DJ/5.95, CM)	Atheneum	(1970)	Haley, Gail E.	100-150	
Holding, James	Three Wishes of Hu (1st, 8vo, 64p, fp color, DJ/2.75)	Putnam	(1965)	Haley, Gail E.	25-40	
Russell, Solveig	Which is Which (1st, 4to, 30p, color, DJ/3.50)	Prentice-Hall	(1966)	Haley, Gail E.	25-40	
Mother Goose	Old Mother Goose in a New Dress (1st, ob4to, [45]p, color, pep)	NY: Laidlaw	1932	Hall, Douglas	120-170	*

AUTHOR	TITLE	PUBLISHER	DATE	ARTIST	PRICE	LC
Townsend, John R.	Pirate's Island (1st AM {std}, 8vo, 159p, b/w, DJ/3.75)	Lippincott	(1968)	Hall, Douglas	25-45	
Hall, Gladys	Cinderella (1st, 4to, [11]p, ibds, color)	Cupples/Leon	1915	Hall, Gladys	80-130	
Metcalf, Suzanne	Annabel (1st [1], 12mo, 231p, grey/gilt, p-o, 6pl)	Reilly/Britton	(1906)	Hall, H. Putnam	600-800	
Madison, Janet (comp)	Sweethearts Always (1st, 8vo, 232p, grey/gilt, teg, uncut, 12pl)	Reilly/Britton	1906	Hall, H. Putnam	85-120	
Omar Khayyam	Rubaiyat of Omar Khayyam (1st, 4to, p-o, teg, [76]p, b/w)	NY: A. Harriman	1911	Hall, Isabel H.	120-200	*
Hall, Albert N.	Wonder Hill (1st, lg8vo, p-o, 271p, 10cp, pep)	Rand/McNally	(1914)	Hall, Norman	180-260	
Scott, Ann H.	Let's Catch a Monster (1st, sm4to, [44]p, 2-color, DJ/3.50)	Lothrop, Lee	(1967)	Hall, Tom	25-45	*
Palmer, Candida	Snow Storm Before Christmas (1st, 8vo, ibds, 32p, b/w, DJ/2.75)	Lippincott	(1965)	Hall, Tom	50-80	
Hallock, Grace T.	Bird in the Bush (1st, ob8vo, 47p, pep, color)	Dutton	1930	Hallock, Grace T.	25-45	*
Hopkins, Wm. J.	Airship Dragonfly (1st, 8vo, 346p, 8pl)	Doubleday/Page	1906	Hallock, Ruth M.	50-80	
Stevenson, Rbt. L.	Child's Garden of Verses (1st, 4to, 96p, p-o, 8cp, pep)	Rand/McNally	(1919)	Hallock, Ruth M.	70-100	
Montgomery, F.T.	Christmas with Santa Claus (1st, lg8vo, 154p, color)	Saalfield	(1905)	Hallock, Ruth M.	70-120	
Washburne, Marion	Every Day Essays (1st, 8vo, 156p, 15pl)	Rand/McNally	(1904)	Hallock, Ruth M.	30-50	
Seegmiller, Wilhelmia	Little Rhymes for Little Readers (1st, lg4to, p-o, 81p, fp color, pep)	Rand/McNally	(1903)	Hallock, Ruth M.	80-125	
Ward, Mrs. H.	Milly & Olly (1st, 8vo, 302p, p-o, 8pl, pep)	Doubleday/Page	1907	Hallock, Ruth M.	30-50	
Gray, Eliz. J.	Sandy (1st, sm8vo, 233p, DJ/2.00, col frn by...)	Viking	1945	Hallock, Ruth M.	25-40	
Dillon, Mary	The Leader (1st, 8vo, 362p, 4pl)	Doubleday/Page	1906	Hallock, Ruth M.	25-40	*
Moulton, Louise C.	Arthur O'Shaughnessy (1st, 12mo, 120p, gilt, teg, cvr by...)	Stone/Kimball	1894	Hallowell, G.H.	80-120	
Carman, Bliss	Low Tide on Grand Pre (2nd, 12mo, gilt, 132p, teg, cvr by...)	Stone/Kimball	1894	Hallowell, G.H.	60-100	
Farrar, Evelyn	Stories from the Bible (1st, 8vo, 243p, gilt, 12pl)	L: Henry Co.	1896	Hallward, Mrs. R.	40-60	*
Stitch, Wilhelmina	Little Book of Singing Rhymes (1st, 12mo, ibds, decor by...)	Volland	(1931)	Halstead, Muriel	50-80	
Russell, Helen R.	Clarion the Killdeer (1st {std}, 8vo, 60p, DJ/3.95)	Hawthorn House	(1970)	Hamberger, John	20-30	
Hamberger, John	Day the Sun Disappeared (1st {std}, 4to, [42]p, color, DJ/3.00)	Norton	(1964)	Hamberger, John	25-40	
Coatsworth, Eliz.	Fox Friend (1st {std}, ob8vo, ibds, [32]p, fp 1-color, DJ/2.95)	Macmillan	(1966)	Hamberger, John	25-40	*
Hamberger, John	Peacock Who Lost his Tail (1st {std}, ob8vo, [48]p, color, DJ/3.25)	Norton	(1967)	Hamberger, John	25-40	*
Siddiqui, Ashraf	Bhombal Dass (1st {std}, sm4to, [28]p, color, DJ/2.75)	Macmillan	(1959)	Hamil, Tom	40-65	*
Hamil, Thomas A.	Brother Alonzo (1st {std}, 4to, [48]p, ibds, color, DJ/2.50)	Macmillan	1957	Hamil, Tom	50-80	R*
Martin, Patricia	Calvin and the Cub Scouts (1st, sm4to, 47p, color, DJ/3.00)	Putnam	(1964)	Hamil, Tom	30-45	
Martin, Patricia	Kumi and the Pearl (1st, 4to, 45p, color, DJ)	Putnam	1968	Hamil, Tom	20-35	
Martin, Patricia	Pumpkin Patch (1st, 8vo, 47p, color, DJ/2.75)	Putnam	(1966)	Hamil, Tom	20-35	
Martin, Patricia	Show and Tell (1st, 8vo, 48p, fp 2-color, DJ/2.00)	Putnam	(1962)	Hamil, Tom	25-45	
Martin, Patricia	There Goes the Tiger! (1st, 8vo, [48]p, color, DJ)	Putnam	1970	Hamil, Tom	20-35	
Goldsmith, Oliver	Comedies of Oliver Goldsmith (1st, 12mo, AEG, gilt, 310p, b/w)	L: G. Allen	1896	Hammond, Chris	75-100	
Austen, Jane	Emma (1st, 12mo, green/gilt, 504p, teg, b/w)	L: G. Allen	1898	Hammond, Chris	55-80	
Edgeworth, Maria	Helen (1st, 12mo, blue/gilt, 490p, AEG, b/w, dep)	L: Macmillan	1896	Hammond, Chris	70-100	
Austen, Jane	Sense and Sensibility (1st, 8vo, AEG, 389p, gilt, b/w)	L: G. Allen	1899	Hammond, Chris	200-300	
Molesworth, Mrs.	Fairies Afield (1st, 8vo, 252p, gilt, teg, 8pl)	L: Macmillan	1911	Hammond, Gertrude D.	60-100	
Molesworth, Mrs.	Fairies of Sorts (1st, 8vo, gilt, 249p, AEG, 8pl)	L: Macmillan	1908	Hammond, Gertrude D.	100-150	*
Molesworth, Mrs.	Jasper, a Story for Children (1st, 12mo, 236p, red/gilt, 8pl)	L: Macmillan	1906	Hammond, Gertrude D.	30-50	
Dawson, L.H. (ed.)	Stories from Faerie Queen (1st, 8vo, 234p)	L: Harrap	1909	Hammond, Gertrude D.	80-130	
Cowie, John	Alliterative Anomalies for Infants & Invalids (1st AM, ob4to, ibds, color)	Dodd	[1914]	Hammond, William	200-300	*
Hample, Stoo	Silly Book (1st, 8vo, [32]p, ipcb, b/w, DJ/1.50)	Harper	(1961)	Hample, Stoo	30-50	*
Krumgold, Joseph	Most Terrible Turk (1st, 8vo, 40p, b/w, DJ/3.75)	Crowell	(1969)	Hampshire, Michael	20-30	
Daringer, Helen F.	Yesterday's Daughter (1st {std}, sm8vo, 156p, b/w, DJ/3.25)	Harcourt	(1964)	Hampshire, Michael	25-45	
Williams, Jay	Cookie Tree (1st, lg8vo, [40]p, fp color, DJ/2.95)	Parents Mag. Pr.	1967	Hampton, Blake	25-40	
Armstrong, William	Animal Tales (1st {std}, 4to, 30p, ibds, color, DJ)	Doubleday	(1970)	Hanak, Mirko	50-80	
Woods, Margaret L.	Come into these Yellow Sands (1st, 4to, ibds, 234p, 16cp, pep)	L: John Lane	1915	Hancock, John	100-175	
Handforth, Thomas	Faraway Meadow (1st {std}, ob4to, [32]p, color, pep, DJ/2.00)	Doubleday/Doran	1939	Handforth, Thomas	60-100	
Handforth, Thomas	Mei Li (1st {std}, 4to, [58]p, orange/gilt, b/w, pep, DJ/2.00, CM)	Doubleday/Doran	1938	Handforth, Thomas	100-170	R
Evernden, Margery	Secret of the Porcelain Fish (1st, 8vo, 147p, b/w, dep, DJ/2.25)	Random	(1947)	Handforth, Thomas	25-45	*
Coatsworth, Eliz.	Toutou in Bondage (1st, 8vo, 56p, dp illus, pep)	Macmillan	1929	Handforth, Thomas	40-60	*
Smith, Susan C.	Tranquilina's Paradise (1st, lg4to, 34p, color, pep)	Minton Balch	(1930)	Handforth, Thomas	75-120	R
Goldsmith, Oliver	Deserted Village (1st, 4to, 99p, gilt, teg, 40 ticp)	L: Constable	1909	Hankey, William L.	100-165	
Hankins, Maude M.	Fermentations of Eliza (1st, 12mo, 203p, 4pl)	Crowell	(1915)	Hankins, C.	55-90	*
Corbett, Scott	Tree House Island (1st {std}, 8vo, 184p, b/w, DJ/3.00)	Little/Brown	(1959)	Hansen, Gordon	25-40	
Robinson, Edwin A.	Children of the Night (1st, 12mo, 123p, tan cl, cvr by...)	Badger	1897	Hapgood, T.B.	200-300	
Lloyd, John U.	Right Side of the Car (1st, 8vo, 59p, teg, green/gilt, cvr by...)	Badger	1897	Hapgood, T.B.	60-100	
Vredenburg, Edric	My Book of Favorite Fairy Tales (1st, 4to, 133p, ibds, 12cp)	Tuck/McKay	[1920]	Harbour, Jennie	120-170	*
Harris, Joel C.	Bishop & Boogerman (1st, 12mo, green cl, 184p, 8cp)	Doubleday/Page	1909	Harding, Charlotte	100-160	
Howells, William D.	Fennel & Rue (1st, 8vo, 130p, green/gilt, 4pl)	Harper	1908	Harding, Charlotte	30-50	
Andrews, Mary S.	Good Samaritan (1st, 12mo, 51p, green cl, 6pl)	McClure	1906	Harding, Charlotte	30-50	*
Eggleston, George C.	Last of the Flatboats (1st, sm8vo, green/gilt, 382p, 4pl)	Lothrop Pub.	(1900)	Harding, Charlotte	30-50	
Jordan, Eliz. G.	May Iverson: Her Book (1st, 8vo, blue cl, 282p, p-o, 8pl)	Harper	1904	Harding, Charlotte	50-80	
Peterson, Maud H.	Potter and the Clay (1st, sm8vo, green/gilt, 348p, teg, 4pl)	Lothrop Pub.	1901	Harding, Charlotte	30-50	
Whitney, Helen H.	Punch and Judy Book (1st, lg sq8vo, ibds, 32p, color)	Duffield	1906	Harding, Charlotte	200-300	
Tappan, Eva M.	Robin Hood: His Book (1st, 8vo, tan cl, 267p, 6cp)	Little/Brown	1903	Harding, Charlotte	60-90	
Hay, Helen	Verses for Jock & Joan (1st, lg sq4to, 32p, ibds, 6cp)	Fox Duffield	1905	Harding, Charlotte	200-300	R
Chodsko, A.	Fairy Tales of Slav Peasants & Herdsmen (1st, 8vo, 353p, gilt, teg, fp b/w)	L: G. Allen	1896	Harding, Emily J.	70-100	
Strettell, Alma	Lullabies of Many Lands (1st, 4to, 127p, gilt, teg, uncut, b/w, dep)	L: G. Allen	1894	Harding, Emily J.	100-170	
Harris, Joel C.	Shadow Between his Shoulder Blades (1st, 12mo, 132p, 4pl)	Small/Maynard	(1909)	Harding, George	120-165	
Gask, Lilian	Quest of the White Merle (1st, 8vo, 282p, p-o, 15pl)	L: Harrap	[1909]	Hardy, Dorothy	100-175	*
N/A	Book for Little People (4to, ibds, 16 chromos)	L: Nister	[1890]	Hardy, E. Stuart	250-400	
Weatherly, Fred E.	Book of Gnomes (1st, sm ob4to, [25]p, ibds, 8 chromos, pep)	L: Nister	[1900]	Hardy, E. Stuart	500-700	
Andersen, Hans C.	Fairy Tales (lg8vo, AEG, 288p, 6 chromos)	L: Nister	[1890]	Hardy, E. Stuart	160-225	
Girvin, Brenda	Queer Cousin Claude (1st, 8vo, 280p, gilt, col frn, 8pl)	L: G. Allen	1912	Hardy, E. Stuart	40-65	
Andersen, Hans C.	Stories from Andersen (4to, 288p, AEG, grey/gilt, 6 chromos)	L: Nister	[1890]	Hardy, E. Stuart	120-180	
Nesbit, Edith	Story of Five Rebellious Dolls (1st, ob folio, ibds, 8cp, pep)	L: Nister	(1904)	Hardy, E. Stuart	350-500	
Carlton, Maud	Tumble Down Pictures (1st, 4to, ibds, unpag, 6 chromos)	Nister/Dutton	[1898]	Hardy, E. Stuart	200-300	

AUTHOR	TITLE	PUBLISHER	DATE	ARTIST	PRICE	LC
Malet, Lucas	Little Peter (1st, 8vo, grey/gilt, 168p, pep, 9pl)	L: Kegan Paul	1888	Hardy, Paul	80-125	
Debenham, Mary H.	Whispering Winds & Tales they Told (1st, 8vo, 195p, gilt, 25pl)	L: Blackie	1895	Hardy, Paul	50-85	
Garst, Shannon	Cowboy Boots (1st, 8vo, 191p, b/w, DJ/2.00)	Abingdon-Cokes.	1946	Hargens, Charles	25-45	
Sabin, Edwin L.	Gold! (1st, 8vo, 336p, fp color, pep)	Macrae-Smith	1929	Hargens, Charles	30-50	
Stigand, Chauncy H.	Black Tales for White Children (1st, 8vo, 200p, b/w)	L: Constable	(1914)	Hargrave, John G.	300-500	
Snedeker, Caroline D.	Theras & his Town (1st {std}, sm8vo, 252p, pep, 4pl)	Doubleday/Page	1924	Haring, Mary W.	80-125	
Harnett, Cynthia	Great House (1st AM {std}, 8vo, 191p, yellow cl, DJ/3.95)	World	1968	Harnett, Cynthia	25-45	
Harnett, Cynthia	Nicholas and the Wool-Pack (1st, 8vo, 184p, b/w, DJ, CgM)	L: Methuen	(1951)	Harnett, Cynthia	60-90	
London, Jack	Valley of the Moon (1st, 8vo, orange/gilt, 530p, col frn by...)	Macmillan	1913	Harper, George	200-300	
Bouve, Edward T.	Centuries Apart (1st, 8vo, 347p, grey/gilt, 6pl, maps)	Little/Brown	1894	Harper, W. St. J.	40-60	
Andersen, Hans C.	Steadfast Tin Soldier (1st, sm4to, ibds, [28]p, color, pep)	NY: Maxton	1946	Harriet	40-60	*
Tarry, Ellen	Hezekiah Horton (1st, lg8vo, ibds, 39p, fp 1-color, pep, DJ/1.00)	Viking	1942	Harrington, Oliver	60-100	
Tarry, Ellen	Runaway Elephant (1st, lg8vo, ibds, 37p, fp 1-color, pep, DJ/1.50)	Viking	1950	Harrington, Oliver	80-140	R
Tennyson, Alfred	Dream of Fair Women (8vo, grey bds, 79p, 8cp, pep)	L: Blackie	[1915]	Harrison, Florence	60-90	
Morris, William	Early Poems of... (1st, 4to, blue/gilt, teg, 194p, 16 ticp, pep)	L: Blackie	1914	Harrison, Florence	180-260	
Morris, William	Early Poems of... (1st AM, 4to, 194p, teg, 16 ticp)	Dodge	(1914)	Harrison, Florence	140-225	
Harrison, Florence	Elfin Song (1st, 8vo, gilt, teg, 142p, 12 ticp, pep)	L: Blackie	(1912)	Harrison, Florence	350-500	
Harrison, Florence	Elfin Song (1st AM, 8vo, teg, gilt, 142p, pep, 12 ticp)	Caldwell	[1912]	Harrison, Florence	300-450	
Rossetti, Christina	Goblin Market (1st, lg8vo, ibds, 79p, 8cp)	L: Blackie	1923	Harrison, Florence	150-220	
Syrett, Netta	Godmother's Garden (1st, 8vo, 222p, ibds, color)	L: Blackie	[1918]	Harrison, Florence	70-130	
Tennyson, Alfred	Guinevere... (1st AM, 4to, 156p, gilt, teg, 24 ticp)	Dana Estes	1912	Harrison, Florence	160-240	
Tennyson, Alfred	Guinevere... (1st, 4to, teg, 156p, gilt, 24 ticp)	L: Blackie	1912	Harrison, Florence	200-300	
Harrison, Florence	In the Fairy Ring (1st, lg4to, 63p, AEG, gilt, pep, 25cp)	L: Blackie	(1908)	Harrison, Florence	280-350	
N/A	Man in the Moon (1st, 4to, bds, 31p, p-o, 12cp, pep)	L: Blackie	[1918]	Harrison, Florence	200-300	
Harrison, Florence	Pixy Book (1st, lg8vo, [31]p, ibds, p-o, 12cp)	L: Blackie	[1918]	Harrison, Florence	250-400	
Rossetti, Christina	Poems by Christina Rossetti (1st AM, 4to, teg, 369p, 36 ticp)	Dana Estes	[1910]	Harrison, Florence	300-450	
Rossetti, Christina	Poems by Christina Rossetti (1st, 4to, gilt, teg, 369p, 36 ticp, pep)	L: Blackie	[1910]	Harrison, Florence	350-500	
Harrison, Florence	Rhyme of a Run... (1st, ob4to, green/gilt, 22 ticp, pep)	L: Blackie	[1907]	Harrison, Florence	400-600	
Harrison, Florence	Rhymes and Reasons (4to, ibds, unpag, fp color)	L: Blackie	[1905]	Harrison, Florence	300-400	
Rossetti, Christina	Shorter Poems of Christina Rossetti (1st, 4to, 79p, ibds, 8cp, pep)	L: Blackie	[1920]	Harrison, Florence	70-125	
Herbertson, Agnes	Tinkler Johnny (1st, sm8vo, 239p, green cl, p-o, 4cp)	L: Blackie	[1915]	Harrison, Florence	40-60	
Mother Goose	Mother Goose Song Book (1st, folio, ibds)	A.& C. Boni	(1926)	Harshberger, Mac	200-300	
Bedier, Joseph	Romance of Tristan and Iseult (1st AM, 12mo, 196p, pcb, gilt, fp b/w)	A.& C. Boni	1927	Harshberger, Mac	60-90	
Harshberger, Kay	Zoological Soliloquies (1st, lg4to, ibds, [44]p, color)	A.& C. Boni	1926	Harshberger, Mac	100-160	
Andersen, Hans C.	Fairy Tales (1st, 8vo, [26]p, ibds, color, pep, DJ/0.60)	Wilcox/Follett	(1945)	Hart, Dick	25-45	
Aiken, Joan	Kingdom and the Cave (1st, ob12mo, 162p, fp b/w, DJ)	L: Abelard-Sch.	(1960)	Hart, Dick	400-650	
Duddington, Natalie	Russian Folk Tales (1st AM {std}, 8vo, 144p, b/w, DJ)	Funk/Wagnalls	(1967)	Hart, Dick	25-40	
Fisher, Murray	Golliwogg's Dream... Little Folks (1st, sm4to, unpag, ibds, color)	L: Cassell	[1910]	Hart, Frank	100-170	*
Jackson, Gabrielle	Wee Winkles and Snowball (1st, 8vo, 147p, 8pl)	Harper	1906	Hart, Mary T.	30-50	
Jackson, Gabrielle	Wee Winkles and Wideawake (1st, 8vo, p-o, 153p, 8pl)	Harper	1905	Hart, Mary T.	30-50	
Hart, Ruby	In the Woods (1st, sm sq4to, wraps, color)	Volland	(1931)	Hart, Ruby	55-80	*
Potter, Beatrix	All About Peter Rabbit (16mo, 47p, bds, p-o, 8cp)	Cupples/Leon	(1914)	Hartley, Dick	60-100	
N/A	All About the Three Bears (12mo, bds, p-o, 47p, color)	Cupples/Leon	(1914)	Hartley, Dick	60-90	
Hartley, Dick	Greta and Peter in the Flower Garden (1st, 16mo, ibds, [22]p, color)	Volland	(1914)	Hartley, Dick	60-90	
Kay, Helen	Magic Mitt (1st, sm4to, 54p, fp b/w, DJ/2.75)	Hastings House	(1959)	Hartman, C.L.	30-50	*
Brown, Margaret W.	Big Red Barn (1st, ob8vo, unpag, 2-color, pep, DJ/2.25)	W.R. Scott	1956	Hartman, Rosella	60-100	
Yates, Elizabeth	Carey Girl (1st, sm8vo, 185p, DJ/2.75, decor by...)	Coward	(1956)	Hartmann, George	20-35	*
Buck, Pearl S.	Yu Lan, Flying Boy of China (1st, 8vo, 60p, fp b/w, DJ/1.50)	NY: John Day	(1945)	Hartmann, George	100-165	R
Hewlett, Maurice	Forest Lovers (1st AM, lg8vo, 384p, teg, uncut, 16 ticp)	Scribner	1909	Hartrick, A.S.	50-80	
Kipling, Rudyard	Soldier Tales (1st, 8vo, AEG, 172p, blue/gilt, 21pl)	L: Macmillan	1896	Hartrick, A.S.	200-300	
Sterling, Helen	Horse that Takes Milk Around (1st, sq8vo, [28]p, ipcb, color, pep, DJ/1.50)	F. Watts	1946	Hartwell, Marjorie	30-45	
Upham, Elizabeth	Little Brown Bear (1st, sm4to, [58]p, 8 fp color, pep, DJ/1.00)	Platt/Munk	(1942)	Hartwell, Marjorie	50-80	
Upham, Elizabeth	Little Brown Bear & His Friends (1st, sm4to, [56]p, color, pep, DJ)	Platt/Munk	(1952)	Hartwell, Marjorie	50-80	
Upham, Elizabeth	Little Brown Bear Goes to School (1st, sm4to, [52]p, fp col, pep, DJ/1.25)	Platt/Munk	(1955)	Hartwell, Marjorie	50-80	
Upham, Elizabeth	Little Brown Monkey (1st, sm4to, ibds, [56]p, color, pep, DJ/1.00)	Platt/Munk	(1949)	Hartwell, Marjorie	50-80	
Scott, Sally	Silly Billy (1st, 8vo, [48]p, b/w, DJ/1.50)	Harcourt	(1945)	Hartwell, Marjorie	20-30	*
Gomme, Alice B.	Old English Singing Games (1st, ob8vo, 56p, ibds, color)	L: G. Allen	1900	Harwood, Edith	140-240	
Lyle, Eugene P.	The Missourian (1st, sm8vo, 519p, 8pl)	Doubleday/Page	1905	Haskell, Ernest	30-60	
Haslewood, C.	Dear Old Nursery Rhymes (1st, 4to, ibds, 48p, 8 chromos)	NY: Warne	[1896]	Haslewood, C.	100-160	
Farrow, George E.	Absurd Ditties (1st, 8vo, blue/gilt, AEG, 224p, b/w)	L: Routledge	1903	Hassall, John	80-130	
G.R.	Alick's Adventures (1st, sm8vo, brown/gilt, 183p, 8 fp b/w)	L: Longmans	1902	Hassall, John	70-130	
N/A	All the Best Nursery Stories & Rhymes (4to, red cl, 6 dp color, 24cp)	L: Blackie	[1908]	Hassall, John	180-225	
Spurr, Harry A.	Bachelor Ballads (1st, sm8vo, 19mo, teg, green cl)	L: Greening	1899	Hassall, John	55-80	
Hartog, Cecile	Barbara's Song Book (1st, ob4to, 55p, ibds, p-o, 8cp)	L: G. Allen	1900	Hassall, John	200-300	
N/A	Dick Whittington & his Cat (4to, ibds, color)	L: Hodder	[1910]	Hassall, John	100-160	
N/A	Dodge's Red Picture Book (8vo, red bds, p-o, fp color, cep)	Dodge	[1912]	Hassall, John	160-220	
Farrow, George E.	Don't Tell (1st, 4to, [56]p, bds, fp color, pep)	L: Alf Cooke	[1905]	Hassall, John	250-400	
Grimm Bros.	Fairy Tales (1st, lg8vo, 305p, 12 illus)	L: Sands	1902	Hassall, John	75-100	*
Westerman, J.M.E.	Fairy Tales/Wonderland (1st, 4to, 160p, orange cl, 4cp, fp b/w)	L: Blackie	[1932]	Hassall, John	100-170	
Byron, May	Friday & Saturday... (1st, ob4to, ibds, unpag, 12 fp color)	L: H. Frowde	[1910]	Hassall, John	170-240	
Girvin, Brenda	Good Queen Bees (1st, ob4to, ibds, unpag, 23cp)	L: D. Nutt	[1907]	Hassall, John	100-180	
N/A	Humpty-Dumpty (4to, wraps, fp color)	L: Blackie	[1910]	Hassall, John	70-100	
Johnson, A.E.	John Hassall, R.I. (1st, 8vo, 44p, 7cp, 28pl)	L: A&C Black	1907	Hassall, John	70-130	
Byron, May	Magic Shop (4to, 36p, ibds, 14 fp color, pep)	L: Alf Cooke	[1905]	Hassall, John	180-240	
Campbell, A.M.	Mercury the Story Teller (4to, ibds, 16cp)	L: T.F. Unwin	[1903]	Hassall, John	250-400	
Orr, Aileen	Miss Manners (1st, 8vo, 99p, AEG, blue cl, 26cp)	L: A. Melrose	1909	Hassall, John	200-300	
Mother Goose	Mother Goose Nursery Rhymes (1st AM, 8vo, 363p, 24cp)	Dodge	(1909)	Hassall, John	150-225	
Mother Goose	Mother Goose Nursery Rhymes (1st, 8vo, gilt, 364p, 24cp)	L: Blackie	1909	Hassall, John	150-200	

AUTHOR	TITLE	PUBLISHER	DATE	ARTIST	PRICE	LC
N/A	Old Nursery Stories & Rhymes (4to, ibds)	L: Bkackie	[1907]	Hassall, John	180-250	
Hamer, Sam H.	Princess & the Dragon (1st AM, 8vo, green cl, p-o, 78p, 12cp)	Dana Estes	[1908]	Hassall, John	80-125	
Hamer, Sam H.	Princess & the Dragon (1st, 8vo, p-o, 78p, 12cp)	L: Duckworth	(1908)	Hassall, John	100-150	
Shirley, Edward	Reggie & I (1st, 4to, 64p, ibds, 8cp)	L: T. Nelson	[1910]	Hassall, John	180-260	
Defoe, Daniel	Robinson Crusoe (1st, 4to, ibds, 80p, col frn, 6 color)	L: Blackie	1916	Hassall, John	100-160	
Farrow, George E.	Round the World ABC (1st, 4to, [54]p, ibds, 26 color)	L: Nister	1904	Hassall, John	200-300	
Byron, May	Ruff and Reddy (1st AM, 4to, ibds, 63p, 26cp)	Stokes	(1911)	Hassall, John	300-500	
N/A	Scampers and Scrapes (1st, sm4to, [20]p, color)	L: T. Nelson	1905	Hassall, John	60-100	*
Shirley, Edward	The Twins (4to, 63p, ibds, 24cp)	L: Nelson	[1905]	Hassall, John	160-240	
Emanuel, Walter	Zoo: A Scamper (4to, 50p, ibds, fp color)	L: Alston Rivers	(1904)	Hassall, John	200-300	
Pratt, Charles S.	Bye O' Baby Ballads (lg8vo, [61]p, ipcb, 14 chromos)	D. Lothrop Co.	(1886)	Hassam, F. Childe	280-400	
Bates, Clara D.	Doll Rosy's Days (1st, ob12mo, ipcb, [31]p, 12cp)	D. Lothrop Co.	(1884)	Hassam, F. Childe	170-240	
Thaxter, Celia	Island Garden (1st, lg4vo, 126p, white/gilt, teg, col frn, b/w)	Houghton	1894	Hassam, F. Childe	350-500	
Dumas, Alexandre	Nutcracker of Nuremberg (1st, lg8vo, black/gilt, 154p, b/w)	McBride	1930	Hasselriis, Else	35-60	
Chrisman, Arthur B.	Shen of the Sea (1st, sm8vo, 252p, red/gilt, silhouettes, pep, NM)	Dutton	(1925)	Hasselriis, Else	60-90	R
Chrisman, Arthur B.	Wind that Wouldn't Blow (1st, sm8vo, 355p, uncut, b/w, pep)	Dutton	(1927)	Hasselriis, Else	35-60	*
Carpenter, Frances	Tales of a Chinese Grandmother (1st, 8vo, 261p, 9cp)	L: Harrap	(1938)	Hasselriis, Malthe	35-60	
Sabin, Edwin L.	Old Jim Badger on the Moccasin Trail (1st, 8vo, 316p, 4cp)	Crowell	(1928)	Hastings, Howard	25-45	*
Haggard, H. Rider	Swallow, Tale of the Great Trek (1st, 8vo, tan/gilt, 348p, b/w pl, cep)	NY: Longmans	1899	Hatherall, William	120-200	
Molesworth, Mrs.	Next-Door House (1st, 8vo, 226p, grey/gilt, 6pl)	L: Chambers	1893	Hatherell, William	40-60	*
Twain, Mark	Prince & the Pauper (1st, 8vo, 285p, gilt, 8cp, pep)	Harper	1909	Hatherell, William	40-60	
Burgess, Thornton	Thornton Burgess Bedtime Stories (1st, lg4to, ibds, 105p, color, pep)	Grosset/Dunlap	(1959)	Hauge, Carl & Mary	30-45	
Lent, Henry B.	Air Pilot (1st, sq16mo, [42]p, color, pep)	Macmillan	1937	Hauman, G.& D.	35-60	
Hauman, George	Buttons (1st, 8vo, 64p, 2-color, pep, DJ/1.35)	Macmillan	1936	Hauman, G.& D.	30-50	*
Molloy, Anne	Decky's Secret (1st, 8vo, 120p, fp color, DJ/2.00)	Houghton	1944	Hauman, G.& D.	25-45	
Coatsworth, Eliz.	Dollar for Luck (1st {std}, 8vo, 151p, b/w, pep, DJ/2.25)	Macmillan	(1951)	Hauman, G.& D.	25-40	
Meigs, Cornelia L.	Dutch Colt (1st {std}, 8vo, 121p, b/w, DJ/2.00)	Macmillan	1952	Hauman, G.& D.	25-40	
Hauman, George	Happy Harbor (1st, 8vo, 60p, 2-color, DJ/1.75)	Macmillan	1939	Hauman, G.& D.	40-65	*
Mason, Miriam E.	Hominy and his Blunt-Nosed Arrow (1st {std}, 8vo, 145p, b/w, DJ/1.75)	Macmillan	1950	Hauman, G.& D.	25-40	
Mason, Miriam E.	Little Jonathan (1st {std}, 8vo, 128p, b/w, DJ/1.25)	Macmillan	1944	Hauman, G.& D.	120-180	
Vaygouny, Margarite	Peter the Stork (1st {std}, 8vo, 109p, fp b/w, DJ/2.25)	Macmillan	1951	Hauman, G.& D.	25-40	*
Andersen, Hans C.	Snow Queen (1st, sm4to, 63p, pep, 6 fp color, DJ/2.00)	Macmillan	1942	Hauman, G.& D.	45-60	
Hauman, George	Surprise for Timmy (1st, 8vo, 78p, fp 1-color, pep, DJ/1.25)	Macmillan	1946	Hauman, G.& D.	30-45	*
Piper, Watty (ed)	Tales from Storyland (1st, lg4to, p-o, [80]p, color)	Platt/Munk	(1941)	Hauman, G.& D.	60-90	
Lent, Henry B.	The Storekeeper (1st, sq16mo, [42]p, color, pep)	Macmillan	1937	Hauman, G.& D.	35-60	
Clark, Ann N.	Blue Canyon Horse (1st, sm4to, 54p, fp color, DJ/2.75)	Viking	1954	Hauser, Allan	65-90	R
Various	Book of Modern Ballads (sm4to, AEG, gilt, 6 chromos)	Hildesheimer	[1890]	Havers, Alice	80-135	*
Andersen, Hans C.	Wild Swans (1st AM, ob4to, 48p, ibds, 14 chromos)	Dutton	[1880]	Havers, Alice	200-270	
Hawes, Judy	Goats Who Killed the Leopard (1st, 8vo, [48]p, fp b/w, DJ/3.75)	Crowell	(1970)	Hawes, Judy	30-45	
De La Mare, Walter	Collected Stories for Children (1st, 8vo, 437p, b/w, DJ, CgM)	L: Faber	1947	Hawkins, Irene	50-80	*
De La Mare, Walter	Dutch Cheese (1st, lg8vo, 143p, gilt, b/w, DJ)	L: Faber	(1946)	Hawkins, Irene	60-100	
De La Mare, Walter	Magic Jacket (1st, sm8vo, 146p, b/w, DJ)	L: Faber	(1943)	Hawkins, Irene	35-60	*
De La Mare, Walter	Old Lion (1st, 8vo, 155p, b/w, DJ)	L: Faber	(1942)	Hawkins, Irene	30-50	
De La Mare, Walter	Scarecrow & other Stories (1st {std}, sm8vo, 128p, fp b/w, DJ)	L: Faber	1945	Hawkins, Irene	30-50	
Hawkins, Sheila	Bruzzy Bear & the Cabin Boy (1st {std}, lg4to, [32]p, color, pep, DJ/1.00)	Harper	(1940)	Hawkins, Sheila	30-50	
Hawkins, Sheila	Little Gray Colo (1st, 8vo, [41]p, ibds, color, pep)	Grosset/Dunlap	(1939)	Hawkins, Sheila	40-65	
Elliot, Geraldine	Long Grass Whispers (1st, 4to, 132p, fp b/w, pep, DJ/2.00)	Putnam	(1939)	Hawkins, Sheila	35-50	
Schlein, Miriam	Billy, the Littlest One (1st, sq12mo, [34]p, fp color, DJ/2.75)	Whitman	(1966)	Hawkinson, Lucy	20-35	
Hawkinson, Lucy	Dance, Dance, Amy Chan! (1st, lg8vo, unpag, color, pep, DJ/2.75)	Whitman	(1964)	Hawkinson, Lucy	20-35	*
Martin, Patricia	One Special Dog (1st, 8vo, 48p, color, DJ/3.95)	Rand/McNally	1968	Hawkinson, Lucy	25-35	
MacDonald, Zillah	Eileen's Adventures in Wonderland (1st, 8vo, p-o, 241p, col frn)	Stokes	(1920)	Hay, Stuart	100-170	*
Bannerman, Helen	Little Black Sambo (lg4to, ipcb, color)	Saalfield	1942	Hays, Ethel	160-225	
Gruelle, Johnny	Raggedy Ann's Adventure (1st, 8vo, [36]p, spiral bds, color)	Saalfield	(1947)	Hays, Ethel	140-200	
Hays, M.G.	Rag Animals ABC (lg4to, stiff wrps, 30p, color)	Donohue	(1913)	Hays, M.G.	200-350	*
Fryer, Jane E.	Mary Frances Cook Book (1st, lg8vo, 175p, blue cl, p-o, color)	Winston	(1912)	Hays/Boyer	200-300	
Haywood, Carolyn	B is for Betsy (1st, 8vo, 159p, b/w, pep, DJ/2.00)	Harcourt	1939	Haywood, Carolyn	30-50	
Haywood, Carolyn	Back to School with Betsy (1st, 8vo, 176p, b/w, DJ/2.00)	Harcourt	(1943)	Haywood, Carolyn	30-50	*
Haywood, Carolyn	Betsy and Billy (1st, 8vo, 156p, b/w, pep, DJ/2.00)	Harcourt	(1941)	Haywood, Carolyn	40-65	*
Haywood, Carolyn	Betsy and the Boys (1st, 8vo, 175p, b/w, DJ/2.00)	Harcourt	(1945)	Haywood, Carolyn	40-65	*
Haywood, Carolyn	Betsy's Little Star (1st, 8vo, 157p, b/w, DJ/2.50)	Wm. Morrow	1950	Haywood, Carolyn	30-50	*
Haywood, Carolyn	Eddie Makes Music (1st, lg8vo, 191p, b/w, DJ/2.95)	Wm. Morrow	1957	Haywood, Carolyn	40-65	*
Haywood, Carolyn	Here's a Penny (1st, 8vo, 158p, b/w, DJ/2.00)	Harcourt	(1944)	Haywood, Carolyn	30-50	*
Haywood, Carolyn	Penny and Peter (1st, 8vo, 160p, b/w, pep, DJ/2.25)	Harcourt	(1946)	Haywood, Carolyn	30-50	*
Haywood, Carolyn	Primrose Day (1st, 8vo, 200p, b/w, DJ/2.00)	Harcourt	(1942)	Haywood, Carolyn	30-50	*
Haywood, Carolyn	Taffy & Melissa Molasses (1st, 8vo, 191p, b/w, DJ/4.25)	Wm. Morrow	(1969)	Haywood, Carolyn	20-40	
Haywood, Carolyn	Two and Two are Four (1st, 8vo, 171p, b/w, pep, DJ/2.00)	Harcourt	(1940)	Haywood, Carolyn	40-65	*
Haywood, Carolyn	When I Grow Up (1st [1st bk.], folio, [20]p, color)	Whitman	(1931)	Haywood, Carolyn	70-120	*
Beim, Lorraine	Blue Jeans (1st, 8vo, 239p, b/w, pep, DJ/2.00)	Harcourt	(1941)	Hazelton, I.B.	120-200	
Burton, John B.	Across the Salt Seas (1st, 12mo, teg, 446p, cvr by...)	Herbert Stone	1897	Hazenplug, Frank	55-90	
Conner, Ralph	Black Rock (1st, 8vo, tan cl, 322p, cvr by...)	Revell	1900	Hazenplug, Frank	30-50	
Adams, Mary J.	Choir Visible (1st, 12mo, 185p, gilt, teg, cvr by...)	Way & Williams	1897	Hazenplug, Frank	100-170	
Crissey, Forrest	Country Boy (1st, 8vo, 300p, gilt, uncut, cvr by...)	Revell	(1903)	Hazenplug, Frank	50-80	
Gould, Katherine C.	Crystal Rood (1st, sm8vo, 306p, cover by....)	NY: J. Lane	1924	Hazenplug, Frank	35-50	
Manners, Robert	Cuba & other Verse (1st, 12mo, 155p, uncut, gilt, teg, cvr by...)	Way & Williams	1898	Hazenplug, Frank	125-200	
Earle, Alice M.	Curious Punishments of Bygone Days (1st, sm8vo, 149p, gilt, teg, uncut)	Herbert Stone	1896	Hazenplug, Frank	70-100	
Baum, L. Frank	Daring Twins (1st [1], sm8vo, 317p, blue cl, cvr by...)	Reilly/Britton	(1911)	Hazenplug, Frank	250-350	
Thwaites, Reuben G.	Down Historic Waterways (1st, sm8vo, gilt, 300p, cvr by...)	McClurg	1902	Hazenplug, Frank	60-90	
Merriman, Henry S.	Dross (1st, 12mo, 54p, teg, cvr by...)	Herbert Stone	1899	Hazenplug, Frank	70-100	

AUTHOR	TITLE	PUBLISHER	DATE	ARTIST	PRICE	LC
D'Annunzio, Gabriele	Episcopo & Co. (1st, 12mo, 122p, green/gilt, teg, cvr by...)	Stone & Kimball	1896	Hazenplug, Frank	65-100	
Lawson, Ellsworth	Euphrosyne & her Golden Book (1st, 8vo, 141p, green/gilt, cvr by...)	Herbert Stone	1901	Hazenplug, Frank	35-50	
Locke, William J.	Fortunate Youth (1st, 12mo, 352p, green/gilt, cvr by...)	NY: John Lane	1914	Hazenplug, Frank	35-60	
Sheffield, Rena C.	Golden Hollow (1st, sm8vo, 214p, col frn, cvr by...)	NY: John Lane	1913	Hazenplug, Frank	50-85	
Boynton, Henry W.	Golfer's Rubaiyat (1st, 12mo, [83]p, bds, cvr by...)	Herbert Stone	1901	Hazenplug, Frank	250-400	
Morier, James	Hajji Baba of Ispahan (1st, 2volumes, tan/gilt, cvr by..)	Stone/Kimball	1895	Hazenplug, Frank	70-100	
Wolf, Alice S.	House of Cards (1st, 12mo, 281p, black/gilt, cvr by...)	Stone/Kimball	1896	Hazenplug, Frank	60-100	
Wilkinson, Florence	Lady of the Flag-Flowers (1st, 12mo, 364p, cvr by...)	Herbert Stone	1899	Hazenplug, Frank	55-90	
Gordon, Samuel	Lesser Destinies (1st, sm8vo, 310p, teg, cvr by...)	Herbert Stone	1899	Hazenplug, Frank	30-50	
Gordon, Charles W.	Man from Glengarry (1st, sm8vo, purple cloth, 473p, cvr by...)	Revell	1901	Hazenplug, Frank	30-50	
Castle, Egerton	Marshfield the Observer (1st, sm8vo, 270p, grey ipcb, cvr by...)	Herbert Stone	1900	Hazenplug, Frank	55-80	
Meyer, Lucy	Mary North (1st, 8vo, 339p, cvr by...)	Revell	(1903)	Hazenplug, Frank	55-80	*
Rossetti, Christina	Maude: Prose & Verse (1st, 12mo, 122p, red pcb, title pg by..)	Herbert Stone	1897	Hazenplug, Frank	50-80	
Percival, Olive	Mexico City: Idler's Note-Book (1st, 12mo, 208p, cvr & designs by...)	Herbert Stone	1901	Hazenplug, Frank	100-170	
Ade, George	More Fables (1st, 16mo, 218p, teg, title page by..)	Herbert Stone	1900	Hazenplug, Frank	35-60	
Gray, William C.	Musings by Campfire & Wayside (1st, 8vo, 337p, black/gilt, cvr by...)	Revell	1902	Hazenplug, Frank	50-80	
Chopin, Kate R.	Night in Acadie (1st, 12mo, 416p, blue/gilt, teg, cvr by...)	Way & Williams	1897	Hazenplug, Frank	400-600	
Johnston, Richard M.	Pearce Amerson's Will (1st, 12mo, teg, 275p, cvr by...)	Way & Williams	1898	Hazenplug, Frank	100-160	
Powell, R.S.	Phyllis in Bohemia (1st, 12mo, 233p, teg, cvr by...)	Herbert Stone	1897	Hazenplug, Frank	45-70	
Peattie, Elia W.	Pippins and Cheese (1st, 12mo, 282p, teg, uncut, cvr by...)	Way & Williams	1897	Hazenplug, Frank	80-120	
LeGallienne, R.	Prose Fancies (1st AM, 12mo, gilt, 201p, cvr by...)	Herbert Stone	1896	Hazenplug, Frank	70-100	
Sharts, Joseph W.	Romance of a Rogue (1st, sm8vo, 249p, designs by...)	Herbert Stone	1902	Hazenplug, Frank	50-80	
Russell, William C.	Rose Island (1st, sm8vo, 359p, teg, cvr by...)	Herbert Stone	1899	Hazenplug, Frank	50-80	
Crowninshield, Mrs.	San Isidro (1st, sm8vo, 312p, yellow cl, cvr by...)	Herbert Stone	1900	Hazenplug, Frank	55-80	
DeKoven, Mrs. R.	Sawdust Doll (1st, 12mo, 237p, blue/gilt, teg, cvr by...)	Stone/Kimball	1895	Hazenplug, Frank	100-165	
Coleman, Oliver	Successful Houses (1st, 8vo, 165p, tan cl, cvr by...)	Herbert Stone	1899	Hazenplug, Frank	60-90	
Carruth, Frances W.	Those Dale Girls (1st, 12mo, 318p, cvr by...)	McClurg	1899	Hazenplug, Frank	50-80	*
James, Henry	What Maisie Knew (1st AM, sm8vo, 470p, teg, grey/gilt, cvr by...)	Herbert Stone	1897	Hazenplug, Frank	150-225	
Helm, Nellie L.	When Jesus was Here Among Men (1st, 8vo, green cl, 205p, cover by...)	Revell	1902	Hazenplug, Frank	50-80	
Healy, Daty	Cat Tales from Many Lands (1st, sq8vo, [64]p, fp 2-color, pep)	Scribner	1932	Healy, Daty	140-220	
Lagerlof, Selma	Wonderful Adventures of Nils (1st AM, 8vo, 430p, 8pl, pep)	Doubleday/Page	1907	Heartt, Harold	100-180	
Eckenstein, Lina	Little Princess and the Great Plot (1st, 16mo, 160p, pep)	L: T.F. Unwin	1892	Heath, Dudley	70-100	*
Akers, Floyd	Boy Fortune Hunters in Alaska (1st [1], sm8vo, 291p, brown cl, 3pl)	Reilly/Britton	(1908)	Heath, Howard	200-300	
Serviss, Garrett P.	Columbus of Space (1st, sm8vo, 298p, green cl, 4pl)	Appleton	1911	Heath, Howard	140-240	
Haldane, Winifred A.	Dream Pal (1st, 8vo, 131p, gilt, 6pl)	Laird & Lee	(1904)	Heath, Howard	70-125	
Barbour, Ralph H.	Finkler's Field (1st, sm8vo, 226p, 4cp)	Appleton	1911	Heath, Howard	50-80	
Fitzgerald, Hugh	Sam Steele's Adventures in Panama (1st, sm8vo, 310p, green cl, 5cp)	Reilly/Britton	(1907)	Heath, Howard	700-900	*
Fitzgerald, Hugh	Sam Steele's Adventures on Land & Sea (1st, sm8vo, 271p, gilt, p-o, 5cp)	Reilly/Britton	(1906)	Heath, Howard	500-700	*
Heath, Irene	An ABC (1st, 4to, unpag, ibds, color)	L: Warne	[1933]	Heath, Irene	100-175	
N/A	Aladdin (1st, 16mo, 61p, pep)	L: J.M. Dent	1895	Heath, Sidney H.	45-80	*
Bingham, Clifton	Dorothy Dimity (4to, ibds, fp 1-color)	L: T.F. Unwin	[1908]	Heatly, E.	100-165	
Gask, Lilian	Pig Tales (1st, 8vo, 64p, color)	Nister/Dutton	[1906]	Heatly, E.	40-60	*
Montgomery, R.	Klepty (1st {std}, 8vo, 83p, b/w, DJ/2.95)	Duell, Sloan	(1961)	Hecathorn, Polly	20-30	
Clifford, Eth	Red is Never a Mouse (1st, 4to, [29]p, fp color, DJ/2.95)	Bobbs-Merrill	1960	Heckler, Bill	30-50	
Zwilgmeyer, Dikken	Four Cousins (1st, sm8vo, 286p, 6cp)	Lothrop, Lee	(1923)	Heiberg, Astri W.	20-35	
Lagerlof, Selma	Further Adventures of Nils (1st {Engl lang.}, 12mo, 339p, 15pl)	Doubleday/Page	1911	Heiberg, Astri W.	90-120	*
Aesopus	Fables of Aesop (1st, 12mo, 222p, gilt, AEG, b/w)	L: Macmillan	1894	Heighway, Richard	100-165	
Whitman, William	Navaho Tales (1st, sm8vo, 217p, b/w, pep)	Houghton	1925	Heins, John P.	40-65	
Stone, A. Harris	Last Free Bird (1st, ob4to, [30]p, fp color, pep, DJ/4.95)	Prentice-Hall	(1967)	Heins, Sheila	30-50	*
Hanemann, Henry W.	As Is (1st, 8vo, ipcb, 190p, uncut, b/w)	Harcourt	(1923)	Held, John	60-100	
Held, John	Danny Decoy (1st, sq8vo, ibds, [83]p, 2-color, pep, DJ/1.00)	A.S. Barnes	(1942)	Held, John	100-165	
Held, John	Dog Stories (1st, 4to, ibds, 124p, fp b/w)	Vanguard Press	1930	Held, John	100-165	
Shay, Frank	Drawn from the Wood (1st, 8vo, 186p, b/w, DJ)	Macaulay	(1929)	Held, John	70-120	
Held, John	Gods were Promiscuous (1st, sm8vo, 248p, DJ/2.00)	Vanguard Press	1937	Held, John	60-90	
Geller, James J.	Grandfather's Follies (1st, lg sq8vo, 218p, b/w)	Macaulay	(1934)	Held, John	50-80	
Gilbreth, Frank	Held's Angels (1st, lg8vo, 211p, fp b/w, DJ/3.95)	Crowell	(1952)	Held, John	50-85	*
Shay, Frank	More Pious Friends (1st, 8vo, 192p, b/w)	Macaulay	(1927)	Held, John	60-100	
Wright, Isa L.	Remarkable Tale of a Whale (1st, 8vo, ibds, color, pep)	Volland	(1920)	Held, John	65-90	
Held, John	Saga of Frankie & Johnny (1st {std}, sm4to, 49p, uncut, red/gilt, fp b/w)	NY: W.V. McKee	(1930)	Held, John	100-160	*
Levy, Newman	Saturday to Monday (1st, sm8vo, uncut, 79p, ipcb, fp b/w)	Knopf	1930	Held, John	50-80	
Helle, Andre	Big Beasts & Little Beasts (1st, ob12mo, p-o, 80p, 20cp)	Stokes	1924	Helle, Andre	140-200	
Brown, Margaret W.	Fables of La Fontaine (1st {std}, 4to, ibds, 39p, color, pep, DJ/1.50)	Harper	(1940)	Helle, Andre	80-125	
Helps, Racey	Barnaby in Search of a House (1st, 16mo, 47p, ibds, color, pep)	L: Collins	1948	Helps, Racey	20-35	
Helps, Racey	Blow Away Balloon (1st, 8vo, 48p, bds, color, pep, DJ/3.50)	Chilton Books	(1967)	Helps, Racey	25-40	
Helps, Racey	Tail of Hunky Dory (1st, 12mo, 46p, ibds, fp color, cep)	L: Collins	1958	Helps, Racey	20-35	
Helps, Racey	Two from a Teapot (1st {std}, 12mo, 48p, 2-color, pep, DJ/2.95)	Chilton Books	(1966)	Helps, Racey	30-50	
Fraser, William A.	Sazada Tales (1st, 8vo, 231p, green/gilt, 24 b/w pl)	Scribner	1905	Heming, Arthur	30-50	*
Fraser, William A.	The Outcasts (1st, 8vo, green/gilt, 138p, teg, 8pl)	Scribner	1901	Heming, Arthur	50-80	
Boston, Lucy M.	House that Grew (1st, 4to, 28p, DJ)	L: Faber	1969	Hemming, Caroline	70-120	
Mitchell, George W.	Little Babs (1st, 12mo, unpag, ibds, pep, color)	Volland	(1919)	Henderson, Arthur	80-135	
Thompson, Ruth P.	Perhappsy Chaps (1st [1st bk.], tall 8vo, [90]p, ibds, color, pep)	Volland	(1918)	Henderson, Arthur	400-600	
Henderson, Dorothy	Danny the Dream Man (1st, sq8vo, ibds, [48]p, color, pep)	Volland	(1928)	Henderson, Dorothy	80-120	
Whitworth, Geoffrey	Book of Whimsies (1st, 8vo, 62p, gilt, teg, uncut, 12cp)	L: J.M. Dent	1909	Henderson, Keith	80-135	
Hudson, Wm. Henry	Green Mansions (1st, lg8vo, 325p, ibds, dp woodcuts)	L: Duckworth	1926	Henderson, Keith	50-80	
Hudson, Wm. Henry	Purple Land (1st, lg8vo, red/gilt, 368p, b/w)	L: Duckworth	1929	Henderson, Keith	45-70	
Hardy, Thomas	Under the Greenwood Tree (1st, 8vo, 271p, green/gilt, teg, 10cp)	L: Chatto	1913	Henderson, Keith	70-120	
Eddison, Eric R.	Worm Ouroboros (1st AM, 8vo, gilt, 445p, b/w, pep)	A.& C. Boni	1926	Henderson, Keith	60-100	
Andersen, Hans C.	Andersen's Best Fairy Tales (1st, 12mo, 200p, color, pep)	Rand/McNally	(1911)	Henderson, W.P.	50-80	

AUTHOR	TITLE	PUBLISHER	DATE	ARTIST	PRICE	LC
Chaucer, Geoffrey	Romaunt of the Rose (4to, grey/gilt, 107p, teg, uncut, 20 ticp)	L: Chatto	1911	Henderson/Wilkinson	150-200	
Means, Florence C.	At the End of Nowhere (1st, 8vo, 232p, white cl, 12pl, DJ/2.00)	Houghton	1940	Hendrickson, David	30-50	*
Allee, Marjorie H.	Off to Philadelphia (1st, 8vo, 214p, col frn, b/w, DJ/2.00)	Houghton	1936	Hendrickson, David	20-30	
Peterkin, Julia	Plantation Christmas (1st, sm8vo, red cl, 26p, p-o, 1-color)	Houghton	1934	Hendrickson, David	50-80	
Allee, Marjorie H.	Runaway Linda (1st, 8vo, 220p, b/w, DJ/2.25)	Houghton	1939	Hendrickson, David	20-35	*
Singmaster, Elsie	Swords of Steel (1st, 8vo, 262p, b/w, pep, NH)	Houghton	1933	Hendrickson, David	40-60	*
Eaton, Jeanette	Young Lafayette (1st, 8vo, 253p, col frn, pep)	Houghton	1932	Hendrickson, David	20-30	
Reynolds, Barbara	Hamlet and Brownswiggle (1st, 8vo, 203p, b/w, DJ/2.50)	Scribner	1954	Henneberger, Rbt.	30-45	*
Brink, Carol R.	Highly Trained Dogs/Professor Pettit (1st {std}, 8vo, 139p, b/w, DJ/2.50)	Macmillan	(1953)	Henneberger, Rbt.	20-35	
Wilson, Hazel	His Indian Brother (1st, 8vo, 188p, b/w, DJ/2.50)	Abingdon-Cokes.	(1955)	Henneberger, Rbt.	50-80	
Dolbier, Maurice	Lion in the Woods (1st {std}, 8vo, 114p, b/w, DJ/2.75)	Little/Brown	(1955)	Henneberger, Rbt.	20-30	
Sheehy, Emma	Molly and the Golden Wedding (1st {std}, 8vo, 159p, b/w, DJ/2.50)	Holt	(1956)	Henneberger, Rbt.	20-30	
Stuart, Jesse	Penny's Worth of Character (1st, 8vo, 61p, b/w, DJ/1.75)	Whittlesey	(1954)	Henneberger, Rbt.	60-90	
Morgan, Nina	Prairie Star (1st, 8vo, 189p, b/w, DJ/2.75)	Viking	1955	Henneberger, Rbt.	25-40	
Stuart, Jesse	Red Mule (1st, 8vo, 123p, b/w, DJ/2.25)	Whittlesey	(1955)	Henneberger, Rbt.	60-90	*
Cameron, Eleanor	Stowaway to the Mushroom Planet (1st {std}, sm8vo, 226p, b/w, DJ/2.75)	Little/Brown	(1956)	Henneberger, Rbt.	150-220	
Dolbier, Maurice	Torten's Christmas Secret (1st {std}, lg8vo, 62p, 2-color, DJ/2.50)	Little/Brown	1951	Henneberger, Rbt.	30-50	
Cameron, Eleanor	Wonderful Flight to Mushroom Planet (1st {std}, sm8vo, 214p, b/w, DJ/2.75)	Little/Brown	(1954)	Henneberger, Rbt.	250-350	
Molesworth, Mrs.	Enchanted Garden: Fairy Stories (1st, 16mo, 221p, teg, b/w)	L: T.F. Unwin	1892	Hennessey, Wm. J.	60-90	
Williams, Jay	Practical Princess (1st, sm ob4to, [42]p, fp color, DJ/3.95)	Parents Mag. Pr.	(1969)	Henstra, Friso	30-45	*
Walker, Barbara	Round Sultan & the Straight Answer (1st, 4to, ibds, [38]p, color, DJ/3.95)	Parents Mag. Pr.	(1970)	Henstra, Friso	30-45	
Putnam, George H.	Little Gingerbread Man (1st, 8vo, 20p, fp color, pep)	Putnam	(1910)	Herbert, Robert	60-90	R*
Harris, Joel C.	Aaron in the Wildwoods (1st [1], 8vo, yellow cl, 270p, 24pl)	Houghton	1897	Herford, Oliver	150-220	
Carroll, Lewis	Alice in Wonderland (1st, sm8vo, 224p, blue/red, b/w)	Ginn & Co.	(1917)	Herford, Oliver	90-120	
Hall, Gertrude	Allegretto (1st, 12mo, beige/gilt, 111p, teg, b/w)	Roberts Bros.	1894	Herford, Oliver	60-100	
Herford, Oliver	Alphabet of Celebrities (1st, lg sq8vo, [58]p, ibds, 26 fp 1-color)	Small/Maynard	1899	Herford, Oliver	120-200	
Herford, Oliver	Artful Antics (1st, sq8vo, tan cl, 100p, b/w)	Century	1894	Herford, Oliver	80-120	*
Herford, Oliver	Astonishing Tale of a Pen & Ink Puppet (1st, ob4to, [62]p, ibds, b/w)	Scribner	1907	Herford, Oliver	100-170	
Herford, Oliver	Bashful Earthquake (1st, 12mo, teg, uncut, ipcb, 126p, b/w)	Scribner	1898	Herford, Oliver	55-90	R
Wells, Carolyn	Bumblepuppy Book (1st, sq8vo, ibds, 82p, fp 1-color)	L: Isbiter	1903	Herford, Oliver	50-80	
Herford, Oliver	Child's Primer of Natural History (1st UK, 95p, sq4to, b/w)	L: John Lane	1900	Herford, Oliver	80-130	
Herford, Oliver	Confessions of a Caricaturist (1st, 12mo, 65p, 9pl)	Scribner	1917	Herford, Oliver	30-50	
Herford, Oliver	Deb's Dictionary (1st {std}, sm8vo, [151]p, cloth, b/w)	Lippincott	1931	Herford, Oliver	35-60	
Herford, Oliver	Excuse it Please (1st {std}, sm8vo, 171p, ipcb, b/w, DJ/2.00)	Lippincott	(1929)	Herford, Oliver	35-60	
Herford, Oliver	Fairy Godmother-in-Law (1st, 12mo, 104p, ipcb, teg, b/w)	Scribner	1905	Herford, Oliver	65-100	
Roche, James J.	Her Majesty the King (1st, 12mo, 149p, 8cp)	R.H. Russell	1902	Herford, Oliver	65-90	
Herford, Oliver	Herford Aesop (1st, 12mo, 90p, col frn, b/w)	Ginn & Co.	(1921)	Herford, Oliver	75-100	
Wells, Carolyn	Idle Idyls (1st, sm8vo, green/gilt, teg, 155p, b/w pl)	Dodd	1900	Herford, Oliver	40-65	
Wells, Carolyn	Jingle Book (1st, sm8vo, 124p, blue cl, teg, b/w)	Macmillan	1899	Herford, Oliver	80-120	R
Wells, Carolyn	Jingle Book (8vo {new ed.}, green cl, p-o, 124p, b/w)	Donohue	(1906)	Herford, Oliver	40-60	*
Herford, Oliver	Kitten's Garden of Verses (1st, 12mo, ipcb, gilt, 59p, 25pl)	Scribner	1911	Herford, Oliver	60-90	
Herford, Oliver	Laughing Willow (1st, sm8vo, ipcb, 134p, col frn)	Doran	(1918)	Herford, Oliver	40-60	*
Herford, Oliver	Little Book of Bores (1st, 12mo, 52p, ipcb, b/w)	Scribner	(1906)	Herford, Oliver	60-90	
Harris, Joel C.	Little Mr. Thimblefinger (1st, lg8vo, 230p, ae green, 32pl, cep)	Houghton	1894	Herford, Oliver	180-240	R
Herford, Beatrice	Monologues (1st, 12mo, 139p, grey cl, 18 b/w)	Scribner	1908	Herford, Oliver	55-80	
Herford, Oliver	More Animals (1st, sq8vo, ibds, 99p, 24pl)	Scribner	1901	Herford, Oliver	90-120	R
Harris, Joel C.	Mr. Rabbit at Home (1st, 8vo, 304p, tan cl, ae green, 25pl, cep)	Houghton	1895	Herford, Oliver	160-220	R
Herford, Oliver	Mythological Zoo (1st, sq8vo, ibds, 45p, 22pl)	Scribner	1912	Herford, Oliver	60-90	
Herford, Oliver	Overheard in a Garden (1st, sm8vo, ibds, teg, 104p, col frn)	Scribner	1900	Herford, Oliver	70-100	
Herford, Oliver	Pen & Inklings (1st [1st bk.], 12mo, tan cl, b/w)	L: G. Allen	1893	Herford, Oliver	120-170	
Herford, Oliver	Peter Pan Alphabet (1st, sq8vo, ibds, [57]p, fp b/w)	Scribner	1907	Herford, Oliver	160-250	
Wells, Carolyn	Phenomenal Fauna (1st, sq8vo, [90]p, ibds, 21cp)	R.H. Russell	1902	Herford, Oliver	100-160	
Herford, Oliver	Rubaiyat of a Persian Kitten (1st, 12mo, [76]p, ibds, 35pl)	Scribner	1904	Herford, Oliver	60-90	
Herford, Oliver	Sea Legs (1st, ob12mo, [55]p, ibds, p-o, 23 fp 2-color)	Lippincott	(1931)	Herford, Oliver	50-80	
Metcalfe, Francis	Side Show Studies (1st, 12mo, 232p, b/w)	Outing	1906	Herford, Oliver	40-65	
Herford, Oliver	Simple Jography (1st, sm8vo, ibds, [100]p, b/w)	Bos: J.W. Luce	(1908)	Herford, Oliver	30-50	
Harris, Joel C.	Story of Aaron (1st, lg8vo, tan/gilt, 198p, 25pl, cep)	Houghton	1896	Herford, Oliver	200-300	R
Herford, Oliver	This Giddy Globe (1st, 8vo, 138p, tan cl, b/w)	Doran	(1919)	Herford, Oliver	25-40	
Herford, Oliver	Cupid's Almanac (1st, narrow 8vo, [58]p, ipcb, col frn, pep)	Houghton	1908	Herford/Clay	40-60	*
Herford, Oliver	Happy Days (1st, 16mo, ipcb, [44]p, color, pep)	Kennerley	1917	Herford/Clay	35-60	
Means, Philip A.	Tupak of the Incas (1st, lg8vo, 136p, b/w, DJ/2.00)	Scribner	1942	Herget, H.M.	30-45	*
Wells, H.G.	First Men in the Moon (1st, 8vo, 312p, blue/gilt, 12pl)	Bowen-Merrill	(1901)	Hering, E.	600-800	
Stevenson, Rbt. L.	Fables (1st AM, 4to, maroon/gilt, teg, 83p, 20pl)	Scribner	1914	Herman, E.R.	100-165	
Travers, Pamela L.	I Go by Sea, I Go by Land (1st {std}, 8vo, 233p, b/w, DJ/2.00)	Harper	(1941)	Hermes, Gertrude	80-125	
Goldsmith, Milton	Dorothy's Dolls... (1st, 8vo, 59p, ibds, 14cp)	NY: Ullman	(1908)	Hermony, N.	75-100	*
Clark, Ann N.	In My Mother's House (1st, 4to, 56p, brown cl, pep, color, DJ/2.00, CH)	Viking	1941	Herrera, Velino	80-125	R
Dalgliesh, Alice	The Hollyberrys (1st, sq12mo, 59p, 12 fp color, cep, DJ/1.50)	Scribner	(1939)	Herric, Pru	30-50	
Marquis, Don	Archy Does His Part (1st {std}, 12mo, p-o, 269p, b/w, pep, DJ/2.00)	Doubleday/Doran	1935	Herriman, George	70-120	
Anderson, Richard C.	Animals in Social Captivity (1st, 8vo, gilt, p-o, 96p, 10cp dep)	Stewart/Kidd	(1914)	Herschede, Lilian N.	55-80	*
Cable, George W.	Old Creole Days (1st, lg8vo, 234p, grey cl, teg, 8pl)	Scribner	1897	Herter, Albert	80-120	
Pease, Eleanor F.	Jolly Little Clown (1st, lg8vo, p-o, gilt, 126p, pep, color)	Whitman	(1927)	Hetherington, M.L.	30-55	
Sidney, Margaret	Five Little Peppers in Little Brown House (1st, sm8vo, 434p, gilt, 8pl)	Lothrop, Lee	1907	Heyer, Hermann	100-160	
Nelson, Margaret W.	Pinky Finds a Home (1st, 12mo, 118p, ibds, col frn, DJ/1.75)	Holiday House	(1940)	Heyneman, Anne	25-45	
Ames, Esther M.	Patsy for Keeps (1st, sm4to, ibds, 95p, doll bk., color)	NY: S. Gabriel	(1932)	Hicks, A.L.	70-100	*
Ames, Esther M.	Twistum Tales (1st, 8vo, 96p, p-o, col frn, fp b/w)	Rand/McNally	(1929)	Hicks, Lorne	30-50	
Gask, Lilian	Babes of the Wild (1st, 4to, 160p, p-o, 5cp)	L: Harrap	1917	Hickson, Wilma	60-100	
Dumas, Alexandre	Three Musketeers (1st, 8vo, p-o, 459p, 5cp, 10pl, pep)	Winston	(1931)	Higgins, Edward R.	30-50	
Asbjornsen, P.C.	East of the Sun, West o/t Moon (1st, lg8vo, 192p, color, p-o, gilt, pep)	Whitman	(1924)	Higgins, Violet M.	50-80	

AUTHOR	TITLE	PUBLISHER	DATE	ARTIST	PRICE	LC
Higgins, Violet M.	Endless Story (1st, 8vo, ibds, 71p, color, pep)	Whitman	(1916)	Higgins, Violet M.	55-80	
Dodge, Mary Mapes	Hans Brinker (1st, 8vo, 320p, p-o, color, pep)	Whitman	1929	Higgins, Violet M.	45-70	
Spyri, Johanna	Heidi (1st, 8vo, 284p, p-o, 1-color, pep)	Whitman	(1924)	Higgins, Violet M.	35-60	*
Higgins, Violet M.	Little Juggler (1st, 8vo, 70p, color, pep)	Whitman	(1917)	Higgins, Violet M.	50-80	
Craik, Dinah	Little Lame Prince (1st, lg8vo, 128p, green/gilt, p-o, 9cp, pep)	Whitman	(1927)	Higgins, Violet M.	50-80	
Higgins, Violet M.	Magic Circus (8vo, [doll bk.], 64p, ibds, color)	Chi: Stanton	1918	Higgins, Violet M.	80-125	
Mother Goose	Mother Goose & her Goslings (1st, lg8vo, 125p, color)	Chi: Stanton	(1918)	Higgins, Violet M.	75-100	*
Collodi, Carlo	Pinocchio (1st, lg8vo, 255p, pep, p-o, fp color)	Whitman	(1926)	Higgins, Violet M.	60-80	*
Higgins, Violet M.	Real Story of a Real Doll (1st, 8vo, 116p, pep, 4cp)	McBride	(1929)	Higgins, Violet M.	35-60	*
Higgins, Violet M.	Silver Ship (1st, lg8vo, ipcb, 63p, color)	Whitman	(1916)	Higgins, Violet M.	50-80	
Beard, Patten	What Happened After Stories (1st, sq4to, 125p, p-o, color, pep)	Whitman	(1929)	Higgins, Violet M.	40-60	
Higgins, Violet M.	Woodcutter's Son (1st, lg8vo, p-o, 68p, 4cp)	Whitman	1917	Higgins, Violet M.	45-70	
Montgomery, F.T.	Zip: Adventures of a Frisky Fox Terrier (1st, 8vo, 77p, ipcb, 4cp)	Saalfield	(1917)	Higgins, Violet M.	60-100	*
Stevenson, Rbt. L.	Kidnapped (1st, 4to, 290p, tan/gilt, 12 ticp, pep)	L: Oxford U.Pr.	1930	Hilder, Rowland	65-100	
Masefield, John	Midnight Folk (1st, 4to, 282p, blue/gilt, 6cp, pep)	L: Heinemann	(1931)	Hilder, Rowland	120-175	
Pratt, Anna	Friends from My Garden (1st, 8vo, AEG, 128p, white/gilt, 12cp)	Stokes	1890	Hill, Laura C.	165-220	
Hill, Mabel B.	Down Along Apple Market Street (1st, ob8vo, p-o, [32]p, color, pep)	Stokes	1934	Hill, Mabel B.	30-50	*
Mother Goose	Most Popular Mother Goose Songs (1st, ob4to, 44p, ipcb, 39cp)	NY: Hinds	(1915)	Hill, Mabel B.	160-240	
Potter, Russell	Little Red Ferry Boat (1st, 8vo, 50p, fp 2-color, pep, DJ/2.00)	Henry Holt & Co.	(1947)	Hill, Marjorie	30-45	*
Hill, William E.	Among Us Cats (1st {std}, lg8vo, p-o, [128]p, col frn, 61pl, pep)	Harper	1926	Hill, William E.	70-120	
White, Stewart E.	Rules of the Game (1st, sm8vo, 644p, 4cp)	Doubleday/Page	1910	Hiller, Lejaren A.	30-50	
Sampson, Martin	Good Giant (1st, 8vo, 218p, col frn, 10pl, pep)	Houghton	1928	Hilton	40-60	*
Thwaite, Ann	Day with the Duke (1st AM {std}, lg8vo, [32]p, color, DJ/4.95)	World	1969	Him, George	30-50	
Herrmann, Frank	Giant Alexander (1st, 4to, 32p, fp color, pep, DJ/3.50)	McGraw-Hill	(1964)	Him, George	30-50	*
Herrmann, Frank	Giant Alexander & the Circus (1st AM, 4to, [32]p, color, pep, DJ/3.75)	McGraw-Hill	(1966)	Him, George	25-40	
Potter, Stephen	Squawky, Advens. of a Clasperchoice (1st, sm4to, 48p, 2-color, DJ/3.75)	Lippincott	1964	Him, George	30-45	*
Sturgis, Edith B.	My Busy Days (1st, folio, 50p, ibds, 8cp)	Appleton	1908	Hinchman, Margaretta	120-200	*
Henty, G.A.	In the Heart of the Rockies (1st, 8vo, grey cl, 352p, 8pl)	L: Blackie	1895	Hindley, Godfrey C.	70-125	
Mabie, Hamilton W.	Under The Trees (1st, 8vo, teg, 165p, green/gilt, 6pl, pep)	Dodd	1902	Hinton, Charles L.	40-60	
Ostrander, Fannie	Baby Goose: His Adventures (1st, lg8vo, ibds, unpag, color)	Laird & Lee	(1900)	Hirchert, R.W.	80-120	*
Mother Goose	Mother Goose (1st, lg8vo, [40]p, color)	Wonder Books	(1946)	Hirsch, Joseph	55-80	*
Hirsh, Marilyn J.	Pink Suit (1st, 4to, [35]p, 2-color, DJ/3.95)	Crown	(1970)	Hirsh, Marilyn	25-40	
Holl, Adelaide	Runaway Hat (1st, 4to, 24p, fp color, pep, DJ)	L.W. Singer	(1969)	Hirsh, Marilyn	30-50	*
Hirsh, Marilyn J.	Where is Yonkela? (1st, 4to, [32]p, fp color, pep, DJ/3.95)	Crown	1969	Hirsh, Marilyn	25-40	*
Twain, Mark	Double-Barrelled Detective Story (1st, 8vo, red/gilt, teg, uncut, 7pl)	Harper	1902	Hitchcock, Lucius	150-250	
Deland, Margaret	Dr. Lavendar's People (1st, 12mo, 370p, 12pl)	Harper	1903	Hitchcock, Lucius	30-50	
Twain, Mark	Horse's Tale (1st, 8vo, red cl, 152p, 5pl)	Harper	1907	Hitchcock, Lucius	120-200	
Hoban, Russell	Baby Sister for Frances (1st, 4to, [31]p, ibds, color, DJ/2.50)	Harper	(1964)	Hoban, Lillian	70-100	
Hoban, Russell	Bargain for Frances (1st, 8vo, 62p, 2-color, DJ/2.50)	Harper	(1970)	Hoban, Lillian	60-100	
Hoban, Russell	Best Friends for Frances (1st, 4to, 31p, color, DJ/2.95)	Harper	(1969)	Hoban, Lillian	30-45	
Hoban, Russell	Birthday for Frances (1st, 4to, 31p, color, DJ/2.95)	Harper	(1968)	Hoban, Lillian	70-120	
Hoban, Russell	Bread & Jam for Frances (1st, 4to, 31p, color, DJ/2.50)	Harper	(1964)	Hoban, Lillian	60-100	
Hoban, Russell	Charlie & the Tramp (1st, 8vo, [48]p, b/w, DJ/2.95)	Four Winds Pr.	(1967)	Hoban, Lillian	60-90	
Hoban, Russell	Goodnight (1st {std}, 8vo, unpag, color, pep, DJ/2.95)	Norton	(1966)	Hoban, Lillian	60-100	
Hoban, Russell	Harvey's Hideout (1st, 4to, [42]p, fp color, DJ/3.50)	Parents Mag. Pr.	(1969)	Hoban, Lillian	70-100	
Hoban, Russell	Henry & the Monstrous Din (1st, sm ob4to, [32]p, fp 3-color, cep, DJ/2.95)	Harper	(1966)	Hoban, Lillian	60-100	
Hoban, Russell	Herman the Loser (1st, 4to, 32p, ibds, b/w, DJ/1.95)	Harper	(1961)	Hoban, Lillian	65-100	
Hoban, Russell	Hester Mouse who Became a Writer (1st {std}, 8vo, 46p, b/w, DJ/2.95)	Norton	(1965)	Hoban, Lillian	70-100	
Fisher, Aileen	In One Door and Out the Other (1st {std}, 8vo, 65p, b/w, DJ/3.75)	Crowell	(1969)	Hoban, Lillian	30-50	
Hoban, Russell	Little Brute Family (1st {std}, 12mo, [30]p, fp 3-color, DJ/2.95)	Macmillan	(1966)	Hoban, Lillian	60-90	
Hoban, Russell	London Men and English Men (1st, lg ob8vo, ipcb, [32]p, b/w, DJ/1.95)	Harper	(1962)	Hoban, Lillian	30-45	
Hoban, Russell	Mole Family's Christmas (1st, 8vo, [39]p, color, cep, DJ/3.50)	Parents Mag. Pr.	(1969)	Hoban, Lillian	60-100	
Hoban, Russell	Mouse and his Child (1st, 8vo, 181p, ibds, b/w, DJ/4.50)	Harper	(1967)	Hoban, Lillian	100-165	
Hoban, Russell	Nothing to Do (1st, sm4to, unpag, ibds, b/w, DJ/2.50)	Harper	(1964)	Hoban, Lillian	30-45	*
Hoban, Russell	Pedaling Man and other Poems (1st {std}, 8vo, 33p, b/w, DJ/3.50)	Norton	(1968)	Hoban, Lillian	70-120	
Hoban, Russell	Save my Place (1st {std}, 8vo, [32]p, color, DJ/3.95)	Norton	(1967)	Hoban, Lillian	70-100	
Hoban, Russell	Some Snow said Hello (1st, ob8vo, [32]p, b/w, DJ/1.95)	Harper	(1963)	Hoban, Lillian	60-100	
Hoban, Russell	Song in my Drum (1st, ob8vo, [32]p, DJ/1.95)	Harper	(1962)	Hoban, Lillian	70-120	
Hoban, Russell	Sorely Trying Day (1st, 4to, [32]p, b/w, DJ/1.95)	Harper	(1964)	Hoban, Lillian	60-100	
Hoban, Russell	Stone Doll of Sister Brute (1st {std}, 12mo, [32]p, color, DJ/2.95)	Macmillan	1968	Hoban, Lillian	60-90	
Hoban, Russell	Tom and the Two Handles (1st, 8vo, 62p, ibds, fp 3-color, DJ/1.95)	Harper	(1965)	Hoban, Lillian	70-100	
Hoban, Russell	Ugly Bird (1st {std}, 8vo, [32]p, color, DJ/3.95)	Macmillan	(1969)	Hoban, Lillian	75-100	
Holman, Felice	Victoria's Castle (1st {std}, sm4to, 40p, color, pep, DJ/3.25)	Norton	(1966)	Hoban, Lillian	50-85	
Hoban, Russell	What Does it Do and How Does it Work? (1st, lg4to, 58p, 2-color, DJ/3.50)	Harper	(1959)	Hoban, Lillian	80-120	
Smith, Robert P.	When I am Big (1st, 8vo, 32p, fp color, cep, DJ/2.50)	Harper	(1965)	Hoban, Lillian	30-50	
Cohen, Miriam	Will I Have a Friend? (1st {std}, ob8vo, unpag, color, DJ/3.50)	Macmillan	(1967)	Hoban, Lillian	25-40	
Wahl, Jan	Wolf of My Own (1st {std}, ob4to, [32]p, fp color, DJ/4.95)	Macmillan	(1969)	Hoban, Lillian	30-45	
Hobbs, Barbara	Alexander's Animals (1st, 4to, 30p, fp 3-color, DJ/2.75)	Houghton	1958	Hobbs, Barbara	40-65	
Hoberman, Mary Ann	All My Shoes Come in Twos (1st {std}, 8vo, 40p, fp color, cep, DJ/2.50)	Little/Brown	(1957)	Hoberman, Norman	50-80	R*
Andersen, Hans C.	Fairy Tales (1st, 12mo, 170p, b/w)	Chi: Flanagan	(1912)	Hodge, H.	35-60	*
Sutcliff, Rosemary	Armourer's House (1st, 8vo, 235p, 11 fp b/w, pep, DJ/2.50)	L: Oxford U.Pr.	1951	Hodges, C. Walter	30-50	
Sutcliff, Rosemary	Brother Dusty-Feet (1st, 8vo, 231p, b/w, DJ)	L: Oxford U.Pr.	1952	Hodges, C. Walter	30-50	
Mayne, William	Chorister's Cake (1st, 8vo, 160p, b/w, DJ)	L: Oxford U.Pr.	1956	Hodges, C. Walter	60-90	
Armstrong, Richard	Cold Hazard (1st, 8vo, 181p, b/w, DJ/2.50)	Houghton	1956	Hodges, C. Walter	20-35	
Sutcliff, Rosemary	Eagle of the Ninth (1st, 8vo, 255p, b/w, DJ)	H.Z. Walck	1961	Hodges, C. Walter	30-50	
Hodges, C. Walter	Flying House (1st, 8vo, 112p, orange/gilt, col frn, b/w, DJ)	L: Benn	1947	Hodges, C. Walter	30-50	
Baker, Margaret	Hannibal and the Bears (1st AM {std}, sm8vo, 115p, b/w, DJ/2.95)	Farrar, Straus	(1966)	Hodges, C. Walter	30-45	
Goudge, Elizabeth	Little White Horse (1st, 12mo, gilt, 286p, 4cp, pep, CgM)	London U. Press	(1946)	Hodges, C. Walter	100-165	

AUTHOR	TITLE	PUBLISHER	DATE	ARTIST	PRICE	LC
Goudge, Elizabeth	Little White Horse (1st AM {std}, 8vo, 280p, blue cl, b/w, pep, DJ/2.50)	Coward	(1947)	Hodges, C. Walter	80-125	
Hodges, C. Walter	Marsh King (1st, 8vo, gilt, 213p, b/w, DJ)	L: G. Bell	(1967)	Hodges, C. Walter	45-70	
Hodges, C. Walter	Marsh King (1st AM, 8vo, 253p, fp b/w, DJ/3.95)	Coward	(1967)	Hodges, C. Walter	30-50	*
Strong, L.A.G.	Mr. Sheridan's Umbrella (1st, 8vo, 215p, col frn, fp b/w, DJ)	L: Nelson	(1935)	Hodges, C. Walter	30-50	
Fenton, Edward	Nine Questions (1st {std}, 8vo, 235p, b/w, DJ/2.95)	Doubleday	(1959)	Hodges, C. Walter	25-40	
Dobbs, Rose	Once-Upon-a-Time Story Book (1st, 4to, 63p, ibds, color, pep, DJ/1.00)	Random	(1958)	Hodges, C. Walter	30-50	
Sutcliff, Rosemary	Queen Elizabeth Story (1st, 8vo, 208p, fp b/w, pep, DJ/2.00)	Oxford U. Pr.	1950	Hodges, C. Walter	30-50	*
Picard, Barbara	Ransom for a Knight (1st AM, 8vo, 314p, b/w, DJ/4.50)	H.Z. Walck	(1967)	Hodges, C. Walter	50-80	*
Sutcliff, Rosemary	Shield Ring (1st {std}, 8vo, 215p, b/w, DJ/3.00)	H.Z. Walck	1957	Hodges, C. Walter	25-45	
Serraillier, Ian	Silver Sword (1st AM, 8vo, 187p, b/w, DJ/3.50)	Criterion Bks.	(1959)	Hodges, C. Walter	25-45	
Goudge, Elizabeth	Sister of the Angels (1st AM, 8vo, blue/gilt, 154p, fp b/w, DJ/1.50)	Coward	(1939)	Hodges, C. Walter	30-50	
Mayne, William	Swarm in May (1st, 8vo, 199p, b/w, pep, DJ)	L: Oxford U.Pr.	1955	Hodges, C. Walter	80-130	
Hodges, C. Walter	The Namesake (1st AM {std}, 8vo, 269p, b/w, pep, DJ/3.95)	Coward	1964	Hodges, C. Walter	30-50	
Brodsky, Mimi	House at 12 Rose Street (1st, 8vo, 157p, fp b/w, DJ/3.50)	Abelard-Schuman	(1966)	Hodges, David	25-40	*
Hoff, Syd	Danny and the Dinosaur (1st, 8vo, 64p, color, DJ/2.50)	Harper	(1958)	Hoff, Syd	30-50	*
Lexau, Joan M.	I Should have Stayed in Bed (1st, 8vo, 48p, color, DJ/2.50)	Harper	(1965)	Hoff, Syd	20-25	*
Lexau, Joan M.	Rooftop Mystery (1st, 8vo, 64p, color, DJ/2.50)	Harper	(1968)	Hoff, Syd	25-45	
Hoff, Syd	Sammy the Seal (1st, 8vo, 64p, color, DJ/2.50)	Harper	(1959)	Hoff, Syd	25-45	
Hoff, Syd	Stanley (1st, 8vo, 64p, ibds, color, DJ/1.95)	Harper	(1962)	Hoff, Syd	30-50	*
Clark, Ann N.	Father Kino: Priest to the Primas (1st, 8vo, 176p, b/w, DJ/2.25)	Farrar, Straus	(1963)	Hoffman, H. Lawrence	20-30	
Guillot, Rene	Elephants of Sargabal (1st AM, 8vo, 170p, b/w, DJ/3.25)	Criterion Bks.	(1957)	Hoffmann, Felix	30-50	
Haviland, Virginia	Favorite Fairy Tales Told in Poland (1st {std}, lg8vo, 90p, color, DJ/2.95)	Little/Brown	1963	Hoffmann, Felix	50-85	R
Grimm Bros.	Four Clever Brothers (1st AM {std}, ob4to, [32]p, color, pep, DJ/4.50)	Harcourt	(1967)	Hoffmann, Felix	40-65	
Grimm Bros.	King Thrushbeard (1st AM {std}, 4to, [32]p, ibds, color, DJ/4.50)	Harcourt	(1970)	Hoffmann, Felix	40-70	
Grimm Bros.	Rapunzel (1st AM {std}, 4to, ibds, unpag, color, DJ/3.75)	Harcourt	(1961)	Hoffmann, Felix	40-65	
Grimm Bros.	Seven Ravens (1st AM {std}, ob4to, [32]p, ibds, color, DJ/3.75)	Harcourt	(1963)	Hoffmann, Felix	40-65	
Grimm Bros.	Sleeping Beauty (1st AM {std}, 4to, ibds, unpag, color, DJ/3.50)	Harcourt	(1960)	Hoffmann, Felix	45-60	
Grimm Bros.	Wolf & the Seven Little Kids (1st AM {std}, ob4to, [32]p, 2-color, DJ/3.75)	Harcourt	(1959)	Hoffmann, Felix	40-65	
Cobb, Lucy M.	Animal Tales from Old North State (1st, 8vo, 200p, b/w, pep, DJ/2.00)	Dutton	1938	Hogan, Inez	30-50	
Hogan, Inez	Bear is a Bear (1st, 8vo, 43p, fp b/w, pep, DJ/2.00)	Dutton	(1953)	Hogan, Inez	50-80	*
Hogan, Inez	Bear Twins (1st {std}, 8vo, [45]p, ipcb, 1-color, pep, DJ/1.00)	Dutton	(1935)	Hogan, Inez	60-100	
Hogan, Inez	Big Ones (1st {std}, 4to, yellow cl, [30]p, b/w, pep, DJ/2.95)	Dutton	(1957)	Hogan, Inez	60-90	
Hogan, Inez	Cubby Bear & the Book (1st {std}, 8vo, [42]p, fp b/w, DJ/2.50)	Dutton	(1961)	Hogan, Inez	45-70	
Hogan, Inez	Dinosaur Twins (1st {std}, 8vo, 39p, DJ/2.25)	Dutton	(1963)	Hogan, Inez	45-70	
Hogan, Inez	Eager Beaver (1st {std}, 8vo, 39p, b/w, DJ/2.25)	Dutton	(1963)	Hogan, Inez	50-80	
Hogan, Inez	Elephant Twins (1st {std}, 8vo, ipcb, [45]p, pep, DJ/1.00)	Dutton	(1936)	Hogan, Inez	50-85	
Bryant, Sara Cone	Epaminondas & his Auntie (1st, sq8vo, ibds, 16p, 2-color, pep, DJ/0.75)	Houghton	1938	Hogan, Inez	100-170	R
Hogan, Erlin	Four Funny Men (1st {std}, 12mo, ibds, [55]p, 1-color, pep, DJ/1.00)	Dutton	(1939)	Hogan, Inez	80-125	
Hogan, Inez	Fox Twins (1st {std}, 8vo, 31p, b/w, DJ/2.25)	Dutton	(1964)	Hogan, Inez	40-65	*
Hogan, Inez	Fraidy Cat (1st {std}, 8vo, 41p, b/w, pep, DJ/2.50)	Dutton	(1962)	Hogan, Inez	40-65	*
Hogan, Inez	Giraffe Twins (1st {std}, 8vo, [48]p, ipcb, 1-color, pep, DJ/1.25)	Dutton	(1948)	Hogan, Inez	70-120	
Hogan, Inez	Kangaroo Twins (1st {std}, 8vo, [49]p, ibds, color, pep, DJ/1.00)	Dutton	(1938)	Hogan, Inez	70-100	
Winlow, Clara V.	Kitten that Grew Too Fat (1st, lg ob8vo, gilt, 93p, 24 fp color)	Macrae Smith	(1929)	Hogan, Inez	80-125	
Hogan, Inez	Koala Bear Twins (1st {std}, 8vo, unpag, color, DJ/1.50)	Dutton	(1955)	Hogan, Inez	60-90	
Hogan, Inez	Listen Hitler! Gremlins are Coming (1st {std} 8vo ibds, b/w [41]p, DJ/1.00)	Dutton	1943	Hogan, Inez	70-120	
Hogan, Inez	Little Black & White Lamb (1st, sm8vo, black/gilt, [103]p, fp color)	Macrae Smith	(1927)	Hogan, Inez	100-165	
Hogan, Inez	Little Lost Bear (1st {std}, lg8vo, [41]p, fp b/w, pep, DJ/2.50)	Dutton	1960	Hogan, Inez	45-70	
Hogan, Inez	Little Ones (1st {std}, 8vo, 45p, b/w, DJ/2.25)	Dutton	(1956)	Hogan, Inez	40-65	*
Hogan, Inez	Little Toy Airplane (1st, ob8vo, [57]p, color, pep)	Macrae Smith	(1930)	Hogan, Inez	60-90	
Hogan, Inez	Littlest Bear (1st {std}, 8vo, 59p, fp b/w, pep, DJ/2.50)	Dutton	1959	Hogan, Inez	40-65	*
Hogan, Inez	Littlest Satellite (1st {std}, 8vo, unpag, b/w, DJ/2.50)	Dutton	1958	Hogan, Inez	50-80	
Hogan, Inez	Lone Wolf (1st {std}, 8vo, [40]p, fp b/w, pep, DJ/2.50)	Dutton	(1961)	Hogan, Inez	50-80	
Hogan, Inez	Me (1st {std}, 8vo, blue cl, 61p, b/w, pep, DJ/2.00)	Dutton	1954	Hogan, Inez	50-80	
Hogan, Inez	Monkey See, Monkey Do (1st {std}, 8vo, [41]p, b/w, pep, DJ/2.50)	Dutton	1960	Hogan, Inez	40-65	
Christopher, Anne	Monkey Twins (1st, ob8vo, [31]p, pep, ipcb, color)	Whitman	(1935)	Hogan, Inez	60-90	*
Hogan, Inez	Monkey Twins, They Saw it All (1st {std}, sm8vo, ipcb, b/w, pep, DJ/1.00)	Dutton	(1943)	Hogan, Inez	50-80	
Hogan, Inez	Mule Twins (1st {std}, 8vo, ibds, [49]p, b/w, pep, DJ/1.00)	Dutton	(1939)	Hogan, Inez	60-100	
Hogan, Inez	Nappy Chooses a Pet (1st {std}, 8vo, [48]p, ipcb, color, DJ/1.00)	Dutton	1946	Hogan, Inez	60-100	
Hogan, Inez	Nappy is a Cowboy (1st {std}, 8vo, ibds, [49]p, fp b/w, pep, DJ/1.25)	Dutton	1949	Hogan, Inez	60-100	
Hogan, Inez	Nappy Planted a Garden (1st {std}, 8vo, ibds, [49]p, b/w, pep, DJ/1.00)	Dutton	1944	Hogan, Inez	60-100	
Hogan, Inez	Nappy Wanted a Dog (1st {std}, 8vo, ibds, [49]p, fp b/w, pep, DJ/1.00)	Dutton	1942	Hogan, Inez	50-70	
Hogan, Inez	Nicodemus & his Gran' Pappy (1st {std}, sm8vo, [49]p, color, pep, DJ/1.00)	Dutton	(1936)	Hogan, Inez	150-250	R
Hogan, Inez	Nicodemus & his Little Sister (1st {std}, 12mo, ibds, [47]p, 1-color)	Dutton	1932	Hogan, Inez	100-165	
Hogan, Inez	Nicodemus & his New Shoes (1st {std} 12mo ibds [49]p, 2-color pep, DJ/1.00)	Dutton	(1937)	Hogan, Inez	150-250	R
Hogan, Inez	Nicodemus & Little Black Pig (1st {std}, sm8vo, [61]p, color, pep)	Dutton	(1934)	Hogan, Inez	120-200	R
Hogan, Inez	Nicodemus & New-Born Baby (1st {std} sm8vo ipcb, 1-col, 53p, pep, DJ/1.00)	Dutton	(1940)	Hogan, Inez	150-250	
Hogan, Inez	Nicodemus & Petunia (1st {std}, sm8vo, [51]p, color, pep, DJ/1.00)	Dutton	(1937)	Hogan, Inez	150-250	R
Hogan, Inez	Nicodemus & the Gang (1st {std}, sm8vo, ibds, [53]p, pep, DJ/1.00)	Dutton	(1939)	Hogan, Inez	150-250	
Hogan, Inez	Nicodemus & the Goose (1st {std}, sm8vo, ibds, [47]p, color pep, DJ/1.00)	Dutton	(1945)	Hogan, Inez	80-140	
Hogan, Inez	Nicodemus & the Houn' Dog (1st {std}, sm8vo, [52]p, ibds, color)	Dutton	(1933)	Hogan, Inez	150-250	R
Hogan, Inez	Nicodemus Helps Uncle Sam (1st {std}, sm8vo, ibds, [48]p, color)	Dutton	1943	Hogan, Inez	100-165	
Hogan, Inez	Nicodemus Laughs (1st {std}, sm8vo, ibds, [40]p, color, pep, DJ/1.00)	Dutton	(1941)	Hogan, Inez	150-250	
Hogan, Inez	Party for Poodles (1st {std}, 4to, [54]p, fp b/w, pep, DJ/2.50)	Dutton	(1952)	Hogan, Inez	50-80	*
Christopher, Anne	Petunia Be Keerful (1st, 8vo, ibds, [41]p, 2-color, pep)	Whitman	(1934)	Hogan, Inez	80-140	
Hogan, Inez	Raccoon Twins (1st {std}, 8vo, [49]p, ibds, b/w, DJ/1.00)	Dutton	(1946)	Hogan, Inez	50-80	*
Hogan, Inez	Read to Me about Charlie (1st {std}, sm4to, ibds, 43p, b/w, pep, DJ/1.25)	Dutton	(1950)	Hogan, Inez	50-80	
Hogan, Inez	Read to Me about Nono, the Baby Elephant (1st {std}, sm4to, 44p, DJ/1.00)	Dutton	(1947)	Hogan, Inez	50-85	
Hogan, Inez	Read to Me about Peter Platypus (1st {std}, lg8vo, ibds, 45p, b/w, DJ/1.25)	Dutton	(1948)	Hogan, Inez	50-85	

AUTHOR	TITLE	PUBLISHER	DATE	ARTIST	PRICE	LC
Hogan, Inez	Runaway Toys (1st {std}, lg8vo, [40]p, pep, color, DJ/1.75)	Dutton	(1950)	Hogan, Inez	60-100	
Hogan, Inez	Sandy, Skip & Man in the Moon (1st, sm8vo, gilt, 93p, color)	Macrae Smith	(1928)	Hogan, Inez	50-85	
Van Vrooman, Maria	Shine (1st {std}, 12mo, 50p, ibds, b/w, pep, DJ/1.00)	Dutton	(1939)	Hogan, Inez	50-80	
Vorse, Mary E.	Skinny Gets Fat (1st, 8vo, ipcb, [41]p, 1-color, pep, DJ/1.00)	W.R. Scott	1940	Hogan, Inez	40-65	
Hogan, Inez	Twin Colts (1st {std}, 8vo, ibds, [49]p, b/w, pep, DJ/1.25)	Dutton	(1944)	Hogan, Inez	60-90	
Hogan, Inez	Twin Kids (1st, 8vo, [50]p, ipcb, 1-color, pep, DJ/1.00)	Dutton	(1937)	Hogan, Inez	100-160	
Hogan, Inez	Twin Kittens (1st {std}, 8vo, [42]p, fp b/w, pep, DJ/2.25)	Dutton	(1958)	Hogan, Inez	50-85	*
Hogan, Inez	Twin Otters and the Indians (1st {std}, 8vo, 41p, b/w, DJ/2.25)	Dutton	(1962)	Hogan, Inez	50-80	
Hogan, Inez	Twin Puppies (1st {std}, 8vo, [40]p, fp b/w, pep, DJ)	Dutton	1959	Hogan, Inez	45-70	
Hogan, Inez	Twin Seals (1st {std}, 8vo, [48]p, ibds, pep, DJ/1.00)	Dutton	(1940)	Hogan, Inez	50-80	
Hogan, Inez	Upside Down Book (1st {std}, sm4to, [46]p, b/w, pep, DJ/2.50)	Dutton	1955	Hogan, Inez	50-80	
Vorse, Mary E.	Wakey Goes to Bed (1st, 8vo, ipcb, [41]p, brown illus, cep, DJ/1.00)	W.R. Scott	1941	Hogan, Inez	40-65	
Hogan, Inez	We are a Family (1st {std}, sm sq4to, 93p, b/w, pep, DJ/2.75)	Dutton	(1952)	Hogan, Inez	50-80	
Hogan, Inez	White Kitten and Blue Plate (1st, ob8vo, [44]p, color, pep)	Macmillan	1930	Hogan, Inez	100-165	*
Hogan, Inez	World Round (1st {std}, 4to, [64]p, blue cl, b/w, pep, DJ/2.50)	Dutton	(1949)	Hogan, Inez	60-100	
Hall, Daniel W.	Arctic Rovings (1st, 8vo, 144p, b/w, DJ/3.95)	Young Scott	1968	Hogarth, William	25-40	
Wister, Owen	Padre Ignacio (1st, 8vo, ibds, 65p, col frn)	Harper	1925	Hogg, Zack	30-45	
Hogner, Dorothy	Daisy (1st, ob8vo, [48]p, ibds, fp b/w, cep, DJ/1.50)	NY: Oxford U.Pr.	1949	Hogner, Nils	30-50	*
Gall, Alice C.	Here and There and Everywhere (1st {std}, 12mo, 56p, 2-color, DJ/1.50)	Oxford U. Pr.	1950	Hogner, Nils	30-50	
Balch, Glenn	Indian Paint (1st, 8vo, 244p, b/w, DJ/2.00)	Crowell	(1942)	Hogner, Nils	30-50	*
Hogner, Dorothy	Snowflake (1st, 12mo, 31p, color, DJ/1.75)	NY: Oxford U.Pr.	1952	Hogner, Nils	30-50	
Gall, Alice C.	Winter Flight (1st, 8vo, 108p, fp b/w, pep, DJ/2.50)	Oxford U. Pr.	1949	Hogner, Nils	25-40	
Leodhas, Sorche	Always Room for One More (1st {std}, ob8vo, [31]p, 2-color, DJ/3.00, CM)	Holt, Rinehart	(1965)	Hogrogian, Nonny	100-160	R*
Fisher, Aileen	Arbor Day (1st, 8vo, [40]p, 1-color, DJ/2.95)	Crowell	(1965)	Hogrogian, Nonny	25-45	
Yulya	Bears are Sleeping (1st, ob12mo, [30]p, blue cl, color, DJ)	Scribner	(1967)	Hogrogian, Nonny	25-40	
DeRegniers, Beatrice	Day Everybody Cried (1st, ob12mo, [32]p, ipcb, 2-color, cep, DJ/2.50)	Viking	(1967)	Hogrogian, Nonny	30-50	
Stephens, James	Deidre (1st {std}, 8vo, 202p, b/w, DJ/5.95)	Macmillan	(1970)	Hogrogian, Nonny	25-45	
Bancroft, Henreitta	Down Come the Leaves (1st, ob8vo, [37]p, 2-color, DJ)	Crowell	(1961)	Hogrogian, Nonny	30-45	
Haviland, Virginia	Favorite Fairy Tales Told in Greece (1st {std}, 8vo, 90p, color, DJ/3.25)	Little/Brown	1970	Hogrogian, Nonny	50-85	
Singer, Isaac B.	Fearsome Inn (1st, 8vo, [46]p, color, DJ, NH)	Scribner	(1967)	Hogrogian, Nonny	40-70	
Leodhas, Sorche	Gaelic Ghosts (1st {std}, lg8vo, 110p, green bds, woodcuts, DJ/3.50)	Holt, Rinehart	(1963)	Hogrogian, Nonny	40-65	
Leodhas, Sorche	Ghosts Go Haunting (1st {std}, lg8vo, 128p, blue bds, b/w, DJ/3.75)	Holt, Rinehart	(1965)	Hogrogian, Nonny	30-50	
Burns, Robert	Hand in Hand We'll Go (1st, 8vo, 28p, fp 2-color, pep, DJ/3.75)	Crowell	(1965)	Hogrogian, Nonny	50-80	R
Hautzig, Esther	In School (1st {std}, sm4to, [36]p, color, DJ/4.95)	Macmillan	(1969)	Hogrogian, Nonny	30-50	*
Meredith, Nicolete	King of the Kerry Fair (1st, 8vo, 56p, 1-color woodcuts, DJ/2.50)	Crowell	(1960)	Hogrogian, Nonny	40-65	
Schiller, Barbara	Kitchen Knight (1st {std}, 8vo, 64p, color, DJ/3.50)	Holt, Rinehart	(1965)	Hogrogian, Nonny	30-45	
Tashjian, Virginia	Once there Was and Was Not (1st {std}, 8vo, 85p, color, DJ/3.50)	Little/Brown	(1966)	Hogrogian, Nonny	30-50	
Whitney, Thomas	Prince Ivan, Firebird & Gray Wolf (1st, ob4to, [32]p, color, cep, DJ)	Scribner	1968	Hogrogian, Nonny	40-65	
Hogrogian, Nonny	Renowned History/Little Red Riding Hood (1st, 24mo, [32]p, color, DJ/2.95)	Crowell	(1967)	Hogrogian, Nonny	30-50	
Fontane, Theodore	Sir Ribbeck of Ribbeck... (1st {std}, ob8vo, ibds, [32]p, color, DJ/4.95)	Macmillan	(1969)	Hogrogian, Nonny	30-50	
Schwartz, Evgeny	Tale of Stolen Time (1st, ob8vo, [32]p, 1-color, dep, DJ/3.75)	Prentice-Hall	1966	Hogrogian, Nonny	25-45	
Hogrogian, Nonny	Thirteen Days of Yule (1st, sq8vo, [31]p, gilt, fp color, cep, DJ/3.95)	Crowell	(1968)	Hogrogian, Nonny	30-50	
Hamilton, Virginia	Time-Ago Tales of Jahdu (1st {std}, 8vo, 61p, b/w, cep, DJ/4.50)	Macmillan	(1969)	Hogrogian, Nonny	25-40	
Whitney, Thomas	Vasilisa the Beautiful (1st {std}, 8vo, [32]p, color, dep, DJ/4.95)	Macmillan	(1970)	Hogrogian, Nonny	40-70	R
O'Neill, Mary	White Palace (1st, 4to, aqua cl, [48]p, fp color, DJ/3.95)	Crowell	(1966)	Hogrogian, Nonny	40-65	
Holberg, Ruth	Bells of Amsterdam (1st, sm4to, 88p, gilt, fp color, DJ/2.00)	Crowell	1940	Holberg, Richard	45-60	
Curtis, Alice B.	Children of the Prairie (1st, 8vo, 198p, color title pg, b/w, DJ/2.00)	Crowell	(1938)	Holberg, Richard	30-45	
Palmer, Elizabeth	Give Me a River (1st, 8vo, 152p, dp color, DJ/1.75)	Scribner	1939	Holberg, Richard	40-65	
Holberg, Ruth	Gloucester Boy (1st {std}, 8vo, [48]p, ipcb, 2-color, pep, DJ/1.00)	Doubleday/Doran	1940	Holberg, Richard	40-65	
Holberg, Ruth	Hester and Timothy, Pioneers (1st {std}, 8vo, 128p, color, pep, DJ/1.50)	Doubleday/Doran	1937	Holberg, Richard	40-65	
Holberg, Ruth	Mitty and Mr. Syrup (1st {std}, 8vo, ibds, [32]p, color, pep, DJ/1.00)	Doubleday/Doran	1935	Holberg, Richard	40-65	
Holberg, Ruth	Mitty on Mr. Syrup's Farm (1st {std}, 4to, ibds, [32]p, color, pep, DJ/1.00)	Doubleday/Doran	1936	Holberg, Richard	40-65	
Holberg, Ruth	Not So Long Ago (1st, 8vo, 131p, dp color, fp b/w, pep, DJ/1.75)	Crowell	1939	Holberg, Richard	35-50	
Holberg, Ruth	Oh Susannah (1st {std}, 8vo, 108p, color, pep, DJ/1.50)	Doubleday/Doran	1939	Holberg, Richard	40-65	
Daniel, Hawthorne	Seal of the White Buddha (1st, 8vo, 271p, col frn, 6pl, DJ/2.00)	Coward	1928	Holberg, Richard	35-50	
Palmer, Elizabeth	Up the River to Danger (1st, 8vo, 183p, b/w, DJ/1.75)	Scribner	1940	Holberg, Richard	25-40	
Flack, Marjorie	Wait for William (1st, ob8vo, ibds, [33]p, color, pep, DJ/1.00)	Houghton	1935	Holberg, Richard	45-70	
Holberg, Ruth	Wee Brigit O'Toole (1st {std}, 8vo, ibds, [32]p, color, DJ/1.00)	Doubleday/Doran	1938	Holberg, Richard	40-70	
Carr, Mary J.	Young Mac of Fort Vancouver (1st, 8vo, 238p, p-o, color, DJ/2.00, NH)	Crowell	1940	Holberg, Richard	45-70	
Holbrook, Ruth	Katy's Quilt (1st {std}, sm4to, [78]p, color, dep, DJ/2.00)	Doubleday/Doran	1940	Holbrook, Ruth	65-90	
Christie, Ella R.	Fairy Tales from England (1st, 8vo, teg, uncut, 232p, 6pl)	L: T.F. Unwin	1896	Holland, Ada	60-100	
Christie, Ella R.	Fairy Tales from Finland (1st, 12mo, 232p, teg, uncut, b/w)	L: T.F. Unwin	1896	Holland, Ada	60-100	
Carroll, Lewis	Alice in Wonderland (1st, sq8vo, ibds, [32]p, color, pep)	Rand/McNally	1951	Holland, Janice	35-60	*
Quigley, Lillian	Blind Men and the Elephant (1st, sm4to, [25]p, color, DJ/2.95)	Scribner	(1959)	Holland, Janice	25-45	
Coblentz, Catherine	Blue Cat of Castle Town (1st {std}, lg8vo, 123p, b/w, pep, DJ/2.75, NH)	Longmans	1949	Holland, Janice	70-120	R
Johnson, Siddie	Cat Hotel (1st {std}, 8vo, 132p, b/w, DJ/2.50)	Longmans	1955	Holland, Janice	30-50	
Watkin, Lawrence	Thomas Jones & his Nine Lives (1st, 8vo, 102p, b/w, pep, DJ/1.50)	Harcourt	1941	Holland, Janice	25-40	
Chambers, Maria C.	Three Kings (1st, 8vo, 38p, color, DJ/1.50)	NY: Oxford U.Pr.	1946	Holland, Janice	25-45	
Bohanon, Paul	Wind and Arabella (1st, 8vo, 70p, 5 fp b/w, DJ/2.00)	Oxford U. Pr.	1947	Holland, Janice	45-70	
Holland, Marion	Big Ball of String (1st {std}, lg8vo, 64p, ibds, fp 2-color, DJ)	Beginner Books	(1958)	Holland, Marion	75-120	
Holland, Marion	Billy Had a System (1st {std}, 8vo, uncut, 184p, b/w, pep, DJ/2.50)	Knopf	1952	Holland, Marion	50-80	*
Holland, Marion	Billy's Clubhouse (1st {std}, 8vo, uncut, 180p, b/w, pep, DJ/2.50)	Knopf	1955	Holland, Marion	50-80	*
Holland, Marion	No Children, No Pets (1st {std}, 8vo, 182p, fp b/w, DJ/2.50)	Knopf	1956	Holland, Marion	30-50	*
Holland, Marion	Teddy's Camp Out (1st, 8vo, 60p, b/w, cep, DJ/2.75)	Knopf	(1963)	Holland, Marion	40-65	*
Holland, Marion	Tree for Teddy (1st {std}, 8vo, 60p, b/w, DJ/2.00)	Knopf	1957	Holland, Marion	80-125	*
Ritter, Elizabeth	You Never Can Tell (1st, lg sq8vo, ibds, [28]p, fp color, pep, DJ/0.50)	Grosset/Dunlap	(1947)	Holland, Marion	80-120	
Memling, Carl	Amazing Advens/Dennis the Menace (1st, 4to, ibds, [62]p, color, pep, DJ/1.95)	Random	(1961)	Holley, Lee	30-50	*
Leavitt, Ann H.	Three Little Indians (1st, 8vo, ipcb, [36]p, fp color, DJ/0.50)	Rand/McNally	1937	Holling, H.C. & L.	40-70	

AUTHOR	TITLE	PUBLISHER	DATE	ARTIST	PRICE	LC
Crawford, Phyllis	Blot: Little City Cat (1st, ob4to, ibds, 56p, b/w)	Cape/Smith	1930	Holling, Holling C.	80-120	
Holling, Holling C.	Book of Cowboys (1st, 4to, orange cl, pep, 126p, color, DJ/1.25)	Platt/Munk	(1936)	Holling, Holling C.	60-90	
Holling, Holling C.	Book of Indians (1st, 4to, 125p, pep, 6cp, DJ/1.25)	Platt/Munk	(1935)	Holling, Holling C.	80-130	
Piper, Watty	Children of Other Lands (1st, lg4to, [85]p, p-o, orange cl, fp color)	Platt/Munk	(1933)	Holling, Holling C.	60-90	
Holling, Holling C.	Choo-Me-Shoo (1st {std}, 8vo, ibds, color, pep)	Volland	(1928)	Holling, Holling C.	65-90	
Holling, Holling C.	Claws of the Thunderbird (1st, 8vo, 128p, gilt, fp color, pep)	Volland	(1928)	Holling, Holling C.	60-100	
Holling, Holling C.	Little Bye-and-Bye (1st, 12mo, [40]p, ibds, color, pep)	Volland	(1926)	Holling, Holling C.	60-90	
Holling, Holling C.	Little Buffalo Boy (1st, sq8vo, ibds, [42]p, color, pep, DJ/1.00)	Garden City	(1939)	Holling, Holling C.	70-120	
Piper, Watty	Little Folks of Other Lands (1st, lg4to, [80]p, gilt, p-o, color, pep)	Platt/Munk	(1929)	Holling, Holling C.	70-100	
Holling, H.C. (ed)	Magic Story Tree (1st, lg4to, 83p, fp color, cep, DJ/2.95)	Platt/Munk	(1964)	Holling, Holling C.	30-45	
Holling, Holling C.	Minn of the Mississippi (1st, 4to, 85p, yellow cl, col, pep, DJ/3.00, NH)	Houghton	1951	Holling, Holling C.	80-135	
Holling, Holling C.	Paddle to the Sea (1st, 4to, beige cl, [63]p, color, pep, DJ/2.50, CH)	Houghton	1941	Holling, Holling C.	200-300	R
Holling, Holling C.	Pagoo (1st, 4to, 86p, green cl, pep, color, DJ/3.00)	Houghton	1957	Holling, Holling C.	50-90	
Piper, Watty (ed)	Road in Storyland (1st, lg4to, [106]p, color, pep)	Platt/Munk	(1932)	Holling, Holling C.	50-85	
Holling, Holling C.	Rocky Billy (1st, 8vo, blue cl, 148p, color, pep)	Macmillan	1928	Holling, Holling C.	55-80	
Holling, Holling C.	Rum-Tum-Tummy... (sq8vo, ibds, unpag, color)	Saalfield	1936	Holling, Holling C.	60-100	
Holling, Holling C.	Seabird (1st, 4to, 58p, blue cl, color, pep, DJ/3.00, NH)	Houghton	1948	Holling, Holling C.	80-125	
Holling, Holling C.	Tree in the Trail (1st, 4to, [70]p, 35 fp color, pep, DJ/3.00)	Houghton	1942	Holling, Holling C.	60-100	
Holling, Holling C.	Twins Who Flew Around the World (1st, lg4to, gilt, 67p, color, pep)	Platt/Munk	(1931)	Holling, Holling C.	70-125	
Bennett, Rowena B.	Around a Toadstool Table (1st, 8vo, ibds, 109p, fp b/w)	Chi: Rockwell	1930	Holling, Lucille W.	65-90	
Bailey, Alice C.	Kimo (1st, lg8vo, ibds, 96p, color, pep)	Volland	(1928)	Holling, Lucille W.	50-75	
Adoff, Arnold (ed)	Black Out Loud (1st {std}, lg8vo, 86p, b/w, DJ/4.95)	Macmillan	(1970)	Hollingsworth, Alvin	25-40	
Tietjens, Eunice H.	Boy of the Desert (1st, 8vo, 182p, green cl, dep, fp b/w)	Coward	1928	Hollingsworth, W.	30-50	*
Coolidge, Olivia	Maid of Artemis (1st {std}, 8vo, 132p, b/w, DJ/3.50)	Houghton	1969	Holmes, Bea	20-30	*
Snyder, Zilpha K.	Black and Blue Magic (1st {std}, 8vo, 186p, b/w, DJ/3.95)	Atheneum	1966	Holtan, Gene	40-65	
Agle, Nan H.	Three Boys & the Remarkable Cow (1st, sm8vo, 127p, b/w, pep, DJ/2.00)	Scribner	(1952)	Honigman, Marion	30-50	
Agle, Nan H.	Three Boys and a Lighthouse (1st, sm8vo, 100p, b/w, pep, DJ/2.00)	Scribner	(1951)	Honigman, Marion	30-50	
Agle, Nan H.	Three Boys and a Tugboat (1st, sm8vo, 121p, b/w, DJ/2.25)	Scribner	(1953)	Honigman, Marion	25-40	
Finger, Charles J.	Bushrangers (1st, 8vo, 216p, color, pep)	McBride	1924	Honore, Paul	50-80	
Finger, Charles J.	Frontier Ballads (1st {std}, lg8vo, 181p, 3cp, b/w, pep)	Doubleday/Doran	1927	Honore, Paul	60-90	*
Finger, Charles (ed)	Heroes from Hakluyt (1st {std}, 4to, 331p, 3-color woodcuts)	Henry Holt & Co.	(1928)	Honore, Paul	30-50	
Finger, Charles J.	Highwaymen... (1st, lg8vo, 258p, tan cl, uncut, 8cp, pep)	McBride	1923	Honore, Paul	50-90	*
Finger, Charles J.	Romantic Rascals (1st, lg8vo, 251p, uncut, 8cp, pep)	McBride	1927	Honore, Paul	40-65	
Finger, Charles J.	Spreading Stain (1st {std}, 8vo, 245p, cep, col frn by...)	Doubleday/Page	1927	Honore, Paul	30-50	
Finger, Charles J.	Tales from Silver Lands (1st {std}, lg8vo, 225p, 10cp, pep, NM)	Doubleday/Page	1924	Honore, Paul	70-100	R
Finger, Charles J.	Tales Worth Telling (1st, lg8vo, 250p, orange cl, pep, 10cp)	Century	1927	Honore, Paul	45-70	
Haggard, H. Rider	Lysbeth: Tale of the Dutch (1st UK, 8vo, 496p, gilt, 26pl, cep)	L: Longmans	1901	Hood, G.P. Jacomb	100-165	
Riggs, Renee	Animal Stories from Eskimo Land (1st, 12mo, 113p, 2-color)	Stokes	1923	Hood, George	30-45	
Eells, Elsie S.	Brazilian Fairy Book (1st, 8vo, 193p, gilt, 6cp, pep)	Stokes	1926	Hood, George	70-100	
Stroebe, C. (ed.)	Danish Fairy Book (1st, 8vo, blue cl, 218p, 6cp, pep)	Stokes	(1922)	Hood, George	70-120	
Martens, Frederick H.	Fairy Tales from Orient (1st, 8vo, 293p, blue cl, 4cp, pep)	McBride	1923	Hood, George	60-90	
Curtin, Jeremiah	Fairy Tales of Eastern Europe (1st, 8vo, 259p, 4cp)	McBride	1914	Hood, George	60-90	
Allen, Frank W.	Golden Road (1st, 8vo, 228p, gilt, teg, col frn, 2pl, pep)	Wessels/Bissell	1910	Hood, George	40-60	
Friedlander, Gerald	Jewish Fairy Book (1st, 8vo, 188p, gilt, 8cp, pep)	Stokes	(1920)	Hood, George	55-90	
Irving, Washington	Legends of the Alhambra (1st, lg8vo, 229p, teg, p-o, 8cp, pep)	Lippincott	1909	Hood, George	60-90	
Bindloss, Harold	Lorimer of the Northwest (1st, 12mo, 384p, cvr by...)	Stokes	(1909)	Hood, George	35-60	
Stroebe, C. (ed.)	Norwegian Fairy Book (1st, 8vo, 304p, 6cp, pep)	Stokes	(1922)	Hood, George	50-90	
Hawthorne, Julian	Rumpty-Dudget's Tower (1st, 8vo, 72p, col frn)	Stokes	1924	Hood, George	30-50	
Segovia, Gertrudis	Spanish Fairy Book (1st, 8vo, 321p, gilt, 8cp, pep)	Stokes	(1918)	Hood, George	100-165	
Lucas, E.V.	The Slowcoach (1st AM, 8vo, 367p, p-o, frn by...)	Macmillan	1910	Hood, George	40-60	
Snell, Roy J.	Told Beneath the Northern Lights (1st, 8vo, 238p, col frn, 4 b/w)	Little/Brown	1925	Hooper, Florence	70-100	
Otis, James	Boy's Revolt (1st, 8vo, 193p, 16pl)	Estes & Lauriat	(1894)	Hooper, Will P.	40-70	
Bouvet, Marguerite	Child of Tuscany (1st, 8vo, 207p, blue cl, 15pl, cep)	McClurg	1895	Hooper, Will P.	25-45	
Stevenson, Rbt. L.	Child's Garden of Verses (16mo, bds, p-o, 127p, color)	Altemus	(1921)	Hoopes, Margaret	40-65	
Almond, Linda S.	Peter Rabbit and the Tinybits (24mo, 62p, cloth, color)	Platt/Munk	(1935)	Hoopes, Margaret	50-80	*
Kauffman, Ruth	Three Little Kittens (12mo, blue cl, 63p, p-o, color, pep)	Platt/Munk	(1935)	Hoopes, Margaret	50-80	
Almond, Linda S.	When Peter Rabbit Went a-Fishing (24mo, ibds, p-o, 64p, 25 color, pep)	Altemus	(1923)	Hoopes, Margaret	30-50	
Tracy, Louis	American Emperor (1st AM, sm8vo, 424p, tan/gilt, 16pl)	Putnam	1897	Hope, E.S.	60-90	
Corbett, Elizabeth T.	3 Wise Old Couples (1st, 4to, ipcb, unpag, 15 chromos)	L: Cassell	(1881)	Hopkins, Everard	90-120	*
Sterne, Laurence	Sentimental Journey/France & Italy (1st, 4to, gilt, teg, 12 ticp)	Putnam	1910	Hopkins, Everard	90-120	
Russell, William C.	Tragedy of Ida Noble (1st UK, 8vo, 315p, blue buckram, b/w)	L: Hutchinson	1893	Hopkins, Everard	70-100	
MacDonald, Betty	Nancy and Plum (1st {std}, 8vo, 190p, b/w, DJ/2.50)	Lippincott	(1952)	Hopkins, Hildegarde	150-250	
Hamp, Sidford F.	Coco Bolo (1st, 12mo, 145p, 12pl)	Badger	1911	Hopp, O.	35-60	*
Whitney, A.D.T.	Mother Goose for Grown Folks (1st {new ed}, 12mo, 204p)	Houghton	1898	Hoppin, Augustus	30-50	*
Phipson, Joan	Family Conspiracy (1st AM {std}, 8vo, 224p, blue cl, b/w, DJ/3.50)	Harcourt	(1964)	Horder, Margaret	20-35	
DeJong, Dola	Picture Story of Holland (1st, 4to, [36]p, color, pep, DJ/2.50)	Reynal/Hitchcock	(1946)	Hordyk, Gerard	40-65	
Washburn, Claude C.	Pages from the Book of Paris (1st, 8vo, pcb, p-o, 276p, b/w)	Houghton	1910	Hornby, Lester G.	30-50	
Saunders, Marshall	Alpatok (1st, 12mo, tan cl, 51p, b/w)	L.C. Page	1906	Horne, Diantha W.	25-40	*
Bailey, Carolyn S.	Firelight Stories (1st, sm8vo, 192p, 9pl)	Milton Bradley	1907	Horne, Diantha W.	25-40	*
Johnston, Annie F.	Mildred's Inheritance (1st, 12mo, blue cl, 74p, 10pl)	L.C. Page	1906	Horne, Diantha W.	40-65	
Sharp, Dallas L.	Roof & Meadow (1st, sm8vo, green cl, 281p, b/w)	Century	1904	Horsfall, Bruce	25-45	
Morris, Kenneth	Book of Three Dragons (1st {std}, 4to, gilt, 206p, 8pl, pep)	Longmans	(1930)	Horvath, Ferdinand	90-120	R
Lansing, Marion	Man's Long Climb (1st, 8vo, 154p, b/w, pep, DJ/1.75)	Little/Brown	1933	Horvath, Ferdinand	40-65	*
Lockhart, Caroline	Lady Doc (1st, 8vo, tan cloth, 339p, 4pl)	Lippincott	1912	Hoskins, Gayle	30-50	
Barbour, Ralph H.	Lady Laughter (1st, 8vo, 176p, teg, p-o, 4cp)	Lippincott	1913	Hoskins, Gayle	30-50	*
Brady, Cyrus T.	Little Angel of Canyon Creek (1st, 8vo, 292p, 6pl)	Revell	1914	Hoskins, Gayle	30-50	
Lockhart, Caroline	Man from the Bitter Roots (1st, 8vo, 327p, red/gilt, 3cp)	Lippincott	1915	Hoskins, Gayle	40-65	
Hopkins, Nevil M.	Raccoon Lake Mystery (1st, sm8vo, blue cl, 319p, 4cp)	Lippincott	1917	Hoskins, Gayle	30-50	

AUTHOR	TITLE	PUBLISHER	DATE	ARTIST	PRICE	LC
Hough, Charlotte	Jim Tiger (1st AM, 8vo, 30p, color, DJ/2.00)	Bobbs-Merrill	(1958)	Hough, Charlotte	25-40	
Clark, Ann N.	Desert People (1st, sm4to, 59p, 3-color, DJ/3.00)	Viking	(1962)	Houser, Allan	30-50	
Coatsworth, Eliz.	The Cave (1st, 8vo, 63p, b/w, DJ/2.50)	Viking	1958	Houser, Allan	30-45	
Rhoads, Dorothy	Bright Feather (1st {std}, 8vo, 196p, uncut, pep, col frn, b/w)	Doubleday/Doran	1932	Houser, Lowell	25-45	
Malkus, Alida S.	Dark Star of Itza (1st {std}, 8vo, 217p, brown cl, 6 fp b/w, NH)	Harcourt	(1930)	Houser, Lowell	50-85	*
Housman, Laurence	All-Fellows & Cloak of Friendship (1st, sm8vo, 192p, green cl, 7pl)	L: J. Cape	(1923)	Housman, Laurence	80-125	
Housman, Laurence	All-Fellows... (1st, 12mo, 138p, green/gilt, uncut, 8pl)	L: Kegan Paul	1896	Housman, Laurence	160-220	
N/A	Aucassin & Nicolette (1st, 12mo, 103p, teg, vellum, 4p)	L: J. Murray	(1902)	Housman, Laurence	140-200	
MacDonald, George	Back of the North Wind (1st, 8vo, 378p, gilt, frn & cvr by...)	L: Blackie	(1899)	Housman, Laurence	160-240	
Housman, Laurence	Bethlehem (1st, 8vo, green/gilt, 85p, cvr by...)	L: Macmillan	1902	Housman, Laurence	100-170	
Housman, Laurence	Blue Moon (1st, 8vo, 210p, teg, blue/gilt, 9pl)	L: J. Murray	1904	Housman, Laurence	120-170	
Housman, Laurence	Cloak of Friendship (1st, 8vo, 192p, buckram/gilt, uncut, cvr by...)	L: J. Murray	1905	Housman, Laurence	90-120	
Hinkson, Katharine	Cuckoo Songs (1st, 12mo, brown/gilt, 105p, cvr & title page by....)	L: E. Mathews	1894	Housman, Laurence	120-180	
Housman, Laurence	Doorway in Fairyland (1st, 8vo, 220p, 14pl)	L: J. Cape	(1922)	Housman, Laurence	140-225	
Barlow, Jane	End of Elfintown (1st, 8vo, gilt, uncut, 77p, AEG, 8pl)	L: Macmillan	1894	Housman, Laurence	350-500	
Housman, Laurence	Farm in Fairyland (1st [1st bk.], 8vo, gilt, 160p, 12pl)	L: Kegan Paul	1894	Housman, Laurence	300-450	
Housman, Laurence	Farm in Fairyland (1st AM, 8vo, teg, 160p, 12pl)	Dodd	1894	Housman, Laurence	200-300	
Housman, Laurence	Field of Clover (1st, 12mo, green/gilt, uncut, 148p, 11pl)	L: Kegan Paul	1898	Housman, Laurence	250-400	
Housman, Laurence	Field of Clover (1st AM, sm8vo, gilt, 148p, teg, 11pl)	NY: J. Lane	1902	Housman, Laurence	200-300	
Meynell, Alice	Flower of the Mind (1st, sm8vo, green/gilt, 348p, cvr by...)	L: Richards	1897	Housman, Laurence	70-100	
Rossetti, Christina	Goblin Market (1st, sm8vo, AEG, 63p, olive/gilt, 12pl)	L: Macmillan	1893	Housman, Laurence	500-700	
Housman, Laurence	Green Arras (1st, 8vo, green/gilt, 90p, uncut, 5pl)	L: John Lane	1896	Housman, Laurence	180-240	
MacDonald, George	Gutta-Percha Willie (1st, 12mo, 212p, blue/gilt, cvr by...)	L: Blackie	[1900]	Housman, Laurence	100-165	
Housman, Laurence	House of Joy (1st, 8vo, 181p, gilt, uncut, 9pl)	L: Kegan Paul	1895	Housman, Laurence	180-250	
Meredith, George	Jump to Glory Jane (1st, 8vo, ipcb, teg, designs by...)	L: Swan	1892	Housman, Laurence	120-200	
Housman, Laurence	Little Land (1st, 8vo, 97p, ipcb, uncut, gilt, 4pl)	L: Richards	1899	Housman, Laurence	200-300	
Housman, Laurence	Moonshine & Clover (1st, 8vo, 220p, blue/silver)	L: J. Cape	(1922)	Housman, Laurence	80-120	
Nesbit, Edith	Pomander of Verse (1st, sm8vo, gilt, teg, 88p, cvr by..)	J. Lane	1895	Housman, Laurence	130-170	
MacDonald, George	Princess & the Goblin (1st, 8vo, 313p, aqua/gilt, cep, cvr by..)	L: Blackie	1900	Housman, Laurence	125-180	
Housman, Laurence	Prunella (1st, sm8vo, 89p, pink/gilt, teg, frn by...)	L: A.H. Bullen	1906	Housman, Laurence	60-85	
Housman, Laurence	Sabrina Warham (1st AM, sm8vo, 439p, teg, brown/gilt)	Macmillan	1904	Housman, Laurence	100-150	
Shelley, Percy B.	Sensitive Plant (1st, 8vo, gilt, 60p, teg, uncut, 12pl)	L: Aldine House	1898	Housman, Laurence	150-220	
Housman, Laurence	Spikenard (1st AM, sm8vo, 53p, brown pcb, gilt)	Badger	1898	Housman, Laurence	100-165	
Bain, Robert N.	Weird Tales from Northern Seas (1st, 8vo, 201p, blue/gilt, 12pl)	L: Kegan Paul	1893	Housman, Laurence	160-240	
Housman, Clemence	Were-Wolf (1st, sq8vo, 124p, pink cl, uncut, 6pl)	L: John Lane	1896	Housman, Laurence	250-400	
Houston, James A.	Akavak, an Eskimo Journey (1st {std}, 8vo, 75p, fp b/w, DJ/3.25)	Harcourt	(1968)	Houston, James	30-50	R*
Houston, James A.	White Archer, an Eskimo Legend (1st {std}, 8vo, 95p, fp b/w, DJ/3.50)	Harcourt	(1967)	Houston, James	30-50	
Edmondson, Norah M.	Lavender Garden (1st, 8vo, 158p, teg, lavender/gilt, 4cp, pep)	L: Warne	1929	Howard, Charles T.	40-65	
Cornwall, Ian W.	Making of Man (1st, 4to, 63p, 1-color, b/w, DJ, CgM)	L: Phoenix House	(1961)	Howard, M. Maitland	50-85	*
Means, Florence C.	Whispering Girl (1st, 8vo, 225p, col frn, pep, DJ/2.00)	Houghton	1941	Howard, Oscar	20-35	
Holl, Adelaide	Bright, Bright Morning (1st, sm ob4to, [36]p, 2-color, DJ/3.75)	Lothrop, Lee	(1969)	Howard, Rob	25-40	
Buckley, Helen E.	Little Pig in the Cupboard (1st, 4to, [32]p, color, DJ/3.50)	Lothrop, Lee	(1968)	Howard, Rob	30-50	*
Buckley, Helen E.	Wonderful Little Boy (1st, 4to, [31]p, color, DJ/4.50)	Lothrop, Lee	(1970)	Howard, Rob	40-65	
Wasson, Mildred	Bill and Nancy (1st {std}, 8vo, 323p, 1-color, DJ/2.00)	Liveright	(1940)	Howe, Gertrude	30-50	
Quigg, Jane	Crispin's Acres (1st, 8vo, 112p, b/w, DJ/1.50)	NY: Oxford U.Pr.	(1941)	Howe, Gertrude	45-70	
Grey, Eve	Elsa's Secret (1st {std}, 8vo, 174p, b/w, DJ/2.25)	Doubleday	1948	Howe, Gertrude	60-100	*
Bohanon, Paul	Golden Kate (1st, 8vo, gilt, 62p, fp b/w, pep, DJ/1.50)	Oxford U. Pr.	(1943)	Howe, Gertrude	40-65	*
Burgwyn, Mebane	Lucky Mischief (1st, 8vo, 246p, fp b/w, DJ/2.50)	NY: Oxford U.Pr.	1949	Howe, Gertrude	150-225	*
Weber, Lenora M.	Meet the Malones (1st, 8vo, 218p, uncut, fp b/w, DJ/3.00)	Crowell	1943	Howe, Gertrude	60-100	
Arason, Steingrimus	Smoky Bay (1st, 8vo, 189p, b/w, pep, DJ/2.00)	Macmillan	1942	Howe, Gertrude	40-65	
Lang, Don	Strawberry Roan (1st, 8vo, 218p, b/w, DJ/2.00)	NY: Oxford U.Pr.	1946	Howe, Gertrude	30-50	
Dalgliesh, Alice	Three from Greenways (1st, sm8vo, 63p, ibds, b/w, DJ/1.00)	Scribner	1941	Howe, Gertrude	30-50	
Lovelace, Maud H.	Trees Kneel at Christmas (1st {std}, sm8vo, 127p, b/w, pep, DJ/2.50)	Crowell	1951	Howe, Gertrude	140-200	
Raabe, Martha	Little Lost Sioux (1st, 8vo, 30p, p-o, color, pep, DJ/1.25)	Whitman	(1942)	Howe, Oscar	40-70	
Various	Peep into Cat-Land (sq8vo, 32p, ibds)	L: Warne	1890	Howell, C.E.	80-120	
Fritz, Jean	Animals of Dr. Schweitzer (1st, 8vo, [62]p, b/w, DJ/3.00)	Coward	(1958)	Howland, Douglas	20-35	
Hoyland, Rosemary	Ethelbert (1st AM, ob folio, [36]p, 2-color, DJ/2.00)	Knopf	1954	Hoyland, Rosemary	40-70	
Hubbard, Eleanore	Cap that Mother Made (1st, 12mo, ibds, unpag, color)	Volland	(1928)	Hubbard, Eleanore	50-85	
Olcott, Julia	Happy Surprises (1st, 8vo, p-o, gilt, 163p, color, pep)	Whitman	1929	Hubbard, Eleanore	30-50	
Beard, Patten	Pantalette Doll (1st, lg8vo, p-o, 160p, color, pep)	Whitman	(1931)	Hubbard, Eleanore	100-165	
May, Robert	Benny the Bunny Liked Beans (1st {std}, 8vo, [25]p, ibds, color, DJ/0.50)	Knopf	(1940)	Hubbell, Harriet	30-50	
Magruder, Julia	Sunny Southerner (1st, 12mo, 194p, teg, b/w pl)	L.C. Page	1901	Hubbell, Henry S.	25-40	
Carroll, Lewis	Alice in Wonderland (1st, 4to, red/gilt, 180p, 12 ticp, pep)	L: Hodder	[1922]	Hudson, Gwynedd	250-400	
Carroll, Lewis	Alice in Wonderland (1st AM, 8vo, gilt, 181p, 12 ticp, pep)	Dodd	(1922)	Hudson, Gwynedd	250-350	
Barrie, James M.	Peter Pan and Wendy (1st, 4to, 272p, blue/gilt, color)	L: Hodder	[1925]	Hudson, Gwynedd	140-200	
Hudson, Alma	Peter Rabbit & the Fairies (sq12mo, 48p, red bds, p-o, 8cp, DJ/1.00)	Cupples/Leon	(1921)	Hudson, Richard	80-125	
Hudson, Alma	Peter Rabbit in Mother Goose Land (1st, 16mo, red bds, p-o, 48p, color)	Cupples/Leon	(1921)	Hudson, Richard	80-125	
Lewis, Eliz. F.	To Beat a Tiger, One Needs a Brother's Help (1st {std}, 8vo, 215p, DJ/2.95)	Winston	(1956)	Huehnergarth, John	20-35	
MacDonald, L.	Babies' Classics (1st, 4to, 79p, blue/gilt, b/w)	L: Longmans	1904	Hughes, Arthur	120-200	
MacDonald, George	Back of the North Wind (new ed., 12mo, 378p, grey/gilt, cep, b/w)	L: Blackie	[1886]	Hughes, Arthur	60-100	
MacDonald, George	Fairy Tales (1st [new ed.], lg8vo, 435p, gilt, 12 b/w)	L: Fifield	1904	Hughes, Arthur	160-240	
MacDonald, George	Gutta-Percha Willie (1st, 12mo, blue cl, 212p, 8pl by...)	L: Blackie	[1900]	Hughes, Arthur	100-165	
MacDonald, George	Magic Crook (1st, 8vo, teg, 273p, b/w)	L: Fifield	1911	Hughes, Arthur	100-170	
MacDonald, George	Phantastes (1st [new ed], 8vo, 320p, blue/gilt, uncut, teg, 33 b/w)	L: A. Fifield	1905	Hughes, Arthur	300-450	
MacDonald, George	Phantastes (8vo, 320p, blue/gilt, uncut, teg, b/w)	L: Dent	[1910]	Hughes, Arthur	200-300	
MacDonald, George	Princess & the Goblin (1st, 8vo, 313p, aqua/gilt, cep, 30 b/w by..)	L: Blackie	1900	Hughes, Arthur	120-200	
Rossetti, Christina	Sing Song (1st [new ed.], 12mo, AEG, 135p, gilt, b/w)	L: Macmillan	1893	Hughes, Arthur	120-200	
Matheson, Annie	As Months Go By (4to, ibds, fp color)	L: R. Tuck	[1900]	Hughes, E.R.	180-250	

AUTHOR	TITLE	PUBLISHER	DATE	ARTIST	PRICE	LC
Meader, Stephen W.	Muddy Road to Glory (1st {std}, 8vo, 190p, b/w, DJ/3.50)	Harcourt	(1963)	Hughes, George	80-125	
Hughes, Shirley	Lucy & Tom's Day (1st, ob4to, tan cl, [27]p, fp color, DJ/2.75)	W.R. Scott	(1960)	Hughes, Shirley	40-65	
Morgan, Helen	Meet Mary Kate (1st, 8vo, 61p, DJ)	L: Faber	1963	Hughes, Shirley	40-65	*
Softly, Barbara	Place Mill (1st AM, 8vo, 190p, b/w, DJ/3.25)	St. Martin's	1963	Hughes, Shirley	20-30	*
Softly, Barbara	Plain Jane (1st AM, 8vo, 256p, b/w, DJ/3.25)	St. Martin's	1962	Hughes, Shirley	20-30	
Baker, Margaret	Porterhouse Major (1st AM, 8vo, 116p, b/w, DJ/3.95)	Prentice-Hall	(1967)	Hughes, Shirley	20-35	
Morgan, Helen	Satchkin Patchkin (1st AM, 8vo, 64p, fp b/w, DJ/3.95)	Macrae Smith	(1970)	Hughes, Shirley	70-100	
Parish, Peggy	Willy is my Brother (1st, ob8vo, [48]p, color, DJ/3.50)	W.R. Scott	(1963)	Hughes, Shirley	25-40	*
Horne, Richard H.	Good-Natured Bear (1st {std}, 12mo, 159p, fp b/w, pep)	Macmillan	1927	Hummel, Lisl	30-50	
White, Eliza O.	Green Door (1st, sm8vo, 212p, silhouettes, DJ/2.00)	Houghton	1930	Hummel, Lisl	40-65	
Fyleman, Rose	Letty (1st AM, 8vo, 142p, fp b/w, pep)	Doran	(1927)	Hummel, Lisl	30-50	
Fyleman, Rose	Little Christmas Book (1st, 8vo, orange ibds, pep, 41p, 2-color)	Doran	(1927)	Hummel, Lisl	25-45	
Thomas, Edith M.	Babes of the Nations (1st, lg8vo, [26]p, ibds, 12cp)	Stokes	1889	Humphrey, Maud	500-700	
Humphrey, Maud	Babes of the Year (1st, sq8vo, ibds, 25p, 12cp)	Stokes	1888	Humphrey, Maud	500-800	
Tucker, Elizabeth S.	Baby Folk (1st, 4to, [26]p, ibds, 6cp)	Stokes	(1898)	Humphrey, Maud	250-400	
Cone, Helen G.	Baby Sweethearts (1st, folio, [26]p, ipcb, 12cp)	Stokes	1890	Humphrey, Maud	600-800	R
N/A	Baby's Record (1st, 4to, green/silver, 12cp)	Stokes	1898	Humphrey, Maud	500-700	
Cone, Helen G.	Bonnie Little People (1st, folio, ibds, 12p, 6cp)	Stokes	1890	Humphrey, Maud	500-700	
Humphrey, Maud	Book of Fairy Tales (1st, 4to, ipcb, [30]p, 12cp)	Stokes	1892	Humphrey, Maud	600-850	
Tucker, Elizabeth S.	Book of Pets (1st, 4to, [48]p, ibds, 12cp)	Stokes	1893	Humphrey, Maud	600-800	
N/A	Book of Pets (lg4to, ibds, 12cp by...)	L: Gardner	1897	Humphrey, Maud	425-600	
N/A	Bride's Book (4to, white/gilt, 4cp by...)	Stokes	1900	Humphrey, Maud	350-500	
Thomas, Edith M.	Children of Spring (4to, wraps, 3 chromos)	Stokes	1888	Humphrey, Maud	350-500	
Humphrey, Maud	Children of the Revolution (1st, 4to, ibds, [24]p, 12cp)	Stokes	1900	Humphrey, Maud	600-850	
Perrault, Charles	Favorite Fairy Tales with New Pictures (1st, 4to, ibds, [25]p, color)	Stokes	1892	Humphrey, Maud	350-500	
Humphrey, Maud	Gallant Little Patriots (1st, 4to, ipcb, 12cp)	Stokes	1899	Humphrey, Maud	600-850	
Humphrey, Maud	Golf Girl (1st, 4to, ibds, color)	Stokes	(1899)	Humphrey, Maud	500-700	
MacDonald, George	Light Princess (1st, 8vo, 305p, tan cl, 7 fp b/w)	Putnam	(1893)	Humphrey, Maud	200-300	
Sage, Agnes C.	Little Colonial Dame (1st, 8vo, 197p, 16pl)	Stokes	(1898)	Humphrey, Maud	60-90	
Humphrey, Mabel	Little Continentals (1st, lg4to, ibds, 6cp)	Stokes	1900	Humphrey, Maud	400-600	
Humphrey, Mabel	Little Folk of '76 (1st, 4to, ibds, 6cp)	Stokes	1900	Humphrey, Maud	400-600	
Tucker, Elizabeth S.	Little Grown-Ups (1st, 4to, [74]p, ibds, 12cp)	Stokes	1897	Humphrey, Maud	500-700	
Humphrey, Maud	Little Heroes & Heroines (1st, 4to, ibds, 6cp)	Stokes	1899	Humphrey, Maud	400-600	
Ogden, Ruth	Little Homespun (1st, 12mo, 127p, 15pl)	Stokes	(1897)	Humphrey, Maud	140-200	
Humphrey, Maud	Little Soldiers & Sailors (1st, 4to, ibds, [19]p, 6cp)	Stokes	(1899)	Humphrey, Maud	400-600	
Tucker, Elizabeth S.	Littlest Ones (1st, lg4to, ibds, 12cp)	Stokes	1898	Humphrey, Maud	500-700	
Tucker, Elizabeth S.	Make-Believe Men & Women (1st, 4to, [26]p, ibds, 6cp)	Stokes	1897	Humphrey, Maud	400-600	
Mother Goose	Mother Goose (1st, 4to, ibds, 24cp)	Stokes	1891	Humphrey, Maud	500-750	
Tucker, Elizabeth S.	Old Youngsters (1st, lg4to, ibds, unpag, 6cp)	Stokes	1897	Humphrey, Maud	500-800	
Cone, Helen G.	One, Two, Three, Four (1st, lg8vo, ibds, [14]p, 4cp)	Stokes	1889	Humphrey, Maud	300-450	
Dobson, L.	Poems by Dobson, Locker & Praed (lg4to, p-o, gilt, 6cp)	Stokes	1892	Humphrey, Maud	400-650	
Humphrey, Maud	Rosebud Stories (1st, 8vo, 24p, ipcb, 6cp)	Holiday Pub.	1906	Humphrey, Maud	350-500	
Booth, Maud B.	Sleepy-Time Stories (1st, sm8vo, 177p, teg, gilt, 17pl)	Putnam	1899	Humphrey, Maud	200-300	
Thomas, Edith M.	Tiny Folk of Sunny Days (1st, sm4to, [14]p, 6cp)	Stokes	1889	Humphrey, Maud	300-500	
Thomas, Edith M.	Tiny Folk of Wintery Days (1st, sm4to, [14]p, 6cp)	Stokes	1889	Humphrey, Maud	300-500	
Humphrey, Maud	Tiny Toddlers (1st, folio, [14]p, color, ibds)	Stokes	1890	Humphrey, Maud	650-900	
Thomas, Edith M.	Treasury of Stories, Jingles & Rhymes (1st, lg8vo, p-o, 251p, b/w)	Stokes	(1894)	Humphrey, Maud	300-425	
Cooper, James F.	The Pathfinder (1st, 12mo, 516p, b/w pl)	Macrae Smith	(1926)	Humphreys, Donald	25-40	*
Townsend, John R.	The Intruder (1st AM {std}, 8vo, 220p, b/w, DJ/4.50)	Lippincott	(1969)	Humphreys, Graham	25-40	
Wiggin, Kate D.	Romance of a Christmas Card (1st, 8vo, 123p, teg, p-o, pep, 5cp)	Houghton	1916	Hunt, Alice E.	45-80	
Lippincott, J.W.	Black Wings (1st {std}, sm8vo, 143p, blue cl, col frn, pep, DJ/2.50)	Lippincott	(1947)	Hunt, Lynn B.	50-80	
Montgomery, R.	Broken Fang (1st, 8vo, red cl, 186p, 10cp, pep)	Donohue	(1935)	Hunt, Lynn B.	45-70	*
Lippincott, J.W.	Red Roan Pony (1st, 8vo, 320p, red cl, col frn, 4pl, pep)	Penn	(1934)	Hunt, Lynn B.	55-80	*
McCracken, Harold	Son of the Walrus King (1st {std}, sm4to, 128p, col frn, DJ/2.50)	Lippincott	(1944)	Hunt, Lynn B.	40-65	
Walker, Margaret C.	Lady Hollyhock & her Friends (1st, 8vo, 153p, color)	Baker/Taylor	(1906)	Hunt, Mary I.	80-120	*
Huntington, Ida M.	Peter Pumpkin in Wonderland (1st, lg sq8vo, 264p, 15pl)	Rand/McNally	(1908)	Hunt, Mary I.	80-120	
Hunt, Wolf R.	Dancing Horses of Acoma (1st {std}, lg8vo, 163p, color, DJ/4.50)	World	(1963)	Hunt, Wolf	80-130	R
Leaf, Munro	Boo, Who Used to be Scared of the Dark (1st, 4to, [40]p, ibds, color, pep)	Random	1948	Hunter, Frances T.	100-160	
Johnson, Burges	Childhood (1st, 4to, [88]p, teg, uncut, tip-in photos by...)	Crowell	(1912)	Hunter/Ogden	140-200	R
Hurd, Edith T.	Annie Moran (1st, ob4to, ibds, [32]p, color, pep, DJ/1.25)	Lothrop, Lee	1942	Hurd, Clement	50-80	
Brown, Margaret W.	Bad Little Duckhunter (1st, sm ob4to, ipcb, [30]p, color, pep, DJ/1.50)	W.R. Scott	(1947)	Hurd, Clement	80-130	
Hurd, Edith T.	Benny the Bulldozer (1st, sm ob4to, [33]p, ibds, 1-color, pep, DJ/1.25)	Lothrop, Lee	1947	Hurd, Clement	50-80	
Hurd, Edith T.	Blue Heron Tree (1st {std}, lg8vo, 66p, fp 1-color, DJ/3.95)	Viking	(1968)	Hurd, Clement	25-40	
Brown, Margaret W.	Bumble Bugs & Elephants (1st, lg sq8vo, ibds, [17]p, color)	W.R. Scott	1938	Hurd, Clement	100-160	
Hurd, Edith T.	Caboose (1st, sm ob4to, [33]p, ibds, 1-color, DJ/1.25)	Lothrop, Lee	1950	Hurd, Clement	50-80	
Hurd, Edith T.	Cat from Telegraph Hill (1st, lg8vo, [32]p, ipcb, pep, color, DJ/2.00)	Lothrop, Lee	(1955)	Hurd, Clement	45-75	
Hurd, Edith T.	Catfish (1st {std}, lg8vo, [63]p, color, DJ/3.50)	Viking	(1970)	Hurd, Clement	30-50	
Hurd, Edith T.	Christmas Eve (1st, ob4to, [48]p, ibds, 1-color, DJ/2.95)	Harper	(1962)	Hurd, Clement	30-50	
Hurd, Edith T.	Come and Have Fun (1st, 8vo, 32p, 2-color, cep, DJ/1.95)	Harper	(1962)	Hurd, Clement	30-50	*
Hurd, Edith T.	Day the Sun Danced (1st, 4to, ibds, [30]p, color, DJ/3.50)	Harper	(1965)	Hurd, Clement	30-45	
Hurd, Edith T.	Devil's Tail (1st {std}, 8vo, 216p, t.e. red, fp b/w, DJ/2.75)	Doubleday	(1954)	Hurd, Clement	30-50	
Brown, Margaret W.	Diggers (1st, ob8vo, unpag, ibds, color, DJ/1.95)	Harper	(1960)	Hurd, Clement	60-100	
Hurd, Edith T.	Engine, Engine No. 9 (1st, sm ob4to, [34]p, ibds, 2-color, pep, DJ/1.25)	Lothrop, Lee	1940	Hurd, Clement	70-100	
Hurd, Edith T.	Faraway Christmas (1st, 8vo, blue cl, [33]p, 1-color, pep, DJ/2.50)	Lothrop, Lee	1958	Hurd, Clement	30-50	
Hurd, Edith T.	Follow Tomas (1st, lg8vo, 61p, fp b/w, dep, DJ/2.95)	Dial Press	(1963)	Hurd, Clement	25-40	
Hurd, Edith T.	Fox in a Box (1st {std}, lg8vo, ibds, [36]p, pep, color, DJ/2.50)	Doubleday	(1957)	Hurd, Clement	45-65	
Brown, Margaret W.	Goodnight Moon (1st, ob8vo, ibds, [31]p, color, DJ/1.75)	Harper	1947	Hurd, Clement	90-150	
Gipson, Morrell	Hello Peter (1st {std}, ob8vo, ibds, [31]p, color, dep, DJ/1.25)	Doubleday	(1948)	Hurd, Clement	60-90	

AUTHOR	TITLE	PUBLISHER	DATE	ARTIST	PRICE	LC
Hurd, Edith T.	It's Snowing (1st, 4to, silver cl, unpag, dep, b/w, DJ/2.50)	NY: Sterling	(1957)	Hurd, Clement	60-100	
Hurd, Edith T.	Johnny Lion's Bad Day (1st, 8vo, 64p, ibds, color, DJ/2.50)	Harper	(1970)	Hurd, Clement	30-45	
Hurd, Edith T.	Johnny Lion's Book (1st, 8vo, 64p, ibds, 2-color, DJ/1.95)	Harper	(1965)	Hurd, Clement	20-35	
Hurd, Edith T.	Johnny Littlejohn (1st, narrow ob8vo, unpag, yellow cl, 1-color, DJ/1.75)	Lothrop, Lee	(1957)	Hurd, Clement	60-100	
Hurd, Edith T.	Last One Home is a Green Pig (1st, 8vo, ibds, 63p, color, DJ/1.95)	Harper	1959	Hurd, Clement	30-50	
Siepmann, Jane	Lion on Scott Street (1st, 12mo, ibds, [32]p, 2-color, DJ/1.75)	Oxford U. Pr.	(1952)	Hurd, Clement	25-40	*
Brown, Margaret W.	Little Brass Band (1st, ob8vo, [25]p, ipcb, dep, color, DJ/2.00)	Harper	(1955)	Hurd, Clement	60-100	
Hurd, Edith T.	Little Dog, Dreaming (1st, ob8vo, [31]p, ibds, 2-color, DJ/2.50)	Harper	(1967)	Hurd, Clement	25-45	
Hurd, Clement	Merry Chase (1st {std}, sm4to, [25]p, yellow cl, pep, color, DJ/1.50)	Random	(1941)	Hurd, Clement	50-85	
Preston, Edna M.	Monkey in the Jungle (1st, sq4to, [32]p, fp color, cep, DJ/4.95)	Viking	(1968)	Hurd, Clement	25-40	
Brown, Margaret W.	My World (1st, ob8vo, [34]p, ibds, color, cep, DJ/1.50)	Harper	1949	Hurd, Clement	60-100	
Hurd, Edith T.	Nino & his Fish (1st, lg8vo, [34]p, ipcb, color, pep, DJ/2.00)	Lothrop, Lee	(1954)	Hurd, Clement	30-50	
Hurd, Edith T.	No Funny Business (1st, 8vo, 62p, 3-color, DJ/1.95)	Harper	(1962)	Hurd, Clement	30-45	*
Hurd, Edith T.	Old Silversides (1st, ob4to, [30]p, ibds, 1-color, pep, DJ/1.50)	Lothrop, Lee	1951	Hurd, Clement	50-80	
Brown, Margaret W.	Peppermint Family (1st, ob8vo, [32]p, ipcb, fp 2-color, dep, DJ/1.75)	Harper	(1950)	Hurd, Clement	80-125	
Hurd, Clement	Race Between the Monkey & the Duck (lg8vo, ibds, [31]p, color, DJ)	Wonder Books	(1946)	Hurd, Clement	30-50	*
Brown, Margaret W.	Runaway Bunny (1st {std}, ob8vo, [40]p, color, pep, DJ/1.50)	Harper	(1942)	Hurd, Clement	180-240	R
Hurd, Edith T.	Sky High (1st, sm ob4to, ibds, [34]p, color, pep, DJ/1.25)	Lothrop, Lee	(1941)	Hurd, Clement	60-100	
Hurd, Edith T.	So-So Cat (1st, sm4to, 32p, fp 1-color, cep, DJ/2.95)	Harper	(1964)	Hurd, Clement	30-45	
Hurd, Edith T.	Somebody's House (1st, 4to, 43p, 2-color, DJ/2.00)	Lothrop, Lee	1953	Hurd, Clement	40-65	
Hurd, Edith T.	Speedy, Hook & Ladder Truck (1st, ob4to, ibds, [36]p, 1-color, pep, DJ/1.00)	Lothrop, Lee	1942	Hurd, Clement	50-80	
Hurd, Edith T.	St. George's Day in Williamsburg (1st, ob8vo, wraps, [32]p, fp 1-color)	(Williamsburg)	1952	Hurd, Clement	40-65	
Hurd, Clement	The Race (1st {std}, sm4to, [27]p, yellow cl, color, pep, DJ/1.50)	Random	(1940)	Hurd, Clement	50-80	
Hurd, Edith T.	Toughy & his Trailer Truck (1st, ob4to, ibds, [34]p, pep, 1-color, DJ/1.25)	Lothrop, Lee	1948	Hurd, Clement	50-80	
Hurd, Edith T.	What Whale? Where? (1st, ob8vo, [44]p, 1-color, cep, DJ/2.95)	Harper	(1966)	Hurd, Clement	25-40	
Valens, Evan G.	Wild Fire (1st {std}, 4to, [32]p, color, DJ/3.75)	World	1963	Hurd, Clement	30-50	
Hurd, Edith T.	Willy's Farm (1st, 4to, 64p, ipcb, color, pep, DJ/2.00)	Lothrop, Lee	(1949)	Hurd, Clement	50-80	
Valens, Evan G.	Wingfin & Topple (1st {std}, sm4to, [32]p, b/w, DJ/3.50)	World	(1962)	Hurd, Clement	45-70	R
Stein, Gertrude	World is Round (1st, 4to, 67p, blue bds, pep, DJ/2.50)	W.R. Scott	1939	Hurd, Clement	150-225	R
Twain, Mark	Adventures of Tom Sawyer (1st, 8vo, 264p, p-o, 4cp, pep)	Winston	(1931)	Hurd, Peter	45-70	
Burglon, Nora	Deep Silver (1st, 8vo, 215p, blue cl, 12pl, DJ/2.00)	Houghton	1938	Hurd, Peter	60-90	
Rollins Philip A.	Gone Haywire (1st, 8vo, 269p, 4 dp b/w, pep, DJ/2.00)	Scribner	1939	Hurd, Peter	40-65	
Horgan, Paul	Habit of Empire (1st {this pub}, 8vo, 114p, 8 dp b/w, DJ/2.00)	Harper	(1939)	Hurd, Peter	30-50	
Dodge, Mary Mapes	Hans Brinker (1st, 8vo, 305p, p-o, 4cp, pep)	Garden City	1932	Hurd, Peter	50-80	
Cooper, James F.	Last of the Mohicans (1st, sm8vo, p-o, 437p, 8cp, pep)	McKay	(1928)	Hurd, Peter	40-65	
Hamilton, Elizabeth	P-Zoo (1st, sm ob4to, ipcb, [32]p, 1-color, pep, DJ/1.00)	Coward	(1945)	Hurd, Peter	120-200	*
Horgan, Paul	Return of the Weed (1st {std}, 8vo, 97p, 7 fp b/w, DJ/2.00)	Harper	1936	Hurd, Peter	50-85	
Baldwin, James	Story of Roland (1st, lg8vo, 347p, p-o, 10cp, pep, SC)	Scribner	(1930)	Hurd, Peter	100-165	
Baldwin, James	Story of Siegfried (1st, lg8vo, p-o, 279p, black cl, 6cp, pep, SC)	Scribner	(1931)	Hurd, Peter	100-165	
Meigs, Cornelia L.	Swift Rivers (1st, 8vo, black cl, p-o, 269p, 6cp, pep, DJ/2.00)	Little/Brown	1937	Hurd, Peter	35-60	*
Hart, Jeanne M.	Scareboy (1st, sm4to, [48]p, fp 3-color, DJ/2.50)	Parnassus Press	(1957)	Hurt, Gerhardt	30-45	
Hurter, Albert	He Drew as He Pleased (1st, 4to, [97]p, b/w, DJ/5.00)	Simon/Schuster	1948	Hurter, Albert	600-900	
Graham, Tom	Hike & the Aeroplane (1st, sm8vo, 275p, 4pl)	Stokes	(1912)	Hutchins, Arthur	1200-2000	R
Hutchins, Pat	Clocks and More Clocks (1st {std}, ob4to, [32]p, color, DJ/4.95)	Macmillan	(1970)	Hutchins, Pat	25-40	*
Hutchins, Pat	Rosie's Walk (1st {std}, ob4to, [32]p, color, DJ/3.95)	Macmillan	(1968)	Hutchins, Pat	25-40	
Hutchins, Pat	Surprise Party (1st {std}, ob4to, [32]p, color, DJ/4.50)	Macmillan	(1969)	Hutchins, Pat	25-40	
Hutchins, Pat	Tom and Sam (1st {std}, ob4to, [32]p, color, DJ/4.50)	Macmillan	(1968)	Hutchins, Pat	25-45	
McNeil, Everett	With Kit Carson in the Rockies (1st, 8vo, 333p, 5pl)	Dutton	(1909)	Hutchinson	30-50	
Budd, Lillian	Bell of Kamela (1st, 8vo, 76p, b/w, pep, DJ/2.95)	Rand/McNally	(1960)	Hutchinson, Paula	20-30	
Winterfeld, Henry	Castaways in Lilliput (1st AM {std}, 8vo, 188p, b/w, DJ/3.00)	Harcourt	(1960)	Hutchinson, Wm.	50-80	*
Young, Miriam	Dollar Horse (1st {std}, 8vo, 128p, b/w, DJ/2.75)	Harcourt	(1961)	Hutchinson, Wm.	50-80	
Uchida, Yoshiko	Mik and the Prowler (1st {std}, 8vo, 122p, b/w, DJ/2.95)	Harcourt	(1960)	Hutchinson, Wm.	30-50	
Uchida, Yoshiko	Takao and Grandfather's Sword (1st {std}, 8vo, 127p, b/w, DJ/2.50)	Harcourt	(1958)	Hutchinson, Wm.	30-50	
Goodrich, Arthur F.	Gleam O'Dawn (1st, sm8vo, gilt, 307p, 4pl)	Appleton	1908	Hutchison, D.C.	25-40	
Chambers, Robert	Anne's Bridge (1st, sm8vo, 161p, green/gilt, col frn, 3pl)	Appleton	1914	Hutt, Henry	30-50	
Hutt, Henry	Girls (1st, 4to, [38]p, blue cl, p-o, 16cp)	Scribner	1910	Hutt, Henry	100-165	
Hutt, Henry	Henry Hutt Picture Book (1st, 4to, [84]p, p-o, 10cp)	Century	1908	Hutt, Henry	100-165	
Ford, Paul L.	His Version of It (1st, 8vo, gilt, teg, 109p, 5cp)	Dodd	1905	Hutt, Henry	30-50	
Hough, Emerson	Mississippi Bubble (1st, sm8vo, 452p, gilt, col frn, 5pl)	Bowen-Merrill	(1902)	Hutt, Henry	40-65	
Lewis, Alfred H.	Peggy O'Neal (1st, 12mo, uncut, 494p, 4cp)	Drexel Biddle	1903	Hutt, Henry	35-60	
Chambers, Robert	Police! (1st, sm8vo, 292p, gilt, p-o, cp)	Appleton	1915	Hutt, Henry	25-40	
Hutt, Henry	Rosebuds (1st, 4to, 27p, 11 ticp)	Bobbs-Merrill	(1912)	Hutt, Henry	130-200	*
Hutt, Henry	She Loves Me (1st, sm4to, p-o, [40]p, 8cp)	Bobbs-Merrill	(1911)	Hutt, Henry	120-170	
London, Jack	The Game (1st, 8vo, 182p, teg, uncut, col frn, 5pl)	Macmillan	1905	Hutt, Henry	450-650	
Tarkington, Booth	Two Vanrevels (1st, sm8vo, 351p, green/gilt, teg, 7pl)	McClure	1902	Hutt, Henry	35-60	
Byng, Douglas	Byng Ballads (1st, 8vo, ibds, [48]p, 8 fp color)	L: John Lane	[1932]	Hutton, Clarke	40-65	
White, Eliza O.	I, Autobiography of a Cat (1st, lg8vo, 114p, b/w, pep, DJ/2.00)	Houghton	1941	Hutton, Clarke	50-85	
Hyde, Elizabeth	Little Brothers to the Scouts (12mo, blu cl, p-o, 72p, 10cp)	Rand/McNally	(1917)	Hyde, Elizabeth	30-50	
Clark, G.O.	Moon Babies (1st, ob4to, ibds, 48p, color)	R.H. Russell	1900	Hyde, Helen	200-325	
Hueffer, F.M.	Cinque Ports... (1st, 4to, 403p, teg, buckram/gilt, 14pl)	L: Blackwood	1900	Hyde, William	425-600	
Aubrey, Frank	Devil-Tree of El Dorado (1st, 8vo, brown/gilt, 392p, 8pl)	L: Hutchinson	1896	Hyland/Ellis	170-240	
Nichols, Ruth	A Walk Out of the World (1st {std}, 8vo, 192p, b/w, DJ/4.25)	Harcourt	(1969)	Hyman, Trina S.	30-50	
Johnson, Elizabeth	All in Free but Janey (1st {std}, lg8vo, 31p, color, DJ/3.95)	Little/Brown	(1968)	Hyman, Trina S.	30-50	
Paley, Claudia	Benjamin the True (1st {std}, 8vo, 88p, color, DJ/3.75)	Little/Brown	(1969)	Hyman, Trina S.	30-45	
Trickey, Edna	Billy Celebrates (1st, 8vo, [48]p, wraps, color)	United Church Pr	(1964)	Hyman, Trina S.	60-90	*
Meyers, Susan	Cabin on the Fjord (1st {std}, 8vo, 128p, b/w, DJ/3.50)	Doubleday	(1968)	Hyman, Trina S.	25-45	
O'Faolain, Eileen	Children of the Salmon (1st {std}, 8vo, 349p, fp b/w, DJ/6.75)	Little/Brown	(1965)	Hyman, Trina S.	40-65	
Moore, John T.	Cinnamon Seed (1st, 8vo, 48p, fp 1-color, DJ/3.25)	Houghton	1967	Hyman, Trina S.	50-85	

AUTHOR	TITLE	PUBLISHER	DATE	ARTIST	PRICE	LC
Blair, Peter	Coming of Pout (1st AM {std}, 8vo, 158p, b/w, DJ/4.50)	Little/Brown	1969	Hyman, Trina S.	25-40	
Warburg, Sandol	Curl up Small (1st, sq8vo, 32p, fp 3-color, DJ/3.00)	Houghton	1964	Hyman, Trina S.	40-70	
McGowen, Tom	Dragon Stew (1st {A & std}, 8vo, 31p, color, DJ/1.95)	Follett	(1969)	Hyman, Trina S.	100-165	
Merriam, Eve	Epaminondas (1st {std}, 8vo, 32p, fp 1-color, DJ/3.95)	Follett	(1968)	Hyman, Trina S.	150-220	
Haviland, Virginia	Fairy Tales from Czechoslovakia (1st {std}, lg8vo, 90p, color, DJ/2.95)	Little/Brown	(1966)	Hyman, Trina S.	50-85	
Townsend, J. David	Five Trials of the Pansy Bed (1st {std}, 8vo, 59p, fp b/w, cep, DJ/3.25)	Houghton	1967	Hyman, Trina S.	60-90	
Turnbull, Agnes S.	George (1st, 8vo, 94p, b/w, cep, DJ/3.00)	Houghton	1965	Hyman, Trina S.	40-65	*
Sobol, Donald J.	Greta the Strong (1st {std}, 8vo, 158p, b/w, DJ/4.95)	Follett	(1970)	Hyman, Trina S.	30-45	
Varney, Joyce	Half-Time Gypsy (1st {std}, 8vo, gilt, 239p, fp b/w, DJ/4.50)	Bobbs-Merrill	(1968)	Hyman, Trina S.	50-85	
Hyman, Trina S.	How Six Found Christmas (1st {std}, 8vo, 27p, color, DJ/2.95)	Little/Brown	(1969)	Hyman, Trina S.	50-85	
Sawyer, Ruth	Joy to the World (1st {std}, 8vo, 102p, fp 1-color, DJ/3.95)	Little/Brown	(1966)	Hyman, Trina S.	30-50	
Serwer, Blanche L.	Let's Steal the Moon (1st {std}, lg8vo, gilt, 88p, color, DJ/3.95)	Little/Brown	(1970)	Hyman, Trina S.	60-90	
Tripp, Paul	Little Red Flower (1st {std}, ob8vo, [49]p, 2-color, cep, DJ/3.95)	Doubleday	1968	Hyman, Trina S.	80-125	*
Varney, Joyce	Magic Maker (1st {std}, 8vo, 176p, b/w, DJ/3.95)	Bobbs-Merrill	(1967)	Hyman, Trina S.	40-65	
Poole, Josephine	Moon Eyes (1st AM {std}, 8vo, 151p, b/w, DJ/4.25)	Little/Brown	(1967)	Hyman, Trina S.	40-65	
Bulla, Clyde R.	Moon Singer (1st, sq8vo, [46]p, fp color, DJ/3.95)	Crowell	(1969)	Hyman, Trina S.	70-100	
Greene, Ellin	Pumpkin Giant (1st, lg8vo, [40]p, fp 1-color, cep, DJ/3.95)	Lothrop, Lee	(1970)	Hyman, Trina S.	40-65	
Krasilovsky, Phyllis	Shy Little Girl (1st {std}, 8vo, 31p, color, DJ/3.75)	Houghton	1970	Hyman, Trina S.	60-100	
McGowen, Tom	Sir Machinery (1st {std}, 8vo, 155p, fp b/w, DJ)	Follett	(1970)	Hyman, Trina S.	140-200	
Johnson, Elizabeth	Stuck with Luck (1st {std}, 8vo, 88p, b/w, DJ/3.50)	Little/Brown	(1967)	Hyman, Trina S.	30-50	
Tripp, Paul	Vi-Daylin Book of Minnie the Mump (1st, 4to, 46p, 3-color)	OH: Ross Labs.	(1970)	Hyman, Trina S.	60-90	*
Hunter, Mollie	Walking Stones (1st, 8vo, 143p, ipcb, 7 fp b/w, DJ/3.95)	Harper	(1970)	Hyman, Trina S.	45-70	
Owen, Betty M.	Wreath of Carols (1st, 8vo, 84p, 1-color, cep, DJ/3.95)	Four Winds Pr.	(1966)	Hyman, Trina S.	50-85	*
Akers, Dwight	King's Mule (1st, 8vo, 173p, black/gilt, b/w, pep)	Minton Balch	(1933)	Illingworth, L.G.	30-50	
Hunt, Mabel L.	Cristy at Skippinghills (1st {std}, 8vo, 139p, b/w, DJ/3.00)	Lippincott	(1959)	Ilsley, Velma	20-30	
Agle, Nan H.	Joe Bean (1st, 8vo, 126p, b/w, DJ/3.25)	Seabury Press	(1967)	Ilsley, Velma	35-50	*
Hunt, Mabel L.	Miss Jellytot's Visit (1st {std}, 8vo, 126p, b/w, DJ/2.50)	Lippincott	(1955)	Ilsley, Velma	20-30	*
Hunt, Mabel L.	Stars for Cristy (1st {std}, 8vo, 141p, b/w, DJ/2.75)	Lippincott	(1956)	Ilsley, Velma	25-45	
Caudill, Rebecca	Time for Lissa (1st, 8vo, 139p, blue cl, b/w, DJ/2.95)	Nelson	(1959)	Ilsley, Velma	20-30	
Field, Michael	Tragic Mary (1st, 8vo, 261p, ipcb, cvr by...)	L: G. Bell	1890	Image, Selwyn	200-300	
L'Engle, Madeleine	Twenty-Four Days before Christmas (1st {std}, lg8vo, 56p, color, DJ/3.25)	Ariel	(1964)	Inga	50-85	
Stein, Evaleen	Child Songs of Cheer (1st, sm8vo, 120p, gilt, 4cp, pep)	Lothrop, Lee	(1918)	Inglis, Antoinette	30-50	*
Dyer, Ruth O.	Daytime Story Book (1st, sm8vo, 152p, col frn, pep)	Lothrop, Lee	(1917)	Inglis, Antoinette	30-50	
Brown, Edna	Silver Bear (1st, 12mo, 166p, cp, pep)	Lothrop, Lee	(1921)	Inglis, Antoinette	25-45	*
Dunham, Curtis	Wurra-Wurra (1st, 12mo, green/gilt, 93p, color, pep)	D. Fitzgerald	(1911)	Innes, John	70-120	*
Hardy, Mary E.	Little Ta-Wish (1st, 8vo, 154p, p-o, gilt, b/w)	Rand/McNally	(1914)	Inukai, Kyohei	30-50	
Beyer, Evelyn	All Babies have Mummies & Daddies Just like You (1st, 8vo, [20]p, color)	W.R. Scott	1946	Ipcar, Dahlov	25-40	
Ipcar, Dahlov	Animal Hide & Seek (1st, lg8vo, [36]p, ipcb, color, pep, DJ/1.50)	W.R. Scott	(1947)	Ipcar, Dahlov	50-80	
Ipcar, Dahlov	Black & White (1st, 4to, [34]p, fp color, pep, DJ/2.95)	Knopf	(1963)	Ipcar, Dahlov	45-70	
Ipcar, Dahlov	Bright Barnyard (1st, 4to, [38]p, color, cep, DJ/3.50)	Knopf	(1966)	Ipcar, Dahlov	45-70	
Ipcar, Dahlov	Brown Cow Farm (1st {std}, ob4to, [44]p, color, pep, DJ/2.50)	Doubleday	1959	Ipcar, Dahlov	40-65	
Ipcar, Dahlov	Calico Jungle (1st, 4to, [40]p, color, pep, DJ/3.50)	Knopf	(1965)	Ipcar, Dahlov	40-65	
Ipcar, Dahlov	Cat at Night (1st {std}, 4to, [48]p, color, DJ/3.95)	Doubleday	(1969)	Ipcar, Dahlov	40-65	
Ipcar, Dahlov	Deep Sea Farm (1st, 4to, [36]p, 2-color, pep, DJ/3.00)	Knopf	(1961)	Ipcar, Dahlov	30-50	
McCullough, John	Good Work! What Will You be when You Grow Up? (1st, 4to, [40]p, color)	W.R. Scott	1948	Ipcar, Dahlov	30-45	*
Ipcar, Dahlov	Horses of Long Ago (1st {std}, 4to, 59p, ibds, color, DJ/3.50)	Doubleday	(1965)	Ipcar, Dahlov	30-45	
Ipcar, Dahlov	I Like Animals (1st, ob4to, [36]p, color, pep, DJ/2.95)	Knopf	(1960)	Ipcar, Dahlov	30-45	*
Ipcar, Dahlov	I Love my Anteater with an A (1st, 4to, [40]p, color, DJ/3.25)	Knopf	(1964)	Ipcar, Dahlov	50-75	R
Brown, Margaret W.	Little Fisherman (1st, lg8vo, ibds, [34]p, color, DJ/1.50)	W.R. Scott	1945	Ipcar, Dahlov	80-120	
Ipcar, Dahlov	Lobsterman (1st, ob4to, [36]p, color, pep, DJ/2.95)	Knopf	(1962)	Ipcar, Dahlov	40-65	*
Ipcar, Dahlov	Marvelous Merry-Go-Round (1st {std}, 4to, [48]p, color, DJ/3.95)	Doubleday	(1970)	Ipcar, Dahlov	45-75	
Ipcar, Dahlov	One Horse Farm (1st {std}, ob4to, ibds, [34]p, color, DJ/2.00)	Doubleday	1950	Ipcar, Dahlov	40-65	
Ipcar, Dahlov	Song of the Day Birds & Night Birds (1st {std}, 4to, [60]p, color, DJ/3.75)	Doubleday	(1967)	Ipcar, Dahlov	30-50	
Ipcar, Dahlov	Stripes & Spots (1st {std}, 4to, [44]p, 2-color, pep, DJ/2.50)	Doubleday	(1961)	Ipcar, Dahlov	40-65	
Ipcar, Dahlov	Ten Big Farms (1st, ob4to, [36]p, 3-color, pep, DJ/2.50)	Knopf	(1958)	Ipcar, Dahlov	40-65	
Ipcar, Dahlov	Whisperings & other Things (1st, 4to, [42]p, fp color, pep, DJ/3.50)	Knopf	(1967)	Ipcar, Dahlov	40-65	
Ipcar, Dahlov	Wild and Tame Animals (1st {std}, ob4to, [48]p, fp 2-color, DJ)	Doubleday	(1963)	Ipcar, Dahlov	40-65	
Ipcar, Dahlov	Wild Whirlwind (1st, sm ob4to, [34]p, fp color, pep, DJ/3.95)	Knopf	(1968)	Ipcar, Dahlov	40-65	
Ipcar, Dahlov	Wonderful Egg (1st, ob4to, [44]p, color, pep, DJ/2.50)	Doubleday	(1958)	Ipcar, Dahlov	40-65	
Ipcar, Dahlov	World Full of Horses (1st {std}, ob4to, [32]p, color, pep, DJ/2.50)	Doubleday	1955	Ipcar, Dahlov	40-65	
Stern, Arthur K.	Fairy Quackenbose (1st, 8vo, 123p, picb, uncut, 4pl)	Phi: Brown Bros.	1913	Iredell, R.W.	100-160	*
Hope, Edward	Alice in the Delighted States (1st AM, 8vo, 303p, 12pl, cep)	MacVeagh/Dial	1928	Irvin, Rea	50-90	
Levy, Newman	Opera Guyed (1st, lg8vo, 87p, b/w, DJ)	Knopf	1923	Irvin, Rea	45-80	
Hyde, Fillmore	Ritz Carltons (1st, 8vo, 157p, pcb, b/w)	NY: Macy	1927	Irvin, Rea	40-65	
Wing, Paul	Unsuccessful Elf (1st, ob4to, ibds, [44]p, 6 fp color, pep, DJ/1.50)	Rinehart	(1947)	Irvin, Rea	80-120	
Lambert, Janet	Glory Be! (1st {std}, 8vo, 207p, b/w, DJ/2.00)	Dutton	1943	Ishmael, Woodi	120-180	
Eaton, Jeanette	Lone Journey (1st, sm8vo, 266p, map, b/w, DJ/2.50, NH)	Harcourt	(1944)	Ishmael, Woodi	40-65	
Eaton, Jeanette	Narcissa Whitman (1st {std}, 8vo, 318p, b/w, pep, DJ/2.50)	Harcourt	(1941)	Ishmael, Woodi	30-50	R*
Ilsley, Velma	Pink Hat (1st, ob8vo, [30]p, fp 1-color, DJ/2.00)	Lippincott	(1956)	Islsey, Velma	30-50	*
Wallace, Lew	Chariot Race of Ben-Hur (1st, lg8vo, gilt, 133p, uncut, teg, 4cp)	Harper	1908	Ivanowski, Sigismond	40-60	
Burnett, Frances H.	Land of the Blue Flower (1st, sm8vo, gilt, 67p, teg, col frn)	Moffat	1909	Ivanowski, Sigismond	40-60	
Cooper, Lettice U.	Bear Who was Too Big (1st AM {std}, 4to, 30p, color, DJ/3.50)	Follett	(1966)	Ives, Ruth	30-50	*
Mother Goose	Mother Goose (1st, 32mo, [41]p, color, pep)	Holiday House	(1939)	Ives, Ruth	55-80	*
Schneider, Nina	Let's Look Inside your House (1st, lg8vo, ibds, 39p, color, DJ/1.50)	W.R. Scott	(1948)	Ivins, Barbara	40-60	
Ewing, Juliana H.	Lob Lie-by-the-Fire ([new ed.], 8vo, 144p, b/w, DJ/1.50)	NY: Oxford U.Pr.	(1937)	Ivins, Florence	25-40	*
Moore, Clement C.	Visit from St. Nicholas (1st, 8vo, ibds, 9p, 3 woodcuts by...)	Atl. Monthly Pr.	1921	Ivins, Florence	80-120	
Matsutani, Miyoko	Crane Maiden (1st, 4to, [32]p, color, DJ/3.50)	Parents Mag. Pr.	(1968)	Iwasaki, Chihiro	25-40	
Matsutani, Miyoko	Fisherman Under the Sea (1st, 4to, 32p, color, DJ/3.50)	Parents Mag. Pr.	(1969)	Iwasaki, Chihiro	25-40	

AUTHOR	TITLE	PUBLISHER	DATE	ARTIST	PRICE	LC
Almond, Linda S.	Peter Rabbit Goes-a-Visiting (1st, 16mo, 60p, ibds, p-o)	Altemus	(1921)	J.L.G.	60-90	
Streamer, Col. D.	Ruthless Rhymes for Heartless Homes (1st, sm8vo, 40p, ibds, b/w, pep)	R.H. Russell	1901	J.W.A.	90-120	
Jack, Marian	Adventures of Bulgy Billy (1st, 8vo, p-o, 42p, 12cp, pep)	Jacobs	(1920)	Jack, Marian	40-65	
Carroll, Lewis	Alice in Wonderland (1st, sm4to, green/gilt, teg, 199p, pep, 16 ticp)	L: H. Frowde	[1915]	Jackson, A.E.	250-400	
Carroll, Lewis	Alice in Wonderland (1st AM, lg8vo, 232p, 16 ticp, pep)	Doran	[1915]	Jackson, A.E.	140-220	*
Carroll, Lewis	Alice in Wonderland (1st {this pub}, 8vo, 216p, 8cp, pep)	Garden City	(1930)	Jackson, A.E.	60-100	*
Swift, Jonathan	Gulliver's Travels (1st, 8vo, blue/gilt, AEG, 332p, 6cp, pep)	Nister/Dutton	[1911]	Jackson, A.E.	80-125	
N/A	Tales from Arabian Nights (1st, lg8vo, 340p, 48cp)	L: Ward Lock	1920	Jackson, A.E.	80-120	*
Lamb, Charles	Tales from Shakespeare (1st, 8vo, 472p, blue cl, p-o, 48cp)	L: Ward Lock	1919	Jackson, A.E.	60-90	
Kingsley, Charles	Water Babies (1st, 4to, teg, blue/gilt, 252p, pep, 16 ticp)	L: Oxford U.Pr.	[1920]	Jackson, A.E.	200-300	
Feld, Freidrich	Mystery of Musical Umbrella (1st AM, lg8vo, 83p, 1-color, pep, DJ/1.95)	Random	(1962)	Jackson, Doris	25-45	
Morgan, Alice	Boy Who Brought Christmas (1st, 12mo, 139p, 4cp)	Doubleday/Page	1911	Jackson, John E.	60-100	*
Page, Thomas N.	On Newfound River (1st, sm8vo, 286p, blue/gilt, teg, 4cp)	Scribner	1906	Jackson, John E.	25-45	
Farley, Walter	Larry and the Undersea Raider (1st {std}, 8vo, 225p, b/w, DJ/1.75)	Random	(1942)	Jackson, P.K.	60-90	*
Judson, Clara I.	Abraham Lincoln (1st {this pub}, 8vo, 29p, color, DJ/1.00)	Follett	(1961)	Jackson, Polly	25-45	
Judson, Clara I.	Christopher Columbus (1st, sm8vo, 29p, color, DJ)	Follett	(1960)	Jackson, Polly	25-45	
Judson, Clara I.	Summer Time (1st, lg8vo, [44]p, color, DJ)	Broadman Press	(1948)	Jackson, Polly	30-50	
Otto, Margaret G.	Syrup (1st {std}, 8vo, 159p, b/w, DJ/2.50)	Holt	(1956)	Jackson, Polly	70-100	
Parkman, Francis	Oregon Trail (1st, lg8vo, 388p, black cl, p-o, 4cp, pep)	Winston	(1931)	Jackson, William H.	45-70	
Codrington, Florence	Chapsticks (1st, 8vo, 154p, b/w)	Macmillan	1929	Jacobs, Helen	25-40	*
Griswold, Florence	Hindu Fairy Tales (1st, 8vo, 186p, 4cp)	L: Harrap	1919	Jacobs, Helen	50-80	
Ewald, Carl	Old Willow-Tree & other Stories (1st, 8vo, 157p, p-o, 4cp by...)	Stokes	(1923)	Jacobs, Helen	50-85	
Page, Thomas N.	Captured Santa Claus (1st, 12mo, 81p, teg, 4cp)	Scribner	1902	Jacobs, William L.	35-60	
Stratton-Porter, Gene	The Harvester (1st, 8vo, 564p, 4cp, pep)	Doubleday/Page	1911	Jacobs, William L.	60-90	
Aiken, Joan	Black Hearts in Battersea (1st {std}, 8vo, 240p, b/w, DJ/3.50)	Doubleday	(1964)	Jacques, Robin	50-80	
Manning-Sanders, Ruth	Book of Dwarfs (1st AM {std}, lg8vo, 127p, b/w, DJ/3.50)	Dutton	(1964)	Jacques, Robin	30-50	
Manning-Sanders, Ruth	Book of Ghosts & Goblins (1st AM {std}, lg8vo, 126p, DJ/3.95)	Dutton	(1969)	Jacques, Robin	30-50	
Manning-Sanders, Ruth	Book of Giants (1st {std}, 8vo, 124p, col frn, b/w, DJ)	L: Methuen	1962	Jacques, Robin	30-50	
Manning-Sanders, Ruth	Book of Mermaids (1st AM {std}, 8vo, 127p, b/w, DJ/3.75)	Dutton	(1968)	Jacques, Robin	40-65	
Manning-Sanders, Ruth	Book of Princes and Princesses (1st, lg8vo, 127p, ibds, col frn, b/w)	L: Methuen	(1969)	Jacques, Robin	30-50	
Skirrow, Desmond	Case of the Silver Egg (1st {std}, 8vo, 239p, b/w, DJ/3.95)	Doubleday	(1968)	Jacques, Robin	20-35	*
Durrell, Gerald M.	Donkey Rustlers (1st AM {std}, 8vo, 158p, b/w, DJ/4.50)	Viking	(1968)	Jacques, Robin	25-40	*
Burton, Hester	Flood at Reedsmere (1st AM {std}, 8vo, 204p, b/w, DJ/3.95)	World	(1968)	Jacques, Robin	25-40	
Swift, Jonathan	Gulliver's Travels (1st, 8vo, 195p, fp 2-color, DJ)	L: Oxford U.Pr.	1955	Jacques, Robin	25-45	
Hampden, John	Gypsy Fiddle (1st, 8vo, 159p, fp b/w, DJ/4.50)	World	(1969)	Jacques, Robin	25-40	*
Coatsworth, Eliz.	Hand of Apollo (1st, 8vo, 77p, b/w, DJ/3.00)	Viking	(1965)	Jacques, Robin	20-35	
Thwaite, Ann	House in Turner Square (1st AM {std}, 8vo, 157p, DJ/2.95)	Harcourt	(1961)	Jacques, Robin	25-40	
La Farge, Phyllis	Jane's Silver Chair (1st, 8vo, 31p, fp 2-color, cep, DJ/3.75)	Knopf	(1969)	Jacques, Robin	30-45	*
Jamison, C.V.	Lady Jane (1st {std}, 8vo, pink cl, 224p, fp b/w, DJ/4.25)	Delacorte Pr.	(1969)	Jacques, Robin	20-25	*
Cross, John K.	Man in the Moonlight (1st, 12mo, 316p, fp b/w, DJ)	L: Westhouse	1947	Jacques, Robin	40-65	
Frame, Janet	Mona Minim & the Smell of the Sun (1st AM, 8vo, 94p, fp color, DJ/4.95)	NY: Braziller	(1969)	Jacques, Robin	30-50	
Aiken, Joan	Nightbirds on Nantucket (1st AM {std}, 8vo, 216p, b/w, pep, DJ/3.25)	Doubleday	1966	Jacques, Robin	80-125	R
Forst, S.	Pipkin (1st {std}, lg8vo, 130p, gilt, fp b/w, DJ/4.50)	Delacorte Pr.	(1970)	Jacques, Robin	20-35	
Ritchie, Rita	Pirates of Samarkand (1st {std}, 8vo, 158p, b/w, DJ/3.75)	Norton	(1967)	Jacques, Robin	30-45	
Wahl, Jan	Prince Who was a Fish (1st {std}, 4to, 62p, color, DJ/4.95)	Simon/Schuster	(1970)	Jacques, Robin	25-45	
Fry, Rosalie K.	Snowed Up (1st, 8vo, 124p, b/w, DJ/3.95)	Farrar, Straus	(1970)	Jacques, Robin	25-40	
Norton, Andre	Steel Magic (1st {std}, 8vo, 155p, blue cl, b/w, DJ/3.50)	World	(1965)	Jacques, Robin	100-150	
Fry, Rosalie K.	Whistler in the Mist (1st, 8vo, 139p, b/w, DJ/3.75)	Farrar, Straus	(1968)	Jacques, Robin	25-45	
Jahn, Mary L.	Deedo and Fawny (1st, ob4to, [32]p, color, pep, DJ/2.00)	Oxford U. Pr.	(1940)	Jahn, Mary L.	30-50	*
N/A	Aucassin & Nicolette (1st, 8vo, 91p, teg, vellum/gilt, 12pl)	L: Routledge	1905	James, Gilbert	80-120	
Petrovitch, W.	Hero Tales & Legends of Serbians (1st, 4to, 394p, uncut, teg, 32cp)	L: Harrap	1914	James, Gilbert	80-125	
Omar Khayyam	Rubaiyat of Omar Khayyam (1st, 4to, 203p, teg, 16cp)	L: A&C Black	1909	James, Gilbert	120-200	
Omar Khayyam	Rubaiyat of Omar Khayyam (8vo, teg, 160p, 12pl)	Elder	1909	James, Gilbert	40-60	
Barfield, Arthur O.	Silver Trumpet (1st, 8vo, green cl, 142p, 8cp)	L: Faber/Gwyer	1925	James, Gilbert	40-60	*
Blue, Rose	How Many Blocks is the World? (1st, 4to, [48]p, b/w, DJ/3.50)	F. Watts	(1970)	James, Harold	30-50	*
Hopkins, Lee B. (comp)	I Think I Saw a Snail (1st, 4to, [39]p, b/w, DJ/3.50)	Crown	(1969)	James, Harold	30-50	*
Jackson, Jesse	Tessie (1st, 8vo, 243p, b/w, DJ/4.95)	Harper	1968	James, Harold	30-50	
Weil, Ann Y.	Betsy Ross: Girl of Old Philadelphia (1st {std}, sm8vo, 192p, b/w, DJ/1.75)	Bobbs-Merrill	(1954)	James, Sandra	30-45	
Steele, William O.	John Sevier, Pioneer Boy (1st {std}, sm8vo, 192p, b/w, DJ/1.75)	Bobbs-Merrill	(1953)	James, Sandra	20-30	
Vipont, Elfrida	Lark in the Morn (1st AM, 8vo, 234p, b/w, DJ/2.50)	Bobbs-Merrill	(1951)	James, Sandra	30-50	
Fisher, Aileen	Over the Hills to Nugget (1st {std}, sm8vo, uncut, 121p, fp b/w, DJ/1.75)	Aladdin	1949	James, Sandra	20-35	*
Govan, Christine	Rachel Jackson, Tennessee Girl (1st {std}, 12mo, 192p, b/w, DJ/1.75)	Bobbs-Merrill	(1955)	James, Sandra	70-120	
Lambert, Janet	Star-Spangled Summer (1st {std}, 8vo, 281p, b/w, pep, DJ/2.00)	Dutton	1941	James, Sandra	100-165	
James, Will	All in the Day's Riding (1st, lg8vo, gilt, 251p, b/w, DJ/2.50)	Scribner	1933	James, Will	200-300	
James, Will	Big-Enough (1st, 8vo, 314p, cloth, b/w, DJ/2.50)	Scribner	1931	James, Will	165-250	
James, Will	Book of Cowboy Stories (1st, 8vo, 242p, fp b/w, DJ/2.50)	Scribner	1951	James, Will	70-100	
James, Will	Cow Country (1st, lg8vo, 242p, brown cl, 28pl, DJ)	Scribner	1927	James, Will	165-220	
James, Will	Cowboys North & South (1st [1st bk.], lg8vo, 217p, 51 fp b/w)	Scribner	1924	James, Will	200-300	
James, Will	Dark Horse (1st, 8vo, green cl, col frn, 306p, DJ/2.50)	Scribner	1939	James, Will	200-300	
James, Will	Drifting Cowboy (1st, lg8vo, 241p, 36 fp b/w)	Scribner	1925	James, Will	150-240	
James, Will	Flint Spears (1st, 8vo, 269p, cloth, col frn, DJ/2.50)	Scribner	1938	James, Will	200-300	
James, Will	Home Ranch (1st, 8vo, 346p, b/w, DJ/2.75)	Scribner	1935	James, Will	200-300	
James, Will	Horses I've Known (1st, 8vo, 280p, 29pl, col frn, DJ/2.50)	Scribner	1940	James, Will	150-225	
James, Will	In the Saddle with Uncle Bill (1st, 8vo, 289p, 33pl, DJ/2.00)	Scribner	1935	James, Will	160-235	
James, Will	Lone Cowboy, My Life Story (1st, 8vo, gilt, uncut, 431p, fp b/w, DJ/2.75)	Scribner	1930	James, Will	140-200	
James, Will	Look-See with Uncle Bill (1st, 8vo, 253p, col frn, DJ/2.00)	Scribner	1938	James, Will	140-200	
James, Will	My First Horse (1st, lg ob8vo, blue cl, [45]p, fp color, DJ/1.50)	Scribner	1940	James, Will	120-170	
James, Will	Sand (1st, 8vo, 328p, green cl, fp b/w, DJ/2.50)	Scribner	1929	James, Will	180-250	

AUTHOR	TITLE	PUBLISHER	DATE	ARTIST	PRICE	LC
James, Will	Scorpion: Good Bad Horse (1st, 8vo, 312p, col frn, b/w, DJ/2.50)	Scribner	1936	James, Will	160-240	
James, Will	Smoky the Cow Horse (1st, 8vo, 310p, b/w, PPP, NM)	Scribner	1926	James, Will	160-225	
James, Will	Smoky the Cow Horse (1st {this fmt}, lg8vo, p-o, gilt, 263p, 6cp, pep, SC)	Scribner	(1929)	James, Will	80-120	
James, Will	Sun Up, Tales of the Cow Camps (1st, lg8vo, p-o, 342p, b/w)	Scribner	1931	James, Will	100-165	
James, Will	Three Mustangeers (1st, 8vo, 338p, green cl, fp b/w)	Scribner	1933	James, Will	100-160	
James, Will	Uncle Bill (1st, 8vo, 241p, orange cl, b/w, DJ/2.00)	Scribner	1932	James, Will	75-120	
Mills, Enos A.	Watched by Wild Animals (1st {std}, 8vo, 243p, 4pl by...)	Doubleday/Page	1922	James, Will	50-80	
Mills, Enos A.	Wild Animal Homesteads (1st {std}, 8vo, 259p, b/w pl)	Doubleday/Page	1923	James, Will	60-85	
James, Will	Will James Cowboy Book (1st, 8vo, 158p, col frn, pep)	Scribner	(1938)	James, Will	500-700	
James, Will	Young Cowboy (1st, lg ob8vo, 72p, p-o, 5cp, DJ/1.50)	Scribner	1935	James, Will	300-500	
Jamieson, M.M.	Little Redskins (sq12mo, [54]p, ibds, chromos)	Nister/Dutton	[1910]	Jamieson, M.M.	100-160	
Sechrist, Eliz. H.	Rufie Had a Monkey! (1st, lg8vo, [46]p, red cl, b/w, cep, DJ/1.00)	McKay	(1939)	Janeway, Hestermary	100-170	*
Janosch	Dear Snowman (1st AM {std}, sq4to, [32]p, color, DJ/4.95)	World	1970	Janosch	30-45	
Prelutsky, Jack	Lazy Blackbird (1st AM {std}, ob4to, [28]p, ibds, fp color, DJ/3.95)	Macmillan	(1969)	Janosch	30-45	
Janosch	Thieves & the Raven (1st AM {std}, ob4to, [32]p, 14cp, DJ/4.50)	Macmillan	(1970)	Janosch	60-90	
Johnson, Osa	Pantaloons (1st, 4to, ibds, 56p, color, pep, DJ/1.50)	Random	(1941)	Jansson, Arthur A.	70-120	
Johnson, Osa	Tarnish: True Story of a Lion Cub (1st, lg8vo, ibds, 59p, color, DJ/1.00)	Wilcox/Follett	(1944)	Jansson, Arthur A.	35-50	
Jansson, Tove	Book About Moomin, Mymble & Little My (1st UK, 4to, ibds, color, DJ)	L: E. Benn	(1953)	Jansson, Tove	170-250	
Jansson, Tove	Comet in Moominland (1st UK, sm8vo, 192p, b/w, DJ)	L: E. Benn	(1951)	Jansson, Tove	90-140	
Jansson, Tove	Exploits of Moominpappa (1st UK, 8vo, 159p, b/w, DJ)	L: E. Benn	(1952)	Jansson, Tove	90-140	
Jansson, Tove	Finn Family Moomintroll (1st UK, 12mo, 170p, b/w, map, DJ)	L: E. Benn	1950	Jansson, Tove	180-220	
Jansson, Tove	Moominpappa at Sea (1st AM {std}, 8vo, 192p, grey cl, b/w, DJ/4.00)	H.Z. Walck	1967	Jansson, Tove	80-140	
Jansson, Tove	Who Will Comfort Toffle? (1st UK, 4to, unpag, red cl, color, DJ)	L: E. Benn	(1960)	Jansson, Tove	160-220	
Michael, Maurice	German Folk and Fairy Tales (1st AM {std}, 8vo, 189p, fp b/w, DJ/2.75)	Putnam	(1963)	Jauss, Anne M.	30-45	
Beattie, Janet	In Came Horace (1st, ob8vo, [32]p, b/w, DJ/2.00)	Lippincott	(1954)	Jauss, Anne M.	40-65	
Belting, Natalia	Moon is a Crystal Ball (1st {std}, 8vo, 150p, pep, DJ/2.50)	Bobbs-Merrill	(1952)	Jauss, Anne M.	30-45	*
Parker, Elinor	Some Dogs (1st, sm4to, ibds, 48p, fp color, DJ/2.50)	Pantheon	(1950)	Jauss, Anne M.	25-45	
Belting, Natalia	Three Apples Fell from Heaven (1st {std}, 8vo, gilt, 158p, pep, DJ/2.50)	Bobbs-Merrill	(1953)	Jauss, Anne M.	30-50	
Jacobs, Joseph	Buried Moon (1st {std}, 4to, [31]p, dp 2-color, DJ/3.95)	Bradbury Press	(1969)	Jeffers, Susan	45-65	
Lincoln, Victoria	Everyhow Remarkable (1st, 8vo, [32]p, b/w, cep, DJ/3.50)	Crowell-Collier	(1967)	Jeffers, Susan	20-35	*
Proddow, Penelope	Spirit of Spring (1st {std}, 8vo, 133p, b/w, DJ/4.75)	Bradbury Press	(1970)	Jeffers, Susan	25-40	
Pomerantz, Charlotte	Why You Look Like You... (1st, 8vo, 64p, fp 2-color, cep, DJ/3.95)	Young Scott	(1969)	Jeffers/Wells	40-65	*
Naylor, Phyllis	Galloping Goat & other Stories (1st, 8vo, 112p, fp color, DJ/3.50)	Abingdon Press	(1965)	Jefferson, Robert	20-35	
Martin, Patricia	Trina's Boxcar (1st, 8vo, 112p, fp 3-color, pep, DJ/3.25)	Abingdon Press	(1967)	Jefferson, Robert	25-40	
Diska, Pat	Andy Says... Bonjour! (1st, 4to, [46]p, fp 1-color, pep, DJ/2.50, NYTBI)	Vanguard Press	(1954)	Jenkyns, Chris	30-50	R
Ingoldsby, Thomas	Misadventures at Margate (folio, ibds, 18p, fp color)	L: Eyre/Spotts.	[1885]	Jessop, Ernest M.	70-100	*
Hill, Frederick T.	Washington: Man of Action (1st, 4to, green/gilt, 329p, 27cp)	Appleton	1914	Job	700-1000	
Leodhas, Sorche	Heather and Broom (1st {std}, 8vo, 128p, b/w, DJ/3.25)	Holt, Rinehart	(1960)	Joerns, Consuelo	30-50	
Wister, Annis L.	Happy-Go-Lucky (1st, 8vo, green/gilt, 115p, teg, 4cp)	Lippincott	1906	Johann, P.G.	35-60	*
Montgomery, Lucy M.	Anne of Ingleside (1st, 12mo, 323p, col frn, DJ/2.00)	Stokes	1939	John, Charles V.	75-125	
Mason, Miriam E.	Three Ships Came Sailing In (1st {std}, 8vo, 246p, b/w, DJ/2.50)	Bobbs-Merrill	(1950)	John, Charles V.	40-65	*
MacKaye, David L.	Far Distant Bugle (1st {std}, 8vo, 264p, b/w, DJ/2.50)	Longmans	1948	Johnson, Avery	30-45	*
White, William C.	Mouseknees (1st, sm8vo, 144p, fp b/w, pep, DJ/1.75)	Random	(1939)	Johnson, Avery	60-100	
Davis, Mary G.	Wakaima & the Clay Man (1st {std}, 8vo, 145p, uncut, b/w, pep, DJ/2.00)	Longmans	(1946)	Johnson, Avery	60-90	
Bangs, John K.	Tiddledywink Tales (1st, 12mo, red/gilt, 236p, b/w)	R.H. Russell	1891	Johnson, Charles H.	90-120	
Bangs, John K.	Tiddledywink's Poetry Book (1st, sm8vo, [64]p, b/w)	R.H. Russell	1892	Johnson, Charles H.	75-100	*
Johnson, Crockett	Barnaby (1st, 12mo, 361p, blue cl, b/w, DJ/2.00)	Henry Holt & Co.	1943	Johnson, Crockett	100-175	
Johnson, Crockett	Barnaby & Mr. O'Malley (1st, 12mo, 328p, b/w, DJ/2.00)	Henry Holt & Co.	(1944)	Johnson, Crockett	100-170	
Johnson, Crockett	Blue Ribbon Puppies (1st, 16mo, ibds, 31p, 2-color, DJ/1.50)	Harper	1958	Johnson, Crockett	140-200	
Krauss, Ruth	Carrot Seed (1st, sm8vo, olive cl, [25]p, fp 2-color, cep, DJ/1.00)	Harper	1945	Johnson, Crockett	50-80	
Johnson, Crockett	Ellen's Lion (1st, 8vo, ibds, 62p, 1-color, DJ/1.75)	Harper	(1959)	Johnson, Crockett	30-50	
Johnson, Crockett	Emperor's Gifts (1st {std}, 8vo, [32]p, color, DJ/3.00)	Holt, Rinehart	(1965)	Johnson, Crockett	30-50	
Johnson, Crockett	Frowning Prince (1st, 8vo, 32p, b/w, DJ/1.50)	Harper	(1959)	Johnson, Crockett	30-50	*
Johnson, Crockett	Harold & the Purple Crayon (1st, 16mo, ibds, [60]p, 1-color, DJ/1.50)	Harper	1955	Johnson, Crockett	150-250	R
Johnson, Crockett	Harold at the North Pole (1st, 24mo, 48p, 1-color, DJ/1.50)	Harper	1958	Johnson, Crockett	50-90	
Johnson, Crockett	Harold's ABC (1st, 24mo, [64]p, ibds, 1-color)	Harper	1963	Johnson, Crockett	50-90	
Johnson, Crockett	Harold's Circus (1st, 16mo, ibds, [61]p, 1-color, DJ/1.50)	Harper	1959	Johnson, Crockett	80-130	
Johnson, Crockett	Harold's Fairy Tale (1st, 24mo, [64]p, ibds, 1-color, DJ/1.95)	Harper	1956	Johnson, Crockett	50-85	*
Krauss, Ruth	How to Make an Earthquake (1st {std}, 8vo, 28p, ipcb, 1-color, DJ/1.75)	Harper	(1954)	Johnson, Crockett	50-85	
Krauss, Ruth	Is This You? (1st, 12mo, ipcb, [40]p, 1-color, cep, DJ/1.50)	W.R. Scott	1955	Johnson, Crockett	50-85	R
Johnson, Crockett	Lion's Own Story (1st, 8vo, 63p, ipcb, fp 1-color, DJ/2.50)	Harper	(1963)	Johnson, Crockett	30-50	
Cook, Bernadine	Little Fish that Got Away (1st, sm8vo, unpag, 2-color, DJ/2.25)	W.R. Scott	1956	Johnson, Crockett	40-60	*
Johnson, Crockett	Merry-Go-Round (1st, 8vo, unpag, color, DJ/1.50)	Harper	1958	Johnson, Crockett	30-50	
Branley, Franklyn	Mickey's Magnet (1st, 8vo, [48]p, yellow cl, color, dep, DJ/2.50)	Crowell	1956	Johnson, Crockett	30-50	
Johnson, Crockett	Picture for Harold's Room (1st, 8vo, 64p, ibds, 1-color, DJ/1.95)	Harper	(1960)	Johnson, Crockett	45-70	*
Johnson, Crockett	Terrible Terrifying Toby (1st, lg8vo, unpag, DJ/2.50)	Harper	1957	Johnson, Crockett	60-100	
Johnson, Crockett	Time for Spring (1st, 8vo, 29p, fp b/w, DJ/1.50)	Harper	1957	Johnson, Crockett	30-50	
Johnson, Crockett	Who's Upside Down? (1st, lg8vo, [24]p, ipcb, b/w, DJ/1.75)	W.R. Scott	1952	Johnson, Crockett	60-95	
Brown, Margaret W.	Willie's Adventures (1st, sm8vo, grey cl, 68p, b/w, DJ/2.00)	W.R. Scott	(1954)	Johnson, Crockett	70-120	R*
Chisholm, Arthur M.	Boss of Wind River (1st, sm8vo, blue cl, 341p, 4cp)	Doubleday/Page	1911	Johnson, F. Tenny	30-50	
Kyne, Peter B.	Long Chance (1st, sm8vo, black/gilt, 313p, 4cp)	H.K. Fly	1914	Johnson, F. Tenny	60-100	
Johnson, Abner M.	Memories and other Rhymes (1st, sm8vo, 78p, tip-in b/w pl)	H.K. Fly	(1924)	Johnson, F. Tenny	25-40	
Sinclair, Harry D.	Out of the Silent North (1st, 12mo, 304p, frn by...)	Macaulay	1923	Johnson, F. Tenny	60-90	
Church, Peggy P.	Burro of Angelitos (1st, 4to, ibds, [42]p, color, pep, DJ/2.00)	Suttonhouse	1936	Johnson, Gigi S.	50-80	
Coatsworth, Eliz.	Desert Dan (1st, lg8vo, 61p, fp b/w, DJ/2.50)	Viking	(1960)	Johnson, Harper	30-50	
Bontemps, Arna	Frederick Douglass... (1st {std}, sm8vo, 177p, b/w, DJ/3.00)	Knopf	1959	Johnson, Harper	35-50	
Schlein, Miriam	Home: the Tale of a Mouse (1st, sq8vo, [58]p, fp 2-color, dep, DJ/2.50)	Abelard-Schuman	1958	Johnson, Harper	30-45	
Zirbes, Laura	How Many Bears? (1st, 8vo, ibds, 64p, fp 2-color, DJ/2.50)	Putnam	(1960)	Johnson, Harper	25-40	

AUTHOR	TITLE	PUBLISHER	DATE	ARTIST	PRICE	LC
Marshall, Catherine	Julie's Heritage (1st {std}, 8vo, 231p, b/w, DJ/3.00)	Longmans	1957	Johnson, Harper	20-30	
Chandler, Ruth F.	Ladder to the Sky (1st, 8vo, 189p, b/w, DJ/3.00)	Abelard-Schuman	(1959)	Johnson, Harper	30-45	
Fisher, Aileen	Lantern in the Window (1st, 8vo, 126p, b/w, DJ/2.75)	Nelson	(1957)	Johnson, Harper	25-40	
Martin, Patricia	Little Brown Hen (1st, 8vo, 23p, 1-color, pep, DJ/2.50)	Crowell	(1960)	Johnson, Harper	30-55	
Worcester, Donald	Lone Hunter's Gray Pony (1st, 8vo, 94p, 1-color, DJ/2.50)	NY: Oxford U.Pr.	1956	Johnson, Harper	40-65	*
Bradley, Duane	Meeting with a Stranger (1st {std}, 8vo, 128p, b/w, DJ/3.75, JABA)	Lippincott	(1964)	Johnson, Harper	25-40	
Stinetorf, Louise	Musa the Shoemaker (1st {std}, 8vo, 183p, b/w, DJ/3.00)	Lippincott	(1959)	Johnson, Harper	20-35	*
Rumsey, Mirian	Seal of Frog Island (1st, 8vo, 48p, fp b/w, DJ/2.50)	Wm. Morrow	1961	Johnson, Harper	30-50	
Bontemps, Arna	Story of George Washington Carver (1st, 8vo, 181p, b/w, pep, DJ/1.50)	Grosset/Dunlap	(1954)	Johnson, Harper	50-80	*
Caudill, Rebecca	Susan Cornish (1st, 8vo, 286p, ipcb, b/w, DJ/2.75)	Viking	1955	Johnson, Harper	20-35	
Kessel, Joseph	The Lion (1st {illus ed. std}, 4to, 186p, fp color, DJ/3.95)	Knopf	(1962)	Johnson, Harper	20-30	
Woolley, Catherine	David's Railroad (1st, 8vo, 159p, b/w, DJ/2.00)	Wm. Morrow	1949	Johnson, Iris B.	25-40	*
Woolley, Catherine	Ginnie and Geneva (1st, 8vo, 191p, fp b/w, DJ/2.00)	Wm. Morrow	1948	Johnson, Iris B.	50-85	*
Woolley, Catherine	Ginnie and the New Girl (1st, 8vo, 159p, fp b/w, DJ/2.50)	Wm. Morrow	1954	Johnson, Iris B.	50-85	
McGowen, Tom	Apple Strudel Soldier (1st {std}, 4to, 48p, fp color, DJ/3.95)	Follett	(1968)	Johnson, John	30-50	
Stephenson, Dorothy	How to Scare a Lion (1st, 4to, 32p, fp color, DJ/2.95)	Follett	(1965)	Johnson, John	25-45	
Wahl, Jan	Howards Go Sledding (1st {std}, ob8vo, [28]p, 1-color, DJ/2.95)	Holt, Rinehart	(1964)	Johnson, John	25-40	
Parish, Peggy	Little Indian (1st, ob8vo, [32]p, color, DJ/3.95)	Simon/Schuster	(1968)	Johnson, John	20-35	*
Stephenson, Dorothy	Night it Rained Toys (1st, lg4to, 32p, fp color, DJ/2.95)	Follett	(1963)	Johnson, John	30-45	
Wahl, Jan	Rickety Rackety Rooster (1st {std}, sq8vo, [39]p, color, DJ/3.95)	Simon/Schuster	(1968)	Johnson, John	20-35	
Parish, Peggy	Snapping Turtle's All Wrong Day (1st {std}, ob8vo, [34]p, color, DJ/3.95)	Simon/Schuster	(1970)	Johnson, John	20-30	*
Richelson, Geraldine	What is a Child? (1st {std}, sq12mo, [32]p, color, DJ/2.95)	Harlin Quist	(1966)	Johnson, John	25-45	
Withers, Carl	World of Nonsense (1st {std}, 8vo, 117p, ibds, b/w, DJ/4.50)	Holt, Rinehart	(1968)	Johnson, John	40-65	*
Johnson, Margaret	Black Bruce (1st, 8vo, 154p, red cl, b/w, pep, DJ/1.75)	Harcourt	(1938)	Johnson, Margaret	125-200	
Johnson, Margaret	Tally-Ho (1st, lg8vo, 120p, b/w, pep, DJ/1.75)	Harcourt	(1936)	Johnson, Margaret	50-80	
Johnson, Margaret	What O'Clock Jingles (1st, ob8vo, ibds, [30]p, 27 b/w)	D. Lothrop Co.	(1887)	Johnson, Margaret	70-100	*
Chapin, Frederic	Pinkey & the Plumed Knight (1st, 4to, tan cl, 207p, 8cp, cep)	Saalfield	(1909)	Johnson, Merle	70-120	
Francis, Philip W.	Remarkable Adventures of Little Boy Pip (1st, 8vo, ibds, 60p, 5cp, pep)	Paul Elder	(1907)	Johnson, Merle	100-185	*
O'Dell, Scott	Black Pearl (1st {std}, 8vo, 140p, black/gilt, fp b/w, cep, DJ/3.25, NH)	Houghton	1967	Johnson, Milton	40-65	
Coolidge, Olivia	Come by Here (1st {std}, 8vo, 239p, b/w, DJ/4.25)	Houghton	1970	Johnson, Milton	25-40	
O'Dell, Scott	Dark Canoe (1st {std}, 8vo, 165p, green cl, b/w, cep, DJ/3.50)	Houghton	1968	Johnson, Milton	30-50	
Haugaard, Erik	Little Fishes (1st, 8vo, 214p, b/w, cep, DJ/3.50, JABA)	Houghton	1967	Johnson, Milton	50-85	R*
Coolidge, Olivia	Lives of Famous Romans (1st {std}, 8vo, 248p, b/w, DJ/3.50)	Houghton	1965	Johnson, Milton	20-30	*
Coolidge, Olivia	Men of Athens (1st, 8vo, 244p, b/w, cep, DJ/3.50, NH)	Houghton	1962	Johnson, Milton	35-50	*
Harris, Christie	You Have to Draw the Line Somewhere (1st {std}, 8vo, 249p, b/w, DJ/3.95)	Atheneum	1964	Johnston, Moira	20-35	
Johnston, Annie F.	Ole Mammy's Torment (1st, 12mo, 118p, fp b/w)	L.C. Page	1897	Johnston/Sacker	70-125	
Doucet, Jerome	Tales of the Spinner (1st, lg8vo, [121]p, teg, uncut, gilt, b/w)	R.H. Russell	1902	Jones, Alfred G.	130-200	R
Young, Miriam	Prance, a Carousel Horse (1st {std}, 8vo, uncut, 116p, b/w, pep, DJ/2.50)	Crowell	(1950)	Jones, Amy	60-100	
Jones, Eliz. O.	Big Susan (1st {std}, sq8vo, ibds, 83p, color, pep, DJ/2.00)	Macmillan	1947	Jones, Eliz. O.	55-80	
Adshead, Gladys	Brownies - Hush! (1st, ob12mo, [64]p, orange cl, 1-color, cep, DJ/1.00)	NY: Oxford U.Pr.	(1938)	Jones, Eliz. O.	50-80	
Jones, Eliz. O.	David: Bible Story with Pictures (1st, 4to, ibds, [64]p, color)	Macmillan	1937	Jones, Eliz. O.	40-60	*
Jones, Jessie O.	Little Child (1st, ob4to, ibds, 38p, pep, fp color, DJ/2.00)	Viking	1946	Jones, Eliz. O.	50-80	
Jones, Eliz. O.	Little Red Riding Hood (1st {A}, 8vo, ibds, [42]p, color, LGB/#42)	Simon/Schuster	(1948)	Jones, Eliz. O.	20-35	
Bridgman, Betty	Lullaby for Eggs (1st {std}, 8vo, ibds, [34]p, fp color, DJ/2.25)	Macmillan	1955	Jones, Eliz. O.	50-80	
Jones, Eliz. O.	Maminka's Children (1st, lg8vo, 107p, fp color, DJ/2.00)	Macmillan	1940	Jones, Eliz. O.	60-100	
Jones, Thomas O.	Minnie the Mermaid (1st, 16mo, [48]p, red cl, color, DJ/0.75)	NY: Oxford U.Pr.	(1939)	Jones, Eliz. O.	35-60	
Hunt, Mabel L.	Peddler's Clock (1st, sq8vo, ipcb, [28]p, pep, color, DJ/0.50)	Grosset/Dunlap	(1943)	Jones, Eliz. O.	30-50	
Field, Rachel	Prayer for a Child (1st, 8vo, [31]p, color, cep, DJ/1.00, CM)	Macmillan	1944	Jones, Eliz. O.	120-200	R
Farjeon, Eleanor	Prayer for Little Things (1st, 8vo, [13]p, color, dep, DJ/1.00)	Houghton	1945	Jones, Eliz. O.	35-60	
Jones, Eliz. O.	Ragman of Paris & his Ragamuffins (1st, 8vo, 82p, fp 2-color, pep, DJ/1.50)	Oxford U. Pr.	(1937)	Jones, Eliz. O.	35-50	
Meigs, Cornelia L.	Scarlet Oak (1st, 8vo, 198p, col frn, pep, 8pl, DJ/2.00)	Macmillan	1938	Jones, Eliz. O.	35-60	
Jones, Jessie O.	Secrets (1st, 8vo, 24p, fp color, DJ/2.00)	Viking	1945	Jones, Eliz. O.	30-50	
Jones, Jessie O.	Small Rain (1st, sm ob4to, ibds, [40]p, 1-color, pep, DJ/2.00, CH)	Viking	1943	Jones, Eliz. O.	60-100	
St. Francis of Assisi	Song of the Sun (1st {std}, sq8vo, [32]p, 11 fp color, pep, DJ)	Macmillan	1952	Jones, Eliz. O.	40-60	
Jones, Jessie O. (ed)	This is the Way (1st, sm ob4to, 62p, 2-color, pep, DJ/3.00)	Viking	1951	Jones, Eliz. O.	40-65	
Trent, Robbie	To Church We Go (1st {this artist}, 4to, [32]p, ibds, 1-color, DJ/2.00)	Follett	(1956)	Jones, Eliz. O.	40-65	
Various	Told Under the Magic Umbrella (1st, lg8vo, 248p, b/w, DJ/2.00)	Macmillan	1939	Jones, Eliz. O.	30-50	
Jones, Eliz. O.	Twig (1st, 8vo, 152p, fp 3-color, pep, DJ/2.00)	Macmillan	1942	Jones, Eliz. O.	200-300	
Adshead, Gladys	What Miranda Knew (1st, 16mo, [48]p, beige cl, color, DJ/1.50)	NY: Oxford U.Pr.	(1944)	Jones, Eliz. O.	40-65	
Lamb, Charles	Essays of Elia (8vo, green/gilt, teg, uncut, 310p, woodcuts)	L: Methuen	1902	Jones, Garth	40-60	
Vipont, Elfrida	Bless this Day (1st AM {std}, lg8vo, 95p, color, DJ/3.25)	Harcourt	(1958)	Jones, Harold	40-65	
Lines, Kathleen	Lavender's Blue (1st AM, 4to, 180p, blue/gilt, color, pep, DJ/6.00)	F. Watts	(1956)	Jones, Harold	80-120	R
Browning, Robert	Pied Piper of Hamelin (1st AM, 4to, [48]p, fp color, cep, DJ/3.00)	F. Watts	(1962)	Jones, Harold	45-70	
Atkinson, Mary E.	Smuggler's Gap (1st, sm8vo, 307p, fp b/w, pep, DJ)	L: Bodley Head	1939	Jones, Harold	60-90	
De La Mare, Walter	This Year: Next Year (1st AM, sm4to, ibds, [64]p, color, pep, DJ/2.50)	Henry Holt & Co.	(1937)	Jones, Harold	90-160	*
Carr, Mary J.	Top of the Morning (1st, ob12mo, [96]p, col frn, DJ/1.50)	Crowell	(1941)	Jones, Henrietta	25-40	*
Bagnold, Enid	Alice and Thomas and Jane (1st AM, 8vo, ibds, 173p, color)	Knopf	1931	Jones, Laurian	30-50	
Bagnold, Enid	National Velvet (1st AM, 8vo, 303p, b/w, pep, DJ/2.50)	Wm. Morrow	(1935)	Jones, Laurian	100-160	
Hall, Bolton	Monkey Shines (1st, sm4to, 78p, ipcb, 10cp)	Wessels	(1904)	Jones, Leon F.	45-70	
Byington, Eloise	Pancake Brownies (1st, 8vo, p-o, 96p, color, pep)	Whitman	(1928)	Jones, Marguerite	50-80	
Wright, Anna R.	Children of the Nineties (1st, lg8vo, ibds, 124p, 3-color, DJ/1.00)	Grosset/Dunlap	1936	Jones, Richard	40-70	
Uchida, Yoshiko	Dancing Kettle (1st {std}, 8vo, 174p, b/w, DJ/2.25)	Harcourt	(1949)	Jones, Richard	25-40	*
Deakin, Irving	Peter and the Wolf (1st, 4to, [48]p, 2-color, DJ/1.75)	Oxford U. Pr.	(1940)	Jones, Richard	20-35	
Maugham, W. Somerset	Princess September & Nightingale (1st, sm4to, [31]p, color, pep, DJ/2.50)	Oxford U. Pr.	(1939)	Jones, Richard	60-90	
Eberle, Irmengarde	Spice on the Wind (1st, 8vo, 56p, brown cl, 2-color, pep, DJ/2.00)	Holiday House	(1940)	Jones, Richard	50-80	R
Buck, Pearl S.	Little Fox in the Middle (1st {std}, 8vo, 31p, b/w, DJ/2.95)	Collier Books	(1966)	Jones, Robert	40-70	R*
Untermeyer, Louis	One and One and One (1st {std}, 4to, [63]p, fp b/w, cep)	Crowell-Collier	(1962)	Jones, Robert	65-100	
McGinley, Phyllis	The B Book (1st {std}, 4to, ibds, [64]p, b/w, cep)	Crowell-Collier	(1962)	Jones, Robert	60-100	

AUTHOR	TITLE	PUBLISHER	DATE	ARTIST	PRICE	LC
Stephens, James	Crock of Gold (1st, 8vo, 298p, green/gilt, 6 fp 2-color, pep)	Macmillan	1922	Jones, Wilfred	40-65	
Kempton, Kenneth P.	Dragon's Thunder (1st, 8vo, 239p, col frn, b/w, pep)	Little/Brown	1931	Jones, Wilfred	20-35	
Harper, Wilhelmina	Harvest Feast (1st {std}, sm8vo, 308p, orange cl, b/w, pep, DJ/2.00)	Dutton	(1938)	Jones, Wilfred	25-45	
Jones, Wilfred	How the Derrick Works (1st, sm4to, black cl, 43p, 2-color, cep)	Macmillan	(1930)	Jones, Wilfred	60-100	
Colum, Padraic	Island of the Mighty (1st, sm8vo, 265p, gilt, 3cp, 19pl)	Macmillan	1924	Jones, Wilfred	50-80	
French, Harry	Lance of Kanana (1st, 8vo, 165p, 4cp, DJ/2.50)	Lothrop, Lee	(1932)	Jones, Wilfred	25-40	
Kempton, Kenneth P.	Loot of the Flying Dragon (1st, 8vo, 269p, col frn, b/w, pep)	Little/Brown	1930	Jones, Wilfred	25-45	
Harper, Wilhelmina	Merry Christmas to You (1st {std}, sm8vo, 276p, b/w, DJ/2.00)	Dutton	(1935)	Jones, Wilfred	25-45	*
Omar Khayyam	Rubaiyat of Omar Khayyam (1st, 16mo, ipcb, gilt, 86p, 8cp)	Harper	1921	Jones, Wilfred	50-80	
Hewes, Agnes D.	Spice Ho! Story of Discovery (1st {std}, 8vo, 198p, grn/gilt, b/w, DJ/1.75)	Knopf	(1941)	Jones, Wilfred	20-35	
Colum, Padraic	The Voyagers (1st, sm8vo, gilt, 188p, 3cp, fp b/w, pep, NH)	Macmillan	1925	Jones, Wilfred	60-90	
Clemens, Nancy	Under Glass (1st {std}, 8vo, 274p, b/w, DJ/2.00)	Longmans	1937	Jones, Wilfred	70-120	
Mirza, Youel B.	Young Tentmaker (1st, 8vo, 192p, b/w, pep, DJ/2.00)	Lothrop, Lee	1935	Jones, Wilfred	25-40	
Sylva, Carmen	Real Queen's Fairy Book (8vo, 279p, gilt, col frn, b/w, pep)	L: G. Newnes	1901	Jones/Nelson	100-165	
Burgess, Thornton	Cubby Finds an Open Door (ob24mo, ibds, [24]p, color)	Whitman	1929	Jordan, Nina	80-140	*
Burgess, Thornton	Farmer Brown's Boy Becomes Curious (ob24mo, ibds, 24p, color)	Whitman	1929	Jordan, Nina	80-140	
Burgess, Thornton	Frightened Baby (1st, ob32mo, ipcb, color)	Whitman	(1929)	Jordan, Nina	70-100	
Tietjens, Eunice H.	Gingerbread Boy (1st, 16mo, ipcb, [57]p, color, pep)	Whitman	(1932)	Jordan, Nina	30-50	
Bannerman, Helen	Little Black Sambo (1st, 16mo, [42]p, ibds, color)	Whitman	(1932)	Jordan, Nina	150-250	*
Jordan, Nina	Mother Goose Handicraft (1st, sm8vo, 149p, fp b/w, DJ/2.00)	Harcourt	(1945)	Jordan, Nina	55-90	
Potter, Beatrix	Story of Peter Rabbit (16mo, ibds, [58]p, color)	Whitman	(1932)	Jordan, Nina	60-100	
N/A	Three Little Pigs (1st, ob8vo, [48]p, color, pep)	Whitman	(1933)	Jordan, Susan	30-60	*
Joyce, Robert	Stray Child (1st {std}, lg ob8vo, 38p, b/w)	Dutton	(1934)	Joyce, Robert	25-45	
Stewart, Anna B.	Three White Cats of Avignon (1st {std}, 12mo, 167p, col frn, pep)	Doubleday/Doran	1929	Joyce, Robert	30-50	
Ziegler, Ursina	Squaps the Moonling (1st AM {std}, ob folio, [27]p, 2-color, DJ/4.95)	Atheneum	(1969)	Jucker, Sita	30-50	
Jungman, B.	Holland (1st, lg8vo, gilt, teg, 212p, 75cp)	L: A&C Black	1904	Jungman, Nico W.	80-120	
Salten, Felix	Perri (1st {std}, 8vo, 228p, b/w, DJ/2.50)	Bobbs-Merrill	(1938)	Jungnickel, L.H.	65-90	
Jupo, Frank	Atu, the Silent One (1st, ob8vo, [32]p, fp 2-color, DJ/3.75)	Holiday House	(1967)	Jupo, Frank	25-40	
Jupo, Frank	Up the Trail/Down the Street (1st {std}, 4to, ipcb, [38]p, color, DJ/2.75)	Macmillan	(1956)	Jupo, Frank	25-45	
Jupo, Frank	Wishing Shoe (1st AM, 8vo, 95p, fp b/w, DJ/2.50)	Abelard-Schuman	(1955)	Jupo, Frank	40-65	
Wiggin, Kate D.	Affair at the Inn (1st, 12mo, tan cl, 220p, 6pl)	Houghton	1904	Justice, B. Martin	40-65	
McCutcheon, George B.	Daughter of Anderson Crow (1st, 8vo, 346p, col frn, 14pl)	Dodd	1907	Justice, B. Martin	30-50	
Malkus, Alida S.	Pirates' Port: Tale of Old New York (1st {std}, 12mo, 251p, col frn, pep)	Harper	(1929)	Justis, Lyle	25-45	
Stevenson, Rbt. L.	Treasure Island (1st, sm4to, 228p, color, pep)	Grosset/Dunlap	(1930)	Justis, Lyle	40-60	*
Means, Florence C.	Rains Will Come (1st, 8vo, 241p, green cl, b/w, DJ/2.50)	Houghton	1954	Kabotie, Fred	30-60	
Byrde, Elsie	Polish Fairy Book (1st, 8vo, 231p, color)	Stokes	(1925)	Kadar, Livia	30-45	
Kahl, Virginia	Away Went Wolfgang (1st, sm ob4to, beige cl, [32]p, color, DJ/2.00)	Scribner	1954	Kahl, Virginia	50-80	R
Kahl, Virginia	Baron's Booty (1st, 4to, [32]p, 3-color, DJ/3.25)	Scribner	1963	Kahl, Virginia	40-65	*
Kahl, Virginia	Droopsi (1st, sm4to, [32]p, fp 3-color, DJ/2.50)	Scribner	1958	Kahl, Virginia	40-65	
Kahl, Virginia	Duchess Bakes a Cake (1st, 4to, [32]p, fp 2-color, DJ/2.00)	Scribner	1955	Kahl, Virginia	80-120	
Kahl, Virginia	Habits of Rabbits (1st, 4to, [32]p, b/w, DJ/2.50)	Scribner	1957	Kahl, Virginia	30-50	
Vacheron, Edith	Here is Henri! (1st, 8vo, 60p, fp color, DJ/2.50)	Scribner	(1959)	Kahl, Virginia	30-50	*
Kahl, Virginia	Maxie (1st, ob4to, [32]p, 3-color, DJ/2.50)	Scribner	1956	Kahl, Virginia	40-65	
Vacheron, Edith	More About Henri! (1st, 8vo, 64p, fp 3-color, DJ/2.75)	Scribner	(1961)	Kahl, Virginia	25-45	
Kahl, Virginia	Perfect Pancake (1st, 4to, [32]p, 2-color, DJ/2.75)	Scribner	1960	Kahl, Virginia	40-65	
Kahl, Virginia	Plum Pudding for Christmas (1st, 4to, grey cl, unpag, color, DJ/2.50)	Scribner	(1956)	Kahl, Virginia	40-65	
Wood, Esther	Belinda Blue (1st {std}, 4to, [31]p, yellow cl, 1-color, DJ/2.00)	Longmans	(1940)	Kalab, Theresa	25-40	
Marshall, Dean	House for Elizabeth (1st {std}, 8vo, 219p, fp b/w, dep, DJ/2.00)	Dutton	1941	Kalab, Theresa	120-180	
Wood, Esther	House in the Hoo (1st {std}, lg8vo, [32]p, fp b/w, pep, DJ/1.50)	Longmans	(1941)	Kalab, Theresa	25-40	*
Kalab, Theresa	Kokwa: Little Koala Bear (1st {std} lg8vo, [29]p, ibds, fp 1-color, DJ/1.00)	Longmans	(1940)	Kalab, Theresa	40-65	*
Walker, Paul E.	Peter Panda (1st, 8vo, 47p, 1-color, pep, DJ/1.50)	Nelson	(1940)	Kalab, Theresa	25-40	
Kalep, Elvy	Air Babies (1st, ob4to, [45]p, ibds, 22 fp color)	Denver: Bradford	(1936)	Kalep, Elvy	200-300	
Jeter, Jacky	Cat and the Fiddler (1st, lg8vo, [41]p, fp color, pep, DJ/3.50)	Parents Mag. Pr.	(1968)	Kalish, Lionel	30-45	
Freschet, Berniece	Beaver on the Sawtooth (1st, 8vo, [39]p, b/w, DJ/3.50)	Crowell	(1969)	Kalmenoff, Matthew	20-35	
Conklin, Gladys	Chimpanzee Roams the Forest (1st, 8vo, 48p, 3-color, DJ/3.95)	Holiday House	(1970)	Kalmenoff, Matthew	20-30	
Kipling, Rudyard	Elephant's Child (1st {std}, ob4to, 48p, color, cep, DJ/3.95)	Follett	(1969)	Kampmann, Ulla	25-35	
McCord, David	Far and Few (1st {std}, 8vo, 99p, gilt, b/w, DJ/2.50)	Little/Brown	(1952)	Kane, Henry B.	30-50	
Harris, Louise D.	Flash, Life of a Firefly (1st {std}, 8vo, 57p, color, DJ/2.95)	Little/Brown	(1966)	Kane, Henry B.	25-45	
McCord, David	For Me to Say (1st {std}, 8vo, 100p, b/w, DJ/4.50)	Little/Brown	(1970)	Kane, Henry B.	20-30	
Carrighar, Sally	One Day on Beetle Rock (1st {std}{1st bk}, 8vo, 196p, gilt, pep, DJ/3.00)	Knopf	1944	Kane, Henry B.	40-65	
McCord, David	Take Sky (1st {std}, 8vo, 107p, fp b/w, DJ/3.50)	Little/Brown	(1962)	Kane, Henry B.	50-80	R
Courlander, Harold	Fire on the Mountain (1st, lg8vo, 141p, 4cp, b/w, DJ/3.00)	Henry Holt & Co.	(1950)	Kane, Robert W.	30-45	
Courlander, Harold	Kantchil's Lime Pit (1st {std}, 8vo, 150p, fp b/w, DJ/2.75)	Harcourt	(1950)	Kane, Robert W.	40-65	
Johnson, Gerald W.	Story of Man's Work (1st, 8vo, 245p, uncut, fp b/w)	Minton Balch	1925	Kappel, Philip	30-50	*
Malory, Thomas	Boy's King Arthur (1st, 8vo, 403p, gilt, 12pl, cep)	Scribner	1880	Kappes, Alfred	120-200	
Eckert, Allan W.	Wild Season (1st {std}, 8vo, 244p, green/gilt, cep, b/w, DJ/4.95)	Little/Brown	(1967)	Karalus, Karl	20-30	
Peters, Fritz	Book of the Year (1st {std}, 8vo, 52p, 12 fp b/w, DJ/2.50)	Harper	(1950)	Karasz, Ilonka	30-45	
Maxwell, William	Heavenly Tenants (1st, 8vo, blue cl, 56p, 1-color, pep, DJ/2.00, NH)	Harper	(1946)	Karasz, Ilonka	120-200	R
McGinley, Phyllis	Merry Christmas, Happy New Year (1st, 8vo, bds, 48p, 3-color, DJ/2.50)	Viking	(1958)	Karasz, Ilonka	30-50	
Karasz, Ilonka	Twelve Days of Christmas (1st, sm4to, [29]p, ibds, fp color, cep, DJ/1.50)	Harper	(1949)	Karasz, Ilonka	30-50	
Moore, Marianne	Puss in Boots, Sleeping Beauty & Cinderella (1st {std}, 8vo, 46p, color)	L: Macmillan	1963	Karlin, Eugene	30-50	
Little, Frances	Little Sister Snow (1st, 12mo, 141p, p-o, 12cp, pep)	Century	1909	Kataoka, Genjiro	40-65	
Watanna, Onoto	Tama (1st, 8vo, 244p, uncut, gilt, teg, 4cp, dep)	Harper	1910	Kataoka, Genjiro	30-50	
Shannon, Monica	Dobry (1st, lg8vo, 176p, grey cl, col frn, pep, DJ/2.00, NM)	Viking	1934	Katchamakoff, A.	100-165	R
Earl of Birkenhead	World in 2030 (1st, lg8vo, 215p, black cl, 9pl)	L: Hodder	(1930)	Kauffer, Edward M.	140-200	
George, Jean C.	Coyote in Manhattan (1st, 8vo, 203p, b/w, DJ/3.95)	Crowell	(1968)	Kaufmann, John	25-40	
Carlson, Natalie S.	Empty Schoolhouse (1st, 8vo, 119p, b/w, DJ/3.50)	Harper	(1965)	Kaufmann, John	20-35	*
Norton, Andre	Fur Magic (1st, 8vo, 174p, fp b/w, DJ/3.95)	World	(1968)	Kaufmann, John	70-120	

ARTIST: 112

AUTHOR	TITLE	PUBLISHER	DATE	ARTIST	PRICE	LC
Baker, Betty	Killer-of-Death (1st {std}, 8vo, 142p, ipcb, b/w, DJ/2.95)	Harper	(1963)	Kaufmann, John	20-35	
Carlson, Natalie S.	Letter on the Tree (1st, 8vo, 116p, fp b/w, cep, DJ/3.50)	Harper	(1964)	Kaufmann, John	20-30	
Farmer, Penelope	Magic Stone (1st {std}, sm8vo, 224p, b/w, DJ/3.75)	Harcourt	(1964)	Kaufmann, John	30-50	*
George, Jean C.	Moon of the Salamanders (1st, 8vo, 39p, fp b/w, DJ/3.25)	Crowell	(1967)	Kaufmann, John	25-40	*
Berry, Erick	Springing of the Rice (1st {std}, 8vo, 89p, b/w, DJ/2.95)	Macmillan	1966	Kaufmann, John	20-25	
Rice, Ethel	Wiggle & Waggle (1st, 4to, bds, [28]p, p-o, color, pep, DJ/1.25)	NY: S. Gabriel	(1939)	Kay, Albert	55-80	
Kay, Gertrude A.	Adventures in Geography (1st, 4to, 157p, orange cl, color, pep)	Volland	(1930)	Kay, Gertrude A.	45-75	
Kay, Gertrude A.	Adventures on our Street (1st, lg8vo, p-o, 130p, 4cp, pep)	McKay	(1925)	Kay, Gertrude A.	60-90	
Carroll, Lewis	Alice in Wonderland (1st, sq8vo, 241p, p-o, gilt, 8cp, pep)	Lippincott	1923	Kay, Gertrude A.	130-200	
Kingsbury, Helen O.	All Aboard for Wonderland (1st, 4to, 190p, 4cp)	Moffat	1917	Kay, Gertrude A.	80-125	
MacDonald, George	Back of the North Wind (1st, 8vo, p-o, 326p, 4cp)	McKay	(1926)	Kay, Gertrude A.	60-90	
Kay, Gertrude A.	Book of Seven Wishes (1st, 8vo, 224p, blue cl, 4cp, pep)	Moffat	1917	Kay, Gertrude A.	60-100	
Addington, Sarah	Boy Who Lived in Pudding Lane (1st, 8vo, 93p, 6cp, pep, p-o)	Atl. Monthly Pr.	(1922)	Kay, Gertrude A.	50-80	
Chater, Melville	Bubble Ballads (1st, lg8vo, p-o, 148p, 16pl)	Century	1914	Kay, Gertrude A.	100-150	
Coatsworth, Eliz.	Cat & the Captain (1st, 16mo, 95p, green cl, 3cp, pep)	Macmillan	1927	Kay, Gertrude A.	35-50	
Helm, Clementine	Cecily (1st, lg8vo, p-o, 298p, 8cp, pep)	Lippincott	(1924)	Kay, Gertrude A.	100-160	
Pyrnelle, Louise C.	Diddie, Dumps & Tot (1st, 8vo, 214p, col frn, cp)	Harper	1930	Kay, Gertrude A.	50-80	
Donahey, Mary D.	Down Spider Web Lane (1st, sm4to, p-o, 130p, 6cp)	Stern	1909	Kay, Gertrude A.	100-150	
Kay, Gertrude A.	Fairy Who Believed in Human Beings (1st, 8vo, 169p, 4cp)	Moffat	1918	Kay, Gertrude A.	80-120	
Kay, Gertrude A.	Friends of Jimmy (1st, lg8vo, ibds, [95]p, color, pep)	Volland	(1926)	Kay, Gertrude A.	60-100	
Addington, Sarah	Grammar Town (1st, 8vo, p-o, 79p, 4cp, pep)	McKay	(1927)	Kay, Gertrude A.	30-60	
Addington, Sarah	Great Adventure of Mrs. Santa Claus (1st, 8vo, 107p, 5cp)	Little/Brown	1923	Kay, Gertrude A.	55-80	
Kay, Gertrude A.	Helping the Weatherman (1st, 8vo, ibds, unpag, color, pep)	Volland	(1920)	Kay, Gertrude A.	60-95	
Barbour, Ralph H.	House in the Hedge (1st, sm8vo, 251p, col frn, 3pl)	Moffat	1911	Kay, Gertrude A.	35-60	*
Hearn, Lafcadio	Japanese Fairy Tales (1st, 8vo, 132p, blue cl, 4cp, pep)	Boni/Liveright	(1924)	Kay, Gertrude A.	80-140	
Addington, Sarah	Jerry Juddikins (1st, 8vo, 65p, p-o, 4cp, pep)	McKay	(1926)	Kay, Gertrude A.	35-60	
Kay, Gertrude A.	Jolly Old Shadow Man (1st, 12mo, ibds, [39]p, color, pep)	Volland	(1920)	Kay, Gertrude A.	70-100	
Lang, Andrew	My Own Fairy Book (1st, sm8vo, 402p, rust cl, p-o, pep, 4cp)	McKay	(1927)	Kay, Gertrude A.	60-90	
Stokely, Edith K.	Pantaloon (1st, lg8vo, 168p, orange cl, 6cp, pep)	Doran	(1927)	Kay, Gertrude A.	40-65	
Kay, Gertrude A.	Peter, Patter & Pixie (1st, lg4to, ibds, 22p, 5cp)	McBride	1931	Kay, Gertrude A.	70-100	
Addington, Sarah	Pied Piper of Pudding Lane (1st, 8vo, p-o, 97p, 4cp, pep)	Atl. Monthly Pr.	(1923)	Kay, Gertrude A.	35-60	
MacDonald, George	Princess & Curdie (1st, sm8vo, p-o, cloth, 274p, 4cp, pep)	McKay	[1926]	Kay, Gertrude A.	50-80	
Addington, Sarah	Round the Year on Pudding Lane (1st, lg8vo, 231p, p-o, 9pl, pep)	Little/Brown	1924	Kay, Gertrude A.	55-80	
Bernard, Florence S.	Through the Cloud Mountain (1st, lg8vo, 215p, gilt, p-o, 8cp, pep)	Lippincott	1922	Kay, Gertrude A.	55-80	
Donahey, Mary D.	Through the Little Green Door (1st, sm8vo, 176p, p-o, 3cp)	Stern	1910	Kay, Gertrude A.	100-150	*
Carroll, Lewis	Through the Looking Glass (1st, 8vo, 235p, red/gilt, 8cp, pep)	Lippincott	(1929)	Kay, Gertrude A.	40-65	
Leet, Frank R.	To the Circus the Children Go (ob folio, wraps, color)	Saalfield	1931	Kay, Gertrude A.	50-85	
Addington, Sarah	Tommy Tingle-Tangle (1st, sq8vo, ibds, 39p, color, pep)	Volland	(1927)	Kay, Gertrude A.	70-100	
Kay, Gertrude A.	Us Kids at the Circus (1st, 8vo, ibds, 120p, color, pep)	Volland	(1927)	Kay, Gertrude A.	70-100	*
Kay, Gertrude A.	When the Sandman Comes (1st, 8vo, 183p, p-o, pep, 4cp)	Moffat	1916	Kay, Gertrude A.	60-90	
Lynch, Patricia	Grey Goose of Kilnevin (1st {std}, sm8vo, 285p, col frn, fp b/w, DJ/2.00)	Dutton	1940	Keating, John	30-50	*
Fisher, Dorothea	And Long Remember... (1st, 4to, 118p, b/w, pep, DJ/3.50)	Whittlesey	(1959)	Keats, Ezra J.	30-50	
Eberle, Irmengarde	Apple Orchard (1st, 8vo, 39p, b/w, DJ/3.00)	H.Z. Walck	1962	Keats, Ezra J.	25-40	
Balch, Glenn	Brave Riders (1st {std}, 8vo, 191p, green cl, b/w, DJ/2.75)	Crowell	(1959)	Keats, Ezra J.	30-50	
Scovel, Myra	Buffalo & the Bell (1st, sm8vo, 127p, b/w, wraps)	Friendship Pr.	(1963)	Keats, Ezra J.	40-65	*
Williams, Jay	Change of Climate (1st {std}, 8vo, 241p, b/w, DJ/3.50)	Random	(1956)	Keats, Ezra J.	30-45	*
Clymer, Eleanor	Chester (1st, 8vo, 141p, red cl, fp b/w, DJ/2.50)	Dodd	1954	Keats, Ezra J.	30-50	
Pine, Tillie S.	Chinese Knew (1st, 4to, 32p, 2-color, DJ/2.50)	Whittlesey	(1958)	Keats, Ezra J.	35-50	
Williams, Jay	Danny Dunn & the Anti-Gravity Paint (1st, 8vo, 154p, b/w, DJ/2.50)	Whittlesey	(1956)	Keats, Ezra J.	25-40	
Williams, Jay	Danny Dunn & the Homework Machine (1st {std}, 8vo, 141p, b/w, DJ/2.95)	Whittlesey	(1958)	Keats, Ezra J.	20-35	
Williams, Jay	Danny Dunn and the Weather Machine (1st {std}, 8vo, 144p, b/w, DJ/2.95)	Whittlesey	(1959)	Keats, Ezra J.	25-40	*
Williams, Jay	Danny Dunn on a Desert Island (1st {std}, 8vo, 159p, b/w, DJ/2.75)	Whittlesey	1957	Keats, Ezra J.	20-35	
Best, Herbert	Desmond's First Case (1st, 8vo, 96p, b/w, DJ/2.50)	Viking	(1961)	Keats, Ezra J.	25-40	
Pine, Tillie S.	Egyptians Knew (1st, 4to, 30p, 2-color, DJ/2.95)	Whittlesey	(1962)	Keats, Ezra J.	35-50	
Pine, Tillie S.	Eskimos Knew (1st, 4to, 32p, 2-color, DJ/2.75)	Whittlesey	(1962)	Keats, Ezra J.	35-50	
Collins, Ruth P.	Flying Cow (1st, 8vo, 123p, fp b/w, DJ/3.50)	H.Z. Walck	1963	Keats, Ezra J.	25-40	
Keats, Ezra J.	God is in the Mountain (1st {std}, ob8vo, [44]p, bds 1-color, pep)	Holt, Rinehart	(1966)	Keats, Ezra J.	40-65	
Keats, Ezra J.	Goggles (1st {std}, ob8vo, [32]p, color, pep, DJ/3.95, CH)	Macmillan	(1969)	Keats, Ezra J.	50-80	
Eberle, Irmengarde	Grasses (1st, lg8vo, green cl, 56p, brown illus, DJ/2.75)	H.Z. Walck	1960	Keats, Ezra J.	45-70	
Swenson, Juliet	Hawaii: Book to Begin On (1st {std}, 8vo, ipcb, [48]p, 3-color, DJ/2.50)	Holt, Rinehart	(1963)	Keats, Ezra J.	30-45	
Keats, Ezra J.	Hi, Cat! (1st {std}, sq8vo, [35]p, ibds, color, DJ/4.50)	Macmillan	(1970)	Keats, Ezra J.	50-80	
Selsam, Millicent	How to Be a Nature Detective (1st, lg8vo, 46p, fp color, DJ/2.95)	Harper	(1966)	Keats, Ezra J.	30-50	
Lewis, Richard	In a Spring Garden (1st, 4to, [31]p, fp color, pep, DJ/3.95)	Dial Press	(1965)	Keats, Ezra J.	50-80	R
Showers, Paul	In the Night (1st, ob8vo, [38]p, fp 2-color, DJ/1.95, CH)	Crowell	(1961)	Keats, Ezra J.	50-85	*
Hautzig, Esther	In the Park (1st {std}, 4to, [32]p, color, pep, DJ/4.95)	Macmillan	(1968)	Keats, Ezra J.	30-50	
Pine, Tillie S.	Indians Knew (1st, sm4to, teal cl, 32p, 2-color, DJ/2.00)	Whittlesey	(1957)	Keats, Ezra J.	45-70	
Keats, Ezra J.	Jennie's Hat (1st, lg ob8vo, unpag, color, DJ/3.95)	Harper	(1966)	Keats, Ezra J.	50-80	
Keats, Ezra J.	John Henry: American Legend (1st, 4to, [31]p, fp color, cep, DJ/3.50)	Pantheon	(1965)	Keats, Ezra J.	45-70	
Lansing, Elisabeth H.	Jubilant for Sure (1st {std}, sm8vo, green cl, 148p, fp b/w, DJ/2.50)	Crowell	(1954)	Keats, Ezra J.	70-120	R
Collins, Ruth P.	Krishna & the White Elephants (1st, 8vo, 119p, dp b/w, DJ/3.00)	H.Z. Walck	1961	Keats, Ezra J.	20-30	
Keats, Ezra J.	Letter to Amy (1st, ob8vo, [36]p, color, DJ/3.95)	Harper, Row	(1968)	Keats, Ezra J.	50-80	R
Davis, Katherine	Little Drummer Boy (1st {std}, ob8vo, 34p, ibds, color, cep, DJ/3.95)	Macmillan	1968	Keats, Ezra J.	30-50	
Balch, Glenn	Little Hawk and the Free Horses (1st {std}, 8vo, 180p, b/w, DJ/2.75)	Crowell	(1957)	Keats, Ezra J.	30-50	
Keats, Ezra J.	My Dog is Lost! (1st, lg8vo, beige cl, [48]p, 1-color, DJ/2.75)	Crowell	(1960)	Keats, Ezra J.	35-50	
Whitney, Phyllis	Mystery on the Isle of Skye (1st, 8vo, 224p, b/w, DJ/2.75)	Westminster Pr.	(1955)	Keats, Ezra J.	30-45	*
Keats, John	Naughty Boy, a Poem (1st, 12mo, 31p, grey cl, 2-color, DJ/2.25)	Viking	(1965)	Keats, Ezra J.	40-65	
Murphey, Eleanor A.	Nihal (1st, lg8vo, aqua cl, 39p, fp 2-color, DJ/3.00)	Crowell	(1960)	Keats, Ezra J.	45-75	
Tooze, Ruth	Our Rice Village in Cambodia (1st, 8vo, 39p, 2-color, DJ/2.75)	Viking	(1963)	Keats, Ezra J.	25-40	

AUTHOR	TITLE	PUBLISHER	DATE	ARTIST	PRICE	LC
Cheney, Cora	Peg-Legged Pirate of Sulu (1st {std}, 8vo, 109p, b/w, cep, DJ/2.75)	Knopf	1960	Keats, Ezra J.	40-65	
Keats, Ezra J.	Peter's Chair (1st, ob8vo, [33]p, color, DJ/3.95)	Harper	(1967)	Keats, Ezra J.	50-80	
Hale, Lucretia	Peterkin Papers (1st, 8vo, 192p, col frn, b/w, pep)	Jr. Deluxe Ed.	(1955)	Keats, Ezra J.	30-50	
Pine, Tillie S.	Pilgrims Knew (1st, 4to, 32p, 2-color, DJ/2.00)	Whittlesey	(1957)	Keats, Ezra J.	30-50	
Martin, Patricia	Rice Bowl Pet (1st, sm4to, [36]p, fp 2-color, dep, DJ/3.50)	Crowell	(1962)	Keats, Ezra J.	30-45	
Keats, Ezra J.	Snowy Day (1st, ob8vo, 32p, color, dep, DJ/3.00, CM)	Viking	(1962)	Keats, Ezra J.	80-140	R
Clark, Billy C.	Song of the River (1st, 8vo, 120p, black cl, b/w, DJ/2.95)	Crowell	(1957)	Keats, Ezra J.	30-50	
Kumin, Maxine	Speedy Digs Downside Up (1st, 8vo, 43p, fp 2-color, DJ/2.75)	Putnam	1964	Keats, Ezra J.	30-45	
Lansing, Elisabeth H.	Sure Thing for Shep (1st {std}, sm8vo, red cl, 177p, b/w, DJ/2.50)	Coward	(1956)	Keats, Ezra J.	35-60	
Albee, George	Three Young Kings (1st {std}, 4to, 47p, yellow cl, 1-color, pep, DJ/2.75)	F. Watts	1956	Keats, Ezra J.	45-60	
Clark, Ann N.	Tia Maria's Garden (1st, 8vo, 47p, color, DJ/3.00)	Viking	1963	Keats, Ezra J.	45-70	
Davis, Verne	Time of the Wolves (1st, 8vo, 127p, b/w, DJ/2.95)	Wm. Morrow	1962	Keats, Ezra J.	30-45	
Williams, Jay	Tournament of the Lions (1st, lg8vo, black/gilt, 120p, 5 fp b/w, DJ/2.75)	H.Z. Walck	1960	Keats, Ezra J.	35-50	
MacKellar, William	Wee Joseph (1st, 8vo, 76p, fp b/w, pep, DJ/2.50)	Whittlesey	(1957)	Keats, Ezra J.	30-45	
Russell, Solveig	What Good is a Tail? (1st {std}, 4to, [32]p, 3-color, DJ/2.50)	Bobbs-Merrill	(1962)	Keats, Ezra J.	30-50	
Keats, Ezra J.	Whistle for Willie (1st, ob8vo, ibds, 33p, fp color, dep, DJ/3.50)	Viking	(1964)	Keats, Ezra J.	50-80	R
Carpenter, Frances	Wonder Tales of Dogs & Cats (1st, lg8vo, 255p, fp b/w, DJ/3.50)	Doubleday	(1955)	Keats, Ezra J.	40-60	
McGovern, Ann	Zoo, Where Are You? (1st, 4to, [20]p, color, pep, DJ/3.50)	Harper, Row	1964	Keats, Ezra J.	30-50	
Cavanah, Frances	Our Country's Story (1st, 8vo, 64p, 2-color, pep, DJ/2.95)	Rand/McNally	(1962)	Keats, Julia	20-35	
Coatsworth, Eliz.	Kitten Stand (1st, 8vo, ipcb, [28]p, color, pep, DJ/0.50)	Grosset/Dunlap	(1945)	Keeler, Katherine	30-50	
Gates, Josephine S.	April Fool Doll (1st, lg8vo, 152p, red cl, p-o, b/w)	Bobbs-Merrill	(1909)	Keep, Virginia	80-125	
Gates, Josephine S.	Little Girl Blue Lives in the Woods... (1st, 16mo, 53p, 4cp)	Houghton	1910	Keep, Virginia	55-90	
Gates, Josephine S.	Little Girl Blue Plays I-Spy (1st, 16mo, 61p, color)	Houghton	1913	Keep, Virginia	55-80	*
Gates, Josephine S.	Little Red, White, Blue (1st, lg8vo, 118p, 9pl)	Bobbs-Merrill	(1906)	Keep, Virginia	60-80	
Goss, Charles F.	Little St. Sunshine (1st, sm8vo, green/gilt, 153p, 6cp)	Bowen-Merrill	(1902)	Keep, Virginia	25-40	
Gates, Josephine S.	Live Doll's Busy Days (1st, lg8vo, 105p, 10pl)	Bobbs-Merrill	(1907)	Keep, Virginia	100-165	
Gates, Josephine S.	Live Doll's House Party (1st, lg8vo, red cl, 102p, p-o, 8pl)	Bobbs-Merrill	(1906)	Keep, Virginia	100-160	
Gates, Josephine S.	Live Doll's Play Days (1st, lg8vo, p-o, red cl, 109p, 9pl)	Bobbs-Merrill	(1908)	Keep, Virginia	100-160	
Gates, Josephine S.	Live Dolls in Fairyland (1st, lg8vo, p-o, 136p, 6cp)	Bobbs-Merrill	(1911)	Keep, Virginia	100-160	
Gates, Josephine S.	Live Dolls in Wonderland (1st, 8vo, 149p, p-o, 5pl)	Bobbs-Merrill	(1912)	Keep, Virginia	100-160	
Krag, Martha A.	Martha-Jane: Nursery Nonsense (1st, ob4to, [24]p, black pgs, AEG, cep)	Bowen-Merrill	1897	Keep, Virginia	140-225	
Gates, Josephine S.	Story of the Live Dolls (1st, lg8vo, 103p, p-o, b/w)	Bowen-Merrill	1901	Keep, Virginia	80-135	
Gates, Josephine S.	Story of the Lost Doll (1st, lg8vo, red cl, p-o, 10pl)	Bobbs-Merrill	(1905)	Keep, Virginia	80-130	
Gates, Josephine S.	Story of the Three Dolls (1st, sm4to, red cl, 148p, p-o, 9pl)	Bobbs-Merrill	(1905)	Keep, Virginia	80-130	
Page, Thomas N.	Two Prisoners (1st, 8vo, 82p, teg, gilt, 5cp)	R.H. Russell	1903	Keep, Virginia	30-50	
Keeping, Charles	Alfie Finds Other Side of World (1st AM {std}, ob4to, [32]p, color, DJ/3.95)	F. Watts	(1968)	Keeping, Charles	40-65	*
Gray, Nicholas S.	Apple Stone (1st AM {std}, 8vo, 229p, b/w, DJ/4.95)	Meredith Press	(1969)	Keeping, Charles	30-45	
Keeping, Charles	Charley, Charlotte & Golden Canary (1st, 4to, [32]p, ibds, color, DJ, KGM)	L: Oxford U.Pr.	1967	Keeping, Charles	100-150	
Keeping, Charles	Christmas Story (1st AM, 4to, [24]p, fp 2-color, DJ/3.95)	F. Watts	1968	Keeping, Charles	40-65	
Sutcliff, Rosemary	Dawn Wind (1st AM {std}, 8vo, 241p, b/w, DJ/3.75)	H.Z. Walck	1962	Keeping, Charles	25-45	
Treece, Henry	Dream Time (1st AM {std}, 8vo, 114p, fp b/w, DJ/3.95)	Meredith Press	(1967)	Keeping, Charles	45-70	
Cooper, Lee	Five Fables from France (1st, 8vo, 86p, brown cl, 2-color, pep, DJ/4.50)	Abelard-Schuman	(1970)	Keeping, Charles	25-40	
Garfield, Leon	God Beneath the Sea (1st, 8vo, 168p, fp b/w, DJ, CgM)	L: Longmans	1970	Keeping, Charles	50-80	
Gray, Nicholas S.	Grimbold's other World (1st AM {std}, 8vo, 184p, b/w, DJ/3.95)	Meredith Press	(1968)	Keeping, Charles	30-50	
Treece, Henry	Horned Helmet (1st AM, 8vo, 118p, b/w, DJ/3.00)	Criterion Bks.	(1963)	Keeping, Charles	45-70	
Keeping, Charles	Joseph's Yard (1st AM {std}, 4to, [32]p, color, DJ/4.95)	F. Watts	1969	Keeping, Charles	40-70	
Holding, James	King's Contest (1st, 8vo, 125p, b/w, DJ/3.25)	Abelard-Schuman	(1964)	Keeping, Charles	25-40	
Sutcliff, Rosemary	Knight's Fee (1st AM, 8vo, 241p, fp b/w, DJ/3.50)	H.Z. Walck	1960	Keeping, Charles	35-50	
Sutcliff, Rosemary	Knight's Fee (1st, 8vo, 241p, fp b/w, DJ)	L: Oxford U.Pr.	1960	Keeping, Charles	50-75	
Miller, Margaret	Knights, Beasts & Wonder (1st AM, 8vo, 127p, 3-color, DJ/3.95)	NY: David White	(1969)	Keeping, Charles	25-40	
Keith, Harold V.	Komantica (1st, 8vo, 299p, b/w, DJ/3.95)	Crowell	(1965)	Keeping, Charles	20-35	
Sutcliff, Rosemary	Lantern Bearers (1st AM {std}, 8vo, 252p, b/w, DJ/3.50)	H.Z. Walck	1959	Keeping, Charles	60-90	
Sutcliff, Rosemary	Lantern Bearers (1st, 8vo, 252p, b/w, DJ, CgM)	L: Oxford U.Pr.	1959	Keeping, Charles	70-125	
Keeping, Charles	Shaun & the Cart Horse (1st AM {std}, ob4to, [32]p, color, DJ/3.95)	F. Watts	(1966)	Keeping, Charles	40-65	
Sutcliff, Rosemary	Silver Branch (1st AM {std}, 8vo, 215p, b/w, DJ/3.50)	H.Z. Walck	(1959)	Keeping, Charles	30-45	
Holding, James	Sky-Eater (1st, 8vo, 124p, fp 1-color, pep, DJ/3.25)	Abelard-Schuman	(1965)	Keeping, Charles	25-40	
Keeping, Charles	Through the Window (1st AM {std}, ob4to, [32]p, color, DJ/4.95)	F. Watts	1970	Keeping, Charles	60-90	
Keeping, Charles	Tinker Tailor Folk Song Tales (1st AM {std}, 4to, [48]p, col, pep, DJ/4.50)	World	1969	Keeping, Charles	30-50	
Chandler, Edna W.	With Books on her Head (1st {std}, 8vo, 154p, ibds, b/w, DJ/3.95)	Meredith Press	(1967)	Keeping, Charles	25-40	
Bell, Lilian	Carolina Lee (1st, 12mo, 352p, gilt, p-o, col frn)	L.C. Page	1906	Keith, Dora W.	50-80	*
Wheeler, Candace	Doubledarling & Dreamspinner (1st, 8vo, 167p, blue cl, p-o, 11cp)	Fox Duffield	1905	Keith, Dora W.	80-120	
Latham, Jean L.	Anchor's Aweigh... (1st, 8vo, 273p, b/w, DJ/4.50)	Harper	(1968)	Keith, Eros	40-65	
Carter, Angela	Donkey Prince (1st AM {std}, 8vo, 40p, fp color, pep, DJ/4.95)	Simon/Schuster	(1970)	Keith, Eros	40-65	
Hamilton, Virginia	House of Dies Drear (1st {std}, 8vo, 246p, fp b/w, DJ/4.95)	Macmillan	(1968)	Keith, Eros	30-50	
Moery, Robert	Kevin (1st {std}, 4to, [32]p, 2-color, DJ/4.75)	Bradbury Press	1970	Keith, Eros	30-45	
Fox, Paula	King's Falcon (1st {std}, 8vo, 56p, fp 1-color, cep, DJ/3.95)	Bradbury Press	(1969)	Keith, Eros	45-70	R*
Carter, Angela	Miss Z: Dark Young Lady (1st {std}, 8vo, 32p, fp color, DJ/3.95)	Simon/Schuster	(1970)	Keith, Eros	50-70	
Keith, Eros	Rrra-ah (1st {std}, 4to, [32]p, color, DJ/4.95)	Bradbury Press	(1969)	Keith, Eros	30-50	*
Aesopus	Aesop's Fables (1st, 4to, 71p, ipcb, color, pep)	Duell, Sloan	(1944)	Kelen, Emery	35-50	
Hough, Emerson	54-40 or Fight (1st, sm8vo, 402p, gilt, 4pl)	Bobbs-Merrill	(1909)	Keller, Arthur I.	40-65	
Mitchell, John A.	Amos Judd (1st, 12mo, teg, 252p, 8cp)	Scribner	1901	Keller, Arthur I.	25-40	
Overton, Gwendolen	Anne Carmel (1st, sm8vo, 335p, teg, 6pl)	Macmillan	1903	Keller, Arthur I.	30-50	
Chambers, Robert	Barbarians (1st, 12mo, 353p, 4pl)	Appleton	1917	Keller, Arthur I.	25-40	
Parrish, Randall	Bob Hampton of Placer (1st, 8vo, 383p, 4cp)	McClurg	1906	Keller, Arthur I.	25-40	
Smith, Francis H.	Caleb West, Master Diver (1st, 12mo, gilt, 378p, 6pl by...)	Houghton	1898	Keller, Arthur I.	30-60	
Dickens, Charles	Christmas Carol (1st, 8vo, 130p, blue/gilt, teg, 12cp)	McKay	(1914)	Keller, Arthur I.	35-60	
Locke, William J.	Fortunate Youth (1st, 12mo, 352p, green/gilt, 8pl by...)	NY: John Lane	1914	Keller, Arthur I.	35-60	
Longfellow, H.W.	Hanging of the Crane (1st, 8vo, [60]p, teg, p-o, 12cp)	Houghton	1907	Keller, Arthur I.	40-70	

AUTHOR	TITLE	PUBLISHER	DATE	ARTIST	PRICE	LC
Harte, Bret	Her Letter (1st, 8vo, p-o, green/gilt, teg, 98p, color, pep)	Houghton	1905	Keller, Arthur I.	50-80	
Green, Anna K.	Initials Only (1st, 12mo, 356p, col frn)	Dodd	1911	Keller, Arthur I.	60-90	
Wilkins, Mary E.	Jerome, A Poor Man (1st, 12mo, 506p, gilt, 26pl)	Harper	1897	Keller, Arthur I.	35-60	
Hough, Emerson	Law of the Land (1st, 8vo, 416p, tan cl, 5pl)	Bobbs-Merrill	(1904)	Keller, Arthur I.	30-50	
Irving, Washington	Legend of Sleepy Hollow (1st, 8vo, gilt, 92p, p-o, pep, 14pl)	Bobbs-Merrill	(1906)	Keller, Arthur I.	90-120	
Nicholson, Meredith	Lords of High Decision (1st, sm8vo, 503p, 4cp)	Doubleday/Page	1909	Keller, Arthur I.	25-40	*
Barnes, James	Loyal Traitor (1st, 12mo, 306p, gilt, 21pl)	Harper	1897	Keller, Arthur I.	30-50	*
Farnol, Jeffery	Money Moon (1st, lg8vo, p-o, teg, 385p, 22pl)	Dodd	1911	Keller, Arthur I.	50-80	
Mitchell, S. Weir	Red City (1st, 8vo, 421p, p-o, 10pl)	Century	1908	Keller, Arthur I.	25-40	
Nesbit, Edith	Red House (1st AM, 12mo, 274p, green cl, b/w)	Harper	1902	Keller, Arthur I.	90-150	
Smith, Francis H.	Romance of an Old Fashioned Gentleman (1st, 8vo, 213p, teg, 5cp)	Scribner	1907	Keller, Arthur I.	25-40	
Lindsey, William	Severed Mantle (1st, lg8vo, 452p, 7cp)	Houghton	1909	Keller, Arthur I.	25-45	
Watson, H.B.M.	The Adventurers (1st, sm8vo, 298p, 20pl)	Harper	1899	Keller, Arthur I.	35-60	*
Dixon, Thomas	The Clansman (1st, 8vo, 374p, red cl, b/w)	Doubleday/Page	1905	Keller, Arthur I.	50-80	
Lowell, James R.	The Courtin' (1st, 8vo, teg, bds/gilt, [58]p, color, pep)	Houghton	1909	Keller, Arthur I.	35-60	
Sinclair, May	The Creators (1st, sm8vo, 517p, b/w)	Century	1910	Keller, Arthur I.	25-40	
Wister, Owen	The Virginian (1st, 8vo, 504p, tan cloth, 8pl)	Macmillan	1902	Keller, Arthur I.	170-240	
Rinehart, Mary R.	Window at the White Cat (1st, sm8vo, 378p, 4pl)	Bobbs-Merrill	(1910)	Keller, Arthur I.	30-50	
Green, Anna K.	Woman in the Alcove (1st, 12mo, beige/gilt, 372p, 5pl)	Bobbs-Merrill	(1906)	Keller, Arthur I.	45-70	
O'Day, James	Daddy Long Legs Fun Songs (1st, folio, [68]p, ibds, color)	Chi: Witmark	1900	Keller, Edgar	140-220	
Boylan, Grace D.	Yama Yama Land (1st, sq8vo, 200p, p-o, 14 fp color)	Reilly/Britton	(1909)	Keller, Edgar	90-150	
Stockton, Frank	Kate Bonnet (1st, 12mo, gilt, 420p, 8pl)	Appleton	1902	Keller/Potter	40-70	
Heady, Eleanor	Brave Johnny O'Hare (1st, sm ob4to, [41]p, fp color, pep)	Parents Mag. Pr.	(1969)	Kellogg, Steven	50-80	*
Young, Miriam	Can't You Pretend? (1st, lg sq8vo, [31]p, color, DJ)	Putnam	(1970)	Kellogg, Steven	70-120	*
Parish, Peggy	Granny & the Desperadoes (1st {std}, 8vo, 40p, color, DJ/4.50)	Macmillan	(1970)	Kellogg, Steven	45-70	*
Mendoza, George	Gwot! Horribly Funny Hairticklers (1st, 8vo, 37p, fp b/w, DJ/2.95)	Harper	(1967)	Kellogg, Steven	70-120	
Copp, Jim	Martha Matilda O'Toole (1st {std}, 4to, [28]p, fp 2-color, cep, DJ/3.95)	Bradbury Press	(1969)	Kellogg, Steven	60-90	*
Belloc, Hilaire	Matilda Who Told Lies... (1st, lg8vo, [32]p, b/w, DJ/3.50, NYTBI)	Dial Press	(1970)	Kellogg, Steven	40-65	*
Loomis, Ruth	Mrs. Purdy's Children (1st {std}, 8vo, 178p, fp b/w, cep, DJ/4.50)	Dial Press	(1970)	Kellogg, Steven	30-50	
Rodgers, Mary	Rotten Book (1st, 8vo, [32]p, b/w, DJ/2.50)	Harper	(1969)	Kellogg, Steven	40-65	
Kellogg, Steven	Wicked Kings of Bloon (1st, sq8vo, [32]p, fp color, cep, DJ/4.50)	Prentice-Hall	(1970)	Kellogg, Steven	50-85	
Kelly, R. Talbot	Egypt (1st, 8vo, gilt, teg, 246p, 75cp)	L: A&C Black	1902	Kelly, Robert G.T.	100-165	
Monath, Norman	Songs of the Pogo (1st, 4to, 152p, bds, color, pep, DJ/3.95)	Simon/Schuster	1956	Kelly, Walt	70-100	
O'Reilly, John	The Glob (1st, 8vo, 63p, b/w, pep, DJ/1.50)	Viking	1952	Kelly, Walt	50-85	
Stevenson, Rbt. L.	Treasure Island (1st, lg8vo, 241p, col frn)	Sears	(1926)	Kelsey, C.W.	30-50	*
Disney, Walt	Disney's Perri (1st, folio, ibds, [24]p, color, pep, GGB)	Simon/Schuster	(1957)	Kelsey, D.	120-180	*
Lincoln, Joseph C.	Cape Cod Ballads (1st [1st bk.], 8vo, yellow/gilt, 198p, b/w)	NJ: Brandt	1902	Kemble, Edward W.	100-150	
Kemble, Edward W.	Comical Coons (1st, ob4to, unpag, ibds, b/w)	R.H. Russell	1898	Kemble, Edward W.	300-450	
Kemble, Edward W.	Coon Alphabet (1st, sm4to, ibds, unpag, b/w)	R.H. Russell	1898	Kemble, Edward W.	450-650	
Kemble, Edward W.	Coontown's 400 (1st, 4to, [63]p, cloth, fp b/w)	NY: Life Pub.	1899	Kemble, Edward W.	350-500	
Harris, Joel C.	Daddy Jake the Runaway (1st, 4to, 145p, cream bds, 19 b/w, cep)	Century	1889	Kemble, Edward W.	600-800	
Marquis, Don	Danny's Own Story (1st, 8vo, green cl, 333p, p-o, 16pl)	Doubleday/Page	1912	Kemble, Edward W.	120-200	
Pratt, Lucy	Ezekiel Expands (1st, 8vo, tan cl, 228p, 6pl)	Houghton	1914	Kemble, Edward W.	100-165	
Dunbar, Paul L.	Folks from Dixie (1st, 12mo, 263p, gilt, p-o, 8pl)	Dodd	1898	Kemble, Edward W.	350-500	
Dunbar, Paul L.	Heart of Happy Hollow (1st, sm8vo, 309p, gilt, 6pl)	Dodd	1904	Kemble, Edward W.	400-650	
Kemble, Edward W.	Kemble's Coons (1st, lg ob4to, ibds, 31pl, b/w)	R.H. Russell	1896	Kemble, Edward W.	400-600	
Kemble, Edward W.	Kemble's Pickaninnies (1st, lg ob4to, 31pl, b/w)	R.H. Russell	1901	Kemble, Edward W.	400-600	
Kemble, Edward W.	Kemble's Sketch Book (1st, lg ob8vo, tan buckram, 30pl)	R.H. Russell	1899	Kemble, Edward W.	250-400	
Dix, Dorothy	Mirandy (1st, 12mo, brown cl, 256p, 21pl)	Hearst	1914	Kemble, Edward W.	80-125	
Dunne, Finley P.	Mr. Dooley's Philosophy (1st, sm8vo, red cl, 263p, b/w by...)	R.H. Russell	1900	Kemble, Edward W.	60-90	
Harris, Joel C.	On the Plantation (1st, sm8vo, orange/gilt, 233p, b/w)	Appleton	1892	Kemble, Edward W.	170-240	
Riley, James W.	Poems Here at Home (1st, 8vo, green cl, 187p, teg, b/w)	Century	1893	Kemble, Edward W.	80-125	
Brown, Kenneth	Putter Perkins (1st, 12mo, green cl, teg, 121p, 10pl)	Houghton	1923	Kemble, Edward W.	50-80	
Dunbar, Paul L.	Strength of Gideon (1st, 12mo, 362p, gilt, 6pl)	Dodd	1900	Kemble, Edward W.	400-600	
Kemble, Edward W.	The Blackberries... (1st, lg ob4to, ibds, [36]p, 16cp)	R.H. Russell	1897	Kemble, Edward W.	500-800	
Carleton, Henry G.	Thompson Street Poker Club (1st, 8vo, 48p, ibds, 11 fp b/w)	White & Allen	1888	Kemble, Edward W.	90-120	*
Edwards, Harry S.	Two Runaways (1st, sm8vo, 246p, gilt, 16pl)	Century	(1889)	Kemble, Edward W.	80-125	
Johnston, Richard M.	Widow Guthrie (1st, sm8vo, blue/gilt, 309p, 6pl, cep)	Appleton	1890	Kemble, Edward W.	35-60	*
Stratton-Porter, Gene	At the Foot of the Rainbow (1st, 8vo, 258p, yellow cl, 4cp)	Outing	1907	Kemp, Oliver	500-700	
Sewell, Anna	Black Beauty (1st, 8vo, 224p, blue/gilt, 24cp, pep)	L: J.M. Dent	1915	Kemp-Welch, Lucy	100-160	
Fletcher, Joseph S.	Making of Matthias (1st, sm8vo, AEG, 141p, blue/gilt, 14pl)	L: John Lane	1898	Kemp-Welch, Lucy	50-85	
Nesbit, Edith	Pussy & Doggy Tales (1st, 12mo, 132p, 1-color title pg, b/w)	L: J.M. Dent	1899	Kemp-Welch, Lucy	160-240	*
Kempner, Carol	Nicholas (1st {std}, 4to, [25]p, fp color, DJ/4.50)	Simon/Schuster	(1968)	Kempner, Carol	30-50	*
Kempson, Frederick C.	Sad End of Erica's Blackamoor (1st, ob folio, ibds, 39p, b/w)	L: E. Arnold	1903	Kempson, F.C.	200-300	
Willett, Edward	Cat's Cradle Rhymes for Children (1st, lg8vo, ibds, 60p, fp color)	Worthington	1881	Kendrick, Charles	100-170	*
Egan, Constance	Epaminondas & the Lettuces (1st, 16mo, 62p, brown bds, fp color, pep)	L: Collins	[1938]	Kennedy, A.E.	80-125	
Egan, Constance	Epaminondas & the Puppy (1st, 12mo, unpag, fp color, pep, DJ)	L: Collins	1959	Kennedy, A.E.	90-130	
Egan, Constance	Epaminondas Helps in the Garden (1st, 16mo, 62p, blue bds)	L: Collins	[1937]	Kennedy, A.E.	80-125	*
Egan, Constance	Epaminondas Helps in the House (12mo, ibds, unpag, color)	L: Collins	[1937]	Kennedy, A.E.	80-120	
Baum, L. Frank	Army Alphabet (1st, lg4to, [60]p, ibds, 29cp)	George Hill	1900	Kennedy, Harry	900-1200	R
Baum, L. Frank	Navy Alphabet (1st, lg4to, [58]p, ibds, color)	George Hill	1900	Kennedy, Harry	900-1200	R
Costello, Charles J.	Old Mother Hubbard (1st, 4to, [96]p, pict cl, fp color)	Chi: Jamieson	1902	Kennedy, Harry	120-200	
Haskell, Helen E.	Billy's Princess (1st, sm8vo, 248p, 7pl)	L.C. Page	1907	Kennedy, Helen M.	80-125	*
Alcott, Louisa M.	Silver Pitchers (1st, 8vo, 365p, 8pl)	Little/Brown	1908	Kennedy, J.W.	35-60	
Chase, Mary Ellen	Dolly Moses: Cat & the Clam Chowder (1st {std}, sm8vo, 58p, b/w, DJ/2.95)	Norton	(1964)	Kennedy, Paul	25-40	
Robertson, Keith	If Wishes Were Horses (1st {std}, 8vo, 246p, b/w, DJ/2.95)	Harper	(1958)	Kennedy, Paul	30-50	
De La Mare, Walter	Penny a Day (1st, 8vo, 209p, uncut, fp b/w, cep, DJ/3.00)	Knopf	1960	Kennedy, Paul	25-40	
Longfellow, H.W.	Skeleton in Armor (1st, lg8vo, [31]p, fp color, DJ/3.50)	Prentice-Hall	(1963)	Kennedy, Paul	20-35	*

AUTHOR	TITLE	PUBLISHER	DATE	ARTIST	PRICE	LC
Nichols, Beverly	Stream that Stood Still (1st, 8vo, 218p, gilt, b/w, pep, DJ)	L: J. Cape	(1948)	Kennedy, Richard	30-50	
Harris, Christie	Forbidden Frontier (1st {std}, 8vo, 210p, b/w, DJ/4.50)	Atheneum	1968	Kenny, Carey	20-35	
Aldington, Richard	All Men are Enemies (1st {std}, 8vo, 574p, gilt, b/w, DJ/2.50)	Doubleday/Doran	1933	Kent, Rockwell	70-120	
Squires, Frederick	Architec-tonics (1st {1st bk.}, 12mo, gilt, 172p, col frn)	Comstock Co.	1914	Kent, Rockwell	300-500	R
Paramore, Edward	Ballad of Yukon Jake (1st, 12mo, [42]p, 2pl, pcb)	Coward	1928	Kent, Rockwell	60-90	
Chappell, George S.	Basket of Poses (1st, sm4to, pcb, p-o, 109p, b/w)	A.& C. Boni	1924	Kent, Rockwell	90-120	
Untermeyer, Louis	Book of Noble Thoughts (1st, 8vo, 121p, ibds, 1-color, dep, DJ/3.00)	A.A. Group	(1946)	Kent, Rockwell	60-95	
Voltaire, J.F.	Candide (1st, 8vo, 111p, maroon/gilt, b/w, pep)	Random	1930	Kent, Rockwell	50-80	
Alexander, Lillie M.	Candy (1st, 8vo, 310p, 5pl, pep, DJ/2.50)	Dodd	1934	Kent, Rockwell	80-140	
Chaucer, Geoffrey	Canterbury Tales (1st, lg8vo, 627p, b/w, pep, DJ)	Garden City	1934	Kent, Rockwell	70-100	
Robinson, Selma	City Child (1st, 8vo, red/gilt, 64p, b/w, DJ/2.00)	Farrar/Rinehart	1931	Kent, Rockwell	70-125	
Rich, Edwin G.	Hans the Eskimo (1st, 8vo, 287p, blue cl, p-o, b/w)	Houghton	1934	Kent, Rockwell	40-70	
Vercel, Roger	In Sight of Eden (1st {std}, 8vo, 254p, DJ/2.50, frn by...)	Harcourt	(1934)	Kent, Rockwell	45-70	
Kent, Rockwell	It's Me O Lord... (1st, lg8vo, gilt, 617p, color, DJ/10.00)	Dodd	(1955)	Kent, Rockwell	70-125	
Melville, Herman	Moby Dick (1st, 12mo, 822p, black/silver, b/w, DJ)	Random	1930	Kent, Rockwell	350-500	
Kent, Rockwell	N by E (1st, 8vo, white cl, 281p, b/w, DJ/3.50)	Brewer/Warren	1930	Kent, Rockwell	90-120	
Kent, Rockwell	Northern Christmas (1st, 12mo, [32]p, ipcb, 1-color, DJ/0.50)	A.A. Group	(1941)	Kent, Rockwell	50-75	
Kent, Rockwell	On Earth Peace... (1st, 16mo, [24]p, ibds, 1-color)	A.A. Group	(1942)	Kent, Rockwell	40-60	
Shephard, Esther	Paul Bunyan (1st, 8vo, gilt, 234p, fp b/w)	Harcourt	(1924)	Kent, Rockwell	90-120	
Kent, Rockwell	Rockwellkentiana (1st {std}, 4to, 64p, col frn, blue cl, DJ/3.75)	Harcourt	1933	Kent, Rockwell	90-120	
Chappell, George S.	Rollo in Society (1st, 16mo, p-o, 178p, woodcuts)	Putnam	1922	Kent, Rockwell	70-100	R
Allen, Ralph B.	Saga of Gisli (1st {std}, lg8vo, 148p, uncut, b/w, DJ/2.50)	Harcourt	(1936)	Kent, Rockwell	100-165	
Kent, Rockwell	Salamina (1st {std}, 8vo, blue/silver, 336p, 23pl, DJ/3.75)	Harcourt	1935	Kent, Rockwell	100-170	R
Kent, Rockwell	This is my Own (1st {std}, lg8vo, cream cl, 393p, fp b/w, DJ/3.50)	Duell, Sloan	(1940)	Kent, Rockwell	120-180	
Kent, Rockwell	Voyaging: Southward... (1st, 4to, yellow cl, teg, 184p, b/w, pep)	Putnam	1924	Kent, Rockwell	120-200	
Kent, Rockwell	Wilderness (1st, 4to, teg, 217p, grey/gilt, b/w, pep)	Putnam	1920	Kent, Rockwell	125-200	
Norris, Charles G.	Zest (1st {std}, 8vo, 445p, pict cl, frn by...)	Doubleday/Doran	1933	Kent, Rockwell	40-60	
Kepes, Juliet A.	Birds (1st, 4to, [53]p, b/w, DJ/4.95, NYTBI)	NY: Walker	1968	Kepes, Juliet A.	40-65	
Smith, William J.	Boy Blue's Book of Beasts (1st {std}, 8vo, 58p, fp 1-color, cep, DJ/2.75)	Little/Brown	(1957)	Kepes, Juliet A.	80-120	R
Kepes, Juliet A.	Five Little Monkeys (1st {1st bk}, sm4to, 32p, col, pep, DJ/2.50, CH, NYT)	Houghton	1952	Kepes, Juliet A.	70-100	
Kepes, Juliet A.	Frogs Merry (1st, lg ob8vo, [32]p, color, DJ/2.95)	Pantheon	(1961)	Kepes, Juliet A.	25-40	
Miller, Mary B.	Give a Guess (1st, 8vo, blue cl, [32]p, 1-color, dep, DJ/2.50)	Pantheon	1957	Kepes, Juliet A.	60-100	R*
Kepes, Juliet A.	Lady Bird, Quickly (1st {std}, lg ob8vo, 47p, color, DJ/3.00)	Little/Brown	(1964)	Kepes, Juliet A.	25-40	
Smith, William J.	Laughing Time (1st {std}, 8vo, 54p, yellow cl, fp 1-color, cep, DJ/2.50)	Little/Brown	(1955)	Kepes, Juliet A.	80-125	R
Smith, William J.	Puptents & Pebbles (1st {std}, 4to, yellow cl, 32p, color, pep, DJ/2.75)	Little/Brown	(1959)	Kepes, Juliet A.	80-125	R
Kepes, Juliet A.	Seed that Peacock Planted (1st {std}, lg8vo, 38p, color, DJ/3.50)	Little/Brown	(1967)	Kepes, Juliet A.	25-40	
McLeod, Emilie	Seven Remarkable Bears (1st, sq8vo, 46p, blue cl, fp 2-col, pep, DJ/2.50)	Houghton	1954	Kepes, Juliet A.	45-70	
Read, Herbert	This Way Delight (1st, lg8vo, 155p, b/w, pep, DJ/3.50)	Pantheon	(1956)	Kepes, Juliet A.	25-45	
Kepes, Juliet A.	Two Little Birds & Three (1st, lg8vo, 62p, fp 1-color, DJ/2.50, NYTBI)	Houghton	1960	Kepes, Juliet A.	75-125	R*
Haggard, H. Rider	Allan Quatermain (1st, 8vo, blue/gilt, 280p, 20pl, pep)	L: Longmans	1887	Kerr, C.H.M.	300-500	
Kerr, Estelle	Little Sam in Volendam (1st, lg8vo, 32p)	Moffat	1908	Kerr, Estelle	80-120	
Baum, L. Frank	Baum's American Fairy Tales (1st, 4to, [223]p, p-o, 16cp)	Bobbs-Merrill	(1908)	Kerr, George F.	500-750	
Dunham, Curtis	Bobbie in Bugaboo Land (1st, lg8vo, grey cl, 215p, 11 pl)	Bobbs-Merrill	(1907)	Kerr, George F.	180-250	
Dunham, Curtis	Golden Goblin (1st, lg8vo, ipcb, 190p, 8cp)	Bobbs-Merrill	(1906)	Kerr, George F.	200-300	
Burgess, Thornton	Mother West Wind's Animal Friends (1st, 12mo, 221p, 6pl)	Little/Brown	1912	Kerr, George F.	120-200	
Burgess, Thornton	Mother West Wind's Children (1st, 12mo, 243p, 7pl)	Little/Brown	1911	Kerr, George F.	120-200	
Burgess, Thornton	Mother West Wind's Neighbors (1st, 12mo, tan cl, 223p, 6pl)	Little/Brown	1913	Kerr, George F.	120-200	
Burgess, Thornton	Old Mother West Wind (1st, 12mo, 169p, 7pl, PPP)	Little/Brown	(1910)	Kerr, George F.	250-400	
Kessler, Ethel	Do Baby Bears Sit in Chairs? (1st {std}, sm4to, 32p, ibds, color, DJ/2.50)	Doubleday	1961	Kessler, E.& L.	30-45	
Kessler, Ethel	All Aboard the Train (1st {std}, ob4to, [46]p, color, DJ/2.95)	Doubleday	1964	Kessler, Leonard	20-30	
Kessler, Ethel	Are You Square? (1st {std}, ob4to, [40]p, ipcb, color, pep, DJ/3.50)	Doubleday	1966	Kessler, Leonard	30-50	
Kessler, Ethel	Big Red Bus (1st {std}, ob4to, [32]p, ibds, 2-color, DJ/2.00, NYTBI)	Doubleday	1957	Kessler, Leonard	60-90	
Branley, Franklyn	Book of Mars for You (1st, ob8vo, 56p, 2-color, DJ/3.95)	Crowell	(1968)	Kessler, Leonard	30-45	*
Scott, Rochelle	Colors, Colors All Around (1st, lg8vo, [41]p, ipcb, color, pep, DJ/1.95)	Grosset/Dunlap	(1965)	Kessler, Leonard	40-65	*
Kessler, Ethel	Crunch, Crunch (1st {std}, sq8vo, unpag, color, DJ/1.50)	Doubleday	1955	Kessler, Leonard	30-50	
Kessler, Ethel	Day Daddy Stayed Home (1st {std}, lg8vo, [32]p, color, DJ/2.00)	Doubleday	1959	Kessler, Leonard	25-45	
Schlein, Miriam	Deer in the Snow (1st, 4to, [42]p, fp 3-color, pep, DJ/2.50)	Abelard-Schuman	1956	Kessler, Leonard	30-50	*
Goldin, Augusta	Ducks Don't Get Wet (1st, 8vo, [40]p, color, DJ/2.95)	Crowell	(1965)	Kessler, Leonard	30-45	
Wood, James P.	Elephant in the Barn (1st, 8vo, 115p, b/w, DJ/2.50)	Harper	(1961)	Kessler, Leonard	20-35	
Schlein, Miriam	Fast is Not a Ladybug (1st, sm8vo, ipcb [34]p, 1-col, pep, DJ/1.75, NYTBI)	W.R. Scott	(1953)	Kessler, Leonard	30-50	
Schlein, Miriam	Heavy is a Hippopotamus (1st sm8vo, ipcb unpag, 1-col, pep, DJ/1.75, NYTBI)	W.R. Scott	1954	Kessler, Leonard	50-80	R
Rukeyser, Muriel	I Go Out (1st, 4to, [32]p, ipcb, color, DJ/2.95)	Harper	1961	Kessler, Leonard	50-80	R*
Kessler, Ethel	I Have Twenty Teeth - Do You? (1st, ob12mo, unpag, DJ/1.95)	Dodd	1959	Kessler, Leonard	30-45	*
Schlein, Miriam	It's About Time (1st, sm8vo, [41]p, ipcb, 1-color, pep, DJ/2.00)	W.R. Scott	1955	Kessler, Leonard	30-50	
Kessler, Leonard	Kick, Pass & Run (1st, 8vo, 64p, 2-color, DJ/1.95)	Harper	1966	Kessler, Leonard	25-40	
Kessler, Ethel	Kim and Me (1st {std}, ob8vo, ipcb, [29]p, fp 2-color, pep, DJ/2.00)	Doubleday	1960	Kessler, Leonard	30-50	
Silverberg, Robert	Lost Race of Mars (1st {std}, 8vo, 120p, b/w, DJ/2.95)	Winston	(1960)	Kessler, Leonard	40-65	
Kessler, Ethel	Peek-a-Boo (1st {std}, lg8vo, [32]p, ipcb, 3-color, pep, DJ/2.00)	Doubleday	1956	Kessler, Leonard	30-50	
Kessler, Ethel	Plink, Plink! (1st {std}, ob8vo, ipcb, [29]p, 3-color, pep, DJ/1.50)	Doubleday	1954	Kessler, Leonard	25-45	
McClintock, Marshall	What Have I Got? (1st, 8vo, ibds, 32p, fp color, DJ/1.50)	Harper	(1961)	Kessler, Leonard	50-80	
Ketchum, Jean	Stick-in-the-Mud (1st, sm8vo, unpag, green cl, pep, 1-color, DJ/1.50, JABA)	W.R. Scott	(1953)	Ketchum, Fred	30-50	
Keto, Emma	Ting-Ling and Mee-Too (1st, 8vo, ipcb, [37]p, color, pep, DJ/0.50)	Grosset/Dunlap	1937	Keto, Emma	30-50	
Keto, Emma	Tonto and Pronto (1st, 8vo, [32]p, ipcb, color, pep, DJ/0.50)	Grosset/Dunlap	(1938)	Keto, Emma	30-50	*
Leacock, Stephen B.	Nonsense Novels (1st, 8vo, 176p, grey bds, gilt, 8 color)	L: J. Lane	1921	Kettelwell, John	70-100	
N/A	Story of Aladdin (1st AM, 4to, yellow cl, 110p, 1-color)	Knopf	1928	Kettelwell, John	100-160	
Fuller, O. Muriel	Book of Dragons (1st, lg8vo, green cl, 181p, 4cp, DJ/2.50)	McBride	1931	Key, Alexander	60-100	
Key, Alexander	Red Eagle (1st, 4to, 95p, ibds, pep, color)	Volland	(1930)	Key, Alexander	40-70	
Key, Alexander	With Daniel Boone on Carolina Trail (1st, 8vo, 223p, gilt, 1-color, DJ/2.00)	Winston	(1941)	Key, Alexander	25-40	

AUTHOR	TITLE	PUBLISHER	DATE	ARTIST	PRICE	LC
Key, Ted	Biggest Dog in the World (1st {std}, 8vo, 72p, fp b/w, pep, DJ/2.50)	Dutton	(1960)	Key, Ted	20-30	
Kidd, Will	Dickydidos (1st, folio, 94p, ibds, 22cp)	L: Richards	[1903]	Kidd, Will	300-450	*
Montgomery, R.	Corey's Sea Monster (1st, sm8vo, 159p, fp b/w, DJ/3.75)	World	(1969)	Kidder, Harvey	25-35	
Rydberg, Ernie	Dark of the Cave (1st, 8vo, 118p, fp b/w, DJ/2.95)	McKay	1965	Kidwell, Carl	70-100	
Hubbard, Ralph	Wolf Song (1st {std}, 8vo, 287p, b/w pl, pep, DJ/2.00)	Doubleday/Doran	1935	Kihn, W. Landgon	40-65	
Scott, Lena B.	Dawn Boy of the Pueblos (1st, 8vo, 198p, 4cp, DJ/2.00)	Winston	1935	Kihn, W. Langdon	30-50	
Gall, Alice C.	Flat Tail (1st, lg8vo, 126p, color, pep, DJ/1.50)	Oxford U. Pr.	1935	Kihn, W. Langdon	40-65	
Latham, Jean L.	Columbia: Power House of North America (1st, 8vo, 96p, color, DJ)	Garrard Pub.	(1967)	Kilem, Fred	30-50	
Kilvert, Cory	Kite Book (1st, 4to, [36]p, ipcb, p-o, fp color)	Dodd	1909	Kilvert, Cory	120-180	
Forrester, Izola	Us Fellers (1st, 8vo, blue cl, p-o, 150p, 7cp)	Jacobs	1907	Kilvert, Cory	55-80	*
Wharton, Edith	Fruit of the Tree (1st, 12mo, 633p, red/gilt, 3pl)	Scribner	1907	Kimball, Alonzo	140-200	
Parrish, Randall	Love Under Fire (1st, 8vo, 400p, 5cp)	McClurg	1911	Kimball, Alonzo	25-40	*
Parrish, Randall	My Lady of the South (1st, 8vo, 360p, tan cl, 4cp)	McClurg	1909	Kimball, Alonzo	25-40	
Smith, Francis H.	Wood Fire in No.3 (1st, sm8vo, 298p, teg, uncut, 9cp)	Scribner	1905	Kimball, Alonzo	25-40	
Leekley, Thomas	World of Manabozho (1st, lg8vo, 128p, DJ/3.50)	Vanguard Press	(1965)	Kimball, Yeffe	25-45	
Hichens, Robert	Flames (1st AM, sm8vo, 523p, teg, pcb, cvr by...)	Herbert Stone	1897	Kimbrough, F.R.	55-80	
Magruder, Julia	Miss Ayr of Virginia (1st, 12mo, green cl, 395p, cvr by..)	Herbert Stone	1896	Kimbrough, F.R.	70-100	
Kinert, Reed	Little Helicopter (1st, sm8vo, [40]p, ipcb, color)	Macmillan	1947	Kinert, Reed	25-45	
Fort, Charles	LO! (1st, 8vo, 411p, 12 illus, DJ/2.50)	NY: Kendall	(1931)	King, Alexander	100-150	
McEvoy, Joseph P.	Slams of Life... (1st, sm4to, 127p, uncut, 10 fp b/w, cep)	Volland	(1919)	King, Frank	75-100	*
N/A	A Carol: Good King Wenceslas (4to, [26]p, wraps, p-o, 12 ticp)	L: L.B. Hill	[1920]	King, Jessie	500-800	
N/A	Arabian Nights (1st, 8vo, 501p, cvr by...)	L: Routledge	1904	King, Jessie	140-200	
Arcambeau, Edme	Book of Bridges (1st, 4to, 149p, teg, green/gilt, p-o, 18cp)	L: Gowans/Gray	1911	King, Jessie	600-800	
King, Jessie M.	Budding Life (1st, 8vo, unpag, wraps, 15pl)	L: Gowans/Gray	[1906]	King, Jessie	350-500	
Milton, John	Comus (1st, 12mo, 83p, teg, gilt, 10pl)	L: Routledge	1906	King, Jessie	350-500	
Morris, William	Defense of Gueneviere (1st, 8vo, teg, 310p, red/gilt, 24pl)	L: John Lane	1904	King, Jessie	500-700	
King, Jessie M.	Dwellings of an Old World Town (8vo, 51p, wraps, 24 b/w)	L: Gowans/Gray	1909	King, Jessie	200-300	
Grimm Bros.	Fairy Tales (1st, 8vo, 511p, cvr by....)	L: Routledge	(1904)	King, Jessie	120-160	
Andersen, Hans C.	Fairy Tales and Stories (1st, 8vo, blue/gilt, 512p, cvr by...)	L: Routledge	1903	King, Jessie	90-120	
Drummond, Florence	Fringes of Paradise (1st, 12mo, ipcb, 48p, 4cp)	L: F. Muller	(1935)	King, Jessie	100-165	
King, Jessie M.	Glasgow: City of the West (1st, 8vo, wraps, [27]p, 24 ticp)	L: Foulis	1910	King, Jessie	150-250	
King, Jessie M.	Grey City of the North (1st, 8vo, 51p, wraps, 26pl)	L: Foulis	(1910)	King, Jessie	150-250	
Evans, Sebastian (tr)	High History of the Holy Grail (1st, 8vo, uncut, gilt, teg, 379p, 22pl)	L: Dent	1903	King, Jessie	700-1000	
Wilde, Oscar	House of Pomegranates (1st, 4to, teg, 162p, gilt, 16 ticp, pep)	L: Methuen	(1915)	King, Jessie	700-900	
Wilde, Oscar	House of Pomegranates (1st AM, 4to, teg, 162p, gilt 16ticp, pep)	Brentano's	[1915]	King, Jessie	600-850	
King, Jessie M.	How Cinderella Was Able to Go to the Ball (1st, 8vo ibds, 57p teg, 16 ticp)	L: Foulis	(1924)	King, Jessie	600-800	
Keats, John	Isabella... (1st, 12mo, 42p, gilt, uncut, 6 ticp)	L: Foulis	1907	King, Jessie	100-175	
Buchanan, George	Jeptha (1st {1st illus bk.}, 8vo, blue/gilt, 130p. 5pl)	L: A. Gardner	[1903]	King, Jessie	300-450	
Hogg, James	Kilmeny (1st, 16mo, 31p, 5cp)	L: Foulis	1911	King, Jessie	150-200	
King, Jessie M.	Legends of Flowers (1st, sm8vo, gilt, teg, p-o, 168p, cvr & b/w by...)	L: Foulis	1908	King, Jessie	150-225	
Hawtrey, Valentina	Life of St. Mary Magdalen (1st, 12mo, gilt, 285p, teg, cvr by...)	L: John Lane	1904	King, Jessie	100-160	
King, Jessie M.	Little White Town of Never Weary (1st, 4to, 155p, 4 ticp, 16pl, cep)	L: Harrap	(1917)	King, Jessie	700-900	
Marion	Mummy's Bedtime Story Book (1st, folio, 55p, ipcb, 12cp, pep)	L: C. Palmer	(1929)	King, Jessie	1500-2500	
Shelley, Percy B.	Poems of Shelley (1st, 16mo, 244p, teg, purple/gilt, 8cp)	L: Jack	(1907)	King, Jessie	150-250	
Yeats, Wm. Butler	Poems of Spenser (1st, 16mo, purple/gilt, uncut, 290p, teg, 8cp)	L: Jack	(1906)	King, Jessie	150-225	
Hogg, James	Songs of Ettrick Shepherd (1st, 12mo, 151p, teg, 7 ticp)	L: Foulis	(1912)	King, Jessie	120-180	
Stowe, Harriet B.	Uncle Tom's Cabin (1st, 8vo, 529p, gilt, cvr by...)	L: Routledge	1904	King, Jessie	170-220	
Hughes, Langston	First Book of Rhythms (1st {std}, 8vo, 63p, color, DJ/1.75)	F. Watts	(1954)	King, Robin	200-300	
King, Alexander	Great Ker-Plunk (1st {std}, ob4to, [48]p, fp 2-color, pep, DJ/2.95)	Simon/Schuster	1962	King, Robin	40-65	*
Shippen, Kath. B.	I Know a City: Story of New York' Growth (1st, 8vo, 192p, b/w, DJ/2.75)	Viking	1954	King, Robin	20-35	*
Berry, Erick	Careers of Cynthia (1st, 8vo, red cl, 320p, 9 fp b/w)	Harcourt	(1932)	King, Ruth	20-35	*
Berry, Erick	Illustrations of Cynthia (1st {std}, 8vo, 205p, 8 fp b/w)	Harcourt	(1931)	King, Ruth	25-40	*
Knox, Esther M.	Swift Flies the Falcon (1st {std}, lg8vo, 245p, b/w, pep, DJ/2.00)	Winston	1939	King, Ruth	25-45	
Malkus, Alida S.	Timber Line (1st, 8vo, 247p, b/w, pep)	Harcourt	(1929)	King, Ruth	25-40	
Terhune, Albert P.	The Woman (1st, 12mo, 341p, gilt, 5pl)	Bobbs-Merrill	(1912)	King, W.B.	60-90	
Oakes, Vanya	Bamboo Gate (1st {std}, 8vo, 157p, red cl, b/w, DJ/2.00)	Macmillan	1946	Kingman, Dong	30-50	*
Bulla, Clyde R.	Johnny Hong of Chinatown (1st, 8vo, 69p, b/w, DJ/2.00)	Crowell	(1952)	Kingman, Dong	25-40	
Rinehart, Mary R.	Amazing Interlude (1st, sm8vo, 317p, 4pl)	Doran	(1918)	Kinneys	30-50	
Kinney, T.& M.	Dance: Its Place in Art & Life (1st, lg8vo, gilt, 334p, col frn, b/w)	Stokes	1914	Kinneys	50-80	
Bennet, Robert A.	For the White Christ (1st, 8vo, p-o, 474p, 4cp)	McClurg	1905	Kinneys	25-40	
Taylor, C. Bryson	Nicanor, Teller of Tales (1st, 8vo, p-o, 422p, pep, 5cp)	McClurg	1906	Kinneys	25-40	
Parrish, Randall	Prisoners of Chance (1st, 8vo, yellow cl, 423p, 4cp)	McClurg	1908	Kinneys	30-50	
Doyle, Arthur Conan	Sir Nigel (1st, sm8vo, green cl, 346p, 6pl)	McClure	1906	Kinneys	100-165	
Parrish, Randall	When Wilderness was King (1st, 8vo, 388p, uncut, 6cp, dep)	McClurg	1904	Kinneys	25-40	
Chandler, Edna W.	Cowboy Andy (1st {std}, lg8vo, 65p, color, pep, DJ/1.95)	Beginner Books	(1959)	Kinstler, Raymond	40-65	
Kipling, Rudyard	Jungle Book (1st, 8vo, blue/gilt, AEG, 212p, b/w)	L: Macmillan	1894	Kipling, J.L.	400-600	
Kipling, Rudyard	Kim (1st AM, 8vo, green/gilt, teg, 460p, uncut, 10pl)	Doubleday/Page	1901	Kipling, J.L.	200-300	
Kipling, Rudyard	Second Jungle Book (1st, 8vo, blue/gilt, AEG, 238p, b/w)	L: Macmillan	1895	Kipling, J.L.	400-600	
Kipling, Rudyard	Tales of the Punjab (1st, 8vo, 359p, black/gilt, 5pl)	L: Macmillan	1894	Kipling, J.L.	200-300	
Kipling, Rudyard	Just So Stories... (1st AM, lg8vo, green cl, 249p, b/w)	Doubleday/Page	1902	Kipling, Rudyard	350-500	R
Kipling, Rudyard	Just So Stories... (1st, sq4to, red/white, 249p, 22pl)	L: Macmillan	1902	Kipling, Rudyard	800-1200	
Berlic-Mazuranic	Croatian Tales of Long Ago (1st UK, 8vo, 258p, 10 ticp)	L: Allen/Unwin	(1924)	Kirin, V.	250-350	
Craik, Dinah	Adventures of a Brownie (1st {Gift ed}, lg8vo, teg, 281p, p-o, 14 ticp)	Lippincott	1922	Kirk, Maria L.	80-130	
Carroll, Lewis	Alice in Wonderland (1st, 8vo, 247p, grey/gilt, 12cp)	Stokes	(1904)	Kirk, Maria L.	160-240	
N/A	All Shakespeare's Tales (1st, lg8vo, gilt, p-o, 453p, 11cp)	Stokes	(1911)	Kirk, Maria L.	125-200	
Perry, Stella G.	Angel of Christmas (1st, 12mo, 112p, p-o, 4cp)	Stokes	1917	Kirk, Maria L.	40-70	
Montgomery, Lucy M.	Anne's House of Dreams (1st, 8vo, 346p, gilt, p-o, col frn)	Stokes	(1917)	Kirk, Maria L.	180-250	
MacDonald, George	Back of the North Wind (1st, 8vo, 352p, gilt, p-o, teg, 12cp)	Lippincott	1909	Kirk, Maria L.	90-120	

AUTHOR	TITLE	PUBLISHER	DATE	ARTIST	PRICE	LC
MacDonald, George	Back of the North Wind (new ed., 8vo, 126p, 6cp)	Lippincott	(1914)	Kirk, Maria L.	25-45	
De La Rame, L.	Bimbi (1st, 8vo, 212p, red/gilt, 8cp)	Lippincott	1910	Kirk, Maria L.	40-60	*
Chaucer, Geoffrey	Canterbury Pilgrims (1st, lg8vo, p-o, gilt, 310p, 12cp, pep)	Stokes	(1914)	Kirk, Maria L.	75-100	
Stevenson, Rbt. L.	Child's Garden of Verses (1st, 8vo, 191p, teg, gilt, 8cp)	Lippincott	1919	Kirk, Maria L.	100-160	
Irving, Washington	Child's Rip Van Winkle (1st, lg8vo, 39p, red cl, p-o, 12cp)	Stokes	(1908)	Kirk, Maria L.	80-120	
Hume, Fergus	Chronicles of Fairy-Land (1st, 8vo, 191p, teg, gilt, pep, 8cp)	Lippincott	1911	Kirk, Maria L.	300-500	
Spyri, Johanna	Cornelli... (1st {Gift ed.}, lg8vo, teg, 275p, p-o, pep, 14 ticp)	Lippincott	1921	Kirk, Maria L.	70-100	
Molesworth, Mrs.	Cuckoo Clock (1st, 8vo, teg, red/gilt, 283p, pep, 8cp)	Lippincott	1914	Kirk, Maria L.	40-60	*
Dowd, Emma C.	Doodles (1st, 12mo, 347p, grey cl, col frn)	Houghton	1915	Kirk, Maria L.	40-60	
Spyri, Johanna	Dora (1st, 8vo, red/gilt, 216p, 8cp)	Lippincott	(1924)	Kirk, Maria L.	35-60	*
Montgomery, Lucy M.	Emily Climbs (1st, sm8vo, green cl, 312p, col frn & p-o by)	Stokes	1925	Kirk, Maria L.	150-250	
Montgomery, Lucy M.	Emily of New Moon (1st, sm8vo, 351p, col frn & p-o by...)	Stokes	1923	Kirk, Maria L.	120-200	
Montgomery, Lucy M.	Emily's Quest (1st, sm8vo, 310p, green cl, p-o & col frn by...)	Stokes	1927	Kirk, Maria L.	120-200	
Longfellow, H.W.	Evangeline (1st, lg8vo, gilt, p-o, 260p, 11cp)	Stokes	(1913)	Kirk, Maria L.	120-180	*
Andersen, Hans C.	Fairy Tales (1st, 8vo, 219p, teg, pep, cp)	Lippincott	1911	Kirk, Maria L.	120-180	
Lounsberry, Alice	Frank & Bessie's Forester (1st, sm8vo, 191p, p-o & frn by...)	Stokes	(1912)	Kirk, Maria L.	35-60	
Spyri, Johanna	Gritli's Children (1st {Gift ed.}, lg8vo, 264p, p-o, teg, 14cp, pep)	Lippincott	(1924)	Kirk, Maria L.	80-120	
Swift, Jonathan	Gulliver's Travels (1st, 8vo, 221p, 8cp, pep)	Lippincott	1918	Kirk, Maria L.	50-85	
Spyri, Johanna	Heidi (1st, 8vo, red/gilt, 318p, 8cp)	Lippincott	1915	Kirk, Maria L.	60-90	
Spyri, Johanna	Heidi (1st {Gift ed.}, sm4to, gilt, 318p, teg, 14 ticp, pep)	Lippincott	(1919)	Kirk, Maria L.	100-165	
Daulton, George	Helter Skelters (1st, sm8vo, 294p, 4cp)	Stokes	1909	Kirk, Maria L.	30-50	
Longfellow, H.W.	Hiawatha (1st, lg8vo, gilt, 313p, p-o, 11cp, pep)	Stokes	(1910)	Kirk, Maria L.	100-175	
Tennyson, Alfred	Idylls of the King (1st, lg8vo, black cl, p-o, 394p, 12cp, pep)	Stokes	(1912)	Kirk, Maria L.	100-160	
Gellibrand, Emma	J. Cole (1st, sm8vo, 86p, beige cl, 4cp)	Lippincott	1917	Kirk, Maria L.	35-60	
Cory, David	Jumble Book (4to, unpag, p-o, 6 ticp)	NY: Sully	(1920)	Kirk, Maria L.	80-140	
Perry, Stella G.	Kind Adventure (1st, 12mo, 318p, green cl, p-o, 4cp)	Stokes	(1914)	Kirk, Maria L.	55-80	
Noseworthy, F.	Land of Play (1st, 4to, 128p, p-o, blue cl, 10cp)	Cupples/Leon	(1911)	Kirk, Maria L.	80-120	
Ogden, Ruth	Little Pierre & Big Peter (1st, 8vo, gilt, p-o, 367p, 5cp, pep)	Stokes	(1915)	Kirk, Maria L.	60-100	
Spyri, Johanna	Mazli (1st {Gift ed.}, lg8vo, 320p, teg, p-o, 14cp, pep)	Lippincott	(1923)	Kirk, Maria L.	90-120	
Spyri, Johanna	Moni the Goat Boy (1st, 12mo, red cl, 72p, 4cp)	Lippincott	1916	Kirk, Maria L.	40-60	*
Ingelow, Jean	Mopsa the Fairy (1st, lg8vo, teg, 257p, 10cp, pep)	Lippincott	1910	Kirk, Maria L.	90-120	
De La Rame, M.	Nurnberg Stove (1st, 12mo, 96p, 4cp)	Lippincott	1916	Kirk, Maria L.	25-40	
Collodi, Carlo	Pinocchio (1st, 8vo, 234p, red/gilt, teg, 8cp)	Lippincott	1916	Kirk, Maria L.	40-65	
Collodi, Carlo	Pinocchio (1st {Gift ed.}, lg8vo, 234p, p-o, teg, 14 ticp, pep)	Lippincott	(1920)	Kirk, Maria L.	160-250	
MacDonald, George	Princess & Curdie (1st, 8vo, 305p, gilt, 12cp)	Lippincott	1908	Kirk, Maria L.	80-120	
MacDonald, George	Princess & the Goblin (1st, 8vo, red/gilt, 305p, teg, pep, 12cp)	Lippincott	1907	Kirk, Maria L.	120-180	
Montgomery, Lucy M.	Rainbow Valley (1st, sm8vo, 341p, col frn & p-o by...)	Stokes	1919	Kirk, Maria L.	100-180	
Montgomery, Lucy M.	Rilla of Ingleside (1st, sm8vo, gilt, 370p, p-o, col frn)	Stokes	(1921)	Kirk, Maria L.	150-225	
Burnett, Frances H.	Secret Garden (1st, 8vo, p-o, teg, 375p, gilt, 4cp)	Stokes	(1911)	Kirk, Maria L.	500-650	
Darby, Ada C.	Skip-Come-a-Lou (1st, sm8vo, 243p, col frn)	Stokes	1928	Kirk, Maria L.	20-30	*
Carroll, Lewis	Through the Looking Glass (1st, 8vo, gilt, p-o, 271p, 12cp)	Stokes	(1905)	Kirk, Maria L.	225-325	
Spyri, Johanna	Vinzi (1st AM, 8vo, 296p, red cl, 8cp, pep)	Lippincott	1923	Kirk, Maria L.	30-50	
Kingsley, Charles	Water Babies (1st, 8vo, teg, 316p, 8cp, pep)	Lippincott	1917	Kirk, Maria L.	80-120	
Sedberry, J. Hamilton	Under the Flag of the Cross (1st, sm8vo, 472p, blue/gilt, 10pl)	C.M. Clark	1908	Kirkpatrick, W.	70-100	
Hudson, Wm. Henry	Disappointed Squirrel (1st, lg8vo, p-o, 144p, 8 ticp, pep)	Doran	(1925)	Kirmse, Marguerite	60-90	
Beattie, Janet	Good for Scuffles (1st, 4to, ibds, 41p, color, DJ/1.50)	Howell/Soskin	1944	Kirmse, Marguerite	30-50	
Atkinson, Eleanor	Greyfriars Bobby (1st, lg8vo, red cl, 269p, uncut, 4pl)	Harper	1929	Kirmse, Marguerite	30-50	
Terhune, Albert P.	Heart of a Dog (1st, 8vo, 249p, 8 ticp)	Doran	(1924)	Kirmse, Marguerite	70-100	
Rechnitzer, F.E.	Jinks of Jayson Valley (1st {std}, 8vo, 216p, b/w, DJ/2.00)	Winston	1950	Kirmse, Marguerite	25-40	
L'Hommedieu, Dorothy	Leo, the Little St. Bernard (1st {std}, 8vo, 62p, color, DJ/2.00)	Lippincott	(1948)	Kirmse, Marguerite	60-90	
Terhune, Albert P.	My Friend the Dog (1st {std}, lg8vo, gilt, 317p, 8 ticp, pep)	Harper	1926	Kirmse, Marguerite	70-100	
L'Hommedieu, Dorothy	Nipper the Little Bull Pup (1st {std}, 8vo, ibds, 58p, color, DJ/2.00)	Lippincott	(1943)	Kirmse, Marguerite	40-65	
Eberle, Irmengarde	Our Oldest Friends (1st, sm8vo, 146p, 1-color, DJ/2.00)	Holiday House	(1942)	Kirmse, Marguerite	40-65	
L'Hommedieu, Dorothy	Robbie, Brave Little Collie (1st {std}, 8vo, 60p, ibds, color, DJ/2.00)	Lippincott	(1946)	Kirmse, Marguerite	60-90	
L'Hommedieu, Dorothy	Rusty, Little Red Dachshund (1st, 8vo, 55p, color, pep, DJ/1.50)	Lippincott	1940	Kirmse, Marguerite	50-80	
L'Hommedieu, Dorothy	Scampy the Little Black Cocker (1st, sm4to, ibds, 62p, pep, color, DJ/1.50)	Lippincott	(1939)	Kirmse, Marguerite	70-100	
Kipling, Rudyard	Teem: A Treasure-Hunter (1st {std}, 12mo, 46p, b/w, DJ/1.00, frn by...)	Doubleday/Doran	1938	Kirmse, Marguerite	60-90	R
L'Hommedieu, Dorothy	Tyke, the Little Mutt (1st {std}, sq8vo, ibds, 63p, color, DJ/2.00)	Lippincott	(1949)	Kirmse, Marguerite	45-70	
Kirn, Ann	Beeswax Catches a Thief (1st {std}, ob4to, [48]p, ibds, color, DJ/3.95)	Norton	(1968)	Kirn, Ann	30-50	
Kirn, Ann	Full of Wonder (1st {std}, 8vo, [30]p, 2-color, DJ/2.75, NYTBI)	World	(1959)	Kirn, Ann	30-50	
Kirn, Ann	I Spy (1st {std}, 8vo, [32]p, color, DJ/2.95)	Norton	(1965)	Kirn, Ann	25-45	
Kirn, Ann	Leopard on a String (1st {std}, sq4to, [30]p, 3-color, DJ/2.75)	World	(1959)	Kirn, Ann	40-70	
Kirn, Ann	Let's Look at Tracks (1st, 8vo, 48p, fp 3-color, DJ)	Putnam	(1969)	Kirn, Ann	30-45	*
Kirn, Ann	Peacock and the Crow (1st, sq sm8vo, [32]p, color, DJ/3.95)	Four Winds Pr.	(1969)	Kirn, Ann	30-50	
Graham, Lynda	Pinky Marie (1st, 4to, ibds, [16]p, color)	Saalfield	1939	Kirn, Ann	30-50	
Kirn, Ann	Tale of a Crocodile (1st {std}, sm ob4to, [32]p, color, DJ/3.75)	Norton	(1968)	Kirn, Ann	30-50	*
Kirn, Ann	Tinkie (1st {std}, lg narrow 4to, [30]p, fp 2-color, cep, DJ/2.75)	World	(1960)	Kirn, Ann	30-50	
Kirn, Ann	Tip for Tap (1st {std}, lg8vo, [32]p, fp 3-color, DJ)	Norton	(1970)	Kirn, Ann	50-80	
Elder, Art	Blue Streak and Doctor Medusa (1st, sm8vo, 248p, b/w, pep, DJ)	Whitman	(1946)	Kirn, Frances	30-50	
Klem, Grace	Mike and his Neighbors (1st {std}, ob8vo, ibds, [28]p, color, DJ/0.75)	Doubleday/Doran	1941	Klem, Grace	35-50	*
Nesbit, Edith	Children's Shakespeare (1st, lg8vo, 128p, fp b/w, DJ/2.00)	Random	(1938)	Klep, Rolf	60-90	*
Borski, Lucia M.	Jolly Tailor (1st {std}, 8vo, 156p, col frn, fp b/w, pep)	Longmans	1928	Klepacki, Kazimir	30-50	*
Wyss, Johann D.	Swiss Family Robinson (8vo, green bds, 291p, gilt, 6cp, 8pl)	Nister/Dutton	[1900]	Kley, H.	75-100	
Montgomery, R.	Out of the Sun (1st, 8vo, 254p, b/w, DJ/2.00)	McKay	1943	Knight, Clayton	20-30	
Montgomery, R.	War Wings (1st, 8vo, 224p, col frn, DJ/2.00)	McKay	(1943)	Knight, Clayton	20-35	
Gallico, Paul	Snowflake (1st, sm8vo, 63p, ipcb, 1-color, DJ)	L: M. Joseph	(1952)	Knight, David	30-50	
Nash, Ogden	Animal Garden (1st, sq8vo, [48]p, dp 1-color, DJ/3.95)	NY: M. Evans	(1965)	Knight, Hilary	40-65	
DeBeaumont, Marie L.	Beauty and the Beast (1st, folio, ibds, 35p, fp color, DJ/1.95)	Macmillan	1963	Knight, Hilary	80-125	

AUTHOR	TITLE	PUBLISHER	DATE	ARTIST	PRICE	LC
Maiden, Cecil	Beginning with Mrs. McBee (1st, lg8vo, [46]p, fp color, cep, DJ/3.00)	Vanguard Press	(1960)	Knight, Hilary	60-90	
Dickens, Charles	Captain Boldheart & Magic Fishbone (1st {std}, 8vo, [48]p, col, DJ/3.50)	Macmillan	(1964)	Knight, Hilary	60-90	
Thompson, Kay	Eloise (1st {std}, 4to, 65p, white cloth, color, pep, DJ/2.95)	Simon/Schuster	1955	Knight, Hilary	250-400	
Thompson, Kay	Eloise at Christmastime (1st {std}, 4to, red ibds, [52]p, color, DJ/3.50)	Random	(1958)	Knight, Hilary	250-400	
Thompson, Kay	Eloise in Moscow (1st {std}, 4to, [66]p, ibds, pep, color, DJ/3.75)	Simon/Schuster	1959	Knight, Hilary	250-400	
Thompson, Kay	Eloise in Paris (1st {std}, 4to, red pcb, [65]p, color, pep, DJ/3.50)	Simon/Schuster	1957	Knight, Hilary	250-400	
MacDonald, Betty	Hello, Mrs. Piggle-Wiggle (1st {std}, 8vo, green cl, 119p, col, DJ/2.50)	Lippincott	(1957)	Knight, Hilary	150-220	
Knight, Hilary	Hilary Knight's Mother Goose (1st, lg4to, ibds, 62p, color, BGB)	Golden Press	1962	Knight, Hilary	45-70	
Bracken, Peg	I Hate to Cook Book (1st {std}, 8vo, 176p, b/w, DJ/3.75)	Harcourt	1960	Knight, Hilary	30-50	*
Scarry, Patricia	Jeremy Mouse Book (1st, lg sq4to, 64p, fp color, cep, DJ/3.95)	Amer. Heritage	1969	Knight, Hilary	65-100	
Maiden, Cecil	Speaking of Mrs. McCluskie (1st, 8vo, 43p, 3-color, DJ/3.00)	Vanguard Press	(1962)	Knight, Hilary	60-90	
Viorst, Judith	Sunday Morning (1st, ob8vo, [32]p, color, DJ/2.95)	Harper	(1968)	Knight, Hilary	30-50	
Knight, Hilary	Sylvia the Sloth (1st, 12mo, [32]p, pep, b/w, DJ/3.50)	Harper	(1969)	Knight, Hilary	40-65	
Henry, Jan	Tiger's Chance (1st {std}, 8vo, 138p, b/w, DJ/2.75)	Harcourt	(1957)	Knight, Hilary	50-80	
Gendel, Evelyn	Tortoise & the Turtle (1st {std}, 4to, ibds, [64]p, color, pep, DJ/2.95)	Simon/Schuster	1960	Knight, Hilary	40-70	
Gendel, Evelyn	Tortoise & Turtle Abroad (1st {std}, 4to, ibds, [55]p, b/w, pep, DJ/3.50)	Simon/Schuster	1963	Knight, Hilary	40-70	
Zolotow, Charlotte	When I Have a Little Girl (1st, 12mo, ibds, 32p, 1-color, pep, DJ/1.95)	Harper	(1965)	Knight, Hilary	25-40	
Zolotow, Charlotte	When I Have a Son (1st, sq24mo, [40]p, 2-color, DJ/1.95)	Harper	(1967)	Knight, Hilary	25-40	
Knight, Hilary	Where's Wallace? (1st, sq8vo, ibds, 40p, color, DJ/3.50)	Harper	1964	Knight, Hilary	25-40	
Gury, Jeremy	Wonderful World of Aunt Tuddy (1st {std}, 4to, ibds unpag, 1-color, DJ/3.50)	Random	(1958)	Knight, Hilary	80-125	
Knight, M. Forster	Mr. Tittlewit's Holiday (1st, 8vo, 153p, col frn, b/w, pep, DJ/1.50)	Lippincott	(1940)	Knight, M. Forster	30-45	
Haines, Alice C.	Boys (1st, lg4to, [18]p, ibds, 8cp)	Stokes	(1905)	Knipe, Emilie B.	80-120	
Knipe, A.A.	Cavalier Maid (1st, sm8vo, 255p, 6pl)	Macmillan	1919	Knipe, Emilie B.	30-50	
Chambers, Robert	Forest-Land (1st, lg8vo, ipcb, 118p, 8cp, pep)	Appleton	1905	Knipe, Emilie B.	150-220	
Haines, Alice C.	Girls (1st, lg4to, [18]p, ipcb, 4cp)	Stokes	(1905)	Knipe, Emilie B.	80-120	
Knipe, A.A.	Luck of Denewood (1st, sm8vo, 359p, brown cl, b/w)	Century	1921	Knipe, Emilie B.	35-60	
Knipe, E.B.	Mayflower Maid (1st, 8vo, 297p, blue cl, 4pl)	Century	1920	Knipe, Emilie B.	35-60	
Knipe, A.A.	Remember Rhymes (1st, 4to, brown/gilt, 80p, 4cp, pep)	Penn	1914	Knipe, Emilie B.	90-120	
Olmsted, Millicent	Land of Never Was (1st, 8vo, p-o, 148p, 12cp, pep)	Jacobs	(1908)	Knipe, Helen A.	70-120	
Olmsted, Millicent	Land of Really True (1st, 8vo, p-o, 187p, 12cp, pep)	Jacobs	(1909)	Knipe, Helen A.	70-120	
Sabin, Elbridge H.	Magical Man of Mirth (1st, 8vo, p-o, 233p, 8cp, pep)	Jacobs	(1910)	Knipe, Helen A.	100-150	
Sabin, Elbridge H.	Queen of the City of Mirth (1st, 8vo, p-o, 164p, 8cp, pep)	Jacobs	(1911)	Knipe, Helen A.	100-165	
Asbjornsen, P.C.	Norse Fairy Tales (1st, sm8vo, 463p, 8cp, 20pl, pep)	L: Freemantle	1910	Knowles, H.& R.	225-325	
Lagerlof, Selma	Christ Legends (1st, 8vo, 244p, blue cl, b/w)	L: E. Mathews	1930	Knowles, Horace J.	40-65	
Stirling, John	For a Little Child Like Me (1st, 8vo, 52p, blue cl, b/w, pep)	Scribner	1934	Knowles, Horace J.	30-50	
Pedley, Muriel	Land of Goodness Knows Where (1st, 8vo, 117p, col frn, b/w)	L: Newnes	(1923)	Knowles, Horace J.	100-150	
Knowles, Horace J.	Peeps into Fairyland (1st, lg4to, 89p, tan/gilt, 6cp, pep)	L: Butterworth	(1924)	Knowles, Horace J.	600-850	
Mother Goose	Mother Goose Rhymes (1st, 8vo, p-o, 199p, b/w)	Baker/Taylor	1911	Knowles, Machan	100-160	*
Mother Goose	Mother Goose Rhymes (1st, 8vo, 206p, cp)	NY: Noble	1917	Knowles, Machan	90-150	R*
Lee, Holme	Legends from Fairyland (1st, 8vo, 276p, blue/gilt, 17pl, pep)	L: Chatto	1907	Knowles, R.L.	200-300	
Asbjornsen, P.C.	Norse Fairy Tales (16mo, ibds, 8cp)	L: Routledge	[1920]	Knowles, R.L.	180-240	
Mason, Eugene (tr)	Old-World Love Stories (1st, 8vo, 282p, gilt, teg, 8 ticp)	L: J.M. Dent	1913	Knowles, R.L.	170-240	
Kennedy, Mildred	Forest Beyond the Woodlands (1st, 8vo, 152p, pcb, 14pl)	Knopf	1921	Knowlton, Vianna	80-120	
Gate, Ethel M.	Fortunate Days (1st, sm8vo, 127p, silhouettes)	Yale U. Press	1922	Knowlton, Vianna	25-40	
Jones, Weyman	Edge of Two Worlds (1st {std}, 8vo, 143p, b/w, DJ/3.95)	Dial Press	(1968)	Kocsis, J.C.	25-40	
Huston, Anne	Trust a City Kid (1st, 8vo, 192p, b/w, DJ/3.75)	Lothrop, Lee	(1966)	Kocsis, J.C.	45-70	*
Molloy, Anne	Celia's Lighthouse (1st, 8vo, 248p, fp b/w, DJ/2.50)	Houghton	1949	Koering, Ursula	40-65	*
Hughes, Langston	First Book of Negroes (1st {std}, sq8vo, gilt, 69p, color, DJ/1.75)	F. Watts	1952	Koering, Ursula	300-450	
Clymer, Eleanor	Little Bear Island (1st, 8vo, 143p, uncut, gilt, b/w, DJ/2.25)	McBride	1945	Koering, Ursula	30-50	*
Wier, Ester A.	Long Year (1st, 8vo, 150p, b/w, DJ/3.95)	McKay	(1969)	Koering, Ursula	20-30	
Gould, Jean	Miss Emily (1st, 8vo, 220p, b/w, DJ/2.50)	Houghton	1946	Koering, Ursula	30-45	
Elting, Mary	Patch (1st {std}, sm8vo, 146p, b/w, pep, DJ/2.00)	Doubleday	1948	Koering, Ursula	30-50	*
O'Neill, Hester	Picture Story of the Philippines (1st, 4to, [49]p, 3-color, pep, DJ/2.50)	McKay	1948	Koering, Ursula	30-50	
Bontemps, Arna	Slappy Hooper... (1st, lg ob8vo, 44p, color, pep, DJ/2.00)	Houghton	1946	Koering, Ursula	140-200	
Wier, Ester A.	The Winners (1st, 8vo, 179p, b/w, DJ/3.95)	McKay	(1968)	Koering, Ursula	20-30	*
Bacheller, Irving	Charge It (1st, 12mo, p-o, 192p, b/w)	Harper	1912	Koerner, W.H.D.	20-35	
Stanovsky, Vladislav	Fairy Tale Tree (1st, lg8vo, 452p, color, DJ/4.95)	Putnam	(1961)	Kolibal, Stanislav	45-70	
Hogan, Carol	Eighteen Cousins (1st, ob8vo, [36]p, fp color, DJ/3.50)	Parents Mag. Pr.	(1968)	Komoda, Beverly	25-45	*
Young, Miriam	Jellybeans for Breakfast (1st, ob8vo, gilt, [40]p, fp color, cep, DJ/3.50)	Parents Mag. Pr.	(1968)	Komoda, Beverly	120-200	*
Wise, Winifred	Revolt of the Darumas (1st, ob8vo, [38]p, fp color, DJ/3.95)	Parents Mag. Pr.	(1970)	Komoda, Beverly	25-40	
Holberg, Ruth	Jill & the Applebird House (1st {std}, 8vo, 161p, DJ/3.50)	Doubleday	(1968)	Komoda, Kiyoaki	20-35	*
George, Jean C.	Moon of the Fox Pups (1st, 8vo, 39p, fp b/w, DJ/3.75)	Crowell	(1968)	Komoda, Kiyoaki	20-35	
Konigsburg, E.L.	About the B'nai Bagels (1st {std}, 8vo, 172p, blue/gilt, b/w, cep, DJ/4.25)	Atheneum	1969	Konigsburg, E.L.	45-70	R
Konigsburg, E.L.	From Mixed-Up Files/Mrs. B. Frankweiler (1st {std} 8vo 162p DJ/3.95, NM)	Atheneum	1967	Konigsburg, E.L.	100-175	
Konigsburg, E.L.	Jennifer, Hecate, Macbeth.... (1st {std}, 8vo, 117p, b/w, DJ, NH)	Atheneum	1967	Konigsburg, E.L.	65-100	
Mendoza, George	Piece of String (1st {std}, 4to, 34p, 1-color, pep, DJ/3.50)	Obolensky	(1966)	Koplin, Norma J.	25-45	
Steele, William O.	Hound Dog Zip to the Rescue (1st, 8vo, 62p, color)	Garrard Pub.	1970	Korach, Mimi	20-25	
Meader, Stephen W.	Skippy's Family (1st {std}, 8vo, 153p, b/w, DJ/2.00)	Harcourt	(1945)	Korn, Elizabeth	80-140	
Krahn, Fernando	First Peko-Neko Bird (1st {std}, sq8vo, [46]p, fp b/w, DJ/3.95)	Simon/Schuster	(1969)	Krahn, Fernando	30-50	
Krahn, Fernando	Flying Saucer Full of Spaghetti (1st {std}, sq12mo, [29]p, color, DJ/3.95)	Dutton	(1970)	Krahn, Fernando	30-45	
Wahl, Jan	Furious Flycycle (1st {std}, 8vo, 114p, blue cl, b/w, DJ/3.50)	Delacorte Pr.	(1968)	Krahn, Fernando	25-40	
Krahn, Fernando	Gustavus and Stop (1st {std}, lg8vo, [40]p, color, DJ/4.50)	Dutton	(1969)	Krahn, Fernando	25-40	
Krahn, Fernando	Hildegarde & Maximilian (1st {std}, 12mo, [41]p, 2-color, DJ/3.50)	Delacorte Pr.	(1970)	Krahn, Fernando	30-45	
Krahn, Fernando	Journeys of Sebastian (1st {std}, ob12mo, [121]p, color, DJ/3.95)	Delacorte Pr.	(1968)	Krahn, Fernando	30-50	
Krahn, Fernando	Life of Numbers (1st {std}, sq8vo, [47]p, color, DJ/3.95)	Simon/Schuster	(1970)	Krahn, Fernando	30-50	
Gardner, Fred	Lioness Who Made Deals (1st {std}, sm4to, [22]p, color, DJ/4.25)	Norton	(1969)	Krahn, Fernando	30-45	*
Newman, Carol	Strella's Children (1st {std}, lg ob8vo, 40p, fp b/w, DJ/3.50)	Atheneum	1966	Krahn, Fernando	30-50	
Krahn, Fernando	Uncle Timothy's Traviata (1st {std}, ob4to, [32]p, color, pep, DJ/3.95)	Delacorte Pr.	(1967)	Krahn, Fernando	30-50	

AUTHOR	TITLE	PUBLISHER	DATE	ARTIST	PRICE	LC
Snow, Jack	Magical Mimics in Oz (1st, 8vo, grey cl, p-o, 243p, b/w, pep, DJ/2.00)	Reilly/Lee	(1946)	Kramer, Frank	350-500	
Snow, Jack	Shaggy Man of Oz (1st, lg8vo, grey cl, p-o, 254p, b/w, pep, DJ/2.00)	Reilly/Lee	(1949)	Kramer, Frank	350-500	
Kraus, Robert	All the Mice Came (1st, sm ob4to, ibds, [32]p, b/w, DJ/1.75)	Harper	(1955)	Kraus, Robert	70-100	
Kraus, Robert	Amanda Remembers (1st, 4to, ipcb, 32p, fp color, DJ/3.50)	Harper	(1965)	Kraus, Robert	30-50	
Kraus, Robert	Daddy Long Ears (1st, 12mo, [32]p, color, DJ/3.50)	Windmill Books	(1970)	Kraus, Robert	30-50	
Kraus, Robert	Hello Hippopotamus (1st, lg8vo, [32]p, color, DJ/3.95)	Windmill Books	(1969)	Kraus, Robert	40-65	
Kraus, Robert	I, Mouse (1st, 12mo, ibds, 32p, b/w, DJ/1.75)	Harper	(1958)	Kraus, Robert	50-85	
Kraus, Robert	Junior, the Spoiled Cat (1st, 4to, [32]p, b/w, pep, DJ/2.00)	Oxford U. Pr.	1955	Kraus, Robert	30-50	
Kraus, Robert	Ladybug, Ladybug (1st, ob4to, ipcb, [30]p, b/w, DJ/1.75)	Harper	(1957)	Kraus, Robert	30-50	
Kraus, Robert	Little Giant (1st, 12mo, [32]p, color, cep, DJ/2.50)	Harper	(1967)	Kraus, Robert	25-45	*
Kraus, Robert	Littlest Rabbit (1st, 8vo, 32p, ipcb, 2-color, DJ/1.95)	Harper	(1961)	Kraus, Robert	20-30	
Kraus, Robert	Miranda's Beautiful Dream (1st, 8vo, [32]p, ibds, fp 3-color, DJ/1.95)	Harper	(1964)	Kraus, Robert	20-35	
Kraus, Robert	My Son the Mouse (1st, ob12mo, ipcb, [32]p, 1-color, DJ/1.95)	Harper	1966	Kraus, Robert	30-45	
Kraus, Robert	Penguin's Pal (1st, 8vo, ibds, 31p, 2-color, DJ/2.50)	Harper	(1964)	Kraus, Robert	20-35	
Stevens, Carla	Rabbit and Skunk & the Scary Rock (1st, ob8vo, [46]p, 1-color, DJ/2.75)	W.R. Scott	1962	Kraus, Robert	30-45	*
Anderson, Paul S.	Red Fox and the Hungry Tiger (1st, lg ob8vo, [48]p, 3-color, DJ/3.50)	W.R. Scott	1962	Kraus, Robert	30-50	*
Kraus, Robert	Trouble with Spider (1st, 8vo, 32p, color, DJ/1.95)	Harper	(1962)	Kraus, Robert	30-50	
Krauss, Ruth	This Thumbprint (1st, 12mo, [30]p, 1-color, cep, DJ/1.95)	Harper	(1967)	Krauss, Ruth	25-40	
Carroll, Lewis	Alice in Wonderland (1st, 8vo, 150p, color)	Random	(1946)	Kredel, Fritz	55-90	*
Roosevelt, Eleanor	Christmas (1st {std}, 24mo, ibds, 42p, 8 fp b/w, dep, DJ/0.50)	Knopf	1940	Kredel, Fritz	30-50	
Eunson, Dale	Day they Gave Babies Away (1st, 8vo, 38p, ibds, b/w, DJ/2.00)	Farrar, Straus	1947	Kredel, Fritz	25-40	
Peet, Creighton	Defending America (1st {std}, 8vo, 160p, color, pep, DJ/1.50)	Harper	(1941)	Kredel, Fritz	30-50	
Murphy, Shirley R.	Elmo Doolan & Search for Golden Mouse (1st {std}, 8vo, 125p, b/w, DJ/4.25)	Viking	(1970)	Kredel, Fritz	20-35	
Grimm Bros.	Fairy Tales (1st, 8vo, 373p, 10cp, cep)	Grosset/Dunlap	(1945)	Kredel, Fritz	50-80	R
Bogan, Louise	Golden Journey (1st, lg8vo, 275p, 1-color, woodcuts, DJ/5.95)	Reilly/Lee	(1965)	Kredel, Fritz	50-80	R*
Steele, William O.	Golden Root (1st {std}, sm8vo, ibds, 76p, fp b/w, DJ/1.75)	Aladdin	1951	Kredel, Fritz	30-50	*
Wheeler, Opal	H.M.S. Pinafore (1st {std}, 4to, ibds, 96p, color, pep, DJ/3.00)	Dutton	1946	Kredel, Fritz	40-65	
Ruskin, John	King of the Golden River (1st {std}, 8vo, 113p, color, pep, DJ/1.25, RC)	World	(1946)	Kredel, Fritz	25-40	
Eaton, Jeanette	Leaders in Other Lands (1st, 8vo, 322p, color, DJ)	D.C. Heath	(1950)	Kredel, Fritz	25-40	
Pauli, Hertha	Little Town of Bethlehem (1st {std} 12mo, [44]p, gilt, color, pep, DJ/2.50)	Duell, Sloan	(1963)	Kredel, Fritz	25-40	
Steele, William O.	Over-Mountain Boy (1st {std}, 8vo, 192p, b/w, DJ/1.75)	Aladdin	1952	Kredel, Fritz	20-30	
Zoff, Otto (ed)	Riddles Around the World (1st, 4to, ibds, [48]p, color, DJ/2.00)	Pantheon	(1946)	Kredel, Fritz	30-50	
Brown, Marion	Silent Storm (1st {A}, 8vo, 250p, fp b/w, DJ/3.25)	Abingdon Press	(1963)	Kredel, Fritz	25-40	*
Hoffmann, Heinrich	Slovenly Peter (1st {std}, lg8vo, ibds, [30]p, color)	Harper	1935	Kredel, Fritz	120-180	*
Latham, Jean L.	Story of Eli Whitney (1st {std}, 8vo, 192p, b/w, DJ/1.75)	Aladdin	1953	Kredel, Fritz	45-70	
Lamb, Charles	Tales from Shakespeare (1st, 8vo, 296p, color, pep, DJ/1.00)	Garden City	1939	Kredel, Fritz	30-50	
Wibberley, Leonard	Time of the Lamb (1st, 16mo, 47p, fp b/w, cep, DJ/2.50)	NY: Washburn	(1961)	Kredel, Fritz	25-45	*
Gurko, Leo	Tom Paine, Freedom's Apostle (1st {std}, 8vo, 213p, b/w, DJ/2.75, NH)	Crowell	(1957)	Kredel, Fritz	50-80	
Snedeker, Caroline D.	White Isle (1st {std}, 8vo, 271p, pep, b/w pl, DJ/2.00)	Doubleday/Doran	1940	Kredel, Fritz	30-50	
Boyle, Kay	Youngest Camel (1st {std}, 8vo, 96p, beige cl, 6cp, DJ/2.00)	Little/Brown	1939	Kredel, Fritz	50-90	R
Schmidt, Sarah L.	Secret of Silver Peak (1st, sm8vo, 334p, rust cl, b/w, DJ/2.00)	Random	(1938)	Kreis, Hans	30-50	*
Eberle, Irmengarde	Visiting Jimpsons (1st, 8vo, 188p, pep, DJ/2.00)	Harcourt	(1946)	Kreps, Ruth	20-35	*
Alexander, Lloyd C.	Border Hawk: August Bondi (1st {std}, 8vo, 182p, b/w, pep, DJ/2.95)	Farrar, Straus	(1958)	Krigstein, Bernard	30-50	
Alexander, Lloyd C.	Flagship Hope and Aaron Lopez (1st, 8vo, 179p, pep, DJ/2.95)	Farrar, Straus	(1960)	Krigstein, Bernard	30-45	
Lampman, Evelyn	Rusty's Space Ship (1st {std}, 8vo, 240p, b/w, DJ/2.95)	Doubleday	1957	Krigstein, Bernard	25-45	*
Fyleman, Rose	Katy Kruse Play Book (1st AM, sm4to, p-o, 32p, 12cp)	McKay	(1930)	Kruse, Katy	120-180	*
Fyleman, Rose	Katy Kruse Play Book (1st, sm4to, ibds, p-o, 32p, 12cp)	L: Harrap	(1930)	Kruse, Katy	125-185	*
Farjeon, Eleanor	Perfect Zoo (1st, ob4to, red cl, p-o, 31p, 12cp)	McKay	(1929)	Kruse, Katy	140-200	
Scott, Sally	Benjie & his Family (1st {std}, 8vo, yellow cl, [62]p, fp b/w, DJ/2.00)	Harcourt	(1952)	Krush, Beth	25-45	
Scott, Sally	Binky's Fire (1st {std}, 8vo, [54]p, fp b/w, DJ/1.75)	Harcourt	(1952)	Krush, Beth	25-40	*
Scott, Sally	Bitsy (1st {std}, 8vo, 41p, b/w, DJ/2.25)	Harcourt	(1957)	Krush, Beth	25-40	*
Scott, Sally	Bobby & his Band (1st {std}, 8vo, [46]p, fp b/w, DJ/2.00)	Harcourt	(1954)	Krush, Beth	25-40	*
Scott, Sally	Brand New Kitten (1st {std}, 8vo, 54p, fp b/w, DJ/2.25)	Harcourt	(1956)	Krush, Beth	25-40	*
Caudill, Rebecca	Higgins and the Great Big Scare (1st {std}, 8vo, 87p, b/w, DJ/2.95)	Holt, Rinehart	(1960)	Krush, Beth	20-35	
Scott, Sally	Jenny & the Wonderful Jeep (1st {std}, 8vo, 47p, b/w, DJ/2.50)	Harcourt	(1963)	Krush, Beth	25-40	
Scott, Sally	Judy's Summer Adventure (1st {std}, 8vo, 61p, b/w, DJ/2.50)	Harcourt	(1960)	Krush, Beth	20-30	*
Scott, Sally	Little Wiener (1st {std}, 8vo, ibds, [48]p, b/w, DJ/1.75)	Harcourt	(1951)	Krush, Beth	30-50	*
Scott, Sally	Mr. Doodle (1st, 8vo, 45p, fp b/w, DJ/1.75)	Harcourt	(1947)	Krush, Beth	25-45	*
Scott, Sally	Rip & Royal (1st {std}, 8vo, 58p, tan cl, b/w, DJ/1.75)	Harcourt	(1950)	Krush, Beth	30-60	*
Welty, Eudora	Shoe Bird (1st {std}, lg8vo, 88p, b/w, DJ/3.50)	Harcourt	(1964)	Krush, Beth	150-225	
Scott, Sally	Sunny Jim the Uppity Kitten (1st {std}, 8vo, 46p, b/w, DJ/2.50)	Harcourt	(1962)	Krush, Beth	25-45	
Scott, Sally	There was Timmy! (1st {std}, 8vo, 46p, b/w, DJ/2.25)	Harcourt	(1959)	Krush, Beth	20-30	*
Scott, Sally	Tinker Takes a Walk (1st {std}, 8vo, 62p, b/w, DJ/2.25)	Harcourt	(1958)	Krush, Beth	20-30	
Scott, Sally	Tippy (1st {std}, 8vo, [48]p, b/w, DJ/1.75)	Harcourt	(1950)	Krush, Beth	20-30	*
Weiss, Edna S.	Truly Elizabeth (1st, 8vo, 178p, b/w, DJ/2.50)	Houghton	1957	Krush, Beth	30-50	*
Scott, Sally	What Susan Wanted (1st {std}, sm8vo, pink cl, 36p, fp b/w, DJ/2.00)	Harcourt	(1956)	Krush, Beth	30-50	
Cameron, Eleanor	Beast with the Magical Horn (1st {std}, 8vo, 73p, color, DJ/3.75)	Little/Brown	1963	Krush, Beth & Joe	140-200	
Norton, Mary	Borrowers Afield (1st AM {std}, 8vo, 215p, green cl, b/w, DJ/2.50)	Harcourt	(1955)	Krush, Beth & Joe	120-185	R
Norton, Mary	Borrowers Afloat (1st AM {std}, 8vo, 191p, b/w, DJ/2.75)	Harcourt	(1959)	Krush, Beth & Joe	100-165	
Norton, Mary	Borrowers Aloft (1st AM {std}, 8vo, 193p, fp b/w, DJ/2.95)	Harcourt	(1961)	Krush, Beth & Joe	100-175	R
Cleary, Beverly	Emily's Runaway Imagination (1st, 8vo, 221p, b/w, DJ/2.95)	Wm. Morrow	1961	Krush, Beth & Joe	25-40	
Cleary, Beverly	Fifteen (1st, 8vo, 254p, b/w, DJ/2.75)	Wm. Morrow	1956	Krush, Beth & Joe	25-40	
Cooper, Elizabeth	Fish from Japan (1st {std}, 4to, [32]p, color, DJ/3.75)	Harcourt	(1969)	Krush, Beth & Joe	25-45	
Enright, Elizabeth	Gone-Away Lake (1st {std}, 8vo, 192p, green cl, b/w, DJ/3.00, NH)	Harcourt	(1957)	Krush, Beth & Joe	70-100	
Cleary, Beverly	Jean & Johnny (1st, 8vo, 284p, b/w, DJ/2.95)	Wm. Morrow	1959	Krush, Beth & Joe	20-35	
Untermeyer, Louis	Magic Circle (1st, 8vo, 288p, fp b/w, DJ/3.00)	Harcourt	(1952)	Krush, Beth & Joe	35-60	*
Fritz, Jean	Magic to Burn (1st, 8vo, 255p, b/w, DJ/3.75)	Coward	(1964)	Krush, Beth & Joe	45-70	
Sorensen, Virginia	Miracles on Maple Hill (1st {std}, 8vo, 180p, b/w, DJ/2.95, NM)	Harcourt	(1956)	Krush, Beth & Joe	60-100	R

AUTHOR	TITLE	PUBLISHER	DATE	ARTIST	PRICE	LC
Hightower, Florence	Mrs. Wappinger's Secret (1st, 8vo, 280p, b/w, DJ/3.00)	Houghton	1956	Krush, Beth & Joe	30-50	*
Cameron, Eleanor	Mysterious Christmas Shell (1st {std}, 8vo, 184p, b/w, DJ/3.25)	Little/Brown	(1961)	Krush, Beth & Joe	80-130	
Courlander, Harold	Piece of Fire (1st {std}, 8vo, 128p, b/w, DJ/3.25)	Harcourt	(1964)	Krush, Beth & Joe	45-70	*
Enright, Elizabeth	Return to Gone-Away (1st {std}, 8vo, 191p, fp b/w, DJ/3.25)	Harcourt	(1961)	Krush, Beth & Joe	60-90	R
Carlsen, Ruth C.	Ride a Wild Horse (1st {std}, 8vo, 164p, b/w, DJ/3.50)	Houghton	1970	Krush, Beth & Joe	50-80	
Cleary, Beverly	Sister of the Bride (1st, 8vo, 288p, b/w, DJ/3.25)	Wm. Morrow	1963	Krush, Beth & Joe	25-35	
Lansing, Elisabeth H.	Small Circus (1st, 8vo, 150p, b/w, DJ/2.50)	Crowell	(1957)	Krush, Beth & Joe	25-45	
Cameron, Eleanor	Spell is Cast (1st {std}, 8vo, 271p, b/w, DJ/3.95)	Little/Brown	(1964)	Krush, Beth & Joe	160-225	
Kramer, Nora	Storybook (1st, lg8vo, 160p, b/w, cep, DJ/2.95)	J. Messner	(1955)	Krush, Beth & Joe	45-75	
Langstaff, John	Swapping Boy (1st {std}, sm4to, [32]p, color, pep, DJ/2.95)	Harcourt	(1960)	Krush, Beth & Joe	30-50	
Cameron, Eleanor	Terrible Churnadryne (1st {std}, 8vo, 125p, b/w, DJ/3.00)	Little/Brown	(1959)	Krush, Beth & Joe	80-130	*
Norton, Mary	The Borrowers (1st AM {std}, 8vo, 180p, blue cl, b/w, DJ/2.50, CgM)	Harcourt	(1953)	Krush, Beth & Joe	180-250	
Naylor, Phyllis	To Make a Wee Moon (1st, 8vo, 190p, b/w, DJ/3.95)	Follett	(1969)	Krush, Beth & Joe	20-35	
Ogburn, Charlton	Big Caesar (1st, 8vo, 118p, b/w, DJ/2.75)	Houghton	1958	Krush, Joe	25-45	*
Chambers, Maria C.	Boy Heroes of Chapultepec (1st {std}, 8vo, 182p, 1-color, pep, DJ/1.50)	Winston	(1953)	Krush, Joe	30-50	*
Scott, Sally	Chica (1st {std}, 8vo, 114p, rust cl, fp b/w, DJ/2.25)	Harcourt	(1954)	Krush, Joe	25-45	
West, Jassamyn	Cress Delahanty (1st {std}, 8vo, 311p, b/w, DJ/3.75)	Harcourt	(1953)	Krush, Joe	25-40	
Norton, Andre	Huon of the Horn (1st {std}, 8vo, 208p, b/w, DJ/2.75)	Harcourt	1951	Krush, Joe	100-175	
Langstaff, John	Ol' Dan Tucker (1st {std}, sm4to, [33]p, color, cep, DJ/2.95)	Harcourt	(1963)	Krush, Joe	30-50	
Welty, Eudora	Ponder Heart (1st {std}, 8vo, ibds, 158p, b/w, DJ/3.00)	Harcourt	(1954)	Krush, Joe	150-225	
Sandburg, Carl	Prairie-Town Boy (1st, 8vo, 179p, b/w, DJ/2.75)	Harcourt	(1955)	Krush, Joe	30-50	
Trease, Geoffrey	Secret Fiord (1st AM {std}, sm8vo, 241p, b/w, DJ/2.50)	Harcourt	(1950)	Krush, Joe	25-45	
Trease, Geoffrey	Trumpets in the West (1st AM {std}, 8vo, 239p, b/w, pep, DJ/2.50)	Harcourt	(1947)	Krush, Joe	30-50	
Kubinyi, Laszlo	Cat and the Flying Machine (1st {std}, 8vo, 48p, fp b/w, DJ/3.95)	Simon/Schuster	(1970)	Kubinyi, Laszlo	25-40	
Kubinyi, Laszlo	Zeki and the Talking Cat (1st {std}, lg8vo, 47p, b/w, DJ/3.95)	Simon/Schuster	1970	Kubinyi, Laszlo	25-40	
Salten, Felix	Bambi's Children (1st, 8vo, [32]p, ibds, color, DJ/0.50)	Grosset/Dunlap	(1948)	Kuhn, Bob	25-45	
Kjelgaard, Jim	Big Red (1st, sm8vo, 231p, tan cl, b/w, pep, DJ/2.00)	Holiday House	(1945)	Kuhn, Bob	25-40	
Taber, Gladys	First Book of Dogs (1st, 8vo, 45p, color, pep, DJ/1.50)	F. Watts	(1949)	Kuhn, Bob	30-50	
Kjelgaard, Jim	Kalak of the Ice (1st, sm8vo, 201p, b/w, DJ/2.50)	Holiday House	(1949)	Kuhn, Bob	150-220	
Enckling, Louise	Toy Maker (1st, 8vo, 16p, p-o, color, pep, DJ/1.00)	Whitman	1935	Kukenthal, Fritz	40-70	
Pratt, Davis	Magic Animals of Japan (1st, ob4to, [32]p, color, dep, DJ/3.95)	Parnassus Press	1967	Kula, Elsa	40-65	
Kunhardt, Dorothy	Brave Mr. Buckingham (1st, sm sq8vo, [63]p, fp 1-color, DJ/1.00)	Harcourt	(1935)	Kunhardt, Dorothy	100-165	
Kunhardt, Dorothy	Junket is Nice (1st, sm ob4to, ibds, [63]p, 1-color)	Harcourt	1933	Kunhardt, Dorothy	200-300	
Kunhardt, Dorothy	Lucky Mrs. Ticklefeather (1st, sm ob4to, ibds, [63]p, 1-color, DJ/1.25)	Harcourt	1935	Kunhardt, Dorothy	100-160	
Kunhardt, Dorothy	Now Open the Box (1st, sm ob4to, [61]p, ipcb, color)	Harcourt	1934	Kunhardt, Dorothy	100-160	
Kunhardt, Dorothy	Wise Old Aard-Vark (1st, ob4to, ibds, 62p, 1-color, DJ/1.00)	Viking	1936	Kunhardt, Dorothy	120-180	
Rockwood, Roy	Through Space to Mars (1st, sm8vo, 248p, blue cl, 4pl)	Cupples/Leon	(1910)	Kuser, G.M.	65-90	
Kuskin, Karla	ABCDEFGHIJKLMNOPQR... (1st, 24mo, [56]p, ipcb, color, pep, DJ/3.75)	Harper	(1963)	Kuskin, Karla	30-50	*
Kuskin, Karla	Alexander Soames (1st, 8vo, [48]p, 1-color, DJ/1.95)	Harper	(1962)	Kuskin, Karla	30-50	
Kuskin, Karla	All Sizes of Noises (1st, ob8vo, ipcb, [32]p, 3-color, DJ/1.95)	Harper	(1962)	Kuskin, Karla	30-45	
Kuskin, Karla	Animals and the Ark (1st, lg ob8vo, ipcb, [32]p, fp 3-color, DJ/2.50)	Harper	(1958)	Kuskin, Karla	30-50	
Kuskin, Karla	Bear Who Saw Spring (1st, 4to, ipcb, [47]p, 3-color, DJ/2.50)	Harper	(1961)	Kuskin, Karla	30-50	
Kafka, Sherry	Big Enough (1st, 12mo, [32]p, 2-color, DJ/3.50)	Putnam	(1970)	Kuskin, Karla	40-65	*
Schmitt, Gladys	Boris the Lopsided Bear (1st {std}, 8vo, 32p, fp b/w, DJ/2.95)	Collier Books	(1966)	Kuskin, Karla	30-50	
Latham, Jean L.	Dog that Lost his Family (1st {std}, 8vo, [32]p, fp 2-color, DJ/2.50)	Macmillan	1961	Kuskin, Karla	30-50	
Levine, Rhoda	Harrison Loved his Umbrella (1st {std}, sq12mo, [46]p, 3-color, cep, DJ)	Atheneum	1964	Kuskin, Karla	30-45	
Kuskin, Karla	In the Flaky Frosty Morning (1st, 8vo, ipcb, [26]p, fp 2-col, dep, DJ/3.95)	Harper	1969	Kuskin, Karla	30-50	
Kuskin, Karla	In the Middle of the Trees (1st, lg4to, 38p, 2-color, cep, DJ/2.50)	Harper	(1958)	Kuskin, Karla	60-100	R
Kuskin, Karla	James & the Rain (1st, sq8vo, [38]p, ibds, 2-color, DJ/2.25)	Harper	(1957)	Kuskin, Karla	30-50	
Kuskin, Karla	Just Like Everyone Else (1st, 24mo, [32]p, fp 1-color, DJ/1.50)	Harper	(1959)	Kuskin, Karla	40-65	
Rudolph, Marguerita	Look at Me (1st, ob12mo, [38]p, color, DJ/2.75)	McGraw-Hill	(1967)	Kuskin, Karla	25-45	
Kuskin, Karla	Roar & More (1st [1st bk.], ob8vo, [45]p, fp 2-color, DJ/2.00)	Harper	(1956)	Kuskin, Karla	70-120	R
Kuskin, Karla	Rose on My Cake (1st, 4to, [42]p, ibds, b/w, DJ/2.50)	Harper	(1964)	Kuskin, Karla	30-45	
Kuskin, Karla	Sand and Snow (1st, ob12mo, ipcb, [32]p, fp color, cep, DJ/2.50)	Harper	(1965)	Kuskin, Karla	30-50	*
Kuskin, Karla	Square as a House (1st, ob8vo, [23]p, fp 2-color, DJ/2.50)	Harper	(1960)	Kuskin, Karla	40-65	
Kuskin, Karla	Walk the Mouse Girls Took (1st, 8vo, 32p, ibds, color, DJ/2.50)	Harper	(1967)	Kuskin, Karla	30-45	
Kuskin, Karla	Watson, Smartest Dog in the USA (1st, lg ob4to, [32]p, color, DJ/3.50)	Harper	(1968)	Kuskin, Karla	30-50	
Winn, Marie	What Shall We Do & Allee Galloo! (1st, 4to, ibds, 87p, 2-color, DJ/5.95)	Harper	(1970)	Kuskin, Karla	30-50	
Kuskin, Karla	Which Horse is William? (1st, ob8vo, [30]p, 2-color, DJ/1.95)	Harper	(1959)	Kuskin, Karla	30-45	
Seidman, Mitzi	Who Woke the Sun? (1st {std}, 12mo, [31]p, fp color, DJ/1.95)	Macmillan	(1960)	Kuskin, Karla	30-50	
Viertel, Violette	Xingu (1st {std}, 8vo, 73p, green cl, 1-color, DJ/2.75)	Macmillan	(1959)	Kuskin, Karla	30-50	
Lang, Andrew	Blue Fairy Book (1st, 8vo, 372p, gilt, 2-color frn, b/w, pep, DJ/2.00)	Longmans	(1948)	Kutcher, Ben	30-50	
Andersen, Hans C.	Fairy Tales (1st, lg8vo, 367p, gilt, p-o, 24cp)	Penn	(1930)	Kutcher, Ben	55-80	*
Wilde, Oscar	House of Pomegranates (1st, 8vo, black/gilt, 180p, 16pl, pep)	Dodd	1925	Kutcher, Ben	55-80	
Moore, Thomas	Lalla Rookh (1st, sm4to, 179p, red/gilt, uncut, 16pl, pep)	MacVeagh/Dial	1930	Kutcher, Ben	55-80	
Maury, Jean W.	Old Raven's World (1st, 8vo, 281p, col frn, 6pl, pep)	Little/Brown	1931	Kutcher, Ben	20-35	
Shakespeare, Wm.	Venus & Adonis (1st, 4to, red/gilt, 112p, pep, 12cp)	Macveagh/Dial	1930	Kutcher, Ben	35-60	*
Clement, Marguerite	All the World is Colour (1st AM, lg4to, [95]p, 2-color, pep)	Farrar/Rinehart	[1930]	L'Hardy, P.& G.	30-50	
Clement, Marguerite	Flowers of Chivalry (1st {std}, 4to, ipcb, 72p, color, cep)	Doubleday/Doran	1934	L'Hardy, P.& G.	60-100	*
Atkins, Elizabeth H.	Pot of Gold (1st, 8vo, p-o, 164p, 4cp, 6pl, pep)	Stokes	1930	LaDow, St. C.	55-80	*
Bowman, James C.	John Henry, Rambling Black Ulysses (1st, 8vo, 288p, 2cp, 12pl, DJ/2.50)	Whitman	1942	LaGrone, Roy	30-50	
Hoffmann, Ernst T.	Tales of Hoffmann (1st, 4to, 207p, 10cp)	L: Harrap	(1932)	Laboccetta, Mario	140-200	
Hoffmann, Ernst T.	Tales of Hoffmann (sm4to, 207p, 10 fp color)	Dodd	[1933]	Laboccetta, Mario	60-85	
Baker, Cornelia	Magic Image from India (1st, sm4to, 163p, 6cp)	Stern	1909	Lachman, Harry B.	65-90	
Adams, Kathleen	Book of Giant Stories (1st, lg8vo, 205p, 8pl, pep)	Dodd	(1926)	Lahr, Robert W.	20-30	
Laird, Rowena	Stuffy (1st, 4to, [32]p, p-o, color, DJ/2.00)	Wm. Morrow	1945	Laird, Rowena	30-50	
Dodge, Louis	Everychild (1st, 8vo, 284p, pep, uncut, 6cp)	Scribner	1921	Laite, B.F.	30-50	
Belting, Natalia	Elves and Ellefolk (1st {std}, lg8vo, 95p, b/w, DJ/3.00)	Holt, Rinehart	(1961)	Laite, Gordon	20-30	

AUTHOR	TITLE	PUBLISHER	DATE	ARTIST	PRICE	LC
Seeger, Elizabeth	Five Sons of King Pandu (1st, 8vo, 340p, fp color, DJ/6.95)	W.R. Scott	(1967)	Laite, Gordon	30-50	
Seeger, Elizabeth	The Ramayana (1st, lg8vo, 244p, fp color, DJ/6.95)	W.R. Scott	(1969)	Laite, Gordon	20-30	
Hewlett, Pia	Grandmother's Fairy Tales (1st, sm4to, 116p, gilt, p-o, 9cp)	L: Heinemann	1915	Lalau, Maurice	120-180	
Mayne, William	Grass Rope (1st {std}, 8vo, 166p, b/w, DJ, CgM)	L: Oxford U.Pr.	1957	Lamb, Lynton	40-65	
Lamb, Tom	Jolly Kid Alphabet (1st, lg ob4to, ibds, color)	Volland	[1930]	Lamb, Tom	225-325	
Higgins, Alice	Runaway Rhymes (1st, 8vo, 127p, red bds, gilt, pep, 14 fp color)	Volland	(1931)	Lamb, Tom	75-100	
Lamb, Tom	Tale of Bingo (1st, 8vo, ibds, 120p, color)	Volland	(1927)	Lamb, Tom	75-100	*
Marguilies, John	Gold Steps, Stone Steps (1st, 4to, [30]p, color, DJ)	Harlin Quist	1969	Lambert, J.K.	40-60	
Lambert, H.G.C.	Peter Pixie at Play (4to, ibds, p-o, 6cp, pep)	L: Gale/Polden	[1910]	Lambert, M.	200-270	*
Perrault, Charles	Bluebeard & other Fairy Tales (1st {std}, folio, ibds, 38p, color, DJ/2.95)	Macmillan	1964	Lambert, Saul	30-50	*
Lambert, Emily	Man Who Drew Cats (1st, ob4to, ipcb, [32]p, 3-color, DJ/2.00)	Harper	(1957)	Lambert, Saul	30-45	*
Fox, Paula	Portrait of Ivan (1st {std}, 8vo, 131p, b/w, cep, DJ/4.50)	Bradbury Press	(1969)	Lambert, Saul	60-90	R*
Frazier, Neta L.	One Long Picnic (1st, 8vo, 179p, b/w, DJ/3.50)	McKay	1962	Lambo, Don	20-35	*
Meader, Stephen W.	Stranger on Big Hickory (1st {std}, 8vo, 186p, b/w, DJ/3.50)	Harcourt	(1964)	Lambo, Don	70-100	
Hewes, Agnes D.	With the Will to Go (1st {std}, 8vo, 244p, DJ/3.75)	Longmans	1960	Lambo, Don	20-30	
Lamkey, Rosemary	Lonely Dwarf (1st, 8vo, 49p, fp color, pep, DJ/1.00)	Henry Holt & Co.	(1939)	Lamkey, Rosemary	60-85	
Duncombe, Frances	Hoo! Hoo! DeWitt! (1st, 8vo, 31p, fp color, DJ/1.25)	Holt	(1939)	Lamont, Jean	35-50	
Dell, Stanley	Three-Four Kittens (1st, 4to, 95p, 2-color, DJ/2.00)	Henry Holt & Co.	(1941)	Lamont, Jean	30-50	
Saint-Exupery, A.	Flight to Arras (1st, 8vo, 255p, 13pl, pep, DJ/2.75)	Reynal/Hitchcock	(1942)	Lamotte, Bernard	300-500	
LeFevre, A.	Puzzling Pair (1st, sq8vo, 144p, b/w)	Revell	1898	Lance, Eveline	25-40	*
Montgomery, R.	Big Brownie (1st, 8vo, 222p, b/w, DJ/2.00)	Henry Holt & Co.	(1944)	Landau, Jacob	25-40	*
Montgomery, R.	Husky: Co-Pilot of the Pilgrim (1st, sm8vo, 271p, b/w, DJ/2.00)	Holt	1942	Landau, Jacob	20-35	
Kjelgaard, Jim	Lion Hound (1st, 8vo, 216p, b/w, DJ/2.75)	Holiday House	(1955)	Landau, Jacob	60-100	
Gates, Doris	River Ranch (1st, 8vo, 160p, b/w, DJ/2.00)	Viking	1949	Landau, Jacob	20-35	
Kjelgaard, Jim	Snow Dog (1st, 8vo, 236p, olive cl, b/w, pep, DJ/2.50)	Holiday House	(1948)	Landau, Jacob	40-65	
Latham, Jean L.	This Dear-Bought Land (1st {std}, 8vo, 246p, b/w, DJ/2.75)	Harper	(1957)	Landau, Jacob	30-50	
Von Volkmann, Richard	Rusted Knight and other Stories (1st, lg8vo, 135p, silhouettes)	Humphries	1933	Landsberger, Marte	50-80	*
Skorpen, Liesel	If I Had a Lion (1st, ob8vo, 32p, ibds, color, DJ/2.50)	Harper	(1967)	Landshoff, Ursula	50-85	
Harris, Isobel	Frosty Snow (1st {std}, 8vo, [26]p, ibds, DJ/1.50)	Holt	(1951)	Lane/Robertson	20-35	*
Clark, Ann N.	Brother Andre of Montreal (1st, 8vo, 173p, b/w, DJ/2.25)	Farrar, Straus	(1967)	Lang, Harold	40-65	*
Dawson, Coningsby	Little House (1st, 8vo, pcb, p-o, 127p, 8pl, pep)	NY: J. Lane	1920	Langdale, Stella	25-40	
Elam, Elizabeth	Chuffer (1st {std}, 8vo, [48]p, ibds, DJ/1.25)	Winston	(1949)	Langford, Dan	25-45	*
Graham, Eleanor	Night Adventures of Alexis (1st, sm4to, 34p, 9cp)	L: Faber/Gwyer	1925	Langlands, Winifred	50-80	*
Langley, Noel	Tale of the Land of Green Ginger (1st AM, lg4to, 143p, color, DJ/2.50)	Wm. Morrow	1938	Langley, Noel	280-400	
Olsen, Aileen	Bernadine & the Water Bucket (1st, 4to, unpag, color, pep, DJ/2.95)	Abelard-Schuman	1966	Langner, Nola	25-45	
Simon, Sidney	Henry the Uncatchable Mouse (1st {std}, ob8vo, [40]p, 1-col, pep, DJ/2.95)	Norton	(1964)	Langner, Nola	30-50	
Pack, Robert	How to Catch a Crocodile (1st, ob4to, [38]p, fp color, cep, DJ/3.25)	Knopf	(1964)	Langner, Nola	30-50	*
Langton, Jane	Majesty of Grace (1st, 8vo, 190p, b/w, DJ/2.95)	Harper	(1961)	Langton, Jane	35-50	
Crawford, Phyllis	Hello, the Boat! (1st, 8vo, 227p, tan cl, fp b/w, pep, DJ/2.00, NH)	Henry Holt & Co.	(1938)	Laning, Edward	40-70	
Bradford, Roark	John Henry (1st {std}, 8vo, 225p, col frn, pep)	Harper	1931	Lankes, Julius J.	30-50	
Potter, Beatrix	Wag by Wall (1st {std}, 16mo, [30]p, buckram, p-o, t-i frn, DJ/1.50)	Horn Book	1944	Lankes, Julius J.	180-250	
Wells, H.G.	When the Sleeper Wakes (1st AM, 8vo, red/gilt, 328p, 3pl)	Harper	1899	Lanos, H.	300-500	
Gates, Doris	Blue Willow (1st, 8vo, 172p, blue cl, 10pl, pep, DJ/2.00, NH)	Viking	1940	Lantz, Paul	60-100	
Davis, Lavinia R.	Clown Dog (1st {std}, lg8vo, 61p, 2-color, pep, DJ/2.75)	Doubleday	(1961)	Lantz, Paul	25-40	
Holdridge, Betty	Island Boy (1st, 8vo, 110p, green cl, 1-color, pep, DJ/2.00)	Holiday House	(1942)	Lantz, Paul	25-45	
Means, Florence C.	Knock at the Door, Emmy (1st, 8vo, 240p, tan cl, b/w, DJ/2.75)	Houghton	1956	Lantz, Paul	30-50	
Clark, Ann N.	Little Navajo Bluebird (1st, 8vo, 143p, b/w, pep, DJ/2.50)	Viking	1943	Lantz, Paul	30-50	
Edmonds, Walter D.	Matchlock Gun (1st {std}, sm4to, 50p, dp color, pep, DJ/2.00, NM)	Dodd	1941	Lantz, Paul	90-140	R
Lampman, Evelyn	Navaho Sister (1st {std}, 8vo, 191p, b/w, DJ/2.75)	Doubleday	(1956)	Lantz, Paul	30-45	
Edmonds, Walter D.	Tom Whipple (1st, lg8vo, blue cl, 70p, dp color, pep, DJ/2.00)	Dodd	1942	Lantz, Paul	60-100	
Koch, Dorothy	When the Cows Got Out (1st, 8vo, [33]p, b/w, pep, DJ/2.50)	Holiday House	(1958)	Lantz, Paul	25-40	*
Steele, William O.	Story of Leif Ericson (1st, 8vo, 181p, b/w, DJ/1.50)	Grosset/Dunlap	(1954)	Lape, Panas	20-35	
Ormondroyd, Edward	Broderick (1st, ob8vo, [32]p, color, dep, DJ/3.50)	Parnassus Press	(1969)	Larrecq, John	30-45	
Ormondroyd, Edward	Theodore (1st, ob12mo, [33]p, fp 2-color, dep, DJ/3.25)	Parnassus Press	(1966)	Larrecq, John	50-75	*
Andersen, Hans C.	Ugly Duckling (1st AM, ob4to, ibds, 54p, 24 fp color, DJ/2.50)	Macmillan	1955	Larsen, Johannes	60-90	*
Flack, Marjorie	Away Goes Jonathan Wheeler (1st {std}, ob8vo, ibds, [32]p, color, DJ/1.00)	Garden City	1944	Larson, Hilma	40-65	*
Flack, Marjorie	I See a Kitty (1st, sq12mo, ibds, [16]p, color)	Garden City	1943	Larsson, Karl	30-50	
Flack, Marjorie	Pedro (1st, 8vo, blue cl, 96p, dp color, pep, DJ/2.25)	Macmillan	1940	Larsson, Karl	55-80	
Flack, Marjorie	Up in The Air (1st, lg8vo, blue cl, [40]p, color, DJ/1.75)	Macmillan	1935	Larsson, Karl	30-50	
Zolotow, Charlotte	Man with the Purple Eyes (1st, 8vo, 60p, 2-color, DJ/2.50)	Abelard-Schuman	(1961)	Lasker, Joe	30-50	*
Simon, Norma	What Do I Do? (1st, lg8vo, [40]p, 2-color, DJ/3.50)	Whitman	(1969)	Lasker, Joe	20-35	
Zolotow, Charlotte	When the Wind Stops (1st, sm4to, [42]p, fp color, pep, DJ/2.75)	Abelard-Schuman	1962	Lasker, Joe	30-50	
Hamlin, John	Beloved Acres (1st, sm8vo, 228p, 4pl)	Century	1925	Lassell, Charles	25-40	
Miles, Miska	Teacher's Pet (1st {std}, lg8vo, 54p, b/w, DJ/3.25)	Little/Brown	(1966)	Lassell, Fen	20-30	
Van Rosen, Rosa	Baker's Dozen (1st, 4to, [31]p, 1-color, DJ/1.50)	Appleton-Century	(1946)	Latham, Barbara	40-65	*
Sears, Paul M.	Downy Woodpecker (1st, 8vo, 43p, 2-color, cep, DJ/2.00)	Holiday House	(1953)	Latham, Barbara	25-45	
Black, Irma S.	Dusty & his Friends (1st, sm8vo, [56]p, b/w, cep, DJ/1.50)	Holiday House	(1950)	Latham, Barbara	25-40	
Latham, Jean L.	Frightened Hero (1st {std}, sm8vo, 97p, 1-color, pep, DJ/3.50)	Chilton Books	(1965)	Latham, Barbara	30-50	
Fiedler, Jean	Green Thumb Story (1st, sm8vo, 38p, red cl, 2-color, pep, DJ/1.75)	Holiday House	1952	Latham, Barbara	20-35	
Adrian, Mary	Honeybee (1st, 8vo, 40p, fp 2-color, cep, DJ/2.00)	Holiday House	(1952)	Latham, Barbara	50-80	R
Gale, Leah	Hurdy Gurdy Holiday (1st {std}, 4to, ipcb, [48]p, color, pep, DJ/1.50)	Harper	1942	Latham, Barbara	80-130	
Conklin, Gladys	I Like Caterpillars (1st, sm4to, yellow cl, [26]p, color, DJ/2.75)	Holiday House	(1958)	Latham, Barbara	25-45	
Black, Irma S.	Maggie, Mischievous Magpie (1st, sm8vo, [61]p, grn cl, b/w, cep, DJ/1.50)	Holiday House	(1949)	Latham, Barbara	60-90	R
Marcher, Marion W.	Monarch Butterfly (1st, 8vo, 42p, green cl, 2-color, DJ/2.00)	Holiday House	(1954)	Latham, Barbara	60-90	R
Duplaix, Lily	Pedro, Nina & Perrito (1st, lg4to, [48]p, ibds, fp color, pep, DJ/1.50)	Harper	1939	Latham, Barbara	90-150	
Latham, Barbara	Perrito's Pup (1st {std}, lg ob8vo, ibds, [32]p, color, DJ/1.25)	Knopf	(1946)	Latham, Barbara	50-80	*
Lowrey, Janette S.	Silver Dollar (1st {std}, lg4to, ibds, [48]p, pep, DJ/1.50)	Harper	1940	Latham, Barbara	45-70	*
Sears, Paul M.	Tree Frog (1st, 8vo, 45p, green cl, 2-color, DJ/2.00)	Holiday House	(1954)	Latham, Barbara	50-80	R

AUTHOR	TITLE	PUBLISHER	DATE	ARTIST	PRICE	LC
Lathbury, M.A.	April Skies (1st, 4to, ibds, [25]p, 12 chromos)	Worthington	1889	Lathbury, M.A.	100-175	
Lathbury, M.A.	Idyls of the Months (4to, ibds, gilt, unpag, AEG, 14 chromos)	L: Routledge	(1885)	Lathbury, M.A.	250-400	
LeFevre, A.	Odd One (1st, sq8vo, uncut, 142p, b/w)	Revell	1898	Lathbury, M.A.	35-60	*
Lathbury, M.A.	Ring-a-Round-a-Rosy (4to, ibds, 13 chromos)	Worthington	1885	Lathbury, M.A.	125-200	
Lathrop, Dorothy	Angel in the Woods (1st {std}, 8vo, red cl, [48]p, fp b/w, cep, DJ/2.00)	Macmillan	1947	Lathrop, Dorothy	60-100	
Fish, Helen D.	Animals of the Bible (1st, sm4to, 65p, gilt, dp color, DJ/2.00, CM)	Stokes	1937	Lathrop, Dorothy	180-250	R
Cabot, Elise	Balloon Moon (1st, 8vo, 99p, blue/gilt, col frn, fp b/w)	Henry Holt & Co.	(1927)	Lathrop, Dorothy	60-100	
De La Mare, Walter	Bells & Grass (1st AM, 8vo, p-o, 144p, b/w, pep, DJ/2.50)	Viking	1942	Lathrop, Dorothy	75-125	
Lathrop, Dorothy	Bouncing Betsy (1st, lg ob8vo, [41]p, 16pl, DJ/1.50)	Macmillan	1936	Lathrop, Dorothy	60-100	
Field, Rachel	Branches Green (1st, 8vo, green cl, 66p, 12 b/w, DJ/1.50)	Macmillan	1934	Lathrop, Dorothy	80-130	
Lathrop, Dorothy	Colt from Moon Mountain (1st, 8vo, [62]p, b/w, pep, DJ/1.75)	Macmillan	1941	Lathrop, Dorothy	140-200	
De La Mare, Walter	Crossings... (1st, lg8vo, 170p, teg, blue/gilt, col frn)	Knopf	1923	Lathrop, Dorothy	90-160	
Dean, Agnes L.	Devonshire Cream (1st, 8vo, wraps, 49p, 3 fp b/w & cvr by...)	Unity Press	1950	Lathrop, Dorothy	70-100	
Lathrop, Dorothy	Dog in the Tapestry Garden (1st {std}, 8vo, ipcb, 42p, fp b/w, DJ/2.50)	Macmillan	1962	Lathrop, Dorothy	60-90	
De La Mare, Walter	Down-Adown-Derry (1st {std}, 4to, 190p, blue/gilt, teg, 3cp, b/w)	L: Constable	(1922)	Lathrop, Dorothy	120-180	
De La Mare, Walter	Down-Adown-Derry (1st AM, 8vo, 195p, gilt, uncut, col frn)	Henry Holt & Co.	1922	Lathrop, Dorothy	80-120	R
De La Mare, Walter	Dutch Cheese (1st {std}, lg8vo, 75p, green/gilt, 4cp)	Knopf	1931	Lathrop, Dorothy	80-130	
Farjeon, Eleanor	Fair of St. James (1st, 8vo, 310p, green/gilt, b/w)	Stokes	1932	Lathrop, Dorothy	60-90	
Lathrop, Dorothy	Fairy Circus (1st {1st bk.}, lg ob8vo, gilt, 67p, 8cp, 12pl, NH)	Macmillan	1931	Lathrop, Dorothy	200-300	
Mukerji, Dhan G.	Fierce Face (1st {std}, 8vo, 77p, green cl, pep, DJ/1.00)	Dutton	1936	Lathrop, Dorothy	100-150	
Lathrop, Dorothy	Follow the Brook (1st {std}, sm4to, blue cl, 40p, fp b/w, DJ/3.25)	Macmillan	(1960)	Lathrop, Dorothy	70-120	
Snedeker, Caroline D.	Forgotten Daughter (1st {std}, 8vo, 309p, col frn, 3pl, pep, NH)	Doubleday/Doran	1933	Lathrop, Dorothy	100-160	
Burlingame, Eugene W.	Grateful Elephant (1st, sm4to, 172p, yellow cl, col frn, 10pl)	Yale U. Press	1923	Lathrop, Dorothy	100-165	
Fleuron, Svend	Grim: Story of a Pike (1st, sm8vo, green cl, 186p, 4pl)	Knopf	1921	Lathrop, Dorothy	60-100	
Mandal, Sant Ram	Happy Flute (1st, lg8vo, 54p, tan cl, 10 fp b/w, pep, DJ/1.50)	Stokes	1939	Lathrop, Dorothy	80-130	
Lathrop, Dorothy	Hide and Go Seek (1st, sm4to, grey cl, [40]p, fp b/w, pep, DJ/1.75)	Macmillan	1938	Lathrop, Dorothy	80-130	
Field, Rachel	Hitty, Her First Hundred Years (1st, sq8vo, 207p, p-o, 3cp, NM, PPPa)	Macmillan	1929	Lathrop, Dorothy	120-200	
Lathrop, Dorothy	Let Them Live (1st {std}, 8vo, orange cl, 80p, fp b/w, cep, DJ/2.00)	Macmillan	1951	Lathrop, Dorothy	70-120	
MacDonald, George	Light Princess (1st, 12mo, 133p, col frn, 12pl, pep)	Macmillan	1926	Lathrop, Dorothy	70-100	
Hudson, Wm. Henry	Little Boy Lost (1st, 4to, teg, 187p, gilt, uncut, pep, 8cp)	Knopf	1920	Lathrop, Dorothy	150-220	
Andersen, Hans C.	Little Mermaid (1st, sm4to, blue/gilt, [48]p, 6 fp color, pep, DJ/2.50)	Macmillan	1939	Lathrop, Dorothy	150-220	
Lathrop, Dorothy	Little White Goat (1st, ob4to, 59p, col frn, 15pl, pep)	Macmillan	1933	Lathrop, Dorothy	100-160	
Lathrop, Dorothy	Littlest Mouse (1st {std}, sm8vo, ibds, 32p, b/w, DJ/2.25)	Macmillan	(1955)	Lathrop, Dorothy	60-90	
Howes, Edith	Long Bright Land (1st, 8vo, 207p, green/gilt, col frn, 12pl, pep)	Little/Brown	1929	Lathrop, Dorothy	65-100	
Lathrop, Dorothy	Lost Merry-Go-Round (1st, sq8vo, 104p, col frn, 10pl, pep)	Macmillan	1934	Lathrop, Dorothy	120-170	
Canfield, Dorothy	Made-to-Order Stories (1st, 8vo, 263p, col frn, b/w)	Harcourt	(1925)	Lathrop, Dorothy	60-90	
Ingelow, Jean	Mopsa the Fairy (1st, 8vo, p-o, 259p, uncut, col frn, 12pl, pep)	Harper	1927	Lathrop, Dorothy	100-160	
De La Mare, Walter	Mr. Bumps & His Monkey (1st, sq8vo, 69p, 7 fp color, DJ/2.00)	Winston	(1942)	Lathrop, Dorothy	100-160	
Lathrop, Dorothy	Presents for Lupe (1st, sm sq4to, orange cl, [40]p, color, dep, DJ/2.00)	Macmillan	1940	Lathrop, Dorothy	60-100	
MacDonald, George	Princess & Curdie (1st, sm8vo, p-o, 265p, gilt, col frn, 12pl, pep)	Macmillan	1927	Lathrop, Dorothy	100-175	
Lathrop, Dorothy	Puffy & Seven Leaf Clover (1st {std}, 8vo, 34p, 2-color, cep, DJ/2.50)	Macmillan	(1954)	Lathrop, Dorothy	50-90	
Lathrop, Dorothy	Puppies for Keeps (1st {std}, lg ob8vo, brown cl, [40]p, color, DJ/2.00)	Macmillan	1943	Lathrop, Dorothy	80-145	
Conkling, Hilda	Silverhorn (1st, 8vo, p-o, 159p, col frn, fp b/w, pep)	Stokes	1924	Lathrop, Dorothy	70-120	
Lathrop, Dorothy	Skittle-Skattle Monkey (1st, lg8vo, red cl, [48]p, fp b/w, DJ/1.75)	Macmillan	1945	Lathrop, Dorothy	100-150	
Lathrop, Dorothy	Snail Who Ran (1st, 16mo, green cl, 57p, col frn, fp b/w)	Stokes	1934	Lathrop, Dorothy	50-90	
Hawthorne, Nathaniel	Snow Image (1st, 16mo, blue cl, 69p, dp color, pep)	Macmillan	1930	Lathrop, Dorothy	50-80	
Teasdale, Sara	Stars Tonight (1st, 8vo, blue cl, p-o, 49p, col frn, 14 fp b/w)	Macmillan	1930	Lathrop, Dorothy	60-90	
Various	Sung Under the Silver Umbrella (1st, lg8vo, 211p, red cl, fp b/w)	Macmillan	1935	Lathrop, Dorothy	30-50	
Gate, Ethel M.	Tales from Enchanted Isles (1st, sq8vo, 118p, green cl, col frn, b/w)	Yale U. Press	1926	Lathrop, Dorothy	70-100	
De La Mare, Walter	Three Mulla Mulgars (1st, lg8vo, blue/gilt, 275p, 8cp, pep)	Knopf	1919	Lathrop, Dorothy	125-200	
De La Mare, Walter	Three Mulla Mulgars (1st UK, 4to, 275p, gilt, 8cp, 4pl)	L: Duckworth	1921	Lathrop, Dorothy	100-160	
Robida, Albert	Treasure of Carcassone (1st {std}, sm8vo, 213p, col frn, 7pl, pep)	Longmans	1928	Lathrop, Dorothy	50-80	
Lathrop, Dorothy	Who Goes There? (1st, sm ob4to, [40]p, 16 fp b/w, pep, DJ/1.50)	Macmillan	1935	Lathrop, Dorothy	100-165	
Robinson, Gertrude	Chee-Chee's Brother (1st {std}, sm4to, green cl, 40p, fp b/w, pep, DJ/1.50)	Dutton	(1937)	Latimer, Glenna M.	30-50	
Lattimore, Eleanor	Bayou Boy (1st {std}, 4to, 128p, b/w, pep, DJ/2.00)	Wm. Morrow	1946	Lattimore, Eleanor	80-130	
Lattimore, Eleanor	Bells for a Chinese Donkey (1st, 8vo, 126p, pep, DJ/2.00)	Wm. Morrow	1951	Lattimore, Eleanor	40-65	
Lattimore, Eleanor	Bittern's Nest (1st, 8vo, 127p, b/w, DJ/2.75)	Wm. Morrow	1962	Lattimore, Eleanor	40-65	*
Lattimore, Eleanor	Christopher and his Turtle (1st, 8vo, 126p, pep, DJ/2.00)	Wm. Morrow	1950	Lattimore, Eleanor	40-70	
Lattimore, Eleanor	Clever Cat (1st, sm8vo, 113p, b/w pl, pep, DJ/1.50)	Harcourt	1936	Lattimore, Eleanor	60-90	*
Lattimore, Eleanor	Cousin Melinda (1st, 8vo, 128p, b/w, pep, DJ/2.75)	Wm. Morrow	1961	Lattimore, Eleanor	30-50	
Lattimore, Eleanor	Davy of the Everglades (1st, 8vo, 127p, b/w, DJ/2.00)	Wm. Morrow	1949	Lattimore, Eleanor	30-50	*
Lattimore, Eleanor	Deborah's White Winter (1st, 8vo, 124p, b/w, DJ/2.00)	Wm. Morrow	1949	Lattimore, Eleanor	25-45	
Lattimore, Eleanor	Happiness for Kimi (1st, 8vo, 126p, b/w, DJ/2.50)	Wm. Morrow	1958	Lattimore, Eleanor	25-45	
Lattimore, Eleanor	Holly in the Snow (1st, 8vo, 125p, b/w, pep, DJ/2.25)	Wm. Morrow	1954	Lattimore, Eleanor	30-45	
Lattimore, Eleanor	Indigo Hill (1st, 8vo, 128p, pep, DJ/2.00)	Wm. Morrow	1950	Lattimore, Eleanor	30-45	
Lattimore, Eleanor	Jasper (1st, 8vo, 128p, b/w, DJ/2.00)	Wm. Morrow	1953	Lattimore, Eleanor	30-50	
Lattimore, Eleanor	Jeremy's Isle (1st, 8vo, 123p, fp b/w, pep, DJ/2.00)	Wm. Morrow	1947	Lattimore, Eleanor	40-65	
Lattimore, Eleanor	Jerry and the Pusa (1st, 8vo, 197p, uncut, fp b/w, pep)	Harcourt	(1932)	Lattimore, Eleanor	200-300	
Lattimore, Eleanor	Junior, Colored Boy of Charleston (1st, 8vo, 129p, dep, fp b/w, DJ/2.00)	Harcourt	(1938)	Lattimore, Eleanor	75-125	
Lattimore, Eleanor	Little Pear (1st [1st bk.], 8vo, 144p, uncut, fp b/w, pep)	Harcourt	(1931)	Lattimore, Eleanor	180-250	
Lattimore, Eleanor	Little Pear and his Friends (1st, 8vo, 178p, red cl, fp b/w, pep)	Harcourt	(1934)	Lattimore, Eleanor	100-170	
Lattimore, Eleanor	Little Pear and the Rabbits (1st, 8vo, 125p, b/w, pep, DJ/2.50)	Wm. Morrow	(1956)	Lattimore, Eleanor	50-85	*
Lattimore, Eleanor	Lost Leopard (1st, sm ob8vo, orange cl, 104p, 8cp, pep, DJ/2.00)	Harcourt	(1935)	Lattimore, Eleanor	60-90	
Lattimore, Eleanor	Molly in the Middle (1st, 8vo, 127p, b/w, pep, DJ/2.25)	Wm. Morrow	1956	Lattimore, Eleanor	30-50	
Lattimore, Eleanor	Peachblossom (1st, 8vo, 96p, fp b/w, pep, DJ/2.00)	Harcourt	(1943)	Lattimore, Eleanor	40-65	*
Lattimore, Eleanor	Questions of Lifu (1st, 8vo, 104p, 1-color, DJ/2.00)	Harcourt	(1942)	Lattimore, Eleanor	45-70	
Lattimore, Eleanor	Seven Crowns (1st, sm8vo, 189p, green cl, fp b/w, pep)	Harcourt	(1933)	Lattimore, Eleanor	180-240	
Mason, Miriam E.	Dan Beard, Boy Scout (1st {std}, 8vo, 192p, b/w, DJ/1.75)	Bobbs-Merrill	(1953)	Laune, Paul	25-45	*

AUTHOR	TITLE	PUBLISHER	DATE	ARTIST	PRICE	LC
Weil, Ann Y.	John Quincy Adams: Boy Patriot (1st {std}, sm8vo, 192p, b/w, DJ/1.75)	Bobbs-Merrill	(1945)	Laune, Paul	25-40	
Schmidt, Sarah L.	Ranching on Eagle Eye (1st {std}, 12mo, 374p, pep, DJ/2.00)	McBride	(1936)	Laune, Paul	30-50	*
Annixter, Jane	The Runner (1st, 8vo, 220p, red cl, pep, DJ/2.75)	Holiday House	(1956)	Laune, Paul	20-35	
Laune, Paul	Thirsty Pony (1st, 4to, [31]p, ibds, color, pep, DJ/0.50)	Grosset/Dunlap	(1940)	Laune, Paul	25-40	
Courlander, Harold	Big Old World of Richard Creeks (1st {std}, 8vo, 118p, b/w, DJ/3.50)	Chilton Books	(1962)	Laurie, Bob	60-90	
Lewis, Hilda	Ship that Flew (1st, 8vo, 320p, b/w, DJ)	L: Oxford U.Pr.	1939	Lavrin, Nora	100-165	*
Demuth, Averil	Trudi and Hansel (1st, 8vo, silver cl, 174p, fp color, pep, DJ/2.00)	Winston	(1938)	Lavrin, Nora	30-50	
Lawrence, C.H.	Santa Claus in Toyland (1st, 4to, 96p, ibds, 8cp, 12pl)	Reilly/Britton	(1915)	Lawrence, C.H.	140-220	
Lawrence, Jacob	Harriet & the Promised Land (1st {std}, lg4to, [32]p, color, DJ/5.95, NYTBI)	Windmill Books	(1968)	Lawrence, Jacob	250-350	R
Lawrence, John	Giant of Grabbist (1st AM, 4to, [32]p, ibds, color, DJ/3.95)	NY: David White	1969	Lawrence, John	45-70	
Lawrence, John	Pope Leo's Elephant (1st AM {std}, 12mo, [32]p, color, DJ/3.95)	World	(1970)	Lawrence, John	25-40	*
MacLeod, Fiona	Hills of Ruel (1st AM, sm4to, gilt, teg, 92p, 8 ticp)	Duffield	1921	Lawrence, Margery	90-120	
Brownjohn, Alan	Brownjohn's Beasts (1st AM, 8vo, 48p, b/w, DJ/3.95)	Scribner	(1970)	Lawson, Carol	20-35	
Lawson, Lizzie	Christmas Roses (lg8vo, [31]p, ibds, 10 chromos, pep)	Nister/Dutton	[1880]	Lawson, Lizzie	170-240	
Spyri, Johanna	Heidi (1st, 8vo, 219p, gilt, teg, uncut, 13 fp color)	Dent/Dutton	(1909)	Lawson, Lizzie	30-50	*
Moore, Clement C.	Night Before Christmas (8vo, [24]p, pep, 12 chromos)	L: Nister	[1885]	Lawson, Lizzie	100-170	*
Mack, Robert E.	Old Father Christmas (4to, ibds, unpag, 14 chromos)	Nister/Dutton	(1888)	Lawson, Lizzie	200-350	
Mack, Robert E.	Old Father Santa Claus (4to, ibds, [40]p, 14 chromos)	Nister/Dutton	[1885]	Lawson, Lizzie	200-300	
Mack, Robert E.	Under the Mistletoe (lg8vo, ibds, [40]p, 14 chromos)	Nister/Dutton	(1890)	Lawson, Lizzie	120-200	
Dickens, Charles	Boots of the Holly Tree Inn (8vo, red/gilt, pep, 44p, b/w)	Harper	1928	Lawson, Marie A.	35-60	*
Malkus, Alida S.	Caravans to Sante Fe (1st {std}, 12mo, 289p, b/w)	Harper	1928	Lawson, Marie A.	35-60	*
Lawson, Marie A.	Dragon John (1st, 8vo, 51p, green cl, 2-color, dep, DJ/1.50)	Viking	1943	Lawson, Marie A.	50-90	
Moore, Colleen	Enchanted Castle (1st, 4to, 63p, ibds, 6 fp 1-color, cep)	Garden City	1935	Lawson, Marie A.	60-100	
Knox, Esther M.	Flags of Dawn (1st {std}, sm8vo, 298p, 10pl, DJ/2.00)	Little/Brown	1944	Lawson, Marie A.	30-50	
Lawson, Marie A.	Hail Columbia (1st {std}, lg8vo, 387p, 7cp, 2-color, pep)	Doubleday/Doran	1931	Lawson, Marie A.	40-65	
Parton, Ethel	Melissa Ann (1st {std}, 8vo, 280p, col frn, fp b/w)	Doubleday/Doran	1931	Lawson, Marie A.	40-65	
Montgomery, Lucy M.	Mistress Pat (1st, 12mo, 338p, col frn, DJ/2.00)	Stokes	1935	Lawson, Marie A.	150-220	
Dubois, Gertrude	Peter & Penny Plant a Garden (1st, sm8vo, 210p, gilt, b/w, DJ/1.25)	Stokes	1936	Lawson, Marie A.	30-50	
Weber, Henriette	Prize Song (1st, lg8vo, 272p, 2-color, pep, DJ/3.00)	Oxford U. Pr.	1935	Lawson, Marie A.	30-50	
Lawson, Marie A.	Sea is Blue (1st, 8vo, 126p, pep, 11 fp 1-color, DJ/2.00)	Viking	1946	Lawson, Marie A.	50-80	
Wheelock, Sarah	Three Little Warrens (1st, 8vo, 227p, b/w, DJ/1.75)	Stokes	1935	Lawson, Marie A.	30-45	
Jewett, Eleanore	Told on the King's Highway (1st, 8vo, 246p, b/w, pep, DJ/2.50)	Viking	1943	Lawson, Marie A.	40-65	
Gray, Eliz. J.	Adam of the Road (1st, lg8vo, 317p, green cl, 23pl, pep, DJ/2.00, NM)	Viking	1942	Lawson, Robert	80-145	R
Aesopus	Aesop's Fables (1st, lg4to, brown/gilt, 134p, 1-color, pep, case)	Heritage Press	(1941)	Lawson, Robert	70-100	
Lawson, Robert	At that Time (1st, lg8vo, 127p, b/w, DJ/2.50)	Viking	1947	Lawson, Robert	60-90	
Lawson, Robert	Ben & Me (1st {std}, sq8vo, 114p, brown cl, b/w, pep, DJ/1.75)	Little/Brown	1939	Lawson, Robert	200-300	R
Bates, Helen D.	Betsy Ross (1st {std}, 8vo, 127p, b/w, pep, DJ/1.00)	Whittlesey	(1936)	Lawson, Robert	40-65	
Lawson, Robert	Captain Kidd's Cat (1st {std}, 8vo, 151p, green cl, b/w, pep, DJ/3.00)	Little/Brown	(1956)	Lawson, Robert	80-145	
Lawson, Robert	Country Colic (1st {std}, sq8vo, 66p, beige cl, b/w, pep, DJ/1.75)	Little/Brown	1944	Lawson, Robert	50-85	
Sterne, Emma G.	Drums of Monmouth (1st, 8vo, 287p, aqua cl, uncut, b/w, pep, DJ/2.50)	Dodd	1935	Lawson, Robert	75-130	
Lawson, Robert	Edward, Hoppy & Joe (1st {std}, 8vo, 122p, fp b/w, pep, DJ/2.50)	Knopf	(1952)	Lawson, Robert	150-225	
Lawson, Robert	Fabulous Flight (1st {std}, lg8vo, 152p, green cl, b/w, pep, DJ/2.75)	Little/Brown	1949	Lawson, Robert	70-120	
Fish, Helen D.	Four & Twenty Blackbirds (1st, sm4to, 104p, 1-color, pep, DJ/1.50, CH)	Stokes	1937	Lawson, Robert	150-250	
Bates, Helen D.	Francis Scott Key (1st {std}, 8vo, 118p, b/w, pep, DJ/1.00)	Whittlesey	(1936)	Lawson, Robert	50-80	
Mason, Arthur	From the Horn of the Moon (1st {std}, lg8vo, 259p, blue cl, b/w, pep)	Doubleday/Doran	1931	Lawson, Robert	70-125	
Brewton, John	Gaily We Parade (1st, lg8vo, 218p, pep, b/w, DJ/2.00)	Macmillan	1940	Lawson, Robert	50-80	
Coatsworth, Eliz.	Golden Horseshoe (1st, 8vo, 151p, gilt, pep, 14pl, DJ/2.00)	Macmillan	1935	Lawson, Robert	70-100	
Lawson, Robert	Great Wheel (1st, lg8vo, 188p, pep, b/w, green cl, DJ/3.00, NH)	Viking	(1957)	Lawson, Robert	80-120	
Robinson, Tom P.	Greylock & the Robins (1st, sm4to, 32p, ibds, color, DJ/2.00)	Viking	1946	Lawson, Robert	80-140	
Marquand, John	Haven's End (1st, 8vo, 341p, uncut, b/w)	Little/Brown	1933	Lawson, Robert	50-80	
Bianco, Margery W.	Hurdy-Gurdy Man (1st, sq12mo, 56p, ibds, cep, b/w)	Oxford U. Pr.	(1933)	Lawson, Robert	100-165	
Lawson, Robert	I Discover Columbus (1st {std}, 8vo, blue cl, 110p, b/w, pep, DJ/1.75)	Little/Brown	1941	Lawson, Robert	100-170	
Barnes, Ruth A.	I Hear America Singing (1st, 8vo, 346p, 1-color, pep, DJ/2.00)	Winston	(1937)	Lawson, Robert	80-140	
N/A	Just for Fun... (1st, 4to, 64p, blue cl, fp b/w, pep, DJ/1.00)	Rand/McNally	(1940)	Lawson, Robert	80-130	
Chester, Geo. R.	Little Prince Toofat (1st, sq4to, 71p, col frn, cp)	McCann	(1922)	Lawson, Robert	200-300	R
Teal, Valentine	Little Woman Wanted Noise (1st, 8vo, [40]p, orange cl, b/w, pep, DJ/1.00)	Rand/McNally	(1943)	Lawson, Robert	80-120	
Potter, Mary A.	Mathematics for Success (1st, 8vo, 439p, b/w)	Ginn & Co.	(1952)	Lawson, Robert	50-80	*
Lawson, Robert	McWhinney's Jaunt (1st {std}, sq8vo, 77p, cloth, fp b/w, DJ/2.50)	Little/Brown	1951	Lawson, Robert	80-140	
Sterne, Emma G.	Miranda is a Princess (1st, 8vo, 221p, yellow cl, b/w, pep, DJ/1.75)	Dodd	1937	Lawson, Robert	70-125	
Atwater, Richard	Mr. Popper's Penguins (1st {std}, 8vo, 138p, 1-color, pep, DJ/1.75, NH)	Little/Brown	1938	Lawson, Robert	100-165	R
Lawson, Robert	Mr. Revere & I (1st {std}, 8vo, 152p, b/w, pep, DJ/3.00)	Little/Brown	(1953)	Lawson, Robert	80-125	R
Lawson, Robert	Mr. Twigg's Mistake (1st {std}, 8vo, 143p, aqua cl, b/w, pep, DJ/2.50)	Little/Brown	1947	Lawson, Robert	80-125	
Lawson, Robert	Mr. Wilmer (1st {std}, sm8vo, 218p, beige cl, b/w, pep, DJ/2.00)	Little/Brown	1945	Lawson, Robert	70-100	
Farjeon, Eleanor	One Foot in Fairyland (1st, 8vo, 261p, gilt, b/w, cep, DJ/2.50)	Stokes	1938	Lawson, Robert	120-200	
Ring, Barbara	Peik (1st, sm8vo, 268p, 15 fp b/w, cep)	Little/Brown	1932	Lawson, Robert	60-90	
Godolphin, Mary	Pilgrims' Progress (1st, sm4to, red cl, 10 fp b/w, 120p, DJ/2.00)	Stokes	1939	Lawson, Robert	60-100	
Forester, C.S.	Poo Poo & the Dragons (1st {std}, 8vo, 142p, green cl, b/w, pep, DJ/1.75)	Little/Brown	1942	Lawson, Robert	450-650	
Twain, Mark	Prince & the Pauper (1st, 8vo, 274p, p-o, gilt, color, pep, DJ)	Winston	(1937)	Lawson, Robert	80-140	
Lang, Andrew	Prince Prigio (1st {std}, sq8vo, green cl, 108p, b/w, pep, DJ/1.75)	Little/Brown	1942	Lawson, Robert	100-160	
Lawson, Robert	Rabbit Hill (1st, lg8vo, 128p, 1-color, pep, DJ/2.50, NM)	Viking	1944	Lawson, Robert	140-220	R
Lawson, Robert	Robbut: Tale of Tails (1st, 4to, ibds, 94p, b/w, pep, DJ/2.50)	Viking	1948	Lawson, Robert	80-140	
Mason, Arthur	Roving Lobster (1st {std}, 8vo, 132p, green cl, 10 fp b/w, cep)	Doubleday/Doran	1931	Lawson, Robert	80-120	
Gale, Elizabeth	Seven Beads of Wampum (1st, 8vo, 298p, 8 fp b/w, pep, DJ/2.00)	Putnam	(1936)	Lawson, Robert	60-90	
Hall, William N.	Shoelace Robin (1st, 8vo, ipcb, [20]p, 1-color, pep, DJ/1.00)	Crowell	1945	Lawson, Robert	60-100	
Haines, William	Slim (1st, 8vo, 414p, 6 fp b/w, pep, DJ/2.50)	Little/Brown	1934	Lawson, Robert	100-165	
Lawson, Robert	Smeller Martin (1st, lg8vo, green cl, 157p, fp b/w, DJ/2.50)	Viking	1950	Lawson, Robert	60-100	
Leaf, Munro	Story of Ferdinand (1st, 8vo, ibds, [81]p, b/w, pep, DJ/1.00)	Viking	1936	Lawson, Robert	900-1400	R
Bowie, Walter R.	Story of Jesus for Young People (1st, 8vo, 125p, blue/gilt, 6cp, DJ/2.00)	Scribner	1937	Lawson, Robert	80-135	

ARTIST: 124

AUTHOR	TITLE	PUBLISHER	DATE	ARTIST	PRICE	LC
Leaf, Munro	Story of Simpson & Sampson (1st, sm4to, [64]p, blue cl, b/w pep, DJ/1.50)	Viking	1941	Lawson, Robert	120-200	
White, Terence H.	Sword in the Stone (1st AM, 8vo, 311p, gilt, DJ/2.50, pep by....)	Putnam	1939	Lawson, Robert	250-400	
Stratton, Clarence	Swords & Statues (1st, 8vo, 254p, gilt, col frn, 7 b/w, cep, DJ/2.00)	Winston	(1937)	Lawson, Robert	120-175	
Lawson, Robert	They Were Strong & Good (1st, 4to, [68]p, fp b/w, pep, DJ/1.50, CM)	Viking	1940	Lawson, Robert	170-250	
Lawson, Robert	Tough Winter (1st, lg8vo, 128p, blue/silver, b/w, pep, DJ/3.00)	Viking	1954	Lawson, Robert	80-125	
Tarn, William W.	Treasure of Isle of Mist (1st, 8vo, gilt, 184p, pep, b/w)	Putnam	(1934)	Lawson, Robert	60-90	
Brewton, John (ed)	Under the Tent of the Sky (1st, 8vo, 205p, blue cl, pep, fp b/w, DJ/2.00)	Macmillan	1937	Lawson, Robert	100-165	
Young, Ella	Unicorn with Silver Shoes (1st {std}, sm8vo, gilt, 214p, 9pl, pep)	Longmans	1932	Lawson, Robert	70-120	R
Lawson, Robert	Watchwords of Liberty (1st {std}, sm4to, 115p, b/w, pep, DJ/2.00)	Little/Brown	1943	Lawson, Robert	60-100	
Leaf, Munro	Wee Gillis (1st, 4to, ipcb, [71]p, 33 fp b/w, pep, DJ/1.50, CH)	Viking	1938	Lawson, Robert	150-250	R
Mason, Arthur	Wee Men of Ballywooden (1st {std}, lg8vo, 266p, pep, 4pl)	Doubleday/Doran	1930	Lawson, Robert	100-165	
Mason, Arthur	Wee Men of Ballywooden (1st {this pub}, 8vo, p-o, 266p, 4pl, pep)	Garden City	(1937)	Lawson, Robert	50-80	
Cormack, Maribelle	Wind of the Vikings (1st, 8vo, 259p, tan cl, 6 fp b/w, pep, DJ/2.00)	Appleton-Century	1937	Lawson, Robert	58-80	*
Dixon, Charles	Fifteen Hundred Miles an Hour (1st, 8vo, 313p, blue/gilt, AEG, 6pl)	L: Bliss Sands	1895	Layard, Arthur	250-400	
Layard, Arthur	Harriet Hare (1st, 16mo, grey bds, 88p, p-o, 20cp)	L: Nisbet	[1907]	Layard, Arthur	70-100	
Haggard, H. Rider	People of the Mist (1st, 12mo, 343p, blue/gilt, 16pl, cep)	L: Longmans	1894	Layard, Arthur	150-250	
Kantor, MacKinley	Lobo (1st {std}, 8vo, 110p, bds, b/w, DJ/2.75)	World	(1957)	Layne, Irene	50-80	
Burch, Robert	Queenie Peavy (1st, 8vo, 159p, fp b/w, DJ/3.50, JABA)	Viking	(1966)	Lazare, Jerry	30-50	
LeCain, Errol	Cabbage Princess (1st, 4to, unpag, ibds, color, pep, DJ)	L: Faber	1969	LeCain, Errol	70-100	
Malory, Thomas	King Arthur... (1st, 12mo, 64p, green wraps, fp b/w)	Penn	1908	LeFanu, B.	40-60	*
Hawthorne, Nathaniel	Wonder Tales (1st, 12mo, 62p, b/w)	Penn	1908	LeFanu, B.	25-40	*
Cocagnac, A.M.	Three Trees of the Samurai (1st, sq4to, 24p, color, DJ/4.25)	Harlin Quist	1969	LeFoll, Alain	30-50	
Roy, Claude	Very Obliging Flowers (1st, ob4to, ibds, 38p, color, DJ/3.95, NYTBI)	Grove Press	(1968)	LeFoll, Alain	50-80	*
Ley, Madeleine	Enchanted Eve (1st, 4to, [52]p, blue cl, 1-color, pep, DJ/2.50)	Howell/Soskin	(1946)	LeGrand, Edy	30-45	
LeMair, H.W.	Auntie's Little Rhyme Book (ob 16mo, ibds, [26]p, 10 color)	Augener/McKay	[1918]	LeMair, H.W.	140-225	
LeMair, H.W.	Baby's Little Rhyme Book (ob 12mo, ibds, [28]p, 10 color)	L: Augener	[1920]	LeMair, H.W.	125-200	
Stevenson, Rbt. L.	Child's Garden of Verses (1st, ob4to, p-o, 89p, gilt, 12cp, pep)	McKay	(1926)	LeMair, H.W.	225-325	
Stevenson, Rbt. L.	Child's Garden of Verses (1st UK, ob4to, ibds, pep, 71p, 12cp)	L: Harrap	(1931)	LeMair, H.W.	200-300	
Elkin, R.H.	Children's Corner (1st AM, lg ob8vo, [30]p, p-o, gilt, 16 ticp)	McKay/Augner	[1915]	LeMair, H.W.	200-300	
LeMair, H.W.	Daddy's Little Rhyme Book (ob 16mo, ibds, [28]p, 10 color)	L: Augener	[1920]	LeMair, H.W.	130-200	
Milne, A.A.	Gallery of Children (1st, lg4to, p-o, 105p, 12cp)	L: Stan. Paul	(1925)	LeMair, H.W.	200-300	
Milne, A.A.	Gallery of Children (1st AM, 4to, 105p, p-o, gilt, 12cp)	McKay	(1925)	LeMair, H.W.	120-200	
LeMair, H.W.	Granny's Little Rhyme Book (ob16mo, [28]p, ibds, 12 color)	L: Augener	(1912)	LeMair, H.W.	125-200	
Elkin, R.H.	Little People (1st AM, lg8vo, [32]p, red/gilt, p-o, 16 fp color)	McKay/Augener	[1915]	LeMair, H.W.	200-300	
Moffat, Alfred	Little Songs of Long Ago (1st, ob4to, 64p, gilt, p-o, 32 fp color)	L: Augener	(1912)	LeMair, H.W.	150-220	
LeMair, H.W.	Mother's Little Rhyme Book (ob 16mo, ibds, [28]p, color)	McKay	[1915]	LeMair, H.W.	120-170	
LeMair, H.W.	Nursie's Little Rhyme Book. (ob16mo, ibds, [26]p, 10 color)	Augener/McKay	[1915]	LeMair, H.W.	140-220	
Elkin, R.H.	Old Dutch Nursery Rhymes (1st, ob4to, gilt, p-o, 31p, 16 fp color)	L: Augener	(1917)	LeMair, H.W.	200-300	
Moffat, Alfred	Our Old Nursery Rhymes (1st, ob4to, 63p, gilt, p-o, 30 fp color)	L: Augener	(1911)	LeMair, H.W.	150-220	
Inayat, Noor	Twenty Jataka Tales (1st, 8vo, blue cl, 138p, col frn, 19pl, DJ)	L: Harrap	(1939)	LeMair, H.W.	120-165	
Inayat, Noor	Twenty Jataka Tales (1st AM, lg8vo, 138p, gilt, col frn, 19pl, DJ/2.00)	McKay	(1939)	LeMair, H.W.	120-170	
LeWitt, Jan	The Vegetabull (1st {std}, 4to, ibds, [32]p, color, DJ/3.00)	Harcourt	1956	LeWitt, Jan	70-130	*
Jackson, Joseph	Christmas Flower (1st {std}, 8vo, 31p, ibds, 1-color, pep, DJ/1.00)	Harcourt	(1951)	Lea, Tom	40-70	
Leaf, Munro	Fair Play (1st, 4to, 94p, blue cl, b/w, DJ/1.50)	Stokes	1939	Leaf, Munro	70-100	
Leaf, Munro	Flock of Watchbirds (1st {std}, sm8vo, [42]p, red cl, color, DJ/1.50)	Lippincott	(1946)	Leaf, Munro	40-65	
Leaf, Munro	Gordon the Goat (1st {std}, 8vo, green cl, 48p, color, DJ/1.00)	Lippincott	(1944)	Leaf, Munro	60-90	
Leaf, Munro	John Henry Davis (1st, 8vo, 56p, red/black, color, pep, DJ/1.00)	Stokes	1940	Leaf, Munro	50-80	
Leaf, Munro	Lucky You (1st {std}, 4to, 47p, red cl, b/w, DJ/2.25)	Lippincott	(1955)	Leaf, Munro	30-50	
Leaf, Munro	Manners Can be Fun (1st, sm4to, 45p, b/w, pep, DJ/1.25)	Stokes	1936	Leaf, Munro	100-150	
Leaf, Munro	Robert Francis Weatherbee (1st, 12mo, 75p, blue cl, color, DJ/1.00)	Stokes	1935	Leaf, Munro	65-90	
Leaf, Munro	Sam and the Superdroop (1st, 8vo, 122p, b/w, DJ/1.50)	Viking	1948	Leaf, Munro	80-120	
Leaf, Munro	Turnabout (1st {std}, 8vo, [34]p, 2-color, DJ/3.75)	Lippincott	1967	Leaf, Munro	30-50	
Thaler, Mike	The Rainbow (1st {std}, ob8vo, [30]p, color, cep, DJ/2.95)	Harlin Quist	(1967)	Leake, Donald	30-50	
Newbolt, Henry J.	Taken From the Enemy (1st [new ed], 8vo, gilt, teg, 170p, p-o, 8cp)	L: Chatto	1911	Leake, Gerald	30-60	
Montgomery, R.	Golden Stallion and the Wolf Dog (1st {std}, sm8vo, 210p, b/w, DJ/3.00)	Little/Brown	(1958)	Leason, Percy	25-40	
Montgomery, R.	Golden Stallion's Advens at Redstone (1st {std}, sm8vo, 198p, b/w DJ/3.00)	Little/Brown	(1959)	Leason, Percy	25-40	
Leavens, Evelyn	Boswell's Life of Boswell (1st, 4to, [26]p, ibds, DJ/1.95)	Simon/Schuster	(1958)	Leavens, Evelyn	30-45	*
Lebeck, Oskar	Diary of Terwilliger Jellico (1st, lg8vo, ibds, [48]p, color, pep, DJ/0.50)	Grosset/Dunlap	1935	Lebeck, Oskar	40-60	
Baum, L. Frank	Wizard of Oz (1st, lg ob8vo, [56]p, ibds, color, pep, DJ/0.50)	Grosset/Dunlap	1939	Lebeck, Oskar	100-175	*
Lebedev, Vladimir	Lion & the Ox (1st, sq4to, 35p, b/w, DJ/1.25)	Macmillan	1932	Lebedev, Vladimir	30-45	
Newman, Robert	Merlin's Mistake (1st {std}, 8vo, 237p, b/w, DJ/5.25)	Atheneum	1970	Lebenson, Richard	20-30	
Criss, Mildred	Malou (1st {std}, 8vo, blue cl, 280p, uncut, col frn, 4 fp b/w)	Doubleday/Doran	1929	Lederer, Charlotte	20-35	
McNeer, May	Tales from the Crescent Moon (1st, lg8vo, 306p, blue/silver, 6cp, DJ)	Farrar/Rinehart	(1930)	Lederer, Charlotte	40-60	
McNeer, May	Tinka Minka & Linka (1st, 8vo, 30p, yellow cl, cep, fp color)	Knopf	1931	Lederer, Charlotte	50-85	
Snedeker, Caroline D.	Town of the Fearless (1st {std}, 8vo, 351p, col frn, 12 fp b/w, pep)	Doubleday/Doran	1931	Lee Manning De V.	30-50	
Koch, Dorothy	Gone is My Goose (1st, lg8vo, green cl, [27]p, 1-color, cep, DJ/2.25)	Holiday House	(1956)	Lee, Doris	45-70	R*
Thurber, James	Great Quillow (1st, 8vo, 54p, p-o, yellow cl, color, DJ/2.00)	Harcourt	(1944)	Lee, Doris	150-250	
Stong, Philip D.	Hired Man's Elephant (1st, 8vo, 149p, beige cl, b/w, DJ/2.00)	Dodd	1939	Lee, Doris	30-50	
Edmonds, Walter D.	Mr. Benedict's Lion (1st, 8vo, 154p, fp b/w, gilt, uncut, DJ/2.75)	Dodd	1950	Lee, Doris	60-90	R*
Read, Helen S.	My Blue Book (1st, sq8vo, [166]p, fp color, pep)	Scribner	1931	Lee, Eleanor	60-90	*
Pease, Leonora	Dollies in Happy-Land (1st, lg8vo, pict cl, [45]p, color)	Whitman	(1914)	Lee, Ella D.	100-160	
Mother Goose	Ella Dolbear Lee Mother Goose (1st, sm4to, 280p, 24cp, pep)	Donohue	(1918)	Lee, Ella D.	120-200	
Lee, Ella D.	Ever Living Fairy Tales (lg8vo, blue/gilt, p-o, 18cp)	Donohue	1924	Lee, Ella D.	50-80	*
Grimm Bros.	Fairy Tales (4to, 229p, p-o, 24cp, pep)	Donohue	(1920)	Lee, Ella D.	90-140	*
Andersen, Hans C.	Fairy Tales (4to, 245p, 16cp, pep)	Donohue	(1926)	Lee, Ella D.	75-120	
McGovern, Mary H.	Fifty Famous Fairy Tales (1st, 8vo, 254p, 7cp)	Whitman	(1917)	Lee, Ella D.	60-100	*
Pease, Leonora	Four & Twenty Dollies (1st, sm sq4to, 94p, ibds, color)	Hamming	(1914)	Lee, Ella D.	80-140	
Keys, Leonora	Happy Dollies (lg8vo, [46]p, color)	Whitman	(1914)	Lee, Ella D.	90-120	

AUTHOR	TITLE	PUBLISHER	DATE	ARTIST	PRICE	LC
Gordon, Elizabeth	Lorraine & Little People of Spring (1st, sm8vo, 64p, color)	Rand/McNally	(1918)	Lee, Ella D.	40-65	
Keys, Leonora	Play Dollies (sm4to, 38p, ibds, color)	Whitman	(1927)	Lee, Ella D.	90-120	*
Lee, Melicent	Pablo and Petra (1st, 8vo, 152p, col frn, b/w, pep)	Crowell	(1934)	Lee, Leslie W.	25-45	
Coatsworth, Eliz.	Aunt Flora (1st {std}, 8vo, 64p, 1-color, DJ/2.00)	Macmillan	1953	Lee, Manning De V.	25-40	
Snedeker, Caroline D.	Beckoning Road (1st {std}, 8vo, 326p, col frn)	Doubleday/Doran	1929	Lee, Manning De V.	25-40	
Snedeker, Caroline D.	Black Arrowhead (1st {std}, 8vo, 279p, col frn, pep)	Doubleday/Doran	1929	Lee, Manning De V.	25-40	
Lang, Andrew	Blue Fairy Book (1st, 8vo, 428p, p-o, 6cp, pep)	Macrae Smith	(1926)	Lee, Manning De V.	30-50	
Coatsworth, Eliz.	Boston Bells (1st {std}, 8vo, 64p, grey cl, DJ/2.00)	Macmillan	1952	Lee, Manning De V.	25-40	
Edmonds, Walter D.	Cadmus Henry (1st, 8vo, 137p, b/w, DJ/2.75)	Dodd	1949	Lee, Manning De V.	60-100	R
Coatsworth, Eliz.	Cherry Ann & the Dragon Horse (1st {std}, 8vo, ipcb, 64p, b/w, DJ/2.00)	Macmillan	(1955)	Lee, Manning De V.	20-30	
Malkus, Alida S.	Colt of Destiny... (1st {std}, 8vo, 244p, b/w, DJ/2.50)	Winston	(1950)	Lee, Manning De V.	25-40	
Edmonds, Walter D.	Corporal Bess: Story of a Boy & a Dog (1st, 8vo, 182p, b/w, DJ/2.75)	Dodd	(1952)	Lee, Manning De V.	40-65	*
Means, Florence C.	Dusky Day: A College Story (1st, 8vo, 271p, b/w, pep)	Houghton	1933	Lee, Manning De V.	25-40	
Kelly, Eric P.	From Star to Star: Story of Krakow (1st {std}, 8vo, 239p, gilt, DJ/2.00)	Lippincott	(1944)	Lee, Manning De V.	25-45	
Allee, Marjorie H.	House of Her Own (1st, 8vo, 220p, b/w, pep, DJ/2.00)	Houghton	1934	Lee, Manning De V.	25-40	
Righter, Linwood	Junior Starke, Poundman (1st {std}, 8vo, 306p, col frn, pep)	Doubleday/Doran	1928	Lee, Manning De V.	20-35	
Coatsworth, Eliz.	Old Whirlwind (1st {std}, 8vo, 64p, 2-color, DJ/2.00)	Macmillan	1953	Lee, Manning De V.	20-30	
Snedeker, Caroline D.	Perilous Seat (1st {std}, sm8vo, 314p, frn by...)	Doubleday/Page	1923	Lee, Manning De V.	30-50	
Lang, Andrew	Red Fairy Book (1st, sm8vo, 399p, p-o, 7cp, pep)	Macrae Smith	[1927]	Lee, Manning De V.	60-90	
Allee, Marjorie H.	Road to Carolina (1st sm8vo, 240p, b/w, DJ/2.00)	Houghton	1932	Lee, Manning De V.	20-30	
Malkus, Alida S.	Sidi: Boy of the Desert (1st {std}, 8vo, 210p, b/w, DJ/2.95)	Winston	(1956)	Lee, Manning De V.	20-35	*
Means, Florence C.	Singing Wood: College Story (1st, 8vo, 241p, b/w, DJ/2.00)	Houghton	1937	Lee, Manning De V.	50-80	*
Allee, Marjorie H.	Smoke Jumper (1st, sm8vo, 160p, b/w, pep, DJ/2.00)	Houghton	1945	Lee, Manning De V.	20-30	
Coatsworth, Eliz.	Sod House (1st {std}, 8vo, 64p, b/w, DJ/2.00)	Macmillan	(1954)	Lee, Manning De V.	20-35	
North, Sterling	Son of the Lamp Maker (1st, 8vo, 60p, 1-color, pep, DJ/2.00)	Rand/McNally	(1956)	Lee, Manning De V.	20-30	
Kauffman, Reginald	Spanish Dollars (1st, 8vo, 299p, gilt, p-o, col frn, 7pl)	Penn	1925	Lee, Manning De V.	25-40	
Govan, Christine	Sweet Possom Valley (1st, 8vo, 202p, b/w, pep, DJ/2.00)	Houghton	1940	Lee, Manning De V.	150-220	
Snedeker, Caroline D.	Uncharted Ways (1st {std}, 8vo, 340p, 14pl, pep, DJ/2.00)	Doubleday/Doran	1935	Lee, Manning De V.	25-45	
Mason, George	Snip and Snap and the Lost Baby (1st, 16mo, ibds, unpag, color)	Volland	(1914)	Lee/Hardy	50-80	
Malkus, Alida S.	Amazon: River of Promise (1st, lg8vo, 128p, DJ/5.95)	McGraw-Hill	(1970)	Leepin, Bruno	20-30	
Belting, Natalia	In Enemy Hands (1st {std}, 8vo, gilt, 168p, b/w, pep, DJ/2.50)	Bobbs-Merrill	(1953)	Lees, Harry	20-30	*
Hoke, Helen	Too Many Kittens (1st, 4to, ibds, [34]p, color, DJ/2.00)	McKay	1947	Lees, Harry	30-50	*
Richards, Laura E.	Merry-Go-Round (1st, sm8vo, 113p, p-o, b/w, DJ/1.50)	Appleton-Century	1935	Lefferts, Winfred E.	30-50	*
Vildrac, Charles	Rose Island (1st, ob8vo, 100p, 1-color, DJ/3.75)	Lothrop, Lee	(1957)	Legrand, Edy	25-40	
Leichman, Seymour	Boy Who Could Sing Pictures (1st {std}, 4to, 59p, 2-color, DJ/3.50)	Doubleday	(1968)	Leichman, Seymour	25-45	
Quick, Herbert	Virginia of the Air Lanes (1st, sm8vo, blue cl, 424p, 5pl)	Bobbs-Merrill	(1909)	Leigh, William R.	40-65	
Moore, Nancy	Unhappy Hippopotamus (1st, 4to, 44p, ibds, fp 1-color, DJ/2.75, NYTBI)	Vanguard Press	(1957)	Leight, Edward	40-65	
Wilder, Thornton	Bridge of San Luis Rey (1st, 8vo, 139p, red/gilt, 16 tip-in woodcuts)	L: Longmans	1929	Leighton, Clare	100-150	
Symington, E.H.	By Light of Sun (1st, 8vo, 196p, buckram, DJ/2.00, fp woodcuts by...)	Putnam	1941	Leighton, Clare	40-65	
Leighton, Clare	Country Matters (1st AM, 4to, 159p, gilt, 70 wood engravings, DJ/3.00)	Macmillan	1937	Leighton, Clare	100-160	R
Plotz, Helen (comp)	Earth is the Lord's (1st {std}, 8vo, 223p, b/w, DJ/5.00)	Crowell	(1965)	Leighton, Clare	30-45	
Leighton, Clare	Farmer's Year... (1st, ob folio, 54p, gilt, 12 fp woodcuts, pep)	L: Collins	1933	Leighton, Clare	200-300	
Nathan, Robert	Fiddler in Barly (1st, 8vo, 137p, 6 woodcuts, DJ)	L: Heinemann	1927	Leighton, Clare	50-80	
Leighton, Clare	Four Hedges... (1st AM, 4to, 167p, blue cl, wood engravings, DJ/3.00)	Macmillan	1935	Leighton, Clare	80-125	
Plotz, Helen	Imagination's Other Place (1st, 8vo, 200p, fp b/w, DJ/3.50)	Crowell	(1955)	Leighton, Clare	30-50	
Brailsford, Mabel	Making of William Penn (1st, 8vo, 367p, gilt, t-i frn by...)	Longmans	1930	Leighton, Clare	35-60	
Leighton, Clare	Musical Box (1st {std}, ob4to, [32]p, ibds, color)	L: Longmans	(1932)	Leighton, Clare	130-185	
Farjeon, Eleanor	Perkin the Pedlar (1st, 8vo, blue cl, 205p, 8cp)	L: Faber	(1932)	Leighton, Clare	75-100	
Tomlinson, H.M.	Sea & the Jungle (1st, 8vo, 343p, green/gilt, 16 woodcuts)	L: Duckworth	1930	Leighton, Clare	60-100	
Parker, Elinor	Singing and the Gold (1st {std}, 4to, 230p, b/w woodcuts, DJ/3.75)	Crowell	(1962)	Leighton, Clare	25-45	
Leighton, Clare	Sometime Never (1st, lg8vo, 178p, b/w, pep, DJ/3.50)	Macmillan	1939	Leighton, Clare	55-80	
Leighton, Clare	Southern Harvest (1st UK, 4to, 123p, blue/gilt, b/w, DJ)	L: Gollancz	1943	Leighton, Clare	60-90	
Roberts, Elizabeth M.	Time of Man (1st, 8vo, 397p, p-o, fp woodcuts, DJ/5.00)	Viking	1945	Leighton, Clare	60-100	
Holme, Constance	Trumpet in the Dust (1st, 8vo, 255p, 6 woodcuts)	L: Nicholson	1934	Leighton, Clare	40-65	
Hardy, Thomas	Under the Greenwood Tree (1st, sm4to, gilt, 236p, wood engravings)	L: Macmillan	1940	Leighton, Clare	55-80	*
Plotz, Helen	Untune the Sky (1st {std}, 8vo, 162p, b/w, DJ/3.50)	Crowell	(1957)	Leighton, Clare	70-120	
Leighton, Clare	Where Land Meets Sea (1st, sm4to, 202p, 4 fp b/w, DJ/4.00)	Rinehart	(1954)	Leighton, Clare	70-125	
Leighton, Clare	Wood that Came Back (1st, ob4to, [33]p, ibds, 2-color)	L: Nicholson	(1934)	Leighton, Clare	100-165	
Bronte, Emily J.	Wuthering Heights (1st {std}, 4to, 325p, 12pl, DJ)	Random	1931	Leighton, Clare	70-100	
Daudet, Alphonse	Letters from my Mill (1st, lg8vo, 236p, tan/gilt, 10cp)	Dodd	1893	Lemaire, Madeleine	35-60	
Meredith, Owen	Lucille (1st, 8vo, teg, 12cp by...)	Stokes	(1897)	Lemaire, Madeleine	70-100	
Andersen, Hans C.	Fairy Tales (1st, lg8vo, 219p, b/w)	L: E. Arnold	1893	Lemann, E.A.	90-120	
Lang, Andrew	Gold of Fairnilee (1st, 4to, gilt, teg, 86p, uncut, 13cp)	L: Arrowsmith	(1888)	Lemann, E.A.	200-300	
Andersen, Hans C.	Snow Queen (1st, 8vo, 232p, 35 illus, AEG)	L: E. Arnold	1894	Lemann, E.A.	90-120	
Bond, Susan	Ride with Me through ABC (1st AM, 4to, [30]p, ibds, color, pep, DJ/3.75)	NY: Scroll Pr.	1968	Lemke, Horst	30-50	
Kastner, Erich	The Simpletons (1st AM, 4to, 69p, fp color, cep, DJ)	J. Messner	1957	Lemke, Horst	35-50	
Hazard, R.H.	House on Stilts (1st, 12mo, red cl, 346p, 4pl)	Dillingham	(1910)	Lemon, J.A.	30-50	
Locke, William J.	Christmas Mystery (1st UK, 4to, 37p, orange cl, 6cp)	L: John Lane	1922	Lendon, Warwick W.	35-60	*
Locke, William J.	Story of the Three Wise Men (1st, 8vo, 38p, gilt, 6cp)	L: John Lane	1922	Lendon, Warwick W.	40-60	
Lenski, Lois	A-Going to the Westward (1st, 8vo, 370p, uncut, b/w, pep, DJ/2.00)	Stokes	1937	Lenski, Lois	90-140	
Lenski, Lois	Alphabet People (1st {std}, lg8vo, 104p, p-o, blue cl, color, pep)	Harper	1928	Lenski, Lois	100-160	
Lenski, Lois	Animals for Me (1st, ob16mo, [48]p, fp 2-color, cep, DJ/0.75)	Oxford U. Pr.	(1941)	Lenski, Lois	60-90	
Lenski, Lois	Arabella & Her Aunts (1st, 16mo, p-o, 115p, 5cp, cep)	Stokes	1932	Lenski, Lois	100-170	
Lenski, Lois	Bayou Suzette (1st {std}, 8vo, 207p, map, fp b/w, pep, DJ/2.00)	Stokes	1943	Lenski, Lois	100-175	
Lenski, Lois	Benny & His Penny (1st ob4to, blue cl, [32]p, color)	Knopf	1931	Lenski, Lois	120-170	
Lenski, Lois	Berries in the Scoop (1st {std}, 8vo, 124p, red cl, b/w, DJ/2.25)	Lippincott	(1956)	Lenski, Lois	80-140	
Lovelace, Maud H.	Betsy-Tacy (1st, 8vo, 112p, pink cl, b/w, pep, DJ/2.00)	Crowell	1940	Lenski, Lois	120-170	
Lovelace, Maud H.	Betsy-Tacy and Tib (1st, 8vo, 127p, b/w, DJ/2.00)	Crowell	1941	Lenski, Lois	150-200	

AUTHOR	TITLE	PUBLISHER	DATE	ARTIST	PRICE	LC
Lenski, Lois	Big Little Davy (1st, ob16mo, 48p, fp 2-color, pep, DJ/1.50)	Oxford U. Pr.	1956	Lenski, Lois	60-90	
Lenski, Lois	Blue Ridge Billy (1st {std}, 8vo, 203p, b/w, pep, DJ/2.50)	Lippincott	(1946)	Lenski, Lois	70-120	
Lenski, Lois	Blueberry Corners (1st, 8vo, blue/gilt, 209p, b/w, pep, DJ/2.00)	Stokes	1940	Lenski, Lois	80-140	
Adams, Kathleen	Book of Enchantment (1st, lg8vo, 23p, pep, gilt, 4cp, pep)	Dodd	1928	Lenski, Lois	60-100	
Adams, Kathleen	Book of Princess Stories (1st, lg8vo, blue/gilt, 223p, 4cp, b/w, pep)	Dodd	1927	Lenski, Lois	100-160	
Lenski, Lois	Boom Town Boy (1st {std}, 8vo, 177p, fp b/w, pep, DJ/2.50)	Lippincott	1948	Lenski, Lois	80-140	
Lenski, Lois	Bound Girl of Cobble Hill (1st, 8vo, 292p, uncut, b/w, dep, DJ/2.25)	Stokes	1938	Lenski, Lois	70-120	
Hutchinson, Veronica	Candle-Light Stories (1st, sm4to, 146p, 6cp, pep)	Minton Balch	1928	Lenski, Lois	80-120	
Hutchinson, Veronica	Chimney Corner Fairy Tales (1st, sm4to, 183p, 6cp, pep)	Minton Balch	1926	Lenski, Lois	80-140	
Hutchinson, Veronica	Chimney Corner Poems (1st, sm4to, 115p, 6cp, pep)	Minton Balch	1929	Lenski, Lois	80-140	
Hutchinson, Veronica	Chimney Corner Stories (1st, sm4to, 149p, 6cp, pep)	Minton Balch	1925	Lenski, Lois	80-140	
Lenski, Lois	Coal Camp Girl (1st {std}, 8vo, 173p, b/w, pep, DJ/3.95)	Lippincott	(1959)	Lenski, Lois	60-90	
Lenski, Lois	Corn-Farm Boy (1st {std}, 8vo, 179p, b/w, pep, DJ/3.00)	Lippincott	(1954)	Lenski, Lois	60-95	
Lenski, Lois	Cotton in My Sack (1st {std}, 8vo, 191p, dp b/w, pep, DJ/2.50)	Lippincott	(1949)	Lenski, Lois	80-125	
Lenski, Lois	Cowboy Small (1st, 12mo, [48]p, fp color, pep, DJ/1.00)	Oxford U. Pr.	(1949)	Lenski, Lois	70-120	
Lenski, Lois	Davy and His Dog (1st, ob16mo, 38p, fp 2-color, pep, DJ/1.50)	Oxford U. Pr.	1957	Lenski, Lois	50-80	
Lenski, Lois	Davy Goes Places (1st, ob16mo, 46p, fp 2-color, pep, DJ/1.75)	H.Z. Walck	1961	Lenski, Lois	50-80	
Lenski, Lois	Davy's Day (1st, ob 16mo, [48]p, color, DJ/0.75)	Oxford U. Pr.	(1943)	Lenski, Lois	50-80	
Lenski, Lois	Debbie and Her Dolls (1st, ob16mo, 48p, fp color, DJ/3.00)	H.Z. Walck	(1970)	Lenski, Lois	50-85	
Lenski, Lois	Debbie and Her Family (1st, ob16mo, 46p, fp color, DJ/3.00)	H.Z. Walck	(1969)	Lenski, Lois	50-85	
Lenski, Lois	Debbie and Her Grandma (1st, ob16mo, 48p, fp color, DJ/2.50)	H.Z. Walck	1967	Lenski, Lois	50-85	
Lenski, Lois	Debbie Goes to Nursery School (1st, ob16mo, 48p, color, DJ/3.00)	H.Z. Walck	(1970)	Lenski, Lois	50-85	
Lenski, Lois	Debbie Herself (1st, ob16mo, 46p, fp color, DJ/3.00)	H.Z. Walck	(1969)	Lenski, Lois	50-85	
Lenski, Lois	Deer Valley Girl (1st {std}, 8vo, 145p, fp b/w, DJ/3.95)	Lippincott	1968	Lenski, Lois	80-120	
Lenski, Lois	Dog Came to School (1st, ob16mo, 46p, 2-color, pep, DJ/1.50)	Oxford U. Pr.	1955	Lenski, Lois	60-95	
Bulla, Clyde R.	Donkey Cart (1st, 8vo, yellow cl, 89p, b/w, pep, DJ/2.25)	Crowell	(1946)	Lenski, Lois	60-100	
Lovelace, Maud H.	Down Town: Betsy-Tacy Story (1st, 8vo, 180p, b/w, DJ/2.00)	Crowell	1943	Lenski, Lois	80-140	
Grahame, Kenneth	Dream Days (1st, 8vo, 192p, 4cp, pep)	L: John Lane	1922	Lenski, Lois	100-165	
Lenski, Lois	Easter Rabbit's Parade (1st, lg8vo, ipcb, [31]p, 3-color, pep, DJ/1.00)	Oxford U. Pr.	(1936)	Lenski, Lois	200-300	
Stong, Philip D.	Edgar: The 7:58 (1st, sm8vo, 101p, pep, b/w, DJ/1.50)	Farrar/Rinehart	1938	Lenski, Lois	80-125	
Hutchinson, Veronica	Fireside Poems (1st, sm4to, 147p, 5cp, pep)	Minton Balch	1930	Lenski, Lois	70-120	
Hutchinson, Veronica	Fireside Stories (1st, sm4to, 150p, 6cp, pep)	Minton Balch	1927	Lenski, Lois	80-130	
Barksdale, Lena	First Thanksgiving (1st {std}, sm8vo, 57p, 6cp, pep, DJ/1.50)	Knopf	1942	Lenski, Lois	60-90	
Whitehead, Roberta	Five & Ten (1st, 8vo, red cl, [41]p, color, pep, DJ/1.00)	Houghton	1943	Lenski, Lois	80-130	
Lenski, Lois	Flood Friday (1st {std}, 8vo, 96p, b/w, DJ/2.50)	Lippincott	1956	Lenski, Lois	100-175	
Grahame, Kenneth	Golden Age (1st [1st bk.], 8vo, uncut, 199p, 4 ticp)	L: John Lane	1921	Lenski, Lois	100-160	
Becker, May L.	Golden Tales of Canada (1st, 8vo, 274p, pep, DJ/2.50, decor by...)	Dodd	1938	Lenski, Lois	50-80	*
Becker, May L.	Golden Tales of Far West (1st, sm8vo, 304p, pep, DJ/2.50, decor by...)	Dodd	1935	Lenski, Lois	50-85	
Becker, May L.	Golden Tales of Prairie States (1st, sm8vo, 355p, pep, decor by...)	Dodd	1932	Lenski, Lois	50-85	
Becker, May L.	Golden Tales of the Southwest (1st, sm8vo, 265p, pep, DJ/2.50, decor by...)	Dodd	1939	Lenski, Lois	50-80	*
Lenski, Lois	Gooseberry Garden (1st {std}, ob8vo, ipcb, [32]p, color, pep)	Harper	1934	Lenski, Lois	100-165	
Lenski, Lois	Grandmother Tippytoe (1st, lg8vo, p-o, 104p, 8cp, dep)	Stokes	1931	Lenski, Lois	100-165	
Birch, Vera B.	Green-Faced Toad (1st AM, lg8vo, 107p, green cl, 8cp, pep)	Stokes	1923	Lenski, Lois	100-150	
Emerson, Caroline	Hat Tub Tale... (1st {std}, 8vo, 185p, blue cl, uncut, b/w, pep)	Dutton	1928	Lenski, Lois	70-120	
Lenski, Lois	High-Rise Secret (1st {std}, sm8vo, 152p, b/w, DJ/3.50)	Lippincott	(1966)	Lenski, Lois	50-80	
Lenski, Lois	Houseboat Girl (1st {std}, 8vo, 175p, bds, b/w, DJ/3.00)	Lippincott	1957	Lenski, Lois	80-125	
Lenski, Lois	I Like Winter (1st, sq24mo, [48]p, 2-color, DJ/1.00)	Oxford U. Pr.	(1950)	Lenski, Lois	70-120	
Bulla, Clyde R.	I Went for a Walk (1st, ob12mo, 48p, 1-color, DJ/2.00)	H.Z. Walck	1958	Lenski, Lois	60-90	
Lenski, Lois	Indian Captive (1st, 8vo, 269p, pep, color, DJ/2.00, NH)	Stokes	1941	Lenski, Lois	70-120	
Rogers, Frances	Indigo Treasure (1st, sm8vo, 291p, col frn, DJ/2.00)	Stokes	(1941)	Lenski, Lois	80-120	
Lenski, Lois	Jack Horner's Pie (1st, lg8vo, 83p, gilt, color)	Harper	1927	Lenski, Lois	100-175	
Lenski, Lois	Johnny Goes to the Fair (1st, ob8vo, [32]p, yellow cl, color)	Minton Balch	1932	Lenski, Lois	80-130	
Piper, Watty (ed)	Jolly Rhymes of Mother Goose (1st, 12mo, [118]p, col frn)	Platt/Munk	(1932)	Lenski, Lois	60-100	
Lenski, Lois	Judy's Journey (1st {std}, 8vo, 212p, b/w, pep, DJ/2.50)	Lippincott	1947	Lenski, Lois	70-120	
Lenski, Lois	Let's Play House (1st, ob8vo, [40]p, fp 2-color, dep, DJ/1.00)	Oxford U. Pr.	1944	Lenski, Lois	80-125	
La Rue, Mabel G.	Letter to Popsey (1st, sq8vo, [28]p, ibds, color, pep, DJ/0.50)	Grosset/Dunlap	1942	Lenski, Lois	60-100	
Lenski, Lois	Life I Live: Collected Poems (1st, 8vo, 238p, gilt, b/w, DJ/7.50)	H.Z. Walck	1965	Lenski, Lois	100-175	
Lenski, Lois	Little Airplane (1st, sq12mo, [48]p, 1-color, pep, DJ/0.75)	Oxford U. Pr.	(1938)	Lenski, Lois	100-165	
Lenski, Lois	Little Auto (1st, sq12mo, [48]p, 1-color, pep)	Oxford U. Pr.	(1934)	Lenski, Lois	80-140	
Lenski, Lois	Little Baby Ann (1st, sq12mo, [47]p, color, pep)	Oxford U. Pr.	(1935)	Lenski, Lois	80-140	
Piper, Watty (ed)	Little Engine that Could (1st, 8vo, [25]p, p-o, color, pep)	Platt/Munk	(1930)	Lenski, Lois	70-100	
Lenski, Lois	Little Family (1st {std}, sq24mo, ibds, [48]p, color, dep)	Doubleday/Doran	1932	Lenski, Lois	80-140	
Lenski, Lois	Little Farm (1st, sq12mo, [48]p, color, pep, DJ/0.75)	Oxford U. Pr.	(1942)	Lenski, Lois	80-130	
Lenski, Lois	Little Fire Engine (1st, ob8vo, red/gilt, [46]p, 1-color, pep, DJ/1.00)	Oxford U. Pr.	1946	Lenski, Lois	70-120	
Lenski, Lois	Little Girl of 1900 (1st, 8vo, 218p, p-o, col frn, 9pl, pep)	Stokes	1928	Lenski, Lois	100-165	R
Phillips, Ethel C.	Little Rag Doll (1st, 8vo, p-o, 173p, 4cp, pep)	Houghton	1930	Lenski, Lois	70-125	
Lenski, Lois	Little Sail Boat (1st, sq12mo, [48]p, color, pep)	Oxford U. Pr.	(1937)	Lenski, Lois	70-125	
Lenski, Lois	Little Sioux Girl (1st {std}, 8vo, 128p, b/w, DJ/2.75)	Lippincott	1958	Lenski, Lois	70-100	
Lenski, Lois	Little Train (1st, ob8vo, [48]p, color, pep, DJ/0.75)	Oxford U. Pr.	(1940)	Lenski, Lois	100-160	
Lenski, Lois	Lois Lenski's Christmas Stories (1st {std}, lg8vo, 152p, gilt b/w, DJ/3.95)	Lippincott	(1968)	Lenski, Lois	80-120	
Mother Goose	Lois Lenski's Mother Goose (1st, 8vo, 83p, fp 2-color)	Harper	(1936)	Lenski, Lois	80-120	
Lenski, Lois	Mama Hattie's Girl (1st {std}, 8vo, 182p, pep, b/w, DJ/3.00)	Lippincott	(1953)	Lenski, Lois	80-135	
Emerson, Caroline	Merry-Go-Round of Modern Tales (1st, 8vo, gilt, 173p, b/w, pep)	Dutton	1927	Lenski, Lois	70-120	*
Drummond, Henry	Monkey that Would not Kill (1st, sm8vo, fp b/w, pep)	Dodd	1925	Lenski, Lois	60-100	*
Meigs, Cornelia L.	Mother Makes Christmas (1st, sq8vo, ibds, [28]p, pep, 14 color, DJ/0.50)	Grosset/Dunlap	1940	Lenski, Lois	70-120	
Lenski, Lois	Mr. and Mrs. Noah (1st, ob16mo, [48]p, fp color, pep, DJ/1.00)	Crowell	(1948)	Lenski, Lois	50-85	*
Emerson, Caroline	Mr. Nip & Mr. Tuck (1st {std}, 8vo, 173p, aqua/gilt, b/w, dep)	Dutton	1930	Lenski, Lois	70-125	
Phillips, Ethel C.	Name for Obed (1st, sm4to, 117p, 1-color, pep, DJ/2.00)	Houghton	1941	Lenski, Lois	80-125	

AUTHOR	TITLE	PUBLISHER	DATE	ARTIST	PRICE	LC
Lenski, Lois	Now It's Fall (1st, ob24mo, [48]p, ibds, color, DJ/1.00)	Oxford U. Pr.	(1948)	Lenski, Lois	100-160	
Lenski, Lois	Ocean-Born Mary (1st, sm8vo, 388p, fp b/w, pep, DJ/2.00)	Stokes	1939	Lenski, Lois	100-165	
Chidsey, Alan	Odysseus, Sage of Greece (1st, sm8vo, 320p, fp b/w, pep)	Minton Balch	1931	Lenski, Lois	50-80	
Lenski, Lois	On a Summer Day (1st, sq16mo, [36]p, color, pep, DJ/1.25)	Oxford U. Pr.	(1953)	Lenski, Lois	70-100	
Thompson, Dorothy	Once on Christmas (1st, 24mo, ipcb, [44]p, pep, 6 fp b/w, DJ/0.50)	NY: Oxford U.Pr.	1938	Lenski, Lois	90-140	R
Lovelace, Maud H.	Over the Big Hill (1st, 8vo, 171p, b/w, pep, DJ/2.00)	Crowell	1942	Lenski, Lois	100-170	
Lenski, Lois	Papa Small (1st, sq12mo, [46]p, 1-color, pep, DJ/1.25)	Oxford U. Pr.	1951	Lenski, Lois	60-90	
Lenski, Lois	Peanuts for Billy Ben (1st {std}, 8vo, 128p, 1-color, pep, DJ/2.00)	Lippincott	1952	Lenski, Lois	70-125	
Colum, Padraic	Peep-Show Man (1st, 12mo, blue cl, 65p, 4cp, pep)	Macmillan	1924	Lenski, Lois	70-120	
Lenski, Lois	Phebe Fairchild (1st, sm8vo, 316p, rust/gilt, b/w, dep, DJ/2.00, NH)	Stokes	1936	Lenski, Lois	100-165	
Collodi, Carlo	Pinocchio (1st, 4to, yellow bds, [65]p, 7 fp color, pep)	Random	(1946)	Lenski, Lois	100-175	
Lenski, Lois	Policeman Small (1st, 12mo, [48]p, fp 1-color, pep, DJ/2.25)	H.Z. Walck	1962	Lenski, Lois	50-85	
Lenski, Lois	Prairie School (1st {std}, 8vo, 196p, fp b/w, pep, DJ/2.75)	Lippincott	(1951)	Lenski, Lois	60-100	
Lenski, Lois	Project Boy (1st {std}, 8vo, 128p, b/w, cep, DJ/2.00)	Lippincott	1954	Lenski, Lois	70-100	
Robins, Elizabeth	Prudence & Peter... (1st, sm8vo, 244p, grey cl, p-o, b/w)	Wm. Morrow	(1928)	Lenski, Lois	60-100	
Lenski, Lois	Puritan Adventure (1st {std}, sm8vo, gilt, 223p, 2-color, DJ/2.00)	Lippincott	1944	Lenski, Lois	100-150	
N/A	Read to Me Storybook (1st, 8vo, 146p, b/w, cep, DJ/2.00)	Crowell	(1947)	Lenski, Lois	45-70	
Chidsey, Alan	Rustam Lion of Persia (1st, 8vo, 271p, blue cl, b/w, pep)	Minton Balch	1930	Lenski, Lois	50-80	*
Lenski, Lois	San Francisco Boy (1st {std}, 8vo, 176p, b/w, pep, DJ/3.00)	Lippincott	(1955)	Lenski, Lois	80-125	
Powers, Tom	Scotch Circus (1st, 8vo, 95p, col frn, 3 dp color)	Houghton	1934	Lenski, Lois	100-165	
Lenski, Lois	Shoo-Fly Girl (1st {std}, 8vo, 176p, b/w, pep, DJ/3.95)	Lippincott	(1963)	Lenski, Lois	70-120	
Lenski, Lois	Skipping Village (1st, sm4to, 179p, blue cl, 4cp, 3pl, pep)	Stokes	1927	Lenski, Lois	175-250	
Bulla, Clyde R.	Songs of Mr. Small (1st, 4to, 40p, 2-color, pep, DJ/2.75)	Oxford U. Pr.	1954	Lenski, Lois	70-125	
Lenski, Lois	Spinach-Boy (1st, 12mo, 91p, p-o, 6cp, pep)	Stokes	1930	Lenski, Lois	80-120	
Lenski, Lois	Spring is Here (1st, ob12mo, [48]p, yellow cl, color, cep, DJ/0.75)	Oxford U. Pr.	(1945)	Lenski, Lois	70-125	
Lenski, Lois	Strawberry Girl (1st {std}, 8vo, 194p, green/gilt, b/w, dep, DJ/2.50, NM)	Lippincott	(1945)	Lenski, Lois	300-450	R
Lenski, Lois	Sugarplum House (1st {std}, lg ob8vo, ipcb, 31p, 2-color, DJ/1.00)	Harper	1935	Lenski, Lois	100-170	
Lenski, Lois	Surprise for Davy (1st, ob16mo, [48]p, fp 3-color, cep, DJ/1.00)	Oxford U. Pr.	1947	Lenski, Lois	60-100	
Lenski, Lois	Surprise for Mother (1st, sq12mo, 91p, yellow cl, col frn, b/w)	Stokes	1934	Lenski, Lois	50-80	
Bonner, Mary G.	Surprise Place (1st {std}, 8vo, 119p, green cl, b/w, DJ/2.00)	Knopf	1945	Lenski, Lois	70-120	
Lenski, Lois	Susie Mariar (1st, ob8vo, [43]p, 3-color, dep, DJ/1.00)	NY: Oxford U.Pr.	(1939)	Lenski, Lois	100-165	
Lenski, Lois	Texas Tomboy (1st {std}, 8vo, 180p, b/w, pep, DJ/2.50)	Lippincott	(1950)	Lenski, Lois	80-130	
Adams, Kathleen	There Were Giants (1st, 8vo, 234p, green cl, 4pl, pep)	Dodd	1929	Lenski, Lois	50-80	
Judson, Clara I.	They Came from France (1st, 8vo, red cl, 245p, fp b/w, pep, DJ/2.00)	Houghton	1943	Lenski, Lois	60-95	
Lenski, Lois	To Be a Logger (1st {std}, 8vo, 174p, b/w, pep, DJ/3.95)	Lippincott	1967	Lenski, Lois	70-100	
Lofting, Hugh	Twilight of Magic (1st, 8vo, p-o, 303p, col frn, b/w, pep)	Stokes	1930	Lenski, Lois	100-175	
Lenski, Lois	Two Brothers & their Animal Friends (1st, ob12mo, 122p, p-o, 12 color, pep)	Stokes	1929	Lenski, Lois	120-200	
Lenski, Lois	Two Brothers & their Baby Sister (1st, ob12mo, 121p, p-o, 12cp, pep)	Stokes	1930	Lenski, Lois	120-200	
Lenski, Lois	Washington Picture Book (1st, ob4to, ibds, [32]p, color, pep)	Coward	1930	Lenski, Lois	120-180	
Bulla, Clyde R.	We Are thy Children (1st {std}, ob4to, 32p, 1-color, pep, DJ/2.75)	Crowell	(1952)	Lenski, Lois	80-145	
Lenski, Lois	We Live in the City (1st {std}, 8vo, 128p, blue cl, b/w, cep, DJ/2.00)	Lippincott	1954	Lenski, Lois	50-80	
Lenski, Lois	Wonder City: Picture Book of New York (1st, ob4to, [32]p, 2-color, pep)	Coward	1929	Lenski, Lois	140-200	
Mother Goose	Mother Goose Rhymes (1st, 4to, p-o, [120]p, 8cp, pep)	Platt/Munk	(1931)	Lenski/Eulalie	50-80	
Piper, Watty (ed)	Stories Children Love (lg4to, green cl, p-o, [71]p, color, cep)	Platt/Munk	(1933)	Lenski/Eulalie	70-100	
Piper, Watty	Tick-Tock Tales (1st, 4to, [118]p, gilt, col frn, b/w, pep)	Platt/Munk	(1931)	Lenski/Eulalie	80-120	
Sleater, William	Angry Moon (1st {std}, sq8vo, blue cl, 45p, color, DJ/4.95, CH)	Little/Brown	(1970)	Lent, Blair	70-125	
Small, Ernest	Baba Yaga (1st, 4to, 48p, fp 3-color, cep, DJ/3.50)	Houghton	(1966)	Lent, Blair	30-50	
Scull, Florence	Bear Teeth for Courage (1st, 8vo, 163p, fp b/w, DJ/3.75)	Van Nostrand	(1964)	Lent, Blair	40-65	*
Branley, Franklyn	Christmas Sky (1st, lg8vo, [46]p, gilt, fp 2-color, DJ/3.75)	Crowell	(1966)	Lent, Blair	45-70	R
Lent, Blair	From King Boggen's Hall to Nothing-At-All (1st {std}, sq8vo, 44p, DJ/3.95)	Little/Brown	(1967)	Lent, Blair	30-50	
Lent, Blair	John Tabor's Ride (1st {std}, sq8vo, 48p, color, DJ/3.75)	Little/Brown	(1966)	Lent, Blair	30-50	
Andersen, Hans C.	Little Match Girl (1st, 4to, 43p, color, DJ/3.50)	Houghton	(1968)	Lent, Blair	40-70	R
Wahl, Jan	May Horses (1st {std}, sq8vo, [41]p, fp color, pep, DJ/4.95)	Delacorte Pr.	(1969)	Lent, Blair	30-50	
Bartlett, Ruth	Miracle of the Talking Jungle (1st, 8vo, 96p, fp 1-color, DJ/3.95)	Van Nostrand	(1965)	Lent, Blair	25-40	
Economakis, Olga	Oasis of the Stars (1st, 8vo, [32]p, dp color, DJ/3.50)	Coward	(1965)	Lent, Blair	30-45	
Lent, Blair	Pistachio (1st {std}, 4to, 30p, color, DJ/2.95)	Little/Brown	(1964)	Lent, Blair	40-65	
Hodges, Margaret	The Wave (1st, lg sq8vo, 45p, fp 1-color, DJ/3.25, CH, NYTBI)	Houghton	1964	Lent, Blair	60-100	R
Mosel, Arlene	Tikki-Tikki Tembo (1st {std}, sm4to, ibds, [45]p, color, DJ/4.50)	Holt, Rinehart	(1968)	Lent, Blair	45-60	
Dayrell, Elphinstone	Why Sun and Moon Live in the Sky (1st {std}, 8vo, 26p, color, DJ/3.25, CH)	Houghton	(1968)	Lent, Blair	60-90	
Lent, Henry B.	Diggers and Builders (1st, 8vo, 68p, silhouettes)	Macmillan	1931	Lent, Henry B.	60-100	
Weil, Ann Y.	Silver Fawn (1st {std}, 8vo, 228p, 1-color, pep, DJ/2.00)	Bobbs-Merrill	(1939)	Leon, E.	25-45	
Sleigh, Barbara	Kingdom of Carbonel (1st AM, 8vo, blue cl, 287p, fp b/w, DJ/3.50)	Bobbs-Merrill	(1960)	Leonard, D.M.	150-225	
Peck, Harry T.	Hilda and the Wishes (1st, sm8vo, 240p, 8pl)	Dodd	1907	Leonard, M.E.	35-60	*
Sautriax [Rabelais]	Gargantua (1st, ob folio, 52p, ibds, 6cp)	Duffield	1921	Leroy, Adrien	120-200	*
Clarke, Pauline	Twelve and the Genii (1st {std}, 8vo, gilt, 185p, b/w, DJ, CgM)	L: Faber	(1962)	Leslie, Cecil	60-100	
Rinehart, Mary R.	Circular Staircase (1st, 12mo, 362p, 7pl)	Bobbs-Merrill	(1908)	Lester, Ralph	80-130	
Stratton-Porter, Gene	White Flag (1st {std}, sm8vo, 483p, col frn, pep)	Doubleday/Page	1923	Lester, Ralph	100-150	
Armstrong, Richard	Sea Change (1st, 8vo, 211p, b/w, DJ, CgM)	L: J.M. Dent	1948	Leszczynski, M.	70-100	*
Buchan, John	Lake of Gold (1st AM, 8vo, 189p, green cl, b/w, pep, DJ/2.00)	Houghton	1941	Levenson, S.	40-60	
Bangs, John K.	Alice in Blunderland (1st, 12mo, 124p, brown cl, p-o, b/w)	Doubleday/Page	1907	Levering, Albert	60-90	
Carryl, Guy W.	Grimm Tales Made Gay (1st, sq8vo, green cl, 142p, b/w)	Houghton	(1902)	Levering, Albert	120-200	R
Ade, George	In Pastures New (1st, 12mo, 309p, red cl, b/w)	McClure	1906	Levering, Albert	30-50	
Bangs, John K.	Jack and the Check Book (1st, 12mo, 236p, green cl, b/w)	Harper	1911	Levering, Albert	60-90	
Ade, George	Knocking the Neighbors (1st, 12mo, 229p, brown cl, 15pl)	Doubleday/Page	1912	Levering, Albert	55-80	R
Bangs, John K.	Molly and The Unwiseman (1st, sm8vo, 198p, 8pl)	Coates	1902	Levering, Albert	70-120	
Bangs, John K.	Olympian Nights (1st, 12mo, red/gilt, 224p, 16pl)	Harper	1902	Levering, Albert	50-80	
George, Jean C.	Moon of the Moles (1st, 8vo, 37p, color, DJ/3.75)	Crowell	(1969)	Levering, Robert	25-40	
Blake, William	Songs of Experience (1st, 8vo, 83p, green cl, uncut, 9pl)	L: D. Nutt	(1902)	Levetus, Celia	85-120	

AUTHOR	TITLE	PUBLISHER	DATE	ARTIST	PRICE	LC
Blake, William	Songs of Innocence (1st, 24mo, pcb, 118p, AEG, designs by...)	L: Wells/Gard.	1899	Levetus, Celia	80-125	*
Kunos, Ignacz	Turkish Fairy Tales... (1st, lg8vo, gilt, 275p, teg, 9pl)	L: Lawrence	1896	Levetus, Celia	80-140	
Hauff, Wilhelm	Heart of Stone (1st {std}, sm4to, unpag, 1-color, DJ/3.50)	Macmillan	(1964)	Levine, David	30-50	
Hawthorne, Nathaniel	Pegasus, the Winged Horse (1st, folio, ibds, 39p, 11 fp color, DJ/1.95)	Macmillan	1963	Levit, Herschel	30-50	
Greene, Sarah P.M.	Power Lot (1st, sm8vo, teg, 396p, 5pl)	Baker/Taylor	1906	Levy, Alex O.	25-40	
Lewicki, Lillian	Golden Book of Christmas Tales (1st {A}, folio, 28p, ipcb, color, BGB)	Simon/Schuster	(1956)	Lewicki, James	60-90	R
Burroughs, Margaret	Jasper the Drummin' Boy (1st {std}, 8vo, 64p, b/w, DJ/2.95)	Follett	(1970)	Lewin, Ted	30-45	
Field, Rachel	Calico Bush (1st, 8vo, 213p, p-o, 1-color, DJ/2.50, NH)	Macmillan	1931	Lewis, Allen	60-90	R
Field, Rachel	Hepatica Hawks (1st, sm8vo, 239p, blue cl, 5 fp woodcuts, NH)	Macmillan	1932	Lewis, Allen	40-65	
Brooks, Charles S.	Journeys to Baghdad (1st, 8vo, bds, p-o, 140p, teg, 27 woodcuts)	Yale U. Press	1915	Lewis, Allen	40-60	*
Stevens, James	Paul Bunyan (1st, 8vo, 245p, woodcuts by...)	Knopf	1925	Lewis, Allen	30-50	
Scott, Ann H.	Big Cowboy Western (1st, sm4to, [28]p, color, cep, DJ/2.95)	Lothrop, Lee	(1965)	Lewis, Richard	50-80	*
Wier, Ester A.	Gift of the Mountains (1st, 8vo, 116p, b/w, DJ/3.25)	McKay	1963	Lewis, Richard	20-30	
Lewis, Richard W.	Summer Adventure (1st, 8vo, 105p, fp b/w, DJ/2.95)	Harper	(1962)	Lewis, Richard	50-80	*
Prelutsky, Jack	Gopher in the Garden (1st {std}, 4to, [32]p, 3-color, DJ/3.95)	Macmillan	(1967)	Leydenfrost, Rbt.	25-40	*
Roethke, Theodore	I Am! Says the Lamb (1st {std}, 8vo, ibds, 70p, b/w, DJ/2.50)	Doubleday	1961	Leydenfrost, Rbt.	150-225	
Leydenfrost, Robert	Other Side of the Mountain (1st {std}, 4to, [28]p, fp 3-color, DJ/4.50)	Macmillan	(1968)	Leydenfrost, Rbt.	25-45	
Kipling, Rudyard	With the Night Mail (1st, 8vo, teg, blue cl, 77p, pep, 4cp)	Doubleday/Page	1909	Leyendecker, F.X.	170-220	
Morris, Margaretta	Bryn Mawr Stories (1st, 8vo, 296p, teg, green/gilt, cvr by...)	Jacobs	(1901)	Leyendecker, J.C.	60-100	
Hudson, Charles B.	Crimson Conquest (1st, 8vo, 454p, cvr by...)	McClurg	1907	Leyendecker, J.C.	50-80	
Lorimer, George H.	False Gods (1st, 8vo, gilt, p-o, 91p, 4pl)	Appleton	1906	Leyendecker, J.C.	40-65	
Brown, Annie G.	Fireside Battles (1st, 8vo, teg, 327p, 8pl)	Laird & Lee	1900	Leyendecker, J.C.	75-100	*
Craig, Alexander	Ionia... (1st, 8vo, grey buckram, 301p, 6pl)	E.A. Weeks	1898	Leyendecker, J.C.	100-165	
Boylan, Grace D.	Kiss of Glory (1st, sm8vo, 298p, col frn & cvr by...)	Dillingham	(1902)	Leyendecker, J.C.	35-50	
Williams, Egerton	Ridolfo (1st, 8vo, p-o, 406p, 4cp)	McClurg	1906	Leyendecker, J.C.	40-70	
Catherwood, Mary	Spanish Peggy (1st, 8vo, uncut, teg, 85p, red cl, p-o, b/w)	Herbert Stone	1899	Leyendecker, J.C.	90-120	
Morris, Gouverneur	Voice in the Rice (1st, 12mo, 158p, 6cp)	Dodd	1910	Leyendecker, J.C.	60-80	
Chambers, Robert	Iole (1st, sm8vo, 142p, p-o, 2pl by...)	Appleton	1905	Leyendeckers	30-50	
Liang, Yen	Dee-Dee's Birthday (1st, sq12mo, [32]p, fp 3-color, DJ/1.75)	NY: Oxford U.Pr.	1952	Liang, Yen	25-45	
Liang, Yen	The Skyscraper (1st, 4to, 48p, blue cl, fp 1-color, DJ/2.95)	Lippincott	(1958)	Liang, Yen	20-35	*
Collodi, Carlo	Adventures of Pinocchio (1st {std}, sm8vo, 280p, col frn)	Doubleday/Doran	1930	Liddell, Mary	60-100	*
Liddell, Mary	Little Machinery (1st, 8vo, 62p, ibds, color)	Doubleday/Page	(1926)	Liddell, Mary	120-200	
Patri, Angelo	Pinocchio in America (1st {std}, 8vo, 255p, col frn, 17pl, pep)	Doubleday/Doran	1928	Liddell, Mary	60-90	
Perera, Lydia	Frisky (1st, sm8vo, [46]p, red cl, color, cep, DJ/2.25)	Holiday House	1955	Liebman, Oscar	25-40	
Baruch, Dorothy W.	Funny Little Boy (1st, sq12mo, [36]p, color, pep, DJ/1.00)	Lothrop, Lee	1936	Lietta	30-50	*
Johnson, Ryerson	Monkey & the Wild, Wild Wind (1st, 4to [40]p, fp col, pep, DJ/2.75, JABA)	Abelard-Schuman	1961	Lignell, Lois	30-50	
Lindberg, Maja	Karl's Journey to the Moon (4to, ibds, 28p, 14 fp color)	Harper	[1927]	Lindberg, Maja	150-225	
Lindman, Maj	Dear Little Deer (1st, sm4to, [27]p, p-o, color, DJ)	Whitman	(1953)	Lindman, Maj	100-160	
Lindman, Maj	Fire Eye (1st, ob4to, ipcb, 32p, color, DJ/1.50)	Whitman	1948	Lindman, Maj	70-100	
Lindman, Maj	Flicka, Ricka, Dicka & Little Dog (1st, lg8vo, p-o, [27]p, color, DJ/1.00)	Whitman	1946	Lindman, Maj	80-130	
Lindman, Maj	Flicka, Ricka, Dicka & Three Kittens (1st, lg8vo, [27]p, p-o, fp color)	Whitman	1941	Lindman, Maj	80-120	
Lindman, Maj	Sailboat Time (1st, 4to, [27]p, p-o, fp color, pep)	Whitman	(1951)	Lindman, Maj	60-100	
Lindman, Maj	Snipp, Snapp, Snurr & Buttered Bread (1st, sm4to, ibds, p-o, [23]p, color)	Whitman	1934	Lindman, Maj	70-120	
Lindman, Maj	Snipp, Snapp, Snurr & Gingerbread (1st, lg8vo, p-o, ibds, [23]p, color, pep)	Whitman	1936	Lindman, Maj	75-120	
Lindman, Maj	Snipp, Snapp, Snurr & the Red Shoes (1st, sm4to, [24]p, bds, p-o, col, pep)	Whitman	1936	Lindman, Maj	90-125	
Lindman, Maj	Snowboot, Son of Fire Eye (1st, ob4to, 26p, ipcb, color)	Whitman	(1950)	Lindman, Maj	60-100	
Lindsay, Norman	Magic Pudding (1st AM, 8vo, orange cl, [159]p, b/w, DJ/1.50)	Farrar/Rinehart	[1936]	Lindsay, Norman	100-165	
Nash, Ogden	Custard the Dragon & Wicked Knight (1st {std}, 8vo, 47p, color, DJ/2.75)	Little/Brown	(1961)	Linell	50-80	R
Cooke, Grace M.	Doings of the Dollivers (1st, 12mo, 174p, 7pl)	Sturgis/Walton	1910	Linnell, Harry	40-60	*
Shakespeare, Wm.	Merchant of Venice (1st, lg8vo, gilt, 143p, 36 ticp)	L: Hodder	[1909]	Linton, James D.	100-180	
Lindsay, Maud	Jock Barefoot (1st, 8vo, 177p, fp b/w, DJ/1.50)	Lothrop, Lee	1939	Linton, Jane	75-125	
Lionni, Leo	Alexander and the Wind-Up Mouse (1st, 4to, [30]p, color, DJ/3.95, CH)	Pantheon	(1969)	Lionni, Leo	40-65	
Lionni, Leo	Alphabet Tree (1st, 4to, ibds, [33]p, color, pep, DJ)	Pantheon	(1968)	Lionni, Leo	60-100	
Lionni, Leo	Biggest House in the World (1st, 4to, [30]p, fp color, DJ/3.50)	Pantheon	1968	Lionni, Leo	45-70	
Lionni, Leo	Fish is Fish (1st, 4to, [32]p, color, DJ)	Pantheon	(1970)	Lionni, Leo	40-60	
Lionni, Leo	Frederick (1st, 4to, [32]p, color, pep, DJ/3.50, CH, NYTBI)	Pantheon	(1967)	Lionni, Leo	65-100	
Lionni, Leo	Inch by Inch (1st, sq4to, ipcb, unpag, color, pep, DJ/3.50, CH, NYTBI)	Obolensky	(1960)	Lionni, Leo	140-200	R
Lionni, Leo	Little Blue & Little Yellow (1st, sq8vo, ibds, [40]p, col, DJ/2.95, NYTBI)	Obolensky	(1959)	Lionni, Leo	200-300	R
Lionni, Leo	On My Beach there are Many Pebbles (1st, ob4to, [32]p, fp b/w, DJ/3.50)	Obolensky	(1961)	Lionni, Leo	60-100	R
Lionni, Leo	Swimmy (1st, 4to, [31]p, ibds, color, dep, DJ/3.50, CH, NYTBI)	Pantheon	(1963)	Lionni, Leo	65-100	R
Lionni, Leo	Tico and the Golden Wings (1st, 4to, ibds, [34]p, fp, color, cep, DJ/3.50)	Pantheon	1964	Lionni, Leo	60-90	
Coolidge, Olivia	Roman People (1st, 8vo, 243p, b/w, DJ/3.00)	Houghton	1959	Lipinsky, Lino	25-40	
Lipman, Michael	Chatterlings in Wordland (8vo, orange cl, 112p, color, pep)	Wise-Parlow	(1935)	Lipman, Michael	40-70	
Lipman, Michael	The Chatterlings (1st, lg8vo, 96p, ibds, color, pep)	Volland	(1928)	Lipman, Michael	60-100	R
Selden, George	Dunkard (1st, 8vo, 47p, 1-color, cep, DJ/2.95)	Harper	(1968)	Lippman, Peter	20-25	
Lippman, Peter J.	New at the Zoo (1st, sm ob4to, 31p, 2-color, DJ/3.50)	Harper	(1969)	Lippman, Peter	25-40	
Selden, George	Oscar Lobster's Fair Exchange (1st, 12mo, 172p, b/w, cep, DJ/3.95)	Harper	(1966)	Lippman, Peter	30-50	
Lippman, Peter J.	Plunkety Plunk (1st {std}, 4to, [46]p, color, cep, DJ/3.25, NYTBI)	Ariel	(1963)	Lippman, Peter	30-50	
Georgiou, Constantine	Proserpina: Duck that Came to School (1st, 4to, 60p, 1-color, pep, DJ/3.50)	Harvey House	(1968)	Lipscomb, Bernard	30-50	
Andersen, Hans C.	Tumble-Bug (1st, lg8vo, green cl, 166p, pep, fp 1-color, DJ/2.00)	Harcourt	(1940)	List, Hertha	50-80	
N/A	Arabian Nights (1st, sm8vo, p-o, 420p, 7cp, pep)	Jacobs	[1918]	Lister, W.H.	30-50	
Jewett, John H.	Con the Wizard (1st AM, narrow 12mo, 123p, ibds, 8cp)	Stokes	(1905)	Little, Edward R.	55-80	
Farjeon, Eleanor	Singing Games for Children (1st, 8vo, 71p, ipcb, fp color)	Dent/Dutton	[1919]	Littlejohns, J.	60-90	
Grimm Bros.	Hansel & Gretel (1st, 12mo, ibds, [32]p, fp 1-color)	Rand/McNally	1937	Livings, Bess	25-45	*
N/A	Little Rabbit (1st, 8vo, [48]p, b/w, pep)	Whitman	(1934)	Livings, Bess	30-45	
Lynch, Patricia	King of the Tinkers (1st {std}, sm8vo, 240p, 8cp, DJ/2.00)	Dutton	1938	Lloyd, Katharine	40-65	
Monjo, Ferdinand N.	Indian Summer (1st, 8vo, 62p, ibds, color, DJ/2.50)	Harper	(1968)	Lobel, Anita	30-45	
Dalgliesh, Alice	Little Wooden Farmer (1st {std} [new ed.], ob8vo, [32]p, color, DJ/3.95)	Macmillan	(1968)	Lobel, Anita	20-35	*

AUTHOR	TITLE	PUBLISHER	DATE	ARTIST	PRICE	LC
Lobel, Anita	Potatoes, Potatoes (1st, ob4to, [40]p, ibds, fp 2-color, DJ/2.95)	Harper	(1967)	Lobel, Anita	30-50	
DeJong, Meindert	Puppy Summer (1st, 8vo, 98p, fp b/w, DJ/3.95)	Harper	(1966)	Lobel, Anita	50-80	R*
Lobel, Anita	Seamstress of Salzburg (1st, ob4to, [49]p, fp color, cep, DJ/4.50)	Harper	(1970)	Lobel, Anita	30-50	
Borack, Barbara	Someone Small (1st, 8vo, 32p, ibds, color, DJ/3.50)	Harper	(1969)	Lobel, Anita	20-35	
Lobel, Anita	Sven's Bridge (1st, ob8vo, ibds, [32]p, color, cep, DJ/2.95, NYTBI)	Harper	(1965)	Lobel, Anita	40-65	
Orgel, Doris	The Uproar (1st, 4to, [40]p, 3-color, DJ/4.95)	McGraw-Hill	(1970)	Lobel, Anita	30-50	
Ginsburg, Mirra	Three Rolls & One Doughnut (1st {std}, 4to, 52p, b/w, DJ/4.50)	Dial Press	(1970)	Lobel, Anita	30-45	
Lobel, Anita	Troll Music (1st, 4to, ibds, [32]p, fp color, DJ/2.95)	Harper	(1966)	Lobel, Anita	30-50	
Lobel, Anita	Under a Mushroom (1st, sm sq8vo, ibds, [40]p, fp b/w, DJ/3.95)	Harper	(1970)	Lobel, Anita	30-50	
Elkin, Benjamin	Wisest Man in the World (1st, sm4to, [46]p, fp color, pep, DJ/3.50)	Parents Mag. Pr.	(1968)	Lobel, Anita	25-40	
N/A	Wishing Penny (1st, 8vo, 69p, fp 1-color, cep, DJ/2.95)	Parents Mag. Pr.	(1967)	Lobel, Anita	30-50	
Myrick, Mildred	Ants are Fun (1st, 8vo, 63p, color, DJ/2.50)	Harper	(1968)	Lobel, Arnold	25-40	
Lobel, Arnold	Bears of the Air (1st, lg8vo, [32]p, ibds, 1-color, cep, DJ/2.50)	Harper	(1965)	Lobel, Arnold	30-50	
Selsam, Millicent	Benny's Animals & How He Put them in Order (1st, 8vo, 60p, color, DJ/1.95)	Harper	(1966)	Lobel, Arnold	25-40	
Martin, Sarah C.	Comic Adventures of Old Mother Hubbard & her Dog (1st, sm8vo, [32]p, DJ)	Bradbury Press	(1968)	Lobel, Arnold	30-50	R
Ressner, Phil	Dudley Pippin (1st, 8vo, 46p, fp b/w, cep, DJ/2.50)	Harper	(1965)	Lobel, Arnold	30-50	
Lear, Edward	Four Little Children/Went around World (1st {std}, 8vo, 44p, DJ/3.95)	Macmillan	(1968)	Lobel, Arnold	30-50	
Lobel, Arnold	Frog and Toad are Friends (1st, 8vo, ibds, 64p, color, DJ/2.50, CH)	Harper	(1970)	Lobel, Arnold	50-80	
Lobel, Arnold	Giant John (1st, 4to, [32]p, ibds, fp 2-color, DJ/2.95)	Harper	1964	Lobel, Arnold	45-70	
Lobel, Arnold	Great Blueness & other Predicaments (1st, 4to, ibds, [32]p, color, DJ/3.95)	Harper	1968	Lobel, Arnold	50-80	
Selsam, Millicent	Greg's Microscope (1st, 8vo, 64p, color, DJ/1.95)	Harper	(1963)	Lobel, Arnold	20-35	
Lobel, Arnold	Holiday for Mister Muster (1st {std}, ob4to, [32]p, 1-color, DJ/2.75, NYT)	Harper	(1963)	Lobel, Arnold	30-50	
Viorst, Judith	I'll Fix Anthony (1st, ob8vo, [32]p, color, DJ/3.50)	Harper	(1969)	Lobel, Arnold	30-40	
Moore, Lilian	Junk Day on Juniper Street (1st, 8vo, 71p, 1-color, DJ/3.95)	Parents Mag. Pr.	(1969)	Lobel, Arnold	20-30	
Parish, Peggy	Let's Be Early Settlers with Daniel Boone (1st, 8vo, 96p, b/w, DJ/2.95)	Harper	(1967)	Lobel, Arnold	25-40	
Parish, Peggy	Let's Be Indians (1st, 8vo, 96p, b/w, DJ/2.75)	Harper	(1962)	Lobel, Arnold	20-35	
Selsam, Millicent	Let's Get Turtles (1st, 8vo, 62p, color, DJ/1.95)	Harper	(1965)	Lobel, Arnold	20-30	
Baker, Betty	Little Runner of the Longhouse (1st, 8vo, 63p, ibds, fp 2-color, DJ/1.95)	Harper	(1962)	Lobel, Arnold	40-65	
Lobel, Arnold	Lucille (1st, 8vo, 64p, color, DJ/1.95)	Harper	(1964)	Lobel, Arnold	30-50	*
Moore, Lilian	Magic Spectacles (1st, 8vo, 70p, fp 1-color, DJ/2.95)	Parents Mag. Pr.	(1965)	Lobel, Arnold	20-30	
Lobel, Arnold	Martha the Movie Mouse (1st, 4to, [32]p, ibds, color, cep, DJ/2.95)	Harper	(1966)	Lobel, Arnold	45-70	
Young, Miriam	Miss Suzy (1st, 4to, ipcb, [42]p, color, pep, DJ/2.75)	Parents Mag. Pr.	(1964)	Lobel, Arnold	60-100	
Lear, Edward	New Vestments (1st {std}, 8vo, [32]p, color, ibds, DJ/3.95)	Bradbury Press	(1970)	Lobel, Arnold	30-45	
Benchley, Nathaniel	Oscar Otter (1st, 8vo, 64p, color, DJ/1.95)	Harper	(1966)	Lobel, Arnold	30-50	
Lobel, Arnold	Prince Bertram the Bad (1st {std}, 4to, [32]p, color, DJ/2.95)	Harper	(1963)	Lobel, Arnold	40-65	
Zolotow, Charlotte	Quarreling Book (1st {std}, sq16mo, unpag, b/w, DJ/1.95)	Harper	(1963)	Lobel, Arnold	25-40	
Benchley, Nathaniel	Red Fox and His Canoe (1st, 8vo, 62p, ibds, fp 2-color, DJ/1.95)	Harper	(1964)	Lobel, Arnold	30-50	
Phleger, Fred	Red Tag Comes Back (1st, 8vo, ipcb, 64p, fp 2-color, DJ/1.95)	Harper	(1961)	Lobel, Arnold	30-45	
Benchley, Nathaniel	Sam, the Minuteman (1st, 8vo, ibds, 62p, fp 2-color, DJ/2.50)	Harper	(1969)	Lobel, Arnold	50-80	R
Myrick, Mildred	Secret Three (1st, 8vo, ibds, 64p, 2-color, DJ/1.95)	Harper	(1963)	Lobel, Arnold	25-45	
Lobel, Arnold	Small Pig (1st, 8vo, 63p, 2-color, DJ/2.50)	Harper	(1969)	Lobel, Arnold	30-50	
Zolotow, Charlotte	Someday (1st, ob8vo, ipcb, [32]p, fp 2-color, DJ/2.50)	Harper	(1965)	Lobel, Arnold	70-100	
Rhinehart, Susan	Something Old, Something New (1st, 8vo, ibds, 32p, 2-color, DJ/1.95)	Harper	(1961)	Lobel, Arnold	35-50	
DiNoto, Andrea	Star Thief (1st {std}, 4to, [30]p, fp 2-color, pep, DJ/3.50)	Macmillan	1967	Lobel, Arnold	40-65	
Benchley, Nathaniel	Strange Disappearance of Arthur Cluck (1st, 8vo, 64p, 2-color, DJ/1.95)	Harper	(1967)	Lobel, Arnold	25-45	
Prelutsky, Jack	Terrible Tiger (1st {std}, 4to, [38]p, color, DJ/4.95)	Macmillan	(1970)	Lobel, Arnold	30-50	
Selsam, Millicent	Terry and the Caterpillars (1st, 8vo, 64p, color, DJ/1.95)	Harper	(1962)	Lobel, Arnold	30-50	
Cathon, Laura	Tot Botot and his Little Flute (1st {std}, 8vo, [32]p, color, DJ/4.50)	Macmillan	(1970)	Lobel, Arnold	30-50	
Holman, Felice	Witch on the Corner (1st {std}, 8vo, 89p, b/w, DJ/3.50)	Norton	(1966)	Lobel, Arnold	30-45	
Lobel, Arnold	Zoo for Mister Muster (1st, sm ob4to, [32]p, ibds, 1-color, cep, DJ/2.75)	Harper	(1962)	Lobel, Arnold	40-65	
Martin, Patricia	Birthday Present (1st {A}, sm8vo, 47p, fp 3-color, DJ/2.25)	Abingdon Press	(1963)	Locke, Margot	25-40	
Martin, Patricia	Broomtail Bronc (1st {A}, 8vo, 64p, b/w, pep, DJ/2.50)	Abingdon Press	(1965)	Locke, Margot	25-40	*
Martin, Patricia	Chandler Chipmunk's Flying Lesson (1st {A}, lg8vo, 64p, color, DJ/2.50)	Abingdon Press	(1960)	Locke, Margot	20-35	
Lockyer, A.M.	Robbers of Squeak (1st, lg ob8vo, [32]p, ibds, chromos)	L: Marcus Ward	[1890]	Lockyer, A.M.	100-165	
Bianco, Margery W.	Franzi and Gizi (1st, 4to, p-o, [56]p, fp color, pep, DJ/2.00)	J. Messner	1941	Loeffler, Gisella	40-65	
Lofting, Hugh	Dr. Dolittle & Green Canary (1st {std}, 8vo, 276p, col frn, pep, DJ/2.75)	Lippincott	(1950)	Lofting, Hugh	100-175	
Lofting, Hugh	Dr. Dolittle & Secret Lake (1st {std}, 8vo, 366p pep, p-o col frn, DJ/3.00)	Lippincott	(1948)	Lofting, Hugh	100-175	
Lofting, Hugh	Dr. Dolittle in the Moon (1st, 8vo, p-o, 307p, col frn, pep)	Stokes	(1928)	Lofting, Hugh	100-175	
Lofting, Hugh	Dr. Dolittle's Birthday Bk. (1st, sq12mo gilt [216]p, col frn, dep, DJ/1.75)	Stokes	(1935)	Lofting, Hugh	200-300	
Lofting, Hugh	Dr. Dolittle's Caravan (1st {std}, 8vo, 342p, p-o, col frn, pep)	Stokes	(1926)	Lofting, Hugh	100-175	
Lofting, Hugh	Dr. Dolittle's Circus (1st, 8vo, 379p, p-o, col frn, pep)	Stokes	(1924)	Lofting, Hugh	100-175	
Lofting, Hugh	Dr. Dolittle's Garden (1st, 8vo, 327p, p-o, col frn, pep)	Stokes	(1927)	Lofting, Hugh	100-175	
Lofting, Hugh	Dr. Dolittle's Post Office (1st, 8vo, 359p, col frn, pep)	Stokes	(1923)	Lofting, Hugh	100-175	
Lofting, Hugh	Dr. Dolittle's Puddleby Advens (1st {std} 8vo, 241p, pep, col frn, DJ/3.00)	Lippincott	(1952)	Lofting, Hugh	100-175	
Lofting, Hugh	Dr. Dolittle's Return (1st, 8vo, p-o, 273p, col frn, b/w, pep)	Stokes	1933	Lofting, Hugh	100-175	
Lofting, Hugh	Dr. Dolittle's Zoo (1st, 8vo, grey cl, p-o, 338p, col frn, pep)	Stokes	(1925)	Lofting, Hugh	100-175	
Lofting, Hugh	Gub Gub's Book (1st, sm8vo, 185p, p-o, 2cp, 6pl, pep)	Stokes	(1932)	Lofting, Hugh	100-185	
Lofting, Hugh	Noisy Nora (1st, 16mo, [53]p, pink cl, p-o, pep, color)	Stokes	(1929)	Lofting, Hugh	100-170	
Lofting, Hugh	Porridge Poetry (1st, ob12mo, [96]p, p-o, yellow cl, color)	Stokes	(1924)	Lofting, Hugh	120-180	
Lofting, Hugh	Story of Dr. Dolittle (1st, 8vo, p-o, 180p, col frn, b/w, pep, PPP)	Stokes	1920	Lofting, Hugh	300-500	
Lofting, Hugh	Story of Mrs. Tubbs (1st, sm ob8vo, p-o, [95]p, color)	Stokes	(1923)	Lofting, Hugh	200-300	
Lofting, Hugh	Tommy, Tilly & Mrs. Tubbs (1st UK, ob12mo, 72p, ibds, color)	L: J. Cape	(1937)	Lofting, Hugh	90-140	
Lofting, Hugh	Voyages of Doctor Dolittle (1st, 12mo, p-o, 364p, 2cp, pep, NM)	Stokes	1922	Lofting, Hugh	120-185	
Carlson, Natalie S.	Chalou (1st, 8vo, 109p, fp b/w, cep, DJ/3.50)	Harper	(1967)	Loh, George	30-45	
Carlson, Natalie S.	Sailor's Choice (1st, 8vo, 140p, b/w, DJ/3.50)	Harper	(1966)	Loh, George	25-40	
Mother Goose	Mother Goose (1st, lg4to, p-o, 113p, color, pep)	Saalfield	(1938)	Lohman, Fred D.	75-100	*
Gridley, Marion	Indians of Yesterday (1st, lg4to, ibds, 63p, 6 fp color, pep, DJ/1.00)	Donohue	(1940)	Lone Wolf	50-80	
Simon, Shirley	Best Friend (1st, 8vo, 191p, b/w, DJ/3.50)	Lothrop, Lee	(1964)	Lonette, Reisie	25-45	*

AUTHOR	TITLE	PUBLISHER	DATE	ARTIST	PRICE	LC
Shank, Margarethe	Coffee Train (1st {std}, sm8vo, 285p, b/w, DJ/3.50)	Doubleday	1953	Lonette, Reisie	20-35	
Fenton, Edward	Hidden Trapezes (1st {std}, 8vo, 239p, b/w, DJ/2.50)	Doubleday	(1950)	Lonette, Reisie	20-35	
Harry, Robert	Island Boy (1st, 8vo, 209p, b/w, DJ/3.00)	Lothrop, Lee	(1956)	Lonette, Reisie	25-40	
Snedeker, Caroline D.	Lysis Goes to the Play (1st, lg8vo, 61p, fp b/w, DJ/3.00)	Lothrop, Lee	(1962)	Lonette, Reisie	40-65	
Oursler, Fulton	String of Blue Beads (1st {std}, 12mo, ibds, [32]p, color, DJ/1.50)	Doubleday	1956	Lonette, Reisie	30-50	
Fenton, Edward	Us and the Duchess (1st {std}, 8vo, 208p, b/w, pep, DJ/2.00)	Doubleday	1947	Lonette, Reisie	25-40	
Crothers, Samuel M.	Miss Muffet's Christmas Party (1st, sm8vo, blue/gilt, 106p, b/w, pep)	Houghton	1902	Long, Olive M.	35-60	
Long, Olive M.	The Lollipops (1st, ob8vo, ipcb, [28]p, b/w)	R.H. Russell	1901	Long, Olive M.	120-180	*
Kilbourne, Charles E.	Baby Elephant & Zoo Man (1st, 8vo, p-o, color, pep)	Penn	1911	Longstreet, Hattie	90-150	*
Kilbourne, Charles E.	Baby Ostrich & Mr. Wise Owl (1st, 16mo, ipcb, p-o, 82p, color, pep)	Penn	1915	Longstreet, Hattie	100-160	R*
Kilbourne, Charles E.	Baby Reindeer & Silver Fox (1st, 16mo, ipcb, p-o, 82p, color, pep)	Penn	1916	Longstreet, Hattie	100-165	R
Barzini, Luigi	Little Match Man (1st, 8vo, 164p, p-o, 5cp, pep)	Penn	1917	Longstreet, Hattie	35-50	
Heide, Florence P.	Day It Snowed in Summer (1st {1}, 4to, [32]p, fp 3-color, dep, DJ/2.95)	Funk/Wagnalls	(1968)	Longtemps, Kenneth	30-50	*
Ipcar, Dahlov	General Felice (1st, 8vo, 159p, b/w, DJ/4.50)	McGraw-Hill	(1967)	Longtemps, Kenneth	50-80	
Heide, Florence P.	Sound of Sunshine, Sound of Rain (1st, lg8vo, [40]p, fp color, DJ/3.95)	Parents Mag. Pr.	(1970)	Longtemps, Kenneth	30-50	
Mother Goose	Familiar Rhymes of Mother Goose (1st, 8vo, 30cp, pcb)	L: Nister	1888	Loomis, Chester B.	200-300	
Loomis, Charles B.	Little Maude & her Mama (1st, 12mo, 43p, brown cl, 4pl)	Doubleday/Page	1909	Loomis, Chester B.	40-65	
Mother Goose	New Mother Goose Pictures (1st, sq4to, ibds)	Russell	1898	Loomis, Chester B.	170-240	
Phleger, Fred	Ann Can Fly (1st {std}, 8vo, 63p, color, pep, DJ/1.95)	Beginner Books	(1959)	Lopshire, Robert	45-70	
Lopshire, Robert M.	I Am Better than You (1st, 8vo, 64p, ibds, fp color, DJ/2.50)	Harper	(1968)	Lopshire, Robert	25-40	
Kelly, Eric P.	Hand in the Picture (1st {std}, 8vo, 241p, b/w, DJ/2.50)	Lippincott	(1947)	Lorentowicz, Irena	25-40	
Maril, Lee	Mr. Bunny Paints the Eggs (1st, ob4to, ibds, [28]p, color, DJ/1.00)	Roy Pub. Co.	(1945)	Lorentowicz, Irena	40-65	*
Deutsch, Babette	Tales of Faraway Folk (1st, 8vo, yellow cl, 68p, b/w, pep, DJ/2.25)	Harper	(1952)	Lorentowicz, Irena	60-100	
Nash, Ogden	Adventures of Isabel (1st {std}, 4to, 32p, 3-color, DJ/2.75)	Little/Brown	(1963)	Lorraine, Walter	200-300	R*
Reid, Alastair	Allth (1st, lg8vo, 51p, 1-color, DJ/3.00)	Houghton	1958	Lorraine, Walter	50-85	R*
Simon, Sidney	Armadillo Who Had No Shell (1st {std}, ob8vo, ipcb, 32p, color, DJ/3.25)	Norton	(1966)	Lorraine, Walter	25-40	
Holt, Margaret	David McCheever's 29 Dogs (1st, sm4to, 48p, 2-color, DJ/2.95)	Houghton	1963	Lorraine, Walter	25-40	
Cunningham, Julia	Dear Rat (1st, 8vo, 125p, fp 1-color, cep, DJ/2.75, NYTBI)	Houghton	1961	Lorraine, Walter	30-50	
Annett, Cora	Dog Who Thought He was a Boy (1st {std}, sm4to, 48p, 2-color, cep, DJ/3.25)	Houghton	1965	Lorraine, Walter	30-45	
Reid, Alastair	I Will Tell You of a Town (1st, 8vo, 36p, fp 3-color, DJ/2.25, NYTBI)	Houghton	1956	Lorraine, Walter	50-80	R
McLeod, Emilie	One Snail and Me (1st {std}, sm ob4to, 32p, color, DJ/2.95)	Little/Brown	1961	Lorraine, Walter	30-50	
Hieatt, Constance	Sir Gawain & the Green Knight (1st, lg8vo, 48p, fp 1-color, DJ/3.50)	Crowell	(1967)	Lorraine, Walter	50-80	*
Nash, Ogden	Untold Adventures of Santa Claus (1st {std}, lg8vo, 47p, color, DJ/2.95)	Little/Brown	(1964)	Lorraine, Walter	40-65	
Loud, Marian V.	Picnic on a Pyramid (1st, 8vo, 114p, grey cl, 4pl)	Saalfield	1904	Loud, Marian V.	80-125	
Kalashnikoff, N.	The Defender (1st, 8vo, 136p, tan cl, 8 fp b/w, DJ/2.00, NH)	Scribner	1951	Louden, C.& G.	60-90	
Henry, Marguerite	Mustang: Wild Spirit o/t West (1st {std}, lg8vo, 222p, color, pep, DJ/3.95)	Rand/McNally	(1966)	Lougheed, Robert	40-65	
Love, Edwin M.	Rocking Island (1st, lg8vo, p-o, 182p, purple/gilt, 6cp, 12pl, pep)	Nelson	(1927)	Love, Edwin M.	50-85	
MacMunn, George F.	Armies of India (1st, 8vo, blue/gilt, 224p, teg, 72cp)	L: A&C Black	1911	Lovett, Alfred C.	150-225	
Low, Joseph	Adam's Book of Odd Creatures (1st {std}, sm ob4to, [32]p, DJ/3.50)	Atheneum	(1962)	Low, Joseph	30-50	*
Rau, Margaret	Band of the Red Hand (1st {std}, 8vo, 250p, b/w, DJ/2.00)	Knopf	1938	Low, Joseph	25-40	
Mendoza, George	Beastly Alphabet (1st, ob4to, [30]p, color, DJ/3.95)	Grosset/Dunlap	(1969)	Low, Joseph	30-50	
Schlein, Miriam	Big Cheese (1st, sm4to, white cl, [48]p, 2-color, DJ/2.95)	W.R. Scott	1958	Low, Joseph	30-50	
De La Iglesia, Maria	Cat and the Mouse (1st, lg8vo, [62]p, color, DJ/3.50)	Pantheon	(1966)	Low, Joseph	25-45	
Swift, Jonathan	Directions to Servants (1st {std}, 8vo, bds, 126p, 2-color, DJ/4.95)	Pantheon	(1964)	Low, Joseph	30-50	
Coolidge, Olivia	Egyptian Adventures (1st, 8vo, 209p, b/w, pep, DJ/3.00)	Houghton	1954	Low, Joseph	35-50	R*
Mendoza, George	Flowers & Grasses & Weeds (1st, ob4to, ibds, [33]p, 2-color, dep, DJ/4.50)	Funk/Wagnalls	(1968)	Low, Joseph	20-35	
Keiser, Melanie E.	God Returns to Vuelta Abajo (1st, lg8vo, 149p, rust/gilt, p-o, 1-color)	W.R. Scott	(1936)	Low, Joseph	80-120	R*
Rugoff, Milton (ed)	Harvest of World Folk Tales (1st, 8vo, 734p, b/w, DJ/3.95)	Viking	1949	Low, Joseph	30-50	*
Bro, Marguerite	How the Mouse Deer Became King (1st {std}, lg8vo, 127p, bds, b/w, DJ/2.95)	Doubleday	(1966)	Low, Joseph	25-40	
De La Mare, Walter	Jack & the Beanstalk (1st, narrow 4to, 52p, fp 3-color, dep, DJ/3.00)	Knopf	(1959)	Low, Joseph	70-100	R
Hieatt, Constance	Knight of the Lion (1st, lg8vo, 68p, fp b/w, DJ/3.95)	Crowell	(1968)	Low, Joseph	30-50	
Tresselt, Alvin	Legend of Willow Plate (1st, ob4to, [43]p, color, pep, DJ/3.50)	Parents Mag. Pr.	1968	Low, Joseph	50-80	R*
Cullen, Countee	Lost Zoo (1st {this pub} {std}, lg8vo, 95p, color, DJ/4.95)	Follett	(1969)	Low, Joseph	30-45	
Mother Goose	Mother Goose Riddle Rhymes (1st {std}, 8vo, [46]p, color, DJ/2.50, NYTBI)	Harcourt	(1953)	Low, Joseph	30-50	R*
Mincieli, Rose	Pulcinella (1st {std}, 4to, [34]p, color, DJ/2.95)	Knopf	(1960)	Low, Joseph	30-50	
Osborne, Maurice M.	Rudi and the Mayor of Naples (1st, 8vo, 48p, b/w, DJ/2.50)	Houghton	1958	Low, Joseph	20-35	
DeHartog, Jan	Sailor's Life (1st {std}, 8vo, 210p, b/w, DJ/3.00)	Harper	1956	Low, Joseph	20-35	
Hawes, Judy	Shrimps (1st, ob8vo, ipcb, [40]p, 2-color, DJ/3.25)	Crowell	(1967)	Low, Joseph	30-45	
Low, Joseph	Smiling Duke (1st, ob4to, ibds, 30p, color, DJ/3.25)	Houghton	1963	Low, Joseph	25-45	
Goldin, Augusta	Spider Silk (1st, ob8vo, [40]p, fp 2-color, DJ/2.75)	Crowell	(1964)	Low, Joseph	30-45	
Burland, Brian	St. Nicholas and the Tub (1st, sm4to, [36]p, 2-color, pep, DJ/3.25)	Holiday House	(1964)	Low, Joseph	30-50	*
Walker, Barbara	Stargazer to the Sultan (1st, sm4to, [41]p, color, pep, DJ/3.50)	Parents Mag. Pr.	1967	Low, Joseph	30-50	
Low, Joseph	There was a Wise Crow (1st {std}, ob4to, [32]p, color, DJ/3.95)	Follett	(1969)	Low, Joseph	25-45	
Zimelman, Nathan	To Sing a Song as Big as Ireland (1st {std}, 4to, 32p, color, cep, DJ/3.95)	Follett	(1967)	Low, Joseph	30-45	*
Hawley, Harriet E.	Story of a Little Tin Soldier (1st, 4to, p-o, 64p, 6cp)	Cupples/Leon	(1914)	Low, Loretta	60-90	
Hawley, Harriet E.	Timothy Toddlekin (1st, 4to, red cl, 64p, p-o, 6cp, 6pl)	Cupples/Leon	(1914)	Low, Loretta	50-80	
Hawley, Harriet E.	Woodland Party (1st, 4to, p-o, 49p, 13cp)	Cupples/Leon	(1913)	Low, Loretta	60-100	
Streatfeild, Noel	New Shoes (1st AM, 8vo, 314p, b/w, DJ/2.95)	Random	1960	Low, Vaike	30-50	
Mabie, Hamilton W.	In Arcady (1st, 8vo, 128p, teg, green/gilt, 4pl, pep)	Dodd	1903	Low, Will H.	40-65	
Stockton, Frank	Bicycle of Cathay (1st, sm8vo, green cl, 240p, 32pl)	Harper	1900	Lowell, Orson	50-80	
Kipling, Rudyard	Brushwood Boy (1st, 8vo, blue/gilt, teg, uncut, 119p, b/w, pep)	Doub./McClure	1899	Lowell, Orson	120-180	
White, William A.	Court of Boyville (1st, sm8vo, 358p, buckram, b/w pl, PPP)	Doub./McClure	1899	Lowell, Orson	140-200	
Webster, Jean	Jerry Junior (1st, sm8vo, green cl, p-o, 282p, 15pl)	Century	1907	Lowell, Orson	25-40	
Ellis, Edward S.	Klondike Nuggets (1st, sm8vo, 255p, 22pl)	Doub./McClure	1898	Lowell, Orson	50-85	
Coatsworth, Eliz.	Bess and the Sphinx (1st {std}, 8vo, ibds, 88p, b/w, cep, DJ/3.75)	Macmillan	(1967)	Lowenstein, Bernice	20-30	
Selsam, Millicent	Birth of an Island (1st, lg8vo, 48p, 2-color, DJ/2.50)	Harper	(1959)	Lubell, Winifred	20-30	*
Sterling, Dorothy	Creatures of the Night (1st {std}, 8vo, 125p, blue bds, b/w, DJ/2.95)	Doubleday	(1960)	Lubell, Winifred	30-45	
George, Jean C.	Moon of the Mountain Lions (1st, 8vo, 39p, fp b/w, DJ/3.75)	Crowell	(1968)	Lubell, Winifred	25-40	

AUTHOR	TITLE	PUBLISHER	DATE	ARTIST	PRICE	LC
Stuart, Mary	Pirate's Bridge (1st, ob4to, unpag, color, DJ/2.95)	Lothrop, Lee	1960	Lubell, Winifred	30-45	
Creswick, Paul	Greypaws... (1st, 8vo, 64p, 5pl)	L: Partridge	[1909]	Lucas, K.	60-80	*
Browne, Frances	Granny's Wonderful Chair (4to, 95p, 15cp)	Dutton	1891	Lucas, Marie S.	80-130	*
Chesterton, G.K.	Innocence of Father Brown (1st, 8vo, 334p, red/gilt, 8pl)	L: Cassell	1911	Lucas, Sydney S.	300-500	
Ludins, Ryah	Wonder Rock (1st, 8vo, [40]p, ibds, 2-color)	Coward	1931	Ludins, Ryah	80-125	
Selsam, Millicent	A Time for Sleep (1st, sm8vo, [57]p, DJ/2.00)	W.R. Scott	1953	Ludwig, Helen	30-45	
Selsam, Millicent	All About Eggs (1st, sm8vo, [62]p, 3-color, DJ/2.00)	W.R. Scott	1952	Ludwig, Helen	30-50	
Kelly, Eric P.	At the Sign of the Golden Compass (1st, 8vo, gilt, 195p, 11pl, pep, DJ/2.50)	Macmillan	1938	Lufkin, Raymond	25-45	
Emerson, Caroline	Magic Tunnel (1st, 8vo, 120p, b/w, DJ/1.75)	Stokes	1940	Lufkin, Raymond	70-100	*
Lide, Alice A.	Ood-Le-Uk: Wanderer (1st, sm8vo, 265p, col frn, 9 fp b/w, pep, NH)	Little/Brown	1930	Lufkin, Raymond	45-70	
Bontemps, Arna	Story of the Negro (1st {std}, 8vo, 239p, b/w, DJ/3.00, NH, JABA)	Knopf	1948	Lufkin, Raymond	80-130	
Kelly, Eric P.	Treasure Mountain (1st, 8vo, 211p, green cl, pep, b/w, DJ/2.00)	Macmillan	1937	Lufkin, Raymond	25-45	
Alger, Horatio	Finding a Fortune (1st, 12mo, 364p, 7pl)	Penn	1904	Lukens, W.S.	60-90	R
Arnold, Edwin	Voyage of Ithobal (1st, 8vo, 226p, teg, blue cl, 8pl)	Dillingham	1901	Lumley, Arthur	25-40	
France, Anatole	Honey-Bee (1st, lg8vo, red/gilt, 172p, uncut, teg, 12cp, pep)	L: John Lane	1911	Lundborg, Florence	70-125	
White, Stewart E.	The Mountains (1st, 8vo, 282p, teg, col frn, 15pl)	McClure	1904	Lungren, Fernand	30-50	
White, Stewart E.	The Pass (1st, 8vo, 198p, blue cl, col frn, 14pl)	Outing	1906	Lungren, Fernand	30-50	
Lupprian, Hildegard	Honey Land (1st, 4to, [30]p, ibds, color)	McLoughlin	1927	Lupprian, Hildegard	100-160	
Bonner, Mary G.	Hundred Trips to Storyland (1st, 8vo, 327p, orange cl, 7cp, pep)	Macaulay	(1930)	Lupprian, Hildegard	55-80	*
Donaldson, Ellen M.	In Blue Bird Time (1st, 8vo, 160p, ibds, fp 2-color, pep)	Milton Bradley	1926	Lupprian, Hildegard	45-70	*
Harrison, Elizabeth	In the Story World (1st, 12mo, 204p, gilt, dep, fp b/w)	Milton Bradley	(1931)	Lupprian, Hildegard	30-50	
Bannerman, Helen	Little Black Sambo (12mo, ibds, color)	McLoughlin	(1938)	Lupprian, Hildegard	100-175	
Hulbert, Homer B.	Omjee, The Wizard (1st, lg8vo, 156p, black cl, color, pep)	Milton Bradley	(1925)	Lupprian, Hildegard	100-180	
Bailey, Carolyn S.	Read Aloud Stories (1st, sm8vo, 215p, red/gilt, 6cp, pep)	Milton Bradley	(1929)	Lupprian, Hildegard	30-50	*
Harraden, Beatrice	New Book of the Fairies (1st, 8vo, 190p, gilt, 10pl, pep)	L: Griffith	[1891]	Lupton, Dorothy	75-100	*
Wyler, Rose	Oil Comes to Us (1st, ob8vo, ibds, [28]p, color, DJ/0.50)	Grosset/Dunlap	1937	Luykx, Th. D.	30-50	
Schwarzman, Marg.	Steel (1st, lg ob8vo, ibds, [28]p, color)	Western Printing	1937	Luykx, Th. D.	30-50	
Rugoff, Milton	Hurly Burly & the Knights (1st AM, 4to, ibds, 31p, color, DJ/1.95, NYTBI)	Platt/Munk	(1963)	Luzzati, Emanuele	45-70	
Lyall, Mary C.	Cubies' ABC (1st, sm ob8vo, p-o, 56p, color)	Putnam	1913	Lyall, Earl H.	200-300	
Lynch, Lorenzo	Hot Dog Man (1st {std}, ob4to, [24]p, color, DJ/5.00)	Bobbs-Merrill	(1970)	Lynch, Lorenzo	30-50	
Lang, Andrew	Johnny Nut & Golden Goose (1st, 4to, 45p, teg, gilt, col frn, b/w, cep)	L: Longmans	1887	Lynen, Amedee	250-350	
Nye, Robert	March Has Horse's Ears (1st AM {std}, 8vo, 88p, fp b/w, cep, DJ/3.75)	Hill & Wang	(1967)	Maas, Dorothy	60-90	R*
Tripp, Paul	Tale of Tubby the Tuba (1st, ob8vo, ibds, [26]p, color, pep, DJ/2.00)	Vanguard Press	(1948)	Maas, George	70-100	*
Hubbell, Patricia	Apple Vendor's Fair (1st {std}, 8vo, 53p, DJ/2.75)	Atheneum	1963	Maas, Julie	20-35	*
Posey, Anita	Rings and Things (1st {std}, 8vo, 32p, fp 1-color, DJ/2.95)	Crowell-Collier	(1967)	Maas, Julie	25-40	
Aiken, Conrad	Tom, Sue and the Clock (1st {std}, 8vo, 24p, fp b/w, DJ/2.95)	Collier Books	(1966)	Maas, Julie	30-50	R
Mabie, Peter	A to Z Book (lg4to, wraps, color)	Whitman	1929	Mabie, Peter	100-160	
Mabie, Peter	Gingerbread Stories (1st, ob4to, ibds, [42]p, color, pep)	Whitman	(1931)	Mabie, Peter	80-130	
Rourke, Constance	Davy Crockett (1st, 8vo, green cl, 276p, 8pl, pep, DJ/2.50, NH)	Harcourt	(1934)	MacDonald, James	40-65	
Hawthorne, Hildegarde	No Road Too Long (1st {std}, 8vo, 261p, b/w, pep, DJ/2.25)	Longmans	1940	MacDonald, James	30-50	
Meader, Stephen W.	Who Rides in the Dark? (1st, sm8vo, 281p, b/w, pep, DJ/2.00)	Harcourt	(1937)	MacDonald, James	80-130	
Rossetti, Dante G.	Blessed Damozel (1st, 8vo, 54p, gilt, teg, uncut)	L: Duckworth	1898	MacDougall, W.B.	130-200	
Bible	Book of Ruth (1st AM, 4to, tan/gilt, 16 designs by...)	Dodd	1896	MacDougall, W.B.	170-240	
Armour, Margaret (ed)	Eerie Book (1st, lg8vo, teg, 211p, uncut, 15pl)	L: Shiells & Co.	1898	MacDougall, W.B.	180-280	
Armour, Margaret (tr)	Fall of the Nibelungs (1st, 8vo, 260p, 16pl)	L: Dent	1897	MacDougall, W.B.	200-300	
Keats, John	Isabella... (1st, 4to, teg, gilt, 8pl)	L: Kegan Paul	1898	MacDougall, W.B.	170-240	
Omar Khayyam	Rubaiyat of Omar Khayyam (1st, 4to, uncut, green/gilt, 43p, b/w)	L: Macmillan	1898	MacDougall, W.B.	120-185	
Armour, Margaret	Shadow of Love (1st, 8vo, 124p, 2 fp b/w)	L: Duckworth	1898	MacDougall, W.B.	75-100	*
Brown, Dr. John	Jeems the Door Keeper (1st, 16mo, teg, uncut, 105p, 8 ticp)	L: Foulis	1912	MacGoun, H.C.P.	60-80	
Brown, Dr. John	Little Book of Children (12mo, 57p, ibds, teg, gilt, 8cp)	L: Foulis	1923	MacGoun, H.C.P.	35-60	*
Parry, Edward A.	Butterscotia... (1st, 8vo, blue/gilt, uncut, 170p, map, 6pl)	L: D. Nutt	1896	MacGregor, Archie	180-270	
Parry, Edward A.	First Book of Krab (1st, lg8vo, green cl, 132p, uncut, b/w)	L: D. Nutt	1897	MacGregor, Archie	125-200	
Parry, Edward A.	Katawampus: Its Treatment & Cure (1st, 8vo, green cl, 96p, b/w)	L: D. Nutt	1895	MacGregor, Archie	120-200	
Squire, Robert	World Wonderful (1st, 8vo, 201p, 10 fp b/w)	L: D. Nutt	1898	MacGregor, Archie	50-80	*
Fezandie, Clement	Through the Earth (1st, sm8vo, tan cl, 238p, 15pl by...)	Century	1898	MacKay, William A.	70-100	
N/A	Aladdin & his Wonderful Lamp (1st, 4to, [17]p, color, DJ)	Macmillan	1935	MacKinstry, Eliz.	100-170	R
Field, Rachel	Eliza & the Elves (1st, sm8vo, green/gilt, 96p, 2cp, pep)	Macmillan	1926	MacKinstry, Eliz.	60-90	
MacKinstry, Eliz.	Fairy Alphabet (1st, lg8vo, [59]p, ibds, 26pl)	Viking	1933	MacKinstry, Eliz.	100-175	
Wiggin, Kate D.	Fairy Ring (1st, 8vo, 445p, col frn, 25pl)	Doubleday/Page	1910	MacKinstry, Eliz.	100-180	
Andersen, Hans C.	Fairy Tales (1st {std}, 4to, 253p, p-o, color, pep, DJ/2.50)	Coward	(1933)	MacKinstry, Eliz.	150-220	
Noyes, Alfred	Forty Singing Seamen (1st, 8vo, ipcb, 124p, 6cp, pep)	Stokes	(1930)	MacKinstry, Eliz.	55-80	
Colum, Padraic	Legend of St. Columbia (1st, 8vo, green cl, 156p, b/w, DJ/2.25)	Macmillan	1935	MacKinstry, Eliz.	50-80	
Johnson, Burges	Little Book of Necessary Nonsense (1st {std}, 16mo, 81p, b/w, dep)	Harper	1929	MacKinstry, Eliz.	30-50	*
Field, Rachel	Magic Pawnshop (1st, 8vo, ibds, 125p, 3-color, DJ)	Dutton	(1927)	MacKinstry, Eliz.	60-100	
Moore, Clement C.	Night Before Christmas (1st, 4to, ibds, [26]p, color)	Dutton	1928	MacKinstry, Eliz.	100-170	R
Ibsen, Henrik	Peer Gynt (1st {std}, sm4to, green bds, p-o, 286p, pep, 10cp)	Doubleday/Doran	1929	MacKinstry, Eliz.	70-100	
MacDonald, George	Princess & the Goblin (1st, lg8vo, 271p, 4cp)	Doubleday/Doran	1928	MacKinstry, Eliz.	70-100	
MacKinstry, Eliz.	Puck in Pasture (1st {std}, 8vo, ibds, 79p, pep, b/w)	Doubleday/Page	1925	MacKinstry, Eliz.	40-60	
White, Hervey	Snake Gold (1st, 12mo, 220p, decor by...)	Macmillan	1926	MacKinstry, Eliz.	25-45	
Wiggin, Kate D.	Tales of Laughter (1st, lg8vo, 331p, black cl, 8cp)	Doubleday/Page	1926	MacKinstry, Eliz.	70-100	
MacKaye, Percy	Tall Tales of Kentucky Mountains (1st, 8vo, 185p, ipcb, p-o, col frn, b/w)	Doran	(1926)	MacKinstry, Eliz.	40-65	
Kilmer, Joyce	Trees (1st, 8vo, [24]p, ipcb, color, DJ)	Doran	(1925)	MacKinstry, Eliz.	60-100	
Geister, Edna	What Shall We Play? (1st, 8vo, 175p, ibds, p-o, col frn, cep)	Doran	(1924)	MacKinstry, Eliz.	50-80	
D'Aulnoy	White Cat... (1st, 4to, ibds, 150p, p-o, 8cp, pep)	Macmillan	1928	MacKinstry, Eliz.	80-140	
Kjelgaard, Jim	Coyote Song (1st, 8vo, 174p, b/w, DJ/4.00)	Dodd	(1969)	MacLean, Robert	50-85	*
Vance, Marguerite	Jeptha and the New People (1st, 8vo, 113p, fp b/w, DJ/2.50)	Dutton	1960	MacLean, Robert	20-35	
Meigs, Cornelia L.	Mystery at the Red House (1st {std}, 8vo, 158p, red cl, b/w, DJ/3.00)	Macmillan	1961	MacLean, Robert	25-40	
Bradbury, Bianca	Two on an Island (1st, 8vo, 139p, b/w, DJ/3.00)	Houghton	1965	MacLean, Robert	25-40	*

AUTHOR	TITLE	PUBLISHER	DATE	ARTIST	PRICE	LC
Sefton, Harriet L.	Dream Imp & Others (1st, 4to, 96p, red/gilt, 10cp)	L: Bickers	[1912]	MacQuigg, Gertrude	140-220	
Polland, Madeleine	Children of the Red King (1st AM {std}, 8vo, 159p, b/w, DJ/3.00)	Holt, Rinehart	(1961)	Macarthur-Onslow, A.	20-30	
Porter, Sheena	Nordy Bank (1st, 8vo, gilt, 144p, b/w, CgM)	L: Oxford U.Pr.	1964	Macarthur-Onslow, A.	70-100	*
Stevenson, Rbt. L.	Dr. Jekyll & Mr. Hyde (1st, lg8vo, gilt, teg, 189p, 8pl)	Scott-Thaw	1904	Macauley, Charles R.	80-120	*
Bangs, John K.	Emblemland (1st, 8vo, 164p, blue/gilt, fp b/w)	R.H. Russell	1902	Macauley, Charles R.	70-100	*
Macauley, Charles R.	Fantasma Land (1st, 8vo, brown/gilt, 204p, b/w)	Bobbs-Merrill	(1904)	Macauley, Charles R.	60-100	
Adams, Samuel H.	Flying Death (1st, 12mo, brown cl, 239p, 4pl)	McClure	1908	Macauley, Charles R.	60-100	
Harper, Vincent	Mortgage on the Brain (1st, 8vo, brown/gilt, 293p, 4pl)	Doubleday/Page	1905	Macauley, Charles R.	30-50	*
Conrad, Joseph	Romance (1st AM, sm8vo, blue/gilt, 428p, 8pl)	McClure	1904	Macauley, Charles R.	200-300	
McGinley, Phyllis	Short Walk from the Station (1st, 8vo, 175p, b/w, DJ/2.75)	Viking	1951	Macdonald, Roberta	30-50	
Tarn, William W.	Treasure of Isle of Mist (1st, 8vo, green/gilt, 163p, fp 1-color)	L: P. Allan	1919	Macdonald, Somerled	80-125	
Mitchell, John A.	Drowsy (1st [1], sm8vo, blue/gilt, 301p, 19pl)	Stokes	(1917)	Macdonall, Agnus	35-60	
Pope, Jessie	Bobbity Flop (1st, ob8vo, unpag, ibds, 24pl)	L: Blackie	[1912]	Macgregor, Angusine	80-125	
Pope, Jessie	Bunny Book (1st, 4to, [36]p, ibds, color)	L: Blackie	[1909]	Macgregor, Angusine	80-130	
Woodhouse, S.C.	Crude Ditties (1st, 16mo, 103p, tan cl, 24 fp color)	Swan/Dutton	1903	Macgregor, Angusine	80-125	*
Clarke, Olive	Freddy Frizzylocks (1st, ob8vo, ibds, unpag, fp color)	L: Blackie	[1914]	Macgregor, Angusine	150-225	
Macgregor, Angusine	Maxims for Mice (1st AM, sq8vo, p-o, unpag, color, pep)	Dodge	[1910]	Macgregor, Angusine	180-300	
Pope, Jessie	Story of Flip & Fuzzy (1st AM, 8vo, ibds, color)	Dodge	[1910]	Macgregor, Angusine	200-300	
Macgregor, Angusine	Story of Snips (1st, lg ob8vo, ibds, [46]p, fp color)	L: Blackie	[1909]	Macgregor, Angusine	150-225	
Smedley, A. Constance	Wizards of Ryetown (1st, 12mo, gilt, 273p, b/w)	Henry Holt & Co.	1905	Macgregor, Angusine	60-90	
Cullen, Countee	My Lives & How I Lost Them (1st {std}, lg8vo, 160p, b/w, DJ/2.00)	Harper	(1942)	Macguire, Robert	200-300	
Machetanz, Sara	Puppy Named Gih (1st, sm4to, [32]p, fp 2-color, DJ/2.75)	Scribner	(1957)	Machetanz, Fred	30-50	
Kredenser, Gail	ABC of Bumptious Beasts (1st {std}, lg8vo, 56p, b/w, pep, DJ/3.75)	Harlin Quist	(1966)	Mack, Stanley	25-40	
Lear, Edward	Four Little Children/Went around World (1st {std}, 4to, [32]p, 1-col, pep)	Harlin Quist	1967	Mack, Stanley	30-50	*
Lear, Edward	Story of the Four Little Children... (1st, 4to, [32]p, b/w, DJ/2.95)	Harlin Quist	1967	Mack, Stanley	50-80	
Wolff, Carolyn	Three People (1st {std}, sq8vo, [46]p, 3-color, cep, DJ/3.95)	Harlin Quist	1968	Mack, Stanley	30-50	
Mack, Robert E.	Little Bright Eyes (1st, sm4to, unpag, ipcb, chromos)	L: Nister	1890	Mack/Bennett	80-125	
Dawson, Forbes	Sensational Trance (1st, 8vo, 178p, red cl, 20pl)	L: Downey	1895	Mackenzie, F.	90-120	
Selden, George	Garden Under the Sea (1st, 8vo, 190p, b/w, DJ/2.75)	Viking	(1957)	Mackenzie, Garry	20-30	
Goudey, Alice	Here Come the Bears! (1st, 12mo, 92p, blue cl, fp 1-color, DJ/2.25)	Scribner	(1954)	Mackenzie, Garry	30-50	R
Montgomery, R.	McGonnigle's Lake (1st {std}, 8vo, 219p, fp b/w, DJ/2.50)	Doubleday	(1953)	Mackenzie, Garry	25-35	
Garrett, Helen	Mr. Flip Flop (1st, sm4to, ibds, 41p, 3-color, DJ/2.00)	Viking	1948	Mackenzie, Garry	30-50	
Ransome, Arthur	Aladdin & his Wonderful Lamp (1st, 4to, [128]p, 12 ticp)	L: J. Nisbet	[1919]	Mackenzie, Thomas B.	300-450	
Ransome, Arthur	Aladdin & his Wonderful Lamp (1st AM, sm4to, [128]p, 12ticp pep)	Brentano's	[1920]	Mackenzie, Thomas B.	250-350	
N/A	Ali Baba & Aladdin (1st, 4to, 128p, ibds, 8cp)	L: Harrap	1918	Mackenzie, Thomas B.	200-300	
Chaundler, Christine	Arthur & His Knights (1st AM, lg8vo, 311p, 8 ticp, pep)	Stokes	[1923]	Mackenzie, Thomas B.	160-240	
Stephens, James	Crock of Gold (1st, 8vo, 227p, red/gilt, 12cp)	L: Macmillan	1926	Mackenzie, Thomas B.	120-175	
Flecker, James E.	Hassan (1st, 4to, 155p, teg, red/gilt, 12 ticp, pep)	L: Heinemann	1924	Mackenzie, Thomas B.	150-225	
Stapp, Emilie B.	Uncle Peter-Heathen (1st, 8vo, 285p, 10cp)	McKay	(1912)	Macy, Harriet	25-40	
Holl, Adelaide	One Kitten for Kim (1st {std}, 8vo, [32]p, 3-color, DJ/4.35)	Addison-Wesley	1969	Madden, Don	20-35	
Hawes, Judy	Why Frogs are Wet (1st, ob8vo, 35p, color, DJ/3.50)	Crowell	(1968)	Madden, Don	25-40	
Moore, Clement C.	Night Before Christmas (1st, folio, ipcb, [18]p, color)	Whitman	1940	Madsen, Eleanora	50-80	
Collodi, Carlo	Pinocchio (1st, 4to, ibds, 96p, cvr & col frn by...)	Saalfield	(1939)	Madsen, Eleanora	90-120	*
Joseph, Alfred W.	Sondo: A Liberian Boy (1st, lg8vo, ibds, pep, 32p, fp b/w, DJ/1.00)	Whitman	(1936)	Magnie, Bernice	60-90	
Langford, George	Stories of the First American Animals (1st, lg8vo, p-o, gilt, 5cp)	Boni/Liveright	(1923)	Mahon, Ty	55-80	*
Lively, Penelope	Astercote (1st [1st bk.], 8vo, gilt, 156p, b/w, DJ)	L: Heinemann	1970	Maitland, Antony	70-120	
Garfield, Leon	Black Jack (1st, 8vo, 243p, b/w, gilt, DJ)	L: Longmans	(1968)	Maitland, Antony	25-40	
Pearce, Philippa	Dog So Small (1st AM {std}, 8vo, 142p, b/w, DJ/2.95)	Lippincott	(1963)	Maitland, Antony	25-40	
Garfield, Leon	Drummer Boy (1st AM, 8vo, 186p, b/w, DJ/4.50)	Pantheon	(1969)	Maitland, Antony	20-30	
Garfield, Leon	Jack Holburn (1st AM {std}, [1st bk.], 8vo, 250p, red cl, b/w, DJ/3.75)	Pantheon	(1965)	Maitland, Antony	40-65	
Pearce, Philippa	Mrs. Cockle's Cat (1st AM {std}, 4to, [32]p, b/w, DJ/3.00, KGM)	Lippincott	(1961)	Maitland, Antony	30-50	
Locke, Elsie	Runaway Settlers (1st AM {std}, 8vo, 190p, b/w, DJ/3.75)	Dutton	(1966)	Maitland, Antony	30-50	*
Garfield, Leon	Smith (1st AM {std}, 8vo, 218p, b/w, DJ/3.95)	Pantheon	(1967)	Maitland, Antony	25-40	
Johnson, Emilie F.	Umbrella Bird & other Verses (1st, lg8vo, 83p, col frn, color, DJ/1.00)	Falmouth Pub.	(1939)	Malcher, Lucretia	30-45	
Malkus, Alida S.	Silver Llama (1st, lg8vo, 107p, fp color, pep, DJ/2.00)	Winston	(1939)	Malkus, Alida S.	30-50	
Mallett, Beatrice	Playmates (4to, ibds, 16 fp color)	L: R. Tuck	[1910]	Mallett, Beatrice	200-350	
Mallison, Clare	Wooster-Poosters (1st, ob4to, p-o, 88p, 15cp, pep)	Stokes	(1931)	Mallison, Clare	150-220	
Justus, May	Near Side and Far (1st {std}, 8vo, 148p, fp b/w, pep)	Suttonhouse	(1936)	Mallon, Grace	30-50	
Dalgliesh, Alice	America Begins... (1st, sq8vo, ibds, [78]p, color, DJ/2.00)	Scribner	(1938)	Maloy, Lois	30-50	
Dalgliesh, Alice	America Builds Homes (1st, sq8vo, ibds, [84]p, color, DJ/2.00)	Scribner	(1938)	Maloy, Lois	35-50	
Maloy, Lois	Arabella of the Merry-Go-Round (1st, lg ob8vo, [64]p, color, DJ/1.50)	Scribner	1935	Maloy, Lois	30-50	
Dalgliesh, Alice	Long Live the King! (1st, sq8vo, ipcb, 76p, color, dep, DJ/1.60)	Scribner	1937	Maloy, Lois	30-50	
Johnson, Richard	Saint George & the Dragon (1st, lg8vo, [30]p, fp b/w, pep, DJ/1.00)	Scribner	1941	Maloy, Lois	30-50	
Maloy, Lois	Tea Party in Plumpudding Street (1st, 8vo, ibds, [54]p, 1-color, pep)	Grosset/Dunlap	(1946)	Maloy, Lois	30-50	
Maloy, Lois	Wooden Shoes in America (1st, sm ob4to, [72]p, color, DJ/1.75)	Scribner	(1940)	Maloy, Lois	50-85	*
Dallam, Helen	Nursery Rhymes and Songs (1st, 4to, ibds, [65]p, fp color, pep)	Whitman	1944	Malvern, Corrine	25-40	
Hall, Rosalys	Out of Provincetown (1st, sm8vo, 296p, fp b/w, DJ/2.00)	Farrar/Rinehart	(1941)	Malvern, Corrine	20-35	
Stanovsky, Vladislav	The Firebird (1st, 8vo, 64p, color, DJ)	L: J.M. Dent	1969	Manasek, Ludek	35-50	
Madison, Janet (comp)	Sweethearts Always (2nd, 8vo, 210p, green/gilt, 8cp)	Reilly/Britton	1907	Manning, Fred S.	50-80	
Meigs, Cornelia L.	Wind in the Chimney (1st, 8vo, 144p, blue cl, col frn, 8pl, cep)	Macmillan	1934	Mansfield, Louise	25-40	
Haines, Alice C.	Japanese Child Life (1st, lg4to, [34]p, ibds, 8cp)	Stokes	(1905)	Mar, Alice	100-165	
Haines, Alice C.	Little Japs at Home (1st, lg4to, [26]p, ibds, 4cp)	Stokes	(1905)	Mar, Alice	200-300	
Collodi, Carlo	Adventures of Pinocchio (1st, folio, ibds, 126p, color, DJ)	Grosset/Dunlap	(1957)	Maraja	45-70	
Goulden, Shirley	Chinese Fairy Tales (1st, 4to, 58p, ibds, color)	Duell, Sloan	(1958)	Maraja	40-60	
March, Eleanor S.	Little White Barbara (1st, 24mo, green cl, 95p, 24cp)	L: Richards	1902	March, Eleanor S.	250-400	
Mighels, Philip V.	Furnace of Gold (1st, sm8vo, 402p, p-o, 12pl)	D. Fitzgerald	(1910)	Marchand, J.N.	25-40	
Garland, Hamlin	Money Magic (1st, sm8vo, pcb, 354p, 8pl)	Harper	1907	Marchand, J.N.	35-60	
Margalit, Avi	Hebrew Alphabet Book (1st, ob4to, [25]p, color, DJ/2.95)	Funk/Wagnalls	(1968)	Margalit, Avi	50-80	*

AUTHOR	TITLE	PUBLISHER	DATE	ARTIST	PRICE	LC
Thompson, Ruth P.	King Kojo (1st, lg8vo, red cl, p-o, 239p, 8cp, pep), DJ/1.50)	McKay	(1938)	Marge	250-350	
Bontemps, Arna	Drums at Dusk (1st {std}, 8vo, 226p, black cl, b/w, cep, DJ/2.50)	Macmillan	1939	Margenta	200-300	
Browne, Frances	Granny's Wonderful Chair (24mo, gilt, 166p, AEG, 12cp)	L: H. Frowde	1908	Margetson, W.H.	100-175	
Clark, Janet M.	Legends of King Arthur & his Knights (8vo, 307p, AEG, 6cp, pep)	L: Nister	[1899]	Margetson, W.H.	70-100	
Henty, G.A.	Tiger of Mysore (1st AM, 12mo, 390p, blue/gilt, 12pl)	Scribner	1895	Margetson, W.H.	120-185	
Peckinpah, Betty	Coco is Coming (1st, sm4to, [26]p, fp color, cep, DJ/2.50)	Lothrop, Lee	1956	Mariana	40-65	*
Mariana	Doki the Lonely Papoose (1st, lg8vo, unpag, color, DJ/2.50)	Lothrop, Lee	(1955)	Mariana	30-45	
Jaszi, Jean	Everybody has Two Eyes (1st, 8vo, [34]p, b/w, DJ/2.50)	Lothrop, Lee	(1956)	Mariana	30-45	
Mariana	Hotspur (1st, 12mo, ibds, [40]p, fp color, DJ/1.25)	Lothrop, Lee	(1953)	Mariana	45-70	
Mariana	Journey of Bangwell Put (1st, sm4to, [38]p, color, DJ/3.50)	Lothrop, Lee	(1965)	Mariana	60-85	
Janice	Little Bear's Sunday Breakfast (1st, lg8vo, [30]p, color, DJ/2.75)	Lothrop, Lee	1958	Mariana	25-45	
Mariana	Miss Flora McFlimsey & Baby New Year (1st, 12mo, ibds, unpag, DJ/1.00)	Lothrop, Lee	(1951)	Mariana	60-90	
Mariana	Miss Flora McFlimsey & Little Laughing Water (1st 12mo [32]p, col, DJ/1.25)	Lothrop, Lee	(1954)	Mariana	60-90	
Mariana	Miss Flora McFlimsey's Easter Bonnet (1st sq12mo ibds, [40]p, col, DJ/1.00)	Lothrop, Lee	(1951)	Mariana	60-90	
Andersen, Hans C.	The Nightingale (1st {std}, 12mo, 20p, color, pep, DJ/1.00)	Harper	1937	Marine, Edmund	40-60	
Brown, Myra B.	Benjy's Blanket (1st {std}, ob8vo, [57]p, 1-color, pep, DJ/1.95)	F. Watts	(1962)	Marino, Dorothy	50-75	*
Marino, Dorothy	Buzzy Bear Goes South (1st {std}, sm4to, [33]p, 1-color, pep, DJ/2.95)	F. Watts	1961	Marino, Dorothy	30-50	
Brown, Myra B.	First Night Away from Home (1st, ob8vo, [60]p, fp 1-color, pep, DJ/2.50)	F. Watts	(1960)	Marino, Dorothy	30-50	
Marino, Dorothy	Good-Bye Thunderstorm (1st, ob8vo, [36]p, 3-color, DJ/2.25)	Lippincott	1958	Marino, Dorothy	30-45	
Marino, Dorothy	Little Angela and her Puppy (1st {std}, ob8vo, [40]p, 1-color, DJ/2.00)	Lippincott	(1954)	Marino, Dorothy	40-65	
Moodey, Marion M.	Here Comes the Peddler! (1st, lg8vo, ipcb, [32]p, b/w, cep, DJ/1.50)	Holiday House	(1947)	Markham, Kyra	30-50	
DeSelincourt, Hugh	Oxford From Within (1st, 4to, 180p, blue/gilt, 12cp)	L: Chatto	1910	Markino, Y.	90-120	
Van Stockum, Hilda	King Oberon's Forest (1st, lg8vo, 151p, fp b/w, pep, DJ/2.75)	Viking	(1957)	Marlin, Brigid	30-45	
Kim, Yong-Ik	Blue in the Seed (1st {std}, 8vo, 117p, b/w, DJ/3.95)	Little/Brown	(1964)	Marokvia, Artur	25-40	*
Kumin, Maxine	Follow the Fall (1st, 8vo, 48p, color, DJ/2.50)	Putnam	(1961)	Marokvia, Artur	50-80	*
Marokvia, Mireille	French School for Paul (1st AM, 4to, ipcb, 47p, 2-color, DJ/3.50)	Lippincott	(1963)	Marokvia, Artur	30-45	*
Conklin, Gladys	I Caught a Lizard (1st, ob8vo, [40]p, color, DJ/3.50)	Holiday House	(1967)	Marokvia, Artur	20-30	
Conklin, Gladys	If I were a Bird (1st, ob8vo, [40]p, color, DJ/3.50)	Holiday House	1965	Marokvia, Artur	20-30	
Marokvia, Mireille	Jannot, a French Rabbit (1st AM, sm4to, 46p, fp color, DJ/3.00)	Lippincott	1959	Marokvia, Artur	30-50	
Kalashnikoff, N.	Toyon: Dog of the North (1st {std}, 8vo, 246p, uncut, b/w, DJ/2.75)	Harper	(1950)	Marokvia, Artur	25-45	
Conklin, Gladys	When Insects are Babies (1st, 8vo, [40]p, color, DJ/4.50)	Holiday House	(1969)	Marokvia, Artur	25-40	
Aiken, Joan	All You've Ever Wanted (1st [1st bk.], 12mo, 191p, gilt, fp b/w, DJ)	L: J. Cape	(1953)	Marriott, Pat	180-250	
Aiken, Joan	More than You Bargained For (1st AM, 8vo, 192p, b/w, DJ/2.50)	Abelard-Schuman	(1957)	Marriott, Pat	50-85	
Aiken, Joan	Wolves of Willoughby Chase (1st AM {std}, 8vo, 168p, b/w, DJ/2.95)	Doubleday	(1963)	Marriott, Pat	50-80	R
Smith, Gertrude	Loveable Tales of Janey, Josey & Joe (1st, 4to, green cl, 157p, 16cp)	Harper	1902	Mars, E.	80-120	
Brink, Carol R.	Andy Buckram's Tin Men (1st, 8vo, 192p, yellow cl, b/w, DJ/3.50)	Viking	(1966)	Mars, Witold T.	30-45	
Krasilovsky, Phyllis	Benny's Flag (1st {std}, 4to, [40]p, b/w, DJ/2.50)	World	(1960)	Mars, Witold T.	25-45	
Kjelgaard, Jim	Boomerang Hunter (1st, 8vo, 172p, b/w, DJ/2.95)	Holiday House	(1960)	Mars, Witold T.	80-120	
Speare, Elizabeth G.	Calico Captive (1st, 8vo, red cl, 274p, b/w, DJ/3.50)	Houghton	1957	Mars, Witold T.	25-45	
Clark, Ann N.	Circle of Seasons (1st, 8vo, 113p, b/w, DJ/3.95)	Farrar, Straus	(1970)	Mars, Witold T.	25-40	*
Best, Herbert	Desmond and Dog Friday (1st, 8vo, 126p, b/w, DJ/3.75)	Viking	(1968)	Mars, Witold T.	20-30	
Wier, Ester A.	Easy Does It (1st, 8vo, 126p, b/w, DJ/3.50)	Vanguard Press	1965	Mars, Witold T.	30-50	
Mayberry, Genevieve	Eskimo of Little Diomede (1st, 8vo, 31p, color, DJ/1.50)	Follett	(1961)	Mars, Witold T.	25-40	
Robertson, Dorothy	Fairy Tales from Viet Nam (1st, lg8vo, 93p, b/w, DJ/3.50)	Dodd	(1968)	Mars, Witold T.	30-50	*
Calhoun, Mary	High Wind for Kansas (1st, 8vo, 45p, b/w, DJ/2.75)	Wm. Morrow	1965	Mars, Witold T.	30-45	*
Johnston, Johanna	Joan of Arc (1st {std}, lg4to, 88p, ibds, color, DJ/2.95)	Doubleday	1961	Mars, Witold T.	25-40	*
Kalnay, Francis	Richest Boy in the World (1st {std}, 8vo, 92p, green cl, fp b/w, DJ/2.75)	Harcourt	(1959)	Mars, Witold T.	30-50	
Johnston, Johanna	Stories of the Norsemen (1st {std}, lg4to, 88p, color, DJ/2.95)	Garden City	1959	Mars, Witold T.	25-45	*
Johnston, Johanna	Story of Hannibal (1st {std}, lg4to, 67p, color, pep, DJ/2.95)	Garden City	(1960)	Mars, Witold T.	20-35	
Wriston, Hildreth T.	Susan's Secret (1st {std}, 8vo, uncut, 126p, fp b/w, DJ/2.75)	Ariel	(1957)	Mars, Witold T.	25-45	
Wier, Ester A.	The Rumptydoolers (1st, 8vo, 159p, b/w, DJ/3.50)	Vanguard Press	(1964)	Mars, Witold T.	30-50	*
Lamb, Charles	Adventures of Ulysses (1st, 4to, 117p, uncut, 16cp, cep)	R.H. Russell	1902	Mars/Squire	200-320	
Stevenson, Rbt. L.	Child's Garden of Verses (1st, lg sq4to, ibds, 115p, 12cp)	R.H. Russell	(1900)	Mars/Squire	400-600	
Stevenson, Rbt. L.	Child's Garden of Verses (1st {this pub}, 8vo, 94p, 9 fp color, b/w)	Rand/McNally	(1902)	Mars/Squire	80-125	
Wells, Carolyn	Children of Our Town (1st, ob folio, ibds, [56]p, color, pep)	R.H. Russell	(1902)	Mars/Squire	750-1000	R
Hobart, George V.	Li'l Verses for Li'l Fellers (1st, 4to, 121p, 7cp, 8pl)	R.H. Russell	1903	Mars/Squire	100-170	*
Smith, Gertrude	Roggie & Reggie Stories (1st, 8vo, 95p, 15cp)	Harper	1900	Mars/Squire	75-100	*
Smith, Gertrude	Stories of Peter & Ellen (1st, 8vo, 137p, 15cp)	Harper	1903	Mars/Squire	75-100	*
Kingsley, Charles	The Heroes (1st, sm4to, blue cl, 186p, uncut, 24cp)	R.H. Russell	1901	Mars/Squire	200-285	R*
N/A	Tot & Tim (1st, lg4to, [52]p, ibds, 16cp)	L: Collins	[1918]	Marsh, H.G.C.	200-300	
Gury, Jeremy	Round and Round Horse (1st, ob4to, [47]p, color, DJ/1.50)	Henry Holt & Co.	(1943)	Marsh, Reginald	80-120	
Mitton, G.E.	Scenery of London (1st, 8vo, 223p, gilt, teg, 75cp)	L: A&C Black	1905	Marshall, Herbert	120-200	
Walker, Augusta	Back-Fence Story (1st {std}, 8vo, 145p, bds, gilt, b/w, DJ/4.95)	Knopf	1967	Martin, David S.	30-50	
Morse, Evangeline	Brown Rabbit, Her Story (1st {std}, 8vo, 191p, b/w, DJ/3.50)	Follett	(1967)	Martin, David S.	25-45	
McGraw, Eloise J.	Merry Go Round in Oz (1st, lg8vo, 303p, fp b/w, pep, DJ/3.95)	Reilly/Lee	(1963)	Martin, Dick	350-500	
Baum, L. Frank	Ozma of Oz (1st, 4to, [61]p, bds, color, DJ)	Reilly/Lee	(1961)	Martin, Dick	200-300	
Gordon, Elizabeth	Sheaf of Roses (1st, lg8vo, [72]p, ipcb, color)	Rand/McNally	(1915)	Martin, F.W.	40-60	*
Jenkins, Marie M.	Moon Jelly Swims through the Sea (1st, 8vo, 46p, color, DJ/3.95)	Holiday House	(1969)	Martin, Rene	30-50	*
Seidler, Ann	Bendemolena (1st {std}, sm4to, 31p, color, pep, DJ/2.95)	Follett	(1967)	Martin, Richard	30-50	
Coatsworth, Eliz.	Ronnie and the Chief's Son (1st {std}, 8vo, 38p, fp 1-color, DJ/3.00)	Macmillan	1962	Martin, Stefan	30-50	R
Coatsworth, Eliz.	Sparrow Bush (1st {std}, lg8vo, 63p, b/w, DJ/3.25)	Norton	(1966)	Martin, Stefan	20-35	
Coatsworth, Eliz.	They Walk in the Night (1st {std}, ob8vo, 60p, b/w, DJ/4.25)	Norton	(1969)	Martin, Stefan	20-30	
Adrian, Mary	Fiddler Crab (1st, 8vo, 40p, aqua cl, 2-color, DJ/2.00)	Holiday House	(1953)	Martinez, Jean	25-45	
Voight, Virginia F.	House in Robin Lane (1st, sm8vo, 220p, yellow, cl, b/w, DJ/2.50)	Holiday House	(1951)	Martinez, Jean	25-45	
Brown, Jeanette	Manuel, Little Boy of Mexico (1st, 24mo, ibds, 61p, fp 2-color)	Friendship Pr.	(1951)	Martinez, Jean	60-90	R*
Brown, Jeanette	Ronnie's Wish (1st, sq8vo, 32p, color, DJ/1.25)	Friendship Pr.	1954	Martinez, Jean	30-45	
Sickels, Evelyn	That Boy Johnny! (1st, 8vo, 120p, b/w, DJ/2.00)	Scribner	(1952)	Martinez, Jean	30-50	*
Muehl, Lois B.	Hidden Year of Devlin Bates (1st, 8vo, 138p, fp b/w, DJ/3.25)	Holiday House	(1967)	Martinez, John	20-30	

AUTHOR	TITLE	PUBLISHER	DATE	ARTIST	PRICE	LC
Cleaver, Vera	Grover (1st {std}, 8vo, 125p, b/w, DJ/3.50)	Lippincott	(1970)	Marvin, Frederic	30-45	
Masani, Shakuntala	Nehru's Story (1st, 8vo, 81p, 2-color, cep)	NY: Oxford U.Pr.	1949	Masani, Shakuntala	40-70	R
Masereel, Franz	Passionate Journey (1st AM, 8vo, [190]p, fp woodcuts, DJ)	NY: Lear Pub.	(1948)	Masereel, Franz	80-125	*
Werner, Jane	Child's Book of Bible Stories (1st, lg4to, ibds, 53p, color, DJ/2.00)	Random	1944	Masha	30-50	
Wyckoff, Marjorie	Child's Book of Hymns (1st, lg4to, ibds, 44p, color, pep, DJ/1.50)	Random	(1945)	Masha	30-50	
Bible	Child's Book of Prayers (1st, lg4to, ibds, 36p, color, pep)	Random	1941	Masha	30-50	
Raymond, Louise	Child's Story of the Nativity (1st, lg4to, [36]p, ibds, color, pep, DJ/1.50)	Random	1943	Masha	40-65	
Nast, Elsa R.	Farm Story (1st {std}, 4to, ibds, [40]p, color, pep, DJ/1.00)	Harper	(1946)	Masha	35-50	
Mother Goose	Masha's Stuffed Mother Goose (1st {std}, 4to, ibds, 64p, color, DJ/1.00)	Garden City	1946	Masha	60-90	*
N/A	Three Little Kittens (1st, sm8vo, ibds, [42]p, color, LGB)	Simon/Schuster	1942	Masha	25-40	R
Duplaix, Lily	White Bunny & his Magic Nose (1st, 4to, [28]p, ipcb, fp color, DJ/1.00)	Simon/Schuster	1945	Masha	30-50	
Gall, Alice C.	Royal Mimkin (1st, lg8vo, 128p, red cl, 1-color)	Oxford U. Pr.	1934	Masline, Camille	25-45	*
Inman, H.E.	Gobbo Bobo (1st, 8vo, 477p, gilt, AEG, b/w)	L: Warne	1900	Mason, E.A.	100-165	*
Hall, A.W. (ed.)	Icelandic Fairy Tales (1st, 12mo, 317p, gilt, 8pl)	L: Warne	1897	Mason, E.A.	70-130	
Inman, H.E.	One-Eyed Griffin... (1st, 12mo, 353p, teg, gilt, 4pl, dep)	L: Warne	1897	Mason, E.A.	120-170	
Inman, H.E.	Owl King... (1st, 12mo, 378p, teg, 4pl, dep)	L: Warne	1898	Mason, E.A.	120-170	
Hendry, Hamish	Holidays & Happy Days (1st, 8vo, teg, 120p, 24cp)	L: Richards	1901	Mason, E.F.	90-140	
Granville, Austyn	Fallen Race (1st, 8vo, blue/gilt, 352p, 5pl)	F.T. Neely	(1892)	Mason, Edward	200-300	
Steele, Robert (tr)	Renaud of Montauban (1st, 8vo, 284p, gilt, uncut 10 fp b/w)	L: G. Allen	1897	Mason, Fred	70-100	
Steele, Robert	Story of Alexander (1st, lg8vo, 226p, uncut, 6pl)	L: D. Nutt	1894	Mason, Fred	80-125	
Balch, Glenn	Hide-Rack Kidnapped (1st, sm8vo, 302p, dp pl, DJ/2.00)	Crowell	1939	Mason, George F.	25-40	*
Schlein, Miriam	Oomi, the New Hunter (1st, 8vo, 109p, b/w, DJ/2.50)	Abelard-Schuman	(1955)	Mason, George F.	20-30	
Massie, Diane R.	Baby Beebee Bird (1st, ob8vo, ipcb, [32]p, 3-color, cep, DJ/2.75)	Harper	(1963)	Massie, Diane R.	20-35	
Massie, Diane R.	King Henry the Mouse (1st {std}, 8vo, 65p, b/w, cep, DJ/3.50)	Atheneum	1968	Massie, Diane R.	25-40	*
Massie, Diane R.	Monstrous Glisson Glop (1st, lg8vo, [39]p, color, DJ/3.95)	Parents Mag. Pr.	(1970)	Massie, Diane R.	20-35	
Massie, Diane R.	Tiny Pin (1st, sm ob8vo, 31p, color, DJ/2.95)	Harper	(1964)	Massie, Diane R.	25-40	*
Harben, William N.	Mam' Linda (1st, 12mo, 387p, green/gilt, 8pl)	Harper	1907	Masters, F.B.	35-60	
Merwin, Samuel	Road Builders (1st, sm8vo, 313p, 10pl, pep)	Macmillan	1905	Masters, F.B.	30-50	
Kozisek, Josef	Forest Story (1st, 4to, ibds, [58]p, color, pep)	Macmillan	1929	Mates, Rudolf	250-350	
Kozisek, Josef	Magic Flutes (1st, lg ob4to, [56]p, ibds, color)	L: Longmans	1929	Mates, Rudolf	350-500	
Sedlacek, Hanus	Nursery Rhymes from Bohemia (1st AM, lg4to, [24]p, ibds, color, pep)	McBride	1929	Mates, Rudolf	150-225	
Heide, Florence P.	Alphabet Zoop (1st, ob4to, [61]p, color, DJ/4.75)	McCall Pub.	(1970)	Mathews, Sally	40-65	*
Heide, Florence P.	Benjamin Budge & Barnaby Ball (1st, ob8vo, [32]p, fp 1-color, DJ/2.95)	Four Winds Pr.	(1967)	Mathews, Sally	50-80	
Proudfit, Isabel	Come and See the Pencil Box Family (1st, 12mo, ibds, [38]p, color)	McKay	(1945)	Matson, Caroline	30-50	
Strong, L.A.G.	Henry of Agincourt (1st, 8vo, 160p, col frn, b/w, DJ)	L: Nelson	(1937)	Matthew, Jack	40-65	
Matthews, Harry B.	Happy Day Fair (folio, ibds, color)	McLoughlin	(1908)	Matthews, Harry B.	200-320	
Mother Goose	Mother Goose: Her Rhymes (lg8vo, blue cl, 142p, 6 ticp, pep)	Saalfield	(1915)	Matthews, Harry B.	100-165	
Carrighar, Sally	One Day at Teton Marsh (1st {std}, 8vo, 239p, b/w woodcuts, DJ/3.50)	Knopf	1947	Mattson, G.& P.	30-45	
Borland, Hal	Rocky Mountain Tipi Tales (1st [1st bk.] {std}, 8vo, 247p, col frn by...)	Doubleday/Page	1924	Mattsson, Esther M.	90-130	
Hosford, Dorothy	By His Own Might (1st {std}, 8vo, 69p, fp b/w, pep, DJ/2.00)	Henry Holt & Co.	(1947)	Matulay, Laszlo	40-60	R
Fillmore, Parker H.	Shoemaker's Apron (1st, 8vo, 280p, col frn, pep)	Harcourt	1920	Matulka, Jan	30-50	*
Mauzey, Merritt	Cotton Farm Boy (1st, 4to, 79p, fp b/w, cep, DJ/2.50)	H. Schuman	(1953)	Mauzey, Merritt	35-50	
Mauzey, Merritt	Salt Boy (1st, 4to, 60p, fp b/w, DJ/3.00)	Abelard-Schuman	(1963)	Mauzey, Merritt	25-45	*
Martin, Patricia	Zachary Taylor (1st, 8vo, 62p, color, DJ)	Putnam	(1969)	Mawicke, Tran	20-35	
Max, Peter	Peter Max Land of Blue (1st, 4to, ibds, [32]p, color, pep)	F. Watts	(1970)	Max, Peter	60-100	
Max, Peter	Peter Max Land of Red (1st, 4to, ibds, [32]p, color, pep)	F. Watts	(1970)	Max, Peter	60-100	
Max, Peter	Peter Max Land of Yellow (1st, 4to, [31]p, ibds, color, pep)	F. Watts	1970	Max, Peter	60-100	
Streatfeild, Noel	Family at Caldicott Place (1st AM {std}, 8vo, 177p, ibds, b/w, DJ/3.95)	Random	(1968)	Maxey, Betty	30-45	
Lear, Edward	Owl & the Pussycat (1st {std}, 4to, [34]p, ibds, color, DJ/3.95)	Follett	1969	Maxey, Dale	25-40	
Kipling, Rudyard	East of Suez (1st, 4to, 72p, blue/gilt, 10cp)	L: Macmillan	1931	Maxwell, Donald	90-120	
Maxwell, Donald	Excursions in Color (1st, lg8vo, blue/gilt, 118p, 89 illus)	L: Cassell	1927	Maxwell, Donald	90-160	
Maxwell, G.S.	Just Beyond London (1st, 8vo, 280p, 18pl)	L: Methuen	1927	Maxwell, Donald	50-80	
Maxwell, Donald	New Lights O'London (1st, lg8vo, 158p, blue/gilt, color)	L: H. Jenkins	1926	Maxwell, Donald	70-100	
Kipling, Rudyard	Sea & Sussex (1st AM {std}, 4to, 94p, teg, blue cl, 24 ticp)	Doubleday/Page	1926	Maxwell, Donald	100-160	
Kipling, Rudyard	Sea & Sussex (1st, 4to, 94p, blue/gilt, teg, 24 ticp)	L: Macmillan	1926	Maxwell, Donald	120-200	
Kipling, Rudyard	Songs of the Sea (1st, sm4to, 99p, blue/gilt, teg, uncut, 12cp)	L: Macmillan	1927	Maxwell, Donald	80-125	
Milne, James	Travels in Hope (1st, sm4to, 190p, blue cl, 22ticp)	L: Hodder	[1926]	Maxwell, Donald	100-150	
Maxwell, Donald	Wembley in Colour (1st, 4to, bds, 112p, 37cp)	L: Longmans	1924	Maxwell, Donald	75-100	
Fenner, Phyllis R.	Yankee Doodle (1st {std}, 8vo, red cl, 214p, uncut, fp b/w, DJ/2.50)	Knopf	1951	Maxwell, John	25-45	
Carroll, Lewis	Alice in Wonderland (1st, 12mo, 198p, col frn, gilt)	L: Routledge	[1907]	Maybank, Thomas	120-185	
Maybank, Thomas	Mirth by Maybank (1st, ob4to, ibds, b/w)	L: Ward Lock	(1937)	Maybank, Thomas	80-120	
Drayton, Michael	Nymphidia (1st, 8vo, blue/gilt, teg, uncut, unpag, 8pl)	L: Routledge	1906	Maybank, Thomas	100-165	*
Herbertson, Agnes	Teddy & Trots in Wonderland (1st, 8vo, 254p, 27 illus)	L: Ward Lock	1910	Maybank, Thomas	80-120	*
Mayer, Henry	Adventures of a Japanese Doll (1st, ob4to, 127p, ibds, 30cp)	L: Richards	1901	Mayer, Henry	500-700	
Mayer, Henry	In Laughland (1st, folio, [58]p)	R.H. Russell	1899	Mayer, Henry	350-500	
Mayer, Henry	Trip to Toyland (lg ob4to, ibds, 127p, 30 fp color)	L: Richards	1900	Mayer, Henry	250-350	
Offit, Sidney	Boy Who Made a Million (1st, 8vo, 148p, b/w, DJ/3.95)	St. Martin's	(1968)	Mayer, Mercer	25-40	
Mayer, Mercer	Boy, a Dog, and a Frog (1st {std}, 32mo, [32]p, ibds, DJ/1.95)	Dial Press	(1967)	Mayer, Mercer	25-40	
Mendoza, George	Crack in the Wall (1st {std}, lg8vo, 54p, b/w, DJ/3.95)	Dial Press	(1968)	Mayer, Mercer	25-45	
Mayer, Mercer	Frog, Where are You? (1st {std}, 32mo, [32]p, ibds, DJ/2.50)	Dial Press	(1969)	Mayer, Mercer	25-40	
Larson, Jean R.	Jack Tar (1st, 8vo, 76p, b/w, DJ/3.95)	Macrae Smith	(1970)	Mayer, Mercer	20-35	
Fine, Warren	Mousechildren & the Famous Collector (1st {std}, 4to, 57p, b/w, DJ/7.50)	Harper	(1970)	Mayer, Mercer	30-50	
Skorpen, Liesel	Outside My Window (1st, 12mo, 32p, color, DJ/2.50)	Harper	(1968)	Mayer, Mercer	30-50	
Mayer, Mercer	Special Trick (1st {std}, sq8vo, 33p, color, DJ/4.50)	Dial Press	(1970)	Mayer, Mercer	50-85	
Mendoza, George	The Gillygoofang (1st, ob4to, ipcb, [32]p, fp color, cep, DJ)	Dial Press	1968	Mayer, Mercer	30-45	
Mayer, Mercer	There's a Nightmare in My Closet (1st {std}, 4to, [30]p, 2-col, cep DJ/3.50)	Dial Press	(1968)	Mayer, Mercer	50-85	
Barrows, Marjorie	Fraidy Cat (1st, 4to, [28]p, ibds, color, DJ/0.50)	Rand/McNally	1942	Maynard, Barbara	40-65	*
Mowat, Farley	Black Joke (1st AM {std}, 8vo, 218p, b/w, DJ/3.75)	Little/Brown	(1963)	Mays, Victor	40-65	

AUTHOR	TITLE	PUBLISHER	DATE	ARTIST	PRICE	LC
Meader, Stephen W.	Blow for Liberty (1st {std}, 8vo, 187p, tan cl, pep, DJ/3.50)	Harcourt	(1965)	Mays, Victor	85-130	
North, Sterling	Mark Twain and the River (1st, 8vo, 184p, 1-color, DJ/1.95)	Houghton	1961	Mays, Victor	20-30	
Meader, Stephen W.	Phantom of the Blockade (1st {std}, 8vo, 190p, red cl, b/w, DJ/3.25)	Harcourt	(1962)	Mays, Victor	70-100	
Latham, Jean L.	Trail Blazer of the Seas (1st, 8vo, 245p, b/w, DJ/2.75)	Houghton	1956	Mays, Victor	40-70	
Latham, Jean L.	Young Man in a Hurry (1st, 8vo, 238p, b/w, DJ/2.95)	Harper	(1958)	Mays, Victor	30-45	
Mazer, Sonia	Yossele's Holiday & Brave Maccabees (1st {std}, sm4to, ibds, 60p, b/w, pep)	Doubleday/Doran	1934	Mazer, Sonia	50-85	*
Collodi, Carlo	Story of a Puppet (1st {Engl. trans.}, 8vo, green/gilt, 232p, teg, b/w)	L: T.F. Unwin	1892	Mazzanti, C.	2000-4000	
Collodi, Carlo	Story of a Puppet (1st AM, sm8vo, 232p, 1-color title pg., b/w, dep)	NY: Cassell	1892	Mazzanti, C.	1800-3000	
Calhoun, Mary	Goblin Under the Stairs (1st, ob8vo, [32]p, color, DJ/3.50)	Wm. Morrow	(1968)	McCaffery, Janet	30-45	*
Calhoun, Mary	Last Two Elves in Denmark (1st, ob8vo, [32]p, fp color, dep, DJ/3.25)	Wm. Morrow	1968	McCaffery, Janet	30-45	
Calhoun, Mary	Pixy & the Lazy Housewife (1st, lg ob8vo, [32]p, color, DJ/3.50)	Wm. Morrow	1969	McCaffery, Janet	20-35	
Laboulaye, E.R.	Laboulaye's Fairy Book (1st, lg8vo, 199p, p-o, 12cp, pep)	Harper	(1920)	McCandlish, Edward	70-100	
McCann, Rebecca	Children's Cheerful Cherub (1st, 12mo, ibds, [63]p, color, pep)	Covici Friede	(1932)	McCann, Rebecca	45-65	
Levine, Edna S.	Little Nemo in Slumberland (1st, 12mo, ibds, [63]p, 12 fp color)	Rand/McNally	(1941)	McCay, Winsor	80-125	
Voight, Virginia F.	Zeke & the Fisher-Cat (1st, sm8vo, 201p, red cl, b/w, pep, DJ/2.50)	Holiday House	(1953)	McChesney, Harry	25-40	
Hays, Wilma P.	Goose that was a Watchdog (1st {std}, 8vo, 41p, b/w, DJ/2.95)	Little/Brown	(1967)	McClary, Nelson	20-30	
Blodgett, Mabel F.	When Christmas Came Too Early (1st, 12mo, 107p, 6cp)	Little/Brown	1912	McClellan, R.	35-60	*
McClelland, Hugh	Magic Lassoo (1st, lg8vo, [38]p, b/w, DJ)	St. Martin's	(1963)	McClelland, Hugh	30-45	
McCloskey, Robert	Blueberries for Sal (1st, ob4to, 54p, fp 1-color, DJ/2.00, CH)	Viking	1948	McCloskey, Robert	140-200	
McCloskey, Robert	Burt Dow, Deep-Water Man (1st, lg4to, 63p, green cl, color, DJ/4.00)	Viking	(1963)	McCloskey, Robert	100-165	
McCloskey, Robert	Centerburg Tales (1st, 8vo, 190p, fp 1-color, DJ/2.50)	Viking	1951	McCloskey, Robert	80-120	
Robertson, Keith	Henry Reed's Baby-Sitting Service (1st, 8vo, 204p, color, DJ/3.50)	Viking	(1966)	McCloskey, Robert	70-100	
Robertson, Keith	Henry Reed's Big Show (1st {std}, 8vo, 206p, color, DJ/4.50)	Viking	(1970)	McCloskey, Robert	50-80	
Robertson, Keith	Henry Reed's Journey (1st, 8vo, 220p, color, DJ/3.25)	Viking	(1963)	McCloskey, Robert	50-80	
Robertson, Keith	Henry Reed, Inc. (1st, 8vo, 239p, b/w, DJ/3.00)	Viking	(1958)	McCloskey, Robert	60-90	R
McCloskey, Robert	Homer Price (1st, lg8vo, 149p, blue cloth, sepia, DJ/2.00)	Viking	1943	McCloskey, Robert	120-180	R
Sawyer, Ruth	Journey Cake, Ho! (1st, 4to, 45p, 2-color, pep, DJ/2.50, CH)	Viking	1953	McCloskey, Robert	250-350	R
White, Anne H.	Junket (1st, lg8vo, 184p, b/w, DJ/2.75)	Viking	1955	McCloskey, Robert	70-100	
McCloskey, Robert	Lentil (1st {1st bk.}, lg4to, beige cl, fp b/w, [61]p, pep, DJ/2.00)	Viking	1940	McCloskey, Robert	140-225	R
McCloskey, Robert	Make Way for Ducklings (1st, lg4to, [70]p, 1-color, pep, DJ/2.00, CM)	Viking	1941	McCloskey, Robert	200-300	R
Bishop, Claire H.	Man Who Lost his Head (1st, lg ob8vo, ibds, pep, [53]p, b/w, DJ/1.00)	Viking	1942	McCloskey, Robert	80-140	
McCloskey, Robert	One Morning in Maine (1st, lg4to, 64p, grey cl, pep, DJ/2.50, CH)	Viking	1952	McCloskey, Robert	250-350	
McCloskey, Robert	Time of Wonder (1st, lg4to, 63p, blue cl, color, DJ/3.50, CM)	Viking	(1957)	McCloskey, Robert	250-350	R
Davis, Robert	Tree Toad (1st [new ed.], 8vo, 276p, b/w, DJ/2.00)	Stokes	1942	McCloskey, Robert	40-65	
Robinson, Tom P.	Trigger John's Son (1st, 8vo, 284p, b/w, DJ/2.50)	Viking	1949	McCloskey, Robert	60-90	
Malcolmson, Anne	Yankee Doodle's Cousins (1st, sm4to, 267p, red cl, fp b/w, pep, DJ/2.50)	Houghton	1941	McCloskey, Robert	100-165	R
Crissey, Forrest	Country Boy (1st, 8vo, 300p, gilt, uncut, 14pl by...)	Revell	(1903)	McClure, Griselda M.	50-80	
Knowles, Robert E.	Dawn at Shanty Bay (1st, 8vo, green/gilt, 156p, col frn, dep)	Revell	(1907)	McClure, Griselda M.	35-60	
Stewart, Mary	Once Upon a Time Tales (1st, 8vo, 275p, pep, 8cp)	Revell	(1912)	McClure, Griselda M.	40-65	
Barr, Amelia E.	Souls of Passage (1st, sm8vo, 327p, 6pl)	Dodd	1901	McConnell, Emlen	25-40	*
Washburne, Heluiz	Little Elephant's Christmas (1st, lg8vo, 30p, p-o, 2-color, DJ/1.00)	Whitman	1938	McConnell, Jean	30-50	
Washburne, Heluiz	Little Elephant's Picnic (1st, lg8vo, 30p, p-o, fp 2-color, pep, DJ/1.00)	Whitman	1939	McConnell, Jean	30-50	
Sewell, Daisy	About Fairies.... (1st, sq8vo, ibds, 76p, 5cp)	L: Allenson	[1930]	McConnell, Jeannie	120-180	
Sewell, Daisy	Visions in Fairyland (1st, sq8vo, ibds, 69p, 3cp)	L: Allenson	[1930]	McConnell, Jeannie	100-170	
Schaefer, Jack W.	Shane (1st {illus. ed}, 8vo, 214p, 16 fp b/w, DJ/2.75)	Houghton	1954	McCormack, John	200-300	
Newbolt, Henry J.	Drake's Drum... (1st, 4to, green cl, 143p, 12 ticp, pep)	L: Hodder	[1914]	McCormick, A.D.	100-165	
Hudson, Wm. Henry	Little Boy Lost (1st, sm8vo, buckram/gilt, teg, 201p, fp b/w pl)	L: Duckworth	1905	McCormick, A.D.	140-200	R
MacGregor, Mary	Romance of the Netherlands (1st, 8vo, teg, 344p, uncut, 12cp)	Jack/Stokes	1907	McCormick, A.D.	60-90	
Poe, Edgar A.	Tales of Mystery... (1st, 8vo, 416p)	L: A. Pearson	1905	McCormick, A.D.	75-100	*
McCoy, Neely	Jupie the Wise Old Owl (1st, 8vo, 95p, 3cp, pep)	Macmillan	1931	McCoy, Neely	25-45	
Stevenson, Rbt. L.	Child's Garden of Verses (1st, 8vo, p-o, gilt, 127p, fp color, pep)	Whitman	(1930)	McCracken, James	30-50	*
Gordon, Elizabeth	Lorraine & Little People of Summer (1st, sm8vo, 64p, color)	Rand/McNally	(1920)	McCracken, James	40-65	
Browning, Robert	Pied Piper of Hamelin (1st, lg8vo, p-o, [64]p, color, pep)	Whitman	1927	McCracken, James	55-90	
Garnett, Louise A.	The Merrymakers (1st, 4to, p-o, 80p, 8 fp color)	Rand/McNally	(1918)	McCracken, James	55-80	
Horn, Madeline D.	Log Cabin Family (1st, lg8vo, 95p, fp color, cep, DJ/2.00)	Scribner	(1939)	McCray, Francis	45-65	
Engdahl, Sylvia	Journey Between Worlds (1st {std}, 8vo, 235p, DJ/5.25, decor by...)	Atheneum	1970	McCrea, J.& R.	25-40	
McCrea, James & Ruth	King's Procession (1st {std}, lg ob8vo, [30]p, color, DJ/3.25)	Atheneum	1963	McCrea, J.& R.	30-50	
McCrea, James & Ruth	Magic Tree (1st {std}, lg sq8vo, [30]p, 2-color, DJ)	Atheneum	1965	McCrea, J.& R.	40-65	R
Hawes, Judy	What I Like about Toads (1st, ob8vo, [40]p, color, DJ/3.50)	Crowell	(1969)	McCrea, J.& R.	25-45	
Chipman, Charles P.	Aerial Runaway (1st, sm8vo, 387p, 3pl)	Lothrop Pub.	(1901)	McCullough, Wm. A.	70-100	
Pratt, Ella	Happy Children (1st, lg4to, 64p, ibds, 8cp)	Crowell	(1896)	McCullough, Wm. A.	120-200	
Pyle/Porter	Theodora (1st, 12mo, 271p, 4pl)	Little/Brown	1907	McCullough, Wm. A.	35-60	*
Sonneborn, Ruth	Friday Night is Papa Night (1st {std}, 8vo, [31]p, 2-color, DJ/3.00)	Viking	(1970)	McCully, Emily	30-50	
Miles, Miska	Gertrude's Pocket (1st {std}, 8vo, 55p, fp b/w, DJ/3.95)	Little/Brown	(1970)	McCully, Emily	25-40	
Borack, Barbara	Gooney (1st, sm4to, [32]p, fp color, pep, DJ/2.95)	Harper	(1968)	McCully, Emily	40-65	*
DeJong, Meindert	Journey from Peppermint Street (1st, sm8vo, 242p, fp b/w, DJ/4.50)	Harper	(1968)	McCully, Emily	30-45	
Carlson, Natalie S.	Luigi on the Streets (1st, 8vo, 144p, b/w, DJ/3.95)	Harper	(1967)	McCully, Emily	30-45	
Kantrowitz, Mildred	Maxie (1st, 8vo, [33]p, fp color, DJ/3.50)	Parents Mag. Pr.	(1970)	McCully, Emily	50-85	
Walker, Barbara	Mouse and the Elephant (1st, 4to, [36]p, color, pep, DJ/3.50)	Parents Mag. Pr.	(1969)	McCully, Emily	40-65	*
Sharmat, Marjorie	Rex (1st, sm ob4to, 32p, fp 2-color, pep, DJ/3.50)	Harper	(1967)	McCully, Emily	30-50	
Panetta, George	Sea Beach Express (1st, lg8vo, 64p, fp b/w, DJ/3.95)	Harper	(1966)	McCully, Emily	45-70	
Neville, Emily C.	Seventeenth Street Gang (1st, 8vo, 148p, b/w, DJ/3.50)	Harper	(1966)	McCully, Emily	30-50	*
Hardendorff, Jeanne	Slip! Slop! Gobble! (1st, 4to, [32]p, color, cep, DJ/4.50)	Lippincott	(1970)	McCully, Emily	30-50	*
Hoffman, Phyllis	Steffie and Me (1st, sm ob4to, 32p, ipcb, fp 3-color, DJ/3.50)	Harper	(1970)	McCully, Emily	50-85	
Gripari, Pierre	Tales of the Rue Broca (1st AM {std}, 8vo, 111p, 14 fp b/w, DJ/4.95)	Bobbs-Merrill	(1969)	McCully, Emily	30-50	
Skorpen, Liesel	That Mean Man (1st, 4to, 32p, fp color, DJ/2.95)	Harper	(1968)	McCully, Emily	50-80	*
Wahl, Jan	The Fishermen (1st {std}, 8vo, [47]p, color, DJ/4.25)	Norton	(1969)	McCully, Emily	40-65	
Lunn, Janet	Twin Spell (1st, 8vo, 158p, pcb, fp b/w, DJ/3.95)	Harper	(1969)	McCully, Emily	40-65	*

AUTHOR	TITLE	PUBLISHER	DATE	ARTIST	PRICE	LC
Bull, Angela	Wayland's Keep (1st AM {std}, 8vo, 198p, b/w, DJ/3.95)	Holt, Rinehart	(1967)	McCully, Emily	25-45	
Holman, Felice	Year to Grow (1st {std}, 8vo, 100p, color, DJ/3.95)	Norton	(1968)	McCully, Emily	30-50	
Ade, George	Artie (1st {1st bk.}, 16mo, 192p, teg, blue cl, b/w)	Herbert Stone	1896	McCutcheon, J.T.	60-90	
McCutcheon, John T.	Congressman Pumphrey (1st, 8vo, 126p, b/w)	Bobbs-Merrill	(1907)	McCutcheon, J.T.	25-40	*
Kiser, Samuel E.	Love Sonnets of an Office Boy (1st, 16mo, ibds, 42p)	Chi: Forbes	1902	McCutcheon, J.T.	30-50	*
Ade, George	People You Know (1st, 12mo, blue cl, 224p, b/w)	R.H. Russell	1903	McCutcheon, J.T.	40-60	
Ade, George	Pink Marsh (1st, 12mo, green cl, 197p, teg, uncut, b/w)	Herbert Stone	1897	McCutcheon, J.T.	70-100	
Crissey, Forrest	Tattlings of a Retired Politician (1st, lg8vo, red/gilt, teg, 487p, b/w)	Chi: Thompson	1904	McCutcheon, J.T.	30-50	
Lippmann, Julie M.	Jock O'Dreams (1st, 8vo, 211p, gilt, b/w)	Roberts Bros.	1891	McDermott, Jessie	40-70	
Sidney, Margaret	Phronsie Pepper (1st, sm8vo, 437p, green/gilt, b/w)	Lothrop, Lee	1897	McDermott, Jessie	70-120	
Sidney, Margaret	Stories Polly Pepper Told (1st, 12mo, green/gilt, 469p, b/w)	Lothrop Pub.	1899	McDermott/Barry	100-165	
Peck, George W.	Peck's Bad Boy & his Chums (ob4to, stiff wraps, color)	Chi: Stanton	1908	McDougall, Walter	250-350	
McDougall, Walter	Rambillicus Book (1st, lg8vo, 239p, 20pl)	Jacobs	(1903)	McDougall, Walter	80-130	*
Martin, Fran	Nine Tales of Coyote (1st, 8vo, 60p, fp color, pep, DJ/2.00)	Harper	(1950)	McEntee, Dorothy	30-45	
McGaw, Jessie B.	How Medicine Man Cured Paleface Women (1st, ob4to, [62]p, 1-col, DJ/2.75)	W.R. Scott	(1956)	McGaw, Jessie B.	40-60	*
Montgomery, R.	Mystery of the Turquoise Frog (1st, sm8vo, 187p, b/w, DJ/2.25)	J. Messner	(1946)	McGee, Millard	20-35	
McGinley, Phyllis	On the Contrary (1st {std}, sm8vo, 119p, gilt, b/w)	Doubleday/Doran	1934	McGinley, Phyllis	30-50	*
Topelius, Zacharias	Canute Whistlewinks... (1st {std}, 8vo, 271p, orange cl, 5cp, dep)	NY: Longmans	1927	McIntosh, Frank	50-80	
Lansing, Marion	Magic Gold (1st, 8vo, 302p, col frn, b/w, pep)	Little/Brown	1928	McIntosh, Frank	25-40	
Coatsworth, Eliz.	Sun's Diary (1st, sq8vo, ibds, [98]p, b/w, cep)	Macmillan	1929	McIntosh, Frank	90-140	R
Palm, Amy	Wanda and Greta at Broby Farm (1st {std}, 8vo, 198p, 6cp, pep)	Longmans	1930	McIntosh, Frank	30-45	*
Fox, Paula	Stone-Faced Boy (1st {std}, 8vo, 106p, b/w, DJ/3.95)	Bradbury Press	(1968)	McKay, Donald	30-50	
Dyer, Caroline	Three Famous Ugly Sisters (1st, sm4to, ibds, [52]p, color, DJ/2.00)	Whittlesey	(1946)	McKay, Donald	25-45	
N/A	Goldilocks & Three Bears (1st, ob4to, [14]p, color)	McLoughlin	1943	McKean, E.C.	45-80	*
McKee, David	Elmer, Story of a Patchwork Elephant (1st, lg8vo, [45]p, color, DJ/4.50)	McGraw-Hill	(1968)	McKee, David	25-45	
Gale, Elizabeth	Circus Babies (1st, sq4to, 100p, fp color, pep)	Rand/McNally	(1930)	McKee, John D.	100-150	
LeSieg, Theo	Eye Book (1st, 8vo, [29]p, ibds, color, pep, DJ/1.95)	Beginner Books	(1968)	McKie, Roy	40-65	*
Sharp, Margery	Melisande (1st {std}, 4to, [88]p, fp b/w, DJ/2.95)	Little/Brown	(1960)	McKie, Roy	25-40	
LeSieg, Theo	Ten Apples Up on Top! (1st, 8vo, 59p, ibds, 2-color, pep, DJ/1.95)	Beginner Books	(1961)	McKie, Roy	40-65	*
Henry, Marguerite	Misty, Wonder Pony: By Misty Herself (1st, 8vo, unpag)	Rand/McNally	1956	McKinley, Clare	50-80	
Ibbotson, M.C.	Robertson, Ugly & Nohow (1st AM, 8vo, 119p, b/w, DJ)	Pantheon	(1968)	McLachlan, Edward	20-35	
Fox, Paula	Dear Prosper (1st, 8vo, 67p, b/w, DJ/3.95)	NY: David White	(1968)	McLachlin, Steve	20-35	
Cavanna, Betty	Secret Passage (1st {std}, 8vo, 216p, col frn, pep, DJ/2.50)	Winston	(1946)	McLaughlin, Jean	30-50	
Sewell, Anna	Black Beauty (1st, lg8vo, 244p, p-o, gilt, col frn, 1-color, pep)	Sears	(1926)	McMann, Jessica S.	40-60	*
Carroll, Lewis	Alice in Wonderland (1st, 4to, 255p, yellow/gilt, 16cp)	Wessels	(1899)	McManus, Blanche	130-200	R
Carroll, Lewis	Alice in Wonderland (sm8vo, green/gilt, 8pl)	L: Ward Lock	[1901]	McManus, Blanche	70-100	
Carroll, Lewis	Alice... & Through... (1st, lg8vo, 255p, yellow cl, 12cp)	Wessels	(1900)	McManus, Blanche	150-225	
Carroll, Lewis	Alice... & Through... (8vo, 255p, beige cl, 16 fp color)	Platt/Peck	(1900)	McManus, Blanche	200-300	
Ervin, Mabel C.	As Told by the Typewriter Girl (1st, 8vo, 245p)	Herrick	(1898)	McManus, Blanche	60-90	
Miltoun, Francis	Automobilist Abroad (1st, 8vo, 381p, gilt, teg, p-o, col frn, pep)	L.C. Page	1907	McManus, Blanche	70-125	
McManus, Blanche	Bachelor Ballads (1st, 8vo, beige cl, 159p, color)	New Amsterdam	1898	McManus, Blanche	60-90	
Mansfield, Richard	Blown Away (1st, 12mo, 180p, teg, cvr by...)	L.C. Page	1897	McManus, Blanche	60-100	
McManus, Blanche	Calendar of Omar Khayaam (4to, ibds, dep, color)	L.C. Page	1904	McManus, Blanche	80-120	*
Miltoun, Francis	Castles & Chateaux of Touraine (1st, 8vo, 347p, teg, gilt, 39pl, pep)	L.C. Page	1906	McManus, Blanche	40-60	
Raymond, Walter	Charity Chance (1st, 12mo, 256p, cvr by..)	Dodd	1896	McManus, Blanche	25-40	*
Porter, Rose	Charm of Birds (1st, 12mo, gilt, 206p, teg, cvr by...)	Herrick	(1897)	McManus, Blanche	40-60	
Watts, Isaac	Childhood Songs of Long Ago (1st, 8vo, 87p, 20pl, pep)	Herrick	(1897)	McManus, Blanche	70-100	
Hawthorne, Nathaniel	In Colonial Days (1st, 8vo, 104p, teg, beige/gilt, cvr by...)	L.C. Page	1906	McManus, Blanche	40-65	
Clemens, Will	Ken of Kipling (1st, 12mo, 141p, orange/gilt, cvr by...)	New Amsterdam	1899	McManus, Blanche	60-90	
McManus, Blanche	Little Dutch Cousin (1st, 12mo, 99p, 6pl)	L.C. Page	1906	McManus, Blanche	25-45	*
McManus, Blanche	Little French Cousin (1st, sm8vo, 116p, 6pl)	L.C. Page	1905	McManus, Blanche	25-45	*
McManus, Blanche	Little Hindu Cousin (1st, sm8vo, 103p, 6pl)	L.C. Page	1907	McManus, Blanche	25-45	*
McManus, Blanche	Little Scotish Cousin (1st, sm8vo, 95p, 6pl)	L.C. Page	1906	McManus, Blanche	25-45	*
Nixon-Roulet	Little Spanish Cousin (1st, sm8vo, 125p, 6pl)	L.C. Page	1906	McManus, Blanche	30-50	
Elton, Emily D.	Mince Pie Dream (1st, 8vo, 75p, cloth, 8cp)	NY: E.R. Herrick	1897	McManus, Blanche	50-80	*
Mother Goose	Mother Goose Nursery Rhymes (1st {this pub}, sq8vo, 136p, b/w)	Platt/Peck	(1912)	McManus, Blanche	70-100	
Miltoun, Francis	Rambles on the Riviera (1st, 8vo, teg, 434p, 32pl)	L.C. Page	1906	McManus, Blanche	35-60	
Omar Khayyam	Rubaiyat of Omar Khayyam (1st, 8vo, 25p, 12 illus)	L: A. Moring	1903	McManus, Blanche	75-120	*
Omar Khayyam	Rubaiyat of Omar Khayyam (1st {this pub}, 12mo, 159p, color)	L.C. Page	1907	McManus, Blanche	40-60	*
Fezandie, Clement	Through the Earth (1st, sm8vo, tan cl, 238p, cvr by...)	Century	1898	McManus, Blanche	70-100	
Carroll, Lewis	Through the Looking Glass (1st, lg8vo, 139p, grey/gilt, 12cp)	Mansfield/Wes.	1899	McManus, Blanche	140-200	
N/A	Told in the Twilight (1st, 8vo, 93p, tan cloth, 9pl, pep)	Herrick	(1898)	McManus, Blanche	75-100	
Mother Goose	True Mother Goose (1st, lg8vo, 138p)	Lamson/Wolffe	1896	McManus, Blanche	120-185	R*
Mother Goose	True Mother Goose (1st, lg8vo, 138p, b/w)	Mansfield/Wes.	1899	McManus, Blanche	100-175	
Hall, Tom	When Cupid Calls (1st, 12mo, 119p, teg, decor by...)	Herrick	1898	McManus, Blanche	25-45	*
Roberts, Chas. G.D.	Young Acadian (1st, 12mo, 139p, 6pl)	L.C. Page	1907	McManus, Blanche	30-50	*
Orgel, Doris	In a Forgotten Place (1st, 8vo, 144p, b/w, cep, DJ/3.95)	Knopf	(1967)	McMullan, Jim	20-35	
Braun, Kathy	Kangaroo and Kangaroo (1st {std}, ob4to, 36p, color, DJ/3.25, NYTBI)	Doubleday	(1965)	McMullan, Jim	40-65	*
DeJong, Meindert	Last Little Cat (1st, 8vo, 66p, b/w, DJ/2.75)	Harper	1961	McMullan, Jim	25-40	
McNagny, Bob	Noah's Nightmare (1st, 4to, p-o, [67]p, 30cp)	Bobbs-Merrill	(1926)	McNagny, Bob	65-100	
Catling, Patrick	Chocolate Touch (1st, 8vo, yellow cl, 95p, fp b/w, DJ/2.50)	Wm. Morrow	1952	McNutt, Mildred	70-100	*
Pollard, Josephine	Boston Tea Party (1st, lg8vo, ipcb, [32]p, color)	Dodd	1882	McVickar, H.W.	90-140	
Plummer, Mary W.	Chronicles of the Cid (1st, sm8vo, 155p, 10pl)	Henry Holt & Co.	1910	McVickar, H.W.	60-100	*
James, Henry	Daisy Miller (1st, 8vo, stripe cl, 294p, teg, uncut, col frn, b/w)	Harper	1892	McVickar, H.W.	100-170	
McVickar, H.W.	Evolution of Woman (1st, sm4to, [94]p, teg, uncut, 1-color)	Harper	1896	McVickar, H.W.	40-65	
Holmes, Oliver W.	Grandmother's Story of Bunker Hill Battle (1st, lg8vo, 32p, chromos, dep)	Dodd	(1883)	McVickar, H.W.	200-300	
Bangs, John K.	Mr. Bonaparte of Corsica (1st, 16mo, 265p, gilt, b/w)	Harper	1895	McVickar, H.W.	70-120	
N/A	Our Amateur Circus (1st, ob8vo, [48]p, black/gilt, color)	Harper	1892	McVickar, H.W.	300-450	

AUTHOR	TITLE	PUBLISHER	DATE	ARTIST	PRICE	LC
Meader, Stephen W.	Down the Big River (1st, sm8vo, 270p, b/w pl, DJ)	Harcourt	(1924)	Meader, Stephen	120-165	
Smith, Gertrude	Beautiful Story of Doris & Julie (1st, lg sq8vo, 167p, 14cp)	Harper	1901	Mears, W.E.	75-100	*
Munroe, Kirk	Blue Dragon (1st, 12mo, 268p, grey cl, 7pl)	Harper	1904	Mears, W.E.	35-60	
Barnes, James	Son of Light Horse (1st, 12mo, 242p, 8pl)	Harper	1904	Mears, W.E.	30-50	*
Roche, James J.	Sorrows of Sap'ed (1st, 8vo, uncut, 195p, p-o, 8cp)	Harper	1904	Mears, W.E.	25-40	
Garland, Hamlin	Tyranny of the Dark (1st, sm8vo, blue/gilt, 438p, 8pl)	Harper	1905	Mears, W.E.	50-80	
Cameron, Eleanor	Time and Mr. Bass (1st {std}, sm8vo, 247p, b/w, DJ/3.95)	Little/Brown	(1967)	Meise, Fred	200-300	
Grover, Eulalie O.	Sunbonnet Babies in Mother Goose Land (1st, lg8vo, 115p, color, pep)	Rand/McNally	(1927)	Melcher, B.C.	120-200	
Grover, Eulalie O.	Overall Boys in Switzerland (1st, sm8vo, beige cl, 160p, pep, color)	Rand/McNally	(1916)	Melcher, Bertha C.	100-160	
Grover, Eulalie O.	Sonbonnet Babies in Holland (1st, 8vo, map, 150p, color, pep)	Rand/McNally	(1915)	Melcher, Bertha C.	100-165	
Grover, Eulalie O.	Sunbonnet Babies ABC Book... (1st, 4to, p-o, 64p, pep, color)	Rand/McNally	(1929)	Melcher, Bertha C.	100-150	
Grover, Eulalie O.	Sunbonnet Babies in Italy (1st, 8vo, 187p, color, pep)	Rand/McNally	(1922)	Melcher/McCracken	70-120	*
Farley, Walter	Black Stallion and Satan (1st {std}, 8vo, 208p, b/w, DJ/2.00)	Random	(1949)	Menasco, Milton	50-80	
Farley, Walter	Black Stallion's Filly (1st {std}, 8vo, 309p, b/w, DJ/2.00)	Random	(1952)	Menasco, Milton	45-70	
Farley, Walter	Blood Bay Colt (1st {std}, 8vo, 307p, fp b/w, DJ/2.00)	Random	(1950)	Menasco, Milton	30-50	
Farley, Walter	Son of the Black Stallion (1st {std}, 8vo, 330p, b/w, DJ/2.00)	Random	(1947)	Menasco, Milton	60-90	
Mendoza, George	World from My Window (1st, 4to, [102]p, color, DJ/4.95)	Hawthorn Books	(1969)	Mendoza, George	20-30	
Menpes, Mortimer	Brittany (1st, 8vo, gilt, 254p, teg, 75cp)	L: A&C Black	1912	Menpes, Mortimer	80-120	
Blake, Henry A.	China (1st, sm4to, 138p, blue/gilt, 16cp)	L: A&C Black	1909	Menpes, Mortimer	70-100	
Menpes, Mortimer	Japan (1st, lg8vo, 207p, teg, blue/gilt, 75cp)	L: A&C Black	1905	Menpes, Mortimer	80-120	
Menpes, Mortimer	Rembrandt (1st, 4to, 50p, teg, gilt, 16cp)	L: A&C Black	1905	Menpes, Mortimer	90-150	
Menpes, Dorothy	World Pictures (1st AM, 8vo, gilt, teg, 332p, color)	R.H. Russell	1902	Menpes, Mortimer	80-120	*
Menpes, Mortimer	World's Children (1st, 8vo, teg, 246p, blue/gilt, 100cp)	L: A&C Black	1903	Menpes, Mortimer	100-170	
Jacberns, Raymond	Crab Cottage (1st, 12mo, 285p, 6pl, cep)	L: Chambers	1905	Menzies, John	60-90	
Gilbert, William	Magic Mirror (1st, 8vo, 253p, purple/gilt, p-o, teg, 20cp)	L: MacLaren	1908	Menzies, John	80-125	
Syrett, Netta	Rachel & the Seven Wonders (1st, 8vo, 172p, p-o, 5cp, pep)	Stokes	(1923)	Mercer, Joyce	75-120	
Ross, Patricia	Hungry Moon (1st {std}, sm4to, 72p, color, DJ/3.00)	Knopf	1946	Merida, Carlos	80-130	
Ross, Patricia	Magic Forest (1st {std}, 8vo, 128p, color, DJ/2.50)	Knopf	1948	Merida, Carlos	120-170	
Lowrey, Janette S.	The Bird (1st, 4to, 32p, color, ibds, pep, DJ/2.00)	Harper	1947	Merida, Carlos	50-85	
Schlein, Miriam	Best Place (1st, 8vo, [32]p, fp color, DJ/3.50)	Whitman	(1968)	Merkling, Erica	25-40	*
Udry, Janice M.	If You're a Bear (1st, 12mo, [32]p, color, DJ/2.95)	Whitman	(1967)	Merkling, Erica	20-35	
Reed, Helen L.	Brenda's Ward (1st, 8vo, 340p, 6pl)	Little/Brown	1906	Merrill, Frank T.	40-70	
Richards, Laura E.	Captain January (1st, sq8vo, teg, 133p, gilt, b/w)	Estes & Lauriat	1893	Merrill, Frank T.	55-80	*
Bynner, Edwin L.	Chase of the Meteor (1st, 8vo, 209p, gilt, 10 b/w)	Little/Brown	1891	Merrill, Frank T.	60-90	
Dickens, Charles	Christmas Carol (8vo, AEG, blue cl)	Putnam	1907	Merrill, Frank T.	35-60	
Otis, James	Fighting for the Empire (1st, 8vo, 466p, 8pl)	Dana Estes	(1900)	Merrill, Frank T.	40-60	
Johnston, Annie F.	Giant Scissors (1st, sm8vo, 201p, blue/gilt, teg, 8cp)	L.C. Page	1906	Merrill, Frank T.	30-50	
Ray, Anna C.	Half a Dozen Boys (1st, 8vo, 318p, 18pl)	Crowell	(1895)	Merrill, Frank T.	30-45	*
Wattles, Wallace D.	Hell-Fire Harrison (1st, sm8vo, 100p, green/gilt, 6cp, pep)	L.C. Page	1910	Merrill, Frank T.	25-40	
Hawthorne, Nathaniel	In Colonial Days (1st, 8vo, 104p, teg, beige/gilt, 7cp by...)	L.C. Page	1906	Merrill, Frank T.	40-65	
Richards, Laura E.	Isla Heron (1st, 8vo, 109p, fp b/w)	Estes & Lauriat	(1896)	Merrill, Frank T.	20-35	
Atkinson, Eleanor	Johnny Apple-Seed (1st, sm8vo, gilt, 340p, b/w)	Harper	1915	Merrill, Frank T.	50-80	
Johnston, Annie F.	Mary Ware of Texas (1st, sm8vo, 385p, pict cl, 8pl)	L.C. Page	1910	Merrill, Frank T.	40-65	
Dix, Beulah M.	Merrylips (1st, sm8vo, 307p, 8pl, PPPa)	Macmillan	1906	Merrill, Frank T.	125-200	*
Richards, Laura E.	Mrs. Tree (1st, 12mo, ipcb, 282p, teg, 4pl)	Dana Estes	(1902)	Merrill, Frank T.	40-65	
Vaile, Charlotte	Orcutt Girls (1st, sm8vo, 316p, green/gilt, 5pl)	W.A. Wilde	(1896)	Merrill, Frank T.	30-50	
Trowbridge, John T.	Pair of Madcaps (1st, 12mo, 359p, 8pl)	Lothrop, Lee	(1909)	Merrill, Frank T.	50-80	*
Irving, Washington	Rip Van Winkle (1st, lg4to, AEG, gilt, 49p, b/w pl)	S.E. Cassino	1888	Merrill, Frank T.	120-185	
Stevenson, Rbt. L.	Treasure Island (1st AM, sm8vo, 292p, mustard cl, 4 fp b/w)	Roberts Bros.	1884	Merrill, Frank T.	350-500	
Porter, Eleanor	Turn of the Tide (1st, sm8vo, 306p, 4pl)	W.A. Wilde	(1908)	Merrill, Frank T.	30-50	*
Peattie, Elia W.	Edda & the Oak (1st, sq8vo, 134p, p-o, color)	Rand/McNally	(1911)	Merrill, Katharine	30-50	
Johnson, Siddie	Susan's Year (1st {std}, 8vo, uncut, 168p, b/w, pep, DJ/2.25)	Longmans	1948	Merriman, Anne	20-35	
Eastwick, Ivy O.	Fairies & Suchlike (1st {std}, sq8vo, 63p, ipcb, 1-color, pep, DJ/1.50)	Dutton	1946	Merwin, Decie	60-100	
Baker, Margaret	Four Farthings and a Thimble (1st {std}, 8vo, 150p, b/w, pep, DJ/2.50)	Longmans	1950	Merwin, Decie	25-40	
Caudill, Rebecca	Happy Little Family (1st {std}, sm8vo, 116p, b/w, pep, DJ/2.00)	Winston	(1947)	Merwin, Decie	20-35	
Turner, Nancy B.	Magpie Lane (1st, sm8vo, 88p, orange cl, silhouettes, dep)	Harcourt	(1927)	Merwin, Decie	30-60	*
Haviland-Taylor, K.	Nursery Nights (1st, lg8vo, 95p, 2-color, DJ/1.50)	Lippincott	(1942)	Merwin, Decie	70-100	
Merwin, Decie	Pink-Tails (1st, 8vo, 103p, 1-color, DJ/2.00)	NY: Oxford U.Pr.	1950	Merwin, Decie	25-45	
Caudill, Rebecca	Schoolhouse in the Woods (1st {std}, sm8vo, 120p, b/w, pep, DJ/2.00)	Winston	(1949)	Merwin, Decie	25-40	
Caudill, Rebecca	Schoolroom in the Parlor (1st {std}, sm8vo, 120p, b/w, pep, DJ/2.95)	Winston	(1959)	Merwin, Decie	25-40	
Adshead, Gladys	Seventeen to Sing (1st, 4to, 39p, 1-color, DJ/2.50)	NY: Oxford U.Pr.	1946	Merwin, Decie	25-45	
Caudill, Rebecca	Up and Down the River (1st {std}, sm8vo, 115p, b/w, pep, DJ/2.00)	Winston	(1951)	Merwin, Decie	20-30	
Shakespeare, Wm.	Romeo & Juliet (1st, 4to, 95p, purple cl, 8 ticp)	L: Batsford	1936	Messel, Oliver	80-120	*
Longfellow, H.W.	Golden Legend (1st, 4to, green/gilt, teg, 153p, 25 ticp)	L: Hodder	[1910]	Meteyard, Sidney	125-200	
Longfellow, H.W.	Golden Legend (1st AM, 4to, 153p, gilt, 25 ticp)	Doran	[1912]	Meteyard, Sidney	120-180	
Stevenson, Rbt. L.	Ebb-Tide (1st, 12mo, 204p, gilt, cvr by...)	Stone/Kimball	1894	Meteyard, Thomas B.	90-150	
Hovey, Richard	Marriage of Guenevere (1st, sm8vo, 179p, teg, cvr by...)	Herbert Stone	1895	Meteyard, Thomas B.	60-100	R
Carman, Bliss	Winter Holiday (1st, 12mo, 43p, cvr by...)	Small/Maynard	1899	Meteyard, Thomas B.	55-80	
Wells, Carolyn	Emily Emmins Papers (1st, sm8vo, 273p, p-o, b/w)	Putnam	1907	Meyer, Josephine	60-90	*
Graves, Robert	Poor Boy Who Followed his Star (1st AM {std}, lg8vo, 43p, b/w, DJ/3.50)	Doubleday	1961	Meyer-Wallace, A.	70-120	
Nesbit, Wilbur D.	Jolly Kid Book (1st, ob4to, ibds, [12]p, color)	Volland	(1926)	Meyers, M.H.	160-240	
Haskett, Edytha	Grains of Pepper (1st, lg8vo, 119p, color, DJ)	John Day	(1967)	Miatta, Musu	30-45	
Michael, A.C.	Artist in Spain (1st, 4to, rust cl, 205p, 26 ticp)	L: Hodder	[1920]	Michael, A.C.	80-125	
Stevenson, Rbt. L.	Catriona (1st, 8vo, 357p, 4cp)	L: Cassell	(1915)	Michael, A.C.	50-80	
Haggard, H. Rider	Child of the Storm (1st AM, 8vo, red cl, 335p, 3pl)	NY: Longmans	1913	Michael, A.C.	80-125	*
Dickens, Charles	Christmas Carol (1st, 4to, red/gilt, 116p, pep, 12 ticp)	L: Hodder	[1911]	Michael, A.C.	120-200	R
Haggard, H. Rider	Ivory Child (1st, 8vo, 344p, col frn, 3pl)	L: Cassell	(1916)	Michael, A.C.	70-120	
Dorrington, Albert	Radium Terrors (1st, sm8vo, red/gilt, 361p, 4pl)	Doubleday/Page	1912	Michael, A.C.	50-80	

AUTHOR	TITLE	PUBLISHER	DATE	ARTIST	PRICE	LC
Haggard, H. Rider	Wanderer's Necklace (1st, 8vo, 328p, brown/gilt, col frn, 3pl)	L: Cassell	1914	Michael, A.C.	100-150	
Wells, H.G.	War in the Air (1st, 8vo, blue/gilt, 389p, uncut, 16pl)	L: G. Bell	1908	Michael, A.C.	500-700	
Montgomery, R.	Golden Stallion & Mysterious Feud (1st {std}, sm8vo, 180p, b/w, DJ/3.95)	Little/Brown	(1967)	Michini, Albert	40-65	
Mighels, Philip V.	Chatwit the Man-Talk Bird (1st, sm8vo, blue cl, 265p, b/w)	Harper	1906	Mighels, Philip W.	30-50	
Hoover, Helen	Great Wolf & the Good Woodsman (1st, ob4to, [42]p, color, DJ/3.50)	Parents Mag. Pr.	(1967)	Mikolaycak, Charles	30-50	
Wyndham, Lee	Mourka: Mighty Cat (1st, sq8vo, [48]p, fp color, cep, DJ)	Parents Mag. Pr.	(1969)	Mikolaycak, Charles	30-45	
Rinkoff, Barbara	Pretzel Hero (1st, 4to, [32]p, fp color, DJ/3.95)	Parents Mag. Pr.	(1970)	Mikolaycak, Charles	20-35	
Dalgliesh, Alice	Along Janet's Road (1st, 8vo, 208p, gilt, pep, DJ/2.50, decor by...)	Scribner	1946	Milhous, Katherine	30-50	
Milhous, Katherine	Appolonia's Valentine (1st, sm4to, red cl, [32]p, color, DJ/2.00)	Scribner	(1954)	Milhous, Katherine	70-120	R
Hunt, Mabel L.	Billy Button's Buttered Biscuit (1st, 12mo, 56p, color, cep, DJ/1.00)	Stokes	1941	Milhous, Katherine	40-70	
Dalgliesh, Alice	Book for Jennifer (1st, 8vo, 114p, uncut, 10cp, DJ/2.00)	Scribner	1940	Milhous, Katherine	50-80	
Milhous, Katherine	Corporal Keeperupper (1st, sm8vo, 62p, ipcb, color, DJ/1.00)	Scribner	1943	Milhous, Katherine	30-50	
Milhous, Katherine	Egg Tree (1st, sm4to, [32]p, aqua cl, color, DJ/2.00, CM)	Scribner	(1950)	Milhous, Katherine	150-250	R
Milhous, Katherine	First Christmas Crib (1st, 12mo, ibds, 47p, fp color, DJ/1.00)	Scribner	1944	Milhous, Katherine	50-90	
Dalgliesh, Alice	Happily Ever After (1st, lg8vo, 60p, 7 fp color, DJ/1.50)	Scribner	(1939)	Milhous, Katherine	70-100	R
Milhous, Katherine	Herodia the Lovely Puppet (1st, 8vo, 193p, red cl, pep, 7cp, DJ/2.00)	Scribner	1942	Milhous, Katherine	60-100	R
Dalgliesh, Alice	Little Angel (1st, 8vo, 70p, 3 dp cp, pep, DJ/2.00)	Scribner	1943	Milhous, Katherine	40-60	
Milhous, Katherine	Lovina (1st, lg ob8vo, [48]p, red cl, color, DJ/1.50)	Scribner	(1940)	Milhous, Katherine	50-85	
Sherwood, Lorraine	Old Abe, American Eagle (1st, sm8vo, 60p, ibds, color, DJ/1.50)	Scribner	1946	Milhous, Katherine	50-80	
Dalgliesh, Alice	Once On a Time (1st, sm4to, 70p, 10 fp color, DJ/1.50)	Scribner	(1938)	Milhous, Katherine	50-80	
Milhous, Katherine	Patrick & the Golden Slippers (1st {std}, 4to, [32]p, color, cep, DJ/2.00)	Scribner	1951	Milhous, Katherine	30-50	
Hunt, Mabel L.	Peter Piper's Pickled Peppers (1st, 16mo, 62p, cep, 4cp, DJ/1.50)	Stokes	1942	Milhous, Katherine	30-50	
Dalgliesh, Alice	Silver Pencil (1st, 8vo, 235p, blue/gilt, b/w, pep, DJ/2.50, NH)	Scribner	1944	Milhous, Katherine	60-90	
Milhous, Katherine	Snow Over Bethlehem (1st, 8vo, 98p, pep, 3 dp color, DJ/2.00)	Scribner	1945	Milhous, Katherine	40-70	
Ewing, Juliana H.	The Brownies (1st, 12mo, ibds, 50p, 3-color, dep, DJ/1.50)	Scribner	1946	Milhous, Katherine	35-60	
Milhous, Katherine	Through These Arches (1st, ob4to, 96p, fp 2-color, DJ/4.50)	Lippincott	1964	Milhous, Katherine	50-80	R
Dalgliesh, Alice	Wings Around South America (1st, lg8vo, 158p, fp color, cep, DJ/2.50)	Scribner	1941	Milhous, Katherine	40-65	
Milhous, Katherine	With Bells On: A Christmas Story (1st, 4to, [32]p, fp 2-color, DJ/2.00)	Scribner	(1955)	Milhous, Katherine	40-70	R
Milius, Winifred	Here Comes Daddy (1st, lg ob8vo, spiral ipcb, [22]p, color)	W.R. Scott	1944	Milius, Winifred	40-60	*
Udry, Janice M.	What Mary Jo Shared (1st, lg8vo, unpag, color, pep, DJ/2.95)	Whitman	(1966)	Mill, Eleanor	20-30	*
Morier, James	Adventures of Hajji Baba (1st, 12mo, 456p, gilt, fp b/w)	L: Macmillan	1895	Millar, H.R.	60-90	
Nesbit, Edith	Book of Dragons (1st, 8vo, teg, 290p, blue/gilt, 16 b/w by...)	L: Harper	1901	Millar, H.R.	450-600	
N/A	Diamond Fairy Book (1st, 8vo, 310p, gilt, AEG, b/w, dep)	L: Hutchinson	(1897)	Millar, H.R.	120-180	
Millar, H.R.	Dreamland Express (1st AM, ob4to, 56p, ibds, 14cp)	Dodd	(1927)	Millar, H.R.	170-250	
Nesbit, Edith	Enchanted Castle (1st, 8vo, teg, 352p, red/gilt, 46pl)	L: T.F. Unwin	1907	Millar, H.R.	300-400	
Nesbit, Edith	Enchanted Castle (1st AM, 12mo, 297p, 8pl)	Harper	1908	Millar, H.R.	250-350	
Kinglake, A.W.	Eothen (1st, 12mo, 305p, teg, uncut, blue cl, b/w)	L: Newnes	1898	Millar, H.R.	70-100	
Quiller-Couch, A.	Fairy Tales from Far & Near (1st, 12mo, teg, 192p)	L: Cassell	1895	Millar, H.R.	120-180	*
Gower, Margaret L.	Fighting Six (1st, 8vo, 250p, b/w)	Harcourt	(1929)	Millar, H.R.	30-50	*
Nesbit, Edith	Five Children and It (1st, 8vo, 301p, teg, red/gilt, 46pl)	L: T.F. Unwin	1902	Millar, H.R.	200-300	
N/A	Golden Fairy Book (1st, lg8vo, 312p, AEG, b/w, gilt)	L: Hutchinson	[1890]	Millar, H.R.	100-175	
Various	Golden Fairy Book (1st AM, 8vo, 312p, gilt, b/w)	Appleton	1894	Millar, H.R.	70-100	
Nesbit, Edith	Harding's Luck (1st, 8vo, 281p, gilt, teg, 16 fp b/w)	L: Hodder	1909	Millar, H.R.	250-350	
Nesbit, Edith	Harding's Luck (1st AM, 12mo, green cl, 308p, 16pl)	Stokes	(1910)	Millar, H.R.	180-280	
Peacock, Thomas L.	Headlong Hall and Nightmare Abbey (1st, sm8vo, 243p, gilt, 40 fp b/w, pep)	L: Macmillan	1896	Millar, H.R.	40-65	
Nesbit, Edith	House of Arden (1st, 8vo, 349p, teg, red/gilt, 33 fp b/w)	L: T.F. Unwin	1908	Millar, H.R.	250-400	
Nesbit, Edith	House of Arden (1st AM, 12mo, 349p, gilt, 33 fp b/w)	Dutton	1909	Millar, H.R.	200-300	
Nesbit, Edith	Magic City (1st, 12mo, red/gilt, teg, 333p, 26pl)	L: Macmillan	1910	Millar, H.R.	300-450	
Nesbit, Edith	Magic World (1st, 12mo, teg, 280p, red/gilt, 24pl)	L: Macmillan	1912	Millar, H.R.	300-425	
Stevenson, Rbt. L.	Merry Men (1st, 8vo, 266p)	L: Macmillan	1928	Millar, H.R.	35-60	*
Kennedy, Howard A.	New World Fairy Book (1st, 8vo, 354p, gilt, teg, uncut, 9pl)	L: Dent	1904	Millar, H.R.	80-120	*
Molesworth, Mrs.	Peterkin (1st, sm8vo, 198p, orange/gilt, 8pl)	L: Macmillan	1902	Millar, H.R.	40-60	
Nesbit, Edith	Phoenix & the Carpet (1st, lg8vo, teg, blue/gilt, 321p, col frn, b/w)	L: Newnes	(1904)	Millar, H.R.	300-425	
Kipling, Rudyard	Puck of Pook's Hill (1st, 8vo, 306p, gilt, teg, 20pl)	L: Macmillan	1906	Millar, H.R.	200-300	
Various	Ruby Fairy Book (1st, 8vo, 281p, AEG, gilt, b/w)	L: Hutchinson	(1900)	Millar, H.R.	80-120	
Marryat, Frederick	Snarleyyow (1st, sm8vo, 405p, blue/gilt, AEG, fp b/w)	L: Macmillan	1897	Millar, H.R.	55-80	
Nesbit, Edith	Story of the Amulet (1st, 12mo, teg, 374p, red/gilt, 48pl)	L: T.F. Unwin	1906	Millar, H.R.	250-350	
Hugo, Victor	Story of the Bold Pecopin (1st, lg8vo, teg, 92p, gilt, 8pl, cep)	L: Smith Elder	1902	Millar, H.R.	65-90	
Haggard, H. Rider	The Brethren (1st AM, sm8vo, 411p, blue/gilt, 16pl)	McClure	1904	Millar, H.R.	80-130	
Harraden, Beatrice	Untold Tales of the Past (1st, 8vo, 273p, uncut, teg, gilt, b/w)	L: Blackwood	1897	Millar, H.R.	70-90	
Nesbit, Edith	Wet Magic (1st, 12mo, teg, red/gilt, 274p, 12pl)	L: T. Laurie	(1913)	Millar, H.R.	160-220	
Nesbit, Edith	Wonderful Garden (1st, 8vo, teg, 402p, red/gilt, 26 fp b/w)	L: Macmillan	1911	Millar, H.R.	200-300	
Nesbit, Edith	Five Children (1st, 8vo, 306p, col frn)	Coward	1930	Millar/Blam	60-100	
Shannon, Monica	California Fairy Tales (1st {std}, sm8vo, 298p, cp, pep)	Doubleday/Page	1926	Millard, C.E.	50-80	
Shannon, Monica	Eyes for the Dark (1st {std}, 8vo, 311p, 4cp, 15pl, pep)	Doubleday/Doran	1928	Millard, C.E.	35-60	
Retner, Beth	Tired Trolley Car (1st {std}, 8vo, 158p, green cl, 4cp, dep)	Doubleday/Page	1926	Millard, C.E.	25-45	
Clifton, Lucille	Black B C's (1st {std}, lg8vo, 45p, fp b/w, cep, DJ/3.95)	Dutton	(1970)	Miller, Don	60-90	*
Miller, Edna	Mousekin's Family (1st, lg8vo, [32]p, color, cep, DJ/4.95)	Prentice-Hall	(1969)	Miller, Edna	20-35	
Miller, Edna	Mouseskin's Woodland Sleepers (1st, 8vo, [32]p, color, cep, DJ/4.50)	Prentice-Hall	(1970)	Miller, Edna	20-30	
Ford, Ford Madox	Queen Who Flew (1st, 8vo, 82p, fp b/w, DJ/3.50)	NY: Braziller	(1965)	Miller, Grambs	25-40	
Sewell, Anna	Black Beauty (1st, 8vo, 96p, p-o, b/w)	Saalfield	(1905)	Miller, Harry L.	35-60	*
Raiker, Alice M.	Dulcibella & the Fairies (1st, 4to, green bds, 54p, p-o, 13cp)	L: C. Faulkner	[1919]	Miller, Hilda T.	200-300	
Saunders, Phyllis	Flame Flower (1st, lg8vo, purple cl, 127p, p-o, 4cp)	L: Butterworth	1922	Miller, Hilda T.	70-125	
De La Mare, Walter	Lucy (1st, 8vo, 40p, ipcb, p-o, b/w)	L: Blackwell	[1927]	Miller, Hilda T.	55-80	R*
Fyleman, Rose	Rose Fyleman Fairy Book (1st, 4to, 102p, blue/gilt, 16 ticp, pep)	L: Methuen	1923	Miller, Hilda T.	300-500	
Hall, Donald	Andrew the Lion Farmer (1st, sm4to, [60]p, color, DJ/2.95)	F. Watts	(1959)	Miller, Jane	50-80	
Wyndham, Lee	Dance for Susie (1st, 8vo, 55p, fp b/w, DJ/2.00)	Dodd	1953	Miller, Jane	20-30	
Hobson, Laura Z.	Dog of his Own (1st, ob8vo, ibds, [40]p, fp 2-color, DJ/1.00)	Viking	1941	Miller, Jane	30-50	*

AUTHOR	TITLE	PUBLISHER	DATE	ARTIST	PRICE	LC
Watts, Mabel	Henrietta & the Hat (1st, 4to, [40]p, ibds, 2-color, DJ/2.75)	Parents Mag. Pr.	(1962)	Miller, Jane	20-35	
Ciardi, John	Scrappy the Pup (1st {std}, 4to, unpag, 1-color, cep, DJ/3.00, NYTBI)	Lippincott	(1960)	Miller, Jane	50-80	
Simon, Norma	Wet World (1st [1st bk.], 8vo, [25]p, fp 1-color, pep, DJ/2.00, NYTBI)	Lippincott	(1954)	Miller, Jane	30-45	*
Brown, Margaret W.	Wonderful House (1st, sm8vo, [42]p, ibds, color, LGB/#76)	Simon/Schuster	1950	Miller, John P.	20-30	
Brown, Margaret W.	Wonderful Story (1st, 4to, ibds, 92p, color, pep, BGB)	Simon/Schuster	(1948)	Miller, John P.	60-90	
Sorensen, Virginia	Curious Missie (1st {std}, 8vo, 208p, b/w, DJ/2.75)	Harcourt	(1953)	Miller, Marilyn	30-50	
Sendak, Jack	Martze (1st, 8vo, 70p, b/w, DJ/3.50)	Farrar, Straus	(1968)	Miller, Mitchell	30-50	*
Lang, Leonora B.	Red Book of Heroes (1st, 8vo, 368p, red/gilt, AEG, 8cp)	L: Longmans	1909	Mills, A. Wallis	140-220	
Harris, Christie	Once Upon a Totem (1st {std}, 8vo, 148p, b/w woodcuts, DJ/3.50, NYTBI)	Atheneum	1963	Mills, John F.	25-45	
Milne-Home, M.P.	Mama's Black Nurse Stories (1st, 12mo, 131p, grey/gilt, 6 fp b/w)	L: Blackwood	1890	Milne-Home, M.P.	130-200	
Flanders, Michael	Creatures Great & Small (1st {std}, 8vo, 42p, color, DJ/3.50)	Holt, Rinehart	(1965)	Minale, Marcello	25-40	
Baker, Karle W.	Garden of the Plynck (1st, lg8vo, ibds, 112p, col frn, b/w)	Yale U. Press	(1920)	Minard, Florence	80-120	*
Nicholson, Meredith	Reversible Santa Claus (1st, sm8vo, blue cl, 176p, 4cp, dep)	Houghton	1917	Minard, Florence	30-50	
Smucker, Barbara	Wigwam in the City (1st {std}, 8vo, 154p, b/w, DJ)	Dutton	(1966)	Miret, Gil	25-40	*
Bible	Favorite Hymns for Children (1st, lg8vo, ibds, [38]p, color, DJ/0.50)	Grosset/Dunlap	(1942)	Miss Elliott	20-30	
Barrie, James M.	Peter Pan (1st, 8vo, 27p, color)	Grosset/Dunlap	1942	Miss Elliott	30-50	*
Bain, Robert N.	Cossack Fairy Tales & Folk Tales (1st, 8vo, 290p, teg, fp b/w)	L: Lawrence/Bul.	1894	Mitchell, E.W.	80-130	
Mitchell, Edith	Otherside Book (1st, 4to, ipcb, [36]p, color)	Reilly/Britton	(1915)	Mitchell, Edith	70-120	*
Mitchell, John A.	Romance of the Moon (1st, ob12mo, [32]p, gilt, 1-color, dep)	Henry Holt & Co.	1886	Mitchell, John A.	60-90	*
Ransome, Arthur	Old Peter's Russian Tales (1st, 8vo, 334p, 6cp, pep)	L: Jack	1916	Mitrokhin, Dmitri	100-165	
Ransome, Arthur	Old Peter's Russian Tales (1st {this pub}, 12mo, 334p, 7cp, DJ)	L: Nelson	[1938]	Mitrokhin, Dmitri	75-100	*
Zolotow, Charlotte	I Have a Horse of My Own (1st, ob8vo, [31]p, 2-color, cep, DJ/2.75)	Abelard-Schuman	1964	Mitsuhashi, Yoko	30-50	
Leister, Mary	Silent Concert (1st {std}, ob4to, [32]p, gilt, cep, color, DJ/5.95)	Bobbs-Merrill	(1970)	Mitsuhashi, Yoko	30-50	
Elkin, Benjamin	Such is the Way of the World (1st, sm4to, [40]p, color, dep, DJ/3.50)	Parents Mag. Pr.	(1968)	Mitsuhashi, Yoko	30-45	
Titus, Eve	Two Stonecutters (1st {std}, ob4to, [48]p, color, DJ/3.95)	Doubleday	(1967)	Mitsuhashi, Yoko	25-40	
Lifton, Betty	Joji and the Amanojaku (1st {std}, sm4to, [64]p, fp b/w, DJ/2.75)	Norton	(1965)	Mitsui, Eiichi	40-65	*
Lifton, Betty	Joji and the Dragon (1st, 4to, [64]p, fp b/w, DJ/2.50)	Wm. Morrow	1957	Mitsui, Eiichi	30-50	*
Lifton, Betty	Kap the Kappa (1st, sm4to, [64]p, b/w, DJ/2.75)	Wm. Morrow	1960	Mitsui, Eiichi	30-45	*
Lifton, Betty	Rice-Cake Rabbit (1st {std}, sm4to, [62]p, fp b/w, DJ/2.75)	Norton	(1966)	Mitsui, Eiichi	30-45	*
Ratel, Simonne	The Weathercock (1st AM, 8vo, 84p, color, DJ/1.75)	Appleton-Century	1939	Mittelman, Gertrude	20-35	
Plasmati, Valdine	Algernon and the Pigeons (1st, 4to, 37p, fp 1-color, DJ/2.50)	Viking	(1963)	Mizumura, Kazue	25-35	
Gray, Eliz. J.	Cheerful Heart (1st, 8vo, 176p, b/w, dep, DJ/2.75)	Viking	(1959)	Mizumura, Kazue	40-65	
Matsuno, Masako	Chie and the Sports Day (1st AM {std}, ob8vo, [28]p, color, DJ/3.00)	World	(1965)	Mizumura, Kazue	70-100	
Mizumura, Kazue	Emperor Penguins (1st, sq8vo, 35p, color, DJ/3.50)	Crowell	(1969)	Mizumura, Kazue	50-85	
Hawes, Judy	Fireflies in the Night (1st, ob8vo, [38]p, 3-color, DJ/2.50)	Crowell	(1963)	Mizumura, Kazue	25-40	
Uchida, Yoshiko	Forever Christmas Tree (1st, lg8vo, gilt, [46]p, fp 1-color, DJ/2.95)	Scribner	(1963)	Mizumura, Kazue	40-65	
Martin, Patricia	Greedy One (1st {A}, 8vo, 64p, color, DJ/2.95)	Rand/McNally	(1964)	Mizumura, Kazue	25-40	
Mizumura, Kazue	I See the Winds (1st, sm ob8vo, 35p, fp color, DJ)	Crowell	(1966)	Mizumura, Kazue	45-70	
Mizumura, Kazue	If I Were a Mother (1st, 4to, [32]p, color, DJ/3.95)	Crowell	(1968)	Mizumura, Kazue	45-70	
Gans, Roma	It's Nesting Time (1st, ob8vo, [40]p, color, DJ/2.75)	Crowell	(1964)	Mizumura, Kazue	30-50	
Freschet, Berniece	Jumping Mouse (1st, 8vo, [48]p, b/w, DJ/3.95)	Crowell	(1970)	Mizumura, Kazue	30-50	*
Lewis, Janet	Keiko's Bubble (1st {std}, lg8vo, 62p, b/w, DJ/2.50)	Doubleday	1961	Mizumura, Kazue	40-65	
George, Jean C.	Moon of the Winter Bird (1st, 8vo, 38p, b/w, DJ/3.75)	Crowell	(1969)	Mizumura, Kazue	25-35	*
Fisher, Aileen	My Mother and I (1st, sm4to, [32]p, fp color, DJ/3.95)	Crowell	(1967)	Mizumura, Kazue	25-40	
Matsuno, Masako	Pair of Red Clogs (1st {std}, lg ob8vo, [28]p, color, DJ/3.00)	World	(1960)	Mizumura, Kazue	80-125	
Serage, Nancy	Prince Who Gave up a Throne (1st, 8vo, 62p, fp b/w, DJ/3.50)	Crowell	(1966)	Mizumura, Kazue	30-50	
Uchida, Yoshiko	Sumi & the Goat and the Tokyo Express (1st, 8vo, [48]p, color, DJ/3.95)	Scribner	(1969)	Mizumura, Kazue	30-50	
Uchida, Yoshiko	Sumi's Prize (1st, lg8vo, [48]p, 1-color, DJ/3.25)	Scribner	(1964)	Mizumura, Kazue	30-50	
Uchida, Yoshiko	Sumi's Special Happening (1st, lg8vo, [46]p, fp color, DJ/3.50)	Scribner	(1966)	Mizumura, Kazue	30-50	
Martin, Patricia	Suzu and the Bride Doll (1st {A}, 8vo, [48]p, color, pep, DJ/2.75)	Rand/McNally	1960	Mizumura, Kazue	30-50	
Matsuno, Masako	Taro and the Tofu (1st AM {std}, sm4to, [26]p, fp color, DJ/3.00)	World	(1962)	Mizumura, Kazue	70-120	*
Stamm, Claus	Three Strong Women (1st, 8vo, 47p, fp 1-color, dep, DJ/2.50)	Viking	(1962)	Mizumura, Kazue	60-100	R
Stamm, Claus	Very Special Badgers (1st, ob4to, 40p, fp b/w, pep, DJ/2.25)	Viking	(1960)	Mizumura, Kazue	30-50	
Mizumura, Kazue	Way of an Ant (1st, narrow 4to, [34]p, fp color, DJ/3.95)	Crowell	(1970)	Mizumura, Kazue	30-45	
Smith, Richard G.	Ancient Tales & Folklore of Japan (1st, 8vo, gilt, teg, 361p, 62cp)	L: A&C Black	1908	Mo-No-Yuki	250-400	
Neville, Emily C.	Traveler from a Small Kingdom (1st, 8vo, 197p, b/w, DJ/3.50)	Harper	(1968)	Mocniak, George	20-35	
Allen, Phil S.	Begging Bear (1st, lg ob4to, 60p, p-o, 20cp)	Reilly/Lee	(1932)	Moe, Louis M.	100-165	
Moe, Louis M.	Kylle Kluk (1st AM, ob4to, [24]p, orange cl, 11 fp color)	NY: Laidlaw	[1931]	Moe, Louis M.	130-225	*
Moe, Louis M.	Peter Kroak (1st AM, ob4to, [17]p, p-o, 8 fp color, cep)	Whitman	1932	Moe, Louis M.	150-220	*
Moe, Louis M.	Vain Pussy Cat (1st, sm ob4to, ipcb, [32]p, b/w, pep)	Coward	(1929)	Moe, Louis M.	125-200	*
Moeschlin, Elsa	Little Boy with Big Apples (1st AM, 4to, ibds, [23]p, color)	Coward	[1932]	Moeschlin, Elsa	90-140	
Moeschlin, Elsa	Red Horse (1st AM, sm4to, ibds, 19p, color, cep, DJ/1.75)	Coward	[1929]	Moeschlin, Elsa	80-120	
Elting, Mary	Hopi Way (1st {std}, lg8vo, 63p, fp 1-color, DJ/3.95)	Lippincott	(1969)	Mofsie, Louis	25-45	*
Manzi, Alberto	White Boy (1st {std}, 8vo, 202p, fp b/w, DJ/3.95)	Macmillan	1963	Molina, Charles	25-40	*
Rasmussen, K.	People of the Frozen North (1st UK, 4to, 358p, 12cp)	L: Trubner	1908	Moltke, H.	120-180	
Stapp, Emilie B.	Bread & Lasses (1st, 8vo, tan cl, 94p, 6pl)	(DeMoines)	1902	Monahan, P.J.	30-60	
England, George A.	Darkness and Dawn (1st, sm8vo, 672p, col frn, 4pl, pep)	Small/Maynard	(1914)	Monahan, P.J.	150-220	*
England, George A.	Flying Legion (1st, 8vo, 394p, frn by...)	McClurg	1920	Monahan, P.J.	60-90	*
London, Jack	Smoke Bellew (1st, 8vo, blue cl, 385p, 8pl)	Century	1912	Monahan, P.J.	250-350	
Van Dyke, Henry	Story of the Other Wise Man (8vo, gold cl, 87p, designs by...)	Harper	(1907)	Monetti, E.	80-120	
Herbertson, Agnes	Busy Broom (1st, 4to, unpag, color)	L: Cassell	[1910]	Monsell, J.R.	75-100	
Darwin, Bernard	Elves & Princes (1st, 8vo, 199p, 6cp)	L: Duckworth	[1913]	Monsell, J.R.	130-200	*
Grimm Bros.	Fairy Tales (1st, 8vo, 336p, 16cp)	L: Cassell	1908	Monsell, J.R.	100-160	*
Monsell, J.R.	Hooded Crow (1st, 8vo, [48]p, yellow cl, 1-color)	L: Blackwell	[1926]	Monsell, J.R.	70-100	*
N/A	Jingle Book (1st, sm ob8vo, ibds, color)	L: Nister	(1905)	Monsell, J.R.	40-65	
Mackenzie, Compton	Kensington Rhymes (1st, sm4to, pcb, gilt, 87p, uncut, 9cp)	L: M. Secker	1912	Monsell, J.R.	100-165	
Monsell, J.R.	Pink Knight (1st, 16mo, 95p, 24cp)	L: Richards	1901	Monsell, J.R.	150-225	
Thackeray, Wm. M.	Rose & the Ring (1st, sq8vo, 128p, gilt, teg, 12 ticp, pep)	L: Kegan Paul	1911	Monsell, J.R.	120-185	

ARTIST: 140

AUTHOR	TITLE	PUBLISHER	DATE	ARTIST	PRICE	LC
Thackeray, Wm. M.	Rose & the Ring (1st AM, 4to, red/gilt, 128p, 12 ticp, pep)	Crowell	[1911]	Monsell, J.R.	100-160	
De La Mare, Walter	Three Mulla Mulgars (1st, 8vo, teg, green/gilt, 312p, 2cp)	L: Duckworth	1910	Monsell, J.R.	200-300	
Williams, Orlando	Three Naughty Children (1st, lg8vo, 110p, fp 2-color)	L: Duckworth	1922	Monsell, J.R.	60-90	*
Housman, Laurence	What-O'Clock Tales (1st, 8vo, 225p, 14 fp b/w)	L: Blackwell	(1932)	Monsell, J.R.	70-100	
Montresor, Beni	A for Angel: Beni Montresor's ABC... (1st, ob4to, [39]p, 3-color, cep, DJ)	Knopf	(1969)	Montresor, Beni	50-85	
Stolz, Mary S.	Belling the Tiger (1st, 8vo, 64p, fp b/w, DJ/2.50, NH)	Harper	(1961)	Montresor, Beni	40-65	
N/A	Cinderella (1st, sm ob4to, unpag, fp color, DJ/3.50)	Knopf	(1965)	Montresor, Beni	80-130	
Rossini, Gioacchino	Cinderella: From the Opera (1st, ob4to, [32]p, fp color, DJ/3.50)	Knopf	(1965)	Montresor, Beni	40-65	R
Stolz, Mary S.	Great Rebellion (1st, 8vo, 63p, fp b/w, DJ/2.50)	Harper	(1961)	Montresor, Beni	30-50	R
Montresor, Beni	House of Flowers, House of Stars (1st {std} 4to, [40]p color, cep, DJ/3.50)	Knopf	(1962)	Montresor, Beni	50-85	
Montresor, Beni	I Saw a Ship A-Sailing (1st, 4to, [38]p, fp 2-color, cep, DJ/3.95)	Knopf	1967	Montresor, Beni	60-90	
Menotti, Gian-Carlo	Last Savage (1st, lg4to, 45p, dp color, b/w, cep, DJ/5.95)	NY Graphic Soc.	(1964)	Montresor, Beni	45-70	
Spender, Stephen	Magic Flute (1st, sm ob4to, [44]p, fp color, cep, DJ/3.95, NYTBI)	Putnam	(1966)	Montresor, Beni	60-90	
DeRegniers, Beatrice	May I Bring a Friend? (1st {std}, lg8vo, [46]p, color, DJ/3.50, CM)	Atheneum	1964	Montresor, Beni	70-120	
Merriam, Eve	Mommies at Work (1st, 4to, [38]p, color, cep, DJ/3.00)	Knopf	(1961)	Montresor, Beni	50-80	R
Mincieli, Rose	Old Neapolitan Fairy Tales (1st, 4to, 123p, fp b/w, gilt, cep, DJ/3.25)	Knopf	(1963)	Montresor, Beni	40-65	
Brown, Margaret W.	On Christmas Eve (1st, 4to, [48]p, color, DJ/3.50)	W.R. Scott	(1961)	Montresor, Beni	120-200	
Johnson, Sally (ed)	Princesses: 16 Stories about Princesses (1st, 8vo 318p, b/w, DJ/4.95, NYTBI)	Harper	(1962)	Montresor, Beni	60-90	*
Stolz, Mary S.	Siri the Conquistador (1st {std}, 8vo, 57p, b/w, DJ/2.50)	Harper	(1963)	Montresor, Beni	25-45	*
Garelick, May	Sounds of a Summer Night (1st, ob8vo, [32]p, 2-color, DJ/3.25)	Young Scott	(1963)	Montresor, Beni	30-45	
DeRegniers, Beatrice	Willy O'Dwyer Jumped in the Fire (1st {std}, 4to, [39]p, col, cep, DJ/4.50)	Atheneum	1968	Montresor, Beni	30-45	
Montresor, Beni	Witches of Venice (1st, 4to, [40]p, 1-color, DJ/3.25)	Knopf	(1963)	Montresor, Beni	50-80	
Moon, Grace P.	Arrow of Tee-May (1st {std}, 8vo, 284p, col frn, b/w, pep)	Doubleday/Doran	1931	Moon, Carl	50-80	
Moon, Grace P.	Book of Nah-Wee (1st {std}, sm sq4to, 59p, ibds, color, pep)	Doubleday/Doran	1932	Moon, Carl	50-80	
Moon, Grace P.	Chi-Wee (1st {std}, 8vo, uncut, 239p, col frn, fp b/w, pep)	Doubleday/Page	1925	Moon, Carl	30-50	
Moon, Grace P.	Chi-Wee and Loki (1st {std}, 8vo, 208p, tan cl, col frn, 18pl)	Doubleday/Page	1926	Moon, Carl	50-80	
Moon, Grace P.	Daughter of Thunder (1st, sm8vo, 184p, col frn, pep, DJ/2.00)	Macmillan	1942	Moon, Carl	50-80	
Moon, Grace P.	Far-Away Desert (1st {std}, sm8vo, 261p, color, pep)	Doubleday/Doran	1932	Moon, Carl	40-65	
Moon, Grace P.	Indian Legends in Rhyme (1st, sm4to, p-o, 54p, 5cp)	Stokes	(1917)	Moon, Carl	70-125	
Moon, Grace P.	Lost Indian Magic (1st, sm8vo, 301p, p-o, 8cp, pep)	Stokes	(1918)	Moon, Carl	80-125	
Moon, Grace P.	Magic Trail (1st {std}, sm8vo, 234p, col frn, 13pl, pep)	Doubleday/Doran	1929	Moon, Carl	50-80	
Moon, Grace P.	Missing Katchina (1st {std}, 8vo, 286p, col frn, b/w, pep)	Doubleday/Doran	1930	Moon, Carl	40-65	
Moon, Grace P.	Nadita (1st {std}, 8vo, 274p, col frn, 16pl, pep)	Doubleday/Doran	1927	Moon, Carl	45-70	
Moon, Grace P.	One Little Indian (1st, lg8vo, [32]p, p-o, fp color, pep, DJ/2.00)	Whitman	1950	Moon, Carl	45-70	
Moon, Carl	Painted Moccasin (1st, 8vo, 318p, green/gilt, col frn, pep)	Stokes	1931	Moon, Carl	70-120	
Moon, Grace P.	Runaway Papoose (1st {std}, 8vo, 264p, col frn, b/w, pep, NH)	Doubleday/Doran	1928	Moon, Carl	40-60	
Moon, Grace P.	Shanty Ann (1st, 8vo, 200p, col frn, DJ/2.00)	Stokes	1935	Moon, Carl	45-70	
Moon, Grace P.	Singing Sands (1st {std}, 8vo, 245p, col frn, b/w, pep, DJ/2.00)	Doubleday/Doran	1936	Moon, Carl	40-65	
Moon, Grace P.	Solita (1st {std}, 8vo, tan cl, 241p, col frn, b/w, pep, DJ/2.00)	Doubleday/Doran	1938	Moon, Carl	60-90	
Moon, Grace P.	Tita of Mexico (1st, sm8vo, 213p, col frn, 4pl, pep)	Stokes	1934	Moon, Carl	40-65	
Moon, Grace P.	White Indian (1st {std}, sm8vo, 221p, col frn, b/w, pep, DJ/2.00)	Doubleday/Doran	1937	Moon, Carl	45-70	
Moon, Grace P.	Wongo & the Wise Old Crow (1st, 8vo, 188p, pep, gilt, col frn)	Reilly/Lee	(1923)	Moon, Carl	50-80	
Grahame, Kenneth	Golden Age (1st, sm4to, gilt, 243p, uncut, 19cp)	L: John Lane	1914	Moony, R.J.E.	100-150	
Bannerman, Helen	Little Black Sambo (1st, lg8vo, ibds, [22]p, color, pep)	Grosset/Dunlap	(1942)	Moore, Robert	200-300	
Gilby/Cuming	George Moorland... (1st, 8vo, 290p, teg, 50cp)	L: A&C Black	1907	Moorland, George	80-120	
Kahmann, Chesley	Sinfi and Little Gypsy Goat (1st {std}, sm4to, 70p, color, pep, DJ/1.50)	Random	(1940)	Mora, F. Luis	50-80	*
Kahmann, Chesley	Tara, Daughter of the Gypsies (1st {std}, 8vo, 288p, b/w, DJ/2.00)	Smith/Haas	1935	Mora, F. Luis	50-80	
Sawyer, Ruth	Tono Antonio (1st, 8vo, 132p, red/gilt, 8 fp b/w, pep)	Viking	1934	Mora, F. Luis	30-50	*
Aesopus	Animals of Aesop (1st, lg8vo, 210p, color)	Dana Estes	1900	Mora, Joseph J.	75-100	*
Andersen, Hans C.	Fairy Tales (1st, lg8vo, 188p, 24pl)	Dana Estes	(1902)	Mora, Joseph J.	180-250	
Quigg, Jane	Looking for Lucky (1st, 8vo, ibds, 29p, 2-color, pep, DJ/1.00)	Howell/Soskin	1946	Moran, Connie	40-70	*
Tucker, Elizabeth S.	Children of Colonial Days (1st, lg4to, ibds, [74]p, 12cp)	Stokes	1894	Moran, E. Percy	180-270	*
Tucker, Elizabeth S.	Rhymes & Stories of Olden Times (1st, lg4to, ibds, [26]p, 6cp)	Stokes	1894	Moran, E. Percy	140-225	*
Boylan, Grace D.	Kids of Many Colors (1st, 8vo, tan cl, 156p, color)	Chi: Jamieson	(1901)	Morgan, Ike	120-200	
N/A	Night Before Christmas & Jingles (sq8vo, 48p, p-o, 12cp by...)	Hurst	(1908)	Morgan, Ike	130-200	*
Reed, Myrtle	Pickaback Songs (1st, 4to, [70]p, ibds, pep, color)	Putnam	1903	Morgan, Ike	350-500	
Boylan, Grace D.	Steps to Nowhere (1st, lg8vo, 230p, p-o, blue cl, 8cp)	Baker/Taylor	1910	Morgan, Ike	120-180	
Baum, L. Frank	Woggle-Bug Book (1st, folio, [48]p, wraps, color)	Reilly/Britton	1905	Morgan, Ike	2000-3000	R
Boylan, Grace D.	Young Folks Uncle Tom's Cabin (1st, 8vo, ipcb, 166p, 16 fp b/w)	Jamieson-Higgins	1901	Morgan, Ike	200-300	*
Wells, Carolyn	Folly in Fairyland (1st, 12mo, 261p, 12pl)	Altemus	(1901)	Morgan, Wallace	60-90	
Molesworth, Mrs.	Lucky Ducks (1st, 8vo, 96p, blue/gilt, color, pep)	L: SPCK	[1891]	Morgan, Walter J.	40-70	*
N/A	Nursery Rhymes & Fables (8vo, ibds, 64p, fp color)	L: SPCK	[1910]	Morgan, Walter J.	100-165	
Bischoff, Julia B.	Dog for David (1st, 8vo, 110p, b/w, DJ)	W.R. Scott	(1966)	Moriarty, Jerome	20-30	*
Stephens, Charles A.	Grandfather's Broadaxe (1st, 8vo, 222p, b/w, DJ/3.95)	W.R. Scott	(1967)	Moriarty, Jerome	25-45	
Gerber, Will	Gooseberry Jones (1st, 8vo, 96p, b/w, DJ/2.00)	Putnam	(1947)	Morris, Dudley	45-70	
Morris, M.	Reign of William and Mary (ob4to, ibds, p-o, 8cp)	Nister/Dutton	[1908]	Morris, M.	280-350	
Haggard, H. Rider	Ancient Allan (1st, sm8vo, 310p, tan/gilt, 8pl)	L: Cassell	1920	Morrow, Albert	150-250	
Jackson, Jacqueline	Chicken Ten Thousand (1st {std}, lg ob8vo, 31p, color, DJ/3.95)	Little/Brown	(1968)	Morrow, Barbara	30-50	*
Church, Alfred J.	Heroes of Chivalry and Romance (1st, sm8vo, 342p, 8cp)	L: Seeley	1898	Morrow, George	50-80	*
Dickson, George S.	Nursery Geography (1st, 8vo, 256p, white cl, 20cp, pep)	L: Jack	[1915]	Morrow, George	60-100	
Evans, F. Gwynne	Puffin, Puma & Co. (1st, sm4to, ipcb, 96p, b/w)	L: Macmillan	1929	Morrow, George	70-100	
Weil, Ann Y.	Eleanor Roosevelt: Courageous Girl (1st, sm8vo, 200p, fp b/w, DJ/2.25)	Bobbs-Merrill	(1965)	Morrow, Gray	25-35	
Means, Florence C.	Borrowed Brother (1st, 8vo, blue cl, 239p, b/w, DJ/3.00)	Houghton	1958	Morse, Dorothy B.	30-50	
Hall, Anna G.	Cyrus Holt and the Civil War (1st, 8vo, 128p, b/w, DJ/3.00)	Viking	(1964)	Morse, Dorothy B.	20-30	
Caudill, Rebecca	Tree of Freedom (1st, 8vo, 279p, green cl, pep, DJ/2.50, NH)	Viking	1949	Morse, Dorothy B.	50-80	
Marshall, Dean	Wish on the Moon (1st {std}, 8vo, 192p, b/w, DJ/2.50)	Dutton	1951	Morse, Dorothy B.	200-300	
Morse, Livingston B.	Road to Nowhere (1st, 12mo, 236p, color)	Harper	1900	Morse, Edna	55-80	*
Sandburg, Helga	Bo & the Old Donkey (1st {std}, sm4to, unpag, 2-color, DJ/3.50)	Dial Press	(1965)	Morton, Marian	25-45	

AUTHOR	TITLE	PUBLISHER	DATE	ARTIST	PRICE	LC
Bourne, Miriam	Raccoons are for Loving (1st, ob4to, 44p, fp 3-color, cep, DJ/3.95)	Random	(1968)	Morton, Marian	30-50	
Carroll, Lewis	Alice... & Through... (1st, 8vo, yellow cl, 317p, col frn, 8pl)	L: Clowes	[1935]	Morton-Sale, J.	40-60	*
Farjeon, Eleanor	Cherrystones (1st AM {std}, 12mo, red/gilt, 58p, fp b/w, DJ/1.25)	Lippincott	(1944)	Morton-Sale, J.	30-45	
Farjeon, Eleanor	Martin Pippin in the Daisy-Field (1st AM {std} 8vo, 320p, col frn, DJ/2.50)	Stokes	1938	Morton-Sale, J.	80-125	
Griggs, Mary	Yellow Cat (1st, 8vo, 110p, yellow cl, 6 doub pg cp)	L: H. Milford	(1936)	Morton-Sale, J.	65-90	
Bailey, Temple	Star in the Well (1st, sm8vo, 46p, wraps, color decor by...)	Volland	(1928)	Moschcowitz, P.	55-80	*
Harris, Joel C.	Wally Wanderoon... (1st, lg8vo, tan cl, 294p, 31pl)	McClure	1903	Moseley, Karl	180-250	
Felton, Harold	Bowleg Bill: Seagoing Cowpuncher (1st, 8vo, 174p, 2-color, DJ/2.95)	Prentice-Hall	1957	Moyers, William	30-50	
Mason, Miriam E.	Broomtail - Brother of Lightning (1st {std}, 8vo, 135p, b/w, DJ/2.00)	Macmillan	1952	Moyers, William	50-80	
Montgomery, R.	Claim Jumpers of Marble Canyon (1st {std}, 8vo, 179p, b/w, DJ/2.50)	Knopf	1956	Moyers, William	20-30	
Warren, Robert P.	Gods of Mount Olympus (1st {std}, 8vo, 52p, fp 1-color, pep, DJ/1.50)	Random	(1959)	Moyers, William	80-130	R
Felton, Harold	New Tall Tales of Pecos Bill (1st, 8vo, 164p, fp 1-color, DJ/2.95)	Prentice-Hall	(1958)	Moyers, William	30-50	
Bialk, Elisa	Taffy's Foal (1st, lg8vo, 179p, beige cl, b/w, DJ/2.25)	Houghton	1949	Moyers, William	45-70	
Malkus, Alida S.	Young Inca Prince (1st {std}, 8vo, 246p, b/w, pep, DJ/3.00)	Knopf	1957	Moyers, William	25-40	
Allen, Merritt	Blow, Bugles, Blow (1st {std}, 8vo, 217p, uncut, DJ/3.00, b/w decor by...)	Longmans	1956	Moyler, Alan	20-35	
Smith, Agnes	Edge of the Forest (1st, 8vo, 192p, DJ/3.00, b/w decor by...)	Viking	(1959)	Moynihan, Roberta	60-90	
Collodi, Carlo	Adventures of Pinocchio (1st, 8vo, 224p, fp color, pep, DJ/2.95)	F. Watts	(1959)	Mozley, Charles	20-30	
France, Anatole	CLIO (1st, sm8vo, 189p, teg, 12 chromos)	Paris: Calmann	1900	Mucha, Alphonse	500-700	
Blackmore, R.D.	Fringilla (1st, 8vo, uncut, 128p, 8pl)	L: E. Mathews	1895	Muckley, Louis F.	300-450	
Cooke, Grace M.	Gourd Fiddle (1st, 12mo, 118p, red cl, 1-color)	Altemus	1904	Mudge/Miles	40-60	
Wyss, Johann D.	Swiss Family Robinson (lg4to, 96p, ibds, col frn, b/w)	Saalfield	(1940)	Muheim, Henry	30-60	*
Schultz, James W.	Gold Dust (1st, 8vo, 243p, b/w, DJ/2.00)	Houghton	1934	Mulford, Stockton	40-60	
Porter, Eleanor	Pollyanna (1st, sm8vo, 310p, pink/gilt, 8pl, PPP)	L.C. Page	1913	Mulford, Stockton	300-500	
Porter, Eleanor	Pollyanna (1st UK, sm8vo, blue/gilt, p-o, 310p, 8pl)	L: I. Pitman	1913	Mulford, Stockton	100-165	
Lamb, Charles	Tales from Shakespeare (1st, lg8vo, 242p, ipcb, gilt, 16 ticp)	L: Rbt. Scott	1915	Mulliner, May	100-150	
Munari, Bruno	Birthday Present (1st AM, lg4to, unpag, ibds, color, DJ/2.00)	World	(1959)	Munari, Bruno	80-125	
Munari, Bruno	Bruno Munari's ABC (1st AM {std}, lg4to, [48]p, color, DJ/3.50, NYTBI)	World	(1960)	Munari, Bruno	100-175	
Munari, Bruno	Bruno Munari's Zoo (1st AM {std}, 4to, ibds, unpag, color, DJ/3.50)	World	(1963)	Munari, Bruno	75-125	
Munari, Bruno	Circus in the Mist (1st AM {std}, sq8vo, ibds, [57]p, color, DJ/4.50, NYT)	World	(1969)	Munari, Bruno	70-120	
Munari, Bruno	Jimmy has Lost his Cap, Where Can it Be? (1st AM lg4to unpag col, DJ/2.00)	World	(1959)	Munari, Bruno	70-100	
Munari, Bruno	Tic, Tac, and Toc (1st AM, folio, ibds, unpag, DJ/2.00)	World	(1957)	Munari, Bruno	75-125	
Munari, Bruno	Who's There? Open the Door! (1st AM, folio, ibds, unpag, color, DJ/2.00)	World	(1957)	Munari, Bruno	70-120	
Sawyer, Ruth	Primrose Ring (1st, 12mo, 186p, 6pl)	Harper	(1915)	Munsell, Fanny	40-65	
Lexau, Joan M.	Archimedes Takes a Bath (1st, 8vo, 56p, b/w, DJ/3.50)	Crowell	(1969)	Murdocca, Salvatore	30-45	
Collodi, Carlo	Adventures of Pinocchio (1st AM, lg4to, 404p, cp, DJ)	Macmillan	(1925)	Mussino, Attilio	250-400	
Nesbit, Wilbur D.	Friend O'Mine (1st, 12mo, ipcb, [12]p, color)	Volland	(1912)	Myers, Marie H.	45-80	*
Nesbit, Wilbur D.	Just Because of You (1st, 12mo, ibds, color)	Volland	(1925)	Myers, Marie H.	40-60	*
Bailey, Alice C.	Skating Gander (1st, 8vo, ibds, 93p, color, pep)	Volland	(1927)	Myers, Marie H.	60-90	
Myller, Rolf	Rolling Round (1st {std}, 8vo, [34]p, 1-color, DJ/2.95)	Atheneum	1963	Myller, Rolf	25-40	
Hall, Conrad	Story of a Little Colored Coon (1st, 8vo, 125p, red cl, color)	L: Hodder	(1902)	Myrtle/Rigby	500-800	
Wilde, Oscar	Fisherman & his Soul (1st, lg8vo, 212p, gilt, 15 ticp, pep)	Farrar/Rinehart	(1929)	Nadejen, Theodore	120-185	
Zeitlin, Ida	Gessar-Khan (1st, sm4to, 203p, gilt, 18 fp color, pep)	Doran	(1927)	Nadejen, Theodore	50-85	
Zeitlin, Ida	King's Pleasure (1st {std}, lg8vo, 230p, blue/gilt, 17cp, cep)	Harper	1929	Nadejen, Theodore	60-90	
Adams, Julia D.	Mountains are Free (1st {std}, 8vo, gilt, 250p, 10pl, NH)	Dutton	(1930)	Nadejen, Theodore	60-90	*
Mirza, Youel B.	Myself when Young (1st {std}, 8vo, 260p, col frn)	Doubleday/Doran	1929	Nadejen, Theodore	40-65	
Zeitlin, Ida	Skazki (1st, 4to, 335p, black/gilt, teg, pep, 24 ticp)	Doran	(1926)	Nadejen, Theodore	70-100	
De La Mare, Walter	Stories from the Bible (1st AM, lg8vo, gilt, 393p, pep, 9cp)	Cosmopolitan	1929	Nadejen, Theodore	55-80	*
Hughes, Ted	Iron Giant (1st, 8vo, 56p, blue ipcb, fp b/w, DJ/2.95)	Harper	(1968)	Nadler, Robert	250-450	R
O'Neill, Mary	Take a Number (1st {std}, lg8vo, 63p, fp 3-color, cep, DJ/3.95)	Doubleday	(1968)	Nagy, Al	30-50	R
Ryder, Arthur	Twenty-Two Goblins (1st, 8vo, 220p, 20cp)	L: Dent	1917	Nahl, Perham	70-100	*
Nakano, Hirotaka	Elephant Blue (1st AM, 4to, 31p, color, cep, DJ/4.50)	Bobbs-Merrill	(1970)	Nakano, Hirotaka	40-65	*
Daudet, Alphonse	Brave Little Goat of Monsieur Seguin (1st AM, 4to, [32]p, color, DJ/3.95)	World	(1968)	Nakatani, Chiyoko	60-80	R*
Nakatani, Chiyoko	Day Chiro Was Lost (1st AM, ob4to, ipcb, 29p, fp color, cep, DJ/3.75)	World	(1969)	Nakatani, Chiyoko	30-50	*
Nakatani, Chiyoko	Fumio and the Dolphins (1st AM {std}, 4to, [42]p, color, DJ/4.95)	World	1970	Nakatani, Chiyoko	30-50	
Jarrell, Randall	Golden Bird (1st AM, folio, 50p, ibds, color, DJ/1.95)	Macmillan	1962	Nardini, Sandro	35-50	*
Andersen, Hans C.	Thumbelina (1st, 4to, 42p, ibds, color, DJ/1.95)	Macmillan	1962	Nardini/Fontana	45-70	
Nash, Ogden	Christmas that Almost Wasn't (1st {std}, lg8vo, 63p, 8 fp color, DJ/3.50)	Little/Brown	(1957)	Nash, Linell	50-80	
Drinkwater, John	Cotswold Characters (1st, 12mo, bds, p-o, 54p, 5 woodcuts)	Yale U. Press	1921	Nash, Paul	160-240	R
Nash, Dorothy	Moon Baby (1st, 4to, ibds, p-o, 87p, 9 ticp)	L: Jarrold	[1917]	Nash/Rudge	120-180	*
Frost, Robert	You Come Too (1st {std}, 8vo, 94p, wood engravings, DJ/3.00)	Holt	(1959)	Nason, Thomas	70-120	R
Nast, Thomas	Christmas Drawings for the Human Race (1st, 4to, [67]p, fp b/w)	Harper	1890	Nast, Thomas	450-600	
Irving, Washington	Rip Van Winkle (sq4to, [11]p, wraps, 6 chromos)	McLoughlin	[1880]	Nast, Thomas	250-400	
Webster, George	Santa Claus & his Works (4to, wraps, 6 chromos)	McLoughlin	1897	Nast, Thomas	220-350	
N/A	Yankee Doodle (4to, wraps, 6 chromos by...)	McLoughlin	[1880]	Nast, Thomas	250-400	
Brown, Marjorie	Pueblo Playmates (1st, 8vo, 61p, color, pep, DJ/1.50)	Whitman	1938	Nay, Carol	30-50	
Nay, Carol	Timmy Rides the China Clipper (1st, 8vo, 94p, p-o, color, pep)	Whitman	1939	Nay, Carol	20-30	
Dimmick, Ruth C.	Bogie Man (1st, lg8vo, ibds, [71]p, fp b/w)	Winston	(1906)	Neale, Marguerite	80-130	
Hawkins, Quail	Androcles & the Lion (1st, ob4to, 48p, 3-color, DJ/4.50)	Coward	(1970)	Negri, Rocco	40-65	
Holladay, Virginia	Bantu Tales (1st {std}, 8vo, 95p, fp b/w, DJ/3.95)	Viking	(1970)	Negri, Rocco	45-70	*
Steele, Mary Q.	Journey Outside (1st, lg8vo, 143p, brown cl, dp b/w, DJ/4.50, NH)	Viking	(1969)	Negri, Rocco	30-50	
Monjo, Ferdinand N.	One Bad Thing About Father (1st, 8vo, ibds, 62p, fp 2-color, DJ/2.50)	Harper	(1970)	Negri, Rocco	25-40	
Byars, Betsy C.	Trouble River (1st, 8vo, 158p, dp fp b/w, DJ/4.50)	Viking	(1969)	Negri, Rocco	40-65	*
Craik, Dinah	Adventures of a Brownie (1st, 16mo, 57p, p-o, fp color)	Reilly/Britton	(1908)	Neill, John R.	70-100	
Sewell, Anna	Black Beauty (sm8vo, red cl, 58p, p-o, color)	Reilly/Britton	1908	Neill, John R.	70-100	
Thompson, Ruth P.	Captain Salt in Oz (1st, lg8vo, 306p, blue cl, p-o, b/w, pep, DJ/1.50)	Reilly/Lee	(1936)	Neill, John R.	400-650	
Stone, Mary	Children's Stories that Never Grow Old (1st, 12mo, 312p, yellow cl, color)	Reilly/Britton	(1908)	Neill, John R.	100-165	
Dickens, Charles	Christmas Carol (12mo, ipcb, p-o, color)	Reilly/Britton	1915	Neill, John R.	60-100	
N/A	Cinderella (1st, 8vo, p-o, 57p, color, pep)	Reilly/Britton	(1908)	Neill, John R.	80-140	

AUTHOR	TITLE	PUBLISHER	DATE	ARTIST	PRICE	LC
Douglas, Amanda M.	Clover's Princess (1st, 12mo, p-o, 95p, blue/gilt, 6pl)	Altemus	(1904)	Neill, John R.	60-90	R
Thompson, Ruth P.	Cowardly Lion of Oz (1st [1], lg8vo, 291p, p-o, pep, 12cp)	Reilly/Lee	(1923)	Neill, John R.	400-600	
Thompson, Ruth P.	Curious Cruise of Captain Santa (1st, lg8vo, 124p, p-o, color)	Reilly/Lee	(1926)	Neill, John R.	300-500	
Baum, L. Frank	Dorothy and the Wizard of Oz (1st [1], lg8vo, p-o, 256p, pep, 16cp)	Reilly/Britton	(1908)	Neill, John R.	700-900	
Baum, L. Frank	Emerald City of Oz (1st [1], lg8vo, 296p, p-o, 16cp, pep)	Reilly/Britton	(1910)	Neill, John R.	750-900	R
James, Hartwell	Enchanted Castle (1st, 12mo, 123p, b/w)	Altemus	(1906)	Neill, John R.	50-75	*
Longfellow, H.W.	Evangeline (1st, sm8vo, teg, p-o, 172p, pep)	Reilly/Britton	(1909)	Neill, John R.	80-125	
Andersen, Hans C.	Fairy Tales (1st, lg8vo, p-o, 180p, blue/gilt, 2cp, b/w)	Cupples/Leon	(1923)	Neill, John R.	150-250	
N/A	Foolish Fox (1st, 16mo, ibds, p-o, 92p, color)	Altemus	(1904)	Neill, John R.	60-100	R
Bangs, John K.	From Pillar to Post (1st, sm8vo, 339p, gilt, b/w)	Century	1916	Neill, John R.	50-80	
Johnston, Annie F.	Georgina of the Rainbows (1st, sm8vo, gilt, 348p, col frn, 3pl)	NY: Britton	(1916)	Neill, John R.	70-100	
Thompson, Ruth P.	Giant Horse of Oz (1st, lg8vo, 283p, p-o, brown cl, pep, 12cp)	Reilly/Lee	(1928)	Neill, John R.	300-500	
Baum, L. Frank	Gingerbread Man (1st, sm4to, ibds, 62p, col frn)	Reilly/Britton	(1917)	Neill, John R.	200-300	
Baum, L. Frank	Glinda of Oz (1st [1], lg8vo, grey cl, p-o, 279p, 12cp, pep)	Reilly/Lee	(1920)	Neill, John R.	600-800	R
Thompson, Ruth P.	Gnome King of Oz (1st, lg8vo, 282p, p-o, green cl, pep, 12cp)	Reilly/Lee	(1927)	Neill, John R.	400-600	
Thompson, Ruth P.	Grampa in Oz (1st, lg8vo, 271p, p-o, 12cp, pep)	Reilly/Lee	(1924)	Neill, John R.	350-500	
Thompson, Ruth P.	Handy Mandy in Oz (1st, lg8vo, 246p, blue cl, p-o, b/w, pep, DJ/1.50)	Reilly/Lee	(1937)	Neill, John R.	400-600	
Grimm Bros.	Hansel & Gretel (1st, 12mo, red bds, 58p, p-o, color)	Reilly/Britton	(1908)	Neill, John R.	80-120	
Longfellow, H.W.	Hiawatha (1st, 8vo, p-o, 208p, teg, 1-color, pep)	Reilly/Britton	(1909)	Neill, John R.	80-140	
Thompson, Ruth P.	Hungry Tiger of Oz (1st [1], 8vo, p-o, 261p, 12cp, pep)	Reilly/Lee	(1926)	Neill, John R.	350-500	
Johnston, Annie F.	It Was the Road to Jericho (1st {std}, sm8vo, [41]p, gilt, pep)	Britton	(1919)	Neill, John R.	50-80	
Thompson, Ruth P.	Jack Pumpkinhead of Oz (1st, 8vo, 252p p-o, 12cp, pep)	Reilly/Lee	(1929)	Neill, John R.	300-500	
Hartwell, James (ed)	Jeweled Sea (1st, 12mo, 102p, aqua cl, b/w)	Altemus	(1906)	Neill, John R.	80-135	
Baum, L. Frank	John Dough and the Cherub (1st [1], lg8vo, tan cl, 314p, color, pep)	Reilly/Britton	(1906)	Neill, John R.	700-900	
Thompson, Ruth P.	Kabumpo in Oz (1st [1], lg8vo, blue cl, 297p, p-o, 12cp, pep)	Reilly/Lee	(1922)	Neill, John R.	350-500	
Bannerman, Helen	Little Black Sambo (sq8vo, ibds, 28p, color)	Reilly/Britton	(1908)	Neill, John R.	200-300	
N/A	Little Red Riding Hood (16mo, ibds, 57p, fp color)	Reilly/Britton	(1908)	Neill, John R.	70-100	
Baum, L. Frank	Little Wizard Stories of Oz (1st [1], sm8vo, p-o, 152p, 42cp)	Reilly/Britton	(1914)	Neill, John R.	400-650	
Thompson, Ruth P.	Lost King of Oz (1st, 8vo, p-o, 280p, 12cp, pep)	Reilly/Lee	(1925)	Neill, John R.	350-500	
Baum, L. Frank	Lost Princess of Oz (1st [1], 8vo, 312p, p-o, 12cp, pep)	Reilly/Britton	(1917)	Neill, John R.	700-900	
Neill, John R.	Lucky Bucky in Oz (1st [1], 8vo, 289p, p-o, blue cl, b/w, pep, DJ/1.50)	Reilly/Lee	(1942)	Neill, John R.	400-650	
Hartwell, James (ed)	Magic Bed (1st, 12mo, 109p, b/w pl)	Altemus	(1906)	Neill, John R.	80-130	
Baum, L. Frank	Magic Cloak... (1st [1], 8vo, 58p, ibds)	Reilly/Britton	(1916)	Neill, John R.	500-700	
James, Hartwell	Magic Jaw Bone (1st, 12mo, 107p, 2-color)	Altemus	(1906)	Neill, John R.	60-100	
Baum, L. Frank	Magic of Oz (1st [1], lg8vo, 265p, p-o, green cl, 12cp, pep)	Reilly/Lee	(1919)	Neill, John R.	500-700	
Jenks, Tudor	Magician for One Day (1st, 24mo, brown ipcb, 107p, color)	Altemus	(1905)	Neill, John R.	80-145	
Baum, L. Frank	Marvelous Land of Oz (1st [1], lg8vo, 287p, green cl, 16cp, pep)	Reilly/Britton	1904	Neill, John R.	900-1400	
Warwick, Charles	Mirabeau & the French Revolution (1st, 8vo, 483p, 15pl)	Lippincott	1905	Neill, John R.	50-90	
Mother Goose	Mother Goose Nursery Tales (12mo, 91p, green cl, p-o, color)	Altemus	(1904)	Neill, John R.	100-165	
Thompson, Ruth P.	Ojo in Oz (1st, 8vo, p-o, 304p, red cl, 12cp, pep)	Reilly/Lee	(1933)	Neill, John R.	300-500	
Baum, L. Frank	Ozma of Oz (1st [1], lg8vo, 270p, tan cl, color, pep)	Reilly/Britton	(1907)	Neill, John R.	700-900	
Thompson, Ruth P.	Ozoplaning with the Wizard of Oz (1st, lg8vo, 272p, p-o, pep, DJ/1.50)	Reilly/Lee	(1939)	Neill, John R.	400-600	
Baum, L. Frank	Patchwork Girl of Oz (1st [1], 8vo, 341p, green cl, color, pep)	Reilly/Britton	(1913)	Neill, John R.	700-900	
Grabo, Carl H.	Peter & the Princess (1st, sm4to, teg, gilt, p-o, 243p, 8cp, pep)	Reilly/Lee	(1920)	Neill, John R.	250-400	
Thompson, Ruth P.	Pirates in Oz (1st [1], 8vo, green cl, p-o, 280p, 12cp, pep)	Reilly/Lee	(1931)	Neill, John R.	350-500	
Thompson, Ruth P.	Purple Prince of Oz (1st [1], lg8vo, p-o, 281p, 12cp, pep)	Reilly/Lee	(1932)	Neill, John R.	350-500	
Jenks, Tudor	Rescue Syndicate (1st, 24mo, ipcb, 110p, b/w, pep)	Altemus	(1905)	Neill, John R.	80-120	
Baum, L. Frank	Rinkitink in Oz (1st [1], lg8vo, blue cl, 314p, p-o, 12cp, pep)	Reilly/Britton	(1916)	Neill, John R.	600-800	
Baum, L. Frank	Road to Oz (1st [1], lg8vo, green cl, b/w, p-o, 261p, pep)	Reilly/Britton	(1909)	Neill, John R.	600-800	
N/A	Robber Kitten (1st, 16mo, 96p, gilt, color)	Altemus	(1904)	Neill, John R.	75-100	
Thompson, Ruth P.	Royal Book of Oz (1st [1], 8vo, 312p, grey cl, p-o, 12cp, pep)	Reilly/Lee	(1921)	Neill, John R.	300-450	
Neill, John R.	Scalawagons of Oz (1st, lg8vo, 309p, p-o, b/w, pep, DJ/1.50)	Reilly/Lee	(1941)	Neill, John R.	500-700	
Baum, L. Frank	Scarecrow of Oz (1st [1], lg8vo, green cl, p-o, 288p, 12cp, pep)	Reilly/Britton	(1915)	Neill, John R.	500-700	
Baum, L. Frank	Sea Fairies (1st [1], lg8vo, p-o, 240p, green cl, 12pl, pep)	Reilly/Britton	(1911)	Neill, John R.	600-850	
Thompson, Ruth P.	Silver Princess in Oz (1st, lg8vo, 255p, p-o, b/w, pep. DJ/1.50)	Reilly/Lee	(1938)	Neill, John R.	450-650	
Baum, L. Frank	Sky Island (1st, lg8vo, blue cl, p-o, 287p, 12cp, pep)	Reilly/Britton	(1912)	Neill, John R.	500-700	
Whittier, John G.	Snowbound (1st, 8vo, p-o, 123p, green cl, 12pl, pep)	Reilly/Britton	(1909)	Neill, John R.	60-90	
Thompson, Ruth P.	Speedy in Oz (1st, lg8vo, p-o, 298p, blue cl, 12cp, pep)	Reilly/Lee	(1934)	Neill, John R.	350-500	
Potter, Beatrix	Story of Peter Rabbit (1st, 24mo, p-o, ibds)	Reilly/Britton	(1911)	Neill, John R.	100-165	
Poe, Edgar A.	The Raven (1st, sm8vo, 110p, b/w pl, pep)	Reilly/Britton	(1910)	Neill, John R.	120-170	
Baum, L. Frank	Tik-Tok of Oz (1st [1], lg8vo, 272p, blue cl, p-o, pep, 12cp)	Reilly/Britton	(1914)	Neill, John R.	700-900	
Jenks, Tudor	Timothy's Magical Afternoon (1st, 24mo, ipcb, 98p, b/w, pep)	Altemus	(1905)	Neill, John R.	100-165	
Baum, L. Frank	Tin Woodman of Oz (1st [1], lg8vo, red cl, 288p, p-o, 12cp, pep)	Reilly/Britton	(1918)	Neill, John R.	500-700	
Andersen, Hans C.	Ugly Duckling (1st, 16mo, bds, p-o, 57p, color)	Reilly/Britton	(1912)	Neill, John R.	70-100	
Wright, Harold Bell	Uncrowned King (1st, 12mo, green/gilt, 118p, 5pl)	Book Supply Co.	1910	Neill, John R.	70-125	
Harris, Credo	Where Souls of Men are Calling (1st, 12mo, 298p, col frn by...)	Britton	(1918)	Neill, John R.	30-50	
Thompson, Ruth P.	Wishing Horse of Oz (1st, lg8vo, grey cl, 298p, p-o, 12cp, DJ/1.50)	Reilly/Lee	(1935)	Neill, John R.	400-600	
Neill, John R.	Wonder City of Oz (1st [1], 8vo, p-o, 318p, b/w, pep, DJ/1.50)	Reilly/Lee	(1940)	Neill, John R.	350-500	
Thompson, Ruth P.	Yellow Knight of Oz (1st, 8vo, 275p, grey cl, p-o, 12cp, pep)	Reilly/Lee	(1930)	Neill, John R.	250-350	
Iogolevitch, Paul	Young Russian Corporal (1st, sm8vo, 327p, frn & b/w by...)	Harper	1919	Neill, John R.	55-80	*
Allen, Phil S.	King Arthur and his Knights (1st, lg8vo, 455p, black cl, p-o, 8cp)	Rand/McNally	(1924)	Neill/Schaeffer	60-90	*
Baring-Gould, Sabine	Amazing Adventures (1st, ob folio, 53p, fp color)	L: Skeffington	[1903]	Neilson, Harry B.	180-260	
Krakemsides, Baron	Careless Chicken (1st, sq12mo, 47p, p-o, fp color)	L: Warne	(1924)	Neilson, Harry B.	45-70	
N/A	Droll Doings (1st, lg4to, [64]p, ibds, 40 color)	L: Blackie	[1900]	Neilson, Harry B.	140-200	
Burnand, Francis	Fox's Frolic (ob4to, ibds, [50]p, color, pep)	L: Collins	[1920]	Neilson, Harry B.	100-165	
Hamer, Sam H.	Jungle School (1st, 4to, 64p, color)	L: Cassell	1900	Neilson, Harry B.	80-125	
Hamer, Sam H.	Micky Magee's Menagerie (1st, lg8vo, ibds, 100p, 8cp)	L: Cassell	1897	Neilson, Harry B.	80-125	
Farrow, George E.	Pixie Pickles (1st, lg4to, ibds, 46p, 20 pl)	L: Skeffington	[1904]	Neilson, Harry B.	170-240	

AUTHOR	TITLE	PUBLISHER	DATE	ARTIST	PRICE	LC
Malkus, Alida S.	There Really Was a Hiawatha (1st, 8vo, 180p, b/w, pep, DJ/2.95)	Grosset/Dunlap	1963	Neilson, Jon	30-50	*
Wordsworth, William	Intimations of Immortality... (1st, lg8vo, gilt, unpag, 12cp)	L: J.M. Dent	[1913]	Neilson-Gray	125-180	
Burglon, Nora	Ghost Ship (1st, sm8vo, 275p, blue cl, 8pl, pep, DJ/2.00)	Little/Brown	1936	Nelson, Arthur R.	30-50	
Farjeon, Eleanor	Wonders of Herodotus (1st, 8vo, 176p, col frn, 6 b/w)	L: Nelson	1937	Nelson, Edmund	40-60	*
Van Dyne, Edith	Aunt Jane's Nieces (1st, 12mo, p-o, 325p, 6pl)	Reilly/Britton	(1906)	Nelson, Emile A.	225-325	
Van Dyne, Edith	Aunt Jane's Nieces Abroad (1st, 12mo, green cl, p-o, 5pl)	Reilly/Britton	(1906)	Nelson, Emile A.	180-250	
Van Dyne, Edith	Aunt Jane's Nieces on Vacation (1st, sm8vo, 305p, tan cl, p-o, frn by....)	Reilly/Britton	(1912)	Nelson, Emile A.	100-150	
Akers, Floyd	Boy Fortune Hunters in China (1st [1], 12mo, brown cl, frn by)	Reilly/Britton	(1909)	Nelson, Emile A.	165-250	*
Akers, Floyd	Boy Fortune Hunters in Egypt (1st [1], 12mo, 291p, 3pl)	Reilly/Britton	(1908)	Nelson, Emile A.	200-300	
Akers, Floyd	Boy Fortune Hunters in the South Seas (1st, 8vo, 263p, tan cl, frn by)	Reilly/Britton	(1911)	Nelson, Emile A.	200-300	
Henderson, L.R.S.	Flight Brothers (1st, 4to, 102p, ibds, 6cp)	Reilly/Britton	(1912)	Nelson, Emile A.	200-300	
Henderson, L.R.S.	Magic Aeroplane (1st, 4to, ibds, 96p, 6cp)	Reilly/Britton	(1911)	Nelson, Emile A.	200-300	
Wiggin & Smith	Talking Beasts (1st, sm8vo, 391p, teg, p-o, col frn, pl)	Doubleday/Page	1911	Nelson, Harold	30-50	
North, Sterling	So Red the Nose (1st, sm8vo, pink cl, [72]p, fp b/w, DJ/1.00)	Farrar/Rinehart	(1935)	Nelson, Roy C.	50-80	
Nerman, Einar	Fairy Tales from the North (1st {std}, lg8vo, 128p, 8cp, pep, DJ/3.00)	Knopf	1946	Nerman, Einar R.	35-50	
Grimm Bros.	Goose Girl (1st, 12mo, tan cl, 165p, 3cp, 10 fp b/w, dep)	Macmillan	1929	Nerman, Einar R.	55-80	*
Andersen, Hans C.	The Swineherd (folio, ibds, unpag, color, pep)	Knopf	[1924]	Nerman, Einar R.	175-300	
Andersen, Hans C.	Thumbelina (1st, 16mo, 79p, fp color, pep)	Macmillan	1928	Nerman, Einar R.	40-60	*
Belting, Natalia	Earth is on a Fish's Back (1st {std}, lg8vo, 91p, b/w, DJ/3.50)	Holt, Rinehart	(1965)	Nesbitt, Esta	20-30	*
Coatsworth, Eliz.	Jon the Unlucky (1st {std}, 8vo, 94p, 1-color, DJ/3.50)	Holt, Rinehart	(1964)	Nesbitt, Esta	50-80	R
Belting, Natalia	Stars are Silver Reindeer (1st {std}, ob8vo, [46]p, color, DJ/3.50)	Holt, Rinehart	(1966)	Nesbitt, Esta	25-40	*
Nesbitt, Philip	Nicholas Needlefoot (1st, 8vo, ibds, [32]p, 1-color, DJ/1.00)	Wilcox/Follett	1944	Nesbitt, Philip	50-80	
Nesbitt, Philip	Trum Peter's Tea-Party (1st, lg8vo, [31]p, 2-color)	Coward	1931	Nesbitt, Philip	30-50	
Robinson, Barbara	Across from Indian Shore (1st, 8vo, 158p, fp b/w, DJ/3.50)	Lothrop, Lee	(1962)	Ness, Evaline	25-40	
Leodhas, Sorche	All in the Morning Early (1st {std}, ob8vo, [30]p, 2-color, DJ/3.50, CH)	Holt, Rinehart	(1963)	Ness, Evaline	80-135	R
Cunningham, Julia	Candle Tales (1st, 8vo, 57p, fp 1-color, DJ/3.25)	Pantheon	(1963)	Ness, Evaline	25-40	
Alexander, Lloyd C.	Coll and His White Pig (1st {std}, sq8vo, [32]p, color, cep, DJ/3.50)	Holt, Rinehart	(1965)	Ness, Evaline	50-80	R
Ness, Evaline M.	Double Discovery (1st, 4to, [32]p, 3-color, DJ/3.25, NYTBI)	Scribner	(1965)	Ness, Evaline	30-50	
Ness, Evaline M.	Exactly Alike (1st, ob4to, [32]p, 3-color, DJ/3.50, NYTBI)	Scribner	1964	Ness, Evaline	30-50	
Haviland, Virginia	Favorite Fairy Tales Told in Italy (1st {std}, lg8vo, 90p, color, DJ/2.95)	Little/Brown	(1965)	Ness, Evaline	50-85	R
Merriam, Eve	Funny Town (1st {std}, lg4to, 63p, ibds, fp color, cep)	Crowell-Collier	1963	Ness, Evaline	45-70	
Ness, Evaline M.	Gift for Sula Sula (1st, 4to, [31]p, fp 3-color, DJ/3.25)	Scribner	1963	Ness, Evaline	50-80	
Ness, Evaline M.	Girl and the Goatherd (1st {std}, 4to, [32]p, color, DJ/4.25)	Dutton	(1970)	Ness, Evaline	40-65	
Ness, Evaline M.	Josefina February (1st, 4to, [32]p, fp 3-color, DJ/3.25)	Scribner	1963	Ness, Evaline	50-85	R
Buckley, Helen E.	Josie and the Snow (1st, lg ob8vo, [32]p, color, DJ/2.95)	Lothrop, Lee	(1964)	Ness, Evaline	30-50	
Buckley, Helen E.	Josie's Buttercup (1st, ob4to, [28]p, 2-color, DJ/3.50)	Lothrop, Lee	1967	Ness, Evaline	30-50	
Leodhas, Sorche	Kellyburn Braes (1st {std}, lg8vo, [30]p, ibds, 3-color, DJ/3.95)	Holt, Rinehart	(1968)	Ness, Evaline	30-45	
Miller, Mary B.	Listen -- the Birds (1st, 8vo, 46p, 3-color, DJ/3.00, NYTBI)	Pantheon	(1961)	Ness, Evaline	30-50	
Mother Goose	London Bridge is Falling Down (1st {std}, ob4to, 32p, color, DJ)	Little/Brown	(1967)	Ness, Evaline	30-50	
Coatsworth, Eliz.	Lonely Maria (1st, 8vo, yellow cl, [38]p, 2-color, DJ/3.25)	Pantheon	(1960)	Ness, Evaline	40-65	
Ness, Evaline M.	Long, Broad and Quickeye (1st, 4to, [39]p, color, pep, DJ/3.95)	Scribner	(1969)	Ness, Evaline	30-50	
Cunningham, Julia	Macaroon (1st, 8vo, 63p, ibds, fp 2-color, DJ/3.00)	Pantheon	(1962)	Ness, Evaline	20-30	
N/A	Mr. Miacca, an English Folktale (1st {std}, ob4to, [32]p, color, DJ/3.75)	Holt, Rinehart	(1967)	Ness, Evaline	30-50	
Osborne, Maurice M.	Ondine (1st, lg8vo, 75p, 2-color, DJ/2.75)	Houghton	1960	Ness, Evaline	25-45	
Ness, Evaline M.	Pavo and the Princess (1st, 4to, [32]p, fp color, DJ/3.25)	Scribner	1964	Ness, Evaline	30-50	
Cassedy, Sylvia	Pierino and the Bell (1st {std}, 4to, 47p, color, DJ/3.25)	Doubleday	(1966)	Ness, Evaline	40-65	*
Caudill, Rebecca	Pocketful of Cricket (1st {std}, 4to, [48]p, color, DJ/3.50, CH)	Holt, Rinehart	(1964)	Ness, Evaline	45-70	
Coatsworth, Eliz.	Princess and the Lion (1st, 8vo, 77p, dp 1-color, cep, DJ/3.50)	Pantheon	(1963)	Ness, Evaline	45-70	R
Ness, Evaline M.	Sam, Bangs & Moonshine (1st {std}, 4to, [41]p, 2-color, pep, DJ/3.95, CM)	Holt, Rinehart	(1966)	Ness, Evaline	150-225	
Leodhas, Sorche	Scottish Songbook (1st {std}, ob4to, 63p, 1-color, DJ/4.50)	Holt, Rinehart	(1969)	Ness, Evaline	30-50	
Pope, Elizabeth M.	Sherwood Ring (1st, 8vo, tan cl, 266p, fp b/w, DJ/3.00)	Houghton	1958	Ness, Evaline	50-80	R
Buckley, Helen E.	Some Cheese for Charles (1st, ob4to, [30]p, ibds, color, cep, DJ/2.95)	Lothrop, Lee	(1963)	Ness, Evaline	30-50	
Clifton, Lucille	Some of the Days/Everett Anderson (1st {std}, ob8vo, [32]p, color, DJ/3.95)	Holt, Rinehart	(1970)	Ness, Evaline	40-65	
Gibbons, Mary	Story of Ophelia (1st {std}, 4to, ibds, [32]p, color, DJ/2.00)	Doubleday	1954	Ness, Evaline	40-65	
Alexander, Lloyd C.	Taran Wanderer (1st {std}, 8vo, 256p, cep, DJ/4.50, b/w map by...)	Holt, Rinehart	(1967)	Ness, Evaline	40-65	
Ogburn, Charlton	The Bridge (1st, lg8vo, 68p, fp 2-color, DJ/2.75)	Houghton	1957	Ness, Evaline	70-100	R
Leodhas, Sorche	Thistle and Thyme... (1st {std}, 8vo, 143p, ibds, b/w, DJ/3.50, NH)	Holt, Rinehart	(1962)	Ness, Evaline	50-80	*
Jacobs, Joseph (ed)	Tom Tit Tot: English Folk Tale (1st, 4to, [32]p, 3-color, DJ/3.25, CH)	Scribner	1965	Ness, Evaline	50-75	
Buckley, Helen E.	Too Many Crackers (1st, 4to, [28]p, color, DJ/3.50)	Lothrop, Lee	(1966)	Ness, Evaline	40-60	*
Robinson, Barbara	Trace through the Forest (1st, 8vo, 219p, b/w, DJ/3.50)	Lothrop, Lee	(1965)	Ness, Evaline	25-40	
Alexander, Lloyd C.	Truthful Harp (1st {std}, sq8vo, [32]p, ibds, color, cep, DJ/3.50)	Holt, Rinehart	(1967)	Ness, Evaline	40-65	
Buckley, Helen E.	Where Did Josie Go? (1st, smob4to, 33p, 3-color, DJ/2.95)	Lothrop, Lee	(1962)	Ness, Evaline	40-65	
Jagendorf, Moritz	In the Days of the Han (1st, lg8vo, gilt, 168p, fp color, pep, DJ/2.50)	Suttonhouse	1936	Neumann, Erwin	45-70	
Lovelace, Maud H.	Betsy and Joe (1st, 8vo, 256p, b/w, DJ/2.50)	Crowell	(1948)	Neville, Vera	100-165	
Lovelace, Maud H.	Betsy and the Great World (1st {std}, 8vo, 305p, b/w, DJ/2.50)	Crowell	1952	Neville, Vera	250-400	
Lovelace, Maud H.	Betsy in Spite of Herself (1st {std}, 8vo, 272p, b/w, DJ/2.50)	Crowell	(1946)	Neville, Vera	100-165	*
Lovelace, Maud H.	Betsy's Wedding (1st {std}, 8vo, 241p, b/w, DJ/2.75)	Crowell	(1955)	Neville, Vera	200-300	
Harper, Wilhelmina	Brownie of the Circus (1st {std}, lg8vo, 107p, fp color, pep, DJ/2.00)	McKay	(1941)	Neville, Vera	40-65	
Untermeyer, Louis	Chip: My Life and Times (1st, ob8vo, 102p, fp b/w, pep)	Harcourt	(1933)	Neville, Vera	60-90	R*
Lovelace, Maud H.	Emily of Deep Valley (1st {std}, 8vo, green cl, 257p, b/w, DJ/2.50)	Crowell	(1950)	Neville, Vera	100-170	
Rains, Marie C.	Lazy Liza Lizard (1st, 8vo, 182p, gilt, fp 2-color, pep, DJ/2.00)	Winston	(1938)	Neville, Vera	300-500	
Rains, Marie C.	Lazy Liza Lizard's Tricks (1st {std}, 8vo, 119p, b/w, DJ/2.00)	Winston	(1953)	Neville, Vera	200-300	
Mason, Miriam E.	Lion for Patsy (1st {std}, lg8vo, ibds, [32]p, color, DJ/1.50)	McKay	(1947)	Neville, Vera	60-90	*
Webber, Frank M.	Peter Painter & the Holidays (1st, lg8vo, [32]p, ibds, 2-color, DJ/1.00)	McKay	(1942)	Neville, Vera	40-60	
Webber, Frank M.	Peter Painter's Merry-Go-Round (1st {std} lg8vo, ibds, [32]p, col, DJ/1.00)	McKay	(1946)	Neville, Vera	45-70	
Woolley, Catherine	Two Hundred Pennies (1st, 8vo, 128p, b/w, DJ/2.00)	Wm. Morrow	1947	Neville, Vera	25-40	
Lovelace, Maud H.	Winona's Pony Cart (1st {std}, 8vo, 117p, b/w, DJ/2.00)	Crowell	(1953)	Neville, Vera	200-300	*
Newberry, Clare T.	April's Kittens (1st {std}, 4to, [32]p, gilt, color, pep, DJ/1.75, CH)	Harper	1940	Newberry, Clare T.	120-180	

ARTIST: 144

AUTHOR	TITLE	PUBLISHER	DATE	ARTIST	PRICE	LC
Newberry, Clare T.	Babette (1st {std}, lg8vo, ibds, 32p, pep, color, DJ/1.50)	Harper	1937	Newberry, Clare T.	85-140	
Newberry, Clare T.	Barkis (1st {std}, lg ob8vo, 31p, color, pep, DJ/1.75, CH)	Harper	1938	Newberry, Clare T.	120-180	
Newberry, Clare T.	Cousin Toby (1st {std}, lg8vo, [32]p, yellow bds, pep, DJ/1.60)	Harper	1939	Newberry, Clare T.	100-165	
Newberry, Clare T.	Frosty (1st, 8vo, 92p, fp b/w, DJ/2.50)	Harper	(1961)	Newberry, Clare T.	40-70	
Newberry, Clare T.	Herbert the Lion (1st, ob4to, [41]p, pep, color, DJ/2.00)	Brewer/Warren	1931	Newberry, Clare T.	180-300	
Newberry, Clare T.	Herbert the Lion (1st {this pub-std}, ob4to, ibds [64]p, pep, col, DJ/2.00)	Harper	1939	Newberry, Clare T.	150-250	
Newberry, Clare T.	Ice Cream for Two (1st, 8vo, 58p, 2-color, cep, DJ/2.50)	Harper	(1953)	Newberry, Clare T.	45-70	
Newberry, Clare T.	Kitten's ABC (1st {std}, folio, ibds, [36]p, color, DJ/2.00)	Harper	(1946)	Newberry, Clare T.	80-125	
Newberry, Clare T.	Lambert's Bargain (1st {std}, lg8vo, 31p, b/w, pep, DJ/1.00)	Harper	1941	Newberry, Clare T.	80-120	
Newberry, Clare T.	Marshmallow (1st {std}, lg ob4to, [31]p, color, DJ/1.75, CH)	Harper	(1942)	Newberry, Clare T.	100-165	
Newberry, Clare T.	Mittens (1st {std}, lg8vo, ibds, [28]p, pep, 12cp, DJ/1.50)	Harper	1936	Newberry, Clare T.	70-120	
Newberry, Clare T.	Pandora (1st {std}, folio, ibds, p-o, [35]p, b/w, DJ/1.75)	Harper	(1944)	Newberry, Clare T.	80-140	
Newberry, Clare T.	Percy, Polly and Pete (1st, lg ob8vo, ibds, [30]p, color, DJ/2.00)	Harper	(1952)	Newberry, Clare T.	50-80	
Newberry, Clare T.	Smudge (1st, 8vo, ibds, [32]p, 1-color, pep, DJ/1.75)	Harper	1948	Newberry, Clare T.	65-90	R
Newberry, Clare T.	T-Bone the Baby-Sitter (1st, lg ob8vo, ibds, [30]p, color pep, DJ/1.75, CH)	Harper	1950	Newberry, Clare T.	120-200	
Newberry, Clare T.	Widget (1st, lg ob8vo, unpag, 1-color, DJ/2.50)	Harper	(1958)	Newberry, Clare T.	60-90	
Ramsden, Helen G.	Smile Within a Tear (1st, sm8vo, 251p, blue/gilt, 8pl)	L: Hutchinson	1897	Newcombe, Bertha	60-100	
Newell, David M.	American Animals (1st, 8vo, blue cl, 80p, 10cp, pep)	Volland	(1929)	Newell, David	70-120	
Stockton, Frank	Afield & Afloat (1st, sm8vo, teg, 422p, 12pl)	Scribner	1900	Newell, Peter	40-60	
Carroll, Lewis	Alice in Wonderland (1st, 8vo, vellum/gilt, 193p, teg, 40pl)	Harper	1901	Newell, Peter	160-225	
Bangs, John K.	Bikey the Skycycle (1st, sm8vo, blue/gilt, 321p, col frn, 7pl)	NY: Riggs	1902	Newell, Peter	80-130	
Reed, Myrtle	Book of Clever Beasts (1st, 8vo, p-o, 231p, col frn, 8pl)	Putnam	1904	Newell, Peter	100-165	
Cobb, Irving	Cobb's Anatomy (1st, 8vo, tan pcb, 141p, 17pl, pep)	Doran	(1912)	Newell, Peter	40-60	
Cobb, Irving	Cobb's Bill of Fare (1st, 8vo, tan, pcb, 148p, 15pl, pep)	Doran	(1913)	Newell, Peter	40-60	
Garnett, Louise A.	Creature Songs (1st, folio, 30p, p-o, green/gilt, 10pl)	NY: Ditson	(1912)	Newell, Peter	200-300	
Bangs, John K.	Enchanted Typewriter (1st, 16mo, 171p, uncut, 10pl)	Harper	1899	Newell, Peter	70-125	
Carryl, Guy W.	Fables for the Frivolous (1st, 8vo, 120p, teg, gilt, 6pl)	Harper	1898	Newell, Peter	70-100	
Carryl, Guy W.	Far from Maddening Girls (1st, 8vo, 185p, 8pl)	McClure	1904	Newell, Peter	60-90	
N/A	Favorite Fairy Tales (1st, 8vo, 355p, gilt, teg, 16pl)	Harper	1907	Newell, Peter	200-300	
Harris, Ada V.	Favorites from Fairyland (1st, 12mo, 129p, blue cl, 130p, 6pl)	Harper	1911	Newell, Peter	170-240	
Stockton, Frank	Great Stone of Sardis (1st, 12mo, 230p, teg, uncut, gilt, 52pl)	Harper	1898	Newell, Peter	80-130	R
Newell, Peter	Hole Book (1st, 8vo, p-o, [51]p, blue cloth, 24 fp color, PPP)	Harper	(1908)	Newell, Peter	300-500	R
Bangs, John K.	House Boat on the Styx (1st, 12mo, green/gilt, 171p, 23pl)	Harper	1896	Newell, Peter	60-100	
Carroll, Lewis	Hunting of the Snark (1st, lg8vo, ibds, teg, 248p, 40pl)	Harper	1903	Newell, Peter	150-200	
Stone, Stuart B.	Kingdom of Why (1st, lg8vo, green cl, 275p, p-o, 9pl)	Bobbs-Merrill	(1913)	Newell, Peter	200-300	
Wells, Carolyn	Merry-Go-Round (1st, sm8vo, gilt, 152p, 11pl)	R.H. Russell	1901	Newell, Peter	180-250	
Carryl, Guy W.	Mother Goose for Grownups (1st, 8vo, gilt, teg, 115p, 3pl by...)	Harper	1900	Newell, Peter	120-200	
Wells, Carolyn	Mother Goose's Menagerie (1st, lg8vo, tan cl, 111p, 12cp)	Noyes/Platt	1901	Newell, Peter	200-300	
Bangs, John K.	Mr. Munchausen (1st, 12mo, 180p, tan cl, 15cp)	Noyes/Platt	1901	Newell, Peter	50-80	
Irwin, Wallace	Nautical Lays of a Landsman (1st, sm8vo, 135p, 5pl, dep)	Dodd	1904	Newell, Peter	70-100	
Johnson, Clifton	Parson's Devil (1st, 8vo, 296p, green cl, 4pl)	Crowell	(1927)	Newell, Peter	70-120	
Browne, Porter E.	Peace at any Price (1st, sm8vo, brown pcb, 70p, p-o, 6pl)	Appleton	1916	Newell, Peter	150-220	
Bailey, Carolyn S.	Peter Newell's Mother Goose (1st, 8vo, 265p, 20pl)	Henry Holt & Co.	1905	Newell, Peter	140-200	
Newell, Peter	Peter Newell's Pictures & Rhymes (1st, ob8vo, tan cl, p-o, 50pl)	Harper	1899	Newell, Peter	200-300	
Bangs, John K.	Pursuit of the House Boat (1st, 12mo, 204p, 24pl)	Harper	1897	Newell, Peter	70-100	
Towne, Charles H.	Rise & Fall of Prohibition (1st, sm8vo, blue/gilt, 220p, 4pl)	Macmillan	1923	Newell, Peter	60-100	
Newell, Peter	Rocket Book (1st, lg8vo, [48]p, p-o, 23 fp color)	Harper	(1912)	Newell, Peter	300-500	R
Bell, Lilian	Runaway Equator (1st, 8vo, 118p, p-o, 16pl)	Stokes	(1911)	Newell, Peter	150-250	
Browne, Porter E.	Scars & Stripes (1st, sm8vo, gilt, 208p, frn by..)	Doran	(1917)	Newell, Peter	30-50	*
Newell, Peter	Shadow Show (1st, ob8vo, ipcb, 72p, color)	Century	1896	Newell, Peter	280-350	
Newell, Peter	Slant Book (1st, 8vo, [47]p, ibds, 22 fp color)	Harper	(1910)	Newell, Peter	250-400	R
Crane, Stephen	The Monster... (1st, 12mo, 188p, orange/gilt, 25pl)	Harper	1899	Newell, Peter	300-500	
Cooke, Grace M.	Their First Formal Call (1st, 8vo, 55p, p-o, gilt, 14pl)	Harper	1906	Newell, Peter	70-120	
Carroll, Lewis	Through the Looking Glass (1st, lg8vo, bds, teg, 211p, 40pl)	Harper	1902	Newell, Peter	125-180	
Lee, Al	Tommy Toodles (1st, 8vo, p-o, blue cl, 192p, 26pl)	Harper	1896	Newell, Peter	180-240	
Newell, Peter	Topsys & Turvys (1st, lg ob8vo, bds, p-o, 31cp)	Century	1893	Newell, Peter	250-400	
Newell, Peter	Topsys & Turvys Number 2 (1st, lg ob8vo, ipcb, 69p, color)	Century	(1894)	Newell, Peter	250-400	
Crane, Stephen	Whilomville Stories (1st, sm8vo, green/gilt, 198p, 34pl)	Harper	1900	Newell, Peter	250-350	
Wilkins, Mary E.	Wind in the Rose Bush (1st, sm8vo, green/gilt, 237p, 8pl)	Doubleday/Page	1903	Newell, Peter	80-140	
Newton, Ruth E.	Kittens and Puppies (1st, linen wraps, [12]p, color)	Whitman	1940	Newton, Ruth	20-35	
Mother Goose	Mother Goose Stories (folio, ibds, 76p, 14 fp color)	L: Collins	[1928]	Newton, Ruth	60-90	
Moore, Clement C.	Night Before Christmas (1st, 4to, [33]p, ipcb, color, pep)	Whitman	(1937)	Newton, Ruth	60-90	R*
Mother Goose	Mother Goose (1st, lg4to, [28]p, 12 fp color, pep)	Whitman	(1934)	Newton/Horn	90-120	*
Means, Florence C.	Emmy & the Blue Door (1st, 8vo, yellow cl, 217p, b/w, DJ/3.00)	Houghton	1959	Nicholas, Frank	25-45	
Jackson, Jesse	Room for Randy (1st, 8vo, 136p, b/w, DJ/2.50)	Friendship Pr.	1957	Nicholas, Frank	35-50	*
Wister, Owen	New Swiss Family Robinson (1st, 4to, 25p, ipcb, b/w)	Duffield	1922	Nichols, F.	65-100	
Harper, Wilhelmina	Dog Show (1st, 8vo, p-o, 182p, fp color, DJ/2.75)	Houghton	1950	Nichols, Marie C.	30-50	
Waldman, Dorothy	Goomer (1st {std}, 8vo, [64]p, b/w, DJ/1.75)	Ariel	(1952)	Nichols, Marie C.	40-65	
Colby, Jean P.	Jim the Cat (1st {std}, lg8vo, yellow cl, 46p, fp b/w, DJ/2.50)	Little/Brown	(1957)	Nichols, Marie C.	30-50	
Bradbury, Bianca	One Kitten too Many (1st, 8vo, 32p, 2-color, DJ/1.50)	Houghton	1952	Nichols, Marie C.	30-50	
Dickens, Charles	Christmas Carol (1st AM, 8vo, 78p, 4cp)	Stokes	[1913]	Nichols, Spencer B.	40-60	*
Wilde, Oscar	Happy Prince (1st, 8vo, p-o, 204p, gilt, 8cp)	Stokes	(1913)	Nichols, Spencer B.	80-125	
Noyes, Alfred	Sherwood (1st, 8vo, 225p, black/gilt, p-o, 4cp)	Stokes	1911	Nichols, Spencer B.	35-60	*
Kipling, Rudyard	Almanac of 12 Sports (1st, 4to, [30]p, ibds, 12cp)	L: Heinemann	1898	Nicholson, Wm.	400-650	
Kipling, Rudyard	Almanac of 12 Sports (1st AM, 4to, [30]p, ipcb, 12cp)	R.H. Russell	1898	Nicholson, Wm.	400-650	
Nicholson, William	An Alphabet (1st, folio, ipcb, 26cp)	L: Heinemann	1898	Nicholson, Wm.	500-700	
Nicholson, William	An Alphabet (1st AM, folio, ibds, 26cp)	R.H. Russell	1898	Nicholson, Wm.	500-700	
Nicholson, William	Book of Blokes (1st, sm8vo, [60]p, green/gilt)	L: Faber	[1929]	Nicholson, Wm.	500-700	

AUTHOR	TITLE	PUBLISHER	DATE	ARTIST	PRICE	LC
Nicholson, William	Clever Bill (1st, ob4to, [23]p, yellow ipcb, 21cp)	L: Heinemann	[1926]	Nicholson, Wm.	500-700	
Nicholson, William	Clever Bill (1st AM, ob sm4to, yellow bds, 23p, color)	Doubleday/Page	[1926]	Nicholson, Wm.	425-600	
Wells, David D.	Her Ladyship's Elephant (1st, sm8vo, 234p, tan cl, cvr by...)	Henry Holt & Co.	1898	Nicholson, Wm.	25-40	
Rook, Clarence	Hooligan Nights (1st, 8vo, 289p, rust cl, col frn by...)	L: Richards	1899	Nicholson, Wm.	60-100	*
Davies, William H.	Hour of Magic (1st, 12mo, pcb, gilt, teg, 34p, pep)	L: J. Cape	(1922)	Nicholson, Wm.	150-225	
Henley, William E.	London Types (1st, folio, [30]p, ipcb, 12cp)	L: Heinemann	1898	Nicholson, Wm.	500-700	
Henley, William E.	London Types (1st AM, folio, ibds, [29]p, 12cp)	R.H. Russell	1898	Nicholson, Wm.	300-450	
Sassoon, Siegfried	Memoirs of a Fox Hunting Man (1st AM, lg8vo, 296p, 7pl)	Coward	1929	Nicholson, Wm.	90-140	
Dunne, Finley P.	Mr. Dooley's Philosophy (1st, sm8vo, 263p, red cl, col frn by...)	R.H. Russell	1900	Nicholson, Wm.	60-90	
Nicholson, William	Pirate Twins (1st, ob4to, 28p, ibds, 32p, fp color, pep)	L: Faber	[1929]	Nicholson, Wm.	400-600	
Nicholson, William	Pirate Twins (1st AM, ob8vo, 28p, ibds, color)	Coward	[1929]	Nicholson, Wm.	275-450	
Gay, John	Polly: An Opera (1st, lg8vo, blue bds, 107p, 8cp)	L: Heinemann	1923	Nicholson, Wm.	100-165	
Waugh, Alec	Square Book of Animals (1st, sq4to, [14]p, ibds, 12cp)	L: Heinemann	1900	Nicholson, Wm.	425-600	
Waugh, Alec	Square Book of Animals (1st AM, sq4to, [14]p, ibds, 12cp)	R.H. Russell	1900	Nicholson, Wm.	350-500	R
Pugh, Edwin W.	Tony Drum (1st, sm8vo, 225p, tan cl, 10cp)	Henry Holt & Co.	1898	Nicholson, Wm.	120-180	
Davies, William H.	True Travellers (1st, 8vo, 53p, grey bds, 2-color)	L: J. Cape	1923	Nicholson, Wm.	140-185	
Williams, Margery	Velveteen Rabbit (1st AM, 8vo, ibds, 33p, 7cp, pep)	Doran	(1922)	Nicholson, Wm.	450-600	
Williams, Margery	Velveteen Rabbit (1st, lg8vo, 19p, ipcb, 7cp, pep)	L: Heinemann	1922	Nicholson, Wm.	500-700	
Carlson, Natalie S.	Alphonse, that Bearded One (1st {std}, 8vo, blue cl, 78p, b/w, DJ/2.50)	Harcourt	(1954)	Nicolas	60-90	R
Mordvinoff, Nicolas	Bear's Land (1st, 8vo, [48]p, ibds, 2-color, DJ/2.50)	Coward	(1955)	Nicolas	45-70	*
Bloch, Marie H.	Big Steve: Doubled Quick Tunnelman (1st, 8vo, 71p, ibds, pep, DJ/2.50)	Coward	1952	Nicolas	30-45	*
Lipkind, Will	Billy the Kid (1st {std}, 4to, unpag, color, DJ/3.25)	Harcourt	(1961)	Nicolas	30-50	*
Lipkind, Will	Boy and the Forest (1st {std}, 4to, [40]p, fp 3-color, DJ/3.25)	Harcourt	1964	Nicolas	30-50	*
Lipkind, Will	Boy of the Islands (1st {std}, 8vo, 55p, fp b/w, DJ/2.50)	Harcourt	(1954)	Nicolas	30-45	
Lipkind, Will	Boy with a Harpoon (1st {std}, 8vo, ibds, 58p, b/w, DJ/2.25)	Harcourt	(1952)	Nicolas	30-45	
Lindquist, Willis	Burma Boy (1st, 8vo, 93p, fp b/w, DJ/2.00)	Whittlesey	1953	Nicolas	40-65	R
Schwalje, Earl	Cezar and the Music-Maker (1st {std}, 8vo, 77p, fp 2-color, DJ/2.50)	Knopf	1951	Nicolas	25-45	
Lipkind, Will	Chaga (1st {std}, 4to, [40]p, fp color, DJ/2.50, NYTBI)	Harcourt	(1955)	Nicolas	30-50	
Lipkind, Will	Christmas Bunny (1st {std}, 4to, [49]p, green cl, color, pep, DJ/2.50)	Harcourt	(1953)	Nicolas	70-120	R
Lipkind, Will	Circus Ruckus (1st {std}, 4to, [48]p, fp 3-color, DJ/2.75, NYTBI)	Harcourt	(1954)	Nicolas	50-90	R
Mordvinoff, Nicolas	Coral Island (1st {std}, 8vo, [41]p, ibds, color, DJ/2.75)	Doubleday	(1957)	Nicolas	40-65	
Steele, William O.	Daniel Boone's Echo (1st {std}, 8vo, 78p, b/w, DJ/2.50)	Harcourt	(1957)	Nicolas	25-40	
Steele, William O.	Davy Crockett's Earthquake (1st {std}, 8vo, 63p, fp b/w, DJ/2.25)	Harcourt	(1956)	Nicolas	25-40	
Carlson, Natalie S.	Evangeline, Pigeon of Paris (1st {std}, 8vo, red cl, 70p, fp b/w, DJ/2.75)	Harcourt	(1960)	Nicolas	35-50	
Lipkind, Will	Even Steven (1st {std}, 4to, unpag, ibds, 2-color, DJ/2.25)	Harcourt	(1952)	Nicolas	40-65	
Lipkind, Will	Finders Keepers (1st {std}, 4to, [32]p, pep, 28 color, DJ/2.00, CM)	Harcourt	(1951)	Nicolas	80-125	
Lipkind, Will	Four-Leaf Clover (1st {std}, 4to, [32]p, color, DJ/3.00)	Harcourt	(1959)	Nicolas	45-70	
Carlson, Natalie S.	Hortense, the Cow for a Queen (1st {std}, 8vo, 94p, b/w, DJ/2.75)	Harcourt	(1957)	Nicolas	30-45	
Lipkind, Will	Little Tiny Rooster (1st {std}, 4to, [30]p, fp 3-color, DJ/3.25)	Harcourt	(1960)	Nicolas	45-70	
Lipkind, Will	Magic Feather Duster (1st {std}, [38]p, 2-color, pep, DJ/3.25, NYTBI)	Harcourt	(1958)	Nicolas	50-80	R
Good, Loren D.	Panchito (1st, 8vo, 159p, b/w, DJ/2.75)	Coward	(1955)	Nicolas	20-30	*
Stone, William S.	Pepe was the Saddest Bird (1st {std}, lg8vo, [62]p, ipcb, b/w, DJ/1.75)	Knopf	1944	Nicolas	80-125	R
Lipkind, Will	Perry the Imp (1st {std}, 4to, [38]p, fp 3-color, DJ/2.95)	Harcourt	1956	Nicolas	50-80	R*
Lipkind, Will	Russet and the Two Reds (1st {std}, 4to, [32]p, 2-color, DJ/3.25)	Harcourt	(1962)	Nicolas	30-50	
Stone, William S.	Ship of Flame (1st {std}, 4to, 164p, bds, col frn, b/w, DJ/7.50)	Knopf	1945	Nicolas	60-100	R
Lipkind, Will	Sleepyhead (1st {std}, 4to, green cl, [38]p, 2-color, pep, DJ/3.00)	Harcourt	(1957)	Nicolas	60-90	
Norton, Andre	Star Man's Son, 2250 A.D. (1st {std}, 8vo, 248p, b/w, DJ/2.75)	Harcourt	(1952)	Nicolas	500-700	
Stone, William S.	Tahiti Landfall (1st, 8vo, 308p, b/w, DJ/3.50)	Wm. Morrow	1946	Nicolas	30-50	
Stone, William S.	Thunder Island (1st {std}, 8vo, 194p, 7cp, DJ/2.00)	Knopf	(1942)	Nicolas	40-65	
Lipkind, Will	Two Reds (1st {std}, 4to, [48]p, color, pep, DJ/2.00, CH)	Harcourt	(1950)	Nicolas	80-120	R
Yates, Elizabeth	Around the Year in Iceland (1st, 8vo, 64p, color, pep)	D.C. Heath	1942	Nielsen, Jon	20-35	*
Craik, Dinah	Little Lame Prince (1st, 8vo, 135p, color, pep, RC, DJ/1.25)	World	(1948)	Nielsen, Jon	20-30	
Bradbury, Bianca	The Undergrounders (1st, 8vo, 120p, b/w, DJ/2.95)	NY: Washburn	(1966)	Nielsen, Jon	40-65	*
Asbjornsen, P.C.	East of the Sun, West o/t Moon (1st AM, 4to, 205p, p-o, 25 ticp pep)	Doran	[1914]	Nielsen, Kay	600-800	
Asbjornsen, P.C.	East of the Sun, West o/t Moon (1st, 4to, gilt, 206p, pep, 25 ticp)	L: Hodder	(1914)	Nielsen, Kay	1400-2000	
Asbjornsen, P.C.	East of the Sun, West o/t Moon (8vo, 204p, p-o, cp, pep, later)	Garden City	[1930]	Nielsen, Kay	80-130	
Andersen, Hans C.	Fairy Tales (1st, 4to, 197p, green/gilt, 12 ticp, pep)	L: Hodder	(1924)	Nielsen, Kay	900-1300	
Andersen, Hans C.	Fairy Tales (1st AM, 4to, p-o, 281p, pep, 12 ticp)	Doran	(1924)	Nielsen, Kay	600-900	
Andersen, Hans C.	Fairy Tales (1st {this pub}, lg8vo, p-o, 272p, 8cp)	Garden City	(1932)	Nielsen, Kay	80-130	
Grimm Bros.	Hansel & Gretel (1st AM, 4to, red cl, p-o, gilt, 310p, 12cp)	Doran	(1925)	Nielsen, Kay	300-425	
Quiller-Couch, A.	In Powder & Crinoline (1st, 4to, 164p, ibds, teg, gilt, 24 ticp)	L: Hodder	[1913]	Nielsen, Kay	750-1000	
Wilson, Romer	Red Magic... (1st, sm8vo, red/gilt, 368p, 8cp)	L: J. Cape	(1930)	Nielsen, Kay	500-700	
Wilson, Romer	Red Magic... (1st AM, 8vo, 368p, black cl, uncut, 8cp)	Harcourt	(1931)	Nielsen, Kay	400-650	
Quiller-Couch, A.	Twelve Dancing Princesses (1st AM, lg8vo, gilt, 244p, 16 ticp, pep)	Doran	[1923]	Nielsen, Kay	400-650	
Quiller-Couch, A.	Twelve Dancing Princesses (lg8vo, 244p, 16cp, pep)	Doubleday/Doran	1930	Nielsen, Kay	125-200	
De La Mare, Walter	Old Joe (1st, lg8vo, 29p, pcb, p-o, b/w)	L: Blackwell	[1927]	Nightingale, C.T.	30-50	
De La Mare, Walter	Readings (1st, lg8vo, 436p, b/w woodcuts by...)	Knopf	1927	Nightingale, C.T.	30-50	
Nightingale, Madeleine	Tony-O'-Dreams (1st, lg8vo, p-o, 160p, 8 ticp, pep)	L: Blackwell	1919	Nightingale, C.T.	70-100	*
Lyons, Dorothy	Midnight Moon (1st, 8vo, 276p, b/w, DJ/2.00)	Harcourt	(1941)	Nims, W.C.	100-165	*
Alexander, Anne	ABC of Cars and Trucks (1st {std}, ob4to, [30]p, ibds, color, pep, DJ/2.50)	Doubleday	1956	Ninon	40-65	
Meadowcroft, Enid	Along the Erie Towpath (1st, 8vo, 227p, fp color, pep, DJ/2.00)	Crowell	(1940)	Ninon	30-50	
Quigg, Jane	Hickory Lane (1st, 8vo, 62p, grey cl, b/w, DJ/1.00)	NY: T. Nelson	1938	Ninon	50-85	
Demuth, Averil	House in the Mountains (1st AM, {std}, 8vo, 240p, col frn, b/w, DJ/2.00)	Harper	(1941)	Ninon	60-90	
Ninon	Kit Koala (1st, 8vo, [32]p, ipcb, fp 1-color, pep, DJ/1.25)	Rinehart	(1948)	Ninon	40-65	
Seyfert, Ella	Little Amish Schoolhouse (1st, lg8vo, 136p, dp color, pep, DJ/2.00)	Crowell	1939	Ninon	30-50	*
McDevitt, Jean	Mr. Apple's Family (1st {std}, 8vo, 118p, fp color, DJ/2.00)	Doubleday	1950	Ninon	25-45	*
Krasilovsky, Phyllis	Scaredy Cat (1st {std}, 8vo, unpag, color, DJ/2.00)	Macmillan	1959	Ninon	30-50	
Bertail, Inez	Time for Bed (1st, ob12mo, ibds, [32]p, color, pep, DJ/0.75)	Doubleday/Doran	1939	Ninon	40-65	*

AUTHOR	TITLE	PUBLISHER	DATE	ARTIST	PRICE	LC
Krasilovsky, Phyllis	Very Little Boy (1st {std}, 8vo, [32]p, color, DJ/1.95)	Doubleday	(1962)	Ninon	30-50	
Krasilovsky, Phyllis	Very Little Girl (1st {std}, 8vo, ibds, unpag, 2-color, DJ/1.50)	Doubleday	(1953)	Ninon	30-50	
Bain, Robert N.	Russian Fairy Tales (1st, lg8vo, teg, p-o, 283p, 4cp, 12pl)	L: Harrap	1915	Nisbet, Noel L.	170-240	
Blyton, Enid	Heyo, Brer Rabbit (1st, sm4to, 127p, green cl, 2-color, pep)	L: Newnes	1938	Nixon, Kathleen I.	100-170	*
Browne, Edgar G.	Puck's Broom (1st AM, sm8vo, 237p, red/gilt, 4cp)	Moffat	1923	Nixon, Kathleen I.	50-85	*
Bailey, Margery	Seven Peas in the Pod (1st UK, 8vo, 201p, 4cp by...)	L: Harrap	(1921)	Nixon, Kathleen I.	70-100	
L'Engle, Madeleine	Arm of the Starfish (1st {std}, 8vo, 243p, uncut, DJ/3.50)	Ariel	(1965)	No Illustrations	60-90	
Ullman, James R.	Banner in the Sky (1st {std}, 8vo, 252p, pep, DJ/2.75, NH)	Lippincott	(1954)	No Illustrations	40-65	
Alexander, Lloyd C.	Black Cauldron (1st {std}, 8vo, 224p, DJ/3.95, NH)	Holt, Rinehart	(1965)	No Illustrations	60-90	R
Speare, Elizabeth G.	Bronze Bow (1st, 8vo, 255p, DJ/3.25, NM)	Houghton	1961	No Illustrations	80-120	
McGraw, Eloise J.	Golden Goblet (1st, 8vo, 248p, DJ/3.50, NH)	Coward	(1961)	No Illustrations	40-65	
Alexander, Lloyd C.	High King (1st {std}, 8vo, 285p, ibds, b/w map, DJ/4.50, NM)	Holt, Rinehart	(1968)	No Illustrations	140-200	
DeTrevino, Elizabeth	I, Juan de Pareja (1st {std}, 8vo, 180p, cep, DJ/3.25, NM)	Farrar, Straus	(1965)	No Illustrations	80-140	R
O'Dell, Scott	Island of the Blue Dolphins (1st, 8vo, 184p, uncut, DJ/2.75, NM)	Houghton	1960	No Illustrations	100-175	R
McGraw, Eloise J.	Mara (1st, 4to, 279p, DJ/3.00)	Coward	(1953)	No Illustrations	50-80	
Harris, Rosemary	Moon in the Cloud (1st, 8vo, 176p, DJ, CgM)	L: Faber	1968	No Illustrations	45-70	*
Sleigh, Barbara	No One Must Know (1st AM, 8vo, 192p, DJ/3.50)	Bobbs-Merrill	(1963)	No Illustrations	40-65	
Ish-Kishor, Salamith	Our Eddie (1st, 8vo, 183p, DJ/4.50, NH)	Pantheon	(1969)	No Illustrations	60-90	
Garner, Alan	Owl Service (1st, 8vo, 157p, DJ, CgM)	L: Collins	1967	No Illustrations	120-200	
Garner, Alan	Owl Service (1st AM {std}, 8vo, 202p, DJ/4.00, CgM)	H.Z. Walck	1968	No Illustrations	90-140	
Keith, Harold V.	Rifles for Watie (1st {std}, 8vo, 332p, DJ/3.75, NM)	Crowell	(1957)	No Illustrations	80-120	R
Schaefer, Jack W.	Shane (1st, sm8vo, 214p, DJ/2.50)	Houghton	1949	No Illustrations	600-800	
O'Dell, Scott	Sing Down the Moon (1st {std}, 8vo, 137p, DJ/3.75, NH)	Houghton	1970	No Illustrations	60-90	
Hunt, Irene	Up a Road Slowly (1st {std}, 8vo, 192p, cloth, DJ/3.95, NM)	Follett	1966	No Illustrations	150-225	
L'Engle, Madeleine	Wrinkle in Time (1st {std}, 8vo, 211p, DJ/3.25, NM)	Ariel	(1962)	No Illustrations	75-125	R
Woole, Rose	Animal Legends of Many Lands (4to, gilt, 144p, 12cp)	Tuck/McKay	[1915]	Noble, Edwin	90-150	
Pycraft, W.P.	Animal Why Book (1st AM, sm4to, 90p, p-o, 31 ticp)	Stokes	[1910]	Noble, Edwin	200-300	
Davidson, Gladys	Helpers Without Hands (1st, sm4to, p-o, bds, 118p, 32cp)	L: Wells/Gard.	(1914)	Noble, Edwin	170-240	
Pycraft, W.P.	Pads, Paws & Claws (1st, 4to, ibds, 123p, p-o, 32 ticp)	L: Wells/Gard.	(1911)	Noble, Edwin	200-300	
Ewald, Carl	Twelve Sisters (1st, 8vo, 143p, b/w)	L: Butterworth	1923	Noble, Edwin	30-50	*
Ewing, Juliana H.	Jacanapes (1st, 12mo, 72p, col frn, 4 fp b/w, dep)	McLoughlin	(1906)	Noble-Ives, Sarah	35-60	*
Noble-Ives, Sarah	Key to Betsy's Heart (1st, 12mo, 225p, green cl, 4pl)	Macmillan	1916	Noble-Ives, Sarah	25-40	
Otis, James	Old Ben (1st, 12mo, ipcb, 188p, 7pl)	Harper	1911	Noble-Ives, Sarah	30-50	
Noble-Ives, Sarah	Songs of the Shining Way (1st, 8vo, tan ipcb, 45p, fp b/w)	R.H. Russell	1899	Noble-Ives, Sarah	75-100	*
Noble-Ives, Sarah	Story of Teddy the Bear (1st, lg4to, [42]p, ibds, 5cp)	McLoughlin	[1907]	Noble-Ives, Sarah	180-250	
Stevenson, Rbt. L.	Child's Garden of Verses (1st, lg8vo, 243p, col frn, b/w, pep)	Sears	(1926)	Noe, Eva	30-50	*
Montgomery, R.	Amikuk (1st {std}, 8vo, 204p, b/w, DJ/2.75)	World	(1955)	Nonnast, Marie	25-35	*
Dalgliesh, Alice	Fourth of July Story (1st, 4to, [30]p, fp color, DJ/2.75)	Scribner	(1956)	Nonnast, Marie	60-90	R
Goudey, Alice	Graywings (1st, 8vo, [63]p, 1-color, DJ/2.95)	Scribner	1964	Nonnast, Marie	30-50	*
Montgomery, R.	Whitetail: Story of a Prairie Dog (1st {std}, 8vo, 64p, b/w, DJ/2.50)	World	(1958)	Nonnast, Marie	20-35	
Perrault, Charles	Puss in Boots (1st {std}, 4to, 34p, color, DJ/4.95)	Doubleday	(1970)	Noonan, Julia	25-40	
Brown, Elinor	Little Story Book (1st, 8vo, 30p, color, pep)	Oxford U. Pr.	1940	Norcross, Grace	30-50	
Parrish, Randall	Don MacGrath (1st, 8vo, 269p, 5pl)	McClurg	1910	Norton, John W.	30-50	
DeJong, Dola	Sand for the Sandmen (1st, sm8vo, 87p, 1-color, DJ/2.00)	Scribner	1946	Norton, Natalie	20-30	
Dow, Ethel C.	Diary of a Birthday Doll (1st, 8vo, 88p, p-o, 6cp)	Stern	1908	Nosworthy, Florence	160-250	
Sawyer, Edith A.	Elsa's Gift Home (1st, 8vo, 229p, 6pl)	L.C. Page	1911	Nosworthy, Florence	25-40	*
Nuckel, Otto	Destiny (1st AM, 8vo, [414]p, red cl, woodcuts)	Farrar/Rinehart	(1930)	Nuckel, Otto	100-165	
Nura	All Aboard: We Are Off (1st, 4to, [40]p, fp color, DJ/2.50)	Studio Pub.	(1944)	Nura	100-165	
Nura	Kitten Who Listened (1st, 4to, ibds, 30p, 1-color, pep, DJ/1.50)	Harper	(1950)	Nura	40-65	*
Nura	Mitty Children Fix Things (1st, 4to, gilt, [40]p, fp color, DJ/2.50)	American Studio	(1946)	Nura	50-80	
Nura	Nura's Garden of Betty & Booth (1st, 4to, [50]p, ibds, fp color, DJ/2.00)	Wm. Morrow	1935	Nura	50-80	
Hurlimann, Bettina	William Tell and his Son (1st AM {std}, lg ob4to, [36]p, color, DJ/4.25)	Harcourt	(1967)	Nussbaumer, Paul	40-65	
Metcalf, Suzanne	Annabel (2nd, 8vo, 213p, green cl, 3pl)	Reilly/Britton	(1912)	Nuyttens, Joseph P.	180-270	
Peattie, Elia W.	Azalea at Sunset Gap (1st, sm8vo, tan cl, 286p, 4pl)	Reilly/Britton	(1914)	Nuyttens, Joseph P.	30-50	*
Mitchell, Lebbeus	Bobby in Search of/Birthday (1st, 12mo, pcb, 64p, p-o, gilt, b/w)	Volland	1916	Nuyttens, Joseph P.	40-60	
Van Dyne, Edith	Flying Girl (1st [1], sm8vo, red cl, 232p, 4pl)	Reilly/Britton	(1911)	Nuyttens, Joseph P.	200-300	
Van Dyne, Edith	Flying Girl & her Chum (1st, 12mo, 313p, p-o, red/white, 4pl)	Reilly/Britton	(1912)	Nuyttens, Joseph P.	220-300	
Stow, Edith	Nancy the Joyous (1st, sm8vo, 253p, col frn, decor by...)	Reilly/Britton	1914	Nuyttens, Joseph P.	40-60	
Baum, L. Frank	Phoebe Daring... (1st, 8vo, 298p, grey cl, 4pl)	Reilly/Britton	(1912)	Nuyttens, Joseph P.	200-300	
Nyce, Vera	Adventures of Greyfur Family (1st, 16mo, 76p, 24cp, pep)	Lippincott	(1917)	Nyce, Helen	50-80	
Field, Eugene	Fiddle Dee-Dee (1st, 8vo, 93p, p-o, color)	Saalfield	(1929)	Nyce, Helen	100-160	
Nyce, Vera	Greyfur's Neighbors (1st, 16mo, 76p, 24cp)	Lippincott	(1917)	Nyce, Helen	55-80	*
Tappan, Eva M.	Prince from Nowhere... (1st, sm8vo, 206p, blue cl, 8cp)	Houghton	1928	Nystrom, J.	30-50	*
Mendel, Florence	Little Polish Cousin (1st, 12mo, 147p, 6pl)	L.C. Page	1912	O'Brien, Harriet	30-50	*
Lowe, Samuel E.	In the Court of King Arthur (1st, 8vo, 223p, blue cl, p-o, 6cp, pep)	Western Printing	(1918)	O'Keefe, Neil	50-80	
Bacon, Josephine D.	Biography of a Boy (1st, 8vo, 322p, blue cl, 14pl)	Harper	1910	O'Neill, Rose	60-90	
Wilson, Harry L.	Boss of the Little Arcady (1st, 8vo, green cl, 371p, 4pl)	Lothrop Pub.	1905	O'Neill, Rose	35-60	
Burnham, Clara L.	Clever Betsy (1st, sm8vo, red/gilt, 402p, 3pl)	Houghton	1910	O'Neill, Rose	40-65	
Brainerd, Eleanor H.	For Love of Mary Ellen (1st, 12mo, 43p, tan cl, 4pl)	Harper	1912	O'Neill, Rose	40-65	
O'Neill, Rose	Garda (1st {std}, sm8vo, blue cl, 305p, pep, DJ/2.50)	Doubleday/Doran	1929	O'Neill, Rose	100-150	
O'Neill, Rose	Goblin Woman (1st {std}, 8vo, 345p, b/w, pep)	Doubleday/Doran	1930	O'Neill, Rose	50-80	
Fillmore, Parker H.	Hickory Limb (1st, 12mo, green cl, 70p, p-o, 4pl)	J. Lane	1910	O'Neill, Rose	55-80	
O'Neill, Rose	Kewpie Kutouts (1st, 4to, bds, p-o, 48p, pep, color)	Stokes	(1914)	O'Neill, Rose	800-1100	
O'Neill, Rose	Kewpie Primer (1st, sq8vo, 118p, color, cep)	Stokes	(1916)	O'Neill, Rose	400-600	
O'Neill, Rose	Kewpies & Dotty Darling (4to, p-o, tan bds, 79p, 1-color, pep)	Stokes	(1912)	O'Neill, Rose	500-700	R
O'Neill, Rose	Kewpies & Dotty Darling (1st, 4to, 88p, tan bds, p-o, 1-color, pep)	Doran	(1912)	O'Neill, Rose	600-900	
O'Neill, Rose	Kewpies & Runaway Baby (1st {std}, 8vo, 111p, red cl, color, cep)	Doubleday/Doran	1928	O'Neill, Rose	250-400	
O'Neill, Rose	Kewpies: Their Book (1st, lg4to, tan bds, p-o, 80p, 1-color, dep)	Stokes	(1913)	O'Neill, Rose	500-700	R

AUTHOR	TITLE	PUBLISHER	DATE	ARTIST	PRICE	LC
O'Neill, Rose	Lady in the White Veil (1st, 12mo, blue cl, 350p, col frn, 4pl)	Harper	1909	O'Neill, Rose	90-140	
Wilson, Harry L.	Lions of the Lord (1st, 8vo, p-o, 520p, 6pl)	Lothrop Pub.	(1903)	O'Neill, Rose	35-60	
Fillmore, Parker H.	Little Question of Ladies' Rights (1st, 12mo, 79p, p-o, b/w)	J. Lane	1916	O'Neill, Rose	40-60	
O'Neill, Rose	Loves of Edwy (1st, sm8vo, tan cl, 432p, b/w)	Lothrop Pub.	(1904)	O'Neill, Rose	60-100	
O'Neill, Rose	Master-Mistress (1st, 8vo, maroon bds, 227p, 9pl)	Knopf	1922	O'Neill, Rose	70-120	
Lee, Agnes	Round Rabbit (1st, 12mo, brown cl, 52p, 6pl)	Copeland & Day	1898	O'Neill, Rose	200-325	
Marks, Gerald	Sing a Song of Safety (1st, lg4to, 71p, spiral wraps, fp 3-color)	NY: I. Caesar	1937	O'Neill, Rose	60-100	
Wilson, Harry L.	The Seeker (1st, 8vo, green cl, 341p, b/w)	Doubleday/Page	1904	O'Neill, Rose	30-50	
O'Neill, George	Tomorrow's House (1st {std}, sq8vo, purple cl, 159p, b/w, pep)	Dutton	1930	O'Neill, Rose	70-100	
Vorse, Mary Heaton	Very Little Person (1st, 12mo, 163p, green/gilt, 8pl)	Houghton	1911	O'Neill, Rose	40-65	
Stevenson, Rbt. L.	Child's Garden of Verses (1st, sm8vo, 131p, cp, pep)	Chi: Flanagan	(1908)	O'Reilly, E.D.	50-80	*
Rollins, Charlene	Christmas Gif' (1st, lg8vo, 119p, fp b/w, cep, DJ/4.95)	Follett	(1963)	O'Sullivan, Tom	50-85	
Sawyer, Ruth	Old Con and Patrick (1st, 8vo, 137p, col frn, b/w, DJ/2.00)	Viking	1946	O'Toole, Cathal	30-50	
Kingsley, Charles	Westward Ho! (1st, lg8vo, 604p, p-o, 14cp, pep)	Jacobs	[1920]	Oakley, Thornton	70-100	
Rives, Amelia	Damsel Errant (1st, 16mo, teg, 211p, uncut, 4pl)	Lippincott	1898	Oakley, Violet	90-120	*
Skinner, Charles M.	Do-Nothing Days (1st, 12mo, 219p, teg, frn by...)	Lippincott	1899	Oakley, Violet	90-120	
Longfellow, H.W.	Evangeline (1st, 8vo, 143p, teg, gilt, 5cp by...)	Houghton	1897	Oakley, Violet	200-300	
King, Charles	From School to Battlefield (1st, 8vo, beige/gilt, 322p, 6pl)	Lippincott	1899	Oakley, Violet	50-85	
Gale, Norman	June Romance (1st, 12mo, teg, blue cl, 193p, b/w)	Stone/Kimball	1899	Oakley, Violet	85-135	
Walford, Lucy B.	Little Legacy (1st, 12mo, blue cl, 344p, teg, frn by...)	Herbert Stone	1899	Oakley, Violet	80-120	
Spofford, Harriet	Maid He Married (1st, 16mo, blue cl, 210p, teg, frn by...)	Stone/Kimball	1899	Oakley, Violet	80-125	
Otis, James	Princess & Joe Potter (1st, sq8vo, 249p, 7pl)	Estes & Lauriat	(1898)	Oakley, Violet	80-120	
Thanet, Octave	Slave to Duty (1st, 12mo, 221p, teg, frn by...)	Herbert Stone	1898	Oakley, Violet	60-100	
Skinner, Charles M.	With Feet to the Earth (1st, 12mo, 231p, teg, frn by...)	Lippincott	1899	Oakley, Violet	100-150	
Whitehorn, Alan L.	Wonder Tales of Old Japan (1st, 8vo, gilt, 173p, p-o, 12cp)	L: Jack	1911	Obata, Shozan	70-100	*
Whitehorn, Alan L.	Wonder Tales of Old Japan (1st AM, 8vo, 173p, teg, p-o, 12cp)	Stokes	(1912)	Obata, Shozan	70-100	*
Kendall, Carol S.	Big Splash (1st, 8vo, 217p, b/w, DJ/3.00)	Viking	(1960)	Obligado, Lilian	30-50	
Best, Herbert	Desmond the Dog Detective (1st, 8vo, 96p, b/w, DJ/2.50)	Viking	(1962)	Obligado, Lilian	20-30	
Best, Herbert	Desmond the Peppermint Ghost (1st, 8vo, 93p, b/w, DJ/3.00)	Viking	1965	Obligado, Lilian	25-40	*
Gates, Doris	Elderberry Bush (1st, 8vo, 160p, fp b/w, DJ/3.50)	Viking	(1967)	Obligado, Lilian	25-40	
Obligado, George	Gaucho Boy (1st, 8vo, 63p, b/w, DJ/2.50)	Viking	(1961)	Obligado, Lilian	20-30	
Coatsworth, Eliz.	Jock's Island (1st, 8vo, 75p, fp b/w, DJ/2.75)	Viking	(1963)	Obligado, Lilian	20-30	
Untermeyer, Louis	Kitten Who Barked (1st, ob4to, ibds, [32]p, color)	Golden Press	(1962)	Obligado, Lilian	40-65	R
MacIntyre, Carlyle F.	Pig that Ate Truffles (1st, sm ob4to, ibds, [25]p, color, pep, DJ/2.95)	Golden Press	(1963)	Obligado, Lilian	50-80	*
Thompson, Vivian L.	Sad Day, Glad Day (1st, sm8vo, [40]p, b/w, DJ/2.50)	Holiday House	1962	Obligado, Lilian	30-50	
Jackson, Jacqueline	Taste of Spruce Gum (1st {std}, 8vo, 212p, b/w, DJ/3.95)	Little/Brown	(1966)	Obligado, Lilian	25-40	*
Cabassa, Victoria	Trixie and the Tiger (1st, sm4to, [41]p, fp color, pep, DJ/3.50)	Abelard-Schuman	1968	Obligado, Lilian	40-65	
Zolotow, Charlotte	White Marble (1st, 4to, unpag, fp 2-color, pep, DJ/2.75)	Abelard-Schuman	1963	Obligado, Lilian	40-65	
Kenny, Herbert A.	Dear Dolphin (1st {std}, 8vo, 174p, blue cl, b/w, DJ/3.95)	Random	(1967)	Oechsli, Kelly	30-45	
Alan, Sandy	Plaid Peacock (1st, ob4to, [40]p, color, cep, DJ/3.95)	Pantheon	(1965)	Oechsli, Kelly	25-40	
Scheer, Julian	Upside Down Day (1st, lg8vo, [32]p, fp color, DJ/3.95)	Holiday House	1968	Oechsli, Kelly	30-50	
Williston, Teresa P.	Japanese Fairy Tales (1st, sm8vo, blue cl, 88p, 8 fp color, pep)	Rand/McNally	(1904)	Ogawa, Sanchi	55-80	
Ogden, Ruth	Little Queen of Hearts (1st, 8vo, 232p, 15 fp b/w, gilt)	Stokes	(1893)	Ogden, Henry A.	40-60	*
Ogden, Ruth	Loyal Little Redcoat (1st, 8vo, 217p, gilt, b/w, PPPa)	Stokes	1890	Ogden, Henry A.	70-125	
Fryer, Alfred C.	Fairy Tales from the Harz Mountains (1st, lg8vo, 206p, gilt, b/w)	L: D. Nutt	1908	Ogders, Alice M.	75-100	*
Fenton, Edward	Big Yellow Balloon (1st {std}, ob4to, [48]p, color, DJ/3.95)	Doubleday	(1967)	Ohlsson, Ib	30-50	
Walters, Marguerite	City-Country ABC (1st {std}, sm8vo, unpag, color, DJ/2.95)	Doubleday	(1966)	Ohlsson, Ib	30-45	
Sachs, Marilyn	Laura's Luck (1st {std}, 8vo, 181p, b/w, DJ/3.25)	Doubleday	(1965)	Ohlsson, Ib	20-30	*
Williams, Jay	Philbert the Fearful (1st {std}, 8vo, 48p, color, DJ/3.25)	Norton	(1966)	Ohlsson, Ib	25-45	*
Lauring, Paul	Stone Daggers (1st AM {std}, 8vo, 160p, b/w, DJ/3.50)	Macmillan	(1964)	Ohlsson, Ib	40-65	
Gilly Bear	Adventures of Peterkin (1st, lg8vo, 153p, brown/gilt, 12cp)	NY: S. Gabriel	(1916)	Ohrenschall, Helen	75-100	
Gilly Bear	Tom Tit Tales (1st, 4to, 155p, purple/gilt, 12cp)	NY: S. Gabriel	(1915)	Ohrenschall, Helen	70-100	
Gordon, Hampden C.	Golden Key (1st, 8vo, 223p, col frn, 5 fp b/w)	L: J. Murray	(1932)	Oldfield, M.	35-60	*
Olds, Elizabeth	Big Fire (1st, lg sq8vo, red cl, [32]p, color, pep, DJ/2.00)	Houghton	1945	Olds, Elizabeth	40-65	
Olds, Elizabeth	Deep Treasure: Story of Oil (1st, 4to, [36]p, fp color, DJ/3.00)	Houghton	1958	Olds, Elizabeth	30-50	
Olds, Elizabeth	Feather Mountain (1st, lg ob8vo, aqua cl, 27p, color, pep, DJ/2.00, CH)	Houghton	1951	Olds, Elizabeth	65-90	
Olds, Elizabeth	Little Una (1st, 4to, [28]p, fp color, DJ/3.25)	Scribner	(1963)	Olds, Elizabeth	30-50	
Olds, Elizabeth	Plop Plop Ploppie (1st, 4to, [30]p, 3-color, DJ/2.95)	Scribner	(1962)	Olds, Elizabeth	30-50	
Olds, Elizabeth	Riding the Rails (1st, lg ob8vo, 43p, color, dep, DJ/2.50)	Houghton	1948	Olds, Elizabeth	40-60	*
Fish, Helen D.	Butterfly Land (1st AM, ob4to, [15]p, p-o, 14p, 7cp)	Stokes	1931	Olfers, Sibylle	150-220	
Fish, Helen D.	When the Root Children Wake Up (1st AM, 4to, [22]p, p-o, 9cp, pep)	Stokes	1930	Olfers, Sibylle	200-300	R
Gratacap, L.P.	New Northland (1st, sm8vo, 391p, blue/gilt, 16pl)	NY: T. Benton	1915	Operti, Albert	120-200	
Aesopus	Aesop's Fables (1st, 8vo, 318p, color)	Lippincott	1916	Opper, Frederick B.	55-80	*
Mother Goose	Mother Goose Nursery Rhymes (1st, sm8vo, 320p, col frn, b/w)	Lippincott	1900	Opper, Frederick B.	60-100	*
Martin, Patricia	Long Ago Christmas (1st, ob4to, ibds, 31p, 2-color)	Putnam	(1968)	Orbaan, Albert	20-30	
Holland, Marion	No Room for a Dog (1st {std}, 8vo, 79p, 1-color, pep, DJ/1.95)	Random	(1959)	Orbaan, Albert	40-65	*
Darwall, Blanche	Martin in Fairyland (1st, 4to, 165p, 10 fp b/w)	L: Simpkin	1924	Ord, E.R.	50-80	
Bowen, William	Solario the Tailor (1st, sm8vo, 232p, gilt, 4cp, pep)	Macmillan	1922	Ormsbee, J.	25-40	
Boylston, Helen D.	Sue Barton: Rural Nurse (1st {std}, 8vo, 244p, b/w, DJ/2.00)	Little/Brown	1939	Orr, Forrest W.	250-400	
Coatsworth, Eliz.	Toast to the King (1st, 8vo, 159p, b/w, pep, DJ/1.50)	Coward	(1940)	Orr, Forrest W.	30-50	
Foley, Dorothy C.	When Our Ship Comes In (1st, 4to, ibds, [34]p, color, pep, DJ/1.00)	Saalfield	1938	Orr, Forrest W.	45-70	
Mother Goose	Mother Goose Nursery Rhymes (1st, 4to, ibds, 128p, 16pl)	L: Jack	[1915]	Orr, Jack	170-220	
N/A	Arabian Nights (1st AM, 8vo, 294p, 15cp)	Henry Holt & Co.	1913	Orr, Monro S.	75-100	
N/A	Arabian Nights (1st, lg8vo, teg, 294p, gilt, 15cp)	L: Harrap	1913	Orr, Monro S.	90-120	
Grimm Bros.	Fairy Tales (1st, 8vo, 333p, p-o, 20cp)	L: Harrap	(1914)	Orr, Monro S.	80-130	
Andersen, Hans C.	Fairy Tales (1st, 8vo, 309p, cream cl, 8cp)	L: Harrap	1925	Orr, Monro S.	60-90	*
Kingsley, Charles	Hereward the Wake (1st, 8vo, 196p, pcb, p-o, 8cp)	L: Jack	[1910]	Orr, Monro S.	75-100	*
Mother Goose	Mother Goose (1st, 4to, teg, 255p, 16cp)	L: Harrap	(1915)	Orr, Monro S.	180-240	

ARTIST: 148

AUTHOR	TITLE	PUBLISHER	DATE	ARTIST	PRICE	LC
Mother Goose	Mother Goose (1st AM, lg8vo, 255p, 16cp)	McKay	(1915)	Orr, Monro S.	100-160	*
Orr, Monro S.	The Alphabet (1st, 4to, ibds, [60]p, 26cp)	L: J.M. Dent	1931	Orr, Monro S.	145-225	
Stevenson, Rbt. L.	Treasure Island (1st, 8vo, red/gilt, 252p, 10cp)	L: Muller	1934	Orr, Monro S.	100-160	
N/A	World's Fairy Book (1st, lg8vo, 256p, 12cp)	L: Harrap	(1930)	Orr, Monro S.	120-170	
Brymer, John	Gammon and Spinach (1st, ob4to, ibds, 103p, fp color)	L: Blackie	[1901]	Orr, Stewart	250-350	
N/A	Two Jolly Mariners (1st, lg ob8vo, [52]p, ibds, 24 fp color)	L: Blackie	(1915)	Orr, Stewart	150-220	
Ort, Jane	Mr. Mogo Mouse (1st, 12mo, ibds, 39p, color, pep)	Volland	(1930)	Ort, Jane	60-100	
Walker, Margaret C.	Tales Come True & Tales Made New (1st, 8vo, 149p, p-o, color)	Baker/Taylor	1910	Orwig, Louise	35-50	
Ciardi, John	I Met a Man (1st, lg8vo, 74p, 1-color, DJ/2.75)	Houghton	1961	Osborn, Robert	40-65	
Nash, Ogden	Santa Go Home (1st {std}, 8vo, 56p, green cl, 2-color, DJ/4.95)	Little/Brown	(1967)	Osborn, Robert	40-65	
Malkus, Alida S.	Animals of the High Andes (1st, 8vo, 160p, DJ/3.50)	Abelard-Schuman	(1965)	Osmond, Edward	20-35	
Osmond, Edward	Valley Grows Up (1st, 4to, ibds, 81p, 10 dp color, CgM)	L: Oxford U.Pr.	1953	Osmond, Edward	50-80	
Browning, Robert	Men and Women (1st, sm8vo, green/gilt, teg, 312p, 15pl)	L: Dent	1903	Ospovat, Henry	70-100	
Arnold, Matthew	Poems (1st, 12mo, brown/gilt, 374p, teg, uncut, 18pl)	J. Lane	1900	Ospovat, Henry	50-80	
Shakespeare, Wm.	Songs (1st, 12mo, 140p, uncut, green/gilt, teg, 11pl)	J. Lane	1901	Ospovat, Henry	60-80	
Mabie, Hamilton W.	Fairy Tales Every Child Should Know (1st, sm8vo, 370p, pep, b/w)	Doubleday/Page	1905	Ostertag, Blanche	100-160	
Muller, F. Max	Memories... (1st [new ed], 8vo, 135p, teg, gilt, p-o, 8pl)	McClurg	1902	Ostertag, Blanche	40-60	
Forsythe, Clarence	Old Songs for Young Americans (1st, ob4to, 46p, green cl, color)	Doubleday/Page	1901	Ostertag, Blanche	100-160	
Adams, Julia D.	Vaino: Boy of New Finland (1st, 8vo, 273p, pep, NH)	Dutton	1929	Ostman, Lempi	50-80	*
Blanchard, Amy E.	Dear Little Girl's Summer Holidays (1st, sm8vo, 283p, 5cp)	Jacobs	(1911)	Otis, E.	30-50	*
Montgomery, R.	Mystery of Crystal Canyon (1st {std}, 8vo, 216p, b/w, DJ/2.50)	Winston	(1951)	Oughton, Taylor	20-30	
Outhwaite, Ida R.	Blossom: A Fairy Story (1st sm4to, p-o, bds/gilt, 94p, 8cp, pep)	L: A&C Black	(1928)	Outhwaite, Ida R.	700-900	
Outhwaite, Ida R.	Bunny & Brownie (1st UK, sm4to, 99p, ibds, 8cp, 8pl, p-o, pep)	L: A&C Black	(1930)	Outhwaite, Ida R.	600-900	
Daskein, Tarella	Chimney Town (1st, lg8vo, 238p, blue cl, color)	L: A&C Black	(1934)	Outhwaite, Ida R.	250-400	
Outhwaite, Grenbry	Enchanted Forest (1st, 4to, 93p, gilt, pep, 16 ticp, 15pl)	L: A&C Black	1921	Outhwaite, Ida R.	700-1000	
Outhwaite, Annie R.	Fairyland (1st AM, folio, 165p, 19cp, pep)	Stokes	1929	Outhwaite, Ida R.	900-1500	
Outhwaite, Ida R.	Fairyland (1st UK, lg4to, blue cl, 128p, 16cp, pep)	L: A&C Black	(1931)	Outhwaite, Ida R.	900-1400	
Danks, Bertha M.	Janet & the Fairies (1st, sm8vo, 64p, 4cp)	L: A&C Black	(1937)	Outhwaite, Ida R.	250-400	
Power, Phyllis	Legends from the Outback (1st, 8vo, 127p, col frn, DJ)	L: J.M. Dent	(1958)	Outhwaite, Ida R.	120-170	
Outhwaite, Ida R.	Little Fairy Sister (1st, 4to, gilt, ibds, 8cp, 8pl)	L: A&C Black	1923	Outhwaite, Ida R.	800-1000	
Outhwaite, Ida R.	Little Fairy Sister (2nd, 4to, 91p, 8cp, pep)	L: A&C Black	1929	Outhwaite, Ida R.	250-400	
Outhwaite, I. & A.	Little Green Road to Fairyland (1st, 4to, 103p, bds, p-o, 8cp)	L: A&C Black	1922	Outhwaite, Ida R.	700-1000	
Outhwaite, I. & A.	Little Green Road to Fairyland (1st AM, 4to, ibds, 102p, 8cp, pep)	Dutton	[1922]	Outhwaite, Ida R.	600-900	
Outhwaite, Ida R.	Sixpence to Spend (1st, 4to, 92p, bds, 5 ticp)	Angus/Robertson	1935	Outhwaite, Ida R.	425-600	
Henty, G.A.	On the Irrawaddy (1st, 12mo, 352p, blue/gilt, 8pl)	L: Blackie	1897	Overend, William H.	140-200	
Nash, Ogden	Musical Zoo (1st {std}, 4to, 47p, cloth, b/w, DJ/2.50)	Little/Brown	1947	Owen, Frank	60-90	
Grimm Bros.	Robber Bridegroom (1st, lg4to, p-o, 39p, pep, 8 ticp)	L: A&C Black	1922	Owen, H.S.	200-300	
Cornish, Sam	Your Hand in Mine (1st {std}, 8vo, 32p, b/w, DJ/3.25)	Harcourt	(1970)	Owens, Carl	50-80	
Mahy, Margaret	Dragon of an Ordinary Family (1st, ob4to, [41]p, color, KGM)	L: Heinemann	1969	Oxenbury, Helen	70-125	
Tolstoy, Alexei	Great Big Enormous Turnip (1st AM, sm8vo, [34]p, color, DJ/3.95)	F. Watts	(1968)	Oxenbury, Helen	30-50	*
Lear, Edward	Quangle Wangle's Hat (1st, 4to, [32]p, color, DJ, KGM)	L: Heinemann	(1969)	Oxenbury, Helen	60-90	
Lear, Edward	Quangle Wangle's Hat (1st AM, 4to, [32]p, color, pep, DJ/4.95, KGM)	F. Watts	(1970)	Oxenbury, Helen	50-85	
Carroll, Lewis	Alice... & Through... (1st, 8vo, ibds, 284p, 2-color, pep)	Whitman	(1955)	Paflin, Roberta	30-50	
Lambert, Janet	Candy Kane (1st {std}, 8vo, 184p, b/w, DJ/2.00)	Dutton	1943	Paflin, Roberta	100-160	
Lambert, Janet	Just Jenifer (1st {std}, sm8vo, 187p, b/w, DJ/2.25)	Dutton	1945	Paflin, Roberta	120-180	
Moore, Clement C.	Night Before Christmas (1st, lg8vo, ibds, [16]p, color, DJ/1.00)	Dutton	(1944)	Paflin, Roberta	50-80	
Andersen, Hans C.	Tales from Andersen (1st {std}, lg8vo, 78p, color, DJ/1.50)	Dutton	1946	Paflin, Roberta	75-100	*
Grimm Bros.	Tales from Grimm (1st {std}, lg8vo, ibds, 78p, color, DJ/1.50)	Dutton	1945	Paflin, Roberta	65-90	
Henty, G.A.	Through the Fray (1st, 8vo, 384p, brown cl, fp b/w)	L: Blackie	1886	Paget, Henry M.	80-140	
Goldsmith, Oliver	Vicar of Wakefield (1st, 8vo, AEG, 224p, green/gilt, 5pl)	L: Nister	[1898]	Paget, Henry M.	60-90	
Doyle, Arthur Conan	Desert Drama (1st AM, sm8vo, 277p, tan cl, 32pl)	Lippincott	1898	Paget, Sidney	120-200	
Doyle, Arthur Conan	Memoirs of Sherlock Holmes (1st, 8vo, AEG, blue/gilt, 279p, b/w)	L: G. Newnes	1894	Paget, Sidney	1000-1600	
N/A	Arabian Nights (1st, 8vo, gilt, AEG, 328p, 6cp, pep)	Nister/Dutton	[1907]	Paget, Walter	120-180	
Henty, G.A.	At Agincourt (1st, 12mo, green cl, 384p, 12pl, cep)	L: Blackie	1897	Paget, Walter	100-175	
Henty, G.A.	Condemned as a Nihilist (1st, 12mo, 352p, gilt, 10pl, cep)	L: Blackie	1893	Paget, Walter	100-170	
Stevenson, Rbt. L.	Master of Ballantrae (1st, 8vo, 349p, 12cp)	L: Cassell	1911	Paget, Walter	40-60	*
Smeaton, William H.	Mystery of the Pacific (1st, 8vo, 335p, red/gilt, 8pl)	L: Blackie	1899	Paget, Walter	70-100	
Jameson, Anna	Shakespeare's Heroines (lg8vo, 308p, gilt, AEG, 6cp, pep)	L: Nister	[1900]	Paget, Walter	100-150	
Lamb, Charles	Tales from Shakespeare (lg8vo, AEG, 319p, gilt, 6cp, pep)	L: Nister	[1901]	Paget, Walter	100-150	
Stevenson, Rbt. L.	Treasure Island (1st AM, 12mo, 388p, fp b/w)	Scribner	1900	Paget, Walter	55-80	*
Henty, G.A.	Treasure of the Incas (1st, 8vo, 340p, green/gilt, 8pl)	L: Blackie	1903	Paget, Walter	80-140	
Henty, G.A.	Under Wellington's Command (1st, 12mo, 386p, blue/gilt, 12pl)	L: Blackie	1899	Paget, Walter	125-200	
Henty, G.A.	With Frederick the Great (1st, 12mo, 384p, red/gilt, 12pl)	L: Blackie	1898	Paget, Walter	150-220	
Paget-Fredericks, J.	Green-Pipes (1st {1st bk.}, lg4to, 50p, green/gilt, 6cp, pep)	Macmillan	1929	Paget-Fredericks, J.	80-140	
Amsden, Dora	Macaroni Tree (1st, 4to, ipcb, 58p, 1-color)	Hebberd	1927	Paget-Fredericks, J.	30-50	
Paget-Fredericks, J.	Miss Pert's Christmas Tree (1st, 4to, red/gilt, 24p, 6cp, pep)	Macmillan	1929	Paget-Fredericks, J.	80-140	
Millay, Edna St. V.	Princess Marries the Page (1st {std}, lg8vo, 50p, bds, col frn)	Harper	1932	Paget-Fredericks, J.	80-140	R
Anderson, Mildred	Sandra and the Right Prince (1st, 8vo, 70p, b/w, DJ/2.50)	Oxford U. Pr.	1951	Paget-Fredericks, J.	25-40	
Asbjornsen, P.C.	Fifteen Norse Tales (1st, 8vo, 180p)	L: Nelson	1931	Pailthorpe, Doris	60-80	*
Aesopus	Aesop's Fables (1st, 4to, ipcb, 92p, color, pep)	Doubleday	1954	Palazzo, Tony	30-45	
Palazzo, Tony	Amerigo, the Wandering Tortoise (1st {std}, 4to, 56p, color, DJ/2.95)	Duell, Sloan	(1965)	Palazzo, Tony	20-35	
Palazzo, Tony	Animal Babies (1st {std}, lg4to, ibds, gilt, 88p, color, DJ/2.50)	Garden City	1960	Palazzo, Tony	30-50	*
Palazzo, Tony	Animal Folk Tales of America (1st {std}, lg4to, ibds, 88p, color, DJ/2.95)	Doubleday	1961	Palazzo, Tony	30-45	
Sharfman, Amalie	Beagle Named Bertram (1st, 8vo, 116p, b/w, DJ/2.50)	Crowell	(1954)	Palazzo, Tony	30-45	
Palazzo, Tony	Bianco and the New World (1st, 4to, 64p, green cl, b/w, pep, DJ/2.75)	Viking	(1957)	Palazzo, Tony	30-50	
Palazzo, Tony	Bird Alphabet (1st {std}, 4to, ibds, [58]p, color, pep, DJ/2.95)	Duell, Sloan	(1966)	Palazzo, Tony	30-45	
Palazzo, Tony	Cat Alphabet (1st {std}, 4to, ibds, [56]p, color, pep, DJ/2.95)	Duell, Sloan	(1966)	Palazzo, Tony	30-45	
Palazzo, Tony	Charley the Horse (1st, sq4to, 56p, color, pep, DJ/2.50)	Viking	1950	Palazzo, Tony	40-65	

AUTHOR	TITLE	PUBLISHER	DATE	ARTIST	PRICE	LC
Thayer, Jane	Chicken in the Tunnel (1st, 8vo, 48p, fp 1-color, pep, DJ/2.00)	Wm. Morrow	1956	Palazzo, Tony	25-45	
Palazzo, Tony	Did You Say Dogs? (1st, lg8vo, 43p, color, DJ/2.50)	Garrard Pub.	(1964)	Palazzo, Tony	25-45	
Palazzo, Tony	Dinosaur Alphabet (1st {std}, 4to, unpag, color, DJ/2.95)	Duell, Sloan	(1963)	Palazzo, Tony	25-45	
Graham, Al	Down with Dinosaurs! (1st {std}, 12mo, 61p, b/w, DJ/2.50)	Duell, Sloan	(1963)	Palazzo, Tony	20-30	
Palazzo, Tony	Elephant Alphabet (1st, 4to, [41]p, color, pep, DJ/2.95)	Duell, Sloan	(1961)	Palazzo, Tony	30-45	
Palazzo, Tony	Federico the Flying Squirrel (1st, 4to, 54p, ipcb, color, pep, DJ/2.50)	Viking	1951	Palazzo, Tony	40-65	
Palazzo, Tony	Fireman: Save My Cat! (1st, sm4to, [42]p, fp color, DJ/2.95)	Abelard-Schuman	1964	Palazzo, Tony	30-50	*
Kjelgaard, Jim	Forest Patrol (1st [1st bk.], 8vo, 293p, rust cl, fp b/w, DJ/2.00)	Holiday House	(1941)	Palazzo, Tony	60-100	
Grimm Bros.	Four Musicians (1st {std}, 4to, ibds, [24]p, fp color, pep, DJ)	Doubleday	1962	Palazzo, Tony	30-45	*
Palazzo, Tony	Giant Nursery Book (1st, lg4to, ibds, 188p, color, pep, DJ/3.95)	Garden City	1957	Palazzo, Tony	55-80	*
Palazzo, Tony	Golden Girl (1st, lg8vo, 43p, color, pep, DJ/2.50)	Garrard Pub.	(1963)	Palazzo, Tony	25-40	
Palazzo, Tony	Goldilocks & the Three Bears (1st {std}, 4to, ibds, [34]p, color, DJ/1.00)	Garden City	1959	Palazzo, Tony	25-45	
Palazzo, Tony	Great Othello (1st, sm ob4to, 48p, blue cl, 1-color, DJ/2.00)	Viking	1952	Palazzo, Tony	40-65	
Palazzo, Tony	Henny-Penny and Chicken Little (1st {std}, 4to, unpag, color, pep, DJ/1.00)	Garden City	1960	Palazzo, Tony	30-50	
Graves, Elizabeth	Hey, Horses! (1st, lg8vo, 42p, color, pep, DJ)	Garrard Pub.	(1965)	Palazzo, Tony	25-40	
Palazzo, Tony	Jan and the Reindeer (1st, lg8vo, 42p, color, pep, DJ/2.50)	Garrard Pub.	(1963)	Palazzo, Tony	25-40	
Palazzo, Tony	Let's Go to the Circus (1st {std}, lg4to, 88p, ibds, color, pep, DJ/2.95)	Doubleday	1961	Palazzo, Tony	25-40	
Palazzo, Tony	Let's Go to the Jungle (1st {std}, lg4to, 88p, ibds, color, pep, DJ/2.95)	Doubleday	(1962)	Palazzo, Tony	25-40	
Bible	Lord is My Shepherd: 23rd Psalm (1st, sm8vo, [32]p, color, DJ/3.75)	H.Z. Walck	1965	Palazzo, Tony	25-40	
Palazzo, Tony	Monkey Alphabet (1st {std}, 4to, [54]p, ibds, color, pep, DJ/2.50)	Duell, Sloan	1962	Palazzo, Tony	30-50	
Mother Goose	Mother Goose Nursery Almanac (1st {std}, folio, ibds, 88p, color, DJ/2.50)	Garden City	1960	Palazzo, Tony	90-160	*
Graham, Al	Mouse with a Small Guitar (1st, lg8vo, 35p, grey cl, color, pep, DJ/1.50)	Welch Pub. Co.	(1947)	Palazzo, Tony	50-80	
Palazzo, Tony	Mr. Whistle's Secret (1st, sm4to, 52p, fp color, DJ/2.50)	Viking	1953	Palazzo, Tony	25-45	
Palazzo, Tony	Noah's Ark (1st, lg4to, ibds, [88]p, color, pep, DJ/2.50)	Garden City	(1955)	Palazzo, Tony	40-65	
Colver, Anne	Old Bet (1st, 4to, [52]p, color, pep, DJ/3.00)	Knopf	(1957)	Palazzo, Tony	25-35	
Liers, Emil	Otter's Story (1st, 8vo, blue cl, 191p, fp b/w, DJ/2.50)	Viking	1953	Palazzo, Tony	55-80	R
Prokofieff, Serge	Peter & the Wolf (1st {std}, lg4to, ibds, 88p, color, pep, DJ/2.95)	Doubleday	1961	Palazzo, Tony	40-65	
Palazzo, Tony	Pig for Tom (1st, lg8vo, 42p, color, pep, DJ/2.50)	Garrard Pub.	(1963)	Palazzo, Tony	25-40	
Palazzo, Tony	Ramona Knew What She Wanted (1st, sm4to, [41]p, 2-color, pep, DJ/2.95)	Abelard-Schuman	(1964)	Palazzo, Tony	30-50	
Graham, Al	Rhymes of Squire O'Squirrel (1st {std}, 4to, 60p, b/w, DJ/2.50)	Duell, Sloan	(1963)	Palazzo, Tony	30-45	
Thomajan, Puzant K.	Runaway House (1st, lg8vo, 45p, color, pep, DJ/1.50)	Rittenhouse	(1941)	Palazzo, Tony	30-50	
Palazzo, Tony	Secret of Alexander's Horse (1st {std}, 4to, [42]p, ibds, color, DJ/2.95)	Duell, Sloan	(1965)	Palazzo, Tony	25-45	
Palazzo, Tony	Simple Simon (1st {std}, 4to, unpag, ibds, color, DJ/1.00)	Garden City	1959	Palazzo, Tony	30-45	
Graham, Al	Songs for a Small Guitar (1st {std}, 4to, ibds, 59p, 1-color, DJ/2.50)	Duell, Sloan	(1962)	Palazzo, Tony	30-45	
White, Anne H.	Story of Serapina (1st, 4to, 128p, orange cl, b/w, DJ/2.50)	Viking	1951	Palazzo, Tony	35-60	*
Palazzo, Tony	Story of Snowmand (1st {std}, 4to, [60]p, 2-color, ipcb, DJ/2.50)	Duell, Sloan	1962	Palazzo, Tony	25-40	
Palazzo, Tony	Susie the Cat (1st, 4to, 50p, color, pep, DJ/2.50)	Viking	1949	Palazzo, Tony	30-50	
Palazzo, Tony	Tales of Don Quixote (1st, lg4to, 84p, dp 2-color, DJ/2.95)	Garden City	1958	Palazzo, Tony	30-45	
Palazzo, Tony	Thai, Kao and Tone: Elephant Story (1st, 4to, [41]p, 1-color, pep, DJ/2.95)	Abelard-Schuman	(1966)	Palazzo, Tony	30-45	
Palazzo, Tony	Three Little Kittens (1st {std}, 4to, [32]p, ibds, color, pep, DJ/1.25)	Doubleday	1961	Palazzo, Tony	25-40	
Graham, Al	Timothy Turtle (1st, lg4to, [30]p, color, pep, DJ/2.00, CH)	Welch Pub. Co.	(1946)	Palazzo, Tony	80-120	*
Palazzo, Tony	Waldo the Wood Chuck (1st {std}, 4to, [42]p, color, DJ/2.95)	Duell, Sloan	(1964)	Palazzo, Tony	40-65	
Palmer, Robin	Wings of the Morning (1st, sq8vo, [29]p, color, DJ/3.75)	H.Z. Walck	1968	Palazzo, Tony	20-35	
Bontemps, Arna	We Have Tomorrow (1st, sm8vo, 131p, DJ/2.50, photos by...)	Houghton	1945	Palfi, Marion	80-140	
Omar Khayyam	Rubaiyat of Omar Khayyam (1st, 4to, 128p, gilt, 12 ticp)	L: L.B. Hill	[1925]	Palmer, Doris M.	170-240	
Hildick, E.W.	Manhattan is Missing (1st {std}, 8vo, 239p, b/w, DJ/3.95)	Doubleday	1969	Palmer, Jan	25-40	
Burgess, Thornton	Tales from Storyteller's House (1st {std}, sq8vo, 195p, 8cp, DJ)	Little/Brown	1937	Palmer, Lemuel	90-150	
Burgess, Thornton	While the Story Log Burns (1st {std}, 8vo, 195p, 8cp, DJ/2.00)	Little/Brown	1938	Palmer, Lemuel	80-130	
Austin, Mary	California: Land of the Sun (1st, lg8vo, 178p, gilt, 32 ticp)	L: A&C Black	1914	Palmer, Sutton	125-200	
Moncrieff, Ascott	Surrey (1st, 8vo, blue/gilt, 252p, teg, 75cp)	L: A&C Black	1906	Palmer, Sutton	80-120	
Lindgren, Astrid	Rasmus & the Vagabond (1st, 8vo, 192p, b/w, DJ/2.75)	Viking	(1960)	Palmquist, Eric	60-100	
Sobol, Donald J.	Lost Dispatch (1st {std}, 8vo, 173p, b/w, DJ/2.95)	F. Watts	(1958)	Palumbo, Anthony	20-35	
Sewell, Anna	Black Beauty (1st, 8vo, p-o, 261p, color)	Dodge	(1907)	Pancoast, C.W.	50-85	
Pancoast, Morris H.	Rejuvenation of Mama & Papa Goose (1st, lg4to, ipcb, [84]p, color)	NY: Britton	(1916)	Pancoast, Morris H.	180-280	*
McMeekin, Isabel	Journey Cake (1st, 8vo, 231p, b/w, DJ/2.00)	J. Messner	1942	Panesis, Nicholas	25-45	*
Turner, Philip	Grange at High Force (1st, 8vo, 220p, b/w, DJ, CgM)	L: Oxford U.Pr.	1965	Papas, William	60-95	
N/A	Arabian Nights (1st, sm8vo, 371p, col frn, b/w)	Macmillan	1923	Pape, Eric	60-90	
Andersen, Hans C.	Fairy Tales and Stories (1st, 8vo, 214p, gilt, col frn, pep)	L: Macmillan	1921	Pape, Eric	75-100	
Austin, Mary	Isidro (1st, sm8vo, 425p, green/gilt, dep, 4cp)	Houghton	1905	Pape, Eric	60-100	
Irving, Washington	Rip Van Winkle (1st, 12mo, blue cl, 183p, 4cp, fp b/w, pep)	Macmillan	1925	Pape, Eric	40-60	*
Groesbeck, Telford	The Incas (1st, lg8vo, green/gilt, 71p, teg, uncut, 14pl)	Putnam	1896	Pape, Eric	70-125	
Wells, H.G.	War in the Air (1st AM, 8vo, 395p, grey/gilt, uncut, 20pl)	Macmillan	1908	Pape, Eric	350-500	
Clark, Alfred	As It is in Heaven (1st, 8vo, 261p, AEG, 8 ticp, pep)	L: Sampson Low	1912	Pape, Frank	60-90	
France, Anatole	At the Sign of the Reine Padauque (1st, 4to, 275p, gilt, 12pl, pep)	L: John Lane	1922	Pape, Frank	50-80	
MacDonald, George	Back of the North Wind (1st, 8vo, 391p, p-o, 12cp)	L: Blackie	1911	Pape, Frank	120-170	
MacDonald, George	Back of the North Wind (1st AM, 8vo, blue cl, teg, p-o, 12 fp color)	Caldwell	[1911]	Pape, Frank	80-140	
Bible	Book of Psalms (1st, sm folio, teg, gilt, 282p, 24cp)	L: Hutchinson	(1912)	Pape, Frank	120-180	
Buckley, Elsie F.	Children of the Dawn (1st, 8vo, 348p, gilt, 24pl)	L: Wells/Gard.	1908	Pape, Frank	90-160	
Buckley, Elsie F.	Children of the Dawn (1st AM, 8vo, 348p, 24pl)	Stokes	(1909)	Pape, Frank	70-100	
Stawell, Mrs. R.	Fairy of Old Spain... (1st AM, 8vo, beige/gilt, 134p, teg, 6cp)	Dent/Dutton	1912	Pape, Frank	65-120	
Andersen, Hans C.	Fairy Tales (1st, sm8vo, 324p, cp)	Nister/Dutton	[1910]	Pape, Frank	70-100	*
Underdown, E.	Gateway to Spenser (1st, 8vo, teg, 399p, 16cp, pep)	L: Nelson	[1911]	Pape, Frank	80-130	
Wilson, Richard	Indian Story Book (1st, 8vo, 272p, blue/gilt, 16cp)	L: Macmillan	1914	Pape, Frank	80-125	
Blackmore, R.D.	Lorna Doone (1st, 4to, 136p, blue cl, col frn)	L: John Lane	1933	Pape, Frank	75-100	
France, Anatole	Mother of Pearl (1st, lg8vo, 291p, black/gilt, uncut, pep, 12pl)	L: John Lane	1929	Pape, Frank	50-85	
Rowsell, Mary	Pedlar & His Dog (8vo, green cl, p-o, 156p, 4cp)	L: Blackie	[1912]	Pape, Frank	50-80	
France, Anatole	Penguin Island (1st, lg8vo, black/gilt, uncut, pep, 12pl)	L: John Lane	1927	Pape, Frank	45-60	
Bunyan, John	Pilgrim's Progress (1st, lg8vo, 315p, green/gilt, 12cp, pep)	L: J.M. Dent	1910	Pape, Frank	100-170	

AUTHOR	TITLE	PUBLISHER	DATE	ARTIST	PRICE	LC
Rix, Herbert	Prince Pimpernel (1st, 8vo, 141p, 8cp)	L: Duckworth	1909	Pape, Frank	100-160	
France, Anatole	Revolt of the Angels (1st, 8vo, 357p, black/gilt, 12pl, pep)	L: John Lane	1924	Pape, Frank	90-120	
Wilson, Richard	Russian Story Book (1st, 8vo, 307p, gilt, 16cp)	L: Methuen	1916	Pape, Frank	80-130	
N/A	Siegfried & Kriemhild (8vo, 96p, p-o, 8cp, pep)	Dana Estes	[1905]	Pape, Frank	120-175	
Reader, Ethel	Story of the Little Merman (1st, 8vo, 274p)	L: Macmillan	1909	Pape, Frank	30-50	*
Grove, F.	Story Without an End (1st, 8vo, 165p, teg, gilt, 8 ticp)	L: Duckworth	(1912)	Pape, Frank	80-125	
Lamb, Charles	Tales from Shakespeare (1st, 8vo, 308p, teg, gilt, 12cp)	L: Warne	1923	Pape, Frank	80-125	
France, Anatole	Thais (1st, lg8vo, black/gilt, 247p, 12pl, pep)	L: Bodley Head	1926	Pape, Frank	50-85	
France, Anatole	Well of St. Clare (1st, 8vo, black/gilt, 302p, gilt, 12pl, pep)	L: John Lane	(1928)	Pape, Frank	50-85	
Benedict, Dorothy	Bandoleer (1st, 8vo, 219p, b/w, DJ/3.50)	Pantheon	(1963)	Papin, Joseph	25-40	
Park, Carton M.	Alphabet of Animals (1st, 4to, ibds, 105p, 26 fp color)	L: Blackie	1899	Park, Carton M.	180-260	
Bicknell, Ethel	Dog Book (1st, 24mo, 119p)	L: G. Richards	1902	Park, Carton M.	60-100	*
Norman	Elfin Rhymes (1st, 4to, unpag, 40 color)	L: Gay & Bird	1900	Park, Carton M.	200-300	
Norman	Elfin Rhymes (1st AM, sm4to, unpag, 40 color)	Stokes	(1900)	Park, Carton M.	140-240	
Brown, John	Little Book of Dogs (1st, 8vo, 91p, gilt, teg, 8 ticp)	L: Foulis	(1911)	Park, Carton M.	60-90	
Spielmann, M.H.	Love Family (1st, 8vo, ibds, 63p, 12cp)	L: G. Allen	(1908)	Park, Carton M.	100-180	
Morris, Alice T.	Old Friends and New Fables (1st AM, 4to, p-o, 52p, 21 ticp)	Dodge	[1916]	Park, Carton M.	170-220	
Morris, Alice T.	Old Friends and New Fables (1st, 4to, 52p, p-o, 21 ticp)	L: Blackie	1916	Park, Carton M.	160-245	
Bates, Herbert E.	Down the River (1st AM, sm4to, 151p, wood engravings, DJ/3.00)	Henry Holt & Co.	1937	Parker, Agnes M.	70-120	
Power, Rhoda	How it Happened (1st, lg8vo, beige cl, 188p, 12pl)	Cambridge U. Pr.	1930	Parker, Agnes M.	55-80	*
Bates, Herbert E.	Through the Woods (1st AM, 4to, gilt, 142p, b/w engravings, DJ/3.00)	Macmillan	1936	Parker, Agnes M.	70-120	
Miller, Arthur	Jane's Blanket (1st {std}, 4to, 64p, ibds, fp 1-color, cep)	Crowell-Collier	(1963)	Parker, Al	200-300	
N/A	Jack & the Beanstalk (1st, 24mo, ibds, [39]p, decor by...)	Holiday House	(1935)	Parker, Arvilla	70-100	R*
Parker, B.	Cinderella at the Zoo (lg4to, ibds, 16 chromos)	L: Chambers	[1900]	Parker, B.	400-600	
Perry, Nora	Flock of Girls & Boys (1st, sm8vo, 323p, grey/gilt, 9pl)	Little/Brown	1895	Parker, C.T.	35-60	
Parker, Edgar	Rogue's Gallery (1st, 4to, 62p, fp b/w, DJ/3.95)	Pantheon	(1969)	Parker, Edgar	20-35	
Terhune, Albert P.	Caleb Conover, Railroader (1st, 12mo, green/gilt, 322p, 4cp)	A.& N. Assoc.	1907	Parker, Frank	80-140	
Little, Jean	Mine for Keeps (1st {std}, 8vo, 186p, b/w, DJ/3.75)	Little/Brown	(1962)	Parker, Lewis	25-45	
Little, Jean	Spring Begins in March (1st {std}, 8vo, 156p, b/w, DJ/3.95)	Little/Brown	(1966)	Parker, Lewis	25-45	
Parker, B.	A's and the K's (lg ob4to, ibds, 12 dp color)	L: Chambers	[1910]	Parker, N.	450-600	
Parker, B.	Arctic Orphans (1st, ob folio, ibds, color, pep)	L: Chambers	[1910]	Parker, N.	400-650	
Parker, B.	Funny Bunnies (lg ob4to, ibds, unpag, 12cp)	L: Chambers	[1905]	Parker, N.	400-650	
Parker, B.	History of the Hoppers (lg4to, ibds, color)	Chambers/Stokes	[1908]	Parker, N.	400-600	
Parker, B.	Hole & Corner Book (lg ob4to, ibds, 12 fp chromos, pep)	L: Chambers	[1910]	Parker, N.	450-600	
Parker, B.& N.	Larder Lodge (lg ob4to, ibds, 14 fp color)	L: Chambers	[1910]	Parker, N.	400-600	
Parker, B.	Lays of the Grays (lg ob4to, ibds, color, pep)	L: Chambers	[1908]	Parker, N.	450-600	
Heddle, Enid	Boomerang Book of Legendary Tales (1st, 8vo, 150p, fp b/w, DJ)	Longmans	(1957)	Parker, Nancy	25-45	
Cole, William	Book of Nature Poems (1st, 8vo, 256p, b/w, DJ/5.95)	Viking	(1969)	Parker, Robert	20-35	
Preston, Edna M.	Pop Corn and Ma Goodness (1st, ob8vo, [35]p, fp color, DJ/4.50, CH)	Viking	(1969)	Parker, Robert	60-100	
Parkes, William T.	Spook Ballads (1st, 12mo, 246p, brown/gilt, b/w, cep)	L: Simpkin	1895	Parkes, William T.	70-100	
Byron, May	Sambo & Susanna (ob4to, ibds, 24 color, [french fold paper])	L: Blackie	[1905]	Parkinson, Ethel	400-600	
MacDonald, George	Rough Shaking (1st, 8vo, 384p, red/gilt, 12pl)	L: Blackie	1891	Parkinson, W.A.	185-265	
Miles, Miska	Apricot ABC (1st {std}, sq8vo, [32]p, color, DJ)	Little/Brown	(1969)	Parnall, Peter	25-40	
Parish, Peggy	Beastly Circus (1st {std}, 12mo, [48]p, fp 1-color, DJ/3.95)	Simon/Schuster	(1969)	Parnall, Peter	25-40	
Borland, Hal	Beyond Your Doorstep (1st {std}, 8vo, 400p, b/w, DJ/5.95)	Knopf	1962	Parnall, Peter	30-45	*
Fisher, Aileen	But Ostriches... (1st, 8vo, [48]p, fp b/w, DJ/3.95)	Crowell	(1970)	Parnall, Peter	50-85	R*
Short, Wayne	Cheechakoes (1st {std}, 8vo, 244p, b/w, DJ/4.95)	Random	(1964)	Parnall, Peter	25-45	*
Abbey, Edward	Desert Solitaire (1st {std}, 8vo, 269p, b/w, DJ/5.95)	McGraw-Hill	(1968)	Parnall, Peter	300-500	
Wahl, Jan	Doctor Rabbit (1st {std}, ob8vo, [48]p, color, DJ/4.95)	Delacorte Pr.	(1970)	Parnall, Peter	40-65	
Griffen, Elizabeth	Dog's Book of Bugs (1st {std}, ob8vo, 63p, b/w, DJ, NYTBI)	Atheneum	1967	Parnall, Peter	30-50	*
Coffin, Patricia	Gruesome Green Witch (1st, lg8vo, 85p, color, DJ/4.50)	NY: Walker	(1969)	Parnall, Peter	40-65	
Mendoza, George	Herman's Hat (1st {std}, ob4to, [48]p, color, DJ/4.50)	Doubleday	(1969)	Parnall, Peter	30-50	
Morey, Walter	Kavik the Wolf Dog (1st {std}, 8vo, 192p, b/w, DJ/4.50)	Dutton	(1968)	Parnall, Peter	25-40	
Moon, Sheila	Knee Deep in Thunder (1st {std}, lg8vo, 307p, b/w, DJ/4.95, NYTBI)	Atheneum	1967	Parnall, Peter	30-50	
Lindsay, Christina	Little Italian Cookbook (1st, 4to, 128p, color)	NY: Walker	(1968)	Parnall, Peter	25-45	*
Cecil, Edward	Malachi Mudge (1st, 8vo, 47p, b/w, DJ/3.95)	McGraw-Hill	(1968)	Parnall, Peter	25-40	
George, Jean C.	Moon of the Wild Pigs (1st, 8vo, 39p, fp b/w, DJ/3.75)	Crowell	(1968)	Parnall, Peter	30-45	
DeChazeau, Eunice	Of Houses and Cats (1st {std}, 8vo, 120p, b/w, DJ/4.95)	Random	(1965)	Parnall, Peter	40-60	
Lindsay, Merrill	One Hundred Great Guns (1st, folio, gilt, 379p, color, pep, DJ)	NY: Walker	(1967)	Parnall, Peter	80-125	
Shura, Mary F.	Tale of Middle Length (1st {std}, 8vo, 105p, green cl, b/w, DJ/3.50)	Atheneum	1966	Parnall, Peter	25-35	
DuMond, Frank	Tall Tales of the Catskills (1st {std}, 8vo, 179p, b/w, DJ/4.95)	Atheneum	1968	Parnall, Peter	30-50	
Mendoza, George	The Inspector (1st {std}, ob8vo, [48]p, color, DJ/3.95)	Doubleday	(1970)	Parnall, Peter	30-45	
Goodwin, Murray	Underground Hideaway (1st, 8vo, 130p, b/w, DJ/3.95)	Harper	(1968)	Parnall, Peter	25-45	
Parrish, A.& D.	Dream Coach (1st, 8vo, 143p, blue/gilt, fp b/w, pep, NH)	Macmillan	1924	Parrish, A.& D.	70-120	
Parrish, A.& D.	Knee-High to a Grasshopper (1st, 8vo, yellow cl, 209p, b/w, pep)	Macmillan	1923	Parrish, A.& D.	45-75	
Parrish, A.& D.	Floating Island (1st {std}, lg8vo, p-o, 265p, 13pl, NH)	Harper	(1930)	Parrish, Anne	80-140	R
Parrish, Anne	Story of Appleby Capple (1st, lg4to, 184p, pep, b/w, DJ/2.75, NH)	Harper	(1950)	Parrish, Anne	70-120	
N/A	Arabian Nights (1st, lg8vo, 339p, teg, p-o, 12cp, pep, SC)	Scribner	1909	Parrish, Maxfield	180-240	R
Read, Opie	Bolanyo (1st, 12mo, tan cl, teg, 309p, uncut, cvr by...)	Way & Williams	1897	Parrish, Maxfield	200-320	
Scudder, Horace E.	Children's Book (sm4to, 444p, p-o by...)	Houghton	(1909)	Parrish, Maxfield	50-80	
Grahame, Kenneth	Dream Days (1st, sq8vo, teg, 228p, gilt, 9pl, pep)	L: John Lane	(1902)	Parrish, Maxfield	125-200	
Skinner, Ada M.	Emerald Story Book (1st, sm8vo, 371p, col frn by...)	Duffield	1915	Parrish, Maxfield	100-135	
Rayner, Emma	Free to Serve (2nd, 8vo, 434p, cover art by..)	Copeland & Day	1897	Parrish, Maxfield	125-200	
Carryl, Guy W.	Garden of Years (1st, 12mo, 129p, uncut, teg, dep, frn by...)	Putnam	1904	Parrish, Maxfield	100-170	R
Grahame, Kenneth	Golden Age (1st, 8vo, red/gilt, 252p, teg, 19pl, pep)	J. Lane	1900	Parrish, Maxfield	150-220	
Grahame, Kenneth	Golden Age (2nd, 8vo, 252p, 18pl)	J. Lane	1904	Parrish, Maxfield	80-135	
Palgrave, Francis T.	Golden Treasury of Songs & Lyrics (1st, lg8vo, p-o, 373p, pep, 8cp)	Duffield	1911	Parrish, Maxfield	200-300	
Longfellow, H.W.	Hiawatha (1st, red/gilt, 8vo, teg, 242p, p-o by...)	Houghton	1911	Parrish, Maxfield	400-600	

AUTHOR	TITLE	PUBLISHER	DATE	ARTIST	PRICE	LC
Irving, Washington	History of New York (1st, folio, bds, teg, p-o, 299p, 8pl)	R.H. Russell	1900	Parrish, Maxfield	700-1000	
Irving, Washington	History of New York (1st {this format}, 4to, 299p, bds, 8 ticp)	Dodd	1915	Parrish, Maxfield	200-300	
Wharton, Edith	Italian Villas and their Gardens (1st, 4to, teg, 270p, gilt, 15cp)	Century	1904	Parrish, Maxfield	700-1000	
Saunders, Louise	Knave of Hearts (1st {hardback}, folio, 46p, p-o, color, pep)	Scribner	1925	Parrish, Maxfield	900-1400	
Hawthorne, Hildegarde	Lure of the Garden (1st, 4to, teg, uncut, 259p, dep, 1cp by...)	Century	1911	Parrish, Maxfield	150-225	
Baum, L. Frank	Mother Goose in Prose (1st [1], 4to, gilt cloth, 265p, 12pl)	Way & Williams	(1897)	Parrish, Maxfield	5000-7000	R
Baum, L. Frank	Mother Goose in Prose (2nd, sm4to, 265p, red cl, 12 fp b/w)	George Hill	1901	Parrish, Maxfield	900-1400	
Baum, L. Frank	Mother Goose in Prose (3rd, sq8vo, 265p, 12pl)	Bobbs-Merrill	(1905)	Parrish, Maxfield	600-800	
Jackson, Gabrielle	Peterkin (1st, lg8vo, p-o, 75p, col frn by...)	Duffield	1912	Parrish, Maxfield	125-200	*
Field, Eugene	Poems of Childhood (1st UK, 8vo, 199p, red/gilt, teg, pep, 8cp)	L: John Lane	1904	Parrish, Maxfield	150-250	
Field, Eugene	Poems of Childhood (1st, lg8vo, p-o, teg, 199p, 8cp, pep, SC)	Scribner	1904	Parrish, Maxfield	200-300	
Schauffler, Rbt. H.	Romantic America (1st, 4to, 339p, gilt, teg, col frn by...)	Century	1913	Parrish, Maxfield	100-170	
Skinner, Ada M.	Topaz Story Book (1st, 12mo, 381p, col frn by...)	Duffield	1917	Parrish, Maxfield	100-150	
Stein, Evaleen	Troubadour Tales (1st, sm8vo, 165p, gilt, col frn by...)	Bobbs-Merrill	(1903)	Parrish, Maxfield	100-150	
Smith, Arthur C.	Turquoise Cup (1st, 8vo, blue bds, 209p, frn by...)	Scribner	1903	Parrish, Maxfield	100-150	
Skinner, Ada M.	Turquoise Story Book (1st, sm8vo, 409p, blue cl, col frn by...)	Duffield	1918	Parrish, Maxfield	100-150	
Hawthorne, Nathaniel	Wonder Book (1st, lg8vo, p-o, 358p, blue/gilt, pep, 10cp)	Duffield	1910	Parrish, Maxfield	250-350	
Winsor, Frederick	Space Child's Mother Goose (1st {std}, 8vo, [88]p, b/w, pep, DJ/3.50)	Simon/Schuster	1958	Parry, Marian	140-225	
Coburn, Grace	Heroes & Wizards (1st, 8vo, 246p, col frn, 8 fp b/w)	L: Nelson	1939	Parsons, Jacynth	30-50	*
Blake, William	Songs of Innocence (1st, 4to, 42p, gilt, 12cp)	L: Medici	1927	Parsons, Jacynth	100-165	
Kraus, Robert	First Robin (1st, 24mo, 48p, ibds, color, DJ/1.99)	Harper	(1965)	Partch, Virgil	25-35	
Dobson, Austin	Proverbs in Porcelain (1st, sq8vo, gilt, teg, 112p, uncut, fp b/w)	L: Kegan Paul	1893	Partridge, J.B.	80-125	
Browning, Robert	Rabbi Ben Ezra... (1st, 4to, 84p, 12 ticp)	L: Hodder	(1915)	Partridge, J.B.	90-120	
Urquhart, Elizabeth	Horace (1st {std}, 8vo, 115p, b/w, DJ/2.00)	Dutton	1951	Pastor, Rosita	40-65	*
Reeves, James	Ragged Robin (1st AM {std}, sm8vo, unpag, color, DJ/3.75)	Dutton	1961	Paton, Jane	20-30	
Williams, Ursula	The Moonball (1st AM {std}, 8vo, pcb, 138p, fp b/w, DJ/3.95)	Meredith Press	(1967)	Paton, Jane	40-65	
Smythe, Gladys	Fairy Scales (1st, 4to, 101p, white cl, p-o, 10cp)	L: Jack	(1917)	Patricchio, C.	140-200	
Butler, William A.	Animal Book (1st {this pub}, 8vo, bds, p-o, 42p, 8cp, pep)	Stokes	(1914)	Pattee, Elsie D.	40-65	
Judson, Clara I.	George Washington (1st, sm8vo, 29p, color, DJ/1.00)	Follett	(1961)	Patterson, Bob	20-35	
Gordon, Hampden C.	Through the Enchanted Wood (1st, 8vo, blue cl, 174p, b/w)	L: Murray	1931	Patterson, Cora	30-50	
France, Anatole	Golden Tales of Anatole France (1st {this fmt}, lg8vo, 352p, gilt, fp b/w)	Dodd	1927	Patterson, M.	60-100	
Freeman, Mae & Ira	You Will Go to the Moon (1st {std}, 8vo, ibds, 54p, color, DJ/1.95)	Beginner Books	(1959)	Patterson, Robert	50-80	
Costantino, Joan	Pepito at Capistrano (1st, lg8vo, p-o, 32p, color, pep, DJ/1.00)	Whitman	1943	Patton, Lucia	20-30	
Friskey, Margaret	Seven Diving Ducks (1st {std}, 4to, ibds, [32]p, 1-color, pep, DJ/1.50)	McKay	(1940)	Patton, Lucia	30-45	
N/A	Aucassin & Nicolette (1st, 4to, 120p, p-o, teg, 13 ticp)	L: Harrap	[1917]	Paul, Evelyn	130-200	
N/A	Aucassin & Nicolette (1st AM, 4to, p-o, unpag, 13 ticp)	Brentano's	[1917]	Paul, Evelyn	100-145	
West, Michael P.	Clair De Lune (1st, lg4to, 137p, teg, brown/gilt, 8 ticp, pep)	L: Harrap	[1913]	Paul, Evelyn	160-220	
Gaskell, Mrs.	Cranford (1st, sm8vo, 247p, gilt, teg, 24cp, pep)	L: Chapman	[1911]	Paul, Evelyn	50-80	
Lindsey, William	Curtain of Forgetfulness (1st, lg8vo, 31p, 11 ticp)	Houghton	1923	Paul, Evelyn	80-120	
Monro, W.D.	India's Gods & Heroes (1st AM, 8vo, uncut, 237p, 16cp)	Crowell	(1910)	Paul, Evelyn	70-100	
Davis, Frederick H.	Myths & Legends of Japan (1st, 8vo, 432p, gilt, 32cp)	L: Harrap	1912	Paul, Evelyn	100-165	
Spence, Lewis	Myths of Babylonia & Assyria (1st AM, 8vo, teg, 411p, 8cp)	Stokes	[1915]	Paul, Evelyn	90-120	
Dante	New Life (1st, lg8vo, 168p, teg, color, pep)	L: Harrap	[1916]	Paul, Evelyn	100-160	
N/A	Romance of Tristam & Isoude (1st, 4to, teg, 12cp, pep)	Brentano's	(1920)	Paul, Evelyn	150-200	
Cunnington, Susan	Stories from Dante (1st, 8vo, p-o, 255p, teg, uncut, gilt, 16cp)	L: Harrap	1910	Paul, Evelyn	80-120	
Bishop, Claire H.	Augustus (1st, sm4to, [32]p, ipcb, color, pep, DJ/1.50)	Viking	1945	Paull, Grace	30-60	
Hunt, Mabel L.	Benjie's Hat (1st, 8vo, 119p, orange cl, pep, b/w, DJ/1.75)	Stokes	1938	Paull, Grace	30-50	
Lampman, Evelyn	Bounces of Cynthiann' (1st {std}, 8vo, 260p, b/w, DJ/2.50)	Doubleday	1950	Paull, Grace	25-45	*
Bailey, Carolyn S.	Children of the Handcrafts (1st, lg8vo, 192p, b/w, dep, DJ/2.00)	Viking	1935	Paull, Grace	30-50	
Bailey, Carolyn S.	Country-Stop (1st, 8vo, 128p, dep, 8 fp color, DJ/2.00)	Viking	1942	Paull, Grace	35-50	
Lampman, Evelyn	Crazy Creek (1st {std}, 8vo, 213p, b/w, DJ/2.50)	Doubleday	1948	Paull, Grace	20-35	*
Coatsworth, Eliz.	Dancing Tom (1st, sq12mo, tan cl, [49]p, 1-color, DJ/1.00)	Macmillan	1938	Paull, Grace	30-50	
Wriston, Hildreth T.	Downstreet with Edith (1st {std}, 8vo, 198p, col frn, pep, DJ/1.50)	Doubleday/Doran	1935	Paull, Grace	40-65	
Meadowcroft, Enid	First Year (1st [new ed.], 8vo, 153p, b/w, pep, DJ/2.00)	Crowell	(1946)	Paull, Grace	20-30	*
Coatsworth, Eliz.	Forgotten Island (1st, 8vo, 65p, tan cl, b/w, DJ/0.50)	Grosset/Dunlap	(1942)	Paull, Grace	30-45	
Paull, Grace	Four Friends (1st, 8vo, [48]p, 2-color, pep)	Grosset/Dunlap	1935	Paull, Grace	30-50	
Paull, Grace	Freddy the Curious Cat (1st {std}, ob4to, unpag, color, pep, DJ/2.75)	Doubleday	1958	Paull, Grace	30-50	
Paull, Grace	Gloomy the Camel (1st, 12mo, [40]p, color, pep, DJ/1.50)	Viking	1938	Paull, Grace	25-45	
Bianco, Margery W.	Good Friends (1st, 8vo, 142p, b/w, DJ/1.75)	Viking	1934	Paull, Grace	60-90	
Bianco, Margery W.	Green Grows the Garden (1st, 12mo, 117p, p-o, pep, DJ/1.50)	Macmillan	1936	Paull, Grace	25-45	
Paull, Grace	Horse to Ride (1st {std}, sq8vo, [32]p, ibds, color, pep, DJ/1.25)	Doubleday	1949	Paull, Grace	30-50	
Darby, Ada C.	Jump Lively, Jeff! (1st, 8vo, 278p, b/w, DJ/2.00)	Stokes	1942	Paull, Grace	30-50	
Koch, Katharine	Katie Meets Buffalo Bill (1st, lg8vo, [28]p, ibds, pep, DJ/0.50)	Grosset/Dunlap	(1947)	Paull, Grace	50-80	
White, Eliza O.	Lending Mary (1st, 8vo, 114p, 7 fp 1-color)	Houghton	1934	Paull, Grace	20-30	
Hunt, Mabel L.	Little Girl with Seven Names (1st, 8vo, 63p, b/w, pep, DJ/1.50)	Stokes	1936	Paull, Grace	30-55	
Coatsworth, Eliz.	Little Haymakers (1st {std}, 8vo, tan cl, 79p, fp b/w, DJ/2.00)	Macmillan	1949	Paull, Grace	30-50	
Paull, Grace	Little Twin (1st {std}, sq8vo, ipcb, 29p, 2-color, pep, DJ/1.50)	Doubleday	(1953)	Paull, Grace	30-50	*
Provines, Mary V.	Liz'beth Ann's Goat (1st, 4to, 40p, ipcb, color, DJ/2.00)	Viking	1947	Paull, Grace	30-50	
Lansing, Elisabeth H.	Lulu's Window (1st {std}, 8vo, 148p, fp b/w, DJ/2.50)	Crowell	(1954)	Paull, Grace	30-50	*
Mason, Miriam E.	Middle Sister (1st {std}, 8vo, 160p, b/w, DJ/1.75)	Macmillan	1947	Paull, Grace	25-45	*
Paull, Grace	Pancakes for Breakfast (1st {std}, ob4to, ibds, [28]p, color, DJ/1.75)	Doubleday	1946	Paull, Grace	40-65	
Paull, Grace	Peanut Butter's Slide (1st, 8vo, ibds, [32]p, fp 3-color, DJ/1.00)	Viking	1939	Paull, Grace	30-50	*
Meade, Julian R.	Peter by the Sea (1st {std}, 8vo, 146p, b/w, pep, DJ/1.50)	Doubleday/Doran	1940	Paull, Grace	35-45	
Paull, Grace	Raspberry Patch (1st {std}, sm4to, ibds, [25]p, color, pep, DJ/1.50)	Doubleday/Doran	1941	Paull, Grace	30-50	
Bulla, Clyde R.	Riding the Pony Express (1st, 8vo, 95p, b/w, pep, DJ/2.25)	Crowell	(1948)	Paull, Grace	30-45	*
Holberg, Ruth	Rowena Carey (1st {std}, 8vo, 242p, fp b/w, DJ/2.50)	Doubleday	1949	Paull, Grace	20-30	*
Holberg, Ruth	Rowena the Sailor (1st {std}, 8vo, 224p, b/w, DJ/2.75)	Doubleday	(1954)	Paull, Grace	20-30	*
Davis, Lavinia R.	Sandy's Spurs (1st {std}, 8vo, red cl, b/w, 246p, DJ/2.50)	Doubleday	(1951)	Paull, Grace	25-45	

AUTHOR	TITLE	PUBLISHER	DATE	ARTIST	PRICE	LC
Bulla, Clyde R.	Secret Valley (1st, sq8vo, 100p, blue cl, fp b/w, DJ/2.25)	Crowell	(1949)	Paull, Grace	30-45	
Urmston, Mary	Seven and Sam (1st, 8vo, 188p, fp b/w, DJ/2.50)	Doubleday	1955	Paull, Grace	25-40	*
Paull, Grace	Squash for the Fair (1st {std}, 4to, ibds, [24]p, color, DJ/1.50)	Doubleday/Doran	1943	Paull, Grace	30-50	
Balch, Glenn	Stallion King (1st, 8vo, 118p, bds, b/w, DJ/2.95)	Crowell	1960	Paull, Grace	30-45	
Vance, Marguerite	Star for Hansi (1st {std}, 8vo, ibds, 30p, 2-color, DJ/1.00)	Harper	1936	Paull, Grace	70-100	
Bianco, Margery W.	Street of Little Shops (1st {std}, 8vo, 111p, uncut, cep, 8cp)	Doubleday/Doran	1932	Paull, Grace	60-90	R
Meade, Julian R.	Teeny & the Tall Man (1st {std}, 8vo, 155p, col frn, b/w, pep, DJ/2.00)	Doubleday/Doran	1936	Paull, Grace	25-40	
Bailey, Carolyn S.	Tops and Whistles (1st, lg8vo, 193p, 20 fp b/w, pep, DJ/2.00)	Viking	1937	Paull, Grace	30-50	
Bacon, Frances A.	Turkey Tale (1st, sq12mo, 48p, ipcb, fp b/w, pep)	Oxford U. Pr.	(1935)	Paull, Grace	25-40	*
Harper, Wilhelmina	Uncle Sam's Story Book (1st {std}, lg8vo, 144p, color, DJ/2.00)	McKay	(1944)	Paull, Grace	30-50	
Curtis, Alice B.	Winter on the Prairie (1st, 8vo, 164p, b/w, DJ/2.50)	Crowell	(1945)	Paull, Grace	25-45	
Hunt, Mabel L.	Wonderful Baker (1st {std}, 8vo, blue cl, 47p, b/w, dep, DJ/1.50)	Lippincott	(1950)	Paull, Grace	30-50	
Maeterlinck, Maurice	Children's Blue Bird (1st, 4to, p-o, 182p, teg, 19pl)	Dodd	1913	Paus, Herbert	100-160	
Maeterlinck, Maurice	Tyltyl (1st, 4to, blue/gilt, p-o, 159p, 8 ticp, pep)	Dodd	1920	Paus, Herbert	120-185	
Maeterlinck, Maurice	Tyltyl (1st UK, sm4to, p-o, 159p, blue/gilt, 8 ticp, pep)	L: Methuen	(1921)	Paus, Herbert	100-165	
Henry, Alfred H.	By Order of the Prophet (1st, 8vo, orange cl, 402p, 5pl)	Revell	1902	Paxon, E.S.	30-50	
Garth, Mary	What Happened to Hannah (1st, 4to, 81p, p-o, color)	L: Goschen	1913	Payne, Irene	50-85	
Payne, Joan B.	Magnificent Milo (1st, 4to, 64p, b/w, DJ/2.75)	Hastings House	(1958)	Payne, Joan B.	40-65	
Justus, May	New Boy in School (1st, 8vo, 56p, b/w, DJ/2.95)	Hastings House	(1963)	Payne, Joan B.	45-70	
Justus, May	New Home for Billy (1st, lg8vo, 55p, b/w, pep, DJ/3.25)	Hastings House	(1966)	Payne, Joan B.	30-50	
Payne, Joan B.	The Raven & other Fairy Tales (1st, 4to, 52p, 1-color, DJ/4.95)	Hastings House	(1969)	Payne, Joan B.	40-65	
Taylor, Anne & Jane	Meddlesome Matty (1st, 8vo, 54p, ibds, color)	L: Bodley Head	1925	Payne, Wyndham	60-90	
Taylor, Anne & Jane	Meddlesome Matty (1st AM, 8vo, ibds, 54p, uncut, color)	Viking	1926	Payne, Wyndham	80-120	R
Beaumont, Cyril W.	Sea Magic... (1st, 8vo, 120p, pcb, gilt, color)	L: Bodley Head	(1928)	Payne, Wyndham	50-85	
Grahame, Kenneth	Wind in the Willows (1st, 8vo, 247p, blue/gilt, teg, 20 fp 1-color)	L: Methuen	(1927)	Payne, Wyndham	125-200	
Carlson, Natalie S.	Ann Aurelia and Dorothy (1st, 8vo, 130p, b/w, DJ/3.95)	Harper	(1968)	Payson, Dale	20-30	
Burgwyn, Mebane	Crackajack Pony (1st {std}, 8vo, uncut, 190p, fp b/w, DJ/3.95)	Lippincott	1969	Payson, Dale	50-80	
Orgel, Doris	Next Door to Xanadu (1st, 8vo, 160p, b/w, DJ/3.95)	Harper	(1969)	Payson, Dale	25-35	*
O'Brien, Robert	Silver Crown (1st {std}, 8vo, 274p, fp b/w, DJ/4.95)	Atheneum	1968	Payson, Dale	100-175	
Mendes, Catulle	Fairy Spinning Wheel (1st, sq8vo, 146p, 14 fp b/w)	Badger	1898	Peabody, Marion L.	120-170	*
Eastman, Elaine G.	Little Brother O'Dream (1st, sm8vo, 191p, cvr by...)	Houghton	1910	Peabody, Marion L.	25-45	
Stringer, Arthur J.	Loom of Destiny (1st, 16mo, 208p, blue/silver, cvr by...)	Small/Maynard	1899	Peabody, Marion L.	55-90	*
Peabody, Josephine	The Wayfarers (1st [1st bk.], sm8vo, 83p, gilt, cvr by...)	Copeland & Day	1898	Peabody, Marion L.	70-100	
Goodwin, Wilder	Up Grade (1st, sm8vo, 321p, gilt, cvr by...)	Little/Brown	1910	Peabody, Marion L.	20-35	
Henty, G.A.	Both Sides of the Border (1st sm8vo, 384p, blue/gilt, 12pl)	L: Blackie	1899	Peacock, Ralph	100-170	
Henty, G.A.	Knight of the White Cross (1st, sm8vo, green/gilt, 392p, 12pl, cep)	L: Blackie	1896	Peacock, Ralph	120-200	
Leighton, Robert	Olaf the Glorious (1st, sm8vo, gilt, 350p, 8 fp b/w)	L: Blackie	1895	Peacock, Ralph	70-100	
Henty, G.A.	Wulf the Saxon (1st AM, 12mo, gilt, 384p, 12pl)	Scribner	1895	Peacock, Ralph	80-125	
Carroll, Lewis	Alice... & Through... (1st UK, 8vo, 264p, blue/gilt, b/w, DJ)	L: Allan Wingate	1954	Peake, Mervyn	200-300	
Drake, Burgess	Book of Lyonne (1st, 12mo, 260p, blue/gilt, 8cp, DJ)	L: Falcon Press	(1952)	Peake, Mervyn	160-220	
Peake, Mervyn	Captain Slaughterboard Drops Anchor (1st, 4to, 48p, cloth, color, DJ)	L: Eyre/Spotts.	1945	Peake, Mervyn	300-500	
Stevenson, Rbt. L.	Dr. Jekyll & Mr. Hyde (1st, 8vo, 148p, gilt, 12 fp b/w)	Folio Society	1948	Peake, Mervyn	80-120	
Peake, Mervyn	Figures of Speech (1st, lg8vo, fp b/w, gilt, [58]p, DJ)	L: Gollancz	(1954)	Peake, Mervyn	150-220	
Grimm Bros.	Household Tales (1st, sm4to, 303p, yellow cl, 6 fp color, DJ)	L: Eyre/Spotts.	(1946)	Peake, Mervyn	160-225	
Carroll, Lewis	Hunting of the Snark (1st, 8vo, red cl, 46p, b/w)	L: Chatto	1941	Peake, Mervyn	150-240	*
Peake, Mervyn	Mr. Pye (1st, 8vo, 278p, blue/gilt, b/w, DJ)	L: Heinemann	(1953)	Peake, Mervyn	150-225	
Judah, Aaron	Pot of Gold (1st, 8vo, 62p, red cloth, fp b/w, DJ)	L: Faber	1959	Peake, Mervyn	60-100	
Laing, Allan M.	Prayers & Graces (1st, sq12mo, 64p, blue/gilt, 30 b/w, DJ)	L: Gollancz	1944	Peake, Mervyn	80-120	
Collis, Maurice	Quest for Sita (1st AM, 8vo, 162p, blue/gilt, uncut, 31 fp b/w, DJ/2.75)	NY: J. Day	(1947)	Peake, Mervyn	100-165	
Peake, Mervyn	Rhymes without Reason (1st, 4to, 39p, yellow cl, 16 fp color, DJ)	L: Eyre/Spotts.	1944	Peake, Mervyn	200-300	
N/A	Ride a Cock-Horse (1st, 4to, 29p, ibds, fp color)	L: Chatto	1940	Peake, Mervyn	350-500	
Peake, Mervyn	Shapes & Sounds (1st, 8vo, 23p, pcb, DJ)	L: Chatto	1941	Peake, Mervyn	200-300	
Peake, Mervyn	Titus Groan (1st AM, 8vo, 430p, b/w, DJ/3.00)	Reynal/Hitchcock	(1946)	Peake, Mervyn	250-400	
Stevenson, Rbt. L.	Treasure Island (1st, 8vo, 246p, gilt, 20 fp b/w, DJ)	L: Eyre/Spotts.	1949	Peake, Mervyn	130-200	
Hole, Christina	Witchcraft in England (1st, 8vo, 167p, maroon/gilt, fp b/w, DJ)	L: Batsford	1945	Peake, Mervyn	100-150	*
Hole, Christina	Witchcraft in England (1st AM, lg8vo, 168p, fp b/w, DJ/3.00)	Scribner	1947	Peake, Mervyn	100-165	
Palmer, Ernest C.	Young Blackbird (1st, 8vo, 62p, b/w, DJ)	L: Allan Wingate	1953	Peake, Mervyn	50-80	
Stacpoole, H.D.	Poppyland (1st, lg8vo, 219p, blue/gilt, 17cp, pep)	L: Bodley Head	1914	Pearce, Leighton	140-220	
Dana, Richard H.	Two Years Before the Mast (1st, 8vo, 415p, 15cp)	L: Macmillan	1915	Pears, Charles	30-50	*
Ash, Fenton	By Airship to Ophir (1st, 8vo, 320p, AEG, red/gilt, 3 color)	L: J.F. Shaw	(1911)	Pearse, Alfred	200-300	
Stables, Gordon	City at the Pole (1st, 8vo, blue cl, 352p, 8pl)	L: J. Nisbet	1906	Pearse, Alfred	60-90	
Henty, G.A.	Maori and Settler (1st, 12mo, 352p, brown/gilt, b/w, cep)	L: Blackie	1891	Pearse, Alfred	120-200	
Heward, Constance	Ameliaranne & Green Umbrella (1st AM, 8vo, 109p, p-o, color, pep)	Jacobs	(1920)	Pearse, Susan B.	70-100	
Heward, Constance	Ameliaranne & the Monkey (1st AM, 8vo, p-o, [63]p, color, pep)	McKay	(1929)	Pearse, Susan B.	60-80	
Joan, Natalie	Ameliaranne and the Big Treasure (1st AM, 8vo, red cl, unpag, p-o, color)	McKay	[1932]	Pearse, Susan B.	55-80	
Farjeon, Eleanor	Ameliaranne and the Magic Ring (1st AM, 8vo, [63]p, p-o, color, pep)	McKay	[1933]	Pearse, Susan B.	50-80	
Gilmour, Margaret	Ameliaranne at the Circus (1st, 12mo, p-o, [63]p, color)	L: Harrap	(1931)	Pearse, Susan B.	80-120	
Heward, Constance	Ameliaranne at the Farm (1st, 8vo, [58]p, ibds, pep)	L: Harrap	1937	Pearse, Susan B.	55-80	
Heward, Constance	Ameliaranne at the Farm (1st AM, 8vo, [58]p, p-o, color, pep)	McKay	(1937)	Pearse, Susan B.	55-90	
Gilmour, Margaret	Ameliaranne at the Seaside (1st, 8vo, unpag, color)	L: Harrap	1935	Pearse, Susan B.	80-120	
Thompson, K.L.	Ameliaranne at the Zoo (1st AM, 8vo, p-o, ibds, color)	McKay	[1936]	Pearse, Susan B.	50-80	
Morris, Ethelberta	Ameliaranne Bridesmaid (1st, 8vo, ibds, unpag, p-o, color)	L: Harrap	(1946)	Pearse, Susan B.	50-85	
Heward, Constance	Ameliaranne Camps Out (1st, 8vo, ibds, unpag, color, pep)	L: Harrap	(1939)	Pearse, Susan B.	60-90	
Heward, Constance	Ameliaranne Cinema Star (1st, 8vo, [60]p, tan bds, p-o, color)	L: Harrap	(1929)	Pearse, Susan B.	60-90	
Gilmour, Margaret	Ameliaranne Gives a Concert (1st, 8vo, unpag, ibds, fp color)	L: Harrap	(1944)	Pearse, Susan B.	80-120	
Heward, Constance	Ameliaranne Gives a Party (1st, 8vo, ibds, pep, 28 color)	L: Harrap	(1938)	Pearse, Susan B.	60-90	
Heward, Constance	Ameliaranne Goes Touring (1st, 4to, ibds, unpag, pep, color)	L: Harrap	(1941)	Pearse, Susan B.	60-90	
Joan, Natalie	Ameliaranne in Town (1st, 12mo, bds, p-o, unpag, color)	L: Harrap	(1930)	Pearse, Susan B.	60-90	

AUTHOR	TITLE	PUBLISHER	DATE	ARTIST	PRICE	LC
Heward, Constance	Ameliaranne Keeps Shop (1st AM, 8vo, ibds, [128]p, color, pep)	McKay	(1928)	Pearse, Susan B.	55-80	
Morris, Ethelberta	Ameliaranne's Moving-Day (1st, 8vo, ibds, [60]p, color, DJ)	L: Harrap	(1950)	Pearse, Susan B.	55-80	
Heward, Constance	Twins & Tabiffa (1st AM, 8vo, 121p, p-o, blue cl, color, pep)	Jacobs	(1923)	Pearse, Susan B.	60-90	
Ottley, Reginald	Boy Alone (1st AM {std}, 8vo, 191p, b/w, DJ/3.50)	Harcourt	(1966)	Pearson, Clyde	25-40	
Carroll, Lewis	Alice in Wonderland (1st {this pub}, 4to, p-o, ibds, 164p, 8cp)	L: Coker	[1915]	Pease, Bessie C.	120-180	
Cooke, Edmund V.	Biography of Our Baby (1st, sm4to, white/gilt, [60]p, color)	Dodge	(1906)	Pease, Bessie C.	170-240	
Stevenson, Rbt. L.	Child's Garden of Verses (1st, 8vo, blue cl, 110p, 21cp, pep)	Dodge	(1905)	Pease, Bessie C.	130-200	
Cooke, Edmund V.	Chronicles of a Little Tot (1st, 8vo, 119p, 3cp)	Dodge	(1905)	Pease, Bessie C.	175-250	
Cooke, Edmund V.	Told to the Little Tot (1st, 8vo, 132p, p-o, teg, 10cp)	Dodge	(1906)	Pease, Bessie C.	160-200	
Leet, Frank R.	Animal Caravan (1st, lg4to, 60p, ibds, 12 fp color)	Saalfield	(1930)	Peat, Fern B.	70-125	
Shankland, Frank	Bird Book (1st, 4to, 60p, ibds, 8 fp color)	Saalfield	(1931)	Peat, Fern B.	50-80	
Boyd, Harriet	Cabbages & Peanuts (1st, 8vo, [40]p, ibds, color, pep)	Saalfield	(1929)	Peat, Fern B.	60-90	
Stevenson, Rbt. L.	Child's Garden of Verses (1st, 4to, ibds, 89p, 7cp, pep)	Saalfield	(1940)	Peat, Fern B.	50-80	
Dickens, Charles	Christmas Carol (1st, 8vo, 249p, blue/gilt, 7cp)	Saalfield	(1929)	Peat, Fern B.	60-90	
Leet, Frank R.	Christmas Carols (1st, 4to, ibds, [70]p, gilt, pep)	Saalfield	(1937)	Peat, Fern B.	60-90	
N/A	Cinderella (sm folio, 16p, wraps, 8cp)	Harter	(1931)	Peat, Fern B.	50-80	
Lefevre, Felicite	Cock, Mouse & Little Red Hen (ob folio, wraps, color)	Saalfield	1931	Peat, Fern B.	60-100	
Dauzet, Marceline	Forest Friends (1st, sq4to, [16]p, ibds, fp color, pep)	Saalfield	1940	Peat, Fern B.	60-100	
Shankland, Frank	Friends of the Forest (1st, lg4to, ibds, 92p, color)	Saalfield	(1932)	Peat, Fern B.	40-65	
N/A	Gingerbread Boy (folio, wraps, 16 color)	Whitman	(1941)	Peat, Fern B.	50-80	
Grimm Bros.	Hansel & Gretel (folio, wraps, color)	Harter	1932	Peat, Fern B.	60-90	
Leet, Frank R.	Hop, Skip & Jump (1st, 4to, ibds, 34p, 6cp)	Saalfield	1936	Peat, Fern B.	70-100	
Mayol, Lurline B.	Jiji Lou (1st, sm4to, p-o, 142p, blue cl, 8 fp color, dep)	Saalfield	1928	Peat, Fern B.	50-80	
N/A	Kittens (1st, folio, [12]p, wraps, 6cp)	Saalfield	1937	Peat, Fern B.	55-80	
Bannerman, Helen	Little Black Sambo (1st {std}, 4to, [20]p, p-o, 6cp)	Harter	(1931)	Peat, Fern B.	300-450	
Bannerman, Helen	Little Black Sambo (8vo, [20]p, ibds, color, pep)	Saalfield	(1932)	Peat, Fern B.	200-300	
Goldsmith, Oliver	Little Goody Two-Shoes (1st, 8vo, [40]p, ibds, pep, color)	Saalfield	(1929)	Peat, Fern B.	55-80	
N/A	Little Housekeepers (folio, wraps, 8cp)	Saalfield	1934	Peat, Fern B.	55-80	
Peat, Fern B.	Magnificent Squeak (1st, 8vo, ibds, 42p, color)	Saalfield	(1929)	Peat, Fern B.	50-80	
Mother Goose	Mother Goose (1st, lg4to, ipcb, [60]p, p-o, 8cp)	Saalfield	(1929)	Peat, Fern B.	80-130	
Mother Goose	Mother Goose: Best Known Rhymes (1st, lg4to, ibds, [34]p, color)	Saalfield	1933	Peat, Fern B.	80-120	
Mother Goose	Mother Goose: Her Rhymes & Riddles (1st, 4to, ipcb, [16]p, color, pep)	Saalfield	1939	Peat, Fern B.	75-100	*
Moore, Clement C.	Night Before Christmas (folio, wraps, unpag, color)	Saalfield	(1932)	Peat, Fern B.	65-100	
N/A	Picture & Rhyme Book (folio, wraps, 20 color)	Saalfield	1941	Peat, Fern B.	70-100	
N/A	Picture Story Book (folio, [18]p, wraps, shape bk., 12 color)	Saalfield	1929	Peat, Fern B.	50-80	
Leet, Frank R.	Purr & Miew (1st, 4to, ibds, 60p, 12 fp color)	Saalfield	(1931)	Peat, Fern B.	70-100	
Treffinger, Carolyn	Rag Doll Jane (1st, lg4to, 59p, ibds, 12cp)	Saalfield	(1930)	Peat, Fern B.	80-125	
Wurth, Anne	Rag Doll Susie (1st, lg sq8vo, [16]p, ibds, 6 color, pep)	Saalfield	1939	Peat, Fern B.	75-100	
Peat, Fern B.	Rags (1st, lg4to, [12]p, wraps, color)	Saalfield	1929	Peat, Fern B.	60-100	
McNeil, Marion	Round the Mulberry Bush (1st, 4to, ibds, 32p, 8cp)	Saalfield	1933	Peat, Fern B.	60-100	
Peat, Fern B.	Stories Children Like (1st, lg4to, [34]p, ibds, 8cp)	Saalfield	1933	Peat, Fern B.	50-85	
Mayol, Lurline B.	Story of a Happy Doll (4to, ibds, 142p, 1cp)	Saalfield	1928	Peat, Fern B.	40-60	
Field, Eugene	Sugar-Plum Tree (1st, 4to, ipcb, [58]p, 12cp)	Saalfield	(1930)	Peat, Fern B.	60-90	R
Potter, Beatrix	Tale of Peter Rabbit (lg4to, wraps, 8 color)	Harter	1931	Peat, Fern B.	75-120	
Barnaby, Horace T.	Tale of the Long-Eared Bat (1st, 4to, [60]p, ibds, 4cp)	Saalfield	(1929)	Peat, Fern B.	70-90	
N/A	Three Little Kittens (1st, 4to, ipcb, [16]p, color, dep)	Saalfield	1940	Peat, Fern B.	50-80	
N/A	Three Little Pigs (folio, wraps, 16p, color)	Saalfield	1933	Peat, Fern B.	50-80	
Semple, Daisy	Tommy & Jane & the Birds (1st, lg8vo, p-o, 94p, color, pep)	Saalfield	(1929)	Peat, Fern B.	55-90	
DuBois, Theodora	Travelling Toys (1st, 8vo, 201p, p-o, 4cp, pep)	Penn	1934	Peat, Fern B.	60-90	
Clinton, Althea L.	Treasure Book of Best Stories (1st, 4to, 92p, ibds, 10 fp color)	Saalfield	(1933)	Peat, Fern B.	50-85	
Andersen, Hans C.	Ugly Duckling (1st, 4to, [40]p, ibds, 5cp, pep)	Saalfield	1931	Peat, Fern B.	60-100	
Randall, Jane	When Toys Could Talk (1st, 4to, [16]p, spiral-bound, 6 fp color)	Saalfield	1939	Peat, Fern B.	80-130	
Hawthorne, Nathaniel	Wonder Book (1st, 12mo, 234p, color)	Saalfield	(1929)	Peat, Fern B.	35-60	*
Field, Eugene	Wynken, Blynken & Nod (1st, folio, wraps, [12]p, color)	Saalfield	1930	Peat, Fern B.	70-120	R
La Rue, Mabel G.	Good-Time Book (1st, 12mo, 111p, 2-color, cep)	Macmillan	1931	Peck, A. Gladys	30-50	*
Newell, Hope	Cinder Ike (1st, 8vo, 121p, b/w, DJ/1.75)	NY: Nelson	1942	Peck, Anne M.	30-50	*
Warde, Margaret	Holiday Book (1st, 8vo, 208p, 5pl)	Little/Brown	1925	Peck, Anne M.	25-40	
Bazin, Rene	Juniper Farm (1st, sm8vo, 180p, color)	Macmillan	1928	Peck, Anne M.	30-45	
Dussauze, Alice	Little Jack Rabbit (1st, 12mo, 125p, col frn)	Macmillan	1927	Peck, Anne M.	30-50	*
Yonge, Charlotte	Little Lucy's Wonderful Globe (1st, 12mo, 103p, col frn, b/w, pep)	Harper	1927	Peck, Anne M.	20-30	
Peck, Anne M.	Manoel & the Morning Star (1st {std}, 8vo, 31p, ipcb, color, pep, DJ/1.75)	Harper	(1943)	Peck, Anne M.	25-40	
Govan, Christine	Mr. Hermit Miser & Neighborly Pumpkin (1st, 8vo, ibds, [46]p, col, DJ/1.75)	Aladdin	(1949)	Peck, Anne M.	70-100	
Wolff, Carl F.	Pale Mountains (1st, 8vo, 204p, 8pl)	Minton Balch	1927	Peck, Anne M.	30-45	
Crownfield, Gertrude	Princess White Flame (1st, 8vo, 229p, gilt, fp b/w)	Dutton	(1920)	Peck, Anne M.	30-45	
Johnson, Enid	Runaway Balboa (1st {std}, 4to, [41]p, ibds, color, pep, DJ/2.00)	Harper	1938	Peck, Anne M.	40-65	*
Newell, Hope	Steppin & Family (1st, 8vo, 198p, color, pep, DJ/2.00)	NY: Oxford U.Pr.	(1942)	Peck, Anne M.	65-90	
Brown, Katharine H.	Hallowell Partnership (1st, sm8vo, 241p, 4pl)	Scribner	1912	Peck, Clara E.	25-40	*
Bacon, Josephine D.	In the Border Country (1st, sm8vo, 130p, 5cp)	Doubleday/Page	1909	Peck, Clara E.	30-50	
Sterling, Sara H.	Lady of King Arthur's Court (1st, 8vo, teg, 262p, p-o, 5cp)	Jacobs	(1907)	Peck, Clara E.	60-95	
Sterling, Sara H.	Shakespeare's Sweetheart (1st, 8vo, 282p, p-o, teg, 5pl, pep)	Jacobs	(1905)	Peck, Clara E.	40-70	
Greene, Sarah P.M.	Deacon Lysander (1st, 12mo, teg, 223p, red/gilt, 4pl)	Baker/Taylor	(1904)	Peck, Henry J.	20-35	
Means, Florence C.	Ranch and Ring (1st, sm8vo, tan cl, 260p, fp b/w, pep)	Houghton	1932	Peck, Henry J.	25-45	
Montgomery, R.	King of the Castle (1st {std}, 8vo, 60p, 1-color, DJ/2.95)	World	(1961)	Pedersen, Russell	30-45	
Peet, Bill	Buford, the Little Bighorn (1st, sm sq4to, 46p, fp color, DJ/3.25)	Houghton	1967	Peet, Bill	30-50	
Peet, Bill	Capyboppy (1st {std}, 8vo, 62p, color, DJ/3.00)	Houghton	1966	Peet, Bill	30-50	
Peet, Bill	Chester, the Worldly Pig (1st, sm sq4to, 48p, fp color, DJ/3.25)	Houghton	1965	Peet, Bill	30-50	
Peet, Bill	Ella (1st, sm sq4to, 48p, fp color, DJ/3.25)	Houghton	1964	Peet, Bill	30-50	
Peet, Bill	Farewell to Shady Glade (1st, lg8vo, 38p, color, pep, DJ/3.25)	Houghton	1966	Peet, Bill	30-50	

AUTHOR	TITLE	PUBLISHER	DATE	ARTIST	PRICE	LC
Peet, Bill	Fly Homer, Fly (1st {std}, lg8vo, 60p, color, DJ/4.50)	Houghton	1969	Peet, Bill	50-75	
Peet, Bill	Hubert's Hair-Raising Adventure (1st, 4to, color, 38p, DJ/3.00)	Houghton	1959	Peet, Bill	35-50	
Peet, Bill	Huge Harold (1st, sm sq4to, [45]p, fp color, DJ/3.00)	Houghton	1961	Peet, Bill	35-50	
Peet, Bill	Jennifer & Josephine (1st, sm sq4to, 46p, fp color, DJ/3.25)	Houghton	1967	Peet, Bill	35-50	*
Peet, Bill	Kermit the Hermit (1st {std}, sm sq4to, 48p, fp color, DJ/3.25)	Houghton	1965	Peet, Bill	35-50	
Peet, Bill	Pinkish, Purplish, Bluish Egg (1st, sm sq4to, 46p, fp color, DJ/3.25)	Houghton	1963	Peet, Bill	35-50	
Peet, Bill	Randy's Dandy Lions (1st, sm sq4to, 48p, fp color, DJ/3.00)	Houghton	1964	Peet, Bill	35-50	
Peet, Bill	Smokey (1st, sm sq4to, 38p, fp color, pep, DJ/3.00)	Houghton	1962	Peet, Bill	35-50	
Peet, Bill	Whingdingdilly (1st {std}, sm4to, 60p, color, cep, DJ/4.95)	Houghton	1970	Peet, Bill	50-75	
Peet, Bill	Wump World (1st {std}, lg8vo, 44p, color, cep, DJ/3.95)	Houghton	1970	Peet, Bill	35-50	
Norton, Mary	Magic Bed-Knob (1st {1st bk}, 4to, ibds, [48]p, fp color, pep, DJ/1.75)	Hyperion Press	(1943)	Peirce, Waldo	200-300	
Staunton, Schuyler	Daughters of Destiny (1st [1], sm8vo, p-o, gilt, 319p, 8cp)	Reilly/Britton	(1906)	Peirce/DeLay	220-300	
Wyllarde, Dolf	Things (1st, lg8vo, blue/gilt, 137p, 4pl)	L: T.F. Unwin	(1915)	Peirse/Vane	80-120	*
Thompson, Maurice	Rosalynde's Lovers (1st, 8vo, p-o, 249p, gilt, teg, 11pl, dep)	Bowen-Merrill	1901	Peirson, G. Alden	25-40	
Wharton, Edith	Italian Backgrounds (1st, lg8vo, 214p, teg, 12pl by…)	Scribner	1905	Peixotto, E.C.	400-600	
Hillert, Margaret	Three Goats (1st, 8vo, 27p, color, DJ/1.00)	Follett	(1963)	Pekarsky, Mel	20-35	
Penfield, Edward	Big Book of Horses & Goats (1st, ob folio, [24]p, color)	R.H. Russell	1901	Penfield, Edward	300-500	*
Bangs, John K.	Dreamers, A Club (1st, 12mo, brown/gilt, 247p, b/w)	Harper	1899	Penfield, Edward	50-85	
Penfield, Edward	Holland Sketches (1st, lg8vo, 147p, ibds, 34 ticp, pep)	Scribner	1907	Penfield, Edward	150-225	
Bangs, John K.	Peeps at People (1st, 12mo, 184p, gilt, 36pl)	Harper	1899	Penfield, Edward	50-80	
Williamson, C.& N.	Princess Passes (1st, 12mo, green cl, 369p, 12 pl by…)	Henry Holt & Co.	1905	Penfield, Edward	30-50	
Penfield, Edward	Spanish Sketches (1st, lg8vo, 146p, yellow bds, 27 ticp, pep)	Scribner	1911	Penfield, Edward	150-225	
Bangs, John K.	The Bicyclers (1st, 12mo, 176p, blue/gilt, 4pl)	Harper	1896	Penfield, Edward	60-100	
Pennell, Joseph	Adventures of an Illustrator (1st, lg4to, buckram/gilt, 372p, col frn)	Little/Brown	1925	Pennell, Joseph	100-185	
Hay, John	Castilian Days (1st, 8vo, 343p, teg, green cl, b/w)	Houghton	1903	Pennell, Joseph	50-80	
James, Henry	English Hours (1st AM, lg8vo, 336p, teg, b/w by…)	Houghton	1905	Pennell, Joseph	200-300	
Pennell, Joseph	French Cathedrals (1st AM, 4to, 424p, teg, 38pl)	Century	1909	Pennell, Joseph	70-125	
James, Henry	Italian Hours (1st AM, 4to, 504p, teg, uncut, 32cp)	Houghton	1909	Pennell, Joseph	200-300	
Pennell, Joseph	Jew at Home (1st, 12mo, red/gilt, 105p, b/w)	Appleton	1892	Pennell, Joseph	200-300	
James, Henry	Little Tour in France (1st AM, 8vo, teg, 345p, b/w)	Houghton	1900	Pennell, Joseph	150-220	
Dodd, Anna B.	On the Broads (1st, 8vo, 331p, gilt, teg, 24 fp b/w)	L: Macmillan	1896	Pennell, Joseph	70-120	
Pennell, Eliz. R.	Our House (1st, 8vo, ipcb, 373p, 10pl)	Houghton	1912	Pennell, Joseph	50-85	
Pennell, Joseph	Our Philadelphia (1st, sm4to, red/gilt, 552p, teg, b/w)	Lippincott	1914	Pennell, Joseph	60-90	
Pennell, Eliz. R.	Over the Alps on a Bicycle (1st, 8vo, 110p, 18 fp b/w)	L: T.F. Unwin	1898	Pennell, Joseph	80-130	
Pennell, Joseph	Pictures of Panama Canal (1st, sm4to, [56]p, brown cl, p-o, 28pl)	Lippincott	1912	Pennell, Joseph	60-100	
Pennell, Joseph	Play in Provence (1st, sm8vo, tan cl, teg, uncut, 202p, b/w)	Century	1892	Pennell, Joseph	80-125	
Crawford, F. Marion	Salve Venetia (1st, 8vo, 2 volumes, gilt)	Macmillan	1905	Pennell, Joseph	55-80	
Irving, Washington	The Alhambra (1st, 12mo, green/gilt, AEG, 436p, b/w, cep)	L: Macmillan	1896	Pennell, Joseph	55-80	
Pennell, Eliz. R.	To Gypsyland (1st, sm8vo, pink cl, 240p, fp b/w)	L: T.F. Unwin	1893	Pennell, Joseph	60-100	
Pennell, Joseph	Wonder of Work (1st, sm4to, [226]p, brown cl, p-o, 52pl)	Lippincott	1916	Pennell, Joseph	70-100	
Eustis, Celestine	Cooking in Old Creole Days (1st, 8vo, ipcb, 129p, 8pl)	R.H. Russell	1903	Pennington, Harper	200-300	R
Biddle, Anthony	Second Froggy Fairy Book (1st, 8vo, 90p, col frn, 11 fp b/w)	Drexel Biddle	1898	Pennock, Anne	100-160	
Irving, Washington	Rip Van Winkle (1st, 8vo, 127p, b/w)	Stokes	1933	Perard, Victor S.	25-45	*
Clark, Ann N.	Little Indian Pottery Maker (1st, sm ob8vo, 31p, fp color, pep)	Melmont Pub.	(1955)	Perceval, Don	30-50	*
Rowntree, Lester	Ronnie (1st, 8vo, 188p, b/w, DJ/2.50)	Viking	1952	Perceval, Don	25-45	*
Fox, Frances M.	Wildling Princess (1st, 8vo, 79p, brown/gilt, 10cp, pep)	Volland	(1929)	Perkins, John E.	80-120	
Aesopus	Aesop's Fables (1st, sm4to, p-o, 111p, 12cp)	Stokes	(1908)	Perkins, Lucy F.	90-150	
Perkins, Lucy F.	American Twins of the Revolution (1st, 8vo, 208p, pep, b/w)	Houghton	1926	Perkins, Lucy F.	35-60	*
Perkins, Lucy F.	Belgian Twins (1st, 8vo, brown cl, 198p, b/w, pep)	Houghton	1917	Perkins, Lucy F.	40-70	R
Perkins, Lucy F.	Book of Joys (1st, lg8vo, 212p, green cl, uncut, p-o, 5cp)	McClurg	1907	Perkins, Lucy F.	50-80	
Perkins, Lucy F.	Cave Twins (1st, 8vo, 164p, b/w)	Houghton	1916	Perkins, Lucy F.	40-60	*
Pease, Leonora	Child You Used to Be (1st, 8vo, 198p, 10pl, pep)	McClurg	1909	Perkins, Lucy F.	45-70	
Perkins, Lucy F.	Chinese Twins (1st, sm8vo, yellow cl, 166p, col frn, b/w, DJ/1.75)	Houghton	1935	Perkins, Lucy F.	50-80	
Baker, Cornelia	Coquo and the King's Children (1st, 8vo, 250p, brown/gilt, 6 color)	McClurg	1902	Perkins, Lucy F.	40-70	
Perkins, Lucy F.	Cornelia (1st, sm8vo, 202p, 8pl)	Houghton	1919	Perkins, Lucy F.	30-50	
Perkins, Lucy F.	Dutch Twins (1st, 8vo, 190p, b/w, PPPa)	Houghton	1911	Perkins, Lucy F.	75-120	
Brown, Julia	Enchanted Peacock (1st, 4to, p-o, 4cp, 4pl)	Rand/McNally	(1911)	Perkins, Lucy F.	75-100	
Blakely, Elizabeth	Fairy Starlight (1st, 12mo, lavender cl, 213p, b/w)	McClurg	1896	Perkins, Lucy F.	70-120	*
Perkins, Lucy F.	Filipino Twins (1st, 8vo, 150p, b/w)	Houghton	1923	Perkins, Lucy F.	35-60	
Harrison, Edith O.	Flaming Sword (1st, sm4to, blue/silver, 133p, 4cp)	McClurg	1908	Perkins, Lucy F.	60-100	
Perkins, Lucy F.	French Twins (1st, 8vo, blue cl, 202p, b/w, pep)	Houghton	1918	Perkins, Lucy F.	40-60	
Wade, Blanche E.	Garden in Pink (1st, 8vo, 201p, p-o, blue cl, 12pl)	McClurg	1905	Perkins, Lucy F.	50-80	
Perkins, Lucy F.	Indian Twins (1st, 8vo, 203p, b/w)	Houghton	1930	Perkins, Lucy F.	35-50	
Perkins, Lucy F.	Irish Twins (1st, 8vo, 206p, b/w)	Houghton	1913	Perkins, Lucy F.	35-50	
Perkins, Lucy F.	Italian Twins (1st, 8vo, green cl, 149p, b/w, pep)	Houghton	1920	Perkins, Lucy F.	30-50	
Perkins, Lucy F.	Japanese Twins (1st, 8vo, 178p, beige cl, b/w, pep)	Houghton	1912	Perkins, Lucy F.	35-60	
English, Thomas D.	Little Giant, Big Dwarf (1st, sm4to, 150p, t.e. yellow, 4 fp b/w)	McClurg	1904	Perkins, Lucy F.	70-100	
Warren, Maude R.	Little Pioneers (1st, 12mo, 253p, b/w, pep)	Rand/McNally	(1916)	Perkins, Lucy F.	30-50	
Van Sickle, James H.	Magic Key (1st, 12mo, blue cl, 270p, 10 fp b/w)	Houghton	(1931)	Perkins, Lucy F.	30-50	*
Perkins, Lucy F.	Mexican Twins (1st, 8vo, tan cl, 186p, b/w)	Houghton	1915	Perkins, Lucy F.	30-50	
Shakespeare, Wm.	MidSummer Night's Dream (1st, sm4to, p-o, 93p, 12cp, pep)	Stokes	(1907)	Perkins, Lucy F.	120-180	
Harrison, Edith O.	Moon Princess (1st, sm4to, 162p, blue cl, 6cp)	McClurg	1905	Perkins, Lucy F.	100-160	
Mother Goose	Mother Goose Book (ob4to, red cl, p-o, 11cp)	Whitman	(1915)	Perkins, Lucy F.	90-140	
Perkins, Lucy F.	Mr. Chick: his Travels & Adventures (1st, ob4to, 117p, p-o, fp b/w)	Houghton	1926	Perkins, Lucy F.	45-70	
Perkins, Eleanor E.	News from Notown (1st, sm4to, 108p, b/w)	Houghton	1919	Perkins, Lucy F.	40-60	
Perkins, Lucy F.	Pickaninny Twins (1st, 8vo, 152p, tan cl, b/w, pep)	Houghton	1931	Perkins, Lucy F.	120-180	
Harrison, Edith O.	Prince Silverwings… (1st, sm4to, blue/silver, 313p, 4cp)	McClurg	1902	Perkins, Lucy F.	80-125	
Perkins, Lucy F.	Puritan Twins (1st, 8vo, 179p, pep, b/w)	Houghton	1921	Perkins, Lucy F.	30-50	

AUTHOR	TITLE	PUBLISHER	DATE	ARTIST	PRICE	LC
N/A	Robin Hood (1st, lg8vo, olive cl, 115p, 12cp)	Stokes	(1906)	Perkins, Lucy F.	60-90	
Perkins, Lucy F.	Spartan Twins (1st, 12mo, 161p, b/w)	Houghton	1920	Perkins, Lucy F.	35-60	
Harrison, Edith O.	Star Fairies (1st, sm4to, 128p, 6cp)	McClurg	1903	Perkins, Lucy F.	80-125	
Perkins, Lucy F.	Swiss Twins (1st, 8vo, 132p, brown cl, b/w, pep)	Houghton	1922	Perkins, Lucy F.	35-60	
Hawthorne, Nathaniel	Wonder Book (1st, lg8vo, p-o, 125p, 12cp)	Stokes	(1908)	Perkins, Lucy F.	70-100	
Valen, Herb	Boy Who Could Enter Paintings (1st {std}, 8vo, 60p, color, DJ/3.50)	Little/Brown	(1968)	Perl, Susan	20-30	
Kravetz, Nathan	Horse of Another Color (1st {std}, 8vo, 57p, color, DJ/2.95)	Little/Brown	(1962)	Perl, Susan	25-40	
Kravetz, Nathan	Monkey's Tale (1st {std}, 8vo, 57p, color, DJ/2.75)	Little/Brown	1964	Perl, Susan	25-40	
Moore, Clement C.	Night Before Christmas (1st, 8vo, [64]p, red/gilt, fp 2-color)	Harlin Quist	1964	Perl, Susan	30-50	
Johnston, Johanna	Story of the Barber of Seville (1st, 4to, 61p, fp color, DJ/3.95)	Putnam	(1966)	Perl, Susan	25-40	
Smaridge, Norah	What a Silly Thing to Do (1st {std}, 8vo, [38]p, 2-color, DJ/2.50)	Abingdon Press	(1967)	Perl, Susan	25-40	
Kennell, Ruth E.	Vanya of the Streets (1st {std}, 8vo, 208p, uncut, b/w, pep, DJ/2.00)	Harper	1931	Perts, Michael	70-125	
D'Aulnoy	Fairy Tales (1st, 8vo, 535p, teg, gilt, b/w by...)	L: Lawrence	1892	Peters, Clinton	150-225	
Bartrug, Carey M.	Mother Goose Etiquette Rhymes (1st, ob8vo, 32p, blue cl, pep)	Whitman	1941	Peters, Marjorie	55-80	*
Palmer, Elizabeth	Nightingale House (1st, 8vo, 122p, orange cl, b/w, DJ/1.75)	Scribner	1937	Peters, Marjorie	20-30	
Judson, Clara I.	People Who Come to Our House (1st {A}, 4to, 48p, color, DJ/1.00)	Rand/McNally	(1940)	Peters, Marjorie	30-50	
Petersham, Maud	Shepherd Psalm (1st {std}, 8vo, 27p, ibds, color, DJ/2.50)	Macmillan	1962	Petersham, Maud	25-40	
Wheeler, Post	Albanian Wonder Tales (1st {std}, 8vo, 282p, col frn, b/w, pep, DJ/2.00)	Doubleday/Doran	1936	Petershams	65-100	
Petershams	America's Stamps... (1st, 4to, 144p, 3 fp color, DJ/3.50)	Macmillan	1947	Petershams	60-90	
Petersham, Maud	American ABC (1st, lg8vo, [56]p, gilt, color, cep, DJ/2.00, CH)	Macmillan	1941	Petershams	100-160	
Petershams	Ark of Father Noah & Mother Noah (1st {std}, sq4to, ibds, color, pep)	Doubleday/Doran	1930	Petershams	70-120	R
Petersham, Maud	Auntie & Celia Jane & Miki (1st {std}, sm4to, ibds, [64]p, color, NH)	Doubleday/Doran	1932	Petershams	100-160	R*
Rowland, Sydney	Beckoning Road (1st, sm8vo, 471p, color, pep)	Winston	(1931)	Petershams	30-50	
La Rue, Mabel G.	Billy Bang Book (1st, 12mo, 176p, 2-color)	Macmillan	1927	Petershams	40-70	*
Franklin, Benjamin	Bird in the Hand (1st {std}, 4to, blue cl, [36]p, color, cep, DJ/2.50)	Macmillan	(1951)	Petershams	45-70	
Petersham, Maud	Box with Red Wheels (1st, sm4to, ibds, [32]p, color, DJ/1.50)	Macmillan	(1949)	Petershams	60-100	*
Petershams	Boy Who Had no Heart (1st {std}, sm4to, ibds, [30]p, color, DJ/2.75)	Macmillan	(1955)	Petershams	70-100	
Lamprey, Louise	Children of Ancient Britain (1st, 12mo, 222p, fp b/w)	Little/Brown	1921	Petershams	40-60	*
Miller, Elizabeth C.	Children of Mountain Eagle (1st {std}, sm8vo, 328p, 3cp, pep)	Doubleday/Doran	1927	Petershams	35-60	*
Petersham, Maud	Christ Child (1st {std}, 4to, ibds, [62]p, color, pep)	Doubleday/Doran	(1931)	Petershams	80-125	R
Petersham, Maud	Circus Baby (1st, sm4to, ibds, [32]p, color, DJ/1.50)	Macmillan	(1950)	Petershams	80-120	
Bowen, William	Enchanted Forest (1st, 12mo, 197p, col frn, fp b/w, pep)	Macmillan	1920	Petershams	80-130	
Adams, Sherred W.	Five Little Friends (1st, 12mo, 139p, color)	Macmillan	1922	Petershams	55-80	
Barringer, Marie	Four and Lena (1st {std}, 8vo, 216p, black cl, 6cp, pep, DJ/2.00)	Doubleday/Doran	1938	Petershams	45-70	
Petersham, Maud	Get-A-Way & Harry Janos (1st, 4to, ibds, p-o, [64]p, 14cp)	Viking	1933	Petershams	140-200	
Spyri, Johanna	Heidi (1st, 8vo, blue cl, p-o, 319p, 4cp, pep)	Garden City	1932	Petershams	40-60	
Kelly, Eric P.	In Clean Hay (1st {std}, 8vo, ibds, 31p, color, cep, DJ/1.25)	Macmillan	1953	Petershams	40-65	
Bible	Jesus' Story (1st, 12mo, 119p, 6 fp color, cep, DJ/1.50)	Macmillan	1942	Petershams	50-80	
Petersham, Maud	Joseph and his Brothers (1st, lg8vo, [32]p, color, pep, DJ/0.90)	Winston	1938	Petershams	40-65	
Johnson, Emilie F.	Little Book of Prayers (1st, 16mo, [47]p, 1-color, pep, DJ/1.00)	Viking	1941	Petershams	55-80	
La Rue, Mabel G.	Little Indians (1st, 12mo, 170p, color)	Macmillan	1930	Petershams	40-65	
Coolidge, Florence C.	Little Ugly Face (1st, 12mo, 181p, 2-color)	Macmillan	1925	Petershams	45-70	
Lamprey, Louise	Long Ago People (1st, 12mo, 222p, fp b/w)	Little/Brown	1921	Petershams	40-60	*
Queen Marie	Magic Doll of Roumania (1st, 8vo, p-o, 319p, 10cp)	Stokes	1929	Petershams	90-145	
Barringer, Marie	Martin the Goose Boy (1st {std}, 8vo, 188p, black cl, 8cp, pep)	Doubleday/Doran	1932	Petershams	50-85	
Petersham, Maud	Miki (1st {std}, sm4to, [63]p, ibds, color, pep)	Doubleday/Doran	1929	Petershams	80-125	
Petersham, Maud	Miki & Mary... (1st, 4to, ibds, [64]p, color, pep, DJ/2.50)	Viking	1934	Petershams	80-120	R
Mason, Miriam E.	Miss Posy Longlegs (1st {std}, 8vo, 54p, 1-color, DJ/2.00)	Macmillan	(1955)	Petershams	40-65	
Petersham, Maud	Moses (1st, lg8vo, blue cl, [32]p, color, pep, DJ/0.90)	Winston	1938	Petershams	60-90	
Miller, Olive B.	Nursery Friends from France (1st, 4to, 190p, gilt, p-o, color, pep)	Book House	(1925)	Petershams	40-65	
Petersham, Maud	Off to Bed (1st {std}, 4to, [30]p, color, DJ/2.25)	Macmillan	(1954)	Petershams	50-80	
Petersham, Maud	Peppernuts (1st {std}, 8vo, 62p, 1-color, DJ/2.50)	Macmillan	(1958)	Petershams	30-50	
Ayer, Jean	Picnic Book (1st, 12mo, 46p, color, wraps)	Macmillan	1934	Petershams	35-60	
Collodi, Carlo	Pinocchio (1st, 8vo, p-o, blue cl, 323p, 4cp, pep)	Garden City	1932	Petershams	65-100	R
Clark, Margery	Poppy Seed Cakes (1st {std}, sm sq8vo, 154p, 16cp, pep)	Doubleday/Page	1924	Petershams	120-180	R
Miller, Elizabeth C.	Pran of Albania (1st {std}, 8vo, 257p, col frn, pep, NH)	Doubleday/Doran	1929	Petershams	60-100	
Rowland, Sydney	Rich Cargoes (1st, sm8vo, 449p, fp 1-color, pep)	Winston	(1931)	Petershams	30-50	
Irving, Washington	Rip Van Winkle & Sleepy Hollow (1st, 8vo, 105p, 1-color, pep, DJ/2.00)	Macmillan	(1951)	Petershams	60-100	
Petersham, Maud	Rooster Crows (1st, sm4to, [64]p, tan cl, color, cep, DJ/2.00, CM)	Macmillan	1945	Petershams	85-140	R
Sandburg, Carl	Rootabaga Pigeons (1st, 8vo, blue cl, 218p, col frn)	Harcourt	(1923)	Petershams	80-120	R
Sandburg, Carl	Rootabaga Stories (1st, 8vo, 230p, blue cl, col frn, PPP)	Harcourt	(1922)	Petershams	100-165	R
Petersham, Maud	Ruth (1st, lg8vo, blue/gilt, [32]p, pep, 8 fp color, DJ/0.90)	Winston	1938	Petershams	50-80	
Petershams	Silver Mace (1st {std}, sm4to, ibds, 38p, fp color, DJ/2.75)	Macmillan	(1956)	Petershams	50-80	
Petersham, Maud	Stories from the Old Testament (1st, lg8vo, [128]p, color, pep, DJ/2.75)	Winston	1938	Petershams	40-65	
Petersham, Maud	Story Book of Clothes (1st, sq8vo, [32]p, p-o, yellow cl, color)	Winston	1933	Petershams	30-50	
Petersham, Maud	Story Book of Cotton (1st, sq8vo, [32]p, p-o, color, DJ/0.50)	Winston	1939	Petershams	30-50	
Petershams	Story Book of Iron and Steel (1st, sq8vo, p-o, [32]p, color, cep, DJ/0.60)	Winston	1935	Petershams	30-50	
Mason, Miriam E.	Susannah: Pioneer Cow (1st, 8vo, yellow cl, 151p, 1-color, cep, DJ/1.25)	Macmillan	1941	Petershams	40-65	
Lamb, Charles	Tales from Shakespeare (1st, sm8vo, 375p, blue cl, 4cp, pep)	Macmillan	1923	Petershams	55-80	
Eells, Elsie S.	Tales of Enchantment from Spain (1st, 8vo, 173p, 4cp)	Harcourt	(1920)	Petershams	50-80	
Miller, Olive B.	Tales Told in Holland (1st, 4to, 190p, p-o, pep, gilt, color)	Book House	(1926)	Petershams	50-85	
Various	Told Under the Christmas Tree (1st {std}, 8vo, 304p, b/w, DJ/3.00)	Macmillan	1948	Petershams	35-50	
Tyler, Anna C.	Twenty-Four Unusual Stories (1st, 12mo, 328p, fp b/w)	Harcourt	1921	Petershams	40-65	
La Rue, Mabel G.	Under the Story Tree (1st, 12mo, 139p, color)	Macmillan	1923	Petershams	50-80	*
Clement, Marguerite	Where Was Bobby? (1st {std}, 8vo, 151p, 19cp, pep)	Doubleday/Doran	1928	Petershams	60-90	
Rowland, Sydney	Wings of Adventure (1st, sm8vo, 500p, color, pep)	Winston	(1931)	Petershams	30-50	
Snowden, James H.	Wonderful Night (1st, 12mo, blue cl, 95p, p-o, designs by...)	Macmillan	1919	Petershams	30-55	
Miller, Elizabeth C.	Young Trajan (1st {std}, 8vo, 232p, black cl, pep, col frn)	Doubleday/Doran	1931	Petershams	30-50	*

AUTHOR	TITLE	PUBLISHER	DATE	ARTIST	PRICE	LC
La Rue, Mabel G.	Zip the Toy Mule (1st, sm4to, 46p, 6cp, pep)	Macmillan	1932	Petershams	50-80	
Zolotow, Charlotte	Bunny Who Found Easter (1st, 12mo, [32]p, 2-color, pep, DJ/2.25)	Parnassus Press	(1959)	Peterson, Betty	30-50	
Peterson, Barbara	Whitefoot Mouse (1st, 8vo, 52p, red cl, 2-color, pep, DJ)	Holiday House	(1959)	Peterson, Russell	25-40	
Byron, May	Land of Nod (ob4to, ibds, 12cp)	NY: Hodder	[1909]	Petherick, Rosa	170-240	
Jewett, John H.	Little Toy Bearkins (16mo, ibds, [78]p, fp color)	L: Nister	[1908]	Petherick, Rosa	120-185	
Byron, May	Little Wee Bear (24mo, ipcb, 24 fp color)	L: H. Milford	[1908]	Petherick, Rosa	120-180	
Byron, May	Teddy Bear Book (sq8vo, ibds, 12cp)	L: H. Frowde	[1911]	Petherick, Rosa	250-400	
Robinson, Geraldine	Toy Bearkins Christmas (12mo, 32p)	L: Nister	[1915]	Petherick, Rosa	130-180	
Lyons, A. Neil	Simple Simon... (1st, 8vo, 344p, red/gilt, 8pl)	L: John Lane	1914	Peto, G.E.	40-60	
Peto, Gladys	China Cow (1st, 4to, p-o, 129p, black/gilt, 8cp)	Houghton	[1926]	Peto, Gladys	80-120	
Hunt, Enid	Fine Lady Upon a White Horse (1st AM, 4to, gilt, 120p, 8cp)	Dodge	[1929]	Peto, Gladys	100-165	
Peto, Gladys	Gladys Peto's Children's Book (lg8vo, ibds, 7cp)	L: Routledge	[1930]	Peto, Gladys	70-100	*
Peto, Gladys	Twilight Stories (1st, 4to, ibds, unpag, 8cp)	L: J.F. Shaw	[1932]	Peto, Gladys	90-140	*
Norwood, Edwin P.	Adventures of Diggeldy Dan (1st, 8vo, p-o, 240p, 8cp)	Little/Brown	1922	Peyton, A. Conway	40-65	
Norwood, Edwin P.	Davy Winkle in Circusland (1st, 8vo, 202p, tan cl, col frn)	Little/Brown	1926	Peyton, A. Conway	40-65	
Norwood, Edwin P.	Friends of Diggeldy Dan (1st, 8vo, 215p, p-o, 8cp)	Little/Brown	1924	Peyton, A. Conway	40-65	
Norwood, Edwin P.	In the Land of Diggeldy Dan (1st, 8vo, p-o, 226p, 8cp)	Little/Brown	1923	Peyton, A. Conway	40-65	
Stratton-Porter, Gene	Laddie (1st, 8vo, 602p, blue cl, 4cp, pep)	Doubleday/Page	1913	Pfeifer, Herman	100-175	
Phillips, Coles	Gallery of Girls (1st, 4to, p-o, [88]p, green cl, 39cp)	Century	1911	Phillips, Coles	450-650	
Atherton, Gertrude	Gorgeous Isle (1st, sm8vo, 223p, orange cl, 4cp, pep)	Doubleday/Page	1908	Phillips, Coles	40-60	
Sinclair, May	Immortal Moment (1st, sm8vo, 315p, white cl, 4pl)	Doubleday/Page	1908	Phillips, Coles	35-60	
Michelson, Miriam	Michael Thwaites's Wife (1st, 8vo, red cl, 402p, 3cp)	Doubleday/Page	1909	Phillips, Coles	25-40	
Nicholson, Meredith	Siege of the Seven Suitors (1st, sm8vo, green cl, 401p, col frn)	Houghton	1910	Phillips, Coles	40-65	
Phillips, Coles	Young Man's Fancy (1st, 4to, [47]p, gilt, 19cp)	Bobbs-Merrill	(1912)	Phillips, Coles	450-650	
Ballard, Martin	Benjie's Portion (1st AM {std}, 8vo, 208p, b/w, DJ/3.95)	World	(1969)	Phillips, Douglas	20-35	
Sabin, Edwin L.	Magic Mashie (1st, sm8vo, 210p, frn by...)	A. Wessels	1902	Phillips, Jay C.	250-350	*
Phillips, Jay C.	Plantation Sketches (1st, ob folio, [58]p, brown ibds, b/w)	R.H. Russell	1899	Phillips, Jay C.	250-400	
Kingsley, Charles	Water Babies (1st, 12mo, blue/gilt, teg, 295p, b/w)	Rand/McNally	(1900)	Phillips, Mary E.	40-65	
Phipps, Mary	All About Patsy (1st {std}, 8vo, red cl, 136p, 16cp, 38pl, pep)	Doubleday/Doran	1930	Phipps, Mary	120-180	
Phipps, Mary	Liza Jane & the Kinkies (1st, 4to, ibds, [90]p, color, pep)	Sears	(1929)	Phipps, Mary	250-350	
Merryman, Mildred P.	Quack! Said Jerusha (1st, lg8vo, ibds, [50]p, 1-color, pep)	Sears	(1930)	Phipps, Mary	140-200	
Piatti, Celestino	Animal ABC (1st AM {std}, ob4to, [26]p, color, DJ/4.50, NYTBI)	Atheneum	1966	Piatti, Celestino	40-70	
Bolliger, Max	Golden Apple (1st AM {std}, lg4to, ibds, [27]p, color, DJ/4.95)	Atheneum	(1970)	Piatti, Celestino	30-50	
Piatti, Celestino	Happy Owls (1st AM {std}, ob4to, [32]p, ibds, color, DJ/4.50, NYTBI)	Atheneum	1964	Piatti, Celestino	40-70	
Von Juchen, Aurel	Holy Night (1st AM {std}, narrow ob4to, [29]p, ibds, color, DJ/4.95)	Atheneum	1968	Piatti, Celestino	30-50	*
Huber, Ursula	Nock Family Circus (1st AM {std}, 4to, ibds, [32]p, color, DJ/4.95)	Atheneum	1968	Piatti, Celestino	25-40	
Aiken, Joan	Necklace of Raindrops (1st AM, lg8vo, 109p, fp color, cep, DJ/3.95)	Doubleday	1968	Pienkowski, Jan	150-225	
DeRegniers, Beatrice	Who Likes the Sun? (1st {std}, 4to, [30]p, 2-color, DJ/3.00)	Harcourt	(1961)	Pierce, Leona	50-80	
Pierson, Clara D.	Tales of a Poultry Farm (1st, sm8vo, 195p, gilt, 9pl)	Dutton	1904	Pierson, Clara D.	70-120	
Hodder, William R.	Daughter of the Dawn (1st, 8vo, green cl, 333p, 12pl)	L: Jarrold	1903	Piffard, Harold	55-80	*
Burnett, Frances H.	Little Princess (1st UK, 8vo, 302p, p-o, 8cp)	L: Warne	(1905)	Piffard, Harold	100-170	
Tracy, Louis	Lost Provinces (1st, 8vo, 380p, olive/gilt, 12pl)	L: C. Pearson	1898	Piffard, Harold	55-80	*
Curtis, Alice T.	Little Maid of Old New York (1st, sm8vo, 224p, p-o, 5pl)	Penn	1921	Pilsbry, Elizabeth	25-45	
Grimm Bros.	Little Red Riding Hood (1st {std}, 8vo, unpag, color, DJ/3.50)	Harcourt	(1968)	Pincus, Harriet	25-40	
Segal, Lore	Tell Me a Mitzi (1st {std}, ob4to, [40]p, color, DJ/4.95)	Farrar, Straus	(1970)	Pincus, Harriet	30-50	
Livingston, Richard	The Hunkendunkens (1st {std}, ob8vo, [36]p, color, DJ/3.25)	Harcourt	(1968)	Pincus, Harriet	30-45	
Durham, Mae	Tit for Tat (1st {std}, 8vo, 126p, b/w, DJ/3.25)	Harcourt	(1967)	Pincus, Harriet	25-40	*
Sandburg, Carl	Wedding Procession/Rag Doll & Broomhandle (1st {std}, ob4to, [30]p, color)	Harcourt	(1967)	Pincus, Harriet	40-65	
Cooper, Elizabeth	Who is Paddy? (1st {std}, 16mo, [32]p, color, DJ/2.95)	Harcourt	1967	Pincus, Harriet	25-40	
Arkhurst, Joyce C.	Adventures of Spider (1st {std}, lg8vo, 58p, color, DJ/2.95)	Little/Brown	(1964)	Pinkney, Jerry	30-50	
Spellman, John W.	Beautiful Blue Jay (1st {std}, lg8vo, 101p, b/w, DJ/3.50)	Little/Brown	(1967)	Pinkney, Jerry	30-50	
Sobol, Ken	Clock Museum (1st, sm4to, 48p, color, DJ/3.75)	McGraw-Hill	(1967)	Pinkney, Jerry	30-50	
Saleh, Harold	Even Tiny Ants Must Sleep (1st, sm ob4to, [31]p, fp 3-color, pep, DJ/3.25)	McGraw-Hill	(1967)	Pinkney, Jerry	40-65	*
Powell, Fern	Porcupine and the Tiger (1st, sm ob4to, [32]p, fp 3-color, cep, DJ/3.75)	Lothrop, Lee	1969	Pinkney, Jerry	30-45	
Salten, Felix	Bambi's Children (1st {std}, sm8vo, 315p, green cl, b/w, DJ/2.50)	Bobbs-Merrill	(1939)	Pinner, Erna	80-140	
Cendrars, Blaise	Little Black Stories for Little White Children (1st, 8vo, 138p, cp)	Payson-Clarke	1929	Pinsard, Pierre	50-80	*
Cherr, Pat	Bear in Fact and Fiction (1st {std}, 8vo, 157p, b/w, DJ/3.25)	Harlin Quist	(1967)	Pinto, Ralph	25-45	
Holman, Felice	Cricket Winter (1st {std}, 8vo, 107p, b/w, gilt, DJ/3.95)	Norton	(1967)	Pinto, Ralph	20-30	
Johnston, Johanna	Eagle in Fact & Fiction (1st {std}, 8vo, 157p, b/w, DJ/3.25)	Harlin Quist	(1966)	Pinto, Ralph	25-40	
Cherr, Pat	Lion in Fact and Fiction (1st {std}, 8vo, 157p, b/w, DJ/3.25)	Harlin Quist	(1966)	Pinto, Ralph	25-45	
Graves, Robert	Two Wise Children (1st {std}, 8vo, [32]p, b/w, DJ/2.75)	Harlin Quist	(1966)	Pinto, Ralph	50-80	
Terry, Richard R.	Old Rhymes with New Tunes (1st, 4to, ibds, 32p, b/w)	Longmans	1912	Pippet, Gabriel	55-80	*
Molesworth, Mrs.	Magic Nuts (1st, 8vo, 194p, orange/gilt, 7pl)	L: Macmillan	1898	Pitman, R.M.M.	55-80	
Molesworth, Mrs.	Ruby Ring (1st, 8vo, 213p, orange cl, 8pl)	L: Macmillan	1904	Pitman, R.M.M.	50-80	
Fouque, La Motte	Undine (1st, 8vo, blue/gilt, 204p, teg, 19pl)	L: Macmillan	1897	Pitman, R.M.M.	80-120	
Fenner, Phyllis R.	Adventure Rare & Magical (1st {std}, 8vo, 178p, b/w, DJ/2.50)	Knopf	1945	Pitz, Henry C.	25-40	
Cooper, Page	Amigo, Circus Horse (1st {std}, 8vo, 238p, yellow cl, uncut, b/w, DJ/2.50)	World	(1955)	Pitz, Henry C.	30-50	
Aspden, Don	Barney's Barges (1st, 8vo, 192p, green cl, fp b/w, pep, DJ/2.00)	Holiday House	(1944)	Pitz, Henry C.	30-50	
Macleod, Mary	Book of King Arthur (1st {std}, 8vo, blue cl, 324p, color, DJ)	Lippincott	(1949)	Pitz, Henry C.	35-60	*
Means, Florence C.	Bowlful of Stars (1st, 8vo, green cl, 247p, b/w, pep)	Houghton	1934	Pitz, Henry C.	30-50	*
Meadowcroft, Enid	By Secret Railway (1st, 8vo, 275p, b/w, pep, DJ/3.00)	Crowell	(1948)	Pitz, Henry C.	30-50	
Finger, Charles J.	Cape Horn Snorter (1st, 8vo, 263p, b/w, pep, DJ/2.00)	Houghton	1939	Pitz, Henry C.	30-50	
Malkus, Alida S.	Citadel of a Hundred Stairways (1st, 8vo, 234p, col frn, pep, DJ/2.00)	Winston	(1941)	Pitz, Henry C.	20-35	
Craine, Edith	Conquistador (1st, 8vo, 288p, gilt, b/w, pep)	Duffield/Green	(1931)	Pitz, Henry C.	25-45	
Watkins, Hope	Cunning Fox (1st {std}, lg8vo, uncut, 118p, fp b/w, DJ/2.00)	Knopf	1943	Pitz, Henry C.	30-50	*
Fenner, Phyllis R.	Demons & Dervishes (1st {std}, 8vo, red cl, 183p, fp b/w, pep, DJ/2.00)	Knopf	(1946)	Pitz, Henry C.	35-60	*
Finger, Charles J.	Distant Prize... (1st, sm8vo, 330p, red/gilt, col frn, pep, DJ/2.50)	Appleton-Century	1935	Pitz, Henry C.	30-50	
Finger, Charles J.	Dog at His Heel (1st, 8vo, 304p, orange cl, dp color, pep, DJ/2.00)	Winston	(1936)	Pitz, Henry C.	30-50	

AUTHOR	TITLE	PUBLISHER	DATE	ARTIST	PRICE	LC
Moore, David	End of Black Dog (1st, 8vo, 198p, b/w, DJ/2.50)	Crowell	(1949)	Pitz, Henry C.	25-40	
Savery, Constance	Enemy Brothers (1st {std}, 8vo, 313p, DJ/2.50, b/w decor by...)	Longmans	1943	Pitz, Henry C.	40-65	
Coblentz, Catherine	Falcon of Eric the Red (1st {std}, 8vo, 211p, 10 dp pl, DJ/2.25)	Longmans	1942	Pitz, Henry C.	30-50	
Fenner, Phyllis R.	Fools and Funny Fellows (1st {std}, 8vo, 185p, b/w, DJ/2.50)	Knopf	1947	Pitz, Henry C.	30-50	*
Fenner, Phyllis R.	Giants & Witches (1st {std}, 8vo, red cl, 208p, fp b/w, pep, DJ/2.50)	Knopf	1943	Pitz, Henry C.	40-60	*
Finger, Charles J.	Give a Man a Horse (1st, 8vo, 340p, col frn, dp b/w, pep, DJ/2.00)	Winston	(1938)	Pitz, Henry C.	30-50	
Finger, Charles J.	High Water in Arkansas (1st, 8vo, ibds, [28]p, color, pep, DJ/0.50)	Grosset/Dunlap	1943	Pitz, Henry C.	30-55	
Davis, Robert	Hudson Bay Express (1st, 8vo, 258p, blue cl, b/w, DJ/2.00)	Holiday House	(1942)	Pitz, Henry C.	25-40	*
Coryell, Hubert	Indian Brother (1st, 8vo, 348p, b/w, pep, DJ/2.00)	Harcourt	(1935)	Pitz, Henry C.	40-65	
Scott, Walter	Ivanhoe (1st, 8vo, red cl, 469p, uncut, 6pl)	Sears	(1928)	Pitz, Henry C.	30-50	*
Juta, Jan	Look Out for the Ostriches! (1st {std}, 8vo, 177p, b/w, DJ/2.50)	Knopf	1949	Pitz, Henry C.	25-45	
Meader, Stephen W.	Lumberjack (1st, 8vo, 277p, b/w pl, pep, DJ/2.00)	Harcourt	(1934)	Pitz, Henry C.	80-135	
Bennett, John	Master Skylark (1st, lg8vo, blue cl, 322p, p-o, 8cp, pep)	Century	1922	Pitz, Henry C.	45-70	
Walsh, Mary R.	Mullingar Heifer (1st {std}, 8vo, [61]p, b/w, pep, DJ/1.75)	Knopf	1946	Pitz, Henry C.	40-65	
Leighton, Robert	Olaf the Glorious (1st, sm8vo, 208p, col frn, 6 fp b/w, pep)	Macmillan	1929	Pitz, Henry C.	25-45	
Fenner, Phyllis R.	Princesses & Peasant Boys (1st {std}, 8vo, 188p, b/w, pep, DJ/2.50)	Knopf	1944	Pitz, Henry C.	30-50	*
Sperry, Armstrong	River of the West (1st {std}, 8vo, 182p, b/w, DJ/1.50)	Winston	(1952)	Pitz, Henry C.	20-35	
Jordan, Mildred	Shoo-Fly Pie (1st {std}, 8vo, 118p, dp color, pep, DJ/2.00)	Knopf	1944	Pitz, Henry C.	30-50	
Lide, Alice A.	Thord Firetooth (1st, 8vo, 226p, b/w, pep, DJ/2.00)	Lothrop, Lee	1937	Pitz, Henry C.	25-40	
Meigs, Cornelia L.	Trade Wind (1st, 8vo, 309p, black cl, p-o, 8cp, pep)	Little/Brown	1927	Pitz, Henry C.	30-45	
Kingsley, Charles	Westward Ho! (1st, 12mo, 342p, col frn, b/w)	Macmillan	1930	Pitz, Henry C.	40-60	*
Finger, Charles J.	When Guns Thundered at Tripoli (1st, sm8vo, 290p, col frn, DJ/2.00)	Henry Holt & Co.	(1937)	Pitz, Henry C.	30-50	
Walsh, Mary R.	Widow Woman and her Goat (1st {std}, lg8vo, [64]p, b/w, DJ/1.75)	Knopf	(1949)	Pitz, Henry C.	20-35	
Watson, Virginia	With LaSalle the Explorer (1st, 8vo, 366p, p-o, col frn, 4pl, pep)	Henry Holt & Co.	1922	Pitz, Henry C.	25-45	
Fenner, Phyllis R.	With Might and Main (1st {std}, 8vo, 190p, b/w, DJ/2.50)	Knopf	1948	Pitz, Henry C.	25-40	
Finger, Charles J.	Yankee Captain in Patagonia (1st, narrow 8vo, 74p, b/w, DJ/0.50)	Grosset/Dunlap	(1941)	Pitz, Henry C.	25-40	
Coatsworth, Eliz.	You Shall Have a Carriage (1st {std}, 8vo, 138p, pep, DJ/2.00)	Macmillan	1941	Pitz, Henry C.	30-45	
O'Neill, Mary	Poor Merlo (1st {std}, ob8vo, [48]p, color, DJ/3.95)	Atheneum	1967	Piussi-Campbell, J.	30-50	*
Campbell, M. Rudolph	Talking Crocodile (1st {std}, 4to, [46]p, color, cep, DJ/4.95)	Atheneum	1968	Piussi-Campbell, J.	30-50	*
Bianco, Margery W.	Bright Morning (1st, 8vo, 143p, b/w, dep, DJ/1.50)	Viking	1942	Platt, Margaret	30-50	
Parton, Ethel	Lost Locket (1st, 8vo, 317p, b/w, pep, DJ/2.00)	Viking	1940	Platt, Margaret	30-50	
Parton, Ethel	Penelope Ellen (1st, 8vo, 300p, b/w, pep, DJ/2.00)	Viking	1936	Platt, Margaret	25-45	
Parton, Ethel	Tabitha Mary (1st, 8vo, 244p, col frn, 4 dp b/w, pep)	Viking	1933	Platt, Margaret	30-45	
Berry, Erick	Leif the Lucky: Discoverer of America (1st, 8vo, 72p, color, DJ/2.25)	Garrard Pub.	(1961)	Plummer, William	25-35	
Johnson, A.E.	Below Zero (1st, lg4to, 61p, 12 tip)	L: Hodder	[1911]	Pocock, Noel	160-220	
Grimm Bros.	Fairy Tales (1st, lg8vo, 346p, 23 ticp)	L: Hodder	(1913)	Pocock, Noel	200-300	
Grimm Bros.	Fairy Tales (1st AM, 4to, blue/gilt, 346p, 23 ticp)	Doran	[1913]	Pocock, Noel	200-300	
Grimm Bros.	Fairy Tales (8vo, green cl, 337p, 8cp, pep)	Garden City	[1930]	Pocock, Noel	55-80	
Defoe, Daniel	Robinson Crusoe (1st, lg8vo, 352p, tan/gilt, 24 ticp, pep)	L: Hodder	(1910)	Pocock, Noel	80-120	
Farrow, George E.	Adventures of a Dodo (1st, 8vo, gilt, 245p, 70 b/w, pep)	L: T.F. Unwin	(1907)	Pogany, Willy	200-300	
Olcott, F.J. (ed)	Adventures of Haroun Er Raschid (1st, 8vo, 363p, gilt, col frn)	Henry Holt & Co.	1923	Pogany, Willy	55-80	*
Colum, Padraic	Adventures of Odysseus (1st, 12mo, 254p, 8cp, pep)	Macmillan	1918	Pogany, Willy	60-90	
Carroll, Lewis	Alice in Wonderland (1st, 8vo, purple/gilt, 192p, pep, b/w)	Dutton	(1929)	Pogany, Willy	160-240	
Heine, Heinrich	Atta Troll (1st, 12mo, 185p, grey bds, gilt, pep, b/w)	L: Sidgwick/Jack	1913	Pogany, Willy	150-225	
Heine, Heinrich	Atta Troll (1st AM, 12mo, 185p, bds, gilt, 3pl)	Huebsch	(1914)	Pogany, Willy	140-200	
Olcott, F.J. (ed)	Bible Stories to Read & Tell (1st, 8vo, blue cl, 486p, 8cp)	Houghton	1916	Pogany, Willy	70-100	
Stacpoole, H.D.	Blue Lagoon (1st, 8vo, blue/gilt, uncut, 326p, 13 ticp)	L: T.F. Unwin	1910	Pogany, Willy	250-400	
Anthony, Joseph	Casanova Jones (1st, sm8vo, gilt, 206p, b/w, pep)	Century	1930	Pogany, Willy	35-50	
Bartruse, Grace	Children in Japan (1st, lg8vo, [32]p, bds, p-o, 16cp)	McBride	1915	Pogany, Willy	200-300	
Colum, Padraic	Children of Odin (1st, sm8vo, gilt, 282p, 4cp, pep)	Macmillan	1920	Pogany, Willy	50-80	
Skinner, Ada M.	Children's Plays (1st, sm8vo, 269p, color)	Appleton	1919	Pogany, Willy	80-125	
Elias, E. (ed.)	Cinderella (1st AM, sm4to, red bds, p-o, 8 dp color)	McBride	1915	Pogany, Willy	200-300	
Ambrose, Blanche A.	Coppa Hamba (1st, 4to, [82]p, orange cl, 3cp, fp b/w, pep)	Suttonhouse	1936	Pogany, Willy	250-350	
Gask, Lilian	Fairies & Christmas Child (1st AM, lg8vo, p-o, 261p, 8cp, pep)	Crowell	(1912)	Pogany, Willy	200-300	
Gask, Lilian	Fairies & Christmas Child (1st, 8vo, 260p, gilt, 8cp, pep)	L: Harrap	(1912)	Pogany, Willy	250-400	
Newman, Isidora	Fairy Flowers (1st AM, 8vo, ibds, 196p, 15 ticp, pep)	Henry Holt & Co.	(1926)	Pogany, Willy	250-350	
Newman, Isidora	Fairy Flowers (1st, 4to, ibds, 160p, 15 ticp, pep)	L: H. Milford	(1926)	Pogany, Willy	200-300	
Goethe	Faust (1st, 4to, red/gilt, teg, 205p, 31 ticp)	L: Hutchinson	1908	Pogany, Willy	250-400	
Newman, Isidora	Flowers, Facts & Fables (1st, 4to, 141p, ibds, 7cp, cep)	NY: Snellgrove	1937	Pogany, Willy	120-170	
Gask, Lilian	Folk Tales from Many Lands (1st, 8vo, red/gilt, teg, 287p, p-o, 8cp)	L: Harrap	1910	Pogany, Willy	150-225	
Gask, Lilian	Folk Tales from Many Lands (1st AM, 8vo, 286p, p-o, teg, uncut, 8cp, pep)	Crowell	(1910)	Pogany, Willy	125-200	
Kunos, Ignacz	Forty-Four Turkish Fairy Tales (1st, 4to, tan cl, teg, 363p, 16 ticp)	L: Harrap	[1913]	Pogany, Willy	250-400	
Colum, Padraic	Frenzied Prince (1st {std}, sm4to, 196p, gilt, 10 fp color, pep, DJ/3.50)	McKay	(1943)	Pogany, Willy	80-140	
Thomas, Margaret L.	George Washington Lincoln Goes Around/World (1st, 8vo, p-o, 205p, pep)	NY: T. Nelson	(1927)	Pogany, Willy	80-120	*
Fable, Leonard	Gingerbread Man (1st AM, 4to, [32]p, p-o, bds, 8cp)	McBride	1915	Pogany, Willy	160-220	
Pushkin, Alexander	Golden Cockerel (1st, lg4to, red/gilt, [48]p, 12cp, pep, DJ/2.50)	NY: Nelson	1938	Pogany, Willy	150-250	
Colum, Padraic	Golden Fleece (1st, sq8vo, 290p, gilt, 8cp, pep, NH)	Macmillan	1921	Pogany, Willy	60-100	
Hawley, Harriet S.	Goose Girl of Nurnberg (1st, 4to, [59]p, col frn, b/w, DJ/1.50)	Suttonhouse	1936	Pogany, Willy	100-140	
Swift, Jonathan	Gulliver's Travels (1st, sm8vo, 296p, blue/gilt, 12cp, pep)	Macmillan	1917	Pogany, Willy	90-120	
Swift, Jonathan	Gulliver's Travels (1st UK, 8vo, 296p, gilt, uncut, 12cp)	L: Harrap	1919	Pogany, Willy	80-120	
Harmon, Margaretta	How Santa Found the Cobbler's Shop (1st, 4to, [46]p, color, pep)	Suttonhouse	1936	Pogany, Willy	180-250	
Pogany, Nebby	Hungarian Fairy Book (1st, 8vo, 287p, blue/gilt, col frn)	L: T.F. Unwin	(1913)	Pogany, Willy	125-200	
Burton, Richard F.	Kasidah of Haji Abdu El-Yezdi (1st, sm4to, gilt, p-o, 129p, 12pl)	McKay	(1931)	Pogany, Willy	80-140	
Colum, Padraic	King of Ireland's Son (1st, 8vo, green/gilt, 316p, 4cp)	Henry Holt & Co.	1916	Pogany, Willy	80-145	
Colum, Padraic	King of Ireland's Son (1st UK, 8vo, 316p, 4cp, 9 fp b/w)	L: Harrap	1920	Pogany, Willy	80-120	
Colum, Padraic	King of Ireland's Son (1st {this pub.}, sq8vo, 316p, 4cp)	Macmillan	1921	Pogany, Willy	60-100	
Newman, Isidora	Legend of the Lilac (1st, 4to, ibds, [23]p, 4cp)	Whitman	1926	Pogany, Willy	60-90	
Newman, Isidora	Legend of the Tulip... (1st, 4to, [24]p, ibds, 5cp)	Whitman	(1926)	Pogany, Willy	60-90	

ARTIST: 158

AUTHOR	TITLE	PUBLISHER	DATE	ARTIST	PRICE	LC
Arnold, Edwin	Light of Asia (1st, sm4to, black/silver, p-o, 182p, 12pl)	McKay	(1932)	Pogany, Willy	120-175	
Mother Goose	Little Mother Goose (1st, sm4to, bds, p-o, [30]p, 16cp)	McBride	1915	Pogany, Willy	225-320	
Crownfield, Gertrude	Little Tailor of Windy Way (1st, sm8vo, 132p, 4cp)	Macmillan	1917	Pogany, Willy	40-65	
Flanders, Helen H.	Looking Out of Jimmie (1st, sm8vo, 92p, gilt, pep, uncut, fp b/w)	Dutton	(1927)	Pogany, Willy	60-90	
Pogany, Nebby	Magyar Fairy Tales (1st {std}, 8vo, green/gilt, 268p, b/w, pep)	Dutton	(1930)	Pogany, Willy	100-170	R
Ward, Mrs. H.	Milly and Olly (2nd ed., 8vo, 352p, b/w)	L: T.F. Unwin	1907	Pogany, Willy	70-120	*
Olcott, F.J. (ed)	More Tales of the Arabian Nights (1st, 8vo, 274p, red/gilt, 12cp)	Henry Holt & Co.	1915	Pogany, Willy	120-180	
Huffard, Grace T.	My Poetry Book (1st, lg8vo, blue cl, 6cp)	(London)	1934	Pogany, Willy	60-100	
Huffard, Grace T.	My Poetry Book (1st AM, lg8vo, 504p, blue/gilt, 6cp, pep)	Winston	(1934)	Pogany, Willy	50-90	
Wagner, Richard	Parsifal (1st AM, 4to, maroon/gilt, teg, 16 ticp, pep)	Crowell	(1912)	Pogany, Willy	275-450	
Wagner, Richard	Parsifal (1st, 4to, [192]p, grey/gilt, 16 ticp, pep)	L: Harrap	(1912)	Pogany, Willy	300-500	
Pogany, Elaine	Peterkin (1st, sm4to, ibds, [75]p, 14 fp color, pep, DJ/1.00)	McKay	1940	Pogany, Willy	130-200	
Johnson, Margaret	Polly & the Wishing Ring (1st, 12mo, 123p, 4cp)	Macmillan	1918	Pogany, Willy	70-100	
Banks, Helen M.	Polly's Garden (1st, sm8vo, 96p, grey cl, 4cp)	Macmillan	1918	Pogany, Willy	60-100	
Coleridge, Samuel T.	Rime of the Ancient Mariner (1st AM, lg4to, gilt, 20 ticp, pep)	Crowell	(1910)	Pogany, Willy	300-500	
Coleridge, Samuel T.	Rime of the Ancient Mariner (1st, lg4to, gilt, teg, pep, 20 ticp)	L: Harrap	(1910)	Pogany, Willy	400-600	
Coleridge, Samuel T.	Rime of the Ancient Mariner (1st {this fmt}, sm4to, teg, gilt, 20 ticp)	Doran	[1915]	Pogany, Willy	200-320	
Capes, Bernard E.	Romance of Lohengrin (1st, 8vo, blue/gilt, 271p, 14pl)	L: Dean	1905	Pogany, Willy	200-300	
Omar Khayyam	Rubaiyat of Omar Khayyam (1st, 4to, ibds, teg, gilt, 24 ticp, pep)	L: Harrap	(1909)	Pogany, Willy	300-450	
Omar Khayyam	Rubaiyat of Omar Khayyam (1st AM, 4to, ibds, teg, 96p, 24 ticp)	Crowell	(1909)	Pogany, Willy	250-400	
Omar Khayyam	Rubaiyat of Omar Khayyam (lg8vo, 96p, green/gilt, teg, 12 ticp)	Crowell	[1920]	Pogany, Willy	200-300	
Omar Khayyam	Rubaiyat of Omar Khayyam (1st [new ed.], 4to, 171p, gilt, teg, 12 ticp)	L: Harrap	(1930)	Pogany, Willy	175-250	
Garrard, Phillis	Running Away with Nebby (1st {std}, lg8vo, 144p, 6cp, 11pl, pep, DJ/2.00)	McKay	(1944)	Pogany, Willy	75-100	
Arnold, Edwin	Song Celestial (1st, sm4to, 135p, black/silver, p-o, 18pl)	McKay	(1934)	Pogany, Willy	100-165	
Browning, Eliz. B.	Sonnets from the Portuguese (1st, lg8vo, 96p, 8 ticp, DJ/2.50)	Crowell	(1936)	Pogany, Willy	60-100	
Bryant, Sara Cone	Stories to Tell the Littlest Ones (1st UK, 12mo, 178p, 6cp, pep)	L: Harrap	1918	Pogany, Willy	100-170	
Tagore, Rabindranath	Stray Birds (1st, sm8vo, blue/gilt, 84p, col frn by...)	L: Macmillan	1917	Pogany, Willy	35-60	
Wagner, Richard	Tale of Lohengrin (1st AM, 4to, grey/gilt, teg, 8 ticp)	Crowell	(1913)	Pogany, Willy	250-350	
Wagner, Richard	Tale of Lohengrin (1st, 4to, brown/gilt, 8 ticp, pep)	L: Harrap	[1913]	Pogany, Willy	250-400	
Olcott, F.J. (ed)	Tales of the Persian Genii (1st, 8vo, gilt, pep, 225p, 4cp)	Houghton	(1917)	Pogany, Willy	70-100	
Olcott, F.J. (ed)	Tales of the Persian Genii (1st UK, 8vo, grey cl, 225p, 4cp)	L: Harrap	1919	Pogany, Willy	70-100	
Hawthorne, Nathaniel	Tanglewood Tales (12mo, red cl, 320p, 4to, 24pl, pep)	L: T.F. Unwin	(1910)	Pogany, Willy	120-170	
Wagner, Richard	Tannhauser (1st AM, lg8vo, black/gilt, unpag, 16 ticp)	Brentano's	[1911]	Pogany, Willy	250-400	
Wagner, Richard	Tannhauser (1st, 4to, [128]p, grey/gilt, 16 ticp)	L: Harrap	(1911)	Pogany, Willy	300-500	
Schwimmer, Rosika	Tisza Tales (1st {std}, lg8vo, 225p, blue/gilt, 8cp, pep, DJ/5.00)	Doubleday/Doran	1928	Pogany, Willy	100-170	
Edgar, M.G.	Treasury of Verse... (1st AM, lg8vo, 261p, teg, gilt, pep, 8cp)	Crowell	(1908)	Pogany, Willy	180-250	
Newman, Isidora	Wee Miss Violet... (1st, 4to, ibds, unpag, 4cp)	Whitman	(1926)	Pogany, Willy	50-80	
Jenkyn-Thomas, W.	Welsh Fairy Book (1st AM, 8vo, blue/gilt, col frn, 303p)	Stokes	[1907]	Pogany, Willy	200-300	
Jenkyn-Thomas, W.	Welsh Fairy Book (1st, 8vo, 312p, blue/gilt, col frn, 9pl, pep)	L: T.F. Unwin	(1907)	Pogany, Willy	250-400	
Mother Goose	Willy Pogany's Mother Goose (1st lg8vo, [152]p, teg, gilt, color, pep)	Nelson	(1928)	Pogany, Willy	250-400	
Various	Wimp & the Woodle (1st, 4to, blue/gilt bds, 180p, 7cp, pep)	Suttonhouse	1935	Pogany, Willy	250-350	R
Young, Gerald	Witch's Kitchen (1st, 8vo, p-o, 223p, gilt, 8cp)	L: Harrap	(1910)	Pogany, Willy	200-300	
Young, Gerald	Witch's Kitchen (1st AM, 8vo, 223p, teg, p-o, 8cp, pep)	Crowell	(1911)	Pogany, Willy	200-300	
Hawthorne, Nathaniel	Wonder Book (1st AM, lg8vo, gilt, 320p, 4cp, pep)	Jacobs	(1909)	Pogany, Willy	120-185	
Holbrook, Florence	Hiawatha Alphabet (1st, 4to, [60]p, p-o, fp color)	Rand/McNally	(1910)	Pohl, H.D.	150-250	
Meader, Stephen W.	Sabre Pilot (1st {std}, 8vo, 173p, b/w, DJ/2.75)	Harcourt	1956	Polgreen, John	70-120	
Alexander, Cecil	All Things Bright and Beautiful (1st, sm4to, [32]p, color, DJ/3.25)	Scribner	1962	Politi, Leo	60-90	
Garrett, Helen	Angelo, the Naughty One (1st, 4to, ipcb, 40p, color, pep, DJ/2.00)	Viking	1944	Politi, Leo	130-200	
Parish, Helen R.	At the Palace Gates (1st, sm4to, ipcb, 64p, fp 2-color, pep, DJ/2.00)	Viking	1949	Politi, Leo	70-125	
Politi, Leo	Boat for Peppe (1st, 4to, [32]p, fp color, DJ/2.00)	Scribner	1950	Politi, Leo	80-125	
Politi, Leo	Butterflies Come (1st, sm4to, yellow cl, [31]p, color, DJ/2.75)	Scribner	(1957)	Politi, Leo	120-200	
Dalgliesh, Alice	Columbus Story (1st, 4to, [30]p, ibds, dp color, DJ/2.75)	Scribner	(1955)	Politi, Leo	80-130	R
Perez, Luis	El Coyote the Rebel (1st {std}, sm8vo, orange cl, 233p, b/w, DJ/2.75)	Henry Holt & Co.	(1947)	Politi, Leo	50-80	
Politi, Leo	Juanita (1st, sm4to, ibds, [31]p, color, DJ/2.00, CH)	Scribner	1948	Politi, Leo	150-220	
Sawyer, Ruth	Least One (1st, sm4to, 88p, 2-color, pep, DJ/2.00)	Viking	1941	Politi, Leo	70-100	
Politi, Leo	Lito and the Clown (1st, 4to, [31]p, fp color, DJ/3.25)	Scribner	(1964)	Politi, Leo	70-100	
Politi, Leo	Little Leo (1st, sm4to, [30]p, color, DJ/2.00)	Scribner	1951	Politi, Leo	150-220	
Politi, Leo	Little Pancho (1st {1st book}, 16mo, [40]p, ibds, color, pep, DJ/0.50)	Viking	1938	Politi, Leo	150-220	
Clark, Ann N.	Looking for Something (1st, 8vo, 53p, dp color, pep, DJ/2.50)	Viking	1952	Politi, Leo	50-85	
Clark, Ann N.	Magic Money (1st, sm4to, 121p, red cl, pep, fp 1-color, DJ/2.50)	Viking	1950	Politi, Leo	50-80	
Politi, Leo	Mieko (1st, lg4to, [31]p, fp color, DJ/4.95)	Golden Gate	(1969)	Politi, Leo	60-90	
Politi, Leo	Mission Bell (1st, ob8vo, [32]p, blue cl, color, DJ/2.25)	Scribner	1953	Politi, Leo	80-125	
Politi, Leo	Moy, Moy (1st, sm4to, [31]p, fp color, DJ/2.95)	Scribner	(1960)	Politi, Leo	100-150	
Coatsworth, Eliz.	Noble Doll (1st, lg8vo, 45p, dp color, pep, DJ/3.00)	Viking	(1961)	Politi, Leo	80-140	
Politi, Leo	Pedro, Angel of Olvera Street (1st, 8vo, [32]p, color, DJ/1.75, CH)	Scribner	1946	Politi, Leo	125-220	
Politi, Leo	Piccolo's Prank (1st, 4to, [32]p, fp color, DJ/3.25)	Scribner	(1965)	Politi, Leo	90-150	
Politi, Leo	Rosa (1st, 4to, [38]p, fp color, DJ/3.25)	Scribner	(1963)	Politi, Leo	100-165	R
Politi, Leo	Song of the Swallows (1st sm4to, [32]p, color, DJ/2.00, CM)	Scribner	1949	Politi, Leo	120-200	R
Politi, Leo	St. Francis & the Animals (1st, sm4to, beige cl, [32]p, dp color, DJ/2.95)	Scribner	1959	Politi, Leo	100-165	
Henius, Frank	Stories from the Americas (1st, lg8vo, orange cl, 115p, fp b/w, DJ/2.75)	Scribner	1944	Politi, Leo	45-70	
Blanton, Catherine	Three Miracles (1st, 8vo, 47p, ipcb, color, DJ/2.00)	John Day	(1946)	Politi, Leo	100-165	
Brown, Abbie F.	Lonesomest Doll (1st, sm8vo, ibds, 76p, 4pl)	Houghton	1901	Pollak, E.	35-60	*
Freschet, Berniece	Flight of the Snow Goose (1st, 8vo, 40p, blue cl, b/w, DJ/3.50)	Crown	(1970)	Polseno, Jo	20-30	*
Cheney, Cora	Plantation Doll (1st {std}, 8vo, 136p, b/w, pep, DJ/2.50)	Holt	(1955)	Polseno, Jo	30-45	
Pons, Helene	Story of Vania (1st, ob4to, 24p, color, pep, DJ/3.50)	Viking	(1963)	Pons, Helene	30-50	
Bishop, Claire H.	Toto's Triumph (1st, 8vo, 127p, b/w, DJ/2.50)	Viking	(1957)	Ponsot, Claude	20-30	
Johnson, Clifton (ed)	Fir-Tree Fairy Book (1st, 8vo, 333p, color, pep)	Little/Brown	1912	Popini, Alexander	60-90	
Russell, Franklin	The Honeybees (1st, 4to, [34]p, fp color, pep, DJ/3.95, NYTBI)	Knopf	(1967)	Portal, Colette	30-50	*

AUTHOR	TITLE	PUBLISHER	DATE	ARTIST	PRICE	LC
Cleary, Beverly	Mitch and Amy (1st, 8vo, 222p, b/w, DJ/3.75)	Wm. Morrow	1967	Porter, George	20-35	
Stokely, Edith K.	Bubbleloon (1st, lg8vo, 201p, blue/gilt, 6cp, pep)	Doran	(1926)	Porter, J. Erwin	80-125	
Brink, Carol R.	Family Grandstand (1st, 8vo, 208p, b/w, pep, DJ/2.50)	Viking	1952	Porter, Jean M.	25-45	*
Kelsey, Vera	Maria Rosa (1st {std}, lg ob4to, [38]p, fp color, pep, DJ/2.00)	Doubleday/Doran	1942	Portinari, Candido	60-100	
King, Charles	Tonio, Son of Sierras (1st, 12mo, 338p, 4cp, 4pl)	Dillingham	(1906)	Post, Charles J.	30-50	
Tietjens, Eunice H.	Jaw Breaker's Alphabet (1st, ob4to, ibds, [111]p, b/w, dep)	A.& C. Boni	1930	Post, Hermann	70-100	*
Blair, Matilda	Bunny Cottontail (1st, lg4to, ibds, 51p, fp color)	McLoughlin	(1908)	Post, May A.	250-350	*
Mother Goose	Mother Goose in Holland (1st, 4to, 90p, color, pep)	Jacobs	(1912)	Post, May A.	120-200	*
Potter, Beatrix	Appley Dapply's Nursery Rhymes (1st, 16mo, p-o, [52]p, ibds, 15cp)	L: Warne	[1917]	Potter, Beatrix	500-750	
Potter, Beatrix	Cecily Parsley's Nursery Rhymes (1st, 16mo, orange bds, p-o, 15cp)	L: Warne	(1922)	Potter, Beatrix	500-700	
Potter, Beatrix	Fairy Caravan (1st, 8vo, green/gilt, p-o, 225p, 6cp)	McKay	(1929)	Potter, Beatrix	400-600	
Potter, Beatrix	Ginger & Pickles (1st, 12mo, 52p, bds, p-o, 10cp, pep)	L: Warne	1909	Potter, Beatrix	500-700	R
Potter, Beatrix	Pie & Patty Pan (1st, 12mo, 52p, p-o, bds, 10cp)	L: Warne	1905	Potter, Beatrix	500-700	
Potter, Beatrix	Roly Poly Pudding (1st, lg8vo, 69p, p-o, 18cp)	L: Warne	1908	Potter, Beatrix	500-700	
Potter, Beatrix	Story of Miss Moppet (1st, 16mo, bds, p-o, 14cp)	L: Warne	1906	Potter, Beatrix	700-950	
Potter, Beatrix	Tailor of Gloucester (1st, 16mo, green bds, 85p, p-o, 27cp)	L: Warne	1903	Potter, Beatrix	500-750	
Lane, Margaret	Tale of Beatrix Potter (1st, 8vo, gilt, 162p, 4cp, 16 b/w, DJ/3.50)	Warne	(1946)	Potter, Beatrix	100-160	
Potter, Beatrix	Tale of Benjamin Bunny (1st, 16mo, 85p, p-o, tan bds, color, pep)	L: Warne	1904	Potter, Beatrix	600-800	
Potter, Beatrix	Tale of Flopsy Bunnies (1st, sm8vo, 85p, bds, p-o, 27cp, pep)	L: Warne	1909	Potter, Beatrix	500-750	R
Potter, Beatrix	Tale of Jemima Puddle Duck (1st, sq16mo, grey bds, p-o, 85p, color, pep)	L: Warne	1908	Potter, Beatrix	500-700	
Potter, Beatrix	Tale of Johnny Town Mouse (1st, 16mo, 85p, bds, p-o)	L: Warne	1918	Potter, Beatrix	400-600	
Potter, Beatrix	Tale of Little Pig Robinson (1st, sq8vo, 141p, p-o, gilt, 6cp)	L: Warne	(1930)	Potter, Beatrix	300-450	
Potter, Beatrix	Tale of Little Pig Robinson (1st AM, 8vo, p-o, 141p, 6cp, pep)	McKay	(1930)	Potter, Beatrix	250-350	
Potter, Beatrix	Tale of Mr. Jeremy Fisher (1st, 24mo, red bds, 85p, p-o, color)	L: Warne	1906	Potter, Beatrix	500-750	
Potter, Beatrix	Tale of Mr. Tod (1st, 16mo, grey bds, p-o, 94p, color)	L: Warne	1912	Potter, Beatrix	500-750	R
Potter, Beatrix	Tale of Mrs. Tiggy-Winkle (1st, 16mo, grey bds, 85p, p-o, color)	L: Warne	1905	Potter, Beatrix	500-700	
Potter, Beatrix	Tale of Mrs. Tittlemouse (1st, 24mo, bds, 85p, p-o, 28cp)	L: Warne	1910	Potter, Beatrix	500-700	
Potter, Beatrix	Tale of Peter Rabbit (1st {trade}, 16mo, 97p, grey bds, p-o 31cp)	L: Warne	(1902)	Potter, Beatrix	700-900	
Potter, Beatrix	Tale of Peter Rabbit (1st {this pub}, 16mo, 127p, green cl, 31cp)	Altemus	1904	Potter, Beatrix	300-500	R*
Potter, Beatrix	Tale of Pigling Bland (1st, 16mo, 94p, bds, p-o, 15cp, pep)	L: Warne	1913	Potter, Beatrix	450-600	
Potter, Beatrix	Tale of Squirrel Nutkin (1st, 16mo, grey bds, p-o, 27cp)	L: Warne	1903	Potter, Beatrix	425-600	R
Potter, Beatrix	Tale of Timmy Tiptoes (1st, sq16mo, 85p, brown bds, p-o, color)	L: Warne	1911	Potter, Beatrix	425-600	
Potter, Beatrix	Tale of Tom Kitten (1st, 16mo, green bds, 85p, p-o, pep, color)	L: Warne	1907	Potter, Beatrix	450-650	
Potter, Beatrix	Tale of Two Bad Mice (1st, 16mo, bds, p-o, 85p, color, pep)	L: Warne	1904	Potter, Beatrix	600-800	
DeJong, Meindert	Big Goose & Little White Duck (1st {std}, 8vo, 160p, 8cp, pep, DJ/2.00)	Harper	1938	Potter, Edna	60-90	
Laboulaye, E.R.	Laboulaye's Fairy Book (1st, 8vo, 363p, black cl, p-o, b/w)	Harper	(1925)	Potter, Edna	35-60	*
Thompson, Mary W.	My Grandpa's Farm (1st, sm8vo, 184p, col frn)	Stokes	1929	Potter, Edna	20-35	
Sickels, Evelyn	Pet Parade (1st, sq12mo, ipcb, 64p, color, pep)	Scribner	1935	Potter, Edna	30-45	
Hunt, Mabel L.	Such a Kind World (1st, sq8vo, [28]p, fp color, pep, DJ/0.50)	Grosset/Dunlap	1947	Potter, Edna	30-50	
Potter, Miriam C.	Goofy Mrs. Goose (1st {std}, sm8vo, 122p, b/w, DJ/2.95)	Lippincott	(1963)	Potter, Miriam C.	100-160	
Potter, Miriam C.	Hello, Mrs. Goose (1st {std}, sm8vo, 150p, b/w, DJ/2.00)	Lippincott	1947	Potter, Miriam C.	100-150	
Potter, Miriam C.	Mrs. Goose and Three Ducks (1st, 12mo, 114p, color, pep, DJ/1.25)	Stokes	1936	Potter, Miriam C.	100-170	
Potter, Miriam C.	The Littlebits (1st {std}, sm8vo, grey cl, 129p, b/w, DJ/1.75)	Lippincott	(1951)	Potter, Miriam C.	120-170	
Childs, Mary F.	De Namin ob De Twins (1st, 8vo, teg, 139p, 7pl)	Dodge	1908	Potthast, Edward	100-165	
Stuart, Ruth M.	George Washington Jones (1st, 12mo, 147p, 5pl)	Altemus	(1903)	Potthast, Edward	35-60	
Stuart, Ruth M.	Holly & Pizen (1st, 12mo, gilt, 216p, 7pl)	Century	1899	Potthast, Edward	50-80	
Stuart, Ruth M.	Napoleon Jackson (1st, 12mo, 132p, red/gilt, 8pl)	Century	1902	Potthast, Edward	60-90	
Stoutenburg, Adrien	American Tall Tales (1st, lg8vo, 112p, fp b/w, DJ/3.50)	Viking	(1966)	Powers, Richard	25-40	
DeRegniers, Beatrice	David and Goliath (1st, 4to, brown cl, unpag, color, DJ/3.75)	Viking	1965	Powers, Richard	20-35	
Fisher, Aileen	Off to the Gold Fields (1st, 8vo, 158p, b/w, DJ/2.75)	Nelson	1955	Powers, Richard	20-30	
Polland, Madeleine	To Tell My People (1st {std}, 8vo, 209p, b/w, DJ/4.50)	Holt, Rinehart	(1968)	Powers, Richard	30-45	*
Praeger, Sophia R.	Adventures of Three Bold Bears (ob4to, ibds, 48p)	L: Longmans	1897	Praeger, Sophia R.	120-200	
Aesopus	Aesop's Fables (1st AM, 16mo, gilt, p-o, 47p, 24cp)	Jack/Dutton	[1910]	Praeger, Sophia R.	70-100	*
Nesbit, Edith	As Happy as a King (1st, ob8vo, unpag)	L: Marcus Ward	[1896]	Praeger, Sophia R.	100-165	
Praeger, Sophia R.	Little Twin Dragons (1st, ob4to, 60p, ibds)	L: Longmans	1900	Praeger, Sophia R.	120-185	
Stevenson, Rbt. L.	Child's Garden of Verses (1st, 4to, 76p, color, pep)	C.E. Graham	(1930)	Pratt, J.C.	35-60	*
Cromie, Robert	From the Cliffs of Croaghaun (1st AM, sm8vo, blue/gilt, 343p, 2pl)	Saalfield	1904	Praut, Victor	35-60	
Prendergast, Mabel	Little Yellow Duckling (1st, ob4to, ibds, 18 fp color)	Cooke/Stokes	(1907)	Prendergast, Mabel	180-260	
Barrie, James M.	My Lady Nicotine (1st {this pub}, sm8vo, teg, 276p)	J. Knight	1896	Prendergast, Mabel	100-165	
Brady, Loretta E.	Green Forest Fairy Book (1st, 8vo, 271p, gilt)	Little/Brown	1920	Preston, Alice B.	80-120	
Bailey, Margery	Seven Peas in the Pod (1st, 8vo, 201p, gilt, 8cp, pep)	Little/Brown	1919	Preston, Alice B.	50-85	
Sandwell, Helen B.	Valley of Color Days (1st, 8vo, tan cl, 299p, 6cp, pep)	Little/Brown	1924	Preston, Alice B.	55-80	
Byron, May	Adventures of Trooper Peek-A-Boo (1st, 8vo, unpag, color)	L: Hodder	[1916]	Preston, Chloe	150-250	
Byron, May	Barbara Peek-A-Boo's Holiday (1st, 4to, ibds, p-o, unpag, 8cp)	L: Hodder	[1914]	Preston, Chloe	250-400	
Byron, May	Peek-a-Boo Farmers (sq4to, bds, p-o, 6cp)	L: H. Milford	[1912]	Preston, Chloe	300-450	
Byron, May	Peek-a-Boo Gipsies (1st, sq4to, ibds, 43p, 6cp)	L: H. Milford	(1923)	Preston, Chloe	300-450	
Preston, Tom	Peek-A-Boo Twins (1st, 4to, tan bds, p-o, 12cp)	L: H. Frowde	[1915]	Preston, Chloe	300-450	
Hoyle, Zoe	Peek-a-Boo's Desert Island (1st, sq4to, ipcb, b/w, pep)	L: H. Milford	[1915]	Preston, Chloe	220-350	
Preston, Tom	Peek-a-Boo's Holiday (4to, ibds, 18cp)	Frowde/Hodder	[1915]	Preston, Chloe	350-500	
Byron, May	Peek-a-Boos at the Zoo (1st, sq4to, ibds, unpag, p-o, 12cp)	L: H. Frowde	[1915]	Preston, Chloe	250-400	
Byron, May	Peek-a-Boos in Town (1st, ob4to, ibds, unpag, 16 fp color)	L: H. Frowde	[1915]	Preston, Chloe	300-500	
Byron, May	Peek-a-Boos in War (sq4to, bds, p-o, 6cp)	L: H. Frowde	[1915]	Preston, Chloe	300-450	
Byron, May	Peek-a-Boos in Winter (ob folio, ibds, 18cp)	L: H. Frowde	[1910]	Preston, Chloe	300-500	
Byron, May	William & Woggs (sq4to, bds, p-o, 6cp)	L: H. Frowde	[1910]	Preston, Chloe	150-225	
Lardner, Ring	Big Town (1st, sm8vo, 244p, green cl, 5 tip-in pl)	Bobbs-Merrill	(1921)	Preston, May W.	100-165	
Lardner, Ring	Gullible's Travels (1st, sm8vo, blue cl, 255p, col frn, pep)	Bobbs-Merrill	(1917)	Preston, May W.	120-170	
Butler, Ellis P.	Incubator Baby (1st, 12mo, 111p, 4cp)	Funk/Wagnalls	1906	Preston, May W.	25-40	
Wodehouse, P.G.	Piccadilly Jim (1st, sm8vo, 363p, orange cl, 8cp)	Dodd	1917	Preston, May W.	400-650	

ARTIST: 160

AUTHOR	TITLE	PUBLISHER	DATE	ARTIST	PRICE	LC
Wells, Carolyn	Rubaiyat of Bridge (1st, 12mo, p-o, [42]p, 1-color)	Harper	1909	Preston, May W.	30-50	
Rinehart, Mary R.	Tish (1st, sm8vo, 371p, 9cp)	Houghton	1916	Preston, May W.	30-50	
Bertol, Roland	Sundiata: Epic of the Lion King (1st, 8vo, 81p, fp b/w, DJ/3.95)	Crowell	(1970)	Prestopino, Gregorio	30-50	
Jewett, Eleanore	Cobbler's Knob (1st, 8vo, 192p, b/w, DJ/2.50)	Viking	1956	Price, Christine	50-85	*
Marshall, Dean	Dig for a Treasure (1st {std}, 8vo, 188p, b/w, pep, DJ/2.50)	Dutton	1949	Price, Christine	100-170	
Price, Christine	Dragon and the Book (1st {std}, 8vo, 196p, b/w, DJ/2.75)	Longmans	1953	Price, Christine	25-40	
Carse, Robert	Great Venture (1st, 8vo, 239p, b/w, DJ/2.50)	Scribner	(1952)	Price, Christine	40-65	
Marshall, Dean	Invisible Island (1st {std}, 8vo, 191p, fp b/w, pep, DJ/2.50)	Dutton	1948	Price, Christine	70-100	
Wibberley, Leonard	King's Beard (1st {std}, 8vo, 198p, pep, DJ/2.75)	Ariel	(1952)	Price, Christine	30-50	
Magoon, Marian	Little Dusty Foot (1st {std}, 8vo, 239p, b/w, pep, DJ/2.50)	Longmans	1948	Price, Christine	25-45	
Savery, Constance	Magic in My Shoes (1st {std}, 8vo, 152p, b/w, DJ/2.75)	Longmans	1958	Price, Christine	40-65	*
Price, Christine	One is God: Two Old Counting Songs (1st, ob4to, [48]p, color, DJ/4.95)	Warne	(1970)	Price, Christine	40-65	*
Boegehold, Betty	Pawpaw's Run (1st {std}, sm ob4to, [32]p, color, DJ/3.95)	Dutton	(1968)	Price, Christine	30-45	*
Treece, Henry	Road to Miklagard (1st AM, 8vo, 254p, b/w, DJ/3.50)	Criterion Bks.	(1957)	Price, Christine	45-70	
Lyon, Elinor	Runaway Home (1st, 8vo, 192p, b/w, DJ/2.50)	Viking	1953	Price, Christine	30-45	
N/A	Santa's Footprints (1st, sm8vo, 154p, uncut, red/gilt, fp b/w, DJ/2.00)	Aladdin	1948	Price, Christine	80-140	
Stone, Eugenia	Secret of the Bog (1st, sm8vo, 217p, b/w, cep, DJ/2.25)	Holiday House	(1948)	Price, Christine	25-40	
Wibberley, Leonard	Secret of the Hawk (1st {std}, 8vo, 214p, b/w, pep, DJ/2.95)	Ariel	(1953)	Price, Christine	40-65	
Caire, Helen	Senor Castillo (1st, lg8vo, 76p, ibds, b/w, DJ/1.50)	Rinehart	(1948)	Price, Christine	25-45	
Wier, Ester A.	The Loner (1st, 8vo, 153p, b/w, DJ/3.75, NH)	McKay	1963	Price, Christine	45-70	
Price, Christine	Three Golden Nobles (1st {std}, 89vo, 239p, b/w, pep, DJ/2.75)	Longmans	(1951)	Price, Christine	20-35	
Riley, Louise	Train for Tiger Lily (1st, 8vo, 186p, fp b/w, pep, DJ/2.50)	Viking	1954	Price, Christine	40-65	R*
Hahn, Lotte K.	Unicorn Who Wanted to be Seen (1st, sm4to, [38]p, fp 2-color, cep, DJ)	Warne	(1961)	Price, Christine	40-65	*
Price, Christine	Valiant Chattee-Maker (1st, sq8vo, [43]p, 2-color, pep, DJ/2.95)	Warne	(1965)	Price, Christine	25-40	
Treece, Henry	Viking's Dawn (1st AM, 8vo, 252p, b/w, DJ/3.00)	Criterion Bks.	(1956)	Price, Christine	40-70	
Treece, Henry	Viking's Sunset (1st AM {std}, 8vo, 182p, b/w, DJ/3.50)	Criterion Bks.	(1961)	Price, Christine	40-70	
Goldberg, Martha	Wait for the Rain (1st, sm8vo, [43]p, blue cl, b/w, cep, DJ/1.50)	Holiday House	(1952)	Price, Christine	25-40	*
Price, Edith B.	Four Winds (1st, 8vo, 181p, col frn, b/w, pep)	Stokes	1927	Price, Edith B.	25-40	
Meigs, Cornelia L.	Rain on the Roof (1st, sm8vo, 308p, b/w, dep)	Macmillan	1925	Price, Edith B.	70-100	
Daringer, Helen F.	Stepsister Sally (1st {std}, 8vo, 182p, b/w, DJ/2.25)	Harcourt	(1952)	Price, Garrett	40-65	
Kiviat, Esther	Paji (1st {std}, sm4to, 56p, color, DJ/2.00)	McGraw-Hill	(1946)	Price, Harold	55-80	
Blanton, Catherine	Pedro's Choice (1st, lg8vo, 64p, b/w, DJ/2.00)	Whittlesey	(1948)	Price, Harold	25-45	
Widdemer, Margaret	Binkie and Bell Dolls (1st, 8vo, tan cl, 146p, p-o, 8cp, pep)	Penn	1923	Price, Hattie L.	55-90	*
Larrimore, Lida	Blossoming of Patricia-The-Less (1st, 8vo, 253p, p-o, 4cp, pep)	Penn	1924	Price, Hattie L.	50-80	
Alcott, Louisa M.	Eight Cousins (1st, 8vo, 278p, 6cp)	Little/Brown	1927	Price, Hattie L.	25-45	
Pleasonton, Louise	Fairyland of Opera (1st, 8vo, 240p, p-o, col frn, b/w, pep)	Penn	1923	Price, Hattie L.	40-65	
Allee, Marjorie H.	Judith Lankester (1st, sm8vo, 241p, b/w, pep)	Houghton	1930	Price, Hattie L.	25-40	
Franchi, Anna	Little Lead Soldier (1st, 8vo, p-o, 186p, 5cp)	Penn	1919	Price, Hattie L.	80-130	
Campbell, Ruth	Runaway Smalls (1st, lg8vo, ibds, 73p, b/w)	Penn	1923	Price, Hattie L.	50-80	
Allee, Marjorie H.	Susanna and Tristram (1st, sm8vo, 220p, b/w, pep)	Houghton	1929	Price, Hattie L.	30-50	
McNeely, Marian H.	Winning Out (1st {std}, 12mo, 308p, b/w)	Longmans	1931	Price, Hattie L.	35-60	*
Singmaster, Elsie	Young Ravenels (1st, 12mo, 214p, blue/gilt, 9pl)	Houghton	1932	Price, Hattie L.	25-45	*
Orton, Helen F.	Little Lost Pigs (1st, ob12mo, 96p, color)	Stokes	1925	Price, Luxor	60-100	
Bonner, Mary G.	Magic Clock (1st, 8vo, yellow cl, 187p, 8cp, pep)	Macaulay	(1931)	Price, Luxor	80-120	
Bonner, Mary G.	Magic Journeys (1st, lg8vo, orange cl, 286p, 16cp, pep)	Macaulay	(1928)	Price, Luxor	80-120	
Bonner, Mary G.	Magic Map (1st, lg8vo, 238p, 17cp, pep)	Macaulay	(1927)	Price, Luxor	80-120	
Bonner, Mary G.	Magic Music Shop (1st, lg4to, orange cl, 95p, color, pep)	Macaulay	(1929)	Price, Luxor	90-140	
Price, Luxor	The Quoks (1st, 4to, 62p, p-o, red cl, color, pep)	Stokes	1924	Price, Luxor	180-270	
Price, Margaret E.	Angora Twinnies (4to, wraps, [12]p, shape book, color)	Stecher	1919	Price, Margaret E.	60-90	
Price, Margaret E.	Betty Fairy Book (folio, [14]p, wraps, shape book, color)	Stecher	1915	Price, Margaret E.	60-90	
N/A	Betty's Painting Book (sq4to, stiff wraps, color)	NY: Stecher	1917	Price, Margaret E.	65-90	
Price, Margaret E.	Child's Book of Myths (1st, 4to, blue cl, p-o, 112p, 6cp)	Rand/McNally	(1924)	Price, Margaret E.	60-90	
Price, Margaret E.	Down Comes the Wilderness (1st {std}, 8vo, 212p, b/w, pep, DJ/1.75)	Harper	1937	Price, Margaret E.	25-45	
Price, Margaret E.	Enchantment Tales for Children (1st, 4to, 118p, p-o, color, pep)	Rand/McNally	(1926)	Price, Margaret E.	70-100	
Grimm Bros.	Hansel & Gretel (folio, shape bk, [12]p, wraps, color)	Stecher	1916	Price, Margaret E.	50-80	
Price, Margaret E.	Land of Nod (folio, wraps, [12]p, shape book, color)	Stecher	1916	Price, Margaret E.	50-80	
Price, Margaret E.	Legends of the Seven Seas (1st {std}, 8vo, 168p, gilt, col frn, pep)	Harper	1929	Price, Margaret E.	40-65	
Price, Margaret E.	Manger Babe (folio, [14]p, wraps, shape bk., color)	Stecher	1916	Price, Margaret E.	55-80	
Price, Margaret E.	Monkey-Do (1st {std}, 8vo, 149p, b/w, dep)	Harper	1934	Price, Margaret E.	30-50	
Price, Margaret E.	Mota & the Monkey Tree (1st {std}, 8vo, 146p, b/w, pep, DJ/1.50)	Harper	1935	Price, Margaret E.	40-65	
Mother Goose	Mother Goose Book of Rhymes (narrow folio, wraps, color)	Stecher	1927	Price, Margaret E.	55-80	
Price, Margaret E.	Myths & Enchantment Tales (1st, lg8vo, 160p, color, DJ/1.00)	Rand/McNally	(1935)	Price, Margaret E.	50-80	
Moore, Clement C.	Night Before Christmas (folio, wraps {shape bk}, color)	NY: Stecher	(1917)	Price, Margaret E.	90-140	
Bates, Katharine L.	Once Upon a Time (1st, 4to, p-o, blue cl, 128p, color, pep)	Rand/McNally	(1921)	Price, Margaret E.	60-90	
N/A	Three Bears (12mo, 63p, color)	Rand/McNally	(1937)	Price, Margaret E.	35-60	*
Price, Margaret E.	Visit to Santa Claus (sm4to, wraps, [16]p, color)	Stecher	[1915]	Price, Margaret E.	70-100	
Dalgliesh, Alice	West Indian Play Days (1st, 12mo, 174p, col frn, b/w, pep)	Rand/McNally	(1926)	Price, Margaret E.	30-45	*
Price, Margaret E.	Windy Shore (1st {std}, lg8vo, brown cl, 181p, col frn, 18pl, pep)	Harper	1930	Price, Margaret E.	50-85	
Kummer, Frederic	Leif Erikson the Lucky (1st, 8vo, 245p, col frn, b/w, pep, DJ/2.00)	Winston	(1939)	Price, Norman	25-40	
Lamb, Charles	Tales from Shakespeare (1st AM, 4to, 324p, gilt, teg, 20cp)	Scribner	[1905]	Price, Norman	70-100	
Stevenson, Rbt. L.	Treasure Island (1st [special ed], lg8vo, 342p, color, DJ/2.00)	Grosset/Dunlap	(1947)	Price, Norman	30-50	
Harrington, John W.	Adventures of Admiral Frog (1st, lg8vo, ipcb, 49p, fp 1-color)	R.H. Russell	1902	Price, Willard B.	100-180	
Godden, Rumer	Creature's Choir (1st AM, 4to, ibds, 69p, gilt, dep, DJ/3.50)	Viking	(1965)	Primrose, Jean	30-45	
Godden, Rumer	Home is the Sailor (1st AM, 8vo, 128p, color, pep, DJ/3.00)	Viking	(1964)	Primrose, Jean	40-65	R
Godden, Rumer	Little Plum (1st AM, 8vo, 97p, fp color, pep, DJ/3.25)	Viking	(1963)	Primrose, Jean	40-70	R
Godden, Rumer	Miss Happiness and Miss Flower (1st AM, 8vo, 81p, fp color, pep, DJ/3.00)	Viking	(1961)	Primrose, Jean	45-70	R
Gasztold, Carmen	Prayers from the Ark (1st, 8vo, 71p, pep, DJ/2.95, decor by...)	Viking	(1962)	Primrose, Jean	25-40	*
Godden, Rumer	St. Jerome and the Lion (1st, lg8vo, 34p, 1-color, pep, DJ/2.50)	Viking	(1961)	Primrose, Jean	30-45	

AUTHOR	TITLE	PUBLISHER	DATE	ARTIST	PRICE	LC
Agle, Nan H.	Maple Street (1st, 8vo, 126p, b/w, DJ/4.50)	Seabury Press	(1970)	Prince, Leonora	25-40	*
Carroll, Lewis	Alice... & Through... (1st, 8vo, 319p, gilt, p-o, 4cp, pep)	Winston	(1923)	Prittie, Edwin J.	60-100	
Fryer, Jane E.	Bible Story Book (1st, lg8vo, blue cl, p-o, 352p, 4cp)	Winston	(1924)	Prittie, Edwin J.	60-90	
Sewell, Anna	Black Beauty (1st, 8vo, green/gilt, p-o, 297p, 4cp, pep)	Winston	(1927)	Prittie, Edwin J.	35-60	
Grimm Bros.	Fairy Tales (1st, 8vo, 310p, cp)	Winston	(1922)	Prittie, Edwin J.	60-90	*
Swift, Jonathan	Gulliver's Travels (1st, 8vo, 274p, p-o, gilt, 3cp, fp b/w, pep)	Winston	(1930)	Prittie, Edwin J.	30-50	
Holmes, Mabel D.	Joan of Arc (1st, sm4to, 300p, gilt, p-o, 4cp, pep)	Winston	(1930)	Prittie, Edwin J.	35-60	
Fryer, Jane E.	Mary Frances Story Book (1st, lg8vo, p-o, 328p, fp 3-color, pep)	Winston	(1921)	Prittie, Edwin J.	200-300	
Fillebrown, R.H.	Rhymes of Happy Childhood (1st, lg8vo, 119p, p-o, 3cp, pep)	Winston	(1908)	Prittie, Edwin J.	50-80	
Engle, Paul	Who's Afraid? (1st {std}, 4to, 64p, 1-color)	Crowell-Collier	1963	Prohaska, Ray	30-50	
Provensen, A.& M.	Animal Fair (1st {A}, folio, 76p, ibds, color, pep, GGB, NYTBI)	Simon/Schuster	1952	Provensen, A.& M.	50-80	
Tennyson, Alfred	Charge of the Light Brigade (1st ob4to, ibds, [25]p, col, DJ/2.95, NYTBI)	Golden Press	1964	Provensen, A.& M.	45-70	
Leanard, Rachel	Funny Bunny (1st, folio, ibds, [25]p, color, BGB)	Simon/Schuster	(1950)	Provensen, A.& M.	80-130	
Mother Goose	Golden Mother Goose (1st, folio, ibds, 96p, color, GGB)	Simon/Schuster	(1948)	Provensen, A.& M.	90-160	*
Untermeyer, Louis	Tales from the Ballet (1st, lg4to, ibds, 91p, fp color, DJ/5.95)	Golden Press	(1968)	Provensen, A.& M.	60-90	
Provensen, A.& M.	What is a Color? (1st, 4to, 32p, ibds, color, DJ/2.95, BGB)	Golden Press	(1967)	Provensen, A.& M.	50-85	
Provensen, A.& M.	Who's in the Egg? (1st, lg4to, ibds, 32p, color, cep)	Golden Press	1970	Provensen, A.& M.	50-85	
Stevenson, Rbt. L.	Child's Garden of Verses (1st, 4to, 76p, ibds, color, pep, BGB)	Simon/Schuster	(1951)	Provensen, A.&M.	70-100	R
Chipman, Charles P.	Last Cruise of the Electra (1st, sm8vo, 268p, 4pl)	Saalfield	1902	Provost, Charles	70-100	*
Kelly, Eric P.	Blacksmith of Vilno (1st, 8vo, 184p, green cl, 3cp)	Macmillan	1930	Pruszynska, Angela	35-60	*
Kelly, Eric P.	Golden Star of Halich (1st, 8vo, green cl, 215p, 3cp, fp b/w)	Macmillan	1931	Pruszynska, Angela	40-60	*
Kelly, Eric P.	Trumpeter of Krakow (1st, 8vo, 218p, blue cl, 3cp, DJ/2.50, NM)	Macmillan	1928	Pruszynska, Angela	80-125	
Nesbit, Edith	These Little Ones (1st, 8vo, gilt, 210p, teg, 10pl)	L: G. Allen	1909	Pryse, Gerald S.	160-240	
Hunt, Irene	Across Five Aprils (1st [1st bk.] {std}, 8vo, 223p, pep, DJ/3.95, NH)	Follett	(1964)	Pucci, Albert	80-120	R
Janeway, Elizabeth	Ivanov Seven (1st, 8vo, 176p, fp b/w, DJ/3.95, pep by...)	Harper	(1967)	Pucci, Albert	45-70	R*
Holmes, Oliver W.	Autocrat at the Breakfast Table (1st, 8vo, teg, 2vols, gilt, 15pl)	Houghton	1894	Pyle, Howard	125-200	
Van Dyke, Henry	Blue Flower (1st, sm8vo, 298p, blue/gilt, teg, 3cp by...)	Scribner	1902	Pyle, Howard	30-50	
Pyle, Howard	Book of American Spirit (1st {std}, lg4to, 344p, ibds, p-o, 23cp)	Harper	1923	Pyle, Howard	250-350	
Pyle, Howard	Book of Pirates (1st, lg4to, 247p, bds, gilt, p-o, 11cp, 25pl)	Harper	1921	Pyle, Howard	250-350	R
Pyle, Howard	Champions of the Round Table (1st, lg8vo, tan/gilt, 328p, b/w)	Scribner	1905	Pyle, Howard	220-300	R
Cabell, James B.	Chivalry (1st, 8vo, red cl, teg, 224p, 12cp, dep)	Harper	1909	Pyle, Howard	100-160	
Holmes, Oliver W.	Dorothy Q. (1st, sm8vo, grey cl, t.e. silver, 131p, b/w)	Houghton	1893	Pyle, Howard	70-100	
Peterson, Henry	Dulcibel (1st, 12mo, grey cl, 402p, teg, p-o, 3cp)	Winston	1907	Pyle, Howard	50-80	
Van Dyke, Henry	First Christmas Tree (1st, 8vo, olive/gilt, 76p, teg, 4pl)	Scribner	1897	Pyle, Howard	70-100	
Cabell, James B.	Gallantry (1st, 8vo, teg, grey/gilt, 334p, 4 ticp, pep)	Harper	1907	Pyle, Howard	100-160	
Pyle, Howard	Garden Behind the Moon (1st, 8vo, green/gilt, 192p, 10pl)	Scribner	1895	Pyle, Howard	150-225	
Wilson, Woodrow	George Washington (1st, 8vo, 333p, teg, 20pl)	Harper	1897	Pyle, Howard	80-120	
Abbott, Charles D.	Howard Pyle: A Chronicle (1st, lg8vo, 249p, grey bds, 6cp)	Harper	1925	Pyle, Howard	125-200	
Janvier, Thomas A.	In Old New York (1st, 12mo, 285p, rust/gilt, b/w by...)	Harper	1894	Pyle, Howard	60-100	
Forman, Justus M.	Island of Enchantment (1st, 8vo, blue/gilt, teg, 106p, 4cp, dep)	Harper	1905	Pyle, Howard	80-125	
Pyle, Howard	Jack Ballister's Fortunes (1st, 8vo, 420p, 14pl)	Harper	1895	Pyle, Howard	90-140	
Tennyson, Alfred	Lady of Shalott (1st, lg8vo, [64]p, blue/gilt, AEG, color, dep)	Dodd	(1881)	Pyle, Howard	350-500	
Cabell, James B.	Line of Love (1st, 8vo, p-o, teg, 291p, uncut, 10cp)	Harper	1905	Pyle, Howard	100-165	
Markham, Edwin	Man With the Hoe... (1st, 8vo, 114p, gilt, teg, b/w)	Doub./McClure	1900	Pyle, Howard	90-120	
Pyle, Howard	Men of Iron (1st, 8vo, 328p, red cl, teg, 15pl)	Harper	1892	Pyle, Howard	160-240	
Pyle, Howard	Merry Adventures of Robin Hood (1st, 4to, leather/gilt, 296p, 23 fp b/w)	Scribner	1883	Pyle, Howard	700-950	R
Pyle, Howard	Modern Aladdin (1st, 8vo, 205p, blue/gilt, b/w)	Harper	1892	Pyle, Howard	160-240	
Deland, Margaret	Old Chester Tales (1st [1], 12mo, 360p, green cl, 16pl)	Harper	1899	Pyle, Howard	140-220	
Holmes, Oliver W.	One-Hoss Shay ([new ed.], 8vo, 78p, teg, gilt, 12cp)	Houghton	1905	Pyle, Howard	100-165	
Pyle, Howard	Otto of the Silver Hand (1st, lg8vo, olive/gilt, 173p, fp b/w, PPP)	Scribner	1888	Pyle, Howard	250-400	
Pyle, Howard	Pepper and Salt (1st, 4to, tan/gilt, 121p, b/w)	Harper	1886	Pyle, Howard	300-450	
Pyle, Howard	Price of Blood (1st, 8vo, ipcb, 98p, A.E. red, 6cp)	Badger	1899	Pyle, Howard	160-240	R
Pyle, Howard	Rose of Paradise (1st, 12mo, green/gilt, 231p, 8pl)	Harper	1888	Pyle, Howard	125-180	
Pyle, Howard	Ruby of Kishmoor (1st, 8vo, teg, 74p, gilt, 10cp)	Harper	1908	Pyle, Howard	130-200	R
Goodwin, Maud W.	Sir Christopher (1st, 12mo, 411p, gilt, frn by...)	Little/Brown	1901	Pyle, Howard	30-50	
Cabell, James B.	Soul of Melicent (1st, 8vo, 216p, gilt, p-o, 4cp)	Stokes	(1913)	Pyle, Howard	100-170	
Twain, Mark	St. Joan of Arc (1st, lg8vo, black/gilt, 32p, p-o, 4 ticp, pep)	Harper	(1919)	Pyle, Howard	140-200	
Pyle, Howard	Stolen Treasure (1st, 12mo, 253p, orange cl, p-o, 8pl)	Harper	1907	Pyle, Howard	100-150	
Howells, William D.	Stops of Various Quills (1st, 8vo, teg, [110]p, gilt, designs by...)	Harper	1895	Pyle, Howard	80-130	
Brooks, Elbridge S.	Storied Holidays (1st, 8vo, 271p, gilt)	D. Lothrop Co.	[1887]	Pyle, Howard	170-220	
Pyle, Howard	Story of Jack Ballister's Fortunes (1st, 8vo, 420p, 14pl)	Century	1895	Pyle, Howard	170-240	
Pyle, Howard	Story of King Arthur... (1st, lg8vo, tan/gilt, 313p, b/w, cep)	Scribner	1903	Pyle, Howard	250-400	
Baldwin, James	Story of Siegfried (1st, 12mo, red/gilt, 306p, teg, PPP)	Scribner	1882	Pyle, Howard	170-240	
Pyle, Howard	Story of Sir Lancelot (1st, lg8vo, 340p, tan/gilt, b/w)	Scribner	1907	Pyle, Howard	180-250	
Baldwin, James	Story of the Golden Age (1st, 12mo, 286p, gilt, uncut, 12pl, PPP)	Scribner	1887	Pyle, Howard	150-250	
Pyle, Howard	Story of the Grail (1st, lg8vo, 258p, tan/gilt, b/w)	Scribner	1910	Pyle, Howard	170-240	R
Seitz, Don C.	The Buccaneers (1st, 8vo, p-o, teg, 52p, frn by...)	Harper	1912	Pyle, Howard	60-100	
Doyle, Arthur Conan	The Parasite (1st AM, 12mo, gilt, 143p, 4pl)	Harper	1895	Pyle, Howard	170-250	
Pyle, Howard	Twilight Land (1st, 8vo, 438p, gilt, b/w)	Harper	1895	Pyle, Howard	140-200	
Pyle, Howard	Wonder Clock (1st, sm4to, grey cl, 318p, b/w)	Harper	1888	Pryle, Howard	250-350	
Pyle, Howard	Yankee Doodle (1st, 4to, 31p, ibds, 8 fp color)	Dodd	1881	Pyle, Howard	400-650	
Reed, Helen L.	Amy in Acadia (1st, 8vo, 344p, blue cl, 6pl)	Little/Brown	1905	Pyle, Katharine	50-80	
Pyle, Katharine	As the Goose Flies (1st, sm8vo, 183p, gilt, 6pl)	Little/Brown	1901	Pyle, Katharine	50-80	
Sewell, Anna	Black Beauty (1st, lg8vo, p-o, 239p, 4cp, 13pl, pep)	Dodd	1923	Pyle, Katharine	100-160	
Pyle, Katharine	Black-Eyed Puppy (1st, 8vo, 89p, p-o, 12cp)	Dutton	1923	Pyle, Katharine	60-100	
White, Eliza O.	Blue Aunt (1st, sm8vo, 144p, col frn & cvr by...)	Houghton	1918	Pyle, Katharine	35-60	
White, Eliza O.	Borrowed Sister (1st, sm8vo, 150p, green cl, p-o, 4pl)	Houghton	1906	Pyle, Katharine	60-90	
Pyle, Katharine	Careless Jane (1st, 12mo, green cl, 110p, b/w)	Dutton	(1902)	Pyle, Katharine	45-70	

AUTHOR	TITLE	PUBLISHER	DATE	ARTIST	PRICE	LC
Pyle, Katharine	Charlemagne & his Knights (1st, 8vo, gilt, 302p, col frn, 7pl)	Lippincott	(1932)	Pyle, Katharine	50-85	
Pyle, Katharine	Christmas Angel (1st, 12mo, green/gilt, teg, 136p, 6pl)	Little/Brown	1900	Pyle, Katharine	70-100	
Pyle, Katharine	Counterpane Fairy (1st [1st bk.], 8vo, green/gilt, uncut, teg, 191p, b/w)	Dutton	1898	Pyle, Katharine	300-450	
Halkett, Sarah P.	Elf King's Flowers (1st, sm4to, 79p, ibds, col frn, pep)	Dutton	(1924)	Pyle, Katharine	40-60	
Sholl, Anna M.	Faery Tales of Weir (1st, 8vo, 172p, purple/gilt, col frn, pep)	Dutton	(1918)	Pyle, Katharine	70-100	
Pyle, Katharine	Fairy Tales from Far & Near (1st, 8vo, green cl, 274p, 7cp)	Little/Brown	1922	Pyle, Katharine	70-120	
Pyle, Katharine	Fairy Tales from India (1st, lg8vo, 229p, red/gilt, 12cp, pep)	Lippincott	1926	Pyle, Katharine	70-120	
Pyle, Katharine	Fairy Tales from Many Lands (1st, 8vo, 316p, col frn)	Dutton	(1911)	Pyle, Katharine	70-120	
Blodgett, Mabel F.	Giant's Ruby (1st, 8vo, 292p, blue cl, 6pl)	Little/Brown	1903	Pyle, Katharine	80-120	
Browne, Frances	Granny's Wonderful Chair (1st, lg8vo, 211p, red/gilt, 6cp, pep)	Dutton	(1916)	Pyle, Katharine	90-120	
Thomas, Edith M.	In Sunshine Land (1st, sm8vo, tan/silver, teg, 152p, b/w pl, cep)	Houghton	1894	Pyle, Katharine	60-90	
Pyle, Katharine	In the Green Forest (1st, lg8vo, green cl, 171p, 5pl)	Little/Brown	1902	Pyle, Katharine	60-90	
Morgan, Harriet	Island Impossible (1st, 12mo, gilt, 206p, 5pl)	Little/Brown	1899	Pyle, Katharine	70-100	
Pyle, Katharine	Katherine Pyle's Book of Fairy Tales (1st, 8vo, 338p, col frn, 28pl)	Dutton	(1925)	Pyle, Katharine	120-200	
Pyle, Katharine	Lazy Matilda... (1st, 8vo, 173p, blue cl, b/w)	Dutton	(1921)	Pyle, Katharine	35-60	*
Pyle, Katharine	Mother's Nursery Tales (1st, lg8vo, gilt, 376p, 7cp, pep)	Dutton	(1918)	Pyle, Katharine	100-180	
Pyle, Katharine	Nancy Rutledge (1st, 8vo, 206p, 6pl)	Little/Brown	1906	Pyle, Katharine	55-80	
White, Eliza O.	Only Child (1st, sm8vo, 167p, grey cl, p-o, 4pl)	Houghton	1905	Pyle, Katharine	40-70	
Pyle, Katharine	Rabbit Witch (1st, lg ob8vo, 81p, 1-color)	Dutton	(1895)	Pyle, Katharine	200-300	
Pyle, Katharine	Six Little Ducklings (1st, 8vo, green cl, p-o, 99p, 24pl, pep)	Dodd	1915	Pyle, Katharine	90-145	
Pyle, Katharine	Tales from Greek Mythology (1st, 8vo, blue cl, 312p, 12pl)	Lippincott	1928	Pyle, Katharine	60-90	
Pyle, Katharine	Tales from Norse Mythology (1st, lg8vo, 256p, 8cp, pep)	Lippincott	(1930)	Pyle, Katharine	55-80	
Pyle, Katharine	Tales of Folk & Fairies (1st, 8vo, blue cl, 288p, 6cp)	Little/Brown	1919	Pyle, Katharine	100-165	
Pyle, Katharine	Tales of Two Bunnies (1st, 8vo, 87p, red cl, b/w, pep)	Dutton	(1913)	Pyle, Katharine	80-120	
Pyle, Katharine	Tales of Wonder & Magic (1st, sm8vo, green cl, 314p, 8cp)	Little/Brown	1920	Pyle, Katharine	65-90	
LeBaron, Grace	Twixt You & Me (1st, 12mo, 296p, decorations by...)	Little/Brown	1898	Pyle, Katharine	40-60	*
Pyle, Katharine	Two Little Mice (1st, 8vo, 108p, grey cl, p-o, 16pl, pep)	Dodd	1917	Pyle, Katharine	80-125	
White, Eliza O.	When Molly was Six (1st, 8vo, 133p, 3pl)	Houghton	1894	Pyle, Katharine	50-80	
Pyle, Katharine	Wonder Tales Retold (1st, 8vo, green/gilt, 322p, 8cp)	Little/Brown	1916	Pyle, Katharine	100-165	
Andersen, Hans C.	Snow Queen (1st, sm8vo, ibds, 49p, fp color)	L: Wells/Gard.	(1883)	Pym, T.	180-250	
McHargue, Georgess	Baker & the Basilisk (1st {std}, ob4to, 31p, color, DJ/4.50)	Bobbs-Merrill	(1970)	Quackenbush, Rbt.	25-40	
Carlson, Natalie S.	Befena's Gift (1st, 8vo, 86p, fp b/w, cep, DJ/3.95)	Harper	(1969)	Quackenbush, Rbt.	25-45	
Young, Miriam	Beware the Polar Bear (1st, 8vo, 35p, color, DJ/3.75)	Lothrop, Lee	(1970)	Quackenbush, Rbt.	20-25	*
Young, Miriam	Billy & Milly (1st, 4to, [32]p, color, DJ/3.50)	Lothrop, Lee	(1968)	Quackenbush, Rbt.	20-35	
Melville, Herman	Billy Bud, Foretopman (1st, 8vo, 126p, fp b/w, DJ/2.95)	F. Watts	(1968)	Quackenbush, Rbt.	20-30	*
McKown, Robin	Boy Who Woke Up in Madagascar (1st, 8vo, 221p, fp b/w, DJ)	Putnam	(1967)	Quackenbush, Rbt.	25-35	
Black, Irma S.	Busy Seeds (1st, 4to, [40]p, 2-color, pep, DJ/4.50)	Holiday House	(1970)	Quackenbush, Rbt.	25-40	
Black, Irma S.	Busy Winds (1st, ob8vo, [32]p, 2-color, pep, DJ/3.95)	Holiday House	(1968)	Quackenbush, Rbt.	25-40	*
DeMaupassant, Guy	Diamond Necklace (1st, 8vo, 82p, fp b/w, DJ/2.95)	F. Watts	(1967)	Quackenbush, Rbt.	20-25	*
Evans, Eva K.	Dirt Book (1st {std}, 8vo, 86p, b/w, DJ/3.75)	Little/Brown	(1969)	Quackenbush, Rbt.	20-30	*
Clymer, Eleanor	Horatio (1st {std}, 12mo, 63p, 3-color, cep, DJ/3.25)	Atheneum	1968	Quackenbush, Rbt.	25-40	
Moore, Lilian	I Feel the Same Way (1st {std}, 12mo, [32]p, color, cep, DJ/3.25)	Atheneum	1967	Quackenbush, Rbt.	20-30	*
Young, Miriam	If I Drove a Truck (1st, ob4to, [31]p, color, DJ/3.50)	Lothrop, Lee	(1967)	Quackenbush, Rbt.	20-35	*
Young, Miriam	If I Flew a Plane (1st, ob4to, [32]p, color, DJ/3.95)	Lothrop, Lee	(1970)	Quackenbush, Rbt.	25-40	*
Stewart, John	Key to the Kitchen (1st, sm4to, ipcb, [32]p, fp color, pep, DJ/3.95)	Lothrop, Lee	1970	Quackenbush, Rbt.	30-45	
Wilde, Oscar	Little Hans (1st, 4to, gilt, 48p, fp 1-color, cep, DJ/4.50)	Bobbs-Merrill	(1969)	Quackenbush, Rbt.	25-40	*
Rice, Inez	Long, Long Time (1st, sm4to, [32]p, fp 3-color, DJ/3.50)	Lothrop, Lee	1964	Quackenbush, Rbt.	25-45	*
Shemin, Margaretha	Mrs. Herring (1st, 8vo, 192p, b/w, DJ/3.95)	Lothrop, Lee	(1967)	Quackenbush, Rbt.	20-35	
Crane, Stephen	Open Boat (1st, 8vo, 85p, b/w, DJ/2.95)	F. Watts	(1968)	Quackenbush, Rbt.	30-45	*
Quackenbush, Robert	Poems for Counting (1st, 8vo, [24]p, color, pep, DJ)	Holt, Rinehart	(1963)	Quackenbush, Rbt.	20-35	*
N/A	Poems for Galloping (1st, 8vo, [25]p, fp color, pep, DJ)	Holt, Rinehart	1963	Quackenbush, Rbt.	20-35	*
McKown, Robin	Rakoto & the Drongo Bird (1st, 4to, 52p, fp color, cep, DJ/3.95)	Lothrop, Lee	(1966)	Quackenbush, Rbt.	25-40	*
Wilde, Oscar	Selfish Giant (1st, 8vo, [40]p, fp color, pep, DJ)	Holt, Rinehart	(1965)	Quackenbush, Rbt.	25-40	*
Andersen, Hans C.	Steadfast Tin Soldier (1st, 8vo, [38]p, 2-color woodcuts)	Holt, Rinehart	1964	Quackenbush, Rbt.	20-35	*
Rowley, Anthony	Sunday in Autumn (1st, 4to, 31p, ibds, color)	L.W. Singer	1967	Quackenbush, Rbt.	20-35	*
Bloch, Marie H.	Two Worlds of Damyan (1st {std}, 8vo, 169p, b/w, DJ/3.95)	Atheneum	1966	Quackenbush, Rbt.	25-40	
Prieto, Mariana	When the Monkeys wore Sombreros (1st, ob4to, 36p, fp color, dep, DJ/3.50)	Harvey House	(1969)	Quackenbush, Rbt.	30-50	*
Collodi, Carlo	Pinocchio's Adventures in Wonderland (1st AM, 12mo, green/gilt, 212p, 4cp)	Jordan Marsh	(1898)	Quentin, R.	350-500	R*
Girvin, Brenda	Mr. Piccolo (1st, 8vo, 247p)	L: G. Allen	1911	Quick, Horace	30-60	*
Girvin, Brenda	Pam & Billy (1st, 8vo, 209p, col frn, 12pl)	L: G. Allen	1910	Quick, Horace	40-60	*
Browning, Robert	Pied Piper of Hamelin (1st, lg4to, [54]p, red/gilt, b/w)	L: Quilter	1898	Quilter, Harry	140-220	
Allee, Marjorie H.	Little American Girl (1st, 8vo, 237p, b/w, pep, DJ/2.00)	Houghton	1938	Quinn, Paul	25-45	*
Means, Florence C.	Penny for Luck: Story of the Rockies (1st, 8vo, 232p, fp b/w, DJ/2.00)	Houghton	1935	Quinn, Paul	30-45	
Bunce, William	Son of the Iroquois (1st {std}, 8vo, 127p, 2-color, pep, DJ/1.50)	Macrae Smith	1936	Quinn, Paul	45-70	
Schlein, Miriam	Four Little Foxes (1st, sm4to, ipcb, unpag, color, pep, DJ/2.00)	W.R. Scott	1953	Quintanilla, Luis	50-85	
Swift, Jonathan	Gulliver's Travels (1st, lg8vo, 358p, 24 engravings, DJ/5.00)	NY: Crown	(1947)	Quintanilla, Luis	60-100	*
Blyton, Enid	Famous Jimmy (1st {std}, 4to, ibds, 58p, 1-color, pep)	Dutton	1937	Rabier, Benjamin	80-140	
Garis, Howard	Uncle Wiggily's Automobile (1st, sm8vo, 184p, color)	Platt/Munk	(1939)	Rache, Elmer	30-50	
Garis, Howard	Uncle Wiggily's Happy Days (1st, lg8vo, 211p, col frn, pep, DJ/1.50)	Platt/Munk	(1947)	Rache, Elmer	40-70	
Aesopus	Aesop's Fables (1st, sm4to, green/gilt, 223p, 13cp, pep)	L: Heinemann	1912	Rackham, Arthur	300-500	
Aesopus	Aesop's Fables (1st AM, sq8vo, 224p, p-o, 13cp)	Doubleday/Page	1912	Rackham, Arthur	225-350	
Aesopus	Aesop's Fables (8vo, gilt, p-o, t.e. red, 13cp)	Garden City	(1939)	Rackham, Arthur	75-100	
Carroll, Lewis	Alice in Wonderland (1st AM, 8vo, p-o, 162p, 13cp, pep)	Doubleday/Page	[1907]	Rackham, Arthur	225-350	
Carroll, Lewis	Alice in Wonderland (1st, 8vo, green/gilt, 161p, 13cp, pep)	L: Heinemann	(1907)	Rackham, Arthur	275-400	
Gosse (intro)	Allies' Fairy Book (1st, 8vo, 121p, blue/gilt, 12cp)	L: Heinemann	(1916)	Rackham, Arthur	280-400	
Kenyon, Charles R.	Argonauts of the Amazon (1st, 8vo, blue/gilt, 305p, 6pl)	L: Chambers	1901	Rackham, Arthur	200-300	
Rackham, Arthur	Arthur Rackham Fairy Book (1st, lg8vo, red cl, 287p, 8cp, pep)	L: Harrap	(1933)	Rackham, Arthur	200-300	
Browne, Maggie	Book of Betty Barber (1st AM, sq8vo, teg, p-o, 130p, 6cp)	Badger	[1910]	Rackham, Arthur	300-500	

AUTHOR	TITLE	PUBLISHER	DATE	ARTIST	PRICE	LC
Browne, Maggie	Book of Betty Barber (1st, 8vo, brown cl, teg, p-o, 129p, 6cp)	L: Duckworth	[1910]	Rackham, Arthur	600-800	
Irving, Washington	Bracebridge Hall (1st, 2 vols, 8vo, teg, 5pl by…)	Putnam	1896	Rackham, Arthur	140-200	
Various	Brains & Bravery (1st, 8vo, 398p, green/gilt, 8pl)	L: Chambers	1903	Rackham, Arthur	300-450	
Weyman, Stanley J.	Castle Inn (1st, 8vo, blue/gilt, 371p, frn by…)	L: Smith Elder	1898	Rackham, Arthur	140-200	
Lever, Charles	Charles O'Malley… (1st, 8vo, 628p, uncut, red/gilt, 16pl)	L: Service	1897	Rackham, Arthur	150-225	
Dickens, Charles	Christmas Carol (1st AM, 8vo, 146p, purple/gilt, 12cp, pep)	Lippincott	(1915)	Rackham, Arthur	250-400	
Dickens, Charles	Christmas Carol (1st, 8vo, olive/gilt, 147p, 12cp, pep)	L: Heinemann	(1915)	Rackham, Arthur	300-500	
N/A	Cinderella (1st AM, 4to, ibds, 100p, DJ)	Lippincott	(1919)	Rackham, Arthur	200-300	
Evans, C.S.	Cinderella (1st, 4to, 110p, cream bds, ti-col frn, dp b/w, pep)	L: Heinemann	(1919)	Rackham, Arthur	250-320	
Walton, Isaac	Compleat Angler (1st, 4to, green/gilt, teg, 12cp, pep)	L: Harrap	(1931)	Rackham, Arthur	250-350	
Walton, Isaac	Compleat Angler (1st AM, sm4to, 224p, gilt, teg, 12cp, pep)	McKay	[1931]	Rackham, Arthur	200-300	
Milton, John	Comus (1st AM, sm4to, teg, green/gilt, 76p, 24 ticp, pep)	Doubleday/Page	[1921]	Rackham, Arthur	200-285	
Burns, Robert	Cotter's Saturday Night (1st, 12mo, ibds, 17p, frn by..)	L: Hewetson	(1908)	Rackham, Arthur	130-200	
Phillpotts, Eden	Dish of Apples (1st, sm4to, lavender cl, teg, 75p, 3 ticp, pep)	Hodder	(1921)	Rackham, Arthur	300-400	
Hope, Anthony	Dolly Dialogues (1st, sm sq8vo, 111p, wraps, 4pl)	(London)	1894	Rackham, Arthur	200-300	
Hope, Anthony	Dolly Dialogues (1st AM, 16mo, 195p, uncut, teg, frn by…)	Henry Holt & Co.	1894	Rackham, Arthur	90-140	
Starkie, Walter	Don Gypsy (1st, 8vo, orange/gilt, 525p, frn by…)	L: J. Murray	(1936)	Rackham, Arthur	60-100	
Steel, Flora A.	English Fairy Tales (1st AM, 8vo, red/gilt, 363p, 16cp, pep)	Macmillan	1918	Rackham, Arthur	200-285	R
Burney, Fanny	Evelina… (1st, sm8vo, teg, blue/gilt, 16 b/w, 416p)	L: Newnes	1898	Rackham, Arthur	200-300	
Rackham, Arthur	Fairy Book (1st {std}, 8vo, 111p, blue/gilt, 11cp)	Doubleday/Page	1923	Rackham, Arthur	180-250	
Grimm Bros.	Fairy Tales (1st, sm8vo, 464p, col frn, pep)	L: Freemantle	1900	Rackham, Arthur	120-200	*
Grimm Bros.	Fairy Tales (1st AM, 4to, ibds, gilt, 325p, 40 ticp)	Doubleday/Page	1909	Rackham, Arthur	700-900	
Grimm Bros.	Fairy Tales (1st, sm4to, 325p, gilt, 40 ticp, pep)	L: Constable	1909	Rackham, Arthur	800-1100	
Andersen, Hans C.	Fairy Tales (1st, 4to, 287p, gilt, teg, uncut, 12cp, pep)	L: Harrap	(1932)	Rackham, Arthur	400-600	
Andersen, Hans C.	Fairy Tales (1st AM, lg8vo, teg, 288p, 12cp, pep)	McKay	(1932)	Rackham, Arthur	350-500	
N/A	Faithful Friends (4to, pict red cl, 6pl by…)	L: Blackie	[1913]	Rackham, Arthur	280-350	
Martineau, Harriet	Feats on the Fjord (1st, 16mo, blue cl, teg, 237p, col frn)	L: Dent	1899	Rackham, Arthur	170-240	
Martineau, Harriet	Feats on the Fjord (1st AM, 12mo, p-o, 128p, 8cp)	Dutton	[1914]	Rackham, Arthur	100-160	
Rossetti, Christina	Goblin Market (1st, 8vo, wraps, 43p, 4cp, pep)	L: Harrap	(1933)	Rackham, Arthur	200-300	
Rossetti, Christina	Goblin Market (1st AM, 8vo, 42p, p-o, red cl, 4cp, pep)	Lippincott	[1933]	Rackham, Arthur	150-250	
Gates, Eleanor	Good Night (1st, sm8vo, 53p, bds, 5cp)	Crowell	(1907)	Rackham, Arthur	400-650	
Niebuhr	Greek Heroes (12mo, 96p, p-o, teg, blue/gilt, 4cp)	L: Cassell	1910	Rackham, Arthur	180-260	
Greene, Mrs.	Grey House on the Hill (1st, sm8vo, pink/gilt, 205p, 8cp)	L: Nelson	[1903]	Rackham, Arthur	200-300	
Merriman, Henry S.	Grey Lady (1st, 8vo, blue/gilt, 342p, 12pl)	L: Smith Elder	1897	Rackham, Arthur	250-350	
Swift, Jonathan	Gulliver's Travels (1st, 8vo, 291p, gilt, teg, 12cp, pep)	L: Dent	1909	Rackham, Arthur	300-450	
Swift, Jonathan	Gulliver's Travels (1st AM, 8vo, gilt, teg, 291p, 12cp, pep)	Dent/Dutton	1909	Rackham, Arthur	250-350	
Grimm Bros.	Hansel & Gretel (1st AM, lg8vo, teg, gilt, 159p, 20 ticp)	Dutton	(1920)	Rackham, Arthur	350-500	R
Grimm Bros.	Hansel & Gretel (1st, lg8vo, blue/gilt, 159p, 20 ticp)	L: Constable	(1920)	Rackham, Arthur	400-600	
Paget, John O.	Hunting (1st, 8vo, 287p, blue/gilt, teg, b/w, pep)	L: Dent	1900	Rackham, Arthur	140-200	
Ford, Julia E.	Imagina (1st, lg8vo, 178p, blue/gilt, 2 fp color, pep)	Duffield	1914	Rackham, Arthur	170-240	
Ingoldsby, Thomas	Ingoldsby Legends (1st, 8vo, teg, 638p, green/gilt, 12cp, pep)	L: Dent	1898	Rackham, Arthur	200-270	
Ingoldsby, Thomas	Ingoldsby Legends (1st AM, 4to, 549p, teg, green/gilt, 24 ticp, pep)	Dent/Dutton	1907	Rackham, Arthur	350-500	
Stephens, James	Irish Fairy Tales (1st, 8vo, 318p, green/gilt, 16cp)	L: Macmillan	1920	Rackham, Arthur	250-350	
Ruskin, John	King of the Golden River (1st AM, 8vo, red cl, 47p, p-o, 4cp)	Lippincott	(1932)	Rackham, Arthur	140-220	
Ruskin, John	King of the Golden River (1st, 8vo, wraps, 47p, 4cp, pep)	L: Harrap	(1932)	Rackham, Arthur	200-270	
N/A	Land of Enchantment (1st, 4to, 144p, olive/gilt, 14pl)	L: Cassell	1907	Rackham, Arthur	250-315	
Irving, Washington	Legend of Sleepy Hollow (1st AM, sm4to, 102p, gilt, teg, p-o, 8cp, pep)	McKay	(1928)	Rackham, Arthur	170-240	
Irving, Washington	Legend of Sleepy Hollow (1st, 4to, gilt, teg, 102p, 8cp, pep)	L: Harrap	(1928)	Rackham, Arthur	270-350	
Grimm Bros.	Little Brother and Little Sister (1st AM, 4to, 251p, 12 ticp)	Dodd	(1917)	Rackham, Arthur	300-450	
Grimm Bros.	Little Brother and Little Sister (1st, 4to, gilt, 251p, uncut, 12 ticp, pep)	L: Constable	(1917)	Rackham, Arthur	400-600	
Barrie, James M.	Little White Bird (1st, 8vo, teg, 242p, 2pl by…)	L: Hodder	1912	Rackham, Arthur	250-350	
Barrie, James M.	Little White Bird (1st AM, 8vo, 286p, teg, uncut, 2pl by…)	Scribner	1912	Rackham, Arthur	150-225	
Brown, Abbie F.	Lonesomest Doll (1st, 8vo, 81p, tan cl, 4pl)	Houghton	(1928)	Rackham, Arthur	250-400	
Shakespeare, Wm.	MidSummer Night's Dream (1st, lg8vo, 134p, grey/gilt, 40 ticp)	L: Heinemann	1908	Rackham, Arthur	425-600	
Merriman, Henry S.	Money Spinner (1st, sm8vo, 242p, gilt, 12pl)	L: Smith Elder	1896	Rackham, Arthur	250-350	
Mother Goose	Mother Goose (1st, sm4to, grey cl, 159p, 13 ticp, pep)	L: Heinemann	(1913)	Rackham, Arthur	400-600	R
Mother Goose	Mother Goose (1st AM, lg8vo, blue/gilt, p-o, 262p, 13cp)	Century	1913	Rackham, Arthur	450-600	R
Moore, Clement C.	Night Before Christmas (1st AM, 8vo, p-o, 37p, 4cp, pep)	Lippincott	[1932]	Rackham, Arthur	170-250	
Nisbet, John	Our Forests & Woodlands (1st, 8vo, teg, gilt, 340p, b/w, pep)	L: J.M. Dent	1900	Rackham, Arthur	100-165	
Ibsen, Henrik	Peer Gynt (1st, 4to, 255p, brown/gilt, 12cp, pep)	L: Harrap	(1936)	Rackham, Arthur	250-350	
Ibsen, Henrik	Peer Gynt (1st AM, 4to, 255p, orange cl, 12cp, pep, DJ/4.00)	Lippincott	[1936]	Rackham, Arthur	350-500	
Drury, William P.	Peradventures of Private Pagett (1st, 12mo, orange cl, 242p, 8pl)	L: Chapman	1904	Rackham, Arthur	250-350	
Barrie, James M.	Peter Pan (1st, sm4to, 125p, red/gilt, 50 ticp)	L: Hodder	1906	Rackham, Arthur	500-700	
Barrie, James M.	Peter Pan (1st AM, lg8vo, 125p, green/gilt, 50 ticp)	Scribner	1906	Rackham, Arthur	500-700	
Browning, Robert	Pied Piper of Hamelin (1st, 8vo, 44p, wraps, 4cp, pep, DJ)	L: Harrap	(1934)	Rackham, Arthur	200-300	
Browning, Robert	Pied Piper of Hamelin (1st AM, 8vo, 45p, p-o, 4cp, pep, DJ/1.50)	Lippincott	[1934]	Rackham, Arthur	150-225	
Bianco, Margery W.	Poor Cecco (1st AM, lg8vo, blue/gilt, 175p, tip-in col frn, 6cp, pep)	Doran	(1925)	Rackham, Arthur	180-260	R
Kipling, Rudyard	Puck of Pook's Hill (1st AM, 8vo, green/gilt, teg, 277p, 4cp)	Doubleday/Page	1906	Rackham, Arthur	100-150	
Rackham, Arthur	Rackham's Book of Pictures (1st, 4to, grey/gilt, 44 ticp)	L: Heinemann	(1913)	Rackham, Arthur	400-600	
Cholmondeley, M.	Red Pottage (1st, 8vo, 202p, tan wraps, 8pl)	L: Newnes	1904	Rackham, Arthur	450-650	
Wagner, Richard	Rhinegold & the Valkyrie (1st, 4to, 160p, gilt, 34 ticp, pep)	L: Heinemann	1910	Rackham, Arthur	400-600	
Wagner, Richard	Rhinegold & the Valkyrie (1st AM, lg8vo, 160p, 34 ticp, pep)	Doubleday/Page	1910	Rackham, Arthur	350-500	
Irving, Washington	Rip Van Winkle (1st AM, 4to, green/gilt, 51 ticp)	Doubleday/Page	1905	Rackham, Arthur	400-600	
Irving, Washington	Rip Van Winkle (1st, 4to, 57p, green/gilt, 51 ticp, dep)	L: Heinemann	1905	Rackham, Arthur	500-700	
Fay, Erica	Road to Fairyland (1st AM, 8vo, grey cl, 218p, col frn by..)	Putnam	(1926)	Rackham, Arthur	170-240	
Pollard, Alfred (ed)	Romance of King Arthur (1st AM, lg8vo, 517p, green/gilt, 16cp)	Macmillan	1917	Rackham, Arthur	250-400	
Wagner, Richard	Siegfried… (1st AM, sm4to, 182p, blue/gilt bds, 30 ticp)	Doubleday/Page	1911	Rackham, Arthur	250-400	
Wagner, Richard	Siegfried… (1st, sm4to, 182p, tan/gilt, 30 ticp, pep)	L: Heinemann	1911	Rackham, Arthur	300-500	

AUTHOR	TITLE	PUBLISHER	DATE	ARTIST	PRICE	LC
Evans, C.S.	Sleeping Beauty (1st, 4to, ibds, 110p, 1 ticp, 4 dp color)	L: Heinemann	(1920)	Rackham, Arthur	200-300	
Ford, Julia E.	Snickerty Nick (1st, lg8vo, 78p, blue cl, 3cp, 10pl)	Moffat	1919	Rackham, Arthur	400-650	
Grimm Bros.	Snowdrop... (1st, lg8vo, 165p, blue/gilt, 20 ticp)	L: Constable	(1920)	Rackham, Arthur	200-300	
Grimm Bros.	Snowdrop.... (1st AM, lg8vo, 165p, teg, 20 ticp)	Dutton	(1920)	Rackham, Arthur	170-220	
N/A	Some British Ballads (1st, 4to, 170p, blue/gilt, 16 ticp)	L: Constable	1919	Rackham, Arthur	180-240	
Starkie, Walter	Spanish Raggle-Taggle (1st, 8vo, 488p, red/gilt, frn by...)	L: J. Murray	(1934)	Rackham, Arthur	70-125	
Swinburne, A.C.	Springtide of Life (1st AM, 4to, 132p, green cl, 8cp, pep)	Lippincott	1918	Rackham, Arthur	200-300	
Swinburne, A.C.	Springtide of Life (1st, 4to, green/gilt, 133p, 8cp, pep)	L: Heinemann	(1918)	Rackham, Arthur	225-300	
Haydon, Arthur L.	Stories of King Arthur (1st, 12mo, 94p, p-o, red/gilt, 4cp by...)	L: Cassell	1910	Rackham, Arthur	200-300	R
Berlyn, Annie	Sunrise-Land (1st, 8vo, 345p, grey cloth, b/w)	L: Jarrold	1894	Rackham, Arthur	225-350	
Brown, Maggie	Surprising Adventures of Tuppy & Tue (1st, sm8vo, gilt, 190p, 4cp)	L: Cassell	1904	Rackham, Arthur	400-600	
Lamb, Charles	Tales from Shakespeare (1st AM, 8vo, gilt, 304p, teg, 12cp, pep)	Dent/Dutton	1909	Rackham, Arthur	225-300	
Lamb, Charles	Tales from Shakespeare (1st, 8vo, 304p, gilt, teg, 12cp, pep)	L: Dent	1909	Rackham, Arthur	300-395	
Irving, Washington	Tales of a Traveller (1st, 2vols, lg8vo, white/gilt, 5pl by...)	Putnam	1895	Rackham, Arthur	150-225	
Poe, Edgar A.	Tales of Mystery... (1st, 4to, 318p, gilt, 12cp, pep)	L: Harrap	(1935)	Rackham, Arthur	250-400	
Poe, Edgar A.	Tales of Mystery... (1st AM, 4to, gilt, 318p, 12cp, pep)	Lippincott	[1935]	Rackham, Arthur	250-350	
Shakespeare, Wm.	The Tempest (1st AM, 4to, grey/gilt, 20 ticp)	Doubleday/Page	(1926)	Rackham, Arthur	250-350	
Shakespeare, Wm.	The Tempest (1st, sm4to, olive/gilt, 185p, 20 ticp)	L: Heinemann	1926	Rackham, Arthur	350-500	
Fouque, La Motte	Undine (1st, sm4to, 136p, blue/gilt, 15 ticp, pep)	L: Heinemann	1909	Rackham, Arthur	250-350	
Fouque, La Motte	Undine (1st AM, 4to, 136p, grey/gilt, 15 ticp, pep)	Doubleday/Page	1909	Rackham, Arthur	200-300	
Goldsmith, Oliver	Vicar of Wakefield (1st AM, lg8vo, gilt, 232p, teg, 12cp, pep)	McKay	[1929]	Rackham, Arthur	160-240	
Goldsmith, Oliver	Vicar of Wakefield (1st, 4to, teg, uncut, gilt, 232p, 12cp, pep)	L: Harrap	(1929)	Rackham, Arthur	200-300	
Harbour, Henry	Where Flies the Flag (1st, 12mo, 286p, gilt, 6cp, cep)	L: Collins	(1904)	Rackham, Arthur	500-700	
Morley, Christopher	Where the Blue Begins (1st AM, smo, blue/gilt, teg, 227p, 4cp, pep)	Doubleday/Page	(1922)	Rackham, Arthur	200-300	
Dewar, G.A.B.	Wild Life in Hampshire Highlands (1st, 8vo, teg, green/gilt, b/w, pep)	L: J.M. Dent	1899	Rackham, Arthur	125-200	
Grahame, Kenneth	Wind in the Willows (1st {this pub}, lg8vo, 190p, 12cp, box)	Heritage Press	(1940)	Rackham, Arthur	120-170	
Hawthorne, Nathaniel	Wonder Book (1st AM, lg8vo, red/gilt, 16 ticp, 8cp)	Doran	[1922]	Rackham, Arthur	250-350	
Hawthorne, Nathaniel	Wonder Book (1st, 4to, 207p, red/gilt, 16 ticp, 8cp, pep)	L: Hodder	[1922]	Rackham, Arthur	270-350	
Hawthorne, Nathaniel	Wonder Book (8vo, later, yellow cl, p-o, 206p, 7cp)	Garden City	[1930]	Rackham, Arthur	90-130	
Fitzgerald, S.	Zankiwank & Bletherwitch (1st AM, 8vo, 188p, gilt, b/w)	Stokes	(1896)	Rackham, Arthur	500-700	
Fitzgerald, S.	Zankiwank & Bletherwitch (1st, 8vo, teg, green/gilt, 188p, fp b/w)	L: J.M. Dent	1896	Rackham, Arthur	700-900	
Radlov, Nicholas	Cautious Carp (1st, ob4to, ibds, [48]p, color, DJ/1.50)	Coward	(1938)	Radlov, Nicholas	60-100	
Larned, William T.	American Indian Fairy Tales (1st, lg8vo, ibds, [88]p, color, pep)	Volland	(1921)	Rae, John	120-185	
Gillmore, Inez H.	Angel Island (1st, sm8vo, blue cl, 351p, 2pl)	Henry Holt & Co.	1914	Rae, John	80-130	
Rae, John	Big Family (1st, ob4to, p-o, 50p, color)	Dodd	1916	Rae, John	100-165	
Gordon, Elizabeth	Buddy Jim (1st, lg8vo, ibds, [93]p, color)	Volland	(1922)	Rae, John	50-80	
N/A	Children at Play in Many Lands (1st, lg ob4to, [16]p, color)	Volland	1922	Rae, John	100-150	
Bible	Christmas Story from Saint Mark (1st, 24mo, ibds, unpag, color)	Volland	(1921)	Rae, John	55-80	*
Rowland, Henry C.	Countess Diane (1st, sm8vo, 149p, uncut, p-o, 5cp, pep)	Dodd	1908	Rae, John	40-60	
Skinner, Constance	Debby Barnes, Trader (1st, 8vo, 244p, col frn, b/w, pep)	Macmillan	1932	Rae, John	30-45	
Cox, Florence T.	Epic of Ebenezer (1st, 12mo, ibds, 72p)	Dodd	1912	Rae, John	25-40	
La Fontaine, J.	Fables in Rhyme for Little Folks (1st, 8vo, 94p, ibds, color)	Volland	(1918)	Rae, John	80-120	
Larned, William T.	Fairy Tales From France (1st, lg8vo, ibds, [93]p, color, pep)	Volland	(1920)	Rae, John	100-170	
Mills, Weymer J.	Girl I Left Behind Me (1st, 4to, 90p, teg, p-o, 11cp, pep)	Dodd	1910	Rae, John	100-175	
Rae, John	Granny Goose (1st, 4to, [48]p, ibds, 21 fp color, pep)	Volland	(1926)	Rae, John	180-260	
Rae, John	Grasshopper Green and the Meadow Mice (1st, 12mo, ibds, [40]p, color)	Volland	(1922)	Rae, John	75-100	
Grimm Bros.	Grimm's Animal Stories (1st, sq8vo, green cl, p-o, 9cp)	Duffield	(1911)	Rae, John	250-350	
Viele, Herman K.	Heartbreak Hill (1st, 12mo, 330p, grey cl, p-o, 6cp, pep)	Duffield	1908	Rae, John	30-50	*
Snyder, Fairmont	Lovely Garden (1st, 12mo, ibds, [38]p, color, color)	Volland	(1919)	Rae, John	70-100	
Rae, John	Lucy Locket... (1st, 8vo, 120p, ibds, color)	Volland	(1928)	Rae, John	70-100	
Meigs, Cornelia L.	Master Simon's Garden (1st, 8vo, 320p, blue cl, col frn, pep)	Macmillan	1929	Rae, John	60-90	R
Marryat, Frederick	Masterman Ready (1st, lg8vo, gilt, 403p, p-o, 6cp)	Harper	1928	Rae, John	35-60	
Gordon, Elizabeth	More Really So Stories (1st, lg8vo, ibds, 95p, color, pep)	Volland	(1929)	Rae, John	70-100	
Wister, Owen	Mother (1st, 8vo, 95p, p-o, uncut, 3cp, 4pl, dep)	Dodd	1907	Rae, John	30-50	
Klein, Charles	Music Master (1st, sm8vo, 341p, p-o, 4cp)	Dodd	1909	Rae, John	30-50	
Rae, John	New Adventures of Alice (1st, lg8vo, ibds, 158p gilt, 12cp, pep)	Volland	(1917)	Rae, John	125-200	
Dorrington, Albert	Our Lady of Darkness (1st, 12mo, 371p, red/gilt, 4pl)	Macaulay	1910	Rae, John	70-100	
Meigs, Cornelia L.	Pool of Stars (1st, 8vo, 203p, blue cl, pep, col frn)	Macmillan	1929	Rae, John	25-40	*
Martin, John	Prayers for Little Men & Women (1st, 8vo, 96p, gilt, 6 ticp)	Harper	1912	Rae, John	60-80	
Gordon, Elizabeth	Really So Stories (1st, lg8vo, ibds, 96p, 11cp, pep)	Volland	(1924)	Rae, John	70-100	
Belasco, David	Return of Peter Grimm (1st, 12mo, 344p, p-o, 3cp)	Dodd	1912	Rae, John	30-50	
Masefield, John	Reynard the Fox (1st, lg8vo, ibds, [94]p, color, pep)	Volland	(1925)	Rae, John	75-100	
Barbour, Ralph H.	Story my Doggie Told to Me (1st, sm8vo, p-o, 182p, fp b/w)	Dodd	1914	Rae, John	35-60	*
Gates, Josephine S.	Story of the Mince Pie (1st, 8vo, 164p, p-o, 16cp)	Dodd	1916	Rae, John	80-130	
Peck, Theodora A.	Sword of Dundee (1st, sm8vo, 398p, p-o, col frn, 6pl)	Duffield	1908	Rae, John	30-45	
Churchill, Winston	The Crossing... (1st, 8vo, green/gilt, 296p, 10pl)	Macmillan	1930	Rae, John	35-60	
Mee, John	Three Little Frogs (1st, 8vo, ibds, color, pep)	Volland	(1924)	Rae, John	60-90	
Mills, Weymer J.	Through the Gates of Old Romance (1st, sm8vo, 281p, teg, b/w)	Lippincott	1903	Rae, John	30-50	
Robins, Elizabeth	Under the Southern Cross (1st, 8vo, teg, p-o, 234p, 4cp, pep)	Stokes	(1907)	Rae, John	35-60	
Mills, Weymer J.	Van Rensselaers of Old Manhattan (1st, 8vo, p-o, 215p, 5cp)	Stokes	(1907)	Rae, John	30-50	
Rae, John	Why: Reflections for Children (1st, lg8vo, unpag, blue cl, p-o, color)	Dodd	1910	Rae, John	200-300	
Snyder, Zilpha K.	Egypt Game (1st {std}, 8vo, 215p, yellow cl, b/w, DJ/3.95, NH)	Atheneum	1967	Raible, Alton	50-85	*
Snyder, Zilpha K.	Eyes in the Fishbowl (1st {std}, 8vo, 168p, b/w, DJ/3.95)	Atheneum	1968	Raible, Alton	40-65	
Martin, Patricia	Rolling the Cheese (1st {std}, ob4to, [46]p, fp 2-color, cep, DJ/3.95)	Atheneum	1966	Raible, Alton	25-40	
Snyder, Zilpha K.	Season of Ponies (1st {std}, 8vo, 133p, b/w, DJ/3.25)	Atheneum	1964	Raible, Alton	30-45	
Snyder, Zilpha K.	The Changeling (1st {std}, 8vo, 220p, yellow cl, cep, DJ/5.25)	Atheneum	1970	Raible, Alton	30-50	
Snyder, Zilpha K.	Velvet Room (1st {std}, 8vo, 216p, b/w, cep, DJ/3.95)	Atheneum	1965	Raible, Alton	30-50	
Hutton, William H.	Hampton Court (1st, lg8vo, 244p, blue bds, teg, gilt, fp b/w)	L: Nimmo	1897	Railton, Herbert	60-90	

AUTHOR	TITLE	PUBLISHER	DATE	ARTIST	PRICE	LC
Hood, Thomas	Haunted House (1st, 12mo, 56p, AEG, green/gilt, b/w)	L: Lawrence	1896	Railton, Herbert	40-60	
Tilney, Frederick C.	Robin Hood & his Merry Outlaws (12mo, green/gilt, 128p, p-o, 8cp)	Dent/Dutton	[1919]	Railton, Ione	35-60	*
Henty, G.A.	At Aboukir and Acre (1st AM, 12mo, 320p, gilt, b/w)	Scribner	1898	Rainey, William	100-165	
Brereton, Frederick	Boy of the Dominion (1st, 8vo, 367p, gilt, 6cp)	L: Blackie	1913	Rainey, William	40-60	
Henty, G.A.	Out with Garibaldi (1st, 12mo, blue/gilt, 352p, 8pl, cep)	L: Blackie	1901	Rainey, William	120-200	
MacGregor, Mary	Story of France (1st AM, lg8vo, gilt, 508p, 20cp)	Stokes	[1920]	Rainey, William	40-60	
Henty, G.A.	With Buller in Natal (1st, 12mo, 384p, blue/gilt, 10pl, cep)	L: Blackie	1901	Rainey, William	100-165	
Twain, Mark	Eve's Diary (1st, 8vo, 109p, red cloth, b/w)	Harper	1906	Ralph, Lester	120-185	
Burgess, Gelett	Heart Line (1st, sm8vo, 584p, p-o, 12pl)	Bobbs-Merrill	(1907)	Ralph, Lester	40-60	
Latham, Jean L.	Jack the Giant-Killer (1st, 8vo, [32]p, p-o, color, DJ/1.95)	Bobbs-Merrill	1961	Ramierz, Pablo	30-50	
Latham, Jean L.	Aladdin (1st, 8vo, [32]p, ipcb, color, DJ/1.95)	Bobbs-Merrill	1961	Ramirez, Pablo	30-50	
Latham, Jean L.	Ali Baba (1st, 8vo, [32]p, ipcb, color, DJ/1.95)	Bobbs-Merrill	1961	Ramirez, Pablo	30-50	
Perrault, Charles	Cinderella (1st, lg8vo, unpag, color, DJ/1.50)	World	(1965)	Ramirez, Pablo	20-30	
Latham, Jean L.	Puss in Boots (1st, 8vo, [32]p, p-o, fp color, DJ/1.95)	Bobbs-Merrill	1961	Ramirez, Pablo	30-50	
Ramsay, Tamara	Toy Workshop in Land of Silvery Blue (1st AM, 4to, p-o, [31]p, color, cep)	Whitman	1932	Ramsay, Tamara	60-100	
Steele, William O.	Andy Jackson's Water Well (1st {std}, 8vo, 80p, fp b/w, DJ/2.75)	Harcourt	(1959)	Ramus, Michael	20-30	
Davis, M.E.M.	Moons of Balbanca (1st, 8vo, 180p, 6pl)	Houghton	1908	Rand, Amy	50-80	
Booth, Maud B.	Twilight Fairy Tales (1st, 8vo, 273p, gilt, teg, 16cp)	Putnam	1906	Rand, Amy	80-125	
Rand, Ann	I Know a Lot of Things (1st {std}, 4to, [32]p, color, cep, DJ/2.75, NYTBI)	Harcourt	(1956)	Rand, Paul	200-300	R
Rand, Ann	Listen! Listen! (1st {std}, 4to, 31p, color, DJ/4.25)	Harcourt	(1970)	Rand, Paul	80-130	
Rand, Ann	Little 1 (1st, 4to, ibds, unpag, color, DJ/3.25)	Harcourt	(1962)	Rand, Paul	150-225	
Rand, Ann	Sparkle & Spin (1st {std}, sm4to, [30]p, color, dep, DJ/2.95, NYTBI)	Harcourt	(1957)	Rand, Paul	250-350	R
Van Derveer, Helen	Little Slam Bang (1st, 8vo, ibds, 38p, color, pep)	Volland	(1928)	Ransom, Fletcher	60-90	
Ransome, Arthur	Big Six (1st AM, 8vo, 353p, b/w, DJ/2.00)	Macmillan	1941	Ransome, Arthur	70-100	
Ransome, Arthur	Missee Lee (1st, 8vo, 336p, gilt, b/w, pep, DJ)	L: J. Cape	1941	Ransome, Arthur	200-300	
Ransome, Arthur	Pigeon Post (1st, 8vo, 383p, b/w, pep, DJ, CgM)	L: J. Cape	(1936)	Ransome, Arthur	160-240	
Ransome, Arthur	Secret Water (1st AM, 8vo, 363p, b/w, pep, DJ/2.00)	Macmillan	1940	Ransome, Arthur	30-45	
Ransome, Arthur	Coot Club (1st AM, 8vo, 342p, 1-color, DJ/2.00)	Lippincott	(1935)	Ransome/Carter	70-125	
Raskin, Ellen	A & The (1st {std}, lg8vo, [32]p, color, DJ/4.95)	Atheneum	1970	Raskin, Ellen	30-50	
Raskin, Ellen	And It Rained (1st {std}, 8vo, [48]p, color, DJ/3.75)	Atheneum	1969	Raskin, Ellen	30-50	
Bartlett, Susan	Books (1st {std}, 8vo, unpag, color, DJ/2.95)	Holt, Rinehart	(1968)	Raskin, Ellen	35-50	*
Thomas, Dylan	Child's Christmas in Wales (1st, ob16mo, wraps, 5 fp b/w)	New Directions	(1959)	Raskin, Ellen	45-70	
Razzell, Arthur	Circles and Curves (1st AM {std}, 8vo, 47p, color, DJ/2.50)	Doubleday	(1969)	Raskin, Ellen	30-50	
Caudill, Rebecca	Come Along! (1st {std}, ob8vo, 30p, ibds, color, DJ/3.95)	Holt, Rinehart	(1969)	Raskin, Ellen	30-45	
Cleaver, Vera	Ellen Grae (1st {std} [1st bk.], 8vo, 89p, fp b/w, cep, DJ/2.95)	Lippincott	(1967)	Raskin, Ellen	30-50	
Raskin, Ellen	Ghost in a Four-Room Apartment (1st {std}, 12mo, [48]p, color, DJ/3.75)	Atheneum	1969	Raskin, Ellen	30-50	
Rossetti, Christina	Goblin Market (1st {std}, ob8vo, ipcb, 32p, color, DJ/4.95)	Dutton	(1970)	Raskin, Ellen	40-65	R
Bishop, Claire H.	Happy Christmas (1st, lg8vo, 287p, fp b/w, pep, DJ/3.00)	S. Daye Press	(1956)	Raskin, Ellen	50-80	*
Morrow, Suzanne	Inatuck's Friend (1st {std}, 4to, 48p, color, DJ/3.50)	Little/Brown	(1968)	Raskin, Ellen	30-45	
Cone, Molly	Jewish Sabbath (1st, 8vo, [38]p, fp 3-color, DJ/2.95)	Crowell	(1966)	Raskin, Ellen	30-50	*
Coolidge, Olivia	King of Men (1st {std}, 8vo, 230p, b/w, cep, DJ/3.50)	Houghton	1966	Raskin, Ellen	50-80	R*
Krauss, Ruth	Mama, I Wish I Was Snow (1st {std}, ob8vo, [28]p, color, cep, DJ/2.50)	Atheneum	1962	Raskin, Ellen	50-85	
Raskin, Ellen	Nothing Ever Happens/my Block (1st {std}, ob8vo, unpag, col, DJ/2.95, NYT)	Atheneum	1966	Raskin, Ellen	45-70	
Weiss, Renee K.	Paper Zoo (1st {std}, sm4to, 38p, fp 2-color, DJ/4.50)	Macmillan	(1968)	Raskin, Ellen	60-90	R
Larrick, Nancy	Piping Down the Valleys Wild (1st {std}, 8vo, 247p, b/w, cep, DJ/4.95)	Delacorte Pr.	(1968)	Raskin, Ellen	20-35	
Razzell, Arthur	Probability: Science of Chance (1st AM {std}, 8vo, 47p, color, DJ/2.50)	Doubleday	(1967)	Raskin, Ellen	30-50	
Brewton, Sara W.	Shrieks at Midnight (1st, sm8vo, 177p, b/w, DJ/3.95)	Crowell	(1969)	Raskin, Ellen	30-50	
Raskin, Ellen	Silly Songs and Sad (1st, sq8vo, [48]p, fp color, DJ/3.75)	Crowell	(1967)	Raskin, Ellen	30-50	
Blake, William	Songs of Innocence (1st {std}, ob4to, 48p, color, DJ/3.50)	Doubleday	(1966)	Raskin, Ellen	30-50	*
Raskin, Ellen	Spectacles (1st {std}, ob12mo, [48]p, color, DJ/3.50, NYTBI)	Atheneum	1968	Raskin, Ellen	60-100	R
Razzell, Arthur	Symmetry (1st AM {std}, 8vo, 47p, color, DJ/2.50)	Doubleday	(1968)	Raskin, Ellen	30-45	
Razzell, Arthur	This is 4: Idea of a Number (1st AM {std}, 8vo, 47p, color, DJ/2.50)	Doubleday	(1967)	Raskin, Ellen	30-50	
Razzell, Arthur	Three and the Shape of Three (1st {std}, 8vo, 47p, color, DJ/2.50)	Doubleday	(1969)	Raskin, Ellen	30-45	
Fisher, Aileen	We Alcotts (1st {std}, 8vo, 278p, b/w, DJ/4.95)	Atheneum	1968	Raskin, Ellen	35-50	
Fisher, Aileen	We Dickinsons (1st {std}, 8vo, 246p, color, DJ/4.50, b/w frn & decor by...)	Atheneum	1965	Raskin, Ellen	30-50	R
Brown, Margaret W.	Fish with a Deep Sea Smile (1st {std}, 8vo, 128p, color, cep, DJ/2.00)	Dutton	(1938)	Rauch, Roberta	70-100	
Wedgwood, Henry A.	Bird Talisman (1st, lg8vo, 70p, gilt, pep, 8cp)	L: Faber	1939	Raverat, Gwen	50-85	
Uttley, Alison	Mustard, Pepper and Salt (1st, 8vo, 230p, b/w, DJ)	L: Faber	1938	Raverat, Gwen	30-50	*
Shippen, Kath. B.	Men of Medicine (1st, 8vo, 220p, b/w, DJ/3.50)	Viking	(1957)	Ravielli, Anthony	25-40	*
Shippen, Kath. B.	Men, Microscopes & Living Things (1st, 8vo, grn cl, fp b/w, DJ/3.00, NH)	Viking	1955	Ravielli, Anthony	50-80	R
Cross, Launcelot	Book of Old Sun Dials (1st, 8vo, ibds, gilt, 102p, 8cp by...)	L: Foulis	(1914)	Rawlings, Alfred	75-120	
Mitford, Mary R.	Our Village (1st, lg8vo, green/gilt, 256p, teg, 16 ticp)	L: Macmillan	1910	Rawlings, Alfred	90-120	
Kjelgaard, Jim	Buckskin Brigade (1st, 8vo, 310p, b/w, pep, DJ/2.50)	Holiday House	(1947)	Ray, Ralph	30-50	
Coatsworth, Eliz.	Captain's Daughter (1st {std}, 8vo, 198p, DJ/2.50, decor by...)	Macmillan	1950	Ray, Ralph	20-30	
Kjelgaard, Jim	Chip the Dam Builder (1st, sm8vo, 233p, b/w, pep, DJ/2.50)	Holiday House	(1950)	Ray, Ralph	30-50	
Judson, Clara I.	City Neighbor: Story of Jane Addams (1st, 8vo, 130p, b/w, DJ/2.50)	Scribner	1951	Ray, Ralph	20-30	
Eaton, Jeanette	David Livingstone: Foe of Darkness (1st, 8vo, 256p, b/w, DJ/3.00)	Wm. Morrow	1947	Ray, Ralph	20-35	
Kjelgaard, Jim	Fire-Hunter (1st, 8vo, 217p, tan cl, b/w, pep, DJ/2.50)	Holiday House	(1951)	Ray, Ralph	30-50	
Coatsworth, Eliz.	First Adventure (1st {std}, 8vo, 60p, color, DJ/1.50)	Macmillan	1950	Ray, Ralph	25-40	
Eaton, Jeanette	Gandhi: Fighter Without a Sword (1st, 8vo, 253p, b/w, pep, DJ/3.00)	Wm. Morrow	1950	Ray, Ralph	25-40	
Adrian, Mary	Garden Spider (1st, sm8vo, 38p, blue cl, 2-color, pep, DJ/2.00)	Holiday House	(1951)	Ray, Ralph	25-45	
Burgwyn, Mebane	River Treasure (1st, 8vo, 150p, blue cl, fp b/w, DJ/2.50)	Oxford U. Pr.	1947	Ray, Ralph	250-350	
Coblentz, Catherine	Sequoya (1st {std}, 8vo, 199p, DJ/2.50, decor by...)	Longmans	1946	Ray, Ralph	25-45	
Eaton, Jeanette	Washington: Nation's First Hero (1st, 8vo, 70p, fp b/w, pep, DJ/2.00)	Wm. Morrow	1951	Ray, Ralph	20-30	
Coatsworth, Eliz.	Wishing Pear (1st {std}, 8vo, 64p, fp 1-color, DJ/2.00)	Macmillan	1951	Ray, Ralph	20-30	
Ray, Wade	Train to Spain (1st, 4to, [38]p, fp dp color, cep, DJ/2.95)	Knopf	(1963)	Ray, Wade	25-40	
Ormondroyd, Edward	David and the Phoenix (1st, 8vo, 173p, b/w, DJ/2.75)	Follett	1957	Raysor, Joan	100-165	
Hornibrook, Isabel	Scout of Today (1st, 8vo, 290p, 5pl)	Houghton	1913	Reading, J.	25-40	*

AUTHOR	TITLE	PUBLISHER	DATE	ARTIST	PRICE	LC
Harrington, Isis	Told in the Twilight (1st {std}, 8vo, 143p, b/w, DJ/1.75)	Dutton	1938	Ream, Glen	25-40	
Judson, Clara I.	They Came from Scotland (1st, sm8vo, 198p, col frn, pep, DJ/2.00)	Houghton	1944	Reardon, Mary	25-45	
London, Jack	Children of the Frost (1st, sm8vo, 261p, blue cl, 8pl)	Macmillan	1902	Reay, Raphael M.	425-600	
Smith, Gertrude	Arabella & Araminta Stories (1st, sq8vo, 103p, uncut, 15pl, PPPa)	Copeland & Day	1895	Reed, Ethel	350-500	
Smith, Gertrude	Arabella & Araminta Stories (8vo, 103p, 15pl, pep, later)	Small/Maynard	1903	Reed, Ethel	100-180	
Blodgett, Mabel F.	Fairy Tales (1st, sm4to, yellow cl, 204p, teg, 12pl, pep)	Lamson/Wolffe	1896	Reed, Ethel	600-850	
Cabot, Carolyn S.	Football Grandma (1st, 8vo, 79p, tan cl, b/w, pep by...)	Small/Maynard	1905	Reed, Ethel	40-60	*
Moulton, Louise C.	In Childhood's Country (1st, 8vo, tan cl, 69p, uncut, 9pl, pep)	Copeland & Day	1896	Reed, Ethel	200-300	R
Bolton, Charles K.	Love Story of Ursula Wolcott (1st, 16mo, ipcb, 31p, pep, designs by..)	Lamson/Wolffe	1895	Reed, Ethel	100-165	*
Dickens, Charles	Christmas Carol (1st, 12mo, 148p, ipcb, uncut, color, DJ/2.00)	Holiday House	(1940)	Reed, Philip	50-85	
Mother Goose	Mother Goose & Nursery Rhymes (1st {std}, 4to, 57p, color, DJ/4.95, CH)	Atheneum	1963	Reed, Philip	60-100	R
N/A	Seven Voyages of Sinbad (1st, 12mo, 71p, ipcb, color)	Holiday House	1939	Reed, Philip	70-100	R*
N/A	Seven Voyages of Sinbad the Sailor (1st {std}, 8vo, 58p, color, DJ/3.25)	Atheneum	1962	Reed, Philip	45-70	
Fisher, Aileen	Cherokee Strip: Race for Land (1st {std}, 8vo, 192p, 1-color, DJ/1.75)	Aladdin	1956	Reed, Walt	20-35	*
Teresah	A Doll, Two Children & Three Storks (1st AM {std}, 8vo, 178p, col frn)	Dutton	(1931)	Reetz, Wilhelm	30-50	
Linklater, Eric	Pirates in the Deep Green Sea (1st, 8vo, 397p, gilt, b/w, pep, DJ/2.75)	Macmillan	1949	Reeves, William	50-80	*
Harris, Christie	Raven's Cry (1st {std}, 8vo, 192p, b/w, DJ/3.95)	Atheneum	1966	Reid, Bill	20-35	*
Borski, Lucia M.	Gypsy and the Bear (1st {std}, 8vo, 129p, b/w, pep)	Longmans	1933	Reid, James	25-45	*
Norton, Andre	Ralestone Luck (1st, sm8vo, 296p, fp b/w, DJ/2.00)	Appleton-Century	1938	Reid, James	500-700	*
Gall, Alice C.	Ringtail (1st, lg8vo, 119p, pep, 1-color)	Oxford U. Pr.	(1933)	Reid, James	30-50	
Goldsmith, Oliver	Deserted Village (1st, ob4to, 59p, vellum/gilt, 14cp, pep)	L: Gowans/Gray	1907	Reid, Stephen	120-200	
Noyes, Alfred (ed)	Magic Casement (1st, 8vo, teg, uncut, 391p, gilt, b/w)	L: Chapman	[1908]	Reid, Stephen	50-80	
Gowans, Adam I.	Treasury of English Verse (1st, 8vo, 303p, green cl, 50pl, pep)	L: Gowans/Gray	1907	Reid, Stephen	80-120	*
Stearns, Monroe	Kasimir's Journey (1st, 4to, [35]p, fp color, DJ/3.00, NYTBI)	Lippincott	1957	Reidel, Marlene	45-70	
Krauss, Ruth	Good Man & his Good Wife (1st, 8vo, [32]p, fp 2-color, DJ/1.50)	Harper	1944	Reinhardt, Adolph	250-400	
Burnett, Frances H.	Pretty Sister of Jose (1st [1], 12mo, 127p, gilt, 12pl)	Scribner	1889	Reinhart, C.S.	100-160	
Smith, Francis H.	Tom Grogan (1st, 12mo, 246p, teg, 19pl)	Houghton	1896	Reinhart, C.S.	30-50	
Gray, Eliz. J.	Fair Adventure (1st, 8vo, 298p, b/w, pep, DJ/2.00)	Viking	1940	Reischer, Alice K.	25-45	
Gianakoulis, T.P.	Fairy Tales of Modern Greece (1st {std}, 8vo, 126p, pep, b/w)	Dutton	1930	Reiss, Henriette	30-50	*
Reiss, John J.	Colors (1st {std}, 4to, [32]p, 2-color, DJ/4.95)	Bradbury Press	(1969)	Reiss, John	40-70	
Linderman, Frank B.	Blackfeet Indians (1st, lg4to, 65p, ibds, 49 color, DJ/3.50)	(St. Paul)	1935	Reiss, Winold	350-500	
Locke, Alain L. (ed)	New Negro (1st, 8vo, ipcb, 445p, col frn, b/w)	A.& C. Boni	1925	Reiss, Winold	400-600	
Barbour, Ralph H.	Captain Chub (1st, sm8vo, 413p, 22pl)	Century	1909	Relyea, Charles M.	100-160	
Seawell, Molly E.	House of Egremont (1st, sm8vo, 515p, gilt, 6pl)	Scribner	1900	Relyea, Charles M.	20-30	
Hughes, Rupert	Lakerim Athletic Club (1st, sm8vo, gilt, 286p, 20pl, PPPa)	Century	1898	Relyea, Charles M.	200-300	
Richmond, Grace S.	On Christmas Day in the Evening (1st, 12mo, 76p, white bds, 4cp)	Doubleday/Page	1910	Relyea, Charles M.	30-50	
Barbour, Ralph H.	On Your Mark (1st, 8vo, 267p, p-o, 4cp)	Appleton	1904	Relyea, Charles M.	25-40	
Riley, James W.	Rubaiyat of Doc Sifers (1st, 12mo, teg, 211p, green/gilt, b/w)	Century	1897	Relyea, Charles M.	60-100	R
Barbour, Ralph H.	Weatherby's Inning (1st, 8vo, gilt, 249p, 6cp)	Appleton	1907	Relyea, Charles M.	70-100	
Wenning, Elizabeth	Christmas Mouse (1st, sm4to, [48]p, fp 2-color, DJ/2.95)	Holt	(1959)	Remington, Barbara	30-55	
Frost, Lesley	Really Not Really (1st, 4to, 61p, cloth, 1-color, DJ/2.75)	Channel Press	(1962)	Remington, Barbara	25-40	
Weik, Mary H.	Scarlet Thread (1st {std}, lg8vo, 109p, red cl, b/w, DJ/4.50)	Atheneum	1968	Remington, Barbara	25-40	
Soule, Jean	Scuttle, the Stowaway Mouse (1st, ob4to, [41]p, color, pep, DJ/3.50)	Parents Mag. Pr.	(1969)	Remington, Barbara	25-40	
Janvier, Thomas A.	Aztec Treasure House (1st, 12mo, 446p, grey/gilt, 19pl, PPPa)	Harper	1890	Remington, Frederic	80-125	
Lewis, Alfred H.	Black Lion Inn (1st, sm8vo, 380p, yellow cl, 16pl)	R.H. Russell	1903	Remington, Frederic	80-140	
Garland, Hamlin	Book of the American Indian (1st {std}, 4to, bds, 274p, p-o, 4cp)	Harper	1923	Remington, Frederic	180-240	
Bigelow, Poultney	Borderland of Czar and Kaiser (1st, 12mo, 8vo, 343p, gilt, 50pl)	Harper	1895	Remington, Frederic	80-125	
Fitzhugh, Percy K.	Boy's Book of Scouts (1st, 8vo, 317p, 3pl by...)	Crowell	(1917)	Remington, Frederic	70-100	*
Remington, Frederic	Crooked Trails (1st, 8vo, 150p, tan cloth, 49pl)	Harper	1898	Remington, Frederic	200-320	
Davis, Richard H.	Cuba in War Time (1st, 12mo, 143p, brown bds, 24pl)	R.H. Russell	1897	Remington, Frederic	200-300	
King, Charles	Daughter of the Sioux (1st, sm8vo, 306p, teg, p-o, 4pl)	Hobart	1903	Remington, Frederic	60-90	
Norris, Frank	Deal in Wheat (1st, 8vo, 272p, red/gilt, teg, 4pl)	Doubleday/Page	1903	Remington, Frederic	60-90	
Remington, Frederic	Done in the Open (1st, folio, [90]p, ibds, 70 b/w)	R.H. Russell	1902	Remington, Frederic	650-850	
Remington, Frederic	Drawings (1st, ob folio, ibds, 60pl)	R.H. Russell	1897	Remington, Frederic	700-1000	
Decker, Karl	Evangelina Cisneros (1st, sm8vo, teg, uncut, 257p, 4pl by...)	Continental	1898	Remington, Frederic	80-130	
Custer, Elizabeth B.	Following The Guidon (1st, sm8vo, gilt, 341p, 2pl by...)	Harper	1890	Remington, Frederic	100-180	
Remington, Frederic	Frontier Sketches (1st, lgob4to, AEG, white pcb, 15pl)	Werner Co.	1898	Remington, Frederic	800-1200	
Longfellow, H.W.	Hiawatha (1st, 8vo, suede/gilt, 242p, teg, 23pl)	Houghton	1891	Remington, Frederic	250-350	
Longfellow, H.W.	Hiawatha (lg8vo, p-o, 193p, 9pl by...)	Riverside	1908	Remington, Frederic	120-180	
Longfellow, H.W.	Hiawatha (1st, 8vo, teg, red/gilt, 242p, b/w illus by...)	Houghton	1911	Remington, Frederic	400-600	
Wister, Owen	Jimmyjohn Boss (1st, 12mo, 333p, gilt, p-o, 5pl by...)	Harper	1900	Remington, Frederic	70-100	
Remington, Frederic	John Ermine of the Yellowstone (1st, 8vo, brown cl, 271p, teg, 7pl)	Macmillan	1902	Remington, Frederic	160-225	
Wister, Owen	Journey in Search of Christmas (1st, 8vo, teg, gilt, 93p, 3pl, pep)	Harper	1904	Remington, Frederic	70-100	
Remington, Frederic	Men with the Bark On (1st, 12mo, 209p, tan/gilt, 32pl)	Harper	1900	Remington, Frederic	200-300	
Inman, Henry	Old Santa Fe Trail (1st, 8vo, 493p, teg, 8pl)	Macmillan	1897	Remington, Frederic	160-225	R
Ralph, Julian	On Canada's Frontier (1st, 8vo, 325p, 60 illus by...)	Harper	1892	Remington, Frederic	150-250	
Whitney, Caspar	On Snow-Shoes/Barren Grounds (1st, lg8vo, gilt, teg, 324p, blue cl, b/w)	Harper	1896	Remington, Frederic	200-300	
Parkman, Francis	Oregon Trail (1st, 8vo, teg, gilt, 411p, 10pl)	Little/Brown	1892	Remington, Frederic	250-400	
Remington, Frederic	Pony Tracks (1st {std bk.}, 8vo, tan/gilt, 269p, 70 illus)	Harper	1895	Remington, Frederic	400-650	
Roosevelt, Theodore	Ranch Life & the Hunting Trail (1st, 4to, tan/gilt, 186p, AEG, b/w)	Century	(1888)	Remington, Frederic	175-240	
Wister, Owen	Red Men & White (1st, 12mo, 280p, gilt, 16pl)	Harper	1896	Remington, Frederic	80-130	
Dodge, Theodore A.	Riders of Many Lands (1st, lg8vo, 486p, brown/gilt, teg, b/w)	Harper	1894	Remington, Frederic	120-200	
Whitney, Caspar	Sporting Pilgrimage (1st, 8vo, 397p, red/gilt, b/w)	Harper	1895	Remington, Frederic	80-125	
Remington, Frederic	Stories of Peace & War (1st, 16mo, blue cl, 98p, 2pl)	Harper	1899	Remington, Frederic	140-200	
Remington, Frederic	Sundown Leflare (1st, 12mo, brown/gilt, 115p, 12pl)	Harper	1899	Remington, Frederic	200-300	
Custer, Elizabeth B.	Tenting on the Plains (1st, lg8vo, 702p, 11 b/w, gilt)	Webster	1887	Remington, Frederic	250-400	
Wister, Owen	The Virginian (1st, 8vo, red cl, p-o, 506p, teg, 10pl by...)	Macmillan	1911	Remington, Frederic	280-350	*
King, Charles	To the Front (1st, sm8vo, ibds, 260p, 4pl)	Harper	1908	Remington, Frederic	70-100	*

AUTHOR	TITLE	PUBLISHER	DATE	ARTIST	PRICE	LC
Remington, Frederic	Way of an Indian (1st, 8vo, red cl, 251p, p-o, 14pl)	Fox Duffield	1906	Remington, Frederic	160-240	
Hough, Emerson	Way to the West (1st, sm8vo, grey cl, 446p, 6pl)	Bobbs-Merrill	(1903)	Remington, Frederic	70-100	
Davis, Richard H.	West From a Car Window (1st, 12mo, blue cl, 242p, gilt, b/w)	Harper	1892	Remington, Frederic	80-140	
Bigelow, Poultney	White Man's Africa (1st, 8vo, 271p, 3pl by...)	Harper	1900	Remington, Frederic	60-100	
Lewis, Alfred H.	Wolfville (1st, 12mo, red cl, 337p, 18pl)	Stokes	(1897)	Remington, Frederic	120-200	
Lewis, Alfred H.	Wolfville Days (1st, 12mo, 311p, frn by...)	Stokes	(1902)	Remington, Frederic	80-125	
King, Charles	Apache Princess (1st, 12mo, 328p, p-o, teg, 8pl)	Hobart	1903	Remington/Deming	80-140	
May, Julian	Why Birds Migrate (1st, ob8vo, [36]p, color, DJ/4.95)	Holiday House	(1970)	Reneson, Chet	20-35	
Yolen, Jane	Gwinellen, Princess Who Could Not Sleep (1st {std} 4to, unpag, col DJ/2.95)	Macmillan	(1965)	Renfro, Ed	25-40	
Heide, Florence P.	Maximilian (1st {1}, 4to, [32]p, fp color, cep, DJ/2.95)	Funk/Wagnalls	(1967)	Renfro, Ed	20-35	
Retan, Walter	Snowplow that Tried to Go South (1st {std}, 4to, [31]p, 2-color, DJ/1.75)	Aladdin	(1950)	Resko, John	30-50	*
Sobol, Donald J.	Double Quest (1st {std}, 8vo, 240p, b/w, DJ/2.95)	F. Watts	1957	Rethi, Lili	25-45	*
Hume, Ruth & Paul	Lion of Poland (1st, 8vo, 192p, b/w, pep, DJ/2.95)	Hawthorn Books	1962	Rethi, Lili	20-35	
Rey, Hans A.	Anybody at Home? (1st AM, ob8vo, [24]p, wraps, color)	Houghton	1942	Rey, Hans A.	120-180	
Rey, Hans A.	Au Clair de la Lune (1st, ob4to, spiral bds, [32]p, fp color)	Greystone Press	(1941)	Rey, Hans A.	250-350	
Rey, Margret E.	Billy's Picture (1st, sm4to, ibds, [22]p, 2-color, DJ/1.00)	Harper	(1948)	Rey, Hans A.	90-130	
Rey, Hans A.	Cecily G. & the 9 Monkeys (1st AM, 4to, 31p, color, DJ/2.00)	Houghton	1942	Rey, Hans A.	140-200	
Rey, Hans A.	Curious George (1st, sm4to, [55]p, color, pep, DJ/2.00)	Houghton	1941	Rey, Hans A.	200-300	
Rey, Hans A.	Curious George Gets a Medal (1st, 4to, 47p, 1-color, DJ/3.25, NYTBI)	Houghton	1957	Rey, Hans A.	100-170	
Rey, Margret E.	Curious George Goes to the Hospital (1st, lg8vo, 48p, fp color, DJ/3.25)	Houghton	1966	Rey, Hans A.	50-80	*
Rey, Hans A.	Curious George Learns the Alphabet (1st, lg8vo, 72p, color, pep, DJ/3.25)	Houghton	1963	Rey, Hans A.	70-125	*
Rey, Hans A.	Curious George Rides a Bike (1st, 4to, 45p, color, DJ/2.75)	Houghton	1952	Rey, Hans A.	100-160	*
Rey, Hans A.	Curious George Takes a Job (1st, 4to, 47p, color, pep, DJ/2.50)	Houghton	1947	Rey, Hans A.	120-180	
Brown, Margaret W.	Don't Frighten the Lion (1st {std}, sq4to, [31]p, p-o, 1-color, DJ/1.75)	Harper	(1942)	Rey, Hans A.	90-150	
Gilbert, Paul T.	Egbert & his Marvelous Adventures (1st {std}, sm8vo, 103p, b/w, DJ/1.50)	Harper	(1944)	Rey, Hans A.	50-80	
Rey, Hans A.	Elizabite (1st {std}, sm4to, ipcb, [32]p, color, DJ/1.50)	Harper	(1942)	Rey, Hans A.	120-180	
Rey, Hans A.	Humpty Dumpty... (1st {std}, ob4to, [23]p, color, DJ/1.00)	Harper	(1943)	Rey, Hans A.	100-160	
Payne, Emmy	Katy No-Pocket (1st, 4to, [32]p, color, pep, DJ/2.00)	Houghton	1944	Rey, Hans A.	100-160	
Rey, Hans A.	Look for the Letters (1st, lg ob8vo, [56]p, ibds, color, DJ/2.00)	Harper	(1945)	Rey, Hans A.	120-200	
Zolotow, Charlotte	Park Book (1st {std}, ob sm4to, [32]p, color, pep, DJ/1.75)	Harper	(1944)	Rey, Hans A.	100-150	R
Brown, Margaret W.	Polite Penguin (1st {std}, sm4to, green cl, 31p, 2-color, pep, DJ/1.75)	Harper	(1941)	Rey, Hans A.	80-130	
Rey, Margret E.	Pretzel (1st {std}-[1st bk.], sm4to, [30]p, color, DJ/1.75)	Harper	(1944)	Rey, Hans A.	200-300	
Rey, Margret E.	Pretzel & the Puppies (1st {std}, sm4to, ibds, [30]p, color, DJ/1.00)	Harper	(1946)	Rey, Hans A.	140-200	
Rey, Hans A.	Raffy & the 9 Monkeys (1st, lg4to, 31p, ibds, color)	L: Chatto	1939	Rey, Hans A.	100-150	
Rey, Margret E.	Spotty (1st, sm4to, [30]p, ibds, p-o, color, DJ/1.75)	Harper	(1945)	Rey, Hans A.	80-125	
Rey, Hans A.	The Stars: New Way to See Them (1st, 4to, blue cl, 143p, 2-color, DJ/4.00)	Houghton	1952	Rey, Hans A.	60-90	
Rey, Hans A.	Tit for Tat (1st {std}, sq4to, ipcb, [30]p, color, DJ/1.50)	Harper	(1942)	Rey, Hans A.	150-225	
Waldstein, Henry F.	We Three Kings (1st {std}, ob4to, ibds, [23]p, color)	Harper	(1944)	Rey, Hans A.	80-120	
Rey, Hans A.	Zebrology (1st, ob8vo, wraps, color)	L: Chatto	[1937]	Rey, Hans A.	150-200	
Rey, Hans A.	Zozo (1st UK, 4to, stiff wraps)	L: Chatto	(1942)	Rey, Hans A.	220-300	
Dickens, Charles	David Copperfield (1st, 4to, gilt, 572p, 20 ticp, pep)	Westminster Pr	(1911)	Reynolds, Frank	170-250	
Dickens, Charles	Mr. Pickwick... (4to, red/gilt, 21 ticp)	(NY & Lon)	[1911]	Reynolds, Frank	170-250	
Dickens, Charles	Old Curiosity Shop (1st, 4to, 359p, teg, red/gilt, 21 ticp)	L: Hodder	1912	Reynolds, Frank	200-270	
Dickens, Charles	Posthumous Papers of the Pickwick Club (1st, 4to, gilt, 534p, 20 ticp)	Westminster Pr	(1912)	Reynolds, Frank	170-240	
Howard, Keble	Smiths of Surbiton (1st, 8vo, 300p, b/w)	L: Chapman/Hall	1906	Reynolds, Frank	50-80	*
Sapte, William	By the Way Ballads (1st, 8vo, 153p, b/w)	L: Sands	1901	Reynolds/Hassall	30-50	
Bunyan, John	Life & Death of Mr. Badman (1st UK, folio, gilt, 143p, teg, 12pl)	L: Heinemann	1900	Rhead Brothers	120-185	
Bunyan, John	Life & Death of Mr. Badman (1st, folio, ibds, teg, 12pl)	R.H. Russell	1900	Rhead Brothers	140-200	
Bunyan, John	Pilgrim's Progress (1st, folio, 184p, ibds, b/w)	Century	1898	Rhead Brothers	120-170	
Bunyan, John	Pilgrim's Progress (1st UK, folio, gilt, 201p)	L: A. Pearson	[1898]	Rhead Brothers	140-200	
Aesopus	Aesop's Fables (1st, 8vo, black/gilt, p-o, 194p, fp color)	Harper	(1927)	Rhead, Louis	50-80	
N/A	Arabian Nights' Entertainment (1st, 8vo, 430p, p-o, 4cp, pep)	Harper	(1916)	Rhead, Louis	50-80	
Conner, Ralph	Black Rock (1st, 8vo, tan cl, 322p, 8pl by...)	Revell	1900	Rhead, Louis	30-50	
Craik, Dinah	Fairy Book (1st, lg8vo, 403p, p-o, col frn, fp b/w)	Harper	(1922)	Rhead, Louis	40-60	*
Grimm Bros.	Fairy Tales (1st, 8vo, 443p, b/w)	Harper	(1917)	Rhead, Louis	40-60	*
Andersen, Hans C.	Fairy Tales and Wonder Stories (1st, 8vo, 442p, b/w, dep)	Harper	1914	Rhead, Louis	70-100	*
Swift, Jonathan	Gulliver's Travels (1st, 8vo, 350p, col frn, b/w, pep)	Harper	1913	Rhead, Louis	35-60	*
Spyri, Johanna	Heidi (1st, lg8vo, 333p, col frn, 23pl, p-o)	Harper	(1925)	Rhead, Louis	30-50	*
Morris, William	History of Over Sea (1st, 4to, 28p, ipcb, 1-color)	R.H. Russell	1902	Rhead, Louis	140-200	
Field, Eugene	Holy Cross (1st, 12mo, blue/gilt, 191p, teg, cep, cvr by...)	Stone & Kimball	1893	Rhead, Louis	50-80	
Tennyson, Alfred	Idylls of the King (1st, lg4to, [114]p, gilt, uncut, 24 woodcuts)	R.H. Russell	1898	Rhead, Louis	150-250	
Stevenson, Rbt. L.	Kidnapped (1st, lg8vo, gilt, 301p, p-o, col frn, b/w, pep)	Harper	(1921)	Rhead, Louis	30-60	*
Sudermann, Hermann	Magda (1st, 12mo, 161p, red/gilt, teg, uncut, cvr by...)	Lamson/Wolffe	1896	Rhead, Louis	80-120	
Brown, Alice	Meadow Grass (1st, 12mo, olive cl, 315p, cvr by...)	Copeland & Day	1895	Rhead, Louis	70-125	
Bible	Psalms of David (1st, sm4to, 284p, red/gilt, 16pl)	Revell	1900	Rhead, Louis	80-120	
Rhead, Louis	Robin Hood (1st, 8vo, black cl, 285p, p-o, col frn, b/w)	Harper	1912	Rhead, Louis	65-90	
Defoe, Daniel	Robinson Crusoe (1st, 8vo, black cl, p-o, 363p, col frn, b/w)	R.H. Russell	1900	Rhead, Louis	60-90	
Wyss, Johann D.	Swiss Family Robinson (1st, 8vo, 602p, red cl, b/w)	Harper	1909	Rhead, Louis	50-80	*
Lamb, Charles	Tales from Shakespeare (1st, 8vo, gilt, 366p, fp b/w)	Harper	(1918)	Rhead, Louis	40-70	
Cooper, James F.	The Deerslayer (1st, 8vo, black cl, p-o, 556p, 4cp)	Harper	(1926)	Rhead, Louis	40-60	
Hughes, Thomas	Tom Brown's School Days (1st, lg8vo, 376p, pict cl, b/w)	Harper	(1911)	Rhead, Louis	60-80	
Stevenson, Rbt. L.	Treasure Island (1st, 8vo, 288p, 35pl, pep)	Harper	(1915)	Rhead, Louis	40-60	*
Goudge, Elizabeth	Linnets and Valderians (1st AM {std}, 8vo, 290p, b/w, DJ/3.95)	Coward	(1964)	Ribbons, Ian	50-80	
Grimm Bros.	Hansel & Gretel (1st, sq12mo, [60]p, color)	McLoughlin	(1943)	Rice, A.	35-60	*
Russell, Walter	Bending of the Twig (1st, 8vo, 297p, teg, p-o, cvr by...)	Dodd	1903	Richards, Anna M.	80-140	
Richards, Anna M.	New Alice in the Old Wonderland (1st, 12mo, 309p, teg, red/gilt, b/w)	Lippincott	1895	Richards, Anna M.	160-220	
Farjeon, Eleanor	Bad Day for Martha (1st, lg8vo, 29p, ipcb, p-o, b/w)	L: Blackwell	[1928]	Richards, Eugenie	30-50	*
Bangs, John K.	Idiot at Home (1st, 12mo, 314p, teg, uncut, b/w pl)	Harper	1900	Richards, F.T.	60-90	

AUTHOR	TITLE	PUBLISHER	DATE	ARTIST	PRICE	LC
Bangs, John K.	The Idiot (1st, 12mo, 115p, gilt, 8pl)	Harper	1895	Richards, F.T.	60-100	
Crockett, Samuel R.	Red Axe (1st, 8vo, 421p, teg, gilt, 8pl)	L: Smith Elder	1898	Richards, Frank	25-40	
Van Doren, Mark	Dick & Tom in Town (1st, 8vo, 80p, col frn, b/w pl)	Macmillan	1932	Richards, George M.	50-80	R*
Mother Goose	Humpty Dumpty (1st, sq12mo, ibds)	Macmillan	1927	Richards, George M.	80-120	
Lindsay, Vachel	Johnny Appleseed (1st, 12mo, green cl, 144p, color, DJ/1.00)	Macmillan	1928	Richards, George M.	50-80	
Andersen, Hans C.	Steadfast Tin Soldier (1st, sq16mo, ibds, [42]p, color, pep)	Macmillan	1927	Richards, George M.	50-80	
Alcott, Louisa M.	Eight Cousins (1st, sm8vo, 292p, gilt, teg, 8pl)	Little/Brown	1904	Richards, Harriet R.	50-80	
Alcott, Louisa M.	Jack and Jill (1st, 8vo, green cl, 334p, 8pl)	Little/Brown	1905	Richards, Harriet R.	35-50	
Bailey, Alice W.	Roberta and her Brothers (1st, sm8vo, 310p, 4pl)	Little/Brown	1906	Richards, Harriet R.	25-40	*
Alcott, Louisa M.	Rose in Bloom (1st, 8vo, gilt, teg, 344p, 8pl)	Little/Brown	1904	Richards, Harriet R.	50-80	
Myers, Jane P.	Stories of Enchantment (1st, 12mo, 215p, b/w)	McClurg	1901	Richards, Harriet R.	25-40	
Ray, Anna C.	Ursula's Freshman (1st, 12mo, 303p, 6pl)	Little/Brown	1903	Richards, Harriet R.	30-50	
Levine, Rhoda	Quiet Story (1st {std}, sq24mo, [32]p, 1-color, cep, DJ/1.95)	Atheneum	1963	Richards, Rosalie	25-35	
Vredenburg, Edric	Golden Locks & Pretty Frocks (1st, 8vo, 136p, ibds, p-o, 12cp)	L: R. Tuck	[1914]	Richardson, Agnes	250-350	
Richardson, Emmeline	Doors... (1st, 8vo, 160p, 12cp)	L: Headley	[1909]	Richardson, Emmeline	140-200	*
Richardson, Emmeline	Songs of Near & Far Away (1st, 4to, tan cl, 80p, color)	L: Cassell	1900	Richardson, Emmeline	120-180	*
Richardson, Emmeline	Sun, Moon & Stars... (1st, 4to, green cl, unpag, b/w)	L: Bodley Head	1899	Richardson, Emmeline	120-185	
Kirkpatrick, Oliver	Naja the Snake & Mangus the Mongoose (1st {std}, ob4to, 40p, col, DJ/4.50)	Doubleday	(1970)	Richardson, Enid	30-50	*
Collodi, Carlo	Adventures of Pinocchio (8vo, 259p, p-o, 8cp)	Winston	(1920)	Richardson, F.	50-80	
Lear, Edward	Alphabet Book (1st, ob8vo, ibds, [55]p, color, pep)	Reilly/Britton	(1915)	Richardson, F.	120-165	
Richardson, Frederick	Book for Children (1st, ob4to, 107p, pep, p-o, 35cp, DJ/1.50)	Donohue	(1938)	Richardson, F.	90-120	
Richardson, Frederick	Book of Drawings (1st, folio, [106]p, grey bds, b/w)	Lakeside Pr.	1899	Richardson, F.	425-600	
Asbjørnsen, P.C.	East of the Sun, West o/t Moon (1st, 12mo, 218p, 9cp)	Row, Peterson	(1912)	Richardson, F.	70-100	
Harrison, Edith O.	Enchanted House (1st, sm8vo, 126p, 5cp)	McClurg	1913	Richardson, F.	70-120	
Andersen, Hans C.	Fairy Tales (1st, 8vo, p-o, 276p, black/gilt, pep, 4cp)	Winston	(1926)	Richardson, F.	50-80	
N/A	Gingerbread Boy (ob12mo, 32p, bds, p-o)	Winston	(1918)	Richardson, F.	40-60	
Green, Allen A.	Good Fairy & the Bunnies (1st, ob4to, ibds, 140p, 11cp)	McClurg	1906	Richardson, F.	200-300	
Faulkner, Georgene	Italian Fairy Tales (1st, 8vo, 95p, gilt, p-o, 5cp, pep)	Chi: Daughaday	(1916)	Richardson, F.	120-165	
Herben, Beatrice S.	Jack O'Health, Peg O'Joy (1st, 12mo, 39p, 10cp)	Scribner	(1921)	Richardson, F.	80-120	
Faulkner, Georgene	Little Peachling (1st, lg8vo, 91p, ibds, color, pep)	Volland	(1928)	Richardson, F.	70-130	
Mother Goose	Mother Goose (1st, lg4to, grey/gilt, [119]p, p-o, color)	Volland	(1915)	Richardson, F.	180-260	
Chambers, Robert	Mountain-Land (1st, lg8vo, ibds, 122p, 8cp, pep)	Appleton	1906	Richardson, F.	150-225	R
Various	Old Old Tales Retold (1st, ob4to, [108]p, blue/gilt, color, pep)	Volland	(1923)	Richardson, F.	120-185	
Collodi, Carlo	Pinocchio (1st, 8vo, 167p, gilt, p-o, 21cp, pep)	Winston	(1923)	Richardson, F.	100-165	*
Collodi, Carlo	Pinocchio (1st, lg8vo, green/gilt, 262p, p-o, 21cp, pep)	Winston	(1927)	Richardson, F.	120-200	
Baum, L. Frank	Queen Zixi of Ix (1st [1], lg8vo, 303p, green cl, 16cp)	Century	1905	Richardson, F.	400-600	
Stockton, Frank	Queen's Museum (1st, lg8vo, 219p, gilt, p-o, teg, 10cp, pep, SC)	Scribner	1906	Richardson, F.	150-220	
Lang, Andrew	Red Fairy Book (1st, 8vo, 386p, gilt, p-o, 4cp)	Winston	(1930)	Richardson, F.	40-70	
Olcott, F.J.	Red Indian Fairy Book (1st, 8vo, 338p, col frn, 5pl)	Houghton	1917	Richardson, F.	120-200	
Fry, John H.	Revolt Against Beauty (1st, 8vo, 212p, ibds, designs by...)	Putnam	1934	Richardson, F.	30-50	*
Faulkner, Georgene	Road to Enchantment (1st, 8vo, 312p, p-o, 8cp)	Sears	(1929)	Richardson, F.	100-160	
Faulkner, Georgene	Squeaky & the Scare Box (1st, 8vo, [32]p, ibds, 4cp, pep)	Grosset/Dunlap	(1931)	Richardson, F.	60-100	
Faulkner, Georgene	Story Lady's Christmas Stories (1st, 8vo, 93p, red cl, 5cp, pep)	Sears	(1927)	Richardson, F.	35-60	*
Faulkner, Georgene	Story Lady's Italian Tales (1st, 8vo, 95p, gilt, uncut, pep, 5cp)	Chi: Daughaday	(1916)	Richardson, F.	75-100	*
N/A	Wee Wee Woman (ob16mo, bds, p-o, 32p, fp color)	Winston	(1918)	Richardson, F.	45-70	
Faulkner, Georgene	White Elephant (1st, lg8vo, ibds, 92p, 10 fp color, pep)	Volland	(1929)	Richardson, F.	60-100	R
Hawthorne, Nathaniel	Wonder Book (1st, 8vo, p-o, 403p, red/gilt, 4cp, pep)	Winston	(1930)	Richardson, F.	40-60	
Forbush, Wm. B.	Wonder Book of Myths & Legends (lg8vo, 337p, blue cl, p-o, 3cp, 11 b/w)	Winston	(1928)	Richardson, F.	25-40	*
Stewart, Anna B.	Bibi the Baker's Horse (1st, 8vo, 190p, color, pep, DJ/2.00)	Lippincott	(1942)	Richter, Catherine	30-50	
Stewart, Anna B.	Two Young Corsicans (1st {std}, 8vo, 261p, color, DJ/2.00)	Lippincott	(1944)	Richter, Catherine	30-45	
Ruck-Pauquet, Gina	Little Hedgehog (1st AM, sm4to, [36]p, color, DJ/2.75)	Hastings House	(1959)	Richter, Marianne	40-65	
Richter, Mischa	Eric and Matilda (1st, 4to, ibds, 32p, 2-color, DJ/2.95)	Harper	(1967)	Richter, Mischa	25-45	
Krauss, Ruth	Great Duffy (1st, sm4to, ibds, [32]p, color, DJ/1.75)	Harper	(1946)	Richter, Mischa	100-165	
Holman, Felice	Solomon's Search (1st, 8vo, [58]p, color, DJ/4.50)	Grosset/Dunlap	(1970)	Richter, Mischa	25-45	*
Symonds, John	In the Key of Blue (1st, 8vo, 302p, blue/gilt, cvr by...)	L: E. Mathews	1893	Ricketts, Charles	200-300	
Shaw, George B.	St. Joan (1st, folio, ibds, 182p, p-o, teg, 16 ticp, 1/750)	L: Constable	(1924)	Ricketts, Charles	200-300	
Wilde, Oscar	Woman of No Importance (1st, 12mo, 102p, pink/gilt, cvr by...)	L: John Lane	1894	Ricketts, Charles	500-700	
Tomlins, William L.	Child's Garden of Song (1st, lg8vo, 72p, red/gilt, color)	McClurg	1895	Ricketts, Ella	120-185	
Burglon, Nora	Lost Island (1st, 8vo, 261p, col frn, b/w, DJ/2.00)	Winston	1939	Ried, James	30-50	
Akers, Floyd	Boy Fortune Hunters in Yucatan (1st, sm8vo, 343p, tan cl, frn by)	Reilly/Britton	(1910)	Rieman, G.A.	200-300	
Rietveld, Jane	ABC Molly (1st {std}, 8vo, 89p, b/w, DJ/3.00)	Norton	(1966)	Rietveld, Jane	20-35	
Rietveld, Jane	Monkey Island (1st, 4to, 54p, 1-color, DJ/2.75)	Viking	(1963)	Rietveld, Jane	30-45	*
Rietveld, Jane	Nicky's Bugle (1st, 4to, 56p, ibds, b/w, dep, DJ/2.00)	Viking	1947	Rietveld, Jane	40-65	
Rietveld, Jane	Wild Dog (1st, 8vo, 189p, b/w, DJ/2.50)	Wilcox/Follett	(1953)	Rietveld, Jane	20-35	*
Killilea, Marie	Wren (1st, lg8vo, 118p, b/w, DJ/3.00)	Dodd	(1954)	Riger, Bob	30-50	
Brett, Edna P.	Circus Day (1st, 12mo, p-o, ibds, 64p, 8 fp color)	Rand/McNally	1922	Riley, Garada C.	30-50	
Greene, Ward	Lady and the Tramp (1st, 8vo, 139p, b/w, DJ/2.95)	Simon/Schuster	(1953)	Rinaldi, Joe G.	150-220	*
Hawes, Charles B.	Dark Frigate (1st, 8vo, yellow cl, 247p, b/w, PPP, NM)	Atl. Monthly Pr.	(1923)	Ripley, A.L.	100-165	
Broun, Heywood	A Shepherd (1st, 8vo, [32]p, color, DJ/4.95)	Prentice-Hall	(1967)	Riswold, Gilbert	25-40	*
Freschet, Berniece	Owl & the Prairie Dog (1st, 8vo, [31]p, color, DJ/3.50)	Scribner	(1969)	Riswold, Gilbert	25-40	
Carlson, Natalie S.	School Bell in the Valley (1st {std}, sm4to, 124p, b/w, DJ/3.00)	Harcourt	(1963)	Riswold, Gilbert	20-30	
Johnson, Annabel	The Grizzly (1st, 8vo, 160p, fp b/w, DJ/3.50)	Harper	(1964)	Riswold, Gilbert	60-90	R*
Fisher, Aileen	Up, Up the Mountain (1st, 4to, [32]p, fp color, DJ/3.95)	Crowell	(1968)	Riswold, Gilbert	30-50	
Donaldson, Lois	Runzel-Punzel (1st, lg8vo, yellow cl, p-o, 16p, fp color, cep)	Whitman	1933	Ritter, Mathilde	50-80	
Young, Louise	Best Foot Forward (1st, lg ob8vo, 32p, fp 3-color, DJ/3.50)	Van Nostrand	(1968)	Rivoli, Mario	40-65	*
Wersba, Barbara	Do Tigers Ever Bite Kings? (1st {std}, lg8vo, [30]p, fp color, DJ/3.50)	Atheneum	1966	Rivoli, Mario	30-45	
Wersba, Barbara	Song for Clowns (1st {std}, lg8vo, 101p, b/w, DJ/3.75)	Atheneum	1965	Rivoli, Mario	25-40	
Collodi, Carlo	Pinocchio (1st, folio, 116p, ibds, color, DGB)	Golden Press	(1963)	Rizzato, Sergio	60-90	

AUTHOR	TITLE	PUBLISHER	DATE	ARTIST	PRICE	LC
Kroeber, Theodora	Ishi, Last of his Tribe (1st, 8vo, 209p, b/w, pep, DJ/3.95)	Parnassus Press	(1964)	Robbins, Ruth	30-50	
Aldridge, Josephine	Penny and a Periwinkle (1st {std}, 4to, [30]p, color, pep, DJ/2.95)	Parnassus Press	(1961)	Robbins, Ruth	30-50	
Fisher, Anne B.	Stories California Indians Told (1st, lg8vo, 109p, fp 1-color, DJ/2.95)	Parnassus Press	(1957)	Robbins, Ruth	25-45	
Le Guin, Ursula K.	Wizard of Earthsea (1st, 8vo, 205p, fp b/w, cep, DJ/3.95)	Parnassus Press	(1968)	Robbins, Ruth	150-225	
Walter, Eleanor D.	Bugs (1st, lg4to, wraps, [16]p, color)	Whitman	1931	Roberts, Helen M.	40-60	
Lorimer, D.& E.	Persian Tales (1st, 8vo, gilt, 354p, 16cp, 8pl)	L: Macmillan	1919	Roberts, Hilda	45-70	
Farrow, George E.	Mysterious Voyage (1st, 12mo, 160p, gilt, 32 illus)	L: Partridge	[1910]	Roberts, K.M.	55-80	*
Harker, L. Allen	Romance of the Nursery (1st, 8vo, 333p, teg, red/gilt, uncut, 8pl)	L: John Lane	1903	Roberts, Katharine	30-50	
Robertson, Lilian	Runaway Rocking Horse (1st, ob4to, [32]p, 3-color, DJ/2.00)	Harcourt	(1948)	Robertson, Lillian	60-100	*
Moore, Ida C.	Lucky Orphan (1st, 8vo, 122p, fp b/w, pep, DJ/2.00)	Scribner	(1947)	Robertson, Primrose	20-30	
Robertson, W.G.	Baby's Day Book (1st, lg8vo, 127p, grey cl, col frn, b/w)	L: John Lane	1908	Robertson, W.G.	170-240	
Robertson, W.G.	Gold, Frankincense & Myrrh (1st, 4to, blue cl, 152p, 12cp)	L: John Lane	1907	Robertson, W.G.	200-300	
Scott-Gatty, Alfred	I Wonder Why? (1st, lg4to, 72p, bds, p-o, 16 ticp)	L: Collins	1920	Robertson, W.G.	125-200	
Chapman, E.R.	Little Child's Wreath (1st, 16mo, 70p, b/w)	L: John Lane	1904	Robertson, W.G.	40-65	
Robertson, W.G.	Masque of May Morning (1st, 4to, green cl, 62p, 12cp)	L: John Lane	1904	Robertson, W.G.	250-350	
Chesterton, G.K.	Napoleon of Notting Hill (1st, 8vo, uncut, 301p, 8pl)	L: John Lane	1904	Robertson, W.G.	160-225	
Cheatham, Kitty	Nursery Garland (1st, lg4to, ibds, 171p, 14cp)	Schirmer	(1917)	Robertson, W.G.	180-250	
N/A	Old English Songs & Dances (1st, sm folio, [62]p, ibds, color)	L: Longmans	1902	Robertson, W.G.	350-500	
N/A	Old English Songs & Dances (folio, ibds, color)	L: Hamish	[1910]	Robertson, W.G.	250-350	
Ewing, Juliana H.	Old Fashioned Fairy Tales (1st, 12mo, 125p, 8cp, pep)	L: G. Bell	(1919)	Robertson, W.G.	200-300	
Robertson, W.G.	Pan's Garden (1st, 8vo, 530p, gilt, b/w woodcuts)	L: Macmillan	1912	Robertson, W.G.	140-200	
Robertson, W.G.	Pinkie and the Fairies (1st, 12mo, 146p, fp b/w)	L: Heinemann	1909	Robertson, W.G.	180-260	
Ollivant, Alfred	Redcoat Captain (1st, 8vo, 203p, fp b/w)	L: J. Murray	1907	Robertson, W.G.	45-70	
Robertson, W.G.	Slippers of Cinderella (1st, 12mo, 130p)	L: Heinemann	1919	Robertson, W.G.	70-100	*
Grahame, Kenneth	Wind in the Willows (1st AM, 8vo, green/gilt, 302p, teg, frn by...)	Scribner	1908	Robertson, W.G.	600-800	
Grahame, Kenneth	Wind in the Willows (1st, sm8vo, 302p, teg, blue/gilt, frn by)	L: Methuen	(1908)	Robertson, W.G.	1200-2000	R
Robertson, W.G.	Year of Songs for a Baby in a Garden (1st, 8vo, 111p, fp b/w)	L: John Lane	1906	Robertson, W.G.	200-300	
Shepard, Odell	Pedlar's Progress (1st, lg8vo, 546p, 5pl, DJ/3.75)	Little/Brown	1937	Robillard, Conrad	30-50	
Andersen, Hans C.	Andersen in German (1st, 8vo, 219p, beige cl, b/w)	L: J.M. Dent	1902	Robinson Brothers	225-325	
Andersen, Hans C.	Fairy Tales (1st, 12mo, 539p, teg, uncut, col frn, b/w, pep)	L: Dent	1899	Robinson Brothers	200-300	
Andersen, Hans C.	Fairy Tales (1st {this fmt}, 16mo, 312p, 12 b/w)	L: Dent	1901	Robinson Brothers	120-180	*
Sage, Betty	Rhymes of If & Why (1st, 4to, 31p, ibds, 4cp)	Duffield	1927	Robinson, Boardman	80-125	
Various	Adventures of Odysseus (1st, 8vo, 227p, green/gilt, teg, 13pl)	Dutton	(1900)	Robinson, Charles	165-220	
Aesopus	Aesop's Fables (1st {1st bk}, 16mo, [60]p, red/gilt, teg, b/w, pep)	L: J.M. Dent	1895	Robinson, Charles	170-240	
Carroll, Lewis	Alice in Wonderland (1st, sm4to, teg, gilt, 179p, 8cp, pep)	L: Cassell	(1907)	Robinson, Charles	500-750	
Carroll, Lewis	Alice in Wonderland (lg8vo, [new ed.], 8cp)	L: Cassell	1928	Robinson, Charles	140-200	
Carrington, Edith	Animals in the Wrong Places (1st, 24mo, 83p, 11 fp b/w)	L: Bell	1896	Robinson, Charles	200-300	*
Copeland, Walter	Awful Airship (1st, ob16mo, 62p, 30cp)	L: Blackie	[1906]	Robinson, Charles	225-325	
Pope, Jessie	Babes & Beasts (1st, 8vo, ibds, unpag, color)	L: Blackie	[1912]	Robinson, Charles	180-270	*
Pope, Jessie	Babes & Birds (1st AM, 8vo, ibds, unpag, 17cp)	Caldwell	(1910)	Robinson, Charles	180-270	
Pope, Jessie	Babes & Birds (1st, 8vo, ibds, unpag, 17cp)	L: Blackie	[1910]	Robinson, Charles	200-300	
Copeland, Walter	Babes & Blossoms (1st AM, sm8vo, ipcb, 16cp)	Caldwell	(1908)	Robinson, Charles	200-300	
Copeland, Walter	Babes & Blossoms (1st, 8vo, ibds, [66]p, 16cp, pep)	L: Blackie	(1908)	Robinson, Charles	250-400	
Pope, Jessie	Babes and Beasts (1st AM, 8vo, ibds, unpag, color)	Caldwell	(1912)	Robinson, Charles	180-250	
Pope, Jessie	Baby Scouts (1st, ob 16mo, unpag)	L: Blackie	[1911]	Robinson, Charles	150-200	*
Bridgman, Clare	Bairn's Coronation Book (1st, 16mo, 120p, 44 fp color, pep)	L: Dent	[1902]	Robinson, Charles	200-300	
France, Anatole	Bee, Princess of the Dwarfs (1st, 8vo, gilt, [128]p, teg, 17 ticp)	L: Dent	1912	Robinson, Charles	250-400	
Jerrold, Walter	Big Book of Fables (1st, lg8vo, 293p, teg, red cl, 28cp, pep)	L: Blackie	1912	Robinson, Charles	300-500	
Jerrold, Walter	Big Book of Fairy Tales (1st AM, 4to, gilt, teg, 344p, 12cp, pep)	Dodge	[1911]	Robinson, Charles	300-500	
Jerrold, Walter	Big Book of Fairy Tales (1st, 4to, 344p, gilt, AEG, 12cp)	L: Blackie	1911	Robinson, Charles	350-500	
Jerrold, Walter	Big Book of Nursery Rhymes (1st, 4to, red/gilt, 320p, AEG, 18cp)	L: Blackie	[1903]	Robinson, Charles	350-500	
Robinson, Charles	Black Bunnies (1st, 16mo, [56]p, blue/gilt, fp silhouettes, pep)	L: Blackie	[1907]	Robinson, Charles	400-650	
Copeland, Walter	Black Cat Book (1st, lg8vo, [48]p, ipcb, p-o, fp 1-color)	L: Blackie	[1905]	Robinson, Charles	450-650	
Copeland, Walter	Black Cat Book (1st AM, 8vo, unpag, p-o, ibds, 1-color)	Dodge	(1905)	Robinson, Charles	500-700	
Robinson, Charles	Black Doggies (16mo, red cloth, silhouettes)	L: Blackie	[1907]	Robinson, Charles	300-425	
Bridgman, Clare	Book of Days for Little Ones (1st, 16mo, 120p, 2-color, pep)	L: Dent	1901	Robinson, Charles	200-300	
Bridgman, Clare	Book of Shops (1st, 16mo, 120p, 2-color, pep)	L: Dent	1902	Robinson, Charles	200-300	
Copeland, Walter	Book of the Zoo (1st, 16mo, 120p, 3-color, pep)	L: Dent	1902	Robinson, Charles	200-300	
Copeland, Walter	Bouncing Babies (ob12mo, green cl, color, pep)	L: J.M. Dent	(1906)	Robinson, Charles	450-600	
Stables, Gordon	Boy's Book of Battleships (lg4to, ibds, 64p, 16 color)	L: Blackie	[1909]	Robinson, Charles	125-200	
Stevenson, Alice M.	Bridget's Fairies (1st, sm8vo, p-o, 131p, b/w)	L: R.T.S.	(1919)	Robinson, Charles	150-240	
Arkwright, Ruth	Brownikins and Other Fancies (1st, 4to, p-o, [82]p, 5 ticp, pep)	L: Wells/Gard.	[1910]	Robinson, Charles	300-425	
Cule, William E.	Child Voices (1st, 8vo, 139p)	L: A. Melrose	1899	Robinson, Charles	60-100	*
Setoun, Gabriel	Child World (1st, 12mo, AEG, gilt, 174p, uncut, 14pl)	L: John Lane	1896	Robinson, Charles	150-220	
Morris, Alice T.	Child's Book of Empire (1st, 4to, unpag)	L: Blackie	[1914]	Robinson, Charles	170-240	*
Sharp, Evelyn	Child's Christmas (1st, lg8vo, 227p, orange/gilt, AEG, 38 color)	L: Blackie	(1906)	Robinson, Charles	400-600	
Sharp, Evelyn	Child's Christmas (1st AM, lg8vo, teg, gilt, 227p, color, pep)	Caldwell	[1907]	Robinson, Charles	300-500	
Stevenson, Rbt. L.	Child's Garden of Verses (1st UK, 8vo, 136p, AEG, gilt, b/w)	L: John Lane	1895	Robinson, Charles	200-300	
Stevenson, Rbt. L.	Child's Garden of Verses (1st, sm8vo, 137p, teg, uncut, gilt, b/w)	Scribner/Lane	1895	Robinson, Charles	250-350	R
Stevenson, Rbt. L.	Child's Garden of Verses (1st {color ed.}, 8vo, gilt, teg, 8cp, pep)	L: Bodley Head	(1908)	Robinson, Charles	200-280	
Rhys, Grace (ed.)	Children's Garland of Verse (1st, 8vo, 296p, 8cp)	L: J.M. Dent	1921	Robinson, Charles	150-220	*
Wallis, I. Henry	Cloud Kingdom (1st, 12mo, green/gilt, 174p, teg, 18pl, pep)	L: John Lane	(1905)	Robinson, Charles	200-300	
Marc, Elizabeth	Doris & David All Alone (1st, 8vo, 259p, red/gilt, 4cp, pep)	L: Hutchinson	[1922]	Robinson, Charles	90-120	
Martinengo-Cesaresco	Fairies' Fountain (1st, 8vo, 268p, blue/gilt, col frn, 15pl)	L: A. Fairbairns	1908	Robinson, Charles	200-285	
Grimm Bros.	Fairy Tales (1st, 8vo, 356p, gilt, p-o, pep, 4cp)	L: Nister	[1910]	Robinson, Charles	220-315	
Perrault, Charles	Fairy Tales (1st, 12mo, brown/gilt, p-o, 128p, 8cp)	L: Dent	(1913)	Robinson, Charles	160-225	
Copeland, Walter	Farm Book (1st, 16mo, 120p, 3-color, pep)	Dent/Dutton	1901	Robinson, Charles	200-300	
Stevenson, John G.	Father Time Stories (1st, 8vo, ibds, 154p, 3cp, pep)	L: R.T.S.	(1921)	Robinson, Charles	140-200	

AUTHOR	TITLE	PUBLISHER	DATE	ARTIST	PRICE	LC
Jerrold, Douglas W.	Fireside Saints (1st, 16mo, teg, 109p, gilt, col frn, 1-color, pep)	L: Blackie	1904	Robinson, Charles	80-120	
Mord, W.	Four Champions of Great Britain & Ireland (1st, 4to, ibds, 16cp)	L: T.F. Unwin	[1905]	Robinson, Charles	250-350	
Handasyde, Emily	Four Gardens (1st AM, 8vo, 161p, purple/gilt, 8cp, pep)	Lippincott	1912	Robinson, Charles	90-120	
Heide, Florence P.	Giants are Very Brave People (1st, sm4to, [42]p, fp color, dep, DJ/3.50)	Parents Mag. Pr.	(1970)	Robinson, Charles	25-40	
Austin, Phyllis	Goldfish Bowl (1st, 8vo, gilt, 254p, 4cp)	L: Hutchinson	[1928]	Robinson, Charles	100-170	
Wilde, Oscar	Happy Prince (1st AM, 4to, 134p, gilt, teg, 12 ticp, pep)	Putnam	(1913)	Robinson, Charles	500-700	
Wilde, Oscar	Happy Prince (1st, 4to, teg, gilt, 134p, 12 ticp, dep)	L: Duckworth	(1913)	Robinson, Charles	675-900	
Bell, John J.	Jack of All Trades (1st, 4to, brown cl, 64p, 32cp)	L: John Lane	1900	Robinson, Charles	200-300	
MacGregor, Barrington	King Longbeard (1st, 8vo, 262p, blue/gilt, 12 fp b/w)	L: John Lane	1898	Robinson, Charles	200-280	
Rands, William B.	Lilliput Lyrics (1st, 12mo, 330p, gilt, col frn, b/w, pep)	L: John Lane	1899	Robinson, Charles	100-160	
Tynan, Katharine	Little Book of Courtesies (1st, 12mo, teg, 57p, gilt, col frn)	L: Dent	1906	Robinson, Charles	80-120	
Dearmer, Percy	Little Lives of the Saints (1st, 12mo, 144p, green/gilt, fp b/w, dep)	L: Wells/Gard.	1900	Robinson, Charles	80-120	*
Field, Eugene	Lullaby Land (1st, 8vo, teg, 229p, green/gilt, b/w)	Scribner	1897	Robinson, Charles	200-300	
Field, Eugene	Lullaby Land (1st UK, sm8vo, 229p, gilt, AEG, b/w)	L: John Lane	1898	Robinson, Charles	200-300	
Copeland, Walter	Mad Motor (1st, ob24mo, [60]p, ibds, fp color, pep)	L: Blackie	(1906)	Robinson, Charles	200-300	
Lowry, H.D.	Make-Believe (1st, 8vo, 177p, teg, green/gilt, b/w)	L: John Lane	1896	Robinson, Charles	100-160	
Fielding-Hall, H.	Margaret's Book (1st AM, 4to, 283p, teg, gilt, 12 ticp, pep)	Stokes	[1913]	Robinson, Charles	250-350	
Fielding-Hall, H.	Margaret's Book (1st, 4to, AEG, red/gilt, 283p, 12 ticp, pep)	L: Hutchinson	(1913)	Robinson, Charles	250-400	
Coleridge, Christabel	Minstrel Dick (1st, 8vo, gilt, 288p, 3pl & cvr by...)	L: Wells/Gard.	1896	Robinson, Charles	100-165	
Mother Goose	Mother Goose Nursery Rhymes (1st, 8vo, 159p)	L: Collins	[1928]	Robinson, Charles	80-120	*
Burn, John H.	Mother's Book of Song (1st, 8vo, 216p, blue/gilt, teg, b/w)	L: Wells/Gard.	(1902)	Robinson, Charles	150-220	
Bell, John J.	New Noah's Ark (1st, 4to, brown cl, 64p, color)	L: John Lane	1899	Robinson, Charles	350-500	
Jerrold, Walter	Nonsense Nonsense! (1st, 4to, [68]p, ibds, 30cp)	L: Blackie	1902	Robinson, Charles	300-450	
Milne, A.A.	Once On a Time (1st, 12mo, gilt, 269p, col frn, pep)	L: Hodder	[1925]	Robinson, Charles	180-250	
Milne, A.A.	Once On a Time (1st AM, sm8vo, 358p, gilt, col frn, pep)	Putnam	1922	Robinson, Charles	150-225	
Thurston, Ernest T.	Open Window (1st, lg8vo, 287p, blue/gilt, 4cp, pep)	L: Chapman	1913	Robinson, Charles	120-175	
Castle, A.& E.	Our Sentimental Garden (1st AM, 8vo, gilt, 304p, 8 ticp, pep)	Lippincott	1914	Robinson, Charles	140-200	
Castle, A.& E.	Our Sentimental Garden (1st, lg8vo, 304p, gilt, 8 ticp, pep)	L: Heinemann	(1914)	Robinson, Charles	160-250	
Stacpoole, H.D.	Pierrette (1st, 8vo, 294p, teg, fp b/w)	L: John Lane	1900	Robinson, Charles	150-225	
N/A	Prince Ahmed & the Fairy Perie Banou (1st, 8vo, 118p, bds, p-o, 5cp)	L: Gay/Hancock	(1915)	Robinson, Charles	180-250	
Nella	Prince Babillon (1st, 8vo, 131p, uncut, gilt, color)	Kennerley	[1910]	Robinson, Charles	160-225	
Spicer, Marion D.	Rainbows (1st, 12mo, 41p, white cl, p-o, b/w, pep)	L: A. Melrose	1913	Robinson, Charles	100-165	
Canton, William	Reign of King Herla (1st, 8vo, AEG, 367p, gilt, col frn, b/w)	L: J.M. Dent	(1900)	Robinson, Charles	150-225	
Jerrold, Walter	Reign of King Oberon (1st, sm8vo, 338p, AEG, col frn, pep)	L: Dent	(1902)	Robinson, Charles	200-300	
Gibbon, James M.	Reign of Old King Cole (8vo, pict cl, 338p)	Dutton	(1911)	Robinson, Charles	150-225	
Irving, Washington	Rip Van Winkle (lg8vo, 68p, col frn, cp)	Stokes	[1915]	Robinson, Charles	100-165	*
Jerrold, Clare	Road, Rail & Sea (1st, 4to, ibds, [80]p, 10cp)	L: Blackie	[1906]	Robinson, Charles	250-400	
Omar Khayyam	Rubaiyat of Omar Khayyam (32mo, leather, teg, 86p, 3 ticp)	L: Collins	[1910]	Robinson, Charles	75-100	
Omar Khayyam	Rubaiyat of Omar Khayyam (1st, 4to, 56p, 4 ticp)	L: Collins	(1929)	Robinson, Charles	120-200	*
Unknown	Rule Britannia (4to, ibds, [66]p, 8 fp color)	L: Hodder	[1916]	Robinson, Charles	225-350	
Radcliffe, Winifred	Saint's Garden (1st, sm8vo, 150p, green/gilt, 8pl)	L: SPCK	1927	Robinson, Charles	120-185	
Burnett, Frances H.	Secret Garden (1st, 8vo, green/gilt, 306p, 8cp, pep)	L: Heinemann	1911	Robinson, Charles	450-650	
Shelley, Percy B.	Sensitive Plant (1st AM, 4to, 127p, gilt, teg, 18 ticp)	Heinemann/Lipp.	[1911]	Robinson, Charles	300-450	
Bridgman, Clare	Shopping Day (1st, 16mo, 120p, color, pep)	Dent/Dutton	1902	Robinson, Charles	150-225	
Baring-Gould, Sabine	Siegfried (1st, 8vo, red/gilt, 351p, col frn, 10 fp b/w)	L: Dean	1904	Robinson, Charles	140-225	
Robinson, Charles	Silly Submarine (1st, ob16mo, ibds, 30 fp color, pep)	L: Blackie	[1906]	Robinson, Charles	200-320	
Fouque, La Motte	Sintram and his Companions (1st, 12mo, 12pl)	L: Dent	1900	Robinson, Charles	160-240	
Unknown	Soldiers of the King (4to, [66]p, ibds, 8cp)	L: Hodder	[1916]	Robinson, Charles	225-350	
Shakespeare, Wm.	Songs & Sonnets (1st AM, 4to, 240p, blue/gilt, 12 ticp, pep)	McKay	[1915]	Robinson, Charles	250-400	
Shakespeare, Wm.	Songs & Sonnets (1st, lg8vo, 240p, blue/gilt, 12 ticp, pep)	L: Duckworth	(1915)	Robinson, Charles	350-500	
Maunder, Irene	Songs of Happy Children (12mo, 110p, teg, b/w)	L: Clark	[1908]	Robinson, Charles	60-90	
Blake, William	Songs of Innocence (1st, 12mo, 56p, teg, gilt, 7cp)	L: Dent	(1911)	Robinson, Charles	140-200	
Matheson, Annie	Songs of Love & Praise (1st, 8vo, unpag, gilt, designs by...)	L: J.M. Dent	1907	Robinson, Charles	75-100	*
Sharp, Evelyn	Story of the Weathercock (1st AM, 4to, 258p, teg, red/gilt, 16cp)	Caldwell	[1907]	Robinson, Charles	200-300	
Sharp, Evelyn	Story of the Weathercock (1st, 4to, 258p, red/gilt, AEG, 16cp, pep)	L: Blackie	(1907)	Robinson, Charles	200-300	
Garstin, Norman	Suitors of Aprille (1st, 12mo, teg, 212p, uncut, 19pl)	L: John Lane	1900	Robinson, Charles	120-200	
Gullick, M.E.	Teddy's Year with the Fairies (1st, lg8vo, 176p, ibds, p-o, 3cp, pep)	L: R.T.S.	(1920)	Robinson, Charles	200-300	
Robinson, Charles	Ten Little Babies (sm4to, ibds, pep, color)	L: SPCK	[1905]	Robinson, Charles	500-700	
Meynell, Alice	The Children (1st, 12mo, gilt, 96p, title page by...)	L: John Lane	1897	Robinson, Charles	80-120	
Curry, Jane L.	The Daybreakers (1st {std}, 8vo, 191p, b/w, DJ/4.95)	Harcourt	(1970)	Robinson, Charles	25-40	
Minnion, W.J.	Topsy Turvey (1st, 4to, 72p, bds, gilt, 5 fp 2-color)	L: Connoisseur	1913	Robinson, Charles	300-400	
Syrett, Netta	Vanishing Princess (1st, 8vo, blue cl, 93p, 10pl)	L: D. Nutt	(1910)	Robinson, Charles	120-180	*
Girvin/Cosens	Wee Men (1st, 12mo, p-o, 160p, 4cp)	L: Hutchinson	[1923]	Robinson, Charles	160-220	
Sharp, Evelyn	What Happened at Christmas (1st, 4to, unpag)	L: Blackie	[1915]	Robinson, Charles	125-200	*
Dunbar, Jennie	Young Hopeful (1st, 8vo, 78p, blue/gilt, b/w, pep)	L: H. Jenkins	1932	Robinson, Charles	90-120	*
Norris, Gunilla	Good Morrow (1st {std}, 8vo, 92p, b/w, DJ/3.75)	Atheneum	1969	Robinson, Chas.	20-35	
Maeterlinck, Maurice	Blue Bird (1st AM, 4to, teg, blue/gilt, 211p, 25 ticp)	Dodd	1911	Robinson, F. Cayley	120-200	
Hodgkin, Lucy V.	Book of Quaker Saints (1st, 8vo, 548p, 7 ticp, pep)	L: Foulis	1917	Robinson, F. Cayley	60-100	
Trine, Ralph W.	In Tune with the Infinite (1st, 8vo, ibds, 254p, 8 ticp)	L: Foulis	(1926)	Robinson, F. Cayley	80-120	*
Webling, Peggy	Saints & their Stories (1st, 8vo, grey cl, 312p, 8cp, pep)	L: J. Nisbet	[1919]	Robinson, F. Cayley	80-120	
Chesterton, G.K.	St. Francis of Assisi (1st, sm8vo, 185p, brown/gilt, p-o, 7 ticp)	L: Hodder	[1926]	Robinson, F. Cayley	80-120	
Carroll, Lewis	Alice in Wonderland (1st, 8vo, 201p, blue/gilt, 6cp)	L: C.H. Kelly	(1916)	Robinson, Gordon	150-225	
Carroll, Lewis	Alice in Wonderland (1st AM, lg8vo, p-o, 48p, 4cp)	NY: S. Gabriel	(1916)	Robinson, Gordon	100-170	*
Andersen, Hans C.	Fairy Tales (1st, 8vo, p-o, 513p, 12cp)	L: Chambers	[1917]	Robinson, Gordon	140-200	
Byron, May	Little Brown Rooster (1st, sm4to, ipcb, color, pep)	Doran	(1922)	Robinson, Gordon	40-70	
Byron, May	Little Brown Rooster (1st, lg8vo, p-o, 60p, orange cl, 6cp, pep)	NY: Nelson	1928	Robinson, Gordon	60-100	
N/A	Little Snow Drop (1st, 8vo, 10p, wraps, 4 fp color)	Sam Gabriel	1911	Robinson, Gordon	30-50	
Malone, Henry	Lost Fairy Tales (1st, 8vo, gilt, 288p, 8cp)	L: C.H. Kelly	(1915)	Robinson, Gordon	80-125	

AUTHOR	TITLE	PUBLISHER	DATE	ARTIST	PRICE	LC
Leigh, Mabel C.	Love Songs & Verses (1st, sm4to, 65p, teg, 4pl)	L: Humphreys	1913	Robinson, Gordon	60-100	
N/A	Sleeping Beauty (1st, 8vo, [6]p, linen wraps, color)	Sam Gabriel	(1908)	Robinson, Gordon	70-100	
Perrault, Charles	Tom Thumb (1st AM, 8vo, 10p, wraps, 4 fp color)	Sam Gabriel	(1911)	Robinson, Gordon	25-45	
Robinson, William W.	Elephants (1st {std}, lg4to, 43p, b/w, DJ/1.75)	Harper	1935	Robinson, Irene	30-50	
Dunne, John W.	Jumping Lions of Borneo (1st AM, lg4to, 60p, dp b/w, pep, DJ)	Henry Holt & Co.	(1938)	Robinson, Irene	30-45	
Emerson, Caroline	Magic Tunnel (1st [this pub.], 8vo, 122p, b/w, DJ)	Four Winds Pr.	(1964)	Robinson, Jerry	40-65	
DeTrevino, Elizabeth	About Bellamy (1st {std}, 8vo, 214p, b/w, uncut, DJ/2.00)	Harper	(1940)	Robinson, Jessie	20-35	*
DeJong, Meindert	Cat that Walked a Week (1st {std}, 8vo, grey cl, 148p, 13 fp bw, DJ/2.00)	Harper	1943	Robinson, Jessie	40-65	
Weil, Ann Y.	My Dear Patsy (1st {std}, 8vo, 315p, b/w, DJ/2.00)	Bobbs-Merrill	(1941)	Robinson, Jessie	25-45	*
Weil, Ann Y.	Very First Day (1st, sm8vo, red cl, [32]p, 1-color, DJ/1.50)	Appleton-Century	(1946)	Robinson, Jessie	25-45	
Robinson, Mary Y.	Songs of the Trees (1st, lg4to, 125p, ibds, 2-color)	Bobbs-Merrill	(1903)	Robinson, Mary Y.	140-200	
Smith, Gertrude	Little Girl & Phillip (1st, lg sq8vo, 187p, 8cp)	Harper	1902	Robinson, Rachael	50-80	*
Sill, Louise M.	Sunnyfield (1st, 8vo, 228p, 4pl)	Harper	1909	Robinson, Rachael	30-50	
Jackson, Gabrielle	Wee Winkles & her Friends (1st, 8vo, 155p, 8pl)	Harper	1907	Robinson, Rachael	35-50	
Carroll, Lewis	Alice in Wonderland (8vo, 190p, red/gilt, 30pl by...)	L: Collins	[1910]	Robinson, Thomas H.	120-180	
Haydon, Arthur L.	Book of Robin Hood (8vo, green cl, 263p, 12cp)	L: Warne	[1931]	Robinson, Thomas H.	60-95	
Macy, S.B.	Book of the Kingdom (1st, lg8vo, 388p, gilt, col frn, fp b/w)	L: Longmans	1912	Robinson, Thomas H.	80-120	*
Canton, William	Child's Book of Saints (1st, 8vo, 257p, teg, col frn, 19 fp b/w)	L: J.M. Dent	1898	Robinson, Thomas H.	70-100	*
Gaskell, Mrs.	Cranford (1st, sm8vo, 316p, blue/gilt, AEG, b/w)	L: Bliss Sands	1896	Robinson, Thomas H.	40-60	*
N/A	Fairy Tales/Arabian Nights (1st, 12mo, 287p, col frn, 12pl)	L: Dent	1899	Robinson, Thomas H.	75-100	*
Oxenham, Elsie J.	Goblin Island (1st, 8vo, 316p, AEG, p-o, col frn, pep)	L: Collins	[1907]	Robinson, Thomas H.	150-225	
Creswick, Paul	Hastings the Pirate (1st, 8vo, 303p, purple cl, 8pl)	Nister/Dutton	(1902)	Robinson, Thomas H.	55-80	*
Boult, Katharine F.	Heroes of the Norselands (1st, 8vo, 211p, 9pl)	L: Dent	1903	Robinson, Thomas H.	55-80	*
Creswick, Paul	In Alfred's Days (sm8vo, teg, gilt, uncut, 304p, 18pl)	L: Nister	[1900]	Robinson, Thomas H.	50-80	
Fenn, Geo. Manville	King's Sons (1st, 8vo, blue cl, 48p, 4pl)	L: Nister	1901	Robinson, Thomas H.	40-65	*
Sylva, Carmen	Legends from River & Mountain (1st, 8vo, blue/gilt, teg, 328p, fp b/w)	L: G. Allen	1896	Robinson, Thomas H.	90-120	
Pollard, Eliza F.	Little Chief (1st, sm8vo, teg, uncut, 236p, 6pl)	L: Nister	(1901)	Robinson, Thomas H.	35-60	
Rinder, Frank	Old World Japan (1st, 8vo, blue/gilt, teg, uncut, 195p, fp b/w, pep)	L: G. Allen	1895	Robinson, Thomas H.	100-180	
Creswick, Paul	Robin Hood & his Adventures (1st, 8vo, gilt, 312p, 4cp, pep)	Nister/Dutton	(1902)	Robinson, Thomas H.	60-90	
Omar Khayyam	Rubaiyat of Omar Khayyam (1st, 12mo, 147p, AEG, blue/gilt, 5 fp color)	Nister/Dutton	[1907]	Robinson, Thomas H.	80-120	
Hawthorne, Nathaniel	Scarlet Letter (1st, 8vo, AEG, blue bds, 8pl)	L: Bliss Sands	1897	Robinson, Thomas H.	70-120	
Sterne, Laurence	Sentimental Journey/France & Italy (1st, 12mo, 442p, blue/gilt, b/w, AEG)	L: Bliss Sands	1897	Robinson, Thomas H.	75-100	
Wyss, Johann D.	Swiss Family Robinson (1st AM, 4to, red/gilt, 25 ticp)	Hodder	[1913]	Robinson, Thomas H.	100-160	
Wyss, Johann D.	Swiss Family Robinson (1st, sm4to, 431p, teg, red/gilt, 25 ticp)	L: H. Milford	[1913]	Robinson, Thomas H.	120-180	
Wyss, Johann D.	Swiss Family Robinson (8vo, 436p, color, pep)	Garden City	(1931)	Robinson, Thomas H.	35-60	*
Marsh, Lewis	Tales of the Homeland (1st, 8vo, buckram, 199p, 6cp)	L: Hodder	[1911]	Robinson, Thomas H.	75-100	*
Kingsley, Charles	The Heroes (1st, 8vo, blue/gilt, AEG, 296p, 6cp, pep)	L: Nister	[1903]	Robinson, Thomas H.	80-120	
Spenser, Edmund	Una & Red Cross Knight (1st, 8vo, teg, 264p, ipcb, col frn)	L: J.M. Dent	1905	Robinson, Thomas H.	70-125	
Creswick, Paul	Under the Black Raven (1st, 8vo, 303p, teg, b/w pl)	Nister/Dutton	[1901]	Robinson, Thomas H.	55-80	*
Aguilar, Grace	Vale of Cedars (1st, 8vo, 428p, uncut, teg, col frn, 11pl, pep)	L: Dent	1902	Robinson, Thomas H.	60-90	
Robinson, W. Heath	Absurdities (1st, lg4to, 96p, ibds, fp b/w illus)	L: Hutchinson	[1934]	Robinson, W. Heath	125-200	
Cervantes	Adventures of Don Quixote (1st, 8vo, 532p, teg, uncut, b/w, pep)	Dent/Dutton	1902	Robinson, W. Heath	120-180	
Robinson, W. Heath	Adventures of Uncle Lubin (1st AM, 8vo, 117p, green cl, b/w)	Brentano's	1902	Robinson, W. Heath	1000-1600	
Robinson, W. Heath	Adventures of Uncle Lubin (1st, sm4to, 117p, col frn, fp b/w, pep)	L: Richards	1902	Robinson, W. Heath	2000-3000	
Robinson, W. Heath	Adventures of Uncle Lubin (new ed, sm4to, 114p, ibds, col frn, 7 b/w, DJ)	L: Chatto	(1934)	Robinson, W. Heath	200-300	
Robinson, W. Heath	Bill the Minder (1st, 4to, green/gilt, 255p, p-o, 16 ticp)	L: Constable	1912	Robinson, W. Heath	500-700	
Robinson, W. Heath	Bill the Minder (1st AM, 4to, p-o, 254p, gilt, 16 ticp)	Henry Holt & Co.	1912	Robinson, W. Heath	450-600	
Robinson, W. Heath	Book of Goblins (1st, 4to, 239p, blue/gilt, 7cp)	L: Hutchinson	(1934)	Robinson, W. Heath	400-600	
Robinson, W. Heath	Child's Arabian Nights (1st, 4to, ibds, 84p, 12cp)	L: Richards	1903	Robinson, W. Heath	700-1000	
Kipling, Rudyard	Collected Verse of... (1st, sm4to, red/gilt, 392p, teg, 17 ticp)	Doubleday/Page	1910	Robinson, W. Heath	200-300	
Shakespeare, Wm.	Comedy of the Twelfth Night (1st, 4to, 144p, green/gilt, 40 ticp)	L: Hodder	[1908]	Robinson, W. Heath	200-325	
Andersen, Hans C.	Danish Fairy Tales (1st {1st bk.}, 8vo, red/gilt, 332p, 16pl)	L: Bliss Sands	1897	Robinson, W. Heath	225-300	
Kipling, Rudyard	Dead King (1st, 8vo, 48p, grey/gilt, designs by...)	L: Hodder	(1910)	Robinson, W. Heath	140-225	
Cervantes	Don Quixote (8vo, red/gilt, 614p, 16 b/w)	Dodd	1925	Robinson, W. Heath	70-100	
Andersen, Hans C.	Fairy Tales (1st AM, 4to, red/gilt, 16 ticp)	Henry Holt & Co.	1913	Robinson, W. Heath	225-300	
Andersen, Hans C.	Fairy Tales (1st, 4to, red/gilt, 289p, 16 ticp)	L: Constable	1913	Robinson, W. Heath	350-500	
Andersen, Hans C.	Fairy Tales (4to, 320p, red/gilt, 16 ticp)	L: Hodder	[1913]	Robinson, W. Heath	180-240	
Andersen, Hans C.	Fairy Tales (1st {this pub}, lg8vo, 355p, color)	Houghton	1931	Robinson, W. Heath	75-100	*
Rouse, W.H.D.	Giant Crab (1st, 8vo, 134p, 7pl)	L: D. Nutt	1897	Robinson, W. Heath	180-265	
Browne, K.R.G.	How to Make a Garden Grow (1st, 12mo, 104p, green cl, dep, DJ)	L: Hutchinson	(1938)	Robinson, W. Heath	80-135	
Robinson, W. Heath	Humours of Golf (1st AM, 4to, ibds, 50p, b/w)	Dodd	1923	Robinson, W. Heath	250-350	
Robinson, W. Heath	Hunlikely! (1st, sm4to, ibds, 24pl)	L: Duckworth	(1916)	Robinson, W. Heath	125-200	
Hunter, Norman	Incredible Adventures/Professor Brawnestawm (1st, lg8vo, 203p, col frn)	L: Bodley Head	(1933)	Robinson, W. Heath	180-300	
Robinson, W. Heath	Jamboree of Laughter (1st, 4to, [24]p, p-o, wraps)	L: Jones & Co.	[1918]	Robinson, W. Heath	250-400	
Shuck, Professor H.	Medieval Stories (1st, 8vo, brown cl, 8pl, pep)	L: Sands	1902	Robinson, W. Heath	120-180	
Patterson, R.F.	Mein Rant (1st, 8vo, 69p, tan cl, b/w)	L: Blackie	1940	Robinson, W. Heath	80-140	
O'Cluny, Thomas	Merry Multifleet & the Mounting Multicorps (1st, 8vo, 206p, 16 illus)	L: J.M. Dent	1904	Robinson, W. Heath	120-170	*
Shakespeare, Wm.	MidSummer Night's Dream (1st AM, 4to, 187p, teg, gilt, 12 ticp)	Henry Holt & Co.	1914	Robinson, W. Heath	350-450	
Shakespeare, Wm.	MidSummer Night's Dream (1st, lg4to, 187p, gilt, 12 ticp)	L: Constable	1914	Robinson, W. Heath	400-600	
Carse, Roland	Monarchs of Merry England (1st, 4to, 52p, p-o, 10cp)	L: T.F. Unwin	1904	Robinson, W. Heath	280-350	
Carse, Roland	More Monarchs of Merry England (1st, 4to, ibds, 129p, 20cp, pep)	L: T.F. Unwin	[1907]	Robinson, W. Heath	300-450	
Perrault, Charles	Old Time Stories (1st AM, 4to, 200p, p-o, gilt, 6 ticp)	Dodd	(1921)	Robinson, W. Heath	250-400	
Perrault, Charles	Old-Time Stories (1st, 4to, red/gilt, 200p, 6 ticp)	L: Constable	1921	Robinson, W. Heath	350-500	
De La Mare, Walter	Peacock Pie (1st, 8vo, 178p, green/gilt, col frn)	L: Constable	(1916)	Robinson, W. Heath	120-170	
De La Mare, Walter	Peacock Pie (1st AM, 8vo, green/gilt, 178p, col frn)	Henry Holt & Co.	[1917]	Robinson, W. Heath	90-160	
Bunyan, John	Pilgrim's Progress (1st, 8vo, 284p, red cl, 24pl)	L: Bliss Sands	1897	Robinson, W. Heath	150-225	*
Poe, Edgar A.	Poems of Edgar Allan Poe (1st, 8vo, 225p, olive/gilt, teg, b/w)	L: G. Bell	1900	Robinson, W. Heath	350-500	
Gomme, George (ed)	Queen's Story Book (1st, 12mo, 446p, teg, blue/gilt, 20pl)	L: Constable	1898	Robinson, W. Heath	100-175	

AUTHOR	TITLE	PUBLISHER	DATE	ARTIST	PRICE	LC
Robinson, W. Heath	Railway Ribaldry (1st, 4to, [96]p, wraps, 88 fp b/w)	G.W. Railway	1935	Robinson, W. Heath	160-220	
Robinson, W. Heath	Some Frightful War Pictures (1st, folio, [54]p, 24 fp b/w, pep)	L: Duckworth	(1915)	Robinson, W. Heath	200-300	
Kipling, Rudyard	Song of the English (1st AM, 4to, [124]p, red/gilt, 30 ticp)	Doubleday/Page	(1909)	Robinson, W. Heath	400-600	
Kipling, Rudyard	Song of the English (1st, lg4to, [124]p, 91p, 30 ticp)	L: Hodder	[1909]	Robinson, W. Heath	450-650	
Kelman, Janet H.	Stories from Chaucer (1st, 12mo, 114p, p-o, gilt, 8cp)	L: Jack	[1906]	Robinson, W. Heath	140-225	
Lang, Jeanie	Stories from the Illiad (12mo, 119p, p-o, 8cp)	L: Jack	[1905]	Robinson, W. Heath	45-65	
N/A	Stories from the Odyssey (16mo, 118p, brown/gilt, p-o)	L: Jack	[1910]	Robinson, W. Heath	80-120	*
Hope, Ascott R.	Tales For Toby (1st, 8vo, 207p, 5pl)	L: Dent	1900	Robinson, W. Heath	120-170	
Lamb, Charles	Tales from Shakespeare (1st, 8vo, red cl, 296p, 16pl)	L: Sands	[1902]	Robinson, W. Heath	140-225	*
Rouse, W.H.D.	Talking Thrush (8vo, 8pl, cvr by...)	L: Dent	1902	Robinson, W. Heath	200-300	
Munro, E.S.	Topsy-Turvey Tales (1st, lg8vo, 180p, 6cp, 16 b/w)	L: John Lane	1923	Robinson, W. Heath	180-270	
Kingsley, Charles	Water Babies (1st, 8vo, 319p, green/gilt, 8cp)	L: Constable	1915	Robinson, W. Heath	400-600	
Kingsley, Charles	Water Babies (1st AM, 8vo, green cl, p-o, 320p, 8cp)	Houghton	(1915)	Robinson, W. Heath	300-500	
Unknown	Wonders of Wilmington (lg4to, [12]p, ibds, 5 fp b/w)	Hull	[1925]	Robinson, W. Heath	220-320	
N/A	Tales from Arabian Nights (1st, 8vo, 128p, p-o, 8cp)	L: Dent	(1914)	Robinson/Curtis	120-170	*
Byron, May	Little Yellow Duckling (1st, sm4to, gilt, 60p, 6cp, pep)	Doran	(1922)	Robinson/Rudge	40-70	*
Macy, S.B.	From Slavery to Freedom (1st, 4to, 299p, green/gilt, 8cp, pep)	L: Longmans	1910	Robinson/Sarg	200-300	
Dyer, Kate G.	Turkey Trott & the Black Santa (1st, 8vo, orange cl, [39]p, 2-color)	Platt/Munk	(1942)	Robson, Janet	140-200	
Roche, A.K.	Clever Turtle (1st, ob8vo, [32]p, fp 2-color, cep, DJ/4.50)	Prentice-Hall	(1969)	Roche, A.K.	35-50	*
Carlson, Natalie S.	Carnival in Paris (1st, 8vo, 152p, fp b/w, cep, DJ/2.95)	Harper	(1962)	Rocker, Fermin	45-70	R
Fall, Thomas	Goat Boy of Brooklyn (1st {std}, 8vo, 192p, b/w, DJ/3.95)	Dial Press	(1968)	Rocker, Fermin	20-30	
Horvath, Betty	Hooray for Jasper (1st {std}, 4to, [32]p, fp 1-color, DJ/2.95)	F. Watts	(1966)	Rocker, Fermin	30-50	
Coatsworth, Eliz.	Indian Mound Farm (1st {std}, 8vo, 62p, fp b/w, DJ/4.50)	Macmillan	(1969)	Rocker, Fermin	25-40	
Horvath, Betty	Jasper Makes Music (1st, 4to, [38]p, fp 1-color, DJ/2.95)	F. Watts	(1967)	Rocker, Fermin	30-50	*
Sorensen, Virginia	Lotte's Locket (1st {std}, sm8vo, 253p, b/w, DJ/3.50)	Harcourt	(1964)	Rocker, Fermin	25-40	*
Henry, Vera	Ong, the Wild Gander (1st {std}, 8vo, 95p, b/w, DJ/3.50)	Lippincott	(1966)	Rocker, Fermin	20-30	
Carlson, Natalie S.	Pet for the Orphelines (1st, sm4to, 97p, fp b/w, DJ/2.95)	Harper	(1962)	Rocker, Fermin	50-80	R
Burchardt, Nellie	Project Cat (1st, 8vo, 66p, yellow cl, fp 1-color, DJ/2.95)	F. Watts	(1966)	Rocker, Fermin	30-50	
Burch, Robert	Simon and the Game of Chance (1st {std}, 8vo, 128p, b/w, DJ/4.50)	Viking	(1970)	Rocker, Fermin	25-45	
Stevens, Eden V.	The Piper (1st {std}, 8vo, 85p, b/w, gilt, cep, DJ/3.95)	Atheneum	1964	Rocker, Fermin	30-50	
Brink, Carol R.	Two are Better than One (1st {std}, 8vo, 180p, b/w, DJ/4.50)	Macmillan	(1968)	Rocker, Fermin	25-45	
Brink, Carol R.	Winter Cottage (1st {std}, 8vo, 178p, b/w, DJ/4.50)	Macmillan	(1968)	Rocker, Fermin	20-35	
Rockwell, Anne	Filippo's Dome (1st {std}, lg8vo, 82p, fp b/w, DJ)	Atheneum	1967	Rockwell, Anne	30-45	
Hopkins, Marjorie	Glass Valentine (1st, sm8vo, [40]p, color, cep, DJ/3.50)	Parents Mag. Pr.	(1968)	Rockwell, Anne	20-35	
Petry, Ann	Legends of the Saints (1st, lg8vo, 47p, fp color, dep, DJ/4.50)	Crowell	(1970)	Rockwell, Anne	80-130	
Hitte, Kathryn	Mexicali Soup (1st, lg8vo, [38]p, color, DJ/3.95)	Parents Mag. Pr.	(1970)	Rockwell, Anne	30-45	*
Yolen, Jane	Minstrel & the Mountain (1st, 12mo, [60]p, gilt, color, cep, DJ/3.50)	World	(1967)	Rockwell, Anne	25-40	
Rockwell, Anne	Stolen Necklace (1st, sm4to, [32]p, color, cep, DJ/3.95)	World	(1968)	Rockwell, Anne	30-45	
Rockwell, Anne	Temple on a Hill (1st {std}, lg8vo, 108p, b/w, cep, DJ/3.95)	Atheneum	1969	Rockwell, Anne	50-80	R*
Hopkins, Marjorie	Three Visitors (1st, ob4to, [40]p, ipcb, color, cep, DJ/2.95)	Parents Mag. Pr.	(1967)	Rockwell, Anne	25-40	
Showers, Paul	What Happened to a Hamburger? (1st, ob8vo, 33p, color, DJ/3.75)	Crowell	(1970)	Rockwell, Anne	25-40	
Rockwell, Anne	Wonderful Eggs of Furicchia (1st, 4to, [32]p, fp color, cep, DJ/3.95)	World	(1969)	Rockwell, Anne	30-45	
Rockwell, Anne	Olly's Polliwogs (1st, 4to, [57]p, color, DJ/3.95)	Doubleday	(1970)	Rockwell, Harlow	30-50	*
May, Elizabeth	Flower Babies (1st, 4to, [100]p, ibds, fp color)	Saalfield	(1905)	Rockwell, Ida M.	250-350	
Twain, Mark	Adventures of Huckleberry Finn (1st, 4to, 346p, gilt, 8 ticp, box)	Heritage Press	(1940)	Rockwell, Norman	90-120	
Twain, Mark	Adventures of Tom Sawyer (1st, 4to, 284p, 8 ticp, box)	Heritage Press	(1937)	Rockwell, Norman	90-120	
Cave, Edward	Boy's Camp Book (1st, 12mo, green cl, 194p, 4 fp b/w)	Doubleday/Page	1914	Rockwell, Norman	80-120	*
Coles, Robert	Dead End School (1st {std}, 8vo, 100p, b/w, DJ/3.95)	Little/Brown	(1968)	Rockwell, Norman	40-65	
Barbour, Ralph H.	Hitting the Line (1st, sm8vo, 322p, 5cp)	Appleton	1917	Rockwell, Norman	90-120	*
Barbour, Ralph H.	Lucky Seventh (1st, sm8vo, 310p, 4cp)	Appleton	1915	Rockwell, Norman	80-120	*
Jackson, Gabrielle	Maid of Middies' Haven (1st, 12mo, 299p, 4pl)	McBride	1912	Rockwell, Norman	170-240	*
Barbour, Ralph H.	Purple Pennant (1st, sm8vo, 322p, 4cp)	Appleton	1916	Rockwell, Norman	250-350	*
Tomlinson, Everett	Scouting with Daniel Boone (1st, sm8vo, 303p, green cl, 8pl)	Doubleday/Page	1914	Rockwell, Norman	120-180	
Barbour, Ralph H.	Secret Play (1st, 12mo, p-o, gilt, 335p, 4cp)	Appleton	1915	Rockwell, Norman	250-350	*
Claudy, C.H.	Tell Me Why Stories (1st, lg8vo, tan cl, 154p, 8cp)	McBride	1912	Rockwell, Norman	600-900	*
Sawyer, Ruth	This Way to Christmas (1st, 12mo, 165p, gilt, frn by...)	Harper	(1916)	Rockwell, Norman	55-80	*
Rockwell, Norman	Willie Was Different (1st, sm4to, cloth, [48]p, color, DJ/3.95)	Funk/Wagnalls	(1969)	Rockwell, Norman	140-200	
Thompson, Wolfe	Moccasins on the Trail (1st {std}, sm8vo, 298p, gilt, DJ/2.00)	Longmans	1935	Rodgers, Richard	30-50	
Hawthorne, Hildegarde	Wheels Toward the West (1st {std}, 8vo, 243p, 5 fp b/w, pep)	Longmans	1931	Rodgers, Richard	20-35	
Bianco, Margery W.	The Candlestick (1st {std}, 8vo, ibds, 46p, color, pep)	Doubleday/Doran	1929	Rodo, Ludovic	30-50	
Brooks, Walter	Ernestine Takes Over (1st, sm8vo, 265p, b/w, DJ/2.00)	Wm. Morrow	1935	Roese, Herbert	80-135	
Phelps, Eliz. S.	Avery... (1st, 12mo, 238p, gilt)	Houghton	1902	Rogers, Bruce	30-50	
Warner, Charles D.	Backlog Studies (1st, 12mo, 257p, title page by...)	Houghton	1899	Rogers, Bruce	30-50	
Bellamy, William	Century of Charades (1st, 16mo, 100p)	Houghton	1901	Rogers, Bruce	30-50	
Chesnutt, Charles	Conjure Woman (1st, 8vo, 229p, green cl, designs by...)	Houghton	1899	Rogers, Bruce	350-500	
Todd, Mabel L.	Corona & Coronet (1st, 8vo, teg, 383p, green/gilt, designs by...)	Houghton	1898	Rogers, Bruce	125-200	
Brown, Alice	Day of His Youth (1st, 12mo, green/gilt, 143p)	Houghton	1897	Rogers, Bruce	50-80	R
James, Henry	English Hours (1st AM, lg8vo, teg, 336p, design by...)	Houghton	1905	Rogers, Bruce	200-300	
Crothers, Samuel M.	Gentle Reader (1st, 12mo, 321p, gilt, teg)	Houghton	1903	Rogers, Bruce	25-40	
Smith, Francis H.	Gondola Days (1st, 12mo, 205p, red/gilt, cvr by...)	Houghton	1897	Rogers, Bruce	50-80	
Aldrich, Thomas B.	Judith of Bethulia (1st, 8vo, gilt, 98p, teg, p-o)	Houghton	1904	Rogers, Bruce	30-50	
Hearn, Lafcadio	Kwaidan (1st, 12mo, 240p, teg, uncut, designs by..)	Houghton	1904	Rogers, Bruce	120-160	
Fiske, John	Life Everlasting (1st, 12mo, 87p, blue cl, teg, designed by...)	Houghton	1901	Rogers, Bruce	25-40	
Sherman, Frank D.	Little Folk Lyrics (1st, sm8vo, 140p, green cl, teg, designs by...)	Houghton	1897	Rogers, Bruce	30-50	
Bell, Lilian	Little Sister to the Wilderness (1st, 16mo, 267p, gilt, teg, cvr by...)	Stone/Kimball	1895	Rogers, Bruce	60-90	
Peattie, Elia W.	Mountain Woman (1st, 12mo, 251p, teg, cvr by...)	Way & Williams	1896	Rogers, Bruce	100-175	
Smith, Francis H.	Other Fellow (1st, 8vo, teg, 218p)	Houghton	1899	Rogers, Bruce	30-50	
Crothers, Samuel M.	Pardoner's Wallet (1st, 12mo, 287p, teg)	Houghton	1905	Rogers, Bruce	25-40	

AUTHOR	TITLE	PUBLISHER	DATE	ARTIST	PRICE	LC
Drachmann, Holger	Paul & Virginia of a Northern Zone (1st, 8vo, 208p, gilt, teg, cvr by...)	Way & Williams	1895	Rogers, Bruce	100-165	
Sherwood, Mary M.	Prince Por Quoi (1st, 12mo, 211p, designs by...)	Houghton	1907	Rogers, Bruce	25-45	
Johnston, Mary	Prisoners of Hope (1st, sm8vo, 378p, green/gilt)	Houghton	1898	Rogers, Bruce	60-100	
James, Henry	Question of Our Speech (1st, sm8vo, gilt, teg, 115p, uncut)	Houghton	1905	Rogers, Bruce	180-250	
Hearn, Lafcadio	Romance of the Milky Way (1st, 12mo, 209p, t.e. yellow)	Houghton	1905	Rogers, Bruce	80-130	
Aldrich, Thomas B.	Sea Turn (1st, 12mo, grey cl, 300p)	Houghton	1902	Rogers, Bruce	30-50	
Muir, John	Stickeen... (1st, 12mo, tan cl, [73]p, designs, PPPa)	Houghton	1909	Rogers, Bruce	120-200	
Brown, Alice	Tiverton Tales (1st, 12mo, green/gilt, 339p, designs by..)	Houghton	1899	Rogers, Bruce	40-65	
Moore, Clement C.	Visit from St. Nicholas (1st, 8vo, ibds, 9p, designed by....)	Atl. Monthly Pr.	1921	Rogers, Bruce	80-120	
Parker, Gilbert	When Valmond Came to Pontiac (1st, 12mo, teg, green/gilt, 222p)	Stone/Kimball	1895	Rogers, Bruce	70-120	
New, Catherine M.	Woman Reigns (1st, 12mo, 112p, gilt, teg, uncut, cvr by...)	Bowen-Merrill	1895	Rogers, Bruce	30-50	
Zimelman, Nathan	Beneath the Oak Tree (1st, lg ob8vo, 31p, b/w, DJ/2.95)	Steck-Vaughn	(1966)	Rogers, Carol	30-50	
Zimelman, Nathan	Once When I was Five (1st, 4to, 31p, fp 1-color, DJ/2.95)	Steck-Vaughn	(1967)	Rogers, Carol	25-40	*
Snedeker, Caroline D.	Triumph for Flavius (1st, lg8vo, 87p, b/w, DJ/3.00)	Lothrop, Lee	(1955)	Rogers, Cedric	20-35	*
Stratton-Porter, Gene	Daughter of the Land (1st, sm8vo, 475p, green cl, col frn)	Doubleday/Page	1918	Rogers, Frances	65-100	
Stratton-Porter, Gene	Michael O'Halloran (1st, 8vo, 560p, green cl, 4pl, pep)	Doubleday/Page	1915	Rogers, Frances	50-85	
Singmaster, Elsie	Little Money Ahead (1st, sm8vo, 194p, b/w pl)	Houghton	1930	Rogers, Hubert	200-300	
Singmaster, Elsie	Loving Heart (1st, 8vo, 244p, col frn, DJ/2.00)	Houghton	1937	Rogers, Hubert	80-120	
Miller, Leo E.	Adrift on the Amazon (1st, 8vo, 263p, olive cl, 4pl)	Scribner	1923	Rogers, W.A.	30-50	*
Munroe, Kirk	Copper Princess (1st, 12mo, 237p, 12pl)	Harper	1898	Rogers, W.A.	40-70	
Munroe, Kirk	Fur-Seal's Tooth (1st, 12mo, 267p, green cl, b/w)	Harper	1894	Rogers, W.A.	70-100	
Otis, James	Jenny Wren's Boarding House (1st, 8vo, blue/gilt, 173p, 12pl, pep, PPP)	Estes & Lauriat	(1893)	Rogers, W.A.	120-180	
Pool, Maria L.	Mrs. Gerald (1st, 12mo, 339p, orange/silver, 13pl)	Harper	1896	Rogers, W.A.	25-45	
Munroe, Kirk	Ready Rangers (1st, sm8vo, 334p, red cl, 6pl)	Lothrop Pub.	(1897)	Rogers, W.A.	40-60	
Munroe, Kirk	Rick Dale (1st, 12mo, 282p, 19pl)	Harper	1899	Rogers, W.A.	30-50	
Otis, James	Teddy & Carrots (1st, 8vo, 225p, 18pl, pep)	Estes & Lauriat	(1896)	Rogers, W.A.	45-70	
Otis, James	Tim & Tip (1st, 16mo, 179p, 13 fp b/w, dep)	Harper	1883	Rogers, W.A.	80-140	R
Otis, James	Toby Tyler (1st, sq8vo, 265p, brown/gilt, 21 fp b/w, PPP)	Harper	1881	Rogers, W.A.	160-240	
Rohmer, Albert	Ivan the Iron Horse (1st, 12mo, 31p, 2-color, DJ/1.25)	Whitman	1944	Rohmer, Albert	35-50	
Bishop, Claire H.	All Alone (1st, lg8vo, 90p, fp b/w, pep, DJ/2.50, NH)	Viking	1953	Rojankovsky, Feodor	60-95	
Duplaix, Georges	Animal Stories (1st {std}, folio, ibds, 91p, color, pep, GGB)	Simon/Schuster	1944	Rojankovsky, Feodor	60-100	
Rojankovsky, Feodor	Animals in the Zoo (1st, 4to, unpag, color, pep, DJ/3.95)	Knopf	(1962)	Rojankovsky, Feodor	70-120	R
Rojankovsky, Feodor	Animals on the Farm (1st, 4to, [32]p, color, pep, DJ/2.95)	Knopf	(1967)	Rojankovsky, Feodor	70-120	
Riesenberg, Felix	Balboa, Swordsman & Conquistador (1st, 8vo, 178p, color, pep, DJ/1.50)	Random	(1956)	Rojankovsky, Feodor	30-45	*
Lida	Bruin the Brown Bear (1st {std}, 4to, ibds, [32]p, color, pep)	Harper	1937	Rojankovsky, Feodor	50-85	
Kipling, Rudyard	Butterfly that Stamped (1st, 8vo, [28]p, ibds, color, pep)	Garden City	(1947)	Rojankovsky, Feodor	25-45	
Fritz, Jean	Cabin Faced West (1st, 8vo, blue cl, 124p, b/w, DJ/3.00)	Coward	(1958)	Rojankovsky, Feodor	30-50	
Averill, Esther	Cartier Sails the St. Lawrence (1st, sm4to, 108p, fp b/w, DJ/3.00)	Harper	(1956)	Rojankovsky, Feodor	40-65	R
Brown, Margaret W.	Children's Year (1st {std}, ob12mo, [26]p, ipcb, pep, color)	Harper	1937	Rojankovsky, Feodor	70-100	
Newcomb, Covelle	Cortez the Conqueror (1st, folio, 106p, fp 1-color, DJ/3.00)	Random	(1947)	Rojankovsky, Feodor	70-100	
Fisher, Aileen	Cricket in a Thicket (1st, 8vo, 63p, ibds, b/w, DJ/3.25)	Scribner	(1963)	Rojankovsky, Feodor	20-35	
Graham, John	Crowd of Cows (1st {std}, 4to, bds, [32]p, color, DJ/3.50)	Harcourt	(1968)	Rojankovsky, Feodor	30-50	
Lida	Cuckoo (1st {std}, 4to, ibds, [32]p, pep, color, DJ/1.25)	Harper	1942	Rojankovsky, Feodor	60-100	
Averill, Esther	Daniel Boone (1st AM {std}, 4to, ipcb, 58p, color, pep, DJ/1.50)	Harper	(1945)	Rojankovsky, Feodor	80-120	R
Coatsworth, Eliz.	Dog Stories (1st {A}, folio, ibds, 66p, color, pep, GGB)	Simon/Schuster	1953	Rojankovsky, Feodor	70-120	*
Kipling, Rudyard	Elephant's Child (1st, lg8vo, ibds, [28]p, color, DJ/0.50)	Garden City	(1942)	Rojankovsky, Feodor	30-50	
Daniels, Guy (tran)	Falcon Under the Hat (1st, 4to, 110p, fp color, DJ/5.95)	Funk/Wagnalls	(1969)	Rojankovsky, Feodor	30-50	
N/A	Favorite Fairy Tales (1st, folio, ibds, [28]p, color, GGB)	Simon/Schuster	(1949)	Rojankovsky, Feodor	55-80	*
Averill, Esther	Flash: Story of a Horse (1st AM, narrow 4to, 32p, color, ibds)	Smith/Haas	(1934)	Rojankovsky, Feodor	150-225	
Duplaix, Georges	Fluff (1st, sq4to, ibds, [40]p, color, pep)	Harper	1937	Rojankovsky, Feodor	100-165	*
Langstaff, John	Frog Went A-Courtin' (1st {std}, 4to, [32]p, color, pep, DJ/2.50, CM)	Harcourt	(1955)	Rojankovsky, Feodor	140-200	R
Duplaix, Georges	Gaston & Josephine (1st {A}, sm8vo, [42]p, ibds, color, LGB/#65)	Simon/Schuster	1948	Rojankovsky, Feodor	25-45	
Werner, Elsa	Golden Bible (1st {std}, folio, 124p, ibds, color, GGB)	Simon/Schuster	(1946)	Rojankovsky, Feodor	30-50	
N/A	Great Big Animal Book (1st, folio, [22]p, ibds, color, pep, GGB/#468)	Simon/Schuster	1950	Rojankovsky, Feodor	40-60	
Kipling, Rudyard	How the Camel Got his Hump (1st {std}, lg8vo, [28]p, ibds, color, pep)	Garden City	(1942)	Rojankovsky, Feodor	30-50	
Kipling, Rudyard	How the Leopard Got his Spots (1st, lg8vo, ibds, [28]p, color)	Garden City	(1942)	Rojankovsky, Feodor	35-50	
Kipling, Rudyard	How the Rhinoceros Got his Skin (1st, lg8vo, ibds, [31]p, color)	Garden City	(1942)	Rojankovsky, Feodor	35-50	
Memling, Carl	I Can Count (1st, folio, ibds, [24]p, fp color, pep)	Golden Press	1963	Rojankovsky, Feodor	40-65	*
Koch, Dorothy	I Play at the Beach (1st, lg8vo, blue cl, [28]p, color, pep, DJ/2.50)	Holiday House	1955	Rojankovsky, Feodor	65-100	*
Rand, Ann	Little River (1st {std}, sm ob4to, ibds, [32]p, color, pep, DJ/2.95)	Harcourt	(1959)	Rojankovsky, Feodor	75-125	
Kalashnikoff, N.	My Friend Yakub (1st, 8vo, 249p, fp b/w, DJ/2.75)	Scribner	(1953)	Rojankovsky, Feodor	30-50	
McGinley, Phyllis	Name for Kitty (1st {A}, sm8vo, ibds, [28]p, color, LGB/#55)	Simon/Schuster	(1948)	Rojankovsky, Feodor	20-35	
Andersen, Hans C.	Old Man is Always Right (1st {std}, sq8vo, ibds, 28p, color, pep)	Harper	(1940)	Rojankovsky, Feodor	50-80	
Nast, Elsa R.	Our Puppy (1st {A}, 8vo, ibds, [28]p, color, LGB/#56)	Simon/Schuster	(1948)	Rojankovsky, Feodor	25-40	
Thayer, Jane	Outside Cat (1st, 4to, [34]p, color, pep, DJ/2.95)	Wm. Morrow	1957	Rojankovsky, Feodor	30-50	
Langstaff, John	Over in the Meadow (1st {std}, 4to, unpag, color, pep, DJ/2.75)	Harcourt	(1957)	Rojankovsky, Feodor	45-70	
Lida	Plouf the Little Wild Duck (1st, 4to, ibds, [40]p, color, pep)	Harper	1936	Rojankovsky, Feodor	50-85	
Lida	Pompom (1st, sq4to, ibds, [38]p, color, pep, DJ/1.00)	Harper	1936	Rojankovsky, Feodor	50-80	
Averill, Esther	Powder (1st AM, 4to, ibds, 29p, color)	Smith/Haas	(1933)	Rojankovsky, Feodor	80-125	
Defoe, Daniel	Robinson Crusoe (1st, folio, ibds, 97p, color, GGB/#698)	Golden Press	1960	Rojankovsky, Feodor	60-100	*
Lida	Scuff the Seal (1st {std}, 4to, ibds, [32]p, color, pep)	Harper	1937	Rojankovsky, Feodor	50-80	
Rand, Ann	So Small (1st {std}, sq12mo, [48]p, fp color, DJ/2.95)	Harcourt	(1962)	Rojankovsky, Feodor	80-125	
Lida	Spiky the Hedgehog (1st {std}, 4to, ibds, [34]p, color, pep, DJ/1.00)	Harper	1938	Rojankovsky, Feodor	80-125	
Mariotti, Jean	Tales of Poindi (1st, 4to, 64p, green/gilt, b/w, DJ/2.50)	Domino Press	(1938)	Rojankovsky, Feodor	80-130	
Mother Goose	Tall Book of Mother Goose (1st {std}, lg4to, 120p, ibds, color, pep)	Harper	(1942)	Rojankovsky, Feodor	80-140	
N/A	Tall Book of Nursery Tales (1st, narrow 4to, ibds, 120p, color, DJ/1.00)	A.& W. Guild	(1944)	Rojankovsky, Feodor	70-100	*
Lida	The Kingfisher (1st {std}, sm sq4to, ibds, [32]p, pep, color, DJ/1.00)	Harper	1940	Rojankovsky, Feodor	70-100	
Lester, Carol E.	To Make a Duck Happy (1st {std}, 8vo, uncut, 148p, b/w, pep, DJ/4.95)	Harper	(1969)	Rojankovsky, Feodor	20-35	*

AUTHOR	TITLE	PUBLISHER	DATE	ARTIST	PRICE	LC
Prishvin, Mikhail	Treasure Trove of the Sun (1st, 4to, 80p, color, pep, DJ/2.75)	Viking	1952	Rojankovsky, Feodor	60-100	R
Tchaika, Florence	Trouble at Beaver Dam (1st, 8vo, 63p, fp 1-color, pep, DJ/1.60)	J. Messner	(1953)	Rojankovsky, Feodor	25-45	
Watson, Jane W.	True Story of Smokey the Bear (1st, folio, ibds, [24]p, pep, BGB/#429)	Golden Press	1955	Rojankovsky, Feodor	50-80	
Andersen, Hans C.	Ugly Duckling (1st, lg8vo, ibds, [32]p, color, DJ/0.50)	Grosset/Dunlap	(1945)	Rojankovsky, Feodor	30-60	
Averill, Esther	Voyages of Jacques Cartier (1st, 4to, 94p, gilt, fp b/w)	Domino Press	(1937)	Rojankovsky, Feodor	100-160	R*
Varley, Dimitry	Whirly Bird (1st, 4to, [32]p, color, pep, DJ/3.00)	Knopf	(1961)	Rojankovsky, Feodor	60-90	
Daly, Kathleen N.	Wild Animal Babies (1st {A}, sm8vo, [28]p, ibds, color, LGB/#332)	Simon/Schuster	1958	Rojankovsky, Feodor	20-35	
Celli, Rose	Wild Animals & their Little Ones (1st AM, folio, [20]p, wraps, 12 color)	A.& W. Guild	(1935)	Rojankovsky, Feodor	50-85	
Reynier, Marguerite	Wild Animals at Home (sq4to, wraps, [16]p, color)	A.& W. Guild	(1934)	Rojankovsky, Feodor	35-60	
Raymond, Evelyn	The Whirligig (1st, 12mo, 351p, 6pl)	Penn	1905	Rollins, R.	35-60	*
Edelstat, Vera	Steam Shovel for Me! (1st, sm4to, orange cl, [56]p, color, pep)	Stokes	1933	Romano	70-120	*
Bannerman, Helen	Little Black Sambo (1st, 8vo, ibds, unpag, color)	NY: Harrison Co.	(1945)	Romyns, Marjorie	200-300	
Cowper, William	Diverting History of John Gilpin (1st, ob4to [36]p, gilt, bds, 8cp)	L: Routledge	[1888]	Rosa, H.	120-180	
Embry, Margaret	Blue-Nosed Witch (1st, 8vo, 45p, yellow cl, b/w, pep, DJ/2.00)	Holiday House	(1955)	Rose, Carl	25-40	
Leaf, Munro	Listen Little Girl (1st, 8vo, 196p, DJ/1.50, decor by...)	Stokes	1938	Rose, Dick	40-60	
Joyce, James	Cat and the Devil (1st UK, 8vo, 32p, color, DJ)	L: Faber	1965	Rose, Gerald	150-250	
Rose, Elizabeth	Old Winkle and the Seagulls (1st, 8vo, unpag, color, DJ, KGM)	L: Faber	1960	Rose, Gerald	50-85	*
Eaton, Jeanette	Leader by Destiny (1st, 8vo, 402p, blue/gilt, 19pl, DJ/3.00, NH)	Harcourt	(1938)	Rose, Jack M.	40-70	
Wright, Ethel B.	Saturday Flight (1st, lg ob8vo, [20]p, spiral bds, color)	W.R. Scott	1944	Rose, Richard	50-80	
Wright, Ethel B.	Saturday Walk (1st, lg ob8vo, [20]p, spiral-bound, color)	W.R. Scott	1941	Rose, Richard	50-80	
Ovington, Mary W.	Hazel (1st, 8vo, 162p, b/w)	NY: Crisis Pub	(1913)	Roseland, Harry	150-200	*
Lightfoot, Beryl H.	Jolly Jack Horner (1st, 8vo, 64p, p-o, 4cp)	Whitman	(1916)	Rosenkrans, Eliz.	35-60	
Paine, Albert B.	Great White Way (1st, sm8vo, blue cl, teg, 327p, 6pl)	J.F. Taylor	1901	Rosenmeyer, B.J.	90-120	
Daskam, Josephine	Imp & The Angel (1st, 8vo, 168p, teg, ivol, 8pl)	Scribner	1901	Rosenmeyer, B.J.	35-60	*
Russell, William C.	Two Captains (1st UK, 8vo, 372p, cloth, b/w)	L: Sampson Low	1897	Rosenmeyer, B.J.	75-100	
Moray, Ann	Gervase (1st, sm8vo, 93p, b/w, DJ/4.50)	Wm. Morrow	1970	Rosier, Lydia	20-30	
Haldane, J.B.S.	My Friend Mr. Leakey (1st AM {std}, 8vo, 179p, b/w, DJ/1.75)	Harper	1938	Rosoman, Leonard	140-200	
Garelick, May	Wild Ducks and Daffodils (1st, lg ob8vo, [48]p, ibds, color, DJ/3.50)	Young Scott	1965	Ross, Clare	20-35	
Martin, John	Children's Munchausen (1st, lg8vo, 185p, p-o, gilt, 8cp)	Houghton	1921	Ross, Gordon	60-100	
Irving, Washington	Christmas Dinner (1st, 8vo, ipcb, 22p, b/w)	NY: W. Rudge	1929	Ross, Gordon	60-90	R
Cooke, Edmund V.	Impertinent Poems (1st, 8vo, p-o, teg, uncut, 103p, 11cp)	Dodge	(1907)	Ross, Gordon	35-60	
Levine, Rhoda	Herbert Situation (1st {std}, ob4to, 32p, gilt, color, DJ/3.95)	Harlin Quist	1969	Ross, Larry	25-45	
Kirkwood, Edith B.	Animal Children (1st, 8vo, yellow ipcb, p-o, 96p, pep, color)	Volland	(1913)	Ross, M.T.	100-180	
Gordon, Elizabeth	Bird Children (1st, lg8vo, 96p, ibds, color, pep)	Volland	(1912)	Ross, M.T.	120-180	
Gordon, Elizabeth	Butterfly Babies' Book (1st, 8vo, 78p, ibds, color)	Rand/McNally	(1914)	Ross, M.T.	80-120	
Scott, Anna M.	Flower Babies' Book (1st, 8vo, 78p, ibds, color)	Rand/McNally	(1914)	Ross, M.T.	120-180	
Gordon, Elizabeth	Flower Children (1st, 8vo, ibds, [92]p, color, pep)	Volland	(1910)	Ross, M.T.	120-180	
Gordon, Elizabeth	I Wonder Why? (1st, sm8vo, 72p, color)	Rand/McNally	(1916)	Ross, M.T.	50-80	
Gordon, Elizabeth	Lorraine & the Little People (1st, 12mo, ibds, 73p, color)	Rand/McNally	(1915)	Ross, M.T.	70-100	
Sadler, Marie C.	Mamma's Angel Child (1st, 8vo, ibds, p-o, 115p, fp color)	Rand/McNally	(1915)	Ross, M.T.	140-200	
Gordon, Elizabeth	Mother Earth's Children (1st, lg8vo, 95p, ibds, color, pep)	Volland	(1914)	Ross, M.T.	150-250	
Gordon, Elizabeth	Some Smiles (1st, 12mo, ibds, [29]p, color)	W.A. Wilde	(1911)	Ross, M.T.	40-60	
Warner, Harriette	Story Song Book (1st, 4to, ibds, 38p, p-o, 10 fp color)	Chi: Cook	(1912)	Ross, M.T.	120-170	
Scott, Anna M.	Year with the Fairies (1st, 8vo, ibds, [100]p, color, pep)	Volland	(1914)	Ross, M.T.	200-300	
Bailey, Alice C.	Katrina and Jan (1st, lg8vo, ibds, [93]p, color, pep)	Volland	(1923)	Rosse, Herman	55-80	*
Olcott, F.J. (ed)	Wonder Tales from Pirate Isles (1st {std}, 8vo, 256p, col frn, b/w, pep)	NY: Longmans	1927	Rosse, Herman	40-60	*
Olcott, F.J. (ed)	Wonder Tales from Windmill Lands (1st, 8vo, 238p, col frn, pep, DJ)	L: Longmans	1926	Rosse, Herman	55-90	
Cole, William	I Went to the Animal Fair (1st {std}, ob4to, 46p, b/w, DJ/2.75)	World	(1958)	Rosselli, Colette	40-65	R*
Rossetti, Christina	Pageant & other Poems (1st, 8vo, 198p, blue/gilt)	L: Macmillan	1881	Rossetti, Daniel G.	200-300	
Rossetti, Dante G.	Pictures & Poems (1st, folio, gilt, teg, [54]p, 14 tipl)	R.H. Russell	1899	Rossetti, Dante G.	300-450	*
Daly, Maureen	Sixteen and other Stories (1st, 8vo, 157p, b/w, DJ/3.00)	Dodd	1961	Rossi, Kendall	20-35	*
Yolen, Jane	Isabel's Noel (1st, sm4to, [30]p, fp 3-color, pep, DJ/2.95)	Funk/Wagnalls	(1967)	Roth, Arnold	30-50	*
Fadiman, Clifton	Wally the Wordworm (1st {std}, 12mo, [63]p, color, DJ/2.95)	Macmillan	(1964)	Roth, Arnold	20-35	
Yolen, Jane	Witch Who Wasn't (1st {std}, 4to, ibds, [36]p, color, DJ/2.95)	Macmillan	1964	Roth, Arnold	20-35	
Hall, Lynn	Ride a Wild Dream (1st {std}, 8vo, 160p, b/w, DJ/3.50)	Follett	(1969)	Roth, George	20-35	*
Hewes, Agnes D.	Two Oceans to Canton (1st {std}, sm8vo, 184p, color, DJ/2.50)	Knopf	1944	Roth, Harry	20-35	
LeBlanc, Georgette	Children's Blue Bird (1st, 8vo, ibds, 172p, 12cp)	L: Methuen	1913	Rothenstein, Albert	80-120	
Farjeon, Eleanor	Country Child's Alphabet (1st, 8vo, stiff wraps, [54]p, b/w)	L: Poetry Bkshp.	1924	Rothenstein, Wm. M.	120-200	
Aesopus	Aesop's Fables (1st, 8vo, 162p, color, DJ/2.50)	Lippincott	(1949)	Rounds, Glen	35-50	
Gage, Wilson	Big Blue Island (1st {std}, lg8vo, 120p, b/w, DJ/3.50)	World	(1964)	Rounds, Glen	40-65	R
Rounds, Glen	Blind Colt (1st, lg8vo, blue cl, [80]p, color, DJ/2.00)	Holiday House	(1941)	Rounds, Glen	30-50	
Rounds, Glen	Buffalo Harvest (1st, 8vo, 141p, b/w, pep, DJ/2.25)	Holiday House	(1952)	Rounds, Glen	20-35	
Caudill, Rebecca	Contrary Jenkins (1st {std}, ob4to, [40]p, b/w, DJ/3.50)	Holt, Rinehart	(1969)	Rounds, Glen	30-50	R
Stoutenburg, Adrien	Crocodile's Mouth (1st, 4to, 64p, fp b/w, DJ/3.00)	Viking	(1966)	Rounds, Glen	30-50	
Gage, Wilson	Dan and the Miranda (1st {std}, 4to, 124p, b/w, DJ/2.95)	World	(1962)	Rounds, Glen	20-30	
Sears, Paul M.	Firefly (1st, sm8vo, 37p, green cl, 2-color, pep, DJ/2.00)	Holiday House	1956	Rounds, Glen	25-45	
Black, Irma S.	Flipper: Sea Lion (1st, 8vo, [50]p, color, pep, DJ/1.75)	Holiday House	1940	Rounds, Glen	30-45	
Crosby, Alexander	Go Find Hanka! (1st, lg8vo, 44p, fp b/w, cep, DJ/3.95)	Golden Gate	(1970)	Rounds, Glen	25-45	
Kjelgaard, Jim	Haunt Fox (1st, sm8vo, 220p, brown cl, b/w, pep, DJ/2.50)	Holiday House	(1954)	Rounds, Glen	45-60	R
Leach, Maria	How the People Sang the Mountains Up (1st, lg8vo, 159p, b/w, DJ/3.75)	Viking	(1967)	Rounds, Glen	20-30	
Seeman, Elizabeth	In the Arms of the Mountain (1st, 8vo, 251p, b/w, DJ/4.00)	Crown	(1961)	Rounds, Glen	20-35	
Conklin, Gladys	Lucky Ladybugs (1st, 4to, [32]p, color, DJ/4.50)	Holiday House	(1968)	Rounds, Glen	25-40	
Rounds, Glen	Lumbercamp (1st, sm8vo, wood bds, 116p, b/w, pep)	Holiday House	1937	Rounds, Glen	45-70	
Gage, Wilson	Mike's Toads (1st, 4to, 93p, fp b/w, DJ/4.50)	World	(1970)	Rounds, Glen	30-45	
Rounds, Glen	Ol' Paul, Mighty Logger (1st, 12mo, beige cl, 132p, b/w, pep, DJ/2.00)	Holiday House	1936	Rounds, Glen	50-85	R
Rounds, Glen	Pay Dirt (1st, 12mo, 148p, b/w, pep, DJ/2.00)	Holiday House	(1938)	Rounds, Glen	30-50	
Rounds, Glen	Prairie Schooners (1st, lg8vo, 95p, b/w, cep, DJ/3.75)	Holiday House	(1968)	Rounds, Glen	30-45	R
Rounds, Glen	Rain in the Woods (1st {std}, lg8vo, 95p, b/w, DJ/3.00)	World	(1964)	Rounds, Glen	20-30	

AUTHOR	TITLE	PUBLISHER	DATE	ARTIST	PRICE	LC
Rounds, Glen	Rodeo: Bulls, Broncs & Buckaroos (1st, 8vo, 157p, b/w, pep, DJ/2.25)	Holiday House	(1949)	Rounds, Glen	25-40	
Rounds, Glen	Snake Tree (1st {std}, lg8vo, 95p, b/w, DJ/3.50)	World	(1966)	Rounds, Glen	20-30	
Rounds, Glen	Stolen Pony (1st, lg8vo, [96]p, b/w, DJ/3.95)	Holiday House	(1969)	Rounds, Glen	20-35	
Rounds, Glen	Strawberry Roan (1st, ob4to, [48]p, 2-color, cep, DJ/4.50)	Golden Gate	(1970)	Rounds, Glen	25-40	
Blair, Walter	Tall Tale America (1st, 8vo, 262p, b/w, DJ/2.50)	Coward	1944	Rounds, Glen	30-45	
Hardy, Martha	Tatoosh (1st {std}, 8vo, 239p, b/w, DJ/3.00)	Macmillan	1946	Rounds, Glen	25-40	
Adams, Andy	Trail Drive (1st, 8vo, 250p, b/w, DJ/3.95)	Holiday House	(1965)	Rounds, Glen	25-40	
Rounds, Glen	Treeless Plains (1st, lg8vo, 95p, b/w, DJ/3.75)	Holiday House	(1967)	Rounds, Glen	20-35	
Webb, Wheaton P.	Uncle Swithin's Inventions (1st, lg8vo, 114p, fp b/w, pep, DJ/2.00)	Holiday House	(1947)	Rounds, Glen	30-50	
Rounds, Glen	Whitey & Jinglebob (1st, sq8vo, [28]p, ibds, pep, color, DJ/0.50)	Grosset/Dunlap	(1946)	Rounds, Glen	35-50	
Rounds, Glen	Whitey & the Blizzard (1st, sm8vo, blue cl, 31p, b/w, cep, DJ/1.25)	Holiday House	(1952)	Rounds, Glen	30-50	
Rounds, Glen	Whitey & the Colt Killer (1st, 8vo, 90p, b/w, DJ/2.50)	Holiday House	(1962)	Rounds, Glen	20-30	*
Rounds, Glen	Whitey & the Rustlers (1st, sm8vo, 32p, b/w, DJ/1.25)	Holiday House	(1951)	Rounds, Glen	25-40	
Rounds, Glen	Whitey Looks for a Job (1st, lg8vo, [28]p, ibds, color, pep, DJ/0.50)	Grosset/Dunlap	(1944)	Rounds, Glen	40-65	
Rounds, Glen	Whitey's First Roundup (1st, lg8vo, [28]p, ibds, color, DJ/0.50)	Grosset/Dunlap	(1942)	Rounds, Glen	35-50	
Rounds, Glen	Whitey's New Saddle (1st, 8vo, 92p, b/w, DJ/2.50)	Holiday House	(1963)	Rounds, Glen	20-30	
Rounds, Glen	Whitey's Sunday Horse (1st, lg8vo, [28]p, ibds, color, pep, DJ/0.50)	Grosset/Dunlap	1943	Rounds, Glen	40-65	
Randolph, Vance	Who Blowed Up the Church House? (1st, 8vo, 232p, b/w, DJ/3.50)	Columbia U. Pr.	1952	Rounds, Glen	50-80	
Gage, Wilson	Wild Goose Tale (1st {std}, sm4to, 112p, blue cl, b/w, DJ/2.95)	World	1961	Rounds, Glen	20-30	
Rounds, Glen	Wild Horses of the Red Desert (1st, ob4to, [48]p, 3-color, cep, DJ/4.95)	Holiday House	(1969)	Rounds, Glen	25-40	
Rounds, Glen	Wild Orphan (1st, lg8vo, [75]p, b/w, cep, DJ/2.95)	Holiday House	(1961)	Rounds, Glen	25-45	
Rountree, Harry	Adventures of Mabel (1st AM, sm4to, 223p, 8cp)	Dodd	1916	Rountree, Harry	60-90	
Aesopus	Aesop's Fables (1st, 8vo, 340p, green cl, p-o, 48cp, pep)	L: Ward Lock	[1920]	Rountree, Harry	140-220	
Carroll, Lewis	Alice in Wonderland (1st, lg8vo, blue/gilt, teg, 246p, 14cp, pep)	L: Nelson	[1908]	Rountree, Harry	600-800	
Carroll, Lewis	Alice... & Through... (4to, 143p, green/gilt, 8 ticp)	L: Collins	[1928]	Rountree, Harry	200-300	
Jefferies, Richard	Bevis, Story of a Boy (1st, 8vo, 464p, ibds, 8cp)	L: Duckworth	(1913)	Rountree, Harry	80-125	
Towers, Alton	Billy Bunce... (1st, 4to, ibds, unpag, 17cp)	L: A. Cooke	(1907)	Rountree, Harry	250-350	
Russ, Patrick	Caesar: Life Story of a Panda Leopard (1st, 8vo, 88p, col frn, b/w)	Putnam	(1930)	Rountree, Harry	30-45	
Dumas, Alexandre	Dumas Fairy Tale Book (8vo, 290p, grey cl, 4cp, 20pl)	L: Warne	1924	Rountree, Harry	80-140	
Hamer, Sam H.	Enchanted Wood (1st, 8vo, 100p, 8cp)	L: Duckworth	1909	Rountree, Harry	100-165	
Hamer, Sam H.	Enchanted Wood (1st AM, 12mo, 101p, p-o, 8cp)	Dana Estes	[1910]	Rountree, Harry	80-130	
Dumas, Alexandre	Fairy Tales by Dumas (1st AM, sm4to, 114p, fp b/w)	Stokes	(1904)	Rountree, Harry	60-95	
Hamer, Sam H.	Forest Foundling (1st AM, lg8vo, p-o, 109p, 8cp)	Dana Estes	[1909]	Rountree, Harry	100-175	R
Hamer, Sam H.	Forest Foundling (1st, lg8vo, 109p, 8cp)	L: Duckworth	1909	Rountree, Harry	120-200	
Bright, A.D.	Fortunate Princeling (1st, 8vo, 68p, color)	L: Duckworth	1909	Rountree, Harry	50-80	
Hamer, Sam H.	Four Glass Balls (1st, 8vo, 109p, color)	L: Duckworth	1911	Rountree, Harry	75-100	*
Darwin, Bernard	Golf Courses of the British Isles (1st, lg8vo, 253p, gilt, teg, 64cp)	L: Duckworth	1910	Rountree, Harry	1200-2000	
Hart, Helen	Little Silver Tail (1st, 8vo, p-o, 96p, fp color)	Whitman	(1916)	Rountree, Harry	120-200	*
Harvey, Baldwin	Magic Dragon (1st, 8vo, 144p)	L: Duckworth	(1911)	Rountree, Harry	30-50	*
Hamer, Sam H.	Magic Wand (lg8vo, 88p, cloth, 12cp)	Dana Estes	[1908]	Rountree, Harry	120-200	
Bayne, C. (ed.)	My Book of Best Fairy Tales (1st AM, lg8vo, blue/gilt, 368p, 16cp)	Funk/Wagnalls	[1915]	Rountree, Harry	120-200	
Bayne, C. (ed.)	My Book of Best Fairy Tales (1st, lg8vo, blue/gilt, 368p, 16cp)	L: Cassell	(1915)	Rountree, Harry	250-350	
Crichton, Frances E.	Peep-in-World (1st, 8vo, 258p, green cl, 4pl)	L: E. Arnold	1908	Rountree, Harry	30-50	*
Rountree, Harry	Peter Pink-Eye (1st AM, 8vo, p-o, 85p, 8cp)	Dana Estes	(1908)	Rountree, Harry	55-90	
St. Mars, F.	Pinion & Paw (1st, sm8vo, green cl, 296p, 12pl)	L: Chambers	1919	Rountree, Harry	55-80	*
Doyle, Arthur Conan	Poison Belt (1st, 8vo, 199p, blue/gilt, uncut, 16pl)	L: Hodder	(1913)	Rountree, Harry	450-650	
Talbot, Alfred J.	Pond Mermaid (1st, 4to, 48p)	L: Cassell	1929	Rountree, Harry	40-65	*
Nesbit, Edith	Pug Peter (1st, 4to, 64p, teg, blue cloth, color)	L: A. Cooke	(1905)	Rountree, Harry	200-300	
Hamer, Sam H.	Quackles Junior (1st, sm4to, 76p, ibds, 4cp)	L: Cassell	1903	Rountree, Harry	120-200	
Rountree, Harry	Rountree's Ridiculous Rabbits (1st AM, 8vo, unpag, ibds, 5 cp, b/w)	LeRoy Phillips	[1915]	Rountree, Harry	200-300	
Steedman, Amy	Stories from Grimm... (16mo, 116p, p-o, 8cp)	Jack/Dutton	[1908]	Rountree, Harry	60-90	
Hamer, Sam H.	Story of the Ring (1st, 8vo, 53p, 4cp)	L: Cassell	1907	Rountree, Harry	120-180	
Hamer, Sam H.	Story of the Ring (1st AM, 8vo, 53p, 4cp)	Dodd	1907	Rountree, Harry	100-165	
Wyss, Johann D.	Swiss Family Robinson (1st, 8vo, 307p, teg, grey/gilt, 12cp)	L: A&C Black	(1907)	Rountree, Harry	120-200	
Hamer, Sam H.	The Dolomites (1st AM, lg8vo, 305p, 16cp, pep)	NY: J. Lane	1910	Rountree, Harry	150-225	
Hamer, Sam H.	The Dolomites (1st, lg8vo, gilt, 305p, 16cp, pep)	L: Methuen	1910	Rountree, Harry	150-225	
Hamer, Sam H.	Transformations of the Truefitts (1st, 4to, ibds, 77p, 4cp)	L: Cassell	1908	Rountree, Harry	150-250	
Harris, Joel C.	Uncle Remus (1st, folio, [111]p, 12cp)	L: Nelson	[1906]	Rountree, Harry	400-600	
Harris, Joel C.	Uncle Remus (4to, 111p, orange cl, 12 cp by...)	L: Raithby	[1939]	Rountree, Harry	250-400	
Dearden, Harold	Wonderful Adventure (1st UK, sm4to, ibds, 52p, b/w)	L: Heinemann	1929	Rountree, Harry	50-85	*
Hamer, Sam H.	Wonderful Isles (1st AM, sm4to, p-o, 107p, 8cp)	Dana Estes	[1908]	Rountree, Harry	150-250	
Hamer, Sam H.	Wonderful Isles (1st, sm4to, 107p, 8cp)	L: Duckworth	1908	Rountree, Harry	200-300	
Gilbert, Paul T.	Bertram and his Fabulous Animals (1st, 8vo, 159p, b/w, pep, DJ/1.00)	Rand/McNally	(1937)	Rousseff/Maynard	70-120	
Verne, Jules	Antarctic Mystery (1st AM, 8vo, 336p, red/silver, 17 fp b/w)	Lippincott	1899	Roux, G.	800-1200	R
Krauss, Ruth	Bears (1st, 4to, [23]p, ibds, 1-color, cep, DJ/1.00)	Harper	(1948)	Rowand, Phyllis	80-120	
Hopkins, Clark	Cyrus Hunts the Cougar (1st {std}, 8vo, 115p, fp b/w, DJ/2.50)	Little/Brown	(1954)	Rowand, Phyllis	40-65	R
Rowand, Phyllis	Day After Yesterday (1st {std}, lg8vo, 54p, fp 2-color, DJ/2.50)	Little/Brown	(1953)	Rowand, Phyllis	40-65	
Rowand, Phyllis	Every Day in the Year (1st {std}, sm4to, 26p, fp 2-color, DJ/2.75)	Little/Brown	(1959)	Rowand, Phyllis	30-45	
Krauss, Ruth	Growing Story (1st, 4to, ibds, [32]p, color, DJ/2.00)	Harper	(1947)	Rowand, Phyllis	60-90	
Rowand, Phyllis	It is Night (1st, 4to, [32]p, ibds, fp 2-color, dep, DJ/1.75)	Harper	(1953)	Rowand, Phyllis	30-50	
Krauss, Ruth	Monkey Day (1st, lg4to, ibds, [26]p, fp 1-color, DJ/2.50)	Harper	(1957)	Rowand, Phyllis	60-90	
Rowand, Phyllis	Watch the Birdie! (1st, lg8vo, ipcb, [40]p, fp 1-color, DJ/1.50)	W.R. Scott	1947	Rowand, Phyllis	60-100	
Raine, William M.	Brand Blotters (1st, sm8vo, 348p, 2pl)	Dillingham	1912	Rowe, Clarence	40-65	
Stevenson, Rbt. L.	Kidnapped (1st, 16mo, 387p, b/w)	Macmillan	(1930)	Rowe, Clarence	30-50	*
Seton, Ernest T.	Preacher of Cedar Mountain (1st, 8vo, 426p, gilt, col frn by...)	Doubleday/Page	1917	Rowe, Clarence	60-90	
Sabin, Edwin L.	Range & Trail (1st, 8vo, 445p, 8pl)	Crowell	(1910)	Rowe, Clarence	50-85	
Seltzer, Charles A.	Range Riders (1st, 8vo, 310p, b/w)	Outing	1911	Rowe, Clarence	60-100	
Sinclair, Bertrand	Raw Gold (1st, sm8vo, 311p, 4pl)	Dillingham	1908	Rowe, Clarence	40-60	

AUTHOR	TITLE	PUBLISHER	DATE	ARTIST	PRICE	LC
Raine, William M.	Wyoming (1st, sm8vo, 353p, 4pl)	Dillingham	1908	Rowe, Clarence	40-60	
Baker, Margaret	Bears Back in Business (1st, 8vo, 116p, b/w, DJ/3.25)	Farrar, Straus	(1967)	Rowles, Daphne	20-30	
Bond, Michael	Here Comes Thursday (1st AM {std}, 8vo, 126p, fp b/w, DJ/3.25)	Lothrop, Lee	(1967)	Rowles, Daphne	30-50	
Baker, Edna D.	Child is Born (1st, folio, ibds, 60p, color, pep)	Reilly/Lee	(1932)	Royt, Mary	50-85	*
Mother Goose	Mother Goose: Her Own Book (1st, folio, [55]p, color, pep)	Reilly/Lee	(1932)	Royt, Mary	120-200	*
Prelutsky, Jack	Three Saxon Nobles (1st AM {std}, lg4to, [23]p, color, DJ/3.95)	Macmillan	(1969)	Rubin, Eva	25-40	
Golding, Harry	Tim Tubby-Toes (16mo, ipcb, p-o, 85p, fp color, pep)	L: Ward Lock	[1912]	Rudge/Braham	70-100	
Lewis, Claudia	Straps the Cat (1st, 12mo, 141p, rust cl, fp b/w, DJ/2.50)	W.R. Scott	(1957)	Ruhtenberg, Cornelis	30-50	
Rukeyser, Muriel	Come Back, Paul (1st, 4to, [32]p, ibds, 3-color, pep, DJ/2.50)	Harper	(1955)	Rukeyser, Muriel	50-85	R*
Nash, Ogden	Cricket of Carador (1st {std}-{1st bk}, sm8vo, 165p, col frn, b/w, pep)	Doubleday/Page	1925	Rule, Christopher	80-145	
Mother Goose	Littlefolks' Mother Goose (1st, 4to, 158p, p-o, 7cp, pep)	Sears	(1926)	Rule, Christopher	70-100	
Kirk, Victorine	Mickey & the Monkeys (1st, sm4to, 175p, col frn, b/w, pep)	Viking	1927	Rule, Christopher	40-60	
Collodi, Carlo	Pinocchio (1st, lg8vo, 236p, p-o, orange cl, col frn, pep)	Sears	(1926)	Rule, Christopher	60-90	
Craddock, Harry (cmp)	Savoy Cocktail Book (1st, 8vo, 287p, pcb, gilt, color)	L: Constable	1930	Rumbold, Gilbert	180-240	
Parry, Edward A.	Scarlet Herring (1st, 8vo, 253p, uncut, green/gilt, fp b/w, AEG)	L: Smith Elder	1899	Rusden, Athelstan	75-100	
Marshall, Helen L.	New Mexican Boy (1st, 8vo, 85p, 9 fp color, cep, DJ/2.00)	Holiday House	(1940)	Rush, Olive	30-50	
Strahorn, Carrie A.	15 Thousand Miles by Stage (1st, lg8vo, 673p, gilt, p-o, teg, 4cp)	Putnam	1911	Russell, Charles M.	500-800	
Jennings, Alphonso	Beating Back (1st, sm8vo, 355p, gilt, 3pl by...)	Appleton	1914	Russell, Charles M.	70-100	*
Freeman, Harry C.	Brief History of Butte Montana (1st, 4to, 123p, pep, 4 illus by..)	H.O. Shepard Co.	1900	Russell, Charles M.	150-250	
Brummitt, Stella W.	Brother Van (1st, sm8vo, 171p, pict cl, 2 illus by...)	NY: M. Ed. Mov.	(1919)	Russell, Charles M.	60-90	
Steedman, Charles J.	Bucking the Sagebrush (1st, 8vo, 270p, map, teg, 9pl)	Putnam	1904	Russell, Charles M.	300-500	
Bower, B.M.	Chip of the Flying-U (1st, 12mo, 264p, red cl, 3cp)	Street & Smith	(1906)	Russell, Charles M.	120-200	
MacKay, Malcolm S.	Cow Range & Hunting Trail (1st, 8vo, gilt, 243p, 3pl by...)	Putnam	1925	Russell, Charles M.	300-500	
Davis, Duke	Flashlights from Mountain & Plain (1st, sm8vo, 266p, 4cp)	(New Jersey)	1911	Russell, Charles M.	125-180	
Russell, Charles M.	Good Medicine (1st [trade ed], 4to, 162p, tan cl, col frn, pep)	Doubleday/Doran	(1930)	Russell, Charles M.	120-200	
Parker, Frances	Hope Hathaway (1st, sm8vo, 408p, green cl, 9pl)	C.M. Clark	1904	Russell, Charles M.	80-125	
Beacom, John	How the Buffalo Lost his Crown (1st, ob folio, 41p, 8 tip-in pl)	Forest/Stream	1894	Russell, Charles M.	2000-3000	
Linderman, Frank B.	Indian Old-Man Stories (1st, 8vo, gilt, p-o, 169p, 9cp)	Scribner	1920	Russell, Charles M.	160-250	
Linderman, Frank B.	Indian Why Stories (1st, 8vo, maroon/gilt, p-o, 236p, 8cp)	Scribner	1915	Russell, Charles M.	160-250	
Bower, B.M.	Lure of the Dim Trails (1st, sm8vo, red cl, 210p, 3cp)	Dillingham	(1907)	Russell, Charles M.	100-180	
Hamilton, William T.	My Sixty Years on the Plains (1st, 8vo, 244p, p-o, 6pl by...)	Forest/Stream	1905	Russell, Charles M.	170-240	
Bower, B.M.	Range Dwellers (1st, 12mo, 356p, 3cp)	Street & Smith	(1907)	Russell, Charles M.	150-200	
Coburn, Wallace D.	Rhymes from a Roundup Camp (1st, 12mo, 138p, 7 b/w)	Ridgley Press	1899	Russell, Charles M.	250-350	
Coburn, Wallace D.	Rhymes from a Roundup Camp ({new ed.}, sm8vo, teg, 137p, 7pl)	Putnam	1903	Russell, Charles M.	150-250	
Hough, Emerson	Story of the Cowboy (1st, 8vo, 349p, 6pl by...)	Appleton	1897	Russell, Charles M.	125-200	
Wister, Owen	The Virginian (1st, 8vo, red cl, p-o, 506p, teg, 42 illus by...)	Macmillan	1911	Russell, Charles M.	280-350	*
Vaughn, Robert	Then & Now (1st, 8vo, 461p, black/gilt, 8pl)	(Minneap)	1900	Russell, Charles M.	250-400	
Russell, Charles M.	Trails Plowed Under (1st {std}, 4to, 210p, 5 dp cp)	Doubleday/Page	1927	Russell, Charles M.	120-200	
Bower, B.M.	Uphill Climb (1st, sm8vo, 283p, 4pl)	Little/Brown	1913	Russell, Charles M.	80-125	
Bannerman, Helen	Little Black Sambo (folio, wraps, color)	NY: S. Gabriel	[1920]	Russell, Mary L.	150-225	
Hubbell-Plummer, B.	Little Homespun Songs (1st, lg4to, 104p, ibds, p-o, 12pl, pep)	Stokes	(1920)	Russell, Mary L.	100-170	
Deihl, Edna G.	Teddy Bear that Prowled the Night (1st, 4to, ibds, 24p, color)	S. Gabriel	(1924)	Russell, Mary L.	80-120	*
Birdsall, Katharine N.	Jacks of All Trades (1st, 8vo, 236p, 6cp)	Appleton	1902	Russell, Walter	30-50	*
Shiel, Matthew P.	Lord of the Sea (1st AM, 12mo, 474p, blue cl, frn by...)	Stokes	(1901)	Russell, Walter	150-250	
Habberton, John	Tiger & the Insect (1st, sm8vo, ipcb, 235p, uncut, 9pl)	R.H. Russell	1902	Russell, Walter	35-60	
Kitt, Tamara	Boy Who Fooled the Giant (1st, 8vo, ibds, 61p, color)	Grosset/Dunlap	1963	Russell, William	25-40	*
Housman, Laurence	Angels & Ministers (1st, sm8vo, 139p, fp b/w)	L: J. Cape	1922	Rutherston, Albert	35-60	*
Colvile, Kathleen	Jason & the Princess (1st AM, 8vo, blue cl, 86p, 4cp)	Houghton	(1926)	Rutherston, Albert	35-60	*
Bragdon, Ollie	Moon Party (1st, 12mo, 122p, p-o, 6pl)	Caldwell	(1904)	Ruyl, Beatrice B.	50-75	
Edey, Birdsall O.	Six Giants & a Griffin (1st, 4to, 46p, 6pl)	R.H. Russell	1903	Ruyl, Beatrice B.	160-240	*
Costain, Thomas B.	Black Rose (1st {illus ed} {std}, lg8vo, 403p, gilt, dp col, pep, DJ/5.00)	Doubleday	1953	Ryman, Herbert	100-170	*
Lewis, Caroline	Clara in Blunderland (1st, 8vo, 150p, green cl, 4pl)	L: Heinemann	1902	S.R.	100-165	
Alcott, Louisa M.	Hole in the Wall (1st, sm8vo, 62p, orange/gilt, cvr by...)	Little/Brown	(1899)	Sacker, Amy	60-90	
Ewing, Juliana H.	Jacanapes (1st, 12mo, 60p, blue cl, b/w)	J. Knight	1895	Sacker, Amy	35-60	*
Robinson, Edith	Little Puritan Rebel (1st, 12mo, 135p, blue/gilt, b/w)	L.C. Page	1898	Sacker, Amy	30-50	
Robinson, Edith	Loyal Little Maid (1st, 12mo, 79p, b/w illus)	J. Knight	1897	Sacker, Amy	25-40	
Sleight, Charles L.	Prince of the Pin Elves (1st, 12mo, 159p, b/w)	L.C. Page	1897	Sacker, Amy	70-100	
Raftery, Gerald	Twenty-Dollar Horse (1st, 8vo, 192p, b/w, DJ/2.75)	J. Messner	(1955)	Safran, Bernard	30-50	*
Newman, Robert	Boy Who Could Fly (1st {std}, 8vo, 121p, fp b/w, cep, DJ)	Atheneum	1967	Sagsoorian, Paul	30-50	*
DeJong, Meindert	Horse Came Running (1st {std}, 8vo, 147p, b/w, DJ/4.95)	Macmillan	(1970)	Sagsoorian, Paul	30-45	
Saint, Lawrence B.	Knight of the Cross (1st, 8vo, 220p, gilt, uncut, p-o, teg, 7 ticp)	Jacobs	(1914)	Saint, Lawrence B.	25-40	
Saint-Exupery, A.	Little Prince (1st AM, sq8vo, 91p, color, DJ/2.50)	Reynal/Hitchcock	(1943)	Saint-Exupery, A.	800-1400	
Godden, Rumer	Doll's House (1st AM, 8vo, 125p, yellow, cl, 4cp, DJ/2.50)	Viking	1948	Saintsbury, Dana	70-120	R
Hearn, Lafcadio	Boy Who Drew Cats (1st, folio, 40p, ibds, fp color, DJ/1.95)	Macmillan	1963	Saito, Manabu	35-50	
Lord Brabourne	Friends & Foes from Fairy Land (1st AM, 8vo, yellow cl, 367p)	Little/Brown	1886	Sambourne, Linley	100-180	
Andersen, Hans C.	Three Tales/Hans Andersen (lg sq8vo, 79p, blue/gilt, 22 b/w)	L: Macmillan	1910	Sambourne, Linley	90-160	
Kingsley, Charles	Water Babies (1st, 8vo, 371p, blue/gilt, AEG, b/w, cep)	L: Macmillan	1885	Sambourne, Linley	120-200	
Kingsley, Charles	Water Babies (1st [new ed.], 8vo, blue/gilt, 330p, b/w)	L: Macmillan	1894	Sambourne, Linley	90-125	
Aesopus	Famous Fables (4to, ibds, 40p, fp b/w)	Harter	(1933)	Sampson, Florence	70-100	
Weil, Ann Y.	John Phillip Sousa: Marching Boy (1st {std}, sm8vo, 192p, b/w, DJ/1.95)	Bobbs-Merrill	(1959)	Sampson, Kath.	25-35	
Samson, Anne S.	Lines, Spines & Porcupines (1st {std}, lg8vo, [64]p, 2-color, DJ/3.50)	Doubleday	(1969)	Samson, Anne	25-40	
Lide, Alice A.	Aztec Drums (1st {std}, sm8vo, 142p, blue cl, fp b/w, pep, DJ)	Longmans	1938	Sanchez, Carlos M.	30-50	
Belpre, Pura	Perez and Martina (1st, lg ob8vo, 79p, 16cp, pep)	Warne	(1932)	Sanchez, Carlos M.	80-140	
Sawyer, Ruth	Picture Tales from Spain (1st, ob12mo, 132p, b/w, DJ/1.25)	Stokes	1936	Sanchez, Carlos M.	40-65	
Lide, Alice A.	Princess of Yucatan (1st {std}, 12mo, tan cl, 187p, b/w, pep, DJ/1.75)	Longmans	1939	Sanchez, Carlos M.	30-50	
Lederer, Joe	Fafan in China (1st, 8vo, 137p, green cl, b/w, pep, DJ/2.00)	Holiday House	(1939)	Sanderson, William	25-40	*
Blodgett, Mabel F.	At the Queen's Mercy (1st, 8vo, 261p, teg, uncut, 5pl)	Lamson/Wolffe	1897	Sandham, Henry	70-100	*
Burnett, Frances H.	Editha's Burglar (1st [1], 12mo, blue/gilt, 64p, 13pl)	J. Marsh	1888	Sandham, Henry	200-300	

AUTHOR	TITLE	PUBLISHER	DATE	ARTIST	PRICE	LC
Jackson, Helen H.	Father Junipero... (1st, 12mo, 159p, b/w)	Little/Brown	1902	Sandham, Henry	35-60	
Lummis, Charles F.	Gold Fish of Gran Chimu (1st, 12mo, gilt, 126p, teg, 7pl)	Lamson/Wolffe	1896	Sandham, Henry	100-175	
Baylor, Frances C.	Juan and Juanita (1st, 8vo, green/gilt, 276p, b/w, pep, PPP)	Ticknor	1888	Sandham, Henry	125-200	
Jacobs, Violet	Golden Heart (1st AM, 8vo, 171p, green/gilt, p-o, 16pl)	Doubleday/Page	1905	Sandheim, May	55-80	*
Rossetti, Christina	Prince's Progress (1st, 8vo, gilt, 146p, teg, fp b/w)	L: A. Melrose	[1900]	Sandheim, May	75-120	
Lexau, Joan M.	Crocodile & Hen (1st, ob4to, [32]p, color, DJ/3.95)	Harper	(1969)	Sandin, Joan	20-35	*
Wojciechowska, Maia	Hey, What's Wrong with This One? (1st, 8vo, 72p, fp b/w, DJ/3.95)	Harper	(1969)	Sandin, Joan	30-50	
Lexau, Joan M.	It All Began with Drip, Drip, Drip (1st {std}, ob4to, [41]p, color, DJ/4.25)	McCall Pub.	(1970)	Sandin, Joan	30-45	*
Little, Jean	Look Through My Window (1st, 8vo, 258p, fp b/w, DJ/3.95)	Harper	(1970)	Sandin, Joan	25-45	
Hull, Eleanor	Trainful of Strangers (1st {std}, 8vo, 114p, b/w, DJ/3.95)	Atheneum	1968	Sandin, Joan	25-45	*
Coolidge, Olivia	Legends of the North (1st, 8vo, 260p, b/w, DJ/3.00)	Houghton	1951	Sandoz, Edouard	20-30	*
Coolidge, Olivia	Trojan War (1st, 8vo, 244p, b/w, DJ/3.00)	Houghton	1952	Sandoz, Edouard	20-30	*
Sandys, Ruth	Numerous Names Nimbly Narrated (1st, 4to, ibds, [58]p, color)	L: Oxford U.Pr.	(1930)	Sandys, Ruth	170-240	
Johnson, Laura R.	Teddy-Bear ABC (1st, sq8vo, [55]p, color, pep)	Caldwell	(1907)	Sanford, Margaret L.	250-350	
Tennyson, Alfred	Morte d'Arthur (1st, sm4to, white bds/gilt, 24p, color)	L: Chatto	1912	Sangorski, Alberto	180-250	
Armstrong, Richard	Mystery of Obadiah (1st, 8vo, 160p, col frn, b/w, DJ)	L: J.M. Dent	1943	Sankey, Marjorie	30-50	
Larom, Henry	Mountain Pony (1st {std}, 8vo, 240p, b/w, pep, DJ/2.00)	Whittlesey	(1946)	Santee, Ross	30-50	
Stephens, William	Hermit Crab Lives in a Shell (1st, 8vo, 46p, color, DJ/3.95)	Holiday House	(1969)	Sapieha, Christine	25-45	*
Boyd, Elizabeth M.	All About David (1st, lg8vo, 117p, pep, b/w, DJ/1.50)	Winston	(1940)	Sarg, Tony	30-50	
Pezet, A. Washington	Aristokia (1st, 8vo, 214p, blue/gilt, 8pl)	Century	1919	Sarg, Tony	40-65	
MacPherson, J.F.	Children For Ever (1st, 8vo, 352p, 16 color)	L: John Long	1908	Sarg, Tony	120-200	
Lefevre, Felicite	Cock, Mouse & Little Red Hen (1st, 8vo, 103p, 24cp)	L: Richards	1907	Sarg, Tony	225-350	
Lefevre, Felicite	Cock, Mouse & Little Red Hen (1st AM, 8vo, 103p, 24cp)	Jacobs	(1907)	Sarg, Tony	180-270	
Cobb, Irving	Fibble, D.D. (1st, 8vo, 279p, blue cl, p-o, b/w, pep)	Doran	(1916)	Sarg, Tony	25-45	
Wells, Carveth	Jungle Man & his Animals (1st, lg4to, ibds, 68p, 12cp)	Duffield	1925	Sarg, Tony	180-240	*
Wells, Carveth	Jungle Man & his Animals (1st {this pub}, 4to, 68p, ibds, 7cp)	McBride	(1925)	Sarg, Tony	170-240	
Mitchell, George W.	Kernel Cob & Little Miss Sweetclover (1st, 8vo, ibds, [96]p, color, pep)	Volland	(1918)	Sarg, Tony	100-160	
Hellman, Sam	Low Bridge & Punk Pungs (1st, 12mo, 111p, 5pl)	Little/Brown	1924	Sarg, Tony	30-50	
White, William A.	Martial Adventures of Henry and Me (1st, 8vo, 340p, red cl, 25 b/w)	Macmillan	1918	Sarg, Tony	30-50	
Spaeth, Sigmund	Maxims to Music (1st {std}, 4to, 64p, color, DJ/2.00)	McBride	1939	Sarg, Tony	130-180	
Marquis, Don	Noah an' Jonah an' Cap'n John Smith (1st, 12mo, 157p, b/w)	Appleton	1921	Sarg, Tony	25-45	
Maniates, Belle	Our Next-Door Neighbors (1st, sm8vo, 280p, 12 fp b/w)	Little/Brown	1917	Sarg, Tony	30-55	
Collodi, Carlo	Pinocchio (1st, 4to, red cl, 122p, pep, 6cp)	Platt/Munk	(1940)	Sarg, Tony	100-160	
Lefevre, Felicite	Soldier Boy (1st, sm8vo, [64]p, orange cl, color, pep)	Greenberg	(1926)	Sarg, Tony	60-100	
Mills, G.R.	Talking Dolls (1st, 4to, [96]p, color, pep)	Greenberg	(1930)	Sarg, Tony	80-130	
Potter, Miriam C.	The Gigglequicks (1st, 12mo, ibds, unpag, color, pep)	Volland	(1918)	Sarg, Tony	90-135	*
Sarg, Tony	Tony Sarg's Book of Animals (4to, green ibds, color, pep)	Greenberg	(1925)	Sarg, Tony	100-150	
Sarg, Tony	Tony Sarg's Book of Tricks (1st, 4to, ibds, [96]p, color, pep)	Greenberg	(1928)	Sarg, Tony	80-120	
Sarg, Tony	Tony Sarg's New York (1st, lg4to, p-o, [60]p, 24cp)	Greenberg	1926	Sarg, Tony	140-200	
Sarg, Tony	Tony Sarg's Wonder Zoo (1st, ob12mo, ibds, [30]p, color)	Greenberg	(1925)	Sarg, Tony	50-80	
Moses, Montrose (ed)	Treasury of Plays for Children (1st, 8vo, 550p, col frn, 8pl, pep)	Little/Brown	1921	Sarg, Tony	60-100	
O'Malley, Frank W.	War-Whirl in Washington (1st, sm8vo, 298p, grey cl, 16pl)	Century	1918	Sarg, Tony	40-60	
Sarg, Tony	Where is Tommy? (1st, sm ob4to, [20]p, ipcb, color)	Greenberg	(1932)	Sarg, Tony	70-120	
Munson, Nelson	Who's Who in Tony Sarg's Zoo (1st, 4to, ibds, [34]p, fp color, pep)	McLoughlin	1937	Sarg, Tony	140-200	
Macy, S.B.	From Slavery to Freedom (1st, 4to, 299p, green/gilt, 8cp, pep)	L: Longmans	1910	Sarg/Robinson	200-300	
Stevens, Frank	Adventures in Hiveland (1st, 8vo, 227p, green/gilt, b/w)	L: Hutchinson	1903	Sargent, L.A.	140-220	
Sargent, Robert	Adventurous Moth (1st {std}, 4to, [32]p, 2-color, DJ/3.50)	Simon/Schuster	(1968)	Sargent, Robert	25-45	
White, Bessie	Bear Named Grumms (1st, lg8vo, 81p, b/w, DJ/2.50)	Houghton	1953	Sari	20-35	
Kissin, Rita	Gramp's Desert Chick (1st, ob4to, ibds, [36]p, fp 2-color, pep, DJ/2.00)	Reynal/Hitchcock	(1946)	Sari	40-70	
Laird, Helene	Nancy Keeps House (1st {std}, 8vo, 189p, b/w, DJ/2.00)	World	(1947)	Sari	25-40	
Govan, Christine	Pink Maple House (1st {std}, sm8vo, 283p, b/w, DJ/2.50)	Aladdin	1950	Sari	80-120	
N/A	Puss in Boots (1st, 16mo, [59]p, fp color)	McLoughlin	(1941)	Sari	25-40	*
Govan, Christine	Surprising Summer (1st {std}, sm8vo, 171p, b/w, DJ/2.25)	Aladdin	1951	Sari	80-120	
Johnson, Enid	Three J's (1st, 8vo, 63p, fp b/w, pep, DJ/1.50)	J. Messner	(1952)	Sari	50-80	*
Govan, Christine	Tilly's Strange Secret (1st {std}, sm8vo, 184p, b/w, DJ/2.25)	Aladdin	1952	Sari	80-125	
Sasek, Miroslav	This is New York (1st, lg4to, ibds, 60p, color, DJ/3.00, NYTBI)	Macmillan	(1960)	Sasek, Miroslav	80-120	
Sasek, Miroslav	This is Paris (1st, lg4to, ibds, 60p, color, DJ/3.00)	Macmillan	(1959)	Sasek, Miroslav	60-100	
Pollard, Josephine	Elfin-Land (1st, ob folio, [40]p, ibds, chromos, dep)	G.W. Harlan	(1882)	Satterlee, Walter	160-240	
Moore, Frank F.	Impudent Comedian (1st, sm8vo, green cl, teg, 274p, 10pl)	Herbert Stone	1897	Sauber, Robert	60-90	
Galsworthy, John	Awakening (1st, sm4to, 63p, color, pep)	Scribner	(1920)	Sauter, R.H.	50-90	R*
Judson, Clara I.	Andrew Carnegie (1st, lg8vo, 157p, b/w, DJ/3.50)	Follett	(1964)	Savage, Steele	20-30	
Webb, Wheaton P.	Twelve Labors of Wimpole Stout (1st, 8vo, 176p, b/w, DJ/3.95)	Abingdon Press	(1970)	Savage, Steele	20-30	
Carlson, Natalie S.	Orphelines in the Enchanted Castle (1st, sm4to, 95p, fp b/w, cep, DJ/3.50)	Harper	(1964)	Saviozzi, Adriana	50-80	R
Meader, Stephen W.	Keep 'Em Rolling (1st {std}, 8vo, 192p, b/w, DJ/3.50)	Harcourt	(1967)	Savitt, Al	80-120	
Kendall, Lace	Little Smoke (1st, lg8vo, unpag, ibds, b/w, DJ/2.75)	Coward	(1961)	Savitt, Sam	25-45	
Young, Miriam	Up and Away (1st {std}, 8vo, 191p, fp b/w, DJ/3.25)	Harcourt	(1960)	Savitt, Sam	30-50	
Haggard, H. Rider	Heart of the World (1st, 12mo, 347p, green/gilt, 13pl)	NY: Longmans	1895	Sawyer, Amy	200-300	
Sawyer, Ruth	Tale of the Enchanted Bunnies (1st {std}, lg8vo, 131p, p-o, fp color)	Harper	(1923)	Sawyer, Ruth	60-100	
Doughtie, Charles	Gabriel Wrinkles (1st, 4to, [46]p, fp 2-color, DJ/2.75)	Dodd	(1959)	Saxon, Charles	40-65	*
Omar Khayyam	Rubaiyat of Omar Khayyam (1st, lg8vo, 149p, gilt, color, pep)	Random	(1947)	Sayah, Mahmoud	45-70	
Nichols, Beverly	Cats' XYZ (1st AM, lg8vo, ibds, 128p, fp color, pep, DJ/3.50)	Dutton	(1961)	Sayer, Derrick	30-50	
Johnston, Johanna	Supposings (1st, 4to, [32]p, fp 3-color, DJ/4.95)	Holiday House	(1967)	Sayers, Rudy	25-40	
Summers, Clara	Sandy Sandman (1st, lg8vo, tan cl, p-o, 155p, 8cp, pep)	Whitman	(1917)	Scannell, Mae	40-70	
La Fontaine, J.	Fables of La Fontaine (1st {std}, 4to, ibds, 60p, color, DJ/3.25)	Doubleday	(1964)	Scarry, Richard	65-100	
Scarry, Richard	Great Big Schoolhouse (1st, folio, 69p, color)	Random	(1969)	Scarry, Richard	50-85	*
Parish, Peggy	My Golden Book of Manners (1st, folio, [24]p, ibds, color)	Golden Press	1962	Scarry, Richard	30-50	*
Brown, Margaret W.	Two Little Miners (1st, sm8vo, [42]p, ibds, color, LGB/#66)	Simon/Schuster	(1949)	Scarry, Richard	25-40	
Scarry, Richard	What Do People Do All Day? (1st, folio, 95p, color, pep)	Random	1968	Scarry, Richard	60-90	

ARTIST: 178

AUTHOR	TITLE	PUBLISHER	DATE	ARTIST	PRICE	LC
Schaad, Hans	Gunpowder Tower (1st AM {std}, ob folio, ibds, unpag, color, DJ/3.75)	Harcourt	(1967)	Schaad, Hans	25-45	
Coolidge, Olivia	Marathon Looks on the Sea (1st {std}, 8vo, 246p, b/w, DJ/3.50)	Houghton	1967	Schachner, Erwin	40-65	R*
Malot, Hector	Adventures of Remi (1st, lg8vo, p-o, 492p, gilt, pep, WS)	Rand/McNally	(1925)	Schaeffer, Mead	40-70	
Meader, Stephen W.	Black Buccaneer (1st, lg8vo, black/gilt, 269p, 8cp, pep)	Harcourt	(1920)	Schaeffer, Mead	70-100	
Dumas, Alexandre	Count of Monte Cristo (lg8vo, 472p, black/gilt, p-o, 8cp, pep)	Dodd	[1920]	Schaeffer, Mead	40-65	
Bullen, Frank T.	Cruise of the Cachalot (1st, lg8vo, 301p, 8cp, pep)	Dodd	1926	Schaeffer, Mead	35-60	
Knipe, A.A.	Everybody's Washington (1st, lg8vo, 282p, gilt, uncut, p-o, 7cp, pep)	Dodd	1931	Schaeffer, Mead	35-60	
Masefield, John	Jim Davis (1st, 8vo, blue/gilt, p-o, 226p, 8cp)	Stokes	1924	Schaeffer, Mead	35-60	*
Hugo, Victor	Les Miserables (lg8vo, black/gilt, 585p, pep, 12cp)	Dodd	[1925]	Schaeffer, Mead	70-100	
Blackmore, R.D.	Lorna Doone (1st, lg8vo, p-o, 646p, black/gilt, 8cp, pep)	Dodd	(1930)	Schaeffer, Mead	45-70	
Melville, Herman	Moby Dick (1st, lg8vo, p-o, 540p, black/gilt, teg, 12cp, pep)	Dodd	1922	Schaeffer, Mead	50-85	
Melville, Herman	Omoo (1st, lg8vo, teg, 299p, black/gilt, 8cp, pep)	Dodd	1924	Schaeffer, Mead	70-125	
Dumas, Alexandre	Three Musketeers (1st, lg8vo, black/gilt, 555p, 8cp)	Dodd	[1929]	Schaeffer, Mead	50-80	
Scott, Michael	Tom Cringle's Log (1st, lg8vo, black/gilt, 384p, p-o, 7cp, pep)	Dodd	1927	Schaeffer, Mead	50-80	
Melville, Herman	Typee (lg8vo, black cl, teg, 283p, 8cp, pep)	Dodd	(1923)	Schaeffer, Mead	60-90	
Tracy, Louis	Wings of the Morning (lg8vo, 319p, p-o, 4cp)	Winston	(1924)	Schaeffer, Mead	35-60	
Tracy, Louis	Wings of the Morning (1st, lg8vo, black/gilt, 320p, teg, 12cp)	E.J. Clode	(1924)	Schaeffer, Mead	35-60	
Schaeffler, Ursula	Thief and the Blue Rose (1st AM {std}, 4to, [25]p, ibds, color, DJ/4.25)	Harcourt	(1967)	Schaeffler, Ursula	40-65	
Sutton, Adah L.	Teddy Bears (1st, lg8vo, 154p, ibds, 6cp)	Saalfield	1907	Schaffer, A.J.	250-400	
Scharen, Beatrix	Gigin and Till (1st AM {std}, ob4to, [27]p, 2-color, DJ/4.95)	Atheneum	1969	Scharen, Beatrix	25-45	
Memling, Carl	Riddles, Riddles from A to Z (1st {A}, 8vo, [24]p, ibds, color, LGB/#490)	Golden Press	(1962)	Schart, Trina	35-50	
Schick, Eleanor	5A and 7B (1st {std}, ob4to, [32]p, fp b/w, ipcb, DJ/2.95)	Macmillan	(1967)	Schick, Eleanor	30-50	
Wahl, Jan	Christmas in the Forest (1st {std}, ob4to, [32]p, 1-color, DJ/3.50)	Macmillan	(1967)	Schick, Eleanor	30-50	
Schick, Eleanor	City in the Summer (1st {std}, ob4to, [32]p, color, DJ/4.50)	Macmillan	(1969)	Schick, Eleanor	30-50	
Schick, Eleanor	City in the Winter (1st {std}, ob4to, [32]p, color, DJ/4.95)	Macmillan	(1970)	Schick, Eleanor	30-50	
Schick, Eleanor	Dancing School (1st, ob12mo, ipcb, [32]p, b/w, DJ/2.25)	Harper	(1966)	Schick, Eleanor	30-50	
Schick, Eleanor	I'm Going to the Ocean (1st {std}, ob8vo, [30]p, fp b/w, DJ/2.50)	Macmillan	(1966)	Schick, Eleanor	30-50	
Schick, Eleanor	Katie Goes to Camp (1st, ob4to, [32]p, b/w, DJ/3.50)	Macmillan	(1968)	Schick, Eleanor	30-50	
Schick, Eleanor	Little School at Cottonwood Corners (1st, ob8vo, [32]p, b/w, DJ/2.25)	Harper	(1965)	Schick, Eleanor	30-50	
Schick, Eleanor	Making Friends (1st {std}, 8vo, [32]p, 1-color, cep, DJ/3.95)	Macmillan	(1969)	Schick, Eleanor	30-50	
Schick, Eleanor	Peggy's New Brother (1st {std}, 8vo, [32]p, color, DJ/4.50)	Macmillan	(1970)	Schick, Eleanor	30-50	
Schick, Eleanor	Surprise in the Forest (1st, ob24mo, [32]p, ibds, b/w, DJ/1.95)	Harper	(1964)	Schick, Eleanor	30-50	
Dahl, Roald	Charlie & the Chocolate Factory (1st, lg8vo, gilt, 162p, b/w, cep, DJ/3.95)	Knopf	(1964)	Schindelman, Joseph	400-650	
Harris, Leon	Great Picture Robbery (1st {std}, ob8vo, [34]p, 2-color, cep, DJ, NYTBI)	Atheneum	1963	Schindelman, Joseph	30-45	*
Merriam, Eve	There is No Rhyme for Silver (1st {std}, 8vo, 70p, b/w, DJ/3.25)	Atheneum	1962	Schindelman, Joseph	30-45	
Andersen, Hans C.	Fir Tree (1st, 4to, ibds, [24]p, color, pep, DJ/1.00)	Grosset/Dunlap	(1947)	Schlesinger, Alice	40-60	*
Grimm Bros.	Three Tales from Grimm (1st AM, 8vo, pink cl, [48]p, color, DJ/1.25)	Macmillan	1938	Schlotter, Brunhild	100-150	
Baumann, Hans	Fenny the Desert Fox (1st, ob4to, [23]p, color, DJ/3.95)	Random	(1970)	Schmid, Eleonore	30-50	
Kesselman, Wendy	Franz Tovey & the Rare Animals (1st {std}, 4to, [32]p, b/w, cep, DJ/3.25)	Harlin Quist	(1968)	Schmid, Eleonore	40-65	
Schmid, Eleonore	Horns Everywhere (1st, sq8vo, [32]p, fp color, cep, DJ/3.95)	Harlin Quist	1968	Schmid, Eleonore	45-70	
Meader, Stephen W.	Bulldozer (1st {std}, 8vo, 239p, b/w, DJ/2.50)	Harcourt	(1951)	Schmidt, Edwin	130-175	
Means, Florence C.	Silver Fleece (1st {std}, 8vo, 213p, b/w, cep, DJ/2.50)	Winston	(1950)	Schmidt, Edwin	20-35	
DeJong, Meindert	Mighty Ones (1st, lg8vo, 282p, b/w, DJ/3.50)	Harper	(1959)	Schmidt, Harvey	30-45	*
Burnham, Clara L.	Jewel's Story Book (1st, 12mo, 343p, green cl, 6pl, pep)	Houghton	1904	Schmitt, Albert	25-40	
Atkinson, Eleanor	Poilu, Dog of Roubaix (1st, sm8vo, 225p, frn by...)	Harper	1918	Schneider, Sophie	60-100	
Mulets, Lenore E.	Stories of the Little Fishes (1st, 8vo, 288p, 6pl)	L.C. Page	1905	Schneider, Sophie	25-40	*
Miles, Miska	Eddie's Bear (1st {std}, sq8vo, 43p, color, DJ/3.95)	Little/Brown	(1970)	Schoenherr, John	25-40	
Miles, Miska	Fox and the Fire (1st {std}, ob4to, 40p, color, DJ/3.50)	Little/Brown	(1966)	Schoenherr, John	25-40	
Morey, Walter	Gentle Ben (1st {std}, 8vo, 191p, fp b/w, DJ/3.95)	Dutton	(1965)	Schoenherr, John	40-70	
Miles, Miska	Hoagie's Rifle Gun (1st {std}, 8vo, 40p, fp b/w, DJ/3.50)	Little/Brown	(1970)	Schoenherr, John	25-40	
Freschet, Berniece	Kangaroo Red (1st, 8vo, [47]p, fp 1-color, DJ/3.25)	Scribner	(1966)	Schoenherr, John	25-40	*
Miles, Miska	Mississippi Possum (1st {std}, lg8vo, 41p, 2-color, DJ/3.00)	Little/Brown	(1965)	Schoenherr, John	40-65	
George, Jean C.	Moon of the Chickarees (1st, 8vo, 40p, fp b/w, DJ/3.75)	Crowell	(1968)	Schoenherr, John	20-35	
Miles, Miska	Nobody's Cat (1st {std}, ob8vo, 43p, 2-color, DJ/3.75)	Little/Brown	(1969)	Schoenherr, John	30-45	
Miles, Miska	Rabbit Garden (1st {std}, 4to, 40p, b/w, DJ/3.50)	Little/Brown	(1967)	Schoenherr, John	25-40	
North, Sterling	Rascal... (1st {std}, 8vo, 189p, pcb, gilt, b/w, pep, DJ/3.95, NH)	Dutton	1963	Schoenherr, John	60-90	R
Schoenherr, John	The Barn (1st {std}, sm4to, 40p, b/w, pep, DJ/3.50)	Little/Brown	(1968)	Schoenherr, John	25-40	*
North, Sterling	The Wolfling (1st {std}, 8vo, ibds, 223p, fp b/w, DJ/5.95)	Dutton	1969	Schoenherr, John	25-40	
Clarke, Arthur	Islands in the Sky (1st {std}, 8vo, 209p, DJ/2.00, pep by...)	Winston	(1952)	Schomburg, Alex	75-120	
Tappan, Eva M.	American Hero Stories (1st, 8vo, 301p, gilt, 4cp)	Houghton	1926	Schoonover, Frank	25-40	
Kauffman, Reginald	Barbary Bo... (1st, 8vo, p-o, 261p, 5pl)	Penn	1929	Schoonover, Frank	30-60	
Paine, Ralph D.	Blackbeard Buccaneer (1st, 8vo, 309p, gilt, p-o, col frn 5pl)	Penn	1922	Schoonover, Frank	35-60	
Fraser, William A.	Blood Lilies (1st, 8vo, 262p, 6pl)	Scribner	1903	Schoonover, Frank	30-50	
Smith, Mary P.W.	Boy Captive of Old Deerfield (1st, 8vo, 295p, p-o, 6cp, gilt, pep)	Little/Brown	1929	Schoonover, Frank	30-50	*
Van Dyke, Henry	Broken Soldier & Maid of France (1st, 8vo, 66p, teg, blue/gilt, 2 ticp)	Harper	1919	Schoonover, Frank	35-60	
Carter, Russell	Crimson Cutlass (1st, 8vo, 302p, col frn, pep)	Penn	(1933)	Schoonover, Frank	25-40	*
McIlwraith, Jean N.	Curious Career of Roderick Campbell (1st, sm8vo, 287p, 4pl)	Houghton	1901	Schoonover, Frank	25-45	
Munroe, Kirk	Flamingo Feather (1st {std}, lg8vo, 222p, p-o, gilt, 10pl, pep)	Harper	(1923)	Schoonover, Frank	50-80	
Swan, Oliver G.	Frontier Days (1st, lg8vo, 512p, 3cp by...)	Macrae Smith	(1928)	Schoonover, Frank	60-90	
Lee, Jennette	Happy Island (1st, 12mo, 330p, frn by...)	Century	1910	Schoonover, Frank	25-40	
Scott, Walter	Ivanhoe (1st, lg8vo, 515p, p-o, blue/gilt, 10cp, pep)	Harper	1922	Schoonover, Frank	60-90	
Tomlinson, Everett	Jersey Boy in the Revolution (1st, sm8vo, 428p, 4pl)	Houghton	1899	Schoonover, Frank	50-85	
Madison, Lucy F.	Joan of Arc (1st, lg8vo, 389p, p-o, blue/gilt, 8cp, pep)	Penn	1918	Schoonover, Frank	60-90	
Frith, Henry	King Arthur & his Knights (1st, 8vo, black cl, p-o, 406p, 4cp)	Garden City	1932	Schoonover, Frank	50-80	
Madison, Lucy F.	Lafayette (1st, lg8vo, p-o, 371p, blue cl, 8cp, pep)	Penn	1921	Schoonover, Frank	60-90	
Parker, Gilbert	Lane that Had No Turning (1st, lg8vo, 215p, teg, uncut, 7pl, pep)	Doubleday/Page	1902	Schoonover, Frank	35-60	
Madison, Lucy F.	Lincoln (1st, lg8vo, p-o, 368p, 8cp, pep)	Penn	1928	Schoonover, Frank	60-90	
Parrish, Randall	Maid of the Forest (1st, 8vo, 427p, 5cp)	McClurg	1913	Schoonover, Frank	30-50	

AUTHOR	TITLE	PUBLISHER	DATE	ARTIST	PRICE	LC
Cummings, Edward	Marmaduke of Tennessee (1st, sm8vo, 371p, 5pl)	McClurg	1914	Schoonover, Frank	30-50	
Burroughs, Edgar R.	Princess of Mars (1st, sm8vo, black cl, 326p, 5pl)	McClurg	1917	Schoonover, Frank	450-650	
Seltzer, Charles A.	Range Boss (1st, sm8vo, green cl, 333p, 4pl)	McClurg	1916	Schoonover, Frank	60-100	
Singmaster, Elsie	Rifles for Washington (1st, 8vo, 321p, color title page, b/w, DJ/2.25)	Houghton	1938	Schoonover, Frank	25-45	
Collier, Virginia M.	Roland the Warrior (1st, 8vo, 237p, gilt, color, pep, DJ/2.75)	Harcourt	(1934)	Schoonover, Frank	60-90	
Sublette, Clifford	Scarlet Cockerel (1st, 8vo, 293p, p-o, gilt, 6cp)	Little/Brown	1931	Schoonover, Frank	25-45	
Adams, Samuel H.	Secret of Lonesome Cove (1st, 12mo, 340p, olive cl, 6pl)	Bobbs-Merrill	(1912)	Schoonover, Frank	20-35	
Schultz, James W.	Seizer of Eagles (1st, sm8vo, 230p, brown cl, 4pl)	Houghton	1922	Schoonover, Frank	30-50	
Voss, Richard	Sigurd Eckdal's Bride (1st, 12mo, 235p, 4pl)	Little/Brown	1900	Schoonover, Frank	30-50	
Schultz, James W.	Skull Head the Terrible (1st, sm8vo, 208p, brown cl, 4pl, pep)	Houghton	1929	Schoonover, Frank	30-50	*
Marsh, George	Sled Trails and White Waters (1st, lg8vo, 298p, gilt, p-o, col frn, 9pl)	Penn	1929	Schoonover, Frank	30-50	
Glasgow, Ellen	The Deliverance (1st, 8vo, 543p, red/gilt, 4cp)	Doubleday/Page	1904	Schoonover, Frank	35-60	
Johnston, Mary	To Have & to Hold (1st {this format}, lg8vo, 331p, 5cp)	Houghton	1931	Schoonover, Frank	30-50	
Marsh, George	Toilers of the Trails (1st, lg8vo, p-o, 245p, col frn, 8pl)	Penn	1921	Schoonover, Frank	35-60	
Madison, Lucy F.	Washington (1st, lg8vo, blue/gilt, p-o, 399p, 8cp, pep)	Penn	1925	Schoonover, Frank	60-90	
Mott, Lawrence	White Darkness (1st, 12mo, blue cl, 308p, 3pl by...)	Outing	1907	Schoonover, Frank	35-60	
Watson, Virginia	With Cortes the Conqueror (1st, lg8vo, p-o, 332p, 8cp, pep)	Penn	1917	Schoonover, Frank	60-100	
Holland, Rupert S.	Yankee Ships in Pirate Waters (1st, lg8vo, p-o, 317p, 5cp, pep)	Macrae Smith	(1931)	Schoonover, Frank	50-80	
Schreiber, Georges	Bambino Goes Home (1st, 4to, 29p, fp color, pep, DJ/3.00)	Viking	(1959)	Schreiber, Georges	50-85	
Schreiber, Georges	Bambino the Clown (1st, sm4to, 30p, ipcb, color, pep, DJ/2.00, CH)	Viking	1947	Schreiber, Georges	80-140	
Sauer, Julia L.	Light at Tern Rock (1st, sm4to, 62p, pep, brown illus, DJ/2.50, NH)	Viking	1951	Schreiber, Georges	80-120	R*
Bishop, Claire H.	Pancakes-Paris (1st, sm4to, 63p, grey cl, 1-color, pep, DJ/2.00, NH)	Viking	1947	Schreiber, Georges	50-85	
Lipkind, Will	Professor Bull's Umbrella (1st, 4to, [38]p, color, pep, DJ/2.50)	Viking	1954	Schreiber, Georges	30-50	
Dalgliesh, Alice	Ride on the Wind (1st, 4to, [32]p, ibds, color, DJ/2.75)	Scribner	1956	Schreiber, Georges	25-40	
Bragdon, Elspeth	That Jud! (1st, 8vo, ivory cl, 126p, fp b/w, DJ/2.50)	Viking	(1957)	Schreiber, Georges	30-50	
Hughes, Richard A.	Gertrude's Child (1st {std}, 8vo, 44p, pcb, fp b/w, pep, DJ/2.95)	Harlin Quist	(1966)	Schreiter, Rick	25-40	
Andersen, Hans C.	Great Claus and Little Claus (1st {std}, folio, 31p, 1-color, DJ/3.95)	Grove Press	(1968)	Schreiter, Rick	45-60	
Hughes, Ted	How the Whale Became (1st AM {std}, lg8vo, 100p, fp b/w, DJ/3.50)	Atheneum	1964	Schreiter, Rick	80-140	
Kastner, Erich	Little Man (1st AM {std}, lg8vo, 183p, bds, b/w, DJ/3.95)	Knopf	(1966)	Schreiter, Rick	30-50	
Andersen, Hans C.	What Good Man Does is Always Right (1st, 4to, [32]p, ibds, color, DJ/3.95)	Dial Press	1968	Schreiter, Rick	25-45	
Coatsworth, Eliz.	Bob Bodden & the Good Shop Rover (1st, 8vo, 48p, color, pep, DJ)	Garrard Pub.	(1968)	Schroeder, Ted	25-40	
Martin, Patricia	Abraham Lincoln (1st, 8vo, 64p, color, DJ/1.95)	Putnam	(1964)	Schrotter, Gustav	20-30	
Farley, Walter	Horse-Tamer (1st {std}, 8vo, 175p, b/w, DJ/2.00)	Random	1958	Schucker, James	45-70	
Farley, Walter	Little Black: A Pony (1st, lg8vo, 60p, ibds, p-o, fp 2-color, DJ/1.95)	Beginner Books	(1961)	Schucker, James	70-100	
Schulz, Charles	Charlie Brown Christmas (1st {std}, sq8vo, 42p, color, DJ/2.50)	World	(1965)	Schulz, Charles	30-50	
Schulz, Charles	Snoopy and the Red Baron (1st {std}, 8vo, [64]p, b/w, DJ/2.00)	Holt, Rinehart	(1966)	Schulz, Charles	35-50	
Thompson, Wolfe	Circle of the Braves (1st, sm8vo, 257p, col frn, b/w)	Stokes	1931	Schuyler, Remington	25-45	
White, Stewart E.	Daniel Boone (1st {std}, sm8vo, 308p, blue cl, p-o, 5pl, PPP)	Doubleday/Page	1922	Schuyler, Remington	90-120	R
Mulford, Clarence	Hopalong Cassidy Returns (1st, sm8vo, 310p, color)	Doubleday/Page	1924	Schuyler, Remington	80-130	
Emerson, Caroline	Indian Hunting Grounds (1st, 8vo, 191p, b/w, DJ/1.75)	Stokes	1938	Schuyler, Remington	40-65	*
Coblentz, Catherine	Scatter the Chipmunk (1st, lg8vo, ipcb, [25]p, 1-color, pep, DJ/1.00)	Children's Press	(1946)	Schwartz, Berta	30-45	
Schwartz, Elizabeth R.	Cottontail Rabbit (1st, 8vo, 45p, olive cl, 2-color, cep, DJ/2.00)	Holiday House	(1957)	Schwartz, Charles	30-50	
Schwartz, Elizabeth R.	When Water Animals are Babies (1st, 4to, [36]p, color, DJ/4.50)	Holiday House	(1970)	Schwartz, Charles	20-35	
Eaton, Jeanette	Story of Light (1st {std}, sm8vo, 79p, col frn)	Harper	1928	Schwartz, Max	25-40	
Scott, Florence E.	Kindergarten Limericks (1st, sm4to, [59]p, 27cp)	Hurst	(1915)	Scott, Arthur O.	160-240	*
Scott, Barbara	Tales of Raindrop, Cloud Fairy (1st {std}, 8vo, 55p, fp 2-color, DJ/2.95)	Vantage Press	1968	Scott, Barbara	30-50	
Skorpen, Liesel	All the Lassies (1st {std}, ob8vo, [32]p, 3-color, cep, DJ/3.50)	Dial Press	(1970)	Scott, Bruce M.	80-130	
N/A	Cinderella (1st, 24mo, [41]p, ipcb, 2-color)	Holiday House	[1938]	Scott, Hilda	55-80	
Andersen, Hans C.	Thumbelina (1st, sq32mo, ipcb, [60]p, color, dep)	Holiday House	(1939)	Scott, Hilda	70-120	R
Jahn, Mary L.	Yelly (1st, lg ob4to, [32]p, color, pep, DJ/2.00)	Oxford U. Pr.	(1941)	Scott, Hilda	45-65	
Mitchell, Edith	Betty, Bobby & Bubbles (1st, 12mo, ibds, [40]p, pep, color)	Volland	(1921)	Scott, Janet L.	70-100	
Stevenson, Rbt. L.	Child's Garden of Verses (1st, 12mo, ipcb, [52]p, color, pep)	Whitman	1947	Scott, Janet L.	30-50	*
McNeil, Marion	Children Across the Sea (1st, ob folio, wraps, unpag, color)	Saalfield	1931	Scott, Janet L.	150-225	
Merryman, Mildred P.	Daddy Domino (1st {std}, 8vo, ibds, 6 fp color, pep)	Volland	(1929)	Scott, Janet L.	80-140	
Graham, Mary N.	Fifty Songs for Boys & Girls (1st, lg ob8vo, ibds, 60p, 2-color)	Whitman	(1935)	Scott, Janet L.	80-120	*
Bowman, John G.	Happy all Day Through (1st, lg ob4to, [32]p, ibds, color)	Volland	(1917)	Scott, Janet L.	90-140	
N/A	Happy Day Begins (lg sq4to, wraps, [12]p, color)	Saalfield	1931	Scott, Janet L.	70-100	
Bender, Eric	I Never Knew that Before (1st, 4to, 123p, ibds, pep, fp color, DJ/1.50)	Saalfield	(1938)	Scott, Janet L.	40-65	*
O'Donnell, T.C.	Ladder of Ricketty Rungs (1st, 8vo, ibds, [85]p, color, pep)	Volland	(1923)	Scott, Janet L.	80-120	
Muter, Gladys N.	Little Bim the Circus Boy (1st, ob folio, color)	Volland	(1924)	Scott, Janet L.	140-220	*
Bonner, Mary G.	Madam Red Apple (1st, 8vo, [123]p, fp color, pep)	Milton Bradley	(1929)	Scott, Janet L.	45-65	
Bonner, Mary G.	Miss Angelina Adorable (1st, 8vo, [102]p, color, pep)	Milton Bradley	(1928)	Scott, Janet L.	40-65	
Bonner, Mary G.	Mrs. Cucumber Green (1st, 8vo, [108]p, pep, color)	Milton Bradley	(1927)	Scott, Janet L.	40-65	
Dauzet, Marceline	One Happy Day (lg sq4to, ibds, [16]p, fp color, pep)	Saalfield	1939	Scott, Janet L.	30-50	
Thompson, Ruth P.	Princess of Cozytown (1st, lg8vo, ibds, [96]p, color, pep)	Volland	(1922)	Scott, Janet L.	250-400	
Addington, Sarah	Pudding Lane People (1st, 8vo, p-o, 183p, 4cp, pep)	Little/Brown	1926	Scott, Janet L.	30-60	
Scott, Janet L.	Round the World We Sail (ob4to, [16]p, ibds, color)	Volland/Buzza	[1930]	Scott, Janet L.	120-165	
Scott, Janet L.	Round the World We Sail (1st, sq4to, spiral bds, [16]p, color, pep)	Saalfield	1939	Scott, Janet L.	50-80	
Chamberlin, Ethel C.	Shoes, Ships & Sealing Wax (1st, 8vo, 123p, ibds, color)	Saalfield	(1928)	Scott, Janet L.	25-45	
Trimpey, Alice	Story of My Dolls (1st, 4to, 76p, ibds, b/w, pep, DJ/0.75)	Whitman	1935	Scott, Janet L.	60-90	
Bonner, Mary G.	Story Teller's Holiday (1st, lg4to, [64]p, red cl, p-o, color)	McLoughlin	(1938)	Scott, Janet L.	100-165	
Gordon, Elizabeth	Turned-Intos (1st, 8vo, ipcb, unpag, color, pep)	Volland	(1920)	Scott, Janet L.	80-125	
Gordon, Elizabeth	Wild Flower Children (1st, lg8vo, ibds, [84]p, color, pep)	Volland	(1918)	Scott, Janet L.	160-250	
Sewell, Anna	Black Beauty (1st, 8vo, 295p, 12cp)	Jacobs	(1910)	Scrivener, M.	50-80	
N/A	Golden Goose (1st, sq16mo, ibds, [42]p, color)	Macmillan	1928	Seaman, Mary L.	60-100	
Dickens, Charles	Christmas Carol (1st {std}, 4to, 110p, dep, color, DJ/4.95)	World	(1961)	Searle, Ronald	25-40	
Cullen, Countee	Lost Zoo (1st {std}, lg8vo, 72p, yellow cl, 16cp, pep, DJ/2.50)	Harper	(1940)	Sebree, Charles	200-300	
Seccombe, Lieut.	Good Old Story of Cinderella (1st AM, sm4to, 48p, gilt, 12cp)	NY: Armstrong	(1882)	Seccombe, Lieut.	120-175	*

AUTHOR	TITLE	PUBLISHER	DATE	ARTIST	PRICE	LC
Deihl, Edna G.	Little Black Hen (1st, 8vo, 61p, p-o, color, pep)	Whitman	1938	Seeley, Sue	35-50	
Dalgliesh, Alice	Gulliver Joins the Army (1st, 8vo, 936p, fp b/w, DJ/1.50)	Scribner	1942	Segner, Ellen	30-50	
Scott, Sally	Molly & the Tool Shed (1st, 8vo, ibds, 40p, b/w, DJ/1.50)	Harcourt	(1943)	Segner, Ellen	20-35	*
Maurois, Andre	Country of 36000 Wishes (1st AM, 4to, ibds, 66p, 11cp, pep)	Appleton	1930	Segur, Adrienne	100-185	R
Ponsot, Marie	Fairy Tale Book (1st, folio, ibds, 156p, color, GGB)	Simon/Schuster	(1958)	Segur, Adrienne	200-300	
Ponsot, Marie (tran)	Snow Queen (1st, folio, 136p, ibds, fp color, DGB)	Golden Press	(1961)	Segur, Adrienne	120-200	
Weigle, Oscar	Story of Noah's Ark (1st, lg4to, [26]p, ipcb, color, pep, DJ/1.95)	Grosset/Dunlap	1957	Seiden, Art	60-90	R*
Brown, Margaret W.	Train to Timbuctoo (1st, sm8vo, ibds, [28]p, color, LGB/#118)	Simon/Schuster	1951	Seiden, Art	20-30	
Seidler, Rosalie	Grumpus and the Venetian Cat (1st {std}, sm4to, 39p, color, DJ/3.50)	Atheneum	1964	Seidler, Rosalie	30-50	
Surany, Anico	Etienne-Henri and Gri-Gri (1st, sq8vo, [35]p, color, DJ/4.50)	Holiday House	(1969)	Selig, Sylvie	25-40	
Thompson, Vivian L.	Hawaiian Legends of Tricksters & Riddlers (1st, 8vo, 103p, color, DJ/4.50)	Holiday House	(1969)	Selig, Sylvie	60-100	
MacGregor, Ellen	Tommy & the Telephone (1st, 8vo, [32]p, p-o, color, pep, DJ/1.25)	Whitman	1947	Selover, Zabeth	30-50	
Chandler, Edna W.	Will You Carry Me? (1st, lg8vo, unpag, color, DJ/2.95)	Whitman	1965	Seltzer, Meyer	25-40	
DeJong, Meindert	Along Came a Dog (1st, 8vo, 172p, b/w, DJ/2.75, NH)	Harper	(1958)	Sendak, Maurice	200-300	R
Jarrell, Randall	Animal Family (1st, 12mo, 179p, green/gilt, b/w, cep, DJ/3.50, NH, NYTBI)	Pantheon	(1965)	Sendak, Maurice	100-170	R
Eidinoff, Maxwell L.	Atomics for the Millions (1st, lg8vo, 281p, blue cl, b/w, DJ/3.50)	Whittlesey	(1947)	Sendak, Maurice	450-600	
Jarrell, Randall	Bat-Poet (1st, 8vo, 42p, brown cl, fp b/w, cep, DJ/2.75, NYTBI)	Macmillan	(1964)	Sendak, Maurice	80-145	R
Stockton, Frank	Bee-Man of Orn (1st {std}, sq8vo, 44p, ibds, color, DJ/3.50)	Holt, Rinehart	(1964)	Sendak, Maurice	120-200	R
Graves, Robert	Big Green Book (1st {std}, 4to, [32]p, green cl, fp b/w)	Crowell-Collier	(1962)	Sendak, Maurice	100-170	
Graves, Robert	Big Green Book (1st {this fmt} {std}, 8vo, [63]p, fp b/w, DJ/3.95)	Crowell-Collier	(1968)	Sendak, Maurice	60-100	
Krauss, Ruth	Birthday Party (1st, ob12mo, ipcb, [23]p, dep, color, DJ/1.50, NYTBI)	Harper	1957	Sendak, Maurice	200-300	R
Krauss, Ruth	Charlotte & White Horse (1st, 16mo, ibds, [20]p, color, dep, DJ/2.00)	Harper	(1955)	Sendak, Maurice	180-250	
Sendak, Jack	Circus Girl (1st, lg8vo, beige cl, [30]p, color, DJ/2.50)	Harper	1957	Sendak, Maurice	180-260	R
Hauff, Wilhelm	Dwarf Long-Nose (1st, lg sq8vo, ipcb, 61p, 1-color, pep, DJ/2.95)	Random	(1960)	Sendak, Maurice	160-220	R
Sendak, Maurice	Fantasy Sketches (1st, 4to, [28]p, wraps, fp b/w)	Rosenbach Found.	1970	Sendak, Maurice	100-170	
Minarik, Else H.	Father Bear Comes Home (1st, 8vo, ibds, 62p, color, DJ/1.95, NYTBI)	Harper	(1959)	Sendak, Maurice	150-220	
DeRegniers, Beatrice	Giant Story (1st, 4to, [29]p, grey cl, fp 2-color, DJ/2.00)	Harper	(1953)	Sendak, Maurice	200-300	
MacDonald, George	Golden Key (1st {std}, 12mo, 85p, gilt, fp b/w, DJ/3.95)	Farrar, Straus	(1967)	Sendak, Maurice	100-170	R
Garvey, Robert	Good Shabbos, Everybody (1st, 4to, [26]p, ibds, color, pep)	United Synagogue	(1951)	Sendak, Maurice	600-900	
Stockton, Frank	Griffin and the Minor Canon (1st {std}, 8vo, 55p, ibds, color, DJ/3.50)	Holt, Rinehart	(1963)	Sendak, Maurice	120-200	R
Chanover, Hyman	Happy Hanukah Everybody (1st, 8vo, unpag, ibds, color)	United Synagogue	(1954)	Sendak, Maurice	650-900	
Sendak, Jack	Happy Rain (1st, sm4to, 40p, blue cl, 8 fp b/w, DJ/2.50)	Harper	(1956)	Sendak, Maurice	350-500	R
Sendak, Maurice	Hector the Protector (1st, ob8vo, [52]p, ibds, color, pep, DJ/4.25)	Harper	(1965)	Sendak, Maurice	100-170	
Sendak, Maurice	Higglety Pigglety Pop! (1st 12mo, p-o, gilt fp 1-color, 69p, cep, DJ/4.95)	Harper	(1967)	Sendak, Maurice	180-250	R
Krauss, Ruth	Hole is to Dig (1st, 12mo [48]p, ibds, green pep, DJ/1.50, NYTBI)	Harper	(1952)	Sendak, Maurice	250-400	R
DeJong, Meindert	House of Sixty Fathers (1st, 8vo, 189p, tan cl, b/w, DJ/2.50, NH)	Harper	(1956)	Sendak, Maurice	250-350	R
Vogel, Amos	How Little Lori Visited Times Square (1st {std}, ob8vo [32]p col, DJ/2.95)	Harper	(1963)	Sendak, Maurice	350-500	
DeJong, Meindert	Hurry Home, Candy (1st, 8vo, 244p, green cl, b/w, DJ/2.50, NH)	Harper	(1953)	Sendak, Maurice	250-350	R
Krauss, Ruth	I Want to Paint My Bathroom Blue (1st, 8vo, [22]p col, cep, DJ/2.50, NYTBI)	Harper	1956	Sendak, Maurice	200-300	R
Krauss, Ruth	I'll Be You & You Be Me (1st, lg8vo, ibds, pep, [38]p, b/w, DJ/1.75, NYTBI)	Harper	(1954)	Sendak, Maurice	250-350	R
Sendak, Maurice	In the Night Kitchen (1st, 4to, p-o, [40]p, color, DJ/4.95, CH, NYTBI)	Harper	(1970)	Sendak, Maurice	250-400	
Sendak, Maurice	Kenny's Window (1st, lg sq8vo, tan cl, [62]p, 1-color, DJ/2.00)	Harper	(1956)	Sendak, Maurice	350-500	R
Minarik, Else H.	Kiss for Little Bear (1st, 8vo, 32p, ibds, color, DJ/2.50, NYTBI)	Harper	(1968)	Sendak, Maurice	180-260	
Udry, Janice M.	Let's Be Enemies (1st, 24mo, [32]p, 3-color, DJ/1.95)	Harper	1961	Sendak, Maurice	80-135	
MacDonald, George	Light Princess (1st, sm8vo, 110p, blue/gilt, fp b/w, DJ/3.95, NYTBI)	Farrar, Straus	(1969)	Sendak, Maurice	100-165	
Minarik, Else H.	Little Bear (1st, 8vo, 63p, ibds, color, DJ/2.50)	Harper	(1957)	Sendak, Maurice	200-300	R
Minarik, Else H.	Little Bear's Friend (1st, 8vo, 57p, ibds, fp 2-color, DJ/1.95)	Harper	(1960)	Sendak, Maurice	150-220	R
Minarik, Else H.	Little Bear's Visit (1st, 8vo, 64p, ibds, color, DJ/1.95, CH)	Harper	(1961)	Sendak, Maurice	150-220	
DeJong, Meindert	Little Cow & the Turtle (1st, 8vo, 178p, b/w, DJ/2.50)	Harper	(1955)	Sendak, Maurice	250-350	
Engvick, Wm. (ed)	Lullabies and Night Songs (1st, folio, 77p, blue/gilt, color, cep, DJ/6.95)	Harper	(1965)	Sendak, Maurice	150-200	
Sawyer, Ruth	Maggie Rose: Her Birthday Christmas (1st {std}, 12mo, 151p, b/w, DJ/2.00)	Harper	1952	Sendak, Maurice	180-250	
Ayme, Marcel	Magic Pictures (1st {std}, 8vo, blue cl, 117p, b/w, DJ/2.50)	Harper	(1954)	Sendak, Maurice	180-250	R
Udry, Janice M.	Moon Jumpers (1st, sm4to, ibds, [31]p, 7 dp color, DJ/2.50, CH)	Harper	(1959)	Sendak, Maurice	300-450	
Zolotow, Charlotte	Mr. Rabbit & the Lovely Present (1st, ob8vo, [32]p, ibds, dep, DJ/2.95, CH)	Harper	(1962)	Sendak, Maurice	100-160	
MacDonald, Betty	Mrs. Piggle-Wiggle's Farm (1st {std}, 8vo, 128p, b/w, DJ/2.00)	Lippincott	(1954)	Sendak, Maurice	250-400	
Tolstoy, Leo	Nikolenka's Childhood (1st, lg8vo, 173p, ibds, b/w, DJ/3.95)	Pantheon	(1963)	Sendak, Maurice	200-300	
Minarik, Else H.	No Fighting! No Biting! (1st, 8vo, 62p, b/w, DJ/2.50)	Harper	1958	Sendak, Maurice	200-300	
Krauss, Ruth	Open House for Butterflies (1st, 16mo, ibds, [46]p, pep, b/w, DJ/1.50, NYT)	Harper	(1960)	Sendak, Maurice	200-320	R
Wahl, Jan	Pleasant Fieldmouse (1st, 8vo, 65p, ibds, b/w, cep, DJ/2.95)	Harper	(1964)	Sendak, Maurice	150-200	
Orgel, Doris	Sarah's Room (1st, 24mo, 46p, ibds, color, DJ/1.95)	Harper	(1963)	Sendak, Maurice	150-220	
Brentano, Clemens	Schoolmaster Whackwell's Wonderful Sons (1st lg8vo ibds 86p, 1-col, DJ/3.50)	Random	(1962)	Sendak, Maurice	200-300	R
Andersen, Hans C.	Seven Tales (1st, 8vo, 128p, blue/gilt, 5cp, fp b/w, DJ/3.95)	Harper	1959	Sendak, Maurice	200-300	R
DeJong, Meindert	Shadrach (1st {std}, 8vo, rust cl, 182p, b/w, DJ/2.50, NH)	Harper	(1953)	Sendak, Maurice	180-250	R
Keeshan, Robert	She Loves Me, She Loves Me Not (1st, 24mo, unpag, ibds, color, DJ/1.95)	Harper	(1963)	Sendak, Maurice	200-300	
Sendak, Maurice	Sign on Rosie's Door (1st, 8vo, grey cl, 47p, 2-color, DJ/2.50)	Harper	(1960)	Sendak, Maurice	250-400	R
Ritchie, Jean	Singing Family of the Cumberlands (1st, 8vo, grn cl, 282p, b/w, DJ/4.00)	NY: Oxford U.Pr.	1955	Sendak, Maurice	200-300	
DeJong, Meindert	Singing Hill (1st, 8vo, 180p, b/w, DJ/2.95, NYTBI)	Harper	(1962)	Sendak, Maurice	120-180	R
Krauss, Ruth	Somebody Else's Nut Tree (1st, sm4to, ibds, 43p, fp b/w, DJ/2.00)	Harper	(1958)	Sendak, Maurice	180-240	
Brentano, Clemens	Tale of Gockel, Hinkel & Gackeliah (1st, lg8vo, 143p, fp b/w, pep, DJ/3.95)	Random	(1961)	Sendak, Maurice	200-300	R
Tripp, Edward	Tin Fiddle (1st, lg ob8vo, pink cl, unpag, brown illus, cep, DJ/2.00)	NY: Oxford U.Pr.	1954	Sendak, Maurice	350-500	R
Sendak, Maurice	Very Far Away (1st, 8vo, green cl, cep, 52p, color, DJ/2.00)	Harper	(1957)	Sendak, Maurice	220-300	R
Krauss, Ruth	Very Special House (1st, sm4to, ibds, [22]p, 1-color, DJ/1.75, CH)	Harper	(1953)	Sendak, Maurice	250-400	R
DeRegniers, Beatrice	What Can You Do with a Shoe? (1st, ob4to, ipcb, [32]p, 1-color, DJ/1.75)	Harper	(1955)	Sendak, Maurice	500-700	
Joslin, Sesyle	What Do You Do, Dear? (1st, ob8vo, [48]p, color, DJ/2.75)	Young Scott	1961	Sendak, Maurice	130-180	
Joslin, Sesyle	What Do You Say, Dear? (1st, ob8vo, [48]p, 1-color, DJ/2.75, CH, NYTBI)	Young Scott	1958	Sendak, Maurice	250-350	
DeJong, Meindert	Wheel on the School (1st, 8vo, 298p, b/w, uncut, DJ/2.75, NM)	Harper	(1954)	Sendak, Maurice	200-300	R LC
Sendak, Maurice	Where the Wild Things Are (1st 4to [40]p, ibds col, dep, DJ/3.50, CM, NYT)	Harper	1963	Sendak, Maurice	800-1200	R
Ayme, Marcel	Wonderful Farm (1st {std}, 8vo, 182p, red cl, b/w, DJ/2.50)	Harper	(1951)	Sendak, Maurice	300-450	R

AUTHOR	TITLE	PUBLISHER	DATE	ARTIST	PRICE	LC
Nash, Ogden	You Can't Get There from Here (1st {std}, 12mo, gilt, 190p, b/w, DJ/3.75)	Little/Brown	(1957)	Sendak, Maurice	120-200	
Singer, Isaac B.	Zlateh the Goat (1st, 8vo, gilt, 90p, fp b/w, DJ/4.50, NH, NYTBI)	Harper	(1966)	Sendak, Maurice	120-200	
Daringer, Helen F.	Adopted Jane (1st, sm8vo, 225p, fp b/w, DJ/2.00)	Harcourt	(1947)	Seredy, Kate	30-50	
Thompson, Blanche J.	Bible Children (1st {std}, 8vo, ibds, [32]p, color, DJ/1.50)	Dodd	(1937)	Seredy, Kate	40-60	
Seredy, Kate	Brand-New Uncle (1st, 8vo, 142p, 1-color, DJ/3.00)	Viking	(1961)	Seredy, Kate	50-80	
Daugherty, Sonia	Broken Song (1st, sm8vo, 270p, b/w, DJ/2.00)	Nelson	1934	Seredy, Kate	25-45	
Brink, Carol R.	Caddie Woodlawn (1st, 8vo, 270p, b/w, cep, DJ/2.00, NM)	Macmillan	1935	Seredy, Kate	80-120	R
Thompson, Blanche J.	Candle Burns for France (1st, 8vo, 80p, col frn, fp b/w, DJ/1.75)	Bruce Pub. Co.	(1946)	Seredy, Kate	40-60	
Seredy, Kate	Chestry Oak (1st, 8vo, 236p, red cl, fp b/w, DJ/2.50)	Viking	1948	Seredy, Kate	75-120	
Sawyer, Ruth	Christmas Anna Angel (1st, 8vo, 48p, color, pep, DJ/2.00, CH)	Viking	1944	Seredy, Kate	80-120	
Gaggin, Eva R.	Ear for Uncle Emil (1st, 8vo, 238p, 83 b/w, pep, DJ/2.00)	Viking	1939	Seredy, Kate	40-65	
Bailey, Carolyn S.	Finnegan II - His Nine Lives (1st, sm4to, red cl, 95p, b/w, pep, DJ/2.50)	Viking	1953	Seredy, Kate	50-85	R
Gates, Arthur	Friendly Stories (1st, 12mo, 226p, fp color, pep)	Macmillan	1930	Seredy, Kate	30-50	
Seredy, Kate	Good Master (1st, sq8vo, 211p, b/w, pep, DJ/2.00, NH)	Viking	1935	Seredy, Kate	70-120	R
Seredy, Kate	Gypsy (1st, 4to, 62p, cloth, 29pl, DJ/3.00)	Viking	1951	Seredy, Kate	70-100	
La Rue, Mabel G.	Hoot-Owl (1st, 12mo, blue cl, 207p, 2-color, pep)	Macmillan	1936	Seredy, Kate	35-60	*
Seredy, Kate	Lazy Tinka (1st, 8vo, 56p, fp color, pep, DJ/2.75)	Viking	(1962)	Seredy, Kate	60-90	
Seredy, Kate	Listening (1st, 8vo, gilt, 157p, pep, 18pl, DJ/2.00)	Viking	1936	Seredy, Kate	60-100	
Gates, Doris	Little Vic (1st, 8vo, 160p, tan cl, b/w, pep, DJ/2.50)	Viking	1951	Seredy, Kate	30-50	
Brink, Carol R.	Mademoiselle Misfortune (1st, 8vo, 267p, 12 fp b/w, cep, DJ/2.00)	Macmillan	1936	Seredy, Kate	80-120	
Daringer, Helen F.	Mary Montgomery, Rebel (1st, 8vo, green cl, 222p, fp b/w, DJ/2.50)	Harcourt	(1948)	Seredy, Kate	40-60	
Hunt, Mabel L.	Michel's Island (1st, lg8vo, 265p, gilt, pep, b/w, DJ/2.00)	Stokes	1940	Seredy, Kate	30-50	
Thompson, Blanche J.	Oldest Story (1st, 8vo, 241p, b/w, DJ/2.50)	Bruce Pub. Co.	(1943)	Seredy, Kate	40-65	
Seredy, Kate	Open Gate (1st, 8vo, blue cl, 280p, fp b/w, pep, DJ/2.50)	Viking	1943	Seredy, Kate	50-80	
Bianco, Margery W.	Other People's Houses (1st, 8vo, 201p, pep, DJ/2.00)	Viking	1939	Seredy, Kate	35-50	
Seredy, Kate	Philomena (1st, lg8vo, 95p, b/w, pep, DJ/2.75)	Viking	1955	Seredy, Kate	50-80	
Daringer, Helen F.	Pilgrim Kate (1st, 8vo, 252p, fp b/w, DJ/2.50)	Harcourt	(1949)	Seredy, Kate	30-50	
Norton, Andre	Prince Commands (1st {std}, sm8vo, 268p red cl, fp b/w)	Appleton-Century	1934	Seredy, Kate	200-300	*
Harper, Wilhelmina	Selfish Giant... (1st, lg8vo, 86p, 6cp, DJ/2.00)	McKay	(1935)	Seredy, Kate	50-80	
Seredy, Kate	Singing Tree (1st, 8vo, 247p, color, 32 fp b/w, pep, DJ/2.50, NH)	Viking	1940	Seredy, Kate	80-120	
Mason, Miriam E.	Smiling Hill Farm (1st, 8vo, 311p, pep, 1-color)	Ginn & Co.	(1937)	Seredy, Kate	80-130	
Seredy, Kate	Tenement Tree (1st, 4to, 96p, fp b/w, pep, DJ/3.00)	Viking	(1959)	Seredy, Kate	60-90	
Harper, Wilhelmina	The Gunniwolf (1st {std}, lg8vo, green/gilt, 104p, fp color, pep, DJ/2.00)	McKay	(1936)	Seredy, Kate	70-100	
Seredy, Kate	Tree for Peter (1st, lg8vo, 102p, 1-color, DJ/2.00)	Viking	1941	Seredy, Kate	120-200	
Seredy, Kate	White Stag (1st, lg8vo, 95p, gilt, b/w, pep, DJ/2.00, NM)	Viking	1937	Seredy, Kate	120-185	R
Bianco, Margery W.	Winterbound (1st, 8vo, blue cl, 234p, pep, DJ/2.00, NH)	Viking	1936	Seredy, Kate	45-60	
Thompson, Blanche J.	With Harp and Lute (1st, sm8vo, 187p, fp b/w, DJ/1.25)	Macmillan	1935	Seredy, Kate	30-45	
Barnes, Nancy	Wonderful Year (1st, 8vo, 185p, b/w, DJ/2.50, NH)	J. Messner	(1946)	Seredy, Kate	40-65	
Gray, Eliz. J.	Young Walter Scott (1st, 8vo, 239p, pep, port. frn, DJ/2.00, NH)	Viking	1935	Seredy, Kate	60-100	*
Kotzwinkle, William	Day the Gang Got Rich (1st {std}, ob4to, [29]p, color, DJ/3.50)	Viking	(1970)	Servello, Joe	50-80	
Kotzwinkle, William	Elephant Boy (1st {std}, 4to, 43p, fp 2-color, cep, DJ/3.95)	Farrar, Straus	(1970)	Servello, Joe	45-70	
Kotzwinkle, William	Ship that Came Down the Gutter (1st, sq8vo, [23]p, fp color, DJ/4.50)	Pantheon	1970	Servello, Joe	30-50	
Preston, Edna M.	Toolittle (1st, lg8vo, 47p, fp 1-color, DJ/2.95)	Viking	(1969)	Servello, Joe	25-45	
Seton, Ernest T.	Animal Heroes (1st, 8vo, green/gilt, 362p, teg, 19pl)	Scribner	1905	Seton, Ernest T.	120-180	
Seton, Ernest T.	Biography of a Grizzly (1st, sq8vo, 167p, 12 tipl, cep)	Century	1900	Seton, Ernest T.	75-120	
Seton, Ernest T.	Biography of a Silver Fox (1st, sm8vo, blue cl, 209p, 10pl)	Century	1909	Seton, Ernest T.	50-80	
Seton, Ernest T.	Bird Portraits (1st, lg4to, 40p, green cl, 20pl)	Ginn & Co.	1901	Seton, Ernest T.	140-200	
Stickney, J.H.	Bird World (1st, 12mo, 214p, green cl, 10pl by...)	Ginn & Co.	1898	Sedak, Ernest T.	100-160	*
Seton, Ernest T.	Book of Woodcraft (1st, 8vo, 567p, green/gilt, b/w)	Doubleday/Page	1912	Seton, Ernest T.	80-125	
Wright, Mabel O.	Four-Footed Americans... (1st, sm8vo, 432p, b/w)	Macmillan	1898	Seton, Ernest T.	75-100	
Seton, Ernest T.	Krag & Johnny Bear (1st, sm8vo, 141p, b/w pl)	Scribner	1902	Seton, Ernest T.	70-100	
Seton, Ernest T.	Lives of the Hunted (1st, 8vo, 360p, green/gilt, teg, b/w)	Scribner	1901	Seton, Ernest T.	100-165	
Seton, Ernest T.	Monarch the Big Bear of Tallac (1st, 8vo, 214p, blue/gilt, p-o, 8pl)	Scribner	1904	Seton, Ernest T.	80-125	
Seton, Grace G.	Nimrod's Wife (1st, 8vo, 406p, teg, 18pl)	Doubleday/Page	1907	Seton, Ernest T.	60-100	
Seton, Ernest T.	Rolf in the Woods (1st, 8vo, 437p, green/gilt, 12pl)	Doubleday/Page	1911	Seton, Ernest T.	120-200	
Seton, Ernest T.	Studies in Art Anatomy of Animals (1st, folio, teg, green/gilt, 96p, 49pl)	L: Macmillan	1896	Seton, Ernest T.	500-800	
Grinnell, George B.	Trail & Camp Fire (1st, 8vo, 353p, 14pl)	Forest/Stream	1897	Seton, Ernest T.	200-300	
Seton, Ernest T.	Trail of the Sandhill Stag (1st, 8vo, teg, 93p, gilt, col frn)	Scribner	1899	Seton, Ernest T.	80-125	
Seton, Ernest T.	Two Little Savages (1st, 8vo, grey/gilt, 552p, 29pl, pep)	Doubleday/Page	1903	Seton, Ernest T.	80-145	
Seton, Ernest T.	Wild Animal Play for Children (1st, sm8vo, green cl, 79p, b/w)	Doubleday/Page	1900	Seton, Ernest T.	100-150	
Seton, Ernest T.	Wild Animals at Home (1st, 8vo, 226p, gilt, b/w)	Doubleday/Page	1913	Seton, Ernest T.	120-170	
Seton, Ernest T.	Wild Animals I Have Known (1st, 8vo, gilt, teg, 359p, b/w, PPP)	Scribner	1898	Seton, Ernest T.	150-220	
Seton, Grace G.	Woman Tenderfoot (1st, 8vo, 361p, teg, b/w)	Doubleday/Page	1900	Seton, Ernest T.	80-130	
Seton, Ernest T.	Woodmyth & Fable (1st, 8vo, 181p, red/gilt, b/w)	Century	1905	Seton, Ernest T.	120-165	
Seuss, Dr.	500 Hats/Bartholomew Cubbins (1st, 4to, ibds, [47]p, pep, 1-color, DJ/1.50)	Vanguard Press	(1938)	Seuss, Dr.	700-1000	R
Seuss, Dr.	And to Think/I Saw It on Mulberry Street (1st, 4to, [32]p, ibds pep)	Vanguard Press	1937	Seuss, Dr.	500-800	R
Seuss, Dr.	Bartholomew & the Oobleck (1st, lg4to, [48]p, blue ibds, pep, DJ/2.00, CH)	Random	(1949)	Seuss, Dr.	500-750	
Abingdon, Alex	Boners (1st, sq16mo, 102p, b/w)	Viking	1931	Seuss, Dr.	250-400	
Seuss, Dr.	Cat in the Hat (1st, lg8vo, 61p, ipcb, 2-color, pep, DJ/2.00)	Random	(1957)	Seuss, Dr.	600-900	R
Seuss, Dr.	Cat in the Hat Comes Back (1st {std}, lg8vo, ibds 61p, color, pep, DJ/1.95)	Beginner Books	(1958)	Seuss, Dr.	400-650	
Seuss, Dr.	Cat in the Hat Songbook (1st, 4to, ibds, [64]p, color, pep, DJ/2.95)	Random	(1967)	Seuss, Dr.	250-400	
Seuss, Dr.	Dr. Seuss's ABC (1st, 8vo, ibds, 63p, color, DJ/1.95)	Beginner Books	(1963)	Seuss, Dr.	250-400	
Seuss, Dr.	Dr. Seuss's Sleep Book (1st, 4to, ibds, [56]p, color, DJ/2.95)	Random	(1962)	Seuss, Dr.	400-650	
Seuss, Dr.	Foot Book (1st, 8vo, ibds, [32]p, color, DJ/1.95)	Beginner Books	(1968)	Seuss, Dr.	250-400	
Seuss, Dr.	Fox in Socks (1st, 8vo, ibds, 61p, color, pep, DJ/1.95)	Beginner Books	(1965)	Seuss, Dr.	250-400	
Seuss, Dr.	Green Eggs & Ham (1st, lg8vo, 62p, ibds, color, DJ/1.95)	Beginner Books	1960	Seuss, Dr.	300-450	
Seuss, Dr.	Happy Birthday to You! (1st, lg4to, [57]p, ibds, color, pep, DJ/2.95)	Random	(1959)	Seuss, Dr.	500-700	
Seuss, Dr.	Hop on Pop (1st, 8vo, 64p, color, DJ/1.95)	Beginner Books	1963	Seuss, Dr.	250-400	

AUTHOR	TITLE	PUBLISHER	DATE	ARTIST	PRICE	LC
Seuss, Dr.	Horton Hatches the Egg (1st {std}, 4to, [55]p, ibds, fp 2-color)	Random	(1940)	Seuss, Dr.	450-600	
Seuss, Dr.	Horton Hears a Who! (1st, 4to, [68]p, ibds, fp 2-color, pep, DJ/2.50)	Random	(1954)	Seuss, Dr.	500-800	
Seuss, Dr.	How the Grinch Stole Christmas (1st, lg4to ibds [62]p, 1-color, pep DJ/2.50)	Random	1957	Seuss, Dr.	800-1200	
Seuss, Dr.	I Can Lick 30 Tigers Today... (1st, 4to, ibds, [65]p, color, pep, DJ/2.95)	Random	(1969)	Seuss, Dr.	300-450	
Seuss, Dr.	I Had Trouble Getting to Solla Sollew (1st, 4to, ibds, color, pep, DJ/2.95)	Random	(1965)	Seuss, Dr.	500-700	
Seuss, Dr.	If I Ran the Circus (1st, lg4to, [64]p, ibds, 3-color, pep, DJ/2.50)	Random	(1956)	Seuss, Dr.	450-650	
Seuss, Dr.	If I Ran the Zoo (1st, lg4to, ibds, [56]p, color, pep, DJ/2.00, CH)	Random	(1950)	Seuss, Dr.	450-650	
Sullivan, Frank	In One Ear (1st, 8vo, red/gilt, 169p, frn by...)	Viking	1933	Seuss, Dr.	150-225	
Seuss, Dr.	King's Stilts (1st, lg4to, [48]p, 1-color, cep)	Random	(1939)	Seuss, Dr.	500-800	
Seuss, Dr.	McElligot's Pool (1st, 4to, [56]p, green cl, color, pep, DJ/2.50, CH)	Random	(1947)	Seuss, Dr.	600-900	
Abingdon, Alex	More Boners (1st, 16mo, green cl, 89p, b/w)	Viking	1931	Seuss, Dr.	250-400	
Seuss, Dr.	Mr. Brown Can Moo: Can You? (1st, 8vo, [27]p, color, pep, DJ)	Random	(1970)	Seuss, Dr.	250-450	
Abingdon, Alex	Omnibus Boners (1st, 16mo, b/w)	Viking	1931	Seuss, Dr.	250-400	
Seuss, Dr.	On Beyond Zebra! (1st, 4to, ibds, unpag, color, DJ/2.50)	Random	(1955)	Seuss, Dr.	500-700	
Seuss, Dr.	One Fish Two Fish Red Fish Blue Fish (1st, lg8vo, 62p, ipcb, col, DJ/1.95)	Beginner Books	1960	Seuss, Dr.	400-650	
Seuss, Dr.	Scrambled Eggs Super (1st, lg4to, ibds, [52]p, color, pep, DJ/2.50)	Random	(1953)	Seuss, Dr.	400-650	
Seuss, Dr.	Seven Lady Godivas (1st {std}, sm4to, [80]p, fp 1-color, pep, DJ)	Random	(1939)	Seuss, Dr.	800-1200	
Seuss, Dr.	Sneetches and other Stories (1st, 4to, ibds, 65p, color, DJ/2.95)	Random	1961	Seuss, Dr.	300-450	
Seuss, Dr.	Thidwick the Big-Hearted Moose (1st, 4to, ibds, [40]p, color, pep, DJ/2.00)	Random	(1948)	Seuss, Dr.	500-750	
Leaf, Munro	This is Ann, She's Dying to Meet You (1st, 24mo, [36]p, wraps, 1-color)	DC: U.S. GPO	(1943)	Seuss, Dr.	650-800	
Seuss, Dr.	Yertle the Turtle (1st, 4to, ibds, [80]p, fp 2-color, pep, DJ/2.95)	Random	(1958)	Seuss, Dr.	500-700	
Corelli, Marie	Devil's Motor (1st, 4to, [100]p, red/gilt, 6 ticp)	L: Hodder	[1910]	Severn, Arthur	200-300	
Chiang, May-Ling	Little Sister Su (1st, lg4to, ibds, [20]p, accordian fold, b/w)	John Day	1942	Sewall, Janet	50-80	
Sewell, A.A.	Ballad of the Prince (1st, lg4to, unpag, 12pl, pep)	R.H. Russell	1900	Sewell, A.A.	180-250	
Sewell, Helen	ABC for Everyday (1st, 4to, ipcb, [28]p, pep, 2-color)	Macmillan	1930	Sewell, Helen	120-180	R*
White, Eliza O.	Ann Frances (1st, 8vo, 126p, blue cl, 7cp, cep, DJ/1.75)	Houghton	1935	Sewell, Helen	35-60	
Coatsworth, Eliz.	Away Goes Sally (1st, lg8vo, 122p, p-o, b/w, pep, DJ/2.00)	Macmillan	1934	Sewell, Helen	50-80	R
Crowley, Maude	Azor (1st, sm8vo, ibds, 54p, b/w, DJ/2.00)	NY: Oxford U.Pr.	1948	Sewell, Helen	40-65	
Crowley, Maude	Azor & the Blue-Eyed Cow (1st, sm8vo, 70p, b/w, DJ/2.25)	NY: Oxford U.Pr.	1951	Sewell, Helen	40-65	
Crowley, Maude	Azor & the Haddock (1st, sm8vo, 63p, grey cl, b/w, DJ/2.00)	NY: Oxford U.Pr.	1949	Sewell, Helen	40-65	
Brink, Carol R.	Baby Island (1st, sm8vo, 172p, pep, 6cp, DJ/2.00)	Macmillan	1937	Sewell, Helen	80-125	
Dalgliesh, Alice	Bears on Hemlock Mountain (1st, 8vo, [64]p, 1-color, DJ/2.00, NH)	Scribner	(1952)	Sewell, Helen	60-100	
Kristoffersen, Eva	Bee in Her Bonnet (1st, 8vo, 168p, b/w, pep, DJ/2.00)	Crowell	1944	Sewell, Helen	30-50	
Sewell, Helen	Belinda the Mouse (1st, sq12mo, grey cl, [61]p, color, DJ/1.25)	Oxford U. Pr.	(1944)	Sewell, Helen	40-65	
Coatsworth, Eliz.	Big Green Umbrella (1st, sq8vo, ibds, [28]p, color, pep, DJ/0.50)	Grosset/Dunlap	(1944)	Sewell, Helen	45-65	
Sewell, Helen	Birthdays for Robin (1st, sq12mo, [46]p, grey cl, fp 3-color, DJ/1.00)	Macmillan	1943	Sewell, Helen	30-50	
Sewell, Helen	Blue Barns (1st, sm sq4to, [46]p, b/w, DJ/1.75)	Macmillan	1933	Sewell, Helen	80-120	R
Sayers, Frances C.	Blue Bonnets for Lucinda (1st, sm sq8vo, ibds, [30]p, color, pep)	Viking	1934	Sewell, Helen	50-85	
Molnar, Ferenc	Blue-Eyed Lady (1st, sm4to, blue cl, 46p, color, pep, DJ/2.00)	Viking	1942	Sewell, Helen	40-60	
Ward, Marion	Boat Children of Canton (1st {std}, sm4to, 92p, color, pep, DJ/2.00)	McKay	(1944)	Sewell, Helen	40-65	
Bulfinch, Thomas	Book of Myths (1st, sm4to, 126p, color, DJ/2.75)	Macmillan	1942	Sewell, Helen	50-80	
Seaman, Louise	Brave Bantam (1st {std}, 8vo, green cl, 48p, b/w, pep, DJ/1.00)	Macmillan	1946	Sewell, Helen	30-50	
Falkberget, Johan	Broomstick & Snowflake (1st, 8vo, blue cl, 88p, b/w, cep)	Macmillan	1933	Sewell, Helen	30-50	
Cautley, Marjorie S.	Building a House in Sweden (1st, sq8vo, 40p, fp brown illus)	Macmillan	1931	Sewell, Helen	35-60	
Tippett, James S.	Christmas Magic (1st, 16mo, ibds, [40]p, fp color, pep)	Grosset/Dunlap	(1944)	Sewell, Helen	30-50	
Smith, Susan C.	Christmas Tree in the Woods (1st, sq12mo, [38]p, color, pep)	Minton Balch	(1932)	Sewell, Helen	35-60	*
N/A	Cinderella (1st, 4to, blue cl, [17]p, color, DJ/1.75)	Macmillan	1934	Sewell, Helen	80-130	R
Evers, Alf	Colonel's Squad (1st {std}, 8vo, blue/gilt, 200p, b/w, DJ/2.75)	Macmillan	1952	Sewell, Helen	30-50	
Langer, Susanne	Cruise of the Little Dipper (1st, 12mo, 176p, gilt, 5cp, pep)	NY: Norcross	(1923)	Sewell, Helen	120-180	
Hughes, Langston	Dream Keeper (1st {std}, 8vo, 77p, blue/silver, b/w)	Knopf	1932	Sewell, Helen	450-600	R
Coatsworth, Eliz.	Fair American (1st, lg8vo, 132p, p-o, pep, 14pl, DJ/2.00)	Macmillan	1940	Sewell, Helen	40-65	
Wilder, Laura I.	Farmer Boy (1st {std}, 8vo, 230p, col frn, b/w, dep)	Harper	1933	Sewell, Helen	200-300	R*
Bible	First Bible (1st, 4to, blue/gilt, 109p, 13pl, pep, DJ/2.50)	Oxford U. Pr.	1934	Sewell, Helen	90-160	
Coatsworth, Eliz.	Five Bushel Farm (1st, lg8vo, 152p, pep, p-o, b/w, DJ/2.00)	Macmillan	1939	Sewell, Helen	30-50	
Sewell, Helen	Head for Happy (1st, ob4to, [56]p, p-o, pep, DJ/2.50)	Macmillan	1931	Sewell, Helen	80-120	
Evers, Alf	In the Beginning (1st, lg8vo, aqua cl, [30]p, 2-color, dep, DJ/2.00)	Macmillan	1954	Sewell, Helen	60-90	R
Bronte, Charlotte	Jane Eyre (1st, 8vo, 576p, pep, fp 1-color, DJ/3.00)	Oxford U. Pr.	(1938)	Sewell, Helen	45-70	
Sewell, Helen	Jimmy & Jemima (1st, 8vo, [47]p, p-o, color, DJ/1.00)	Macmillan	1940	Sewell, Helen	40-60	
Milne, A.A.	Magic Hill (1st {this pub}, 4to, 40p, ibds, 8 fp color, pep)	Grosset/Dunlap	(1937)	Sewell, Helen	90-160	
Miller, Mary B.	Menagerie (1st, sq8vo, 124p, col frn, 8pl, pep)	Macmillan	1928	Sewell, Helen	35-60	
Sewell, Helen	Ming & Mehitable (1st, 16mo, yellow cl, [60]p, dep, color, DJ/0.75)	Macmillan	1936	Sewell, Helen	30-50	
Rhys, Mimpsy	Mr. Hermit Crab (1st, 8vo, green cl, 190p, col frn, 6pl, pep)	Macmillan	1929	Sewell, Helen	30-50	
Cregan, Mairin	Old John (1st, 8vo, 183p, 11pl, pep, DJ/2.00)	Macmillan	1936	Sewell, Helen	50-80	
Kunhardt, Dorothy	Once there was a Little Boy (1st, lg8vo, 66p, fp color, DJ/2.50)	Viking	1946	Sewell, Helen	40-70	
Sewell, Helen	Peggy & the Pony (1st, sq8vo, blue cl, [47]p, 2-color, DJ/1.25)	Oxford U. Pr.	(1936)	Sewell, Helen	55-90	
Sewell, Helen	Peggy & the Pup (1st, sq8vo, [46]p, beige cl, fp 2-color, DJ/1.25)	Oxford U. Pr.	(1941)	Sewell, Helen	35-60	*
Jones, Viola M.	Peter & Gretchen of Old Nuremberg (1st, 4to, p-o, 96p, color, pep, DJ/2.00)	Whitman	1935	Sewell, Helen	40-65	
Collodi, Carlo	Pinocchio (1st, sm8vo, rust cl, 282p, 13 fp b/w)	Appleton-Century	(1935)	Sewell, Helen	35-60	*
Milne, A.A.	Princess & the Apple Tree (1st, 4to, ibds, 40p, 8 fp color, pep, DJ/1.00)	Grosset/Dunlap	(1937)	Sewell, Helen	80-120	
Noble, Thomas T.	Round of Carols (1st {std}, 4to, red/gilt, 72p, b/w, pep, DJ/2.00)	Oxford U. Pr.	1935	Sewell, Helen	40-65	
Potter, Miriam C.	Sally Gabble & the Fairies (1st, 12mo, 87p, col frn, b/w, DJ/1.00)	Macmillan	1929	Sewell, Helen	80-120	
Sayers, Frances C.	Tag-Along Tooloo (1st, lg8vo, 87p, pep, 8 fp color, DJ/1.50)	Viking	1941	Sewell, Helen	40-65	
Farjeon, Eleanor	Ten Saints (1st AM {std}, lg8vo, 124p, 10 fp color, pep, DJ/2.50)	NY: Oxford U.Pr.	1936	Sewell, Helen	60-90	
Dalgliesh, Alice	Thanksgiving Story (1st, 4to, red cl, [28]p, fp color, DJ/2.50, CH)	Scribner	(1954)	Sewell, Helen	70-100	R
Evers, Alf	Three Kings of Saba (1st, 4to, [30]p, color, DJ/2.50, NYTBI)	Lippincott	1955	Sewell, Helen	50-80	R
Sewell, Helen	Three Tall Tales (1st {std}, sq4to, ibds, [40]p, color, DJ/1.50)	Macmillan	1947	Sewell, Helen	50-80	
White, Eliza O.	Where is Adelaide? (1st, 8vo, 155p, orange cl, b/w, dep)	Houghton	1933	Sewell, Helen	30-50	
Coatsworth, Eliz.	White Horse (1st {std}, 8vo, 164p, p-o, 14 fp b/w, pep, DJ/2.00)	Macmillan	1942	Sewell, Helen	40-65	

AUTHOR	TITLE	PUBLISHER	DATE	ARTIST	PRICE	LC
Coatsworth, Eliz.	Wonderful Day (1st {std}, 8vo, yellow cl, 126p, p-o, pep, DJ/2.25)	Macmillan	1946	Sewell, Helen	40-65	
Sewell, Helen	Words to the Wise (1st, ob8vo, [64]p, 1-color, tan cl, dep)	Dodd	(1932)	Sewell, Helen	40-65	
Jarden, Mary L.	Young Brontes (1st, 8vo, 279p, blue cl, 2-color, pep, DJ/2.50)	Viking	1938	Sewell, Helen	30-45	
Wilder, Laura I.	By the Shores of Silver Lake (1st {std}, 8vo, 260p, col frn, DJ/2.00, NH)	Harper	1939	Sewell/Boyle	600-800	R
Wilder, Laura I.	Little House in Big Woods (1st {1st bk} {std}, 8vo, 176p, col frn, dep, NH)	Harper	1932	Sewell/Boyle	250-400	R
Wilder, Laura I.	Little House on the Prairie (1st {std}, sq8vo, 200p, col frn, dep, DJ/2.00)	Harper	1935	Sewell/Boyle	300-500	R
Wilder, Laura I.	Little Town on the Prairie (1st {std} 8vo, 288p, col frn, dep, DJ/2.00, NH)	Harper	(1941)	Sewell/Boyle	600-800	R
Wilder, Laura I.	Long Winter (1st {std}, 8vo, 325p, col frn, dep, DJ/2.00, NH)	Harper	1940	Sewell/Boyle	600-800	R
Wilder, Laura I.	On the Banks of Plum Creek (1st {std}, 8vo, 239p, col frn, DJ/2.00, NH)	Harper	1937	Sewell/Boyle	600-800	
Wilder, Laura I.	These Happy Golden Years (1st {std}, 8vo, 299p, col frn, DJ/2.00)	Harper	(1943)	Sewell/Boyle	200-300	R
Grimm Bros.	Grimm's Tales (1st, 8vo, 142p, 2-color, pep, DJ/3.50)	NY: Oxford U.Pr.	1954	Sewell/Gekiere	50-80	R*
Chase, Mary	Mrs. McThing: A Play (1st, lg8vo, 141p, blue cl, b/w, DJ/3.00)	Oxford U. Pr.	1952	Sewell/Gekiere	40-65	
Carson, Norma B.	Children's Own Story Book (1st, lg8vo, yellow cl, 160p, color)	Reilly/Britton	(1916)	Sewsmith, Hazeltine	55-80	*
Morse, Elizabeth	Siamese Cat (1st, sm8vo, 62p, b/w, pep, DJ/1.50)	Dutton	(1929)	Seymour, Ruth	30-50	
Shackelford, L.T.	As I See It (1st {std}, ob8vo, ibds, 96p, b/w, DJ/1.50)	Knopf	1943	Shackelford, L.T.	50-80	
Engdahl, Sylvia	Enchantress from the Stars (1st {std}, lg8vo, 275p, b/w, cep, DJ/5.95, NH)	Atheneum	1970	Shackell, Rodney	65-100	
Ish-Kishor, Salamith	Boy of Old Prague (1st, 8vo, 90p, fp b/w, pep, DJ/3.95)	Pantheon	(1963)	Shahn, Ben	45-70	R
Porter, Katherine A.	Christmas Story (1st {std}, sq16mo, [32]p, ibds, fp b/w, pep, DJ/2.95)	Delacorte Pr.	(1967)	Shahn, Ben	50-80	R
Samstag, Nicholas	Kay-Kay Comes Home (1st, ob8vo, wraps, [44]p, fp b/w, DJ)	NY: Valentin	1952	Shahn, Ben	65-100	
Samstag, Nicholas	Kay-Kay Comes Home (1st {this pub} {std}, 8vo, bds 47p, b/w DJ/2.95, NYT)	Obolensky	(1962)	Shahn, Ben	30-50	
Reid, Alastair	Ounce, Dice, Trice (1st {std}, 4to, 57p, fp b/w, DJ/3.50)	Little/Brown	(1958)	Shahn, Ben	60-90	R
Cook, Bernadine	Looking for Susie (1st, ob8vo, [48]p, fp 1-color, DJ/2.50)	Young Scott	1959	Shahn, Judith	25-45	
Livingston, Myra C.	Moon and a Star (1st {std}, 12mo, 48p, b/w, DJ/2.50)	Harcourt	(1965)	Shahn, Judith	20-35	*
Smith, Thorne	Lazy Bear Lane (1st {std}, 8vo, 240p, green cl, pep, b/w, DJ/2.00)	Doubleday/Doran	1931	Shanks, George	120-185	
Bloch, Bertram	Little Laundress & the Fearful Knights (1st {std}, 8vo, 122p, b/w, DJ/2.50)	Doubleday	1954	Shanks, George	30-45	
Wilde, Oscar	House of Pomegranates (1st, 8vo, 158p, gilt, uncut, dep, 4pl)	L: McIlvanie	1891	Shannon/Ricketts	700-1000	
Bontemps, Arna (comp)	Golden Slippers (1st {std}, 8vo, 220p, b/w pl, DJ/2.50)	Harper	(1941)	Sharon, Henrietta	45-65	
Caldwell, Erskine	Molly Cottontail (1st {std}, 8vo, 31p, fp 2-color, DJ/2.50)	Little/Brown	1958	Sharp, William	80-125	R
Vance, Eleanor G.	Tall Book of Fairy Tales (1st, lg4to, ibds, 124p, color, pep, DJ/1.00)	Harper	(1947)	Sharp, William	60-100	
Steel, Flora A.	Adventures of Akbar (1st AM, 8vo, 204p, gilt, 8cp)	Stokes	(1913)	Shaw, Byam	80-120	
Steel, Flora A.	Adventures of Akbar (1st, 8vo, 204p, gilt, 8cp)	L: Heinemann	1913	Shaw, Byam	80-120	
Sidgwick, Frank (ed)	Ballads & Lyrics of Love (1st, lg8vo, teg, 178p, uncut, 10cp)	L: Chatto	1908	Shaw, Byam	70-100	
Reade, Charles	Cloister & Hearth (1st, 4to, 663p, violet/gilt, teg, 20cp)	L: Chatto	1909	Shaw, Byam	60-90	
Tennyson, Alfred	Geraint & Enid (1st, 16mo, blue/gilt, 4cp)	L: Jack	[1906]	Shaw, Byam	80-125	
Sidgwick, Frank (ed)	Legendary Ballads (1st, lg8vo, 180p, red/gilt, uncut, teg, 10cp)	L: Chatto	1908	Shaw, Byam	70-100	
N/A	Old King Cole's Book of Nursery Rhymes (4to, ibds, fp color)	L: Macmillan	[1906]	Shaw, Byam	200-300	
Hadden, James C.	Operas of Richard Wagner (1st, 8vo, gilt, teg, 246p, 24cp)	L: Jack	1908	Shaw, Byam	80-125	
Bunyan, John	Pilgrim's Progress (sm4to, gilt, 393p, teg, 29cp, pep)	L: Jack	[1910]	Shaw, Byam	70-125	
MacGregor, Mary	Pilgrim's Progress told to Children (24mo, 120p, p-o, 8cp)	L: Jack	[1910]	Shaw, Byam	25-40	
Garnett (ed.)	Poems by Robert Browning (1st, 8vo, 377p, gilt, b/w)	L: Bell	1900	Shaw, Byam	70-100	
Poe, Edgar A.	Selected Tales of Mystery (1st AM, 4to, 334p, teg, 16cp)	Lippincott	1909	Shaw, Byam	100-165	
Jacobs (ed.)	Tales from Boccaccio (1st, sq8vo, gilt, teg, 117p, 20pl)	L: G. Allen	1899	Shaw, Byam	90-120	
Lamb, Charles	Tales from Shakespeare (1st, sm8vo, 363p, gilt, teg, 24pl)	L: G. Bell	1903	Shaw, Byam	60-90	
Scott, William R.	Apple that Jack Ate (1st, sm ob4to, ipcb, [25]p, color, dep, DJ/1.50)	W.R. Scott	1951	Shaw, Charles G.	45-70	
Brown, Margaret W.	Black and White (1st, 4to, ibds, [32]p, fp b/w, DJ/1.25)	Harper	1944	Shaw, Charles G.	100-165	
Shaw, Charles G.	Blue Guess Book (1st, 8vo, ipcb, [48]p, color, DJ/1.00)	W.R. Scott	(1942)	Shaw, Charles G.	50-80	
McCullough, John	Dark is Dark (1st, lg8vo, [34]p, ibds, color, cep, DJ/1.50)	W.R. Scott	1947	Shaw, Charles G.	30-50	
Shaw, Charles G.	Giant of Central Park (1st, lg8vo, ipcb, [64]p, fp b/w, DJ/1.50)	W.R. Scott	(1940)	Shaw, Charles G.	50-80	
Shaw, Charles G.	Guess Book (1st, 8vo, [48]p, ipcb, color, DJ/1.00)	W.R. Scott	(1941)	Shaw, Charles G.	50-80	
Scott, William R.	This is the Milk that Jack Drank (1st, sm ob4to, ipcb, [24]p, color)	W.R. Scott	1944	Shaw, Charles G.	40-65	
Scott, William R.	Water that Jack Drank (1st, sm ob4to, ipcb, [24]p, color, pep, DJ/1.50)	W.R. Scott	1950	Shaw, Charles G.	45-70	
Brown, Margaret W.	Winter Noisy Book (1st, 8vo, [42]p, ipcb, pep, color, DJ/1.50)	W.R. Scott	1947	Shaw, Charles G.	70-125	
Shecter, Ben	Conrad's Castle (1st, sm4to, [32]p, color, DJ/3.50)	Harper	(1967)	Shecter, Ben	30-50	
Lexau, Joan M.	Every Day a Dragon (1st, 12mo, 32p, b/w, DJ/1.95)	Harper	(1967)	Shecter, Ben	20-25	*
Borack, Barbara	Grandpa (1st, lg8vo, 32p, color, cep, DJ/2.95)	Harper	(1967)	Shecter, Ben	30-50	
Zolotow, Charlotte	Hating Book (1st, ob sm8vo, 32p, ibds, color, DJ/2.95)	Harper	(1969)	Shecter, Ben	30-50	
Lexau, Joan M.	Millicent's Ghost (1st, 8vo, [32]p, 2-color, pep, DJ/2.75)	Dial Press	(1962)	Shecter, Ben	20-30	*
Zolotow, Charlotte	My Friend John (1st, ob 12mo, ipcb, 32p, fp 2-color, DJ/2.50)	Harper, Row	(1968)	Shecter, Ben	25-45	*
Shecter, Ben	Partouche Plants a Seed (1st, ob8vo, ipcb, 32p, 2-color, DJ/2.50)	Harper	(1966)	Shecter, Ben	25-45	*
Staunton, Schuyler	Fate of a Crown (1st, sm8vo, 306p, red/gilt, 6pl)	Reilly/Britton	(1905)	Sheffer, G.C.	350-500	
Zolotow, Charlotte	River Winding (1st, 8vo, 32p, 2-color)	Abelard-Schuman	(1970)	Shekerjian, Regina	25-45	*
Tietjens, Eunice H.	Boy of the South Seas (1st, 8vo, 193p, 20 fp b/w, pep, NH)	Coward	(1931)	Sheldon, Marian	55-80	*
Stevenson, Rbt. L.	Child's Garden of Verses (12mo, 96p, col frn, fp b/w)	Donohue	(1916)	Sheldon, Marian	35-50	
Tarry, Ellen	Janie Belle (1st, 4to, [30]p, ibds, fp 1-color, DJ/0.50)	Garden City	1940	Sheldon, Marian	80-120	
Mills, Freya	Susan's Surprise (1st, 8vo, [31]p, color, pep, DJ/1.50)	Oxford U. Pr.	1946	Sheldon, Marian	30-45	
Jones, Paul	Alphabet of Aviation (1st, lg8vo, blue cl, [62]p, gilt, 28 fp color)	Macrae Smith	(1928)	Shenton, Edward	140-225	*
Meader, Stephen W.	Bat: Story of a Bull Terrier (1st, 8vo, 273p, b/w pl, DJ/2.00)	Harcourt	(1939)	Shenton, Edward	80-140	
Meader, Stephen W.	Behind the Ranges (1st {std}, 8vo, 222p, b/w, pep, DJ/2.50)	Harcourt	(1947)	Shenton, Edward	120-185	
Peeples, Edwin A.	Blue Boy (1st, 8vo, 176p, b/w, DJ/3.00)	Houghton	1964	Shenton, Edward	30-50	
Meader, Stephen W.	Blueberry Mountain (1st, 8vo, 309p, b/w pl, pep, DJ/2.00)	Harcourt	(1941)	Shenton, Edward	100-165	
Meader, Stephen W.	Boy with a Pack (1st, 8vo, 297p, brown cl, b/w, pep, DJ/2.00, NH)	Harcourt	(1939)	Shenton, Edward	100-170	
Meader, Stephen W.	Buckboard Stranger (1st {std}, 8vo, 213p, b/w, DJ/2.75)	Harcourt	(1954)	Shenton, Edward	100-160	
Bialk, Elisa	Colt of Cripple Creek (1st {std}, 8vo, 180p, b/w, DJ/2.50)	World	(1953)	Shenton, Edward	25-40	
Rawlings, Marjorie K.	Cross Creek (1st, 8vo, 368p, gilt, b/w, pep, DJ/2.50)	Scribner	1942	Shenton, Edward	150-250	
Meader, Stephen W.	Fish Hawk's Nest (1st {std}, 8vo, 236p, b/w, pep, DJ/2.50)	Harcourt	(1952)	Shenton, Edward	100-170	
Meader, Stephen W.	Jonathan Goes West (1st {std}, 8vo, 241p, b/w, DJ/2.25)	Harcourt	(1946)	Shenton, Edward	120-185	
Kalashnikoff, N.	Jumper (1st, 8vo, blue/silver, 224p, b/w, DJ/2.75)	Scribner	1944	Shenton, Edward	30-50	
Coatsworth, Eliz.	Last Fort (1st {std}, 8vo, 250p, b/w, DJ/2.75)	Winston	(1952)	Shenton, Edward	30-45	*

AUTHOR	TITLE	PUBLISHER	DATE	ARTIST	PRICE	LC
DeJong, Meindert	Little Stray Dog (1st {std}, 8vo, 51p, b/w, DJ/1.50)	Harper	(1943)	Shenton, Edward	35-60	
Meader, Stephen W.	Long Trains Roll (1st, 8vo, 259p, black cl, b/w, pep, DJ/2.00)	Harcourt	(1944)	Shenton, Edward	80-120	
Latham, Jean L.	On Stage, Mr. Jefferson! (1st {std}, 8vo, 266p, grey cl, DJ/2.95)	Harper	(1958)	Shenton, Edward	30-50	
Shenton, Edward	Riders of the Winds (1st, lg8vo, 205p, gilt, 16cp, pep, DJ/2.50)	Macrae Smith	(1929)	Shenton, Edward	50-80	
Meader, Stephen W.	River of the Wolves (1st {std}, 8vo, 248p, b/w, pep, DJ/2.50)	Harcourt	(1948)	Shenton, Edward	80-120	
Meader, Stephen W.	Sea Snake (1st, 8vo, 255p, b/w, pep, DJ/2.00)	Harcourt	(1943)	Shenton, Edward	80-135	
Meader, Stephen W.	Shadow in the Pines (1st, 8vo, 281p, b/w, pep, DJ/2.00)	Harcourt	(1942)	Shenton, Edward	80-135	
Taber, Gladys	Stillmeadow Road (1st {std}, 8vo, 287p, b/w, DJ/4.95)	Lippincott	(1962)	Shenton, Edward	25-40	
Kjelgaard, Jim	Swamp Cat (1st, 8vo, 175p, b/w, DJ/3.00)	Dodd	(1957)	Shenton, Edward	50-80	
Meader, Stephen W.	T-Model Tommy (1st, 8vo, 305p, b/w pl, DJ/2.00)	Harcourt	(1938)	Shenton, Edward	120-180	
Rawlings, Marjorie K.	The Yearling (1st, 8vo, 428p, beige cl, b/w, DJ/2.50)	Scribner	1938	Shenton, Edward	400-600	
Meader, Stephen W.	Whaler 'Round the Horn (1st {std}, 8vo, 244p, b/w, pep, DJ/2.50)	Harcourt	(1950)	Shenton, Edward	80-120	
Sawyer, Ruth	Year of Jubilo (1st, 8vo, 266p, b/w, pep, DJ/2.00)	Viking	1940	Shenton, Edward	30-45	
Lucas, E.V.	As the Bee Sucks (1st, 8vo, 169p, pink cl, b/w, DJ)	L: Methuen	(1937)	Shepard, Ernest H.	30-50	
Shepard, Ernest	Ben and Brock (1st AM {std}, sm8vo, 91p, gilt, b/w, DJ/2.95)	Doubleday	(1966)	Shepard, Ernest H.	30-50	
Grahame, Kenneth	Bertie's Escapade (1st AM, sm8vo, 41p, grey cl, b/w, DJ/1.50)	Lippincott	(1949)	Shepard, Ernest H.	60-90	R
Grahame, Kenneth	Bertie's Escapade (1st, 12mo, pink bds, 42p, b/w, DJ)	L: Methuen	(1949)	Shepard, Ernest H.	80-120	
Shepard, Ernest	Betsy and Joe (1st AM {std}, 12mo, 78p, b/w, DJ/3.25)	Dutton	(1967)	Shepard, Ernest H.	50-80	
Jefferies, Richard	Bevis, Story of a Boy (1st, 8vo, 519p, b/w, pep, DJ)	L: J. Cape	(1932)	Shepard, Ernest H.	80-120	
Squire, John (ed)	Cheddar Gorge (1st, 4to, 181p, yellow/gilt, fp b/w)	L: Collins	(1937)	Shepard, Ernest H.	60-100	*
Drinkwater, John	Christmas Poems (1st, sq8vo, 18p, orange wraps, uncut, 6 b/w)	L: Sidgwick	1931	Shepard, Ernest H.	70-100	
Milne, A.A.	Christopher Robin Birthday Book (1st, 16mo, 215p, orange/gilt, b/w)	L: Methuen	(1930)	Shepard, Ernest H.	300-450	
Milne, A.A.	Christopher Robin Story Book (1st AM, sm8vo, gilt, 171p, b/w)	Dutton	(1929)	Shepard, Ernest H.	250-400	
Milne, A.A.	Christopher Robin Story Book (1st, sm8vo, 171p, blue/gilt, b/w)	L: Methuen	(1929)	Shepard, Ernest H.	300-400	
Milne, A.A.	Christopher Robin Verses (1st AM {std}, 8vo, 210p, 12cp)	Dutton	(1932)	Shepard, Ernest H.	140-225	*
Milne, A.A.	Christopher Robin Verses (1st, 8vo, 210p, blue/gilt, 12cp)	L: Methuen	(1932)	Shepard, Ernest H.	200-300	
Chalmers, Patrick	Cricket in the Cage (1st, 8vo, 77p, gilt, fp b/w, DJ)	L: A&C Black	1933	Shepard, Ernest H.	100-165	
Rugh, Belle Dorman	Crystal Mountain (1st [1st bk.], 8vo, 208p, b/w, DJ/2.75)	Houghton	1955	Shepard, Ernest H.	50-85	R
Grahame, Kenneth	Dream Days (1st AM, 8vo, 172p, gilt, pep)	Dodd	1931	Shepard, Ernest H.	40-60	
Morshead, O.F.	Everybody's Pepys (1st, 8vo, blue cl, 615p, b/w, pep)	Harcourt	1926	Shepard, Ernest H.	40-65	
Rieu, E.V.	Flattered Flying Fish (1st AM {std}, sm8vo, 101p, b/w, DJ/2.95)	Dutton	(1962)	Shepard, Ernest H.	35-50	
Colling, Susan	Frogmorton (1st AM {std}, 8vo, 148p, grey cl, b/w, pep, DJ/2.50)	Knopf	1956	Shepard, Ernest H.	40-70	
Milne, A.A. (intro)	Fun & Fantasy (1st, lg4to, 87p, ibds, color)	L: Methuen	(1927)	Shepard, Ernest H.	180-270	
Farjeon, Eleanor	Glass Slipper (1st, 8vo, 175p, b/w, DJ)	L: Oxford U.Pr.	1955	Shepard, Ernest H.	55-80	
Farjeon, Eleanor	Glass Slipper (1st AM, 8vo, 187p, red cl, b/w, DJ/2.75)	Viking	1956	Shepard, Ernest H.	35-60	
Grahame, Kenneth	Golden Age (1st, 12mo, 166p, beige/gilt, t.e. pink, b/w, DJ)	L: John Lane	(1928)	Shepard, Ernest H.	120-185	
Grahame, Kenneth	Golden Age (1st AM, sm8vo, 170p, b/w, pep)	Dodd	1929	Shepard, Ernest H.	75-100	
Housman, Laurence	Golden Sovereign (1st, 8vo, green/gilt, 349p, b/w, DJ)	L: J. Cape	(1937)	Shepard, Ernest H.	60-100	
Housman, Laurence	Gracious Majesty (1st, 8vo, 222p, gilt, b/w, DJ)	L: J. Cape	1941	Shepard, Ernest H.	60-90	
Dickens, Charles	Holly Tree... (1st AM, sm4to, green cloth, 192p, 30pl)	Scribner	(1925)	Shepard, Ernest H.	55-80	
Milne, A.A.	House at Pooh Corner (1st [1], 12mo, 178p, teg, pink/gilt, b/w, pep)	L: Methuen	(1928)	Shepard, Ernest H.	450-650	
Fraser-Simson, H.	Hums of Pooh (1st AM, lg4to, 67p, ibds, p-o, b/w decor by...)	Dutton	[1930]	Shepard, Ernest H.	80-140	
Pertwee, Rowland	Islanders (1st, 8vo, gilt, 267p, b/w, pep, DJ/3.00)	Bobbs-Merrill	(1956)	Shepard, Ernest H.	30-55	
Walpole, Hugh	Jeremy (1st AM, 8vo, 304p, col frn, b/w, pep)	Doran	(1919)	Shepard, Ernest H.	30-50	
Milne, A.A.	King's Breakfast (1st, lg8vo, bds, 17p, b/w, DJ)	L: Methuen	(1925)	Shepard, Ernest H.	140-200	
Agnew, Georgette	Let's Pretend (1st, 12mo, 63p, blue/gilt, teg, b/w, pep)	L: J. Saville	1927	Shepard, Ernest H.	70-100	
Armstrong, Anthony	Livestock in Barracks (1st, 12mo, 153p, gilt, 20 fp b/w)	L: Methuen	(1929)	Shepard, Ernest H.	30-50	
Green, Roger L.	Modern Fairy Stories (1st AM {std}, 8vo, 270p, 8cp, DJ/2.95)	Dent/Dutton	(1955)	Shepard, Ernest H.	75-100	*
Struther, Jan	Modern Struwwelpeter (1st, lg8vo, ibds, 37p, color)	L: Methuen	1936	Shepard, Ernest H.	200-300	
Fraser-Simpson, H.	More Very Young Songs (1st, lg4to, p-o, 40p, bds, b/w)	L: Methuen	(1928)	Shepard, Ernest H.	150-225	
Lucas, E.V.	Mr. Punch's Country Songs (1st, lg4to, 92p, ibds, p-o, b/w)	L: Methuen	1928	Shepard, Ernest H.	100-165	
Milne, A.A.	Now We Are Six (1st, 12mo, 103p, maroon/gilt, teg, b/w, pep)	L: Methuen	(1927)	Shepard, Ernest H.	450-650	
Milne, A.A.	Now We Are Six (1st AM, sm8vo, buckram, 103p, gilt, b/w)	Dutton	(1927)	Shepard, Ernest H.	250-400	
Milne, A.A.	Old Sailor (1st AM, lg8vo, ipcb, [23]p, 1-color, pep, DJ/0.50)	Dutton	(1947)	Shepard, Ernest H.	100-160	*
Avery, Harold	Play the Game (1st, 8vo, 343p, gilt, 4cp)	L: T. Nelson	[1906]	Shepard, Ernest H.	60-90	
Lucas, E.V.	Playtime & Company (1st, 4to, ibds, b/w, 95p, pep, DJ)	L: Methuen	(1925)	Shepard, Ernest H.	120-200	
Ellison, Virginia	Pooh Cook Book (1st {std}, 8vo, yellow cl, 120p, DJ/4.50)	Dutton	(1969)	Shepard, Ernest H.	25-40	
Grahame, Kenneth	Reluctant Dragon (1st, 8vo, [57]p, cloth, b/w, DJ/1.25)	Holiday House	(1938)	Shepard, Ernest H.	60-100	
Goulden, Shirley	Royal Reflections (1st, 12mo, 136p, ibds, 7 fp b/w, DJ)	L: Methuen	1956	Shepard, Ernest H.	55-80	
Farjeon, Eleanor	Silver Curlew (1st, 8vo, 192p, b/w, DJ)	L: Oxford U.Pr.	1953	Shepard, Ernest H.	60-90	
Milne, A.A.	Sneezles (1st AM, lg sq8vo, ibds, [23]p, 2-color, pep, DJ/0.50)	Dutton	(1947)	Shepard, Ernest H.	80-120	
Fraser-Simpson, H.	Songs from Now We are Six (1st, sm folio, 33p, bds, p-o, b/w)	L: Methuen	(1927)	Shepard, Ernest H.	170-240	
Struther, Jan	Sycamore Square (1st AM, 8vo, 63p, b/w, DJ/1.25)	Oxford U. Pr.	1932	Shepard, Ernest H.	45-60	
Struther, Jan	Sycamore Square (1st, 8vo, green/gilt, 63p, fp b/w)	L: Methuen	(1932)	Shepard, Ernest H.	50-80	
Milne, A.A.	Teddy Bear & other Songs (1st, lg4to, bds, p-o, 43p, b/w)	L: Methuen	(1926)	Shepard, Ernest H.	130-200	
Milne, A.A.	Teddy Bear & other Songs (1st AM, lg4to, bds, p-o, 43p, b/w)	Dutton	(1926)	Shepard, Ernest H.	140-225	
Milne, A.A.	Very Young Verses (1st, sm8vo, 88p, blue cl, 6pl)	L: Methuen	(1929)	Shepard, Ernest H.	120-180	*
Milne, A.A.	When We Were Very Young (1st, 12mo, 100p, gilt, AEG, b/w)	L: Methuen	(1924)	Shepard, Ernest H.	500-700	
Milne, A.A.	When We Were Very Young (1st AM, 12mo, 100p, red/gilt, b/w, pep)	Dutton	(1924)	Shepard, Ernest H.	350-500	
Grahame, Kenneth	Wind in the Willows (1st, 12mo, green/gilt, 312p, b/w, pep)	L: Methuen	(1931)	Shepard, Ernest H.	200-300	
Grahame, Kenneth	Wind in the Willows (1st AM, 8vo, 312p, blue/gilt, b/w, pep)	Scribner	1933	Shepard, Ernest H.	150-225	
Milne, A.A.	Winnie-the-Pooh (1st, 12mo, 158p, gilt, teg, b/w, pep)	L: Methuen	(1926)	Shepard, Ernest H.	700-1000	
Milne, A.A.	Winnie-the-Pooh (1st AM, 12mo, 158p, gilt, b/w, pep)	Dutton	(1926)	Shepard, Ernest H.	500-700	
George, Jean C.	Moon of the Bears (1st, 8vo, 38p, b/w, DJ/3.25)	Crowell	(1967)	Shepard, Mac	20-30	*
Travers, Pamela L.	Mary Poppins (1st AM, 12mo, 206p, blue cl, b/w, pep, DJ/1.50)	Reynal/Hitchcock	(1934)	Shepard, Mary	250-400	R
Travers, Pamela L.	Mary Poppins Comes Back (1st AM, 12mo, 268p, grn cl, b/w, pep, DJ/1.50)	Reynal/Hitchcock	(1935)	Shepard, Mary	180-275	
Travers, Pamela L.	Mary Poppins Comes Back (1st, sm8vo, 303p, beige cl, b/w, DJ)	L: Lovat/Dicks	(1935)	Shepard, Mary	300-425	
Travers, Pamela L.	Mary Poppins from A to Z (1st {std}, sm sq8vo, [58]p, b/w, pep, DJ/2.95)	Harcourt	(1962)	Shepard, Mary	80-125	

AUTHOR	TITLE	PUBLISHER	DATE	ARTIST	PRICE	LC
Travers, Pamela L.	Mary Poppins in the Park (1st, sm8vo, 212p, brown/gilt, b/w, DJ)	L: P. Davies	1952	Shepard, Mary	180-260	
Travers, Pamela L.	Mary Poppins in the Park (1st AM {std}, 12mo, 235p, b/w, dep, DJ/2.50)	Harcourt	(1952)	Shepard, Mary	120-185	
Milne, A.A.	Prince Rabbit & Princess Who Could Not Laugh (1st {std} 4to 72p color DJ)	Dutton	(1966)	Shepard, Mary	40-65	
Travers, Pamela L.	Mary Poppins Opens the Door (1st, sm8vo, 239p, grey cl, b/w, DJ/1.75)	Reynal/Hitchcock	(1943)	Shepard/Sims	100-165	
Harris, Joel C.	Nights with Uncle Remus (1st, 8vo, 367p, b/w)	L: A. Moring	[1907]	Shepherd, J.A.	200-300	*
Rostand, Edmond	Story of Chanticleer (1st AM, 8vo, 144p, 12cp)	Stokes	(1913)	Shepherd, J.A.	60-90	
Rostand, Edmond	Story of Chanticleer (1st, 8vo, 144p, gilt, 12cp, pep)	L: Heinemann	1913	Shepherd, J.A.	75-100	
Cuming, E.W.D.	Three Jovial Puppies (1st, folio, bds, 36p, p-o, color)	L: Blackie	[1908]	Shepherd, J.A.	250-350	
Harris, Joel C.	Uncle Remus (1st, 8vo, 288p, teg, 9cp, fp b/w)	L: Richards	1901	Shepherd, J.A.	100-165	
Cuming, E.W.D.	Wonders in Monsterland (1st, 12mo, AEG, 257p, 4cp, 14pl)	L: G. Allen	1901	Shepherd, J.A.	125-170	*
Shepherd, J.A.	Zig Zag Fables (1st, ob4to, 36p, ibds, color)	L: Gardner	1897	Shepherd, J.A.	170-240	
Daley, C.F.	Sundials (1st, 4to, ibds, 12cp)	Worthington	(1891)	Shepley, Annie B.	120-180	
Wiggin, Kate D.	Diary of a Goose Girl (1st, 12mo, 117p, tan cl, b/w)	Houghton	1902	Shepperson, Claude	30-50	
Wells, H.G.	First Men in the Moon (1st UK, 8vo, 342p, blue/gilt, 12pl, cep)	L: G. Newnes	1901	Shepperson, Claude	600-800	
Lucas, E.V.	Open Road (1st, 4to, blue/gilt, 301p, teg, 16ticp)	Henry Holt & Co.	1913	Shepperson, Claude	100-160	
Tracy, Louis	Final War (1st UK, sq8vo, 372p, grey/gilt, 16pl)	L: C. Pearson	1896	Sherie, Ernest F.	60-90	*
MacMillan, Cyrus	Canadian Wonder Tales (1st, sm4to, 199p, 17pl, pep)	L: John Lane	1918	Sheringham, George	100-170	
Beerbohm, Max	Happy Hypocrite (1st, 4to, 70p, white/gilt, uncut, 24cp, dep)	L: John Lane	(1915)	Sheringham, George	120-200	
Sheridan, Richard B.	The Duenna (1st, lg8vo, 105p, bds, gilt, 12cp)	L: Constable	1925	Sheringham, George	60-90	
Montgomery, R.	Ghost Town Adventure (1st, 12mo, 252p, dp pl, pep, DJ/2.00)	Henry Holt & Co.	(1942)	Sherman, Russell	25-40	
Crawford, Phyllis	Walking on Gold (1st, 8vo, 284p, dp b/w, pep, DJ/2.00)	J. Messner	(1940)	Sherman, Russell	20-35	
Black, Irma S.	Big Puppy & Little Puppy (1st, 8vo, yellow cl, [33]p, b/w, pep, DJ/2.50)	Holiday House	1960	Sherman, Theresa	25-40	
Govan, Christine	Delectable Mountain (1st {std}, 8vo, 187p, b/w, DJ/2.95)	World	(1962)	Sherman, Theresa	25-40	
Schlein, Miriam	Little Rabbit the High Jumper (1st, 8vo, [46]p, 2-color, DJ/2.25)	W.R. Scott	1957	Sherman, Theresa	30-50	
Holland, Marion	Muggsy (1st, 8vo, [32]p, ibds, 1-color, pep, DJ/2.50)	Knopf	(1959)	Sherman, Theresa	30-50	*
Selsam, Millicent	Nature Detective (1st, ob8vo, [48]p, color, DJ)	W.R. Scott	1958	Sherman, Theresa	30-45	
Todd, Ruthven	Tan's Fish (1st {std}, 8vo, 58p, color, DJ/2.75)	Little/Brown	(1958)	Sherman, Theresa	20-35	
Sherrill, Dorothy	Little White Teddy Bear... (1st {std}, 12mo, [62]p, color)	Farrar/Rinehart	(1931)	Sherrill, Dorothy	70-90	
Sherrill, Dorothy	Story of a Little Duck (1st, 12mo, [50]p, ibds, color)	Merrill	(1934)	Sherrill, Dorothy	60-80	
Sherrill, Dorothy	Story of Roly & Poly (1st {std}, 24mo, [63]p, fp color, cep, DJ/1.50)	Crowell	(1952)	Sherrill, Dorothy	50-80	
Sherwood, E. Hugh	Bobbie Bubbles (1st, sq8vo, 78p, ibds, color)	Rand/McNally	(1916)	Sherwood, E. Hugh	70-100	
Sherwood, E. Hugh	Jack Jingling in Jungleland (1st, lg ob8vo, 80p, ibds, fp color)	Rand/McNally	(1918)	Sherwood, E. Hugh	100-170	
Carroll, Lewis	Verses from Alice (1st, 4to, blue/gilt, [34]p, color, DJ)	L: Collins	(1944)	Sherwood, G.S.	100-165	
Puzo, Mario	Runaway Summer of Davie Shaw (1st, 8vo, 186p, b/w, DJ/2.95)	Platt/Munk	(1966)	Sherwood, Stewart	50-80	
Nash, Ogden	Boy is a Boy (1st {std}, sm4to, unpag, 1-color, DJ/2.95)	F. Watts	(1960)	Shilstone, Arthur	40-65	R
Stong, Philip D.	Forty Pounds of Gold (1st {std}, sm8vo, 218p, b/w, DJ/2.50)	Doubleday	1951	Shilstone, Arthur	25-45	
Montgomery, R.	Hurricane Yank (1st, 8vo, 250p, col frn, b/w, DJ/2.00)	McKay	(1942)	Shimer, James	25-40	
Selsam, Millicent	All Kinds of Babies (1st, ob8vo, [40]p, 2-color, DJ/3.75)	Four Winds Pr.	(1969)	Shimin, Symeon	25-40	*
Hoover, Helen	Animals Near & Far (1st, 8vo, 64p, color, DJ/4.50)	Parents Mag. Pr.	(1970)	Shimin, Symeon	20-30	
May, Julian	Before the Indians (1st, 4to, [40]p, color, DJ/3.95)	Holiday House	(1969)	Shimin, Symeon	30-45	
L'Engle, Madeleine	Dance in the Desert (1st {std}, 8vo, [55]p, color, gilt, pep, DJ/4.95)	Farrar, Straus	(1969)	Shimin, Symeon	60-90	
Schlein, Miriam	Elephant Herd (1st, lg8vo, ipcb, [40]p, 1-color, cep, DJ/2.00)	W.R. Scott	1954	Shimin, Symeon	30-50	
Schlein, Miriam	Go With the Sun (1st, lg8vo, ipcb, [40]p, fp 2-color, cep, DJ/2.00)	W.R. Scott	1952	Shimin, Symeon	25-40	
Cone, Molly	House in the Tree (1st, 8vo, 40p, b/w, DJ/3.75)	Crowell	(1968)	Shimin, Symeon	25-40	
Schneider, Herman	How Big is Big? (1st {this fmt}, sm4to, ibds, [40]p, color, DJ/1.75)	W.R. Scott	1950	Shimin, Symeon	30-60	*
Singer, Isaac B.	Joseph and Koza (1st {std}, lg4to, [38]p, fp 2-color, DJ/4.95)	Farrar, Straus	(1970)	Shimin, Symeon	40-65	
Lexau, Joan M.	Kite Over 10th Avenue (1st {std}, 8vo, 94p, gilt, 1-color, pep, DJ/2.95)	Doubleday	(1967)	Shimin, Symeon	30-45	
Coatsworth, Eliz.	Lighthouse Island (1st {std}, 8vo, 62p, 2-color, DJ/4.25)	Norton	(1968)	Shimin, Symeon	30-45	*
Fisher, Aileen	Listen Rabbit (1st, 4to, [36]p, 2-color, pep, DJ/3.50)	Crowell	(1964)	Shimin, Symeon	40-65	R
Schweitzer, Byrd B.	Man Who Talked to a Tree (1st {std}, sm4to, [47]p, color, DJ/4.50)	Dutton	(1968)	Shimin, Symeon	40-70	
Schweitzer, Byrd B.	One Small Blue Bead (1st {std}, 4to, 40p, 2-color, DJ/3.50)	Macmillan	(1965)	Shimin, Symeon	35-50	
Krumgold, Joseph	Onion John (1st {std}, 8vo, 248p, b/w, DJ/3.00, NM)	Crowell	(1959)	Shimin, Symeon	80-125	
Scott, Ann H.	Sam (1st, 4to, [33]p, 1-color, DJ/3.95)	McGraw-Hill	(1967)	Shimin, Symeon	50-80	R*
Belpre, Pura	Santiago (1st, 4to, 31p, ibds, color, DJ/3.95)	Warne	(1969)	Shimin, Symeon	25-40	*
Fisher, Aileen	Sing, Little Mouse (1st, 4to, [36]p, color, pep, DJ/3.95)	Crowell	(1969)	Shimin, Symeon	25-45	
Brown, Margaret W.	Young Kangaroo (1st, 8vo, 42p, 2-color, pep, DJ/2.25)	W.R. Scott	(1955)	Shimin, Symeon	100-165	R
Hamilton, Virginia	Zeely (1st {std}, [1st bk.], 8vo, 122p, fp b/w, DJ/3.95)	Macmillan	(1967)	Shimin, Symeon	45-70	R
Bannerman, Helen	Little Black Sambo (1st, lg8vo, p-o, 63p, col frn, color, pep)	Whitman	(1925)	Shinn, Cobb X.	180-300	
Bible	Christ Story (1st {std}, sm4to, [41]p, color, pep, DJ)	Winston	(1943)	Shinn, Everett	30-50	
Dickens, Charles	Christmas Carol (1st {std}, lg8vo, 132p, red/gilt, teg, cep, 12 fp color)	Winston	1938	Shinn, Everett	100-165	R*
Dickens, Charles	Christmas in Dickens (1st, 8vo, 63p, ibds, color, pep, DJ/1.00)	Garden City	(1941)	Shinn, Everett	35-50	
Dickens, Charles	David Copperfield (1st {std}, 8vo, 423p, color, DJ/3.50)	Winston	(1948)	Shinn, Everett	40-60	*
Maurois, Andre	Frederic Chopin (1st {std}, 8vo, 91p, 13 fp color, pep, DJ/1.75)	Harper	(1942)	Shinn, Everett	50-80	
Wilde, Oscar	Happy Prince (1st, lg8vo, blue/gilt, teg, 148p, pep, 12cp, DJ/3.50)	Winston	(1940)	Shinn, Everett	50-80	
Dickens, Charles	Life of Our Lord (1st, lg8vo, 125p, gilt, 12 color, pep)	Garden City	(1939)	Shinn, Everett	40-65	
Moore, Clement C.	Night Before Christmas (1st, sm4to, [24]p, ibds, color, DJ/1.25)	Winston	(1942)	Shinn, Everett	70-100	
Riley, James W.	Poems of Childhood (1st, 8vo, [36]p, ibds, color, pep, DJ/0.50)	Grosset/Dunlap	(1943)	Shinn, Everett	30-50	
Irving, Washington	Rip Van Winkle (1st, lg4to, ibds, [40]p, fp color, DJ/1.00)	Garden City	(1939)	Shinn, Everett	70-120	
Bible	Sermon on the Mount (1st {std}, 4to, [40]p, 18cp, pep, DJ)	Winston	(1946)	Shinn, Everett	45-70	
Otis, James	Toby Tyler (1st, 8vo, 212p, p-o, fp color, pep, DJ/1.00)	Winston	1937	Shinn, Everett	30-50	
Howells, William D.	Flight of Pony Baker (1st, 12mo, red/silver, 223p, 8pl, PPP)	Harper	1902	Shinn, Florence S.	120-200	R
Rice, Alice H.	Lovey Mary (1st, 8vo, teg, uncut, 236p, 24pl)	Century	1903	Shinn, Florence S.	25-40	
Hurd, Edith T.	Hurry Hurry (1st, 8vo, ipcb, 45p, 1-color, cep)	W.R. Scott	(1938)	Shipman, M.D.	50-80	
Uchida, Yoshiko	Makoto, the Smallest Boy (1st, 8vo, 41p, b/w, DJ/3.75)	Crowell	(1970)	Shirakawa, Akihito	30-50	*
Shirk, Jeannette C.	Mr. Baxter's Dandelion Garden (1st {std}, 4to, 58p, fp b/w, dep, DJ/1.50)	Dutton	1940	Shirk, Jeanette C.	30-50	
Spyri, Johanna	Heidi (1st, 12mo, 305p, p-o, gilt, 7 fp color)	Macrae Smith	(1925)	Shoemaker, Edna C.	40-65	
Montgomery, Lucy M.	Magic for Marigold (1st, sm8vo, 328p, p-o, col frn)	Stokes	1929	Shoemaker, Edna C.	150-225	
Clymer, Eleanor	Big Pile of Dirt (1st {std}, ob4to, [32]p, 1-color, DJ/3.95)	Holt, Rinehart	1968	Shore, Robert	25-45	

ARTIST: 186

AUTHOR	TITLE	PUBLISHER	DATE	ARTIST	PRICE	LC
Morey, Walter	Home is the North (1st {std}, 8vo, 223p, b/w, DJ/3.95)	Dutton	(1967)	Shore, Robert	20-35	
Shuttlesworth, Dorothy	ABC of Buses (1st {std}, ob4to, ipcb, fp 3-color, cep, DJ/3.25)	Doubleday	(1965)	Shortall, Leonard	40-65	*
Shortall, Leonard	Andy, the Dog Walker (1st, 8vo, 48p, 2-color, pep, DJ/2.95)	Wm. Morrow	(1968)	Shortall, Leonard	20-35	*
Robinson, Mabel L.	Back-Seat Driver (1st, 8vo, 68p, fp b/w, DJ/2.00)	Random	(1949)	Shortall, Leonard	30-50	*
Bond, Gladys B.	Blue Chimney (1st, sm8vo, 164p, red cl, b/w, pep, DJ/2.75)	Holiday House	(1959)	Shortall, Leonard	25-40	
Stolz, Mary S.	Bully of Barkham Street (1st {std}, 8vo, 194p, fp b/w, cep, DJ/3.50)	Harper	(1963)	Shortall, Leonard	25-40	
Beim, Jerrold	Country Train (1st, 8vo, [48]p, color, DJ/2.00)	Wm. Morrow	1950	Shortall, Leonard	30-50	
Govan, Christine	Curious Clubhouse (1st {std}, 8vo, 159p, b/w, DJ/3.75)	World	(1967)	Shortall, Leonard	30-50	
Corbett, Scott	Cutlass Island (1st {std}, 8vo, 151p, b/w, DJ/3.25)	Little/Brown	(1962)	Shortall, Leonard	20-35	
Stolz, Mary S.	Dog on Barkham Street (1st, 8vo, 184p, fp b/w, DJ/2.50)	Harper	(1960)	Shortall, Leonard	25-45	
Fritz, Jean	How to Read a Rabbit (1st, 8vo, [60]p, fp b/w, DJ/2.50)	Coward	(1959)	Shortall, Leonard	30-50	*
Elkin, Benjamin	King's Wish (1st {std}, lg8vo, 59p, color, DJ/1.95)	Beginner Books	1960	Shortall, Leonard	50-85	
Cameron, Eleanor	Mystery for Mr. Bass (1st {std}, sm8vo, 229p, b/w, DJ/3.00)	Little/Brown	(1960)	Shortall, Leonard	200-300	
Moore, Lilian	Old Rosie, the Horse Nobody Understood (1st, 4to, 33p, fp 1-color, DJ/1.95)	Random	(1960)	Shortall, Leonard	30-50	
Felton, Harold	Pecos Bill & the Mustang (1st, 4to, [30]p, fp 2-color, cep, DJ/3.50)	Prentice-Hall	(1965)	Shortall, Leonard	30-50	
Shortall, Leonard	Peter in Grand Central Station (1st, 8vo, 46p, color, DJ/3.25)	Wm. Morrow	(1969)	Shortall, Leonard	20-35	
Govan, Christine	Phinny's Fine Summer (1st {std}, 8vo, 158p, b/w, DJ/3.75)	World	(1968)	Shortall, Leonard	25-40	
Robinson, Mabel L.	Riley Goes to Obedience School (1st, 8vo, 80p, fp b/w, DJ/2.50)	Random	(1956)	Shortall, Leonard	25-40	
Sobol, Donald J.	Secret Agents Four (1st, sm8vo, 142p, b/w, DJ)	Four Winds Pr.	(1967)	Shortall, Leonard	20-30	
Lansing, Elisabeth H.	Secret of Dark Entry (1st {std}, 8vo, 186p, b/w, DJ/3.00)	Crowell	(1961)	Shortall, Leonard	20-30	
Robinson, Mabel L.	Skipper Riley: Terrier Dog (1st, 8vo, blue cl, 90p, b/w, DJ/2.50)	Random	(1955)	Shortall, Leonard	25-45	
Corbett, Scott	Susie Sneakers (1st {std}, 8vo, 216p, b/w, DJ/2.75)	Crowell	(1956)	Shortall, Leonard	40-65	
Fritz, Jean	Tap, Tap, Lion - 1 2 3 (1st, 8vo, [48]p, fp 1-color, DJ/2.75)	Coward	(1962)	Shortall, Leonard	40-65	*
Moore, Lilian	Terrible Mr. Twitmeyer (1st {std}, 8vo, 62p, fp b/w, pep, DJ/2.00)	Random	(1952)	Shortall, Leonard	30-45	*
Govan, Christine	Trash Pile Treasure (1st {std}, 8vo, 126p, b/w, DJ/4.50)	World	(1970)	Shortall, Leonard	25-40	
Faber, Doris	Wonderful Tumble of Timothy Smith (1st {std}, 8vo, 84p, b/w, DJ/2.50)	Knopf	1958	Shortall, Leonard	20-35	*
Ish-Kishor, Salamith	Carpet of Solomon (1st, lg8vo, 57p, b/w, DJ/3.25)	Pantheon	(1966)	Shulevitz, Uri	45-70	
Hays, Daniel	Charley Sang a Song (1st, ob8vo, 46p, fp color, DJ/2.95)	Harper	(1964)	Shulevitz, Uri	40-65	
Ransome, Arthur	Fool of the World & Flying Ship (1st, ob4to, [48]p, color, pep, DJ/4.50, CM)	Farrar, Straus	(1968)	Shulevitz, Uri	60-100	R
Stolz, Mary S.	Maximilian's World (1st, 8vo, 57p, ibds, fp b/w, DJ/2.95)	Harper	(1966)	Shulevitz, Uri	40-65	R
Nathan, Dorothy	Month Brothers (1st {std}, 8vo, 95p, b/w, DJ/3.95)	Dutton	(1967)	Shulevitz, Uri	30-45	
Shulevitz, Uri	Moon in My Room (1st {std}, [1st bk.], 8vo, [30]p, color, DJ/2.50)	Harper	1963	Shulevitz, Uri	60-90	
Stolz, Mary S.	Mystery of the Woods (1st, 8vo, 46p, fp 2-color, DJ/2.95)	Harper	(1964)	Shulevitz, Uri	30-50	
Shulevitz, Uri	One Monday Morning (1st, 4to, [46]p, color, DJ)	Scribner	(1967)	Shulevitz, Uri	30-50	
Shulevitz, Uri	Rain Rain Rivers (1st, ob4to, [32]p, fp 2-color, pep, DJ/4.50)	Farrar, Straus	(1969)	Shulevitz, Uri	60-90	R*
Zolotow, Charlotte	Rose, a Bridge & Wild Black Horse (1st {std}, ob8vo, [33]p, color, DJ/2.95)	Harper	(1964)	Shulevitz, Uri	30-50	
Wahl, Jan	Runaway Jonah... (1st {std}, 8vo, 42p, ibds, 2-color, DJ/3.95)	Macmillan	1968	Shulevitz, Uri	30-50	
Sendak, Jack	Second Witch (1st, 8vo, 94p, fp b/w, DJ/2.95)	Harper	(1965)	Shulevitz, Uri	30-45	
Larson, Jean R.	Silkspinners (1st, 8vo, 93p, b/w, DJ/3.95)	Scribner	(1967)	Shulevitz, Uri	25-40	
Biber, Yehoash	Treasure of the Turkish Pasha (1st, 8vo, 128p, b/w, DJ/3.50)	Scribner	(1968)	Shulevitz, Uri	35-50	
Grimm Bros.	Twelve Dancing Princesses (1st, 8vo, [30]p, color, cep, DJ/3.25)	Scribner	(1966)	Shulevitz, Uri	30-50	
Wahl, Jan	Wonderful Kite (1st {std}, 4to, 92p, color, DJ/4.95)	Delacorte Pr.	(1970)	Shulevitz, Uri	30-45	
Russell, William C.	Lady Maud (1st {this pub}, 8vo, 312p, b/w pl)	Fenno	(1896)	Shute, A.B.	100-175	*
Meader, Stephen W.	Commodore's Cup (1st {std}, 8vo, 192p, b/w, DJ/2.95)	Harcourt	(1958)	Sibley, Don	100-165	
Coatsworth, Eliz.	Dog from Nowhere (1st, 8vo, 80p, b/w, DJ/2.20)	Row, Peterson	(1958)	Sibley, Don	20-30	
Street, Julia M.	Fiddler's Fancy (1st, 8vo, 157p, b/w, DJ/2.50)	Follett	(1955)	Sibley, Don	20-35	
Feagles, Anita M.	Genie and Joe Maloney (1st, sm8vo, 62p, b/w, DJ/2.75)	W.R. Scott	(1962)	Sibley, Don	20-35	
Young, Miriam	Marco's Chance (1st {std}, 8vo, 190p, b/w, DJ/3.00)	Harcourt	(1959)	Sibley, Don	30-50	*
Meader, Stephen W.	Snow on Blueberry Mountain (1st {std}, 8vo, 189p, b/w, DJ/3.25)	Harcourt	(1961)	Sibley, Don	80-125	
Meader, Stephen W.	Sparkplug of the Hornets (1st {std}, 8vo, 245p, b/w, DJ/2.75)	Harcourt	(1953)	Sibley, Don	80-120	
Kinsey, Elizabeth	This Cat Came to Stay (1st {std}, sm8vo, 157p, b/w, pep, DJ/2.50)	F. Watts	(1955)	Sibley, Don	70-100	*
Richardson, W.C.F.	India Rubber Jack (1st, 16mo, blue cl, [124]p, 28 color)	L: Swan/Sonn.	[1902]	Sichel, Gerald	120-180	
Woodhouse, S.C.	Miss Bounce (1st, 16mo, 111p, color)	S. Sonnenschein	1903	Sichel, Gerald	100-160	
DeMille, W.M.C.	Forest Ring (1st, lg8vo, 180p, gilt, p-o, 10cp)	Doran	(1914)	Sichel, Harold	60-90	*
Bancroft, Alberta	Goblins of Haubeck (1st, 12mo, 117p, green/gilt, pep, col frn)	McBride	1925	Sichel, Harold	30-50	
Burnett, Frances H.	Good Wolf (1st, 8vo, gilt, 125p, 5cp)	Moffat	1908	Sichel, Harold	30-50	
Rinehart, Mary R.	Truce of God (1st, 8vo, 96p, gilt, col frn, pep)	Doran	(1920)	Sichel, Harold	25-40	
Olcott, F.J. (ed)	Wonder Tales from Goblin Hills (1st {std}, 8vo, 268p, col frn, pep)	NY: Longmans	1930	Sichel, Harold	40-60	*
Holl, Adelaide	Journey to the Sea (1st, ob8vo, 32p, fp 1-color, cep, DJ)	L.W. Singer	1968	Sickles, Noel	25-40	
Robbins, Ruth	Baboushka & Three Kings (1st, sq12mo, [28]p, col, pep, DJ/2.50, CM, NYT)	Parnassus Press	(1960)	Sidjakov, Nicolas	100-165	R*
Robbins, Ruth	Emperor & the Drummer Boy (1st, lg8vo, [38]p, fp color, DJ/3.25, NYTBI)	Parnassus Press	(1962)	Sidjakov, Nicolas	60-90	*
Baker, Laura N.	Friendly Beasts (1st, 12mo, [24]p, ibds, 3-color, dep, DJ/1.50, NYTBI)	Parnassus Press	(1957)	Sidjakov, Nicolas	40-65	R*
Robbins, Ruth	Harlequin and Mother Goose (1st, 4to, 32p, color, DJ/3.75)	Parnassus Press	(1965)	Sidjakov, Nicolas	45-70	
Elmer, Irene	Lodestone and Toadstone (1st, 4to, [40]p, fp color, cep, DJ/4.50)	Knopf	(1969)	Sidjakov, Nicolas	20-35	
Shideler, Ross (tran)	Staffan (1st, 12mo, [25]p, grey cl, color, DJ/3.25)	Parnassus Press	(1970)	Sidjakov, Nicolas	35-50	*
Parish, Peggy	Amelia Bedelia (1st, 8vo, 64p, ipcb, fp 3-color, DJ/1.95)	Harper	(1966)	Siebel, Fritz	20-30	
Minarik, Else H.	Cat and Dog (1st, 8vo, ibds, 32p, fp 2-color, DJ/1.50)	Harper	(1960)	Siebel, Fritz	30-50	
McClintock, Marshall	Fly Went By (1st {std}, 8vo, ibds, 62p, color, pep, DJ/1.95)	Beginner Books	(1958)	Siebel, Fritz	60-100	
Parish, Peggy	Thank You, Amelia Bedelia (1st, 8vo, [32]p, color, DJ/1.95)	Harper	(1964)	Siebel, Fritz	20-30	*
Towne, Robert D.	Teddy Bears in a Smashup (1st, 12mo, ibds, [16]p, color)	Reilly/Britton	(1907)	Sieber, C.A.	80-145	
Towne, Robert D.	Teddy Bears in Hot Water (1st, 12mo, [16]p, ibds, color)	Reilly/Britton	(1907)	Sieber, C.A.	80-145	
Towne, Robert D.	Teddy Bears on a Lark (1st, 12mo, ibds, [16]p, color)	Reilly/Britton	(1907)	Sieber, C.A.	80-145	
Siegel, William	Around the World in a Mailbag (1st, 8vo, ibds, [30]p, color, pep)	McBride	1932	Siegel, William	40-60	*
McNeely, Marian H.	Jumping-Off Place (1st {std}, sm8vo, 308p, b/w, pep, NH)	Longmans	1929	Siegel, William	55-80	*
Whitney, Elinor	Mystery Club (1st, sm8vo, 252p, b/w pl)	Stokes	1933	Siegel, William	25-40	*
Sherwood, Merriam	Road to Cathay (1st, lg8vo, 251p, gilt, col frn, pep)	Macmillan	1928	Siegel, William	25-45	
Cole, William	Birds and the Beasts were There (1st {std}, 8vo, 320p, woodcuts, DJ/4.95)	World	(1963)	Siegl, Helen	30-45	
Walker, Barbara	Dancing Palm Tree (1st, 8vo, 112p, fp b/w, pep, DJ/3.95)	Parents Mag. Pr.	(1968)	Siegl, Helen	25-40	*

AUTHOR	TITLE	PUBLISHER	DATE	ARTIST	PRICE	LC
Hauff, Wilhelm	The Caravan (1st, 8vo, 220p, b/w, DJ/4.50)	Crowell	(1964)	Silverman, Burt	20-35	
Silverman, Mel	Good-for-Nothing Burro (1st {std}, 8vo, [39]p, 1-color, pep, DJ/2.50)	World	1958	Silverman, Mel	20-35	
Silverman, Mel	Hymie's Fiddle (1st {std}, sm4to, 46p, b/w, DJ/2.50)	World	(1960)	Silverman, Mel	25-45	
Shippen, Kath. B.	Portals to the Past (1st, 8vo, 255p, b/w, DJ/4.50)	Viking	(1963)	Silverman, Mel	25-40	*
Behn, Harry	Roderick (1st {std}, 8vo, 63p, DJ/2.75)	Harcourt	(1961)	Silverman, Mel	25-40	
Allstrom, Elizabeth	Songs Along the Way (1st, lg8vo, 64p, 2-color, pep, DJ/2.50)	Abingdon Press	(1961)	Silverman, Mel	25-40	
Behn, Harry	Two Uncles of Pablo (1st {std}, 8vo, 96p, b/w, DJ/3.00)	Harcourt	(1959)	Silverman, Mel	25-40	*
Silverstein, Shel	Giving Tree (1st, 8vo, [57]p, ibds, b/w, DJ/2.50)	Harper	(1964)	Silverstein, Shel	70-100	
Silverstein, Shel	Take Ten (1st [1st bk.], 12mo, ibds, [126]p, b/w)	Stars & Stripes	1955	Silverstein, Shel	150-250	
Silverstein, Shel	Uncle Shelby's a Giraffe and a Half (1st, 4to, unpag, b/w, DJ/2.95)	Harper	(1964)	Silverstein, Shel	50-85	
Silverstein, Shel	Uncle Shelby's ABZ Book (1st {std}, 4to, [76]p, wraps, b/w)	Simon/Schuster	1961	Silverstein, Shel	60-100	
Silverstein, Shel	Uncle Shelby's Story of Lafcadio (1st {std}, 8vo, [100]p, b/w, DJ/2.95)	Harper	1963	Silverstein, Shel	50-85	
Silverstein, Shel	Uncle Shelby's Zoo... (1st {std}, 8vo, [62]p, color, DJ/3.95)	Simon/Schuster	(1964)	Silverstein, Shel	60-90	
Silverstein, Shel	Who Wants a Cheap Rhinoceros? (1st, ob8vo, [48]p, fp b/w, DJ/2.00)	Macmillan	1964	Silverstein, Shel	60-90	*
Simbari, Nicola	Gennarino (1st, 4to, [32]p, color, DJ/3.95)	Lippincott	(1962)	Simbari, Nicola	40-65	*
Sime, Sidney H.	Bogey Beasts (1st, 4to, ibds, 62p, 15pl)	L: Goodwin	(1923)	Sime, Sidney	275-450	
Lord Dunsany	Book of Wonder (1st, 8vo, 98p, brown pcb, p-o, 10pl)	L: Heinemann	1912	Sime, Sidney	250-350	
Lord Dunsany	Dreamer's Tales (1st, sm8vo, 252p, blue/gilt, teg, uncut, 9pl)	L: G. Allen	1910	Sime, Sidney	160-220	
Lord Dunsany	Gods of Pegana (1st, 8vo, 94p, grey bds, uncut, 8pl)	L: E. Mathews	1905	Sime, Sidney	250-350	
Lord Dunsany	Sword of Welleran (1st, 4to, 243p, green/gilt, teg, 10pl)	L: G. Allen	1908	Sime, Sidney	150-225	
Lord Dunsany	Time & the Gods (1st AM, 8vo, bds, 179p, p-o, 10pl)	Bos: J.W. Luce	[1913]	Sime, Sidney	80-140	
Shakespeare, Wm.	Hamlet (1st, lg4to, 165p, gilt, 30 ticp)	L: Hodder	[1900]	Simmonds, W.G.	250-400	
Gannett, Ruth S.	Katie and the Sad Noise (1st, 8vo, [64]p, 2-color, pep, DJ/1.95)	Random	(1961)	Simmons, Ellie	30-50	
Simmons, Ellie	Mary the Mouse Champion (1st, 8vo, [32]p, b/w, DJ/2.75)	McKay	(1963)	Simmons, Ellie	25-40	
Simmons, Henry B.	Jingle Jangle Rhyme Book (1st, ob4to, [38]p, ibds, 18cp)	Stokes	1898	Simmons, Henry B.	150-220	
Weatherly, Fred E.	Happy Childhood (12mo, ibds, fp color)	L: Hildesheimer	[1892]	Simmons/West	50-85	
Weatherly, Fred E.	Rhymes and Roses (4to, ibds, 32p, 8 chromos)	L: Hildesheimer	[1888]	Simmons/Wilson	80-140	
Simon, Ellen	Critter Book (1st, sm ob4to, ibds, [48]p, color, DJ/1.50)	Holiday House	(1940)	Simon, Ellen	45-70	
Stone, Caroline R.	Inga of Porcupine Mine (1st, sm8vo, 212p, blue cl, b/w, DJ/2.00)	Holiday House	(1942)	Simon, Ellen	25-45	
Judson, Clara I.	Railway Engineer (1st, 8vo, 171p, b/w pl, pep, DJ/1.50)	Scribner	(1941)	Simon, Eric M.	30-45	
Knight, Marjorie	Alexander's Christmas Eve (1st {std}, 8vo, 92p, color, pep, DJ/1.75)	Dutton	1938	Simon, Howard	30-50	
Beim, Lorraine	Burro that Had a Name (1st, 8vo, [63]p, fp 1-color, pep, DJ/1.50)	Harcourt	1939	Simon, Howard	30-50	
Lewiton, Mina	Candita's Choice (1st, sm8vo, 184p, b/w, DJ/2.95)	Harper	(1959)	Simon, Howard	30-50	
Beim, Lorraine	Little Igloo (1st, 8vo, [72]p, fp 1-color, pep, DJ/1.50)	Harcourt	(1941)	Simon, Howard	30-45	*
Beim, Lorraine	Lucky Pierre (1st, 8vo, [61]p, fp 2-color, pep, DJ/1.50)	Harcourt	(1940)	Simon, Howard	30-45	*
Justus, May	Mr. Songcatcher & Co. (1st {std}, 8vo, 237p, 2-color, DJ/2.00)	Doubleday/Doran	1940	Simon, Howard	20-35	
Simont, Marc	Afternoon in Spain (1st, 8vo, 64p, ibds, color, DJ/3.95)	Wm. Morrow	1965	Simont, Marc	25-40	
Withers, Carl	American Riddle Book (1st, 8vo, 157p, b/w, DJ/2.75)	Abelard-Schuman	(1954)	Simont, Marc	25-45	*
Krauss, Ruth	Backward Day (1st, 8vo, ibds, [31]p, color, DJ/1.50)	Harper	1950	Simont, Marc	50-85	
Krauss, Ruth	Big World & Little House (1st, sm4to, ibds, [41]p, color, pep, DJ/2.00)	NY: Schuman	1949	Simont, Marc	70-130	R
DeJong, Meindert	Billy & the Unhappy Bull (1st {std}, 4to, 206p, brown cl, b/w, DJ/2.00)	Harper	(1946)	Simont, Marc	40-65	
Owen, Ruth	Castle in Silver Wood (1st, 8vo, 181p, blue cl, col frn, pep, DJ/2.00)	Dodd	1939	Simont, Marc	30-50	
Cooke, Alistair	Christmas Eve (1st AM {std}, 8vo, 56p, bds, 1-color, DJ/2.00)	Knopf	(1952)	Simont, Marc	40-60	
Simont, Marc	Contest at Paca (1st, 8vo, ibds, 60p, 3-color, DJ/2.00)	Harper	(1959)	Simont, Marc	25-40	
Lansing, Elisabeth H.	Deer Mountain Hideaway (1st {std}, 8vo, 153p, b/w, DJ/2.50)	Crowell	(1953)	Simont, Marc	25-40	*
Lansing, Elisabeth H.	Deer River Raft (1st, 8vo, 191p, b/w, DJ/2.50)	Crowell	(1955)	Simont, Marc	25-40	*
Alger, Leclaire	Dougal's Wish (1st {std}, 4to, 244p, rust cl, fp b/w, DJ/2.00)	Harper	1942	Simont, Marc	60-90	
Kjelgaard, Jim	Duck-Footed Hound (1st, 8vo, 184p, b/w, DJ/2.95)	Crowell	(1960)	Simont, Marc	50-80	
McCord, David	Every Time I Climb a Tree (1st {std}, 4to, [48]p, color, cep, DJ/3.95)	Little/Brown	(1967)	Simont, Marc	60-90	R*
Trent, Robbie	First Christmas (1st, 12mo, ipcb, [32]p, color, pep, DJ/1.00)	Harper	1948	Simont, Marc	40-65	
Brown, Margaret W.	First Story (1st, lg8vo, [31]p, ibds, 1-color, pep, DJ/1.75)	Harper	(1947)	Simont, Marc	70-100	
Fritz, Jean	Fish Head (1st, sm4to, tan cl, [38]p, fp 3-color, pep, DJ/2.75)	Coward	(1954)	Simont, Marc	50-80	
Vinton, Iris	Flying Ebony (1st, sm8vo, 289p, olive cl, b/w, DJ/2.50)	Dodd	1947	Simont, Marc	30-50	
Udry, Janice M.	Glenda (1st, lg8vo, 55p, b/w, DJ/3.50)	Harper	(1969)	Simont, Marc	25-40	*
DeJong, Meindert	Good Luck Duck (1st, lg8vo, yellow cl, 57p, color, pep, DJ/2.00)	Harper	(1950)	Simont, Marc	40-65	
Krauss, Ruth	Good Man & his Good Wife (1st, 8vo, 30p, 1-color, DJ/1.95)	Harper	(1962)	Simont, Marc	100-160	
Krauss, Ruth	Happy Day (1st, lg4to, ipcb, [33]p, b/w, DJ/1.75, CH)	Harper	1949	Simont, Marc	80-130	
Simont, Marc	How Come Elephants? (1st, 12mo, [44]p, fp 2-color, cep, DJ/2.50)	Harper	1965	Simont, Marc	30-50	
Simont, Marc	How to Get to First Base (1st, 8vo, [62]p, wraps, b/w)	Schuman	(1952)	Simont, Marc	25-40	
Schwartz, Julius	I Know a Magic House (1st, sm4to, 32p, 2-color, pep, DJ/2.00)	Whittlesey	(1956)	Simont, Marc	25-45	
Powell, Miriam	Jareb (1st {std}, sm8vo, grey cl, 241p, cep, DJ/2.50)	Crowell	(1952)	Simont, Marc	30-50	
Simont, Marc	Lovely Summer (1st, sm4to, blue cl, [46]p, b/w, DJ/2.00)	Harper	(1952)	Simont, Marc	60-90	
Carr, Albert	Men of Power (1st, 8vo, red cl, 272p, fp b/w, DJ/2.50)	Viking	1940	Simont, Marc	30-50	*
Simont, Marc	Mimi (1st, 8vo, beige cl, 55p, b/w, DJ/2.00)	Harper	(1954)	Simont, Marc	45-60	
Streeter, Edward	Mr. Robbins Rides Again (1st, 8vo, 155p, b/w, pep, DJ/3.00)	Harper	(1958)	Simont, Marc	25-45	
Walsh, Chad	Nellie & her Flying Crocodile (1st {std}, 8vo, 179p, b/w, DJ/2.50)	Harper	(1956)	Simont, Marc	30-50	
Schwartz, Julius	Now I Know (1st, 4to, 32p, 2-color, pep, DJ/2.00)	Whittlesey	(1955)	Simont, Marc	30-50	
Simont, Marc	Opera Souffle: 60 Pictures in Bravura (1st, 4to, [89]p, b/w, pep, DJ/2.50)	Schuman	(1950)	Simont, Marc	30-50	
Liggett, Thomas	Pigeon, Fly Home! (1st, 8vo, 189p, tan cl, b/w, pep, DJ/2.75)	Holiday House	(1956)	Simont, Marc	25-40	*
Sterne, Emma G.	Pirate of Chatham Square (1st, 8vo, 213p, b/w, pep, DJ/2.00)	Dodd	1939	Simont, Marc	25-45	
Simont, Marc	Plumber Out of the Sea (1st, lg8vo, ipcb, 39p, 2-color, pep, DJ/2.00)	Harper	(1955)	Simont, Marc	45-70	
Simont, Marc	Polly's Oats (1st, sm4to, [46]p, fp b/w, DJ/1.75)	Harper	(1951)	Simont, Marc	40-65	
Leach, Maria	Rainbow Book of American Folk Tales (1st {std}, 4to, 318p, color)	World	(1958)	Simont, Marc	50-85	
Lang, Andrew	Red Fairy Book (1st [new ed.], 8vo, 364p, color, DJ/2.00)	Longmans	(1948)	Simont, Marc	30-50	*
Jackson, Charlotte	Sarah Deborah's Day (1st, sm4to, ipcb, 74p, 2-color, pep, DJ/2.00)	Dodd	1941	Simont, Marc	40-65	
Ladas, Alexis	Seal that Couldn't Swim (1st {std}, lg8vo, 55p, blue cl, 3-color, DJ/2.75)	Little/Brown	(1959)	Simont, Marc	40-65	
Deutsch, Babette	The Welcome (1st {std}, 8vo, 197p, blue cl, 9 fp b/w, DJ/2.00)	Harper	(1942)	Simont, Marc	100-165	R
Thurber, James	Thirteen Clocks (1st, 8vo, ibds, 124p, color, pep, DJ/2.50)	Simon/Schuster	(1950)	Simont, Marc	120-200	R

AUTHOR	TITLE	PUBLISHER	DATE	ARTIST	PRICE	LC
Paradis, Marjorie	Timmy and the Tiger (1st {std}, 8vo, 246p, fp b/w, DJ/2.50)	Harper	(1952)	Simont, Marc	30-50	
Gipson, Fred B.	Trail-Driving Rooster (1st, 8vo, grey cl, 79p, b/w, DJ/2.25)	Harper	(1955)	Simont, Marc	30-50	
Udry, Janice M.	Tree is Nice (1st, 4to, ibds, [30]p, fp color, DJ/2.50, CM)	Harper	1956	Simont, Marc	130-180	R
Chenery, Janet	Wolfie (1st, 8vo, 63p, fp 2-color, DJ/2.50)	Harper	(1969)	Simont, Marc	40-65	R
Thurber, James	Wonderful O. (1st {std}, 8vo, bds, 72p, 2-color, dep, DJ/3.50)	Simon/Schuster	(1957)	Simont, Marc	80-140	
N/A	Aucassin & Nicolette (1st, narrow 12mo, 106p, color)	Holiday House	1936	Simpson, Maxwell	70-100	R*
Perrault, Charles	Once Upon a Time (1st, sm4to, 115p, 8cp)	L: O'Connor	1922	Sinclair, Helen	90-160	*
Lea, John	Queerie at the Pole (1st, 4to, ibds, 82p, 16cp)	L: A. Melrose	1911	Sinclair, James R.	250-350	
Byron, May	Teddy Bearoplane (1st AM, sm4to, ibds, 12cp)	NY: Hodder	[1909]	Sinclair, James R.	250-400	
Skaar, Grace M.	All About Dogs, Dogs, Dogs (1st, lg ob8vo, wraps, [20]p, color)	Young Scott	1947	Skaar, Grace M.	60-90	
Skaar, Grace M.	Boy and his Horse (1st, 8vo, 141p, b/w, DJ/2.95)	Young Scott	(1958)	Skaar, Grace M.	50-80	
Skaar, Grace M.	Little Red House (1st, ob8vo, [32]p, fp 2-color, DJ/2.00)	Young Scott	1955	Skaar, Grace M.	30-50	
Skaar, Grace M.	Nothing But Cats, Cats, Cats (1st, ob8vo, ipcb, [20]p, color)	Young Scott	1947	Skaar, Grace M.	70-120	
Skaar, Grace M.	Very Little Dog (1st, ob8vo, [20]p, ipcb, 2-color, DJ/1.00)	Young Scott	1949	Skaar, Grace M.	70-100	
Skaar, Grace M.	What Do they Say! (1st, ob8vo, ibds, [20]p, color, DJ/1.00)	W.R. Scott	1950	Skaar, Grace M.	70-100	
Wiig, Hanna	Tale of Tiny Tutak (1st AM, 16mo, [55]p, 2-color, pep, DJ/1.25)	Lippincott	[1957]	Skauge, Sven	30-50	
James, Harry A.	Oddland and other Fairy Tales (1st, 8vo, gilt, 352p, 4pl)	L: G. Newnes	(1901)	Skeaping, K.M.	80-120	
Jerome, Jerome K.	Told After Supper (1st, 12mo, 169p, teg, uncut)	Field & Tuer	1891	Skeaping, K.M.	70-100	
Marshall, Henrietta	Our Empire Story (1st AM, lg8vo, gilt, teg, 493p, 8cp, maps)	Stokes	(1908)	Skelton, Joseph R.	60-100	
Jackson, Shirley	Famous Sally (1st {std}, 8vo, [40]p, ibds, gilt, color, DJ/3.50)	Harlin Quist	(1966)	Slackman, Charles	70-100	
England, George A.	Air Trust (1st, sm8vo, 333p, red/gilt, 6pl)	Phila: P. Wagner	(1915)	Sloan, John	130-200	
Bergengren, Ralph	Gentlemen All and Merry Companions (1st {std}, 12mo, 247p, fp b/w)	Bos: Brimmer	1922	Sloan, John	60-80	*
England, George A.	Golden Blight (1st, sm8vo, 350p, brown/gilt, 5pl)	H.K. Fly	(1916)	Sloan, John	75-100	*
Crane, Stephen	Great Battles of the World (1st, 8vo, red/gilt, 278p, 7pl)	Lippincott	1901	Sloan, John	250-350	R
Daly, Thomas A.	Madrigali (1st, sm8vo, 169p, gilt, teg, fp b/w)	McKay	(1912)	Sloan, John	60-90	*
Gaboriau, Emile	Within an Inch of His Life (1st AM, 8vo, teg, 608p, gilt, 4pl)	Scribner	1913	Sloan, John	45-70	
Sloane, Eric	ABC Book of Early Americana (1st {std}, 4to, gilt, [68]p, b/w, DJ/2.95)	Doubleday	(1963)	Sloane, Eric	35-50	
Sloane, Eric	Return to Taos (1st, 4to, 120p, 4cp, DJ/6.50)	Funk/Wagnalls	(1960)	Sloane, Eric	45-60	
Sloane, Eric	Reverence for Wood (1st, 4to, 110p, b/w, DJ/6.50)	Wilfred Funk	(1965)	Sloane, Eric	45-60	
Sloane, Eric	Second Barrel (1st, 4to, 104p, fp b/w, DJ/5.95)	Funk/Wagnalls	(1969)	Sloane, Eric	45-60	
Sloane, Eric	Sound of Bells (1st {std}, lg8vo, 58p, b/w, DJ/2.75)	Doubleday	(1966)	Sloane, Eric	60-90	
Slobodkin, Louis	Adventures of Arab (1st, lg8vo, 128p, color, cep, DJ/2.50)	Macmillan	1946	Slobodkin, Louis	45-70	
Twain, Mark	Adventures of Tom Sawyer (1st {std}, 8vo, 302p, col frn, fp b/w, pep)	World	(1946)	Slobodkin, Louis	25-40	
Slobodkin, Louis	Amiable Giant (1st {std}, sm4to, 33p, color, DJ/2.75)	Macmillan	(1955)	Slobodkin, Louis	40-65	
Upington, Marion	Beautiful Culpeppers (1st {std}, 8vo, 113p, 2-color, DJ/2.95)	F. Watts	(1963)	Slobodkin, Louis	45-70	
Slobodkin, Louis	Big Circus April 1st (1st {std}, sm8vo, 90p, b/w, DJ/2.25)	Macmillan	(1953)	Slobodkin, Louis	30-50	
Slobodkin, Louis	Bixxy & the Secret Message (1st {std}, 8vo, 94p, b/w, pep, DJ/2.00)	Macmillan	1949	Slobodkin, Louis	30-45	
Friedrich, Otto	Clean Clarence (1st, 8vo, [40]p, fp color, pep, DJ/2.95)	Lothrop, Lee	(1959)	Slobodkin, Louis	30-50	
Slobodkin, Louis	Clear the Track for Michael's Magic Train (1st ob8vo [48]p, color, DJ/1.50)	Macmillan	(1945)	Slobodkin, Louis	30-50	
Slobodkin, Louis	Colette and the Princess (1st {std}, 4to, 46p, color, DJ/3.50)	Dutton	(1965)	Slobodkin, Louis	30-50	
Slobodkin, Florence	Cowboy Twins (1st, 4to, [28]p, color, DJ/2.95)	Vanguard Press	1960	Slobodkin, Louis	30-50	
Slobodkin, Louis	Dinny & Danny (1st {std}, sm4to, ibds, [30]p, color, pep, DJ/2.00)	Macmillan	(1951)	Slobodkin, Louis	40-65	
Eberle, Irmengarde	Evie & Cookie (1st, 8vo, 122p, 1-color, pep, DJ/2.75)	Knopf	(1957)	Slobodkin, Louis	25-40	
Eberle, Irmengarde	Evie & the Wonderful Kangaroo (1st, 8vo, 128p, 1-color, pep, DJ/2.50)	Knopf	(1955)	Slobodkin, Louis	25-40	
Slobodkin, Louis	Excuse Me! Certainly! (1st, sm4to, [32]p, color, DJ/2.75)	Vanguard Press	(1959)	Slobodkin, Louis	30-50	
Slobodkin, Louis	First Book of Drawing (1st {std}, 8vo, 68p, b/w, DJ/1.95)	F. Watts	1958	Slobodkin, Louis	25-40	
Slobodkin, Louis	Friendly Animals (1st, ob4to, [25]p, ibds, 2-color, DJ/1.50)	Vanguard Press	1944	Slobodkin, Louis	60-90	
Baker, Nina B.	Garibaldi (1st, 8vo, 315p, b/w, DJ/2.50)	Vanguard Press	(1944)	Slobodkin, Louis	25-40	*
Glendinning, Marg.	Gertie the Horse Who Thought & Thought (1st, 8vo, 88p, b/w, pep, DJ/2.25)	Whittlesey	(1951)	Slobodkin, Louis	25-40	*
Slobodkin, Louis	Gogo: French Seagull (1st {std}, 4to, [46]p, fp color, DJ)	Macmillan	(1960)	Slobodkin, Louis	50-80	
Slobodkin, Louis	Good Place to Hide (1st {std}, lg8vo, 29p, color, DJ/2.50)	Macmillan	(1961)	Slobodkin, Louis	30-50	
Slobodkin, Louis	Horse with the High-Heeled Shoes (1st, 4to, 30p, fp color, DJ/2.50)	Vanguard Press	(1954)	Slobodkin, Louis	30-50	
Estes, Eleanor	Hundred Dresses (1st, 8vo, 80p, red cl, color, DJ/2.50, NH)	Harcourt	(1944)	Slobodkin, Louis	90-140	
Slobodkin, Louis	Hustle & Bustle (1st, sm ob4to, [36]p, 1-color, DJ/1.50)	Macmillan	1948	Slobodkin, Louis	50-80	
Blanck, Jacob	Jonathan & the Rainbow (1st, 4to, ibds, 48p, color, DJ/2.00)	Houghton	1948	Slobodkin, Louis	45-65	
Blanck, Jacob	King & Noble Blacksmith (1st, sm4to, yellow cl, 48p, color, DJ/2.25)	Houghton	1950	Slobodkin, Louis	55-80	
Slobodkin, Louis	Late Cuckoo (1st, sm4to, [38]p, fp color, cep, DJ/3.00)	Vanguard Press	(1962)	Slobodkin, Louis	30-50	
Baker, Nina B.	Lenin (1st, 8vo, 257p, col frn, b/w, DJ/2.50)	Vanguard Press	(1945)	Slobodkin, Louis	25-40	
Slobodkin, Louis	Little Mermaid Who Could Not Sing (1st {std}, sm4to, 38p, color, DJ/2.75)	Macmillan	(1956)	Slobodkin, Louis	40-65	
Unnerstad, Edith	Little O (1st {std}, 8vo, 150p, b/w, DJ/2.50)	Macmillan	(1957)	Slobodkin, Louis	40-65	*
Kasdan, Sara	Love and Knishes (1st, 8vo, 191p, ipcb, b/w, DJ/3.50)	Vanguard Press	(1956)	Slobodkin, Louis	50-85	
Slobodkin, Louis	Luigi and the Long-Nosed Soldier (1st {std}, 4to, 32p, 2-color, DJ/2.95)	Macmillan	(1963)	Slobodkin, Louis	30-50	
Dickens, Charles	Magic Fishbone (1st, sm4to, ibds, 36p, color, DJ/2.50)	Vanguard Press	(1953)	Slobodkin, Louis	70-120	R
Slobodkin, Louis	Magic Michael (1st, ob8vo, ibds, [48]p, 2-color, pep, DJ/1.50)	Macmillan	(1944)	Slobodkin, Louis	60-90	
Thurber, James	Many Moons (1st, sm4to, red cl, [47]p, color, pep, DJ/2.00, CM)	Harcourt	(1943)	Slobodkin, Louis	170-250	R
Friedrich, Otto	Marshmallow Ghosts (1st, 8vo, 38p, color, DJ/2.95)	Lothrop, Lee	(1960)	Slobodkin, Louis	30-50	*
Davis, Reda	Martin's Dinosaur (1st, 4to, [40]p, 1-color, DJ/3.50)	Crowell	(1959)	Slobodkin, Louis	30-50	
Kasdan, Sara	Mazel Tov Y'All (1st, 8vo, 195p, b/w, DJ/4.95)	Vanguard Press	(1968)	Slobodkin, Louis	30-50	*
Slobodkin, Louis	Melvin the Moose Child (1st {std}, sm4to, 32p, color, DJ/2.50)	Macmillan	(1957)	Slobodkin, Louis	30-50	
Estes, Eleanor	Middle Moffat (1st, 8vo, 317p, p-o, b/w, pep, DJ/2.00, NH)	Harcourt	(1942)	Slobodkin, Louis	90-140	
Slobodkin, Louis	Millions & Millions & Millions! (1st, 4to, ipcb, [32]p, color, pep, DJ/2.50)	Vanguard Press	(1955)	Slobodkin, Louis	30-50	
Slobodkin, Louis	Moon Blossom and the Golden Penny (1st, 8vo, [61]p, fp color, cep, DJ/3.25)	Vanguard Press	(1963)	Slobodkin, Louis	30-45	
Slobodkin, Louis	Mr. Mushroom (1st {std}, sq16mo, ipcb, [32]p, color, DJ/1.25)	Macmillan	(1950)	Slobodkin, Louis	30-50	
Slobodkin, Florence	Mr. Papadilly and Willy (1st, 4to, [38]p, fp color, cep, DJ/3.50)	Vanguard Press	(1964)	Slobodkin, Louis	40-65	*
Slobodkin, Louis	Mr. Petersand's Cats & Kittens (1st {std}, 8vo, 63p, col, cep, DJ/2.25)	Macmillan	(1954)	Slobodkin, Louis	30-50	
Packard, Andrew	Mr. Spindles and the Spiders (1st {std}, sm4to, [32]p, 1-color, DJ/3.00)	Macmillan	1961	Slobodkin, Louis	40-65	
Slobodkin, Louis	Nomi and the Lovely Animals (1st, 8vo, [32]p, color, cep, DJ/2.50)	Vanguard Press	(1960)	Slobodkin, Louis	50-80	
Slobodkin, Louis	One is Good, but Two are Better (1st, 4to, [23]p, color, pep, DJ/2.50)	Vanguard Press	1956	Slobodkin, Louis	40-65	

AUTHOR	TITLE	PUBLISHER	DATE	ARTIST	PRICE	LC
Slobodkin, Louis	Our Friendly Friends (1st, ob4to, ibds, [27]p, 2-color, pep, DJ/2.00)	Vanguard Press	(1951)	Slobodkin, Louis	40-65	
Baker, Nina B.	Peter the Great (1st, 8vo, 310p, fp b/w, DJ/2.50)	Vanguard Press	(1943)	Slobodkin, Louis	30-45	
Slobodkin, Louis	Polka-Dot Goat (1st {std}, 4to, 34p, 2-color, DJ/2.95)	Macmillan	(1964)	Slobodkin, Louis	35-50	
Unnerstad, Edith	Pysen (1st {std}, 8vo, 172p, b/w, DJ/2.50)	Macmillan	(1955)	Slobodkin, Louis	30-45	
Slobodkin, Louis	Read About the Busman (1st, 8vo, 70p, 1-color, DJ/2.65)	F. Watts	(1967)	Slobodkin, Louis	30-45	
Slobodkin, Louis	Read About the Fireman (1st, 8vo, 71p, 1-color, DJ/2.65)	F. Watts	(1967)	Slobodkin, Louis	30-45	
Slobodkin, Louis	Read About the Policeman (1st, 8vo, 168p, 1-color, DJ/2.65)	F. Watts	(1966)	Slobodkin, Louis	30-45	
Slobodkin, Louis	Read About the Postman (1st, 8vo, 67p, 1-color, DJ/2.65)	F. Watts	(1966)	Slobodkin, Louis	30-45	
Eager, Edward	Red Head (1st [1st bk.], 8vo, 24p, fp color, pep, DJ/1.25)	Houghton	1951	Slobodkin, Louis	60-100	*
McSpadden, J.W.	Robin Hood & his Merry Outlaws (1st {std}, 8vo, 285p, color, DJ/1.25, RC)	World	1946	Slobodkin, Louis	55-80	*
Slobodkin, Louis	Round-Trip Space Ship (1st {std}, sm8vo, 167p, b/w, DJ/4.50)	Macmillan	(1968)	Slobodkin, Louis	80-130	
Estes, Eleanor	Rufus M. (1st, 8vo, 320p, red cl, b/w, pep, DJ/2.00, NH)	Harcourt	(1943)	Slobodkin, Louis	80-130	
Slobodkin, Florence	Sarah Somebody (1st, 8vo, 71p, 1-color, DJ/3.95)	Vanguard Press	(1970)	Slobodkin, Louis	35-50	
Unnerstad, Edith	Saucepan Journey (1st {std}, 8vo, 180p, b/w, DJ/2.50)	Macmillan	1951	Slobodkin, Louis	25-45	
Slobodkin, Louis	Seaweed Hat (1st, 8vo, ibds, [48]p, color, DJ/2.00)	Macmillan	1947	Slobodkin, Louis	40-65	
Bill, Helen	Shoes Fit for a King (1st {std}, 4to, [42]p, color, DJ/2.75)	F. Watts	(1956)	Slobodkin, Louis	40-65	
Slobodkin, Louis	Space Ship Returns to Apple Tree (1st {std}, 8vo, 128p, b/w, DJ/2.50)	Macmillan	(1958)	Slobodkin, Louis	100-160	
Slobodkin, Louis	Space Ship Under Apple Tree (1st {std}, 8vo, 116p, blue cl, b/w, DJ/2.50)	Macmillan	(1952)	Slobodkin, Louis	100-175	
Estes, Eleanor	Sun, Wind & Mr. Todd (1st, 4to, [92]p, brown cl, 1-color, pep, DJ/2.00)	Harcourt	(1943)	Slobodkin, Louis	70-100	
Slobodkin, Louis	Thank You, You're Welcome (1st, ob4to, [30]p, color, dep, DJ/2.75)	Vanguard Press	(1957)	Slobodkin, Louis	30-50	
Estes, Eleanor	The Moffats (1st [1st bk.], 8vo, pink cl, 290p, b/w, DJ/2.00)	Harcourt	(1941)	Slobodkin, Louis	80-125	R
Slobodkin, Louis	Three-Seated Space Ship (1st {std}, 8vo, 126p, b/w, DJ/2.75)	Macmillan	1962	Slobodkin, Louis	70-120	
Slobodkin, Florence	Too Many Mittens (1st, 4to, [32]p, blue cl, fp 3-color, DJ/2.75)	Vanguard Press	(1958)	Slobodkin, Louis	40-65	
Slobodkin, Louis	Trick or Treat (1st {std}, 4to, [29]p, fp 3-color, DJ/2.25)	Macmillan	(1959)	Slobodkin, Louis	30-55	
Slobodkin, Louis	Up High and Down Low (1st {std}, sm4to, [32]p, color, DJ/2.50)	Macmillan	(1960)	Slobodkin, Louis	25-45	
Murphy, Robert	Warm-Hearted Polar Bear (1st {std}, 4to, 47p, blue cl, color, DJ/2.95)	Little/Brown	(1957)	Slobodkin, Louis	35-50	
Slobodkin, Louis	Wide-Awake Owl (1st {std}, sm4to, [32]p, color, DJ/2.50)	Macmillan	(1958)	Slobodkin, Louis	30-50	
Slobodkin, Louis	Yasu and the Strangers (1st {std}, ob4to, 34p, color, DJ/2.95)	Macmillan	(1965)	Slobodkin, Louis	30-45	
Hunt, Mabel L.	Young Man of the House (1st {std}, 8vo, 171p, 10 fp b/w, DJ/2.50)	Lippincott	(1944)	Slobodkin, Louis	30-50	
Slobodkina, Esphyr	Caps for Sale (1st, 8vo, ibds, [43]p, color, pep, DJ/1.00)	W.R. Scott	1940	Slobodkina, Esphyr	40-65	
Slobodkina, Esphyr	Flame, the Breeze & the Shadow (1st {std}, lg8vo, 62p, fp color, DJ/3.95)	Rand/McNally	1969	Slobodkina, Esphyr	25-40	
Slobodkina, Esphyr	Jack and Jim (1st, sm4to, [42]p, color, DJ/2.75)	Abelard-Schuman	1961	Slobodkina, Esphyr	25-40	
Brown, Margaret W.	Little Cowboy (1st, lg8vo, ipcb, [33]p, color, pep, DJ/1.50)	W.R. Scott	(1948)	Slobodkina, Esphyr	70-125	
Slobodkina, Esphyr	Little Dinghy (1st, 4to, [41]p, color, DJ/2.50)	Abelard-Schuman	(1958)	Slobodkina, Esphyr	30-50	
Brown, Margaret W.	Little Farmer (1st, sm4to, [38]p, ipcb, color, DJ/1.50)	W.R. Scott	1948	Slobodkina, Esphyr	70-130	
Brown, Margaret W.	Little Fireman (1st, 8vo, ibds, [34]p, color, cep, p-o, DJ/1.50)	W.R. Scott	(1938)	Slobodkina, Esphyr	90-140	
Slobodkina, Esphyr	Pinky and the Petunias (1st, 4to, [39]p, fp color, pep, DJ/2.75)	Abelard-Schuman	(1959)	Slobodkina, Esphyr	40-70	*
Brown, Margaret W.	Sleepy ABC (1st, lg8vo, ibds, unpag, color, dep, DJ/2.00)	Lothrop, Lee	1953	Slobodkina, Esphyr	60-100	
Slobodkina, Esphyr	Wonderful Feast (1st, lg sq8vo, ipcb, [26]p, color, DJ/2.00)	Lothrop, Lee	1955	Slobodkina, Esphyr	40-65	
Slocum, Rosalie	Breakfast with the Clowns (1st, 8vo, ibds, [32]p, color, DJ/1.00)	Viking	1937	Slocum, Rosalie	40-65	
Slocum, Rosalie	Key to New York (1st {std}, 8vo, 312p, b/w, pep, DJ/2.00)	Harper	1939	Slocum, Rosalie	40-65	
Todd, Ann	No Time for Funnies (1st, sm8vo, 54p, fp color, DJ/1.25)	Oxford U. Pr.	(1942)	Slocum, Rosalie	30-50	
Todd, Ann	Umbrella that Got Wet (1st, sm8vo, 55p, color, pep, DJ/1.25)	Oxford U. Pr.	(1938)	Slocum, Rosalie	35-50	
Brown, Margaret W.	When the Wind Blew (1st {std}-[1st Bk], lg8vo, [31]p, ibds, color, DJ/1.50)	Harper	1937	Slocum, Rosalie	120-180	
Howells, William D.	Coast of Bohemia (1st, 12mo, red/gilt, 340p, 8pl)	Harper	1893	Small, F.O.	55-80	
Means, Florence C.	Across the Fruited Plain (1st, sm8vo, 113p, fp b/w, cep, DJ/1.00)	Friendship Pr.	(1940)	Smalley, Janet	30-50	
Smalley, Janet	Animals Came In (1st, 8vo, [88]p, ibds, 2-color, pep)	Wm. Morrow	(1930)	Smalley, Janet	60-90	
Porter, Jane	Biffy Buffalo (1st, 8vo, 63p, color, pep, DJ/2.00)	Wm. Morrow	1942	Smalley, Janet	50-80	
Smalley, Janet	Do You Know about Fishes? (1st, narrow ob8vo, 45p, ibds, color, pep)	Wm. Morrow	(1936)	Smalley, Janet	50-80	
Smalley, Janet	Do You Know? (1st, narrow ob8vo, 44p, color, pep)	Wm. Morrow	(1934)	Smalley, Janet	50-80	
Butters, Dorothy	Enchanted Caravan (1st, 8vo, 207p, b/w, DJ/2.50)	Macrae Smith	(1949)	Smalley, Janet	40-65	
Howes, Edith	Enchanted Road (1st, 8vo, 246p, blue cl, col frn, b/w)	Wm. Morrow	1927	Smalley, Janet	60-100	*
Benet, William R.	Flying King of Kurio (1st, 8vo, 289p, 4cp, pep)	Doran	(1926)	Smalley, Janet	70-120	
Smalley, Janet	How It All Began (1st, 8vo, ibds, 94p, color)	Wm. Morrow	(1932)	Smalley, Janet	50-80	
Whitney, Phyllis	Mystery of the Gulls (1st, 8vo, 202p, b/w, DJ/2.50)	Westminster Pr.	(1949)	Smalley, Janet	30-50	
Smalley, Janet	Now and Then... (1st, 8vo, 91p, ibds, color, pep)	Wm. Morrow	(1931)	Smalley, Janet	70-120	
Means, Florence C.	Peter of the Mesa (1st, sm8vo, p-o, 120p, fp b/w, DJ/1.00)	Friendship Pr.	(1944)	Smalley, Janet	25-45	
Smalley, Janet	Plum to Plum Jam (1st, 8vo, 87p, ibds, color, pep)	Wm. Morrow	(1929)	Smalley, Janet	70-120	
Smalley, Janet	Rice to Rice Pudding (1st, smsq8vo, 85p, ibds, color, pep)	Wm. Morrow	(1928)	Smalley, Janet	70-120	
Acker, Helen	School Train (1st, 8vo, 122p, b/w, DJ/2.00)	Abelard Press	(1953)	Smalley, Janet	20-35	
Twain, Mark	Dog's Tale (1st AM, 8vo, red cl, teg, 36p, 4cp)	Harper	1904	Smedley, W.T.	120-200	
James, Henry	Julia Bride (1st, 8vo, 83p, teg, 4pl)	Harper	1909	Smedley, W.T.	140-200	
Bangs, John K.	Rebellious Heroine (1st, 12mo, 225p, yellow/gilt, 8pl)	Harper	1896	Smedley, W.T.	40-65	
Krumgold, Joseph	Henry 3 (1st, 8vo, gilt, 268p, fp b/w, cep, DJ/4.75)	Atheneum	1967	Smith, Alvin	20-35	
Carlson, Natalie S.	Marchers for the Dream (1st, 8vo, 130p, fp b/w, ipcb, DJ/3.50)	Harper	(1969)	Smith, Alvin	30-50	
Bonham, Frank	Mystery of the Fat Cat (1st {std}, 8vo, 160p, b/w, DJ/3.95)	Dutton	(1968)	Smith, Alvin	20-30	
Bonham, Frank	Nitty Gritty (1st {std}, 8vo, 156p, b/w, DJ/3.95)	Dutton	(1968)	Smith, Alvin	25-45	
Wojciechowska, Maia	Odyssey of Courage (1st {std}, 8vo, 182p, b/w, DJ/3.75)	Atheneum	1965	Smith, Alvin	30-45	
Wojciechowska, Maia	Shadow of a Bull (1st {std}, 8vo, 165p, red cl, fp b/w, DJ/3.50, NM)	Atheneum	1964	Smith, Alvin	70-100	R
Rice, Inez	Tree this Tall (1st, lg8vo, [32]p, 3-color, DJ/3.95)	Wm. Morrow	(1970)	Smith, Alvin	30-50	
Tobias, Doris G.	Zoo's Who (1st, ob4to, ibds, [28]p, 1-color, DJ/2.00)	Vanguard Press	1948	Smith, Barbara	30-50	
Fish, Helen D.	Little Book of Colors (1st {std}, 8vo, [28]p, color, DJ/1.00)	Lippincott	(1944)	Smith, Catharine	25-40	
Justus, May	Honey Jane (1st {std}, 8vo, 202p, cp, pep, DJ/2.00)	Doubleday/Doran	1935	Smith, Charles	20-35	
Baring-Gould, Sabine	Book of Ghosts (1st, 8vo, 383p, gilt, 8pl)	L: Methuen	1904	Smith, D. Murray	150-250	*
Aubrey, Frank	Queen of Atlantis (1st AM, 8vo, red/gilt, 391p, 8pl)	Lippincott	1900	Smith, D. Murray	125-200	
Price, Pattie	Bantu Tales (1st {std}, 8vo, ibds, 64p, 3-color, pep, DJ/1.00)	Dutton	1938	Smith, Desmond	40-65	
Anderson, Rbt. G.	Half-Past Seven Stories (1st, lg8vo, p-o, 251p, 16cp)	Putnam	(1922)	Smith, Dorothy H.	35-60	*
Cocke, Sarah J.	Bypaths in Dixie (1st, 8vo, blue/gilt, 317p, 7pl)	Dutton	(1911)	Smith, Duncan	55-80	*

AUTHOR	TITLE	PUBLISHER	DATE	ARTIST	PRICE	LC
Aesopus	Aesop's Fables (1st, 8vo, 172p, teg, brown/gilt, 6pl)	Century	1911	Smith, E. Boyd	120-185	
Smith, E. Boyd	After they Came Out of the Ark (1st, ob4to, ibds, 48p, 22cp)	Putnam	(1918)	Smith, E. Boyd	250-350	
Mother Goose	Boyd Smith Mother Goose (1st, 4to, red/gilt, 223p, 20cp)	Putnam	(1919)	Smith, E. Boyd	200-300	
Smith, E. Boyd	Chicken World (1st, ob4to, ibds, [28]p, color)	Putnam	1910	Smith, E. Boyd	250-350	
Marryat, Frederick	Children of the New Forest (1st, 8vo, 397p, p-o, 8cp)	Henry Holt & Co.	1911	Smith, E. Boyd	75-100	
Smith, E. Boyd	Circus & All About It (1st, 4to, p-o, 62p, 16cp, pep)	Stokes	(1909)	Smith, E. Boyd	250-350	
Brown, Abbie F.	Curious Book of Birds (1st, 8vo, gilt, 191p, 8pl)	Houghton	1903	Smith, E. Boyd	60-100	
Smith, E. Boyd	Early Life of Mr. Man before Noah (1st, ob4to, ibds, [50]p, 23cp, pep)	Houghton	1914	Smith, E. Boyd	250-400	
Oxley, James M.	Family on Wheels (1st AM, sm8vo, 219p, 4pl)	Crowell	(1905)	Smith, E. Boyd	30-50	
Pine, F.W. (ed.)	Franklin's Autobiography (1st, lg8vo, green cl, 341p, 10cp)	Henry Holt & Co.	1916	Smith, E. Boyd	60-100	
Smith, E. Boyd	Fun in the Radio World (1st, ob4to, [30]p, p-o, 12cp, pep)	Stokes	1923	Smith, E. Boyd	250-350	
Holbrook, Florence	Hiawatha Primer (1st, sm8vo, 139p, green cl, 148p, 8cp)	Houghton	1898	Smith, E. Boyd	70-120	
Brown, Abbie F.	In the Days of Giants (1st, 12mo, gilt, 259p, 6pl)	Houghton	1902	Smith, E. Boyd	100-160	R
Smith, E. Boyd	In the Land of Make-Believe (1st, sm ob4to, ibds, [28]p, 12cp, pep)	Henry Holt & Co.	(1916)	Smith, E. Boyd	250-400	R
Scott, Walter	Ivanhoe (1st, 8vo, red cl, 676p, teg, 16cp)	Houghton	1913	Smith, E. Boyd	100-160	
Brown, Abbie F.	John of the Woods (1st, sm8vo, 189p, 15pl)	Houghton	1909	Smith, E. Boyd	50-80	
Austin, Mary	Land of Little Rain (1st, 8vo, green/gilt, 281p, p-o, teg, 4pl)	Houghton	1903	Smith, E. Boyd	280-400	
Cooper, James F.	Last of the Mohicans (1st, 8vo, p-o, 523p, 8cp)	Henry Holt & Co.	(1910)	Smith, E. Boyd	70-120	
Smith, E. Boyd	Lions 'n' Elephants & Everything (1st, ob4to, [32]p, ibds, 12cp)	Putnam	(1929)	Smith, E. Boyd	250-350	
Adams, Andy	Log of a Cowboy (1st, 8vo, 387p, gilt, 6pl, map, PPPa)	Houghton	1903	Smith, E. Boyd	150-225	
Smith, E. Boyd	My Village (1st [1st bk], 12mo, teg, 325p, b/w)	Scribner	1896	Smith, E. Boyd	90-120	
Harris, Joel C.	Plantation Pageants (1st, sq8vo, green cl, 247p, 20pl, cep)	Houghton	1899	Smith, E. Boyd	160-240	R
Smith, E. Boyd	Pocahontas & Captain Smith (1st, lg ob4to, ibds, [56]p, color, pep)	Houghton	1906	Smith, E. Boyd	250-400	
Smith, E. Boyd	Railroad Book (1st, ob4to, [28]p, p-o, 12cp, pep)	Houghton	1913	Smith, E. Boyd	250-400	R
Defoe, Daniel	Robinson Crusoe (1st, 8vo, blue/gilt, 435p, p-o, 12cp)	Houghton	1909	Smith, E. Boyd	60-100	
Smith, E. Boyd	Santa Claus & All About Him (1st, ob4to, ibds, 62p, 16 fp color, pep)	Stokes	(1908)	Smith, E. Boyd	250-400	
Smith, E. Boyd	Seashore Book (1st, ob4to, [30]p, ibds, 12cp, pep)	Houghton	1912	Smith, E. Boyd	250-350	R
Anderson, Rbt. G.	Seven O'Clock Stories (1st, lg8vo, 180p, gilt, p-o, 20cp, pep)	Putnam	(1920)	Smith, E. Boyd	120-200	
Schultz, James W.	Sinopah, the Indian Boy (1st, 8vo, 154p, 4pl)	Houghton	1913	Smith, E. Boyd	45-70	
Smith, E. Boyd	So Long Ago (1st, lg8vo, green cl, 36p, color, DJ/2.00)	Houghton	1944	Smith, E. Boyd	100-160	
Smith, E. Boyd	Story of Noah's Ark (1st, ob4to, ibds, [56]p, p-o, 26cp, pep)	Houghton	1905	Smith, E. Boyd	250-350	R
Smith, E. Boyd	Story of our Country (1st, ob4to, ibds, 44p, fp color)	Putnam	1920	Smith, E. Boyd	80-135	
Phelps, Eliz. S.	Supply at St. Agatha's (1st, sm8vo, 38p, uncut, teg, 2pl by...)	Houghton	1896	Smith, E. Boyd	35-60	
Harris, Joel C.	Tales of Home Folks in Peace & War (1st, sm8vo, gilt, 417p, 4pl, cep)	Houghton	1898	Smith, E. Boyd	140-220	
Knibbs, Henry H.	Tang of Life (1st, sm8vo, 393p, 4cp)	Houghton	1918	Smith, E. Boyd	40-60	
Adams, Andy	Texas Matchmaker (1st, 12mo, 355p, 6pl)	Houghton	1904	Smith, E. Boyd	100-150	
Austin, Mary	The Flock (1st, 8vo, 266p, brown/gilt, teg, frn by...)	Houghton	1906	Smith, E. Boyd	100-165	
Austin, Mary	The Ford (1st, sm8vo, 440p, 4pl)	Houghton	1917	Smith, E. Boyd	60-90	
Adams, Andy	The Outlet (1st, 8vo, 371p, brown/gilt, 6pl)	Houghton	1905	Smith, E. Boyd	100-150	
Dutton, Maude B. (tr)	Tortoise and the Geese (1st, sm8vo, 124p, 12pl)	Houghton	1908	Smith, E. Boyd	60-90	*
Dana, Richard H.	Two Years Before the Mast (1st, lg8vo, 533p, p-o, 10cp, pep)	Houghton	1911	Smith, E. Boyd	80-125	
Meigs, Cornelia L.	Willow Whistle (1st, ob8vo, 144p, yellow cl, col frn, 10pl)	Macmillan	1931	Smith, E. Boyd	200-300	R
N/A	Aucassin & Nicolette (1st, lg4to, teg, [138]p, gilt, 3 ticp, 14pl)	L: Melrose	1914	Smith, Eileen L.	120-180	
Russell, Robert H.	Delft Cat (1st, 16mo, 71p, uncut, b/w)	R.H. Russell	1896	Smith, F. Berkeley	80-120	*
Smith, F. Berkeley	Real Latin Quarter (1st, 8vo, 204p, b/w photos, frn by...)	Funk/Wagnalls	1901	Smith, F. Hopkinson	50-80	
Smith, Francis H.	Charcoals of New & Old New York (1st, 4to, 142p, bds, 23 tipl)	Doubleday/Page	1912	Smith, Francis H.	90-120	
Smith, Francis H.	Day at Laguerre's... (1st, 8vo, tan cl, 190p, teg)	Houghton	1892	Smith, Francis H.	70-120	
Smith, Francis H.	In Dickens' London (1st, 4to, bds, 199p, teg, 22 tipl)	Scribner	1914	Smith, Francis H.	75-100	
Smith, Francis H.	Old Lines & New in Black & White (1st, ob folio, [28]p, p-o, 12pl)	Houghton	1886	Smith, Francis H.	125-200	*
Smith, Francis H.	Outdoor Sketching (1st, sm8vo, pcb, 145p, 3pl)	Scribner	1915	Smith, Francis H.	30-60	
Lucas, E.V.	Cat Book (1st, 16mo, 121p, fp b/w)	L: G. Richards	1900	Smith, H. Officer	50-85	
Dickens, Charles	David Copperfield (1st, 12mo, 506p, b/w pl)	Macmillan	1925	Smith, Harriet S.	30-50	*
Mother Goose	Mother Goose: Her Book (1st, lg8vo, 48p, color, pep)	Duffield	(1906)	Smith, Harry L.	60-100	*
Ade, George	True Bills (1st, 16mo, 154p, b/w)	Harper	1904	Smith, Harry L.	35-60	
Asbjornsen, P.C.	Tales from the Field (1st AM, 8vo, 403p, gilt, 11pl)	Putnam	1896	Smith, J. Moyr	60-100	
Daldorne, Evan	Wooing of the Water-Witch (1st, 8vo, gilt, 132p, b/w, AEG)	Henry Holt & Co.	1880	Smith, J. Moyr	70-100	*
MacDonald, George	Back of the North Wind (1st, 4to, p-o, teg, 342p, 8cp, pep)	McKay	1919	Smith, Jessie W.	140-220	
Whitney, Helen H.	Bed-Time Book (1st, lg4to, ipcb, 31p, 6cp, pep)	Duffield	1907	Smith, Jessie W.	350-500	
Long, John L.	Billy Boy (1st, sm8vo, blue cl, 74p, teg, p-o, uncut, 4pl, pep)	Dodd	1906	Smith, Jessie W.	160-220	
Franchot, Annie W.	Bobs, King of Fortunate Isle (1st, 8vo, 210p, blue cl, col frn)	Dutton	(1928)	Smith, Jessie W.	40-60	*
Humphrey, Mabel	Book of the Child (1st, folio, ibds, 3cp by...)	Stokes	(1903)	Smith, Jessie W.	750-1000	
Smith, Nora A.	Boys & Girls of Bookland (1st, lg4to, p-o, 100p, 11cp, cep)	Cosmopolitan	1923	Smith, Jessie W.	125-200	
Smith, Nora A.	Boys & Girls of Bookland (lg4to, 100p, brown pcb, 11cp, later)	McKay	(1923)	Smith, Jessie W.	120-200	
Reed, Helen L.	Brenda's Summer at Rockley (1st, 8vo, blue/gilt, 376p, 5pl)	Little/Brown	1901	Smith, Jessie W.	200-300	
Reed, Helen L.	Brenda, Her School & her Club (1st, sm8vo, 328p, gilt, 5pl)	Little/Brown	1900	Smith, Jessie W.	160-220	
Skinner, Ada M.	Child's Book of Country Stories (1st, lg8vo, gilt, 265p, p-o, 4cp)	Duffield	1925	Smith, Jessie W.	180-250	
Skinner, Ada M.	Child's Book of Country Stories (1st {this pub}, 8vo, p-o, 4cp)	Dial	1935	Smith, Jessie W.	90-120	
Skinner, Ada M.	Child's Book of Modern Stories (1st, lg8vo, gilt p-o, 340p, 8cp)	Duffield	1920	Smith, Jessie W.	160-240	
Skinner, Ada M.	Child's Book of Modern Stories (4to, gilt, 341p, p-o, 8cp)	Dial	1935	Smith, Jessie W.	80-120	
Smith, Jessie W.	Child's Book of Old Verses (1st, lg8vo, p-o, teg, 124p, 10cp, pep)	Duffield	1910	Smith, Jessie W.	200-300	
Coussens, Penrhyn W.	Child's Book of Stories (1st, lg8vo, gilt, p-o, 463p, 10cp, pep)	Duffield	1911	Smith, Jessie W.	300-400	
Stevenson, Rbt. L.	Child's Garden of Verses (1st, lg8vo, p-o, 125p, teg uncut, 12cp, SC)	Scribner	1905	Smith, Jessie W.	170-245	
Toogood, Cora C.	Child's Prayer (1st, lg8vo, [16]p, blue/gilt, col frn)	McKay	(1925)	Smith, Jessie W.	100-175	*
Various	Child's Stamp Book of Old Verses (1st, 8vo, bds, p-o, 12 color stamps)	Duffield	1915	Smith, Jessie W.	350-500	
Crothers, Samuel M.	Children of Dickens (1st, lg8vo, p-o, 259p, 10cp, pep, SC)	Scribner	1925	Smith, Jessie W.	100-150	
Cox, Florence T.	Chronicles of Rhoda (1st, 12mo, 287p, red/gilt, 2cp)	Small/Maynard	(1909)	Smith, Jessie W.	80-120	
Chabot, Adrien	Dancing-Master (1st, 12mo, teg, green cl, 139p, 4pl)	Lippincott	1901	Smith, Jessie W.	200-300	*
Dickens, Charles	Dickens' Children (1st, lg8vo, [48]p, gilt, p-o, teg, 10cp)	Scribner	1912	Smith, Jessie W.	170-240	

AUTHOR	TITLE	PUBLISHER	DATE	ARTIST	PRICE	LC
Higgins, Aileen C.	Dream Blocks (1st, lg8vo, p-o, 47p, beige cl, 15cp, pep)	Duffield	1908	Smith, Jessie W.	350-550	
Longfellow, H.W.	Evangeline (1st, 8vo, 143p, teg, gilt, 5cp by...)	Houghton	1897	Smith, Jessie W.	200-300	
Chapin, Anna A.	Everyday & Nowaday Fairy Book (lg4to, 160p, ibds, 8cp)	L: Coker	[1920]	Smith, Jessie W.	200-300	
Chapin, Anna A.	Everyday Fairy Book (1st, 4to, 160p, p-o, 7cp)	Dodd	1915	Smith, Jessie W.	300-400	
Chapin, Anna A.	Everyday Fairy Book (1st UK, 4to, 160p, p-o, 7cp)	L: Harrap	1917	Smith, Jessie W.	200-300	
Keyes, Angela M.	Five Senses (1st, 8vo, ivory cl, 252p, 5cp)	Moffat	1911	Smith, Jessie W.	280-400	
Goodwin, Maud W.	Head of a Hundred (1st, 12mo, green/gilt, 225p, teg, 2pl by...)	Little/Brown	1897	Smith, Jessie W.	200-300	
Goodwin, Maud W.	Head of a Hundred (1st {new ed}, 8vo, 221p, red/gilt, 2pl)	Little/Brown	1900	Smith, Jessie W.	100-160	
Spyri, Johanna	Heidi (1st, lg8vo, 380p, teg, p-o, blue cl, 10cp, pep)	McKay	1922	Smith, Jessie W.	140-250	
Burnett, Frances H.	In the Closed Room (1st, 8vo, green/gilt, teg, 130p, 8cp, dep)	McClurg	1904	Smith, Jessie W.	140-200	
Mother Goose	Jessie W. Smith Mother Goose (1st, ob4to, 173p, p-o, 12cp, 5pl, pep)	Dodd	(1914)	Smith, Jessie W.	600-800	
Bell, Louise P.	Kitchen Fun (1st, lg8vo, ibds, 28p, cvr by...)	Harter Pub. Co.	1932	Smith, Jessie W.	45-70	
Skinner, Ada M.	Little Child's Book of Stories (1st, lg8vo, 258p, gilt, 8cp, pep)	Duffield	1922	Smith, Jessie W.	180-270	*
Taylor, Mary I.	Little Mistress Goodhope (1st, 12mo, gilt, p-o, 186p, col frn)	McClurg	1902	Smith, Jessie W.	250-350	
Mother Goose	Little Mother Goose (1st, ob8vo, p-o, 176p, gilt, 12cp)	Dodd	(1918)	Smith, Jessie W.	250-400	
Alcott, Louisa M.	Little Women (1st, 8vo, p-o, 617p, green/gilt, 8cp, pep)	Little/Brown	1915	Smith, Jessie W.	180-250	
Shelby, Annie B.	Lullaby Book (1st, 8vo, blue/gilt, 183p, col frn by...)	Duffield	1921	Smith, Jessie W.	80-125	
Moore, Clement C.	Night Before Christmas (1st, ob8vo, [32]p, ibds, 12cp, pep)	Houghton	(1912)	Smith, Jessie W.	200-300	
Chapin, Anna A.	Nowadays Fairy Book (1st, lg4to, ibds, 159p, 6 ticp)	Dodd	1911	Smith, Jessie W.	350-500	
Alcott, Louisa M.	Old-Fashioned Girl (1st, sm8vo, green/gilt, teg, 371p, 12pl)	Little/Brown	1902	Smith, Jessie W.	100-165	
MacDonald, George	Princess & the Goblin (1st, 4to, gilt, p-o, teg, 203p, 8cp, pep)	McKay	1920	Smith, Jessie W.	160-240	
Sill, S.C.	Reminiscences/Chest of Drawers (1st, sm8vo, [40]p, AEG, 6pl)	Lippincott	1900	Smith, Jessie W.	100-165	
Sage, Betty	Rhymes of Real Children (1st, sq4to, 32p, ibds, 6cp)	Fox/Duffield	1903	Smith, Jessie W.	300-450	
Wells, Carolyn	Seven Ages of Childhood (1st, sm4to, gilt, 56p, p-o, 7cp, pep)	Moffat	1909	Smith, Jessie W.	350-500	
Richards, Laura E.	Silver Crown (1st, 8vo, 105p, teg, grey/gilt, cvr by...)	Little/Brown	1906	Smith, Jessie W.	60-90	
Stuart, Ruth M.	Sonny's Father (1st, 12mo, teg, 240p, uncut, 2pl by...)	Century	1910	Smith, Jessie W.	70-100	
Bacon, Josephine D.	Ten to Seventeen (1st, sm8vo, 261p, green/gilt, p-o, 3pl by...)	Harper	1908	Smith, Jessie W.	60-90	
McCall, Sidney	Truth Dexter (1st, 8vo, 375p, blue cloth, frn by...)	Little/Brown	1903	Smith, Jessie W.	35-60	
Skinner, Ada M.	Very Little Child's Book of Stories (1st, lg8vo, 232p, gilt, 8cp)	Duffield	1923	Smith, Jessie W.	180-270	*
Kingsley, Charles	Water Babies (1st, sm4to, p-o, teg, gilt, 362p, 12cp, pep)	Dodd	(1916)	Smith, Jessie W.	400-600	
Kingsley, Charles	Water Babies (1st {this format}, 12mo, gilt, 270p, p-o, 8cp, pep)	Dodd	1916	Smith, Jessie W.	140-225	*
Kingsley, Charles	Water Babies (1st UK, 4to, 240p, gilt, 12 ticp)	L: Boots	[1918]	Smith, Jessie W.	280-350	
Stewart, Mary	Way to Wonderland (1st, lg8vo, 144p, gilt, 194p, p-o, 6cp, pep)	Dodd	(1917)	Smith, Jessie W.	180-260	
Stewart, Mary	Way to Wonderland (1st UK, lg8vo, 144p, blue/gilt, 6 ticp, pep)	L: Hodder	[1918]	Smith, Jessie W.	250-350	
Underwood, P.	When Christmas Comes Around (1st, 4to, ipcb, 26p, 6cp, pep)	Duffield	1915	Smith, Jessie W.	700-900	
Smith, Mary P.W.	Young Puritans in Captivity (1st, 12mo, grey cl, 323p, 6pl, dep)	Little/Brown	1899	Smith, Jessie W.	120-200	
Nash, Ogden	Boy & his Room (1st, sm ob4to, yellow cl, unpag, b/w, DJ/2.95)	F. Watts	(1963)	Smith, Lawrence	40-65	
Nash, Ogden	Girls are Silly (1st {std}, ob4to, [38]p, 1-color, pep, DJ/2.95)	F. Watts	(1961)	Smith, Lawrence	50-80	R
Meyer, Franklyn	Me & Caleb (1st {std}, 8vo, 160p, b/w, DJ/3.25)	Follett	(1962)	Smith, Lawrence	140-200	
Mother Goose	Mother Goose Song Book (1st, ob4to, 100p, color)	Garden City	(1948)	Smith, Marion F.	90-160	*
Farjeon, Eleanor	Westwoods (1st AM, 8vo, ibds, [44]p, b/w, pep)	A.& W. Guild	(1935)	Smith, May	30-50	
Smith, Pamela C.	Annancy Stories (1st, folio, 79p, ibds, b/w)	R.H. Russell	1899	Smith, Pamela	200-300	
Smith, Pamela C.	Golden Vanity & Green Bed (1st, folio, [26]p, p-o, green cl, 12cp)	Doub./McClure	1899	Smith, Pamela	250-350	
Brown, Alice	Secret of the Clan (1st, sm8vo, blue/gilt, 314p, 12pl)	Macmillan	1912	Smith, Sarah K.	30-50	
Bannerman, Helen	Little Black Sambo (folio, wraps, [16]p, color)	Whitman	[1915]	Smith, T.& M.	200-300	
Beaman, Emeric H.	Ozmar the Mystic (1st, 8vo, 378p, blue/gilt, 12pl)	L: Bliss Sands	1896	Smith, Thomas	50-85	*
Smith, Wallace	Little Tigress (1st, 8vo, 209p, teg, 15pl, pep)	Putnam	1923	Smith, Wallace	30-50	
Buck, Pearl S.	Chinese Children Next Door (1st, lg ob8vo, red cl, 62p, 1-color, DJ/2.00)	John Day	1942	Smith, William A.	80-125	R*
Buck, Pearl S.	Water-Buffalo Children (1st, 8vo, ipcb, 59p, b/w, DJ/1.50)	NY: John Day	(1943)	Smith, William A.	80-125	R
Sandburg, Carl	Wind Song (1st {std}, 8vo, 127p, b/w, DJ/3.00)	Harcourt	(1960)	Smith, William A.	30-50	
Smith, William J.	Typewriter Town (1st {std}, lg8vo, 32p, 3-color, dep, DJ/2.95)	Dutton	(1960)	Smith, William J.	60-85	R
Gomme, Alice B.	Children's Singing Games (1st, ob8vo, 70p, ibds, b/w)	Nutt/Macmillan	1894	Smith, Winifred	125-200	*
Carr, Alice V.	Fairy of the Rhone (1st, 12mo, 69p, woodcuts)	L.C. Page	1901	Smith, Winifred	30-50	
Jackson, Gabrielle	By Love's Sweet Rule (1st, 12mo, 320p, b/w, pep)	Winston	1906	Smith, Wuanita	30-50	
Unknown	Christmas Letter (1st, 12mo, 85p, 13pl)	Cupples/Leon	1902	Smith, Wuanita	50-80	
Blanchard, Amy E.	Four Corners (1st, sm8vo, 387p, green cl, 5pl)	Jacobs	(1906)	Smith, Wuanita	30-60	*
Grimm Bros.	Golden Bird (1st, sm8vo, 116p, color, pep)	Jacobs	(1922)	Smith, Wuanita	60-90	*
Curtis, Alice T.	Grandpa's Little Girls & Friends (1st, 12mo, p-o, 190p, 5pl, pep)	Penn	1910	Smith, Wuanita	30-50	
Curtis, Alice T.	Grandpa's Little Girls at School (1st, 12mo, 195p, p-o, 5pl)	Penn	1908	Smith, Wuanita	30-50	
Swift, Jonathan	Gulliver's Travels (1st, sm8vo, 370p, cp)	Jacobs	[1923]	Smith, Wuanita	30-50	*
Byrne, Mary Agnes	One Too Many (1st, 8vo, green cl, 191p, 4pl)	Saalfield	(1912)	Smith, Wuanita	35-60	*
Lefferts, Sara T.	Pansy Wedding (1st, sq16mo, ipcb, 86p, color, pep)	Cupples/Leon	(1909)	Smith, Wuanita	60-100	
Lefferts, Sara T.	Patriotic Jubilee (1st, sq16mo, ipcb, 84p, color, pep)	Cupples/Leon	(1910)	Smith, Wuanita	60-100	
Grimm Bros.	Snow White & Seven Dwarfs (1st, sm8vo, 115p, col frn, cp, pep)	Jacobs	(1922)	Smith, Wuanita	55-80	*
Franchot, Annie W.	Bugs, Wings & other Things (1st, 8vo, 99p, green/gilt, 7cp, pep)	Dutton	(1918)	Smith/Cady	170-220	
Barrows, Marjorie	Ezra the Elephant (1st, sq8vo, ibds, [44]p, color, pep)	Grosset/Dunlap	1934	Smock, Nell S.	25-40	
King, Marian	Piccolino (1st, 8vo, 32p, p-o, color, pep, DJ/1.00)	Whitman	1939	Smock, Nell S.	25-45	
Biggers, Earl D.	Love Insurance (1st, 12mo, 402p, brown cl, 8pl)	Bobbs-Merrill	(1914)	Snapp, Frank	100-150	
Biggers, Earl D.	Seven Keys to Baldpate (1st, sm8vo, blue/gilt, 408p, 5pl)	Bobbs-Merrill	(1913)	Snapp, Frank	120-180	
La Prade, E.	Alice in Orchestralia (1st {std}, sm8vo, 171p, 1-color frn, b/w)	Doubleday/Page	1925	Snell, Carroll	40-65	
Mother Goose	Mother Goose (1st, sm4to, ipcb, 380p, color, pep)	Whitman	(1941)	Snow, Dorothea J.	35-60	*
De La Iglesia, Maria	Oak that Would not Pay (1st, lg8vo, [39]p, fp b/w, cep, DJ/3.50)	Pantheon	(1968)	Snyder, Jerome	30-50	
Rand, Ann	Umbrellas, Hats & Wheels (1st {std}, 4to, [31]p, color, DJ/3.25, NYTBI)	Harcourt	(1961)	Snyder, Jerome	80-135	
Elkin, Benjamin	Why the Sun was Late (1st, 4to, [48]p, fp color, cep, DJ/2.95)	Parents Mag. Pr.	1966	Snyder, Jerome	25-40	
Fritz, Jean	121 Pudding Street (1st, 8vo, 219p, b/w, DJ/2.75)	Coward	(1955)	Sofia	45-70	
Nash, Ogden	Happy Days (1st, 8vo, 161p, p-o, fp b/w)	Simon/Schuster	1933	Soglow, Otto	80-120	
Nash, Ogden	Hard Lines (1st [1st bk.], 12mo, 99p, gilt, b/w)	Simon/Schuster	1931	Soglow, Otto	80-130	
Soglow, Otto	Little King (1st, 4to, [67]p, yellow cl, b/w, DJ/2.00)	Farrar/Rinehart	(1933)	Soglow, Otto	70-125	

AUTHOR	TITLE	PUBLISHER	DATE	ARTIST	PRICE	LC
Nash, Ogden	Primrose Path (1st, 8vo, 354p, gilt, b/w, DJ/2.50)	Simon/Schuster	1935	Soglow, Otto	60-90	
Varner, Velma	Animal Frolic (1st, ob8vo, [48]p, b/w, DJ/2.75, NYTBI)	Putnam	(1954)	Sojo, Toba	40-65	*
Miller, Mary B.	All Aboard: Poems (1st {std}, 8vo, 47p, 1-color, cep, DJ/2.75, NYTBI)	Pantheon	(1958)	Sokol, Bill	30-50	
DeRegniers, Beatrice	Cats Cats Cats Cats Cats (1st {std}, lg4to, [30]p, 2-color, cep, DJ/2.95)	Pantheon	(1958)	Sokol, Bill	50-80	R
DeRegniers, Beatrice	Child's Book of Dreams (1st {std}, 12mo, [46]p, fp 2-color, DJ/2.25)	Harcourt	1957	Sokol, Bill	40-65	R
Andersen, Hans C.	Emperor and the Nightingale (1st, lg ob8vo, [32]p, dp color, b/w, DJ/2.95)	Pantheon	1959	Sokol, Bill	40-65	*
Alexander, Lloyd C.	Time Cat... (1st {std}, 8vo, 191p, b/w, DJ/3.50)	Holt, Rinehart	(1963)	Sokol, Bill	30-50	
McKim, Audrey	Andy and the Gopher (1st {std}, 8vo, 119p, b/w, DJ/2.75)	Little/Brown	(1959)	Solbert, Ronni	20-30	
Merrill, Jean	Black Sheep (1st, lg8vo, 73p, fp 1-color, cep, DJ/3.95)	Pantheon	(1969)	Solbert, Ronni	25-40	
Merrill, Jean	Blue's Broken Heart (1st, 8vo, [24]p, 1-color, pep, DJ/2.25)	Whittlesey	1960	Solbert, Ronni	25-45	
Merrill, Jean	Boxes (1st, 4to, [32]p, fp 3-color, pep, DJ/2.50)	Coward	(1953)	Solbert, Ronni	30-50	
Brooks, Gwendolyn	Bronzeville Boys & Girls (1st, 8vo, grey cl, 40p, b/w, cep, DJ/2.00)	Harper	(1956)	Solbert, Ronni	100-160	R
Merrill, Jean	Elephant Who Liked to Smash Small Cars (1st, ob4to, [32]p, color, DJ/3.50)	Pantheon	(1967)	Solbert, Ronni	60-100	*
Merrill, Jean	Emily Emerson's Moon (1st {std}, 8vo, 32p, 2-color, DJ/2.75)	Little/Brown	(1960)	Solbert, Ronni	25-40	*
Haviland, Virginia	Favorite Fairy Tales Told in Sweeden (1st {std}, lg8vo, 95p, color, DJ/2.95)	Little/Brown	(1966)	Solbert, Ronni	50-85	
Merrill, Jean	Henry, the Hand-Painted Mouse (1st, sm4to, [40]p, ibds, b/w, cep, DJ/1.75)	Coward	(1951)	Solbert, Ronni	30-50	*
Merrill, Jean	Pushcart War (1st, 8vo, 222p, fp b/w, DJ/3.95)	W.R. Scott	(1964)	Solbert, Ronni	40-70	R*
Merrill, Jean	Shan's Lucky Knife (1st, sm4to, [48]p, 2-color, DJ)	W.R. Scott	1960	Solbert, Ronni	30-50	
Low, Elizabeth	Snug in the Snow (1st {std}, 8vo, 63p, color, DJ/2.95)	Little/Brown	(1963)	Solbert, Ronni	25-40	*
Merrill, Jean	Superlative Horse (1st, lg8vo, 79p, 1-color, DJ/3.00)	W.R. Scott	(1961)	Solbert, Ronni	25-40	*
Merrill, Jean	The Woover (1st, 8vo, 31p, fp 1-color, cep, DJ/2.00)	Coward	(1952)	Solbert, Ronni	25-40	*
Johnson, Elizabeth	Three-in-One Prince (1st {std}, lg8vo, 58p, fp color, DJ/2.75)	Little/Brown	(1961)	Solbert, Ronni	25-40	*
Merrill, Jean	Tree House of Jimmy Domino (1st, ob4to, [38]p, 1-color, pep, DJ/2.50)	NY: Oxford U.Pr.	(1955)	Solbert, Ronni	30-45	*
Neville, Mary	Woody and Me (1st, lg8vo, [60]p, b/w, DJ/2.95)	Pantheon	(1966)	Solbert, Ronni	25-45	
Martin, Dahris	Little Lamb (1st {std}, ob4to, [32]p, color, pep, DJ/1.50)	Harper	1938	Somppi, Lilly	45-70	*
Fleury, Barbara	Runaway Deer (1st, 8vo, [32]p, p-o, b/w, DJ/1.00)	Macmillan	1938	Somppi, Lilly	30-50	*
Carroll, Lewis	Alice in Wonderland (1st AM, sq8vo, 192p, teg, 192p, 6 ticp, pep)	Baker/Taylor	(1911)	Soper, George	100-165	
Carroll, Lewis	Alice in Wonderland (1st, sq8vo, 192p, red cl, 6 ticp)	L: Headley	(1911)	Soper, George	250-350	
Carroll, Lewis	Alice in Wonderland (lg8vo, 192p, red cl, 6 ticp)	Small/Maynard	[1911]	Soper, George	100-170	
N/A	Arabian Nights (1st, 8vo, 295p, 6cp)	L: Allen/Unwin	(1913)	Soper, George	70-100	
Grimm Bros.	Fairy Tales (1st AM, 8vo, 278p, 6cp, b/w)	Doran	[1924]	Soper, George	55-80	*
Lamb, Charles	Tales from Shakespeare (lg8vo, 323p, 14cp, pep)	Baker/Taylor	[1924]	Soper, George	30-50	
Hawthorne, Nathaniel	Tanglewood Tales (1st, 8vo, 242p, 6cp, pep)	L: Allen/Unwin	1912	Soper, George	70-125	
Kingsley, Charles	The Heroes (sm4to, 6cp, pep)	Doran	[1920]	Soper, George	40-60	
Kingsley, Charles	Water Babies (lg8vo, teg, 4cp)	Baker/Taylor	[1910]	Soper, George	40-60	
Agle, Nan H.	Princess Mary of Maryland (1st, 8vo, 108p, tan cl, b/w, DJ/2.50)	Scribner	(1956)	Sopher, Aaron	45-70	
Cowley, Joy	Duck in the Gun (1st {std}, sm8vo, [40]p, ibds, color, pep, DJ/2.95)	Doubleday	(1969)	Sorel, Edward	30-45	
Miller, Warren	Goings on at Little Wishful (1st {std}, ob4to, [30]p, 2-col, cep, DJ/2.75)	Little/Brown	(1959)	Sorel, Edward	70-100	R
Sherman, Nancy	Gwendolyn & Weathercock (1st, ob4to, unpag, ibds color, pep, DJ/3.50, NYT)	Golden Press	1963	Sorel, Edward	120-200	
Sherman, Nancy	Gwendolyn, the Miracle Hen (1st, ob4to, [25]p, ibds, color, pep, DJ/2.95)	Golden Press	1961	Sorel, Edward	120-200	R
Miller, Warren	King Carlo of Capri (1st {std}, sm4to, [32]p, 2-color, pep, DJ/2.95)	Harcourt	(1958)	Sorel, Edward	70-100	R
Miller, Warren	Pablo Paints a Picture (1st {std}, ob4to [28]p, 1-color, pep, DJ/2.75, NYT)	Little/Brown	(1959)	Sorel, Edward	60-90	
Sotomayor, Antonio	Khasa Goes to the Fiesta (1st {std}, 4to, 57p, color, DJ/3.25)	Doubleday	(1967)	Sotomayor, Antonio	20-35	
Perrault, Charles	Story of Blue-Beard (1st, 8vo, green cl, 61p, b/w)	L: Lawrence	1895	Southall, Joseph	65-90	
Mitchison, Naomi	The Hostages (1st AM, 8vo, 332p, 16 fp b/w)	Harcourt	(1931)	Southby, Logi	25-40	*
Carroll, Lewis	Alice in Wonderland (1st, 8vo, teg, p-o, gilt, 166p, 12cp, pep)	L: Chatto	1907	Sowerby, Millicent	250-350	
Carroll, Lewis	Alice in Wonderland (1st AM, 8vo, p-o, 165p, 12cp)	Duffield	1908	Sowerby, Millicent	200-300	
Carroll, Lewis	Alice in Wonderland (1st {this fmt}, sq12mo, 157p, p-o, 8cp)	L: H. Frowde	1913	Sowerby, Millicent	70-120	
Carroll, Lewis	Alice in Wonderland (new ed., 12mo, bds, 157p, 8cp)	L: H. Milford	(1919)	Sowerby, Millicent	180-260	
Sowerby, Githa	Bonnie Book (1st, 8vo, p-o, 12cp)	L: Oxford U.Pr.	1918	Sowerby, Millicent	150-220	
Stevenson, Rbt. L.	Child's Garden of Verses (1st, 4to, blue/gilt, teg, 12ticp, pep)	L: Chatto	1908	Sowerby, Millicent	200-300	
Stevenson, Rbt. L.	Child's Garden of Verses (1st AM, 4to, 125p, teg, 12cp, pep)	Scribner	1908	Sowerby, Millicent	200-300	
Sowerby, Githa	Childhood (4to, bds, gilt, 12cp)	L: Chatto	(1907)	Sowerby, Millicent	200-300	
Sowerby, Millicent	Childhood (1st AM, lg8vo, 44p, p-o, 12cp)	Duffield	1907	Sowerby, Millicent	140-200	
N/A	Cinderella (4to, ipcb, teg, 62p, gilt, 12 ticp)	L: Hodder	[1915]	Sowerby, Millicent	200-300	
Sowerby, Githa	Dainty Book (1st, sq8vo, ibds, unpag, 12cp)	Hodder	[1915]	Sowerby, Millicent	120-180	
Grimm Bros.	Fairy Tales (1st, 4to, gilt, p-o, teg, 255p, 12cp)	L: Richards	1909	Sowerby, Millicent	250-400	
Grimm Bros.	Fairy Tales (1st AM, 8vo, 255p, 12cp, dep)	Stokes	(1910)	Sowerby, Millicent	200-300	
Sowerby, Githa	Gay Book (1st {this pub.}, 8vo, [29]p, ibds, 12 fp color)	A.& W. Guild	(1935)	Sowerby, Millicent	35-60	
Joan, Natalie	Glad Book (1st, 8vo, [48]p, gilt, ibds, 12 fp color)	L: H. Milford	[1921]	Sowerby, Millicent	100-160	
Sowerby, Githa	Glad Book (1st {this pub.}, 8vo, [29]p, ibds, 12 fp color)	A.& W. Guild	(1935)	Sowerby, Millicent	35-60	
Sowerby, Githa	Little Stories for Little People (1st, lg8vo, 72p)	L: H. Frowde	[1910]	Sowerby, Millicent	75-100	*
Sowerby, Githa	Merry Book (1st, sm sq4to, white bds, 12cp)	L: Hodder	[1911]	Sowerby, Millicent	150-220	
Sowerby, Githa	Poems of Childhood (1st, 4to, 46p, teg, ibds, gilt, 12 ticp, dep)	L: H. Frowde	[1912]	Sowerby, Millicent	200-300	
Sowerby, Githa	The Bumbletoes (1st, 12mo, ibds, 60p, 12cp)	L: Chatto	1907	Sowerby, Millicent	160-250	
Strang, Herbert	What Baby Reads (1st AM, 12mo, bds, gilt, p-o, [32]p, 6cp)	NY: Hodder	[1910]	Sowerby, Millicent	100-160	
Sowerby, Githa	Wise Book (1st AM, 12mo, ipcb, 13cp)	Dent/Dutton	1906	Sowerby, Millicent	120-175	
Sowerby, Githa	Yesterday's Children (1st AM, 4to, 47p, p-o, 12cp)	Duffield	1909	Sowerby, Millicent	80-120	
Streatfeild, Noel	First Book of the Ballet (1st AM, sm4to, 93p, 2-color, DJ/1.75)	F. Watts	1953	Soyer, Moses	30-50	
Livingston, Myra C.	Crazy Flight (1st {std}, 8vo, 48p, b/w, DJ/3.50)	Harcourt	(1969)	Spanfeller, James	25-35	
Cunningham, Julia	Dorp Dead (1st, 8vo, 88p, b/w, DJ/3.50)	Pantheon	(1965)	Spanfeller, James	20-35	
Bulla, Clyde R.	Indian Hill (1st, 8vo, 74p, fp b/w, DJ/3.75)	Crowell	(1963)	Spanfeller, James	20-30	
Farmer, Penelope	Summer Birds (1st {std}, 8vo, 155p, b/w, DJ/2.95)	Harcourt	(1962)	Spanfeller, James	30-50	
Cleaver, Vera	Where the Lilies Bloom (1st {std}, 8vo, ipcb, 174p, fp b/w, cep, DJ/3.95)	Lippincott	(1970)	Spanfeller, James	30-45	
Mason, Francis E.	Daddy Gander (1st, 4to, ibds, [90]p, color)	NY: F.E. Mason	(1900)	Spedon	80-140	
Lyall, Edna	Autobiography of a Slander (1st, 8vo, blue/gilt, AEG, 146p, b/w)	L: Longmans	1892	Speed, Lancelot	60-100	
Knowles, J. (arr.)	King Arthur & his Knights (1st, 8vo, 340p, 8cp)	L: Warne	(1912)	Speed, Lancelot	75-100	
Holland, R. (ed.)	King Arthur & Knights of Roundtable (1st AM, sm8vo, 360p, p-o, 7cp pep)	Jacobs	(1919)	Speed, Lancelot	50-85	

AUTHOR	TITLE	PUBLISHER	DATE	ARTIST	PRICE	LC
Chambers, Robert	Maker of Moons (1st, 12mo, blue/gilt, teg, 401p, frn by...)	Putnam	1896	Speed, Lancelot	120-200	
Speed, Flora	The Limbersnigs (1st, 4to, 75p, 4cp, dep)	L: Lawrence/Jell	(1896)	Speed, Lancelot	80-125	
Mayne, William	Blue Boat (1st AM {std}, 8vo, 173p, b/w, DJ/2.95)	Dutton	1960	Spence, Geraldine	50-80	
Spencer, Ann	Cat Who Tasted Cinnamon Toast (1st {std}, 4to, 68p, ibds, b/w, DJ/4.95)	Knopf	1968	Spencer, Ann	30-45	
Sperry, Armstrong	All About the Arctic and Antarctic (1st, 8vo, 146p, color, pep, DJ/1.95)	Random	(1957)	Sperry, Armstrong	20-30	
Sperry, Armstrong	All About the Jungle (1st {std}, 8vo, 141p, b/w, pep, DJ/1.95)	Random	(1959)	Sperry, Armstrong	20-30	
Sperry, Armstrong	All Sail Set (1st, sm4to, 175p, pep, b/w, DJ/2.00, NH)	Winston	(1935)	Sperry, Armstrong	50-80	R
Sperry, Armstrong	Amazon: River Sea of Brazil (1st, 8vo, 96p, 1-color, pep, DJ/2.50)	Garrard Pub.	(1961)	Sperry, Armstrong	30-50	
Sperry, Armstrong	Bamboo: The Grass Tree (1st, sm8vo, [47]p, 1-color, pep, DJ/1.00)	Macmillan	1942	Sperry, Armstrong	60-100	
Sperry, Armstrong	Black Falcon (1st {std}, 8vo, 218p, DJ/2.50)	Winston	(1949)	Sperry, Armstrong	25-40	
Judson, Clara I.	Boat Builder (1st, 8vo, tan cl, 121p, fp b/w, pep, DJ/1.50)	Scribner	1940	Sperry, Armstrong	30-50	
Sperry, Armstrong	Boy Who Was Afraid (1st UK, 8vo, 95p, b/w, pep, DJ)	L: John Lane	1942	Sperry, Armstrong	30-45	
Carter, Russell	Brothers of the Frontier (1st, sm8vo, 205p, tan cl, b/w, DJ/2.00)	Appleton-Century	1938	Sperry, Armstrong	30-50	
Sperry, Armstrong	Call it Courage (1st, 8vo, 95p, beige cl, 1-color, pep, DJ/1.75, NM)	Macmillan	1940	Sperry, Armstrong	80-130	R
Kahmann, Chesley	Carmen: Silent Partner (1st, sm8vo, 249p, uncut, b/w, pep)	Dodd	1934	Sperry, Armstrong	50-80	*
Sperry, Armstrong	Coconut: Wonder Tree (1st, 8vo, blue cl, [47]p, 1-color, pep, DJ/1.00)	Macmillan	1942	Sperry, Armstrong	30-50	
Hewes, Agnes D.	Codfish Musket (1st {std}, 8vo, 390p, pep, DJ/2.00, NH)	Doubleday/Doran	1936	Sperry, Armstrong	45-70	
Kummer, Frederic	Courage Over the Andes (1st, 8vo, 251p, col frn, fp b/w, pep, DJ/2.00)	Winston	(1940)	Sperry, Armstrong	30-45	
Sperry, Armstrong	Danger to the Windward (1st {std}, 8vo, 241p, b/w, DJ/2.50)	Winston	(1947)	Sperry, Armstrong	30-45	
Heal, Edith	Dogie Boy (1st, lg8vo, 79p, brown cl, pep, 11 fp color, DJ/2.00)	Whitman	1943	Sperry, Armstrong	50-80	
Sperry, Armstrong	Frozen Fire (1st {std}, 8vo, 192p, green cl, b/w, DJ/2.75)	Doubleday	(1956)	Sperry, Armstrong	25-45	
Longfellow, H.W.	Hiawatha (1st, 4to, ibds, [68]p, fp color, pep, DJ/1.00)	Random	1951	Sperry, Armstrong	40-60	
Follett, Helen T.	House Afire! (1st, 8vo, 102p, b/w, pep, DJ/1.50)	Scribner	1941	Sperry, Armstrong	30-50	
Sperry, Armstrong	Hull-Down for Action (1st {std}, 8vo, 213p, pep, DJ/2.00)	Doubleday/Doran	1945	Sperry, Armstrong	40-70	
Sperry, Armstrong	John Paul Jones: Fighting Sailor (1st, 8vo, 180p, fp b/w, pep, DJ/1.50)	Random	(1953)	Sperry, Armstrong	50-80	R*
Pease, Howard	Jungle River (1st {std}, 8vo, 295p, col frn, pep, DJ/2.00)	Doubleday/Doran	1938	Sperry, Armstrong	70-125	
Coryell, Hubert	Klondike Gold (1st, 8vo, 319p, blue cl, pep, b/w, DJ/2.00)	Macmillan	1938	Sperry, Armstrong	40-60	
Sperry, Armstrong	Little Eagle: A Navaho Boy (1st, lg8vo, 102p, color, pep, DJ/2.00)	Winston	(1938)	Sperry, Armstrong	50-80	
Follett, Helen T.	Magic Portholes (1st, lg8vo, 321p, orange cl, fp b/w, pep)	Macmillan	1932	Sperry, Armstrong	30-45	
Lansing, Marion	Nicholas Arnold, Toolmaker (1st {std}, 8vo, 277p, b/w pl, DJ/1.00)	Doubleday/Doran	1941	Sperry, Armstrong	30-50	*
Follett, Helen T.	Ocean Outposts (1st, 4to, 133p, DJ/2.00, maps by...)	Scribner	1942	Sperry, Armstrong	30-50	
Sperry, Armstrong	One Day with Jambi in Sumatra (1st, sm4to, ibds, [65]p, fp color, pep)	Winston	(1934)	Sperry, Armstrong	45-70	R
Sperry, Armstrong	One Day with Manu (1st [1st bk.], sm4to, ibds, [64]p, color, pep)	Winston	(1933)	Sperry, Armstrong	60-90	R
Sperry, Armstrong	One Day with Tuktu (1st, sm4to [66]p, blue/gilt, 10 dp color, pep, DJ/2.00)	Winston	1935	Sperry, Armstrong	60-90	
Sperry, Armstrong	Pacific Islands Speaking (1st {std}, 8vo, 220p, b/w, DJ/3.00)	Macmillan	1955	Sperry, Armstrong	25-40	
Sperry, Armstrong	Rain Forest (1st, 8vo, 190p, green cl, pep, fp 1-color, DJ/2.50)	Macmillan	1947	Sperry, Armstrong	40-65	
Means, Florence C.	Shuttered Windows (1st, 8vo, 206p, 8pl, DJ/2.00)	Houghton	1938	Sperry, Armstrong	45-60	
Lloyd, Trevor	Sky Highways: Geography from the Air (1st, 4to, 61p, color, DJ/2.50)	Houghton	1945	Sperry, Armstrong	30-50	
Sperry, Armstrong	South of Cape Horn... (1st {std}, 8vo, 180p, b/w, DJ/2.95)	Winston	(1958)	Sperry, Armstrong	40-60	*
Follett, Helen T.	Stars to Steer By (1st, sm8vo, blue cl, 257p, fp b/w)	Macmillan	1934	Sperry, Armstrong	35-60	*
Sperry, Armstrong	Storm Canvas (1st {std}, 8vo, pep, 301p, col frn, pep, DJ/2.50)	Winston	(1944)	Sperry, Armstrong	30-50	
Holbrook, Stewart	Tall Timber (1st {std}, 8vo, 179p, fp b/w, pep, DJ/1.50)	Macmillan	1941	Sperry, Armstrong	40-65	*
Stone, William S.	Teri Taro from Bora Bora (1st {std}, 8vo, 133p, 8cp, pep, DJ/1.75)	Knopf	1940	Sperry, Armstrong	50-80	
Sperry, Armstrong	Thunder Country (1st {std}, 8vo, 150p, b/w, DJ/2.75)	Macmillan	1952	Sperry, Armstrong	25-40	
Pease, Howard	Thunderbolt House (1st {std}, sm8vo, 287p, b/w, pep, DJ/2.00)	Doubleday/Doran	1944	Sperry, Armstrong	80-125	
Brown, Rose	Two Children of Brazil (1st {std}, 8vo, 229p, b/w, pep, DJ/2.00)	Lippincott	(1940)	Sperry, Armstrong	30-45	
Sperry, Armstrong	Voyages of Christopher Columbus (1st, 8vo, 186p, color, pep, DJ/1.50)	Random	(1950)	Sperry, Armstrong	30-50	
Sperry, Armstrong	Wagons Westward (1st, 8vo, 276p, orange cl, pep, b/w, DJ/2.00)	Winston	1936	Sperry, Armstrong	30-50	
Bowman, James C.	Winabojo (1st, 8vo, 296p, orange cl, col frn, 12pl, pep, DJ/2.50)	Whitman	1941	Sperry, Armstrong	30-50	
Jackson, Jesse	Anchor Man (1st {std}, 8vo, 142p, red cl, fp b/w, DJ/2.00)	Harper	(1947)	Spiegel, Doris	70-100	
Jackson, Jesse	Call Me Charley (1st {std}, 8vo, 156p, b/w, DJ/2.00)	Harper	(1945)	Spiegel, Doris	55-80	*
Spiegel, Doris	Danny and Company 92 (1st, ob8vo, ibds, [32]p, color, DJ/1.00)	Coward	(1945)	Spiegel, Doris	40-70	*
Woolley, Catherine	I Like Trains (1st {std}, 12mo, ipcb, [32]p, color)	Harper	(1944)	Spiegel, Doris	30-45	
Bishop, Claire H.	King's Day (1st, lg8vo, [47]p, ipcb, fp b/w, cep, DJ/1.50)	Coward	1940	Spiegel, Doris	30-60	
Humphrey, Mabel	Bright Days... (lg4to, 36p, ibds, 12cp)	Stokes	1901	Spiegle, F.	200-300	
DeJong, David C.	Squirrel and the Harp (1st {std}, 8vo, 46p, b/w, DJ/2.95)	Macmillan	(1966)	Spier, Jo	20-35	
Malkus, Alida S.	Story of Louis Pasteur (1st, 8vo, 178p, b/w, DJ/1.50)	Grosset/Dunlap	(1952)	Spier, Jo	25-40	
Mother Goose	And So My Garden Grows (1st {std}, ob8vo, [44]p, ibds, color, DJ/3.95)	Doubleday	1969	Spier, Peter E.	30-50	
Hubbard, Margaret	Boss Chambale (1st, 8vo, 185p, b/w, DJ/2.75)	Crowell	1957	Spier, Peter E.	25-40	
Grant, George H.	Boy Overboard! (1st {std}, 8vo, 199p, b/w, DJ/3.00)	Little/Brown	(1961)	Spier, Peter E.	25-40	
Amrein, Vera A.	Cabin for the Mary Christmas (1st {std}, 8vo, 183p, b/w, DJ/2.75)	Harcourt	(1955)	Spier, Peter E.	20-35	*
Vetter, Marjorie	Cargo for Jennifer (1st {std}, 8vo, 240p, DJ/3.00, decor by...)	Longmans	1954	Spier, Peter E.	100-165	
Otto, Margaret G.	Cocoa (1st {std}, 8vo, 90p, b/w, DJ/2.00)	Holt	(1953)	Spier, Peter E.	30-50	*
Krasilovsky, Phyllis	Cow Who Fell in the Canal (1st {std}, ob4to, [34]p, color, DJ/2.75)	Doubleday	1957	Spier, Peter E.	45-70	R*
Spier, Peter E.	Erie Canal (1st {std}, ob4to, ibds, [36]p, color, pep, DJ/4.50)	Doubleday	(1970)	Spier, Peter E.	50-85	R*
Fairholme, Elizabeth	Esmeralda Ahoy! (1st AM {std}, 8vo, 212p, DJ/2.95)	Doubleday	1959	Spier, Peter E.	25-40	
Boni, Margaret B.	Favorite Christmas Carols (1st, 4to, 128p, color, DJ/2.95)	Simon/Schuster	(1957)	Spier, Peter E.	50-80	
N/A	Fox Went Out on Chilly Night (1st {std}, ob4to, [32]p, color, DJ/2.95, CH)	Doubleday	1961	Spier, Peter E.	30-50	
Dodge, Mary Mapes	Hans Brinker (1st, 8vo, 345p, DJ/3.50)	Scribner	(1958)	Spier, Peter E.	30-50	*
Dodson, Kenneth	Hector the Stowaway Dog (1st {std}, 8vo, 144p, b/w, DJ/3.00)	Little/Brown	(1958)	Spier, Peter E.	30-50	*
Parker, Elinor	Here and There... (1st {std}, 8vo, 170p, b/w, DJ/4.50)	Crowell	(1967)	Spier, Peter E.	30-45	*
Anderson, Joy	Hippolyte: Crab King (1st {std}, 8vo, 39p, b/w, DJ/2.25)	Harcourt	(1956)	Spier, Peter E.	25-40	*
Mother Goose	Hurrah, We're Outward Bound! (1st {std}, ob8vo, [41]p, ipcb, col, DJ/3.95)	Doubleday	(1968)	Spier, Peter E.	25-40	
Davis, Lavinia R.	Island City (1st {std}, 8vo, 256p, b/w, DJ/2.95)	Doubleday	(1961)	Spier, Peter E.	20-35	
Reynolds, Jessica	Jessica's Journal (1st {std}, 8vo, 191p, b/w, DJ/3.00)	Holt	(1958)	Spier, Peter E.	25-40	
Brown, Frieda	Last Hurdle (1st {std}, 8vo, 202p, b/w, DJ/2.50)	Crowell	(1953)	Spier, Peter E.	30-45	
DeJong, Dola	Level Land (1st, 8vo, 176p, b/w, DJ/2.95)	Scribner	(1961)	Spier, Peter E.	30-50	
Angus, Douglas	Lions Fed the Tigers (1st {std}, 8vo, 176p, b/w, DJ/3.00)	Houghton	1958	Spier, Peter E.	25-40	

AUTHOR	TITLE	PUBLISHER	DATE	ARTIST	PRICE	LC
Shemin, Margarteha	Little Riders (1st, lg8vo, 60p, b/w, DJ/3.00)	Coward	(1963)	Spier, Peter E.	30-50	*
Mother Goose	London Bridge is Falling Down (1st {std} ob8vo ibds, [41]p, color, DJ/3.95)	Doubleday	(1967)	Spier, Peter E.	40-70	R
Watkins, Richard	Mystery of Willet (1st, 8vo, 167p, b/w, DJ/2.95)	Nelson	(1959)	Spier, Peter E.	30-50	
Spier, Peter E.	Of Dikes and Windmills (1st {std}, 4to, 187p, color, DJ/5.95)	Doubleday	(1969)	Spier, Peter E.	50-80	R
Flakkeberg, Ardo	Sea Broke Through (1st AM {std}, 8vo, 179p, b/w, DJ/2.75)	Knopf	1960	Spier, Peter E.	30-45	*
Holberg, Ruth	Tam Morgan (1st {std}, 8vo, 224p, b/w, DJ/2.50)	Doubleday	(1953)	Spier, Peter E.	30-50	*
Nicholls, Elizabeth	Thunder Hill (1st {std}, 8vo, 248p, b/w, DJ/3.00)	Doubleday	1953	Spier, Peter E.	35-50	
Mother Goose	To Market! To Market! (1st, ob8vo, [41]p, color, DJ/3.95)	Doubleday	(1967)	Spier, Peter E.	60-90	*
Carpenter, Frances	Wonder Tales of Seas and Ships (1st {std}, 8vo, 285p, b/w, DJ/3.50)	Doubleday	(1959)	Spier, Peter E.	30-55	
Sage, Michael	Careful Carlos (1st, ob8vo, [30]p, b/w, DJ/2.25)	Holiday House	(1967)	Spilka, Arnold	25-40	
Russell, Solveig	Lines and Shapes (1st, 8vo, 31p, b/w, DJ/2.75)	H.Z. Walck	1965	Spilka, Arnold	30-45	
Spilka, Arnold	Lion I Can Do Without (1st, ob4to, [40]p, fp 1-color, cep, DJ/3.50)	H.Z. Walck	1964	Spilka, Arnold	30-45	*
Sage, Michael	Tree and Me (1st, lg8vo, [29]p, fp color, DJ/4.25)	H.Z. Walck	(1970)	Spilka, Arnold	25-40	
Spilka, Arnold	Whom Shall I Marry? (1st, 8vo, pink cl, [33]p, 1-color, DJ)	Holiday House	1960	Spilka, Arnold	25-45	
Spina, Paul	Tree Grew & Birds Flew (1st, ob4to, [40]p, gilt, fp 3-color, DJ/2.95)	Harlin Quist	(1967)	Spina, Paul	30-50	
Chisholm, Louey	Golden Staircase (1st, lg8vo, 361p, uncut, gilt, teg, 16cp)	L: Jack	(1906)	Spooner, M.D.	150-225	
Steedman, Amy	Margot and the Golden Fish (1st, sm8vo, 96p, AEG, p-o, 8cp)	L: Jack	(1908)	Spooner, M.D.	50-80	
Steedman, Amy	Our Island Saints (1st AM, 8vo, p-o, teg, 178p, 8 ticp)	Putnam	(1912)	Spooner, M.D.	50-90	
Merriam, Eve	It Doesn't Always Have to Rhyme (1st {std}, 8vo, 83p, DJ/3.25)	Atheneum	1964	Spooner, Malcolm	20-30	
Streatfeild, Noel	Circus is Coming (1st, sm8vo, 314p, b/w, CgM)	L: J.M. Dent	(1938)	Spurrier, Steven	50-85	
Williams, Wilbur H.	Fairy Tales from Folk Lore (1st, sm8vo, 288p, b/w)	Moffat	1908	Squire, Maud H.	40-60	
Williston, Teresa P.	Hindu Stories (1st, 8vo, 111p, p-o, brown cl, 9cp, pep)	Rand/McNally	(1925)	Squire, Maud H.	50-85	
Andersen, Hans C.	Ugly Duckling (1st, sm4to, 24p, ibds, 3 fp color)	Moffat	1905	Squire, Maud H.	125-200	R*
Kelly, Ethel M.	When I was Little (1st, 8vo, p-o, 96p, fp color)	Rand/McNally	(1915)	Squire, Maud H.	60-90	
Carroll, Lewis	Alice in Wonderland (1st, 8vo, gilt, teg, 6cp, pep)	McClurg	1915	St. John, J. Allen	170-240	
Burroughs, Edgar R.	Beasts of Tarzan (1st, sm8vo, 336p, b/w)	McClurg	1916	St. John, J. Allen	450-650	
McCarter, Margaret	Corner Stone (1st, 8vo, 100p, wraps, col frn, b/w, pep)	McClurg	1915	St. John, J. Allen	40-65	
St. John, J. Allen	Face in the Pool (1st, 4to, 156p, grey/gilt, 4cp)	McClurg	1905	St. John, J. Allen	120-180	
Mason, Edith H.	Great Plan (1st, 8vo, green/white, 308p, 5pl)	McClurg	1913	St. John, J. Allen	70-100	
Burroughs, Edgar R.	Tarzan & the Jewels of Opar (1st, 8vo, green/gilt, 350p, 8pl)	McClurg	1918	St. John, J. Allen	350-500	
Munroe, Kirk	White Conquerors (1st, 12mo, 326p, uncut, gilt, 8pl)	Harper	1893	Stacey, Walter S.	40-60	
Stahl, Ben	Blackbeard's Ghost (1st {std}, lg8vo, 184p, fp b/w, cep, DJ/3.50)	Houghton	1965	Stahl, Ben	60-100	R
Swift, Jonathan	Gulliver's Travels (1st, sm8vo, 64p)	Chi: Rockwell	1931	Stahl, Ben	55-80	*
Weber, Lenora M.	Rocking Chair Ranch (1st, 8vo, 210p, uncut, 4pl, DJ/2.00)	Houghton	1936	Stahley, Joseph	60-90	
Marais, Josef	Koos the Hottentot (1st {std}, 8vo, ibds, 188p, color, DJ/2.50)	Knopf	1945	Stahlhut, Henry	70-125	R
Atkey, Bertram	Easy Money (1st, 8vo, p-o, 311p, b/w)	Dana Estes	(1908)	Stampa, George L.	25-40	
Standon, Anna	Singing Rhinoceros (1st AM, sm4to, [32]p, fp color, DJ/3.00)	Coward	(1963)	Standon, Edward	30-50	
Carroll, Lewis	Alice... & Through... (1st, 8vo, 246p, 8 color, DJ/2.95)	Dutton	(1954)	Stanley, Diana	35-50	
Norton, Mary	Borrowers Afloat (1st, sm8vo, 176p, blue cl, col frn, b/w, DJ)	L: Dent	(1959)	Stanley, Diana	120-200	
Norton, Mary	The Borrowers (1st, 8vo, 159p, b/w, DJ, CgM)	L: J.M. Dent	(1952)	Stanley, Diana	250-400	
Crew, Alice C.	Mary & her Kitchen Garden (1st, lg8vo, 52p, p-o, 9cp, pep)	Doran	(1917)	Stanley, Lee W.	30-50	
Mijatovich, Elodie	Serbian Fairy Tales (1st, 8vo, gilt, 204p, 8cp)	L: Heinemann	(1917)	Stanley, Sidney	80-125	
Mijatovich, Elodie	Serbian Fairy Tales (1st AM, 8vo, black cl, 204p, 8cp, 8pl)	McBride	1918	Stanley, Sidney	75-100	
Parker, Gilbert	March of the White Guard (1st, 12mo, gilt, 133p, b/w)	Fenno	1902	Starkweather, W.	30-50	
Harrison, T. Milner	Modern Arms and a Feudal Throne (1st, 12mo, 376p, green cl, 4pl)	Fenno	1904	Starkweather, W.	80-125	
Disney, Walt	Bongo (1st {std}, folio, [26]p, ibds, color, GGB)	Simon/Schuster	(1947)	Starr, Edgar	60-90	
Huckel, Oliver	Wagner's Parsifal (1st, 12mo, 71p, teg, red/gilt, 5cp)	Crowell	1903	Stassen, Franz	35-50	
Swift, Jonathan	Gulliver's Travels (1st, 8vo, 235p, 8cp, pep)	L: Sidgwick	(1912)	Staynes, Percy A.	35-60	*
Swift, Jonathan	Gulliver's Travels (1st AM, 8vo, 235p, 8cp, pep)	Henry Holt & Co.	(1912)	Staynes, Percy A.	35-60	*
Damjan, Mischa	False Flamingoes (1st AM, 4to, ibds, [31]p, fp color, DJ)	NY: Scroll Pr.	(1970)	Steadman, Ralph	60-95	
Damjan, Mischa	Little Prince and the Tiger Cat (1st AM, 4to, [32]p, color, DJ/4.50)	McGraw-Hill	(1968)	Steadman, Ralph	80-145	
Steadman, Ralph	Little Red Computer (1st AM, 4to, [32]p, color, DJ/4.50)	McGraw-Hill	(1969)	Steadman, Ralph	40-65	
Mother Goose	Baby's Mother Goose (1st, sq16mo, [16]p, color, pep)	Grosset/Dunlap	1938	Stearns, Sharon	55-80	*
Andersen, Hans C.	Favorite Fairy Tales (1st, lg8vo, ibds, [33]p, fp color, DJ/1.00)	Wilcox/Follett	(1946)	Stearns, Sharon	50-80	
Grimm Bros.	Snow White & Seven Dwarfs (1st, 4to, ibds, [38]p, color, DJ/1.00)	Wilcox/Follett	(1946)	Stearns, Sharon	25-45	
Porter, Eleanor	Cross Currents (1st, 12mo, 207p, 4pl)	W.A. Wilde	(1907)	Stecher, William	30-50	*
N/A	Jack & the Beanstalk (1st, 12mo, [31]p, color)	NY: Sully	(1920)	Stecher, William	35-60	*
Steedman, Amy	Madonna of the Goldfinch (1st, 8vo, 194p, uncut, 8 ticp)	L: Jack	[1917]	Steedman, E.M.	60-90	
Pratt, Lucy	Ezekiel (1st, 12mo, 254p, red cl, 16pl)	Doubleday/Page	1909	Steele, Frederic D.	60-100	
Davis, Richard H.	Scarlet Car (1st, 8vo, tan cl, 166p, uncut, 12pl)	Scribner	1907	Steele, Frederic D.	40-70	
Sabin, Edwin L.	When You Were a Boy (1st, sm8vo, 302p, green cl, b/w)	Baker/Taylor	(1905)	Steele, Frederic D.	30-50	
Goudge, Elizabeth	Henrietta's House (1st, 8vo, 252p, green cl, b/w, DJ)	L: Hodder	1942	Steele, Lorna	140-200	
Davis, Richard H.	In the Fog (1st, 8vo, 155p, gilt, 1-color)	Russell	1901	Steele/Peirce	80-125	
Steen, Elizabeth	Red Jungle Boy (1st, lg sq8vo, 82p, fp 2-color, pep, DJ/2.00)	Harcourt	(1937)	Steen, Elizabeth	30-50	
Steig, William	About People (1st {std}, 8vo, 105p, buckram, b/w, DJ/2.50)	Random	(1939)	Steig, William	70-120	*
Steig, William	Agony in the Kindergarten (1st {std}, lg8vo, [124]p, bds, b/w, DJ/1.50)	Duell, Sloan	(1950)	Steig, William	80-120	*
Steig, William	All Embarrassed (1st {std}, 8vo, 101p, b/w, DJ/2.00)	Duell, Sloan	(1944)	Steig, William	60-90	
Steig, William	Bad Island (1st {std}, lg4to, [32]p, fp color, DJ/5.95)	Windmill Books	(1969)	Steig, William	50-80	
Steig, William	Bad Speller (1st {std}, sq12mo, ipcb, [48]p, b/w, DJ)	Windmill Books	(1970)	Steig, William	40-65	
Steig, William	CDB! (1st, sq12mo, [48]p, ibds, b/w, DJ/2.95)	Windmill Books	1968	Steig, William	30-50	
Steig, William	Continuous Performance (1st {std}, lg8vo, 95p, b/w, DJ/1.95)	Duell, Sloan	(1963)	Steig, William	30-50	*
Cuppy, Will	Decline & Fall of Practically Everybody (1st {std}, 8vo, 230p, b/w, DJ/3.00)	Holt	(1950)	Steig, William	30-50	
Steig, William	Dreams of Glory (1st {std}, lg8vo, 147p, b/w, DJ/2.95)	Knopf	(1953)	Steig, William	50-85	
Steig, William	Eye for Elephants (1st, sq12mo, [48]p, 1-color, DJ/2.95)	Windmill Books	(1970)	Steig, William	30-50	
Fenner, Phyllis R.	Giggle Box (1st {std}, lg8vo, yellow cl, 144p, uncut, b/w, pep, DJ/2.50)	Knopf	1950	Steig, William	45-80	*
Cuppy, Will	How to Become Extinct (1st, sm8vo, 181p, cream cl, b/w, DJ/2.00)	Farrar/Rinehart	(1941)	Steig, William	40-65	
Steig, William	Lonely Ones (1st {std}, sm8vo, 102p, ibds, fp b/w, DJ/1.00)	Duell, Sloan	(1942)	Steig, William	85-140	
Steig, William	Man About Town (1st, 4to, [98]p, cartoons)	NY: Long/Smith	1932	Steig, William	80-125	

AUTHOR	TITLE	PUBLISHER	DATE	ARTIST	PRICE	LC
Hodgins, Eric	Mr. Blanding Builds his Dream House (1st, 8vo, 237p, b/w, DJ/2.75)	Simon/Schuster	(1946)	Steig, William	30-45	
Steig, William	Persistent Faces (1st {std}, 12mo, brown cl, [186]p, b/w, DJ/1.50)	Duell, Sloan	(1945)	Steig, William	60-90	
Steig, William	Rejected Lovers (1st {std}, lg8vo, 152p, b/w, DJ/2.95)	Knopf	1951	Steig, William	45-70	
Steig, William	Roland the Minstrel Pig (1st, lg4to, 32p, color, cep, DJ/4.95)	Windmill Books	(1968)	Steig, William	70-100	R
Steig, William	Small Fry (1st, ob12mo, [128]p, b/w, DJ/1.50)	Duell, Sloan	(1944)	Steig, William	55-90	
Steig, William	Small Fry (1st {this fmt}, lg8vo, ipcb, [64]p, b/w, DJ/1.00)	Duell, Sloan	(1951)	Steig, William	45-70	
Steig, William	Sylvester & the Magic Pebble (1st, lg4to, ibds, [32]p, color, DJ/4.95, CM)	Windmill Books	(1969)	Steig, William	140-200	
Steig, William	Till Death Do Us Part (1st {std}, 8vo, [128]p, b/w, DJ/2.00)	Duell, Sloan	(1947)	Steig, William	50-80	
Means, Florence C.	Carver's George (1st, 8vo, 176p, b/w, DJ/2.50)	Houghton	1952	Stein, Harve	25-40	
Havighurst, Marion	First Book of California Gold Rush (1st {std}, 8vo, 61p, 1-color, DJ/1.95)	F. Watts	(1962)	Stein, Harve	25-45	
Havighurst, Marion	First Book of Pioneers (1st {std}, 8vo, 69p, fp 1-color, pep, DJ/1.95)	F. Watts	(1959)	Stein, Harve	30-45	
Alcott, Louisa M.	Little Women (1st, lg8vo, green cl, p-o, 475p, 8cp)	Garden City	1932	Stein, Harve	30-50	
Kelly, Eric P.	On the Staked Plain (1st, 8vo, 250p, b/w, DJ/2.00)	Macmillan	1940	Stein, Harve	25-40	
Coatsworth, Eliz.	Sword of the Wilderness (1st, 8vo, 160p, b/w, pep, DJ/2.00)	Macmillan	1936	Stein, Harve	25-40	
North, Sterling	Thoreau of Walden Pond (1st, 8vo, 183p, b/w, DJ/1.95)	Houghton	1959	Stein, Harve	20-30	
Zolotow, Charlotte	All that Sunlight (1st, 8vo, [31]p, ibds, color, DJ)	Harper	1967	Stein, Walter	20-35	
Steiner, Charlotte	ABC (1st, lg4to, [27]p, ibds, color, DJ/0.50)	F. Watts	1946	Steiner, Charlotte	50-80	
Steiner, Charlotte	Annie's ABC Kitten (1st, 4to, [31]p, color, cep, DJ/3.25)	Knopf	(1965)	Steiner, Charlotte	30-50	
Steiner, Charlotte	Big Laughing Book (1st, lg4to, ibds, [58]p, color, DJ/1.00)	Grosset/Dunlap	1949	Steiner, Charlotte	45-70	*
Steiner, Charlotte	Birthdays are for Everyone (1st {std}, sm8vo, 32p, color, DJ/2.95)	Doubleday	(1964)	Steiner, Charlotte	50-80	
Steiner, Charlotte	Daddy Comes Home (1st {std}, ob8vo, ibds, [24]p, 2-color, DJ/1.25)	Doubleday/Doran	1944	Steiner, Charlotte	30-50	
Steiner, Charlotte	Kiki & Muffy (1st {std}, ob8vo, ibds, [26]p, 2-color, cep, DJ/1.25)	Doubleday/Doran	1943	Steiner, Charlotte	60-90	
Steiner, Charlotte	Kiki Dances (1st {std}, ob8vo, ibds, [32]p, color, DJ/1.25)	Doubleday	(1949)	Steiner, Charlotte	60-90	
Steiner, Charlotte	Kiki is an Actress (1st {std}, lg8vo, unpag, ibds, color, DJ/2.00)	Doubleday	(1958)	Steiner, Charlotte	70-100	
Steiner, Charlotte	Kiki Skates (1st {std}, ob8vo, ibds, [34]p, color, DJ/1.25)	Doubleday	(1950)	Steiner, Charlotte	50-80	
Steiner, Charlotte	Kiki's Play House (1st {std}, ob4to, [29]p, color, DJ/2.50)	Doubleday	1962	Steiner, Charlotte	40-65	
Steiner, Charlotte	Listen to my Seashell (1st, ob4to, 32]pg, color, pep, DJ)	Knopf	(1959)	Steiner, Charlotte	40-65	
Steiner, Charlotte	Lulu (1st {std}, sm ob4to, ibds, [38]p, color, DJ/1.00)	Doubleday/Doran	1939	Steiner, Charlotte	60-90	
Steiner, Charlotte	Lulu's Play School (1st {std}, ob8vo, ibds, [32]p, color, DJ/1.25)	Doubleday	(1948)	Steiner, Charlotte	45-70	*
Barksdale, Lena	Milly and her Dogs (1st {std}, ob4to, ibds, [31]p, color, DJ/1.25)	Doubleday/Doran	1942	Steiner, Charlotte	40-70	
Steiner, Charlotte	My Bunny Feels Soft (1st, ob4to, [33]p, color, pep, DJ/2.75)	Knopf	(1958)	Steiner, Charlotte	50-80	
Steiner, Charlotte	My Slippers are Red (1st, ob4to, [32]p, color, pep, DJ/2.75)	Knopf	(1957)	Steiner, Charlotte	60-90	
Steiner, Charlotte	Patsy's Pet (1st {std}, ob8vo, ibds, [30]p, 2-color, DJ/1.50)	Doubleday	(1955)	Steiner, Charlotte	45-70	
Steiner, Charlotte	Pete and Peter (1st {std}, sq8vo, ipcb, [26]p, color, DJ/1.25)	Doubleday/Doran	1941	Steiner, Charlotte	60-90	
Steiner, Charlotte	Pete's Puppets (1st {std}, 8vo, unpag, ibds, color, DJ/1.25)	Doubleday	(1952)	Steiner, Charlotte	35-50	
Steiner, Charlotte	Polka Dot (1st {std}, ob8vo, ibds, [34]p, color, dep, DJ/1.25)	Doubleday	1947	Steiner, Charlotte	30-50	
Steiner, Charlotte	Red Riding Hood Goes Sledding (1st {std}, sq8vo, 26p, fp color, DJ/2.50)	Macmillan	1962	Steiner, Charlotte	30-45	
Steiner, Charlotte	Sleepy Quilt (1st {std}, sq12mo, [16]p, ibds, color, cep, DJ/1.00)	Doubleday/Doran	(1945)	Steiner, Charlotte	30-50	
Steiner, Charlotte	Wake Up! Wake Up! (1st, ob8vo, ibds, [25]p, color, DJ/0.50)	Grosset/Dunlap	(1946)	Steiner, Charlotte	30-50	
Hall, William N.	Watch the Pony Grow (1st, ob4to, [30]p, spiral bds, color)	Crowell	1942	Steiner, Charlotte	30-50	
Herford, Oliver	Capers, his Haps and Mishaps (1st, lg4to, unpag, p-o, color, pep)	Devin-Adair	1914	Steinigans, Wm. J.	80-130	
Mukerji, Dhan G.	Hari: The Jungle Lad (1st, 8vo, 220p, b/w)	Dutton	(1924)	Steinmetz, Morgan	20-30	
N/A	Cinderella (1st, lg8vo, [16]p, color, pep)	Grosset/Dunlap	(1939)	Stenberg-Masolle, A.	40-60	*
Deland, Margaret	An Encore (1st {std}, 8vo, teg, 79p, 3pl)	Harper	1907	Stephens, Alice B.	35-60	
Deland, Margaret	Around Old Chester (1st, sm8vo, 378p, p-o, 6pl)	Harper	1915	Stephens, Alice B.	35-60	
Walcott, Earle A.	Blindfolded (1st, sm8vo, tan cl, 400p, 8pl)	Bobbs-Merrill	(1906)	Stephens, Alice B.	30-50	
Reed, Helen L.	Brenda's Cousin at Radcliffe (1st, 8vo, 318p, 5pl)	Little/Brown	1902	Stephens, Alice B.	35-60	*
Robinson, Edith	Captain of the School (1st, sm8vo, 258p, grey cl, 15pl)	Little/Brown	1901	Stephens, Alice B.	25-45	
Laughlin, Clara E.	Felicity (1st, sm8vo, green/gilt, 426p, 4cp)	Scribner	1907	Stephens, Alice B.	30-50	
Abbott, Charles C.	Freedom of the Fields (1st, 12mo, 233p, gilt, teg, frn by...)	Lippincott	1898	Stephens, Alice B.	40-60	
Kingsley, Florence M.	Glass House (1st, sm8vo, 312p, 4pl)	Dodd	1909	Stephens, Alice B.	30-50	*
Ray, Anna C.	Hearts & Creeds (1st, sm8vo, 320p, 4pl)	Little/Brown	1906	Stephens, Alice B.	30-50	
Martin, H.R.	His Courtship (1st, 8vo, uncut, 322p, 4pl)	McClure	1907	Stephens, Alice B.	30-50	*
Gilson, Roy R.	In the Morning Glow (1st, 8vo, gilt, 187p, p-o, 16pl)	Harper	1902	Stephens, Alice B.	35-60	
Ray, Anna C.	Janet: Her Winter in Quebec (1st, 12mo, blue cl, 370p, 4pl)	Little/Brown	1906	Stephens, Alice B.	30-50	
Gilson, Roy R.	Katrina (1st, 8vo, green cl, 316p, teg, 6cp)	Baker/Taylor	(1906)	Stephens, Alice B.	35-60	
Alcott, Louisa M.	Little Women (8vo, 617p, teg, 15pl)	Little/Brown	1914	Stephens, Alice B.	40-70	
Green, Anna K.	Mayor's Wife (1st, sm8vo, gilt, 389p, p-o, b/w)	Bobbs-Merrill	(1907)	Stephens, Alice B.	40-70	
Gilson, Roy R.	Mother & Father (1st, 8vo, teg, 63p, green cl, b/w)	Harper	1903	Stephens, Alice B.	55-80	
Wiggin, Kate D.	Mother Carey's Chickens (1st, sm8vo, green cl, 356p, 10pl)	Houghton	1911	Stephens, Alice B.	50-80	
Ray, Anna C.	Nathalie's Sister (1st, 12mo, gilt, 290p, 6pl)	Little/Brown	1904	Stephens, Alice B.	35-60	*
Deland, Ellen D.	Oakleigh (1st, 12mo, green cl, 233p, 19pl)	Harper	1896	Stephens, Alice B.	35-60	
Wiggin, Kate D.	Old Peabody Pew (1st, 8vo, p-o, grey/gilt, teg, 143p, col frn, 5pl, pep)	Houghton	1907	Stephens, Alice B.	35-60	
Sidney, Margaret	Our Davie Pepper (1st, sm8vo, 492p, green/gilt, 6 tipl)	Lothrop, Lee	(1916)	Stephens, Alice B.	60-100	
Freeman, Mary E.W.	People of Our Neighborhood (1st, 12mo, 161p, gilt, teg, 14pl)	Doub./McClure	1898	Stephens, Alice B.	30-50	
Ray, Anna C.	Sidney: Summer on St. Lawrence (1st, 12mo, 332p, blue/gilt, 4pl)	Little/Brown	1905	Stephens, Alice B.	35-60	
Dyer, Ruth O.	Sleepy-Time Story Book (1st, sm8vo, 147p, gilt, pep, col frn)	Lothrop, Lee	(1915)	Stephens, Alice B.	35-60	*
Garland, Hamlin	Son of the Middle Border (1st, sm8vo, 467p, 16pl)	Macmillan	1917	Stephens, Alice B.	70-100	
Taylor, Sophie C.	Story of a Little Poet (1st, sm8vo, 390p, green cl, 8pl)	Little/Brown	1901	Stephens, Alice B.	30-50	
Brown, Alice	Story of Thyrza (1st, 8vo, gilt, 326p, col frn)	Houghton	1909	Stephens, Alice B.	30-50	
Cutting, Mary S.	Suburban Whirl (1st, 12mo, green cl, uncut, 202p, 7pl)	McClure	1907	Stephens, Alice B.	25-40	
Warner, Anne	Susan Clegg & the Man in the House (1st, 12mo, 279p, grey cl, 4pl)	Little/Brown	1907	Stephens, Alice B.	25-40	
Cutting, Mary S.	The Wayfarers (1st, 8vo, 374p, 16pl)	McClure	1908	Stephens, Alice B.	25-45	
Blanchard, Amy E.	Three Pretty Maids (1st, 12mo, 243p, b/w plates)	Lippincott	1897	Stephens, Alice B.	25-40	
Abbott, Charles C.	Travels in a Treetop (1st, 12mo, 215p, frn by...)	Lippincott	1898	Stephens, Alice B.	40-60	
Henry, O.	Trimmed Lamp (1st, 12mo, 260p, frn by...)	McClure	1907	Stephens, Alice B.	75-100	
Alcott, Louisa M.	Under the Lilacs (1st, 8vo, 302p, green/gilt, teg, 8pl)	Little/Brown	1905	Stephens, Alice B.	60-90	*
Deland, Margaret	Way to Peace (1st, 8vo, grey/gilt, teg, uncut, 93p, 7pl, dep)	Harper	1910	Stephens, Alice B.	40-65	

AUTHOR	TITLE	PUBLISHER	DATE	ARTIST	PRICE	LC
Deland, Margaret	Where Laborers are Few (1st, 8vo, 86p, gilt, teg, 3pl)	Harper	1909	Stephens, Alice B.	40-65	
Various	Whole Family (1st, sm8vo, 314p, blue/gilt, 12pl)	Harper	1908	Stephens, Alice B.	60-90	
Pidgin, Charles F.	Blennerhassett (1st, sm8vo, 442p, blue cl, teg, 12pl)	C.M. Clark	1901	Stephens, Charles H.	25-40	
Stockton, Frank	Captain Chap (1st, sm8vo, 298p, tan cl, 6pl)	Lippincott	1897	Stephens, Charles H.	40-60	
Sabin, Edwin L.	Gold Seekers of '49 (1st, sm8vo, 335p, tan cl, col frn, 4pl by)	Lippincott	1915	Stephens, Charles H.	60-100	R*
Tilton, Dwight	Miss Petticoats (1st, 12mo, 377p, tan cl, teg, 7cp)	C.M. Clark	1902	Stephens, Charles H.	20-40	
Sabin, Edwin L.	On the Plains with Custer (1st, sm8vo, 308p, tan cl, 5cp)	Lippincott	1913	Stephens, Charles H.	25-45	
Bannerman, Helen	Little Black Sambo (ob12mo, 95p, ibds, color)	Winston	(1930)	Stephenson, Eunice	100-175	*
Alcott, Louisa M.	Under the Lilacs (1st, 8vo, 282p, p-o, 12cp, pep)	Winston	1934	Stephenson, Eunice	50-80	
Cadby, Carine	Brownies in Switzerland (1st AM, lg8vo, p-o, 137p, 6cp)	Macaulay	(1924)	Stephensons	55-90	*
Steptoe, John	Stevie (1st, 8vo, [24]p, fp color, cep, DJ/3.50)	Harper	(1969)	Steptoe, John	60-100	R
Steptoe, John	Uptown (1st, 8vo, [24]p, ipcb, color, DJ/3.50)	Harper	(1970)	Steptoe, John	65-90	
Bible	Favorite Psalms for Children (1st, lg8vo, ibds, [38]p, color, DJ/0.50)	Grosset/Dunlap	1942	Stern, Marie	20-35	
N/A	Arabian Nights (1st, 4to, 308p, black cl, p-o, 16cp, pep)	Penn	(1928)	Sterrett, Virginia	250-400	R
DeSegur, Sophie	Old French Fairy Tales (1st, 4to, 279p, gilt, p-o, 8cp, pep)	Penn	(1920)	Sterrett, Virginia	250-400	
Hawthorne, Nathaniel	Tanglewood Tales (1st, 4to, p-o, 261p, gilt, pep)	Penn	(1921)	Sterrett, Virginia	250-400	R
Ziner, Feenie	Little Sailor's Big Pet (1st, lg8vo, [40]p, 1-color, pep, DJ/2.75)	Parnassus Press	(1958)	Steven, Leslie	30-50	
Stevens, Eden V.	Abba (1st {std}, 8vo, 116p, fp b/w, cep, DJ/3.00)	Atheneum	1962	Stevens, Anthony	40-65	
Yonge, Charlotte	Little Duke (1st, 8vo, 240p, red/gilt, 4cp)	Duffield	1923	Stevens, Beatrice	35-60	
Boult, Ella M.	Romance of Cinderella (1st, sm4to, 146p, color)	R.H. Russell	1902	Stevens, Beatrice	200-300	*
Carter, Russell	White Plume of Navarre (1st, 8vo, p-o, 192p, fp color, pep)	Volland	(1928)	Stevens, Beatrice	60-90	
Hager, Alice R.	Canvas Castle (1st, 8vo, 179p, b/w, pep, DJ/2.50)	J. Messner	(1949)	Stevens, Mary	30-50	
Guilfoile, Elizabeth	Nobody Listens to Andrew (1st, 8vo, 27p, fp color, DJ)	Follett	(1957)	Stevens, Mary	20-35	*
Lawrence, Mildred	Peachtree Island (1st, 8vo, 224p, fp b/w, DJ/2.25)	Harcourt	(1948)	Stevens, Mary	50-80	
Cleary, Beverly	Real Hole (1st, sm ob4to, [32]p, 2-color, pep, DJ/2.75)	Wm. Morrow	1960	Stevens, Mary	25-40	
Steele, Mary Q.	Secret of Crossbone Hill (1st {std}, 8vo, 183p, b/w, DJ/2.95)	World	(1959)	Stevens, Mary	20-30	*
Gage, Wilson	Secret of Fiery Gorge (1st {std}, 8vo, 185p, b/w, DJ/2.95)	World	(1960)	Stevens, Mary	20-35	*
Gage, Wilson	Secret of Indian Mound (1st {std}, 8vo, 186p, b/w, DJ/2.75)	World	(1958)	Stevens, Mary	20-30	
Otto, Margaret G.	Stephen's Train (1st {std}, ob4to, unpag, 1-color, DJ/2.00)	Holt	1953	Stevens, Mary	25-45	
Cleary, Beverly	Two Dog Biscuits (1st, sm ob4to, unpag, color, pep, DJ/2.75)	Wm. Morrow	1961	Stevens, Mary	20-35	
Govan, Christine	Willow Landing (1st {std}, 8vo, 190p, b/w, DJ/2.95)	World	1961	Stevens, Mary	30-50	
Richards, Laura E.	Quicksilver Sue (1st, 12mo, 177p, 7pl)	Century	1899	Stevens, W.D.	20-35	
Uncle Frank	Uncle Frank's Visit to Fairy-Land (1st, 12mo, 241p, b/w)	Doub./McClure	1897	Stevens, W.D.	200-300	*
MacManus, Seamus	Donegal Wonder Book (1st, 8vo, green/gilt, 283p, b/w)	Stokes	1926	Stevens, William	120-200	
Wister, Owen	Dragon of Wantley (1st, sm4to, teg, blue/gilt, 149p, b/w, pep)	Lippincott	1892	Stewardson, John	100-160	R
Grierson, Eliz. W.	Children's Tales from Scottish Ballads (1st, 4to, 326p, teg, 12cp)	L: A&C Black	1906	Stewart, Allan	140-200	*
Finnemore, John	Robin Hood & his Merry Men (1st AM, 4to, 272p, green/gilt, 8cp)	Macmillan	1929	Stewart, Allan	120-165	
Finnemore, John	Robin Hood & his Merry Men (1st, 4to, 272p, gilt, 8cp)	L: A&C Black	1929	Stewart, Allan	130-180	
McSpadden, J.W.	Robin Hood & his Merry Outlaws (1st, 8vo, green cl, 320p, teg, 12cp)	Crowell	(1923)	Stewart, Allan	40-60	*
Zolotow, Charlotte	New Friend (1st, ob8vo, [31]p, fp color, cep, DJ/3.50)	Abelard-Schuman	1968	Stewart, Arvis	30-50	*
Picard, Barbara	Faun & the Woodcutter's Daughter (1st AM, 8vo, 255p, b/w, DJ/3.50)	Criterion Bks.	(1964)	Stewart, Charles	25-40	
Picard, Barbara	Lady of the Linden Tree (1st AM {std}, 8vo, 214p, b/w, DJ/3.50)	Criterion Bks.	1962	Stewart, Charles	30-45	
N/A	Homes in the Wilderness (1st, 8vo, 74p, p-o, maps)	W.R. Scott	(1939)	Stewart, Mary W.	60-90	
Moodie, Susanna	Roughing It in the Bush (1st, 8vo, 568p, uncut, teg, 17 ticp)	L: G. Bell	1913	Stewart, R.A.	60-90	
Pyle, Katharine	Childhood (1st, sm4to, ibds, 46p, 21cp)	Dutton	(1904)	Stilwell, Sarah	160-240	
Welsh, Richard	Kiddie-Kar Book (lg ob4to, ibds, p-o, 9cp)	Lippincott	(1920)	Stilwell, Sarah	170-265	*
Martin, Edward S.	Lucid Intervals (1st, 12mo, 263p, teg, blue cl, 6pl)	Harper	1900	Stilwell, Sarah	55-80	
Martin, Edward S.	Luxury of Children (1st, lg8vo, 213p, green/gilt, p-o, teg, 8cp)	Harper	1904	Stilwell, Sarah	70-100	
Stilwell, Sarah	Musical Tree (1st, 4to, [66]p, tan cloth, fp color, pep)	Penn	1925	Stilwell, Sarah	70-120	
Dodge, Mary Mapes	Rhymes & Jingles (1st, sm8vo, gilt, teg, uncut, 222p, b/w)	Scribner	1904	Stilwell, Sarah	90-120	
Reed, Langford	Sausages & Sundials (1st, lg8vo, 131p, ibds, b/w)	L: Jarrold	[1927]	Stimpson, Murdock	35-60	
Terhune, Albert P.	Lochinvar Luck (1st, sm8vo, 309p, frn by...)	Doran	(1923)	Stinemetz, Morgan	60-100	
Besser, Marianne	Cat Book (1st, 8vo, 91p, b/w, DJ/3.75)	Holiday House	(1967)	Stirnweis, Shannon	25-45	
Polland, Madeleine	Beorn the Proud (1st AM, 8vo, 176p, fp b/w, DJ/3.00)	Holt, Rinehart	(1962)	Stobbs, William	40-60	*
Manning-Sanders, Ruth	Bundle of Ballads (1st AM, 8vo, 245p, b/w, DJ/3.00, KGM)	Lippincott	(1959)	Stobbs, William	30-50	
Cass, Joan E.	Cat Thief (1st, 8vo, [40]p, fp color, dep, DJ/2.75)	Abelard-Schuman	(1961)	Stobbs, William	40-65	*
Coolidge, Olivia	Ceasar's Gallic War (1st, sm8vo, 245p, b/w, DJ/3.50)	Houghton	1961	Stobbs, William	20-30	*
Syme, Ronald	Columbus, Finder of the New World (1st, 8vo, 70p, dp b/w, DJ/2.00)	Wm. Morrow	1952	Stobbs, William	25-45	*
N/A	Frog He Would a Wooing Go (1st AM, 12mo, blue bds, color, pep, DJ)	Follett	1969	Stobbs, William	30-45	
Chekhov, Anton	Kashtanka (1st AM {std}, sm4to, 48p, fp color, DJ/2.75, KGM)	H.Z. Walck	1961	Stobbs, William	30-50	
Welch, Ronald	Knight Crusader (1st, 8vo, 272p, fp b/w, pep, DJ, CgM)	L: Oxford U.Pr.	1954	Stobbs, William	40-65	
Hewett, Anita	Little White Hen (1st AM, lg ob8vo, 32p, fp 2-color, DJ/2.75)	Whittlesey	1963	Stobbs, William	25-45	
Baumann, Hans	Son of Columbus (1st {std}, lg8vo, 248p, b/w, DJ)	L: Oxford U.Pr.	1957	Stobbs, William	25-40	
Stobbs, William	Story of the Three Bears (1st AM, lg ob8vo, 32p, fp 3-color, pep, DJ/2.75)	Whittlesey	1965	Stobbs, William	25-40	
Clarke, Mollie	Three Brothers (1st {std}, 8vo, 32p, color, DJ/1.95)	Follett	1967	Stobbs, William	30-50	
MacArthur, David	Thunderbolt Men (1st, 8vo, blue/gilt, 229p, fp b/w, DJ)	L: P. Lunn	1947	Stobbs, William	30-50	
Stokes, Vernon	Blobbs at the Sea Side (lg4to, 64p, ibds, 11 chromos, pep)	L: Chambers	[1908]	Stokes, Vernon	250-400	
N/A	Cinderella (1st, lg8vo, ibds, [33]p, color)	Wilcox/Follett	(1948)	Stolberg, Doris	35-60	*
Stolper, Joel	Patches (1st, 8vo, 100p, 1-color, DJ/1.75)	Harcourt	(1940)	Stolper, Joel	30-45	*
Kissin, Rita	Pete the Pelican (1st, lg8vo, 31p, p-o, b/w, pep, DJ/1.00)	Lippincott	(1937)	Stolper, Joel	55-80	*
Heisenfelt, Kathryn	About Customs (1st, 4to, ibds, 42p, color, pep, DJ/1.00)	Grosset/Dunlap	(1938)	Stone, Charlotte	65-100	
Windsor, Mary	About Things (1st, lg4to, ibds, 51p, color, pep, DJ/1.00)	Grosset/Dunlap	(1935)	Stone, Charlotte	65-100	
McGowen, Tom	Hammet and the Highlanders (1st {std}, 8vo, 47p, b/w, DJ/3.50)	Follett	(1970)	Stone, David	40-65	*
McGinley, Phyllis	All Around the Town (1st {std}, sm4to, ibds, [63]p, fp color, DJ/2.00, CH)	Lippincott	(1948)	Stone, Helen	80-140	
Krauss, Ruth	Bundle Book (1st, lg ob8vo, ipcb, [32]p, pep, color, DJ/1.75)	Harper	(1951)	Stone, Helen	60-100	
Lockridge, Frances	Cats & People (1st {std}, 8vo, 286p, b/w, DJ/3.50)	Lippincott	(1950)	Stone, Helen	30-50	
Burton, Earl & L.	Exciting Adventures of Waldo (1st, sm4to, 64p, grey cl, fp col, DJ/2.00)	Whittlesey	(1945)	Stone, Helen	45-60	
McGinley, Phyllis	Horse Who had Picture in Paper (1st {std}, sm4to, 48p, color, DJ/2.00)	Lippincott	(1951)	Stone, Helen	40-65	*

AUTHOR	TITLE	PUBLISHER	DATE	ARTIST	PRICE	LC
McGinley, Phyllis	Horse Who Lived Upstairs (1st {std}, sm4to, [48]p, color, cep, DJ)	Lippincott	(1944)	Stone, Helen	45-70	
Koch, Dorothy	Let it Rain (1st, 4to, [27]p, green cl, color, cep, DJ)	Holiday House	(1959)	Stone, Helen	30-50	
Stirling, Monica	Little Ballet Dancer (1st, lg8vo, ipcb, 61p, 2-color, pep, DJ/2.50)	Lothrop, Lee	1952	Stone, Helen	30-50	
Tate, Elizabeth	Little Flower Girl (1st, lg8vo, aqua cl, [40]p, 3-color, pep, DJ/2.50)	Lothrop, Lee	(1956)	Stone, Helen	40-65	
Bennett, Anna E.	Little Witch (1st [1st bk.] {std}, 8vo, 127p, green cl, b/w, DJ/2.50)	Lippincott	(1953)	Stone, Helen	350-500	
McGinley, Phyllis	Lucy McLockett (1st, sm4to, [32]p, color, DJ/3.00)	Lippincott	(1959)	Stone, Helen	60-90	
McGinley, Phyllis	Most Wonderful Doll in the World (1st, 8vo, 61p, color, cep, DJ/1.75, CH)	Lippincott	(1950)	Stone, Helen	60-90	
McGinley, Phyllis	Plain Princess (1st {std}, 8vo, gilt, 62p, color, DJ/1.50)	Lippincott	(1945)	Stone, Helen	30-50	
Brown, Margaret W.	Pussycat's Christmas (1st, sq12mo, yellow cl, [32]p, color, dep, DJ/1.50)	Crowell	1949	Stone, Helen	120-200	
Weiss, Edna S.	Sally Saucer (1st, 8vo, 179p, yellow cl, b/w, DJ/2.75)	Houghton	1956	Stone, Helen	25-45	
Branley, Franklyn	Snow is Falling (1st, ob8vo, ibds, [40]p, fp 2-color, DJ/2.50)	Crowell	(1963)	Stone, Helen	30-50	
Burton, Earl & L.	Taffy & Joe (1st, sm4to, green cl, 60p, dp col frn, b/w, DJ/2.25)	Whittlesey	1947	Stone, Helen	40-65	
Foster, Doris	Tell Me, Mister Owl (1st, 4to, [29]p, ibds, color, DJ/2.75)	Lothrop, Lee	1957	Stone, Helen	40-65	R*
Simon, Norma	Tree For Me (1st, lg8vo, green cl, [26]p, 1-color, dep, DJ/2.00)	Lippincott	(1956)	Stone, Helen	30-50	
Goldberg, Martha	Twirly Skirt (1st, 8vo, 45p, green cl, fp b/w, pep, DJ/1.75)	Holiday House	1954	Stone, Helen	40-65	R
Kennedy, Mary	Violets are Blue (1st, 8vo, 154p, blue cl, fp b/w, DJ/2.00)	Lothrop, Lee	(1951)	Stone, Helen	25-45	
Hawes, Judy	Watch Honeybees with Me (1st, sq8vo, [40]p, fp 2-color, DJ/2.75)	Crowell	(1964)	Stone, Helen	30-45	*
Stewart, Anna B.	Young Miss Burney (1st {std}, 8vo, green/gilt, 270p, b/w, DJ/2.50)	Lippincott	1947	Stone, Helen	30-50	
Jackson, Helen H.	Ramona (1st [Gift Ed.], lg8vo, 447p, col frn, DJ/2.75)	Little/Brown	1932	Stoops, Herbert M.	30-50	
Linderman, Frank B.	Red Mother (1st, 8vo, 256p, green/gilt, b/w, pep)	John Day	(1932)	Stoops, Herbert M.	100-165	
Malkus, Alida S.	Stone Knife Boy (1st, 8vo, 270p, b/w pl, pep)	Harcourt	(1933)	Stoops, Herbert M.	30-45	
Means, Florence C.	Tangled Waters (1st, 8vo, 212p, col frn, DJ/2.00)	Houghton	1936	Stoops, Herbert M.	25-45	
Stevenson, Rbt. L.	Child's Garden of Verses (1st, 8vo, 115p, 8cp)	Scribner	1909	Storer, Florence	50-80	
Field, Eugene	Christmas Tales and Christmas Verse (1st, 4to, 119p, gilt, 8cp)	Scribner	1912	Storer, Florence	80-120	
Van Dresser, Jasmine	How to Find Happyland (1st, lg8vo, 122p, p-o, AEG, 10cp)	Putnam	1907	Storer, Florence	45-70	
Fraser, Beatrice	Arturo and Mr. Bang (1st {std}, 4to, unpag, b/w, DJ/2.50)	Bobbs-Merrill	1963	Storrs, William	30-45	
Gilbert, Paul T.	Bertram's Trip to the North Pole (1st, sm8vo, 127p, fp b/w, pep, DJ/1.00)	Rand/McNally	(1940)	Stossel, Anne	60-90	
Gilbert, Paul T.	Elmer Buys a Circus (1st, 8vo, ibds, 71p, b/w, pep)	Grosset/Dunlap	(1941)	Stossel, Anne	30-50	
Gilbert, Paul T.	With Bertram in Africa (1st {A}, sm8vo, 127p, b/w, pep, DJ/1.00)	Rand/McNally	1939	Stossel, Anne	100-160	
Stevenson, Rbt. L.	Kidnapped (1st, 8vo, 343p, 8cp)	L: Cassell	1913	Stott, W.R.S.	55-80	*
Lewis, Eliz. F.	Portraits from a Chinese Scroll (1st {std}, 8vo, 267p, gilt, 1-col, DJ/2.50)	Winston	(1938)	Stout, Virginia	25-40	
Fenton, Edward	Phantom of Walkaway Hill (1st {std}, 8vo, 260p, b/w, DJ/2.95)	Doubleday	1961	Stover, Jo Ann	50-85	
Strang, William	Book of Giants (1st, 8vo, 56p, 12pl)	L: Unicorn Press	1898	Strang, William	250-400	
Bunyan, John	Pilgrim's Progress (1st, 4to, 379p, teg, uncut, black/gilt, fp b/w)	L: Nimmo	1895	Strang, William	90-120	
N/A	Sinbad the Sailor (1st, 8vo, 279p)	L: Lawrence	1896	Strang/Clark	60-90	*
Davidson (ed.)	Ali Baba & the Forty Thieves (folio, ibds, 9 fp color)	L: Blackie	[1900]	Stratton, Helen	70-100	
N/A	Arabian Nights (8vo, 352p, 29cp)	L: Blackie	[1910]	Stratton, Helen	55-90	*
Campbell, Walter D.	Beyond the Border (1st AM, 12mo, gilt, AEG, 456p, 38pl)	R.H. Russell	1898	Stratton, Helen	100-160	
Lang, Jeanie	Book of Myths (1st, 8vo, gilt, 340p, teg, uncut, 20cp)	L: Jack	1914	Stratton, Helen	100-160	
Andersen, Hans C.	Fairy Tales (1st, 4to, white/gilt, AEG, 320p, col frn, b/w)	L: G. Newnes	1899	Stratton, Helen	180-250	
Andersen, Hans C.	Fairy Tales (1st AM, 4to, blue/gilt, AEG, 320p, b/w, cep)	NY: Truslove	1899	Stratton, Helen	150-220	*
Andersen, Hans C.	Fairy Tales (1st AM, 8vo, 380p, green/gilt, 28cp)	Dodge	[1905]	Stratton, Helen	200-300	
Andersen, Hans C.	Fairy Tales (4to, ibds, [86]p, 24cp)	L: Blackie	[1905]	Stratton, Helen	180-250	
Grimm Bros.	Fairy Tales (1st, 8vo, 336p, 20cp)	L: Blackie	[1905]	Stratton, Helen	200-300	
Andersen, Hans C.	Fairy Tales (sm8vo, 441p, col frn, dep)	Lippincott	(1908)	Stratton, Helen	50-90	*
Andersen, Hans C.	Fairy Tales (8vo, 380p, ibds, 16cp)	L: Blackie	[1920]	Stratton, Helen	150-200	
Grimm Bros.	Fairy Tales (8vo, 336p, green cl, 29cp)	Dodge	[1920]	Stratton, Helen	100-150	
Grimm Bros.	Grimm's & Andersen's Fairy Tales (1st, folio, [176]p, color, cep)	L: Blackie	[1906]	Stratton, Helen	200-300	R*
Herbertson, Agnes	Heroic Legends (1st, 8vo, 253p, AEG, gilt, 16cp, cep)	L: Blackie	1908	Stratton, Helen	120-200	
Sylva, Carmen	Lily of Life (1st, 4to, gilt, teg, 146p, p-o, 18 ticp)	L: Hodder	[1910]	Stratton, Helen	400-550	
Dearmer, Mabel	Playmate, A Christmas Mystery (1st, 8vo, 31p, 4 illus)	L: A. Mowbray	1910	Stratton, Helen	80-125	
MacDonald, George	Princess & Curdie (1st, 8vo, 304p, blue/gilt, 31 b/w, cep)	L: Blackie	1900	Stratton, Helen	125-180	
MacDonald, George	Princess & Curdie (new ed., 8vo, 320p, p-o, gilt, teg, 12cp, pep)	L: Blackie	1912	Stratton, Helen	90-140	
MacDonald, George	Princess & the Goblin (1st AM, 8vo, 308p, teg, blue/gilt, p-o, 12cp)	Caldwell	[1911]	Stratton, Helen	160-220	
MacDonald, George	Princess & the Goblin (1st, 8vo, teg, 308p, p-o, gilt, 12cp)	L: Blackie	1911	Stratton, Helen	170-250	
Gomme, George L.	Princess's Story Book (1st, 12mo, gilt, teg, 443p, 23pl)	L: Constable	1901	Stratton, Helen	100-170	*
Chaundler, Christine	Ronald's Burglar (1st, 16mo, 62p, col frn, b/w)	L: Nelson	(1919)	Stratton, Helen	30-50	*
Thomson, Clara L.	Selections from LeMorte D'arthur (1st, 8vo, 240p)	L: H. Marshall	1902	Stratton, Helen	80-130	
Gale, Norman	Songs for Little People (1st, 8vo, teg, 110p, uncut, gilt, 8pl)	L: Constable	1896	Stratton, Helen	125-185	
Andersen, Hans C.	Tales from Andersen (1st, 12mo, 194p, gilt, 1-color title pg, 5pl)	L: Constable	1896	Stratton, Helen	120-180	*
Hewes, Agnes D.	Sword of Roland Arnot (1st, 8vo, red cl, 206p, 4cp, DJ/2.50)	Houghton	1939	Strayer, Paul	30-50	
Kipling, Rudyard	Tales of India (1st, lg8vo, p-o, 320p, black cl, 5cp, pep, WS)	Rand/McNally	(1935)	Strayer, Paul	50-80	
Streatfeild, Noel	Dennis the Dragon (1st, 8vo, 32p)	L: Dent	1939	Streatfeild, Ruth	30-45	
Hall, Eliza C.	Aunt Jane of Kentucky (1st, 12mo, 283p, col frn, decor by...)	Little/Brown	1907	Strong, Beulah	25-40	
Burgess, Thornton	Bride's Primer (1st, lg4to, ipcb, [62]p, 24 fp color)	NY: Phelps	(1905)	Strothmann, F.	300-500	R*
Twain, Mark	Extracts from Adam's Diary (1st, 8vo, red cl, 89p, b/w)	Harper	1904	Strothmann, F.	200-300	
Wells, Carolyn	In the Reign of Queen Dick (1st, 8vo, tan cl, 229p, 8pl)	Appleton	1904	Strothmann, F.	30-50	
Twain, Mark	Jumping Frog (1st, 8vo, 65p, 11pl)	Harper	1903	Strothmann, F.	70-120	
Gulliver, Lemeul	Over the Nonsense Road (1st, 8vo, 234p, orange cl, 8cp)	Appleton	1910	Strothmann, F.	60-100	
Hoover, Bessie R.	Pa Flickinger's Folks (1st, 12mo, grey cl, 274p, 10pl)	Harper	1909	Strothmann, F.	50-80	
Wells, Carolyn	Rubaiyat of a Motor Car (1st, 12mo, [60]p, ibds, 14cp)	Dodd	1906	Strothmann, F.	55-80	*
Pattee, Fred L.	House of the Black Ring (1st, sm8vo, 324p, cvr by...)	Henry Holt & Co.	1905	Stuart, Bertha	60-90	
Hopkins, Lee B. (comp)	Me! A Book of Poems (1st {std}, lg ob8vo, 30p, fp 1-color, DJ/3.95)	Seabury Press	(1970)	Stubis, Talivaldis	25-40	
Chandler, Edna W.	Five Cent, Five Cent (1st, 4to, unpag, color, DJ/2.95)	Whitman	(1967)	Stull, Betty	30-45	
Underhill, Andrew F.	Goochy Goggles & Pollywog Named Woggles (1st, lg8vo, [93]p, ibds, color)	McLoughlin	(1926)	Sturges, Katharine	50-80	
Miller, Olive B.	Little Pictures of Japan (1st, 4to, 191p, p-o, pep, color)	Book House	(1925)	Sturges, Katharine	50-80	
Sturges, Katharine	Mimi, Momo and Miss Tabby Tibbs (1st, 12mo, ibds, [42]p, color)	Volland	(1927)	Sturges, Katharine	80-120	
Chamberlin, Ethel C.	Omar the Discontented Cat (1st, 12mo, [39]p, ipcb, pep, color)	Volland	(1925)	Sturges, Katharine	40-60	*

AUTHOR	TITLE	PUBLISHER	DATE	ARTIST	PRICE	LC
Potter, Beatrix	Sister Anne (1st, sm8vo, 154p, gilt, b/w)	McKay	(1932)	Sturges, Katharine	400-600	
Alden, Raymond M.	Why the Chimes Rang (1st, 8vo, 148p, orange cl, p-o, 8cp)	Bobbs-Merrill	(1924)	Sturges, Katharine	55-80	*
Sturges, Lilian B.	Runaway Toys (1st, 12mo, [64]p, black cl, p-o, color)	Rand/McNally	(1920)	Sturges, Lilian B.	70-100	
Sturges, Lilian B.	Toys of Nuremberg (1st, sm8vo, p-o, [80]p, color)	Rand/McNally	(1915)	Sturges, Lilian B.	70-100	
Stutters, Percival	How Percival Caught the Python (1st, sq24mo, [89]p, fp color)	Holiday House	(1937)	Stutters, Percival	50-85	
Stutters, Percival	How Percival Caught the Tiger (1st, sq24mo, [89]p, fp color)	Holiday House	(1936)	Stutters, Percival	50-85	
Ford, Lauren	Ageless Story (1st, sq4to, blue/gilt, [40]p, color, DJ/2.00, CH)	Dodd	1939	Suba, Susanne	65-100	
Malvern, Gladys	Dancing Star (1st, lg8vo, 280p, b/w, pep, DJ/2.50)	J. Messner	1942	Suba, Susanne	30-50	
Petry, Ann	Drugstore Cat (1st, lg8vo, 87p, red cl, fp b/w, pep, DJ/2.00)	Crowell	1949	Suba, Susanne	250-400	
Haviland, Virginia	Favorite Fairy Tales Told in Germany (1st {std}, lg8vo, 83p, DJ/2.75)	Little/Brown	(1959)	Suba, Susanne	50-85	
McCracken, Russell	Gentle Giraffe (1st {std}, sm4to, ibds, 31p, color, DJ/1.00)	Rand/McNally	(1945)	Suba, Susanne	45-70	
Moses, Horace S.	Here Comes the Circus (1st, lg8vo, 47p, color, DJ/1.75)	Houghton	1941	Suba, Susanne	40-65	
Edwards, May	Hobo Hound (1st {std}, sm4to, ibds, [32]p, color, DJ/1.25)	Rand/McNally	1947	Suba, Susanne	40-65	
Fox, Frances M.	Little Cat that Could Not Sleep (1st {std}, 8vo, [31]p, pep, col, DJ/1.50)	Dutton	1941	Suba, Susanne	75-100	*
Suba, Susanne	Man with the Bushy Beard (1st {std}, ob4to, [35]p, color, DJ/4.95)	Viking	(1969)	Suba, Susanne	30-45	
Suba, Susanne	Monkeys and the Pedlar (1st {std}, ob4to, [32]p, color, DJ/5.95)	Viking	(1970)	Suba, Susanne	30-45	
Morrow, Elizabeth	My Favorite Age (1st, sm8vo, 220p, green cl, fp b/w, cep, DJ/2.00)	Macmillan	1943	Suba, Susanne	30-50	
McCracken, Russell	Mystery of Carmen the Cow (1st, sm4to, ibds, 31p, 3-color, DJ/1.00)	Rand/McNally	1946	Suba, Susanne	45-70	
Streatfeild, Noel	Osbert (1st {std}, 8vo, 30p, ipcb, fp 2-color)	Rand/McNally	(1950)	Suba, Susanne	50-80	*
Morrow, Elizabeth	Pint of Judgment (1st {std}, 24mo, ibds, 43p, dep, DJ/0.50)	Knopf	(1939)	Suba, Susanne	30-50	
Withers, Carl (comp)	Rocket in My Pocket (1st {std}, lg8vo, 248p, ipcb, b/w, DJ/3.50)	Henry Holt & Co.	1948	Suba, Susanne	30-50	R*
Otto, Margaret G.	Roly-Poly Snowman (1st {std}, 8vo, blue cl, 83p, fp b/w, DJ/2.00)	Holt	(1954)	Suba, Susanne	40-65	
Lansing, Elisabeth H.	Shoot for a Mule (1st {std}, 8vo, 121p, b/w, DJ/2.00)	Crowell	(1951)	Suba, Susanne	30-50	
Baker, Elizabeth W.	Sonny-Boy Sim (1st {std}, lg8vo, ipcb, 31p, fp 2-color, DJ/1.00)	Rand/McNally	(1948)	Suba, Susanne	40-70	R
Govan, Christine	String & the No-Tail Cat (1st, 4to, 40p, 2-color, DJ/1.50)	Houghton	1939	Suba, Susanne	100-165	
Streatfeild, Noel	Theatre Cat (1st {std}, lg8vo, ipcb, 30p, fp color, DJ/1.25)	Rand/McNally	(1951)	Suba, Susanne	45-65	R*
Herzog, Elizabeth	Tinkers of Turntable (1st, 8vo, grey cl, 125p, b/w, DJ/1.75)	W.R. Scott	(1940)	Suba, Susanne	30-50	
Burch, Robert	Traveling Bird (1st, 8vo, green cl, 42p, b/w, DJ/3.50)	McDowell/Obl.	(1959)	Suba, Susanne	20-30	
Walters, Marguerite	Up & Down and All Around (1st {std}, lg4to, unpag, 2-color, DJ/2.95)	F. Watts	1960	Suba, Susanne	40-60	
Cumming, Marian	Valentine for Candy (1st {std}, 8vo, 160p, DJ/3.00)	Harcourt	(1959)	Suba, Susanne	25-40	
Latham, Jean L.	Far Voyager: Story of James Cook (1st, 8vo, 242p, b/w, DJ/4.50)	Harper	(1970)	Suecklen, Karl	30-50	
Sachs, Marilyn	Amy and Laura (1st {std}, 8vo, 189p, b/w, DJ/3.25)	Doubleday	(1966)	Sugarman, Tracy	20-25	
Gill, Joan	Hush, Jon! (1st {std}, lg8vo, 47p, b/w, DJ/3.50)	Doubleday	(1968)	Sugarman, Tracy	30-50	
Uchida, Yoshiko	New Friends for Susan (1st, sm8vo, 185p, b/w, DJ/2.00)	Scribner	1951	Sugimoto, Henry	40-65	
Beach, Stewart	Good Morning, Sun's Up (1st AM {std}, lg sq8vo, [27]p, color, cep)	NY: Scroll Pr.	(1970)	Sugita, Yutaka	60-90	
Tennyson, Alfred	Dream of Fair Women (1st, lg8vo, teg, 197p, gilt, b/w)	Page/Richards	1900	Sullivan, Edmund J.	100-165	
Borrow, George H.	Lavengro (1st, 8vo, teg, green/gilt, 655p, 12 ticp, cep)	L: Foulis	(1914)	Sullivan, Edmund J.	55-80	
Tennyson, Alfred	Maud (1st, sm4to, 103p, uncut, 8cp)	L: Macmillan	1922	Sullivan, Edmund J.	70-90	
Wells, H.G.	Modern Utopia (1st, 8vo, red/gilt, uncut, teg, 393p, 7pl)	L: Chapman	1905	Sullivan, Edmund J.	200-300	
Marryat, Frederick	Newton Foster (1st, 12mo, 393p, blue/gilt, 40 b/w, pep)	L: Macmillan	1897	Sullivan, Edmund J.	55-80	
Omar Khayyam	Rubaiyat of Omar Khayyam (1st AM, 4to, red/gilt, unpag, teg, col frn)	Dutton	(1913)	Sullivan, Edmund J.	100-170	
Omar Khayyam	Rubaiyat of Omar Khayyam (1st, 4to, red/gilt, unpag, uncut, col frn)	L: Methuen	1913	Sullivan, Edmund J.	120-180	
Carlyle, Thomas	Sartor Resartus (1st, sm8vo, AEG, 352p, blue/gilt, b/w, dep)	L: G. Bell	1898	Sullivan, Edmund J.	100-165	
Fouque, La Motte	Sintram and his Companions (1st, 8vo, 193p, uncut, olive/gilt, teg, 20pl)	L: Methuen	(1908)	Sullivan, Edmund J.	80-125	
Sheridan, Richard B.	The Rivals (1st, 8vo, 365p, b/w)	(London)	1896	Sullivan, Edmund J.	70-100	
Hughes, Thomas	Tom Brown's School Days (1st, 12mo, green/gilt, b/w)	L: Macmillan	1897	Sullivan, Edmund J.	60-90	
Goldsmith, Oliver	Vicar of Wakefield (1st AM, sm4to, 345p, blue/gilt, 16cp)	Henry Holt & Co.	1914	Sullivan, Edmund J.	100-160	
Goldsmith, Oliver	Vicar of Wakefield (1st, 4to, 345p, green/gilt, teg, 16cp)	L: Constable	1914	Sullivan, Edmund J.	120-200	
Lucas, E.V.	Cat Book (1st, lg8vo, 37p, ibds, b/w)	Harper	1927	Sullivan, Pat	60-90	
Stratton-Porter, Gene	Her Father's Daughter (1st, sm8vo, 486p, pep, col frn by...)	Doubleday/Page	1921	Summers, D.G.	100-180	
Belting, Natalia	Cat Tales (1st {std}, 8vo, 95p, b/w, DJ/2.50)	Holt	(1959)	Summers, Leo	20-30	*
Farley, Walter	Horse that Swam Away (1st {std}, 8vo, 75p, b/w, DJ/1.95)	Random	(1965)	Summers, Leo	50-85	*
Wier, Ester A.	Space Hut (1st, 8vo, 94p, b/w, DJ/3.95)	Stackpole Bks.	(1967)	Summers, Leo	20-30	
Foque, De La Motte	Sintram & his Companions (1st, 8vo, gilt, 124p, AEG, b/w)	L: Seeley	1883	Sumner, Heywood	60-90	
Heide, Florence P.	How Big am I? (1st {std}, 8vo, [32]p, color, DJ/1.95)	Follett	(1968)	Suyeoka, George	20-35	
Malkus, Alida S.	Eastward Sweeps the Current (1st, 8vo, 394p, b/w, pep, DJ/2.00)	Winston	(1937)	Sweeney, Dan	20-30	
Roethke, Theodore	Party at the Zoo (1st {std}, 4to, ibds, 62p, fp color, cep)	Crowell-Collier	(1963)	Swiller, Al	80-130	
Swinnerton, James	Canyon Country Kiddies (1st {std}, 4to, blue cl, 74p, color)	Doubleday/Page	1923	Swinnerton, James	80-120	
Dix, Dorothy	Fables of the Elite (1st, 12mo, teg, 261p, b/w pl)	Fenno	1902	Swinnerton, James	70-125	*
Defoe, Daniel	Robinson Crusoe (8vo, 472p, teg, bds, 16cp, pep)	L: J.M. Dent	1895	Symington, J.A.	85-130	
Scott, Michael	Tom Cringle's Log (1st, 8vo, 569p, AEG, blue/gilt, 42 b/w)	L: Macmillan	1895	Symington, J.A.	40-60	
Syrett, Netta	Garden of Delight (1st, sq8vo, green/gilt, 218p, 10pl)	Hurst/Blackett	1898	Syrett, Nellie	70-120	*
Sharp, Evelyn	Other Side of the Sun (1st, 12mo, 188p, 8cp)	L: John Lane	1900	Syrett, Nellie	150-250	
Krasilovsky, Phyllis	Girl Who was a Cowboy (1st {std}, sm8vo, 31p, 1-color, DJ/2.75)	Doubleday	(1965)	Szekeres, Cyndy	20-30	
Parish, Peggy	Jumper Goes to School (1st {std}, ob4to, [29]p, color, DJ/3.95)	Simon/Schuster	(1969)	Szekeres, Cyndy	20-30	
Ormondroyd, Edward	Michael, the Upstairs Dog (1st {std}, ob4to, [40]p, 1-color, cep, DJ/3.50)	Dial Press	(1967)	Szekeres, Cyndy	50-80	*
Holl, Adelaide	Moon Mouse (1st, ob4to, 34p, 1-color, cep, DJ/3.50)	Random	(1969)	Szekeres, Cyndy	30-45	
Lampman, Evelyn	Mrs. Updaisy (1st {std}, 8vo, 215p, fp b/w, DJ/3.25)	Doubleday	(1963)	Szekeres, Cyndy	25-40	
Flack, Marjorie	Walter the Lazy Mouse (1st {std}, lg8vo, 95p, 2-color, DJ/2.95)	Doubleday	(1963)	Szekeres, Cyndy	50-80	
Latham, Jean L.	When Homer Honked (1st {std}, 8vo, [32]p, 1-color, DJ/2.50)	Macmillan	1961	Szekeres, Cyndy	30-45	
Andersen, Hans C.	Fairy Tales (1st, 8vo, 343p, color, DJ/1.25)	Grosset/Dunlap	(1945)	Szyk, Arthur	70-120	R
Lewisohn, Ludwig	Last Days of Shylock (1st, 8vo, 221p, b/w pl)	Harper	1931	Szyk, Arthur	40-70	
Szyk, Arthur	New Order (1st, sm4to, [76]p, 8 fp color, DJ/1.50)	Putnam	(1941)	Szyk, Arthur	120-200	
Omar Khayyam	Rubaiyat of Omar Khayyam (4to, blue ibds, gilt, [40]p, 8 ticp)	Heritage Press	1940	Szyk, Arthur	160-225	
Joslin, Sesyle	Please Share that Peanut (1st {std}, 8vo, [64]p, fp b/w, DJ/2.50, NYTBI)	Harcourt	(1965)	Taback, Simms	30-50	
McGovern, Ann	Too Much Noise (1st, sm ob4to, 44p, fp 3-color, cep, DJ/3.25)	Houghton	1967	Taback, Simms	30-50	
Kipling, Rudyard	Captains Courageous (1st AM, 8vo, green/gilt, 323p, teg, 21pl)	Century	1897	Taber, I.W.	400-600	
Kipling, Rudyard	Captains Courageous (1st, sm8vo, 245p, blue/gilt, AEG, fp b/w)	L: Macmillan	1897	Taber, I.W.	500-700	

AUTHOR	TITLE	PUBLISHER	DATE	ARTIST	PRICE	LC
Gordon, Elizabeth	Book of Bow-Wows (8vo, [40]p, ibds, fp color, pep)	Donohue	(1913)	Tad	90-140	
Kiyooka, Chiyono	Chiyo's Return (1st {std}, 8vo, 342p, pep, DJ/2.00)	Doubleday/Doran	1935	Tagawa, Bunji	30-45	
Strack, Lilian H.	Swords and Iris (1st {std}, 8vo, 125p, col frn, fp b/w, pep, DJ/2.00)	Harper	1937	Tagawa, Bunji	60-100	
Bradley-Birt, F.	Bengal Fairy Tales (1st, lg8vo, 209p, gilt, 6 fp color)	L: John Lane	1920	Tagore, A.N.	90-120	
Omar Khayyam	Rubaiyat of Omar Khayyam (1st, 8vo, 63p, 7 ticp)	L: L.B. Hill	(1920)	Tagore, A.N.	120-170	*
Lloyd, Marion	Penny & Peter of the Island (1st, 4to, [60]p, fp 1-color, pep, DJ/2.00)	J. Messner	(1941)	Tait, Agnes	30-50	*
Clark, Ann N.	Summer is for Growing (1st {std}, 8vo, 180p, fp b/w, DJ/3.50)	Farrar, Straus	(1968)	Tait, Agnes	20-30	*
Martin, Patricia	Pocahontas (1st, 8vo, 63p, color, DJ/1.95)	Putnam	(1964)	Takajian, Portia	20-35	
Black, Irma S.	Barbara's Birthday (1st, 8vo, ibds, 44p, color, DJ/1.25)	W.R. Scott	1946	Takis, Nicholas	45-65	
Tamburine, Jean	I Think I will Go to the Hospital (1st, 4to, cloth, 48p, 3-color, DJ/2.95)	Abingdon Press	(1965)	Tamburine, Jean	20-30	
Barrows, Marjorie	Pudgy: The Little Bear (1st AM, 4to, [22]p, ibds, color, pep)	Rand/McNally	1964	Tamburine, Jean	25-40	
Martin, Patricia	Andrew Jackson (1st, 8vo, 62p, color, DJ)	Putnam	(1966)	Tamer, Salem	20-30	
Voight, Virginia F.	Cuff, a Baby Bear (1st, 8vo, 64p, 1-color, DJ)	Putnam	(1969)	Tamer, Salem	30-50	
Martin, Patricia	Jefferson Davis (1st, 8vo, 63p, color, DJ)	Putnam	(1966)	Tamer, Salem	25-35	*
Martin, Patricia	John Marshall (1st, 8vo, 63p, color, DJ)	Putnam	(1967)	Tamer, Salem	25-35	
Rowe, Dorothy	Rabbit Lantern (1st, 8vo, 98p, 8cp, pep)	Macmillan	1925	Tang, Ling Jui	30-45	
Sykes, M'Cready	Poe's Run.... (1st, 8vo, teg, green cl, 84p, b/w)	Cannon Press	1904	Tarkington, Booth	40-60	
Carroll, Lewis	Alice in Wonderland (1st, sm4to, p-o, 340p, blue/gilt, 48cp, pep)	L: Ward Lock	1916	Tarrant, Margaret	200-300	
Carroll, Lewis	Alice in Wonderland (1st AM, lg8vo, p-o, 332p, 48cp, pep)	Platt/Peck	1916	Tarrant, Margaret	170-240	
Farjeon, Eleanor	Alphabet of Magic (1st, lg8vo, 57p, green cl, b/w)	L: Medici	1928	Tarrant, Margaret	30-50	
Hayes, Nancy M.	Book of Games (1st, 8vo, ibds, 144p, p-o, dep, 24cp)	L: Ward Lock	1920	Tarrant, Margaret	150-240	
Golding, Harry	Book of the Clock (1st, 8vo, p-o, 140p, 27cp)	L: Ward Lock	1920	Tarrant, Margaret	90-120	
Collett, Marjorie	Elizabeth in Toyland (1st, 12mo, bds, 46p, 4cp)	L: Harrap	1925	Tarrant, Margaret	70-100	
Andersen, Hans C.	Fairy Stories (1st, sm4to, 340p, blue cl, p-o, 48cp, pep)	L: Ward Lock	1917	Tarrant, Margaret	200-300	
Andersen, Hans C.	Fairy Tales (4to, ibds, 176p, 24cp)	L: Ward Lock	[1920]	Tarrant, Margaret	100-150	
Andersen, Hans C.	Fairy Tales (1st [this fmt.], 12mo, 127p, gilt, 8cp, pep)	L: Ward Lock	[1935]	Tarrant, Margaret	30-50	
Webb, M. St. John	Forest Fairies (1st, 16mo, 41p, ibds, 6 ticp)	L: Mod.Art.Soc	(1932)	Tarrant, Margaret	70-125	
Wilman, Stanley	Games for Playtime & Parties (1st, 4to, 82p, ibds, color)	Jack	[1914]	Tarrant, Margaret	100-180	
Webb, M. St. John	Insect Fairies (1st, 12mo, beige bds, p-o, 42p, 6 ticp)	L: Mod.Art.Soc	(1925)	Tarrant, Margaret	100-160	
Tarrant, Margaret	Joan in Flowerland (1st, 8vo, 60p, blue cl, 16cp, pep, DJ)	L: Warne	(1935)	Tarrant, Margaret	250-350	
Webb, M. St. John	Little One in Between (1st, 12mo, 59p, blue/gilt, 4cp)	L: Harrap	1929	Tarrant, Margaret	45-60	
Adcock, Marion	Littlest One (1st, 4to, 41p, ibds, 4 ticp)	L: Harrap	1914	Tarrant, Margaret	70-100	
Adcock, Marion	Littlest One (1st AM, 8vo, ibds, p-o, 4 ticp)	Stokes	[1915]	Tarrant, Margaret	60-90	
Webb, M. St. John	Littlest One Again (1st, 4to, p-o, bds, 4cp)	L: Harrap	1926	Tarrant, Margaret	70-100	
Herbertson, Agnes	Lucy-Mary (1st, 8vo, 203p, 6cp)	L: Blackie	1910	Tarrant, Margaret	55-80	*
Webb, M. St. John	Magic Lamplighter (1st, 8vo, 167p, 7cp, pep)	L: Medici	1926	Tarrant, Margaret	60-90	
Rhys, Grace (ed.)	Magic Wood Beyond the World (1st, 8vo, ibds, 4cp)	L: Harrap	1931	Tarrant, Margaret	50-80	
Tarrant, Margaret	Margaret Tarrant's Christmas Garland (1st, sq8vo, 125p, 19 ticp)	Hale-Cushman	(1942)	Tarrant, Margaret	55-80	*
Mother Goose	Mother Goose (1st, 4to, ibds, 74p, 16cp, DJ)	L: Coker	(1920)	Tarrant, Margaret	120-160	
Mother Goose	Mother Goose Nursery Rhymes (1st, 4to, 176p, 24cp)	L: Ward Lock	[1929]	Tarrant, Margaret	90-120	*
Peacocke, Isabel M.	My Friend Phil (1st, 8vo, p-o, 320p, 6cp)	L: Ward Lock	1915	Tarrant, Margaret	60-90	*
N/A	Nursery Rhymes (1st, 8vo, 340p, blue/gilt, p-o, 44cp, pep)	L: Ward Lock	1914	Tarrant, Margaret	200-300	
Golding, Harry	Our Animal Friends (4to, ibds, 176p, p-o, 24cp)	L: Ward Lock	[1920]	Tarrant, Margaret	75-100	
Cole, Frank (ed.)	Picture Birthday Book for Boys & Girls (1st, 16mo, gilt, unpag, 12cp)	L: Harrap	(1915)	Tarrant, Margaret	60-90	
Browning, Robert	Pied Piper of Hamelin (1st, 8vo, 41p, green/gilt, teg, 8cp)	L: J.M. Dent	1912	Tarrant, Margaret	60-100	
Webb, M. St. John	Pond Fairies (1st, 16mo, 41p, grey bds, p-o, 6 ticp)	L: Mod.Art.Soc	(1932)	Tarrant, Margaret	80-125	
N/A	Rhymes of Old Times (1st, 8vo, 107p, teg, 16 ticp, pep)	L: Medici	1925	Tarrant, Margaret	70-120	
Webb, M. St. John	Sea-Shore Fairies (1st, 16mo, 48p, tan bds, p-o, 6 fp color)	L: Mod.Art.Soc	(1925)	Tarrant, Margaret	200-300	
Webb, M. St. John	Seed Fairies (1st, 12mo, 39p, bds, p-o, 6 ticp)	L: Mod.Art.Soc	[1923]	Tarrant, Margaret	180-260	
Stevenson, Rbt. L.	Songs with Music of Child's Garden of Verses (1st, 4to, 55p, pcb, 12cp)	L: Jack	[1915]	Tarrant, Margaret	90-120	
Leighton, Mary	Three Chums (1st, 8vo, 144p, red cl, col frn, 3pl, DJ/1.50)	Chapman/Grimes	(1939)	Tarrant, Margaret	50-90	
Kingsley, Charles	Water Babies (1st, 8vo, 284p, uncut, p-o, teg, 12cp, pep)	L: Dent	1908	Tarrant, Margaret	80-120	
Webb, M. St. John	Wild Fruit Fairies (1st, 12mo, 41p, ibds, 6 ticp)	L: Medici	[1932]	Tarrant, Margaret	100-165	
Golding, Harry	Willie Winkie... (16mo, 96p, ibds, 24 fp color, pep)	L: Ward Lock	[1920]	Tarrant, Margaret	75-100	
Golding, Harry	Zoo Days (1st, lg8vo, 334p, p-o, 48cp, pep)	L: Ward Lock	(1919)	Tarrant, Margaret	70-100	
Scott, Walter	Quentin Durward (1st, lg8vo, uncut, 499p, 16cp)	Dodd	1923	Tarrant, Percy	35-60	*
Judson, Clara I.	Yankee Clippers: Story of Donald McKay (1st, 8vo, 158p, b/w, DJ/3.50)	Follett	(1965)	Tashiro, Chiyo	25-40	
Tashlin, Frank	Bear that Wasn't (1st {std}, sm4to, [60]p, ibds, b/w, DJ/1.25)	Dutton	1946	Tashlin, Frank	25-40	
Hoke, Helen	Furry Bear (1st, 8vo, [16]p, color, DJ/1.25)	J. Messner	1943	Tate, Sally	30-50	
Gaskell, Mrs.	Cranford (1st, sm8vo, 289p, grey/gilt, 8 fp color)	A.& C. Black	1914	Tawse, Sybil	40-70	
Mother Goose	Mother Goose (1st, 4to, 224p, ibds, 12pl)	L: Harrap	1932	Tawse, Sybil	90-120	
Porter, Eleanor	Pollyanna (1st {this pub.}, 8vo, 255p, 8pl)	L: Harrap	1938	Tawse, Sybil	55-80	*
Kingsley, Charles	The Heroes (1st, 8vo, 221p, 8cp)	L: A&C Black	1915	Tawse, Sybil	40-70	
Moore, Clement C.	Night Before Christmas (4to, [16]p, wraps, fp color)	Whitman	(1943)	Taylor, Ethel	30-50	*
Stranathan, May	Silhouette Stories (1st, 8vo, 198p, brown cl, 14 fp b/w)	Moffat	1921	Taylor, Ethel C.	35-60	*
Ransome, Arthur	Bohemia in London (1st AM, 8vo, 293p, teg, uncut, 16pl)	Dodd	1907	Taylor, Fred	70-125	
Montgomery, Lucy M.	Anne of the Island (1st, sm8vo, 326p, col frn & p-o)	L.C. Page	1915	Taylor, H. Weston	200-300	
Barbour, Ralph H.	Hearts Content (1st, 8vo, teg, 204p, p-o, 4cp)	Lippincott	1915	Taylor, H. Weston	40-65	
Porter, Eleanor	Pollyanna Grows Up (1st, sm8vo, 308p, gilt, 8pl)	L.C. Page	1915	Taylor, H. Weston	45-70	
Borton, Elizabeth	Pollyanna in Hollywood (1st, sm8vo, gilt, 341p, col frn)	L.C. Page	(1931)	Taylor, H. Weston	30-45	
Smith, Harriet L.	Pollyanna of the Orange Blossoms (1st, sm8vo, p-o, 313p, 6pl)	L.C. Page	1924	Taylor, H. Weston	30-50	
Smith, Harriet L.	Pollyanna's Jewels (1st, sm8vo, 328p, blue cl, p-o, 6pl)	L.C. Page	(1925)	Taylor, H. Weston	30-50	
Lewis, Alfred H.	Sandburrs (1st, 12mo, 318p, 16pl)	Stokes	(1900)	Taylor, H. Weston	50-80	
Andersen, Hans C.	Fairy Tales (1st, 4to, blue/silver, 56p, color, pep, DJ/2.50)	Duell, Sloan	(1946)	Taylor, John A.	35-50	
Lyons, Dorothy	Silver Birch (1st, 8vo, 308p, b/w, DJ/2.00)	Harcourt	(1939)	Taylor, John A.	80-140	
Burroughs, Margaret	Jasper the Drummin' Boy (1st, lg8vo, ibds, 63p, fp b/w, DJ/1.75)	Viking	1947	Taylor, Margaret	70-100	
Taylor, Paul B.	Tippletappleteven Town (1st, sq8vo, [12]p, ibds, color, pep)	Henry Holt & Co.	(1931)	Taylor, P.B.	65-90	
Pratt, Charles S.	Baby's Lullaby Book (folio, [64]p, 16 t-i chromos, dep)	Prang Co.	1888	Taylor, W.L.	450-600	

ARTIST: 200

AUTHOR	TITLE	PUBLISHER	DATE	ARTIST	PRICE	LC
Sidney, Margaret	Five Little Peppers Midway (1st, 12mo, 512p, gilt, 20pl)	D. Lothrop Co.	(1890)	Taylor, W.L.	70-100	
Maunder, Irene	Plain Princess (1st, 4to, 95p, brown cl, 14pl, dep)	L: Longmans	1905	Taylor/Baxter	100-160	
Farjeon, Eleanor	Tale of Tom Tiddler (1st, 8vo, 191p, gilt, color)	L: Collins	(1929)	Tealby, Norman	75-100	*
N/A	Three Bears (1st, sq4to, [18]p, color, pep)	Grosset/Dunlap	(1938)	Tedder, Elizabeth	30-50	*
Andersen, Hans C.	Fairy Tales (1st AM, lg4to, 524p, gilt, 85pl)	Century	1900	Tegner, Hans	250-350	R
Andersen, Hans C.	Fairy Tales (1st, 4to, 2 volumes, bds, gilt, b/w)	L: Heinemann	1900	Tegner, Hans	250-400	
Wyatt, Horace	Malice in Kulturland (1st AM, 12mo, 84p, ipcb, p-o, b/w)	Dutton	(1917)	Tell, W.	60-100	
Uttley, Alison	Fuzzypeg Goes to School (1st, 8vo, blue cl, 100p, p-o, color, pep)	L: Collins	(1938)	Tempest, Margaret	130-175	
Uttley, Alison	Gray Rabbit Finds a Shoe (1st, 12mo, 63p, ipcb, color, pep)	L: Collins	(1960)	Tempest, Margaret	30-50	
Uttley, Alison	Great Adventure of Hare (1st, 8vo, 107p, ipcb, p-o, color, pep)	L: Heinemann	1931	Tempest, Margaret	50-80	
Uttley, Alison	Grey Rabbit & the Circus (1st, 12mo, ibds, 61p, color)	L: Collins	(1961)	Tempest, Margaret	35-50	
Uttley, Alison	Grey Rabbit's May Day (1st, 12mo, 63p, ipcb, color)	L: Collins	1963	Tempest, Margaret	30-50	
Uttley, Alison	Hare & the Easter Egg (1st, sq12mo, 80p, green bds, 16 fp color)	L: Collins	(1952)	Tempest, Margaret	40-60	
Uttley, Alison	Hare and the Easter Eggs (1st, 12mo, ibds, 80p, fp color, DJ)	L: Collins	1952	Tempest, Margaret	40-65	
Uttley, Alison	Hare Goes Shopping (1st, 12mo, ibds, 63p, color)	L: Collins	(1965)	Tempest, Margaret	35-50	
Uttley, Alison	How Little Grey Rabbit Got Back her Tail (1st, 8vo, 109p, ipcb, p-o, color)	L: Heinemann	1930	Tempest, Margaret	50-80	
Uttley, Alison	Knot Squirrel Tied (1st, 8vo, 101p, grey pcb, p-o, 23 fp color, pep)	L: Collins	1937	Tempest, Margaret	60-90	
Uttley, Alison	Little Grey Rabbit & Weasels (1st, 80p, pcb, p-o, color, pep)	L: Collins	1947	Tempest, Margaret	50-85	
Uttley, Alison	Little Grey Rabbit Goes to Sea (1st, 12mo, ibds, 80p, fp color)	L: Collins	(1954)	Tempest, Margaret	35-50	
Uttley, Alison	Little Grey Rabbit's Christmas (1st, sq8vo, 104p, ibds, color)	L: Collins	1939	Tempest, Margaret	50-85	
Uttley, Alison	Little Grey Rabbit's Pancake Day (1st, 12mo, 63p, ipcb, color, DJ)	L: Collins	1967	Tempest, Margaret	30-50	
Uttley, Alison	Little Grey Rabbit's Party (1st, 12mo, ibds, 112p, fp color, pep)	L: Collins	(1936)	Tempest, Margaret	60-90	
Uttley, Alison	Little Grey Rabbit's Valentine (1st, 8vo, 92p, ibds, color)	L: Collins	(1953)	Tempest, Margaret	40-65	
Uttley, Alison	Moldy Warp the Mole (1st, 12mo, ibds, 88p, color)	L: Collins	(1940)	Tempest, Margaret	50-70	
Evans, Myfanwy	No Rubbish Here (1st, 4to, green ibds, 34p, color)	L: Collins	(1936)	Tempest, Margaret	70-100	
Kaye, Mollie	Potter Pinner Meadow (1st, sq4to, [48]p, ibds, color)	L: Collins	1937	Tempest, Margaret	60-90	
Uttley, Alison	Squirrel Goes Skating (1st, sq8vo, 112p, p-o, color, pep)	L: Collins	1934	Tempest, Margaret	50-80	
Uttley, Alison	Story of Fuzzypeg the Hedgehog (1st, 8vo, 98p, ipcb, p-o, color, pep)	L: Heinemann	1932	Tempest, Margaret	60-90	
Kaye, Mollie	Willow Witches Brook (1st, 12mo, ibds, 46p, color)	L: Collins	(1944)	Tempest, Margaret	60-85	
Uttley, Alison	Wise Owl's Story (1st, 12mo, 108p, ipcb, p-o, pep)	L: Collins	1935	Tempest, Margaret	55-80	
Duplaix, Georges	Big Brown Bear (1st, 4to, ibds, [52]p, color, pep, BGB)	Simon/Schuster	(1947)	Tenggren, Gustaf	80-120	
Hewes, Agnes D.	Boy of the Lost Crusade (1st, 8vo, p-o, 279p, gilt, 4cp, pep)	Houghton	1923	Tenggren, Gustaf	40-65	
Fitinghoff, Laura M.	Children of the Moor (1st, 8vo, 282p, col frn, 3pl, pep)	Houghton	1927	Tenggren, Gustaf	30-50	
Rihbany, Abraham M.	Christ Story for Boys & Girls (1st, 8vo, gilt, p-o, 239p, 4cp)	Houghton	(1923)	Tenggren, Gustaf	55-80	
D'Aulnoy	D'Aulnoy's Fairy Tales (1st, 4to, gilt, teg, p-o, 457p, 9cp, pep)	McKay	1923	Tenggren, Gustaf	160-225	
Woodruff, Elizabeth	Dickey Bird (1st, lg4to, black cl, 146p, 6 ticp, pep)	Milton Bradley	(1928)	Tenggren, Gustaf	280-400	
Andersen, Hans C.	Fairy Tales (1st, sm8vo, 224p, tan cl, 13 fp b/w, DJ/1.50)	Appleton-Century	(1935)	Tenggren, Gustaf	60-100	
Jackson, Kathryn	Farm Stories (1st {std}, folio, ibds, 91p, color, pep, GGB)	Simon/Schuster	(1946)	Tenggren, Gustaf	80-120	
Various	Good Dog Book (1st, 8vo, blue cl, 264p, p-o, 5cp)	Houghton	1924	Tenggren, Gustaf	50-80	
Spyri, Johanna	Heidi (1st, 8vo, 356p, blue cl, p-o, 4cp)	Houghton	1923	Tenggren, Gustaf	60-100	
Muller, Charles G.	How they Carried the Goods (1st, lg8vo, 318p, 4cp, 9pl)	Sears	(1932)	Tenggren, Gustaf	40-60	
Baylor, Frances C.	Juan and Juanita (1st, 8vo, 300p, blue cl, p-o, 4cp, pep)	Houghton	1926	Tenggren, Gustaf	70-100	
Bannerman, Helen	Little Black Sambo (1st {A}, sm8vo, ibds, [42]p, color, LGB/#57)	Simon/Schuster	(1948)	Tenggren, Gustaf	50-80	
Andersen, Hans C.	Little Match Girl (1st, 4to, ibds, [24]p, pep, fp color, DJ/1.00)	Grosset/Dunlap	(1944)	Tenggren, Gustaf	60-90	
Mother Goose	Mother Goose (1st, 4to, 136p, color, pep, DJ/2.00)	Little/Brown	1940	Tenggren, Gustaf	100-170	
Bertail, Inez	New Illustrated Book of Favorite Hymns (1st, folio, 44p, fp color, pep)	Garden City	1941	Tenggren, Gustaf	60-85	
Moore, Clement C.	Night Before Christmas (1st, 4to, ibds, unpag, color, BGB)	Simon/Schuster	(1951)	Tenggren, Gustaf	100-165	
Hunt, Clara W.	Peggy's Playhouses (1st, sm8vo, 123p, p-o, b/w, pl)	Houghton	1924	Tenggren, Gustaf	30-50	*
Rodgers, Carolyn	Pirate's Loot (1st, 8vo, yellow cl, 282p, 30 fp 1-color)	Sears	1931	Tenggren, Gustaf	55-80	
Lowrey, Janette S.	Poky Little Puppy (1st {A}, 12mo, [42]p, ibds, color, LGB/#8)	Simon/Schuster	1942	Tenggren, Gustaf	40-60	
Lang, Andrew	Red Fairy Book (1st, lg8vo, 285p, p-o, teg, red cl, 8cp, pep)	McKay	(1924)	Tenggren, Gustaf	200-300	
Henderson, Gertrude	Ring of the Nibelung (1st {std}, lg8vo, 218p, col frn, 12 fp b/w)	Knopf	1932	Tenggren, Gustaf	60-100	
Schrank, Joseph	Seldom & the Golden Cheese (1st, 8vo, 160p, uncut, col frn, 7pl, pep)	Dodd	1933	Tenggren, Gustaf	150-250	
Wheeler, Opal	Sing for America (1st {std}, 4to, 127p, ibds, fp color, pep, DJ/3.75)	Dutton	(1944)	Tenggren, Gustaf	60-90	
Wheeler, Opal	Sing for Christmas (1st {std}, 4to, ibds, 127p, 12cp, pep, DJ/3.75)	Dutton	1943	Tenggren, Gustaf	80-120	
Campbell, Ruth	Small Fry and the Winged Horse (1st, 8vo, ibds, 28p, 10cp, pep)	Volland	(1927)	Tenggren, Gustaf	80-130	
Dike, Helen	Stories from Great Metropolitan Operas (1st, lg8vo, 247p, 12cp, DJ/2.00)	Random	(1943)	Tenggren, Gustaf	30-50	
Woodruff, Elizabeth	Stories from the Magic World (1st, lg4to, 130p, p-o, 5cp, DJ/1.25)	McLoughlin	(1938)	Tenggren, Gustaf	250-350	
Overbeck, Alice	Sven the Wise & Svea the Kind (1st, 8vo, 171p, 2cp, b/w, pep)	Harper	1932	Tenggren, Gustaf	60-85	
Gibson, Katharine	Tenggren Tell-It-Again Book (1st, 4to, 199p, fp color, pep, DJ/2.50)	Little/Brown	(1942)	Tenggren, Gustaf	100-165	
Jackson, Kathryn	Tenggren's Cowboys & Indians (1st, folio, ibds, 96p, color, GGB)	Simon/Schuster	(1948)	Tenggren, Gustaf	80-125	
Tenggren, Gustaf	Tenggren's Story Book (1st {std}, folio, 89p, ibds, color, pep, GGB)	Simon/Schuster	1944	Tenggren, Gustaf	80-125	
Hawthorne, Nathaniel	Wonder Book (1st, 8vo, p-o, gilt, 421p, 4cp)	Houghton	1923	Tenggren, Gustaf	35-60	
Girvin, Brenda	Girl Scout (1st, sm8vo, 319p, blue/gilt, 6cp)	L: H. Frowde	1913	Tenison, Nell M.	45-70	
Stanley, H.M.	London Street Arabs (1st, 4to, 67p, green cl, AEG, 28pl)	L: Cassell	1890	Tennant, Dudley	120-170	
Wilcox, Ella W.	Poems of Passion & Pleasure (4to, 267p, white/gilt, teg, 20 ticp, pep)	L: Gay/Hancock	(1912)	Tennant, Dudley	200-300	
Carroll, Lewis	Alice in Wonderland (sm4to, tan cl, 160p, 4cp)	Altemus	(1897)	Tenniel, John	100-165	
Carroll, Lewis	Alice in Wonderland (1st, 12mo, 179p, color)	NY: McKibbin	1899	Tenniel, John	80-120	*
Carroll, Lewis	Alice in Wonderland (16mo, ibds, p-o, 126p, 30cp, pep)	Altemus	[1900]	Tenniel, John	80-120	
Carroll, Lewis	Alice in Wonderland (32mo, 127p, 32 color)	L: Macmillan	1903	Tenniel, John	90-160	*
Carroll, Lewis	Alice in Wonderland (sm8vo, ibds, 202p, pep)	Caldwell	[1904]	Tenniel, John	90-160	*
Carroll, Lewis	Alice in Wonderland (1st, 12mo, ipcb, [56]p, 8 fp color)	McLoughlin	(1940)	Tenniel, John	80-120	*
Carroll, Lewis	Alice... & Through... (1st [combined], 12mo, 383p, green cl)	L: Macmillan	1887	Tenniel, John	250-350	
Carroll, Lewis	Alice... & Through... (8vo, teg, 351p, b/w)	Altemus	1895	Tenniel, John	100-165	*
Carroll, Lewis	Alice... & Through... (4to, blue/gilt, col frn, b/w)	McLoughlin	[1910]	Tenniel, John	120-200	*
Carroll, Lewis	Alice... & Through... (1st [color ed.], 8vo, 292p, gilt, 16cp)	L: Macmillan	1911	Tenniel, John	175-260	
Carroll, Lewis	Alice... & Through... (1st {this pub}, 4to, p-o, 59p, cep, color)	Platt/Munk	(1938)	Tenniel, John	100-165	*
Carroll, Lewis	Alice... Through... & Hunting (1st, 8vo, 351p, teg, uncut, b/w)	Boni/Liveright	1925	Tenniel, John	120-180	*

AUTHOR	TITLE	PUBLISHER	DATE	ARTIST	PRICE	LC
Herrick, Christina	Lewis Carroll Birthday Book (16mo, white cl, [255]p, b/w)	Wessels	(1905)	Tenniel, John	120-185	
Carroll, Lewis	Nursery Alice (1st, 4to, ibds, 56p, 20 color, cep)	L: Macmillan	1890	Tenniel, John	700-900	
Carroll, Lewis	Through the Looking Glass (12mo, 175p, grey/gilt, 4 chromos)	DeWolfe/Fiske	1898	Tenniel, John	150-220	
Carroll, Lewis	Through the Looking Glass (1st {this pub}, 4to, ibds, 98p, 2-color)	Whittlesey	[1946]	Tenniel, John	40-60	*
Carroll, Lewis	Alice... & Through... (1st {this pub}, sm8vo, 317p, col frn)	Collier	1903	Tenniel/Stevens	70-100	*
Winfrey, Guy	Bunny Bearskin (1st, 8vo, ibds, color, pep)	Milton Bradley	(1926)	Tessin, Louise D.	80-120	
Winfrey, Guy	Pussy Purr-Mew (1st, 8vo, [126]p, ibds, color, pep)	Milton Bradley	(1927)	Tessin, Louise D.	100-160	
Thackeray, Lance	Light Side of Egypt (1st, ob4to, ibds, [80]p, 36cp)	L: A&C Black	1908	Thackeray, Lance	125-200	
Stratton-Porter, Gene	Magic Garden (1st {std}, sm8vo, 272p, pep, designs by...)	Doubleday/Page	1927	Thayer, Lee	120-170	
Comstock, Harriet T.	Princess Rags & Tatters (1st, sm8vo, grey cl, 112p, 4cp)	Doubleday/Page	1912	Thayer, Lee	35-60	
Woolf, Rose	Children's Stories from Arabian Nights (1st, lg8vo, 144p, 10cp)	L: R. Tuck	[1914]	Theaker, Harry G.	70-100	*
Kato, N. (tr.)	Children's Stories from Japanese Fairy Tales (1st, lg8vo, 134p, ibds, 10cp)	L: R. Tuck	[1918]	Theaker, Harry G.	100-170	
Cervantes	Don Quixote (1st, lg8vo, 340p, 48cp, pep)	L: Ward Lock	1910	Theaker, Harry G.	60-90	*
Grimm Bros.	Fairy Tales (1st, lg8vo, 344p, 48cp)	L: Ward Lock	1920	Theaker, Harry G.	80-120	*
Swift, Jonathan	Gulliver's Travels (1st, lg8vo, 338p, p-o, 48cp)	L: Ward Lock	(1923)	Theaker, Harry G.	70-100	
Ingoldsby, Thomas	Ingoldsby Legends (1st, 8vo, blue/gilt, a.e. blue, 546p, 16cp)	L: Macmillan	1911	Theaker, Harry G.	100-160	
Winder, Blanche	King Arthur & his Knights (8vo, 340p, p-o, 48cp, pep)	L: Ward Lock	[1925]	Theaker, Harry G.	100-165	
Kingsley, Charles	Water Babies (1st, 8vo, 340p, grey cl, p-o, 48cp, pep)	L: Ward Lock	1916	Theaker, Harry G.	120-180	
Martin, Patricia	Dog and the Boat Boy (1st, 4to, 44p, color, DJ)	Putnam	(1969)	Thollander, Earl	20-35	
Cleary, Beverly	Hullabaloo ABC (1st, 4to, [36]p, color, pep, DJ/2.95)	Parnassus Press	1960	Thollander, Earl	25-40	*
Martin, Patricia	Jump Frog Jump (1st, sm4to, 47p, color, DJ/2.75)	Putnam	(1965)	Thollander, Earl	25-35	
Martin, Patricia	Mrs. Grumble and Fire Engine Number 7 (1st, 4to, 48p, color, DJ)	Putnam	(1966)	Thollander, Earl	40-65	
Martin, Patricia	No, No Rosina (1st, 8vo, 48p, color, DJ/2.75)	Putnam	(1964)	Thollander, Earl	20-35	*
Ritchie, Barbara	To Catch a Mongoose (1st AM, 4to, 61p, fp color, DJ/3.75)	Parnassus Press	(1963)	Thollander, Earl	25-40	*
Brown, Myra B.	Where's Jeremy? (1st, 4to, [48]p, 1-color, cep, DJ/3.75)	Golden Gate	(1968)	Thollander, Earl	30-45	
Berger, Josef	Sleepy Steve (1st, 8vo, 200p, uncut, fp b/w, pep)	Minton Balch	(1931)	Thomas, Dorothy G.	25-45	*
Richards, Dorothy	Adventures in an Old Shoe House (1st, 12mo, 30p, ibds, 6cp)	L: Faber	[1948]	Thomas, Elsie	40-60	
Richards, Dorothy	Roma Rabbit's Picnic (1st, 16mo, 30p, ibds, 6cp)	L: Faber	1948	Thomas, Elsie	40-60	
Stowe, Harriet B.	Uncle Tom's Cabin (1st, 8vo, 529p, gilt, illus by...)	L: Routledge	1897	Thomas, George H.	170-220	
Warner, Anne	The Panther (1st, 8vo, teg, uncut, 91p, col frn, 3pl)	Small/Maynard	1908	Thomas, Paul K.	30-50	
White, Anne T.	David the Giant Killer (1st, 8vo, 131p, fp b/w, DJ/4.50)	Crowell	(1970)	Thomas, Phero	40-65	*
Crockett, Davy	Adventures of Davy Crockett (1st, 8vo, black/gilt, 258p, p-o, 3cp)	Scribner	1934	Thomason, John W.	100-160	
Thomason, John W.	Fix Bayonets! (1st, lg8vo, 245p, gilt, bds, p-o, col frn, b/w)	Scribner	1926	Thomason, John W.	70-125	
Page, Thomas N.	Two Little Confederates (1st, sm4to, 189p, gilt, p-o, col frn)	Scribner	1932	Thomason, John W.	70-120	
Reed, Helen L.	Brenda's Bargain (1st, 8vo, 251p, 6pl)	Little/Brown	1903	Thompson, E.B.	35-60	
Ray, Anna C.	Nathalie's Chum (1st, 12mo, 289p, 6pl)	Little/Brown	1902	Thompson, E.B.	30-50	
LeBaron, Grace	Twixt You & Me (1st, 12mo, 296p, 5pl by...)	Little/Brown	1898	Thompson, E.B.	40-60	*
Bingham, Clifton	Airship in Animal Land (ob4to, ibds, 8 chromos)	L: Nister	[1910]	Thompson, G.H.	400-600	
Bingham, Clifton	Animal's Rebellion (1st, ob4to, ibds, [36]p, 8 chromos, pep)	Nister/Dutton	(1911)	Thompson, G.H.	200-300	*
Braine, Sheila E.	Animals' Touring Club (ob4to, ibds, unpag, 8 chromos)	Nister/Dutton	[1900]	Thompson, G.H.	100-170	
Bingham, Clifton	Animals' Trip to Sea (1st, ob4to, ibds, [36]p, fp color)	Nister/Dutton	[1900]	Thompson, G.H.	250-350	
Bingham, Clifton	Funny Doings in Animal Land (ob4to, ibds, 8 chromos, pep)	L: Nister	[1910]	Thompson, G.H.	500-800	
Wood, Helen J.	Funny Friends (8vo, ibds, color)	L: Nister	[1889]	Thompson, G.H.	100-165	
Fletcher, David	Confetti for Cortorelli (1st {std}, 8vo, 147p, b/w, DJ/2.75)	Pantheon	(1957)	Thompson, George	30-45	*
Coatsworth, Eliz.	White Room (1st, 8vo, 143p, b/w, DJ/2.75)	Pantheon	(1958)	Thompson, George	25-45	
Howell, Virginia	Who Likes the Dark? (1st, 8vo, [40]p, ibds, color, DJ/1.50)	Howell/Soskin	1945	Thompson, Marjorie	30-50	*
Lang, Andrew	Story of the Golden Fleece (1st, 8vo, 93p, 6pl)	Altemus	(1903)	Thompson, Mills	75-100	*
Yezback, Steven	Pumpkinseeds (1st {std}, 4to, [30]p, 1-color, DJ/4.50)	Bobbs-Merrill	(1969)	Thompson, Mozelle	40-65	
Molloy, Anne	Blanche of the Blueberry Barrens (1st, 8vo, 168p, fp b/w, dep, DJ/2.95)	Hastings House	(1959)	Thomson, Arline K.	30-50	
Carroll, Lewis	Three Sunsets... (1st, sq8vo, green/gilt, AEG, 68p, 12 fp b/w)	L: Macmillan	1898	Thomson, E. Gertrude	300-500	
Barrie, James M.	Admirable Crichton (1st, 4to, 235p, gilt, 21 ticp)	L: Hodder	[1914]	Thomson, Hugh	130-200	
Shakespeare, Wm.	As You Like It (1st, 4to, ibds, 143p, gilt, 40 ticp)	L: Hodder	[1909]	Thomson, Hugh	125-200	
Dobson, Austin	Ballad of Beau Brocade (1st, 8vo, 89p, uncut, gilt, teg, b/w)	L: Kegan Paul	1892	Thomson, Hugh	70-100	
Dobson, Austin	Coridon's Song (1st, 12mo, green/gilt, AEG, 163p, b/w, cep)	L: Macmillan	1894	Thomson, Hugh	100-170	
Gaskell, Mrs.	Cranford (1st {color ed.}, 12mo, teg, gilt, 298p, 40cp)	L: Macmillan	1898	Thomson, Hugh	70-100	
Burney, Fanny	Evelina... (1st, 8vo, 477p, gilt, b/w)	L: Macmillan	(1903)	Thomson, Hugh	60-90	
Gwynn, Stephen L.	Fair Hills of Ireland (1st, 8vo, 416p, uncut, color)	L: Macmillan	1906	Thomson, Hugh	50-80	
Thackeray, Wm. M.	History of Henry Esmond (1st, 12mo, 402p, gilt, AEG, 50 b/w)	L: Macmillan	1905	Thomson, Hugh	60-100	
Spielmann, M.H.	Hugh Thomson: His Art (1st, lg8vo, 269p, gilt, 12cp)	L: A&C Black	1931	Thomson, Hugh	100-170	
Thomson, Hugh	Jack the Giant Killer (1st, sq8vo, [32]p, wraps, 16 color)	L: Macmillan	1898	Thomson, Hugh	200-350	
Allen, James L.	Kentucky Cardinal Aftermath (1st AM [new ed], 12mo, gilt, 276p, AEG, b/w)	Macmillan	1900	Thomson, Hugh	70-100	
Shakespeare, Wm.	Merry Wives of Windsor (1st AM, 4to, 170p, red/gilt, teg, 40 ticp)	Stokes	(1910)	Thomson, Hugh	165-250	
Shakespeare, Wm.	Merry Wives of Windsor (1st, 4to, gilt, 172p, 40 ticp)	L: Heinemann	1910	Thomson, Hugh	200-300	
Spielmann, M.H.	My Son & I (1st, 8vo, red/gilt, teg, 307p, uncut, col frn, 9pl)	L: G. Allen	1908	Thomson, Hugh	60-90	
Austen, Jane	Northanger Abbey (1st, 12mo, AEG, 444p, red/gilt, b/w)	L: Macmillan	1897	Thomson, Hugh	100-165	
N/A	Old English Songs (1st, sm8vo, 163p, AEG, green/gilt)	L: Macmillan	1894	Thomson, Hugh	60-90	
Mitford, Mary R.	Our Village (1st, sm8vo, 256p, AEG, green/gilt, b/w, cep)	L: Macmillan	1893	Thomson, Hugh	60-100	
Reade, Charles	Peg Woffington (1st, 12mo, 298p, green/gilt, AEG, b/w)	L: G. Allen	1899	Thomson, Hugh	75-100	
Reade, Charles	Peg Woffington (1st AM, 12mo, green/gilt, 298p, AEG, b/w)	Doub./McClure	1899	Thomson, Hugh	60-90	
Browning, Robert	Pied Piper of Hamelin (1st, 8vo, 64p, uncut, 12pl)	L: Heinemann	1893	Thomson, Hugh	100-160	
Austen, Jane	Pride and Prejudice (1st, 12mo, 476p, AEG, green/gilt, b/w, cep)	L: G. Allen	1894	Thomson, Hugh	200-300	
Barrie, James M.	Quality Street (1st, 4to, 198p, blue/gilt, 22 ticp, pep)	L: Hodder	[1913]	Thomson, Hugh	150-240	
Hawthorne, Nathaniel	Scarlet Letter (1st, 4to, uncut, 296p, gilt, teg, 31 ticp)	L: Methuen	(1920)	Thomson, Hugh	170-250	
Hawthorne, Nathaniel	Scarlet Letter (1st AM, sm4to, 296p, ibds, 31 ticp)	Doran	[1920]	Thomson, Hugh	170-240	
Eliot, George	Scenes from Clerical Life (1st, 12mo, 429p, green/gilt, AEG, 16cp)	L: Macmillan	1906	Thomson, Hugh	60-100	
Sheridan, Richard B.	School for Scandal (1st, 4to, gilt, teg, 196p, 25 ticp, pep)	L: Hodder	(1911)	Thomson, Hugh	180-250	
Goldsmith, Oliver	She Stoops to Conquer (1st, 4to, 198p, gilt, 25 ticp)	L: Hodder	(1912)	Thomson, Hugh	140-200	
Dobson, Austin	Story of Rosina (1st, sm8vo, AEG, 120p, gilt, 28pl, cep)	L: Kegan Paul	1895	Thomson, Hugh	75-100	

AUTHOR	TITLE	PUBLISHER	DATE	ARTIST	PRICE	LC
Edgeworth, Maria	Tales from.... (1st AM, 8vo, brown/gilt, teg, 412p, uncut, b/w)	Stokes	(1903)	Thomson, Hugh	85-130	
Somerville, William	The Chase (1st, lg sq8vo, 87p, gilt, teg, 9 fp b/w)	L: Redway	1896	Thomson, Hugh	70-100	
Dickens, Charles	The Chimes (1st, 8vo, 137p, red/gilt, 7 ticp, pep)	L: Hodder	[1912]	Thomson, Hugh	200-300	
Molesworth, Mrs.	This & That (1st, 12mo, 212p, orange/gilt, 8pl)	L: Macmillan	1899	Thomson, Hugh	60-80	
Goldsmith, Oliver	Vicar of Wakefield (1st, 8vo, 305p, AEG, gilt, b/w)	L: Macmillan	1890	Thomson, Hugh	70-125	
Malory, Thomas	King Arthur... (1st, 12mo, 335p, gilt, cp)	Macmillan	1916	Thomson, Rodney	40-60	*
Bradley, Arthur G.	Highways & Byways of North Wales (1st, 8vo, gilt, 474p, b/w)	L: Macmillan	1898	Thomson/Pennell	75-100	*
Terhune, Albert P.	Columbia Stories (1st {1st bk.}, sm8vo, 214p, b/w)	Dillingham	1897	Thornburgh, F.	120-200	*
Bradbury, Bianca	Antique Cat (1st {std}, sq8vo, [64]p, fp 1-color, pep)	Winston	(1945)	Thorne, Diana	40-65	
Shurtleff, Bertrand	Awol the Courier (1st {std}, 8vo, 272p, b/w, DJ/2.50)	Bobbs-Merrill	(1951)	Thorne, Diana	40-65	*
Henry, Marguerite	Boy & a Dog (1st, sm4to, [42]p, ibds, 2-color, pep, DJ/1.00)	Wilcox/Follett	1944	Thorne, Diana	60-100	
Thorne, Diana	Cats & More Cats (1st, 8vo, ibds, [32]p, 2-color, DJ/1.00)	Wilcox/Follett	1945	Thorne, Diana	30-45	
Hoke, Helen	Doctor, the Puppy Who Learned (1st, sq8vo, [18]p, ibds, 1-color, DJ/1.00)	J. Messner	1944	Thorne, Diana	35-50	
Thorne, Diana	Dog Book (1st, 4to, 89p, ibds, 12 fp color)	Saalfield	(1932)	Thorne, Diana	100-165	
Cooper, Page (ed)	Famous Dog Stories (1st {std}, 8vo, 336p, b/w, DJ/3.50)	Doubleday	1948	Thorne, Diana	30-45	
Walden, Jane B.	Igloo (1st, 8vo, 211p, col frn, b/w)	Putnam	1931	Thorne, Diana	30-50	
Garner, Elvira	Little Cat Lost (1st, sm sq4to, ibds, [28]p, 2-color, pep, DJ/2.00)	J. Messner	(1943)	Thorne, Diana	80-130	
Henry, Marguerite	Little Fellow (1st, 4to, [64]p, color, pep, DJ/2.00)	Winston	(1945)	Thorne, Diana	50-85	
Hoke, Helen	Major and the Kitten (1st, 4to, ibds, 36p, 1-color, DJ/2.00)	Henry Holt & Co.	(1941)	Thorne, Diana	30-50	
Hilles, Helen	Mile of Freedom (1st, sm8vo, 248p, b/w, DJ/2.00)	Macmillan	1932	Thorne, Diana	25-40	
Hoke, Helen	Mrs. Silk (1st, 4to, [24]p, ibds, color, DJ/1.00)	Veritas Press	1945	Thorne, Diana	30-45	
Orton, Ruth	Pepito the Colt (1st, ob4to, ibds, 36p, b/w, pep)	Houghton	1933	Thorne, Diana	50-80	*
Thorne, Diana	Peter the Goat (1st, sq8vo, ibds, [48]p, fp b/w, DJ/1.00)	McKay	(1940)	Thorne, Diana	30-50	
Terhune, Albert P.	Real Tales of Real Dogs (1st, lg4to, ibds, 92p, b/w, DJ/1.00)	Saalfield	(1935)	Thorne, Diana	80-125	
Salten, Felix	Renni the Rescuer (1st {std}, 8vo, 326p, b/w, DJ/2.50)	Bobbs-Merrill	1940	Thorne, Diana	40-60	
Genevoix, Maurice	Rrou (1st, 8vo, 224p, blue cl, b/w, cep)	Minton Balch	1932	Thorne, Diana	25-45	
Hoke, Helen	Shep and the Baby (1st, sq8vo, ibds, [17]p, color, DJ/1.00)	J. Messner	1944	Thorne, Diana	30-50	*
Terhune, Albert P.	True Dog Stories (1st, 12mo, 60p, b/w)	Saalfield	1936	Thorne, Diana	50-80	
Inchfawn, Fay	Who Goes to the Wood (1st, 8vo, 229p, col frn, b/w, DJ/2.00)	Winston	(1942)	Thorne, Diana	25-45	
Knecht, Klara	Wild Animals as I Know Them (1st, lg4to, ibds, 90p, 12 fp color)	Saalfield	(1933)	Thorne, Diana	50-80	
Farjeon, Eleanor	Heroes & Heroines (1st AM, lg8vo, 79p, ibds, fp color, DJ)	Dutton	(1933)	Thornycroft, R.	60-100	
Farjeon, Eleanor	Italian Peepshow (1st, 8vo, gilt, p-o, 146p, 12 fp color, pep)	Stokes	1926	Thornycroft, R.	35-60	*
Farjeon, Eleanor	Kings & Queens (1st AM, lg8vo, 79p, color, DJ)	Dutton	1932	Thornycroft, R.	50-90	
Farjeon, Eleanor	Kings & Queens (1st, 8vo, 79p, ibds, 38cp, DJ)	L: Gollancz	(1932)	Thornycroft, R.	60-90	
Farjeon, Eleanor	Kings & Queens (sm4to, red cl, 86p, 40 fp color, DJ/2.50)	Dent/Dutton	(1940)	Thornycroft, R.	35-60	*
Farjeon, Eleanor	Kings & Queens (sm4to, ibds, 86p, 40 color, DJ)	Lippincott	[1940]	Thornycroft, R.	35-60	
Farjeon, Eleanor	Nuts & May (1st, 4to, p-o, 263p, color)	L: Collins	1926	Thornycroft, R.	90-160	*
Thurber, James	Further Fables of Our Time (1st {std}, 8vo, 174p, bds, gilt, b/w, DJ/3.50)	Simon/Schuster	1956	Thurber, James	65-100	
Hawes, Elizabeth	Men Can Take It (1st {std}, 8vo, blue cl, 275p, 14pl, DJ/2.00)	Random	(1939)	Thurber, James	75-100	*
Thurber, James	Owl in the Attic (1st {std}, 8vo, 151p, yellow cl, b/w)	Harper	1931	Thurber, James	140-220	R
Thurston, Clara B.	Discontented Stuffed Cat (1st, 4to, ibds, b/w)	Saalfield	(1910)	Thurston, Clara B.	150-225	
Thurston, Clara B.	Jingle of a Jap (1st, lg8vo, [64]p, p-o, color, pep)	Caldwell	(1906)	Thurston, Clara B.	100-165	
N/A	New Story of Little Black Sambo (16mo, grey bds, unpag, color, pep)	Whitman	1926	Thurston/Vetsch	100-165	
Gibson, Eva K.	Zauberlinda: Wise Witch (1st, 8vo, 256p, blue cl, 1-color, pep)	Chi: R. Smith	(1901)	Tibbitts, Mabel	180-250	
Tice, Clara	ABC Dogs (1st, folio, ibds, [32]p, color, pep, DJ/2.00)	NY: Wilfred Funk	1940	Tice, Clara	200-300	
Sinclair, Upton	The Gnomobile (1st [this pub.], 8vo, 191p, color, DJ/3.50)	Bobbs-Merrill	1962	Tillard, Marcel	80-120	
Chilvers, Hedley A.	Out of the Crucible (1st, 8vo, 273p, gilt, 16 illus)	L: Cassell	1929	Timlin, William M.	120-170	*
Timlin, William M.	Ship that Sailed to Mars (1st, lg4to, gilt, 48p, ibds, 48 ticp)	L: Harrap	(1923)	Timlin, William M.	2000-3000	
Saroyan, William	Me (1st, 4to, [64]p, ibds, color)	Crowell-Collier	(1963)	Tinkelman, Murray	80-120	
George, Jean C.	Moon of the Monarch Butterflies (1st, 8vo, 40p, b/w, DJ/3.75)	Crowell	(1968)	Tinkelman, Murray	20-35	
Stolz, Mary S.	Pigeon Flight (1st, 8vo, 54p, fp b/w, DJ/2.50)	Harper	(1962)	Tinkelman, Murray	40-65	R
N/A	Old Woman & her Pig (1st, 24mo, [41]p, ibds, 1-color)	Holiday House	[1937]	Tinker, Jack H.	40-70	
Collodi, Carlo	Pinocchio (1st {Gift ed.}, lg8vo, 234p, 10cp)	Lippincott	(1930)	Tinker, Jack H.	75-100	*
Thackeray, Wm. M.	Rose & the Ring (lg8vo, 161p, p-o, 9cp, cep)	Brentano's	[1920]	Tinker, Jack H.	80-135	
Tittle, Walter	Colonial Holidays (1st, sm4to, gilt, teg, 73p, p-o, 22cp)	Doubleday/Page	1910	Tittle, Walter	60-90	
Tittle, Walter	First Nantucket Tea-Party (1st, sm4to, [82]p, teg, tan cl, p-o, 23cp)	Doubleday/Page	(1907)	Tittle, Walter	70-125	
Dixon, Thomas	Foolish Virgin (1st, sm8vo, 352p, b/w pl)	Appleton	1915	Tittle, Walter	30-45	*
Abbott, Eleanor H.	Molly Make-Believe (1st, 12mo, 211p, 14pl)	Century	1910	Tittle, Walter	25-45	
Tittle, Walter	My Country (1st, lg4to, unpag, ipcb, chromos)	Tandy-Thomas	(1909)	Tittle, Walter	200-300	
Beach, Rex	The Net (1st, 12mo, 333p, gilt, p-o, 4pl)	Harper	1912	Tittle, Walter	30-45	
Scott, Sally	Judy's Baby (1st {std}, 8vo, 45p, b/w, DJ/1.75)	Harcourt	1949	Toan, Jane	20-30	*
Sewell, Anna	Black Beauty (1st, sm8vo, 200p, grey/silver, 22 illus)	NY: Hovendon	1894	Toaspern, H.	200-300	
Adams, Veotta M.	Captain Joe & the Eskimo (1st, lg8vo, ipcb, [40]p, 1-color, DJ/1.35)	W.R. Scott	1943	Tobey, Barney	75-100	
Fleming, Ian	Chitty Chitty Bang Bang! (1st, 8vo, 63p, ibds, color)	Beginner Books	(1968)	Tobey, Barney	40-65	
LeSieg, Theo	I Wish that I Had Duck Feet (1st, 8vo, 64p, ibds, fp color, cep, DJ/1.95)	Beginner Books	(1965)	Tobey, Barney	40-65	*
Goldberg, Martha	Lunch Box Story (1st, sm8vo, red cl, [30]p, b/w, DJ/1.25)	Holiday House	1951	Tobias, Beatrice	20-35	
Judson, Clara I.	Mr. Justice Holmes (1st, lg8vo, 192p, b/w, DJ/3.50, NH)	Follett	(1956)	Todd, Robert	75-100	*
Johnson, Siddie	Rabbit Fires (1st {std}, lg ob8vo, 32p, b/w, pep)	TX: Highland Pr.	(1951)	Toepperwein, Emilie	50-80	*
Reesink, Maryke	Golden Treasure (1st AM {std}, 4to, [32]p, fp color, cep, DJ/3.95)	Harcourt	(1968)	Tol, Jaap	35-60	
Van Anrooy, Frans	Sea Horse (1st AM {std}, 4to, [32]p, color, DJ/3.75)	Harcourt	1968	Tol, Jaap	30-50	*
Hightower, Florence	Dark Horse of Woodfield (1st, 8vo, 233p, b/w, DJ/3.25)	Houghton	1962	Tolford, Joshua	25-45	*
Chase, Richard	Jack and the Three Sillies (1st, sq8vo, 39p, color, pep, DJ/2.00)	Houghton	1950	Tolford, Joshua	30-45	*
Molloy, Anne	Monkey's Fist (1st, 8vo, 227p, 1-color, DJ/2.50)	Houghton	1953	Tolford, Joshua	30-50	
Molloy, Anne	Uncle Andy's Island (1st, 8vo, 243p, b/w, DJ/2.50)	Houghton	1950	Tolford, Joshua	30-45	
Tolkien, J.R.R.	The Hobbit (1st AM, sm8vo, 310p, beige cl, 4cp, pep, DJ)	Houghton	1938	Tolkien, J.R.R.	3000-5000	R
Fisher, Aileen	In the Woods, In the Meadow, In the Sky (1st, 8vo, 64p, b/w, DJ/3.25)	Scribner	1965	Tomes, Margaret	30-45	
Wersba, Barbara	Boy Who Loved the Sea (1st, lg8vo, unpag, 1-color, DJ/2.50)	Coward	(1961)	Tomes, Margot	30-45	
Wersba, Barbara	Brave Balloon of Benjamin Buckley (1st {std}, 8vo, 66p, b/w, DJ/2.95)	Atheneum	1963	Tomes, Margot	30-45	

AUTHOR	TITLE	PUBLISHER	DATE	ARTIST	PRICE	LC
Oleson, Claire	For Pepita, An Orange Tree (1st {std}, 4to, ibds, [44]p, col, cep, DJ/3.50)	Doubleday	(1967)	Tomes, Margot	30-45	*
Goudge, Elizabeth	I Saw Three Ships (1st AM {std}, 8vo, 60p, b/w, DJ/3.95)	Coward	(1969)	Tomes, Margot	30-50	R
Wersba, Barbara	Land of Forgotten Beasts (1st {std}, lg8vo, 88p, b/w, DJ/3.50)	Atheneum	1964	Tomes, Margot	30-45	*
Edmonds, Walter D.	Wedding Journey (1st {std}, 8vo, 118p, color, DJ/2.50)	Little/Brown	1947	Tompkins, Alan	30-45	*
Bible	Book of Job (1st, 4to, teg, 102p, gilt, 8 ticp)	L: C. Palmer	1916	Tongue, C. Mary	80-140	
Bontemps, Arna	Lonesome Boy (1st, 8vo, blue cl, 28p, fp b/w, cep, DJ/2.00)	Houghton	1955	Topolski, Feliks	60-100	
Yeats, Wm. Butler	Irish Fairy and Folk Tales (1st AM, 4to, 326p, AEG, 12pl, pep)	Scott/Scribner	1895	Torrance, James	140-200	
Ceder, Georgiana	Ann of Bethany (1st, 8vo, 95p, b/w, DJ/2.00)	Abingdon-Cokes.	(1951)	Torrey, Helen	20-35	
DuBois, Theodora	Banjo the Crow (1st, lg8vo, 142p, pep, b/w, DJ/2.00)	Houghton	1943	Torrey, Helen	30-50	
Ceder, Georgiana	Ethan, the Shepherd Boy (1st, 8vo, 94p, b/w, DJ/2.00)	Abingdon-Cokes.	1948	Torrey, Helen	20-35	
Thompson, Blanche J.	Golden Trumpets (1st, sm8vo, 163p, blue/gilt, 2-color)	Macmillan	1927	Torrey, Helen	30-50	
Kelsey, Alice	I Give You my Colt (1st {std}, 8vo, 160p, b/w, DJ/2.75)	Longmans	1956	Torrey, Helen	25-40	
Gall, Alice C.	Little Black Ant (1st, 8vo, 128p, b/w, pep, DJ/1.50)	Oxford U. Pr.	(1936)	Torrey, Helen	30-50	
Bianco, Margery W.	More About Animals (1st, sm8vo, 115p, fp b/w, pep)	Macmillan	1934	Torrey, Helen	25-40	
Morrow, Elizabeth	Shannon (1st {std}, 24mo, ipcb, 68p, fp b/w, DJ/0.50)	Macmillan	1941	Torrey, Helen	25-45	
Savery, Constance	Welcome Santza (1st {std}, 8vo, 166p, b/w, DJ/2.75)	Longmans	1956	Torrey, Helen	30-50	
Carroll, Lewis	Alice in Wonderland (1st, 4to, 64p, p-o, 15 fp color, pep, DJ/2.95)	Random	1955	Torrey, Marjorie	60-90	
Torrey, Marjorie	Artie & the Princess (1st, lg8vo, 80p, green cl, 5cp, pep, DJ/2.00)	Howell/Soskin	(1945)	Torrey, Marjorie	25-45	
Philbrook, Elizabeth	Far From Marlborough Street (1st, 8vo, 302p, b/w, DJ/2.00)	Viking	1944	Torrey, Marjorie	30-50	
Torrey, Marjorie	Merriweathers (1st, 8vo, 254p, grey cl, b/w, DJ/2.50)	Viking	1949	Torrey, Marjorie	40-65	
Torrey, Marjorie	Penny (1st, lg8vo, 126p, fp color, pep, DJ/3.00)	Howell/Soskin	1944	Torrey, Marjorie	40-65	
Barrie, James M.	Peter Pan (1st, lg4to, 64p, fp color, DJ/2.95)	Random	1957	Torrey, Marjorie	40-65	*
Gates, Doris	Sarah's Idea (1st, 8vo, orange cl, 146p, fp b/w, pep, DJ/1.50)	Viking	1938	Torrey, Marjorie	30-50	
Gates, Doris	Sensible Kate (1st, 8vo, yellow cl, 189p, b/w, pep, DJ/2.00)	Viking	1943	Torrey, Marjorie	30-50	
Wheeler, Opal	Sing in Praise (1st {std}, 4to, 94p, ibds, color, pep, DJ/3.75, CH)	Dutton	1946	Torrey, Marjorie	60-90	
Wheeler, Opal	Sing Mother Goose (1st {std}, 4to, 102p, ibds, color, DJ/3.75, CH)	Dutton	1945	Torrey, Marjorie	65-90	
Torrey, Marjorie	Three Little Chipmunks (1st, 4to, ipcb, [40]p, color, pep, DJ/1.00)	Grosset/Dunlap	(1947)	Torrey, Marjorie	50-85	
Gates, Doris	Trouble for Jerry (1st, 8vo, 179p, rust cl, fp b/w, pep, DJ/2.00)	Viking	1944	Torrey, Marjorie	30-50	
Tousey, Sanford	Airplane Andy (1st {std}, ob8vo, 43p, ipcb, color, DJ/1.75)	Doubleday/Doran	1942	Tousey, Sanford	25-45	
Tousey, Sanford	Bob & the Railroad (1st {std}, lg8vo, ibds, 53p, pep, color, DJ/1.00)	Doubleday/Doran	1941	Tousey, Sanford	30-50	
Steffens, Lincoln	Boy on Horseback (1st, 8vo, 258p, b/w, DJ/2.00)	Harcourt	(1935)	Tousey, Sanford	30-50	*
Tousey, Sanford	Buffalo Bill (1st, lg8vo, [36]p, map, ibds, color, pep, DJ/0.50)	Rand/McNally	1938	Tousey, Sanford	30-50	
Tousey, Sanford	Chinky Joins the Circus (1st {std}, lg ob8vo, [56]p, ibds, color, DJ/1.00)	Doubleday/Doran	1938	Tousey, Sanford	45-70	
Tousey, Sanford	Chinky: Banker Pony (1st {std}, ob8vo, ibds, [56]p, color, pep)	Doubleday/Doran	1937	Tousey, Sanford	40-60	
Tousey, Sanford	Cowboy Tommy (1st {std}, lg ob8vo, ibds, [56]p, pep, color)	Doubleday/Doran	1932	Tousey, Sanford	35-60	
Tousey, Sanford	Cowboy Tommy's Roundup (1st {std}, lg ob8vo, [56]p, pep, color)	Doubleday/Doran	1934	Tousey, Sanford	40-60	*
Tousey, Sanford	Cowboys of America (1st, 8vo, [36]p, ibds, color)	Rand/McNally	1937	Tousey, Sanford	30-50	
Tousey, Sanford	Daniel Boone (1st, lg8vo, [36]p, map, color, DJ/0.50)	Rand/McNally	1939	Tousey, Sanford	35-60	*
Tousey, Sanford	Davy Crockett (1st, lg8vo, 48p, cloth, p-o, color, DJ/1.50)	Whitman	1948	Tousey, Sanford	30-50	
Tousey, Sanford	Dick & the Canal Boat (1st {std}, lg8vo, [41]p, ipcb, color, DJ/1.50)	Doubleday/Doran	1943	Tousey, Sanford	30-50	
Tousey, Sanford	Fisherman Tommy (1st, sm4to, 47p, pep, color, DJ/1.50)	Houghton	1940	Tousey, Sanford	40-65	
Tousey, Sanford	Indians & Cowboys (1st, lg8vo, [76]p, color, pep, DJ/1.00)	Rand/McNally	(1940)	Tousey, Sanford	30-50	
Tousey, Sanford	Indians of the Plains (1st, 8vo, ipcb, [36]p, 1-color, DJ/0.50)	Rand/McNally	1940	Tousey, Sanford	30-50	
Tousey, Sanford	Jack Finds Gold (1st {std}, 8vo, ibds, 41p, 8 fp color, pep, DJ/1.50)	Doubleday	(1947)	Tousey, Sanford	30-50	
Tousey, Sanford	Jerry & Pony Express (1st {std}, ob8vo, [56]p, pep, color, DJ/1.00)	Doubleday/Doran	1936	Tousey, Sanford	30-50	
Tousey, Sanford	Little Bear's Pinto Pony (1st, lg8vo, 29p, p-o, col frn, DJ/1.00)	Whitman	1943	Tousey, Sanford	30-50	
Tousey, Sanford	Lumberjack Bill (1st, lg8vo, blue cl, 47p, color, pep, DJ/1.75)	Houghton	1943	Tousey, Sanford	40-65	
Tousey, Sanford	Ned & the Rustlers (1st, lg8vo, 32p, color, pep, DJ/1.00)	Whitman	1941	Tousey, Sanford	30-50	
Tousey, Sanford	Old Blue (1st, 8vo, p-o, 32p, fp color, pep, DJ/1.00)	Whitman	1942	Tousey, Sanford	30-50	
Hawthorne, Hildegarde	On the Golden Trail (1st {std}, 8vo, 302p, b/w, pep, DJ/2.00)	Longmans	1936	Tousey, Sanford	30-50	
Tousey, Sanford	Stagecoach Sam (1st {std}, 8vo, ibds, 53p, color, pep, DJ/1.50)	Doubleday/Doran	1940	Tousey, Sanford	65-90	
Tousey, Sanford	Steamboat Billy (1st {std}, lg ob8vo, ibds, [56]p, color, pep, DJ/1.50)	Doubleday/Doran	1935	Tousey, Sanford	50-80	
Tousey, Sanford	Tinker Tim (1st {std}, 8vo, ibds, 41p, color, pep, DJ/1.50)	Doubleday	1946	Tousey, Sanford	35-60	
Tousey, Sanford	Treasure Cave (1st, lg8vo, 32p, orange cl, p-o, color, DJ/1.25)	Whitman	1946	Tousey, Sanford	30-50	
Tousey, Sanford	Trouble in the Gulch (1st, 8vo, p-o, 32p, fp color, pep, DJ/1.25)	Whitman	1944	Tousey, Sanford	35-60	
Tousey, Sanford	White Prince, the Arabian Horse (1st, 8vo, p-o, 32p, 2-color, DJ/1.25)	Whitman	1945	Tousey, Sanford	30-50	
Tousey, Sanford	Wild Bill Hickok - Frontier Marshall (1st, 8vo, 46p, p-o, color, DJ/1.50)	Whitman	(1952)	Tousey, Sanford	30-50	
Norris, June	Dotzie the Dancey Duck (1st, sq8vo, ibds, color)	Volland	(1927)	Tower, Lew	55-80	*
Norris, June	Katherine the Komical Kow (1st, 12mo, ibds, unpag, color, pep)	Volland	(1926)	Tower, Lew	60-90	
Kipling, Rudyard	Brushwood Boy (1st AM, 8vo, 73p, gilt, p-o, teg, 12cp)	Doubleday/Page	1907	Townsend, F.H.	60-100	
Kipling, Rudyard	Brushwood Boy (1st, 8vo, 91p, grey/gilt, teg, 12cp)	L: Macmillan	1907	Townsend, F.H.	70-100	
Barclay, Florence	Following of the Star (1st, sm8vo, 426p, teg, 8cp by...)	Putnam	1911	Townsend, F.H.	40-65	*
Peacock, Thomas L.	Gryll Grange (1st, sm8vo, 292p, gilt, uncut, AEG, b/w)	L: Macmillan	1896	Townsend, F.H.	55-80	
Marryat, Frederick	King's Own (1st, 12mo, blue cl, AEG, 429p, 40pl, pep)	L: Macmillan	1896	Townsend, F.H.	50-80	
Peacock, Thomas L.	Maid Marian & Crotchet Castle (1st, 12mo, AEG, gilt, 321p, dep)	L: Macmillan	1895	Townsend, F.H.	75-100	
Peacock, Thomas L.	Melincourt (1st, sm8vo, 326p, AEG, gilt, 40 illus)	L: Macmillan	1896	Townsend, F.H.	75-100	
Peacock, Thomas L.	Misfortunes of Elphin & Rhododaphne (1st, 12mo, AEG, 262p, gilt, b/w)	L: Macmillan	1897	Townsend, F.H.	50-85	
Kipling, Rudyard	They (1st, 8vo, 80p, white/gilt, [160]p, 15cp)	L: Macmillan	1905	Townsend, F.H.	120-200	
Kipling, Rudyard	They (1st AM, 8vo, [160]p, p-o, teg, uncut, 15cp)	Doubleday/Page	1906	Townsend, F.H.	80-125	
Kipling, Rudyard	They and Brushwood Boy (1st, 8vo, 160p, red/gilt, teg, 27cp)	L: Macmillan	1925	Townsend, F.H.	45-70	
Townsend, Kenneth	Felix the Bald-Headed Lion (1st AM {std}, 8vo, [32]p, color, DJ/3.95)	Delacorte Pr.	(1968)	Townsend, Kenneth	20-30	
Meader, Stephen W.	Cedar's Boy (1st {std}, 8vo, 234p, b/w, DJ/2.50)	Harcourt	(1949)	Townsend, Lee	70-120	
Rankin, Louise S.	Gentling of Jonathan (1st, 8vo, 223p, green cl, b/w, pep, DJ/2.50)	Viking	1950	Townsend, Lee	30-50	
Meader, Stephen W.	King of the Hills (1st, 8vo, 250p, b/w, DJ/2.00)	Harcourt	(1933)	Townsend, Lee	120-180	
Frost, Frances	Maple Sugar for Windy Foot (1st, 8vo, 184p, fp b/w, DJ/2.00)	Whittlesey	(1950)	Townsend, Lee	60-100	
Meader, Stephen W.	Red Horse Hill (1st {std}, 8vo, 244p, b/w pl, pep)	Harcourt	(1930)	Townsend, Lee	70-100	
Coryell, Hubert	Tan-Ta-Ka (1st, 8vo, 305p, b/w, pep)	Little/Brown	1934	Townsend, Lee	30-45	
Farjeon, Eleanor	Joan's Door (1st, 8vo, 127p, gilt, teg, b/w)	L: Collins	(1926)	Townsend, Will	30-50	

AUTHOR	TITLE	PUBLISHER	DATE	ARTIST	PRICE	LC
Uttley, Alison	Moonshine & Magic (1st, 8vo, 208p, cloth, 8cp)	L: Faber	1932	Townsend, William	60-90	
Baring-Gould, Sabine	Bladys of the Stewponey (1st, 8vo, 319p)	L: Methuen	1897	Townsend/Munns	55-80	*
Tozer, Katharine	Mumfie's Magic Box (1st, 8vo, 221p, ibds, 8cp)	L: J. Murray	1938	Tozer, Katharine	40-65	
Farjeon, Eleanor	Paladins in Spain (1st, 8vo, 168p, col frn, 5pl)	L: T. Nelson	1937	Tozer, Katharine	30-50	*
Gordon, Hampden C.	Paradoc to the Rescue (1st, 8vo, 206p, col frn, fp b/w)	L: J. Murray	(1939)	Tozer, Katharine	40-65	*
Wilson, Augusta	Devota (1st, 8vo, teg, p-o, 122p, red/gilt, 4cp, dep)	Dillingham	(1907)	Travis, Stuart	25-40	
Treadgold, Mary	We Couldn't Leave Dinah (1st, 8vo, 272p, b/w, DJ, CgM)	L: J. Cape	1941	Tresilian, S.	80-125	*
Trez, Denise	Maila and the Flying Carpet (1st, 4to, [32]p, yellow cl, fp color, DJ)	Viking	(1969)	Trez, Alain	25-40	
Trez, Denise	Good Night Veronica (1st, 4to, 32p, yellow cl, fp color, DJ/3.95)	Viking	(1968)	Trez, D.& A.	20-35	*
Pomerantz, Charlotte	Moon Pony (1st, sq4to, [32]p, fp color, DJ/3.95)	Young Scott	(1967)	Trezzo, Loretta	30-45	
Coblentz, Catherine	Martin and Abraham Lincoln (1st, lg8vo, ibds, [24]p, color, pep, DJ/1.00)	Children's Press	(1947)	Trientja	50-80	R*
Trier, Walter	10 Little Negroes (1st, ob8vo, [32]p, ibds, color, pep)	L: Sylvan Press	1944	Trier, Walter	180-250	
Kastner, Erich	Animal's Conference (1st AM, 4to, ibds, [62]p, color, DJ)	McKay	(1949)	Trier, Walter	120-180	
Kastner, Erich	Baron Munchausen (1st AM, sm4to, 68p, fp color, cep, DJ)	J. Messner	1957	Trier, Walter	50-75	
Kastner, Erich	Emil & the Detectives (1st AM {std}, 8vo, 224p, yellow cl, color)	Doubleday/Doran	1930	Trier, Walter	80-130	
Kastner, Erich	Emil & the Three Twins (1st UK, 8vo, 251p, ibds, 8 illus)	L: Cape	1935	Trier, Walter	80-125	
Kastner, Erich	Flying Classroom (1st UK, 8vo, 223p, ibds, 10 fp illus)	L: Cape	1934	Trier, Walter	75-100	
Kastner, Erich	Lisa and Lottie (1st AM {std}, 8vo, 137p, red cl, b/w, DJ/2.50)	Little/Brown	1951	Trier, Walter	35-50	
Kastner, Erich	Puss in Boots (1st AM, 4to, ibds, 66p, fp color)	J. Messner	(1957)	Trier, Walter	60-90	
Bond, Susan	Eric... (1st {std}, lg ob4to, 42p, color, pep, DJ/3.95)	Grove Press	(1968)	Trinkle, Sally	30-50	
Preussler, Otfried	Little Ghost (1st AM, 8vo, 126p, b/w, DJ/2.00)	Abelard-Schuman	(1967)	Tripp, F.J.	20-30	
Preussler, Otfried	Robber Hotzenplotz (1st AM, 8vo, 128p, b/w, DJ/3.00)	Abelard-Schuman	(1965)	Tripp, F.J.	20-30	
Holman, Felice	Holiday Rat & Utmost Mouse (1st {std}, 8vo, ipcb, 80p, b/w, DJ/3.95)	Norton	(1969)	Tripp, Wallace	25-40	
Guillot, Rene	Little Dog Lost (1st, sq8vo, 64p, b/w, DJ/3.75)	Lothrop, Lee	(1970)	Tripp, Wallace	20-30	
Erwin, John	Mrs. Fox (1st, 8vo, 127p, b/w, DJ/3.95)	Simon/Schuster	(1969)	Tripp, Wallace	20-35	
Brock, Betty	No Flying in the House (1st, 8vo, 139p, b/w, DJ/3.95)	Harper	(1970)	Tripp, Wallace	40-65	
Monjo, Ferdinand N.	Pirates in Panama (1st {std}, lg8vo, 59p, fp 1-color, DJ/4.50)	Simon/Schuster	(1970)	Tripp, Wallace	40-65	
Carlsen, Ruth C.	Sam Bottleby (1st, 8vo, 152p, b/w, cep, DJ/3.50)	Houghton	1968	Tripp, Wallace	30-40	
Tripp, Wallace	Tale of a Pig (1st, sm4to, 32p, color, DJ/3.50)	McGraw-Hill	(1968)	Tripp, Wallace	20-30	
Forster, Frederick J.	On the Road to Make-Believe (1st, lg4to, 128p, p-o, color, pep)	Rand/McNally	(1924)	Trippe, Uldene	60-90	
Forster, Frederick J.	Tippytoes Comes to Town (1st, 4to, p-o, 96p, color)	Rand/McNally	(1926)	Trippe, Uldene	50-80	
Atkins, Elizabeth H.	Toby's Goblin (1st, lg ob8vo, 96p, brown cl, b/w)	Rand/McNally	(1930)	Trippe, Uldene	30-40	
Bolliger, Max	The Fireflies (1st AM {std}, lg4to, ibds, [43]p, fp color, DJ/4.95)	Atheneum	(1970)	Trnka, Jiri	40-65	
Troy, Hugh	Chippendale Dam (1st, sm4to, 45p, fp 2-color, DJ/1.50)	Oxford U. Pr.	1941	Troy, Hugh	50-85	
Sawyer, Ruth	Enchanted Schoolhouse (1st, lg8vo, green cl, 128p, fp b/w, pep, DJ/2.50)	Viking	1956	Troy, Hugh	30-50	
Sawyer, Ruth	Year of the Christmas Dragon (1st, lg8vo, red cl, 88p, b/w, pep, DJ/2.50)	Viking	(1960)	Troy, Hugh	30-50	
Baker, Augusta	Golden Lynx (1st {std}, 8vo, 160p, red cl, fp b/w, DJ/3.00)	Lippincott	(1960)	Troyer, Johannes	40-65	
Baker, Augusta	Talking Tree (1st {std}, 8vo, 255p, maroon cl, b/w, DJ/3.00)	Lippincott	(1955)	Troyer, Johannes	40-65	
Parrish, Randall	Last Voyage of the Donna Isabel (1st, 8vo, blue cl, 366p, 4cp)	McClurg	1908	True, Allen	30-45	
Mulford, Clarence	The Orphan (1st, sm8vo, 399p, 4cp)	Outing	1908	True, Allen	100-165	
Browne, Frances	Granny's Wonderful Chair (1st, sm8vo, gilt, 213p, 8cp)	McClure	1904	Truman, Edith	35-60	
N/A	Book of Pets (lg4to, ibds, 12cp by...)	L: Gardner	1897	Tucker, Eliz. S.	425-600	
Tucker, Elizabeth S.	Bubbles (4to, 12p, ibds, 6cp)	Worthington	(1892)	Tucker, Eliz. S.	100-160	
Tucker, Elizabeth S.	Cup of Tea (ob4to, [22]p, ibds, chromos)	Worthington	1892	Tucker, Eliz. S.	120-200	
Tucker, Elizabeth S.	Favorite Pets (1st, 4to, [24]p, ibds, 12cp)	Stokes	1893	Tucker, Eliz. S.	120-170	
Tucker, Elizabeth S.	Little Ways & Great Plays (4to, ibds, 12 chromos)	Worthington	1892	Tucker, Eliz. S.	150-220	
Tucker, Elizabeth S.	Royal Little People (1st, 4to, unpag, ibds, 12cp)	Stokes	(1895)	Tucker, Eliz. S.	120-170	
Tudor, Bethany	Skiddycock Pond (1st, ob8vo, [31]p, ibds, fp color, pep, DJ/2.75)	Lippincott	(1965)	Tudor, Bethany	60-90	
Tudor, Tasha	1 Is One (1st, lg ob8vo, unpag, pep, pink cl, color, DJ/2.75, CH)	NY: Oxford U.Pr.	1956	Tudor, Tasha	200-300	
Tudor, Tasha	A is for Annabelle (1st, lg ob8vo, unpag, grn/gilt, 27 col, pep, DJ/2.50)	NY: Oxford U.Pr.	1954	Tudor, Tasha	180-260	
McCready, Thomas L.	Adventures of a Beagle (1st, 8vo, [48]p, fp color, pep, DJ/2.75)	Ariel	(1959)	Tudor, Tasha	200-300	
Tudor, Tasha	Alexander the Gander (1st, 24mo, green cl, [47]p, color, pep, DJ/0.75)	Oxford U. Pr.	(1939)	Tudor, Tasha	300-450	
Tudor, Tasha	Amanda & the Bear (1st, 12mo, unpag, p-o, blue cl, color, dep, DJ/1.75)	NY: Oxford U.Pr.	1951	Tudor, Tasha	200-300	
Bible	And It Was So (1st, sq8vo, 48p, color, pep, DJ)	Westminster Pr.	(1958)	Tudor, Tasha	70-120	
Tudor, Tasha	Around the Year (1st, lg ob8vo, [54]p, cloth, color, DJ/3.00)	NY: Oxford U.Pr.	1957	Tudor, Tasha	150-250	R
Tudor, Tasha	Becky's Birthday (1st, 8vo, 47p, yellow cl, color, DJ/3.00)	Viking	(1960)	Tudor, Tasha	170-240	
Tudor, Tasha	Becky's Christmas (1st, 4to, 45p, color, pep, DJ/3.00)	Viking	(1961)	Tudor, Tasha	200-300	
McCready, Thomas L.	Biggity Bantam (1st, sq8vo, yellow cl, 49p, color, pep, DJ/2.50)	Ariel	(1954)	Tudor, Tasha	140-220	
Shute, Henry A.	Brite & Fair (1st, sm8vo, 286p, b/w, pep, DJ/4.50)	Noone House	1968	Tudor, Tasha	70-100	
Stevenson, Rbt. L.	Child's Garden of Verses (1st, 8vo 118p, grn cl, p-o, 15cp, pep, DJ/2.50)	Oxford U. Pr.	1947	Tudor, Tasha	200-300	
Tudor, Tasha	County Fair (1st, 24mo, [47]p, red/white, pep, color, DJ/0.75)	Oxford U. Pr.	1940	Tudor, Tasha	350-500	
Tudor, Tasha	Doll's Christmas (1st, sq12mo, red cl, [29]p, pep, p-o, color, DJ/1.50)	NY: Oxford U.Pr.	1950	Tudor, Tasha	250-400	
Godden, Rumer	Doll's House (1st, 8vo, tan cl, 136p, color, pep, DJ/2.75)	Viking	(1962)	Tudor, Tasha	120-185	
Tudor, Tasha	Dorcas Porkus (1st, 24mo, [35]p, orange cl, color, DJ/0.75)	NY: Oxford U.Pr.	(1942)	Tudor, Tasha	300-500	
Tudor, Tasha	Edgar Allan Crow (1st, 12mo, gilt, p-o, unpag, fp color, pep, DJ/1.75)	Oxford U. Pr.	1953	Tudor, Tasha	250-400	
Andersen, Hans C.	Fairy Tales (1st, 8vo, blue cl, 273p, 10 fp color, DJ/3.50)	NY: Oxford U.Pr.	(1945)	Tudor, Tasha	180-250	
Tudor, Tasha	First Delights (1st, 8vo, ibds, [32]p, color, pep, DJ/2.50)	Platt/Munk	(1966)	Tudor, Tasha	80-145	
Bible	First Graces (1st, 32mo, blue cl, 47p, p-o, color, pep, DJ/1.75)	NY: Oxford U.Pr.	1955	Tudor, Tasha	120-180	
Tudor, Tasha	First Poems of Childhood (1st, 8vo, gilt, 45p, color, cep, DJ/1.95)	Platt/Munk	(1967)	Tudor, Tasha	140-200	
Bible	First Prayers (1st, 32mo, 48p, blue cl, p-o, color, DJ/1.50)	NY: Oxford U.Pr.	(1952)	Tudor, Tasha	250-350	
McCready, Thomas L.	Increase Rabbit (1st, sq8vo, yellow cl, unpag, color, pep, DJ/2.75)	Ariel	(1958)	Tudor, Tasha	300-500	
Ewing, Juliana H.	Jacanapes (1st, sm8vo, green/gilt, 62p, color, pep, DJ/2.00)	Oxford U. Pr.	1948	Tudor, Tasha	250-350	
Tudor, Tasha	Linsey Woolsey (1st, sq24mo, [43]p, yellow bds, color, DJ/0.75)	NY: Oxford U.Pr.	1946	Tudor, Tasha	350-500	
Burnett, Frances H.	Little Princess (1st, 8vo, 240p, gilt, fp color, DJ/5.00)	Lippincott	(1963)	Tudor, Tasha	120-185	R
Alcott, Louisa M.	Little Women (1st, 8vo, 544p, red/gilt, 8 fp color, DJ/5.95)	World	(1969)	Tudor, Tasha	200-300	
Clarke, Sara K.	Lord Will Love Thee (1st, sq8vo, 48p, color, pep, DJ/2.50)	Westminster Pr.	(1959)	Tudor, Tasha	70-120	
Bible	More Prayers (1st, 32mo, 38p, blue cl, color, DJ/1.95)	H.Z. Walck	1967	Tudor, Tasha	80-135	
Mother Goose	Mother Goose (1st, sm sq8vo, green cl, 87p, color, pep, DJ/2.00, CH)	NY: Oxford U.Pr.	(1944)	Tudor, Tasha	250-400	

AUTHOR	TITLE	PUBLISHER	DATE	ARTIST	PRICE	LC
McCready, Thomas L.	Mr. Stubbs (1st, sm8vo, 48p, red cl, color, pep, DJ/2.50)	Ariel	(1956)	Tudor, Tasha	180-240	
Campbell, Mary M.	New England Butt'ry Shelf Almanac (1st {std}, sq12mo, 302p, 6cp, DJ/6.95)	World	(1970)	Tudor, Tasha	80-125	
McCready, Thomas L.	Pekin White (1st, sm8vo, green cl, 49p, color, pep, DJ/2.50)	Ariel	(1955)	Tudor, Tasha	300-500	
Tudor, Tasha	Pumpkin Moonshine (1st, 24mo, blue cl, [41]p, color, pep, DJ/0.75)	Oxford U. Pr.	(1938)	Tudor, Tasha	300-500	R
Shute, Henry A.	Real Diary of a Real Boy (1st, sm8vo, 194p, red cl, 12 b/w, DJ/3.95)	R.R. Smith Co.	(1967)	Tudor, Tasha	70-100	
Alcott, Louisa M.	Round Dozen Stories by Louisa M. Alcott (1st, 8vo, 256p, b/w, DJ/4.00)	Viking	(1963)	Tudor, Tasha	150-220	
Burnett, Frances H.	Secret Garden (1st, 8vo, 256p, red/gilt, fp color, DJ/5.00)	Lippincott	(1962)	Tudor, Tasha	120-185	
Tudor, Tasha	Snow Before Christmas (1st, sq12mo, [37]p, pep, p-o, color, DJ/1.00)	NY: Oxford U.Pr.	(1941)	Tudor, Tasha	300-500	
Tudor, Tasha (ed)	Take Joy! Tasha Tudor Christmas Book (1st, ob4to, 157p, color, DJ/4.95)	World	(1966)	Tudor, Tasha	100-165	
Tudor, Tasha	Tale for Easter (1st, sq12mo, [33]p, dep, p-o, color, DJ/1.00)	NY: Oxford U.Pr.	(1941)	Tudor, Tasha	250-400	
Tudor, Tasha (ed)	Tasha Tudor Book of Fairy Tales (1st, lg4to, 92p, color, DJ/3.95)	Platt/Munk	(1961)	Tudor, Tasha	140-185	
Tudor, Tasha	Tasha Tudor's Favorite Stories (1st {std}, sm4to, 131p, ibds, col, DJ/3.95)	Lippincott	(1965)	Tudor, Tasha	100-165	
Tudor, Tasha	Thistly B. (1st, sq12mo, [27]p, color, DJ/1.50)	NY: Oxford U.Pr.	1949	Tudor, Tasha	200-300	
Tudor, Tasha	White Goose (1st, sq12mo, grey cl, p-o, [27]p, color, DJ/1.00)	Oxford U. Pr.	(1943)	Tudor, Tasha	250-400	
Grahame, Kenneth	Wind in the Willows (1st, 8vo, 255p, gilt, 16 fp color, pep, DJ/4.95)	World	(1966)	Tudor, Tasha	140-200	
Tudor, Tasha (comp)	Wings from the Wind (1st {std}, lg8vo, 119p, color, DJ/3.95)	Lippincott	(1964)	Tudor, Tasha	120-200	
Tufts, Georgia	Catrina & the Cats (1st, sm4to, [38]p, fp color, DJ/2.75)	Lothrop, Lee	(1959)	Tufts, Georgia	30-45	
Tunis, Edwin B.	Frontier Living (1st {std}, lg4to, 165p, ibds, b/w, DJ/5.95, NH)	World	(1961)	Tunis, Edwin B.	50-80	
Tunis, Edwin B.	Indians (1st {std}, lg4to, 157p, ipcb, b/w, DJ/4.95)	World	(1959)	Tunis, Edwin B.	60-90	R
Tunis, Edwin B.	Oars, Sails & Steam (1st {std}, lg4to, 78p, ivory cl, b/w, DJ/3.50)	World	(1952)	Tunis, Edwin B.	50-90	R
Tunis, Edwin B.	Shaw's Fortune (1st, ob4to, 63p, fp b/w, DJ/3.95, NYTBI)	World	(1966)	Tunis, Edwin B.	30-50	
Rogerson, Sidney	Both Sides of the Road (1st, 4to, red cl, 183p, 23cp)	L: Collins	1949	Tunnicliffe, C.F.	55-80	
Williams, Harcourt	Tales from Ebony (1st, 8vo, 258p, 32cp)	L: Putnam	(1934)	Tunnicliffe, C.F.	140-200	
Sandburg, Helga	Anna and the Baby Buzzard (1st {std}, 8vo, [48]p, color, DJ/4.75)	Dutton	(1970)	Turkle, Brinton	30-50	
Hawkins, Quail	Aunt-Sitter (1st, 8vo, 35p, yellow cl, b/w, pep, DJ/2.50)	Holiday House	(1958)	Turkle, Brinton	25-40	*
Braucher, Bettye	Belinda and Me (1st, ob24mo, [24]p, fp b/w, dep, DJ/1.95)	Viking	(1966)	Turkle, Brinton	30-45	*
Thompson, Vivian L.	Camp in the Yard (1st, 8vo, [32]p, b/w, pep, DJ/2.50)	Holiday House	1961	Turkle, Brinton	30-50	
Annixter, Paul	Cat that Clumped (1st, lg8vo, [36]p, fp b/w, pep, DJ/2.95)	Holiday House	(1966)	Turkle, Brinton	25-40	
DeRegniers, Beatrice	Catch a Little Fox (1st {std}, ob8vo, [41]p, fp 1-color, DJ/3.95)	Seabury Press	1970	Turkle, Brinton	30-50	*
Williams, Jay	Danny Dunn and the Fossil Cave (1st {std}, 8vo, 146p, b/w, DJ/2.95)	Whittlesey	1961	Turkle, Brinton	20-35	
Williams, Jay	Danny Dunn on the Ocean Floor (1st {std}, 8vo, 156p, b/w, DJ/2.95)	Whittlesey	(1960)	Turkle, Brinton	20-35	
York, Carol B.	Doll in the Bakeshop (1st {std}, 8vo, 98p, fp b/w, DJ/3.50)	F. Watts	(1965)	Turkle, Brinton	30-45	
Caudill, Rebecca	Far-Off Land (1st, sm8vo, 287p, b/w, DJ/3.50)	Viking	(1964)	Turkle, Brinton	25-40	*
Turkle, Brinton	Fiddler of High Lonesome (1st, 8vo, 44p, fp 1-color, DJ/3.50)	Viking	(1968)	Turkle, Brinton	30-50	
Cenac, Claude	Four Paws into Adventure (1st AM {std}, 8vo, 159p, b/w, DJ/3.50)	F. Watts	(1965)	Turkle, Brinton	60-100	*
Parish, Peggy	Granny and the Indians (1st {std}, 8vo, 39p, color, DJ/3.95)	Macmillan	(1969)	Turkle, Brinton	25-40	
May, Charles P.	High-Noon Rocket (1st, ob8vo, [39]p, fp 1-color, DJ/2.95)	Holiday House	(1966)	Turkle, Brinton	30-50	
DeRegniers, Beatrice	How Joe the Bear & Sam the Mouse... (1st, 4to, [40]p, color, pep, DJ/2.95)	Parents Mag. Pr.	1965	Turkle, Brinton	60-90	
Tavo, Gus	Hunt the Mountain Lion (1st {std}, 8vo, 209p, b/w, DJ/3.00)	Knopf	1959	Turkle, Brinton	30-50	
McGovern, Ann	If You Grew Up with Abraham Lincoln (1st, ob8vo, 79p, color, pep, DJ/2.95)	Four Winds Pr.	(1966)	Turkle, Brinton	30-50	
McGovern, Ann	If You Lived in Colonial Times (1st, ob8vo, 79p, color, pep, DJ/2.95)	Four Winds Pr.	(1966)	Turkle, Brinton	30-50	
Farquhar, Margaret	Indian Children of America (1st {std}, 8vo, [48]p, color, DJ/2.50)	Holt, Rinehart	(1964)	Turkle, Brinton	50-80	*
Kitt, Tamara	Jake (1st, sm4to, [41]p, fp 2-color, dep, DJ/3.75)	Abelard-Schuman	(1969)	Turkle, Brinton	40-65	
Agnew, Edith	Larry (1st, 8vo, 125p, gilt, b/w, cep, DJ/2.95)	Friendship Pr.	(1960)	Turkle, Brinton	25-40	*
Agnew, Edith	Leo of Alaska (1st, 8vo, 114p, b/w, DJ/2.95)	Friendship Pr.	(1958)	Turkle, Brinton	30-45	*
Sonneborn, Ruth	Lollipop Party (1st, sq8vo, ipcb, [32]p, fp 1-color, DJ/2.75)	Viking	(1967)	Turkle, Brinton	30-45	
Turkle, Brinton	Magic of Millicent Musgrave (1st, 4to, ibds, [40]p, 1-color, pep, DJ/3.50)	Viking	(1967)	Turkle, Brinton	30-45	
Randall, Janet	Miracle of Sage Valley (1st {std}, 8vo, 185p, DJ/2.75, b/w decor by...)	NY: Longmans	1958	Turkle, Brinton	40-65	*
Turkle, Brinton	Mooncoin Castle (1st {std}, lg8vo, 141p, b/w, DJ/3.95)	Viking	(1970)	Turkle, Brinton	30-50	
Embry, Margaret	Mr. Blue (1st, 8vo, 71p, b/w, DJ/2.75)	Holiday House	(1963)	Turkle, Brinton	30-50	
Bonham, Frank	Mystery of the Red Tide (1st {std}, 8vo, 127p, b/w, DJ/3.50)	Dutton	(1966)	Turkle, Brinton	25-40	*
Urmston, Mary	New Boy (1st {std}, 8vo, 207p, b/w, DJ/2.25)	Doubleday	(1950)	Turkle, Brinton	30-45	
Foltz, Mary Jane	Nicolau's Prize (1st, 8vo, 91p, b/w, DJ/3.25)	McGraw-Hill	(1967)	Turkle, Brinton	50-80	*
Turkle, Brinton	Obadiah the Bold (1st, ob8vo, [36]p, fp color, DJ/3.50)	Viking	(1965)	Turkle, Brinton	30-50	
Smaridge, Norah	Peter's Tent (1st, 8vo, [32]p, fp 1-color, DJ/2.50)	Viking	(1965)	Turkle, Brinton	30-50	
Kitt, Tamara	Sam and the Impossible Thing (1st {std}, ob4to, [40]p, color, DJ/3.25)	Norton	(1967)	Turkle, Brinton	40-65	*
Turkle, Brinton	Sky Dog (1st, lg8vo, [31]p, fp 2-color, DJ/3.95)	Viking	(1969)	Turkle, Brinton	25-45	*
Kitt, Tamara	Special Birthday/Someone Very Special (1st {std}, 12mo, unpag, col, DJ/2.95)	Norton	(1966)	Turkle, Brinton	30-50	*
Merriam, Eve	Story of Ben Franklin (1st, 8vo, 78p, green cl, fp 1-color, DJ)	Four Winds Pr.	(1965)	Turkle, Brinton	40-65	*
Heide, Florence P.	That's What Friends are For (1st, ob8vo, [39]p, color, DJ/3.95)	Four Winds Pr.	(1968)	Turkle, Brinton	30-45	
Turkle, Brinton	Thy Friend Obadiah (1st, ob8vo, [37]p, fp color, DJ/3.95, CH)	Viking	(1969)	Turkle, Brinton	50-80	R*
Stoutenburg, Adrien	Timber Line Treasure (1st, 8vo, 218p, b/w, DJ/2.50)	Westminster Pr.	(1951)	Turkle, Brinton	25-40	*
Rinkoff, Barbara	Troublesome Tuba (1st, 8vo, 80p, fp b/w, DJ/3.25)	Lothrop, Lee	(1967)	Turkle, Brinton	25-45	*
Burt, Nathaniel	War Cry of the West (1st {std}, 8vo, 86p, b/w, cep, DJ/3.00)	Holt, Rinehart	(1964)	Turkle, Brinton	30-55	
Coatsworth, Eliz.	You Say You Saw a Camel? (1st, 8vo, 72p, fp b/w, DJ/2.20)	Row, Peterson	(1958)	Turkle, Brinton	20-35	*
Harris, Leon	Yvette (1st, 4to, 36p, fp 1-color, DJ/4.95)	McGraw-Hill	(1970)	Turkle, Brinton	50-80	*
Proctor, Beth	Tale of a Lucky Dog (1st, lg8vo, [59]p, fp color)	Jordan Pub. Co.	(1924)	Turpin, Fay	40-65	*
Reeves, James	Trojan Horse (1st AM, 4to, [32]p, fp color, DJ/4.95)	F. Watts	1969	Turska, Krystyna	40-70	*
Lindgren, Barbo	Hilding's Summer (1st AM {std}, 8vo, 138p, b/w, DJ/3.75)	Macmillan	(1967)	Tusan, Stan	20-30	
Eaton, Seymour	Prince Domino & Muffles (1st, sq8vo, p-o, 146p, 7cp)	Stern	1910	Twelvetrees, C.	200-300	
Shippen, Kath. B.	Lightfoot: Story of an Indian Boy (1st, 8vo, 122p, b/w, DJ/2.00)	Viking	1950	Two-Arrows, Tom	30-50	*
Coonley, Lydia A.	Singing Verses for Children (1st, ob4to, 80p, p-o, gilt, color)	Macmillan	1897	Tyler, Alice K.	200-300	
Hurst, Edward H.	Mystery Island (1st, sm8vo, 313p, uncut, gilt, col frn by...)	L.C. Page	1907	Tyng, Griswold	25-40	*
Borton, Elizabeth	Pollyanna's Golden Horseshoe (1st, sm8vo, 339p, gilt, col frn, DJ/2.00)	L.C. Page	(1939)	Tyng, Griswold	25-40	*
Uchida, Yoshiko	Full Circle (1st, 8vo, 135p, b/w, DJ/2.50)	Friendship Pr.	(1957)	Uchida, Yoshiko	30-50	
Uchida, Yoshiko	Magic Listening Cap (1st {std}, 8vo, 146p, b/w, DJ/2.50)	Harcourt	(1955)	Uchida, Yoshiko	30-45	
Black, Irma S.	This is the Bread that Betsy Ate (1st, lg ob8vo, ibds, [26]p, col, DJ/1.50)	W.R. Scott	1945	Ullman, Allen	40-65	*
Martin, Patricia	That Cat! 1-2-3 (1st, sm ob4to, [48]p, color, DJ)	Putnam	1969	Unada	25-35	

AUTHOR	TITLE	PUBLISHER	DATE	ARTIST	PRICE	LC
Parrish, Randall	Air Pilot (1st, 8vo, 318p, p-o, 3cp)	McClurg	1913	Underwood, C.F.	30-60	
Underwood, C.F.	American Types (1st, 4to, p-o, red cl, 16cp)	Stokes	(1912)	Underwood, C.F.	80-120	
Chamberlain, Esther	Coast of Chance (1st, sm8vo, tan/gilt, 464p, 4pl)	Bobbs-Merrill	(1908)	Underwood, C.F.	25-40	*
N/A	Comin' Thro the Rye (1st, lg8vo, p-o, 6cp)	Bobbs-Merrill	(1909)	Underwood, C.F.	50-80	
N/A	Famous Love Songs (1st, lg8vo, blue cl, p-o, 17cp)	Bobbs-Merrill	(1909)	Underwood, C.F.	70-100	
Barbour, Ralph H.	Golden Heart (1st, 8vo, gilt, 219p, teg, p-o, 5cp, pep)	Lippincott	1910	Underwood, C.F.	30-45	
Nesbit, Edith	Incomplete Amorist (1st AM, 8vo, p-o, 356p, 8pl)	Doubleday/Page	1906	Underwood, C.F.	100-165	
N/A	Love Songs Old & New (1st, sm4to, p-o, unpag, 18cp)	Bobbs-Merrill	(1909)	Underwood, C.F.	70-100	
Seawell, Molly E.	Loves of Lady Arabella (1st, 8vo, p-o, 244p, 12cp)	Bobbs-Merrill	(1906)	Underwood, C.F.	25-40	
Warner, Anne	Taming of Amorette (1st, sm8vo, 210p, green/gilt, 6pl)	Little/Brown	1915	Underwood, C.F.	20-25	
Bianco, Margery W.	Adventures of Andy (1st, lg8vo, 227p, 8cp, pep)	Doran	(1927)	Underwood, Leon	40-60	
Ungerer, Tomi	Adelaide (1st, 4to, ibds, 40p, 2-color, DJ/2.75)	Harper	(1959)	Ungerer, Tomi	70-120	
Ungerer, Tomi	Ask Me a Question (1st, 8vo, 32p, ibds, 2-color, DJ/2.50)	Harper	(1968)	Ungerer, Tomi	50-85	
Cole, William	Beastly Boys and Ghastly Girls (1st {std}, lg8vo, 124p, b/w, DJ/3.75)	World	(1964)	Ungerer, Tomi	80-140	
Hollander, John	Book of Various Owls (1st {std}, lg4to, unpag, ibds, 3-color, DJ/3.00)	Norton	1963	Ungerer, Tomi	50-80	*
Cole, William	Cat-Haters Handbook (1st, 8vo, [60]p, ibds, b/w, DJ/2.50)	Dial Press	1963	Ungerer, Tomi	25-40	
Ungerer, Tomi	Christmas Eve at the Mellops (1st, ob8vo, [32]p, fp 2-color, DJ/2.50)	Harper	(1960)	Ungerer, Tomi	60-90	
Beatty, Jerome	Clambake Mutiny (1st, lg8vo, 68p, 2-color, DJ/3.50)	Young Scott	(1964)	Ungerer, Tomi	40-65	
Hodeir, Andre	Cleopatra Goes Sledding (1st {std}, 4to, [32]p, color, DJ/3.95)	Grove Press	(1968)	Ungerer, Tomi	50-80	
Ungerer, Tomi	Crictor (1st, 4to, green ibds, 32p, 2-color, DJ/2.50)	Harper	(1958)	Ungerer, Tomi	65-100	R
Showalter, Jean B.	Donkey Ride (1st {std}, ob4to, [40]p, color, DJ/3.95)	Doubleday	(1967)	Ungerer, Tomi	30-50	
Ungerer, Tomi	Emile (1st, 4to, 32p, ibds, 2-color, DJ/2.50)	Harper	(1960)	Ungerer, Tomi	70-120	
Brown, Jeff	Flat Stanley (1st, 8vo, [44]p, color, DJ/2.50)	Harper	1964	Ungerer, Tomi	35-50	
Cole, William	Frances Face-Maker (1st {std}, 8vo, [30]p, fp color, DJ/2.95)	World	(1963)	Ungerer, Tomi	30-50	*
Stolz, Mary S.	Fredou (1st, 8vo, 118p, b/w, DJ/2.95)	Harper	(1962)	Ungerer, Tomi	25-40	
Ungerer, Tomi	Horrible (1st, lg4to, tan cl, [102]p, fp color, DJ/10.00)	Atheneum	1960	Ungerer, Tomi	80-130	
Lear, Edward	Lear's Nonsense Verses (1st, 4to, [42]p, color, DJ/1.25)	Grosset/Dunlap	(1967)	Ungerer, Tomi	45-70	*
Ungerer, Tomi	Mellops Go Diving for Treasure (1st, lg8vo, ibds, unpag, 2-color, DJ/2.00)	Harper	(1957)	Ungerer, Tomi	50-90	
Ungerer, Tomi	Mellops Go Flying (1st, lg ob8vo, ibds, [32]p, 2-color, DJ/2.00)	Harper	(1957)	Ungerer, Tomi	60-100	R
Ungerer, Tomi	Mellops Go Spelunking (1st, ob8vo, ibds, [32]p, color, DJ/2.50)	Harper	(1963)	Ungerer, Tomi	50-85	
Ungerer, Tomi	Mellops Strike Oil (1st, ob8vo, 32p, fp 2-color, DJ/2.00)	Harper	(1958)	Ungerer, Tomi	50-85	
Ungerer, Tomi	Moon Man (1st, folio, 40p, color, DJ/4.50)	Harper	(1967)	Ungerer, Tomi	70-120	
Brenner, Barbara	Mr. Tall & Mr. Small (1st, 8vo, [32]p, 3-color, pep, DJ/3.75)	Young Scott	(1966)	Ungerer, Tomi	30-50	
Cole, William	Oh What Nonsense! (1st, 8vo, 80p, b/w, DJ/2.95)	Viking	(1966)	Ungerer, Tomi	50-85	
Cole, William	Oh, How Silly! (1st {std}, lg8vo, 94p, b/w, DJ/3.50)	Viking	(1970)	Ungerer, Tomi	30-50	*
Ungerer, Tomi	Orlando the Brave Vulture (1st, 4to, 32p, 2-color, ibds, DJ/3.50)	Harper	(1966)	Ungerer, Tomi	40-60	
Ungerer, Tomi	Rufus (1st, lg4to, 32p, ibds, color, DJ/2.95)	Harper	1961	Ungerer, Tomi	60-100	
Selsam, Millicent	Seeds & More Seeds (1st, 8vo, ibds, 60p, 2-color, DJ/2.50)	Harper	(1959)	Ungerer, Tomi	50-80	
Ungerer, Tomi	Snail, Where are You? (1st, 8vo, [32]p, fp color, DJ/2.25)	Harper	(1962)	Ungerer, Tomi	50-80	R
Cole, William	That Pest Jonathan (1st, sm8vo, [32]p, ibds, color, DJ/3.50)	Harper	(1970)	Ungerer, Tomi	30-50	
Ungerer, Tomi	The Hat (1st, 4to, [32]p, ipcb, p-o, fp color, cep, DJ/3.50)	Parents Mag. Pr.	(1970)	Ungerer, Tomi	45-70	
Ungerer, Tomi	Three Robbers (1st {std}, 4to, 39p, color, cep, DJ/3.50, NYTBI)	Atheneum	(1962)	Ungerer, Tomi	100-165	
Ungerer, Tomi	Underground Sketchbook (1st {std}, ob8vo, ibds, [148]p, b/w, DJ/3.95)	Viking	(1964)	Ungerer, Tomi	45-70	
Hodeir, Andre	Warwick's 3 Bottles (1st {std}, 4to, [32]p, color, DJ/3.95)	Grove Press	(1966)	Ungerer, Tomi	50-80	
Ungerer, Tomi	Zeralda's Ogre (1st, 4to, ibds, [32]p, color, DJ/3.95)	Harper	(1967)	Ungerer, Tomi	50-80	
Sigsgaard, Jens	Nils All Alone (1st AM, 8vo, [47]p, fp color, DJ/1.75)	Oxford U. Pr.	1947	Ungermann, Arne	30-50	
Twain, Mark	$30000 Bequest (1st, 8vo, 522p, red/gilt, 8pl)	Harper	1906	Unknown	200-300	
Nesbit, Wilbur D.	A Friend or Two (1st, 16mo, [14]p, ibds, color)	Volland	(1910)	Unknown	75-100	*
N/A	Aladdin (1st, sq4to, wraps, [15]p, chromos)	McLoughlin	1898	Unknown	45-80	*
Girvin, Brenda	Alice & the White Rabbit (1st, 8vo, 160p, 33 b/w illus)	L: Partridge	(1909)	Unknown	75-100	*
Farrow, George E.	All About the Wallypug (1st, folio, unpag)	L: R. Tuck	[1904]	Unknown	120-200	*
Haggard, H. Rider	Allan the Hunter (1st, 8vo, 111p, red cl, 2pl)	Lothrop Pub.	(1898)	Unknown	120-200	
Baum, L. Frank	Animal ABC (1st, 32mo, ibds, 124p, color)	Reilly/Britton	1905	Unknown	100-165	R
Altsheler, Joseph A.	Apache Gold (1st, sm8vo, 382p, cp)	Appleton	1913	Unknown	120-200	
Streamer, Col. D.	Baby's Baedeker (1st, sm8vo, 56p, uncut, ibds, 9pl)	R.H. Russell	1902	Unknown	80-120	*
Alcott, Louisa M.	Candy Country (1st, 12mo, 52p, 3pl)	Little/Brown	(1900)	Unknown	70-100	R
Stuart, Ruth M.	Carlotta's Intended (1st, 12mo, 277p, 11pl)	Harper	1894	Unknown	30-50	
Alcott, Louisa M.	Christmas Dream (1st, 12mo, green cl, 55p, 3pl)	Little/Brown	(1901)	Unknown	60-90	*
Howells, William D.	Christmas Every Day... (1st, 12mo, 150p, rust cl, 14 b/w)	Harper	1893	Unknown	70-100	R
Huntington, Ida M.	Christmas Party for Santa Claus (1st, lg8vo, 102p, p-o, 6cp)	Rand/McNally	(1912)	Unknown	80-120	*
Hughes, Rupert	Colonel Crockett's Cooperative Christmas (1st, sm8vo, 66p, 6cp)	Jacobs	(1906)	Unknown	25-40	
Munroe, Kirk	Coral Ship (1st, sm8vo, 261p, 14pl)	Putnam	1893	Unknown	30-50	
Pyrnelle, Louise C.	Diddie, Dumps & Tot (1st, 12mo, green cl, 217p, 12 fp b/w, PPP)	Harper	1882	Unknown	250-400	
Muter, Gladys N.	Duck's Adventure (1st, sm sq4to, color)	Volland	(1927)	Unknown	55-80	*
Spyri, Johanna	Erick and Sally (1st, 8vo, 173p, gilt, teg, 3cp)	Bos: Beacon Pr.	1921	Unknown	40-65	
Cain, Neville	Fairies' Circus (1st, lg4to, ibds, [16]p, calligraphy, color)	R.H. Russell	1903	Unknown	120-185	*
Grimm Bros.	Fairy Tales (1st, 32mo, gilt, 127p, ibds, fp color, pep)	Reilly/Britton	1905	Unknown	200-300	
N/A	Father Tuck's Bird ABC (4to, wraps, [14]p, 4cp)	L: R. Tuck	1895	Unknown	100-150	
Stockton, Frank	Floating Prince... (1st, 8vo, 199p, PPP, b/w)	Scribner	1881	Unknown	225-350	
Altsheler, J.A.	Free Rangers (1st, 8vo, 365p, 4cp)	Appleton	1909	Unknown	120-200	
Brine, Mary D.	Funnyland Boys (1st, sm8vo, 54p, ipcb, col frn, b/w)	Drexel Biddle	1903	Unknown	70-120	*
Stuart, Ruth M.	Gobolinks (1st, ob8vo, ibds, 73p, b/w)	Century	1896	Unknown	100-165	
Atkinson, Eleanor	Greyfriars Bobby (1st, 12mo, 291p, gilt, frontis, PPPa)	Harper	1912	Unknown	80-125	
Seegmiller, Wilhelmia	Hand Clasp (1st, narrow 16mo, [8]p)	Volland	(1911)	Unknown	50-80	*
Spyri, Johanna	Heidi (1st {this pub}, 12mo, red cl, 338p, b/w pl)	Crowell	(1902)	Unknown	30-50	*
Wharton, Anne H.	Heirlooms in Miniatures (1st, 8vo, 259p, uncut, teg, col frn)	Lippincott	1898	Unknown	25-40	
Vivienne	Hop, Skippy & Jump (1st, 12mo, ipcb, [32]p, color, pep)	Whitman	1947	Unknown	20-25	
Copley, Frank B.	Impeachment of President Israels (1st, 12mo, blue/gilt, 124p, 3pl)	NY: Macmillan	1913	Unknown	40-65	

AUTHOR	TITLE	PUBLISHER	DATE	ARTIST	PRICE	LC
Warren, Ina R.	In Cupid's Court (1st, 12mo, 79p, white/gilt, fp b/w)	R.H. Russell	1900	Unknown	75-100	*
Wodehouse, P.G.	Intrusion of Jimmy (1st, sm8vo, 314p, black/gilt, p-o, col frn)	NY: Watt	(1910)	Unknown	700-1000	
Scott, Walter	Ivanhoe (1st, sm8vo, 346p, 4cp)	Appleton	1910	Unknown	25-45	*
Whittier, John G.	Jack in the Pulpit (1st, sq9vo, [38]p, color)	NY: S. Tilton	1883	Unknown	70-120	*
Hardy, Thomas	Jude the Obscure (1st AM, 8vo, 488p, gilt, 12pl)	Harper	1896	Unknown	150-220	
Gordon, Elizabeth	Just You (1st, sq16mo, ipcb, [20]p, pep)	Volland	(1920)	Unknown	30-50	*
Grey, Zane	Light of Western Stars (1st, sm8vo, 389p, gilt, col frn)	Harper	1914	Unknown	125-180	
Blanchard, Amy E.	Little Miss Mouse (1st, sm8vo, 230p, p-o, 5cp, pep)	Jacobs	(1906)	Unknown	30-50	
Gordon, Armistead	Maje: A Love Story (1st, sm8vo, ipcb, uncut, 119p, 4pl)	Scribner	1914	Unknown	40-60	*
Bangs, John K.	Mantel-Piece Minstrels (1st, 16mo, 84p, pcb, p-o, b/w)	R.H. Russell	1896	Unknown	60-100	
Alcott, Louisa M.	May Flowers (1st, 12mo, grey/gilt, 56p, b/w)	Little/Brown	(1899)	Unknown	60-90	
Cawein, Madison J.	Message of the Lilies (1st, narrow 8vo, [16]p, pcb, color, pep)	Volland	(1913)	Unknown	60-100	R*
Spyri, Johanna	Moni the Goat Boy (1st, 12mo, 43p, 3cp, pep)	Crowell	(1914)	Unknown	30-50	
Gugu	Mother Duck's Children (1st, sq4to, 48p, ibds, color)	R.H. Russell	1900	Unknown	170-240	
LeGallienne, R.	Mr. Sun & Mrs. Moon (1st, folio, bds, [62]p, 12pl)	R.H. Russell	1902	Unknown	220-280	R
Deihl, Edna G.	My Twin Kitties (1st, 8vo, [24]p, ibds, color, pep)	S. Gabriel	(1924)	Unknown	40-65	
Van Valkenburgh, H.	Myself & I (1st, 12mo, [36]p, color)	Volland	(1918)	Unknown	35-60	*
Tregarthen, Enys	North Cornwall Fairies and Legends (1st, 8vo, 192p, teg, gilt, b/w)	L: Wells/Gard.	1906	Unknown	50-85	*
Bowen, William	Old Tobacco Shop (1st, sm8vo, 236p, green/gilt, p-o, fp b/w, NH)	Macmillan	1921	Unknown	60-90	
Gates, Josephine S.	One Day in Betty's Life (1st, ob4to, gilt, [56]p, 2-color)	Bobbs-Merrill	(1913)	Unknown	100-150	*
McNamara, John F.	Playing Airplane (1st, ob8vo, 128p, col frn, b/w, pep)	Macmillan	1930	Unknown	60-90	
Wright, Henrietta	Princess Liliwinkins (1st, 12mo, 220p, 9pl)	Harper	1889	Unknown	70-120	
Gordon, Adam L.	Racing Rhymes (1st, 12mo, 146p, uncut, b/w)	R.H. Russell	1901	Unknown	75-100	*
Bangs, John K.	Real Thing… (1st, sm8vo, 135p, brown/gilt, uncut, 4pl)	Harper	1909	Unknown	50-80	
Asbjornsen, P.C.	Round the Yule Log (1st, sm8vo, 316p, b/w)	L: Sampson Low	1881	Unknown	80-120	*
Bianco, Margery W.	Rufus the Fox (1st, folio, ibds, [44]p, color, DJ/2.00)	Harper	1937	Unknown	100-165	
Phillips, Ethel C.	Santa Claus Brownies (1st, 8vo, 139p, col frn, pep)	Houghton	1928	Unknown	30-45	
Nesbit, Wilbur D.	Sermons in Song (1st, 12mo, ibds, 96p, 1-color, pep)	Volland	(1929)	Unknown	35-60	*
Kipling, Rudyard	Seven Seas (1st {illus ed}, 8vo, teg, uncut, 209p, 8pl)	Appleton	1905	Unknown	50-80	
Haggard, H. Rider	She (1st, 8vo, 317p, gilt, b/w pl, pep)	L: Longmans	1887	Unknown	650-900	
Cawein, Madison J.	So Many Ways (1st, 12mo, pcb, gilt, [12]p, color)	Volland	(1911)	Unknown	60-100	R*
Foley, James W.	Some One Like You (1st, 16mo, gilt, ibds, color, pep)	Volland	(1916)	Unknown	50-80	
Malloch, Douglas	Someone to Care (1st, sq16mo, [22]p, ibds, color)	Volland	(1920)	Unknown	35-60	
Lovelace, Richard	Songs & Sonnets (1st, sm8vo, 57p, uncut, 1-color)	R.H. Russell	1901	Unknown	80-120	*
Barrie, James M.	Story of Peter Pan (4to, ibds, 6 fp color, pep)	C.E. Graham	(1926)	Unknown	60-100	
Ade, George	Sultan of Sulu (1st, 12mo, 127p, b/w)	R.H. Russell	1903	Unknown	55-80	*
N/A	Tales & Talks About Animals (4to, 29cp, pcb, p-o)	Caldwell	[1901]	Unknown	60-100	*
Brown, Abbie F.	Tales of the Red Children (1st, sm8vo, 125p, tan cl, fp b/w)	Appleton	1909	Unknown	40-65	
Evers, Helen	This Little Pig (1st, 8vo, [32]p, ibds, fp 1-color, pep)	Farrar/Rinehart	(1932)	Unknown	50-80	*
Foley, James W.	Through All the Years (1st, sq16mo, pep, [22]p, color)	Volland	(1920)	Unknown	30-50	
Moerleim, G.	Trip Around the World (1st, 4to, AEG, red/gilt, 100 chromos)	Burgheim	1880	Unknown	170-240	
Gotch, Phyllis M.	Tuffy and the Merboo (4to, ibds, fp color)	L: R.B. Johnson	[1904]	Unknown	140-200	*
Burnett, Frances H.	Way to the House of Santa Claus (1st, lg ob4to, p-o, [25]p, color)	Harper	1916	Unknown	120-175	
Meigs, Cornelia L.	Windy Hill (1st, sm8vo, 210p, frontis, NH)	Macmillan	1921	Unknown	60-90	
Field, Eugene	Wynken, Blyken and Nod (1st, lg4to, [34]p, ipcb, color, pep)	C.E. Graham	(1925)	Unknown	80-130	
Yates, Elizabeth	Amos Fortune, Free Man (1st {std}, 8vo, 181p, b/w, DJ/2.50, NM)	Aladdin	1950	Unwin, Nora S.	100-165	R
Dorian, Edith	Ask Dr. Christmas (1st, 8vo, 144p, b/w, DJ/2.25)	Whittlesey	(1951)	Unwin, Nora S.	20-30	
Yates, Elizabeth	Carolina's Courage (1st, 8vo, 94p, b/w, DJ/2.95)	Dutton	(1964)	Unwin, Nora S.	30-45	
Yates, Elizabeth	Children of the Bible (1st {std}, sm8vo, 92p, b/w, DJ/2.00)	Aladdin	1950	Unwin, Nora S.	40-65	
Yates, Elizabeth	Christmas Story (1st {std}, lg8vo, gilt, 54p, b/w, DJ/2.00)	Aladdin	1949	Unwin, Nora S.	40-65	
Hunt, Mabel L.	Cupola House (1st {std}, 8vo, 122p, DJ/3.25)	Lippincott	(1961)	Unwin, Nora S.	20-35	
Eastwick, Ivy O.	Deck the Stable (1st {std}, 4to, [26]p, 1-color, pep, DJ/2.75)	McKay	(1960)	Unwin, Nora S.	30-45	
Tregarthen, Enys	Doll Who Came Alive (1st, sq12mo, 75p, fp 3-color, DJ/2.00)	NY: J. Day	(1942)	Unwin, Nora S.	60-100	
Unwin, Nora S.	Doughnuts for Lin (1st {std}, ob8vo, ibds, [46]p, color, DJ/1.75)	Aladdin	(1950)	Unwin, Nora S.	30-50	*
Yates, Elizabeth	Easter Story (1st {std}, 8vo, 127p, DJ/3.50)	Dutton	(1967)	Unwin, Nora S.	30-50	
Baker, Margaret	Family that Grew and Grew (1st, 8vo, 121p, b/w, DJ/2.25)	Whittlesey	(1952)	Unwin, Nora S.	30-45	*
Nesbit, Edith	Five of Us & Madeline (1st, sm8vo, 310p, red cl, col frn, 6pl)	L: T.F. Unwin	1925	Unwin, Nora S.	125-180	
Yates, Elizabeth	Lighted Heart (1st, 8vo, 251p, b/w, DJ/4.50)	Dutton	1960	Unwin, Nora S.	25-45	
Kyle, Elisabeth	Lost Karin (1st AM, 8vo, 266p, b/w, pep, DJ/2.50)	Houghton	1948	Unwin, Nora S.	50-80	
Unwin, Nora S.	Lucy & Little Red Horse (1st, 4to, 36p, p-o, gilt, 8 fp color, DJ)	L: A. Moring	(1943)	Unwin, Nora S.	55-80	
Snedeker, Caroline D.	Luke's Quest (1st {std}, sm8vo, blue cl, 208p, uncut, b/w, DJ/2.00)	Doubleday	1947	Unwin, Nora S.	30-50	
Yates, Elizabeth	Mountain Born (1st, 8vo, 118p, brown cl, b/w, pep, DJ/2.50, NH)	Coward	(1943)	Unwin, Nora S.	50-80	
Yates, Elizabeth	Next Fine Day: A Novel (1st, 8vo, 191p, b/w, DJ/3.75)	John Day	(1962)	Unwin, Nora S.	20-35	
Yates, Elizabeth	Once in the Year (1st, 8vo, red cl, p-o, [64]p, 1-color, DJ/2.00)	Coward	(1947)	Unwin, Nora S.	30-50	
Barrie, James M.	Peter Pan (1st, 8vo, 242p, pink cl, fp b/w, DJ/2.50)	Scribner	1950	Unwin, Nora S.	40-65	R
Barrie, James M.	Peter Pan (1st UK, 8vo, 192p, red/gilt, 23 b/w illus, DJ)	L: Hodder	1951	Unwin, Nora S.	55-80	
Yates, Elizabeth	Place for Peter (1st, 8vo, 184p, b/w, DJ/2.50)	Coward	(1952)	Unwin, Nora S.	25-35	
Unwin, Nora S.	Poquito, Little Mexican Duck (1st, sm ob4to, [32]p, 1-color, DJ/2.75)	McKay	1959	Unwin, Nora S.	30-50	
MacDonald, George	Princess & Curdie (1st, 8vo, 240p, 1-color, DJ/2.00)	Macmillan	(1954)	Unwin, Nora S.	30-60	*
MacDonald, George	Princess & the Goblin (1st, 8vo, olive cl, 249p, 1-color, pep, DJ/2.00)	Macmillan	(1951)	Unwin, Nora S.	30-50	
Yates, Elizabeth	Prudence Crandall, Woman of Courage (1st {std}, 8vo, 246p, b/w, DJ/3.00)	Aladdin	1955	Unwin, Nora S.	30-45	
Goudge, Elizabeth	Reward of Faith (1st AM, 8vo, blue cl, 186p, b/w, DJ/2.75)	Coward	(1950)	Unwin, Nora S.	30-50	
Burnett, Frances H.	Secret Garden (1st, 8vo, 284p, 4 dp color, b/w, DJ/2.50)	Lippincott	(1949)	Unwin, Nora S.	25-40	
Unwin, Nora S.	Sinbad the Cygnet (1st, ob8vo, [48]p, 2-color, DJ/4.50)	John Day	1970	Unwin, Nora S.	35-50	
Coatsworth, Eliz.	Summer Green (1st {std}, 8vo, ibds, 86p, b/w, DJ/2.00)	Macmillan	1948	Unwin, Nora S.	20-35	
Yates, Elizabeth	Under the Little Fir (1st, 8vo, 96p, 2-color, pep, DJ/2.00)	Coward	(1942)	Unwin, Nora S.	25-40	
Unwin, Nora S.	Way of the Shepherd (1st, sm4to, 32p, fp 2-color, pep, DJ/2.50)	McGraw-Hill	(1963)	Unwin, Nora S.	25-45	
Chase, Mary Ellen	White Gate (1st {std}, 8vo, 185p, b/w, pep, DJ/3.00)	Norton	(1954)	Unwin, Nora S.	30-50	

ARTIST: 208

AUTHOR	TITLE	PUBLISHER	DATE	ARTIST	PRICE	LC
Tregarthen, Enys	White Ring (1st, sq8vo, 65p, fp b/w, DJ/2.00)	Harcourt	(1949)	Unwin, Nora S.	40-65	
Yates, Elizabeth	With Pipe, Paddle and Song (1st {std}, 8vo, 256p, b/w, DJ/4.95)	Dutton	(1968)	Unwin, Nora S.	20-30	
Yates, Elizabeth	Your Prayers and Mine (1st, sm8vo, 64p, 1-color, DJ/2.00)	Houghton	1954	Unwin, Nora S.	20-30	
Brown, Abbie F.	Fresh Posies (1st, sq8vo, 199p, p-o, 4cp)	Houghton	1908	Upjohn, Anna M.	40-60	*
Upjohn, Anna M.	Friends in Strange Garments (1st, 8vo, 148p, 4cp)	Houghton	1927	Upjohn, Anna M.	25-40	
Byrne, Miriam	House of the Red Fox (1st, sq12mo, 116p, 8pl)	Stokes	(1907)	Upjohn, Anna M.	25-45	*
Jewett, John H.	Little Christmas (1st, sm narrow 8vo, 113p, ibds, 8cp)	Stokes	(1906)	Upjohn, Anna M.	40-60	*
Burnham, Clara L.	Quest Flower (1st, sm8vo, 132p, red/gilt, 4cp)	Houghton	1908	Upjohn, Anna M.	55-80	
Jewett, John H.	Snuggy Bedtime Stories (1st, 12mo, 126p, ibds, 8cp)	Stokes	(1906)	Upjohn, Anna M.	55-90	
Byrne, Miriam	Would-Be Witch (1st, sq12mo, 127p, 8pl)	Stokes	(1906)	Upjohn, Anna M.	20-35	
Upton, Florence	Adventures of Borbee & the Wisp (1st, lg sq8vo, ibds, [67]p, 31 color)	L: Longmans	1908	Upton, Florence	300-500	R
Upton, Bertha	Adventures of Two Dutch Dolls & Golliwogg (1st, ob4to, 64p, ibds, 29cp, pep)	Longmans	(1895)	Upton, Florence	500-700	
Alden, William L.	Among the Freaks (1st, 195p, 45 illus)	Longmans	1896	Upton, Florence	200-350	
Upton, Bertha	Golliwogg at Sea-Side (1st, ob4to, ibds, 63p, color, pep)	L: Longmans	1898	Upton, Florence	450-600	R
Upton, Bertha	Golliwogg in Holland (1st, ob4to, 64p, ibds, 31 fp color, dep)	L: Longmans	1904	Upton, Florence	450-650	R
Upton, Bertha	Golliwogg in War! (1st, ob4to, 65p, ibds, color)	L: Longmans	1899	Upton, Florence	400-600	R
Upton, Florence	Golliwogg's Air-Ship (1st, ob4to, ipcb, 65p, color)	L: Longmans	1902	Upton, Florence	400-600	R
Upton, Bertha	Golliwogg's Auto Go Cart (1st, ob4to, ibds, 66p, color)	L: Longmans	1901	Upton, Florence	400-650	R
Upton, Bertha	Golliwogg's Bicycle Club (1st, ob4to, 62p, ibds, fp color)	L: Longmans	1896	Upton, Florence	500-700	
Upton, Bertha	Golliwogg's Christmas (1st, ob4to, 62p, ipcb, 31 fp color)	L: Longmans	1907	Upton, Florence	450-700	R
Upton, Bertha	Golliwogg's Circus (1st, ob4to, ibds, 31 fp color)	L: Longmans	1903	Upton, Florence	500-700	R
Upton, Bertha	Golliwogg's Desert Island (1st, ob4to, ibds, 64p, color)	L: Longmans	1906	Upton, Florence	450-650	
Upton, Bertha	Golliwogg's Fox Hunt (1st, ob4to, 66p, ipcb, 32 fp color)	L: Longmans	1905	Upton, Florence	300-500	
Upton, Bertha	Golliwogg's Polar Adventures (1st, ob4to, 63p, ibds, color)	L: Longmans	1900	Upton, Florence	450-650	R
Upton, Bertha	Little Hearts (4to, ibds, 62p, color)	L: Routledge	1897	Upton, Florence	500-750	
Beckman, Ernst	Pax and Carlino (1st, 8vo, 196p, 6pl, pep)	L: T.F. Unwin	1894	Upton, Florence	100-165	
Brine, Mary D.	Poor Sally/her Christmas (1st, 8vo, 182p, b/w pl)	Dutton	1898	Upton, Florence	150-225	
Upton, Bertha	Vege-Men's Revenge (1st, ob4to, ibds, 63p, color)	L: Longmans	1897	Upton, Florence	500-700	R
Lampman, Evelyn	City Under the Back Steps (1st {std}, 8vo, 210p, b/w, DJ/2.95)	Doubleday	1960	Valintcourt, Honore	25-40	*
Van Doren, Mark	Transparent Tree (1st, 4to, ipcb, 87p, 2-color, pep, DJ/1.50)	Henry Holt & Co.	(1940)	Van Doren, Margaret	70-100	R
Van Dresser, Jasmine	Gibby of Clamshell Alley (1st, sm8vo, 378p, p-o, 8pl, pep)	Dodd	1916	Van Dresser, Wm.	25-45	*
Mason, Arthur	Fossil Fountain (1st {std}, 8vo, 198p, col frn, 4pl, pep)	Doubleday/Doran	1928	Van Everen, Jay	20-30	
Colum, Padraic	Fountain of Youth (1st, sm8vo, 206p, b/w, pep)	Macmillan	1927	Van Everen, Jay	45-70	
Fillmore, Parker H.	Laughing Prince (1st, 8vo, 286p, col frn, pep)	Harcourt	1921	Van Everen, Jay	30-50	
Moore, Ann C.	Nicholas (1st, 12mo, red/gilt, 331p, col frn, pep, NH)	Putnam	1924	Van Everen, Jay	70-100	
Moore, Ann C.	Nicholas & Golden Goose (1st, 12mo, 259p, blue/gilt, color, pep)	Putnam	1932	Van Everen, Jay	40-65	
Adams, Katharine	Red Caps and Lilies (1st, sm8vo, 351p, b/w pl)	Macmillan	1924	Van Everen, Jay	25-40	
Davis, Mary G.	Truce of the Wolf (1st, lg8vo, uncut, 125p, fp b/w, dep, NH)	Harcourt	(1931)	Van Everen, Jay	40-60	*
Andersen, Hans C.	Ugly Duckling (1st, 4to, unpag, color)	L: D. Nutt	1894	Van Hoytema, T.	80-120	*
Van Loon, Hendrik	Adventures & Escapes/Gustavas Vasa (1st {std} lg8vo 136p, col, pep, DJ/2.50)	Dodd	1945	Van Loon, Hendrik	30-50	
Van Loon, Hendrik	Elephant Up a Tree (1st, 8vo, p-o, 206p, 3cp, pep)	Simon/Schuster	1933	Van Loon, Hendrik	50-80	
Van Loon, Hendrik	Folk Songs of Many Lands (1st, 4to, ibds, 96p, color)	Simon/Schuster	1938	Van Loon, Hendrik	30-60	
Van Loon, Hendrik	History with a Match (1st, sm4to, 126p, p-o, color)	McKay	1917	Van Loon, Hendrik	55-90	
Van Loon, Hendrik	Message of the Bells (1st {std}, 12mo, ibds, gilt, pep, 16p, color)	(Garden City)	(1942)	Van Loon, Hendrik	55-80	*
Van Loon, Hendrik	Story of Mankind (1st, lg8vo, 479p, gilt, p-o, NM, PPPa)	Boni/Liveright	(1921)	Van Loon, Hendrik	100-150	
Van Loon, Hendrik	Wilbur the Hat (1st, sm4to, ibds, 110p, p-o, fp color, pep)	H.B. Liveright	(1925)	Van Loon, Hendrik	80-120	R
Mother Goose	Tiny Book of Nursery Rhymes (1st, 12mo, ipcb, 61p, color, pep)	Harter	(1934)	Van Nortwick, C.	40-60	*
Van Hichtum, Ninke	Afke's Ten (1st, 8vo, 255p, col frn, b/w, DJ/2.00)	Lippincott	(1936)	Van Stockum, Hilda	40-65	
Van Stockum, Hilda	Andries (1st, 8vo, 192p, grey cl, 1 dp color, fp b/w, DJ/2.00)	Viking	1942	Van Stockum, Hilda	30-50	
Van Stockum, Hilda	Angel's Alphabet (1st, lg8vo, [64]p, ipcb, fp b/w, DJ/1.50)	Viking	1948	Van Stockum, Hilda	50-80	
Coblentz, Catherine	Beggar's Penny (1st {std}, 8vo, 269p, b/w, map, DJ/2.50)	Longmans	1943	Van Stockum, Hilda	30-50	
Coblentz, Catherine	Bells of Leyden Sing (1st {std}, 8vo, 259p, pep, b/w, DJ/2.25)	Longmans	1944	Van Stockum, Hilda	30-50	
Goetz, Delia	Burro of Burnegat Road (1st, 8vo, 205p, b/w, pep, DJ/2.00)	Harcourt	(1945)	Van Stockum, Hilda	25-45	*
Van Stockum, Hilda	Canadian Summer (1st, 8vo, 190p, fp b/w, DJ/2.50)	Viking	1948	Van Stockum, Hilda	25-45	*
Van Stockum, Hilda	Cottage at Bantry Bay (1st, 8vo, 252p, fp b/w, pep, DJ/2.50)	Viking	1938	Van Stockum, Hilda	30-50	
Van Stockum, Hilda	Day on Skates (1st {std}, ob4to, 40p, 8cp, pep, DJ/2.50, NH)	Harper	1934	Van Stockum, Hilda	100-175	
Van Stockum, Hilda	Francie on the Run (1st, 8vo, 303p, pep, b/w, DJ/2.50)	Viking	1939	Van Stockum, Hilda	30-50	
Van Stockum, Hilda	Friendly Gables (1st, 8vo, 186p, b/w, DJ/2.75)	Viking	(1960)	Van Stockum, Hilda	25-40	
Van Stockum, Hilda	Gerrit & the Organ (1st, 8vo, 178p, col frn, fp b/w, DJ/2.50)	Viking	1943	Van Stockum, Hilda	30-50	
Dodge, Mary Mapes	Hans Brinker (1st, 8vo, 335p, color, DJ/1.25, RC)	World	(1946)	Van Stockum, Hilda	20-30	*
Van Stockum, Hilda	Kersti and St. Nicholas (1st, 4to, 70p, p-o, color, DJ/2.00)	Viking	1940	Van Stockum, Hilda	30-45	
Van Stockum, Hilda	Little Old Bear (1st, lg8vo, 32p, b/w, DJ/1.75)	Viking	(1962)	Van Stockum, Hilda	25-45	*
Van Stockum, Hilda	Mogo's Flute (1st, 8vo, 88p, fp b/w, DJ/3.50)	Viking	(1966)	Van Stockum, Hilda	25-40	
Van Stockum, Hilda	Patsy & the Pup (1st, sm8vo, 82p, ipcb, fp b/w, DJ/1.50)	Viking	1950	Van Stockum, Hilda	30-45	
Van Stockum, Hilda	Pegeen (1st, 8vo, 268p, b/w, pep, DJ/2.00)	Viking	1941	Van Stockum, Hilda	30-50	
Becker, May (ed)	Rainbow Book of Bible Stories (1st, 8vo, 220p, color, RC, DJ/1.25)	World	(1948)	Van Stockum, Hilda	20-35	
Van Stockum, Hilda	The Mitchells (1st, 8vo, 246p, b/w, DJ/2.50)	Viking	1945	Van Stockum, Hilda	25-45	
Voorhoeve, Rudolf	Tilio, Boy of Papua (1st, 8vo, 219p, col frn, DJ/1.75)	Lippincott	(1937)	Van Stockum, Hilda	30-50	
Van Stockum, Hilda	Winged Watchman (1st, 8vo, 204p, b/w, DJ/3.25)	Farrar, Straus	(1962)	Van Stockum, Hilda	25-45	
MacDonald, George	Fairy Fleet (1st, 8vo, [52]p, pattern cl, 1-color, DJ/1.25)	Holiday House	1936	Van Veen, Stuyvesant	60-90	R
Wellman, Manly W.	Rebel Mail Runner (1st, sm8vo, 221p, red cl, b/w, pep, DJ/2.75)	Holiday House	(1954)	Van Veen, Stuyvesant	30-50	
Adams, Darwin	Adventures of Monte & Molly (1st, 4to, blue cl, 152p, fp color, DJ/2.00)	Macaulay	(1938)	Van Zelm, Franklin	90-120	
Keeler, David B.	Memoirs of Simple Simon (1st, 4to, [56]p, color)	R.H. Russell	(1901)	Vandevort, C.S.	250-400	
Dillon, Eilis	Cat's Opera (1st AM, 4to, 63p, fp b/w, DJ/2.75)	Bobbs-Merrill	(1963)	Vanecek, Kveta	30-50	
Varga, Judy	Janko's Wish (1st, ob8vo, [32]p, fp 3-color, pep, DJ/3.50)	Wm. Morrow	(1969)	Varga, Judy	20-30	
Varga, Judy	Miss Lollipop's Lion (1st, 8vo, unpag, color, DJ/2.75)	Wm. Morrow	1963	Varga, Judy	20-30	
Varga, Judy	Pig in the Parlor (1st, sm4to, [32]p, fp 2-color, pep, DJ/2.75)	Wm. Morrow	1963	Varga, Judy	25-45	
Abbot, Alice B.	Frigate's Namesake (1st, sm8vo, 204p, blue cl, 17pl)	Century	1901	Varian, George	30-50	*

AUTHOR	TITLE	PUBLISHER	DATE	ARTIST	PRICE	LC
Hammond, Harold	Further Fortunes of Pinkey Perkins (1st, sm8vo, 391p, 22pl)	Century	1906	Varian, George	40-70	
Hawes, Charles B.	Great Quest (1st, 8vo, 359p, 5pl, pep, NH)	Little/Brown	(1921)	Varian, George	50-80	*
Murai, Gensai	Kibun Daizin (1st, 12mo, 164p, 12pl)	Century	1904	Varian, George	35-60	*
Schultz, James W.	Lone Bull's Mistake (1st, 8vo, 207p, p-o, 4pl)	Houghton	1918	Varian, George	70-120	
Nichols, William T.	Making Good (1st, sm8vo, 293p, p-o, gilt, color)	Appleton	1915	Varian, George	20-30	
Hammond, Harold	Pinkey Perkins, Just a Boy (1st, 8vo, 327p, b/w, PPPa)	Century	1905	Varian, George	60-100	
Schultz, James W.	Plumed Snake Medicine (1st, 8vo, 244p, p-o, 4pl)	Houghton	1924	Varian, George	70-100	
Scott, Walter	Quentin Durward (1st, sm8vo, 348p, 4cp)	Appleton	1910	Varian, George	25-45	*
Schultz, James W.	Quest of the Fish-Dog Skin (1st, 8vo, 219p, tan cl, p-o, 4pl)	Houghton	1913	Varian, George	70-100	
Serviss, Garrett P.	Second Deluge (1st, sm8vo, 399p, aqua cl, 4pl)	McBride	1912	Varian, George	170-240	
London, Jack	Tales of the Fish Patrol (1st, 8vo, teg, 243p, map, 7pl)	Macmillan	1905	Varian, George	250-450	
Kennan, George	Tragedy of Pelee (1st, 8vo, 257p, teg, gilt, 7pl)	Outlook	1902	Varian, George	50-80	
Stevenson, Rbt. L.	Treasure Island (1st, sm8vo, 306p, 7cp, fp b/w)	Scribner	1918	Varian, George	60-100	*
Schultz, James W.	With the Indians in the Rockies (1st, 8vo, p-o, 227p, 6pl)	Houghton	1912	Varian, George	70-100	
Seidelman, James	14th Dragon (1st, ob4to, [31]p, fp color, cep, DJ/3.95)	Harlin Quist	(1968)	Various	50-85	
N/A	All About Story Book (1st, sq4to, 63p, orange/gilt, color)	Cupples/Leon	(1929)	Various	80-120	*
Baum, L. Frank	American Fairy Tales (1st, 8vo, [205]p, teg, cloth, b/w)	George Hill	1901	Various	600-900	*
N/A	Arabian Nights (1st, 4to, 472p, green cl, b/w)	L: Newnes	1899	Various	120-160	*
N/A	Arabian Nights (1st, lg8vo, 435p)	L: Constable	(1908)	Various	75-100	*
N/A	Arabian Nights (8vo, 435p, gilt, col frn)	Dodge	(1910)	Various	25-45	*
Smith, Francis H.	Arm-Chair at the Inn (1st, sm8vo, green/gilt, uncut, 357p, 8pl)	Scribner	1912	Various	30-50	
Cobb, Irving	Back Home (1st, 8vo, gilt, 348p, 10pl)	Doran	(1912)	Various	55-80	
Wharton, Thomas I.	Bobbo and other Fancies (1st, 12mo, gilt, 182p, uncut, 11pl)	Harper	1897	Various	40-70	
Baring-Gould, Sabine	Book of Nursery Songs and Rhymes (1st, 8vo, 160p, gilt, uncut, teg, 16pl)	L: Methuen	1895	Various	150-250	
Baring-Gould, Sabine	Book of Pictured Carols (1st, 8vo, ibds, uncut, 75p, wood engravings)	L: G. Allen	1893	Various	140-200	
N/A	Book of Sweethearts (1st, lg4to, [32]p, p-o, 8cp)	Bobbs-Merrill	(1908)	Various	140-200	
Wharton, Edith	Book of the Homeless (1st, 4to, gilt, 155p, bds, 8cp, 13pl)	Scribner	1916	Various	200-300	
Towers, Alton	Bunny & Bobbie (1st, 4to, unpag)	Cooke/Stokes	[1907]	Various	80-120	*
Stephens, Robert N.	Captain Ravenshaw (1st, 12mo, 369p, teg, blue/gilt, 7pl)	L.C. Page	1901	Various	35-60	
Squire, Charles	Celtic Myth & Legend (1st, 8vo, 446p, teg, gilt, 4cp)	L: Gresham	[1912]	Various	100-180	
Coatsworth, Eliz.	Children Come Running (1st, 8vo, 96p, ipcb, color, cep, DJ/2.95)	Golden Press	(1960)	Various	25-45	
Riis, Jacob A.	Children of the Tenements (1st, sm8vo, green cl, 387p, 8pl)	Macmillan	1903	Various	70-120	
Sherman, Henry	Children's Bible (1st, lg8vo, 329p, black cl, p-o, 15cp, pep, SC)	Scribner	1922	Various	100-165	
Longfellow, H.W.	Children's Longfellow (1st, lg8vo, 334p, p-o, 8cp)	Houghton	1908	Various	50-80	*
Fox, John Jr.	Christmas Eve on Lonesome (1st, sm8vo, 234p, teg, 8cp)	Scribner	1904	Various	25-40	
Thackeray, Wm. M.	Chronicle of the Drum (1st, 4to, AEG, 70p, brown/gilt, 32pl)	Scribner	1882	Various	150-225	
Chesterton, G.K.	Club of Queer Trades (1st, sm8vo, red/gilt, 270p, 6pl)	Harper	1905	Various	200-300	
Gates, Eleanor	Cupid the Cowpunch (1st, sm8vo, 316p, p-o, 8pl)	McClure	1907	Various	45-80	
Swan, Oliver G.	Deep Water Days (1st, lg8vo, 506p, p-o, 11cp, pep)	Macrae Smith	(1929)	Various	60-90	
Ralph, Julian	Dixie (1st, lg8vo, 411p, gilt, b/w)	Harper	1896	Various	60-100	
Morrison, Lucile P.	Doll Dreams (1st, 8vo, p-o, 121p, fp b/w, pep)	Hollycrofters	(1932)	Various	120-200	
Carleton, Katherine	Dorothy, the Motor Girl (1st, sm8vo, 386p, 33pl)	Century	1911	Various	30-50	
Freeman, Mary E.W.	Fair Lavinia (1st, 12mo, 308p, lavender/gilt, 8pl)	Harper	1907	Various	40-65	
Craik, Dinah	Fairy Book (1st, 8vo, 416p, gilt, teg, 32cp)	L: Nelson	(1913)	Various	165-225	
Djurklou, Baron G.	Fairy Tales from Sweedish (1st UK, 8vo, gilt, 178p, 20 fp b/w)	L: Heinemann	1901	Various	125-200	
Piper, Watty (ed)	Famous Rhymes/Mother Goose (4to, blue/gilt, p-o, color)	Platt/Munk	(1923)	Various	50-80	
Asquith, C. (ed.)	Flying Carpet (1st, 4to, 200p, cloth, 4 ticp)	Scribner	(1925)	Various	35-60	
Underdown, E.	Gateway to Romance (1st, 4to, 299p, teg, 16cp, pep)	L: Nelson	[1909]	Various	90-120	
Bangs, John K.	Ghosts I Have Met (1st, 16mo, 191p, uncut, 23pl)	Harper	1898	Various	50-80	
Cutler, Carl	Greyhounds of the Sea (1st {std}, 4to, 592p, gilt, 8cp, photos, pep)	Putnam	1930	Various	100-160	
Bangs, John K.	Half-Hours with Jimmie-Boy (1st, 12mo, green cl, 212p, b/w)	R.H. Russell	1893	Various	60-80	
Stuart, Ruth M.	Haunted Photograph (1st, 12mo, gilt, 168p, 10pl)	Century	1911	Various	60-100	
N/A	Ideal Heads (1st, folio, brown/gilt, AEG, 20cp)	Sunshine	1890	Various	350-500	
Thaxter, Celia	Idyls and Pastorals (1st, 8vo, AEG, 58p, gilt, 24pl)	D. Lothrop Co.	(1886)	Various	90-120	*
Glave, E.J.	In Savage Africa (1st, lg8vo, 247p, grey cl, b/w)	R.H. Russell	(1892)	Various	120-200	*
Stuart, Ruth M.	In Simpkinsville (1st, 12mo, 244p, tan/gilt, 8pl)	Harper	1897	Various	50-80	
Kipling, Rudyard	Indian Tales (1st AM, 8vo, teg, gilt, 750p, 16pl)	Caldwell	(1899)	Various	100-160	
N/A	King Albert's Book (1st, 4to, 187p, pcb, 17 ticp)	L: Hodder	(1914)	Various	120-185	
Hamilton, Myra	Kingdoms Curious (1st, 8vo, 248p, tan/gilt, 8pl)	L: Heinemann	1905	Various	140-200	
Nesbit, Wilbur D.	Land of Make-Believe (1st, 8vo, green cl, 98p, 5pl)	Harper	1907	Various	35-60	*
Dodge, Mary Mapes	Land of Pluck (1st, sm8vo, 313p, gilt, teg, b/w)	Century	1894	Various	55-80	
Laboulaye, E.R.	Last Fairy Tales (1st AM, 12mo, 382p, gilt, fp b/w)	Harper	1885	Various	80-130	
Toland, M.B.M.	Legend Laymone (1st, 4to, 61p, gilt, teg, 10pl, dep)	Lippincott	1890	Various	75-100	*
Kemble, Edward W.	Life's Book of Animals (1st, ob4to, 80p, buckram, b/w)	Doub./McClure	1898	Various	90-120	
Spielmann, M.H.	Littledom Castle (1st, sm8vo, 377p, gilt, col & b/w, AEG)	L: Routledge	1903	Various	350-450	
N/A	Lovely Woman (1st, 4to, [50]p, p-o, 9cp)	Bobbs-Merrill	(1910)	Various	150-225	
Moore, Janet G.	Many Ways of Seeing (1st, 4to, 141p, color, DJ/7.95, NH)	World	(1968)	Various	80-130	
N/A	Merry Children's Nursery Rhymes (1st, 4to, ipcb, t-i frn)	L: Nister	[1890]	Various	90-120	
Waylett, Richard	Mixed Pickles (1st, 12mo, ibds, 48p, p-o, 10cp)	L: Gale/Polden	[1916]	Various	35-60	
Munkittrick, R.K.	Moon Prince & Other Nabobs (1st, 12mo, 340p, aqua/gilt, b/w)	Harper	1893	Various	55-80	*
Loomis, Charles B.	More Cheerful Americans (1st, 8vo, green/gilt, 284p, 12pl)	Henry Holt & Co.	1904	Various	30-50	
Brine, Mary D.	Mother & Baby (1st, 4to, uncut, 48p, 14pl)	R.H. Russell	1901	Various	180-240	*
Staver, Mary W.	New & True (1st, sm4to, 136p, green/gilt, 4pl, dep)	Lee & Shepard	1892	Various	180-250	
Parker, Gilbert	Northern Lights (1st, 12mo, green/gilt, 352p, 16pl)	Harper	1909	Various	35-60	
McCook, Henry C.	Old Farm Fairies (1st, 8vo, 392p, woodcuts)	L: Hodder	1895	Various	70-100	*
Bates, Clara D.	On the Tree Top (1st, 4to, [90]p, ibds, 4cp)	D. Lothrop Co.	(1891)	Various	100-160	
Brown, Alice	One-Footed Fairy (1st, 8vo, p-o, yellow cl, 182p, 12pl)	Houghton	1911	Various	60-100	*
Johnson, Gerald W.	Pattern for Liberty (1st, ob4to, gilt, 146p, fp color, DJ/7.50)	McGraw-Hill	(1952)	Various	50-80	

AUTHOR	TITLE	PUBLISHER	DATE	ARTIST	PRICE	LC
LeGallienne, R.	Perseus & Andromeda (1st, 8vo, teg, gilt, p-o, uncut, 53p, 6pl)	R.H. Russell	1902	Various	50-90	R
Hiatt, Charles	Picture Posters (1st, 8vo, teg, 367p, 151pl)	L: G. Bell	1895	Various	400-600	
Pollard, Percival	Posters in Miniature (1st, 8vo, [255]p, 250pl)	R.H. Russell	1896	Various	200-300	
N/A	Queen Mab's Fairy Realm (1st, 8vo, AEG, 310p, gilt, 27pl, pep)	L: G. Newnes	1901	Various	200-270	
Spielmann, M.H.	Rainbow Book (1st, 8vo, 289p, teg, red/gilt, col frn, 15pl, pep)	L: Chatto	1909	Various	250-400	
Carson, Thomas	Ranching Sport and Travel (1st AM, 8vo, gilt, 319p, teg, 16pl)	Scribner	(1912)	Various	250-400	
Davis, Richard H.	Ranson's Folly (1st, sm8vo, red/gilt, teg, 345p, uncut, 16pl)	Scribner	1902	Various	35-60	
Brady, Cyrus T.	Reuben James (1st, sm8vo, 158p, pict cl, b/w)	Appleton	1900	Various	25-40	
Fyleman, Rose	Round the Mulberry Bush (1st, sm4to, 192p, red cl, 6cp)	Dodd	(1928)	Various	50-80	
Asquith, C. (ed.)	Sails of Gold (1st AM, 4to, 166p, ticp)	Scribner	(1927)	Various	35-60	*
Whittier, John G.	Snowbound (lg8vo, gilt, teg, 96p, color)	Houghton	1906	Various	45-70	
Chisholm, Louey	Staircase of Stories (1st, sm4to, 527p, p-o, 31cp)	L: Jack	(1919)	Various	100-160	*
Tileston, Mary W.	Sugar & Spice & all that's Nice (1st, 12mo, red/gilt, 239p, b/w)	Little/Brown	(1910)	Various	35-60	*
Layard, George S.	Suppressed Plates... (1st, 8vo, 254p, gilt, b/w)	L: A&C Black	1907	Various	140-200	
Molesworth, Mrs.	Tales Told in the Twilight (1st, 8vo, 152p, ibds, chromos)	Nister/Dutton	[1911]	Various	70-120	
James, Ahlee	Tewa Firelight Tales (1st {std}, 8vo, 247p, 11cp, pep)	Longmans	1927	Various	70-120	
Richards, Laura E.	The Piccolo (1st, lg8vo, 121p, color, pep)	Dana Estes	(1906)	Various	30-50	*
Johnston, Mary	To Have & to Hold (1st, 8vo, green cl, 403p, 8pl)	Houghton	1900	Various	40-70	
Harris, Joel C.	Told by Uncle Remus (1st, 8vo, gilt, p-o, teg, 295p, uncut, 19pl)	McClure	1905	Various	250-350	
Willcox, Louise C.	Torch: Book of Poems for Boys (1st {std}, lg8vo, 514p, gilt, 7cp)	Harper	1924	Various	60-90	
Asquith, C. (ed.)	Treasure Cave (1st, 4to, 144p, 5 ticp)	Scribner	(1928)	Various	35-60	
Asquith, C. (ed.)	Treasure Ship (1st, 4to, 198p, 4 ticp)	Scribner	(1926)	Various	35-60	
Lang, Andrew	True Story Book (1st, 8vo, blue/gilt, 337p, AEG, 9pl, cep)	L: Longmans	1893	Various	200-300	
Dodge, Mary Mapes	When Life is Young (1st, 12mo, green/gilt, teg, 255p, b/w)	Century	1894	Various	35-60	
Snow, Jack	Who's Who in Oz (1st, lg8vo, 277p, gilt, 1-color, pep, DJ/3.75)	Reilly/Lee	(1954)	Various	250-400	
N/A	Yours Truly (ob folio, ibds, b/w)	(NY)	1907	Various	100-170	
Henty, G.A.	Yuletide Yarns (1st AM, sm8vo, beige cl, 370p, teg)	Longmans	1899	Various	120-200	
Brough, James	Dog Who Lives at the Waldorf (1st {std}, 8vo, gold bds, 68p, b/w, DJ)	Little/Brown	(1964)	Vasiliu, Mircea	30-45	
Corbett, Scott	Ever Ride a Dinosaur? (1st {std}, 8vo, 113p, b/w, DJ/3.95)	Holt, Rinehart	(1969)	Vasiliu, Mircea	25-40	*
Sherman, Nancy	Miss Agatha's Lark (1st {std}, 4to, [32]p, color, DJ/3.50)	Bobbs-Merrill	(1968)	Vasiliu, Mircea	30-45	*
Gallico, Paul	Mrs. 'Arris Goes to New York (1st AM {std}, 12mo, 192p, b/w, DJ/2.50)	Doubleday	1960	Vasiliu, Mircea	25-40	
Alexander, Lloyd C.	My Love Affair with Music (1st, 8vo, 274p, DJ/3.95, decor by...)	Crowell	(1960)	Vasiliu, Mircea	20-35	
Carlson, Natalie S.	Wings Against the Wind (1st, 8vo, 51p, fp b/w, DJ/2.50)	Harper	(1955)	Vasiliu, Mircea	20-35	
Vassos, Ruth	Contempo (1st, lg4to, [50]p, woodcuts)	Dutton	1929	Vassos, John	120-180	
Gray, Thomas	Elegy in a Country Church Yard (1st, 4to, 75p, ibds, 18pl)	Dutton	(1931)	Vassos, John	80-130	
Wilde, Oscar	Harlot's House (1st, sm4to, ibds, 105p, 16pl, DJ)	Dutton	1929	Vassos, John	120-180	
Vassos, Ruth	Humanities (1st, lg4to, 140p, 24 fp b/w)	Dutton	1935	Vassos, John	80-120	
Coleridge, Samuel T.	Kubla Kahn (1st {std}, 4to, [46]p, gilt, 13 fp brown illus)	Dutton	1933	Vassos, John	100-150	
Wilde, Oscar	Salome... (1st, 8vo, bds, 57p, 13pl)	Dutton	(1927)	Vassos, John	120-180	
Vassos, Ruth	Ultimo (1st, lg8vo, [52]p, ibds, 22pl)	Dutton	1930	Vassos, John	100-165	
Douglas, Emily	Appleseed Farm (1st, 8vo, 127p, b/w, pep, DJ/1.50)	Abingdon-Cokes.	1948	Vaughan, Anne	20-30	*
Smith, Eugene C.	Kongo the Elephant (1st {std}, lg8vo, 78p, color, pep, DJ/2.00)	Knopf	(1939)	Vaughan, Anne	30-50	
DeLeeuw, Adele	Nobody's Doll (1st, 8vo, 86p, fp color, pep, DJ/2.00)	Little/Brown	1946	Vaughan, Anne	70-120	
Bergengren, Ralph	Susan and the Butterbees (1st {std}, 8vo, 175p, b/w, pep, DJ/2.00)	Longmans	1947	Vaughan, Anne	30-50	
Mother Goose	Mother Goose (1st, 12mo, [52]p, 2-color)	Whitman	1950	Vaughan, E.F.	35-60	*
Coatsworth, Eliz.	Hide and Seek (1st, 12mo, [32]p, ipcb, fp 1-color, pep, DJ/2.00)	Pantheon	(1956)	Vaughan-Jackson, G.	35-50	*
Coatsworth, Eliz.	Mouse Chorus (1st, sm8vo, ibds, unpag, 1-color, pep, DJ/2.00)	Pantheon	(1955)	Vaughan-Jackson, G.	25-40	
Steele, William O.	We Were There on the Oregon Trail (1st, 8vo, 182p, b/w, DJ/1.95)	Grosset/Dunlap	(1955)	Vaughn, Frank	20-30	
Riley, James W.	Book of Joyous Children (1st, 8vo, gilt, teg, 176p, uncut, b/w)	Scribner	1902	Vawter, J. Will	50-85	
Riley, James W.	Boys of the Old Glee Club (1st, lg8vo, [56]p, 13pl)	Bobbs-Merrill	(1907)	Vawter, J. Will	60-100	R
Riley, James W.	Defective Santa Claus (1st, 12mo, green/gilt, 77p, b/w)	Bobbs-Merrill	(1904)	Vawter, J. Will	70-120	R
Riley, James W.	Riley Fairy Tales (1st, lg8vo, 96p, p-o, color)	Bobbs-Merrill	(1923)	Vawter, J. Will	140-200	
Burdette, Robert J.	Smiles Yoked with Sighs (1st, sm8vo, 180p, green/gilt, b/w)	Bowen-Merrill	(1900)	Vawter, J. Will	25-40	
Nesbit, Wilbur D.	Trail to Boyland (1st, sm8vo, tan/gilt, uncut, 163p, 5pl)	Bobbs-Merrill	(1904)	Vawter, J. Will	35-60	*
Omar Khayyam	Rubaiyat of Omar Khayyam (folio, teg, brown/gilt, unpag, 56pl, pep)	Houghton	1884	Vedder, Elihu	400-600	
Omar Khayyam	Rubaiyat of Omar Khayyam (3rd, sm4to, brown/gilt, b/w)	Houghton	1894	Vedder, Elihu	90-140	
Crockett, Samuel R.	Red Cap Tales (1st, 8vo, 413p, yellow cl, teg, 16cp)	L: A&C Black	1904	Vedder, Simon H.	50-80	
Stowe, Harriet B.	Uncle Tom's Cabin (1st, 8vo, 508p, 8cp)	L: A&C Black	1904	Vedder, Simon H.	80-120	*
Damjan, Mischa	Wolf and the Kid (1st AM, 4to, green cl, [32]p, color, cep, DJ/4.50)	McGraw-Hill	1967	Velthuijs, Max	30-50	
Holl, Adelaide	Have You Seen my Puppy? (1st, 8vo, 32p, color, DJ/1.50)	Random	(1968)	Veno, Joe	25-40	*
Pothast-Gimberg, C.	Corso the Donkey (1st AM {std}, 8vo, 123p, b/w, DJ)	Dutton	(1963)	Ver Beek, Elly	25-40	
VerBeck, Frank	Acrobatic Animals (1st, lg ob4to, ibds, [58]p, b/w)	R.H. Russell	1899	VerBeck, Frank	250-400	
Macvane, Edith	Adventures of Joujou (1st, sq8vo, 302p, teg, p-o, 15cp, pep)	Lippincott	1906	VerBeck, Frank	100-160	
Paine, Albert B.	Arkansaw Bear (1st, 8vo, 118p, ibds, b/w)	R.H. Russell	1898	VerBeck, Frank	200-300	
Hay, Helen	Beasts & Birds (1st, lg4to, ibds, 15 fp illus)	R.H. Russell	1900	VerBeck, Frank	200-300	
VerBeck, Frank	Book of Bears (1st, lg4to, ibds, [85]p, color)	Lippincott	1906	VerBeck, Frank	250-400	
Heaton, John L.	Book of Lies (1st, 12mo, black/silver, 175p, b/w)	NY: Morse	1896	VerBeck, Frank	45-70	
MacManus, Seumas	Donegal Fairy Stories (1st, sm8vo, 256p, 34pl)	McClure	1900	VerBeck, Frank	80-130	
Willard, Charles D.	Fall of Ulysses (1st, 8vo, grey pcb, gilt, [80]p, 4cp, dep)	Doran	1912	VerBeck, Frank	70-100	*
VerBeck, Frank	Hand-Book of Golf for Bears (1st, lg8vo, ipcb, [59]p, 1-color)	R.H. Russell	1900	VerBeck, Frank	425-600	*
Bannerman, Helen	Little Black Sambo & Baby Elephant (24mo, 62p, ibds, p-o, 30 color, pep)	Platt/Munk	1925	VerBeck, Frank	100-160	
VerBeck, Frank	Little Black Sambo & Monkey People (1st, 24mo, 62p, ibds, fp color, pep)	Altemus	(1928)	VerBeck, Frank	120-200	
VerBeck, Frank	Little Black Sambo & the Tiger Kitten (1st, 24mo, 62p, ibds, fp color, pep)	Altemus	(1926)	VerBeck, Frank	120-200	
Bannerman, Helen	Little Black Sambo Story Book (1st, sm4to, 63p, col frn)	Altemus	(1930)	VerBeck, Frank	250-350	R
Bannerman, Helen	Little Black Sambo Story Book (4to, 63p, ipcb, color)	Platt/Munk	(1935)	VerBeck, Frank	120-180	
Baum, L. Frank	Magical Monarch of Mo (1st [1], lg8vo, 237p, p-o, 12cp, pep)	Bobbs-Merrill	(1903)	VerBeck, Frank	600-850	R
Baum, L. Frank	New Wonderland (1st [1], 4to, [189]p, cloth, 16cp, pep)	R.H. Russell	1900	VerBeck, Frank	2500-4000	
Rion, H.	Smiling Road (1st, 8vo, green cl, 191p, 10pl)	E.J. Clode	(1910)	VerBeck, Frank	30-50	*

AUTHOR	TITLE	PUBLISHER	DATE	ARTIST	PRICE	LC
VerBeck, Frank	The Dumpies (1st, ob12mo, 119p, b/w)	R.H. Russell	1897	VerBeck, Frank	160-225	
VerBeck, Frank	Three Bears (1st, lg4to, [60]p)	R.H. Russell	(1899)	VerBeck, Frank	400-650	
VerBeck, Frank	VerBeck's Bears in Mother Goose-Land (4to, gilt, bds, 3cp)	L: H. Milford	[1900]	VerBeck, Frank	225-300	
Tybout, Ella M.	Poketown People (1st, 8vo, 356p, 6cp)	Lippincott	1904	VerBeck/Moore	100-170	
Velvin, Ellen	Rataplan, a Rogue Elephant (1st, 12mo, red/gilt, 328p, p-o, 12cp)	Altemus	(1902)	Verbeek, Gustave	50-85	
Weil, Ann Y.	Animal Families (1st ob4to, [31]p, color, pep, DJ/1.50)	Greenberg	(1946)	Vernam, Roger	30-50	
Spyri, Johanna	Heidi (1st, lg4to, 284p, ibds, col frn, b/w, pep)	Whitman	(1934)	Vernon, Ethel	40-60	
Defoe, Daniel	Picture Book of Robinson Crusoe (1st, 4to, 51p, fp color, pep)	Macmillan	1931	Verpilleux, E.A.	70-120	
Lynch, Patricia	Brogeen and the Bronze Lizard (1st AM {std}, 8vo, 180p, b/w, DJ/4.95)	Macmillan	(1970)	Vestal, Herman B.	30-45	
Vinton, Iris	Look Out for Pirates! (1st, lg8vo, ibds, 63p, fp color, pep, DJ/1.95)	Beginner Books	1961	Vestal, Herman B.	50-85	
Malkus, Alida S.	Story of Winston Churchill (1st, 8vo, 181p, b/w, DJ/1.95)	Grosset/Dunlap	(1957)	Vestal, Herman B.	25-35	
Robinson, Mabel L.	Robin and Heather (1st, 8vo, 214p, col frn, b/w)	Macmillan	1932	Vibberts, Eunice	20-30	
Vickers, Vincent C.	Google Book (1st, lg4to, 53p, ibds, p-o, 24cp)	L: Medici	(1931)	Vickers, Vincent C.	350-500	
Lederer, William J.	Story of Pink Jade (1st {std}, 8vo, 83p, b/w, pep, DJ/2.95)	Norton	(1966)	Victor, Joan B.	25-40	*
Edmonds, Walter D.	Time to Go House (1st {std}, 8vo, 137p, tan cl, b/w, DJ/4.25)	Little/Brown	(1969)	Victor, Joan B.	30-50	
Faure, Gabriel	Gardens of Rome (1st AM, folio, p-o, 100p, cp)	Brentano's	1924	Vignal, Pierre	100-160	
Fast, Howard (ed)	Tony and the Wonderful Door (1st {std}, lg8vo, 64p, b/w, DJ)	Blue Heron Pr.	1952	Vigoda, William	40-65	
Mills, Enos A.	Animal Trainer (1st, ob8vo, 31p, p-o, 6cp)	Duffield	1910	Vimar, Auguste	70-100	
Guizou, P.	Animals in the Ark (1st, ob8vo, p-o, 31p, 7cp)	Duffield	(1909)	Vimar, Auguste	70-120	R
Vimar, Auguste	Curly-Haired Hen (1st, sm4to, 95p, p-o, b/w)	D. Fitzgerald	(1914)	Vimar, Auguste	30-45	
Vinson, Pauline	Willie Goes to the Seashore (1st {std}, 4to, [32]p, color, cep, DJ/2.25)	Macmillan	1954	Vinson, Pauline	50-80	
Vogel, Ilse-Margret	Don't Be Scared Book (1st {std}, ob8vo, [48]p, fp b/w, cep, DJ/2.95)	Atheneum	1964	Vogel, Ilse-Margret	20-35	*
N/A	Little Plays for Little People (1st, ob4to, 56p, fp 1-color, DJ/3.50)	Parents Mag. Pr.	(1965)	Vogel, Ilse-Margret	30-50	*
Vogel, Ilse-Margret	Willy, Willy, Don't Be Silly (1st {std}, sq4to, [38]p, 1-color, DJ/3.50)	Atheneum	1965	Vogel, Ilse-Margret	30-50	
Von Gottschalck, O.	Innocent Industries (1st, 4to, 100p, ibds, [50]p, b/w)	R.H. Russell	1903	Von Gottschalck	170-240	*
Gail, Otto W.	By Rocket to the Moon (1st AM, 8vo, black cl, 303p, te red, 8pl)	Sears	(1931)	Von Grunberg, R.	70-120	
Carroll, Lewis	Alice in Wonderland (1st, 8vo, 48p, color)	Barse/Hopkins	[1910]	Von Hofsten, H.	60-100	*
Montgomery, F.T.	Billy Whiskers' Grandchildren (1st, lg8vo, 152p, 6cp)	Saalfield	(1909)	Von Hofsten, H.	80-125	
Sewell, Anna	Black Beauty (1st, sm8vo, 45p, 6cp, pep)	Brewer/Barse	(1907)	Von Hofsten, H.	40-70	
Montgomery, F.T.	Cats & Kitts (1st, 8vo, 63p, p-o, 6cp)	Brewer/Barse	(1908)	Von Hofsten, H.	70-100	*
Stevenson, Rbt. L.	Child's Garden of Verses (12mo, ibds, 92p)	Barse/Hopkins	[1910]	Von Hofsten, H.	40-60	
Dickens, Charles	Christmas Carol (1st, 8vo, 48p, 6cp, pep)	Brewer/Barse	(1907)	Von Hofsten, H.	30-50	*
Montgomery, F.T.	Horses & Colts (1st, 8vo, 62p, red cl, p-o, 8cp)	Barse/Hopkins	(1911)	Von Hofsten, H.	45-70	
Mother Goose	Mother Goose Jungle Book (1st, 4to, 63p, color)	Madison Book Co.	1903	Von Hofsten, H.	70-120	*
Stowe, Harriet B.	Uncle Tom's Cabin (brown cl, p-o, 12mo, 46p, 6 color)	Barse/Hopkins	[1915]	Von Hofsten, H.	60-90	*
Fleischman, Sid	Chancy and the Grand Rascal (1st {std}, 8vo, 179p, b/w, DJ/4.25)	Little/Brown	(1966)	Von Schmidt, Eric	25-40	
Fleischman, Sid	Mr. Mysterious and Company (1st {std}, 8vo, 151p, b/w, DJ/3.25)	Little/Brown	(1962)	Von Schmidt, Eric	25-40	
Hubbard, Ralph	Queer Person (1st {std}, 8vo, 336p, doub. plates, pep, NH)	Doubleday/Doran	1930	Von Schmidt, H.	60-100	*
Miers, Earl S.	Billy Yank and Johnny Reb (1st, 8vo, 256p, b/w, DJ/3.50)	Rand/McNally	(1959)	Vosburgh, Leonard	25-40	
Fisher, Aileen	My Cousin Abe (1st, 8vo, 285p, fp b/w, DJ/3.50)	Nelson	(1962)	Vosburgh, Leonard	25-40	
Yolen, Jane	Pirates in Petticoats (1st [1st bk.], 8vo, 118p, DJ/3.25)	McKay	(1963)	Vosburgh, Leonard	60-95	
Wier, Ester A.	Straggler: Adventures of a Sea Bird (1st, 8vo, 85p, b/w, DJ/3.75)	McKay	(1970)	Vosburgh, Leonard	20-35	
Malkus, Alida S.	We Were There at Battle of Gettysburg (1st, 8vo, 176p, b/w, pep, DJ/1.75)	Grosset/Dunlap	(1955)	Vosburgh, Leonard	20-35	
Norton, Andre	Yankee Privateer (1st {std}, 8vo, 300p, b/w, DJ/2.75)	World	(1955)	Vosburgh, Leonard	200-300	*
Heinlein, Robert	Rocket Ship Galileo (1st [1st bk.], 8vo, 212p, b/w, DJ/2.00)	Scribner	(1947)	Voter, Thomas	800-1000	
Coatsworth, Eliz.	House of the Swan (1st {std}, 8vo, 165p, b/w, pep, DJ/2.50)	Macmillan	1948	Voute, Kathleen	25-40	
Carr, Mary J.	Peggy & Paul & Laddy (1st, 8vo, 207p, brown cl, b/w, pep, DJ/1.75)	Crowell	(1936)	Voute, Kathleen	25-40	*
Ryan, Marah E.	Druid Path (1st, 8vo, 321p, green/gilt, b/w, uncut)	McClurg	1917	Vreeland, Will	60-90	
Littledale, Harold	Alexander (1st, sm4to, [43]p, ipcb, color, pep, DJ/2.75)	Parents Mag. Pr.	1964	Vroman, Tom	30-50	
Tresselt, Alvin	An Elephant is Not a Cat (1st, 8vo, [46]p, color, DJ/2.95)	Parents Mag. Pr.	1962	Vroman, Tom	20-35	
Waber, Bernard	Anteater Named Arthur (1st {std}, 4to, 46p, fp 2-color, DJ/3.25)	Houghton	1967	Waber, Bernard	40-65	R
Waber, Bernard	Cheese (1st, 24mo, ipcb, [32]p, fp 1-color, DJ/1.50)	Houghton	1967	Waber, Bernard	30-50	
Waber, Bernard	Firefly Named Torchy (1st {std}, 4to, [29]p, color, DJ/4.95)	Houghton	1970	Waber, Bernard	30-50	
Waber, Bernard	House on E. 88th Street (1st, 4to, 48p, fp 3-color, DJ/3.00)	Houghton	1962	Waber, Bernard	40-65	R
Waber, Bernard	How to Go about Laying an Egg (1st, 12mo, 32p, color, DJ/2.50)	Houghton	1963	Waber, Bernard	25-40	
Waber, Bernard	Just Like Abraham Lincoln (1st, 4to, 40p, fp color, pep, DJ/3.25)	Houghton	1964	Waber, Bernard	30-50	R
Waber, Bernard	Lorenzo (1st, 12mo, [47]p, fp 1-color, DJ/1.95)	Houghton	1961	Waber, Bernard	30-45	
Waber, Bernard	Lovable Lyle (1st {std}, 4to, 48p, color, DJ/3.95)	Houghton	1969	Waber, Bernard	40-65	*
Waber, Bernard	Lyle & the Birthday Party (1st, 4to, 48p, fp color, DJ/3.25)	Houghton	1966	Waber, Bernard	40-65	
Waber, Bernard	Lyle, Lyle, Crocodile (1st, 4to, 48p, color, DJ/3.25)	Houghton	1965	Waber, Bernard	40-65	
Waber, Bernard	Rich Cat, Poor Cat (1st, 4to, 48p, fp color, DJ/3.25)	Houghton	1963	Waber, Bernard	40-65	
Waber, Bernard	Rose for Mr. Bloom (1st {std}, lg8vo, 31p, color, DJ/3.25)	Houghton	1968	Waber, Bernard	30-50	
Waber, Bernard	You Look Ridiculous (1st, 8vo, 32p, color, DJ/3.25)	Houghton	1966	Waber, Bernard	30-50	
Hay, Timothy	Horses (1st {std}, sm ob4to, [32]p, ipcb, fp b/w, DJ/1.50)	Harper	(1944)	Wag	120-200	
Hamill, Katharine F.	Rhymes for Wee Sweethearts (1st, lg8vo, 181p, p-o, 5cp)	Jacobs	(1906)	Wager-Smith, Curtis	50-90	*
McNeil, Everett	Dickon Bend-The-Bow (1st, lg8vo, 126p, fp color, pep)	Saalfield	1903	Wagner, Rob	80-130	
Hunt, Blanche S.	Little Brown Koko has Fun (1st, sm4to, 96p, ibds, 1-color)	Amer. Colortype	(1945)	Wagstaff, Dorothy	80-130	
Hunt, Blanche S.	Stories of Little Brown Koko (1st, 4to, bds, 96p, 1-color, pep, DJ/1.00)	Amer. Colortype	1940	Wagstaff, Dorothy	90-140	
Wagstaff, Hester	Doings of Dicky Daw (1st, sm4to, [45]p, ibds, fp 2-color, DJ/1.50)	Coward	(1940)	Wagstaff, Hester	30-45	
Wahn, J.& G.	Edgar, Runaway Elephant (1st, 4to, ipcb, [38]p, color, DJ/2.00)	W.R. Scott	(1941)	Wahn, J.& G.	60-100	
Hurrell, Marian I.	Adventures of Friskers & His Friends (1st, L: R. Culley	1907	Wain, Louis	500-750	
Bingham, Clifton	All Sorts of Comical Cats (1st, 4to, [62]p, ibds, chromo frn, 2-col, pep)	L: Nister	[1902]	Wain, Louis	450-650	
Wain, Louis	Big Dogs Little Dogs Cats & Kittens (1st, folio, ibds, [36]p, gilt, color)	L/NY: R. Tuck	[1900]	Wain, Louis	700-1000	
Pope, Jessie	Cat Scouts (1st, sm4to, ibds, [48]p, p-o, 6cp)	L: Blackie	[1912]	Wain, Louis	600-900	
Byron, May	Cat's Cradle (1st, sm4to, ibds, [48]p, color)	L: Blackie	[1908]	Wain, Louis	650-900	
Wain, Louis	Cats at Play (folio, [12]p, color)	L: Blackie	[1918]	Wain, Louis	250-450	
Woodhouse, S.C.	Cats at School (1st, 4to, french fold, 21cp)	L: Routledge	[1911]	Wain, Louis	1000-1500	*
Grimalkin	Cats! (1st, 4to, blue cl, 47p, color)	L: Sands	[1901]	Wain, Louis	450-650	

AUTHOR	TITLE	PUBLISHER	DATE	ARTIST	PRICE	LC
N/A	Cinderella (4to, ibds, color)	L: Gale/Polden	[1917]	Wain, Louis	700-1000	
Wain, Louis	Daddy Cat (1st AM, sm4to, 36p, ibds, color)	Dodge	[1915]	Wain, Louis	500-750	
Bingham, Clifton	Dandy Lion (4to, ibds, t-i col frn, b/w)	L: Nister	[1900]	Wain, Louis	300-500	
Wain, Louis	Flossy & Fluffy (narrow 4to, wraps, shape book, [14]p, fp 2-color)	L: Valentine	(1919)	Wain, Louis	500-700	
Bingham, Clifton	Fun and Frolic (1st, sm4to, 143p, ibds, 6cp)	L: Nister	[1900]	Wain, Louis	700-900	
N/A	Fun for the Little Ones (4to, ibds, [36]p, t-i col frn, fp b/w)	L: Nister	[1900]	Wain, Louis	180-250	
Bingham, Clifton	Funny Favorites (1st, sm4to, [44]p, ibds, tip-in col frn)	L: Nister	(1904)	Wain, Louis	400-650	
Wain, Louis	Happy Hours with Louis Wain (4to, bds, p-o, 6 ticp)	L: J.F. Shaw	(1913)	Wain, Louis	600-900	
N/A	Happy Times (4to, ibds, 8 fp color)	L: R. Tuck	[1900]	Wain, Louis	750-1000	
Wain, Louis	In Cat & Dog Land (lg4to, 36p, ibds, 12pl)	L: R. Tuck	[1900]	Wain, Louis	500-800	
Braine/Floyd	In Nurseryland (1st, 4to, ibds, [48]p, color)	L: R. Tuck	[1900]	Wain, Louis	800-1200	
Bingham, Clifton	Jingles, Jokes & Funny Folks (sm4to, wraps, b/w)	McLoughlin	[1908]	Wain, Louis	250-400	
Hannon, John	Kings and the Cats (1st, 8vo, 78p, b/w)	L: Burns & Oates	1908	Wain, Louis	120-200	
Wain, Louis	Kits and Cats (folio, wraps, 4 fp color)	L: R. Tuck	(1919)	Wain, Louis	600-850	
Bingham, Clifton	Kittenland (sm folio, ipcb, 8cp)	L: Collins	(1903)	Wain, Louis	700-1000	
Watson, Emily R.	Lament of Billy Villy (1st, lg sq8vo, wraps, 8cp)	L: R. Tuck	[1894]	Wain, Louis	500-700	
Crommelin, May	Little Soldiers (1st, 4to, ipcb, 94p, 39 color)	L: Hutchinson	[1916]	Wain, Louis	600-900	
Wain, Louis	Louis Wain Kitten Book (sq16mo, 87p, tan cl, fp color)	L: A. Treherne	1904	Wain, Louis	700-900	
Wain, Louis	Louis Wain's Baby Picture Book (1st, 4to, ibds, unpag, b/w)	L: Clarke	1903	Wain, Louis	250-450	
Wain, Louis	Louis Wain's Cats & Dogs (1st, folio, [28]p, ibds, color)	L: R. Tuck	(1903)	Wain, Louis	700-900	
Wain, Louis	Louis Wain's Children's Book (1st, 4to, 95p, ibds, 17pl)	L: Hutchinson	[1923]	Wain, Louis	400-650	
Wain, Louis	Louis Wain's Father Christmas (8vo, ibds, p-o, 5 ticp)	L: J.F. Shaw	(1912)	Wain, Louis	450-650	
Wain, Louis	Louis Wain's Painting Book (4to, bds, p-o, 4 ticp)	L: J. Shaw	[1910]	Wain, Louis	800-1200	
Keiro	Mephistopheles (8vo, 158p, green/gilt, 4pl)	L: Jarrold	(1907)	Wain, Louis	200-300	
Various	Merry Times (sm folio, [48]p, ibds, color & b/w)	L: R. Tuck	[1900]	Wain, Louis	450-600	
N/A	Miss Lovemouse's Letters (1st, ob4to, 21p, wraps, fp b/w)	L: T. Nelson	1896	Wain, Louis	300-500	
Bingham, Clifton	Mixed Pickles (4to, cloth, col frn, 1-color)	L: R. Tuck	[1910]	Wain, Louis	400-600	
Drummond, Henry	Monkey that Would not Kill (1st, 8vo, 115p, AEG, gilt, 16 fp b/w)	L: Hodder	1898	Wain, Louis	250-400	
Drummond, Henry	Monkey that Would not Kill (1st AM, 12mo, 115p, 16 fp b/w)	Dodd	1898	Wain, Louis	200-300	
Bingham, Clifton	More Jingles, Jokes & Funny Folks (4to, wraps, b/w)	McLoughlin	[1909]	Wain, Louis	250-400	
Wain, Louis	Music in Pussytown (ob4to, wraps, [12]p, color)	L: R. Tuck	[1915]	Wain, Louis	900-1300	
Wain, Louis	Nursery Cats (4to, ibds, 6 fp color)	L: R. Tuck	[1908]	Wain, Louis	700-1000	
Owen, Mary A.	Old Rabbit the Voodoo (1st, 8vo, blue/gilt, 310p, uncut, b/w)	L: T.F. Unwin	1893	Wain, Louis	250-400	
Father Tuck	Pa Cats, Ma Cats & their Kittens (1st, lg4to, ibds, [36]p, gilt, 12cp)	L: R. Tuck	[1901]	Wain, Louis	800-1200	
Freckles	Pat & Pips (4to, wraps, color, b/w)	L: Gale/Polden	[1905]	Wain, Louis	500-700	
Morley, Charles	Peter, a Cat O' One Tail (1st AM, 8vo, 110p, ibds, b/w)	Putnam	1892	Wain, Louis	250-350	
Bingham, Clifton	Ping Pong (ob narrow 4to, wraps, 6cp)	L: R. Tuck	[1903]	Wain, Louis	400-650	
Wain, Louis	Pussies & Puppies (1st, 4to, ibds, 96p, color & b/w)	L: Partridge	[1899]	Wain, Louis	800-1200	
Wain, Louis	Somebody's Pussies (4to, ibds, 13cp)	L: R. Tuck	[1920]	Wain, Louis	1000-1500	
Duppa, C.M.	Stories from Lowly Life (1st, lg8vo, 95p, uncut, red/gilt, b/w)	L: Macmillan	1898	Wain, Louis	120-200	
Kitty Cat	Tabbykin Town in School & at Play (1st, lg8vo, 12p, wraps, p-o, color)	L: Faulkner	[1920]	Wain, Louis	500-800	
N/A	Tale of Little Priscilla Purr (16mo, red bds, p-o, 13cp, pep)	L: Valentine	[1915]	Wain, Louis	300-450	
Ruthley, Cecily	Tale of the Tabby Twins (1st, 16mo, bds, p-o, fp color)	L: Valentine	(1920)	Wain, Louis	500-700	
Vredenburg, Edric	Tinker, Tailor (1st, sm4to, 136p, bds, p-o, 12cp)	L: R. Tuck	[1914]	Wain, Louis	900-1200	
Bingham, Clifton	To Nursery Land (1st, 4to, [56]p, ibds, 16 2-color)	L: R. Tuck	[1900]	Wain, Louis	700-900	
Woodhouse, S.C.	Two Cats at Large (1st, 4to, ibds, 24 fp color)	L: Routledge	[1910]	Wain, Louis	800-1200	
Chesson, Nora	With Louis Wain to Storyland (lg4to, cloth, 12 fp color)	L: R. Tuck	[1910]	Wain, Louis	900-1300	
Owen, Mary A.	Voodoo Tales (1st, 8vo, 310p, b/w)	Putnam	1893	Wain/Owen	300-500	
Dixon, Royal	Human Side of Birds (1st, 8vo, 246p, green cl, p-o, 4 ticp)	Stokes	(1917)	Wainwright, S.H.	40-65	
Johnson, Burges	Bashful Ballads (1st, 8vo, teg, 145p, b/w)	Harper	1911	Walker, A.B.	30-50	
Macleod, Mary	King Arthur & Noble Knights (1st, 8vo, 418p, teg, gilt, 35 fp b/w)	L: Wells/Gard.	(1900)	Walker, Arthur G.	150-240	
Macleod, Mary	King Arthur & Noble Knights (1st AM, 4to, 417p, teg, gilt, 35 fp b/w)	Stokes	[1900]	Walker, Arthur G.	150-220	
MacDonald, George	Lost Princess (1st, 8vo, 258p, blue/gilt, 6pl)	L: Wells/Gard.	(1895)	Walker, Arthur G.	180-250	
Macleod, Mary	Red Cross Knight & Sir Guyan (1st, 8vo, 128p)	L: Wells/Gard.	1908	Walker, Arthur G.	40-60	*
Darton, F.J.H.	Wonder Book of Old Romance (1st, sm8vo, 424p, teg, gilt, b/w)	L: Wells/Gard.	1907	Walker, Arthur G.	60-100	
Colum, Padraic	Boy Apprenticed to an Enchanter (1st, sm8vo, 168p, 5 fp b/w, dep)	Macmillan	1920	Walker, Dugald S.	80-130	
Colum, Padraic	Boy Who Knew what the Birds Said (1st, 12mo, 178p, b/w)	Macmillan	1918	Walker, Dugald S.	45-70	
Colum, Padraic	Children Who Followed the Piper (1st, 12mo, 152p, col frn, fp b/w)	Macmillan	1922	Walker, Dugald S.	55-80	
Ingraham, Corinne	Cottontail & Wishing-Fairy (1st, lg8vo, pcb, 39p, p-o, 2cp, pep)	Brentano's	(1921)	Walker, Dugald S.	100-165	
Walker, Dugald S.	Dream Boats (1st, lg8vo, 219p, 4cp, 16pl, pep)	Doubleday/Page	1918	Walker, Dugald S.	125-200	
Ingraham, Corinne	Elephant & Wishing Fairy (1st, lg8vo, bds, [45]p, p-o, 2cp, pep)	Brentano's	(1921)	Walker, Dugald S.	100-165	
Andersen, Hans C.	Fairy Tales (1st, lg8vo, p-o, gilt, 267p, 12cp)	Doubleday/Page	1914	Walker, Dugald S.	150-225	
Andersen, Hans C.	Fairy Tales (1st UK, lg8vo, 268p, p-o, 12cp, 20pl, pep)	L: Harrap	(1914)	Walker, Dugald S.	200-270	
Stewart, Anna B.	Gentlest Giant (1st {1st bk}, lg8vo, 142p, blue bds, color)	NY: Wayne	1915	Walker, Dugald S.	100-165	
Stewart, Anna B.	Gentlest Giant (1st {this pub}, 8vo, blue cl, 148p, uncut, b/w, dep)	McBride	1929	Walker, Dugald S.	50-85	
Colum, Padraic	Girl Who Sat by the Ashes (1st, sm8vo, 175p, col frn, b/w)	Macmillan	1919	Walker, Dugald S.	45-70	
Olcott, F.J.	Go! Champions of Light (1st, 8vo, 226p, b/w, pep, DJ/1.75)	Revell	(1933)	Walker, Dugald S.	50-80	
Hutchinson, W.M.L.	Golden Porch (1st [new ed], sm8vo, 302p, pep, col frn, fp b/w)	NY: Longmans	1925	Walker, Dugald S.	70-100	
Ingelow, Jean	Mopsa the Fairy (1st, 8vo, 259p, blue cl, col frn, pep)	Macmillan	1927	Walker, Dugald S.	100-160	
Hutchinson, W.M.L.	Orpheus with his Lute (1st, sm8vo, 300p, col frn, b/w, pep)	NY: Longmans	1926	Walker, Dugald S.	60-90	*
Ingraham, Corinne	Peacock & Wishing-Fairy (1st, lg8vo, p-o, pcb, [42]p, 2cp, pep)	Brentano's	(1921)	Walker, Dugald S.	100-165	
Teasdale, Sara	Rainbow Gold (1st, 8vo, 267p, blue/gilt, col frn, b/w, pep)	Macmillan	1922	Walker, Dugald S.	50-80	
Walker, Dugald S.	Sally's ABC (1st, 4to, [58]p, buckram, 2-color, pep)	Harcourt	1929	Walker, Dugald S.	120-160	R
Colum, Padraic	Six Who were Left in a Shoe (1st, sq8vo, ibds, unpag, color, pep)	Volland	(1923)	Walker, Dugald S.	50-80	
Garrott, Hal	Snythergen (1st, lg8vo, blue/gilt, 157p, 4cp, 16pl, pep)	McBride	1923	Walker, Dugald S.	80-125	
Garrott, Hal	Squiffer (1st {std}, 8vo, 226p, green/gilt, uncut, 4cp, pep)	McBride	1924	Walker, Dugald S.	70-120	
MacKay, Helen	Stories for Pictures (1st, 8vo, ibds, uncut, teg, 168p, 8cp, pep)	Duffield	1912	Walker, Dugald S.	80-120	
Andersen, Hans C.	The Mermaid (1st, sm4to, p-o, green cl, color)	Doubleday/Page	1923	Walker, Dugald S.	60-85	

AUTHOR	TITLE	PUBLISHER	DATE	ARTIST	PRICE	LC
Andersen, Hans C.	Thumbelisa... (1st, lg8vo, [80]p, p-o, 3cp)	Doubleday/Page	1923	Walker, Dugald S.	75-100	*
Ingraham, Corinne	Wishing Fairy's Animal Friends (1st, lg8vo, 141p, p-o, 8cp)	Brentano's	(1921)	Walker, Dugald S.	100-165	
Olcott, F.J.	Wonder Tales from China Seas (1st, 8vo, 238p, col frn, b/w, pep)	Longmans	1925	Walker, Dugald S.	50-80	
Ingraham, Corinne	Zebra & the Wishing Fairy (1st, lg8vo, [45]p, color, pep)	Brentano's	(1921)	Walker, Dugald S.	100-165	
Ford, Margaret	David and the Magic Powder (1st, lg8vo, ibds, [32]p, color, pep, DJ/1.50)	Random	(1946)	Walker, Nedda	25-45	
Savery, Constance	Good Ship Red Lily (1st {std}, 8vo, 197p, b/w, pep, DJ/2.25)	Longmans	1944	Walker, Nedda	50-80	
Vance, Marguerite	Martha, Daughter of Virginia (1st {std}, 8vo, 190p, col frn, b/w, DJ/2.50)	Dutton	1947	Walker, Nedda	20-30	
Clark, Billy C.	Mooneyed Hound (1st, 8vo, 128p, fp b/w, DJ/2.75)	Putnam	(1958)	Walker, Nedda	40-60	
Carroll, Lewis	Alice in Wonderland (1st, 12mo, blue/gilt, AEG, p-o, 152p, 8cp)	L: John Lane	(1907)	Walker, W.H.	200-300	
Carroll, Lewis	Alice in Wonderland (sm8vo, uncut, 152p, 8cp)	L/NY: J. Lane	[1911]	Walker, W.H.	90-120	*
Young, Charles	Night-Caps for the Babies (1st, 8vo, 126p, 8cp)	L: John Lane	(1907)	Walker, W.H.	60-90	
Uncle Milton	Bennie & Jennie (ob8vo, ibds, fp color)	Cupples/Leon	1907	Wall, Bernhardt	65-90	
Uncle Milton	Little Karl (1st, lg8vo, unpag, 8 fp color)	Cupples/Leon	1908	Wall, Bernhardt	50-80	*
Parry, David M.	Scarlet Empire (1st, sm8vo, red/gilt, 400p, 10pl)	Bobbs-Merrill	(1906)	Wall, Hermann C.	65-100	
Johnston, Harry	Pioneers in Canada (1st, 8vo, 328p, gilt, 8cp)	L: Blackie	1912	Wall-Cousins, E.	50-85	
Tunis, John R.	All-American (1st, 8vo, 245p, b/w, pep, DJ/2.00)	Harcourt	(1942)	Walleen, Hans A.	20-35	
Doone, Radko	Nuvat the Brave (1st, 8vo, green cl, 194p, fp b/w)	Macrae-Smith	(1934)	Walleen, Hans A.	25-45	*
Van Vrooman, Maria	Ju-Ju and his Friends (1st, lg8vo, 126p, color, pep, DJ/2.00)	Whitman	1939	Wallower, Lucille	25-40	
Bowman, James C.	Mystery Mountain (1st, 8vo, 293p, blue cl, 4cp, 10pl, pep, DJ/1.75)	Whitman	1940	Wallower, Lucille	30-45	
Wallower, Lucille	Roll of Drums (1st, 8vo, 111p, col frn, pep, DJ/2.00)	Whitman	1945	Wallower, Lucille	50-75	
Ryland, Lee	Gordon & the Glockenspiel (1st, 4to, [26]p, ibds, color)	Whitman	1966	Walters, Audrey	20-30	
Andersen, Hans C.	Fairy Tales (1st, 4to, black/gilt, teg, 431p, 24cp, pep)	L: Jack	1911	Walton, Cecile	225-325	
Andersen, Hans C.	Fairy Tales (1st AM, sm4to, blue/gilt, teg, 431p, uncut, 24cp)	Stokes	[1911]	Walton, Cecile	180-250	R
Glinski, Antoni J.	Polish Fairy Tales (1st, 4to, 96p, gilt, 20cp, pep)	L: John Lane	1920	Walton, Cecile	80-125	
Doob, Leonard W.	Crocodile has Me by the Leg (1st, 8vo, [54]p, fp 1-color, DJ/2.95)	NY: Walker	(1967)	Wangboje, Solomon I.	40-70	R*
Cooper, James F.	The Pathfinder (1st, 8vo, blue cl, p-o, 430p, 6cp, pep)	Minton Balch	1928	Ward, E.F.	40-60	
Catherwood, Mary	Story of Tonty (1st, 12mo, 227p, b/w)	McClurg	1890	Ward, Enoch	50-85	
Farley, Walter	Black Stallion (1st {std}, 8vo, 275p, fp b/w, DJ/2.00)	Random	(1941)	Ward, Keith	50-85	*
Lear, Edward	Duck & the Kangaroo (1st, 12mo, [56]p, pep, color)	Western Printing	(1932)	Ward, Keith	55-80	*
Gilbert, Helen E.	Go-to-Sleep Book (1st, sm sq4to, wraps, fp color)	Rand/McNally	(1936)	Ward, Keith	40-65	
Gaggin, Eva R.	Jolly Animals (1st, sq4to, p-o, 110p, 7 fp color, pep)	Rand/McNally	(1930)	Ward, Keith	100-160	
Bannerman, Helen	Little Black Sambo (1st, folio, [16]p)	Whitman	(1935)	Ward, Keith	250-350	*
Barrows, Marjorie	Muggins Mouse (1st, folio, black cl, p-o, 60p, color)	Reilly/Lee	(1932)	Ward, Keith	100-170	*
Moore, Clement C.	Night Before Christmas (4to, [16]p, wraps, color)	Whitman	(1935)	Ward, Keith	60-90	
Moore, Clement C.	Night Before Christmas (4to, wraps, [12]p, color)	Whitman	1939	Ward, Keith	50-80	
Lear, Edward	Owl & the Pussycat (1st, ob8vo, [56]p, color, pep)	Whitman	(1932)	Ward, Keith	35-60	*
Judson, Clara I.	People Who Work in Country & City (1st {A}, sm4to, 94p, col, pep, DJ/2.00)	Rand/McNally	(1943)	Ward, Keith	40-60	
Judson, Clara I.	People Who Work Near our House (1st {A}, sm4to, 48p, ipcb, 2-col, DJ/1.00)	Rand/McNally	(1942)	Ward, Keith	40-60	*
Turner, Nancy B.	Ray Coon to the Rescue (1st, lg8vo, 80p, ipcb, b/w, pep)	Rand/McNally	(1931)	Ward, Keith	55-90	*
Owens, Harry J.	Scandalous Advens. of Reynard the Fox (1st {std}, 8vo, 115p, b/w, DJ/3.00)	Knopf	1945	Ward, Keith	45-65	
N/A	Story of Little Red Hen (1st, folio, red ipcb, [16]p, b/w)	Whitman	(1935)	Ward, Keith	90-140	*
Meyer, Edith P.	Tim Chick (1st, sm sq4to, 42p, p-o, color)	Rand/McNally	1932	Ward, Keith	40-60	
North, Sterling	Zipper ABC Book (1st, 12mo, ipcb, [59]p, 2-color)	Rand/McNally	(1937)	Ward, Keith	60-100	R*
McNeer, May	Alaska Gold Rush (1st {std}, 8vo, 186p, 1-color, pep, DJ/1.95)	Random	(1960)	Ward, Lynd	25-45	
Peattie, Donald C.	Almanac for Moderns (1st, 8vo, 396p, b/w, DJ/3.00)	Putnam	(1935)	Ward, Lynd	50-85	
McNeer, May	America's Abraham Lincoln (1st, lg8vo, 119p, blue cl, fp color, DJ/3.50)	Houghton	1957	Ward, Lynd	50-75	R
Holbrook, Stewart	America's Ethan Allen (1st, lg8vo, 95p, color, pep, DJ/2.50, CH)	Houghton	1949	Ward, Lynd	60-90	
McNeer, May	America's Mark Twain (1st, lg8vo, 159p, dp color, DJ/3.75)	Houghton	1962	Ward, Lynd	30-50	
Forbes, Esther	America's Paul Revere (1st, 4to, 46p, color, red cl, DJ/2.50)	Houghton	1946	Ward, Lynd	55-80	
Commager, Henry	America's Robert E. Lee (1st, lg8vo, 112p, color, pep, DJ/3.00)	Houghton	1951	Ward, Lynd	30-50	*
McNeer, May	American Indian Story (1st {std}, 4to, 95p, fp color, pep, DJ/4.25)	Ariel	(1963)	Ward, Lynd	30-50	
Scribner, Grace	American Pilgrimage (1st, 12mo, 89p, 4 woodcuts)	Vanguard Press	(1927)	Ward, Lynd	55-80	*
Colum, Padraic (ed)	Arabian Nights (1st, 8vo, 344p, color, pep, DJ/2.50)	Macmillan	(1953)	Ward, Lynd	30-50	*
McNeer, May	Armed with Courage (1st, lg8vo, 112p, blue/silver, b/w, pep, DJ/2.50)	Abingdon Press	(1957)	Ward, Lynd	40-65	
Rowe, Dorothy	Begging Deer (1st, sm8vo, 109p, tan cl, 8cp, pep)	Macmillan	1928	Ward, Lynd	35-60	*
Ward, Lynd	Biggest Bear (1st, 4to, 84p, beige cl, b/w, DJ/2.75, CM)	Houghton	1952	Ward, Lynd	200-300	R
Halle, Louis J.	Birds Against Men (1st, 8vo, 228p, b/w, DJ/2.50)	Viking	1938	Ward, Lynd	40-65	
Ward, Nanda	Black Sombrero (1st {std}, 12mo, grey cl, unpag, color, pep, DJ/1.75)	Ariel	(1952)	Ward, Lynd	45-60	
Peattie, Donald C.	Book of Hours (1st, 8vo, 246p, 202p, b/w, DJ/2.50, cvr by...)	Putnam	1937	Ward, Lynd	40-60	*
Fritz, Jean	Brady (1st, 8vo, 223p, b/w, DJ/3.50)	Coward	(1960)	Ward, Lynd	30-50	*
Knight, Ruth A.	Brave Companions (1st {std}, 8vo, blue cl, 215p, col frn, DJ/2.00)	Doubleday/Doran	1945	Ward, Lynd	40-65	
Robinson, Mabel L.	Bright Island (1st, 8vo, 268p, silver cl, b/w, pep, DJ/2.00, NH)	Random	(1937)	Ward, Lynd	60-90	
Laing, Alexander	Cadaver of Gideon Wyck (1st, 8vo, 376p, frn by...)	Farrar/Rinehart	1934	Ward, Lynd	50-75	
McNeer, May	California Gold Rush (1st {std}, 8vo, 184p, 2-color, pep, DJ/1.50)	Random	1950	Ward, Lynd	25-40	
Austin, Mary	Can Prayer Be Answered? (1st, 8vo, 55p, black/silver, 3pl)	Farrar/Rinehart	1934	Ward, Lynd	50-80	
McNeer, May	Canadian Story (1st {std}, 4to, 96p, fp color, pep, DJ/4.25)	Ariel	(1958)	Ward, Lynd	30-45	
Coatsworth, Eliz.	Cat Who Went to Heaven (1st, lg8vo, red cl, 57p, 12 fp b/w, NM)	Macmillan	1930	Ward, Lynd	75-100	R
Marryat, Frederick	Children of the New Forest (1st, 8vo, 322p, green cl, 10 fp b/w)	Macmillan	1930	Ward, Lynd	40-60	
Howard, Alice W.	Ching-Li & the Dragons (1st, sm4to, blue/silver, 55p, 10pl)	Macmillan	1931	Ward, Lynd	70-120	
Mann, Thomas	Christmas Poem (1st, sm8vo, wraps, [8]p, 1-color)	Equinox	1932	Ward, Lynd	50-80	*
Dawson, Carley	Dragon Run (1st, 8vo, 282p, b/w, DJ/2.75)	Houghton	1955	Ward, Lynd	200-300	
Barnouw, Victor	Dream of the Blue Heron (1st {std}, 8vo, 191p, b/w, cep, DJ/4.50)	Delacorte Pr.	(1966)	Ward, Lynd	30-50	
Fritz, Jean	Early Thunder (1st, 8vo, 255p, b/w, pep, DJ/4.50)	Coward	(1967)	Ward, Lynd	25-40	
Swift, Hildegarde H.	Edge of April: Biography of John Burroughs (1st, 8vo, 316p, b/w, DJ/3.95)	Wm. Morrow	1957	Ward, Lynd	30-45	
Clark, Leonard	Explorer's Digest (1st, 8vo, 256p, b/w, DJ/3.00)	Houghton	1955	Ward, Lynd	50-80	
Goethe	Faust (1st, 8vo, 262p, 6pl, DJ/2.50)	Cape/Smith	(1930)	Ward, Lynd	90-120	
Brinig, Myron	Flutter of an Eyelid (1st, 12mo, 310p)	Farrar/Rinehart	1933	Ward, Lynd	40-65	R
Sauer, Julia L.	Fog Magic (1st, 8vo, grey cl, 107p, b/w frn, pep, DJ/2.00, NH)	Viking	1943	Ward, Lynd	60-100	R

AUTHOR	TITLE	PUBLISHER	DATE	ARTIST	PRICE	LC
Shelley, Mary W.	Frankenstein (1st, lg8vo, 259p, 15 b/w)	Smith/Haas	1934	Ward, Lynd	180-250	
Swift, Hildegarde H.	From the Eagle's Wing (1st, 8vo, 287p, b/w, DJ/3.95)	Wm. Morrow	1962	Ward, Lynd	25-40	
Henry, Marguerite	Gaudenzia (1st {A}, lg8vo, 237p, red/gilt, 7 fp color, pep, DJ/3.95)	Rand/McNally	(1960)	Ward, Lynd	40-65	
McNeer, May	Give Me Freedom (1st, lg8vo, 128p, fp b/w, DJ/3.00)	Abingdon Press	(1964)	Ward, Lynd	30-45	
Ward, Lynd	God's Man (1st, 8vo, woodcuts, ipcb, 293p, cep)	Cape/Smith	(1929)	Ward, Lynd	200-320	
McNeer, May	Gold Rush (1st, 8vo, ibds, 31p, color, pep, DJ/0.50)	Grosset/Dunlap	(1944)	Ward, Lynd	40-65	
McNeer, May	Golden Flash (1st, 8vo, 227p, pep, color, DJ/3.00)	Viking	1947	Ward, Lynd	30-50	
Faulkner, William	Green Bough (1st, 8vo, green cl, 67p, title page by...)	Smith/Haas	1933	Ward, Lynd	180-300	*
Laing, Alexander (ed)	Haunted Omnibus (1st, 8vo, 848p, fp b/w)	Farrar/Rinehart	(1937)	Ward, Lynd	70-120	
Ward, Nanda	Hi, Tom (1st, sm4to, 48p, tan cl, 3-color, DJ/3.00)	Hastings House	(1962)	Ward, Lynd	25-45	
Ward, Nanda	High Flying Hat (1st, 8vo, [56]p, color, pep, DJ/2.50)	Ariel	(1956)	Ward, Lynd	40-70	
Parsons, Arthur	Horn that Stopped the Band (1st {std}, 4to, [48]p, b/w, dep, DJ/2.50)	F. Watts	1954	Ward, Lynd	50-80	R
Waugh, Alec	Hot Countries (1st, 8vo, 304p, gilt, b/w)	Farrar/Rinehart	(1930)	Ward, Lynd	45-70	
Swift, Hildegarde H.	House by the Sea (1st, 8vo, 245p, blue cl, 8pl, pep, DJ/2.00)	Harcourt	(1938)	Ward, Lynd	40-60	
Powys, Llewelyn	Impassioned Clay (1st {std}, 8vo, bds, 120p, tp-in frn, DJ/2.00)	Longmans	1931	Ward, Lynd	120-170	
Ward, Harry F.	In Place of Profit (1st, 8vo, green cl, 460p, gilt, woodcuts)	Scribner	1933	Ward, Lynd	40-60	
O'Connor, Winfield	Jockeys, Crooks and Kings (1st, 8vo, 219p, b/w decor by...)	NY: Cape/Smith	1930	Ward, Lynd	60-90	*
McNeer, May	John Wesley (1st, lg8vo, 96p, fp color, pep, DJ/2.50)	Abingdon Press	1951	Ward, Lynd	30-50	
Forbes, Esther	Johnny Tremain (1st, 8vo, 256p, col frn, pep, DJ/3.00, NM)	Houghton	1943	Ward, Lynd	100-175	R
Peattie, Donald C.	Journey into America (1st, 8vo, 276p, color, pep, DJ/3.00)	Houghton	1943	Ward, Lynd	30-50	
Stevenson, Rbt. L.	Kidnapped (1st [special ed.], 8vo, 340p, fp color, pep, DJ/2.00)	Grosset/Dunlap	(1948)	Ward, Lynd	25-40	*
Genevoix, Maurice	Last Hunt (1st {std}, 8vo, p-o, 281p, 10 fp 1-color, pep, DJ/2.50)	Random	(1940)	Ward, Lynd	60-90	
McNeer, May	Little Baptiste (1st, lg8vo, [50]p, 1-color, DJ/2.50)	Houghton	1954	Ward, Lynd	30-45	
Swift, Hildegarde H.	Little Blacknose (1st, sm8vo, 149p, 2-color, pep, DJ/2.00, NH)	Harcourt	(1929)	Ward, Lynd	60-100	
Swift, Hildegarde H.	Little Red Lighthouse & Great Gray Bridge (1st, 8vo, [56]p, color, DJ/1.75)	Harcourt	(1942)	Ward, Lynd	40-65	
Rideout, Henry M.	Lola the Bear (1st, 8vo, 159p, gilt, col frn, 3pl, DJ/1.75)	Duffield	1928	Ward, Lynd	50-80	
Ward, Lynd	Mad-Man's Drum (1st, 8vo, ipcb, [257]p, woodcuts, cep)	Cape/Smith	(1930)	Ward, Lynd	200-300	
Cowen, William J.	Man with Four Lives (1st, sm8vo, 277p, b/w pl, DJ/2.00)	Farrar/Rinehart	(1934)	Ward, Lynd	50-80	
Jones, Jessie O. (ed)	Many Mansions (1st, lg8vo, 134p, 1-color, DJ/3.00)	Viking	1947	Ward, Lynd	30-50	
McNeer, May	Martin Luther (1st, lg8vo, 95p, rust cl, pep, color, DJ/2.50)	Abingdon Press	(1953)	Ward, Lynd	55-80	R
McNeer, May	Mexican Story (1st {std}, 4to, 96p, fp color, pep, DJ/3.95)	Ariel	(1953)	Ward, Lynd	40-65	R
Wilhelmson, Carl	Midsummer Night (1st, 8vo, uncut, 305p, 10pl)	Farrar/Rinehart	1930	Ward, Lynd	70-120	
Waugh, Alec	Most Women (1st, 8vo, gilt, 323p, 6 fp woodcuts)	Farrar/Rinehart	(1931)	Ward, Lynd	80-125	
Dawson, Carley	Mr. Wicker's Window (1st, lg8vo, 272p, gilt, 2-color, DJ/3.25)	Houghton	1952	Ward, Lynd	200-300	
McNeer, May	My Friend Mac (1st, lg8vo, 78p, 1-color, DJ/2.75)	Houghton	1960	Ward, Lynd	30-50	
Ward, Lynd	Nic of the Woods (1st {std}, 4to, 95p, fp 1-color, cep, DJ/3.75)	Houghton	1965	Ward, Lynd	40-65	R
Swift, Hildegarde H.	North Star Shining (1st, 4to, 44p, 10 fp color, DJ/2.50)	Wm. Morrow	(1947)	Ward, Lynd	80-130	
Hicks, Granville	One of Us (1st {std}, lg8vo, [64]p, 30 b/w illus, DJ/2.00)	Equinox	(1935)	Ward, Lynd	60-100	
Emblen, Don L.	Palomino Boy (1st, 8vo, blue cl, 189p, pep, DJ/2.00, decor by...)	Viking	1948	Ward, Lynd	40-65	
Johnson, Annabel	Peculiar Magic (1st {std}, 8vo, 246p, b/w, DJ/3.25)	Houghton	1965	Ward, Lynd	25-40	
Sabin, Edwin L.	Pirate Waters (1st, 8vo, 338p, b/w, pep, DJ/2.00)	Lippincott	(1941)	Ward, Lynd	40-65	
Howard, F. Martin	Porpoise of Pirate Bay (1st, lg8vo, 152p, 8 fp b/w, pep, DJ/1.00)	Random	(1938)	Ward, Lynd	40-65	
Chase, Stuart	Primer of Economics (1st, lg8vo, 60p, 1-color, DJ/1.00)	Row, Peterson	(1941)	Ward, Lynd	30-55	
McNeer, May	Prince Bantam (1st, lg8vo, 229p, aqua cl, col frn, 15 fp b/w)	Macmillan	1929	Ward, Lynd	40-60	
Robinson, Mabel L.	Runner of the Mountain Tops (1st {std}, 8vo, blue/gilt, col, DJ/3.00, NH)	Random	(1939)	Ward, Lynd	60-100	
Clark, Ann N.	Santiago (1st, 8vo, 189p, color, pep, DJ/2.75)	Viking	1955	Ward, Lynd	40-65	
Kingman, Lee	Secret Journey of the Silver Reindeer (1st {std}, 8vo, 93p, color, DJ/3.50)	Doubleday	(1968)	Ward, Lynd	30-45	
Dawson, Carley	Sign of the Seven Seas (1st, 8vo, 287p, b/w, DJ/2.50)	Houghton	1954	Ward, Lynd	200-300	
Madariaga, Salvador	Sir Bob (1st {std}, lg8vo, 202p, fp b/w)	Harcourt	(1930)	Ward, Lynd	35-60	*
Saint-Exupery, A.	Southern Mail (1st AM, 8vo, 253p, pep, 1-color lithos by...)	Smith/Haas	1933	Ward, Lynd	80-130	
Hewes, Agnes D.	Spice & Devil's Cave (1st, sm8vo, 331p, gilt, b/w, pep, DJ/2.50, NH)	Knopf	1930	Ward, Lynd	50-80	
Steen, Margarite	Stallion (1st, sm8vo, 315p, 1-color title page by....)	Little/Brown	1933	Ward, Lynd	25-40	
Rourke, Thomas	Stallion from the North (1st, sm8vo, 266p, pep)	Farrar/Rinehart	(1932)	Ward, Lynd	30-45	
McNeer, May	Stop Tim! (1st, ob8vo, ibds, [39]p, 2-color, pep)	Farrar/Rinehart	1930	Ward, Lynd	55-80	
Diller, Angela	Story of Siegfried (1st, 4to, 33p, col frn)	Cape/Smith	(1931)	Ward, Lynd	70-100	
Robinson, Mabel L.	Strong Wings (1st {std}, 8vo, 249p, blue cl, b/w, DJ/2.75)	Random	(1951)	Ward, Lynd	35-50	
Wyss, Johann D.	Swiss Family Robinson (1st [deluxe ed.], 8vo, 388p, 9cp, DJ/3.00)	Grosset/Dunlap	(1949)	Ward, Lynd	40-65	
Golding, Louis	The Pursuer (1st, sm8vo, 275p, uncut, pep, DJ/2.00)	Farrar/Rinehart	(1936)	Ward, Lynd	50-80	*
Masters, Edgar L.	The Sangamon (1st, 8vo, 258p, fp b/w, pep, DJ/2.50)	Farrar/Rinehart	(1942)	Ward, Lynd	50-80	
Waugh, Alec	Thirteen Such Years (1st, 8vo, 277p, green/gilt, b/w, frn by...)	Farrar/Rinehart	(1932)	Ward, Lynd	25-45	
Medary, Marjorie	Topgallant: A Herring Gull (1st {std}, 8vo, 159p, p-o, pep, b/w, DJ/1.75)	Smith/Haas	(1935)	Ward, Lynd	50-85	
Rowe, Dorothy	Traveling Shops (1st, sm8vo, yellow cl, 109p, col frn, pep)	Macmillan	1929	Ward, Lynd	30-60	*
McNeer, May	Up a Crooked River (1st, 8vo, 222p, b/w, pep, DJ/2.50)	Viking	1952	Ward, Lynd	25-45	
Ward, Lynd	Vertigo (1st, 8vo, 231p, woodcuts)	Random	1937	Ward, Lynd	200-300	
McNeer, May	Waif Maid (1st, 8vo, p-o, 212p, col frn, woodcuts, cep)	Macmillan	1930	Ward, Lynd	40-60	
Colum, Padraic	White Sparrow (1st, sq8vo, 46p, grey cl, 1-color, pep, DJ/2.00)	Macmillan	1933	Ward, Lynd	55-80	
Ward, Lynd	Wild Pilgrimage (1st, lg8vo, [190]p, p-o, woodcuts)	Smith/Haas	1932	Ward, Lynd	180-250	
McNeer, May	Wolf of Lambs Lane (1st {std}, lg8vo, 64p, 2-color, DJ/3.50)	Houghton	1967	Ward, Lynd	30-50	
Barry, Mary E.	Wonder Flights of Long Ago (1st, sm8vo, 218p, col frn, b/w, pep)	Appleton	(1930)	Ward, Lynd	30-50	
Sturton, Hugh	Zomo the Rabbit (1st {std}, lg8vo, 128p, b/w, DJ/3.95)	Atheneum	1966	Warner, Peter	25-40	
Warner, Sunny B.	Tobias & his Big Red Satchel (1st 4to ibds [32]p fp 1-color, dep, DJ/3.00)	Knopf	(1961)	Warner, Sunny	30-45	*
Maniates, Belle	Little Boy Bear (1st, 12mo, blue/white, 54p, 5pl)	Pilgrim Press	(1917)	Warren, Elizabeth	25-40	
Stong, Philip D.	Long Lane (1st, 8vo, 308p, b/w, DJ/2.50)	Farrar/Rinehart	(1939)	Warren, F.E.	25-45	*
Yoda, Junichi	Rolling Rice Ball (1st AM, 4to, [32]p, color, cep, DJ/3.50)	Parents Mag. Pr.	1969	Watanabe, Saburo	30-50	*
Baruch, Dorothy W.	I Like Animals (1st {std}, 16mo, ipcb, 48p, b/w, dep)	Harper	1933	Waterall, Corinne P.	25-45	*
Berry, Erick	When Wagon Trains Rolled to Sante Fe (1st, lg8vo, 95p, color, pep, DJ)	Garrard Pub.	1966	Waterhouse, Charles	30-50	
Nesbit, Edith	Cat Tales (1st, 12mo, 62p, grey cl, 4 fp color)	Nister/Dutton	[1904]	Watkin, Isabel	140-200	
Seeger, Elizabeth	Pageant of Chinese History (1st {std}, 8vo, 386p, b/w, pep, NH)	Longmans	1934	Watkins, Bernard	45-70	

AUTHOR	TITLE	PUBLISHER	DATE	ARTIST	PRICE	LC
Howes, Edith	Fairy Rings (1st, 12mo, 248p, p-o, gilt, 4cp)	L: Cassell	1911	Watkins, Frank	80-125	*
Carmichael, Philip	Man from the Moon (1st, 8vo, 296p, blue/gilt, 8cp)	L: Richards	1909	Watkins, Frank	90-135	
Howes, Edith	Sun's Babies (1st [1st bk.], sm8vo, gilt, p-o, 236p, 4cp)	L: Cassell	1910	Watkins, Frank	70-100	
N/A	Our Darlings (4to, 288p, ibds, 24 ticp, pep)	L: J.F. Shaw	[1905]	Watkins, Jessie	100-165	
B.B.	Little Grey Men (1st, lg8vo, 203p, b/w, DJ, CgM)	L: Eyre/Spotts.	1942	Watkins-Pitchford, D	200-300	
B.B.	Little Grey Men (1st AM, 8vo, 248p, b/w, DJ/2.50, CgM)	Scribner	(1949)	Watkins-Pitchford, D	150-225	
Fyleman, Rose	Adventure Club (1st, 12mo, 80p, blue/gilt, 10 b/w)	L: Methuen	1925	Watson, A.H.	40-65	
Fyleman, Rose	Adventure Club (1st AM, 8vo, p-o, 138p, col frn, b/w)	Doran	(1926)	Watson, A.H.	30-50	*
Strang, Herbert	Big Book of Fairy Stories (1st, 8vo, 191p, ibds, 4cp, pep)	L: H. Milford	(1929)	Watson, A.H.	80-120	
Milne, A.A.	Gallery of Children (1st AM {this fmt}, 12mo, 125p, b/w, DJ)	McKay	[1939]	Watson, A.H.	65-100	
Strang, Mrs. H.	Our Old Fairy Stories (1st, 8vo, 223p, 4cp, b/w)	L: Oxford U.Pr.	(1930)	Watson, A.H.	30-50	
Mackenzie, Compton	Santa Claus in Summer (1st, 8vo, 298p, b/w)	L: Constable	1924	Watson, A.H.	50-80	
De La Mare, Walter	Told Again (1st AM, 8vo, 248p, red/gilt, 8cp, b/w)	Knopf	1927	Watson, A.H.	45-70	
De La Mare, Walter	Told Again (1st, 8vo, 320p, blue/gilt, 8cp)	L: Blackwell	1927	Watson, A.H.	70-100	
Robinson, Mabel L.	All the Year Round (1st {std}, 8vo, 150p, b/w, DJ/2.50)	Harper	(1954)	Watson, Aldren A.	20-30	*
Watson, Nancy D.	Annie's Spending Spree (1st, sm4to, 45p, color, pep, DJ/2.50)	Viking	1957	Watson, Aldren A.	25-40	
Frost, Frances	Christmas in the Woods (1st {std}, 16mo, ibds, 28p, fp 1-color, DJ/1.00)	Harper	(1942)	Watson, Aldren A.	30-50	R
Watson, Nancy D.	Fairy Tale Picture Book (1st {std}, lg4to, 91p, color, DJ/2.95)	Garden City	1957	Watson, Aldren A.	60-90	
Leodhas, Sorche	Golden Summer (1st {std}, 8vo, 205p, b/w, DJ/2.00)	Harper	(1942)	Watson, Aldren A.	30-50	*
Swift, Jonathan	Gulliver's Travels (1st [special ed], 8vo, 306p, color, DJ/2.00)	Grosset/Dunlap	(1947)	Watson, Aldren A.	40-60	*
Brooks, Walter	Henry's Dog Henry (1st, 8vo, [30]p, fp 1-color, cep, DJ/2.95)	Knopf	(1965)	Watson, Aldren A.	50-85	
Felton, Harold	John Henry and his Hammer (1st {std}, lg8vo, 82p, fp b/w, pep, DJ/2.50)	Knopf	(1950)	Watson, Aldren A.	80-120	R
O'Faolain, Eileen	Miss Pennyfeather & the Pooka (1st {std}, lg8vo, 154p, 1-col, cep, DJ/2.00)	Random	(1946)	Watson, Aldren A.	30-50	
Muehl, Lois B.	My Name Is... (1st, sm8vo, tan cl, [55]p, 2-color, DJ)	Holiday House	(1959)	Watson, Aldren A.	25-45	
Felton, Harold	Pecos Bill, Texas Cowpuncher (1st {std}, 8vo, 177p, b/w, DJ/2.50)	Knopf	1949	Watson, Aldren A.	60-90	R
Watson, Nancy D.	Sugar on Snow (1st, ob8vo, 43p, fp 1-color, DJ/3.00)	Viking	(1964)	Watson, Aldren A.	25-40	
Watson, Nancy D.	Toby and Doll (1st {std}, 8vo, 125p, 4cp, b/w, pep, DJ/2.75)	Bobbs-Merrill	1955	Watson, Aldren A.	20-30	
DeJong, Meindert	Wheels Over the Bridge (1st {std}, 8vo, 219p, pep, 10pl, DJ/2.00)	Harper	(1941)	Watson, Aldren A.	40-65	
Watson, Nancy D.	When is Tomorrow? (1st, sm ob4to, [32]p, ibds, color, pep, DJ/2.00)	Knopf	(1955)	Watson, Aldren A.	20-35	
Martin, Dahris	Wonder Cat (1st, 8vo, 59p, 1-color, DJ/1.75)	Crowell	1942	Watson, Aldren A.	20-35	
Holton, Priscilla	Chuck Martinez (1st {std}, 8vo, 312p, b/w, pep, DJ/2.25)	Longmans	1940	Watson, Eva A.	30-45	*
Paine, Albert B.	Tent Dwellers (1st, 8vo, uncut, 272p, b/w)	Outing	1908	Watson, Hy	150-220	
Nash, Ogden	Cruise of the Aardvark (1st {std}, 8vo, unpag, b/w, DJ/3.95)	M. Evans	1967	Watson, Wendy	30-50	*
Grimm Bros.	Hedgehog and the Hare (1st, lg ob8vo, 30p, fp 1-color, pep, DJ/3.95)	World	(1969)	Watson, Wendy	30-50	*
Calhoun, Mary	Magic in the Alley (1st {std}, 8vo, 167p, orange cl, cep, DJ/4.50)	Atheneum	1970	Watson, Wendy	25-40	
Tripp, Paul	Strawman Who Smiled by Mistake (1st {std}, ob8vo, 40p, color, pep, DJ/3.95)	Doubleday	1967	Watson, Wendy	30-50	
Miles, Miska	Uncle Fonzo's Ford (1st {std}, 8vo, 54p, b/w, DJ/3.25)	Little/Brown	(1968)	Watson, Wendy	20-35	
Hitte, Kathryn	When Noodlehead Went to the Fair (1st ob4to, ibds, [42]p, color, DJ/3.50)	Parents Mag. Pr.	(1968)	Watson, Wendy	25-45	*
Weatherly, Fred E.	Out of Town (1st, 8vo, 64p, ibds, 12 chromos, dep)	Dutton	[1884]	Watt, Linnie	100-175	
Weston, Jessie L.	Sir Gleges/Sir Libeaus Desconus (1st AM, 16mo, 77p, gilt, b/w)	New Amsterdam	1902	Watts, Caroline	60-100	
Waugh, Dorothy	Among the Leaves & Grasses (1st, sm4to, orange cl, 93p, color)	Henry Holt & Co.	1931	Waugh, Dorothy	100-170	
Waugh, Frederick	Clan of Munes (1st, ob folio, blue cl, 58p, 8 fp color)	Scribner	1916	Waugh, Frederick	400-650	R
Neally, Amy	Baby Days... (1st, 4to, gilt, AEG, 6 chromos)	Dutton	[1890]	Waugh, Ida	200-320	
Waugh, Ida	Becky Longnose... (4to, wraps, 8cp)	McLoughlin	(1882)	Waugh, Ida	80-140	
Mathews, Joanna H.	Belle's Pink Boots (1st, AEG, green/gilt, 16cp)	Dutton	1881	Waugh, Ida	180-280	
Blanchard, Amy E.	Bonny Bairns (1st, 4to, 48p, ibds, 25cp)	Worthington	(1888)	Waugh, Ida	200-270	
N/A	Christmas Card (8vo, wraps, 8cp)	Dutton	1883	Waugh, Ida	100-175	
Newberry, Fanny E.	Everyday Honor (1st, 12mo, 429p, b/w)	Jacobs	1898	Waugh, Ida	25-45	*
Marshall, Caroline	Girl Ranchers of San Coulee (1st, 12mo, 322p, 4pl)	Penn	1897	Waugh, Ida	35-60	
Elmslie, Theodora C.	His Lordship's Puppy (1st, 8vo, 205p, gilt, 4pl)	Penn	1900	Waugh, Ida	30-50	
Waugh, Ida	Holly Berries (1st, lg8vo, 48p, ibds, fp color, cep)	Dutton	(1881)	Waugh, Ida	150-220	
Blanchard, Amy	Ida Waugh's Alphabet Book (1st, 4to, [56]p, ibds, 26 illus)	Lippincott	1888	Waugh, Ida	250-350	
Waugh, Ida	Ideal Heads (1st, folio, brown/gilt, [51]p, AEG, 20 chromos)	Sunshine Co.	1890	Waugh, Ida	700-1000	
Blanchard, Amy E.	Janet's College Career (1st, 8vo, 365p, 5pl)	Jacobs	1904	Waugh, Ida	25-40	*
Waugh, Ida	Little Chicks and Baby Tricks (1st, 4to, ibds, 44p)	Dutton	1885	Waugh, Ida	100-170	
Gould, Elizabeth L.	Little Polly Prentiss (1st, sm8vo, 192p, 5pl)	Penn	1902	Waugh, Ida	30-50	
Blanchard, Amy E.	Mammy's Baby (4to, [16]p, ipcb, chromos)	Worthington	(1890)	Waugh, Ida	125-200	
Blanchard, Amy E.	My Own Dolly (1st, 8vo, ipcb, 64p, 15cp)	Dutton	1882	Waugh, Ida	120-200	
Waugh, Ida	Over the Hills (1st, 4to, ibds, [48]p, chromos)	McLoughlin	(1882)	Waugh, Ida	160-250	
Lippmann, Julie M.	Sweet P's (1st, 12mo, 192p, 5pl, pep)	Penn	1902	Waugh, Ida	30-50	
Blanchard, Amy E.	Tangles & Curls (1st, 4to, [16]p, ibds, 9pl)	Worthington	1888	Waugh, Ida	120-200	
Blanchard, Amy E.	Tell Me a Story (1st, lg sq8vo, [15]p, ibds, 10 fp color)	Worthington	1888	Waugh, Ida	130-200	
Blanchard, Amy E.	Twenty Little Maidens (1st, lg8vo, 160p, 18pl)	Lippincott	1893	Waugh, Ida	50-80	
Marshall, Caroline	Two Wyoming Girls (1st, 12mo, 329p, brown/gilt, b/w)	Penn	1899	Waugh, Ida	30-50	*
Lovell, Lucille	Walcott Twins (1st, sm8vo, 211p, 5pl)	Penn	1900	Waugh, Ida	30-50	
Blanchard, Amy E.	Wee Babies (1st, 4to, ibds, [48]p, color)	Dutton	(1882)	Waugh, Ida	160-225	
Fleckenstein, Alfred	Prince of Gravas (1st, sm8vo, 270p, grey/gilt, 3pl)	Jacobs	1898	Waugh, J.	50-80	
Stevenson, Rbt. L.	Child's Garden of Verses (1st, 4to, p-o, 140p, color, pep)	Whitman	(1917)	Weage, Josephine	60-90	*
Weaver, Annie V.	Boochy's Wings (1st, ob12mo, 122p, color)	Stokes	1931	Weaver, Annie V.	50-85	*
Weaver, Annie V.	Frawg (1st, ob12mo, p-o, 128p, color, pep)	Stokes	1930	Weaver, Annie V.	160-240	
Webb, Clifford	Jungle Picnic (1st, lg8vo, 75p, 24 fp color, pep)	Warne	(1934)	Webb, Clifford	40-65	
Baker, Cornelia	Court Jester (1st, 8vo, 259p, gilt, b/w pl)	Bobbs-Merrill	(1906)	Webb, Margaret E.	25-40	*
Converse, Florence	House of Prayer (1st, 12mo, 276p, gilt, teg, uncut, 8pl)	L: Dent	1908	Webb, Margaret E.	30-50	
Washburne, Marion	Old Fashioned Fairy Tales (1st, lg8vo, brown/gilt, 102p, 3cp, pep)	Rand/McNally	(1909)	Webb, Margaret E.	70-100	*
Webber, Irma E.	Anywhere in the World (1st, 8vo, ipcb, 64p, color, DJ/1.50)	W.R. Scott	(1947)	Webber, Irma	60-90	
Webber, Irma E.	Bits that Grow Big (1st, sm8vo, ipcb, 64p, 2-color, DJ/1.65)	W.R. Scott	(1949)	Webber, Irma	60-90	
Webber, Irma E.	It Looks Like This (1st, sm8vo, ibds, [40]p, b/w, DJ/1.00)	W.R. Scott	1949	Webber, Irma	50-80	
Webber, Irma E.	Thanks to Trees (1st, sm8vo, grey cl, 60p, 3-color, pep, DJ/2.00)	W.R. Scott	(1952)	Webber, Irma	50-80	

AUTHOR	TITLE	PUBLISHER	DATE	ARTIST	PRICE	LC
Webber, Irma E.	Travelers All (1st, sm8vo, ibds, [32]p, color, DJ/1.35)	W.R. Scott	1944	Webber, Irma	50-80	
Webber, Irma E.	Up Above & Down Below (1st, sm8vo, ibds, [31]p, color, DJ/1.00)	W.R. Scott	(1943)	Webber, Irma	70-100	
Mukerji, Dhan G.	Master Monkey (1st {std}, 8vo, aqua/gilt, 261p, pep, 5pl)	Dutton	(1932)	Weber, Florence	35-60	*
Alcott, Louisa M.	Old-Fashioned Girl (1st, 8vo, 319p, color, pep, RC, DJ/1.25)	World	(1947)	Weber, Nettie	20-30	
Webster, Jean	Daddy Long Legs (1st, 12mo, blue cl, 304p, b/w, PPP)	Century	1912	Webster, Jean	55-80	
Webster, Jean	Dear Enemy (1st, sm8vo, 350p, blue cl, b/w)	Century	1915	Webster, Jean	50-80	
Mother Goose	Mother Goose Rhymes (1st, 12mo, ipcb, [62]p, fp color)	Rand/McNally	(1942)	Wedde, Junice	40-60	*
Weeden, Howard	Bandanna Ballads (1st, 8vo, green/gilt, uncut, 90p, 24pl)	Doub./McClure	1899	Weeden, Howard	90-160	
Maurois, Andre	Fattypuffs & Thinifers (1st AM {std}, sm4to, 87p, b/w, DJ/3.95)	Knopf	(1969)	Wegner, Fritz	40-65	
Winterfeld, Henry	Star Girl (1st {std}, 8vo, 191p, b/w, DJ/2.75)	Harcourt	(1957)	Wegner, Fritz	200-300	
Henty, G.A.	Cat of the Bubastes (1st, 12mo, 352p, blue/gilt, 8pl, cep)	L: Blackie	1889	Weguelin, John R.	150-250	
Andersen, Hans C.	Little Mermaid (1st, 8vo, 384p, gilt, teg, uncut, fp b/w)	L: Lawrence/Bul.	1893	Weguelin, John R.	120-185	
Grimm Bros.	Fairy Tales (1st, 8vo, 511p, red cl, 4cp)	L: Routledge	(1904)	Wehnert, Edward H.	120-160	
Mother Goose	Mother Goose (1st, 12mo, [53]p, wraps, color)	Whitman	1944	Weihs, Erika	35-60	*
Baker, Michael	Mountain and the Summer Stars (1st AM {std}, 8vo, 124p, b/w, DJ/3.95)	Harcourt	(1969)	Weihs, Erika	25-40	
Weil, Lisl	Alphabet of Puppy Care (1st, 4to, [41]p, fp 2-color, cep, DJ/3.75)	Abelard-Schuman	1968	Weil, Lisl	30-50	
Furth, Dori	Back in Time for Supper (1st {std}, ob4to, [33]p, color, DJ/2.50)	McKay	(1947)	Weil, Lisl	50-80	
Weil, Lisl	Bill the Brave (1st {std}, 8vo, 32p, color, DJ/1.50)	Houghton	(1948)	Weil, Lisl	30-50	
Weil, Lisl	Bitzli and the Big Bad Wolf (1st, sm4to, 47p, fp color, DJ/3.00)	Houghton	1960	Weil, Lisl	30-50	*
Weil, Lisl	Busiest Boy in Holland (1st, sm4to, 38p, 1-color, DJ/2.75)	Houghton	1959	Weil, Lisl	30-45	
Holberg, Ruth	Catnip Man (1st {std}, 8vo, 114p, fp b/w, pep, DJ/2.50)	Crowell	(1951)	Weil, Lisl	30-45	*
Commager, Henry	Chestnut Squirrel (1st, lg8vo, 122p, b/w, DJ/2.00)	Houghton	1952	Weil, Lisl	25-40	
Joslin, Sesyle	Doctor George Owl (1st {std}, 4to, 45p, color, DJ/3.75)	Houghton	(1970)	Weil, Lisl	25-40	
Weil, Lisl	Eyes So-O Big (1st, sm sq4to, 48p, fp 1-color, DJ/3.25)	Houghton	1964	Weil, Lisl	30-50	*
Weil, Lisl	Fantastic Toy Shop (1st, 4to, 47p, color, DJ/3.50)	Abelard-Schuman	(1966)	Weil, Lisl	30-50	
Weil, Lisl	Golden Spinning Wheel (1st {std}, 4to, [40]p, color, DJ/4.95)	Macmillan	(1969)	Weil, Lisl	30-45	
Weil, Lisl	Happy Birthday in Barcelona (1st, sm sq4to, 48p, 1-color, cep, DJ/3.25)	Houghton	1965	Weil, Lisl	30-45	*
Weil, Lisl	Happy Ski ABC (1st, ob4to, 64p, fp 2-color, DJ/3.50)	Putnam	(1964)	Weil, Lisl	30-50	
Weil, Lisl	Hopping Knapsack (1st {std}, sm4to, [32]p, color, DJ/4.50)	Macmillan	1970	Weil, Lisl	30-45	
Weil, Lisl	I Wish, I Wish (1st, sm4to, 38p, 1-color, DJ/2.50)	Houghton	1957	Weil, Lisl	30-50	*
Weil, Lisl	Jacoble Tells the Truth (1st, 8vo, [20]p, color, DJ/1.00)	Houghton	1946	Weil, Lisl	40-65	*
Weil, Lisl	Lionhearted One (1st, sm4to, 47p, fp 1-color, DJ/3.00)	Houghton	1962	Weil, Lisl	30-45	
Duryea, Elizabeth	Long Christmas Eve (1st, 8vo, 44p, color, DJ/2.00)	Houghton	1954	Weil, Lisl	20-30	
Weil, Lisl	Melissa (1st {std}, sm4to, [32]p, 2-color, DJ/3.25)	Macmillan	1966	Weil, Lisl	30-50	
Weil, Lisl	Melissa's Friend Fabrizzio (1st {std}, 4to, [32]p, color, DJ/3.95)	Macmillan	(1967)	Weil, Lisl	25-40	
Weil, Lisl	Mimi (1st, 4to, 48p, 3-color, DJ/3.00)	Houghton	1961	Weil, Lisl	30-50	
French, Marion	Mr. Bear Goes to Boston (1st, sm4to, 32p, 1-color, DJ/2.00)	Follett	(1955)	Weil, Lisl	100-160	
Weil, Lisl	Pudding's Wonderful Bone (1st, sm ob4to, [30]p, fp 1-color, cep, DJ/2.50)	Crowell	(1956)	Weil, Lisl	40-65	
Kingman, Lee	Sheep Ahoy! (1st, 8vo, 68p, fp b/w, pep, DJ/2.75)	Houghton	1963	Weil, Lisl	25-45	
Weil, Lisl	Shivers... (1st, 4to, 40p, fp 2-color, cep, DJ/3.25)	Houghton	1967	Weil, Lisl	30-50	
Govan, Christine	Super Duper Car (1st, 8vo, green cl, 78p, b/w, pep, DJ/2.00)	Houghton	1952	Weil, Lisl	70-120	
Weil, Lisl	Things that Go Bang (1st, 4to, 40p, color, DJ/4.50)	McGraw-Hill	(1969)	Weil, Lisl	30-50	*
Forbes, Katherine	Thirsty Lion (1st, lg8vo, 88p, fp b/w, pep, DJ/2.00)	Crowell	(1950)	Weil, Lisl	30-50	
Holberg, Ruth	Three Birthday Wishes (1st, 8vo, 121p, b/w, pep, DJ/2.50)	Crowell	(1953)	Weil, Lisl	25-40	
Clark, Electa	Tony for Keeps (1st {std}, 8vo, 186p, b/w, DJ/2.00)	Winston	(1955)	Weil, Lisl	30-45	*
Johnson, Ryerson	Upstairs & Downstairs (1st, sq8vo, [40]p, fp 2-color, DJ/2.50)	Crowell	(1962)	Weil, Lisl	35-50	*
Olds, Helen D.	What Will I Wear? (1st, 8vo, [33]p, 1-color, pep, DJ/2.50)	Knopf	(1961)	Weil, Lisl	20-35	
Brown, Pamela	Windmill Family (1st {std}, 8vo, 262p, b/w, DJ/2.75)	Crowell	(1954)	Weil, Lisl	30-45	*
Rosenblum, Robert	Eight Lights: Story of Chanukah (1st {std}, 4to, 94p, 2-color, DJ/4.95)	Doubleday	1967	Weil, Shraga	30-50	
Haig-Brown, R.L.	Whale People (1st AM {std}, 8vo, 256p, b/w, DJ/3.25)	Wm. Morrow	1963	Weiler, Mary	30-50	
Unterecker, John	Dreaming Zoo (1st, sm4to, [30]p, 3-color, DJ/3.50)	H.Z. Walck	1965	Weinheimer, George	30-50	*
N/A	Wonderful Kittens (sq4to, ibds, 5cp)	Worthington	1883	Weir, H.	150-220	
Evers, Alf	Abner's Cabin (1st {std}, 4to, [42]p, fp b/w, pep, DJ/2.95)	F. Watts	1957	Weisgard, Leonard	40-70	
Dalgliesh, Alice	Adam & the Golden Cock (1st, sm8vo, 64p, grey cl, 1-color, DJ/2.50)	Scribner	(1959)	Weisgard, Leonard	30-50	
Carroll, Lewis	Alice... & Through... (1st, 4to, 159p, ibds, 24 fp color, pep, DJ/3.50)	Harper	(1949)	Weisgard, Leonard	75-120	
Davis, Lavinia R.	Americans Every One (1st {std}, sm8vo, 123p, color, DJ/1.50)	Doubleday/Doran	1942	Weisgard, Leonard	35-60	
Weisgard, Leonard	Athenians in the Classical Period (1st, 4to, 61p, 1-color, DJ/3.95)	Coward	(1963)	Weisgard, Leonard	40-65	
Joslin, Sesyle	Baby Elephant & Secret Wishes (1st {std}, 12mo, ibds, 3-color, DJ/2.50)	Harcourt	(1962)	Weisgard, Leonard	40-65	
Joslin, Sesyle	Baby Elephant Goes to China (1st {std}, 12mo, [45]p, 1-color, DJ/2.50)	Harcourt	(1963)	Weisgard, Leonard	40-65	
Joslin, Sesyle	Baby Elephant's Baby Book (1st {std}, 12mo, [48]p, 1-color, DJ/2.50)	Harcourt	(1964)	Weisgard, Leonard	40-65	
Joslin, Sesyle	Baby Elephant's Trunk (1st {std}, 12mo, unpag, 1-color, DJ/2.50)	Harcourt	(1961)	Weisgard, Leonard	40-65	
Kumin, Maxine	Beach Before Breakfast (1st, ob8vo, grey cl, 46p, color, DJ/3.50)	Putnam	(1964)	Weisgard, Leonard	50-80	R
Weisgard, Leonard	Beginnings of Cities (1st {std}, 4to, 61p, brown illus, DJ)	Coward	(1968)	Weisgard, Leonard	30-50	*
Vance, Marguerite	Beloved Friend (1st, 8vo, 120p, fp b/w, gilt, DJ/3.50)	Holt, Rinehart	(1963)	Weisgard, Leonard	25-45	
Various	Big Book of Train Stories (1st, folio, ibds, unpag, color)	Grosset/Dunlap	1955	Weisgard, Leonard	40-65	
MacDonald, Golden	Big Dog, Little Dog (1st, lg sq8vo, [36]p, red cl, b/w, dep, DJ/1.25)	Doubleday/Doran	(1943)	Weisgard, Leonard	60-90	
Andreas, Evelyn	Big Treasure Book of Fairy Tales (1st, folio, unpag, color, DJ/1.00)	Grosset/Dunlap	1954	Weisgard, Leonard	40-65	
Fry, Christopher	Boat that Mooed (1st {std}, ob4to, 30p, fp 1-color, DJ/3.50)	Macmillan	(1965)	Weisgard, Leonard	60-90	R*
Fitch, Florence	Book About God (1st, 4to, ibds, [28]p, color, DJ/2.00)	Lothrop, Lee	1953	Weisgard, Leonard	50-85	
Joslin, Sesyle	Brave Baby Elephant (1st {std}, 12mo, [48]p, color, DJ/2.50)	Harcourt	(1960)	Weisgard, Leonard	45-70	
Wayne, Elaine	Bucky Bear Who Would not take his Nap (1st, sq12mo, [41]p, col, DJ/1.00)	Lothrop, Lee	(1944)	Weisgard, Leonard	45-70	
Fitch, Florence	Child Jesus (1st, 4to, [32]p, grey cl, fp color, pep, DJ/2.50)	Lothrop, Lee	1955	Weisgard, Leonard	40-65	
N/A	Cinderella (1st, 4to, ibds, [32]p, color, dep)	Garden City	1938	Weisgard, Leonard	80-140	
Gipson, Morrell	City Country ABC (1st, 4to, [48]p, ibds, color, pep, DJ/0.50)	Garden City	1946	Weisgard, Leonard	80-125	
Weisgard, Leonard	Clean Pig (1st, ob4to, [34]p, fp brown illus, pep, DJ/2.00)	Scribner	1952	Weisgard, Leonard	50-85	
Brown, Margaret W.	Country Noisy Book (1st, 8vo, [44]p, bds, color, pep, DJ/1.25)	W.R. Scott	(1940)	Weisgard, Leonard	140-220	
Dalgliesh, Alice	Courage of Sarah Noble (1st, 8vo, 52p, 7 fp illus, DJ/2.00, NH)	Scribner	(1954)	Weisgard, Leonard	60-100	R
Kramer, Nora	Cozy Hour Story Book (1st, 4to, 63p, yellow cl, color, pep, DJ/2.95)	Random	1960	Weisgard, Leonard	45-70	

AUTHOR	TITLE	PUBLISHER	DATE	ARTIST	PRICE	LC
Freeman, Jean T.	Cynthia and the Unicorn (1st {std}, 4to, [32]p, color, DJ/3.75)	Norton	1967	Weisgard, Leonard	40-65	
Brown, Margaret W.	Dark Wood o/t Golden Birds (1st, 8vo, ibds, [58]p, 2-color, pep, DJ/1.75)	Harper	(1950)	Weisgard, Leonard	100-165	R
Redman, Sylvia	Do You Want to Hear a Secret? (1st, 4to, [28]p, fp 2-color, DJ/2.75)	Lothrop, Lee	(1960)	Weisgard, Leonard	35-50	*
Howard, Elizabeth	Dorinda (1st, sm8vo, 303p, beige cl, fp b/w, pep, DJ/2.00)	Lothrop, Lee	(1944)	Weisgard, Leonard	30-50	
Weisgard, Leonard	Down Huckleberry Hill (1st, ob4to, ibds, [31]p, fp 1-color, pep, DJ/2.00)	Scribner	1947	Weisgard, Leonard	50-80	
Haviland, Virginia	Favorite Fairy Tales Told in Norway (1st {std}, 8vo, 88p, color, DJ/2.95)	Little/Brown	(1961)	Weisgard, Leonard	50-85	
Ferris, Helen	Favorite Poems Old and New (1st {std}, lg8vo, 598p, fp b/w, DJ/4.75)	Doubleday	(1957)	Weisgard, Leonard	35-50	*
Ames, Gerald	First Days of the World (1st, sm4to, 48p, ibds, fp color, DJ/2.95)	Harper	(1958)	Weisgard, Leonard	50-80	
Pape, Lee	First Doll in the World (1st, 4to, [30]p, ibds, fp 2-color, DJ/2.75)	Lothrop, Lee	1961	Weisgard, Leonard	50-85	
Weisgard, Leonard	First Farmers in the New Stone Age (1st, 4to, 63p, fp color, DJ)	Coward	(1966)	Weisgard, Leonard	30-50	*
Ames, Gerald	First People in the World (1st, sm4to, ibds, 48p, fp color, DJ/2.95)	Harper	(1958)	Weisgard, Leonard	30-50	*
Hays, Wilma P.	French Are Coming (1st, 8vo, 102p, fp b/w, gilt, DJ/3.50)	Holt, Rinehart	(1965)	Weisgard, Leonard	25-40	
Green, Adam	Funny Bunny Factory (1st, folio, [26]p, ibds, color, DJ/1.00)	Grosset/Dunlap	1950	Weisgard, Leonard	50-80	
Duncan, Lois	Giving Away Suzanne (1st, 4to, 46p, fp 1-color, DJ/3.00)	Dodd	(1963)	Weisgard, Leonard	45-70	
Brown, Margaret W.	Golden Bunny (1st, folio, ibds, [25]p, color, pep, GGB)	Simon/Schuster	(1953)	Weisgard, Leonard	60-90	R
Brown, Margaret W.	Golden Egg Book (1st, folio, ibds, [28]p, color, GGB)	Simon/Schuster	(1947)	Weisgard, Leonard	60-90	
Parish, Peggy	Good Hunting, Little Indian (1st, lg ob8vo, [32]p, color, DJ/3.00)	Young Scott	1962	Weisgard, Leonard	40-65	
Davis, Lavinia R.	Grab Bag (1st {std}, 8vo, 312p, b/w, pep, DJ/2.00)	Doubleday/Doran	1941	Weisgard, Leonard	40-65	
Swift, Jonathan	Gulliver's Travels (1st, 8vo, 272p, b/w, DJ)	Garden City	(1954)	Weisgard, Leonard	20-35	
O'Neill, Mary	Hailstones & Halibut Bones (1st {std}, 8vo, 59p, bds, pep, color, DJ/2.95)	Doubleday	1961	Weisgard, Leonard	40-65	
Frankel, Bernice	Half-as-Big and the Tiger (1st {std}, 8vo, [44]p, 2-color, pep, DJ/2.95)	F. Watts	(1961)	Weisgard, Leonard	40-65	
Thompson, Vivian L.	Hawaiian Myths of Earth, Sea & Sky (1st, 8vo, 83p, 2-color, DJ/3.00)	Holiday House	(1966)	Weisgard, Leonard	60-100	*
Spyri, Johanna	Heidi (1st {std}, 8vo, 334p, color, DJ/1.25, RC)	World	(1946)	Weisgard, Leonard	30-50	R*
Breckenfeld, Vivian	High Trail (1st {std}, 8vo, uncut, 214p, b/w, DJ/2.50)	Doubleday	1948	Weisgard, Leonard	25-40	
Brown, Margaret W.	Important Book (1st, 4to, ibds, [21]p, color, DJ/1.50)	Harper	1949	Weisgard, Leonard	80-140	
Zolotow, Charlotte	Indian, Indian (1st, sm8vo, ibds, [28]p, color, LGB/#149)	Simon/Schuster	(1952)	Weisgard, Leonard	25-40	
Brown, Margaret W.	Indoor Noisy Book (1st, 8vo, ipcb, [44]p, color, DJ/1.25)	W.R. Scott	(1942)	Weisgard, Leonard	120-180	
O'Dell, Scott	Journey to Jericho (1st {std}, lg8vo, 40p, 2-color, DJ/3.75)	Houghton	1969	Weisgard, Leonard	40-65	
Hazeltine, Alice	Just for Fun: Humerous Stories & Poems (1st, 8vo, 332p, b/w, DJ/2.75)	Lothrop, Lee	(1948)	Weisgard, Leonard	30-45	
Weisgard, Leonard	Just Like Me (1st, 8vo, [28]p, ibds, color, pep)	Treasure Books	(1954)	Weisgard, Leonard	30-50	*
Fisher, Aileen	Like Nothing at All (1st, 4to, [38]p, fp 1-color, DJ/3.50)	Crowell	(1962)	Weisgard, Leonard	30-50	
Brown, Margaret W.	Little Chicken (1st {std}, ob8vo, [39]p, color, DJ/1.50)	Harper	(1943)	Weisgard, Leonard	80-130	
Jackson, Charlotte	Little Eskimo (1st, 8vo, [28]p, ibds, color, LGB/#155)	Simon/Schuster	(1952)	Weisgard, Leonard	25-45	
Brown, Margaret W.	Little Frightened Tiger (1st {std}, ob4to, ibds, [35]p, color, DJ/2.50)	Doubleday	1953	Weisgard, Leonard	80-140	
MacDonald, Golden	Little Island (1st {std}, sm ob4to, [42]p, ibds, color, pep, DJ/2.50, CM)	Doubleday	1946	Weisgard, Leonard	120-180	R
Clark, Dorothy	Little Joe (1st, lg ob8vo, ibds, [31]p, 3-color, DJ/1.00)	Lothrop, Lee	1940	Weisgard, Leonard	70-100	
MacDonald, Golden	Little Lost Lamb (1st {std}, 4to, 48p, ibds, color, pep, DJ/2.00, CH)	Doubleday/Doran	1945	Weisgard, Leonard	100-160	
Tresselt, Alvin	Little Lost Squirrel (1st, folio, ibds, [26]p, color, pep, DJ/1.00)	Grosset/Dunlap	1950	Weisgard, Leonard	40-65	
Freschet, Berniece	Little Woodcock (1st, lg8vo, unpag, ipcb, 1-color, DJ)	Scribner	(1967)	Weisgard, Leonard	30-45	
Garelick, May	Look at the Moon (1st, 4to, [32]p, fp 2-color, DJ/3.95)	W.R. Scott	(1969)	Weisgard, Leonard	50-80	
Burnett, Frances H.	Lost Prince (1st, 8vo, 342p, t.e. red, fp b/w, cep, DJ/3.95)	Lippincott	(1967)	Weisgard, Leonard	30-45	
Cavanah, Frances	Louis of New Orleans (1st, lg8vo, ipcb, 36p, color, pep, DJ/1.00)	McKay	(1941)	Weisgard, Leonard	60-90	
Bevans, Margaret	McCall's Read-Me-a-Story Book (1st, 4to, 256p, DJ/3.95)	Putnam	(1961)	Weisgard, Leonard	30-45	*
Phelan, Mary K.	Midnight Alarm: Story of Paul Revere's Ride (1st, 8vo, 131p, b/w, DJ/4.50)	Crowell	(1968)	Weisgard, Leonard	25-40	*
Titus, Eve	Mouse and the Lion (1st, 4to, unpag, 1-color, pep, DJ/2.75)	Parents Mag. Pr.	1962	Weisgard, Leonard	30-50	
Weisgard, Leonard	Mr. Peaceable Paints (1st, ob4to, [32]p, dp color, DJ/2.75)	Scribner	1956	Weisgard, Leonard	60-100	
Delafield, Celia	Mrs. Mallard's Ducklings (1st, 4to, [24]p, fp color, pep, DJ/2.00)	Lothrop, Lee	1946	Weisgard, Leonard	70-100	
Weisgard, Leonard	My First Picture Book (1st, folio, [24]p, ibds, color, pep, DJ/1.00)	Grosset/Dunlap	(1953)	Weisgard, Leonard	50-85	
Campbell, Elizabeth	Nails to Nickels (1st {std}, 4to, 58p, 1-color, DJ/3.00)	Little/Brown	(1960)	Weisgard, Leonard	30-50	
Perrine, Mary	Nannabah's Friend (1st {std}, 8vo, [23]p, color, DJ/3.75)	Houghton	1970	Weisgard, Leonard	40-70	
Baum, L. Frank	New Wizard of Oz (1st, 8vo, 192p, t.e. blue, fp b/w, pep)	Jr. Deluxe Ed.	(1955)	Weisgard, Leonard	50-80	R*
Brown, Margaret W.	Nibble Nibble (1st, 4to, ibds, [64]p, 1-color, DJ/3.75)	W.R. Scott	(1959)	Weisgard, Leonard	50-85	
Brown, Margaret W.	Night and Day (1st {std}, sm4to, [32]p, color, DJ/1.50)	Harper	(1942)	Weisgard, Leonard	120-180	
Moore, Clement C.	Night Before Christmas (1st, lg4to, ibds, [28]p, color, pep, DJ/1.00)	Grosset/Dunlap	1949	Weisgard, Leonard	65-100	
Brown, Margaret W.	Noisy Bird Book (1st, 8vo, ibds, [41]p, color, DJ/1.25)	W.R. Scott	1943	Weisgard, Leonard	70-100	
Brown, Margaret W.	Noisy Book (1st, sq8vo, [42]p, ibds, color, pep, DJ/1.25)	W.R. Scott	(1939)	Weisgard, Leonard	80-120	
Brown, Margaret W.	Noon Balloon (1st, lg8vo, ibds, [32]p, fp 3-color, pep, DJ/2.00)	Harper	1952	Weisgard, Leonard	120-200	
Orgel, Doris	On the Sand Dune (1st, ob8vo, 30p, fp 1-color, DJ/3.50)	Harper	(1968)	Weisgard, Leonard	40-65	
Cavanah, Frances	Pedro of Santa Fe (1st, lg8vo, ipcb, [35]p, 3-color, pep, DJ/1.00)	McKay	(1941)	Weisgard, Leonard	50-80	
Weisgard, Leonard	Pelican Here, Pelican There (1st, sm4to, [30]p, 6 dp color, pep, DJ/2.00)	Scribner	1948	Weisgard, Leonard	60-90	R
Johnston, Johanna	Penguins' Way (1st {std}, lg8vo, [44]p, 2-color, DJ/2.50)	Doubleday	1962	Weisgard, Leonard	30-45	*
Potter, Beatrix	Peter Rabbit (1st, 4to, unpag, color, DJ/1.00)	Grosset/Dunlap	1955	Weisgard, Leonard	50-80	
Colman, Hila	Peter's Brownstone House (1st, 8vo, [46]p, fp 1-color, pep, DJ/2.95)	Wm. Morrow	1963	Weisgard, Leonard	30-50	
Reno, Esther W.	Pick the Vegetables (1st, 4to, [18]p, wraps, color)	Lothrop, Lee	1944	Weisgard, Leonard	70-100	*
Lacey, Marion	Picture Book of Musical Instruments (1st, 4to, ibds, 55p, b/w, DJ/2.00)	Lothrop, Lee	(1942)	Weisgard, Leonard	45-70	
Weisgard, Leonard	Plymouth Thanksgiving (1st {std}, 4to, [64]p, dp color, DJ/3.95)	Doubleday	1967	Weisgard, Leonard	45-70	R
Brown, Margaret W.	Poodle & the Sheep (1st {std}, lg ob8vo, [55]p, ibds, 1-color, DJ/1.50)	Dutton	1941	Weisgard, Leonard	80-130	
Brown, Margaret W.	Punch and Judy (1st, lg8vo, [41]p, color)	W.R. Scott	(1940)	Weisgard, Leonard	60-100	
Reno, Esther W.	Pup Called Cinderella (1st {std}, 8vo, [32]p, ibds, 1-color, b/w, DJ/1.25)	Bobbs-Merrill	(1939)	Weisgard, Leonard	60-100	
Brown, Margaret W.	Pussy Willow (1st, lg4to, [25]p, color, pep, GGB)	Simon/Schuster	1951	Weisgard, Leonard	50-90	
Brown, Margaret W.	Quiet Noisy Book (1st, 4to, ipcb, [34]p, pep, color, DJ/1.50)	Harper	1950	Weisgard, Leonard	100-165	R
Tresselt, Alvin	Rabbit Story (1st, sm4to, unpag, fp 1-color, DJ/2.50)	Lothrop, Lee	1957	Weisgard, Leonard	70-100	R
Martin, Patricia	Raccoon and Mrs. McGinnis (1st, 8vo, 45p, fp 1-color, pep, DJ/2.00)	Putnam	(1961)	Weisgard, Leonard	30-45	
Tresselt, Alvin	Rain Drop Splash (1st, 4to, [29]p, ipcb, fp color, pep, DJ/1.50, CH)	Lothrop, Lee	(1946)	Weisgard, Leonard	120-200	R
MacDonald, Golden	Red Light Green Light (1st {std}, sm ob4to, ibds, [40]p, col, cep, DJ/2.00)	Doubleday/Doran	(1944)	Weisgard, Leonard	80-120	R
Jackson, Charlotte	Round the Afternoon (1st, sm4to, blue cl, [63]p, pep, color, DJ/2.25)	Dodd	1946	Weisgard, Leonard	50-85	
Perrine, Mary	Salt Boy (1st {std}, 4to, 31p, 2-color, cep, DJ/3.25)	Houghton	1968	Weisgard, Leonard	45-70	R
Meadowcroft, Enid	Scarab for Luck: Story of Ancient Egypt (1st, 8vo, 229p, fp b/w, DJ/3.75)	Crowell	(1964)	Weisgard, Leonard	30-45	

AUTHOR	TITLE	PUBLISHER	DATE	ARTIST	PRICE	LC
Brown, Margaret W.	Seashore Noisy Book (1st, 8vo, ibds, [42]p, color, pep, DJ/1.25)	W.R. Scott	(1941)	Weisgard, Leonard	70-125	
Rawlings, Marjorie K.	Secret River (1st, 8vo, [57]p, b/w, brown pages, DJ/2.50, NH)	Scribner	(1955)	Weisgard, Leonard	150-225	R
Selsam, Millicent	See Along the Shore (1st, 8vo, ipcb, [48]p, color, cep, DJ/2.95)	Harper	1961	Weisgard, Leonard	30-45	
Joslin, Sesyle	Senor Baby Elephant the Pirate (1st {std}, 12mo, unpag, 1-color, DJ/2.50)	Harcourt	(1962)	Weisgard, Leonard	30-50	
Weisgard, Leonard	Silly Willy Nilly (1st, sm4to, [32]p, 8 fp color, DJ/2.50)	Scribner	1953	Weisgard, Leonard	60-90	R
Holl, Adelaide	Sir Kevin of Devon (1st, lg4to, [29]p, 1-color, pep, DJ/2.95)	Lothrop, Lee	1963	Weisgard, Leonard	30-45	
Nathan, Robert	Snowflake & the Starfish (1st {std}, 8vo, 68p, fp 2-color, pep, DJ/2.95)	Knopf	(1959)	Weisgard, Leonard	40-70	
Bible	Son of God... (1st, 8vo, blue cl, 122p, fp 1-color, pep)	Seabury Press	(1957)	Weisgard, Leonard	45-70	
Hazeltine, Alice	Stories of Love (1st, 8vo, 308p, b/w, DJ/3.00)	Lothrop, Lee	(1951)	Weisgard, Leonard	20-35	*
Hays, Wilma P.	Story of Valentine (1st, 8vo, 55p, 1-color, DJ/2.50)	Coward	(1956)	Weisgard, Leonard	25-40	
Johnson, Doris	Su An (1st {std}, sm8vo, 30p, b/w, DJ/3.50)	Follett	(1968)	Weisgard, Leonard	30-50	
Weisgard, Leonard	Suki the Siamese Pussy (1st, 4to, [32]p, fp 2-color, DJ/2.00)	NY: Nelson	1937	Weisgard, Leonard	70-125	
Brown, Margaret W.	Summer Noisy Book (1st, sm4to, [36]p, ibds, color, pep, DJ/1.75)	Harper	1951	Weisgard, Leonard	100-160	
Martin, Patricia	Sylvester Jones & Voice in the Forest (1st, 4to, [32]p, 2-color, DJ/2.75)	Lothrop, Lee	(1958)	Weisgard, Leonard	30-50	
Bro, Marguerite	Three & Domingo (1st {std}, sm8vo, 127p, b/w, DJ/2.00)	Doubleday	1953	Weisgard, Leonard	30-50	
Eberle, Irmengarde	Through the Harbor from Everywhere (1st {std}, 8vo, 158p, pep, DJ/1.50)	Bobbs-Merrill	(1938)	Weisgard, Leonard	50-80	
Williams, Gwen M.	Timid Timothy (1st, sm ob8vo, ibds, [68]p, fp 1-color, pep, DJ/1.25)	W.R. Scott	1944	Weisgard, Leonard	40-70	
Otis, James	Toby Tyler (1st, 8vo, 223p, col frn, b/w, pep)	Jr. Deluxe Ed.	(1958)	Weisgard, Leonard	20-30	
Weisgard, Leonard	Treasures to See (1st {std}, sm4to, [32]p, rust cl, color, DJ/3.00)	Harcourt	(1956)	Weisgard, Leonard	50-80	R
Shakespeare, Wm.	Under the Greenwood Tree (1st, 4to, black/gilt, 51p, color, DJ)	NY: Oxford U.Pr.	[1940]	Weisgard, Leonard	45-65	
Bulla, Clyde R.	Valentine Cat (1st, sm4to, [62]p, pink cl, 2-color, DJ/3.00)	Crowell	(1959)	Weisgard, Leonard	50-80	
Chambers, Maria C.	Water-Carrier's Secrets (1st, 8vo, 157p, 29 fp 1-color, pep, DJ/2.00)	Oxford U. Pr.	(1942)	Weisgard, Leonard	40-65	
Johnston, Johanna	Whale's Way (1st {std}, ob4to, 45p, color, DJ/2.95)	Doubleday	1965	Weisgard, Leonard	30-45	
Garelick, May	What Makes a Bird a Bird? (1st {std}, sm4to, ibds, [32]p, color, DJ/.3.95)	Follett	(1969)	Weisgard, Leonard	25-40	
Jackson, Kathryn	Wheels (1st, 8vo, [28]p, ibds, color, pep, LGB/#141)	Simon/Schuster	(1952)	Weisgard, Leonard	30-50	
McNulty, Faith	When a Boy Goes to Bed at Night (1st, 4to, [32]p, 2-color, pep, DJ/3.00)	Knopf	(1963)	Weisgard, Leonard	30-50	
McNulty, Faith	When a Boy Wakes Up in the Morning (1st, 4to, [32]p, 2-color, dep, DJ/2.95)	Knopf	(1962)	Weisgard, Leonard	30-45	
Lewis, Claudia	When I Go to the Moon (1st {std}, 4to, [32]p, fp color, DJ/3.00)	Macmillan	1961	Weisgard, Leonard	30-50	*
Eberstadt, Isabel	Where Did Tuffy Hide? (1st {std}, 8vo, [32]p, fp 2-color, DJ/2.50)	Little/Brown	1957	Weisgard, Leonard	30-50	
MacDonald, Golden	Whistle for the Train (1st {std}, ob4to, [28]p, fp 3-color, pep, DJ/2.50)	Doubleday	1956	Weisgard, Leonard	50-80	
Bulla, Clyde R.	White Bird (1st, 8vo, 79p, b/w, DJ/3.75)	Crowell	1966	Weisgard, Leonard	25-40	
Weisgard, Leonard	Who Dreams of Cheese? (1st, 4to, black cl, [32]p, color, DJ)	Scribner	1950	Weisgard, Leonard	60-100	R
Vaughan, Samuel	Who Ever Heard of Kangaroo Eggs? (1st {std}, 4to, unpag, color, DJ/2.75)	Doubleday	(1957)	Weisgard, Leonard	50-80	
Eberstadt, Isabel	Who Is at the Door? (1st {std}, 8vo, [32]p, fp 2-color, DJ/2.50)	Little/Brown	(1960)	Weisgard, Leonard	30-50	
Weisgard, Leonard	Whose Little Bird Am I? (1st, 24mo, ibds, [39]p, fp 1-color, pep, DJ/1.00)	Crowell	(1944)	Weisgard, Leonard	30-50	
Franchere, Ruth	Willa (1st {std}, 8vo, 168p, DJ/3.00, b/w, decor by...)	Crowell	(1958)	Weisgard, Leonard	45-70	R*
Weisgard, Leonard	Would You Like to be a Monkey? (1st, sm8vo, ibds, [32]p, color, DJ/1.00)	Crowell	(1945)	Weisgard, Leonard	30-50	*
McGinley, Phyllis	Wreath of Christmas Legends (1st {std}, ob8vo, 62p, ibds, b/w, DJ/3.95)	Macmillan	(1967)	Weisgard, Leonard	30-45	
Hall, Rosalys	Dog's Boy (1st, 8vo, 42p, b/w, DJ/2.75)	Lothrop, Lee	(1962)	Weiss, Emil	30-45	*
Neville, Emily C.	It's Like this, Cat (1st {std}, 8vo, ibds, 180p, b/w, DJ/3.50, NM)	Harper	(1963)	Weiss, Emil	50-80	R
Schlein, Miriam	Amazing Mr. Pelgrew (1st, sm4to, [42]p, fp 3-color, pep, DJ/2.50)	Abelard-Schuman	1957	Weiss, Harvey	25-45	
Schlein, Miriam	Big Talk (1st, lg sq8vo, olive cl, [36]p, 2-color, pep, DJ/2.25)	W.R. Scott	1955	Weiss, Harvey	30-50	
Schlein, Miriam	Bumblebee's Secret (1st, sq8vo, 51p, fp color, pep, DJ/2.50)	Abelard-Schuman	(1958)	Weiss, Harvey	30-45	
Schlein, Miriam	Fisherman's Day (1st, lg8vo, [32]p, color, DJ/2.00)	Whitman	1959	Weiss, Harvey	20-35	*
Schlein, Miriam	Here Comes Night (1st, lg8vo, p-o, [32]p, fp color, pep, DJ/2.00)	Whitman	(1957)	Weiss, Harvey	25-40	
Schlein, Miriam	Lazy Day (1st, ob8vo, [38]p, fp 2-color, DJ/2.00)	W.R. Scott	1955	Weiss, Harvey	25-40	
Lexau, Joan M.	Olaf is Late (1st, 8vo, [32]p, fp 1-color, pep, DJ/2.75)	Dial Press	(1963)	Weiss, Harvey	20-35	
Lexau, Joan M.	Olaf Reads (1st [1st bk.], 8vo, 53p, 3-color, pep, DJ/2.75)	Dial Press	(1961)	Weiss, Harvey	30-50	
Rice, Alice H.	Captain June (1st, 8vo, blue cl, 120p, 8pl)	Century	1907	Weldon, C.D.	25-45	
Bunner, H.C.	Three Operettas (1st, ob4to, 163p, gilt, b/w)	Harper	1897	Weldon/Taylor	60-100	
Carroll, Lewis	Alice... & Through... (1st, 4to, 236p, gilt, p-o, col frn)	Sears	(1926)	Welling, G.	120-200	*
Spyri, Johanna	Heidi (1st, 4to, 243p, col frn, 1-color)	Sears	(1926)	Welling, G.	25-40	*
Wells, H.G.	Adventures of Tommy (1st AM, 4to, red cl, [46]p, p-o, color)	Stokes	1929	Wells, H.G.	120-180	
Wells, H.G.	Adventures of Tommy (1st, lg4to, 45p, bds, color)	L: Harrap	(1929)	Wells, H.G.	200-285	
Wells, H.G.	Adventures of Tommy (1st [this fmt.], 4to, 26p, wraps, color)	A.& W. Guild	1935	Wells, H.G.	30-50	
Wells, Peter	Mr. Tootwhistle's Invention (1st, 8vo, [32]p, orange cl, color, DJ/1.25)	Winston	(1942)	Wells, Peter	30-50	
Wells, Peter	Pirate's Apprentice (1st {std}, lg8vo, bds, [48]p, color, pep, DJ/0.75)	Winston	(1943)	Wells, Peter	25-40	
English, James W.	Tailbone Patrol (1st, 8vo, 186p, grey cl, fp b/w, pep, DJ/2.75)	Holiday House	(1955)	Wells, Peter	30-50	*
Wells, Rhea	Ali the Camel (1st {std}, sm8vo, 136p, fp color, pep)	Doubleday/Doran	1931	Wells, Rhea	30-55	
Wells, Rhea	Andy and Polly (1st {std}, lg ob8vo, [32]p, color)	Doubleday/Doran	1931	Wells, Rhea	60-90	R*
Wells, Rhea	Beppo the Donkey (1st {std}, 12mo, 135p, 15cp, pep)	Doubleday/Doran	1930	Wells, Rhea	30-50	
Wells, Rhea	Coco the Goat (1st {std}, sm8vo, 135p, dp color, pep)	Doubleday/Doran	1929	Wells, Rhea	30-50	
Joos, Dorothy H.	Golden Prince (1st, 4to, 129p, p-o, dp color, pep)	Duffield	1928	Wells, Rhea	40-65	
Dane, George E.	Once There Was and was Not (1st {std}, 8vo, 269p, col frn, b/w, pep)	Doubleday/Doran	1931	Wells, Rhea	30-50	*
Wells, Rhea	Peppi the Duck (1st {std}, sm8vo, 118p, cp, pep)	Doubleday/Doran	1927	Wells, Rhea	30-50	
Wells, Rhea	Zeke the Raccoon (1st, sm8vo, green cl, 159p, 8cp, pep)	Viking	1933	Wells, Rhea	30-50	*
Gilbert & Sullivan	Duke of Plaza Toro (1st {std}, 8vo, [32]p, color, DJ/3.95)	Macmillan	(1969)	Wells, Rosemary	25-45	
Wells, Rosemary	First Child (1st {std}, lg8vo, [32]p, color, DJ/4.25)	Hawthorn Books	(1970)	Wells, Rosemary	25-40	
Fox, Paula	Hungry Fred (1st {std}, 4to, [39]p, color, DJ/3.95)	Bradbury Press	(1969)	Wells, Rosemary	25-40	
Wells, Rosemary	John and the Rarey (1st {1}, 4to, bds, 42p, 2-color, cep, DJ/3.50)	Funk/Wagnalls	(1969)	Wells, Rosemary	30-50	
Wells, Rosemary	Martha's Birthday (1st {std}, lg8vo, [31]p, color, DJ/4.25)	Bradbury Press	(1970)	Wells, Rosemary	35-50	
Rosen, Winifred	Marvin's Manhole (1st {std}, 4to, ipcb, [32]p, fp color, cep, DJ/3.95)	Dial Press	(1970)	Wells, Rosemary	30-45	
Wells, Rosemary	Michael and the Mitten Test (1st {std}, 12mo, [35]p, color, DJ/3.50)	Bradbury Press	(1969)	Wells, Rosemary	25-40	
Wells, Rosemary	Miranda's Pilgrims (1st {std}, lg ob8vo, [32]p, color, DJ/4.50)	Bradbury Press	(1970)	Wells, Rosemary	30-50	*
Reinheimer, Sophie	Flower Heaven (1st AM, 4to, ibds, [16]p, color, cep)	Harper	1931	Wenz-Vietor, Else	120-180	
Wharton, Edith	House of Mirth (1st, 8vo, 533p, gilt, teg, uncut, 8pl)	Scribner	1905	Wenzell, A.B.	140-200	
Keller, Frances	Contented Little Pussy Cat (1st, 4to, [52]p, ibds, color)	Platt/Munk	(1949)	Werber/Laslo	25-40	
Keller, Frances	Curious Little Owl (1st, sm4to, [48]p, ipcb, color, pep, DJ/1.50)	Platt/Munk	(1957)	Werber/Laslo	25-40	

AUTHOR	TITLE	PUBLISHER	DATE	ARTIST	PRICE	LC
Asbjornsen, P.C.	Fairy Tales from the Far North (1st AM, 8vo, 303p, b/w)	A.C. Armstrong	1897	Werenskiold, E.	100-160	*
Asbjornsen, P.C.	Fairy Tales from the Far North (1st, 8vo, 303p, b/w pl)	L: D. Nutt	1897	Werenskiold, E.	120-200	
Duarte, Margarida	Legend of the Palm Tree (1st, lg4to, ibds, [47]p, color, DJ/1.00)	Grosset/Dunlap	(1940)	Werneck, Paulo	150-220	
Carden, Priscilla	Aldo's Tower (1st {std}, lg8vo, 63p, color, DJ/2.75)	Ariel	(1954)	Werth, Kurt	25-45	
Buck, Pearl S.	Beech Tree (1st, 8vo, 60p, b/w, DJ/2.50)	John Day	(1955)	Werth, Kurt	80-125	R
Hall, Rosalys	Bright and Shining Breadboard (1st, sm4to, [32]p, fp color, cep, DJ/3.75)	Lothrop, Lee	(1969)	Werth, Kurt	30-50	
Ross, Geraldine	Elf Who Didn't Believe in Himself (1st, lg8vo, 32p, color, DJ/2.95)	Steck-Vaughn	(1966)	Werth, Kurt	30-50	
Daringer, Helen F.	Golden Thorn (1st {std}, 8vo, 181p, b/w, DJ/2.75)	Harcourt	(1956)	Werth, Kurt	30-50	
Martin, Patricia	Happy Piper and the Goat (1st, 8vo, 38p, color, DJ/2.75)	Lothrop, Lee	(1960)	Werth, Kurt	20-30	
Curren, Polly	Hear Ye of Boston (1st, sq4to, 39p, color, pep, DJ/3.95)	Lothrop, Lee	(1964)	Werth, Kurt	30-45	
Schneider, Nina	Hercules: Gentle Giant (1st, sm4to, ibds, [40]p, dp 2-color, pep)	Roy Publishers	(1947)	Werth, Kurt	45-70	*
Budney, Blossom	Huff Puff Hickory Hill (1st, 4to, [29]p, color, pep, DJ/2.50)	Lothrop, Lee	1955	Werth, Kurt	30-50	
Margolis, Ellen	Idy, the Fox-Chasing Cow (1st {std}, 8vo, 64p, b/w, DJ/2.95)	World	(1962)	Werth, Kurt	25-40	*
Bason, Lillian	Isabelle and the Library Cat (1st, lg8vo, unpag, color, pep, DJ/3.25)	Lothrop, Lee	(1966)	Werth, Kurt	30-50	
Buck, Pearl S.	Johnny Jack & his Beginnings (1st, 8vo, 47p, green cl, 1-color, DJ/2.50)	NY: John Day	(1954)	Werth, Kurt	80-125	R
Werth, Kurt	King Thrushbeard (1st, sm4to, [32]p, fp color, DJ/3.95)	Viking	(1968)	Werth, Kurt	30-50	*
Werth, Kurt	Lazy Jack (1st {std}, lg8vo, [32]p, color, DJ/3.75)	Viking	(1970)	Werth, Kurt	30-45	*
Frost, Frances	Little Naturalist (1st, lg8vo, 47p, 3-color, pep, DJ/2.50)	Whittlesey	(1959)	Werth, Kurt	20-35	*
Tate, Elizabeth	Little Teddy & the Big Sea (1st, 4to, [32]p, fp color, pep, DJ/2.50)	Lothrop, Lee	1954	Werth, Kurt	60-100	
Leach, Maria	Luck Book (1st {std}, 8vo, 111p, b/w, DJ/2.95)	World	(1964)	Werth, Kurt	20-35	
Fleischman, Sid	McBroom and the Big Wind (1st {std}, 8vo, [46]p, color, DJ/3.25)	Norton	(1967)	Werth, Kurt	25-40	
Fleischman, Sid	McBroom Tells the Truth (1st {std}, 8vo, 47p, color, DJ/3.25)	Norton	(1966)	Werth, Kurt	25-40	
Fleischman, Sid	McBroom's Ear (1st {std}, 8vo, [48]p, color, DJ/4.25)	Norton	(1969)	Werth, Kurt	25-40	
Hall, Rosalys	Miranda's Dragon (1st, sm4to, green cl, 39p, color, DJ/3.95)	McGraw-Hill	(1968)	Werth, Kurt	30-45	
Werth, Kurt	Monkey, the Lion & the Snake (1st, 8vo, ipcb, 31p, fp color, DJ/3.50)	Viking	(1967)	Werth, Kurt	30-45	*
Hall, Rosalys	No Ducks for Dinner (1st {std}, 8vo, 40p, color, DJ/2.50)	NY: Oxford U.Pr.	1953	Werth, Kurt	30-45	
Leach, Maria	Noodles, Nitwits and Numskulls (1st {std}, sm4to, 96p, b/w, DJ/2.95)	World	(1961)	Werth, Kurt	25-40	*
Preston, Edna M.	One Dark Night (1st, ob8vo, [28]p, fp 1-color, DJ/3.50)	Viking	(1969)	Werth, Kurt	30-45	*
Kay, Helen	One Mitten Lewis (1st, 4to, ibds, [32]p, color, DJ/2.00)	Lothrop, Lee	(1955)	Werth, Kurt	50-80	
Butters, Dorothy	Papa Dolphin's Table (1st {std}, 8vo, 88p, fp b/w, DJ/2.00)	Knopf	1955	Werth, Kurt	50-80	
Varble, Rachel	Pepys' Boy (1st {std}, 8vo, 253p, b/w, DJ/2.75)	Doubleday	1955	Werth, Kurt	30-50	
Hall, Rosalys	Seven for St. Nicholas (1st {std}, 8vo, 156p, b/w, DJ/3.00)	Lippincott	(1958)	Werth, Kurt	25-45	
Holberg, Ruth	Smugglers of Sandy Bay (1st {std}, 8vo, uncut, 192p, fp b/w, DJ/2.75)	Doubleday	1957	Werth, Kurt	20-35	*
Fenner, Phyllis R.	Stories of the Sea (1st {std}, lg8vo, beige cl, 178p, b/w, DJ/3.00)	Knopf	1953	Werth, Kurt	30-50	*
Holberg, Ruth	Tabitha's Hill (1st {std}, 8vo, 223p, b/w, DJ/2.75)	Doubleday	(1956)	Werth, Kurt	20-35	*
Zolotow, Charlotte	Tiger Called Thomas (1st, sm4to, [32]p, fp 2-color, pep, DJ/2.95)	Lothrop, Lee	(1963)	Werth, Kurt	25-45	
Mantle, Winifred	Tinker's Castle (1st {std}, 8vo, 222p, b/w, DJ/3.75)	Holt, Rinehart	(1964)	Werth, Kurt	20-35	
Selsam, Millicent	Tony's Birds (1st, 8vo, 64p, 3-color, DJ/1.95)	Harper	(1961)	Werth, Kurt	20-30	
Wier, Ester A.	Wind Chasers (1st, 8vo, 154p, b/w, DJ/3.50)	McKay	1967	Werth, Kurt	20-35	*
Tague, Lola	Wonderful Merry Go Gound (1st, lg8vo, 46p, fp b/w, DJ/2.95)	Lothrop, Lee	(1961)	Werth, Kurt	20-30	
McGinley, Phyllis	Year Without a Santa Claus (1st, sm4to, tan cl, [32]p, color, cep, DJ/3.00)	Lippincott	1957	Werth, Kurt	30-50	
Spyri, Johanna	New Year's Carol (1st, 12mo, ipcb, 34p, col frn, 3pl)	Houghton	(1924)	Wesson, G.E.	30-45	
Perez-Guerra, A.	Poppy, Adventures of a Fairy (1st, lg8vo, ibds, 80p, pep, b/w)	Rand/McNally	(1931)	West, Benton	100-160	*
Schaefer, Jack W.	Old Ramon (1st, 8vo, 102p, b/w, uncut, DJ/2.50, NH)	Houghton	1960	West, Harold	120-200	
Penney, Grace	Tales of the Cheyennes (1st, lg8vo, 117p, b/w, DJ/2.25)	Houghton	1953	West, Walter	20-35	
Pasma, Henry K.	Enchanted Sword (1st {std}, sm8vo, 275p, 6 fp b/w, pep)	Longmans	1932	Westmacott, Bernard	25-40	
Singmaster, Elsie	You Make Your Own Luck (1st {std}, 8vo, 255p, b/w pl)	Longmans	1929	Westmacott, Bernard	25-40	
Omar Khayyam	Rubaiyat of Omar Khayyam (1st, 8vo, 159p, 8cp)	L: Kegan Paul	(1923)	Weston, H.	55-80	*
Judson, Clara I.	Michael's Victory (1st, 8vo, 192p, b/w, pep, DJ/2.00)	Houghton	1946	Wexler, Elmer	25-45	
Duval, Elizabeth	This Earth We Live On (1st, lg8vo, 157p, color, pep)	Stokes	1927	Wharton, Percival	20-35	
Kohn, Bernice	Beachcomber's Book (1st, ob8vo, 96p, fp b/w, DJ/3.75)	Viking	(1970)	Wheatley, Arobelle	25-35	
Evans, Florence A.	Alice's Adventures in Pictureland (1st, sm4to, 192p, b/w pl)	Dodge	(1900)	Wheelan, A.R.	100-180	
Terhune, Anice	Chinese Child's Day (1st, lg4to, 33p, ibds, 15 color)	NY: Schirmer	[1910]	Wheelan, A.R.	120-200	
Terhune, Anice	Dutch Ditties for Children (1st, lg4to, 31p, ibds, 15 color)	NY: Schirmer	[1910]	Wheelan, A.R.	100-170	
McElhone, Helen K.	Secrets of the Elves (1st, sq 12mo, green cloth, p-o, color)	Devin-Adair	1913	Wheelan, A.R.	140-220	
McElhone, Helen K.	Surprise Book (1st, lg ob4to, yellow cl, 33pl)	Stokes	1901	Wheelan, A.R.	140-220	
Broadwood, Lucy	English Nursery Rhymes (lg4to, 63p, gilt, p-o, color, pep)	L: A&C Black	(1916)	Wheeler, Dorothy M.	125-180	
Swift, Jonathan	Gulliver's Travels (1st, 8vo, 414p, 12cp)	L: Routledge	1895	Wheeler, Edward J.	70-100	
Pritchard, Myron T.	Upward Path (1st, sm8vo, 255p)	Harcourt	(1920)	Wheeler, Laura	80-120	
F.M.H.	War of the Wooden Soldiers (1st, 12mo, ipcb, [76]p, color)	Rand/McNally	(1915)	Wheeler, M.& W.	50-80	R
Wimberley, L. (comp)	Famous Cats of Fairyland (1st {std}, 8vo, 246p, DJ/2.50)	Dutton	1938	Wheeler, Nina B.	45-70	
Whyte, Christina	Adventures of Merry Wink (1st, 8vo, 199p, 12 fp b/w)	L: Hodder	[1906]	Wheelhouse, Mary V.	200-300	
Ewing, Juliana H.	Flat Iron for a Farthing (1st, 12mo, 235p, teg, uncut, 8cp, pep)	L: G. Bell	1908	Wheelhouse, Mary V.	35-60	*
Alcott, Louisa M.	Good Wives (1st UK, 12mo, teg, 316p, 8cp, pep)	L: G. Bell	1911	Wheelhouse, Mary V.	30-50	
Baldwin, May	Holly House and Ridges Row (1st, 8vo, 339p, AEG, red/gilt, 12cp)	L: Chambers	1908	Wheelhouse, Mary V.	40-65	
Ewing, Juliana H.	Jan of the Windmill (1st, 12mo, 307p, teg, uncut, 8cp, pep)	L: G. Bell	1909	Wheelhouse, Mary V.	40-60	*
Ewing, Juliana H.	Mrs. Overtheway's Rememberances (1st, 8vo, 195p, teg, 8cp, pep)	L: G. Bell	1909	Wheelhouse, Mary V.	45-70	
MacDonald, George	Ronald Bannerman's Boyhood (1st, 8vo, 335p, teg, p-o, gilt, 12cp)	L: Blackie	(1911)	Wheelhouse, Mary V.	90-145	
Ewing, Juliana H.	Six to Sixteen (1st, 12mo, green cl, 237p, teg, 8cp)	L: G. Bell	1908	Wheelhouse, Mary V.	30-50	
Gaskell, Mrs.	Sylvia's Lovers (1st, sm8vo, 542p, gilt, teg, 8cp, pep)	L: G. Bell	1910	Wheelhouse, Mary V.	40-65	
Lucas, E.V.	The Slowcoach (1st, 8vo, brown cl, 284p, 16cp, pep)	L: Wells/Gard.	(1910)	Wheelhouse, Mary V.	45-80	
Phillips, Mary E.	Tommy Tregennis (1st, lg8vo, gilt, uncut, teg, 209p, 7cp)	L: Constable	1912	Wheelhouse, Mary V.	60-100	*
Ewing, Juliana H.	We & the World (1st, 12mo, rust cl, 315p, teg, 8cp, pep)	L: G. Bell	1910	Wheelhouse, Mary V.	30-50	
Gaskell, Mrs.	Wives and Daughters (1st, 12mo, 646p, gilt, teg, 8cp)	L:Herbert/Daniel	1912	Wheelhouse, Mary V.	40-70	
Price, Eleanor C.	Adventures of King Arthur (1st, sm4to, ibds, 153p, 8cp, p-o)	L: Coker	1931	Wheelwright, Rowland	40-60	*
Hugo, Victor	Hunchback of Notre-Dame (1st, 8vo, 424p, 16cp)	Dodd	1928	Wheelwright, Rowland	45-70	
Sterling, Sara H.	Robin Hood & his Merry Men (8vo, brown cl, 118p, 7cp)	L: Coker	[1933]	Wheelwright, Rowland	35-60	*
Black, Irma S.	Spoodles, Puppy Who Learned (1st, ob8vo, [48]p, ipcb, 1-color, DJ/1.25)	W.R. Scott	(1948)	Whistle, Johnny	40-60	*

AUTHOR	TITLE	PUBLISHER	DATE	ARTIST	PRICE	LC
Cary, Elisabeth L.	Works of James McNeill Whistler (1st, sm4to, bds, 302p, uncut, 31pl)	Moffat	1907	Whistler, James M.	120-200	
De La Mare, Walter	Desert Islands & Robinson Crusoe (1st AM, lg8vo, 299p, b/w)	Farrar/Rinehart	1930	Whistler, Rex	60-100	*
De La Mare, Walter	Desert Islands & Robinson Crusoe (1st {std}, 4to, 285p, teg, gilt, b/w)	L: Faber	1930	Whistler, Rex	80-120	*
Andersen, Hans C.	Fairy Tales and Legends (1st, 8vo, gilt, 470p, a.e. red, 10 b/w)	L: Cobden	(1935)	Whistler, Rex	200-300	R
Andersen, Hans C.	Fairy Tales and Legends (1st AM, 8vo, 470p, gilt, fp b/w, pep, DJ/2.50)	NY: Oxford U.Pr.	1936	Whistler, Rex	100-165	
De La Mare, Walter	Lord Fish (1st, 8vo, mauve/gilt, 289p, 3cp, pep)	L: Faber	(1933)	Whistler, Rex	60-90	
Aberconway, Christabel	Story of Mr. Korah (1st, sm4to, [42]p, gilt, 3 ticp, b/w, DJ)	L: M. Joseph	(1954)	Whistler, Rex	60-100	
Nichols, Beverly	Thatched Roof (1st, 8vo, 285p, red cl, b/w, pep)	L: J. Cape	1933	Whistler, Rex	30-45	
Montgomery, F.T.	Billy Whiskers in an Aeroplane (1st, lg8vo, 219p, 6cp)	Saalfield	(1912)	White, Constance	200-300	*
Montgomery, F.T.	Billy Whiskers in Panama (1st, lg8vo, 168p, color)	Saalfield	(1914)	White, Constance	100-165	
Montgomery, F.T.	Billy Whiskers in Town (1st, lg8vo, 200p, color)	Saalfield	(1913)	White, Constance	70-120	
White, Constance	Flip Flop Show (folio, bds, fp color)	Donohue	(1909)	White, Constance	70-120	
Berger, Terry	Black Fairy Tales (1st {std}, lg8vo, 137p, b/w, DJ/4.75)	Atheneum	1969	White, David O.	30-50	
Bacon, Martha	Sophia Scrooby Preserved (1st {std}, 8vo, 227p, b/w, DJ/4.95)	Little/Brown	(1968)	White, David O.	25-40	
N/A	Peter Pan's ABC (8vo, ibds, p-o, gilt, 25cp)	L: H. Frowde	[1912]	White, Flora	200-320	
Meigs, Cornelia L.	Kingdom of the Winding Road (1st, sm8vo, blue cl, 238p, 6cp)	Macmillan	1915	White, Frances	50-80	
Herr, Charoltte	Brownie Robinson Crusoe (1st, 8vo, 163p, p-o, 8cp)	Dodd	1920	White, Orrin A.	25-45	
White, Terence H.	Ill-Made Knight (1st, 8vo, 291p, DJ/2.50, decor by...)	Putnam	1940	White, Terence H.	400-600	
White, Terence H.	Ill-Made Knight (1st UK, 8vo, 296p, red/gilt, b/w, DJ)	L: Collins	1941	White, Terence H.	350-500	
White, Terence H.	Sword in the Stone (1st, 8vo, 339p, black cl, b/w, DJ)	L: Collins	1938	White, Terence H.	250-450	
White, Terence H.	Sword in the Stone (1st AM, 8vo, 311p, gilt, b/w, DJ/2.50)	Putnam	1939	White, Terence H.	250-400	
White, Terence H.	Witch in the Wood (1st, 8vo, blue/gilt bds, 270p, b/w, DJ/2.50)	Putnam	1939	White, Terence H.	350-500	
Proudfit, Isabel	Come & See the Bottle Family (1st, sq12mo, ibds, 38p, color, DJ/0.50)	McKay	(1938)	Whitehead, Caroline	30-50	
Proudfit, Isabel	Come & See the Broom Closet Family (1st, sq12mo, ibds, [38]p, color)	McKay	(1938)	Whitehead, Caroline	35-50	
Frank, Mabel L.	Child's Day in Song (1st, lg4to, ibds, 31p, 12cp)	Schirmer	(1916)	Whitelaw, Norah	75-100	*
Whitney, Elinor	Tyke-Y: His Book & his Mark (1st, 8vo, 78p, silhouettes)	Macmillan	1925	Whitney, Elinor	25-40	
Rhys, Ernest (ed.)	English Fairy Book (1st, 8vo, 318p, gilt, col frn, 1-color, pep)	L: T.F. Unwin	1912	Whitney, Frederic C.	50-90	
Gray, Eliz. J.	Penn (1st, 8vo, red cl, 298p, maps, b/w, pep, DJ/2.50, NH)	Viking	1938	Whitney, George	50-85	
Allee, Marjorie H.	Winter's Mischief (1st, 8vo, 216p, b/w, pep, DJ/2.00)	Houghton	1942	Whitney, George	20-35	*
Randolph, Althea	Bouquet of Rhymes for Children (1st, folio, ibds, 6cp)	Bonnell/Silver	(1909)	Whitney, Isabel	140-220	*
Teall, Edna A.	Batter and Spoon Fairies (1st {std}, 8vo, p-o, 279p, b/w, pep)	Harper	1929	Whittemore, C.	70-100	
Spyri, Johanna	Heidi (1st, 8vo, 433p, pep, 12cp)	Crowell	(1927)	Whittemore, C.	30-50	*
Almond, Linda S.	Mary Redding Takes Charge (1st, 8vo, 310p, col frn, cp)	Crowell	(1926)	Whittemore, C.	25-40	*
Moore, Clement C.	Visit from St. Nicholas (1st, 16mo, 53p, gilt, pep, color)	Macmillan	1925	Whittemore, C.	50-80	R*
Wodehouse, P.G.	Gold Bat (1st, 8vo, 277p, red/gilt, 8pl)	L: A&C Black	1904	Whitwell, T.M.R.	700-1000	
Wodehouse, P.G.	Mike (1st, 8vo, 339p, olive cl, 12pl)	L: A&C Black	1909	Whitwell, T.M.R.	900-1500	
Wodehouse, P.G.	Psmith in the City (1st, 8vo, 266p, blue cl, 12pl)	L: A&C Black	1910	Whitwell, T.M.R.	800-1200	
Farjeon, Eleanor	Old Nurse's Stocking Basket (1st AM, 8vo, 154p, col frn, b/w)	Stokes	1931	Whydale, E. Herbert	35-60	
Aflalo, F.G.	Fisherman's Weather (1st, 8vo, teg, gilt, 256p, 8cp)	L: A&C Black	1906	Whymper, Charles	60-100	
Wiberg, Harald	Christmas at Totem's Farm (1st AM, 4to, [30]p, fp 3-color, pep, DJ/4.50)	Coward	(1968)	Wiberg, Harald	70-120	*
Lindgren, Astrid	Christmas in the Stable (1st, ob4to, [28]p, fp color, DJ/2.95)	Coward	(1962)	Wiberg, Harald	60-100	
Lindgren, Astrid	The Tomten (1st UK, ob4to, [30]p, color)	L: Constable	1962	Wiberg, Harald	50-85	
Lindgren, Astrid	Tomten and the Fox (1st AM, ob4to, [32]p, fp color, DJ/3.50)	Coward	1966	Wiberg, Harald	60-90	
Peterson, Hans	When Peter Was Lost in the Forest (1st AM, ob4to, [32]p, fp color, DJ)	Coward	1970	Wiberg, Harald	50-80	*
Wiederseim, Grace	Baby's Day (1st, 4to, ibds, 11 fp color)	Stokes	1910	Wiederseim, Grace	200-300	R
Wiederseim, Grace	Dolly Drake (1st, 4to, ibds, [16]p, shape book, color)	Stokes	(1909)	Wiederseim, Grace	200-300	*
Wiederseim, Grace	Ducky Daddles (folio, shape bk, 16p, ibds, color)	Stokes	(1911)	Wiederseim, Grace	150-225	
Wiederseim, Grace	Fido (shape book, folio, ibds, 16p, color)	Stokes	(1910)	Wiederseim, Grace	150-225	R
Hays, M.G.	Kaptin Kiddo & Puppo (1st, ob4to, ibds, color)	L: Chambers	(1913)	Wiederseim, Grace	600-800	
Hays, M.G.	Kiddie Land (1st, 4to, [52]p, tan bds, p-o, 12cp, pep)	Jacobs	(1910)	Wiederseim, Grace	350-500	
Hays, M.G.	Kiddie Rhymes (1st, 4to, [52]p, ibds, p-o, 6cp, pep)	Jacobs	(1911)	Wiederseim, Grace	300-500	*
Hays, M.G.	Little Pets Book (1st, 4to, ibds, 6cp)	Jacobs	(1911)	Wiederseim, Grace	300-450	
Bangs, John K.	Molly and Unwiseman Abroad (1st, 8vo, p-o, 262p, teg, 10cp)	Lippincott	1910	Wiederseim, Grace	150-220	
Mother Goose	Nursery Rhymes from Mother Goose (1st, lg4to, [48]p, color)	Scribner	1907	Wiederseim, Grace	150-220	
Hays, M.G.	Rosy Childhood (1st, 4to, ibds, 6 fp color, pep)	Jacobs	(1911)	Wiederseim, Grace	200-300	
Wiederseim, Grace	Tiny Tots: their Adventures (1st, 4to, ibds, 12 fp color)	Stokes	(1909)	Wiederseim, Grace	250-350	
Hays, M.G.	Vegetable Verselets (1st, 12mo, 60p, ibds, 20 fp 1-color)	Lippincott	1911	Wiederseim, Grace	250-350	R
Risley, Eleanor	Abandoned Orchard (1st, 8vo, 284p, b/w)	Little/Brown	1932	Wiese, Kurt	25-40	*
Meadowcroft, Enid	Abraham Lincoln (1st, lg8vo, 191p, fp b/w, DJ/2.00)	Crowell	(1942)	Wiese, Kurt	30-45	
Hutter, Donald	Abraham: Iterant Mouse (1st, lg8vo, 70p, fp 1-color, pep, DJ/2.50)	Dodd	1947	Wiese, Kurt	40-70	
Gatti, Attilio	Adventure in Black and White (1st, 8vo, 172p, b/w, pep, DJ/1.75)	Scribner	1943	Wiese, Kurt	60-90	
Bonsels, Waldemar	Adventures of Mario (1st, 8vo, 239p, b/w, DJ/3.00)	A.& C. Boni	1930	Wiese, Kurt	25-40	
Nevins, Albert J.	Adventures of Pancho of Peru (1st, 8vo, 246p, gilt, b/w, DJ/2.75)	Dodd	1953	Wiese, Kurt	25-40	*
Henry, Marguerite	Alaska in Story and Pictures (1st, ob8vo, [28]p, color, DJ/0.50)	Whitman	1941	Wiese, Kurt	30-45	
Brown, Marion	Alexander: Tale of a Monkey (1st {std}, sm8vo, 193p, pep)	Bobbs-Merrill	(1934)	Wiese, Kurt	30-50	*
Hayes, Marjorie A.	Alice-Albert Elephant (1st {std}, 8vo, 134p, pep, fp b/w, DJ/1.75)	Little/Brown	1938	Wiese, Kurt	45-70	
Kipling, Rudyard	All the Mowgli Stories (1st {std} 8vo, 299p, col frn 9 fp b/w, pep, DJ/2.50)	Doubleday/Doran	1936	Wiese, Kurt	30-50	
Glenn, Morris	Amandus, who Was Much Too Big (1st, ob8vo, 63p, fp 1-col, pep, DJ/1.50)	Macrae Smith	(1939)	Wiese, Kurt	45-70	
Guillaume, Jeanette	Amat and the Water-Buffalo (1st, sq8vo, 48p, color, DJ/2.75)	Coward	1962	Wiese, Kurt	25-45	
Hewes, Agnes D.	Anabel's Windows (1st, 8vo, orange cl, 240p, b/w, DJ/2.50)	Dodd	1949	Wiese, Kurt	30-45	*
Kantor, MacKinlay	Angleworms on Toast (1st, lg ob8vo, [32]p, color, ibds, DJ/1.50)	Coward	1942	Wiese, Kurt	60-100	
Pratt, Alice	Animal Babies (1st, 8vo, 148p, ibds, color, DJ/1.75)	Beacon Press	(1941)	Wiese, Kurt	25-40	
Coblentz, Catherine	Animal Pioneers (1st, 8vo, green cl, 241p, b/w, DJ/2.00)	Little/Brown	1936	Wiese, Kurt	35-60	*
Pratt, Alice	Animals of a Sage Brush Ranch (1st, lg8vo, p-o, 208p, 3cp, pep)	Rand/McNally	(1931)	Wiese, Kurt	50-80	
MacPherson, Margaret	Australia Calling (1st, 8vo, 199p, b/w, DJ/2.50)	Dodd	1946	Wiese, Kurt	25-45	
Ross, Margaret I.	Back of Time (1st {std}, 8vo, 271p, pep, b/w)	Harper	1932	Wiese, Kurt	30-50	
Salten, Felix	Bambi: Life in the Woods (1st AM {std}, 12mo, 293p, green/gilt, b/w, pep)	Simon/Schuster	1928	Wiese, Kurt	120-200	R
Stong, Philip D.	Beast Called an Elephant (1st, 8vo, 123p, b/w, DJ/2.75)	Dodd	1955	Wiese, Kurt	25-40	

AUTHOR	TITLE	PUBLISHER	DATE	ARTIST	PRICE	LC
Hollister, Mary	Beggars of Dreams (1st, 8vo, 234p, b/w pl, pep, DJ/2.00)	Dodd	1937	Wiese, Kurt	50-85	
DeJong, Meindert	Bells of the Harbor (1st {std}, 8vo, 289p, pep, b/w, DJ/2.00)	Harper	1941	Wiese, Kurt	40-65	
Tompkins, Jane	Black Bear Twins (1st {std}, 8vo, 112p, b/w, DJ/2.25)	Lippincott	(1952)	Wiese, Kurt	25-45	
Harris, Leila	Blackfellow Bundi... (1st, lg8vo, 63p, pep, p-o, color, DJ/1.50)	Whitman	1939	Wiese, Kurt	50-80	
Hutchinson, Ruth	Blue Butterfly Goes to South America (1st, 4to, 111p, ibds, color, DJ/2.00)	Whitman	1940	Wiese, Kurt	30-50	
Holton, Priscilla	Blue Junk (1st {std}, sm8vo, 178p, blue cl, b/w, pep, DJ/1.75)	Longmans	1931	Wiese, Kurt	40-65	
Reely, Mary K.	Blue Mittens (1st, 8vo, 153p, green cl, b/w, pep, DJ/2.00)	Grosset/Dunlap	1935	Wiese, Kurt	35-60	*
Seaman, Augusta	Book of Mysteries (1st {std}, sm8vo, 224p, col frn, b/w)	Doubleday/Doran	1929	Wiese, Kurt	30-50	*
Booth, Esma	Bright Pathways (1st, sm8vo, 125p, b/w, DJ/2.00)	Friendship Pr.	(1955)	Wiese, Kurt	25-40	
Wiese, Kurt	Buddy the Bear (1st, lg8vo, ibds, color, [32]p, pep, DJ/1.50)	Coward	1936	Wiese, Kurt	60-100	
Mukerji, Dhan G.	Bunny, Hound and Clown (1st {std}, 8vo, gilt, 124p, b/w, pep, DJ/2.50)	Dutton	(1931)	Wiese, Kurt	25-45	
Ratzesberger, Anna	Camel Bells (1st, 4to, ipcb, 80p, color, pep, DJ/2.00)	Whitman	1935	Wiese, Kurt	50-85	
Stong, Philip D.	Captain Kidd's Cow (1st, 8vo, 122p, color, DJ/2.50)	Dodd	1941	Wiese, Kurt	40-65	*
Harris, May V.	Carnival Time at Strobeck (1st, lg8vo, p-o, 64p, fp color, pep, DJ/1.50)	Whitman	1938	Wiese, Kurt	45-75	
La Rue, Mabel G.	Cats for the Tooseys (1st, lg4to, 40p, ipcb, b/w, DJ/1.00)	Nelson	1939	Wiese, Kurt	50-80	
Stong, Philip D.	Censored, the Goat (1st, lg8vo, 78p, ibds, color, DJ/2.50)	Dodd	1945	Wiese, Kurt	50-80	*
Lau, Josephine	Cheeky: A Prairie Dog (1st, lg8vo, 62p, p-o, color, pep, DJ/1.50)	Whitman	1937	Wiese, Kurt	40-65	
Washburne, Heluiz	Children of the Blizzard (1st, 8vo, 192p, b/w, DJ/2.50)	John Day	(1952)	Wiese, Kurt	25-40	
Williams, Herschel	Children of the Clouds (1st, 8vo, 224p, col frn, 10 b/w, pep)	NY: Nelson	1929	Wiese, Kurt	40-65	
Henry, Marguerite	Chile in Story and Pictures (1st, ob8vo, [28]p, color, DJ/0.50)	Whitman	1941	Wiese, Kurt	25-45	
Lewis, Eliz. F.	China Quest (1st, 8vo, 301p, gilt, 4cp, pep, DJ/2.00)	Winston	(1937)	Wiese, Kurt	30-50	
Wiese, Kurt	Chinese Ink Stick (1st {std}, 8vo, 199p, 4cp, pep, DJ/2.00)	Doubleday/Doran	1929	Wiese, Kurt	80-125	
Brooks, Walter	Clockwork Twin (1st {std}, 8vo, 241p, 7 fp b/w, pep, DJ/2.00)	Knopf	1937	Wiese, Kurt	250-400	
Brooks, Walter	Collected Poems of Freddy the Pig (1st {std}, 8vo, 81p, b/w, DJ/2.50)	Knopf	(1953)	Wiese, Kurt	180-250	*
Donaldson, Lois	Colombia in Story and Pictures (1st, ob8vo, [28]p, color, pep, DJ/0.75)	Whitman	1944	Wiese, Kurt	30-50	*
Barr, Stringfellow	Copydog in India (1st, lg8vo, 127p, b/w, DJ/2.75)	Viking	1955	Wiese, Kurt	30-50	
Hunt, Mabel L.	Corn-Belt Billy (1st, lg8vo, ibds, [26]p, pep, color, DJ/0.50)	Grosset/Dunlap	(1942)	Wiese, Kurt	45-70	
O'Brien, Jack	Corporal Corey... (1st, 8vo, gilt, 276p, col frn, DJ/2.00)	Winston	(1936)	Wiese, Kurt	40-65	
Stong, Philip D.	Cowhand Goes to Town (1st {std}, sm4to, ibds, 85p, dp color, pep, DJ/2.50)	Dodd	1939	Wiese, Kurt	50-80	
Lowell, Joan	Cradle of the Deep (1st, lg8vo, 261p, pep, b/w)	Simon/Schuster	1929	Wiese, Kurt	40-65	
Bond, Elizabeth	Crunch: The Squirrel (1st, ob4to, ibds, [48]p, 1-color, pep, DJ/1.50)	Dodd	1939	Wiese, Kurt	70-100	*
Wiese, Kurt	Cunning Turtle (1st, ob4to, 32p, fp 1-color, pep, DJ/2.00)	Viking	1956	Wiese, Kurt	40-65	*
Taber, Gladys	Daisy and Dobbin (1st, 8vo, [62]p, 2-color, DJ/2.00)	Macrae Smith	(1948)	Wiese, Kurt	25-45	*
Rankin, Louise S.	Daughter of the Mountains (1st, lg8vo, 191p, fp b/w, pep, DJ/2.50, NH)	Viking	1948	Wiese, Kurt	60-100	R
Lewis, Alice H.	Day after Tomorrow (1st, 8vo, 117p, b/w, cep, DJ/2.50)	Friendship Pr.	(1956)	Wiese, Kurt	25-40	*
DeJong, Meindert	Dirk's Dog Bello (1st {std}, 8vo, 296p, color, pep, DJ/2.00)	Harper	1939	Wiese, Kurt	40-60	
Wiese, Kurt	Dog, the Fox and the Fleas (1st, sm ob4to, [32]p, fp 2-color, DJ/2.25)	McKay	(1953)	Wiese, Kurt	30-50	*
Terhune, Albert P.	Dogs (1st, 4to, ipcb, 60p, col frn, fp b/w)	Saalfield	(1940)	Wiese, Kurt	45-70	
Grey, Zane	Don: Story of Lion Dog (1st {std}, 12mo, 69p, col frn, 4pl, pep)	Harper	1928	Wiese, Kurt	250-400	
Ratzesberger, Anna	Donkey Beads (1st, lg8vo, 62p, p-o, pep, color, DJ/1.50)	Whitman	1938	Wiese, Kurt	80-125	
Kellock, Harold	Down in the Grass (1st, 12mo, 247p, uncut, col frn, 25 fp b/w)	Coward	1929	Wiese, Kurt	70-100	
Smith, Irene	Down the Road with Johnny (1st, 8vo, 64p, fp b/w, pep, DJ/1.75)	Whittlesey	(1951)	Wiese, Kurt	30-50	
Paschang, Adolph	Dragon Treasure (1st {std}, sm8vo, 265p, 5 fp b/w, pep)	Longmans	1932	Wiese, Kurt	30-50	
Glenn, Elsie	Dumblebum (1st, ob8vo, [63]p, fp color, pep, DJ/2.00)	Macrae Smith	(1947)	Wiese, Kurt	50-80	*
Gall, Alice C.	Each in his Way (1st {std}, 8vo, 180p, bds, p-o, 1-color, pep, DJ/2.00)	Oxford U. Pr.	(1937)	Wiese, Kurt	45-70	
Oldrin, John	Eight Rings on his Tail (1st, 4to, 79p, b/w, DJ/2.50)	Viking	1956	Wiese, Kurt	20-35	
Lie, Haakon	Ekorn (1st, sm8vo, 150p, fp color)	Laidlaw	1931	Wiese, Kurt	40-65	*
Wiese, Kurt	Ella the Elephant (1st, lg8vo, p-o, [31]p, 2-color, pep)	Coward	1931	Wiese, Kurt	40-65	
Hayes, Florence	Eskimo Hunter (1st, sm8vo, 275p, col frn, DJ/2.25)	Random	(1945)	Wiese, Kurt	25-45	
MacMillan, Miriam	Etuk: The Eskimo Hunter (1st, 8vo, 177p, b/w, DJ/2.75)	Dodd	(1950)	Wiese, Kurt	50-85	
Jacobs, Joseph (ed)	Fables of Aesop (1st, 8vo, 174p, 2-color, DJ)	Macmillan	(1950)	Wiese, Kurt	50-80	*
Stong, Philip D.	Farm Boy (1st {std}, sm4to, ibds, col frn, 80p, pep)	Doubleday/Doran	1934	Wiese, Kurt	50-80	
Bishop, Claire H.	Ferryman (1st, ob lg8vo, [64]p, ipcb, 1-color, pep, DJ/1.50)	Coward	1941	Wiese, Kurt	40-65	
Smither, Ethel	First to Be Called Christians (1st {A}, 8vo, 80p, fp color, pep, DJ/1.50)	Abingdon Press	(1955)	Wiese, Kurt	30-50	
Wiese, Kurt	Fish in the Air (1st, ob4to, ipcb, [32]p, color, pep, DJ/2.00, CH)	Viking	1948	Wiese, Kurt	90-150	R*
Bishop, Claire H.	Five Chinese Brothers (1st, lg ob8vo, ipcb, [52]p, 1-color, pep, DJ/1.50)	Coward	(1938)	Wiese, Kurt	70-100	
MacKay, Margaret	Flowered Donkey (1st, 8vo, 91p, b/w, DJ/2.25)	John Day	(1950)	Wiese, Kurt	25-45	
Gallant, Kathryn	Flute Player of Beppu (1st, sq8vo, 43p, fp color, DJ/2.75)	Coward	1960	Wiese, Kurt	30-50	
Hoffmann, Eleanor	Four Friends (1st {std}, 8vo, 105p, fp b/w, DJ/2.00)	Macmillan	1946	Wiese, Kurt	30-45	*
Brooks, Walter	Freddy and Mr. Camphor (1st {std}, 8vo, 244p, b/w, pep, DJ/2.50)	Knopf	1944	Wiese, Kurt	200-300	
Brooks, Walter	Freddy and Simon the Dictator (1st {std}, 8vo, 244p, b/w, DJ/3.00)	Knopf	1956	Wiese, Kurt	160-225	
Brooks, Walter	Freddy and the Baseball Team from Mars (1st {std}, 8vo 241p, b/w, DJ/3.00)	Knopf	1955	Wiese, Kurt	150-200	
Brooks, Walter	Freddy and the Bean Home News (1st {std}, sm8vo, 230p, fp b/w, DJ/2.50)	Knopf	1943	Wiese, Kurt	200-300	
Brooks, Walter	Freddy and the Flying Saucer Plans (1st {std}, 8vo, 243p, b/w, DJ/3.00)	Knopf	1957	Wiese, Kurt	200-300	
Brooks, Walter	Freddy and the Ignoramus (1st {std}, sm8vo, 286p, b/w, DJ/2.00)	Knopf	1941	Wiese, Kurt	250-350	
Brooks, Walter	Freddy and the Men from Mars (1st {std}, 8vo, 246p, pep, b/w, DJ/3.00)	Knopf	1954	Wiese, Kurt	200-300	
Brooks, Walter	Freddy and the Perilous Adventure (1st {std}, 8vo, 245p, b/w, DJ/2.00)	Knopf	1942	Wiese, Kurt	200-300	
Brooks, Walter	Freddy and the Popinjay (1st {std}, sm8vo, 244p, red cl, b/w, DJ/2.50)	Knopf	1945	Wiese, Kurt	200-300	
Brooks, Walter	Freddy and the Spaceship (1st {std}, sm8vo, 262p, b/w, pep, DJ/3.00)	Knopf	1953	Wiese, Kurt	200-300	
Brooks, Walter	Freddy Goes Camping (1st {std}, 8vo, 258p, b/w, DJ/2.50)	Knopf	1948	Wiese, Kurt	200-300	
Brooks, Walter	Freddy Goes to Florida (1st, 8vo, 196p, b/w, DJ/2.50)	Knopf	1949	Wiese, Kurt	200-300	
Brooks, Walter	Freddy Goes to the North Pole (1st {std}, 8vo, 306p, b/w, DJ/2.50)	Knopf	1951	Wiese, Kurt	200-300	
Brooks, Walter	Freddy Plays Football (1st {std}, 8vo, 265p, grey cl, b/w, DJ/2.50)	Knopf	1949	Wiese, Kurt	200-300	
Brooks, Walter	Freddy Rides Again (1st {std}, 8vo, 240p, b/w, DJ/2.50)	Knopf	1951	Wiese, Kurt	200-300	
Brooks, Walter	Freddy the Cowboy (1st {std}, sm8vo, 233p, red cl, b/w, DJ/2.50)	Knopf	1950	Wiese, Kurt	200-300	
Brooks, Walter	Freddy the Detective (1st {std}, 8vo, 264p, b/w, pep)	Knopf	1932	Wiese, Kurt	150-220	
Brooks, Walter	Freddy the Magician (1st {std}, 8vo, red cl, 258p, b/w, DJ/2.50)	Knopf	1947	Wiese, Kurt	200-300	
Brooks, Walter	Freddy the Pied Piper (1st {std}, 8vo, 253p, b/w, DJ/2.50)	Knopf	1946	Wiese, Kurt	200-300	

AUTHOR	TITLE	PUBLISHER	DATE	ARTIST	PRICE	LC
Brooks, Walter	Freddy the Pilot (1st {std}, sm8vo, 247p, b/w, pep, DJ/3.00)	Knopf	1952	Wiese, Kurt	200-300	
Brooks, Walter	Freddy the Politician (1st, 8vo, 252p, red cl, fp b/w, pep, DJ/2.50)	Knopf	1948	Wiese, Kurt	200-300	
Brooks, Walter	Freddy's Cousin Weedly (1st {std}, sm8vo, 283p, b/w, pep, DJ/2.00)	Knopf	1940	Wiese, Kurt	200-300	
Pease, Eleanor F.	Gay Pippo (1st, sm4to, p-o, 80p, color, pep)	Whitman	1936	Wiese, Kurt	50-80	
Hamilton, Elizabeth	Go West, Young Bear (1st, lg8vo, 94p, fp b/w, pep, DJ/2.50)	Coward	(1948)	Wiese, Kurt	40-65	*
Pauli, Hertha	Golden Door (1st {std}, 8vo, 155p, b/w, pep, DJ/2.50)	Knopf	1949	Wiese, Kurt	60-80	
Morley, Christopher	Goldfish Under the Ice (1st {std}, sm8vo, 69p, 14 b/w, cep, DJ/1.00)	Doubleday/Doran	1932	Wiese, Kurt	50-85	
Osborne, Nancy C.	Good Wind & Good Water (1st, 8vo, 248p, red cl, b/w, pep, DJ/2.00)	Viking	1934	Wiese, Kurt	25-45	
North, Sterling	Greased Lightning (1st, sm4to, [93]p, dp color, pep, DJ/2.00)	Winston	(1940)	Wiese, Kurt	60-90	
Johnston, Johanna	Great Gravity the Cat (1st {std}, 8vo, 66p, b/w, DJ/2.50)	Knopf	1958	Wiese, Kurt	30-50	
Wiese, Kurt	Groundhog and his Shadow (1st, ob4to, 32p, color, pep, DJ/2.25)	Viking	(1959)	Wiese, Kurt	30-50	
Weber, Lenora M.	Gypsy Bridle (1st, 8vo, 275p, col frn, fp b/w, pep)	Little/Brown	1930	Wiese, Kurt	250-400	
Black, Irma S.	Hamlet: A Cocker Spaniel (1st, 12mo, [72]p, red cl, fp b/w, DJ/1.50)	Holiday House	(1938)	Wiese, Kurt	30-50	*
Wiese, Kurt	Happy Easter (1st, ob8vo, ibds, 32p, color, DJ/1.50)	Viking	1952	Wiese, Kurt	40-70	
Litchfield, Sarah	Hello, Alaska! (1st, narrow 8vo, p-o, 31p, color, pep, DJ/1.25)	Whitman	1945	Wiese, Kurt	30-45	
Malone, Mary	Here's Howie (1st, 8vo, 173p, uncut, b/w, DJ/3.00)	Dodd	1962	Wiese, Kurt	25-40	
Benet, Laura	Hidden Valley (1st, 8vo, 207p, b/w, pep, DJ/2.00)	Dodd	1938	Wiese, Kurt	25-45	*
Stong, Philip D.	High Water (1st {std}, sm4to, ibds, 79p, color, pep, DJ/2.00)	Dodd	1937	Wiese, Kurt	50-80	
Stong, Philip D.	Hirum, the Hillbilly (1st, 8vo, 104p, b/w, DJ/2.75)	Dodd	1951	Wiese, Kurt	25-45	
Harper, Theodore A.	His Excellency & Peter (1st {std}, 8vo, 313p, col frn, pep uncut)	Doubleday/Doran	1930	Wiese, Kurt	40-60	
Lewis, Eliz. F.	Ho-Ming, Girl of New China (1st, 8vo, 266p, gilt, pep, 4cp)	Winston	1934	Wiese, Kurt	30-50	
Stong, Philip D.	Honk! the Moose (1st {std}, sm4to, ibds, 80p, color, pep, DJ/2.00, NH)	Dodd	1935	Wiese, Kurt	90-140	R
Mason, Miriam E.	Hoppity (1st {std}, 8vo, 76p, fp 1-color, cep, DJ/1.50)	Macmillan	1947	Wiese, Kurt	30-45	
Stong, Philip D.	Horses and Americans (1st, 4to, 333p, col frn, DJ/5.00)	Stokes	1939	Wiese, Kurt	30-55	
Salten, Felix	Hound of Florence (1st, 8vo, 236p, gilt, b/w)	Simon/Schuster	1930	Wiese, Kurt	30-50	
Adelson, Leone	House with Red Sails (1st, 8vo, 185p, fp b/w, DJ/2.50)	McKay	(1951)	Wiese, Kurt	20-30	
Bailey, Bernadine	Iceland in Story and Pictures (1st, ob8vo, [28]p, color, pep, DJ/0.50)	Whitman	1942	Wiese, Kurt	45-70	
Waldeck, Theodore	Jamba the Elephant (1st, 8vo, 224p, b/w, DJ/2.00)	Viking	1942	Wiese, Kurt	25-45	
Ratzesberger, Anna	Jasmine: A Story of Present Day Persia (1st, 8vo, 286p, 6cp, pep, DJ/2.00)	Whitman	1937	Wiese, Kurt	30-50	
Kahmann, Chesley	Jasper the Gypsy Dog (1st, 8vo, yellow cl, 93p, b/w, pep, DJ/1.50)	J. Messner	(1938)	Wiese, Kurt	30-50	
DeLeeuw, Hendrik	Java Jungle Tales (1st {std}, 8vo, 311p, col frn, pep)	Doubleday/Doran	1933	Wiese, Kurt	35-60	*
Medary, Marjorie	Joan & the Three Deer (1st {std}, 8vo, 160p, b/w, DJ/2.00)	Random	(1939)	Wiese, Kurt	30-50	
Wiese, Kurt	Joe Buys Nails (1st {std}, lg ob8vo, ibds, [54]p, color, pep)	Doubleday/Doran	1931	Wiese, Kurt	60-90	
Williams, Herschel	Jolly Old Whistle (1st, 8vo, 187p, purple cl, col frn, fp b/w, pep)	Nelson	1927	Wiese, Kurt	40-65	
Wyckoff, Charlotte C.	Jothy: Story of South Indian Jungle (1st {std}, 8vo, 305p, b/w, pep)	Longmans	1933	Wiese, Kurt	30-50	*
Lathrop, West	Juneau: Sleigh Dog (1st {std}, 8vo, 279p, blue/silver, b/w, DJ/2.00)	Random	(1942)	Wiese, Kurt	25-40	
Kipling, Rudyard	Jungle Book (1st, 8vo, green/gilt, 303p, uncut, col frn, 18pl)	Doubleday/Doran	1932	Wiese, Kurt	45-70	*
Waldeck, JoBesse	Jungle Journey (1st, 8vo, 255p, b/w, pep, DJ/2.50)	Viking	1946	Wiese, Kurt	30-45	
Roberts, Irma	Jungle Twins (1st {std}, 8vo, 127p, ibds, fp 1-color, DJ/2.25)	Coward	(1951)	Wiese, Kurt	25-45	
Wiese, Kurt	Karoo the Kangaroo (1st {1st bk.}, sm4to, [35]p, color, pep)	Coward	1929	Wiese, Kurt	55-80	
Hollister, Mary	Kee-Kee and Company (1st, 8vo, 192p, 5pl, pep, DJ/2.00)	Dodd	1938	Wiese, Kurt	40-60	
Craine, Edith	Ki-Ki: Circus Trouper (1st, lg8vo, 64p, p-o, color, pep, DJ/1.50)	Whitman	1937	Wiese, Kurt	40-65	
Haig-Brown, R.L.	Ki-Yu: Story of Panthers (1st, 8vo, 213p, b/w, cep, DJ/2.50)	Houghton	1934	Wiese, Kurt	80-130	
Norris, Faith	Kim of Korea (1st, 8vo, 157p, b/w, DJ/2.75)	J. Messner	(1955)	Wiese, Kurt	25-40	
O'Brien, Jack	King and the Princess (1st, sm ob4to, ibds, [24]p, color, pep, DJ/0.50)	Grosset/Dunlap	1940	Wiese, Kurt	30-50	
Black, Irma S.	Kip: Young Rooster (1st, 12mo, [68]p, purple cl, b/w, DJ/1.50)	Holiday House	(1939)	Wiese, Kurt	25-45	
Wiese, Kurt	Kurt Wiese's Picture Book of Animals (1st, lg8vo, [99]p, color, pep)	Coward	(1937)	Wiese, Kurt	50-70	
Smith, Helen	Laughing Matter (1st, 8vo, 166p, b/w, DJ/2.50)	Scribner	1949	Wiese, Kurt	20-35	
Clapp, Estelle	Laurie (1st {std}, 8vo, 255p, b/w, DJ/2.50)	Doubleday	1953	Wiese, Kurt	30-45	*
Treffinger, Carolyn	Li Lun: Lad of Courage (1st {A}, 8vo, 93p, 1-color, pep, DJ/2.50, NH)	Abingdon-Cokes.	(1947)	Wiese, Kurt	50-85	
Wiese, Kurt	Liang & Lo (1st {std}, sm ob4to, ibds, [56]p, color, pep)	Doubleday/Doran	1930	Wiese, Kurt	45-70	
Matzdorff, Hyde	Limpy: Tale of a Monkey Hero (1st, 8vo, 87p, fp b/w, DJ/2.50)	John Day	(1957)	Wiese, Kurt	30-45	
Eldridge, Ethel	Ling, Grandson of Yen-Foh (1st, lg8vo, 29p, color, pep, DJ/1.00)	Whitman	1936	Wiese, Kurt	40-70	
Voight, Virginia F.	Lions in the Barn (1st, sm8vo, 95p, yellow cl, b/w, pep, DJ/2.25)	Holiday House	1955	Wiese, Kurt	25-45	
Waldeck, Theodore	Lions on the Hunt (1st, 8vo, 251p, b/w, DJ/2.00)	Viking	1942	Wiese, Kurt	30-45	*
Wiese, Kurt	Little Boy Lost in Brazil (1st, ob8vo, [56]p, fp color, pep, DJ/2.00)	Dodd	1942	Wiese, Kurt	40-65	
Barr, Jene	Little Circus Dog (1st, 8vo, [32]p, p-o, color, pep)	Whitman	1949	Wiese, Kurt	30-50	
Jacobs-Bond, Carrie	Little Monkey with the Sad Face (1st, 8vo, 48p, 8cp, cep, DJ/1.50)	John Day	(1930)	Wiese, Kurt	30-50	
Kunhardt, Dorothy	Little Ones (1st, sm4to, red cl, 78p, color, pep, DJ/2.00)	Viking	1935	Wiese, Kurt	60-90	
Barr, Jene	Little Prairie Dog (1st, 8vo, [32]p, p-o, color, pep)	Whitman	1949	Wiese, Kurt	30-50	
Peary, Marie A.	Little Tooktoo (1st, 8vo, ibds, 62p, pep, 5cp)	Wm. Morrow	(1930)	Wiese, Kurt	50-80	*
Hilton, James	Lost Horizon (1st, sm8vo, 277p, b/w, DJ/1.25)	World	(1948)	Wiese, Kurt	25-40	
Smith, Irene	Lucky Days for Johnny (1st, 8vo, 64p, fp b/w, pep, DJ/1.75)	Whittlesey	(1950)	Wiese, Kurt	30-50	
Spencer, Cornelia	Made in China (1st {std}, 8vo, 258p, 8cp, DJ/3.50)	Knopf	1943	Wiese, Kurt	30-50	*
Dawson, Micthell	Magic Firecrackers (1st, 8vo, 192p, b/w, DJ/2.50)	Viking	1949	Wiese, Kurt	50-80	*
McKown, Wendell	Me an' Pete (1st {std}, sm8vo, 88p, b/w pl)	Doubleday/Doran	1934	Wiese, Kurt	25-40	
North, Sterling	Midnight & Jeremiah (1st {std}, 8vo, 125p, tan cl, color, pep, DJ/2.00)	Winston	(1943)	Wiese, Kurt	30-50	
Stong, Philip D.	Mike: Story of a Young Circus Acrobat (1st, 8vo, 126p, b/w, DJ/3.00)	Dodd	1957	Wiese, Kurt	30-50	
Stong, Philip D.	Missouri Canary (1st, lg8vo, 77p, ibds, color, DJ/2.50)	Dodd	1943	Wiese, Kurt	40-65	
Tompkins, Jane	Moo-Wee: The Musk-Ox (1st, 8vo, blue cl, 103p, 11 fp b/w, pep, DJ/1.50)	Stokes	1938	Wiese, Kurt	80-125	
Brooks, Walter	More To and Again (1st, 8vo, 306p, col frn, 8 fp b/w, DJ/2.00)	Knopf	1930	Wiese, Kurt	250-350	
Pauli, Hertha	Most Beautiful House... (1st {std}, 8vo, 114p, color, DJ/2.50)	Knopf	1949	Wiese, Kurt	30-50	
Clymer, Eleanor	Mr. Piper's Bus (1st, 8vo, 92p, b/w, DJ/3.00)	Dodd	1961	Wiese, Kurt	20-30	
Robinson, Tom P.	Mr. Red Squirrel (1st, sm4to, ibds, [32]p, color, pep, DJ/1.50)	Viking	1943	Wiese, Kurt	30-50	
MacDonald, Betty	Mrs. Piggle-Wiggle's Magic (1st {std}, 8vo, 126p, col frn, b/w, DJ/2.00)	Lippincott	(1949)	Wiese, Kurt	100-165	
Bird, Zenobia	Muffy: Tale of a Muskrat (1st, 8vo, 46p, p-o, color, pep, DJ/1.25)	Whitman	1941	Wiese, Kurt	45-70	
Hollister, Mary	Mulberry Village (1st, 8vo, 287p, b/w, pep, DJ/1.75)	Dodd	1936	Wiese, Kurt	30-50	
Stafford, Marie A.	Muskox: Little Tootoo's Friend (1st, 8vo, 64p, color, pep)	Wm. Morrow	(1931)	Wiese, Kurt	55-80	*

AUTHOR	TITLE	PUBLISHER	DATE	ARTIST	PRICE	LC
Graham, Stephen	New York Nights (1st, 8vo, 288p, bds, 14 b/w)	Doran	(1927)	Wiese, Kurt	40-60	*
Meyer, Ann	Nibby (1st, ob4to, 31p, p-o, 1-color, pep, DJ/2.25)	Coward	(1952)	Wiese, Kurt	50-80	*
Lang, Don	Nibs: Orphan Deer of the Adirondacks (1st, 8vo, 66p, b/w, DJ/0.50)	Grosset/Dunlap	(1942)	Wiese, Kurt	30-45	*
Hawkes, Hester	Ning's Pony (1st, 8vo, [29]p, 1-color, DJ/2.00)	Coward	(1953)	Wiese, Kurt	30-50	
Stong, Philip D.	No-Sitch: the Hound (1st {std}, sm4to, 80p, col frn, pep, DJ/2.00)	Dodd	1936	Wiese, Kurt	60-80	
King, Julius	Odie Seeks a Friend (1st, ob8vo, [32]p, b/w, pep)	Coward	(1934)	Wiese, Kurt	40-70	
Waldeck, Theodore	On Safari (1st, 8vo, 208p, b/w, DJ/2.50)	Viking	1940	Wiese, Kurt	30-45	
Stafford, Marie A.	Ootah and his Puppy (1st, 8vo, 64p, 2-color, pep)	D.C. Heath	1942	Wiese, Kurt	25-40	
Glick, Carl	Oswald's Pet Dragon (1st, 4to, [32]p, ibds, color, DJ/1.75)	Coward	(1943)	Wiese, Kurt	45-70	
Tompkins, Jane	Otter Twins (1st {std}, 8vo, 120p, b/w, DJ/2.50)	Lippincott	(1955)	Wiese, Kurt	25-40	
Monsell, Helen	Paddy's Christmas (1st, ob8vo, [48]p, ibds, fp 2-color, DJ/1.00)	Knopf	1942	Wiese, Kurt	40-70	
Jenkins, Alexandra	Pal: Story of an Airedale (1st, sm8vo, 95p, fp b/w, pep)	Appleton	1930	Wiese, Kurt	30-45	
Baker, Olaf	Panther Magic (1st, 8vo, gilt, 312p, 8cp, pep)	Dodd	1928	Wiese, Kurt	30-50	
Wiese, Kurt	Parrot Dealer (1st {std}, 8vo, 239p, b/w, pep)	Coward	(1932)	Wiese, Kurt	35-60	*
Peck, Leigh	Pecos Bill & Lightning (1st, 8vo, 68p, color, cep, DJ/1.75)	Houghton	1940	Wiese, Kurt	50-80	
Jones, Inis	Peetie: Story of a Real Cat (1st {std}, 8vo, 90p, b/w, DJ/1.50)	McBride	(1935)	Wiese, Kurt	40-70	
Tompkins, Jane	Penguin Twins (1st, 8vo, 116p, b/w, pep, DJ/2.00)	Stokes	1939	Wiese, Kurt	25-40	
Stong, Philip D.	Phil Stong's Big Book (1st, 8vo, 159p, 2-color, DJ/3.50)	Dodd	(1961)	Wiese, Kurt	25-45	*
Hahn, Emily	Picture Story of China (1st, 4to, [52]p, color, pep, DJ/2.50)	Reynal/Hitchcock	(1946)	Wiese, Kurt	50-80	
Meeker, Col. S.P.	Pierre of the Big Top (1st, 8vo, 208p, DJ/3.00)	Dodd	1956	Wiese, Kurt	40-65	
Collodi, Carlo	Pinocchio (1st, 8vo, red/gilt, 239p, 6cp, pep)	T. Nelson	1928	Wiese, Kurt	70-100	
MacKay, Margaret	Poetic Parrot (1st, 8vo, 96p, b/w, DJ/2.50)	John Day	(1951)	Wiese, Kurt	20-35	
Tompkins, Jane	Polar Bear Twins (1st, 8vo, 106p, b/w, DJ/1.50)	Stokes	1937	Wiese, Kurt	30-50	
Mackall, Lawton	Poodle-Oodle on Doodle Farm (1st, ob12mo, p-o, 137p, color, pep)	Stokes	1929	Wiese, Kurt	60-90	R
Stong, Philip D.	Positive Pete (1st, sm4to, ibds, 64p, color, pep, DJ/2.75)	Dodd	1947	Wiese, Kurt	40-60	
Stong, Philip D.	Prince and the Porker (1st, lg8vo, 67p, ibds, color, DJ/2.75)	Dodd	1950	Wiese, Kurt	35-50	
Hawkins, Quail	Puppy for Keeps (1st, 8vo, [28]p, b/w, pep, DJ/1.00)	Holiday House	(1943)	Wiese, Kurt	25-40	
Andrews, Roy	Quest in the Desert (1st, 8vo, 192p, b/w, DJ/2.50)	Viking	1950	Wiese, Kurt	60-90	*
Andrews, Roy	Quest of the Snow Leopard (1st, 8vo, 190p, b/w, DJ/2.75)	Viking	1955	Wiese, Kurt	50-80	*
Wiese, Kurt	Rabbit Bros. Circus: One Night Only (1st ob4to, 38p, fp 3-color, DJ/3.00)	Viking	1963	Wiese, Kurt	50-80	
Wiese, Kurt	Rabbit's Revenge (1st, lg ob8vo, ibds, [48]p, fp 1-color, pep, DJ/1.50)	Coward	(1940)	Wiese, Kurt	50-80	
Tompkins, Jane	Raccoon Twins (1st, 8vo, 126p, orange cl, b/w, pep, DJ/1.60)	Stokes	1942	Wiese, Kurt	30-50	
Strong, Charles	Ranger's Arctic Patrol (1st {std}, 8vo, 214p, b/w, DJ/2.50)	Winston	(1952)	Wiese, Kurt	25-40	*
Kent, Louise A.	Red Rajah (1st, sm8vo, 290p, blue cl, 6 fp b/w, pep)	Houghton	1933	Wiese, Kurt	30-50	*
Tompkins, Jane	Red Squirrel Twins (1st {std}, 8vo, tan cl, 123p, b/w, DJ/2.25)	Stokes	(1950)	Wiese, Kurt	50-80	
Tompkins, Jane	Reindeer Twins (1st {std}, 8vo, 125p, b/w, DJ/2.65)	Lippincott	(1956)	Wiese, Kurt	25-45	
O'Brien, Jack	Return of Silver Chief (1st {std}, 8vo, 211p, col frn, b/w, pep, DJ/2.00)	Winston	(1943)	Wiese, Kurt	30-45	
Beecroft, John	Rocco Came In (1st, sm4to, red cl, [30]p, fp color, DJ/3.00)	Dodd	1959	Wiese, Kurt	30-50	
Jackson, Charlotte	Roger and the Fishes (1st, 4to, 76p, ibds, color, DJ/2.00)	Dodd	1943	Wiese, Kurt	40-65	
Voight, Virginia F.	Rolling Show (1st, 8vo, 188p, red cl, b/w, cep, DJ/2.50)	Holiday House	1956	Wiese, Kurt	30-50	
Conger, Marion	Rosie the Rhino (1st, 8vo, [32]p, ibds, 1-color, DJ/1.00)	Abingdon Press	(1948)	Wiese, Kurt	30-50	
Oldrin, John	Round Meadow (1st, 4to, 80p, fp 1-color, DJ/2.50)	Viking	1951	Wiese, Kurt	20-35	
Hubbard, Freeman	Roundhouse Cat and other Railroad Animals (1st, 8vo, 124p, b/w, DJ/2.00)	Whittlesey	(1951)	Wiese, Kurt	30-50	
Connor, J. Hall	Sandy, Tin Soldier of the A.E.F. (1st, 8vo, 114p, color)	Laidlaw	1931	Wiese, Kurt	30-50	
Gatti, Attilio	Saranga the Pygmy (1st, 8vo, 226p, color, pep, DJ/2.00)	Scribner	1939	Wiese, Kurt	40-65	
Gilfillan, Archer B.	Sheep (1st, 8vo, 272p, green cl, b/w)	Little/Brown	1929	Wiese, Kurt	40-70	
Wood, Esther	Silk and Satin Lane (1st {std}, sm8vo, 255p, b/w, DJ/1.75)	Longmans	1939	Wiese, Kurt	25-40	
O'Brien, Jack	Silver Chief (1st, 8vo, blue/silver, 218p, col frn, 14pl, pep)	Winston	(1933)	Wiese, Kurt	40-65	
O'Brien, Jack	Silver Chief to the Rescue (1st, 8vo, 235p, fp color, pep, DJ/2.00)	Winston	(1937)	Wiese, Kurt	45-70	
Tooze, Ruth	Silver from the Sea (1st, 8vo, 40p, fp 3-color, pep, DJ/2.75)	Viking	(1962)	Wiese, Kurt	30-50	
Shaffer, Robert	Skeeter: Story of an Arabian Gazelle (1st, 8vo, 192p, b/w, DJ/2.75)	Dodd	(1952)	Wiese, Kurt	30-50	*
Pollock, Katherine	Sly Mongoose (1st, 8vo, 78p, b/w, pep, DJ/1.75)	Scribner	1943	Wiese, Kurt	30-45	
Bowen, Vernon	Snow for Christmas (1st, 8vo, [32]p, 2-color, DJ/2.50)	McKay	1953	Wiese, Kurt	30-50	*
Tompkins, Jane	Snowshoe Twins (1st, 8vo, 118p, b/w, DJ/2.00)	Stokes	(1941)	Wiese, Kurt	30-45	*
Russell, Arthur	Snowy for Luck (1st, 8vo, p-o, 128p, col frn, pep)	Whitman	1934	Wiese, Kurt	30-50	
Smither, Ethel	Stories of Jesus (1st, 24mo, 80p, fp color, pep, DJ/1.50)	Abingdon Press	(1954)	Wiese, Kurt	30-50	
Flack, Marjorie	Story about Ping (1st, lg8vo, ipcb, [32]p, color)	Viking	1933	Wiese, Kurt	170-225	R
Brooks, Walter	Story of Freginald (1st {std}, lg8vo, 249p, pep, 10 fp b/w, DJ/2.00)	Knopf	1936	Wiese, Kurt	400-600	
Brown, Margaret W.	Streamlined Pig (1st {std}, ob4to, [32]p, color, pep, DJ/1.75)	Harper	1938	Wiese, Kurt	100-165	
Bro, Marguerite	Su-Mei's Golden Year (1st {std}, 8vo, 246p, beige cl, b/w, DJ/2.50)	Doubleday	1950	Wiese, Kurt	30-50	
Tschiffely, Aime	Tale of Two Horses (1st AM, 8vo, 220p, pep, b/w, DJ/2.00)	Simon/Schuster	1935	Wiese, Kurt	30-50	
Nathan, Robert	Tapiola's Brave Regiment (1st {std}, 8vo, 137p, b/w, pep, DJ/1.75)	Knopf	1941	Wiese, Kurt	25-40	
Lips, Julius	Tents in the Wilderness (1st, 8vo, 297p, b/w, pep, DJ/2.25)	Stokes	1942	Wiese, Kurt	25-45	
Kuh, Charlotte	The Deliveryman (1st, 16mo, [42]p, color)	Macmillan	1929	Wiese, Kurt	40-65	
Kuh, Charlotte	The Engineer (1st, 16mo, [42]p, ibds, color)	Macmillan	1929	Wiese, Kurt	40-65	
Kuh, Charlotte	The Fireman (1st, 16mo, [42]p, ibds, color)	Macmillan	1929	Wiese, Kurt	40-65	
Kuh, Charlotte	The Motorman (1st, 16mo, [42]p, ibds, color)	Macmillan	1929	Wiese, Kurt	40-65	
Kuh, Charlotte	The Policeman (1st, 16mo, [42]p, ibds, color)	Macmillan	1929	Wiese, Kurt	45-60	
Wiese, Kurt	Thief in the Attic (1st, 8vo, 43p, blue cl, color, DJ/3.00)	Viking	(1965)	Wiese, Kurt	25-40	
Cothren, Marion	This is the Moon (1st, lg8vo, 87p, fp b/w, DJ/2.00)	Coward	(1946)	Wiese, Kurt	30-45	*
N/A	Three Little Kittens (1st, 16mo, [42]p, ibds, color)	Macmillan	1928	Wiese, Kurt	40-60	
Hawkes, Hester	Three Seeds (1st, 8vo, [41]p, fp 1-color, pep, DJ/2.25)	Coward	(1956)	Wiese, Kurt	30-50	*
Spencer, Cornelia	Three Sisters (1st, 8vo, blue/silver, 279p, b/w, DJ/2.00)	John Day	(1939)	Wiese, Kurt	40-65	*
Jackson, Charlotte	Tito: Pig of Guatemala (1st, 4to, 73p, ibds, color, pep, DJ/2.00)	Dodd	1940	Wiese, Kurt	45-75	
Black, Irma S.	Toby: A Curious Cat (1st, sm8vo, rust cl, [63]p, b/w, cep, DJ/1.50)	Holiday House	1948	Wiese, Kurt	30-50	
Bridges, William	Toco Toucan (1st {std}, 8vo, [32]p, color, DJ/1.00)	Harper	(1940)	Wiese, Kurt	30-50	
Clymer, Eleanor	Tommy's Wonderful Airplane (1st, 8vo, 212p, b/w, DJ/2.75)	Dodd	(1951)	Wiese, Kurt	25-40	*
Hawkins, Quail	Too Many Dogs (1st, 8vo, [57]p, olive cl, fp b/w, pep, DJ/1.50)	Holiday House	(1946)	Wiese, Kurt	25-40	

AUTHOR	TITLE	PUBLISHER	DATE	ARTIST	PRICE	LC
La Rue, Mabel G.	Tooseys (1st, 8vo, yellow cl, 127p, fp b/w, DJ/1.50)	Nelson	1938	Wiese, Kurt	30-50	*
Hubbard, Freeman	Train that Never Came Back (1st, 8vo, 127p, b/w, DJ/2.25)	Whittlesey	(1952)	Wiese, Kurt	30-45	
Lang, Don	Tramp: The Sheep Dog (1st, sq8vo, [28]p, ibds, color, pep, DJ/0.50)	Grosset/Dunlap	(1938)	Wiese, Kurt	45-60	
Bishop, Claire H.	Twenty-Two Bears (1st, ob4to, 31p, 1-color, pep, DJ/2.50)	Viking	(1964)	Wiese, Kurt	30-45	
O'Brien, Jack	Valiant, Dog of the Timberline (1st, 8vo, 218p, col frn, 5cp, pep, DJ/2.00)	Winston	(1935)	Wiese, Kurt	40-65	
Davis, Lavinia R.	Very Special Pet (1st, 8vo, ibds, [28]p, color, pep, DJ/0.50)	Grosset/Dunlap	1944	Wiese, Kurt	30-50	
Gall, Alice C.	Wagtail (1st, 8vo, 131p, 1-color, pep)	Oxford U. Pr.	1932	Wiese, Kurt	40-65	
Hall, William N.	Walking Hat (1st {std}, 4to, ibds, [32]p, color, DJ/1.50)	Knopf	(1950)	Wiese, Kurt	50-80	
Wiese, Kurt	Wallie the Walrus (1st, lg8vo, [31]p, p-o, 3-color)	Coward	1930	Wiese, Kurt	40-65	
Stong, Philip D.	Way Down Cellar (1st, 8vo, 159p, color, pep, DJ/2.50)	Dodd	1942	Wiese, Kurt	150-220	
Denison, Carol	What Every Young Rabbit Should Know (1st, ob4to, [64]p, 1-color, DJ/2.25)	Dodd	1948	Wiese, Kurt	50-85	
Beecroft, John	What? Another Cat! (1st, 4to, [30]p, color, DJ/3.00)	Dodd	(1960)	Wiese, Kurt	30-50	
Lewis, Eliz. F.	When the Typhoon Blows (1st, 8vo, 273p, orange cl, col frn, pep, DJ/2.00)	Winston	(1942)	Wiese, Kurt	30-50	
Denison, Carol	Where Any Young Cat Might Be (1st, ob4to, [54]p, fp b/w, pep, DJ/2.50)	Dodd	1956	Wiese, Kurt	60-85	
Fletcher, Inglis	White Leopard: Tale of the African Bush (1st {std}, 8vo, 304p, b/w)	Bobbs-Merrill	(1931)	Wiese, Kurt	30-50	
Waldeck, Theodore	White Panther (1st, 8vo, 193p, b/w, pep, DJ/2.00)	Viking	1941	Wiese, Kurt	80-125	
Isasi, Miriam	White Stars of Freedom (1st, 8vo, 308p, col frn, DJ/2.50)	Whitman	1942	Wiese, Kurt	30-50	
Brooks, Walter	Wiggins for President (1st {std}, 8vo, 252p, yellow cl, fp b/w, DJ/2.00)	Knopf	1939	Wiese, Kurt	200-300	
Millen, Muriel	Wild West Bill Rides Home (1st, 8vo, 32p, p-o, fp color, pep, DJ/1.00)	Whitman	1946	Wiese, Kurt	30-50	
Weber, Lenora M.	Wind on the Prairie (1st, 8vo, 276p, pep, col frn, b/w)	Little/Brown	1929	Wiese, Kurt	100-160	
Lin, Yutang	With Love and Irony (1st, 8vo, 291p, b/w, DJ/2.75)	John Day	(1940)	Wiese, Kurt	40-65	
Grey, Zane	Wolf-Tracker (1st, 12mo, orange cl, 98p, col frn, b/w, pep)	Harper	1930	Wiese, Kurt	150-220	
Bowen, Vernon	Wonderful Adventures of Ting Ling (1st, 8vo, [40]p, b/w, pep, DJ/2.00)	McKay	1952	Wiese, Kurt	25-40	*
Clark, Ann N.	World Song (1st, 8vo, 140p, b/w, DJ/2.75)	Viking	(1960)	Wiese, Kurt	20-35	
Eldridge, Ethel	Yen-Foh, a Chinese Boy (1st, lg8vo, gilt, 29p, p-o, color, pep, DJ/1.00)	Whitman	1935	Wiese, Kurt	45-70	
Lide, Alice A.	Yinka-Tu the Yak (1st, 4to, ibds, 63p, color, pep, DJ/2.00)	Viking	1938	Wiese, Kurt	60-90	
Wiese, Kurt	You Can Write Chinese (1st, ob4to, ibds, [64]p, color, DJ/2.00, CH)	Viking	1945	Wiese, Kurt	120-180	
Lewis, Eliz. F.	Young Fu of the Upper Yangtze (1st, 8vo, 265p, black cl, 4cp, pep, NM)	Winston	1932	Wiese, Kurt	60-100	R
Stong, Philip D.	Young Settler (1st {std}, sm4to, ibds, 80p, 20 fp color, pep, DJ/2.50)	Dodd	1938	Wiese, Kurt	60-90	
McGinley, Phyllis	Blunderbus (1st {std}, sm4to, 47p, yellow cl, 1-color, DJ/2.00)	Lippincott	(1951)	Wiesner, William	35-60	*
Wiesner, William	Grabbit, the Rascal (1st, lg8vo, 46p, 3-color, DJ/3.75)	Viking	(1969)	Wiesner, William	25-40	
Wiesner, William	Green Noses (1st, sm ob4to, [37]p, fp color, pep, DJ/3.95)	Four Winds Pr.	(1969)	Wiesner, William	40-65	
Wiesner, William	Happy-Go-Lucky (1st, ob4to, [28]p, color, DJ/4.50)	Seabury Press	(1970)	Wiesner, William	30-45	*
Potter, Charles F.	More Tongue Tanglers & a Rigamarole (1st {std}, 12mo, 42p, color, DJ/2.95)	World	(1964)	Wiesner, William	50-80	R
Leach, Maria	Riddle Me, Riddle Me, Ree (1st {std}, lg8vo, 142p, DJ/3.95)	Viking	(1970)	Wiesner, William	25-40	
Harper, Wilhelmina	The Gunniwolf (1st, lg8vo, [32]p, color, DJ/3.95)	Dutton	(1967)	Wiesner, William	70-100	*
Wiesner, William	Three Good Friends (1st, sm4to, [31]p, ibds, fp color, DJ/1.50)	Harper	(1946)	Wiesner, William	30-45	
Wiesner, William	Tower of Babel (1st {std}, 4to, [32]p, color, DJ/3.95)	Viking	(1968)	Wiesner, William	25-40	
Anderson, Neil	Tina and the Too-Big Doll (1st, sm4to, 44p, color, pep, DJ/2.50)	Crowell	(1956)	Wiggins, Mary C.	30-50	
Blue, Rose	Black, Black, Beautiful Black (1st, 4to, 43p, fp b/w, DJ/3.95)	F. Watts	(1969)	Wigglesworth, Emmett	30-50	*
Smith, Emma	Emily, the Traveling Guinea Pig (1st AM, 8vo, 76p, 8cp, DJ/2.75)	McDowell/Obl.	1959	Wigglesworth, Kath.	35-50	
Uttley, Alison	Flower Show (1st, 12mo, ibds, 65p, fp color)	L: Heinemann	(1955)	Wigglesworth, Kath.	30-50	
Uttley, Alison	Going to the Fair (1st, 12mo, ibds, 72p, color)	L: Heinemann	(1951)	Wigglesworth, Kath.	35-50	
Uttley, Alison	Mouse Telegrams (1st, 12mo, ibds, 65p, fp color)	L: Heinemann	(1955)	Wigglesworth, Kath.	30-50	
Uttley, Alison	Mrs. Mouse Spring-Cleans (1st, 12mo, 70p, bds, p-o, color)	L: Heinemann	(1952)	Wigglesworth, Kath.	40-65	
Uttley, Alison	Snug & the Chimney-Sweeper (1st, 12mo, ibds, 69p, fp color)	L: Heinemann	(1953)	Wigglesworth, Kath.	30-50	
Uttley, Alison	Snug and Serena Pick Cowslips (1st, 12mo, bds, p-o, 72p, fp color)	L: Heinemann	1950	Wigglesworth, Kath.	40-65	
Uttley, Alison	Toad's Castle (1st, 12mo, 70p, bds, p-o, fp color)	L: Heinemann	(1951)	Wigglesworth, Kath.	40-65	
Wightman, Francis P.	Jingle Jangle Jumbly Lays... (1st, lg4to, [26]p, color)	NY: Blanchard	1899	Wightman, Francis P.	300-500	*
Baum, L. Frank	Last Egyptian (1st, 12mo, blue cl, p-o, 287p, 8cp)	Stern	1908	Wightman, Francis P.	250-350	
Wightman, Francis P.	Little Leather Breeches (1st, 4to, ibds, [48]p, color)	J.F. Taylor	1899	Wightman, Francis P.	250-350	
Bibbins, Ruthella	Mammy 'mongst the Wild Nations (1st, sm8vo, 305p, 8pl)	Stokes	(1904)	Wightman, Francis P.	100-150	*
Eaton, Seymour	Teddy-B & Teddy-G/Bear Detectives (4to, ipcb, 152p, p-o, 15cp)	Barse/Hopkins	(1909)	Wightman, Francis P.	250-400	
Eaton, Seymour	Teddy-B & Teddy-G/Bear Detectives (1st, 4to, bds, p-o, 15cp)	Stern	1909	Wightman, Francis P.	400-650	
Lindgren, Astrid	Cherry Time at Bullerby (1st UK, 12mo, cloth, 93p, DJ)	L: Methuen	1964	Wikland, Ilon	30-50	
Lindgren, Astrid	Children of Noisy Village (1st, 8vo, 124p, b/w, DJ/2.50)	Viking	(1962)	Wikland, Ilon	60-90	
Lindgren, Astrid	Children on Troublemaker Street (1st {std}, 8vo, 102p, b/w, DJ/3.25)	Macmillan	(1964)	Wikland, Ilon	50-80	
Lindgren, Astrid	Christmas in Noisy Village (1st AM, ob4to, 30p, green cl, color, DJ/3.00)	Viking	(1964)	Wikland, Ilon	60-100	
Peterson, Hans	Erik & the Christmas Horse (1st AM {std}, ob4to, [32]p, color, DJ/3.95)	Lothrop, Lee	(1970)	Wikland, Ilon	45-70	*
Lindgren, Astrid	Happy Times in Noisy Village (1st AM, 8vo, 122p, b/w, DJ/2.50)	Viking	1963	Wikland, Ilon	60-90	
Lindgren, Astrid	Lotta on Troublemaker Street (1st AM, 8vo, 57p, DJ/3.50)	Macmillan	1963	Wikland, Ilon	50-85	
Lindgren, Astrid	Madicken (1st UK, 8vo, 142p, b/w, DJ)	L: Oxford U.Pr.	1963	Wikland, Ilon	50-85	
Peterson, Hans	Magnus & the Wagon Horse (1st AM {std}, 8vo, 138p, b/w, DJ/3.25)	Pantheon	(1966)	Wikland, Ilon	20-35	
Lindgren, Astrid	Mio, my Son (1st, 8vo, 179p, blue cl, fp b/w, DJ/2.50)	Viking	(1956)	Wikland, Ilon	70-120	*
Lindgren, Astrid	Springtime in Noisy Village (1st, ob4to, ibds, 28p, fp color, DJ/3.50)	Viking	(1966)	Wikland, Ilon	60-90	
Barry, Robert E.	Mr. Willowby's Christmas Tree (1st, 4to, 32p, 1-color, pep, DJ/2.50)	Whittlesey	(1963)	Wilde, George	50-80	
Carruth, Hayden	Voyage of the Rattletrap (1st, 12mo, gilt, 207p, b/w, PPPa)	Harper	1897	Wilder, H.M.	65-100	
Richardson, Alfred	King of the Grizzlies (1st, sm8vo, 242p, p-o, col frn, b/w, pep)	Rand/McNally	(1925)	Wildering, Walter	30-50	
Marton, Gregory	Boy & his Friend the Blizzard (1st {std} sm8vo, 126p, 2-color, pep, DJ/3.50)	Harper	(1962)	Wildsmith, Brian	30-45	
Wildsmith, Brian	Brian Wildsmith's ABC (1st, lg ob8vo, [57]p, color, DJ, KGM)	L: Oxford U.Pr.	1962	Wildsmith, Brian	60-100	
Wildsmith, Brian	Brian Wildsmith's ABC (1st AM {std}, lg ob8vo, color, pep, DJ/2.95, KGM)	F. Watts	1963	Wildsmith, Brian	50-75	
Wildsmith, Brian	Brian Wildsmith's Birds (1st AM, lg ob8vo, [34]p, color, DJ/4.95. NYTBI)	F. Watts	(1967)	Wildsmith, Brian	60-100	
Wildsmith, Brian	Brian Wildsmith's Circus (1st AM, sm4to, [34]p, color, DJ/4.95)	F. Watts	(1970)	Wildsmith, Brian	50-85	
Wildsmith, Brian	Brian Wildsmith's Fishes (1st AM, ob4to, [34]p, color, DJ/4.95)	F. Watts	(1968)	Wildsmith, Brian	50-80	
Stevenson, Rbt. L.	Child's Garden of Verses (1st AM {std}, 4to, ibds, 96p, color, DJ/5.95)	F. Watts	(1966)	Wildsmith, Brian	30-55	
La Fontaine, J.	Hare & the Tortoise (1st AM, 4to, pink cl, unpag, color, DJ/3.95)	F. Watts	(1967)	Wildsmith, Brian	70-100	R
Morgan, Carol	Hunt for the Yule Log (1st, 8vo, 159p, b/w, DJ/2.75)	Abelard-Schuman	(1957)	Wildsmith, Brian	20-35	
Williamson, Joanne	Iron Charm (1st {std}, 8vo, 201p, b/w, DJ/3.50)	Knopf	(1964)	Wildsmith, Brian	25-40	

AUTHOR	TITLE	PUBLISHER	DATE	ARTIST	PRICE	LC
Berna, Paul	Knights of King Midas (1st AM, 8vo, 187p, orange cl, b/w, DJ/3.00)	Pantheon	(1961)	Wildsmith, Brian	40-65	
La Fontaine, J.	Lion and the Rat (1st AM, 4to, [32]p, fp color, cep, DJ/3.95)	F. Watts	(1963)	Wildsmith, Brian	70-100	
La Fontaine, J.	North Wind and the Sun (1st AM, 4to, [32]p, color, cep, DJ/3.95)	F. Watts	1964	Wildsmith, Brian	60-90	
Blishen, Ed (comp)	Oxford Book of Poetry for Children (1st, 4to, 167p, ibds, color, DJ)	L: Oxford U.Pr.	1963	Wildsmith, Brian	50-80	
La Fontaine, J.	Rich Man and the Shoemaker (1st AM, 4to, [32]p, fp color, cep, DJ/3.95)	F. Watts	(1965)	Wildsmith, Brian	50-80	
Chauncy, Nan	Tangara (1st {std}, 8vo, 180p, bds, b/w, DJ)	L: Oxford U.Pr.	1960	Wildsmith, Brian	20-30	*
Spielmann, M.H.	Child of the Air (1st, 8vo, blue/gilt, 125p, teg, 6cp, pep)	L: Duckworth	1910	Wilhelm, M.H.C.	70-120	
Voight, Virginia F.	Apple Tree Cottage (1st, sm8vo, 157p, green cl, b/w, cep, DJ/2.25)	Holiday House	(1949)	Wilkin, Eloise B.	50-80	
Buntain, Ruth J.	Birthday Story (1st, sm8vo, [47]p, fp 2-color, DJ/2.00)	Holiday House	(1953)	Wilkin, Eloise B.	50-80	
Dalgliesh, Alice	Choosing Book (1st, 16mo, [56]p, red cl, color)	Macmillan	1932	Wilkin, Eloise B.	40-65	*
Johnson, Florence	Christmas ABC (1st, sm8vo, ibds, unpag, color, LGB/#478)	Golden Press	1962	Wilkin, Eloise B.	30-50	
Werner, Jane	Christmas Story (1st, sm8vo, [28]p, ibds, color, LGB/#158)	Simon/Schuster	(1952)	Wilkin, Eloise B.	30-50	
Osswald, Edith	Come Play House (1st {A}, sm8vo, ibds, [42]p, color, LGB/#44)	Simon/Schuster	(1948)	Wilkin, Eloise B.	50-80	*
Pitts, Lilla B.	First Grade Book (lg4to, 206p, red cl, 4 fp color by...)	Ginn & Co.	(1949)	Wilkin, Eloise B.	50-85	*
Young, Miriam	Georgie Finds Grandpa (1st {A}, 8vo, ibds, color, LGB/#196)	Simon/Schuster	(1954)	Wilkin, Eloise B.	50-85	
Stone, Amy W.	Going-on-Nine (1st, 8vo, 128p, 6 fp color, b/w, pep, DJ/2.00)	Lothrop, Lee	(1939)	Wilkin, Eloise B.	70-130	
Holl, Adelaide	Jamie Looks (1st {A}, sm8vo, ibds, unpag, color, LGB/#522)	Golden Press	1963	Wilkin, Eloise B.	40-65	
Quigg, Jane	Jenny Jones and Skid (1st, 8vo, 99p, green cl, fp b/w, DJ/2.00)	NY: Oxford U.Pr.	1947	Wilkin, Eloise B.	70-100	
Bacon, Frances A.	Kitty Come Down (1st, sq12mo, 30p, b/w, DJ/1.25)	NY: Oxford U.Pr.	1944	Wilkin, Eloise B.	70-120	
Wilkin, Esther B.	Linda & her Little Sisters (1st {A}, sm8vo, unpag, ibds, color, LGB/#214)	Simon/Schuster	(1954)	Wilkin, Eloise B.	60-90	
Margo, Jan	Make-Believe Parade (1st, 8vo, ipcb, unpag, color)	Wonder Books	(1949)	Wilkin, Eloise B.	60-90	*
Burns, Esther	Mrs. Peregrine & the Yak (1st, 12mo, ibds, [53]p, 2-color, pep, DJ/1.00)	Henry Holt & Co.	(1938)	Wilkin, Eloise B.	80-140	
Burns, Esther	Mrs. Peregrine at the Fair (1st, 12mo, [55]p, ibds, color, pep, DJ/1.00)	J. Messner	(1939)	Wilkin, Eloise B.	70-120	
Scarry, Patricia	My Dolly and Me (1st {A}, sm8vo, ibds, [24]p, color, LGB/#418)	Golden Press	1960	Wilkin, Eloise B.	50-80	*
Scarry, Patricia	My Snuggly Bunny (1st {A}, sm8vo, [24]p, ibds, color, LGB/#250)	Simon/Schuster	1956	Wilkin, Eloise B.	40-65	
Shane, Ruth & Harold	New Baby (1st {A}, sm8vo, [42]p, ibds, color, LGB/#41)	Simon/Schuster	1948	Wilkin, Eloise B.	30-50	
Crampton, Gertrude	Noises & Mr. Flibberty-Jib (1st {A}, sm8vo, [42]p, ibds, color, LGB/#29)	Simon/Schuster	(1947)	Wilkin, Eloise B.	60-100	*
Wilkin, Esther B.	Play with Me (1st {A}, sm8vo, ibds, [24]p, color, pep, LGB/#567)	Golden Press	1967	Wilkin, Eloise B.	40-65	
Kiser, Martha G.	Rainbow for Me (1st, 8vo, 126p, 5 fp b/w, DJ/2.00)	Random	(1948)	Wilkin, Eloise B.	70-100	
Robinson, Mabel L.	Robin & Angus (1st, 8vo, green cl, 186p, col frn, fp b/w)	Macmillan	1931	Wilkin, Eloise B.	40-65	*
Reely, Mary K.	Seatmates (1st, 8vo, 237p, fp b/w, pep, DJ/2.00)	F. Watts	(1949)	Wilkin, Eloise B.	60-100	
Richardson, Myra	Sheep Wagon Family (1st {std}, 8vo, 217p, fp b/w, pep, DJ/2.00)	McBride	1941	Wilkin, Eloise B.	65-100	*
Wilkin, Esther B.	So Big (1st {A}, sm8vo, ibds, [24]p, color, LGB/#574)	Golden Press	1968	Wilkin, Eloise B.	30-50	
Kiser, Martha G.	Sunshine for Merrily (1st, 8vo, 130p, b/w, DJ/2.00)	Random	(1949)	Wilkin, Eloise B.	60-90	*
Shane, Ruth & Harold	The Twins (1st {A}, 12mo, ibds, [28]p, color, LGB/#227)	Simon/Schuster	(1955)	Wilkin, Eloise B.	70-100	
Lovelace, Maud H.	Tune is in the Tree (1st, 8vo, 177p, fp b/w, pep, DJ/2.50)	Crowell	(1950)	Wilkin, Eloise B.	100-160	
Cushman, Jean	We Help Mommy (1st {A}, sm8vo, [24]p, ibds, color, pep, LGB/#352)	Golden Press	1959	Wilkin, Eloise B.	40-65	*
Woodcock, Louise	Wiggles (1st {A}, sm8vo, [24]p, ibds, color, LGB/#166)	Simon/Schuster	1953	Wilkin, Eloise B.	50-75	*
Perrault, Charles	Puss in Boots (1st AM {std}, sm ob4to, [25]p, color, DJ/3.95)	World	1969	Wilkinson, Barry	25-40	
Morley, Christopher	Don't Open Until Christmas (1st {std}, 8vo, ibds, 26p, b/w)	Doubleday/Doran	1931	Willard, Howard	25-45	*
Morrow, Elizabeth	Rabbit's Nest (1st {std}, 24mo, 43p, ipcb, 1-color, pep, DJ/0.50)	Macmillan	1940	Willard, Howard	35-50	
Caudill, Rebecca	Barrie and Daughter (1st [1st bk], sm8vo, 314p, b/w, pep, DJ/2.00)	Viking	1943	Williams, Berkeley	20-35	
Bishop, Claire H.	Christopher the Giant (1st, 8vo, 54p, color, DJ/1.50)	Houghton	1950	Williams, Berkeley	20-35	
Dixon, Thomas	Leopard's Spots (1st, sm8vo, bds, teg, gilt, 465p, 8pl)	Doubleday/Page	1902	Williams, C.D.	50-80	
Long, John L.	Seffy (1st, sm8vo, 144p, green/gilt, 8cp)	Bobbs-Merrill	(1905)	Williams, C.D.	30-50	
Dixon, Thomas	The Traitor (1st, 8vo, red cl, 331p, 4cp)	Doubleday/Page	1907	Williams, C.D.	45-70	
Bacon, Josephine D.	Luck O'Lady Joan (1st, 12mo, 58p, frn by)	F.G. Browne	1913	Williams, C.E.	25-40	*
Kingsley, Charles	Water Babies (1st, 8vo, 104p, b/w)	Saalfield	(1905)	Williams, Carll B.	35-60	*
Naylor, James B.	Witch Crow & Barney Bylow (1st, lg8vo, ipcb, 118p, 6cp)	Saalfield	1906	Williams, Carll B.	50-85	
Arkle, Phyllis	Magic at Midnight (1st AM, ob8vo, 80p, b/w, cep, DJ/3.50)	Funk/Wagnalls	(1968)	Williams, Eccles	20-35	*
Williams, Emery	Alphabet of Indians (1st, folio, ipcb, [57]p, fp 1-color)	R.H. Russell	1900	Williams, Emery	275-450	*
Sewell, Anna	Black Beauty (1st, 8vo, p-o, 234p, col frn, b/w)	Saalfield	(1924)	Williams, Florence	25-45	*
Bannerman, Helen	Little Black Sambo (sq8vo, ibds, [42]p, color)	Saalfield	[1920]	Williams, Florence	250-350	
Williams, Garth	Adventures of Benjamin Pink (1st, 8vo, 151p, green cl, b/w, DJ/2.00)	Harper	(1951)	Williams, Garth	60-90	
Schweitzer, Byrd B.	Amigo (1st {std}, 4to, 41p, color, DJ/3.95)	Macmillan	1963	Williams, Garth	50-85	
Williams, Garth	Baby Animals (1st {A}, 8vo, [24]p, ibds, color, LGB/#274)	Simon/Schuster	1952	Williams, Garth	25-40	R
Hoban, Russell	Bedtime for Frances (1st, sm4to, [31]p, ibds, 1-color, DJ/2.50)	Harper	(1960)	Williams, Garth	140-200	
Colver, Anne	Bread & Butter Indian (1st {std}, 8vo, 96p, ibds, b/w, cep, DJ/2.95)	Holt, Rinehart	1964	Williams, Garth	30-50	
Colver, Anne	Bread & Butter Journey (1st {std}, 8vo, 101p, fp b/w, DJ/3.95)	Holt, Rinehart	(1970)	Williams, Garth	30-50	
Carlson, Natalie S.	Brother for the Orphelines (1st, sm4to, 100p, fp b/w, DJ/2.95)	Harper	(1959)	Williams, Garth	40-65	
White, Elwyn B.	Charlotte's Web (1st {std}, 8vo, 184p, b/w, pep, DJ/2.50, NH)	Harper	(1952)	Williams, Garth	500-800	R
Williams, Garth	Chicken Book (1st, lg ob8vo, ibds, [31]p, color, DJ/1.50)	Howell/Soskin	(1946)	Williams, Garth	100-150	
Williams, Garth	Chicken Book (1st {std}, lg ob8vo, [31]p, color, DJ/4.50)	Delacorte Pr.	(1970)	Williams, Garth	50-80	*
Selden, George	Cricket in Times Square (1st, lg8vo, 151p, fp b/w, DJ/3.50, NH)	Ariel	(1960)	Williams, Garth	70-100	
Zolotow, Charlotte	Do You Know What I'll Do? (1st, 4to, ibds, [27]p, fp 2-color, DJ/2.50)	Harper	(1958)	Williams, Garth	50-80	R
Lothar, Ernest	Door Opens (1st AM {std}, 12mo, 188p, b/w, DJ/2.00)	Doubleday/Doran	1945	Williams, Garth	30-50	
Werner, Jane	Elves & Fairies (1st, sm folio, ibds, 76p, color, pep, GGB)	Simon/Schuster	(1951)	Williams, Garth	180-240	
Stolz, Mary S.	Emmett's Pig (1st, 8vo, ibds, 61p, 2-color, DJ/2.50)	Harper	(1959)	Williams, Garth	50-80	
Carlson, Natalie S.	Family Under the Bridge (1st, 8vo, 99p, green cl, 11 fp b/w, DJ/2.95, NH)	Harper	(1958)	Williams, Garth	65-100	R
Wilder, Laura I.	Farmer Boy (1st [new ed.], 8vo, 372p, b/w, uncut, cep, DJ/2.75)	Harper	(1953)	Williams, Garth	80-120	R
LeGallienne, Eva	Flossie & Bossie (1st {std}, sm8vo, 210p, 30 fp b/w, DJ/2.00)	Harper	(1949)	Williams, Garth	60-100	R
Jarrell, Randall	Gingerbread Rabbit (1st {std}, 8vo, 55p, b/w, DJ/2.95)	Macmillan	(1964)	Williams, Garth	70-120	
Lindquist, Jennie	Golden Name Day (1st, 8vo, blue cl, 247p, pep, b/w, DJ/2.75, NH)	Harper	(1955)	Williams, Garth	80-135	R
Carlson, Natalie S.	Happy Orpheline (1st, sm4to, blue cl, 96p, fp b/w, DJ/2.95)	Harper	(1957)	Williams, Garth	45-70	
Brown, Margaret W.	Home for a Bunny (1st {A}, folio, ibds, [28]p, color, GGB)	Simon/Schuster	1956	Williams, Garth	80-130	
Runyon, Damon	In Our Town (1st, 8vo, 120p, uncut, fp b/w, DJ/2.00)	NY: Creative Age	(1946)	Williams, Garth	40-65	
Garson, Eugenia	Laura Ingalls Wilder Songbook (1st, 4to, 160p, ibds, b/w, cep, DJ/5.95)	Harper, Row	(1968)	Williams, Garth	50-85	*
Brown, Margaret W.	Little Fur Family (1st {this format}, 8vo, [37]p, b/w, DJ/1.50)	Harper	1946	Williams, Garth	90-150	

AUTHOR	TITLE	PUBLISHER	DATE	ARTIST	PRICE	LC
Minarik, Else H.	Little Giant Girl & Elf Boy (1st, 8vo, [31]p, ibds, color, DJ/2.95)	Harper	1963	Williams, Garth	70-120	
Wilder, Laura I.	Little House in the Big Woods (1st [new ed.], 8vo, 237p, b/w, DJ/2.75)	Harper	1953	Williams, Garth	140-200	R
Wilder, Laura I.	Little House on the Prairie (1st [new ed.], 8vo, 334p, b/w, DJ/2.75)	Harper	(1953)	Williams, Garth	100-175	R
Lindquist, Jennie	Little Silver House (1st, sm8vo, 213p, green cl, fp b/w, DJ/2.75)	Harper	(1959)	Williams, Garth	50-85	
Sharp, Margery	Miss Bianca (1st {std}, 8vo, 138p, grey cl, fp b/w, DJ)	L: Collins	1962	Williams, Garth	50-85	
Sharp, Margery	Miss Bianca in the Salt Mines (1st AM {std}, 8vo, 148p, b/w, DJ/3.95)	Little/Brown	(1966)	Williams, Garth	50-80	R
Brown, Margaret W.	Mister Dog (1st, sm8vo, unpag, ibds, color, LGB/#128)	Simon/Schuster	(1952)	Williams, Garth	25-40	
Wilder, Laura I.	On the Banks of Plum Creek (1st [new ed.], 8vo, 338p, color, DJ/2.75)	Harper	1953	Williams, Garth	80-130	
Zolotow, Charlotte	Over and Over (1st, 4to, ibds, unpag, fp color, DJ/2.75)	Harper	(1957)	Williams, Garth	60-100	
Wahl, Jan	Push Kitty (1st, 4to, [32]p, ibds, color, DJ/3.50)	Harper	(1968)	Williams, Garth	40-60	
Williams, Garth	Rabbit's Wedding (1st, lg4to, ibds, unpag, 2-color, DJ/2.50)	Harper	(1958)	Williams, Garth	120-200	
Sharp, Margery	Rescuers: a Fantasy (1st {std}, 8vo, blue cl, 149p, b/w, DJ/3.50)	Little/Brown	(1959)	Williams, Garth	140-220	
Gilbert, Henry	Robin Hood (1st {std}, 8vo, 398p, fp 2-color, DJ/2.50)	Lippincott	(1948)	Williams, Garth	30-50	
Zolotow, Charlotte	Sky Was Blue (1st {std}, 4to, ibds, [31]p, color, DJ/2.95)	Harper	1963	Williams, Garth	70-100	
White, Elwyn B.	Stuart Little (1st {std}, 8vo, tan cl, b/w, 131p, pep, DJ/2.00)	Harper	(1945)	Williams, Garth	500-800	R
Werner, Jane	Tall Book of Make-Believe (1st, narrow 4to, ibds, 92p, color, pep, DJ/1.00)	Harper	(1950)	Williams, Garth	100-160	
Sharp, Margery	The Turret (1st AM {std}, 8vo, 138p, fp b/w, DJ/3.95)	Little/Brown	(1963)	Williams, Garth	60-100	R
Brown, Margaret W.	Three Little Animals (1st, lg4to, ibds, [30]p, color, DJ/2.50)	Harper	(1956)	Williams, Garth	120-185	R
Selden, George	Tucker's Countryside (1st {std}, 8vo, 166p, b/w, DJ/3.95)	Farrar, Straus	(1969)	Williams, Garth	30-50	
Brown, Margaret W.	Wait Till the Moon is Full (1st, sm4to, ibds, [32]p, 1-color, DJ/1.75)	Harper	(1948)	Williams, Garth	120-170	
Williams, C.A.	ABC of Animals (1st, 4to, 17p, color, cep)	Stokes	(1911)	Williams, George A.	120-180	
Williams, C.A.	Bettijak Book (1st, 4to, p-o, color)	Stokes	(1914)	Williams, George A.	250-400	
Sweetser, Kate D.	Book of Indian Braves (1st, lg8vo, 183p, p-o, col frn, 6pl)	Harper	1913	Williams, George A.	55-80	
Williams, George A.	Boy's Book of Indians & Wild West (1st, lg ob4to, p-o, 47p, 11cp)	Stokes	1911	Williams, George A.	80-120	
Williams, George A.	Boy's Book of Pirates & Great Sea Rovers (1st, ob4to, ibds, 47p, 11cp)	Stokes	1913	Williams, George A.	120-185	
Sweetser, Kate D.	Boys & Girls from George Eliot (1st, lg8vo, 212p, 8pl)	Duffield	1906	Williams, George A.	55-80	*
Sweetser, Kate D.	Boys & Girls from Thackeray (1st, lg8vo, 355p, p-o, 7pl)	Duffield	1907	Williams, George A.	45-70	
Dickens, Charles	Christmas Carol (1st, lg8vo, 198p, gilt, col frn, 9pl)	Baker/Taylor	(1905)	Williams, George A.	70-100	*
Dickens, Charles	Holly Tree Inn (1st, lg8vo, 139p, gilt, teg, 10cp)	Baker/Taylor	(1907)	Williams, George A.	60-90	
Williams, C.A.	Magic Book (1st, 4to, 64p, color)	Stokes	(1912)	Williams, George A.	120-200	
Williams, C.A.	Mammy's Lil'l Chillums (1st, lg8vo, [63]p, ibds, fp color)	Stokes	(1904)	Williams, George A.	180-240	R
Dickens, Charles	Mr. Pickwick's Christmas (1st, lg8vo, p-o, AEG, 149p, 6cp)	Baker/Taylor	(1906)	Williams, George A.	60-90	
Williams, C.A.	Stories that Glue Told (1st, ob folio, [36]p, ibds, color)	Stokes	1907	Williams, George A.	130-200	*
Williams, C.A.	Story Book of Silhouettes (ob folio, ibds, b/w)	Stokes	(1914)	Williams, George A.	150-240	
Sweetser, Kate D.	Ten Boys from Dickens (1st, lg8vo, 223p, uncut, b/w pl)	R.H. Russell	1901	Williams, George A.	60-100	
Sweetser, Kate D.	Ten Boys from History (1st, lg8vo, 210p, p-o, col frn, 3pl)	Duffield	1910	Williams, George A.	45-70	
Sweetser, Kate D.	Ten Girls from Dickens (1st, lg8vo, 236p, p-o, uncut, 11pl)	Baker/Taylor	1902	Williams, George A.	60-90	
Dickens, Charles	The Chimes (1st, lg8vo, p-o, 210p, col frn, 9pl)	Baker/Taylor	(1908)	Williams, George A.	40-60	*
LeGallienne, R.	Wagner's Tristan & Isolde (1st, 4to, 358p, black/gilt, teg, 7cp)	Stokes	(1909)	Williams, George A.	120-200	
Marshall, Bernard G.	Cedric the Forester (1st, 8vo, 278p, 18pl, NH)	Appleton	1921	Williams, J. Scott	80-130	
Sawyer, Ruth	Doctor Danny (1st, sm8vo, 410p, ibds, pep, 8pl)	Harper	1918	Williams, J. Scott	40-65	
Parker, Louis N.	Pomander Walk (1st, 8vo, 267p, 16pl)	J. Lane	1911	Williams, J. Scott	60-90	
King, Ben	Jane Jones and Some Others (1st, 8vo, green/gilt, 94p, 16cp)	Chi: Forbes	1909	Williams, John A.	80-120	
Emerson, Willis G.	Smoky God (1st, 12mo, 186p, blue cl, 11cp)	Chi: Forbes	1908	Williams, John A.	70-100	*
MacDonell, Anne	Italian Fairy Book (1st AM, 8vo, gilt, 307p, col frn, 17 fp b/w, pep)	Stokes	[1911]	Williams, Morris M.	165-250	
MacDonell, Anne	Italian Fairy Book (1st, 8vo, 403p, green/gilt, col frn, 1-color)	L: T.F. Unwin	(1911)	Williams, Morris M.	220-300	
Grierson, Eliz. W.	Scottish Fairy Book (1st, 8vo, 384p, gilt, col frn, b/w, pep)	L: T.F. Unwin	1910	Williams, Morris M.	70-120	
Sawyer, Edith A.	Christmas Maker's Club (1st, 8vo, 275p, 6pl)	L.C. Page	1908	Williamson	25-40	*
Gilchrist, Beth B.	Helen and the Fifth Cousins (1st, 12mo, 334p, b/w)	Penn	1915	Williamson, Ada C.	40-65	
Canfield, Dorothy	Understood Betsy (1st, sm8vo, 271p, green cl, 11pl, PPP)	Henry Holt & Co.	1917	Williamson, Ada C.	80-120	
Henderson, Bernard	Wonder Tales of Ancient Wales (1st, 8vo, gilt, 166p, teg, 8cp)	L: P. Allan	(1921)	Williamson, Doris	100-170	
Young, Miriam	Mother Wore Tights (1st, 8vo, 255p, b/w, DJ/2.50)	Whittlesey	(1944)	Williamson, Howard	50-85	
Almond, Linda S.	Peter Rabbit and the Little Girl (1st, 24mo, 58p, col frn)	Altemus	(1930)	Willis, Bess G.	35-60	*
Potter, Beatrix	Peter Rabbit Story Book (lg8vo, 62p, p-o, col frn)	Platt/Munk	(1935)	Willis, Bess G.	80-120	*
Willoughby, Rachel	Tunes for Tiny Troubadours (1st, lg4to, ibds, 31p, color, DJ/2.50)	Putnam	(1936)	Willoughby, Walter	60-90	
Hoke, Helen	Mr. Sweeny (1st, 4to, [76]p, 1-color, pep, DJ/1.50)	Henry Holt & Co.	1940	Wills, William	30-50	
Harland, Henry	Cardinal's Snuff-Box (1st, sm8vo, red/gilt, uncut, 263p, teg, 20pl)	J. Lane	1903	Wilmshurst, G.C.	50-90	
Annixter, Jane	Buffalo Chief (1st, 8vo, 219p, red cl, DJ/2.95, pep by...)	Holiday House	(1958)	Wilson, Charles B.	30-50	*
Davis, Robert	Gid Granger (1st, sm8vo, 179p, tan cl, fp b/w, DJ/2.25)	Holiday House	(1945)	Wilson, Charles B.	25-45	
Neyhart, Louise A.	Henry's Lincoln (1st, lg8vo, 49p, ipcb, 9 fp b/w, pep, DJ/1.50)	Holiday House	(1945)	Wilson, Charles B.	50-80	R
Kjelgaard, Jim	Rebel Siege (1st, 8vo, 221p, b/w, DJ/2.00)	Holiday House	(1943)	Wilson, Charles B.	30-50	
Harrison, Edith O.	Glittering Festival (1st, 4to, 176p, gilt, p-o, 4cp)	McClurg	1911	Wilson, Clara P.	80-125	
Judson, Clara I.	Good-Night Stories (1st, 12mo, pict cl, 131p, b/w)	McClurg	1916	Wilson, Clara P.	25-45	*
Smith, Laura R.	Pixie in the House (1st, sm8vo, 123p, pep)	McClurg	1915	Wilson, Clara P.	30-50	*
Britton, Fay A.	Shakespearian Fairy Tales (1st, 8vo, ibds, 143p, 8cp)	Reilly/Britton	(1907)	Wilson, Clara P.	60-90	
Peltier, Florence	Through the Rainbow (1st, 8vo, blue cl, p-o, 117p, 7cp)	Revell	(1917)	Wilson, Clara P.	60-100	
Schneider, Nina	While Susie Sleeps (1st, sm4to, [32]p, ibds, color, DJ/1.50)	W.R. Scott	(1948)	Wilson, Dagmar	40-65	
Mother Goose	Everychild's Mother Goose (1st, 12mo, 308p, 64 fp 1-color)	Macmillan	1918	Wilson, Edith R.	60-100	*
Coolidge, Olivia	Cromwell's Head (1st, 8vo, 262p, b/w, DJ/3.00)	Houghton	1955	Wilson, Edward A.	20-30	*
Wilson, Edward A.	Pirate's Treasure (1st, 8vo, ibds, [96]p, color, pep)	Volland	(1926)	Wilson, Edward A.	50-85	
Wilson, Eleanore H.	About Ricco (1st, 4to, pep, 123p, p-o, color, pep, DJ/2.00)	Whitman	1937	Wilson, Eleanore H.	60-100	
Wilson, Eleanore H.	Flyaway Flippety (1st {std}, lg8vo, 104p, pep, 14cp)	Harper	1932	Wilson, Eleanore H.	30-50	*
Chester, Geo. R.	The Jingo (1st, sm8vo, grey/gilt, 394p, 10pl)	Bobbs-Merrill	(1912)	Wilson, F. Vaux	50-85	
Rinehart, Mary R.	Where There's a Will (1st, sm8vo, blue/gilt, 352p, 5pl)	Bobbs-Merrill	(1912)	Wilson, F. Vaux	30-50	
Beatty, Jerome	Bob Fulton's Amazing Soda-Pop Stretcher (1st, 8vo, 239p, b/w, DJ/3.50)	Young Scott	(1963)	Wilson, Gahan	20-30	*
Beatty, Jerome	Matthew Looney in the Outback (1st, 8vo, 223p, b/w, DJ/3.95)	W.R. Scott	(1969)	Wilson, Gahan	20-30	*
Beatty, Jerome	Matthew Looney's Voyage to the Earth (1st, 8vo, 131p, b/w, DJ/2.75)	Young Scott	(1961)	Wilson, Gahan	20-30	*
Mendoza, George	Good Luck Spider (1st {std}, 8vo, 47p, b/w, DJ/3.50)	Doubleday	(1970)	Wilson, Galan	25-40	

AUTHOR	TITLE	PUBLISHER	DATE	ARTIST	PRICE	LC
Wilson, Julia	Becky (1st, 4to, [40]p, fp 2-color, DJ/3.75)	Crowell	(1967)	Wilson, John	40-65	
George, Jean C.	Spring Comes to the Ocean (1st, 8vo, 109p, b/w, DJ/3.50)	Crowell	(1965)	Wilson, John	20-25	
Lexau, Joan M.	Striped Ice Cream (1st {std}, 8vo, 95p, b/w, DJ/3.25)	Lippincott	(1968)	Wilson, John	25-40	*
Tovey, Doreen	Cats in Cahoots (1st AM {std}, 8vo, 147p, b/w, DJ/2.95)	Doubleday	1960	Wilson, Maurice	40-65	
Tovey, Doreen	Donkey Work (1st AM {std}, 8vo, 138p, b/w, DJ/3.50)	Doubleday	1963	Wilson, Maurice	30-50	
Tovey, Doreen	New Boy (1st AM, 8vo, 162p, b/w, DJ/4.95)	Norton	(1970)	Wilson, Maurice	40-65	
Tovey, Doreen	Raining Cats and Donkeys (1st AM, 8vo, 156p, b/w, DJ/4.50)	Norton	(1968)	Wilson, Maurice	40-65	
Bible	Daniel in the Lion's Den (1st, 16mo, 98p, blue stripe cl, color)	L: G. Richards	1903	Wilson, Patten	100-160	
Gask, Lilian	Legends of our Little Brothers (1st, 8vo, 268p, 15pl)	L: Harrap	1912	Wilson, Patten	55-80	*
Gask, Lilian	Legends of our Little Brothers (1st AM, 8vo, p-o, 268p, 15pl)	Crowell	(1912)	Wilson, Patten	40-60	
Fletcher, Joseph S.	Life in Arcadia (1st, sm8vo, 265p, green/gilt, cvr by...)	L: John Lane	1896	Wilson, Patten	60-90	
Appiah, Peggy	Ananse the Spider (1st, lg8vo, 152p, b/w, DJ/3.75, NYTBI)	Pantheon	(1966)	Wilson, Peggy	30-50	*
Byars, Betsy C.	Clementine (1st [1st bk.], 8vo, 70p, fp 1-color, DJ/2.75)	Houghton	1962	Wilton, Charles	40-65	
Stratton-Porter, Gene	Jesus of the Emerald (1st, lg8vo, [44]p, white bds, col frn)	Doubleday/Page	1923	Winchell, Everett	500-700	
Brown, Abbie F.	Kisington Town (1st, 8vo, p-o, 213p, col frn, 5pl)	Houghton	1915	Winckler, Ruby	30-50	*
Wibberley, Leonard	Beware of the Mouse (1st, 8vo, 189p, uncut, fp b/w, DJ/3.50)	Putnam	(1958)	Wing, Ronald	70-100	
Lippmann, Julie M.	Dearie Dot and the Dog (1st, sm8vo, 194p, 5pl)	Penn	1903	Winner, Margaret	25-40	*
Davis, Norman	Picken's Exciting Summer (1st, lg8vo, 46p, ibds, 1-color, DJ/2.00)	Oxford U. Pr.	(1949)	Winslade	40-70	
Davis, Norman	Picken's Treasure Hunt (1st, 8vo, 64p, 2-color, DJ/2.50)	Oxford U. Pr.	1955	Winslade	40-65	
Lent, Henry B.	Bus Driver (1st, sq16mo, [42]p, color, pep)	Macmillan	1937	Winslow, Earle	35-60	*
Lent, Henry B.	The Captain (1st, sq16mo, [42]p, color, pep)	Macmillan	1937	Winslow, Earle	35-60	*
Verne, Jules	20 Thousand Leagues under the Sea (1st, lg8vo, 495p, p-o, color, WS)	Rand/McNally	(1922)	Winter, Milo	30-50	*
Craik, Dinah	Adventures of a Brownie (1st, 8vo, p-o, 128p, color)	Rand/McNally	(1923)	Winter, Milo	60-100	
Malot, Hector	Adventures of Perrine (1st, lg8vo, 284p, black cl, p-o, 5cp, pep, WS)	Rand/McNally	(1932)	Winter, Milo	50-80	
Aesopus	Aesop for Children (1st, 4to, p-o, 112p, color, pep)	Rand/McNally	(1919)	Winter, Milo	100-160	
Carroll, Lewis	Alice... & Through... (1st, lg8vo, 242p, p-o, 14cp, pep)	Rand/McNally	(1916)	Winter, Milo	150-240	
Evans, Lawton	America First (1st, 8vo, 447p, p-o, pep, col frn, 9pl)	Milton Bradley	1920	Winter, Milo	40-60	*
Moe, Virginia	Animal Inn (1st, lg8vo, grey cl, 174p, b/w, DJ/2.50)	Houghton	1946	Winter, Milo	25-40	
N/A	Arabian Nights (1st, lg8vo, 293p, p-o, 16cp, pep, WS)	Rand/McNally	(1914)	Winter, Milo	70-100	
Winter, Milo	Billy Popgun (1st, 4to, ibds, p-o, 61p, 8cp, pep)	Houghton	1912	Winter, Milo	170-240	R
Olcott, F.J.	Book of Elves & Fairies (1st, 8vo, 303p, p-o, 3cp by...)	Houghton	1918	Winter, Milo	90-120	
Olcott, F.J.	Book of Elves & Fairies (1st UK, 8vo, 303p, 3cp by...)	L: Harrap	1919	Winter, Milo	80-120	*
Dickens, Charles	Christmas Carol (1st, 12mo, 157p, tan cl, 12pl)	Rand/McNally	(1912)	Winter, Milo	40-60	*
Barton, Olive R.	Cloud Boat Stories (1st, 8vo, 138p, blue cl, p-o, 4cp)	Houghton	1917	Winter, Milo	60-90	
Hinkle, Thomas C.	Dr. Rabbit & Ki-Yi Coyote (1st, 12mo, 106p, yellow bds, color)	Rand/McNally	(1918)	Winter, Milo	40-65	
Snell, Roy J.	Eskimo Island & Penguin Land (1st, 8vo, [256]p, cloth, p-o by...)	Whitman	1928	Winter, Milo	30-50	
Grimm Bros.	Fairy Tales (1st, lg8vo, 275p, p-o, 12cp)	Rand/McNally	(1913)	Winter, Milo	80-140	
Andersen, Hans C.	Fairy Tales (1st, lg8vo, 286p, p-o, gilt, 15cp, pep, WS)	Rand/McNally	(1916)	Winter, Milo	120-170	
Bigham, Madge A.	Goober Village (1st, sm8vo, 184p, color)	Rand/McNally	(1936)	Winter, Milo	50-80	
Swift, Jonathan	Gulliver's Travels (1st, lg8vo, 344p, gilt, p-o, 12cp, pep, WS)	Rand/McNally	(1912)	Winter, Milo	100-150	
Loveland, Mrs. S.	Illustrated Bible Story Book (1st, lg4to, 126p, p-o, 12cp, pep)	Rand/McNally	(1923)	Winter, Milo	60-90	
Scott, Walter	Ivanhoe (1st, lg8vo, p-o, 637p, blue/gilt, 14cp, pep, WS)	Rand/McNally	(1918)	Winter, Milo	60-100	
Townsend, Ralph M.	Journey to the Garden Gate (1st, lg8vo, p-o, gilt, 127p, 8cp, pep)	Houghton	1919	Winter, Milo	70-120	
Stevenson, Rbt. L.	Kidnapped (1st, lg8vo, 262p, p-o, 8cp, WS)	Rand/McNally	(1916)	Winter, Milo	60-100	
Bell, Lilian	Land of Don't-Want-To (1st, lg8vo, 212p, blue cl, p-o, 10cp)	Rand/McNally	(1916)	Winter, Milo	70-100	
Gill, Frances	Little Days (1st, 8vo, ibds, 50p, col frn, b/w)	Houghton	1917	Winter, Milo	75-100	
Hardy, Mary E.	Little King and the Princess True (1st, 8vo, p-o, gilt, 182p, 4pl)	Rand/McNally	(1912)	Winter, Milo	80-125	
DeWolf, Wallace L.	Mardo's Animal Rhymes (1st, sq8vo, p-o, 44p, 4cp)	Rand/McNally	(1916)	Winter, Milo	55-80	
Deihl, Edna G.	Mother Brown Earth's Children (1st, 8vo, 111p, pep, p-o by...)	Whitman	(1927)	Winter, Milo	60-90	
Harris, Joel C.	Nights with Uncle Remus (1st, lg8vo, gilt, p-o, 338p, 12cp, pep)	Houghton	1917	Winter, Milo	150-225	
Kellogg, Vernon L.	Nuova or the New Bee (1st, 8vo, 150p, col frn, 14pl, pep)	Houghton	1920	Winter, Milo	45-75	
Faulkner, Georgene	Old English Nursery Tales (1st, 8vo, 91p, black/gilt, p-o, 8cp)	Chi: Daughaday	(1916)	Winter, Milo	100-150	
Spiegelberg, Flora	Princess Goldenhair & the Wonderful Flower (1st, 8vo, 176p, p-o, 8cp)	Rand/McNally	(1915)	Winter, Milo	100-165	
Spiegelberg, Flora	Princess Goldenhair & the Wonderful Flower (8vo, 176p, green cl, p-o, 8cp)	World	(1932)	Winter, Milo	50-85	
Mother Goose	Real Mother Goose (lg4to, p-o, gilt, color, pep)	Rand/McNally	(1928)	Winter, Milo	70-120	
Garis, Howard	Rick & Ruddy in Camp (1st, sm8vo, 254p, tan cl, 4pl)	Milton Bradley	1921	Winter, Milo	30-50	*
Warren, Maude R.	Robin Hood & his Merry Men (1st, 12mo, 290p, fp b/w)	Rand/McNally	(1914)	Winter, Milo	70-100	
Defoe, Daniel	Robinson Crusoe (1st, lg8vo, 382p, p-o, 16cp, pep, WS)	Rand/McNally	(1914)	Winter, Milo	60-100	
Heal, Edith	Siegfried (1st, 8vo, 368p, 5cp, pep)	Chi: Rockwell	1930	Winter, Milo	50-80	
Hinkle, Thomas C.	Snowy Tail: Champion Jack Rabbit (1st, 12mo, ibds, 64p, color)	Rand/McNally	(1921)	Winter, Milo	40-65	
Faulkner, Georgene	Story Lady's Nursery Tales (1st, 8vo, 241p, p-o, 8cp, pep)	Sears	(1927)	Winter, Milo	75-100	*
Dopp, Katharine E.	Story of the Early Sea People (1st, sm8vo, 219p, col frn, p-o by...)	Rand/McNally	(1913)	Winter, Milo	30-50	*
Wyss, Johann D.	Swiss Family Robinson (1st, lg8vo, 441p, 14cp, pep, WS)	Rand/McNally	(1916)	Winter, Milo	70-100	
Hawthorne, Nathaniel	Tanglewood Tales (1st, lg8vo, p-o, gilt, 283p, 10cp, pep, WS)	Rand/McNally	(1913)	Winter, Milo	90-160	
Hawthorne, Nathaniel	Tanglewood Tales (1st UK, lg8vo, 283p, blue/gilt, 10cp)	L: Duckworth	1914	Winter, Milo	80-120	
Dumas, Alexandre	Three Musketeers (1st, 8vo, 545p, p-o, 8cp, pep, WS)	Rand/McNally	(1923)	Winter, Milo	60-100	
Austin, Mary	Trail Book (1st, 8vo, 304p, p-o, 4cp)	Houghton	1918	Winter, Milo	50-80	
Stevenson, Rbt. L.	Treasure Island (1st, lg8vo, 258p, p-o, cp, pep, WS)	Rand/McNally	(1915)	Winter, Milo	70-120	
Barrows, Marjorie	Who's Who in the Zoo (1st, folio, 60p, p-o, pep, 25 fp color)	Reilly/Lee	(1932)	Winter, Milo	60-100	
Hawthorne, Nathaniel	Wonder Book (1st, lg8vo, p-o, gilt, 254p, 8cp, pep, WS)	Rand/McNally	(1913)	Winter, Milo	70-120	
Olcott, F.J.	Wonderful Garden (1st, 12mo, 483p, p-o, 4cp)	Houghton	1919	Winter, Milo	70-90	
Sharp, Edith L.	Nkwala (1st {std}, 8vo, 125p, b/w, DJ/3.00)	Little/Brown	(1958)	Winter, William	30-50	R*
Coatsworth, Eliz.	The Enchanted, an Incredible Tale (1st, 8vo, 157p, b/w, DJ/2.50)	Pantheon	1951	Winthrop, Robert	30-50	*
Sidney, Margaret	Ben Pepper (1st, sm8vo, 474p, green/gilt, 6pl)	Lothrop Pub.	1905	Wireman, Eugenie	100-160	
Donahey, Mary D.	Magical House of Zur (1st, 4to, 124p, p-o, 6cp)	Barse/Hopkins	(1914)	Wireman, Eugenie	100-165	
Blaisdell, Mary F.	Pretty Polly Flinders (1st, 12mo, green cl, 188p, 4cp)	Little/Brown	1914	Wireman, Eugenie	70-100	
Dow, Ethel C.	Proud Roxana (1st, 8vo, 130p, p-o, 6cp)	Stern	1909	Wireman, Eugenie	130-200	
N/A	Children's Story Garden (1st, sm8vo, 247p, blue cl, col frn, 9pl)	Lippincott	1920	Wireman, K.& E.	45-70	

AUTHOR	TITLE	PUBLISHER	DATE	ARTIST	PRICE	LC
Wiggin, Kate D.	Birds' Christmas Carol (1st, 8vo, 91p, green/gilt, color)	Houghton	1912	Wireman, Katharine	50-85	R
Brown, Jeanette	Wishes Come True (1st, 8vo, 128p, color, DJ/1.50)	Friendship Pr.	(1948)	Wireman, Katharine	40-65	*
Garis, Howard	Joie, Tommie & Kittie Kat (1st, 8vo, 202p, brown cl, col frn, 8pl)	NY: Fenno	1913	Wisa, Louis	80-120	
Davis, Alice V.	Timothy Turtle (1st, lg8vo, [32]p, 2-color, DJ/1.50)	Harcourt	(1940)	Wiser, Guy B.	60-95	
Almond, Linda S.	Little Glad Heart (1st, sm8vo, 317p, 6pl)	L.C. Page	1922	Withington, Eliz.	25-40	*
Withington, Eliz.	Lullabies of Many Lands (1st, 8vo, [32]p, ibds, 24 color, pep)	Caldwell	(1908)	Withington, Eliz.	80-120	
Montgomery, R.	Rough Riders Ho! (1st, 8vo, 228p, b/w, DJ/1.00)	McKay	(1946)	Wittmack, E.F.	20-30	
Montgomery, R.	Sea Raiders Ho! (1st, 8vo, 224p, b/w, DJ/2.00)	McKay	(1945)	Wittmack, E.F.	20-30	
Montgomery, R.	Thunderboats Ho! (1st, 8vo, 256p, col frn, DJ/2.00)	McKay	(1945)	Wittmack, E.F.	25-40	
Keith, Harold V.	Boy's Life of Will Rogers (1st, 8vo, 271p, pep, fp b/w, DJ/2.00)	Crowell	(1937)	Woerner, Karl	25-40	
Thayer, Jane	Andy & Mr. Cunningham (1st, 8vo, 48p, color, DJ/3.25)	Wm. Morrow	(1969)	Wohlberg, Meg	20-30	
Thayer, Jane	Andy & the Runaway Horse (1st, 8vo, 48p, 2-color, pep, DJ/2.75)	Wm. Morrow	1963	Wohlberg, Meg	20-35	*
Pomerantz, Charlotte	Bear Who Couldn't Sleep (1st, sm4to, [30]p, fp color, pep, DJ/2.95)	Wm. Morrow	1965	Wohlberg, Meg	25-45	*
Horn, Gladys	Bounce - Story of a Kitten (1st, 8vo, [32]p, color, pep, DJ/1.25)	Winston	(1941)	Wohlberg, Meg	35-60	
Thayer, Jane	Contrary Little Quail (1st, 4to, [32]p, color, pep, DJ/3.25)	Wm. Morrow	(1968)	Wohlberg, Meg	20-35	
Woolley, Catherine	Lunch for Lennie (1st, 8vo, 48p, b/w, DJ/2.00)	Wm. Morrow	1952	Wohlberg, Meg	25-40	*
Walters, Marguerite	Real Santa Claus (1st, 4to, 31p, ibds, color, DJ/1.00)	Lothrop, Lee	1950	Wohlberg, Meg	25-40	
Beim, Jerrold	Smallest Boy in Class (1st, 8vo, [47]p, 2-color, DJ/2.00)	Wm. Morrow	1949	Wohlberg, Meg	30-50	
Goudey, Alice	Smokey, the Well-Loved Kitten (1st, 8vo, 114p, b/w, DJ/2.50)	Lothrop, Lee	(1952)	Wohlberg, Meg	20-35	*
Baruch, Dorothy W.	Blimps and Such (1st, lg4to, 80p, ibds, col frn, b/w, DJ/2.00)	Harper	1932	Wolcott, Elizabeth	60-100	
Lownsbery, Eloise	Boy Knight of Rheims (1st, 8vo, 332p, col frn, gilt, b/w, pep)	Houghton	1927	Wolcott, Elizabeth	25-45	
Lownsbery, Eloise	Camel for a Throne (1st, 8vo, 305p, b/w, DJ/2.50)	Houghton	1941	Wolcott, Elizabeth	20-35	*
Tippett, James S.	Counting the Days (1st {std}, 24mo, ibds, 66p, DJ/0.75)	Harper	(1940)	Wolcott, Elizabeth	25-45	*
Lownsbery, Eloise	Out of the Flame (1st {std}, sm8vo, 352p, pep, b/w, NH)	NY: Longmans	1931	Wolcott, Elizabeth	50-85	
Kent, Louise A.	Two Children of Tyre (1st, 8vo, 233p, col frn, b/w, pep)	Houghton	1932	Wolcott, Elizabeth	20-35	
Wolf, Ingrid	Pajaro-Cu-Cu (1st AM {std}, ob4to, [24]p, ibds, color, DJ/4.95)	Atheneum	(1967)	Wolf, Ingrid	25-40	*
Wolff, Robert	Feeling Blue (1st, 8vo, [32]p, fp color, cep, DJ)	Scribner	(1968)	Wolff, Robert	45-70	
Doyle, Arthur Conan	Adventures of Gerard (1st AM, 8vo, green cl, 297p, uncut, 16pl)	McClure	1903	Wollen, W.B.	70-100	
Wolo	Amanda (1st, 4to, 37p, color, pep, DJ/2.00)	Wm. Morrow	1941	Wolo	80-125	
Wolo	Secret of the Ancient Oak (1st, 4to, 40p, color, pep, DJ/2.00)	Wm. Morrow	1942	Wolo	100-165	
Wolo	Tweedles, Be Brave! (1st, 4to, 31p, ibds, color, DJ/2.50)	Wm. Morrow	1943	Wolo	90-140	
Caudill, Rebecca	Saturday Cousins (1st {std}, 8vo, 120p, b/w, DJ/2.50)	Winston	(1953)	Woltemate, Nancy	20-30	*
Wondriska, William	123 - A Book to See (1st, 12mo, [26]p, fp 1-color, dep, DJ/2.50)	Pantheon	(1959)	Wondriska, William	60-90	R
Wondriska, William	All the Animals Were Angry (1st {std}, 8vo, ipcb, [36]p, b/w, dep, DJ/2.95)	Holt, Rinehart	(1970)	Wondriska, William	30-45	*
Budney, Blossom	Cat Can't Count (1st, lg8vo, [32]p, color, dep, DJ/2.95)	Lothrop, Lee	(1962)	Wondriska, William	25-40	
Wondriska, William	John John Twilliger (1st {std}, sm ob4to, unpag, ibds, 1-color, DJ/3.50)	Holt, Rinehart	(1966)	Wondriska, William	20-35	
Wondriska, William	Long Piece of String (1st {std}, ob8vo, [44]p, color, DJ/2.75)	Holt, Rinehart	1963	Wondriska, William	25-40	
Wondriska, William	Mr. Brown and Mr. Grey (1st {std}, sq8vo, 39p, color, cep, DJ/3.95)	Holt, Rinehart	(1968)	Wondriska, William	30-45	
Wondriska, William	Puff (1st, sm4to, unpag, 1-color, pep, DJ/2.75)	Pantheon	(1960)	Wondriska, William	30-50	
Wondriska, William	Tomato Patch (1st {std}, 4to, [35]p, color, pep, DJ/3.50)	Holt, Rinehart	(1964)	Wondriska, William	60-90	R
Buck, Pearl S.	Fairy Tales of the Orient (1st {std}, 8vo, 320p, ibds, color, DJ/5.95)	Simon/Schuster	(1965)	Wong, Jeanyee	50-80	
Meigs, Cornelia L.	Fair Wind to Virginia (1st {std}, 8vo, blue cl, 198p, b/w, DJ/2.75)	Macmillan	1955	Wonsetler, Jon	30-50	
Coatsworth, Eliz.	Thief Island (1st {std}, 8vo, 118p, blue cl, b/w, pep, DJ/1.75)	Macmillan	1943	Wonsetler, Jon	30-50	
Wood, Esther	Great Sweeping Day (1st {std}, 12mo, 158p, b/w, pep, DJ/1.75)	Longmans	1936	Wood, Esther	30-50	
Wood, Esther	Pedro's Coconut Skates (1st {std}, sm8vo, 191p, pep, DJ/1.50)	Longmans	1938	Wood, Esther	25-40	
Horn, Madeline D.	Farm on the Hill (1st, lg8vo, 78p, blue cl, 8cp, pep, DJ/2.00)	Scribner	1936	Wood, Grant	175-300	
Hallock, Grace T.	Boy Who Was (1st {std}, lg8vo, 153p, ipcb, 10cp, pep, NH)	Dutton	(1928)	Wood, Harrie	70-125	
Pease, Howard	Gypsy Caravan (1st {std}, 8vo, 254p, col frn, pep)	Doubleday/Doran	1930	Wood, Harrie	80-125	
Hallock, Grace T.	Petersham's Hill (1st, sm8vo, green cl, 132p, 5 fp b/w, pep)	Dutton	(1927)	Wood, Harrie	35-60	*
N/A	Bedtime Story Book (lg4to, wraps, 16cp)	L: Birn Bros.	(1943)	Wood, Lawson	150-225	
Kernahan, John C.	Bow-Wow Book (1st, 4to, 84p, ipcb, b/w pl)	L: J. Nesbit	1912	Wood, Lawson	60-90	
Raiker, Alice M.	Brontos and the Tootle-Bird (4to, green cl, p-o, 16 fp color)	Valentine	[1904]	Wood, Lawson	400-600	
Wood, Lawson	Lawson Wood's Animal Book (4to, stiff wraps, unpag, color)	Whitman	1936	Wood, Lawson	80-130	
N/A	Old Nursery Rhymes (4to, 142p, beige cl, 24cp)	L: Nelson	[1933]	Wood, Lawson	200-300	
Wood, Lawson	Prehistoric Proverbs (sm folio, ibds, p-o, 12 ticp)	L: Collier	[1905]	Wood, Lawson	300-450	
Finnemore, John	Red Men of the Dusk (1st AM, 12mo, 328p, ibds, 8pl)	Lippincott	1900	Wood, Lawson	50-80	*
Hinkson, Henry A.	Splendid Knight (1st, 8vo, 262p, grey cl, b/w)	L: F.V. White	1905	Wood, Lawson	150-220	
Tracy, Louis	The Invaders (1st, 8vo, maroon cl, 428p, 4pl)	L: C. Pearson	1901	Wood, Lawson	75-100	*
Bond, Michael	Thursday Ahoy! (1st AM {std}, 8vo, 130p, b/w, DJ/3.95)	Lothrop, Lee	(1970)	Wood, Leslie	30-50	
Wood, Marni & Harrie	Something Perfectly Silly (1st, sm sq4to, ibds, [66]p, color, pep)	Knopf	1930	Wood, M.& H.	100-160	*
Wood, Nancy	Little Wrangler (1st {std}, 4to, 49p, DJ/3.25, b/w photos by...)	Doubleday	(1966)	Wood, Myron	25-40	
Hyne, Charles J.	Adventures of Captain Kettle (1st, sm8vo, 318p, red/gilt, 14pl)	L: Pearson	1898	Wood, Stanley	80-140	
Henty, G.A.	No Surrender! (1st AM, 12mo, 345p, red/gilt, b/w)	Scribner	1899	Wood, Stanley	100-165	
Fenn, Geo. Manville	Old Gold (1st, sm8vo, 416p, teg, gilt, 8pl)	L: Nister	(1900)	Wood, Stanley	60-90	
Jewett, Sarah O.	Deephaven (1st, 8vo, gilt, 305p, teg, b/w)	Houghton	1894	Woodbury, C.& M.	80-125	
Keith, Harold V.	Pair of Captains (1st {std}, 8vo, 100p, b/w, DJ/2.50)	Crowell	(1951)	Woodbury, Mabel	25-40	*
Crawford, Phyllis	Secret Brother (1st, sm8vo, 238p, b/w, DJ/1.50)	Henry Holt & Co.	(1941)	Woodbury, Mabel	25-40	
Keith, Harold V.	Shotgun Shaw: A Baseball Story (1st, 8vo, 163p, b/w, DJ/2.00)	Crowell	(1949)	Woodbury, Mabel	25-40	*
Lang, Andrew	Book of Dreams & Ghosts (1st, sm8vo, 303p, gilt, teg, cvr by...)	L: Longmans	1897	Woodroffe, Paul	100-175	
Steedman, C.M.	Child's Life of Jesus (1st, 8vo, 423p, white/gilt, 30cp, pep)	L: Jack	[1906]	Woodroffe, Paul	100-180	
Lemon, Mark	Enchanted Doll (1st, 8vo, 64p, p-o, 4cp)	L: Jack	[1915]	Woodroffe, Paul	40-70	*
Mourat, Joseph	Humpty Dumpty & other Songs (1st, sq4to, ibds, 32p, 7 fp b/w)	L: Blackwell	1920	Woodroffe, Paul	200-285	
Shakespeare, Wm.	The Tempest (1st, 4to, gilt, teg, 130p, 20 ticp, pep)	L: Chapman	1908	Woodroffe, Paul	170-240	
Moorat, Joseph	Thirty Old-Time Nursery Songs (1st, lg4to, 32p, ibds, color, pep)	L: Jack	[1895]	Woodroffe, Paul	200-300	
Moorat, Joseph	Ye Booke of Nursery Rhymes (1st, lg ob4to, [47]p, ipcb, b/w)	L: G. Bell	(1895)	Woodroffe, Paul	160-240	
Moorat, Joseph	Ye Second Book of Nursery Rhymes (1st, ob4to, ipcb, 54p, b/w)	L: G. Allen	1896	Woodroffe, Paul	100-175	
Woodruff, Helen S.	Mis' Beauty (1st, 12mo, 163p, p-o, 5cp)	A. Harriman	1911	Woodruff, Helen S.	80-120	*
Smith, Gertrude	Wonderful Stories of Jane & John (1st, 8vo, 74p, 10cp)	Herbert Stone	1899	Woods, Alice	100-150	

AUTHOR	TITLE	PUBLISHER	DATE	ARTIST	PRICE	LC
King, Edith H.	Adventures in Toyland (1st, 4to, blue/gilt, AEG, 152p, 8cp)	L: Blackie	[1897]	Woodward, Alice B.	170-240	
Carroll, Lewis	Alice in Wonderland (1st, 8vo, 161p, 8cp)	L: Bell	1914	Woodward, Alice B.	80-120	
N/A	Banbury Cross... (1st, 8vo, unpag, red cl, 29pl)	L: Dent	1893	Woodward, Alice B.	55-80	*
Sewell, Anna	Black Beauty (1st, 8vo, 224p, 8cp)	L: Bell	1931	Woodward, Alice B.	55-80	
Jerrold, Walter	Bon-Mots of the Eighteenth Century (1st, 16mo, 195p, gilt, b/w)	L: Dent	1897	Woodward, Alice B.	60-90	
Sigerson, Dora	Do-Well & Do-Little (1st, 8vo, 210p, p-o, 4cp)	L: Cassell	(1913)	Woodward, Alice B.	70-100	
Morris, Alice T.	Elephant's Apology (1st, sm8vo, AEG, 152p, blue/gilt, b/w, cep)	L: Blackie	1899	Woodward, Alice B.	100-160	
Countess of Jersey	Eric Prince of Lorlonia (1st, 8vo, gilt, AEG, 182p, 8 fp b/w)	L: Macmillan	1895	Woodward, Alice B.	120-200	
Molesworth, Mrs.	House that Grew (1st, 12mo, 206p, orange/gilt, 7pl)	L: Macmillan	1900	Woodward, Alice B.	75-100	
Ewing, Juliana H.	Lob Lie-by-the-Fire (1st, sq8vo, teg, 189p, 8cp)	L: Bell	1909	Woodward, Alice B.	50-80	
Clark, Mary S.	Lost Legends of the Nursery Songs (1st, 12mo, 278p, uncut, 8cp, pep)	L: G. Bell	1920	Woodward, Alice B.	60-90	
Gatty, Mrs. Alfred	Parables from Nature (1st, 8vo, green cl, 350p, 8pl, pep)	L: G. Bell	1910	Woodward, Alice B.	60-80	
Barrie, James M.	Peter Pan (1st, sm8vo, blue cl, 73p, 16 illus, pep)	Silver Burdette	(1916)	Woodward, Alice B.	70-100	
Barrie, James M.	Peter Pan Picture Book (1st, lg8vo, 62p, p-o, 28cp, pep)	L: G. Bell	1907	Woodward, Alice B.	200-300	
Gilbert, W.S.	Pinafore Picture Book (1st, 4to, 131p, blue cl, 16cp, pep)	L: G. Bell	1908	Woodward, Alice B.	90-160	
Braine, Sheila E.	Princess of Hearts (1st, 8vo, AEG, 172p, green/gilt, col frn)	L: Blackie	1899	Woodward, Alice B.	70-100	
Howes, Edith	Rainbow Children (1st, 8vo, blue/gilt, p-o, 250p, 4cp)	L: Cassell	1912	Woodward, Alice B.	70-100	
Hendry, Hamish	Red Apple & Silver Bells (1st, 8vo, 151p, AEG, red/silver, 20cp)	L: Blackie	(1897)	Woodward, Alice B.	90-140	
Sharp, Evelyn	Round the World to Wympland (1st, sm8vo, 235p, 8pl)	L: John Lane	1901	Woodward, Alice B.	80-120	
Gilbert, W.S.	Story of the Mikado (1st, sm4to, ibds, 114p, 6cp, pep)	L: O'Connor	1921	Woodward, Alice B.	55-80	
Braine, Sheila E.	To Tell the King the Sky is Falling (1st, 8vo, AEG, 171p, 8pl, cep)	L: Blackie	(1896)	Woodward, Alice B.	60-100	
Morris, Alice T.	Troubles of Tatters (1st, lg8vo, 155p, gilt, 8 fp b/w, cep)	L: Blackie	[1898]	Woodward, Alice B.	80-120	
Kingsley, Charles	Water Babies (1st, 12mo, red/gilt, 256p, 4cp)	L: Blackie	1909	Woodward, Alice B.	60-90	*
Dalgliesh, Alice	America Travels... (1st, 8vo, 121p, b/w)	Macmillan	1933	Woodward, Hildegarde	25-40	
Dalgliesh, Alice	Blue Teapot (1st, 8vo, 73p, col frn, pep)	Macmillan	1931	Woodward, Hildegarde	35-60	
Wasson, Valentina P.	Chosen Baby (1st {A}, ob8vo, blue cl, [48]p, color, pep)	Carrick/Evans	(1939)	Woodward, Hildegarde	55-80	*
Wasson, Valentina P.	Chosen Baby (1st {revised ed}, 8vo, 46p, color, DJ/2.00)	Lippincott	(1950)	Woodward, Hildegarde	30-50	
Dalgliesh, Alice	Christmas (1st, 8vo, 232p, col frn, b/w, pep)	Scribner	1934	Woodward, Hildegarde	40-60	
Coatsworth, Eliz.	Country Neighborhood (1st {std}, 8vo, 181p, DJ/2.50, decor by...)	Macmillan	1944	Woodward, Hildegarde	25-45	
Davis, Lavinia R.	Danny's Luck (1st, ob4to, ipcb, [46]p, fp 2-color, pep, DJ/2.50)	Doubleday	1953	Woodward, Hildegarde	45-60	
Woodward, Hildegard	Everyday Children (1st, sq12mo, ipcb, [48]p, 1-color, pep, DJ/1.00)	NY: Oxford U.Pr.	(1935)	Woodward, Hildegarde	30-60	*
Wright, Isa L.	Having Fun (1st, 12mo, 124p, color)	Houghton	(1929)	Woodward, Hildegarde	35-60	*
Stone, Amy W.	Here's Juggins (1st, sm8vo, 162p, blue cl, 6cp, pep, DJ/2.00)	Lothrop, Lee	1936	Woodward, Hildegarde	40-65	
Stone, Amy W.	P-Penny & his Little Red Cart (1st, sm8vo, 165p, color, pep)	Lothrop, Lee	1934	Woodward, Hildegarde	50-80	
Kingman, Lee	Philippe's Hill (1st {std}, 8vo, 86p, b/w, DJ/2.00)	Doubleday	1950	Woodward, Hildegarde	30-45	*
Dalgliesh, Alice	Relief's Rocker (1st, 8vo, 62p)	Macmillan	1932	Woodward, Hildegarde	30-45	
Davis, Lavinia R.	Roger & the Fox (1st {std}, ob4to, [43]p, ipcb, dep, color, DJ/2.00, CH)	Doubleday	1947	Woodward, Hildegarde	60-100	
Davis, Lavinia R.	Round Robin (1st, 8vo, 147p, b/w, DJ/1.50)	Scribner	1943	Woodward, Hildegarde	25-45	
Dalgliesh, Alice	Roundabout (1st, 8vo, 64p, b/w, pep, DJ/1.75)	Macmillan	1934	Woodward, Hildegarde	30-50	
Davis, Lavinia R.	Summer is Fun (1st {std}, sm ob4to, ibds, 48p, color, pep, DJ/2.50)	Doubleday	1951	Woodward, Hildegarde	35-60	
Davis, Lavinia R.	Wild Birthday Cake (1st {std}, ob4to, [50]p, ibds, pep, color, DJ/2.50, CH)	Doubleday	1949	Woodward, Hildegarde	70-120	
Bryant, Bernice M.	Yammy Buys a Bicycle (1st, 8vo, 168p, pep, 5cp, DJ/1.75)	Whitman	1940	Woodward, Hildegarde	30-45	
N/A	Golden Ship... (1st, 8vo, 98p, green bds, gilt, b/w)	(London)	1900	Woodward/Bell	140-200	*
Worm, Piet	3 Little Horses (1st, narrow 4to, red bds, 62p, pep, DJ/2.95)	Random	(1954)	Worm, Piet	100-165	
Bawden, Nina	Three on the Run (1st AM {std}, 8vo, 224p, b/w, DJ/3.75)	Lippincott	(1965)	Worth, Wendy	20-30	
Dixon, Thomas	Fall of a Nation (1st, 12mo, red/gilt, 362p, 6pl)	Appleton	1916	Wrenn, Charles	40-65	
Jewett, Eleanore	Judith and Jane (1st, sm8vo, 318p, p-o, color)	Barse/Hopkins	1925	Wrenn, Charles	25-45	
Service, Robert W.	Rhymes of a Red Cross Man (1st, 8vo, 192p, red/gilt, 8cp)	Barse/Hopkins	1916	Wrenn, Charles	30-50	
Judson, Clara I.	Virginia Lee (1st, sm8vo, gilt, 308p, 4pl, DJ)	Barse/Hopkins	(1926)	Wrenn, Charles	30-45	
Claudy, C.H.	Tell Me Why Stories (1st {this fmt}, 8vo, blue cl, 209p, 8cp)	McBride	1914	Wrenn, Thomas	25-40	*
Farrow, George E.	Adventures in Wallypug-Land (1st, 8vo, AEG, gilt, 186p, b/w)	L: Methuen	1898	Wright, Alan	120-200	
Farrow, George E.	Adventures in Wallypug-Land (1st AM, 8vo, blue cl, AEG, b/w)	New Amsterdam	1899	Wright, Alan	100-165	*
Farrow, George E.	Baker Minor & Dragon (1st, lg8vo, blue/gilt, AEG, 210p, b/w)	L: A. Pearson	1902	Wright, Alan	120-170	*
Wright, Alan	Bingo and Babs (1st, 4to, bds, p-o, 12cp)	L: Blackie	(1919)	Wright, Alan	150-200	
Farrow, George E.	Little Panjandrum's Dodo (1st, 8vo, 210p, gilt, b/w)	L: Skeffington	1899	Wright, Alan	70-100	
Farrow, George E.	Mandarin's Kite (1st, 8vo, 154p)	L: Skeffington	1900	Wright, Alan	60-90	*
Farrow, George E.	New Panjandrum (1st, 8vo, 199p, gilt, AEG, b/w)	L: A. Pearson	1902	Wright, Alan	90-120	
Lowe, Samuel E.	New Story of Peter Rabbit (1st, 16mo, tan bds, unpag, 8cp, pep)	Whitman	1926	Wright, Alan	80-120	
Farrow, George E.	Professor Philanderpan (1st, 8vo, 216p, green/gilt, AEG, b/w)	L: A. Pearson	1904	Wright, Alan	60-100	*
Low, Frances H.	Queen Victoria's Dolls (1st, 4to, [86]p, gilt, AEG, 39cp)	L: Newnes	1894	Wright, Alan	250-400	
Herbertson, Agnes	Sing Song Stories (4to, ibds, 111p, p-o, 3cp by...)	L: H. Milford	[1922]	.Wright, Alan	100-170	
Farrow, George E.	Wallypug at Play (folio, ibds, 12 chromos)	L: R. Tuck	[1895]	Wright, Alan	400-650	
Farrow, George E.	Wallypug Birthday Book (1st, sq8vo, gilt, AEG, 143p, 12cp)	L: Routledge	1904	Wright, Alan	180-270	
Farrow, George E.	Wallypug in Fogland (1st, 8vo, 207p, blue/gilt, AEG, b/w)	L: A. Pearson	1904	Wright, Alan	200-300	
Farrow, George E.	Wallypug in London (1st, 8vo, 174p, uncut, b/w)	L: Methuen	1898	Wright, Alan	200-300	
Farrow, George E.	Wallypug in the Moon (1st AM, 8vo, 256p, AEG, blue/gilt, b/w)	Lippincott	1905	Wright, Alan	200-300	
Farrow, George E.	Wallypug in the Moon (1st, 8vo, AEG, 256p, grey/gilt, fp b/w)	L: A. Pearson	1905	Wright, Alan	200-300	
Farrow, George E.	Wallypug Tales (1st, sm folio, [35]p, grey ibds, fp color)	L: R. Tuck	[1904]	Wright, Alan	500-750	
N/A	Cinderella (1st, 4to, [10]p, wraps, color)	Rand/McNally	(1912)	Wright, Blanche F.	100-150	
Rippey, Sarah C.	Goody-Naughty Book (1st, 12mo, tan cl, p-o, [62]p, color)	Rand/McNally	(1913)	Wright, Blanche F.	50-85	
Mother Goose	Jolly Mother Goose (1st, folio, [66]p, p-o, 19cp)	Rand/McNally	(1916)	Wright, Blanche F.	100-170	
Jackson, Leroy F.	Peter Patter Book (1st, lg4to, 110p, color, pep)	Rand/McNally	(1918)	Wright, Blanche F.	70-100	
Mother Goose	Real Mother Goose (1st, lg4to, [132]p, color, pep)	Rand/McNally	(1916)	Wright, Blanche F.	100-170	*
Mother Goose	Real Mother Goose ([new ed.], lg4to, 134p, color, DJ/2.00)	Rand/McNally	(1941)	Wright, Blanche F.	50-80	*
Rippey, Sarah C.	Sunny-Sulky Book (1st, sm8vo, [40]p, p-o, 12cp)	Rand/McNally	(1915)	Wright, Blanche F.	45-80	
Hunt, Mabel L.	Boy Who Had no Birthday (1st, 8vo, orange cl, 259p, fp b/w, DJ/1.75)	Stokes	1935	Wright, Cameron	40-65	
Hunt, Mabel L.	Lucinda: Little Girl of 1860 (1st, sm8vo, 233p, blue cl, b/w)	Stokes	1934	Wright, Cameron	25-40	*
Bailey, Carolyn S.	Stories and Rhymes for a Child (1st, 8vo, 194p, col frn, p-o, 5pl)	Milton Bradley	1909	Wright, Cameron	25-40	*

AUTHOR	TITLE	PUBLISHER	DATE	ARTIST	PRICE	LC
Reeves, William P.	New Zealand (1st, 8vo, gilt, teg, 241p, 75cp)	L: A&C Black	1908	Wright, F.& W.	100-165	
Barske, Charlotte	King Cotton (1st, folio, wraps, 23p, color)	A.& W. Guild	1938	Wright, George	100-165	
Mabie, Hamilton W.	Norse Stories (1st, 8vo, green/gilt, 250p, 10cp)	Dodd	1901	Wright, George	80-130	
Rice, Alice H.	Romance of Billy-Goat Hill (1st, 12mo, green/gilt, 404p, 8pl)	Century	1912	Wright, George	30-45	
Kingsley, Charles	Water Babies (1st, lg8vo, 231p, 8cp, pep)	Wessels	1900	Wright, George	70-100	
Goldsmith, Oliver	Vicar of Wakefield (1st, 8vo, green/gilt, 260p, teg, 13cp)	L: A&C Black	1903	Wright, John M.	100-160	
Robinson, Mabel L.	All by Ourselves (1st, sm8vo, 254p, decor by...)	Dutton	(1924)	Wright, Mary S.	25-40	*
Paine, Albert B.	Beacon Prize Medals (1st, 12mo, 325p, 6pl)	Baker/Taylor	1899	Wright/Huestis	40-60	*
Wyants, Miche	Giraffe of King Charles X (1st, 12mo, 54p, color, DJ/2.50, NYTBI)	McGraw-Hill	(1964)	Wyants, Miche	30-50	*
Coburn, John B.	Anne and the Sand Dobbies (1st, 8vo, 121p, DJ/3.50, pep by...)	Seabury Press	1964	Wyeth, Andrew	30-50	
Malory, Thomas	Arthur Pendragon of Britain (1st, 8vo, 542p, uncut, 4pl, pep, DJ/5.00)	Putnam	(1943)	Wyeth, Andrew	170-250	*
White, Robb	Smuggler's Sloop (1st {std}, 8vo, 249p, 4 fp b/w, DJ/1.75)	Little/Brown	1937	Wyeth, Andrew	80-130	*
White, Robb	Smuggler's Sloop (1st [this pub.], 8vo, 249p, 4 fp b/w, DJ/1.00)	Doubleday	1947	Wyeth, Andrew	45-70	*
Johnson, Edna	Anthology of Children's Literature (1st, 4to, 917p, 15cp, pep, DJ/5.00)	Houghton	1940	Wyeth, N.C.	250-400	
White, Stewart E.	Arizona Nights (1st, 8vo, gilt, p-o, 351p, 7cp)	McClure	1907	Wyeth, N.C.	80-130	
Mulford, Clarence	Bar 20 (1st [1st bk.], sm8vo, 382p, 2pl by...)	Outing	1907	Wyeth, N.C.	250-400	
Parrish, Randall	Beth Norvell (1st, 8vo, 341p, tan cl, col frn by...)	McClurg	1907	Wyeth, N.C.	60-90	
Stevenson, Rbt. L.	Black Arrow (1st, lg8vo, teg, p-o, 328p, 14cp, pep, SC)	Scribner	1916	Wyeth, N.C.	170-240	
Nordhoff, Charles	Bounty Trilogy (1st, 8vo, 903p, 12cp, pep, DJ/3.50)	Little/Brown	1940	Wyeth, N.C.	180-250	
Malory, Thomas	Boy's King Arthur (1st, lg8vo, p-o, teg, 321p, 14cp, pep, SC)	Scribner	1917	Wyeth, N.C.	200-300	
Pier, Arthur S.	Boys of St. Timothy's (1st, sm8vo, 284p, gilt, 3pl, PPPa)	Scribner	1904	Wyeth, N.C.	70-100	
Sabatini, Rafael	Captain Blood (1st, 12mo, black cl, 356p, col frn by...)	Houghton	1922	Wyeth, N.C.	80-140	*
Longfellow, H.W.	Courtship of Miles Standish (1st, lg8vo, 148p, gilt, p-o, 8cp, pep)	Houghton	1920	Wyeth, N.C.	170-240	
Connolly, James B.	Crested Seas (1st, sm8vo, 311p, gilt, teg, 2pl by..)	Scribner	1907	Wyeth, N.C.	40-65	
Stevenson, Rbt. L.	David Balfour (1st, lg8vo, p-o, 356p, 9cp, pep, SC)	Scribner	1924	Wyeth, N.C.	200-300	
Boyd, James	Drums (1st, lg8vo, gilt, p-o, 409p, 17cp, pep, SC)	Scribner	1928	Wyeth, N.C.	200-300	
Hewes, Agnes D.	Glory of the Seas (1st {std}, sm8vo, 315p, blue cl, col frn, NH)	Knopf	1933	Wyeth, N.C.	45-70	
Longfellow, H.W.	Hiawatha (1st, 8vo, red/gilt, teg, 242p, frn by...)	Houghton	1911	Wyeth, N.C.	400-600	
Connolly, James B.	Hiker Joy (1st, sm8vo, red/gilt, uncut, 244p, 4pl)	Scribner	1920	Wyeth, N.C.	50-80	
Rollins, Philip A.	Jinglebob (1st, lg8vo, black cl, 263p, p-o, 4cp, pep, SC)	Scribner	1930	Wyeth, N.C.	250-350	
Stevenson, Rbt. L.	Kidnapped (1st, lg8vo, map, teg, 289p, 14cp, pep, SC)	Scribner	1913	Wyeth, N.C.	250-350	
Boyles, Kate	Langford of the Three Bars (1st, 8vo, 278p, 4cp)	McClurg	1907	Wyeth, N.C.	70-100	
Doyle, Arthur Conan	Last Galley (1st AM, 12mo, red cl, 321p, col frn by...)	Doubleday/Page	1911	Wyeth, N.C.	250-400	
Cooper, James F.	Last of the Mohicans (1st, lg8vo, 370p, p-o, 14cp, pep, SC)	Scribner	1919	Wyeth, N.C.	200-300	
Bulfinch, Thomas	Legends of Charlemagne (1st, lg8vo, gilt, teg, p-o, 273p, 8cp, pep)	Cosmopolitan	1924	Wyeth, N.C.	200-300	
Stewart, Elinore	Letters of a Woman Homesteader (1st, 12mo, 282p, 6pl)	Houghton	1914	Wyeth, N.C.	200-300	
Fox, John Jr.	Little Shepherd of Kingdom Come (1st, lg8vo, 322p, p-o, 14cp, pep, SC)	Scribner	1931	Wyeth, N.C.	250-350	
Johnston, Mary	Long Roll (1st, 8vo, 683p, grey/gilt, 4cp, pep)	Houghton	1911	Wyeth, N.C.	40-65	
Van Dyke, Henry	Lost Boy (1st, 12mo, 69p, green/gilt, 3pl by...)	Harper	1914	Wyeth, N.C.	30-50	
Thoreau, Henry D.	Men of Concord (1st, lg8vo, 255p, green/silver, 10cp, pep, DJ/4.50)	Houghton	1936	Wyeth, N.C.	250-400	
Verne, Jules	Michael Strogoff (1st, lg8vo, p-o, 397p, 9cp, pep, SC)	Scribner	1927	Wyeth, N.C.	200-300	
Verne, Jules	Mysterious Island (1st, lg8vo, 493p, gilt, p-o, 14cp, pep, SC)	Scribner	1918	Wyeth, N.C.	250-350	
Twain, Mark	Mysterious Stranger (1st, lg8vo, 151p, gilt, teg, p-o, 7cp)	Harper	(1916)	Wyeth, N.C.	200-300	
Spearman, Frank	Nan of Music Mountain (1st, 12mo, green/gilt, 430p, 4cp)	Scribner	1916	Wyeth, N.C.	70-125	
Palmer, G. (tr)	Odyssey of Homer (1st, 4to, red/gilt, 314p, p-o, 16cp, pep)	Houghton	1929	Wyeth, N.C.	250-350	
Parkman, Francis	Oregon Trail (1st, 8vo, 364p, p-o, 5cp, pep)	Little/Brown	1925	Wyeth, N.C.	130-200	
Cadman, S. Parkes	Parables of Jesus (1st, lg8vo, p-o, 163p, purple/gilt, pep, 8cp)	McKay	(1931)	Wyeth, N.C.	500-750	
Hay, John	Pike County Ballads (1st, 8vo, p-o, 45p, 6cp, pep)	Houghton	(1912)	Wyeth, N.C.	150-225	
Matthews, Brander	Poems of American Patriotism (1st, lg8vo, 222p, p-o, 14cp, pep, SC)	Scribner	1922	Wyeth, N.C.	250-350	
Irving, Washington	Rip Van Winkle (1st, lg8vo, 86p, teg, gilt, p-o, 8cp, pep)	McKay	(1921)	Wyeth, N.C.	250-400	
N/A	Robin Hood (1st, lg8vo, green/gilt, p-o, teg, 362p, 8cp, pep)	McKay	1917	Wyeth, N.C.	175-250	
Defoe, Daniel	Robinson Crusoe (1st, lg8vo, teg, p-o, 368p, 13cp, pep)	Cosmopolitan	1920	Wyeth, N.C.	250-350	
Marriott, Crittenden	Sally Castleton, Southerner (1st, sm8vo, uncut, 312p, col frn, 5pl)	Lippincott	1913	Wyeth, N.C.	70-125	
Wiggin, Kate D.	Scottish Chiefs (1st, lg8vo, p-o, gilt, 503p, 17cp, pep, SC)	Scribner	1921	Wyeth, N.C.	200-300	
Merwin, Samuel	Silk (1st, 12mo, 266p, red/gilt, pep, col frn by...)	Houghton	1923	Wyeth, N.C.	40-60	
Wiggin, Kate D.	Susanna & Sue (1st, 8vo, 225p, teg, p-o, dep, b/w designs by...)	Houghton	1909	Wyeth, N.C.	80-145	
Cheney, Warren	The Challenge (1st, 12mo, 386p, red cl, 4pl)	Bobbs-Merrill	(1906)	Wyeth, N.C.	30-50	
Cooper, James F.	The Deerslayer (1st, lg8vo, p-o, 462p, 9cp, pep, SC)	Scribner	1925	Wyeth, N.C.	160-240	
Andrews, Mary S.	The Militants (1st, 12mo, 379p, teg, 2pl by...)	Scribner	1907	Wyeth, N.C.	55-80	
White, Stewart E.	The Riverman (1st, sm8vo, p-o, 368p, 12pl)	McClure	1908	Wyeth, N.C.	70-100	
Baldwin, James	The Sampo (1st, 8vo, green/gilt, 368p, 4cp)	Scribner	1912	Wyeth, N.C.	150-220	
Lewis, Alfred H.	The Throwback (1st, 12mo, 347p, green/gilt, 4cp)	Outing	1906	Wyeth, N.C.	60-100	
Rawlings, Marjorie K.	The Yearling (1st {Pulitzer ed.}, 8vo, 400p, 14cp, DJ)	Scribner	1939	Wyeth, N.C.	175-275	
Rawlings, Marjorie K.	The Yearling (1st {this fmt}, lg8vo, 400p, p-o, 12cp, pep, SC)	Scribner	1940	Wyeth, N.C.	160-240	
Stevenson, Rbt. L.	Treasure Island (1st, lg8vo, p-o, gilt, teg, 273p, 14cp, pep, SC)	Scribner	1911	Wyeth, N.C.	350-500	
Roberts, Kenneth L.	Trending into Maine (1st, lg8vo, 394p, tan cl, 14cp, pep, DJ/4.00)	Little/Brown	1938	Wyeth, N.C.	175-250	
Quick, Herbert	Vandemark's Folly (1st, 12mo, gilt, 420p, 8pl)	Bobbs-Merrill	(1922)	Wyeth, N.C.	30-50	
Long, John L.	War (1st, 12mo, red/gilt, 371p, 4cp)	Bobbs-Merrill	(1913)	Wyeth, N.C.	60-100	
Kingsley, Charles	Westward Ho! (1st, lg8vo, 413p, gilt, p-o, 14cp, pep, SC)	Scribner	1920	Wyeth, N.C.	180-270	
Spearman, Frank	Whispering Smith (1st, 12mo, red cl, 421p, 4cp)	Scribner	1906	Wyeth, N.C.	80-140	
Doyle, Arthur Conan	White Company (1st, lg8vo, 363p, teg, p-o, 13cp, pep)	Cosmopolitan	1922	Wyeth, N.C.	180-240	
Yamaguchi, Tohr	Golden Crane (1st {std}, 4to, [37]p, fp b/w, DJ/3.00)	Holt, Rinehart	(1963)	Yamaguchi, Marianne	30-50	*
Larson, Jean R.	Palace in Bagdad (1st, sm4to, 94p, b/w, DJ/3.50)	Scribner	(1966)	Yamaguchi, Marianne	30-45	*
Uchida, Yoshiko	Sea of Gold (1st AM, lg8vo, 136p, b/w, DJ/3.50)	Scribner	(1965)	Yamaguchi, Marianne	30-50	
Yamaguchi, Tohr	Two Crabs and the Moonlight (1st {std}, 8vo, [32]p, b/w, pep, DJ/3.00)	Holt, Rinehart	(1965)	Yamaguchi, Marianne	25-45	
Yap, Weda	Abigail's Private Reason (1st, 12mo, 70p, col frn, b/w, pep, DJ/1.00)	Macmillan	1932	Yap, Weda	30-45	
Li, Ling-ai	Children of the Sun in Hawaii (1st, 8vo, 80p, color, pep)	D.C. Heath	(1944)	Yap, Weda	35-50	*
Pitman, Norman	Chinese Fairy Tales (1st, sm8vo, 230p, uncut, fp 1-color, pep)	Crowell	(1945)	Yap, Weda	40-60	*

AUTHOR	TITLE	PUBLISHER	DATE	ARTIST	PRICE	LC
Poston, Martha L.	Ching-Li (1st, 8vo, 40p, color, pep, DJ/1.50)	T. Nelson	(1941)	Yap, Weda	35-50	*
Coatsworth, Eliz.	Cricket & the Emperor's Son (1st, sq8vo, dep, 112p, b/w)	Macmillan	1932	Yap, Weda	55-80	*
Waldeck, JoBesse	Exploring the Jungle (1st, 8vo, 56p, p-o, color, pep)	D.C. Heath	1941	Yap, Weda	25-40	*
Clark, Dorothy	Peter on the Min (1st, 8vo, 170p, 2-color, pep, DJ/2.00)	Lothrop, Lee	(1942)	Yap, Weda	40-65	
McDonald, Lucile S.	Sheker's Lucky Piece (1st, 8vo, 79p, fp color, pep, DJ/1.75)	Oxford U. Pr.	(1941)	Yap, Weda	40-65	
Buck, Pearl S.	Stories for Little Children (1st, ob8vo, [48]p, 10 fp 2-color, DJ/1.50)	NY: John Day	(1940)	Yap, Weda	100-165	R
Chrisman, Arthur B.	Treasures Long Hidden (1st {std}, 8vo, blue cl, 302p, b/w, pep, DJ/2.50)	Dutton	1941	Yap, Weda	30-60	*
Stratton, Elenore	Wild Pasture (1st {std}, 8vo, [32]p, fp 2-color, pep, DJ/1.50)	Harper	1940	Yap, Weda	30-45	*
Oakes, Vanya	Willy Wong, American (1st, 8vo, 174p, fp b/w, pep, DJ/2.50)	J. Messner	(1951)	Yap, Weda	25-40	
Johnson, Gerald W.	Little Night-Music (1st {std}, 8vo, gilt, 125p, b/w, DJ/1.50)	Harper	1937	Yardley, Richard	80-130	
Bloch, Marie (tran)	Ivanko and the Dragon (1st {std}, lg sq8vo, [46]p, color, DJ)	Atheneum	1969	Yaroslava	30-50	
Tresselt, Alvin	The Mitten (1st, sm4to, [32]p, color, DJ/2.95)	Lothrop, Lee	1964	Yaroslava	25-45	
Yashima, Taro	Crow Boy (1st, lg4to, 37p, brown cl, color, DJ/2.75, CH)	Viking	1955	Yashima, Taro	100-175	
Kubota, Hikoho	Golden Footprints (1st {std}, 8vo, 50p, blue cl, 1-color, pep, DJ/2.95)	World	(1960)	Yashima, Taro	80-120	R
Yashima, Taro	Horizon is Calling (1st, 8vo, 276p, b/w, DJ/3.50)	Henry Holt & Co.	(1947)	Yashima, Taro	45-70	
Yashima, Taro	Momo's Kitten (1st, lg ob8vo, 33p, color, pep, DJ/2.50)	Viking	(1961)	Yashima, Taro	50-80	
Yashima, Taro	New Sun (1st, 8vo, 310p, b/w, DJ/2.75)	Henry Holt & Co.	(1943)	Yashima, Taro	50-70	
Yashima, M. & T.	Plenty to Watch (1st, sm4to, 39p, color, DJ/2.50)	Viking	1954	Yashima, Taro	80-140	R
Yashima, Taro	Seashore Story (1st, ob4to, [42]p, color, dep, DJ/4.95, CH, NYTBI)	Viking	(1967)	Yashima, Taro	60-100	
Behrens, June	Soo Ling Finds a Way (1st lg ob8vo, [31]p, 2-color, DJ/2.95)	Golden Gate	(1965)	Yashima, Taro	30-50	
Bulla, Clyde R.	Sugar Pear Tree (1st, 8vo, 54p, b/w, dep, DJ/2.75)	Crowell	(1961)	Yashima, Taro	30-50	
Yashima, Taro	Umbrella (1st, sm ob4to, 32p, pep, fp color, DJ/2.50, CH)	Viking	(1958)	Yashima, Taro	100-165	R
Yashima, Taro	Village Tree (1st, 4to, grey cl, 34p, fp color, dep, DJ/2.50)	Viking	1953	Yashima, Taro	80-125	R
Jewett, Eleanore	Which was Witch? (1st, 8vo, 160p, yellow cl, b/w, pep, DJ/2.50)	Viking	1953	Yashima, Taro	60-90	R
Yashima, Taro	Youngest One (1st, lg ob8vo, 33p, color, pep, DJ/2.75)	Viking	1962	Yashima, Taro	50-80	*
Steiner, Stan	Last Horse (1st {std}, 8vo, 71p, color, DJ/3.00)	Macmillan	(1961)	Yazz, Beatien	20-30	
Colum, Padraic	Big Tree of Bunlahy (1st, 8vo, 166p, col frn, DJ/2.25, NH)	Macmillan	1933	Yeats, Jack B.	100-165	
Colum, Padraic	Boy in Eirinn (1st AM, sm8vo, 255p, blue/gilt, col frn, 4pl)	Dutton	(1913)	Yeats, Jack B.	120-180	*
Colum, Padraic	Boy in Eirinn (1st UK, 8vo, bds, 255p, 6pl)	L: Dent	(1916)	Yeats, Jack B.	160-225	
N/A	Irish Fairy Tales (1st, 12mo, 236p, 2pl)	L: T.F. Unwin	1892	Yeats, Jack B.	300-450	
Lynch, Patricia	Turf-Cutter's Donkey (1st AM {std}, sm8vo, 245p, 5cp, dep, DJ/2.00)	Dutton	1935	Yeats, Jack B.	80-120	
Gregor, Arthur	Animal Babies (1st, 4to, [37]p, DJ/2.75, b/w, NYTBI, photos by…)	Harper	1959	Ylla	30-50	*
Bonsall, Crosby	I'll Show You Cats (1st, lg4to, unpag, DJ/2.95, NYTBI, b/w photos by…)	Harper	(1964)	Ylla	40-65	
Koffler, Camilla	Little Elephant (1st {std}, lg4to, [30]p, ibds, cep, photos by…)	Harper	1956	Ylla	60-90	R*
Brown, Margaret W.	The Duck (1st AM {std}, 4to, ibds, [40]p, DJ/2.50, b/w photos by…)	Harper	(1953)	Ylla	80-130	
Thompson, Maurice	Alice of Old Vincennes (1st [1], 8vo, 419p, green/gilt, 6pl)	Bobbs-Merrill	(1900)	Yohn, F.C.	30-50	
Smith, Francis H.	Colonel Carter's Christmas (1st, 8vo, teg, gilt, 159p, 8cp)	Scribner	1903	Yohn, F.C.	25-40	
London, Jack	Daughter of the Snows (1st, 12mo, 334p, gilt, 4cp)	Lippincott	1902	Yohn, F.C.	350-500	
Burnett, Frances H.	Dawn of a To-Morrow (1st, 12mo, brown/gilt, 156p, 8cp)	Scribner	1906	Yohn, F.C.	45-70	
Fox, John Jr.	Heart of the Hills (1st, 12mo, red/gilt, 396p, 7pl)	Scribner	1913	Yohn, F.C.	25-40	
Thomas, Lowell	Hero of Vincennes (1st, 8vo, 195p, p-o, 8cp, pep)	Houghton	1929	Yohn, F.C.	35-50	
Nicholson, Meredith	Hoosier Chronicle (1st, sm8vo, 606p, brown/gilt, 4cp)	Houghton	1912	Yohn, F.C.	25-40	
Fox, John Jr.	In Happy Valley (1st, sm8vo, 229p, red/gilt, 8pl)	Scribner	1917	Yohn, F.C.	30-50	
Lytton, Edward B.	Last Days of Pompeii (1st, lg8vo, p-o, 425p, 9cp, pep, SC)	Scribner	1926	Yohn, F.C.	70-120	
Wiggin, Kate D.	New Chronicles of Rebecca (1st, 12mo, p-o, 278p, 8pl)	Houghton	1907	Yohn, F.C.	30-50	
Parrish, Randall	Sword of the Old Frontier (1st, 8vo, 407p, tan cl, 4cp)	McClurg	1905	Yohn, F.C.	30-50	
Fox, John Jr.	Trail of the Lonesome Pine (1st, 12mo, 422p, teg, uncut, gilt, fp b/w)	Scribner	1908	Yohn, F.C.	40-65	
Dalrymple, Leona	Uncle Noah's Christmas Inspiration (1st, 12mo, 124p, pep, 4cp)	McBride	1912	Yohn, F.C.	35-60	*
Weiss, Renee K.	Bird from the Sea (1st, ob4to, [31]p, gilt, color, cep, DJ/4.50)	Crowell	(1970)	Young, Ed	30-50	
Mother Goose	Chinese Mother Goose Rhymes (1st {std}, ob4to, [48]p, color, DJ/3.95)	World	(1968)	Young, Ed	40-70	*
Yolen, Jane	Emperor and the Kite (1st, ob8vo, [31]p, color, cep, DJ/3.95, CH)	World	(1967)	Young, Ed	60-90	
Krueger, Kermit	Golden Swans (1st, 4to, gilt, 32p, fp color, cep, DJ/3.95)	World	(1969)	Young, Ed	60-90	R*
Udry, Janice M.	Mean Mouse & other Mean Stories (1st, ob8vo, unpag, ibds, 1-color, DJ/2.50)	Harper	(1962)	Young, Ed	30-50	
Jacobs, Leland (ed)	Poetry for Young Scientists (1st {std}, 8vo, [42]p, color, DJ)	Holt, Rinehart	1964	Young, Ed	35-50	
Yolen, Jane	Seventh Mandarin (1st, 4to, gilt, [34]p, color, cep, DJ/4.95)	Seabury Press	(1970)	Young, Ed	30-50	
Evans, Melvin	Tiniest Sound (1st {std}, 8vo, [48]p, color, DJ/3.50)	Doubleday	(1969)	Young, Ed	30-50	
Hillert, Margaret	Yellow Boat (1st {std}, 8vo, 27p, color, DJ/1.00)	Follett	1966	Young, Ed	20-35	*
Beard, Patten	Billy Cory, Adventurer (1st, 8vo, 196p, p-o, color, pep, DJ/1.50)	Whitman	1936	Young, Eleanor M.	40-65	
Pease, Josephine	Nimbo (1st, 8vo, p-o, 64p, color)	Whitman	(1934)	Young, Eleanor M.	100-165	
Taylor, Florance	With Fife and Drum (1st, 8vo, 129p, p-o, col frn, b/w, pep, DJ/1.50)	Whitman	1936	Young, Eleanor M.	30-50	
Young, Evelyn	Wu & Lu & Li (1st, sq12mo, [31]p, green cl, color, DJ/0.75)	NY: Oxford U.Pr.	(1939)	Young, Evelyn	40-60	
Bigham, Madge A.	Bad Little Rabbit (1st, sq12mo, 155p, color)	Little/Brown	1927	Young, Florence L.	30-50	*
Lindsay, Maud	Bobby & the Big Road (1st, 12mo, 112p, blue cl, 16cp, pep)	Lothrop, Lee	(1920)	Young, Florence L.	50-85	
Zwilgmeyer, Dikken	Inger Johanne's Lively Doings (1st, sm8vo, green cl, 261p, 8cp)	Lothrop, Lee	(1926)	Young, Florence L.	50-80	
Zwilgmeyer, Dikken	Johnny Blossom (1st, 8vo, 163p, p-o, gilt, 4cp, pep)	Pilgrim Press	(1912)	Young, Florence L.	30-50	
Lindsay, Maud	Little Missy (1st, sq8vo, 188p, 8cp, pep)	Lothrop, Lee	(1922)	Young, Florence L.	70-100	
Lindsay, Maud	Silverfoot (1st, sq8vo, 223p, 8cp, pep)	Lothrop, Lee	(1924)	Young, Florence L.	60-90	
Smith, Eleanor	Song Devices & Jingles (1st, lg sq8vo, 65p, 6cp)	Lothrop, Lee	(1920)	Young, Florence L.	30-50	*
Lindsay, Maud	Story-Teller (1st, sm sq8vo, 117p, 12cp)	Lothrop, Lee	(1915)	Young, Florence L.	60-90	
Lindsay, Maud	Toy Shop (1st, 12mo, 158p, col frn, b/w, pep)	Lothrop, Lee	(1926)	Young, Florence L.	50-80	
Kingsley, Charles	Water Babies (1st, 12mo, 280p, b/w)	Ginn & Co.	(1916)	Young, Florence L.	30-50	*
Zwilgmeyer, Dikken	What Happened to Inger Johanne (1st, sm8vo, grey cl, 283p, color)	Lothrop, Lee	(1919)	Young, Florence L.	30-45	
Grimm Bros.	Fairy Tales (1st, sm4to, ibds, 282p, col frn, b/w, pep)	Whitman	1934	Young, Goldy	40-65	
Uttley, Alison	Adventures of Peter & Judy in Bunnyland (4to, ibds, 39p, 8cp)	L: Collins	(1935)	Young, Lennie	130-200	
Young, Lillian E.	Adventures of Tommy Cat the Sailor (1st, lg8vo, 165p, 20 fp color)	Sears	(1928)	Young, Lillian E.	70-100	
Young, Lillian E.	Pussy Willow's Naughty Kittens (1st, 4to, p-o, 54p, color)	Funk/Wagnalls	(1924)	Young, Lillian E.	80-150	
Dickens, Charles	Christmas Carol (1st, 4to, ibds, 74p, 11 fp color, pep, DJ/1.00)	Grosset/Dunlap	(1939)	Young, William	40-65	
Baum, Frank J.	Laughing Dragon of Oz (1st [Big-Little bk.], sq32mo, 425p, ibds, b/w)	Whitman	(1934)	Youngren, Milt	300-500	

AUTHOR	TITLE	PUBLISHER	DATE	ARTIST	PRICE	LC
Zacharias, Thomas	But Where is the Green Parrot? (1st AM {std}, 8vo, [20]p, color, DJ/3.50)	Delacorte Pr.	1968	Zacharias, Wanda	30-45	*
Sherman, Stuart P.	Critical Woodcuts (1st, 8vo, 348p, 15 fp b/w, DJ)	Scribner	1926	Zadig, Bertrand	55-80	
Finger, Charles J.	David Livingstone: Explorer and Prophet (1st, 8vo, 300p, uncut, b/w)	Doubleday/Doran	1930	Zaidenberg, Arthur	20-35	
Mendoza, George	Digger Wasp (1st {std}, ob8vo, 48p, b/w, DJ/3.95)	Dial Press	(1969)	Zallinger, Jean	25-40	
George, Jean C.	Moon of the Deer (1st, 8vo, 40p, b/w, DJ/3.75)	Crowell	(1969)	Zallinger, Jean	20-30	
George, Jean C.	Moon of the Owls (1st, 8vo, 40p, b/w, DJ/3.25)	Crowell	(1967)	Zallinger, Jean	20-30	
Hutchins, Ross	The Mayfly (1st {std}, 8vo, 48p, color, DJ)	Addison-Wesley	(1970)	Zallinger, Jean	20-35	
George, Jean C.	Moon of the Alligators (1st, 8vo, 40p, b/w, DJ/3.75)	Crowell	(1969)	Zanazanian, Adrina	20-35	
Northrup, Mili	Watch Cat (1st {std}, ob4to, [32]p, color, DJ/3.50)	Bobbs-Merrill	(1968)	Zanazanian, Adrina	45-70	
Graham, Ruth M.	Happy Sound (1st {std}, 4to, [32]p, color, DJ/4.95)	Follett	(1970)	Zander, Hans	30-50	*
Watanna, Onoto	Japanese Blossom (1st, 8vo, 263p, gilt, uncut, teg, 4cp, dep)	Harper	1906	Zeigler, Lee W.	40-65	
Barr, Amelia E.	Thyra Varrick (1st, sm8vo, green cl, 343p, 12pl)	J.F. Taylor	1903	Zeigler, Lee W.	25-40	
Zemach, Harve	Awake and Dreaming (1st {std}, ob4to, [46]p, color, DJ/4.95)	Farrar, Straus	(1970)	Zemach, Margot	40-65	R
Grimm Bros.	Fisherman and his Wife (1st {std}, 4to, [48]p, fp 2-color, pep, DJ/3.25)	Norton	1966	Zemach, Margot	30-50	
Mincieli, Rose	Harlequin (1st, 4to, 75p, bds, 1-color, DJ)	Knopf	1968	Zemach, Margot	50-80	
Zemach, Harve	Hat with a Rose (1st, ob8vo, [32]p, 1-color, cep, DJ/1.95)	Dutton	1961	Zemach, Margot	40-65	*
Sendak, Jack	King of the Hermits (1st {std}, 8vo, red cl, 105p, b/w, DJ/3.75)	Farrar, Straus	(1966)	Zemach, Margot	40-65	
Blitch, Fleming	Last Dragon (1st, 8vo, [48]p, fp b/w, DJ/3.50)	Lippincott	(1964)	Zemach, Margot	30-50	
Zemach, Margot	Little Tiny Woman (1st, sq24mo, [30]p, fp 2-color, DJ/1.95)	Bobbs-Merrill	1965	Zemach, Margot	25-45	
Singer, Isaac B.	Mazel and Shlimazel (1st, ob4to, 42p, red cl, fp color, DJ/4.50)	Farrar, Straus	(1967)	Zemach, Margot	50-80	R
Zemach, Harve	Mommy, Buy Me a China Doll (1st {std}, ob4to, 32p, color, cep, DJ/3.95)	Follett	(1966)	Zemach, Margot	30-50	R
Zemach, Harve	Nail Soup: Swedish Folktale (1st, 4to, 32p, color, DJ/2.50)	Follett	(1964)	Zemach, Margot	30-50	
Williams, Jay	Question Box (1st {std}, lg8vo, beige cl, 46p, fp 3-color, DJ/2.95)	Norton	1965	Zemach, Margot	40-65	*
Zemach, Harve	Salt, a Russian Tale (1st, ob4to, 32p, color, DJ/3.50)	Follett	(1965)	Zemach, Margot	30-50	
Zemach, Harve	Small Boy is Listening (1st [1st bk.], 8vo, 30p, 1-color, DJ/2.75)	Houghton	1959	Zemach, Margot	50-80	
Zemach, Harve	Speckled Hen (1st {std}, ob8vo, [36]p, color, DJ/3.50)	Holt, Rinehart	(1966)	Zemach, Margot	40-65	*
Hahn, Hannelore	Take a Giant Step (1st, narrow lg4to, 32p, color, DJ/2.75)	Little/Brown	1960	Zemach, Margot	40-70	
Zemach, Harve	The Judge: An Untrue Tale (1st {std}, ob4to, [46]p, color, DJ/4.50, CH)	Farrar, Straus	(1969)	Zemach, Margot	50-80	
Zemach, Margot	Three Sillies: A Folk Tale (1st {std}, ob8vo, [32]p, color, DJ/3.25)	Holt, Rinehart	(1963)	Zemach, Margot	30-50	
Zemach, Harve	Too Much Nose... (1st {std}, 8vo, [44]p, ibds, 2-color, DJ/3.95)	Holt, Rinehart	(1967)	Zemach, Margot	30-45	
Zemach, Harve	Tricks of Master Dabble (1st {std}, 8vo, [32]p, ibds, color, DJ/3.50)	Holt, Rinehart	(1965)	Zemach, Margot	30-50	
Singer, Isaac B.	When Shlemiel Went to Warsaw (1st, 8vo, 115p, fp b/w, DJ/4.50, NH)	Farrar, Straus	(1968)	Zemach, Margot	60-90	
Melcher, Marguerite	Why Don't You Draw a Dog (1st {std}, 8vo, 28p, fp color, DJ/2.95)	Little/Brown	(1962)	Zemach, Margot	30-50	*
Stafford, Kay	Ling Tang & the Lucky Cricket (1st, 4to, 80p, red cl, color, DJ/2.00)	Whittlesey	(1944)	Zibold, Louise	35-50	
Zimnik, Reiner	Bear on the Motorcycle (1st AM {std}, 4to, [38]p, fp color, cep, DJ/3.25)	Atheneum	1963	Zimnik, Reiner	40-65	
Zimnik, Reiner	Jonah, the Fisherman (1st AM, lg4to, [62]p, fp b/w, pep, DJ/3.00, NYTBI)	Pantheon	(1956)	Zimnik, Reiner	50-85	R
Zimnik, Reiner	Little Owl (1st AM {std}, 4to, [32]p, color, cep, DJ/3.50, NYTBI)	Atheneum	1962	Zimnik, Reiner	30-50	
Zimnik, Reiner	Little Roaring Tiger (1st AM {std}, 8vo, 57p, b/w, DJ/3.00)	Pantheon	(1961)	Zimnik, Reiner	40-65	
Zimnik, Reiner	Proud Circus Horse (1st AM, lg4to, [32]p, fp b/w, cep, DJ/2.75)	Pantheon	(1957)	Zimnik, Reiner	30-50	*
DeRegniers, Beatrice	Snow Party (1st {std}, sm4to, unpag, color, DJ/2.75)	Pantheon	(1959)	Zimnik, Reiner	65-100	R
Zimnik, Reiner	The Crane (1st AM, lg8vo, 94p, ibds, b/w, DJ/3.50)	Harper	(1970)	Zimnik, Reiner	30-50	
Streatfeild, Noel	Party Shoes (1st AM {std}, 8vo, 333p, grey cl, fp b/w, DJ/2.50)	Random	(1947)	Zinkeisen, Anna	30-50	
Munroe, Kirk	Brethren of the Coast (1st, 12mo, 303p, 8pl)	Scribner	1900	Zogbaum, Rufus F.	50-85	*
King, Charles	Cadet Days (1st, 12mo, 293p, blue/gilt, 25pl, PPP)	Harper	1894	Zogbaum, Rufus F.	100-175	
Zogbaum, Rufus F.	Horse, Foot & Dragoons (1st, lg8vo, 176p, teg, b/w pl)	Harper	1888	Zogbaum, Rufus F.	200-300	
Zogbaum, Rufus F.	Junior Officer of the Watch (1st, sm8vo, 311p, 4pl)	Appleton	1908	Zogbaum, Rufus F.	30-50	
Davis, Rebecca H.	Kent Hampden (1st, 12mo, gilt, 152p, 4pl)	Scribner	1892	Zogbaum, Rufus F.	70-100	*
Barnes, James	Ships and Sailors (1st, ob folio, 124p, 12cp)	Stokes	1898	Zogbaum, Rufus F.	160-240	
Munroe, Kirk	Son of Satsuma (1st, 12mo, green cl, 306p, 8pl)	Scribner	1901	Zogbaum, Rufus F.	40-70	
Forsyth, George A.	Thrilling Days in Army Life (1st, sm8vo, 196p, 16pl)	Harper	1900	Zogbaum, Rufus F.	125-200	
Barnes, James	Yankee Ships and Yankee Sailors (1st, sm8vo, gilt, 281p, 13pl)	Macmillan	1897	Zogbaum, Rufus F.	30-50	
Bond, Jean C.	Brown is a Beautiful Color (1st, 4to, 39p, fp 1-color, DJ/3.50)	F. Watts	(1969)	Zuber, Barbara	40-65	*
Barker, Mrs. S.	Feathered and Four-Footed Friends (1st, sq8vo, 96p, 24cp)	L: Routledge	1883	Zwecker, John B.	80-120	*
Fryer, Jane E.	Mary Frances Garden Book (1st, lg8vo, p-o, gilt, 378p, color, pep)	Winston	(1916)	Zwirner, William F.	200-300	

Section 3

Title Cross-Reference

$30000 Bequest, (Twain, Mark)
'A' is for Anything, (Barry, Katharina)
1 Is One, (Tudor, Tasha)
10 Little Negroes, (Trier, Walter)
100 Best Fairy Tales, (N/A)
1000 Poems for Children, (Ingpen, Roger)
121 Pudding Street, (Fritz, Jean)
123 - A Book to See, (Wondriska, William)
13th Is Magic, (Howard, Joan)
14th Dragon, (Seidelman, James)
15 Thousand Miles by Stage, (Strahorn, Carrie A.)
170 Cats, (Crespi, Pachita)
20 Years of Hus'ling, (Johnson, J.P.)
2002: Childlife 100 Years from Now, (Fessenden, L.D.)
26 Ways to be Somebody Else, (Boxer, Devorah)
3 Little Horses, (Worm, Piet)
3 Wise Old Couples, (Corbett, Elizabeth T.)
365 Bedtime Stories, (Bonner, Mary G.)
40 Big Pages of Mickey Mouse, (Disney, Walt)
40 Good-Night Tales, (Fyleman, Rose)
50 Caricatures, (Beerbohm, Max)
50 Secrets of Magic Craftmanship, (Dali, Salvador)
50,000 Names for Jeff
500 Hats of Bartholomew Cubbins, (Seuss, Dr.)
51 New Nursery Rhymes, (Fyleman, Rose)
54-40 or Fight, (Hough, Emerson)
5A and 7B, (Schick, Eleanor)
69th Grandchild, (Hunt, Mabel L.)
9 Magic Wishes, (Jackson, Shirley)
900 Buckets of Paint, (Becker, Edna)
A & The, (Raskin, Ellen)
A Apple Pie, (Greenaway, Kate)
A Carol: Good King Wenceslas, (N/A)
A Friend or Two, (Nesbit, Wilbur D.)
A Man & a Woman, (Waterloo, Stanley)
A Rhinoceros? Preposterous!, (Schatz, Letta)
A Shepherd, (Broun, Heywood)
A Survey, (Beerbohm, Max)
A Time for Sleep, (Selsam, Millicent)
A Walk Out of the World, (Nichols, Ruth)
A Wish for Mimi, (Gag, Flavia)
A for Angel: Beni Montresor's ABC..., (Montresor, Beni)
A for the Ark, (Duvoisin, Roger)
A is for Always, (Anglund, Joan W.)
A is for Annabelle, (Tudor, Tasha)
A to Z Book, (Mabie, Peter)
A's and the K's, (Parker, B.)
A-Going to the Westward, (Lenski, Lois)
ABC, (Steiner, Charlotte)
ABC Book, (Falls, Charles B.)
ABC Book of Early Americana, (Sloane, Eric)
ABC Book of People, (Cole, Walter)
ABC Bunny, (Gag, Wanda)
ABC Dogs, (Tice, Clara)
ABC Mickey Mouse Alphabet Book, (Disney, Walt)
ABC Molly, (Rietveld, Jane)
ABC Mother Goose, (Frisbie, William A.)
ABC for Everyday, (Sewell, Helen)
ABC of Animals, (Williams, C.A.)
ABC of Bumptious Beasts, (Kredenser, Gail)
ABC of Buses, (Shuttlesworth, Dorothy)
ABC of Cars and Trucks, (Alexander, Anne)
ABCDEFGHIJKLMNOPQR..., (Kuskin, Karla)
Aaron in the Wildwoods, (Harris, Joel C.)
Abandoned Orchard, (Risley, Eleanor)
Abba, (Stevens, Eden V.)
Abby in the Gobi, (Choate, Florence)
Abe Lincoln Grows Up, (Sandburg, Carl)

Abe Lincoln: Log Cabin to White House, (North, Sterling)
Abecedarian Book, (Ferguson, Charles)
Abigail's Private Reason, (Yap, Weda)
Abner's Cabin, (Evers, Alf)
About Bellamy, (DeTrevino, Elizabeth)
About Customs, (Heisenfelt, Kathryn)
About Fairies...., (Sewell, Daisy)
About Harriet, (Hunt, Clara W.)
About Paris, (Davis, Richard H.)
About People, (Steig, William)
About Ricco, (Wilson, Eleanore H.)
About Things, (Windsor, Mary)
About the B'nai Bagels, (Konigsburg, E.L.)
Abraham Lincoln, (D'Aulaire, I.& E.)
Abraham Lincoln, (Daugherty, James)
Abraham Lincoln, (Foster, Genevieve)
Abraham Lincoln, (Judson, Clara I.)
Abraham Lincoln, (Martin, Patricia)
Abraham Lincoln, (Meadowcroft, Enid)
Abraham Lincoln's World, (Foster, Genevieve)
Abraham Lincoln, Friend of People, (Judson, Clara I.)
Abraham: Iterant Mouse, (Hutter, Donald)
Abroad, (Crane, Thomas)
Absurd Ditties, (Farrow, George E.)
Absurdities, (Robinson, W. Heath)
Abysmal Brute, (London, Jack)
According to Season..., (Parsons, Frances T.)
Achilles and Hector, (Gale, Agnes C.)
Achilles the Donkey, (Bates, Herbert E.)
Acorn Tree, (Angelo, Valenti)
Acrobatic Animals, (VerBeck, Frank)
Across Five Aprils, (Hunt, Irene)
Across from Indian Shore, (Robinson, Barbara)
Across the Cotton Patch, (Credle, Ellis)
Across the Fruited Plain, (Means, Florence C.)
Across the Salt Seas, (Burton, John B.)
Across the Sea, (Goffstein, M.B.)
Ad Astra, (Dante)
Adam & the Golden Cock, (Dalgliesh, Alice)
Adam Bede, (Eliot, George)
Adam of the Road, (Gray, Eliz. J.)
Adam's Balm, (Martin, Bill)
Adam's Book of Odd Creatures, (Low, Joseph)
Add-a-Line Alphabet, (Freeman, Don)
Adelaide, (Ungerer, Tomi)
Admirable Crichton, (Barrie, James M.)
Admiral Wags of USS Lexington, (Sherman, Fanny J.)
Admiral's Caravan, (Carryl, Charles E.)
Adopted Jane, (Daringer, Helen F.)
Adrift on the Amazon, (Miller, Leo E.)
Adventure Club, (Fyleman, Rose)
Adventure Rare & Magical, (Fenner, Phyllis R.)
Adventure Under Sapphire Skies, (Finger, Charles J.)
Adventure for Beginners, (Friskey, Margaret)
Adventure in Black and White, (Gatti, Attilio)
Adventure in Photography, (Thanet, Octave)
Adventure of Lady Ursula, (Hope, Anthony)
Adventure of a Happy Dolly, (Donahey, Mary D.)
Adventures & Escapes of Gustavas Vasa, (Van Loon, H.)
Adventures Every Child Should Know, (Collodi, Carlo)
Adventures in Geography, (Kay, Gertrude A.)
Adventures in Hiveland, (Stevens, Frank)
Adventures in Toyland, (King, Edith H.)
Adventures in Wallypug-Land, (Farrow, George E.)
Adventures in a Dishpan, (Groth, Eleanor)
Adventures in an Old Shoe House, (Richards, Dorothy)
Adventures in the Open, (Putnam, Nina W.)
Adventures of Admiral Frog, (Harrington, John W.)

Adventures of Akbar, (Steel, Flora A.)
Adventures of Alcassim, (Pickard, William B.)
Adventures of Andy, (Bianco, Margery W.)
Adventures of Arab, (Slobodkin, Louis)
Adventures of Benjamin Pink, (Williams, Garth)
Adventures of Benjamin and Christabel, (Austin, C.F.)
Adventures of Bob White, (Burgess, Thornton)
Adventures of Bobby Coon, (Burgess, Thornton)
Adventures of Borbee & the Wisp, (Upton, Florence)
Adventures of Bulgy Billy, (Jack, Marian)
Adventures of Buster Bear, (Burgess, Thornton)
Adventures of Captain Horn, (Stockton, Frank)
Adventures of Captain Kettle, (Hyne, Charles J.)
Adventures of Chatterer the Red Squirrel, (Burgess, T.)
Adventures of Davy Crockett, (Crockett, Davy)
Adventures of Diggeldy Dan, (Norwood, Edwin P.)
Adventures of Don Quixote, (Cervantes)
Adventures of Egbert the Easter Egg, (Armour, Richard)
Adventures of Esteban, (Butterfield, Marguerite)
Adventures of Francois, (Mitchell, S. Weir)
Adventures of Friskers & His Friends, (Hurrell, M.I.)
Adventures of Gerard, (Doyle, Arthur Conan)
Adventures of Grandfather Frog, (Burgess, Thornton)
Adventures of Gremlin, (Jones, DuPre)
Adventures of Greyfur Family, (Nyce, Vera)
Adventures of Hajji Baba, (Morier, James)
Adventures of Harlequin, (Bickley, Francis L.)
Adventures of Haroun Er Raschid, (Olcott, F.J. (ed))
Adventures of Hatim Tai, (Ensor, Dorothy)
Adventures of Herr Baby, (Molesworth, Mrs.)
Adventures of Homer Fink, (Offit, Sidney)
Adventures of Huckleberry Finn, (Twain, Mark)
Adventures of Isabel, (Nash, Ogden)
Adventures of Jack, (N/A)
Adventures of Jack Ninepins, (Averill, Esther)
Adventures of Jerry Muskrat, (Burgess, Thornton)
Adventures of Jimmy Skunk, (Burgess, Thornton)
Adventures of Johnny Appleseed, (Chapin, Harry)
Adventures of Johnny Chuck, (Burgess, Thornton)
Adventures of Johnny T. Bear, (McElroy, Margaret)
Adventures of Joujou, (Macvane, Edith)
Adventures of King Arthur, (Price, Eleanor C.)
Adventures of Kitty Cobb, (Flagg, James M.)
Adventures of Mabel, (Rountree, Harry)
Adventures of Mario, (Bonsels, Waldemar)
Adventures of Maya the Bee, (Bonsels, Waldemar)
Adventures of Merry Wink, (Whyte, Christina)
Adventures of Mickey Mouse, (Disney, Walt)
Adventures of Mickey Mouse Book # 2, (Disney, Walt)
Adventures of Monte & Molly, (Adams, Darwin)
Adventures of Mr. Horace Hedgehog, (Ardley, P.B.)
Adventures of Mr. Mocker, (Burgess, Thornton)
Adventures of Mr. Mouse, (N/A)
Adventures of Nip & Tuck, (Mitchell, Muriel M.)
Adventures of No Ordinary Rabbit, (Uttley, Alison)
Adventures of Odysseus, (Colum, Padraic)
Adventures of Odysseus, (Various)
Adventures of Ol' Mistah Buzzard, (Burgess, Thornton)
Adventures of Old Mr. Toad, (Burgess, Thornton)
Adventures of Paddy Pork, (Goodall, John S.)
Adventures of Pancho of Peru, (Nevins, Albert J.)
Adventures of Perrine, (Malot, Hector)
Adventures of Peter & Judy in Bunnyland, (Uttley, A.)
Adventures of Peter Cottontail, (Burgess, Thornton)
Adventures of Peter Whiffen, (Meadowcroft, Enid)
Adventures of Peter and Lotta, (Beskow, Elsa)
Adventures of Peterkin, (Gilly Bear)
Adventures of Pinocchio, (Collodi, Carlo)

Adventures of Poor Mrs. Quack, (Burgess, Thornton)
Adventures of Prickly Porky, (Burgess, Thornton)
Adventures of Reddy Fox, (Burgess, Thornton)
Adventures of Remi, (Malot, Hector)
Adventures of Rinaldo, (Holt, Isabella)
Adventures of Sammy Jay, (Burgess, Thornton)
Adventures of Sonny Bear, (Fox, Frances M.)
Adventures of Spider, (Arkhurst, Joyce C.)
Adventures of Theodore Roosevelt, (Emerson, Edwin)
Adventures of Three Bold Bears, (Praeger, Sophia R.)
Adventures of Tittletom, (Credle, Ellis)
Adventures of Tom Bombadil, (Tolkien, J.R.R.)
Adventures of Tom Sawyer, (Twain, Mark)
Adventures of Tommy, (Wells, H.G.)
Adventures of Tommy Cat the Sailor, (Young, Lillian E.)
Adventures of Trooper Peek-A-Boo, (Byron, May)
Adventures of Two Dutch Dolls & Golliwogg, (Upton, B.)
Adventures of Ulysses, (Lamb, Charles)
Adventures of Ulysses, (Le Marchand, Jacques)
Adventures of Uncle Billy Possum, (Burgess, Thornton)
Adventures of Uncle Lubin, (Robinson, W. Heath)
Adventures of Willy & Nilly, (Morris, Phyllis)
Adventures of a Beagle, (McCready, Thomas L.)
Adventures of a Brownie, (Craik, Dinah)
Adventures of a Dodo, (Farrow, George E.)
Adventures of a Doll, (Smith, Nora A.)
Adventures of a Japanese Doll, (Mayer, Henry)
Adventures of a Wee Mouse, (McKenna, Dolores)
Adventures of an Illustrator, (Pennell, Joseph)
Adventures of the Bunny-Boys, (McKenna, Dolores)
Adventures of the Ink Spots, (Dyer, Ruth O.)
Adventures of the Traveling Bears, (Eaton, Seymour)
Adventures on our Street, (Kay, Gertrude A.)
Adventurous Moth, (Sargent, Robert)
Adzuma, (Arnold, Edwin)
Aerial Runaway, (Chipman, Charles P.)
Aesop's Fables for Little Readers, (Brookfield, Mrs. A.)
Aesop's Fables in Rhyme, (White, Richardson)
Aesop... [Most titles], (Aesopus)
Affair at the Inn, (Wiggin, Kate D.)
Afield & Afloat, (Stockton, Frank)
Afke's Ten, (Van Hichtum, Ninke)
Afloat and Ashore on the Mediterranean, (Meriwether, Lee)
African Crafts, (Kerina, Jane)
African Wonder Tales, (Carpenter, Frances)
Africans Knew, (Pine, Tillie S.)
After they Came Out of the Ark, (Smith, E. Boyd)
Afternoon in Spain, (Simont, Marc)
Afternoon in the Attic, (Kobler, John)
Ageless Story, (Ford, Lauren)
Agony Column, (Biggers, Earl D.)
Agony in the Kindergarten, (Steig, William)
Ahmeek, (Annixter, Jane)
Air Babies, (Kalep, Elvy)
Air Pilot, (Lent, Henry B.)
Air Pilot, (Parrish, Randall)
Air Trust, (England, George A.)
Airplane Andy, (Tousey, Sanford)
Airplane Spider, (Murray, Gilbert)
Airship Dragonfly, (Hopkins, Wm. J.)
Airship in Animal Land, (Bingham, Clifton)
Akavak, an Eskimo Journey, (Houston, James A.)
Ake & his World, (Malmberg, Bertil)
Aladdin, (Latham, Jean L.)
Aladdin & his Wonderful Lamp, (Ransome, Arthur)
Aladdin's Picture Book, (Crane, Walter)
Aladdin... [Most titles], (N/A)
Alanna, (Crew, Helen)

Alaska Gold Rush, (McNeer, May)
Alaska in Story and Pictures, (Henry, Marguerite)
Alay-Oop, (Gropper, William)
Albanian Wonder Tales, (Wheeler, Post)
Alberic the Wise, (Juster, Norton)
Album of Horses, (Henry, Marguerite)
Aldo's Tower, (Carden, Priscilla)
Aleko's Island, (Fenton, Edward)
Alexander, (Littledale, Harold)
Alexander & the Magic Mouse, (Sanders, Martha)
Alexander Soames, (Kuskin, Karla)
Alexander and the Wind-Up Mouse, (Lionni, Leo)
Alexander the Gander, (Tudor, Tasha)
Alexander's Animals, (Hobbs, Barbara)
Alexander's Christmas Eve, (Knight, Marjorie)
Alexander: Tale of a Monkey, (Brown, Marion)
Alfie Finds Other Side of World, (Keeping, Charles)
Algernon and the Pigeons, (Plasmati, Valdine)
Ali, (O'Neill, Mary)
Ali Baba, (Latham, Jean L.)
Ali Baba & Aladdin, (N/A)
Ali Baba & the Forty Thieves, (Davidson (ed.))
Ali Baba and the Forty Thieves, (N/A)
Ali Hassan of Hamadan, (Ratzesberger, Anna)
Ali Lives in Iran, (Singer, Caroline)
Ali the Camel, (Wells, Rhea)
Ali's Elephant, (Creekmore, Raymond)
Alice & the White Rabbit, (Girvin, Brenda)
Alice Ann, (Judson, Clara I.)
Alice and Thomas and Jane, (Bagnold, Enid)
Alice in Blunderland, (Bangs, John K.)
Alice in Elephantland, (Bradley, Mary H.)
Alice in Jungleland, (Bradley, Mary H.)
Alice in Orchestralia, (La Prade, E.)
Alice in Wonderland, (Carroll, Lewis)
Alice in the Delighted States, (Hope, Edward)
Alice of Old Vincennes, (Thompson, Maurice)
Alice's Adventures in Pictureland, (Evans, Florence A.)
Alice-Albert Elephant, (Hayes, Marjorie A.)
Alice-All-by-Herself, (Coatsworth, Eliz.)
Alice... & Through..., (Carroll, Lewis)
Alice... Through... & Hunting, (Carroll, Lewis)
Alicia, (Means, Florence C.)
Alick's Adventures, (G.R.)
All Aboard for Wonderland, (Kingsbury, Helen O.)
All Aboard the Train, (Kessler, Ethel)
All Aboard!, (Duvoisin, Roger)
All Aboard: Poems, (Miller, Mary B.)
All Aboard: We Are Off, (Nura)
All About Cinderella, (Gruelle, Johnny)
All About David, (Boyd, Elizabeth M.)
All About Dogs, Dogs, Dogs, (Skaar, Grace M.)
All About Eggs, (Selsam, Millicent)
All About Hansel & Gretel, (Gruelle, Johnny)
All About Horses, (Henry, Marguerite)
All About Little Boy Blue, (Sterne, Emma G.)
All About Little Red Riding Hood, (Gruelle, Johnny)
All About Me, (Drinkwater, John)
All About Mother Goose, (Gruelle, Johnny)
All About Patsy, (Phipps, Mary)
All About Peter Pan, (Sterne, Emma G.)
All About Peter Rabbit, (Potter, Beatrix)
All About Pets, (Bianco, Margery W.)
All About Story Book, (N/A)
All About the Arctic and Antarctic, (Sperry, Armstrong)
All About the Fairies, (N/A)
All About the Jungle, (Sperry, Armstrong)
All About the Little Small Red Hen, (Gruelle, Johnny)

All About the Stars, (White, Anne T.)
All About the Three Bears, (N/A)
All Alone, (Bishop, Claire H.)
All Around Robin Hood's Barn, (Dyer, Walter A.)
All Around the Clock, (Mack, Robert E.)
All Around the Sun-Dial, (Hofman, Caroline)
All Around the Town, (Flack, Marjorie)
All Around the Town, (McGinley, Phyllis)
All Babies have Mummies & Daddies... (Beyer, Evelyn)
All Embarrassed, (Steig, William)
All Falling Down, (Zion, Gene)
All Kinds of Babies, (Selsam, Millicent)
All Kinds of Neighbors, (Wellesley, Howard)
All Kinds of Time, (Behn, Harry)
All Men are Enemies, (Aldington, Richard)
All My Shoes Come in Twos, (Hoberman, Mary Ann)
All Over Town, (Brink, Carol R.)
All Round the Farm, (Collins, Charles)
All Sail Set, (Sperry, Armstrong)
All Shakespeare's Tales, (N/A)
All Sizes & Shapes of Monkeys and Apes, (Armour, R.)
All Sizes of Noises, (Kuskin, Karla)
All Sorts of Comical Cats, (Bingham, Clifton)
All Sorts of Stories Book, (Lang, Leonora B.)
All Things Bright and Beautiful, (Alexander, Cecil)
All Things New, (Daugherty, Sonia)
All Those Buckles, (Gaggin, Eva R.)
All Through the Night, (Field, Rachel)
All You've Ever Wanted, (Aiken, Joan)
All by Ourselves, (Robinson, Mabel L.)
All in Free but Janey, (Johnson, Elizabeth)
All in a Suitcase, (Morse, Samuel)
All in the Day's Riding, (James, Will)
All in the Morning Early, (Leodhas, Sorche)
All in the Same Boat, (Flagg, James M.)
All on a Summer's Day, (Fischer, Marjorie)
All that Sunlight, (Zolotow, Charlotte)
All the Animals Were Angry, (Wondriska, William)
All the Best Nursery Stories & Rhymes, (N/A)
All the Days Were Antonia's, (McKown, Gretchen)
All the Lassies, (Skorpen, Liesel)
All the Mice Came, (Kraus, Robert)
All the Mowgli Stories, (Kipling, Rudyard)
All the Way to Fairyland, (Sharp, Evelyn)
All the World Over, (Lucas, E.V.)
All the World is Colour, (Clement, Marguerite)
All the Year Round, (Riley, James W.)
All the Year Round, (Robinson, Mabel L.)
All-American, (Tunis, John R.)
All-Fellows & Cloak of Friendship, (Housman, Laurence)
All-Fellows..., (Housman, Laurence)
Allan Quatermain, (Haggard, H. Rider)
Allan the Hunter, (Haggard, H. Rider)
Allegretto, (Hall, Gertrude)
Allies' Fairy Book, (Gosse (intro))
Alligator Case, (DuBois, W.P.)
Alligator Smiling in the Sawgrass, (Ironmonger, Ira)
Alliterative Alphabet..., (Elliot, Huger)
Alliterative Anomalies for Infants & Invalids, (Cowie, J.)
Allth, (Reid, Alastair)
Almanac for Moderns, (Peattie, Donald C.)
Almanac of 12 Sports, (Kipling, Rudyard)
Almena's Dogs, (Woody, Regina)
Along Came a Dog, (DeJong, Meindert)
Along Janet's Road, (Dalgliesh, Alice)
Along Sandy Trails, (Clark, Ann N.)
Along the Bosphorus, (Wallace, Susan A.)
Along the Coast, (Colmont, Marie)

Along the Erie Towpath, (Meadowcroft, Enid)
Alpatok, (Saunders, Marshall)
Alphabet Book, (Lear, Edward)
Alphabet People, (Lenski, Lois)
Alphabet Tale, (Garten, Jan)
Alphabet Tree, (Lionni, Leo)
Alphabet Zoop, (Heide, Florence P.)
Alphabet for Boys & Girls, (Field, Rachel)
Alphabet for Gourmets, (Fisher, M.F.K.)
Alphabet for Joanna, (Gregory, Horace)
Alphabet of Animals, (Park, Carton M.)
Alphabet of Aviation, (Jones, Paul)
Alphabet of Celebrities, (Herford, Oliver)
Alphabet of Indians, (Williams, Emery)
Alphabet of Magic, (Farjeon, Eleanor)
Alphabet of Puppy Care, (Weil, Lisl)
Alphonse, that Bearded One, (Carlson, Natalie S.)
Alpine Flowers & Gardens, (Flemwell, George)
Alsace-Lorraine, (Edwards, George W.)
Alvin Steadfast on Vernacular Island, (Jacobs, Frank)
Always Reddy, (Henry, Marguerite)
Always Room for One More, (Leodhas, Sorche)
Amabel and Crispin, (Clayton, Margaret)
Amahl & Night Visitors, (Menotti, Gian-Carlo)
Amanda, (Wolo)
Amanda & the Bear, (Tudor, Tasha)
Amanda Remembers, (Kraus, Robert)
Amandus, Who Was Much Too Big, (Glenn, Morris)
Amat and the Water-Buffalo, (Guillaume, Jeanette)
Amateur Gentleman, (Farnol, Jeffery)
Amazing Adventures, (Baring-Gould, Sabine)
Amazing Adventures of Dennis the Menace, (Memling, Carl)
Amazing Advens. of Letitia Carberry, (Rinehart, Mary R.)
Amazing Interlude, (Rinehart, Mary R.)
Amazing Mr. Pelgrew, (Schlein, Miriam)
Amazon: River Sea of Brazil, (Sperry, Armstrong)
Amazon: River of Promise, (Malkus, Alida S.)
Amelia Bedelia, (Parish, Peggy)
Ameliaranne Bridesmaid, (Morris, Ethelberta)
Ameliaranne Gives a Concert, (Gilmour, Margaret)
Ameliaranne and the Big Treasure, (Joan, Natalie)
Ameliaranne and the Magic Ring, (Farjeon, Eleanor)
Ameliaranne at the Circus, (Gilmour, Margaret)
Ameliaranne at the Seaside, (Gilmour, Margaret)
Ameliaranne at the Zoo, (Thompson, K.L.)
Ameliaranne in Town, (Joan, Natalie)
Ameliaranne's Moving-Day, (Morris, Ethelberta)
Ameliaranne... [Many titles], (Heward, Constance)
America, (Tooze, Ruth)
America Before Man, (Baity, Eliz. C.)
America Begins..., (Dalgliesh, Alice)
America Builds Homes, (Dalgliesh, Alice)
America First, (Evans, Lawton)
America Grows Up, (Johnson, Gerald W.)
America Moves Forward, (Johnson, Gerald W.)
America Travels..., (Dalgliesh, Alice)
America is Born, (Johnson, Gerald W.)
America's Abraham Lincoln, (McNeer, May)
America's Ethan Allen, (Holbrook, Stewart)
America's Mark Twain, (McNeer, May)
America's Own Mark Twain, (Eaton, Jeanette)
America's Paul Revere, (Forbes, Esther)
America's Robert E. Lee, (Commager, Henry)
America's Stamps..., (Petershams)
American ABC, (Petersham, Maud)
American Animal Life, (Deming, Therese O.)
American Animals, (Newell, David M.)
American Beauties, (Fisher, Harrison)

American Belles, (Fisher, Harrison)
American Claimant, (Twain, Mark)
American Emperor, (Tracy, Louis)
American Fairy Tales, (Baum, L. Frank)
American Folk & Fairy Tales, (Field, Rachel)
American Girl, (Christy, Howard C.)
American Girl, (Fisher, Harrison)
American Girls in Miniature, (Fisher, Harrison)
American Hero Stories, (Tappan, Eva M.)
American Indian Fairy Tales, (Larned, William T.)
American Indian Story, (McNeer, May)
American Pilgrimage, (Scribner, Grace)
American Riddle Book, (Withers, Carl)
American Sea Fights, (Gibbs, George)
American Songs for Children, (Palmer, Winthrop)
American Stage of Today, (N/A)
American Tall Tales, (Stoutenburg, Adrien)
American Twins of the Revolution, (Perkins, Lucy F.)
American Types, (Underwood, C.F.)
Americans, (Gibson, Charles D.)
Americans Before Columbus, (Baity, Eliz. C.)
Americans Every One, (Davis, Lavinia R.)
Amerigo, the Wandering Tortoise, (Palazzo, Tony)
Amiable Giant, (Slobodkin, Louis)
Amigo, (Schweitzer, Byrd B.)
Amigo, Circus Horse, (Cooper, Page)
Amikuk, (Montgomery, R.)
Amnon, Lad of Palestine, (King, Marian)
Among Us Cats, (Hill, William E.)
Among the Daisies, (Weatherly, Fred E.)
Among the Forest People, (Pierson, Clara D.)
Among the Freaks, (Alden, William L.)
Among the Leaves & Grasses, (Waugh, Dorothy)
Among the Meadow People, (Pierson, Clara D.)
Among the Night People, (Pierson, Clara D.)
Among the Pond People, (Pierson, Clara D.)
Among the... [Many titles], (Pierson, Clara D.)
Amos Fortune, Free Man, (Yates, Elizabeth)
Amos Judd, (Mitchell, John A.)
Amos and the Moon, (Balet, Jan B.)
Amy Moves In, (Sachs, Marilyn)
Amy and Laura, (Sachs, Marilyn)
Amy in Acadia, (Reed, Helen L.)
An ABC, (Heath, Irene)
An Alphabet, (Nicholson, William)
An Artist's Reminiscences, (Crane, Walter)
An Elephant is Not a Cat, (Tresselt, Alvin)
An Encore, (Deland, Margaret)
Anabel's Windows, (Hewes, Agnes D.)
Ananse the Spider, (Appiah, Peggy)
Anansi the Spider Man, (Sherlock, Philip)
Anatole & his Donkey, (DeBrunhoff, Laurent)
Anatole... [Most titles], (Titus, Eve)
Anchor Man, (Jackson, Jesse)
Anchor's Aweigh..., (Latham, Jean L.)
Ancient Allan, (Haggard, H. Rider)
Ancient Tales & Folklore of Japan, (Smith, Richard G.)
And It Rained, (Raskin, Ellen)
And It Was So, (Clarke, Sara K.)
And Long Remember..., (Fisher, Dorothea)
And Now Miguel, (Krumgold, Joseph)
And So My Garden Grows, (Mother Goose)
And There was America, (Duvoisin, Roger)
And Thus He Came, (Brady, Cyrus T.)
And a Good Fat Hen, (Williams, Eleanor)
And the Jackal Played the Masinko, (Hopkins, Marjorie)
And to Think I Saw It on Mulberry Street, (Seuss, Dr.)
Andiron Tales, (Bangs, John K.)

Andrew Carnegie, (Judson, Clara I.)
Andrew Carnegie & Age of Steel, (Shippen, Kath. B.)
Andrew Jackson, (Martin, Patricia)
Andrew the Lion Farmer, (Hall, Donald)
Andries, (Van Stockum, Hilda)
Androcles & the Lion, (Hawkins, Quail)
Andy & Mr. Cunningham, (Thayer, Jane)
Andy & the Lion, (Daugherty, James)
Andy & the Runaway Horse, (Thayer, Jane)
Andy Buckram's Tin Men, (Brink, Carol R.)
Andy Jackson's Water Well, (Steele, William O.)
Andy Says... Bonjour!, (Diska, Pat)
Andy and Polly, (Wells, Rhea)
Andy and the Gopher, (McKim, Audrey)
Andy, the Dog Walker, (Shortall, Leonard)
Angel Child, (Teal, Valentine)
Angel Island, (Gillmore, Inez H.)
Angel and the Donkey, (Reeves, James)
Angel in the Woods, (Lathrop, Dorothy)
Angel of Christmas, (Perry, Stella G.)
Angel's Alphabet, (Van Stockum, Hilda)
Angela of Angel Court, (Rogers, Elizabeth)
Angeline Goes Traveling, (Fox, Frances M.)
Angelino and Barefoot Saint, (Angelo, Valenti)
Angelique, (Janice)
Angelo and Rosaline, (Bettina)
Angelo, the Naughty One, (Garrett, Helen)
Angels & Ministers, (Housman, Laurence)
Angleworms on Toast, (Kantor, MacKinlay)
Angora Twinnies, (Price, Margaret E.)
Angry Moon, (Sleater, William)
Angry Waters, (Morey, Walter)
Angus... [All titles], (Flack, Marjorie)
Animal ABC, (Baum, L. Frank)
Animal ABC, (Piatti, Celestino)
Animal Alphabet, (N/A)
Animal Babies, (Gregor, Arthur)
Animal Babies, (Palazzo, Tony)
Animal Babies, (Pratt, Alice)
Animal Book, (Butler, William A.)
Animal Book and Campfire Stories, (Beard, Dan C.)
Animal Caravan, (Leet, Frank R.)
Animal Children, (Kirkwood, Edith B.)
Animal Fair, (Provensen, A.& M.)
Animal Families, (Weil, Ann Y.)
Animal Family, (Jarrell, Randall)
Animal Folk Songs for Children, (Seeger, Ruth C.)
Animal Folk Tales of America, (Palazzo, Tony)
Animal Folk of Wood & Plain, (Deming, Therese O.)
Animal Frolic, (Varner, Velma)
Animal Frolics, (Byron, May)
Animal Garden, (Nash, Ogden)
Animal Heroes, (Seton, Ernest T.)
Animal Hide & Seek, (Ipcar, Dahlov)
Animal Inn, (Moe, Virginia)
Animal Land Where... are No People, (Corbet, K.& S.)
Animal Legends of Many Lands, (Woole, Rose)
Animal Pioneers, (Coblentz, Catherine)
Animal Stories, (Duplaix, Georges)
Animal Stories from Eskimo Land, (Riggs, Renee)
Animal Story Book, (Lang, Andrew)
Animal Story Book, (Piper, Watty (ed))
Animal Story Book, (Toon, Gladys E.)
Animal Tales, (Armstrong, William)
Animal Tales from Old North State, (Cobb, Lucy M.)
Animal Trainer, (Mills, Enos A.)
Animal Why Book, (Pycraft, W.P.)
Animal's Christmas, (Eaton, Anne T.)

Animal's Conference, (Kastner, Erich)
Animal's Rebellion, (Bingham, Clifton)
Animal-Alphabet Book, (Fallon, Sara W.)
Animals Came First, (Welch, Jean L.)
Animals Came In, (Smalley, Janet)
Animals Everywhere, (D'Aulaire, I.& E.)
Animals Here and There, (Doane, Pelagie)
Animals Made by Me, (Brown, Margery)
Animals Near & Far, (Hoover, Helen)
Animals and the Ark, (Kuskin, Karla)
Animals at the Fair, (Blaisdell, E. Ward)
Animals for Me, (Lenski, Lois)
Animals from Snow White & Seven Dwarfs, (Disney, W.)
Animals in Social Captivity, (Anderson, Richard C.)
Animals in the Ark, (Guizou, P.)
Animals in the Wrong Places, (Carrington, Edith)
Animals in the Zoo, (Rojankovsky, Feodor)
Animals of Dr. Schweitzer, (Fritz, Jean)
Animals of a Sage Brush Ranch, (Pratt, Alice)
Animals of the Bible, (Fish, Helen D.)
Animals of the High Andes, (Malkus, Alida S.)
Animals on the Ceiling, (Armour, Richard)
Animals on the Farm, (N/A)
Animals on the Farm, (Rojankovsky, Feodor)
Animals to Africa, (Hall, Rosalys)
Animals' Touring Club, (Braine, Sheila E.)
Animals' Trip to Sea, (Bingham, Clifton)
Animosities, (Bacon, Peggy)
Ann Anderson's Fairy Tale Book, (Anderson, Anne)
Ann Aurelia and Dorothy, (Carlson, Natalie S.)
Ann Can Fly, (Phleger, Fred)
Ann Frances, (White, Eliza O.)
Ann at Highwood Hall, (Graves, Robert)
Ann of Bethany, (Ceder, Georgiana)
Ann's Surprising Summer, (Allee, Marjorie H.)
Anna Amelia's Apteryx, (O'Neill, Mary)
Anna and the Baby Buzzard, (Sandburg, Helga)
Anna and the King of Siam, (Landon, Margaret)
Anna the Horse, (Fatio, Louise)
Annabel, (Metcalf, Suzanne)
Annals of the Parish, (Galt, John)
Annancy Stories, (Smith, Pamela C.)
Anne Carmel, (Overton, Gwendolen)
Anne and the Sand Dobbies, (Coburn, John B.)
Anne of... [All titles], (Montgomery, Lucy M.)
Anne's Bridge, (Chambers, Robert)
Anne's House of Dreams, (Montgomery, Lucy M.)
Annie Moran, (Hurd, Edith T.)
Annie's ABC Kitten, (Steiner, Charlotte)
Annie's Spending Spree, (Watson, Nancy D.)
Another Book of Verses for Children, (Lucas, E.V.)
Another Brownie Book, (Cox, Palmer)
Another Day, (Ets, Marie H.)
Another Flock of Girls, (Perry, Nora)
Another Hardy Garden Book, (Ely, Helena R.)
Ant Ventures, (Wade, Blanche E.)
Antarctic Mystery, (Verne, Jules)
Anteater Named Arthur, (Waber, Bernard)
Anthology of Children's Literature, (Johnson, Edna)
Anthony Overman, (Michelson, Miriam)
Antigone, (Bourget, Paul)
Antique Cat, (Bradbury, Bianca)
Anton and Anne, (Carigiet, Alois)
Ants are Fun, (Myrick, Mildred)
Anybody at Home?, (Rey, Hans A.)
Anything Can Happen on a River, (Brink, Carol R.)
Anywhere in the World, (Webber, Irma E.)
Apache Gold, (Altsheler, Joseph A.)

Apache Princess, (King, Charles)
Ape in a Cape, (Eichenberg, Fritz)
Apple Orchard, (Eberle, Irmengarde)
Apple Pie..., (Steedman, Amy)
Apple Stone, (Gray, Nicholas S.)
Apple Strudel Soldier, (McGowen, Tom)
Apple Tree, (Bianco, Margery W.)
Apple Tree Cottage, (Voight, Virginia F.)
Apple Vendor's Fair, (Hubbell, Patricia)
Apple and the Arrow, (Buff, M.& C.)
Apple that Jack Ate, (Scott, William R.)
Apples of Istakhar, (Lindsey, William)
Appleseed Farm, (Douglas, Emily)
Appley Dapply's Nursery Rhymes, (Potter, Beatrix)
Appolonia's Valentine, (Milhous, Katherine)
Apprentice of Florence, (Kyle, Anne D.)
Apricot ABC, (Miles, Miska)
April Baby's Book of Tunes, (Russell, Mary A.)
April Fool Doll, (Gates, Josephine S.)
April Skies, (Lathbury, M.A.)
April Umbrella, (Friedrich, Priscilla)
April's Kittens, (Newberry, Clare T.)
Arabella & Araminta Stories, (Smith, Gertrude)
Arabella & Her Aunts, (Lenski, Lois)
Arabella of the Merry-Go-Round, (Maloy, Lois)
Arabian Nights, (Colum, Padraic (ed))
Arabian Nights, (N/A)
Arabian Nights Retold for Children, (Davidson, Gladys)
Arabian Nights' Entertainment, (N/A)
Araminta, (Evans, Eva K.)
Araminta's Goat, (Evans, Eva K.)
Arbor Day, (Fisher, Aileen)
Archie Angel, (Austin, Margot)
Archimedes Takes a Bath, (Lexau, Joan M.)
Architec-tonics, (Squires, Frederick)
Archy Does His Part, (Marquis, Don)
Arctic Orphans, (Parker, B.)
Arctic Prairies, (Seton, Ernest T.)
Arctic Rovings, (Hall, Daniel W.)
Are You Hungry, Are You Cold?, (Bemelmans, Ludwig)
Are You Square?, (Kessler, Ethel)
Are You my Friend?, (Mendoza, George)
Argonauts of the Amazon, (Kenyon, Charles R.)
Argosy of Fables, (Cooper, Frederic T.)
Aristide, (Tibber, Robert)
Aristokia, (Pezet, A. Washington)
Arizona Nights, (White, Stewart E.)
Ark Book, (Derrick, Freda)
Ark of Father Noah & Mother Noah, (Petershams)
Arkansas Planter, (Read, Opie)
Arkansaw Bear, (Paine, Albert B.)
Arm in Arm, (Charlip, Remy)
Arm of the Starfish, (L'Engle, Madeleine)
Arm-Chair at the Inn, (Smith, Francis H.)
Armadillo Who Had No Shell, (Simon, Sidney)
Armed with Courage, (McNeer, May)
Armenian Legends & Poems, (Boyajian, Zabelle C.)
Armfield's Animal Book, (Armfield, Constance)
Armies of India, (MacMunn, George F.)
Armitage, Armitage, Fly Away Home, (Aiken, Joan)
Armourer's House, (Sutcliff, Rosemary)
Army Alphabet, (Baum, L. Frank)
Army Mule, (Downey, Fairfax)
Around Old Chester, (Deland, Margaret)
Around a Toadstool Table, (Bennett, Rowena B.)
Around and About, (Chute, Marchette)
Around the Corner, (Showalter, Jean B.)
Around the House, (N/A)

Around the World in a Mailbag, (Siegel, William)
Around the World with Santa Claus, (N/A)
Around the Year, (Tudor, Tasha)
Around the Year in Iceland, (Yates, Elizabeth)
Arrow of Tee-May, (Moon, Grace P.)
Art of Living, (Grant, Robert)
Art of Walt Disney, (Field, Robert)
Art of Walter Crane, (Konody, Paul G.)
Artful Antics, (Herford, Oliver)
Arthur & His Knights, (Chaundler, Christine)
Arthur Bonnicastle, (Holland, Josiah G.)
Arthur O'Shaughnessy, (Moulton, Louise C.)
Arthur Pendragon of Britain, (Malory, Thomas)
Artie, (Ade, George)
Artie & the Princess, (Torrey, Marjorie)
Artist in Spain, (Michael, A.C.)
Artist's Models, (Aldin, Cecil)
Arturo and Mr. Bang, (Fraser, Beatrice)
As Children Do, (Nesbit, Wilbur D.)
As Happy as a King, (Nesbit, Edith)
As I See, (Artzybasheff, Boris)
As I See It, (Shackelford, L.T.)
As Is, (Hanemann, Henry W.)
As It is in Heaven, (Clark, Alfred)
As Months Go By, (Matheson, Annie)
As Told by the Typewriter Girl, (Ervin, Mabel C.)
As You Like It, (Shakespeare, Wm.)
As the Bee Sucks, (Lucas, E.V.)
As the Goose Flies, (Pyle, Katharine)
Ashes of Empire, (Chambers, Robert)
Asinette, (Frazer, Mrs. J.G.)
Ask Dr. Christmas, (Dorian, Edith)
Ask Me a Question, (Ungerer, Tomi)
Ask Mr. Bear, (Flack, Marjorie)
Ask the Windy Sea, (Pomerantz, Charlotte)
Associate Hermits, (Stockton, Frank)
Assorted Sisters, (Means, Florence C.)
Astercote, (Lively, Penelope)
Astonishing Tale of a Pen & Ink Puppet, (Herford, O.)
At Aboukir and Acre, (Henty, G.A.)
At Agincourt, (Henty, G.A.)
At Daddy's Office, (Misch, Robert J.)
At Flower Farm, (Holloway, Jane)
At Great Aunt Martha's, (Ainslie, Kathleen)
At Home, (Crane, Thomas)
At Home, a Visit in Four Languages, (Hautzig, Esther)
At Midsummer Time, (Brock, Emma)
At Our House, (McCullough, John)
At Paddy the Beaver's Pond, (Burgess, Thornton)
At War with Pontiac, (Munroe, Kirk)
At that Time, (Lawson, Robert)
At the Big House, (Culbertson, Anne V.)
At the End of Nowhere, (Means, Florence C.)
At the Foot of Windy Low, (Justus, May)
At the Foot of the Rainbow, (Stratton-Porter, Gene)
At the Gateways of the Day, (Colum, Padraic)
At the Palace Gates, (Parish, Helen R.)
At the Queen's Mercy, (Blodgett, Mabel F.)
At the Relton Arms, (Sharp, Evelyn)
At the Sign of the Golden Anchor, (Holberg, Ruth)
At the Sign of the Golden Compass, (Kelly, Eric P.)
At the Sign of the Reine Padauque, (France, Anatole)
At the Smiling Pool, (Burgess, Thornton)
At the Top of my Voice, (Holman, Felice)
Athelwold, (Rives, Amelia)
Athenians in the Classical Period, (Weisgard, Leonard)
Atlas & Beyond, (Coatsworth, Eliz.)
Atomics for the Millions, (Eidinoff, Maxwell L.)

Atta Troll, (Heine, Heinrich)
Attic Boarders, (Jacberns, Raymond)
Attic of the Wind, (Lund, Doris)
Atu, the Silent One, (Jupo, Frank)
Au Clair de la Lune, (Rey, Hans A.)
Aubrey Beardsley, (Ross, Robert B.)
Aubrey Beardsley, (Symons, Arthur)
Aucassin & Nicolette, (N/A)
Auction Block, (Beach, Rex)
Auction Pony, (Smith, Linell)
August Explains, (Ressner, Phil)
Augustus, (Bishop, Claire H.)
Augustus Ceasar's World, (Foster, Genevieve)
Auno and Tauno, (Henry, Marguerite)
Aunt Amity's Silver Wedding, (Stuart, Ruth M.)
Aunt Bella's Umbrella, (Cole, William)
Aunt Brown's Birthday, (Beskow, Elsa)
Aunt Flora, (Coatsworth, Eliz.)
Aunt Green, Aunt Brown & Aunt Lavender, (Beskow, Elsa)
Aunt Jane of Kentucky, (Hall, Eliza C.)
Aunt Jane's Nieces... [All titles], (Van Dyne, Edith)
Aunt Louisa's Choice Present, (N/A)
Aunt Sally's Friends in Fur, (Burgess, Thornton)
Aunt-Sitter, (Hawkins, Quail)
Auntie & Celia Jane & Miki, (Petersham, Maud)
Auntie's Little Rhyme Book, (LeMair, H.W.)
Aurelie, (Hardy, Arthur S.)
Australia Calling, (MacPherson, Margaret)
Autobiography of Methuselah, (Bangs, John K.)
Autobiography of a Slander, (Lyall, Edna)
Autocrat at the Breakfast Table, (Holmes, Oliver W.)
Automobiles for Mice, (Ets, Marie H.)
Automobilist Abroad, (Miltoun, Francis)
Autumn Harvest, (Tresselt, Alvin)
Autumn Songs with Music, (Linnell, Olive)
Ave Maria, (Disney, Walt)
Avery..., (Phelps, Eliz. S.)
Avion My Uncle Flew, (Fisher, Cyrus)
Awake and Dreaming, (Zemach, Harve)
Awakening, (Galsworthy, John)
Awakening of Helena Richie, (Deland, Margaret)
Away Goes Jonathan Wheeler, (Flack, Marjorie)
Away Goes Sally, (Coatsworth, Eliz.)
Away We Go, (Harris, Laura)
Away We Go!, (McEwen, Catherine)
Away Went Wolfgang, (Kahl, Virginia)
Away to Sea, (Meader, Stephen W.)
Away to the Moon, (Symonds, John)
Awful Airship, (Copeland, Walter)
Awol the Courier, (Shurtleff, Bertrand)
Azalea at Sunset Gap, (Peattie, Elia W.)
Azor... [Most titles], (Crowley, Maude)
Aztec Drums, (Lide, Alice A.)
Aztec Treasure House, (Janvier, Thomas A.)
B is for Betsy, (Haywood, Carolyn)
Bab Ballads, (Gilbert, W.S.)
Baba Yaga, (Small, Ernest)
Babar... [All titles], (DeBrunhoff, J. or L.)
Babes & Beasts, (Pope, Jessie)
Babes & Birds, (Pope, Jessie)
Babes & Blossoms, (Copeland, Walter)
Babes and Beasts, (Pope, Jessie)
Babes in Birdland, (Bancroft, Laura)
Babes in Toyland, (MacDonough, Glen)
Babes in the Wood, (N/A)
Babes of the Nations, (Thomas, Edith M.)
Babes of the Wild, (Gask, Lilian)
Babes of the Year, (Humphrey, Maud)

Babette, (Newberry, Clare T.)
Babies' Classics, (MacDonald, L.)
Baboushka & Three Kings, (Robbins, Ruth)
Baby Animals, (Brown, Margaret W.)
Baby Animals, (Williams, Garth)
Baby Bear, (Williamson, Hamilton)
Baby Bears & their Wishing Rings, (Drayton, Grace)
Baby Beebee Bird, (Massie, Diane R.)
Baby Days, (Corbett, Bertha)
Baby Days..., (Neally, Amy)
Baby Elephant & Zoo Man, (Kilbourne, Charles E.)
Baby Elephant... [Most titles], (Joslin, Sesyle)
Baby Folk, (Tucker, Elizabeth S.)
Baby Goose: His Adventures, (Ostrander, Fannie)
Baby House, (Simon, Norma)
Baby Island, (Brink, Carol R.)
Baby Ostrich & Mr. Wise Owl, (Kilbourne, Charles E.)
Baby Reindeer & Silver Fox, (Kilbourne, Charles E.)
Baby Roo, (Bannon, Laura)
Baby Scouts, (Pope, Jessie)
Baby Sister for Frances, (Hoban, Russell)
Baby Sweethearts, (Cone, Helen G.)
Baby Weems, (Grant, Joseph P.)
Baby Whale, Sharp Ears, (Beaty, John Y.)
Baby and Me!, (Tucker, Elizabeth S.)
Baby's Animal Book, (N/A)
Baby's Baedeker, (Streamer, Col. D.)
Baby's Biography, (Kaplan, A.O.)
Baby's Birthday Book, (N/A)
Baby's Book, (N/A)
Baby's Book, (Taylor, Ida Scott)
Baby's Bouquet, (Crane, Walter)
Baby's Day, (Wiederseim, Grace)
Baby's Day Book, (Robertson, W.G.)
Baby's Little Rhyme Book, (LeMair, H.W.)
Baby's Lullaby Book, (Pratt, Charles S.)
Baby's Record, (N/A)
Bachelor Ballads, (McManus, Blanche)
Bachelor Ballads, (Spurr, Harry A.)
Bachelor Belles, (Fisher, Harrison)
Bachelor's Christmas, (Grant, Robert)
Back Home, (Cobb, Irving)
Back Home, (Wood, Eugene)
Back in Time for Supper, (Furth, Dori)
Back of Time, (Ross, Margaret I.)
Back of the North Wind, (MacDonald, George)
Back to School with Betsy, (Haywood, Carolyn)
Back to the Local, (Gorham, Maurice)
Back-Fence Story, (Walker, Augusta)
Back-Seat Driver, (Robinson, Mabel L.)
Backboard Magic, (Brier, Howard M.)
Backbone of the King, (Brown, Marcia)
Backlog Studies, (Warner, Charles D.)
Backward Day, (Krauss, Ruth)
Bad Boy, Good Boy, (Ets, Marie H.)
Bad Child's Book of Beasts, (Belloc, Hilaire)
Bad Day for Martha, (Farjeon, Eleanor)
Bad Island, (Steig, William)
Bad Little Duckhunter, (Brown, Margaret W.)
Bad Little Rabbit, (Bigham, Madge A.)
Bad Mrs. Ginger, (Appleton, Honor)
Bad Parents' Garden of Verse, (Nash, Ogden)
Bad Penny, (Wheelwright, John T.)
Bad Speller, (Steig, William)
Bag of Smoke: Story of First Balloon, (Anderson, Lonzo)
Baggage to the Enemy, (Ardizzone, Edward)
Bairn's Coronation Book, (Bridgman, Clare)
Baker & the Basilisk, (McHargue, Georgess)

Baker Minor & Dragon, (Farrow, George E.)
Baker's Dozen, (Davis, Mary G.)
Baker's Dozen, (Van Rosen, Rosa)
Balboa, Swordsman & Conquistador, (Riesenberg, Felix)
Bald Face & other Animal Stories, (Evarts, Hal G.)
Baldy of Nome, (Darling, Esther B.)
Ball of Fire, (Miers, Earl S.)
Ballad of Beau Brocade, (Dobson, Austin)
Ballad of Burglar of Babylon, (Bishop, Elizabeth)
Ballad of Tangle Street, (Bacon, Peggy)
Ballad of Yukon Jake, (Paramore, Edward)
Ballad of the Lost Hare, (Sidney, Margaret)
Ballad of the Prince, (Sewell, A.A.)
Ballads & Lyrics of Love, (Sidgwick, Frank (ed))
Ballads & Songs, (Thackeray, Wm. M.)
Ballads of the Be-Ba-Boes, (Stevens, D.K.)
Ballet Shoes, (Streatfeild, Noel)
Ballet for Mary, (Brock, Emma)
Ballet of the Nations, (Lee, Vernon)
Balloon Moon, (Cabot, Elise)
Bam Bam Clock, (McEvoy, Joseph P.)
Bambi Picture Book, (Disney, Walt)
Bambi's Children, (Salten, Felix)
Bambi: Life in the Woods, (Salten, Felix)
Bambino Goes Home, (Schreiber, Georges)
Bambino the Clown, (Schreiber, Georges)
Bamboo Gate, (Oakes, Vanya)
Bamboo: The Grass Tree, (Sperry, Armstrong)
Banana Tree House, (Garrard, Phillis)
Banbury Cross..., (N/A)
Band of Mirth, (Meade, L.T.)
Band of the Red Hand, (Rau, Margaret)
Bandanna Ballads, (Weeden, Howard)
Bandit Jim Crow, (Bancroft, Laura)
Bandoleer, (Benedict, Dorothy)
Bandy Boy's Treasure Island, (Fry, Rosalie K.)
Bang Bang, You're Dead, (Fitzhugh, Louise)
Banjo Billy and Mr. Bones, (Justus, May)
Banjo Talks, (Culbertson, Anne V.)
Banjo the Crow, (DuBois, Theodora)
Banner in the Sky, (Ullman, James R.)
Bantu Tales, (Holladay, Virginia)
Bantu Tales, (Price, Pattie)
Bar 20, (Mulford, Clarence)
Bar Sinister, (Davis, Richard H.)
Bar-20 Days, (Mulford, Clarence)
Barbara Peek-A-Boo's Holiday, (Byron, May)
Barbara's Birthday, (Black, Irma S.)
Barbara's Song Book, (Hartog, Cecile)
Barbara, Woman of the West, (Whitson, John H.)
Barbarians, (Chambers, Robert)
Barbary Bo..., (Kauffman, Reginald)
Bargain for Frances, (Hoban, Russell)
Barkis, (Newberry, Clare T.)
Barn Swallow, (Sears, Paul M.)
Barnaby, (Johnson, Crockett)
Barnaby & Mr. O'Malley, (Johnson, Crockett)
Barnaby Lee, (Bennett, John)
Barnaby Rudge, (Dickens, Charles)
Barnaby and the Horses, (Pender, Lydia)
Barnaby in Search of a House, (Helps, Racey)
Barney's Adventure, (Austin, Margot)
Barney's Barges, (Aspden, Don)
Baron Munchausen, (Kastner, Erich)
Baron Verdigris, (Quilp, Jocelyn)
Baron's Booty, (Kahl, Virginia)
Barrie and Daughter, (Caudill, Rebecca)
Bartholomew & the Oobleck, (Seuss, Dr.)

Bascombe, Fastest Hound Alive, (Goodman, George)
Baseball Trick, (Corbett, Scott)
Bases of Design, (Crane, Walter)
Bashful Ballads, (Johnson, Burges)
Bashful Earthquake, (Herford, Oliver)
Basil & the Lost Colony, (Titus, Eve)
Basil of Baker Street, (Titus, Eve)
Basket of Poses, (Chappell, George S.)
Bastable Children, (Nesbit, Edith)
Bat-Poet, (Jarrell, Randall)
Bat: Story of a Bull Terrier, (Meader, Stephen W.)
Batter and Spoon Fairies, (Teall, Edna A.)
Battle of France, (Maurois, Andre)
Battle of Life, (Dickens, Charles)
Battle of the Frogs and Mice, (Barlow, Jane)
Battle of the Kegs, (Hopkinson, Frances)
Bayou Boy, (Lattimore, Eleanor)
Bayou Suzette, (Lenski, Lois)
Be Good, Harry, (Chalmers, Mary)
Be Nice to Spiders, (Graham, Margaret B.)
Be-Wee the Gnome..., (Herbertson, Agnes)
Beach Before Breakfast, (Kumin, Maxine)
Beachcomber Bobbie, (Bourgeois, Florence)
Beachcomber's Book, (Kohn, Bernice)
Beacon Prize Medals, (Paine, Albert B.)
Beady Bear, (Freeman, Don)
Beagle Named Bertram, (Sharfman, Amalie)
Beanie, (Carroll, Ruth)
Bear Called Paddington, (Bond, Michael)
Bear Cub, (Clark, Ann N.)
Bear Facts, (Culbertson, Polly)
Bear Named Grumms, (White, Bessie)
Bear Party, (DuBois, W.P.)
Bear Scouts, (Berenstain, Stan)
Bear Teeth for Courage, (Scull, Florence)
Bear Twins, (Hogan, Inez)
Bear Who Couldn't Sleep, (Pomerantz, Charlotte)
Bear Who Never was Cross, (Herr, Charlotte)
Bear Who Saw Spring, (Kuskin, Karla)
Bear Who was Too Big, (Cooper, Lettice U.)
Bear in Fact and Fiction, (Cherr, Pat)
Bear is a Bear, (Hogan, Inez)
Bear on the Motorcycle, (Zimnik, Reiner)
Bear that Wasn't, (Tashlin, Frank)
Bear's Famous Invasion of Sicily, (Buzzati, Dino)
Bear's Land, (Mordvinoff, Nicolas)
Bear's Vacation, (Berenstain, Stan)
Bear's Water Picnic, (Yeoman, John)
Bears, (Krauss, Ruth)
Bears Back in Business, (Baker, Margaret)
Bears are Sleeping, (Yulya)
Bears in My Kitchen, (Merrill, Margaret)
Bears of the Air, (Lobel, Arnold)
Bears on Hemlock Mountain, (Dalgliesh, Alice)
Beasley's Christmas Party, (Tarkington, Booth)
Beast Book, (Wahl, Jan)
Beast Called an Elephant, (Stong, Philip D.)
Beast with the Magical Horn, (Cameron, Eleanor)
Beast, Bird & Fish, (Morrow, Elizabeth)
Beastly Alphabet, (Mendoza, George)
Beastly Boys and Ghastly Girls, (Cole, William)
Beastly Circus, (Parish, Peggy)
Beasts & Birds, (Hay, Helen)
Beasts & Men, (DeBosschere, Jean)
Beasts & Nonsense, (Ets, Marie H.)
Beasts and Saints, (Waddell, Helen (tr))
Beasts of Tarzan, (Burroughs, Edgar R.)
Beasts of the Chase, (Edwards, Lionel)

Beating Back, (Jennings, Alphonso)
Beaufort Chums, (Sabin, Edwin L.)
Beauties, (Wells, Carolyn)
Beautiful Blue Jay, (Spellman, John W.)
Beautiful Culpeppers, (Upington, Marion)
Beautiful Joe's Paradise, (Saunders, Marshall)
Beautiful Story of Doris & Julie, (Smith, Gertrude)
Beauty & the Beast, (Dowson, Ernest)
Beauty & the Beast, (N/A)
Beauty & the Beast Picture Book, (N/A)
Beauty and the Beast, (DeBeaumont, Marie L.)
Beaver Pond, (Tresselt, Alvin)
Beaver Water, (Montgomery, R.)
Beaver on the Sawtooth, (Freschet, Berniece)
Beckoning Road, (Rowland, Sydney)
Beckoning Road, (Snedeker, Caroline D.)
Becky, (Wilson, Julia)
Becky Longnose..., (Waugh, Ida)
Becky's Birthday, (Tudor, Tasha)
Becky's Christmas, (Tudor, Tasha)
Bed-Knob & Broomstick, (Norton, Mary)
Bed-Time Book, (Whitney, Helen H.)
Bedtime Stories, (Wetmore, Claude H.)
Bedtime Story Book, (N/A)
Bedtime for Frances, (Hoban, Russell)
Bee Who Would Not Work, (Herr, Charlotte)
Bee in Her Bonnet, (Kristoffersen, Eva)
Bee, Princess of the Dwarfs, (France, Anatole)
Bee-Man of Orn, (Stockton, Frank)
Beech Tree, (Buck, Pearl S.)
Bees and Beelines, (Hawes, Judy)
Beeswax Catches a Thief, (Kirn, Ann)
Beezus and Ramona, (Cleary, Beverly)
Befena's Gift, (Carlson, Natalie S.)
Before Adam, (London, Jack)
Before You Came this Way, (Baylor, Byrd)
Before the Indians, (May, Julian)
Beggar's Opera, (Gay, John)
Beggar's Penny, (Coblentz, Catherine)
Beggars of Dreams, (Hollister, Mary)
Begging Bear, (Allen, Phil S.)
Begging Deer, (Rowe, Dorothy)
Beginning of the World, (Burne-Jones, Edward)
Beginning with A, (Bianco, Pamela)
Beginning with Mrs. McBee, (Maiden, Cecil)
Beginnings of Cities, (Weisgard, Leonard)
Behind Moroccan Walls, (Morris, Constance)
Behind the Dark Pines, (Young, Martha)
Behind the Ranges, (Meader, Stephen W.)
Bela the Juggler, (Shirk, Jeannette C.)
Belgian Playmates, (Pollock, Nellie)
Belgian Twins, (Perkins, Lucy F.)
Belgium, (Omond, George W.)
Belgium, (Stokes, Hugh)
Belinda Blue, (Wood, Esther)
Belinda and Me, (Braucher, Bettye)
Belinda the Mouse, (Sewell, Helen)
Belinda's New Spring Hat, (Clymer, Eleanor)
Bell for Ursli, (Chonz, Selina)
Bell of Kamela, (Budd, Lillian)
Belle's Pink Boots, (Mathews, Joanna H.)
Belling the Tiger, (Stolz, Mary S.)
Bells & Grass, (De La Mare, Walter)
Bells for a Chinese Donkey, (Lattimore, Eleanor)
Bells of Amsterdam, (Holberg, Ruth)
Bells of Bleecker Street, (Angelo, Valenti)
Bells of Heaven: Story of Joan of Arc, (Bick, Christopher)
Bells of Leyden Sing, (Coblentz, Catherine)

Bells of the Harbor, (DeJong, Meindert)
Beloved Acres, (Hamlin, John)
Beloved Belindy, (Gruelle, Johnny)
Beloved Friend, (Vance, Marguerite)
Beloved Vagabond, (Locke, William J.)
Below Zero, (Johnson, A.E.)
Ben & Me, (Lawson, Robert)
Ben King's Verse, (Waterman, Nixon (ed))
Ben Pepper, (Sidney, Margaret)
Ben and Brock, (Shepard, Ernest)
Bendemolena, (Seidler, Ann)
Bending of the Twig, (Russell, Walter)
Beneath the Hill, (Curry, Jane L.)
Beneath the Oak Tree, (Zimelman, Nathan)
Bengal Fairy Tales, (Bradley-Birt, F.)
Benita, an African Romance, (Haggard, H. Rider)
Benjamin Budge & Barnaby Ball, (Heide, Florence P.)
Benjamin Franklin, (D'Aulaire, I.& E.)
Benjamin Franklin, (Judson, Clara I.)
Benjamin West & his Cat Grimalkin, (Henry, Marguerite)
Benjamin the True, (Paley, Claudia)
Benjie, (Lexau, Joan M.)
Benjie & his Family, (Scott, Sally)
Benjie Goes into Business, (Martin, Patricia)
Benjie on His Own, (Lexau, Joan M.)
Benjie's Hat, (Hunt, Mabel L.)
Benjie's Portion, (Ballard, Martin)
Benjy's Blanket, (Brown, Myra B.)
Benjy, a Ferocious Fairy Tale, (O'Connor, Edwin)
Bennie & Jennie, (Uncle Milton)
Benny & His Penny, (Lenski, Lois)
Benny the Bulldozer, (Hurd, Edith T.)
Benny the Bunny Liked Beans, (May, Robert)
Benny's Animals... (Selsam, Millicent)
Benny's Flag, (Krasilovsky, Phyllis)
Beorn the Proud, (Polland, Madeleine)
Beppo, (Brock, Emma)
Beppo the Donkey, (Wells, Rhea)
Beppy Marlowe of Charles Town, (Gray, Eliz. J.)
Berkshire Vale, (Howe-Nurse, Wilfred)
Bermuda Verses, (Chittenden, Wm. L.)
Bernadine & the Water Bucket, (Olsen, Aileen)
Bernardo and Laurette, (Bouvet, Marguerite)
Berries in the Scoop, (Lenski, Lois)
Bertie's Escapade, (Grahame, Kenneth)
Bertram and his Fabulous Animals, (Gilbert, Paul T.)
Bertram's Trip to the North Pole, (Gilbert, Paul T.)
Bess and the Sphinx, (Coatsworth, Eliz.)
Best Christmas, (Kingman, Lee)
Best Foot Forward, (Young, Louise)
Best Friend, (Simon, Shirley)
Best Friends, (Brown, Myra B.)
Best Friends for Frances, (Hoban, Russell)
Best Man, (MacGrath, Harold)
Best Place, (Schlein, Miriam)
Best Stories to Tell Children, (Bryant, Sara Cone)
Best Teddy Bear in the World, (Cradock, H.C.)
Best of Luck, (Brown, Myra B.)
Best of Times, (Bemelmans, Ludwig)
Best-Loved Doll, (Caudill, Rebecca)
Beth Norvell, (Parrish, Randall)
Bethlehem, (Housman, Laurence)
Betsy Ross, (Bates, Helen D.)
Betsy Ross: Girl of Old Philadelphia, (Weil, Ann Y.)
Betsy and Billy, (Haywood, Carolyn)
Betsy and Joe, (Lovelace, Maud H.)
Betsy and Joe, (Shepard, Ernest)
Betsy and the Boys, (Haywood, Carolyn)

Betsy and the Great World, (Lovelace, Maud H.)
Betsy in Spite of Herself, (Lovelace, Maud H.)
Betsy's Little Star, (Haywood, Carolyn)
Betsy's Napoleon, (Eaton, Jeanette)
Betsy's Wedding, (Lovelace, Maud H.)
Betsy-Tacy, (Lovelace, Maud H.)
Betsy-Tacy and Tib, (Lovelace, Maud H.)
Better Known as Johnny Appleseed, (Hunt, Mabel L.)
Better Treasure, (Andrews, Mary S.)
Bettijak Book, (Williams, C.A.)
Bettina's Bonnet, (N/A)
Betty Book, (Anderson, Anne)
Betty Fairy Book, (Price, Margaret E.)
Betty Leicester's Christmas, (Jewett, Sarah O.)
Betty at Fort Blizzard, (Seawell, Molly E.)
Betty of Mackinaw, (Fox, Frances M.)
Betty's Diary, (Russell, Dorothy)
Betty's Painting Book, (N/A)
Betty, Bobby & Bubbles, (Mitchell, Edith)
Betty-Bide-at-Home, (Dix, Beulah M.)
Between Planets, (Heinlein, Robert)
Beverly of Graustark, (McCutcheon, George B.)
Bevis, Story of a Boy, (Jefferies, Richard)
Beware of the Mouse, (Wibberley, Leonard)
Beware the Polar Bear, (Young, Miriam)
Bewitched Lamp, (Molesworth, Mrs.)
Beyond Your Doorstep, (Borland, Hal)
Beyond the Border, (Campbell, Walter D.)
Beyond the Pawpaw Trees, (Brown, Palmer)
Beyond the Wier Bridge, (Burton, Hester)
Bhimsa the Dancing Bear, (Weston, Christine)
Bhombal Dass, (Siddiqui, Ashraf)
Bianco and the New World, (Palazzo, Tony)
Bib Ballads, (Lardner, Ring)
Bibi the Baker's Horse, (Stewart, Anna B.)
Bible Children..., (Thompson, Blanche J.)
Bible Days, (DeJong, Meindert)
Bible Stories to Read & Tell, (Olcott, F.J. (ed))
Bible Story Book, (Fryer, Jane E.)
Bicycle of Cathay, (Stockton, Frank)
Biffy Buffalo, (Porter, Jane)
Big Bad Wolf & Little Red Riding Hood, (Disney, Walt)
Big Ball of String, (Holland, Marion)
Big Basketball Prize, (Renick, Marion)
Big Beasts & Little Beasts, (Helle, Andre)
Big Blue Island, (Gage, Wilson)
Big Book of Animal Fables, (Green, Margaret (ed))
Big Book of Fables, (Jerrold, Walter)
Big Book of Fairy Stories, (Strang, Herbert)
Big Book of Fairy Tales, (Jerrold, Walter)
Big Book of Horses & Goats, (Penfield, Edward)
Big Book of Nursery Rhymes, (Jerrold, Walter)
Big Book of Train Stories, (Various)
Big Brother, (Bannon, Laura)
Big Brother Danny, (Fiedler, Jean)
Big Brown Bear, (Duplaix, Georges)
Big Brownie, (Montgomery, R.)
Big Caesar, (Ogburn, Charlton)
Big Cheese, (Schlein, Miriam)
Big Circus April 1st, (Slobodkin, Louis)
Big City, (Hader, B.& E.)
Big Cowboy Western, (Scott, Ann H.)
Big Dipper, (Branley, Franklyn)
Big Dog, Little Dog, (MacDonald, Golden)
Big Dogs Little Dogs Cats & Kittens, (Wain, Louis)
Big Doin's on Razorback Ridge, (Credle, Ellis)
Big Enough, (Kafka, Sherry)
Big Family, (Rae, John)

Big Fellow at Work, (Baruch, Dorothy W.)
Big Fire, (Olds, Elizabeth)
Big Fish, (Olsen, Aileen)
Big Flight, (Buck, Pearl S.)
Big Fraid, Little Fraid, (Credle, Ellis)
Big Goose & Little White Duck, (DeJong, Meindert)
Big Green Book, (Graves, Robert)
Big Green Thing, (Schlein, Miriam)
Big Green Umbrella, (Coatsworth, Eliz.)
Big Indian and Little Bear, (Evatt, Harriet)
Big John's Secret, (Jewett, Eleanore)
Big Jump, (Elkin, Benjamin)
Big Laughing Book, (Steiner, Charlotte)
Big Little Davy, (Lenski, Lois)
Big Little Island, (Angelo, Valenti)
Big Loop, (Bishop, Claire H.)
Big Mose, (Shippen, Kath. B.)
Big Old World of Richard Creeks, (Courlander, Harold)
Big Ones, (Hogan, Inez)
Big Pile of Dirt, (Clymer, Eleanor)
Big Puppy & Little Puppy, (Black, Irma S.)
Big Rain, (Francoise)
Big Red, (Anderson, C.W.)
Big Red, (Kjelgaard, Jim)
Big Red Barn, (Brown, Margaret W.)
Big Red Bus, (Kessler, Ethel)
Big Road Walker, (Duncan, Eula G.)
Big Sister, and Little Sister, (Zolotow, Charlotte)
Big Six, (Ransome, Arthur)
Big Snow, (Hader, B.& E.)
Big Splash, (Kendall, Carol S.)
Big Steve: Doubled Quick Tunnelman, (Bloch, Marie H.)
Big Susan, (Jones, Eliz. O.)
Big Talk, (Schlein, Miriam)
Big Tiger and Christian, (Muhlenweg, Fritz)
Big Town, (Lardner, Ring)
Big Treasure Book of Fairy Tales, (Andreas, Evelyn)
Big Tree, (Buff, Mary)
Big Tree of Bunlahy, (Colum, Padraic)
Big World & Little House, (Krauss, Ruth)
Big Yellow Balloon, (Fenton, Edward)
Big and Little, Up & Down, (Berkley, Ethel S.)
Big-Enough, (James, Will)
Biggest Bear, (Ward, Lynd)
Biggest Bear on Earth, (McCracken, Harold)
Biggest Dog in the World, (Key, Ted)
Biggest House in the World, (Lionni, Leo)
Biggest Toot in Toozelburg, (McGowen, Tom)
Biggety Chameleon, (Pope, Edith)
Biggity Bantam, (McCready, Thomas L.)
Bikey the Skycycle, (Bangs, John K.)
Bill Bergson & White Rose Rescue, (Lindgren, Astrid)
Bill Bergson Lives Dangerously, (Lindgren, Astrid)
Bill Truetell, (Brennan, George H.)
Bill and Nancy, (Wasson, Mildred)
Bill the Brave, (Weil, Lisl)
Bill the Minder, (Robinson, W. Heath)
Billy & Milly, (Young, Miriam)
Billy & the Unhappy Bull, (DeJong, Meindert)
Billy Bang Book, (La Rue, Mabel G.)
Billy Barnicoat, (MacDonald, Greville)
Billy Bounce, (Denslow, W.W.)
Billy Boy, (Long, John L.)
Billy Bud, Foretopman, (Melville, Herman)
Billy Bunce..., (Towers, Alton)
Billy Bunny's Fortune, (Gordon, Elizabeth)
Billy Butter, (Hader, B.& E.)
Billy Button's Buttered Biscuit, (Hunt, Mabel L.)

Billy Celebrates, (Trickey, Edna)
Billy Cory, Adventurer, (Beard, Patten)
Billy Had a System, (Holland, Marion)
Billy Mink, (Burgess, Thornton)
Billy Popgun, (Winter, Milo)
Billy Robin, (Judson, Clara I.)
Billy Whiskers at the Circus, (Wheeler, F.G.)
Billy Whiskers... [Most titles], (Montgomery, F.T.)
Billy Yank and Johnny Reb, (Miers, Earl S.)
Billy and Blaze, (Anderson, C.W.)
Billy and the Bear, (Bannon, Laura)
Billy the Barber, (Kunhardt, Dorothy)
Billy the Kid, (Lipkind, Will)
Billy's Clubhouse, (Holland, Marion)
Billy's Picture, (Rey, Margret E.)
Billy's Princess, (Haskell, Helen E.)
Billy, the Littlest One, (Schlein, Miriam)
Bimbi, (De La Rame, L.)
Bimby, (Burchard, Peter)
Bingo and Babs, (Wright, Alan)
Bingo is My Name, (Stoddard, Anne)
Binkie and Bell Dolls, (Widdemer, Margaret)
Binky, (Beale, Will)
Binky's Fire, (Scott, Sally)
Biography of Our Baby, (Cooke, Edmund V.)
Biography of a Boy, (Bacon, Josephine D.)
Biography of a Grizzly, (Seton, Ernest T.)
Biography of a Silver Fox, (Seton, Ernest T.)
Biquette, the White Goat, (Francoise)
Bird Alphabet, (Palazzo, Tony)
Bird Began to Sing, (Field, Rachel)
Bird Book, (Shankland, Frank)
Bird Children, (Gordon, Elizabeth)
Bird Diary, (Harrison, Godfrey)
Bird Portraits, (Seton, Ernest T.)
Bird Talisman, (Wedgwood, Henry A.)
Bird World, (Stickney, J.H.)
Bird from the Sea, (Weiss, Renee K.)
Bird in the Bush, (Hallock, Grace T.)
Bird in the Hand, (Franklin, Benjamin)
Bird's Christmas Tree, (Brock, Emma)
Birds, (Kepes, Juliet A.)
Birds & Beasts, (Lemonnier, Camille)
Birds Against Men, (Halle, Louis J.)
Birds Eat and Eat and Eat, (Gans, Roma)
Birds and the Beasts were There, (Cole, William)
Birds at Night, (Gans, Roma)
Birds in Town & Village, (Hudson, Wm. Henry)
Birds of the Bible, (Stratton-Porter, Gene)
Birds' Christmas Carol, (Wiggin, Kate D.)
Birth of an Island, (Selsam, Millicent)
Birth of the Opal, (Allen, Daphne)
Birthday Book for Children, (Barker, Mrs. S.)
Birthday Party, (Krauss, Ruth)
Birthday Present, (Martin, Patricia)
Birthday Present, (Munari, Bruno)
Birthday Story, (Buntain, Ruth J.)
Birthday for Frances, (Hoban, Russell)
Birthday of Little Jesus, (North, Sterling)
Birthday of Obash, (Chalmers, Audrey)
Birthday of the Infanta, (Wilde, Oscar)
Birthdays are for Everyone, (Steiner, Charlotte)
Birthdays for Robin, (Sewell, Helen)
Birthdays of Freedom, (Foster, Genevieve)
Bishop & Boogerman, (Harris, Joel C.)
Bits and Pieces, (Gay, Zhenya)
Bits that Grow Big, (Webber, Irma E.)
Bitsy, (Scott, Sally)

Bitter Green of the Willow, (Cost, March)
Bittern's Nest, (Lattimore, Eleanor)
Bitzli and the Big Bad Wolf, (Weil, Lisl)
Bixby of Boston, (Fitzgerald, John T.)
Bixxy & the Secret Message, (Slobodkin, Louis)
Black & White, (Brown, Paul)
Black & White, (Ipcar, Dahlov)
Black Arrow, (Stevenson, Rbt. L.)
Black Arrowhead, (Snedeker, Caroline D.)
Black B C's, (Clifton, Lucille)
Black Barque, (Hains, T. Jenkins)
Black Bay and Chestnut, (Anderson, C.W.)
Black Bear Twins, (Tompkins, Jane)
Black Beauty, (Sewell, Anna)
Black Bruce, (Johnson, Margaret)
Black Buccaneer, (Meader, Stephen W.)
Black Bunnies, (Robinson, Charles)
Black Cat Book, (Copeland, Walter)
Black Cats and the Tinker's Wife, (Baker, Margaret)
Black Cauldron, (Alexander, Lloyd C.)
Black Doggies, (Robinson, Charles)
Black Face, (Bell, Thelma H.)
Black Fairy Tales, (Berger, Terry)
Black Falcon, (Sperry, Armstrong)
Black Folk Tales, (Berry, Erick)
Black Folktales, (Lester, Julius B.)
Black Fox of Lorne, (DeAngeli, Marguerite)
Black Friday, (Isham, Frederic S.)
Black Gold, (Henry, Marguerite)
Black Heart of Indri, (Hoge, Dorothy)
Black Hearts in Battersea, (Aiken, Joan)
Black Jack, (Garfield, Leon)
Black Joke, (Mowat, Farley)
Black Lion Inn, (Lewis, Alfred H.)
Black Maria, (Addams, Charles)
Black Misery, (Hughes, Langston)
Black Opal, (Ash, Fenton)
Black Out Loud, (Adoff, Arnold (ed))
Black Pearl, (O'Dell, Scott)
Black Princess, (Young, Christie (ed))
Black Rock, (Conner, Ralph)
Black Rose, (Costain, Thomas B.)
Black Sheep, (Merrill, Jean)
Black Sombrero, (Ward, Nanda)
Black Stallion... [Most titles], (Farley, Walter)
Black Tales for White Children, (Stigand, Chauncy H.)
Black Wings, (Lippincott, J.W.)
Black and Blue Magic, (Snyder, Zilpha K.)
Black and White, (Brown, Margaret W.)
Black is Beautiful, (McGovern, Ann)
Black to Nature, (Cohen, Octavus R.)
Black, Black, Beautiful Black, (Blue, Rose)
Black-Eyed Puppy, (Pyle, Katharine)
Blackbeard Buccaneer, (Paine, Ralph D.)
Blackbeard's Ghost, (Stahl, Ben)
Blackbird in the Lilac, (Reeves, James)
Blackboard Bear, (Alexander, Martha G.)
Blackfeet Indians, (Linderman, Frank B.)
Blackfellow Bundi..., (Harris, Leila)
Blackie, His Friends and Enemies, (Bigham, Madge A.)
Blacklegs and Others, (Cowham, Hilda)
Blacksmith & the Birds, (Rickert, Edith)
Blacksmith of Vilno, (Kelly, Eric P.)
Blackthorn, (Adams, Katharine)
Blacky the Crow, (Burgess, Thornton)
Bladys of the Stewponey, (Baring-Gould, Sabine)
Blampied Edition of Peter Pan, (Barrie, James M.)
Blanche of the Blueberry Barrens, (Molloy, Anne)

Blaze... [Most titles], (Anderson, C.W.)
Blennerhassett, (Pidgin, Charles F.)
Bless this Day, (Vipont, Elfrida)
Blessed Damozel, (Rossetti, Dante G.)
Blimps and Such, (Baruch, Dorothy W.)
Blind Colt, (Rounds, Glen)
Blind Men and the Elephant, (Quigley, Lillian)
Blind Men and the Elephants, (Saxe, John)
Blind Mice & other Numbers, (Chermayeff, Ivan)
Blindfolded, (Walcott, Earle A.)
Blobbs at the Sea Side, (Stokes, Vernon)
Blonk from Beneath the Sea, (Bendick, Jeanne)
Blood Bay Colt, (Farley, Walter)
Blood Lilies, (Fraser, William A.)
Blossom: A Fairy Story, (Outhwaite, Ida R.)
Blossoming of Patricia-The-Less, (Larrimore, Lida)
Blot: Little City Cat, (Crawford, Phyllis)
Blow Away Balloon, (Helps, Racey)
Blow for Liberty, (Meader, Stephen W.)
Blow, Bugles, Blow, (Allen, Merritt)
Blown Away, (Mansfield, Richard)
Blue & Silver Necklace, (Coblentz, Catherine)
Blue Aspic, (Gorey, Edward)
Blue Aunt, (White, Eliza O.)
Blue Barns, (Sewell, Helen)
Blue Bells on the Lea, (Ewing, Juliana H.)
Blue Bird, (Maeterlinck, Maurice)
Blue Boat, (Mayne, William)
Blue Bonnets for Lucinda, (Sayers, Frances C.)
Blue Boy, (Peeples, Edwin A.)
Blue Butterfly Goes to South America, (Hutchinson, Ruth)
Blue Canyon Horse, (Clark, Ann N.)
Blue Cat of Castle Town, (Coblentz, Catherine)
Blue Chimney, (Bond, Gladys B.)
Blue Danube, (Bemelmans, Ludwig)
Blue Dragon, (Munroe, Kirk)
Blue Elephant and the Pink Pig, (McNeil, Marion)
Blue Fairy Book, (Lang, Andrew)
Blue Flower, (Van Dyke, Henry)
Blue Goops & Red, (Burgess, Gelett)
Blue Grass and Rhododendron, (Fox, John Jr.)
Blue Guess Book, (Shaw, Charles G.)
Blue Heron Tree, (Hurd, Edith T.)
Blue Jeans, (Beim, Lorraine)
Blue Junk, (Holton, Priscilla)
Blue Lagoon, (Stacpoole, H.D.)
Blue Mittens, (Reely, Mary K.)
Blue Moon, (Housman, Laurence)
Blue Mountain, (Lewis, Beth H.)
Blue Mystery, (Benary-Isbert, Margot)
Blue Poetry Book, (Lang, Andrew)
Blue Ribbon Puppies, (Johnson, Crockett)
Blue Ridge Billy, (Lenski, Lois)
Blue Rose, (Ross, Eulalie (ed))
Blue Smoke, (Lyons, Dorothy)
Blue Streak and Doctor Medusa, (Elder, Art)
Blue Teapot, (Dalgliesh, Alice)
Blue Willow, (Gates, Doris)
Blue and Red...., (Ewing, Juliana H.)
Blue in the Seed, (Kim, Yong-Ik)
Blue's Broken Heart, (Merrill, Jean)
Blue-Eyed Lady, (Molnar, Ferenc)
Blue-Nosed Witch, (Embry, Margaret)
Bluebeard & other Fairy Tales, (Perrault, Charles)
Blueberries for Sal, (McCloskey, Robert)
Blueberry Corners, (Lenski, Lois)
Blueberry Mountain, (Meader, Stephen W.)
Blueberry Muffin, (Thompson, Mary W.)

Blunderbus, (McGinley, Phyllis)
Bo & the Old Donkey, (Sandburg, Helga)
Boat Builder, (Judson, Clara I.)
Boat Children of Canton, (Ward, Marion)
Boat for Peppe, (Politi, Leo)
Boat that Mooed, (Fry, Christopher)
Boats Finds a House, (Chalmers, Mary)
Boats on the River, (Flack, Marjorie)
Bob & the Railroad, (Tousey, Sanford)
Bob Bodden & Good Shop Rover, (Coatsworth, Eliz.)
Bob Fulton's Amazing Soda-Pop Stretcher, (Beatty, J.)
Bob Hampton of Placer, (Parrish, Randall)
Bob and the Guides, (Andrews, Mary S.)
Bobbie Bubbles, (Sherwood, E. Hugh)
Bobbie and Jock and the Mailman, (Finger, Charles J.)
Bobbie in Bugaboo Land, (Dunham, Curtis)
Bobbity Flop, (Pope, Jessie)
Bobbo and other Fancies, (Wharton, Thomas I.)
Bobby & his Band, (Scott, Sally)
Bobby & the Big Road, (Lindsay, Maud)
Bobby Goes Riding, (Baruch, Dorothy W.)
Bobby Wanted a Pony, (Bryan, Dorothy)
Bobby in Search of a Birthday, (Mitchell, Lebbeus)
Bobcat, (Anderson, C.W.)
Bobo the Barrage Balloon, (McConnell, Margaret)
Bobo's Dream, (Alexander, Martha G.)
Bobs, King of Fortunate Isle, (Franchot, Annie W.)
Bobtail Puppy Book, (Aldin, Cecil)
Bogey Beasts, (Sime, Sidney H.)
Bogie Man, (Dimmick, Ruth C.)
Bohemia in London, (Ransome, Arthur)
Bola and the Oba's Drummers, (Schatz, Letta)
Bolanyo, (Read, Opie)
Bold Dragoon, (Irving, Washington)
Bold Robin, (Brown, Caroline V.)
Bolivar, (Gramatky, Hardie)
Bon-Mots of C. Lamb & D. Jerrold, (Jerrold, Walter)
Bon-Mots of the Eighteenth Century, (Jerrold, Walter)
Bonaventure, (Cable, George W.)
Bonbon & Bonbonette, (Merryman, Mildred P.)
Bone for Bone, (Cosgrove, Margaret)
Boners, (Abingdon, Alex)
Bonfires and Broomsticks, (Norton, Mary)
Bongo, (Disney, Walt)
Bonhomme, (DeBrunhoff, Laurent)
Bonnie Bess, Weathervane Horse, (Tresselt, Alvin)
Bonnie Book, (Sowerby, Githa)
Bonnie Little People, (Cone, Helen G.)
Bonny Bairns, (Blanchard, Amy E.)
Bonny Birds, (Veale, E.)
Bonny's Wish, (Gay, Romney)
Bony Pony, (Martin, Patricia)
Boo, Who Used to be Scared of the Dark, (Leaf, M.)
Boo-Boos at the Seaside, (Attwell, Mabel L.)
Boochy's Wings, (Weaver, Annie V.)
Book About God, (Fitch, Florence)
Book About Moomin, Mymble/Little My, (Jansson, T.)
Book for Children, (Richardson, Frederick)
Book for Jennifer, (Dalgliesh, Alice)
Book for Little People, (N/A)
Book of 50 Drawings, (Beardsley, Aubrey)
Book of American Spirit, (Pyle, Howard)
Book of Animal Tales, (Southwold, Stephen)
Book of Baby Beasts, (Dugdale, Florence E.)
Book of Baby Birds, (Dugdale, Florence E.)
Book of Baby Dogs, (Kaberry, Charles J.)
Book of Baby Pets, (Dugdale, Florence E.)
Book of Bargains, (O'Sullivan, Vincent)

Book of Bears, (VerBeck, Frank)
Book of Betty Barber, (Browne, Maggie)
Book of Blokes, (Nicholson, William)
Book of Bow-Wows, (Gordon, Elizabeth)
Book of Bridges, (Arcambeau, Edme)
Book of Bridges, (Sparrow, Walter S.)
Book of Cheerful Cats, (Francis, J.G.)
Book of Christmas, (Mabie, Hamilton W.)
Book of Christmas Verse, (Beeching (ed.))
Book of Christopher Columbus, (Claudel, Paul)
Book of Clever Beasts, (Reed, Myrtle)
Book of Cowboy Stories, (James, Will)
Book of Cowboys, (Holling, Holling C.)
Book of Days for Little Ones, (Bridgman, Clare)
Book of Discoveries, (Masefield, John)
Book of Dogs, (Nesbit, Edith)
Book of Dragons, (Fuller, O. Muriel)
Book of Dragons, (Nesbit, Edith)
Book of Drawings, (Frost, A.B.)
Book of Drawings, (Richardson, Frederick)
Book of Dreams & Ghosts, (Lang, Andrew)
Book of Dwarfs, (Manning-Sanders, Ruth)
Book of Elves & Fairies, (Olcott, F.J.)
Book of Enchantment, (Adams, Kathleen)
Book of Fables, (Aesopus)
Book of Fairy Poetry, (Owen, Dora)
Book of Fairy Tales, (Baring-Gould, Sabine)
Book of Fairy Tales, (Humphrey, Maud)
Book of Fairy Tales, (N/A)
Book of Famous Dogs, (Terhune, Albert P.)
Book of Flower Fairies, (Barker, Cicely M.)
Book of Games, (Hayes, Nancy M.)
Book of Ghosts, (Baring-Gould, Sabine)
Book of Ghosts & Goblins, (Manning-Sanders, Ruth)
Book of Giant Stories, (Adams, Kathleen)
Book of Giants, (Manning-Sanders, Ruth)
Book of Giants, (Strang, William)
Book of Gilly, (Lawless, Emily)
Book of Gnomes, (Weatherly, Fred E.)
Book of Goblins, (Robinson, W. Heath)
Book of Good Tidings, (Anglund, Joan W.)
Book of Happy Gnomes, (Herbertson, Agnes)
Book of Hours, (Peattie, Donald C.)
Book of Indian Braves, (Sweetser, Kate D.)
Book of Indians, (Holling, Holling C.)
Book of Job, (Bible)
Book of Joyous Children, (Riley, James W.)
Book of Joys, (Perkins, Lucy F.)
Book of King Arthur, (Macleod, Mary)
Book of Lies, (Heaton, John L.)
Book of Lovat Claud Fraser, (MacFall, Haldane)
Book of Lyonne, (Drake, Burgess)
Book of Mars for You, (Branley, Franklyn)
Book of Mermaids, (Manning-Sanders, Ruth)
Book of Modern Ballads, (Various)
Book of Mysteries, (Seaman, Augusta)
Book of Myths, (Bulfinch, Thomas)
Book of Myths, (Lang, Jeanie)
Book of Nah-Wee, (Moon, Grace P.)
Book of Nature, (Doane, Pelagie)
Book of Nature Poems, (Cole, William)
Book of New Fairy Tales, (N/A)
Book of Nimble Beasts, (English, Doug)
Book of Noble Thoughts, (Untermeyer, Louis)
Book of Nonsense Verse, (Reed, Langford)
Book of Nursery Rhymes, (Barlow, Jane (tran))
Book of Nursery Songs and Rhymes, (Baring-Gould, Sabine)
Book of Old Ballads, (Nichols, Beverly)

Book of Old English Love Songs, (Edwards, George W.)
Book of Old Ships, (Culver, Henry B.)
Book of Old Sun Dials, (Cross, Launcelot)
Book of Penny Toys, (Dearmer, Mabel)
Book of Pets, (N/A)
Book of Pets, (Tucker, Elizabeth S.)
Book of Pictured Carols, (Baring-Gould, Sabine)
Book of Pirates, (Pyle, Howard)
Book of Ponies, (Wilding, Suzanne)
Book of Princes & Princesses, (Lang, Andrew)
Book of Princes & Princesses, (Manning-Sanders, Ruth)
Book of Princess Stories, (Adams, Kathleen)
Book of Psalms, (Bible)
Book of Quaker Saints, (Hodgkin, Lucy V.)
Book of Robin Hood, (Haydon, Arthur L.)
Book of Romance, (Lang, Andrew)
Book of Ruth, (Bible)
Book of Saints & Friendly Beasts, (Brown, Abbie F.)
Book of Saints & Heroes, (Lang, Leonora B.)
Book of Seven Wishes, (Kay, Gertrude A.)
Book of Shops, (Bridgman, Clare)
Book of Shops, (Lucas, E.V.)
Book of Sweethearts, (N/A)
Book of Tales for Little Folks, (Bruce, Marjory)
Book of Three Dragons, (Morris, Kenneth)
Book of Various Owls, (Hollander, John)
Book of Wedding Days, (Reid, K.E.J.)
Book of Whimsies, (Whitworth, Geoffrey)
Book of Wonder, (Lord Dunsany)
Book of Wonder Voyages, (Jacobs, Joseph (ed))
Book of Woodcraft, (Seton, Ernest T.)
Book of the American Indian, (Garland, Hamlin)
Book of the Cat, (Humphrey, Mabel)
Book of the Child, (Humphrey, Mabel)
Book of the Clock, (Golding, Harry)
Book of the Happy Warrior, (Newbolt, Henry J.)
Book of the Homeless, (Wharton, Edith)
Book of the Kingdom, (Macy, S.B.)
Book of the Little Past, (Peabody, Josephine)
Book of the Poodle, (Tracy, Thomas H.)
Book of the Sagas, (Hoffman, Alice S.)
Book of the Year, (Peters, Fritz)
Book of the Zoo, (Copeland, Walter)
Books, (Bartlett, Susan)
Boom Town Boy, (Lenski, Lois)
Boomba Lives in Africa, (Singer, Caroline)
Boomer, (Clark, Denis)
Boomerang Book of Legendary Tales, (Heddle, Enid)
Boomerang Hunter, (Kjelgaard, Jim)
Booming of Acre Hill, (Bangs, John K.)
Boots of the Holly Tree Inn, (Dickens, Charles)
Boppet, Please Stop It, (Binney, Ida)
Border Hawk: August Bondi, (Alexander, Lloyd C.)
Border Iron, (Best, Herbert)
Borderland of Czar and Kaiser, (Bigelow, Poultney)
Boris and his Balalaika, (Slobodkina, Esphyr)
Boris the Lopsided Bear, (Schmitt, Gladys)
Borka, (Burningham, John)
Born to Trot, (Henry, Marguerite)
Borrowed Brother, (Means, Florence C.)
Borrowed Sister, (White, Eliza O.)
Borrowed Summer, (Enright, Elizabeth)
Borrowers Afield, (Norton, Mary)
Borrowers Afloat, (Norton, Mary)
Borrowers Aloft, (Norton, Mary)
Boss Chambale, (Hubbard, Margaret)
Boss of Wind River, (Chisholm, Arthur M.)
Boss of the Little Arcady, (Wilson, Harry L.)

Boston Bells, (Coatsworth, Eliz.)
Boston Tea Party, (Pollard, Josephine)
Boswell's Life of Boswell, (Leavens, Evelyn)
Both Sides of the Border, (Henty, G.A.)
Both Sides of the Road, (Rogerson, Sidney)
Bottom of the Sea, (Goldin, Augusta)
Bottom's Dream, (Updike, John)
Botts: The Naughty Otter, (Freeman, Don)
Bounce · Story of a Kitten, (Horn, Gladys)
Bounce and the Bunnies, (Carroll, Ruth)
Bounces of Cynthiann', (Lampman, Evelyn)
Bouncing Babies, (Copeland, Walter)
Bouncing Betsy, (Lathrop, Dorothy)
Bound Girl of Cobble Hill, (Lenski, Lois)
Bountiful Cow, (Czaja, Helen)
Bounty Trilogy, (Nordhoff, Charles)
Bouquet of Littles, (Krauss, Ruth)
Bouquet of Rhymes for Children, (Randolph, Althea)
Bow Bells, (Gibson, Katharine)
Bow-Wow Book, (Kernahan, John C.)
Bower Book of Simple Poems...., (Littlewood, Letty)
Bowleg Bill: Seagoing Cowpuncher, (Felton, Harold)
Bowlful of Stars, (Means, Florence C.)
Bows Against the Barons, (Trease, Geoffrey)
Bowser the Hound, (Burgess, Thornton)
Box Turtle Lives in Armor, (May, Charles P.)
Box of Daylight, (Hillyer, William)
Box with Red Wheels, (Petersham, Maud)
Boxcar Children, (Warner, Gertrude)
Boxes, (Merrill, Jean)
Boy & a Dog, (Henry, Marguerite)
Boy & his Friend the Blizzard, (Marton, Gregory)
Boy Alone, (Ottley, Reginald)
Boy Apprenticed to an Enchanter, (Colum, Padraic)
Boy Blue's Book of Beasts, (Smith, William J.)
Boy Captive of Old Deerfield, (Smith, Mary P.W.)
Boy Emigrants, (Brooks, Noah)
Boy Fortune Hunters... [All titles], (Akers, Floyd)
Boy Heroes of Chapultepec, (Chambers, Maria C.)
Boy Jones, (Gordon, Patricia)
Boy King of the Cannibal Islands, (Ducorron, C.A.F.)
Boy Knight of Rheims, (Lownsbery, Eloise)
Boy Life on the Prairie, (Garland, Hamlin)
Boy Lives on our Farm, (Riley, James W.)
Boy Overboard!, (Grant, George H.)
Boy Scouts in a Trappers' Camp, (Burgess, Thornton)
Boy Scouts of Woodcraft Camp, (Burgess, Thornton)
Boy Who Brought Christmas, (Morgan, Alice)
Boy Who Could Do Anything, (Brenner, Anita)
Boy Who Could Enter Paintings, (Valen, Herb)
Boy Who Could Fly, (Newman, Robert)
Boy Who Could Sing Pictures, (Leichman, Seymour)
Boy Who Drew Cats, (Hearn, Lafcadio)
Boy Who Fooled the Giant, (Kitt, Tamara)
Boy Who Had no Birthday, (Hunt, Mabel L.)
Boy Who Had no Heart, (Petershams)
Boy Who Knew what the Birds Said, (Colum, Padraic)
Boy Who Lived in Pudding Lane, (Addington, Sarah)
Boy Who Loved the Sea, (Wersba, Barbara)
Boy Who Made a Million, (Offit, Sidney)
Boy Who Was, (Hallock, Grace T.)
Boy Who Was Afraid, (Sperry, Armstrong)
Boy Who Woke Up in Madagascar, (McKown, Robin)
Boy Who Wouldn't Talk, (Bouchard, Lois K.)
Boy and a Secret, (Jacberns, Raymond)
Boy and his Horse, (Skaar, Grace M.)
Boy and his Room, (Nash, Ogden)
Boy and the Dolphin, (Rothberg, Abraham)

Boy and the Forest, (Lipkind, Will)
Boy at Bat, (Renick, Marion)
Boy in Eirinn, (Colum, Padraic)
Boy is a Boy, (Nash, Ogden)
Boy of Old Prague, (Ish-Kishor, Salamith)
Boy of the Desert, (Tietjens, Eunice H.)
Boy of the Dominion, (Brereton, Frederick)
Boy of the Islands, (Lipkind, Will)
Boy of the Lost Crusade, (Hewes, Agnes D.)
Boy of the South Seas, (Tietjens, Eunice H.)
Boy on Horseback, (Steffens, Lincoln)
Boy with a Billion Pets, (Mann, Peggy)
Boy with a Harpoon, (Lipkind, Will)
Boy with a Pack, (Meader, Stephen W.)
Boy with the Parrot, (Coatsworth, Eliz.)
Boy's Book of Battleships, (Stables, Gordon)
Boy's Book of Indians & Wild West, (Williams, George A.)
Boy's Book/Pirates & Great Sea Rovers, (Williams, G.A.)
Boy's Book of Scouts, (Fitzhugh, Percy K.)
Boy's Camp Book, (Cave, Edward)
Boy's King Arthur, (Malory, Thomas)
Boy's Life of Will Rogers, (Keith, Harold V.)
Boy's Mabinogion, (Lanier, Sidney)
Boy's Revolt, (Otis, James)
Boy's Town, (Howells, William D.)
Boy, a Dog, and a Frog, (Mayer, Mercer)
Boyhood Adventures of Our Presidents, (Cavanah, Frances)
Boys, (Haines, Alice C.)
Boys & Girls from George Eliot, (Sweetser, Kate D.)
Boys & Girls from Thackeray, (Sweetser, Kate D.)
Boys & Girls of Bookland, (Smith, Nora A.)
Boys & Girls of Brantham, (Raymond, Evelyn)
Boys and Girls from Dickens, (Dickens, Charles)
Boys of Marmiton Prairie, (Smith, Gertrude)
Boys of Other Countries, (Taylor, Bayard)
Boys of St. Timothy's, (Pier, Arthur S.)
Boys of the Andes, (Desmond, Alice C.)
Boys of the Old Glee Club, (Riley, James W.)
Boys' Book of Dogs, (Barbour, Ralph H.)
Bracebridge Hall, (Irving, Washington)
Brady, (Fritz, Jean)
Brains & Bravery, (Various)
Bramble, (Colman, Margery)
Branches Green, (Field, Rachel)
Brand Blotters, (Raine, William M.)
Brand New Kitten, (Scott, Sally)
Brand-New Uncle, (Seredy, Kate)
Brave Balloon of Benjamin Buckley, (Wersba, Barbara)
Brave Bantam, (Seaman, Louise)
Brave Companions, (Knight, Ruth A.)
Brave Cowboy, (Anglund, Joan W.)
Brave John Henry, (Austin, Margot)
Brave Johnny O'Hare, (Heady, Eleanor)
Brave Little Goat of Monsieur Seguin, (Daudet, Alphonse)
Brave Mr. Buckingham, (Kunhardt, Dorothy)
Brave Riders, (Balch, Glenn)
Brave Soldier Janosh, (Ambrus, Victor G.)
Bravest of them All, (Hohler, Mrs. Edwin)
Brayhard, (Allen, F.M.)
Brazilian Fairy Book, (Eells, Elsie S.)
Bread & Butter Indian, (Colver, Anne)
Bread & Butter Journey, (Colver, Anne)
Bread & Jam for Frances, (Hoban, Russell)
Bread & Lasses, (Stapp, Emilie B.)
Breakfast with the Clowns, (Slocum, Rosalie)
Bred in the Bone, (Page, Thomas N.)
Bred in the Bone, (Singmaster, Elsie)
Breman Band, (N/A)

Bremen Town Musicians, (Grimm Bros.)
Brenda... [All titles], (Reed, Helen L.)
Brer Rabbit Rides the Fox, (Harris, Joel C.)
Brer Rabbit and his Tricks, (Rees, Ennis)
Brethren of the Coast, (Munroe, Kirk)
Breton Folk, (Blackburn, Henry G.)
Briar Rose Book of Old Fairy Tales, (N/A)
Bric-a-Brac Stories, (Harrison, Mrs. Burton)
Bride's Book, (N/A)
Bride's Primer, (Burgess, Thornton)
Bridge of San Luis Rey, (Wilder, Thornton)
Bridge of the Gods, (Balch, Frederic H.)
Bridget's Fairies, (Stevenson, Alice M.)
Bridgman's Kewts, (Bridgman, L.J.)
Bridle for Pegasus, (Shippen, Kath. B.)
Bridled with Rainbows, (Brewton, Sara W.)
Brief History of Butte Montana, (Freeman, Harry C.)
Brier-Patch Philosophy, (Long, William J.)
Bright April, (DeAngeli, Marguerite)
Bright Barnyard, (Ipcar, Dahlov)
Bright Days..., (Humphrey, Mabel)
Bright Feather, (Rhoads, Dorothy)
Bright Hunter of the Skies, (Best, Herbert)
Bright Island, (Robinson, Mabel L.)
Bright Islands, (Colum, Padraic)
Bright Morning, (Bianco, Margery W.)
Bright Pathways, (Booth, Esma)
Bright Spurs, (Tempski, Armine)
Bright and Shining Breadboard, (Hall, Rosalys)
Bright, Bright Morning, (Holl, Adelaide)
Brighty of the Grand Canyon, (Henry, Marguerite)
Brimful Book, (Piper, Watty)
Brite & Fair, (Shute, Henry A.)
British Barbarians, (Allen, Grant)
British Empire, (Johnson, Gerald W.)
British Fairy & Folk Tales, (Glover, William J.)
Brittany, (Menpes, Mortimer)
Broad Highway, (Farnol, Jeffery)
Broderick, (Ormondroyd, Edward)
Brogeen and the Bronze Lizard, (Lynch, Patricia)
Broken Fang, (Montgomery, R.)
Broken Soldier & Maid of France, (Van Dyke, Henry)
Broken Song, (Daugherty, Sonia)
Bronto, (Beatty, Hetty B.)
Brontos and the Tootle-Bird, (Raiker, Alice M.)
Bronze Bell, (Vance, Louis J.)
Bronze Bow, (Speare, Elizabeth G.)
Bronzeville Boys & Girls, (Brooks, Gwendolyn)
Brookie and her Lamb, (Goffstein, M.B.)
Brookline Trunk, (Kent, Louise A.)
Brooklyn Story, (Mathis, Sharon B.)
Broom-Squire, (Baring-Gould, Sabine)
Broomstick & Snowflake, (Falkberget, Johan)
Broomsticks & other Fairy Tales, (De La Mare, Walter)
Broomtail - Brother of Lightning, (Mason, Miriam E.)
Broomtail Bronc, (Martin, Patricia)
Brother Alonzo, (Hamil, Thomas A.)
Brother Andre of Montreal, (Clark, Ann N.)
Brother Dusty-Feet, (Sutcliff, Rosemary)
Brother Rabbit, (Bryant, Sara Cone)
Brother Van, (Brummitt, Stella W.)
Brother for the Orphelines, (Carlson, Natalie S.)
Brother of the Birds, (Green, Louisa M.)
Brothers of the Frontier, (Carter, Russell)
Brown Cow Farm, (Ipcar, Dahlov)
Brown Fairy Book, (Lang, Andrew)
Brown Rabbit, Her Story, (Morse, Evangeline)
Brown is a Beautiful Color, (Bond, Jean C.)

Brownie, (Peterson, Hans)
Brownie Clown of Brownie Town, (Cox, Palmer)
Brownie Primer, (Banta, Nathaniel M.)
Brownie Robinson Crusoe, (Herr, Charoltte)
Brownie Year Book, (Cox, Palmer)
Brownie of the Circus, (Harper, Wilhelmina)
Brownie: Engineer of Beaver Brook, (Chaffee, Allen)
Brownies & Prince Florimel, (Cox, Palmer)
Brownies & Rose-Leaves, (White, Roma)
Brownies - Hush!, (Adshead, Gladys)
Brownies Abroad, (Cox, Palmer)
Brownies Around the World, (Cox, Palmer)
Brownies Through the Union, (Cox, Palmer)
Brownies and the Goblins, (Banta, Nathaniel M.)
Brownies at Home, (Cox, Palmer)
Brownies in Fairyland, (Cox, Palmer)
Brownies in Switzerland, (Cadby, Carine)
Brownies in the Philippines, (Cox, Palmer)
Brownies: Their Book, (Cox, Palmer)
Brownikins and Other Fancies, (Arkwright, Ruth)
Brownjohn's Beasts, (Brownjohn, Alan)
Bruin the Brown Bear, (Lida)
Brushwood Boy, (Kipling, Rudyard)
Bruzzy Bear & the Cabin Boy, (Hawkins, Sheila)
Bryn Mawr Stories, (Morris, Margaretta)
Bubble Ballads, (Chater, Melville)
Bubble and Squeak, (Robinson, Philip S.)
Bubbleloon, (Stokely, Edith K.)
Bubbles, (Tucker, Elizabeth S.)
Bubo: Great-Horned Owl, (George, Jean C.)
Buccaneer Islands, (Cochran, Hamilton)
Buck Peters, Ranchman, (Mulford, Clarence)
Buckboard Stranger, (Meader, Stephen W.)
Bucking the Sagebrush, (Steedman, Charles J.)
Buckskin Brigade, (Kjelgaard, Jim)
Bucky Bear Who Would Not Take his Nap, (Wayne, E.)
Budd's Noisy Wagon, (Shaw, Richard)
Budding Life, (King, Jessie M.)
Buddy Jim, (Gordon, Elizabeth)
Buddy and the Old Pro, (Tunis, John R.)
Buddy the Bear, (Wiese, Kurt)
Buddy's Adventures in Blueberry Patch, (Beskow, Elsa)
Buffalo & the Bell, (Scovel, Myra)
Buffalo Bill, (D'Aulaire, I.& E.)
Buffalo Bill, (Garst, Shannon)
Buffalo Bill, (Tousey, Sanford)
Buffalo Chief, (Annixter, Jane)
Buffalo Harvest, (Rounds, Glen)
Buffalo Knife, (Steele, William O.)
Buffalo and Beaver, (Meader, Stephen W.)
Buffin, (Barrett, Leone)
Buford, the Little Bighorn, (Peet, Bill)
Bug Book, (Gorey, Edward)
Bugaboo Men, (Bascom, Louise R.)
Bugs, (Walter, Eleanor D.)
Bugs, Wings & other Things, (Franchot, Annie W.)
Building a House in Sweden, (Cautley, Marjorie S.)
Built-Upon House, (Heath, Janet F.)
Bull Calf, (Frost, A.B.)
Bull of the Kraal, (Kidd, Dudley)
Bulldozer, (Meader, Stephen W.)
Bully of Barkham Street, (Stolz, Mary S.)
Bumble Bugs & Elephants, (Brown, Margaret W.)
Bumble Pup, (Carroll, Ruth)
Bumblebee's Secret, (Schlein, Miriam)
Bumblebuzz, (Fry, Rosalie K.)
Bumblepuppy Book, (Wells, Carolyn)
Bumps & Thumps, (N/A)

Bun, a Wild Rabbit, (Lippincott, J.W.)
Bunch Book, (Douglas, James)
Bunch of Cousins, (Meade, L.T.)
Bundle Book, (Krauss, Ruth)
Bundle of Ballads, (Manning-Sanders, Ruth)
Bungling Pedro & other Majorcan Tales, (Mehdevi, A.)
Bunnie Bear, (Gee, John)
Bunny & Bobbie, (Towers, Alton)
Bunny & Brownie, (Outhwaite, Ida R.)
Bunny Bearskin, (Winfrey, Guy)
Bunny Book, (Pope, Jessie)
Bunny Brothers, (Clayton, John)
Bunny Cottontail, (Blair, Matilda)
Bunny Stories, (Jewett, John H.)
Bunny Who Found Easter, (Zolotow, Charlotte)
Bunny's House, (Bridgman, L.J.)
Bunny, Hound and Clown, (Mukerji, Dhan G.)
Bunnyborough, (Aldin, Cecil)
Buried Moon, (Jacobs, Joseph)
Burlap, (Dennis, Morgan)
Burma Boy, (Lindquist, Willis)
Burnish Me Bright, (Cunningham, Julia)
Burro Boy and his Big Trouble, (Bannon, Laura)
Burro of Angelitos, (Church, Peggy P.)
Burro of Burnegat Road, (Goetz, Delia)
Burro that Had a Name, (Beim, Lorraine)
Burt Dow, Deep-Water Man, (McCloskey, Robert)
Bus Driver, (Lent, Henry B.)
Busby & Co., (Coggins, Herbert)
Bushbabies, (Stevenson, William)
Bushrangers, (Finger, Charles J.)
Busiest Boy in Holland, (Weil, Lisl)
Busiest Man in Town, (Artzybasheff, Boris)
Buster Bear's Twins, (Burgess, Thornton)
Busy Broom, (Herbertson, Agnes)
Busy Brownies, (Veale, E.)
Busy Seeds, (Black, Irma S.)
Busy Winds, (Black, Irma S.)
But Not Billy, (Zolotow, Charlotte)
But Ostriches..., (Fisher, Aileen)
But Soft - We are Observed, (Belloc, Hilaire)
But Where is the Green Parrot?, (Zacharias, Thomas)
Buttercup's Visit..., (Clarkson, L.)
Butterflies Come, (Politi, Leo)
Butterfly Babies' Book, (Gordon, Elizabeth)
Butterfly Land, (Fish, Helen D.)
Butterfly Man, (McCutcheon, George B.)
Butterfly Time, (Goudey, Alice)
Butterfly that Stamped, (Kipling, Rudyard)
Butterfly's Ball & Grasshopper's Feast, (Roscoe, William)
Butterscotia..., (Parry, Edward A.)
Buttons, (Hauman, George)
Buttons, (Robinson, Tom P.)
Buttonwood Island, (Davis, Lavinia R.)
Buz-Buz, (Pratt, Charles S.)
Buzzy Bear Goes South, (Marino, Dorothy)
By Airship to Ophir, (Ash, Fenton)
By His Own Might, (Hosford, Dorothy)
By Light of Sun, (Symington, E.H.)
By Loch and Lin, (Leodhas, Sorche)
By Love's Sweet Rule, (Jackson, Gabrielle)
By Order of the Prophet, (Henry, Alfred H.)
By Pike and Dike, (Henty, G.A.)
By Rocket to the Moon, (Gail, Otto W.)
By Secret Railway, (Meadowcroft, Enid)
By the Shores of Silver Lake, (Wilder, Laura I.)
By the Way Ballads, (Sapte, William)
Bye O' Baby Ballads, (Pratt, Charles S.)

Bylow Hill, (Cable, George W.)
Byng Ballads, (Byng, Douglas)
Bypaths in Dixie, (Cocke, Sarah J.)
Byrd Flam in Town, (Armstrong, Leroy)
CDB!, (Steig, William)
CLIO, (France, Anatole)
Cabbage Moon, (Wahl, Jan)
Cabbage Princess, (LeCain, Errol)
Cabbages & Peanuts, (Boyd, Harriet)
Cabin Faced West, (Fritz, Jean)
Cabin for the Mary Christmas, (Amrein, Vera A.)
Cabin on the Fjord, (Meyers, Susan)
Cabita's Rancho, (Crespi, Pachita)
Caboose, (Hurd, Edith T.)
Cactus, (Armer, Laura A.)
Cadaver of Gideon Wyck, (Laing, Alexander)
Caddie Woodlawn, (Brink, Carol R.)
Cadet Days, (King, Charles)
Cadmus Henry, (Edmonds, Walter D.)
Caesar: Life Story of a Panda Leopard, (Russ, Patrick)
Calderon's Prisoner, (Miller, Alice D.)
Caleb Conover, Railroader, (Terhune, Albert P.)
Caleb Cottontail, (Cady, Harrison)
Caleb West, Master Diver, (Smith, Francis H.)
Caleb's Luck, (Benet, Laura)
Calendar Moon, (Belting, Natalia)
Calendar of Omar Khayaam, (McManus, Blanche)
Calico, (Phillips, Ethel C.)
Calico Bush, (Field, Rachel)
Calico Captive, (Speare, Elizabeth G.)
Calico Cat, (Thompson, Charles M.)
Calico Jungle, (Ipcar, Dahlov)
Calico the Wonder Horse, (Burton, Virginia L.)
California Fairy Tales, (Shannon, Monica)
California Gold Rush, (McNeer, May)
California Indian Days, (Bauer, Helen)
California: Land of the Sun, (Austin, Mary)
Call Me Bandicoot, (DuBois, W.P.)
Call Me Charley, (Jackson, Jesse)
Call it Courage, (Sperry, Armstrong)
Call of the Mountain, (Meigs, Cornelia L.)
Call of the Wild, (London, Jack)
Calvacade of Queens, (Farjeon, Eleanor)
Calvin and the Cub Scouts, (Martin, Patricia)
Camel Bells, (Ratzesberger, Anna)
Camel Who Took a Walk, (Tworkov, Jack)
Camel for a Throne, (Lownsbery, Eloise)
Camel in the Sea, (Goetz, Lee G.)
Camel with Wrinkled Knees, (Gruelle, Justin)
Cammie's Challenge, (McIlvaine, Jane)
Camp and Trail, (White, Stewart E.)
Camp at Westlands, (Allee, Marjorie H.)
Camp in the Yard, (Thompson, Vivian L.)
Can Prayer Be Answered?, (Austin, Mary)
Can't You Pretend?, (Young, Miriam)
Canadian Fairy Tales, (Macmillan, Cyrus)
Canadian Story, (McNeer, May)
Canadian Summer, (Van Stockum, Hilda)
Canadian Wonder Tales, (MacMillan, Cyrus)
Canalboat to Freedom, (Fall, Thomas)
Candide, (Voltaire, J.F.)
Candita's Choice, (Lewiton, Mina)
Candle Burns for France, (Thompson, Blanche J.)
Candle Light, (Durston, Georgia R.)
Candle Tales, (Cunningham, Julia)
Candle in the Mist, (Means, Florence C.)
Candle-Light Stories, (Hutchinson, Veronica)
Candle-Lightin' Time, (Dunbar, Paul L.)

Candy, (Alexander, Lillie M.)
Candy Basket, (Angelo, Valenti)
Candy Country, (Alcott, Louisa M.)
Candy Floss, (Godden, Rumer)
Candy Kane, (Lambert, Janet)
Cannonball Simp, (Burningham, John)
Canterbury Pilgrims, (Chaucer, Geoffrey)
Canterbury Tales, (Chaucer, Geoffrey)
Canterville Ghost, (Wilde, Oscar)
Cantilever Rainbow, (Krauss, Ruth)
Canute Whistlewinks..., (Topelius, Zacharias)
Canvas Castle, (Hager, Alice R.)
Canyon Country Kiddies, (Swinnerton, James)
Cap for Mul Chand, (Batchelor, Julie)
Cap that Mother Made, (Hubbard, Eleanore)
Cape Cod, (Thoreau, Henry D.)
Cape Cod Ballads, (Lincoln, Joseph C.)
Cape Horn Snorter, (Finger, Charles J.)
Cape May Packet, (Meader, Stephen W.)
Capers, his Haps and Mishaps, (Herford, Oliver)
Capital Ship, (Carryl, Charles E.)
Cappy Ricks, (Kyne, Peter B.)
Caps for Sale, (Slobodkina, Esphyr)
Captain Blood, (Sabatini, Rafael)
Captain Boldheart & Magic Fishbone, (Dickens, Charles)
Captain Chap, (Stockton, Frank)
Captain Chub, (Barbour, Ralph H.)
Captain January, (Richards, Laura E.)
Captain Jinks, Hero, (Crosby, Ernest)
Captain Joe & the Eskimo, (Adams, Veotta M.)
Captain June, (Rice, Alice H.)
Captain Kidd's Cat, (Lawson, Robert)
Captain Kidd's Cow, (Stong, Philip D.)
Captain Kitty Colonial, (Madison, Lucy F.)
Captain Lettarblair, (Merington, Marguerite)
Captain Macklin, (Davis, Richard H.)
Captain Pottle's House, (Cooney, Barbara)
Captain Ramsay's Daughter, (Torjesen, Elizabeth)
Captain Ravenshaw, (Stephens, Robert N.)
Captain Salt in Oz, (Thompson, Ruth P.)
Captain Sandman, (Potter, Miriam C.)
Captain Serafina, (DeBrunhoff, Laurent)
Captain Slaughterboard Drops Anchor, (Peake, Mervyn)
Captain of the School, (Robinson, Edith)
Captain of the School Team, (Earl, John P.)
Captain's Daughter, (Coatsworth, Eliz.)
Captains Courageous, (Kipling, Rudyard)
Captivating Stories/Animals, (Veale, E.)
Captives of the Kaid, (Marchant, Bessie)
Captured Cruiser, (Hyne, Charles J.)
Captured Santa Claus, (Page, Thomas N.)
Capyboppy, (Peet, Bill)
Caravan Tales, (Hauff, Wilhelm)
Caravans to Sante Fe, (Malkus, Alida S.)
Carbonel, King of Cats, (Sleigh, Barbara)
Cardinal's Snuff-Box, (Harland, Henry)
Careers of Cynthia, (Berry, Erick)
Careful Carlos, (Sage, Michael)
Careless Chicken, (Krakemsides, Baron)
Careless Jane, (Pyle, Katharine)
Carey Girl, (Yates, Elizabeth)
Cargo for Jennifer, (Vetter, Marjorie)
Caricatures of 25 Gentlemen, (Beerbohm, Max)
Carlo, (Frost, A.B.)
Carlo's Cricket, (Reid, Barbara)
Carlota, (Barnes, Nancy)
Carlotta's Intended, (Stuart, Ruth M.)
Carmen, (Merimee, Prosper)

Carmen: Silent Partner, (Kahmann, Chesley)
Carnival Time at Strobeck, (Harris, May V.)
Carnival in Paris, (Carlson, Natalie S.)
Carol on Tour, (Boylston, Helen D.)
Carolina Caravan, (Govan, Christine)
Carolina Lee, (Bell, Lilian)
Carolina's Courage, (Yates, Elizabeth)
Caroline of Courtlandt Street, (Mills, Weymer J.)
Carpet from Bagdad, (MacGrath, Harold)
Carpet of Flowers, (DeTrevino, Elizabeth)
Carpet of Solomon, (Ish-Kishor, Salamith)
Carrier Boy, (Taylor, Florance)
Carrot Seed, (Krauss, Ruth)
Carry On, Mr. Bowditch, (Latham, Jean L.)
Cartier Sails the St. Lawrence, (Averill, Esther)
Cartoons: Second Childhood of John Bull, (Beerbohm, Max)
Carved Lions, (Molesworth, Mrs.)
Carver's George, (Means, Florence C.)
Casanova Jones, (Anthony, Joseph)
Case of the Cat's Meow, (Bonsall, Crosby)
Case of the Dumb Bells, (Bonsall, Crosby)
Case of the Hungry Stranger, (Bonsall, Crosby)
Case of the Silver Egg, (Skirrow, Desmond)
Case-Record from a Sonnetorium, (Moore, Merrill)
Casey Joins the Circus, (Dobias, Dorathea F.)
Casey at the Bat, (Thayer, Ernest)
Castaways in Lilliput, (Winterfeld, Henry)
Castilian Days, (Hay, John)
Castle Comedy, (Buchanan, Thompson)
Castle Inn, (Weyman, Stanley J.)
Castle Number Nine, (Bemelmans, Ludwig)
Castle in Silver Wood, (Owen, Ruth)
Castle in the Sand, (Bettina)
Castle of Grumpy Grouch, (Donahey, Mary D.)
Castle of Yew, (Boston, Lucy M.)
Castles & Chateaux of Touraine, (Miltoun, Francis)
Castles in the Sand, (Johnson, Crockett)
Castors Away!, (Burton, Hester)
Cat & the Captain, (Coatsworth, Eliz.)
Cat & the Kitten, (Hader, B.& E.)
Cat Alphabet, (Palazzo, Tony)
Cat Book, (Besser, Marianne)
Cat Book, (Lucas, E.V.)
Cat Book, (Lucas, E.V.)
Cat Calls, (Bacon, Peggy)
Cat Came Fiddling, (Kapp, Paul (adap))
Cat Can't Count, (Budney, Blossom)
Cat Club, (Averill, Esther)
Cat Had Nine Lives, (Abdullah, Achmed)
Cat Hotel, (Johnson, Siddie)
Cat Next Door, (Shepard, Birse)
Cat Scouts, (Pope, Jessie)
Cat Tales, (Belting, Natalia)
Cat Tales, (Nesbit, Edith)
Cat Tales from Many Lands, (Healy, Daty)
Cat Thief, (Cass, Joan E.)
Cat Who Couldn't Purr, (Cameron, Polly)
Cat Who Liked to Pretend, (Chalmers, Mary)
Cat Who Rode Cows, (Lockridge, Frances)
Cat Who Tasted Cinnamon Toast, (Spencer, Ann)
Cat Who Went to Heaven, (Coatsworth, Eliz.)
Cat Whose Whiskers Slipped, (Campbell, Ruth)
Cat and Dog, (Minarik, Else H.)
Cat and Mrs. Cary, (Gates, Doris)
Cat and the Devil, (Joyce, James)
Cat and the Fiddler, (Jeter, Jacky)
Cat and the Flying Machine, (Kubinyi, Laszlo)
Cat and the Mouse, (De La Iglesia, Maria)

Cat at Night, (Ipcar, Dahlov)
Cat from Telegraph Hill, (Hurd, Edith T.)
Cat in the Hat... [All titles], (Seuss, Dr.)
Cat of Paris, (Hoffmann, Eleanor)
Cat of the Bubastes, (Henty, G.A.)
Cat that Clumped, (Annixter, Paul)
Cat that Joined the Club, (Thayer, Jane)
Cat that Jumped Out of the Story, (Hecht, Ben)
Cat that Walked a Week, (DeJong, Meindert)
Cat that Went to College, (Frost, Frances)
Cat's Cradle, (Byron, May)
Cat's Cradle Rhymes for Children, (Willett, Edward)
Cat's Elegy, (Burgess, Gelett)
Cat's Fairy Land..., (Johnson, Mary)
Cat's Opera, (Dillon, Eilis)
Cat's Pajamas, (Brundage, Frances)
Cat-Haters Handbook, (Cole, William)
Catch a Little Fox, (DeRegniers, Beatrice)
Catch a Little Rhyme, (Merriam, Eve)
Catfish, (Hurd, Edith T.)
Catharine Susan('s)... [All titles], (Ainslie, Kathleen)
Cathedral Courtship, (Wiggin, Kate D.)
Cathedrals & Abbey Churches of England, (Aldin, Cecil)
Cathy is Company, (Lexau, Joan M.)
Catnip Man, (Holberg, Ruth)
Catrina & the Cats, (Tufts, Georgia)
Catriona, (Stevenson, Rbt. L.)
Cats, (Bronson, Wilfrid S.)
Cats & Bats & Things with Wings, (Aiken, Conrad)
Cats & Kittens, (Tucker, Elizabeth S.)
Cats & Kitts, (Montgomery, F.T.)
Cats & More Cats, (Thorne, Diana)
Cats & People, (Lockridge, Frances)
Cats Cats Cats Cats Cats, (DeRegniers, Beatrice)
Cats Who Stayed for Dinner, (Rowand, Phyllis)
Cats and Rosemary, (Swinnerton, Frank)
Cats at Play, (Wain, Louis)
Cats at School, (Woodhouse, S.C.)
Cats for the Tooseys, (La Rue, Mabel G.)
Cats in Cahoots, (Tovey, Doreen)
Cats of Destiny, (Downey, Fairfax)
Cats of the Eiffel Tower, (Roselli, Auro)
Cats!, (Grimalkin)
Cats' XYZ, (Nichols, Beverly)
Cattle-Ranch To College, (Doubleday, Russell)
Cautionary Tales for Children, (Belloc, Hilaire)
Cautious Carp, (Radlov, Nicholas)
Cavalier Maid, (Knipe, A.A.)
Cavalry Mount, (Downey, Fairfax)
Cave Twins, (Perkins, Lucy F.)
Ceasar's Gallic War, (Coolidge, Olivia)
Cecil Aldin's Happy Family, (Byron, May)
Cecil Aldin's Merry Party, (Byron, May)
Cecily, (Helm, Clementine)
Cecily G. & the 9 Monkeys, (Rey, Hans A.)
Cecily Parsley's Nursery Rhymes, (Potter, Beatrix)
Cedar Deer, (Burbank, Addison)
Cedar's Boy, (Meader, Stephen W.)
Cedric the Forester, (Marshall, Bernard G.)
Celia's Lighthouse, (Molloy, Anne)
Celtic Dragon Myth, (Campbell, John F.)
Celtic Fairy Tales, (Jacobs, Joseph (ed))
Celtic Myth & Legend, (Squire, Charles)
Celtic Wonder World, (Thomson, Clara L.)
Censored, the Goat, (Stong, Philip D.)
Centerburg Tales, (McCloskey, Robert)
Centuries Apart, (Bouve, Edward T.)
Century of Charades, (Bellamy, William)

Certain Small Shepherd, (Caudill, Rebecca)
Cezar and the Music-Maker, (Schwalje, Earl)
Chaga, (Lipkind, Will)
Challenge Stories/Courage & Love for Girls, (Ferris, H.)
Chalou, (Carlson, Natalie S.)
Champion's Choice, (Tunis, John R.)
Champions of the Round Table, (Pyle, Howard)
Chancy and the Grand Rascal, (Fleischman, Sid)
Chandler Chipmunk's Flying Lesson, (Martin, Patricia)
Chang Chee, (Lee, Melicent)
Chang of the Siamese Jungle, (Morse, Elizabeth)
Change of Climate, (Williams, Jay)
Change-Child, (Curry, Jane L.)
Chanticleer & the Fox, (Chaucer, Geoffrey)
Chapsticks, (Codrington, Florence)
Charcoals of New & Old New York, (Smith, Francis H.)
Charge It, (Bacheller, Irving)
Charge of the Light Brigade, (Tennyson, Alfred)
Chariot Race of Ben-Hur, (Wallace, Lew)
Chariot in the Sky, (Bontemps, Arna)
Charity Chance, (Raymond, Walter)
Charlemagne & his Knights, (Pyle, Katharine)
Charles Dickens Birthday Book, (Hawksley, E.D.)
Charles O'Malley..., (Lever, Charles)
Charley Sang a Song, (Hays, Daniel)
Charley and the New Car, (Thayer, Jane)
Charley the Horse, (Palazzo, Tony)
Charley, Charlotte & Golden Canary, (Keeping, Charles)
Charlie & the Chocolate Factory, (Dahl, Roald)
Charlie & the Tramp, (Hoban, Russell)
Charlie Brown Christmas, (Schulz, Charles)
Charlotte & White Horse, (Krauss, Ruth)
Charlotte Sometimes, (Farmer, Penelope)
Charlotte's Web, (White, Elwyn B.)
Charm of Birds, (Porter, Rose)
Charms & Dreams from Pedlar's Pack, (Adam, H.D.)
Chase of the Golden Plate, (Futrelle, Jacques)
Chase of the Meteor, (Bynner, Edwin L.)
Chateau of Montplaisir, (Seawell, Molly E.)
Chateaux of Touraine, (Lansdale, M.H.)
Chatterlings in Wordland, (Lipman, Michael)
Chatwit the Man-Talk Bird, (Mighels, Philip V.)
Checked Love Affair, (Ford, Paul L.)
Cheddar Gorge, (Squire, John (ed))
Chee-Chee's Brother, (Robinson, Gertrude)
Cheechakoes, (Short, Wayne)
Cheeky: A Prairie Dog, (Lau, Josephine)
Cheerful, (Brown, Palmer)
Cheerful Cricket..., (Marks, Jeannette)
Cheerful Heart, (Gray, Eliz. J.)
Cheery Scarecrow, (Gruelle, Johnny)
Cheese, (Waber, Bernard)
Chef's Holiday, (Jones, Idwal)
Cherokee Animal Tales, (Scheer, George)
Cherokee Strip: Race for Land, (Fisher, Aileen)
Cherry Ann & the Dragon Horse, (Coatsworth, Eliz.)
Cherry Time at Bullerby, (Lindgren, Astrid)
Cherrystones, (Farjeon, Eleanor)
Chessie, (Carroll, Ruth)
Chessie and her Kittens, (Carroll, Ruth)
Chester, (Bracker, Charles)
Chester, (Clymer, Eleanor)
Chester, the Worldly Pig, (Peet, Bill)
Chestnut Squirrel, (Commager, Henry)
Chestry Oak, (Seredy, Kate)
Chi Ming & the Writing Lesson, (Marquand, Josephine)
Chi Ming and the Tiger Kitten, (Marquand, Josephine)
Chi-Wee, (Moon, Grace P.)

Chi-Wee and Loki, (Moon, Grace P.)
Chica, (Scott, Sally)
Chickabiddy Stories, (Mitchell, Edmund)
Chicken Book, (Williams, Garth)
Chicken Little & Little Half Chick, (N/A)
Chicken Ten Thousand, (Jackson, Jacqueline)
Chicken World, (Smith, E. Boyd)
Chicken in the Tunnel, (Thayer, Jane)
Chie and the Sports Day, (Matsuno, Masako)
Chief of the Herd, (Mukerji, Dhan G.)
Child Amy, (Magruder, Julia)
Child Characters from Dickens, (Weedon, Lucy L.)
Child Jesus, (Fitch, Florence)
Child Life in Colonial Days, (Earle, Alice M.)
Child Songs of Cheer, (Stein, Evaleen)
Child Thoughts in Picture and Verse, (Westcott, M.K.)
Child Voices, (Cule, William E.)
Child World, (Setoun, Gabriel)
Child You Used to Be, (Pease, Leonora)
Child is Born, (Baker, Edna D.)
Child of Tuscany, (Bouvet, Marguerite)
Child of the Age, (Adams, Francis)
Child of the Air, (Spielmann, M.H.)
Child of the Sea, (Littlewood, Samuel R.)
Child of the Storm, (Haggard, H. Rider)
Child of the Sun, (Banks, Charles E.)
Child's Aesop, (Towers, Alton)
Child's Arabian Nights, (Robinson, W. Heath)
Child's Book of Bible Stories, (Werner, Jane)
Child's Book of Country Stories, (Skinner, Ada M.)
Child's Book of Dreams, (DeRegniers, Beatrice)
Child's Book of Empire, (Morris, Alice T.)
Child's Book of Hymns, (Wyckoff, Marjorie)
Child's Book of Modern Stories, (Skinner, Ada M.)
Child's Book of Myths, (Price, Margaret E.)
Child's Book of Nonsense, (Cameron, Polly)
Child's Book of Old Verses, (Smith, Jessie W.)
Child's Book of Poems, (Fujikawa, Gyo)
Child's Book of Prayers, (Bible)
Child's Book of Saints, (Canton, William)
Child's Book of Stories, (Coussens, Penrhyn W.)
Child's Book of Warriors, (Canton, William)
Child's Calendar, (Updike, John)
Child's Christmas, (Sharp, Evelyn)
Child's Christmas in Wales, (Thomas, Dylan)
Child's Day, (De La Mare, Walter)
Child's Day Book, (Sidney, Margaret)
Child's Day in Song, (Frank, Mabel L.)
Child's Dream of the Zoo, (Manning, William)
Child's Garden of Song, (Tomlins, William L.)
Child's Garden of Verses, (Stevenson, Rbt. L.)
Child's Good Morning, (Brown, Margaret W.)
Child's Good Night Book, (Brown, Margaret W.)
Child's Life of Christ, (Dearmer, Mabel)
Child's Life of Jesus, (Steedman, C.M.)
Child's Prayer, (Toogood, Cora C.)
Child's Primer of Natural History, (Herford, Oliver)
Child's Rip Van Winkle, (Irving, Washington)
Child's Stamp Book of Old Verses, (Various)
Child's Story of the Nativity, (Raymond, Louise)
Child's Story of the World, (Peattie, Donald C.)
Childhood, (Johnson, Burges)
Childhood, (Pyle, Katharine)
Childhood, (Sowerby, Githa)
Childhood, (Sowerby, Millicent)
Childhood Songs of Long Ago, (Watts, Isaac)
Childhood is a Time of Innocence, (Anglund, Joan W.)
Children Across the Sea, (McNeil, Marion)

Children All, (N/A)
Children Come Running, (Coatsworth, Eliz.)
Children For Ever, (MacPherson, J.F.)
Children Sing in the Far West, (Austin, Mary)
Children Who Followed the Piper, (Colum, Padraic)
Children at Play in Many Lands, (N/A)
Children in Japan, (Bartruse, Grace)
Children in Verse, (Burke, Thos. (ed.))
Children in the Wood Stories, (Marks, Jeannette)
Children of Ancient Britain, (Lamprey, Louise)
Children of Colonial Days, (Tucker, Elizabeth S.)
Children of Dickens, (Crothers, Samuel M.)
Children of Mountain Eagle, (Miller, Elizabeth C.)
Children of Noisy Village, (Lindgren, Astrid)
Children of North Africa, (Stinetorf, Louise)
Children of Odin, (Colum, Padraic)
Children of Other Lands, (Piper, Watty)
Children of Our Town, (Wells, Carolyn)
Children of Spring, (Thomas, Edith M.)
Children of the Arctic, (Peary, Josephine)
Children of the Bible, (Yates, Elizabeth)
Children of the Blizzard, (Washburne, Heluiz)
Children of the Castle, (Molesworth, Mrs.)
Children of the Clouds, (Williams, Herschel)
Children of the Cold, (Schwatka, Fred)
Children of the Covered Wagon, (Carr, Mary J.)
Children of the Dawn, (Buckley, Elsie F.)
Children of the Frost, (London, Jack)
Children of the Green Knowe, (Boston, Lucy M.)
Children of the Handcrafts, (Bailey, Carolyn S.)
Children of the Housetops, (Mirza, Youel B.)
Children of the Moor, (Fitinghoff, Laura M.)
Children of the New Forest, (Marryat, Frederick)
Children of the Night, (Robinson, Edwin A.)
Children of the Nineties, (Wright, Anna R.)
Children of the North Lights, (D'Aulaire, I.& E.)
Children of the Prairie, (Curtis, Alice B.)
Children of the Red King, (Polland, Madeleine)
Children of the Revolution, (Humphrey, Maud)
Children of the Salmon, (O'Faolain, Eileen)
Children of the Sea, (Bronson, Wilfrid S.)
Children of the Soil, (Burglon, Nora)
Children of the Sun in Hawaii, (Li, Ling-ai)
Children of the Tenements, (Riis, Jacob A.)
Children of the White House, (Cavanah, Frances)
Children of the Wild, (Deming, Therese O.)
Children of the World from A to Z, (Stevens, Thomas)
Children on Troublemaker Street, (Lindgren, Astrid)
Children's Bells, (Farjeon, Eleanor)
Children's Bible, (Sherman, Henry)
Children's Blue Bird, (LeBlanc, Georgette)
Children's Blue Bird, (Maeterlinck, Maurice)
Children's Book, (Scudder, Horace E.)
Children's Book of Hymns, (Barker, Cicely M.)
Children's Cheerful Cherub, (McCann, Rebecca)
Children's Corner, (Elkin, R.H.)
Children's Garland of Verse, (Rhys, Grace (ed.))
Children's King Arthur, (Lee, Frank H.)
Children's Munchausen, (Martin, John)
Children's Own Story Book, (Carson, Norma B.)
Children's Plays, (Skinner, Ada M.)
Children's Plutarch, (Gould, Frederick J.)
Children's Shakespeare, (Hoffman, Alice S.)
Children's Shakespeare, (Nesbit, Edith)
Children's Singing Games, (Gomme, Alice B.)
Children's Stories from Arabian Nights, (Woolf, Rose)
Children's Stories from French Fairy Tales, (Ashley, Doris)
Children's Stories/Japanese Fairy Tales, (Kato, N. (tr.))

Children's Stories that Never Grow Old, (Stone, Mary)
Children's Story Garden, (N/A)
Children's Tales from Scottish Ballads, (Grierson, E.W.)
Children's Year, (Brown, Margaret W.)
Chile in Story and Pictures, (Henry, Marguerite)
Chimney Corner... [All titles], (Hutchinson, Veronica)
Chimney Farm Bedtime Stories, (Beston, Henry)
Chimney Town, (Daskein, Tarella)
Chimp and the Clown, (Carroll, Ruth)
Chimpanzee Roams the Forest, (Conklin, Gladys)
Chin Ling & Chinese Cricket, (Stilwell, Alison)
China, (Blake, Henry A.)
China Cow, (Peto, Gladys)
China Quest, (Lewis, Eliz. F.)
Chinese Boy and Girl, (Headland, I.T.)
Chinese Bug, (Schweitzer, Byrd B.)
Chinese Child's Day, (Terhune, Anice)
Chinese Children Next Door, (Buck, Pearl S.)
Chinese Fairy Tales, (Goulden, Shirley)
Chinese Fairy Tales, (Pitman, Norman)
Chinese Ink Stick, (Wiese, Kurt)
Chinese Knew, (Pine, Tillie S.)
Chinese Mother Goose Rhymes, (Headland, I.T.)
Chinese Twins, (Perkins, Lucy F.)
Chinese Wonder Book, (Pitman, Norman)
Ching-Li, (Poston, Martha L.)
Ching-Li & the Dragons, (Howard, Alice W.)
Chinky Joins the Circus, (Tousey, Sanford)
Chinky: Banker Pony, (Tousey, Sanford)
Chip of the Flying-U, (Bower, B.M.)
Chip the Dam Builder, (Kjelgaard, Jim)
Chip's Dogs, (Bellew, Frank P.)
Chip: My Life and Times, (Untermeyer, Louis)
Chipmunk that Went to Church, (Bromhall, Winifred)
Chippendale Dam, (Troy, Hugh)
Chiquita, (Tileston, Mary W.)
Chisel-Tooth Tribe, (Bronson, Wilfrid S.)
Chitty Chitty Bang Bang!, (Fleming, Ian)
Chivalry, (Cabell, James B.)
Chiyo's Return, (Kiyooka, Chiyono)
Chloris of the Island, (Watson, H.B.M.)
Chocolate Touch, (Catling, Patrick)
Choir Visible, (Adams, Mary J.)
Choo-Choo, (Burton, Virginia L.)
Choo-Me-Shoo, (Holling, Holling C.)
Choochee: Story of an Eskimo Boy, (Averill, Naomi)
Chooky, (Faulkner, John)
Choosing Book, (Dalgliesh, Alice)
Chorister's Cake, (Mayne, William)
Chosen Baby, (Wasson, Valentina P.)
Chouchou, (Francoise)
Christ Child, (Petersham, Maud)
Christ Legends, (Lagerlof, Selma)
Christ Story, (Bible)
Christ Story for Boys & Girls, (Rihbany, Abraham M.)
Christ's Secret of Happiness, (Abbott, Lyman)
Christabel's Fairyland, (Whyte, Adam G.)
Christmas, (Dalgliesh, Alice)
Christmas, (Roosevelt, Eleanor)
Christmas ABC, (Johnson, Florence)
Christmas Angel, (Brown, Abbie F.)
Christmas Angel, (Pyle, Katharine)
Christmas Anna Angel, (Sawyer, Ruth)
Christmas Book: Gospel of St. Luke, (Bible)
Christmas Bower, (Redford, Polly)
Christmas Bunny, (Lipkind, Will)
Christmas Cake, (Duvoisin, Roger)
Christmas Card, (N/A)

Christmas Carol, (Dickens, Charles)
Christmas Carols, (Leet, Frank R.)
Christmas Child, (Molesworth, Mrs.)
Christmas Dinner, (Irving, Washington)
Christmas Drawings for the Human Race, (Nast, Thomas)
Christmas Dream, (Alcott, Louisa M.)
Christmas Eve, (Cooke, Alistair)
Christmas Eve, (Day-Lewis, Cecil)
Christmas Eve, (Hurd, Edith T.)
Christmas Eve at the Mellops, (Ungerer, Tomi)
Christmas Eve on Lonesome, (Fox, John Jr.)
Christmas Every Day..., (Howells, William D.)
Christmas Flower, (Jackson, Joseph)
Christmas Folk, (Belting, Natalia)
Christmas Forest, (Fatio, Louise)
Christmas Gif', (Rollins, Charlene)
Christmas House..., (Turner, Thyra)
Christmas Kitten, (Carroll, Ruth)
Christmas Letter, (Unknown)
Christmas Magic, (Tippett, James S.)
Christmas Maker's Club, (Sawyer, Edith A.)
Christmas Mouse, (Wenning, Elizabeth)
Christmas Mystery, (Locke, William J.)
Christmas Nightingale, (Kelly, Eric P.)
Christmas Party for Santa Claus, (Huntington, Ida M.)
Christmas Poem, (Mann, Thomas)
Christmas Poems, (Drinkwater, John)
Christmas Pony, (Hall, William N.)
Christmas Posy, (Molesworth, Mrs.)
Christmas Prayer, (Foley, James W.)
Christmas Pudding, (Veale, E.)
Christmas Reindeer, (Burgess, Thornton)
Christmas Roses, (Lawson, Lizzie)
Christmas Sky, (Branley, Franklyn)
Christmas Stocking Rhymes, (Bonte, George W.)
Christmas Stories from Dickens, (Dickens, Charles)
Christmas Story, (Chalmers, Mary)
Christmas Story, (Keeping, Charles)
Christmas Story, (Mencken, H.L.)
Christmas Story, (Porter, Katherine A.)
Christmas Story, (Werner, Jane)
Christmas Story, (Yates, Elizabeth)
Christmas Story from Saint Mark, (Bible)
Christmas Tales and Christmas Verse, (Field, Eugene)
Christmas Tales of Flanders, (DeBosschere, Jean)
Christmas Time, (Field, Rachel)
Christmas Tree Forest, (Alden, Raymond M.)
Christmas Tree for Lydia, (Enright, Elizabeth)
Christmas Tree in the Woods, (Smith, Susan C.)
Christmas Whale, (Duvoisin, Roger)
Christmas at Bracebridge Hall, (Irving, Washington)
Christmas at Totem's Farm, (Wiberg, Harald)
Christmas in Dickens, (Dickens, Charles)
Christmas in Noisy Village, (Lindgren, Astrid)
Christmas in the Barn, (Brown, Margaret W.)
Christmas in the Forest, (Wahl, Jan)
Christmas in the Stable, (Lindgren, Astrid)
Christmas in the Woods, (Frost, Frances)
Christmas is a Time of Giving, (Anglund, Joan W.)
Christmas on the Mayflower, (Hays, Wilma P.)
Christmas that Almost Wasn't, (Nash, Ogden)
Christmas with Santa Claus, (Montgomery, F.T.)
Christmas-Tree Land, (Molesworth, Mrs.)
Christopher Columbus, (Judson, Clara I.)
Christopher Robin... [All titles], (Milne, A.A.)
Christopher and his Turtle, (Lattimore, Eleanor)
Christopher the Giant, (Bishop, Claire H.)
Chronicle of the Drum, (Thackeray, Wm. M.)

Chronicles of Aunt Minervy Ann, (Harris, Joel C.)
Chronicles of Avonlea, (Montgomery, Lucy M.)
Chronicles of Fairy-Land, (Hume, Fergus)
Chronicles of Rhoda, (Cox, Florence T.)
Chronicles of a Little Tot, (Cooke, Edmund V.)
Chronicles of the Cid, (Plummer, Mary W.)
Chubby Bear, (Barto, Emily N.)
Chubby's First Year, (Gag, Flavia)
Chucaro, Wild Pony of Pampa, (Kalnay, Francis)
Chuck Martinez, (Holton, Priscilla)
Chuck-a-Luck & his Reindeer, (Hader, B.& E.)
Chuffer, (Elam, Elizabeth)
Chuggins, (Hancock, H. Irving)
Chuggy & Blue Caboose, (Freeman, Don)
Chums, (Pool, Maria L.)
Churchmouse Stories, (Austin, Margot)
Cian of the Chariots, (Babcock, William H.)
Ciderville Folks, (Brown, Elijah P.)
Cinder Ike, (Newell, Hope)
Cinderella, (Elias, E. (ed.))
Cinderella, (Evans, C.S.)
Cinderella, (Hall, Gladys)
Cinderella, (N/A)
Cinderella, (Perrault, Charles)
Cinderella at the Zoo, (Parker, B.)
Cinderella's Picture Book, (N/A)
Cinderella: From the Opera, (Rossini, Gioacchino)
Cinders, (Gibson, Katharine)
Cindy's Sad and Happy Tree, (Orgel, Doris)
Cindy's Snowdrops, (Orgel, Doris)
Cinnabar: One O'Clock Fox, (Henry, Marguerite)
Cinnamon Seed, (Moore, John T.)
Cinque Ports..., (Hueffer, F.M.)
Circle of Seasons, (Clark, Ann N.)
Circle of the Braves, (Thompson, Wolfe)
Circles and Curves, (Razzell, Arthur)
Circular Staircase, (Rinehart, Mary R.)
Circus & All About It, (Smith, E. Boyd)
Circus ABC, (Willson, Dixie)
Circus Babies, (Gale, Elizabeth)
Circus Baby, (Petersham, Maud)
Circus Comes to Town, (Hutchinson, Veronica)
Circus Day, (Brett, Edna P.)
Circus Girl, (Sendak, Jack)
Circus Parade, (Fenner, Phyllis R.)
Circus Ruckus, (Lipkind, Will)
Circus School, (Brown, Paul)
Circus Shoes, (Streatfeild, Noel)
Circus Time, (Conger, Marion)
Circus in Peter's Closet, (Randolph, Jane)
Circus in the Mist, (Munari, Bruno)
Circus is Coming, (Streatfeild, Noel)
Circus of Dr. Lao, (Finney, Charles G.)
Citadel of a Hundred Stairways, (Malkus, Alida S.)
City Child, (Robinson, Selma)
City Country ABC, (Gipson, Morrell)
City Curious, (DeBosschere, Jean)
City Neighbor: Story of Jane Addams, (Judson, Clara I.)
City People, (Flagg, James M.)
City Rhythms, (Grifalconi, Ann)
City Spreads its Wings, (Hopkins, Lee B. (comp))
City Springtime, (Kay, Helen)
City Under the Back Steps, (Lampman, Evelyn)
City at the Pole, (Stables, Gordon)
City in All Directions, (Adoff, Arnold)
City in the Summer, (Schick, Eleanor)
City in the Winter, (Schick, Eleanor)
City-Country ABC, (Walters, Marguerite)

Claim Jumpers of Marble Canyon, (Montgomery, R.)
Clair De Lune, (West, Michael P.)
Clambake Mutiny, (Beatty, Jerome)
Clan of Munes, (Waugh, Frederick)
Clara in Blunderland, (Lewis, Caroline)
Clarion the Killdeer, (Russell, Helen R.)
Claws of the Thunderbird, (Holling, Holling C.)
Claymore and Kilt, (Leodhas, Sorche)
Clean Clarence, (Friedrich, Otto)
Clean Pig, (Weisgard, Leonard)
Clear for Action!, (Meader, Stephen W.)
Clear the Track/Michael's Magic Train, (Slobodkin, L.)
Clearing Weather, (Meigs, Cornelia L.)
Clearing in the Forest, (Carrick, Carol)
Clementine, (Byars, Betsy C.)
Cleopatra, (Haggard, H. Rider)
Cleopatra Goes Sledding, (Hodeir, Andre)
Clever Betsy, (Burnham, Clara L.)
Clever Bill, (Nicholson, William)
Clever Cat, (Lattimore, Eleanor)
Clever Turtle, (Roche, A.K.)
Climb a Lofty Ladder, (Havighurst, Marion)
Cloak of Friendship, (Housman, Laurence)
Clock Museum, (Sobol, Ken)
Clocks Tell the Time, (Reck, Alma)
Clocks and More Clocks, (Hutchins, Pat)
Clockwork Twin, (Brooks, Walter)
Cloister & Hearth, (Reade, Charles)
Closed Door, (DeBosschere, Jean)
Cloud Boat Stories, (Barton, Olive R.)
Cloud Kingdom, (Wallis, I. Henry)
Cloud with the Silver Lining, (Palmer, C. Everard)
Clover's Princess, (Douglas, Amanda M.)
Clown Dog, (Davis, Lavinia R.)
Clown Town, (Willson, Dixie)
Club of Queer Trades, (Chesterton, G.K.)
Clue of the Faded Dress, (Chapman, Maristan)
Coal Camp Girl, (Lenski, Lois)
Coast of Bohemia, (Howells, William D.)
Coast of Chance, (Chamberlain, Esther)
Cobb's Anatomy, (Cobb, Irving)
Cobb's Bill of Fare, (Cobb, Irving)
Cobbler's Knob, (Jewett, Eleanore)
Cobweb Castle, (Wahl, Jan)
Cock Robin, (N/A)
Cock and the Ghost Cat, (Lifton, Betty)
Cock, Mouse & Little Red Hen, (Lefevre, Felicite)
Cock-a-Doodle-Doo, (Emberley, Edward)
Cock-a-Doodle-Doo, (Hader, B.& E.)
Cockyolly Bird, (Dearmer, Mabel)
Coco Bolo, (Hamp, Sidford F.)
Coco is Coming, (Peckinpah, Betty)
Coco the Goat, (Wells, Rhea)
Cocoa, (Otto, Margaret G.)
Cocoa Dancer, (Rue, Flora)
Cocolo Comes to America, (Bettina)
Cocolo's Home, (Bettina)
Coconut Thieves, (Fournier, Catherine)
Coconut: Wonder Tree, (Sperry, Armstrong)
Codfish Musket, (Hewes, Agnes D.)
Coffee Train, (Shank, Margarethe)
Cold Hazard, (Armstrong, Richard)
Cold-Blooded Penguin, (Disney, Walt)
Colette & Baba in Timbuctoo, (Seabrook, Katie)
Colette and the Princess, (Slobodkin, Louis)
Coll and His White Pig, (Alexander, Lloyd C.)
Collected Stories for Children, (De La Mare, Walter)
Collected Verse of..., (Kipling, Rudyard)

College Girls, (Goodloe, Abbe C.)
College on Horseback, (Hall, Esther G.)
Colombia in Story and Pictures, (Donaldson, Lois)
Colonel Carter's Christmas, (Smith, Francis H.)
Colonel Crockett's Cooperative Christmas, (Hughes, Rupert)
Colonel's Squad, (Evers, Alf)
Colonial Dame, (Fessenden, Laura D.)
Colonial Days in Old New York, (Earle, Alice M.)
Colonial Holidays, (Tittle, Walter)
Colorado: River of Mystery, (Buff, M.& C.)
Colors, (Reiss, John J.)
Colors, Colors All Around, (Scott, Rochelle)
Coloured Lands, (Chesterton, G.K.)
Colt from Moon Mountain, (Lathrop, Dorothy)
Colt from the Dark Forest, (Loken, Anna B.)
Colt of Cripple Creek, (Bialk, Elisa)
Colt of Destiny..., (Malkus, Alida S.)
Columbia Stories, (Terhune, Albert P.)
Columbia's Courtship, (Crane, Walter)
Columbia: Power House/North America, (Latham, Jean L.)
Columbian Ode, (Monroe, Harriet)
Columbus, (D'Aulaire, I.& E.)
Columbus Day, (Showers, Paul)
Columbus Story, (Dalgliesh, Alice)
Columbus of Space, (Serviss, Garrett P.)
Columbus, Finder of the New World, (Syme, Ronald)
Comanche..., (Appel, David)
Come & See the Bottle Family, (Proudfit, Isabel)
Come & See the Broom Closet Family, (Proudfit, Isabel)
Come Again, Pelican, (Freeman, Don)
Come Along!, (Caudill, Rebecca)
Come Back, Paul, (Rukeyser, Muriel)
Come Christmas, (Farjeon, Eleanor)
Come Hither, (De La Mare, Walter)
Come Over to My House, (LeSieg, Theo)
Come Play House, (Osswald, Edith)
Come Play with Me, (Miller, Olive B.)
Come Play with Mickey Mouse, (Disney, Walt)
Come Unto these Yellow Sands, (Woods, Margaret L.)
Come and Have Fun, (Hurd, Edith T.)
Come and See the Pencil Box Family, (Proudfit, Isabel)
Come by Here, (Coolidge, Olivia)
Come for a Walk with Me, (Chalmers, Mary)
Comedies of Courtship, (Hope, Anthony)
Comedies of Oliver Goldsmith, (Goldsmith, Oliver)
Comedy of the Twelfth Night, (Shakespeare, Wm.)
Comet in Moominland, (Jansson, Tove)
Comic Advens. of Old Mother Hubbard... (Martin, Sarah C.)
Comic Yarns, (Cox, Palmer)
Comical Coons, (Kemble, Edward W.)
Comin' Thro the Rye, (N/A)
Coming of Cassidy, (Mulford, Clarence)
Coming of Pout, (Blair, Peter)
Coming of the Dragon Ships, (Everson, Howard)
Commodore's Cup, (Meader, Stephen W.)
Companionable Books, (Van Dyke, Henry)
Compleat Angler, (Walton, Isaac)
Complete Fairy Tales, (Thomas, Edward)
Complete Poetical Works of..., (Chaucer, Geoffrey)
Comus, (Milton, John)
Con the Wizard, (Jewett, John H.)
Conceited Puppy..., (Emanuel, Walter)
Condemned as a Nihilist, (Henty, G.A.)
Confessions of a Caricaturist, (Herford, Oliver)
Confessions of a Daddy, (Butler, Ellis P.)
Confetti for Cortorelli, (Fletcher, David)
Congo and Coasts of Africa, (Davis, Richard H.)
Congressman Pumphrey, (McCutcheon, John T.)

Conjure Woman, (Chesnutt, Charles)
Conjuror's House, (White, Stewart E.)
Conny and Uncle Dick, (Gay, Romney)
Conquest of Montezuma's Empire, (Lang, Andrew)
Conquest of the Atlantic, (D'Aulaire, I.& E.)
Conquistador, (Craine, Edith)
Conrad's Castle, (Shecter, Ben)
Constantinople, (Crawford, F. Marion)
Constantinople, (Van Millingen)
Contempo, (Vassos, Ruth)
Contented Little Pussy Cat, (Keller, Frances)
Contest at Paca, (Simont, Marc)
Continuous Performance, (Steig, William)
Contrary Jenkins, (Caudill, Rebecca)
Contrary Little Quail, (Thayer, Jane)
Contrary Woodrow, (Felt, Sue)
Cookie Tree, (Williams, Jay)
Cookie, the Rabbit, (Lowe, Edith)
Cooking in Old Creole Days, (Eustis, Celestine)
Coon Alphabet, (Kemble, Edward W.)
Coontown's 400, (Kemble, Edward W.)
Coot Club, (Ransome, Arthur)
Coppa Hamba, (Ambrose, Blanche A.)
Copper Khan, (Lyons, Dorothy)
Copper Princess, (Munroe, Kirk)
Copper Sun, (Cullen, Countee)
Copper-Toed Boots, (DeAngeli, Marguerite)
Coppertop, (Gaze, Harold)
Copydog in India, (Barr, Stringfellow)
Coquo and the King's Children, (Baker, Cornelia)
Coral Island, (Mordvinoff, Nicolas)
Coral Ship, (Munroe, Kirk)
Corduroy, (Freeman, Don)
Corey's Sea Monster, (Montgomery, R.)
Coridon's Song, (Dobson, Austin)
Corky's Pet Parade, (Fiedler, Maggi)
Corn Grows Ripe, (Rhoads, Dorothy)
Corn-Belt Billy, (Hunt, Mabel L.)
Corn-Farm Boy, (Lenski, Lois)
Cornelia, (Perkins, Lucy F.)
Cornelli..., (Spyri, Johanna)
Corner Stone, (McCarter, Margaret)
Corner in Women, (Masson, Thomas L.)
Corona & Coronet, (Todd, Mabel L.)
Corporal Bess... (Edmonds, Walter D.)
Corporal Corey..., (O'Brien, Jack)
Corporal Keeperupper, (Milhous, Katherine)
Corrie and the Yankee, (Levy, Mimi C.)
Corso the Donkey, (Pothast-Gimberg, C.)
Cortez the Conqueror, (Newcomb, Covelle)
Coryston Family, (Ward, Mrs. H.)
Cosel: With Geronimo on His Last Raid, (Deming, T.O.)
Cossack Fairy Tales & Folk Tales, (Bain, Robert N.)
Costumes of Colonial Times, (Earle, Alice M.)
Cosy-Time Tales, (Joan, Natalie)
Cotswold Characters, (Drinkwater, John)
Cottage at Bantry Bay, (Van Stockum, Hilda)
Cottage for Betsy, (Sawyer, Ruth)
Cotter's Saturday Night, (Burns, Robert)
Cotton Farm Boy, (Mauzey, Merritt)
Cotton Tails, (Beckenbaugh, G.)
Cotton Woolleena, (Housman, Laurence)
Cotton in My Sack, (Lenski, Lois)
Cottontail & Wishing-Fairy, (Ingraham, Corinne)
Cottontail Rabbit, (Schwartz, Elizabeth R.)
Count Billy, (MacDonald, Greville)
Count of Monte Cristo, (Dumas, Alexandre)
Counterpane Fairy, (Pyle, Katharine)

Countess Diane, (Rowland, Henry C.)
Counting Carnival, (Ziner, Feenie)
Counting the Days, (Tippett, James S.)
Country Boy, (Crissey, Forrest)
Country Bunny & Little Gold Shoes, (Heyward, DuBose)
Country Child's Alphabet, (Farjeon, Eleanor)
Country Colic, (Lawson, Robert)
Country Cousin, (Disney, Walt)
Country Cousins, (Dyer, Walter A.)
Country Garage, (Beim, Jerrold)
Country Kittens, (Clymer, Eleanor)
Country Matters, (Leighton, Clare)
Country Neighborhood, (Coatsworth, Eliz.)
Country Noisy Book, (Brown, Margaret W.)
Country School, (Beim, Jerrold)
Country Train, (Beim, Jerrold)
Country of 36000 Wishes, (Maurois, Andre)
Country of the Dwarfs, (DuChaillu, Paul)
Country of the Hawk, (Derleth, August)
Country-Stop, (Bailey, Carolyn S.)
County Christmas, (Fox, Frances M.)
County Fair, (Tudor, Tasha)
Courage Over the Andes, (Kummer, Frederic)
Courage of Sarah Noble, (Dalgliesh, Alice)
Courageous Companions, (Finger, Charles J.)
Court Jester, (Baker, Cornelia)
Court of Boyville, (White, William A.)
Court of King Arthur, (Frost, William H.)
Courtship of Miles Standish, (Longfellow, H.W.)
Cousin Anthony and I, (Martin, Edward S.)
Cousin Melinda, (Lattimore, Eleanor)
Cousin Toby, (Newberry, Clare T.)
Cousin from Clare, (Sackett, Rose M.)
Covered Bridge, (Meigs, Cornelia L.)
Covered Bridge, (Surany, Anico)
Cow Country, (James, Will)
Cow Range & Hunting Trail, (MacKay, Malcolm S.)
Cow Who Fell in the Canal, (Krasilovsky, Phyllis)
Cow's Party, (Ets, Marie H.)
Cow-Tail Switch, (Courlander, Harold)
Cowardice Court, (McCutcheon, George B.)
Cowardly Lion of Oz, (Thompson, Ruth P.)
Cowboy Andy, (Chandler, Edna W.)
Cowboy Boots, (Garst, Shannon)
Cowboy Lyrics, (Carr, Robert V.)
Cowboy Small, (Lenski, Lois)
Cowboy Tommy, (Tousey, Sanford)
Cowboy Tommy's Roundup, (Tousey, Sanford)
Cowboy Twins, (Slobodkin, Florence)
Cowboy and his Friend, (Anglund, Joan W.)
Cowboys North & South, (James, Will)
Cowboys of America, (Tousey, Sanford)
Cowhand Goes to Town, (Stong, Philip D.)
Coyote Song, (Kjelgaard, Jim)
Coyote in Manhattan, (George, Jean C.)
Coyotes, (Bronson, Wilfrid S.)
Cozy Corner Stories, (Molesworth, Mrs.)
Cozy Hour Story Book, (Kramer, Nora)
Cozy Lion, (Burnett, Frances H.)
Crab Cottage, (Jacberns, Raymond)
Crack in the Wall, (Mendoza, George)
Crackajack Pony, (Burgwyn, Mebane)
Cradle Ship, (Howes, Edith)
Cradle of the Deep, (Lowell, Joan)
Crane Maiden, (Matsutani, Miyoko)
Cranes Flying South, (Karazin, N.N.)
Cranford, (Gaskell, Mrs.)
Crazy Creek, (Lampman, Evelyn)

Crazy Dog, (Ware, Leon)
Crazy Flight, (Livingston, Myra C.)
Crazy Kill Range, (Montgomery, R.)
Crazy Quilt, (Brown, Paul)
Creaking Stair, (Coatsworth, Eliz.)
Cream Hill, (Gannett, Lewis)
Creature Songs, (Garnett, Louise A.)
Creature's Choir, (Godden, Rumer)
Creatures, (Colum, Padraic)
Creatures Great & Small, (Flanders, Michael)
Creatures of Darkness, (Baskin, Esther)
Creatures of the Night, (Sterling, Dorothy)
Creeper's Jeep, (Gramatky, Hardie)
Cress Delahanty, (West, Jassamyn)
Crested Seas, (Connolly, James B.)
Cricket, (Hader, B.& E.)
Cricket & the Emperor's Son, (Coatsworth, Eliz.)
Cricket Winter, (Holman, Felice)
Cricket in Times Square, (Selden, George)
Cricket in a Thicket, (Fisher, Aileen)
Cricket in the Cage, (Chalmers, Patrick)
Cricket of Carador, (Nash, Ogden)
Cricket on the Hearth, (Dickens, Charles)
Crictor, (Ungerer, Tomi)
Crimson Conquest, (Hudson, Charles B.)
Crimson Cutlass, (Carter, Russell)
Crimson Fairy Book, (Lang, Andrew)
Crispin's Acres, (Quigg, Jane)
Crissy at the Wheel, (Lawrence, Mildred)
Cristy at Skippinghills, (Hunt, Mabel L.)
Critical Woodcuts, (Sherman, Stuart P.)
Critter Book, (Simon, Ellen)
Croatian Tales of Long Ago, (Berlic-Mazuranic)
Crock of Gold, (Baring-Gould, Sabine)
Crock of Gold, (Stephens, James)
Crocodile, (Deutsch, Babette (tr))
Crocodile & Hen, (Lexau, Joan M.)
Crocodile Tears, (Francois, Andre)
Crocodile has Me by the Leg, (Doob, Leonard W.)
Crocodile's Mouth, (Stoutenburg, Adrien)
Cromwell's Head, (Coolidge, Olivia)
Crooked Apple Tree, (Meigs, Cornelia L.)
Crooked Colt, (Anderson, C.W.)
Crooked Little Path, (Burgess, Thornton)
Crooked Man, (Mother Goose)
Crooked Trails, (Remington, Frederic)
Cross Creek, (Rawlings, Marjorie K.)
Cross Creek Cookery, (Rawlings, Marjorie K.)
Cross Currents, (Porter, Eleanor)
Crossings..., (De La Mare, Walter)
Crow Boy, (Yashima, Taro)
Crowd of Cows, (Graham, John)
Crows of Pearblossom, (Huxley, Aldous)
Crucifixion of Philip Strong, (Sheldon, Charles)
Crude Ditties, (Woodhouse, S.C.)
Cruikshank's Portraits of Himself, (Layard, George S.)
Cruikshank's Water Colours, (Grego, Joseph)
Cruise Under the Crescent, (Stoddard, Charles W.)
Cruise in the Acorn, (Jerrold, A.)
Cruise of the Aardvark, (Nash, Ogden)
Cruise of the Cachalot, (Bullen, Frank T.)
Cruise of the Little Dipper, (Langer, Susanne)
Cruise of the Rickety-Robin, (Gruelle, Johnny)
Cruise of the Snark, (London, Jack)
Crumb that Walked... (Norman, C.)
Crunch, Crunch, (Kessler, Ethel)
Crunch: The Squirrel, (Bond, Elizabeth)
Crystal Ball, (Gordon, Mary D.)

Crystal Ball, (Sargant, Alice)
Crystal Locket, (Rowe, Nellie)
Crystal Mountain, (Rugh, Belle Dorman)
Crystal Rood, (Gould, Katherine C.)
Crystal Tree, (Lindquist, Jennie)
Cuba & other Verse, (Manners, Robert)
Cuba in War Time, (Davis, Richard H.)
Cubby Bear & the Book, (Hogan, Inez)
Cubby Finds an Open Door, (Burgess, Thornton)
Cubies' ABC, (Lyall, Mary C.)
Cuckoo, (Lida)
Cuckoo Calls, (Burglon, Nora)
Cuckoo Clock, (Molesworth, Mrs.)
Cuckoo Songs, (Hinkson, Katharine)
Cuckoo that Couldn't Count, (Latham, Jean L.)
Cucumber: Story of a Siamese Cat, (Colfer, Enid)
Cuddly-Kitty Book, (N/A)
Cuff, a Baby Bear, (Voight, Virginia F.)
Cultural Slag, (Lamport, Felicia)
Cunning Fox, (Watkins, Hope)
Cunning Turtle, (Wiese, Kurt)
Cup of Sun, (Anglund, Joan W.)
Cup of Tea, (Tucker, Elizabeth S.)
Cupid the Cowpunch, (Gates, Eleanor)
Cupid's Almanac, (Herford, Oliver)
Cupid's Cyclopedia, (Clay/Herford)
Cupola House, (Hunt, Mabel L.)
Curious Book of Birds, (Brown, Abbie F.)
Curious Career/Roderick Campbell, (McIlwraith, Jean N.)
Curious Clubhouse, (Govan, Christine)
Curious Cruise of Captain Santa, (Thompson, Ruth P.)
Curious George Goes to the Hospital, (Rey, Margret E.)
Curious George... [Most titles], (Rey, Hans A.)
Curious Little Kitten, (Cook, Bernadine)
Curious Little Owl, (Keller, Frances)
Curious Missie, (Sorensen, Virginia)
Curious Punishments of Bygone Days, (Earle, Alice M.)
Curious, Furious Chipmunk, (Thayer, Jane)
Curl up Small, (Warburg, Sandol)
Curly Heads & Long Legs, (Vredenburg, Edric)
Curly Heads and Long Legs, (Cowham, Hilda)
Curly-Haired Hen, (Vimar, Auguste)
Curtain of Forgetfulness, (Lindsey, William)
Custard the Dragon & Wicked Knight, (Nash, Ogden)
Cutlass Island, (Corbett, Scott)
Cynthia and the Unicorn, (Freeman, Jean T.)
Cyrano the Crow, (Freeman, Don)
Cyrus Holt and the Civil War, (Hall, Anna G.)
Cyrus Hunts the Cougar, (Hopkins, Clark)
Daddies: What They Do All Day, (Puner, Helen)
Daddles: Story of a Plain Hound-Dog, (Sawyer, Ruth)
Daddy Cat, (Wain, Louis)
Daddy Comes Home, (Steiner, Charlotte)
Daddy Darwin's Dovecot, (Ewing, Juliana H.)
Daddy Days, (Simon, Norma)
Daddy Domino, (Merryman, Mildred P.)
Daddy Gander, (Hankins, Maude M.)
Daddy Gander, (Mason, Francis E.)
Daddy Jake the Runaway, (Harris, Joel C.)
Daddy Long Ears, (Kraus, Robert)
Daddy Long Legs, (Cowham, Hilda)
Daddy Long Legs, (Webster, Jean)
Daddy Long Legs Fun Songs, (O'Day, James)
Daddy Long-Legs, (Kent, Kathleen)
Daddy is Home!, (Blomquist, David)
Daddy'Do-Funny's Wisdom Jingles, (Stuart, Ruth M.)
Daddy's Bedtime Fairy Stories, (Bonner, Mary G.)
Daddy's Girl, (Meade, L.T.)

Daddy's Little Rhyme Book, (LeMair, H.W.)
Daffy Taffy, (Brown, Paul)
Dainty Book, (Sowerby, Githa)
Daisy, (Hogner, Dorothy)
Daisy Days, (N/A)
Daisy Dells, (Denton, Clara J.)
Daisy Miller, (James, Henry)
Daisy and Dobbin, (Taber, Gladys)
Dame Wiggin of Lee, (Ruskin. John (ed.))
Damsel Errant, (Rives, Amelia)
Dan Beard, Boy Scout, (Mason, Miriam E.)
Dan and the Miranda, (Gage, Wilson)
Dance for Susie, (Wyndham, Lee)
Dance in the Desert, (L'Engle, Madeleine)
Dance of Death, (Charlot, Jean)
Dance of the Hours, (Choate, Florence)
Dance of the Hours, (Disney, Walt)
Dance of the Seasons, (Monroe, Harriet)
Dance, Dance, Amy Chan!, (Hawkinson, Lucy)
Dance: Its Place in Art & Life, (Kinney, T.& M.)
Dancing Camel, (Byars, Betsy C.)
Dancing Cloud, (Buff, Mary)
Dancing Faun, (Farr, Florence)
Dancing Horses of Acoma, (Hunt, Wolf R.)
Dancing Kettle, (Uchida, Yoshiko)
Dancing Palm Tree, (Walker, Barbara)
Dancing School, (Schick, Eleanor)
Dancing Shoes, (Streatfeild, Noel)
Dancing Star, (Malvern, Gladys)
Dancing Tom, (Coatsworth, Eliz.)
Dancing in the Moon, (Eichenberg, Fritz)
Dancing-Master, (Chabot, Adrien)
Dandelion, (Freeman, Don)
Dandy Lion, (Bingham, Clifton)
Dandy-Andy Book, (N/A)
Danger to the Windward, (Sperry, Armstrong)
Dangerous Day for Mrs. Doodlepunk, (Dodworth, D.)
Daniel Boone, (Averill, Esther)
Daniel Boone, (Daugherty, James)
Daniel Boone, (Martin, Patricia)
Daniel Boone, (Tousey, Sanford)
Daniel Boone, (White, Stewart E.)
Daniel Boone's Echo, (Steele, William O.)
Daniel in the Lion's Den, (Bible)
Danish Fairy Book, (Stroebe, C. (ed.))
Danish Fairy Tales, (Andersen, Hans C.)
Danny & Fanny, (Gillilan, Strickland)
Danny Decoy, (Held, John)
Danny Dunn [All titles], (Williams, Jay)
Danny and Company 92, (Spiegel, Doris)
Danny and Prue, (Tallant, Edith)
Danny and the Dinosaur, (Hoff, Syd)
Danny and the Poi Pup, (Carroll, Ruth)
Danny the Dream Man, (Henderson, Dorothy)
Danny's Luck, (Davis, Lavinia R.)
Danny's Own Story, (Marquis, Don)
Daphne of Fitzroy Street, (Nesbit, Edith)
Daphnis & Chloe, (Thornley, G. (tr.))
Daring Twins, (Baum, L. Frank)
Dark Canoe, (O'Dell, Scott)
Dark Circle of Branches, (Armer, Laura A.)
Dark Frigate, (Hawes, Charles B.)
Dark Hollow, (Green, Anna K.)
Dark Horse, (James, Will)
Dark Horse of Woodfield, (Hightower, Florence)
Dark Star of Itza, (Malkus, Alida S.)
Dark Venture, (Beyer, Audrey W.)
Dark Wood of the Golden Birds, (Brown, Margaret W.)

Dark is Dark, (McCullough, John)
Dark of the Cave, (Rydberg, Ernie)
Darkness and Dawn, (England, George A.)
Dash and Dart, (Buff, Mary)
Dash of Pepper, (Bell, Thelma H.)
Daughter of Anderson Crow, (McCutcheon, George B.)
Daughter of New France, (Crowley, Mary C.)
Daughter of Raasay, (Raine, William M.)
Daughter of Thunder, (Moon, Grace P.)
Daughter of the Dawn, (Hodder, William R.)
Daughter of the Land, (Stratton-Porter, Gene)
Daughter of the Mountains, (Rankin, Louise S.)
Daughter of the Rich, (Waller, Mary Ella)
Daughter of the Seine, (Eaton, Jeanette)
Daughter of the Sioux, (King, Charles)
Daughter of the Snows, (London, Jack)
Daughter of the Stars, (Crary, Mary)
Daughters of Destiny, (Staunton, Schuyler)
Davenports & Cherry Pie, (Dalgliesh, Alice)
Davenports are at Dinner, (Dalgliesh, Alice)
David Balfour, (Stevenson, Rbt. L.)
David Blaize and the Blue Door, (Benson, E.F.)
David Copperfield, (Dickens, Charles)
David Glasgow Faragut..., (Latham, Jean L.)
David Has his Day, (Borie, Lysbeth)
David Hotfoot, (Totheroh, Dan)
David Livingstone... (Finger, Charles J.)
David Livingstone: Foe of Darkness, (Eaton, Jeanette)
David McCheever's 29 Dogs, (Holt, Margaret)
David and Goliath, (DeRegniers, Beatrice)
David and the Magic Powder, (Ford, Margaret)
David and the Phoenix, (Ormondroyd, Edward)
David in Silence, (Robinson, Veronica)
David the Dreamer, (Bergengren, Ralph)
David the Giant Killer, (White, Anne T.)
David's Little Indian, (Brown, Margaret W.)
David's Railroad, (Woolley, Catherine)
David: Bible Story with Pictures, (Jones, Eliz. O.)
Davy Crockett, (Rourke, Constance)
Davy Crockett, (Tousey, Sanford)
Davy Crockett's Earthquake, (Steele, William O.)
Davy Goes Places, (Lenski, Lois)
Davy Winkle in Circusland, (Norwood, Edwin P.)
Davy and His Dog, (Lenski, Lois)
Davy of the Everglades, (Lattimore, Eleanor)
Davy's Day, (Lenski, Lois)
Dawn Boy of the Pueblos, (Scott, Lena B.)
Dawn Wind, (Sutcliff, Rosemary)
Dawn at Shanty Bay, (Knowles, Robert E.)
Dawn of Fear, (Cooper, Susan)
Dawn of a To-Morrow, (Burnett, Frances H.)
Day After Yesterday, (Rowand, Phyllis)
Day Chiro Was Lost, (Nakatani, Chiyoko)
Day Daddy Stayed Home, (Kessler, Ethel)
Day Everybody Cried, (DeRegniers, Beatrice)
Day It Snowed in Summer, (Heide, Florence P.)
Day Jean-Pierre was Pignapped, (Gallico, Paul)
Day We Saw the Sun Come Up, (Goudey, Alice)
Day Without Wind, (Mayne, William)
Day after Tomorrow, (Lewis, Alice H.)
Day and Night, (Duvoisin, Roger)
Day at Laguerre's..., (Smith, Francis H.)
Day in a Child's Life, (Foster, Myles B.)
Day in the Jungle, (Lowrey, Janette S.)
Day of His Youth, (Brown, Alice)
Day of Pleasure, (Singer, Isaac B.)
Day of Summer, (Miles, Betty)
Day of Winter, (Miles, Betty)

Day of the Dog, (McCutcheon, George B.)
Day on Skates, (Van Stockum, Hilda)
Day the Cow Sneezed, (Flora, James)
Day the Gang Got Rich, (Kotzwinkle, William)
Day the Guinea-Pig Talked, (Gallico, Paul)
Day the Sun Danced, (Hurd, Edith T.)
Day the Sun Disappeared, (Hamberger, John)
Day they Gave Babies Away, (Eunson, Dale)
Day with The Gnomes, (Endres, Ernest)
Day with the Duke, (Thwaite, Ann)
Daybreak, (Cowan, James)
Days Off, (Van Dyke, Henry)
Days of Sunshine, Days of Rain, (Frye, Dean)
Daytime Story Book, (Dyer, Ruth O.)
De Namin ob De Twins, (Childs, Mary F.)
DeSoto, Child of the Sun: Search for Gold, (Steele, W.O.)
Deacon Lysander, (Greene, Sarah P.M.)
Dead Bird, (Brown, Margaret W.)
Dead End School, (Coles, Robert)
Dead King, (Kipling, Rudyard)
Deal in Wheat, (Norris, Frank)
Dealings with Fairies, (MacDonald, George)
Dear Dolphin, (Kenny, Herbert A.)
Dear Enemy, (Webster, Jean)
Dear Friends, (Gay, Zhenya)
Dear Garbage Man, (Zion, Gene)
Dear Little Deer, (Lindman, Maj)
Dear Little Girl's Summer Holidays, (Blanchard, Amy E.)
Dear Old Nursery Rhymes, (Haslewood, C.)
Dear Prosper, (Fox, Paula)
Dear Rat, (Cunningham, Julia)
Dear Readers & Riders, (Henry, Marguerite)
Dear Snowman, (Janosch)
Dear Sooky, (Crosby, Percy L.)
Dear Uncle Looy, (Gulick, Peggy)
Dearie Dot and the Dog, (Lippmann, Julie M.)
Deb's Dictionary, (Herford, Oliver)
Debbie... [All titles], (Lenski, Lois)
Debby Barnes, Trader, (Skinner, Constance)
Deborah's White Winter, (Lattimore, Eleanor)
Deccan Nursery Tales, (Kincaid, Charles A.)
Deck the Stable, (Eastwick, Ivy O.)
Decky's Secret, (Molloy, Anne)
Decline & Fall of Practically Everybody, (Cuppy, Will)
Decorative Plaques, (Wilkins, Mary E.)
Dee-Dee's Birthday, (Liang, Yen)
Deedo and Fawny, (Jahn, Mary L.)
Deeds of Daring done by Girls, (Moore, Hannah)
Deenie Folks and Friends of Theirs, (McMahon, Jo)
Deep Sea Farm, (Ipcar, Dahlov)
Deep Silver, (Burglon, Nora)
Deep Through the Heart, (Anderson, C.W.)
Deep Treasure: Story of Oil, (Olds, Elizabeth)
Deep Water Days, (Swan, Oliver G.)
Deep in the Forest, (Fry, Rosalie K.)
Deephaven, (Jewett, Sarah O.)
Deer Mountain Hideaway, (Lansing, Elisabeth H.)
Deer River Raft, (Lansing, Elisabeth H.)
Deer Valley Girl, (Lenski, Lois)
Deer in the Snow, (Schlein, Miriam)
Defective Santa Claus, (Riley, James W.)
Defending America, (Peet, Creighton)
Defense of Guenevere, (Morris, William)
Deidre, (Stephens, James)
Delafield Affair, (Kelly, Florence)
Delectable Mountain, (Govan, Christine)
Delft Cat, (Russell, Robert H.)
Delicia and Adolphus, (Newman, Gertrude)

Dem Good Ole Times, (Dooley, Mrs.)
Demons & Dervishes, (Fenner, Phyllis R.)
Dennis the Dragon, (Streatfeild, Noel)
Deportmental Ditties, (Graham, Harry)
Deric in Mesa Verde, (Nusbaum, Deric)
Desert Dan, (Coatsworth, Eliz.)
Desert Drama, (Doyle, Arthur Conan)
Desert Gold, (Grey, Zane)
Desert Islands & Robinson Crusoe, (De La Mare, W.)
Desert People, (Clark, Ann N.)
Desert Solitaire, (Abbey, Edward)
Deserted Village, (Goldsmith, Oliver)
Desire of the Moth, (Rhodes, Eugene M.)
Desmond... [All titles], (Best, Herbert)
Destiny, (Nuckel, Otto)
Devil Tales, (Boyle, Virginia F.)
Devil's Motor, (Corelli, Marie)
Devil's Tail, (Hurd, Edith T.)
Devil-Tree of El Dorado, (Aubrey, Frank)
Devonshire Cream, (Dean, Agnes L.)
Devota, (Wilson, Augusta)
Dewdrops from Fairyland, (Scott, Lucy M.)
Dhan of the Pearl Country, (Sowers, Phyllis A.)
Diamond Fairy Book, (N/A)
Diamond King...., (Wesselhoeft, Lily)
Diamond Necklace, (DeMaupassant, Guy)
Diamond Princess, (Cramer, Marie)
Diamond Spider & other Stories, (Butler, Elinor B.)
Diamond in the Window, (Langton, Jane)
Diamonds & Toads, (N/A)
Diana and her Rhinoceros, (Ardizzone, Edward)
Diary of Terwilliger Jellico, (Lebeck, Oskar)
Diary of a Birthday Doll, (Dow, Ethel C.)
Diary of a Goose Girl, (Wiggin, Kate D.)
Diary of a Mouse, (Dunham, Edith)
Dick & Tom in Town, (Van Doren, Mark)
Dick & the Canal Boat, (Tousey, Sanford)
Dick Bruna's Cinderella, (Bruna, Dick)
Dick Foote & Shark, (Babbitt, Natalie)
Dick Whittington, (Lines, Kathleen)
Dick Whittington & his Cat, (N/A)
Dickens' Children, (Dickens, Charles)
Dickens' Year Book, (Prentiss, Lois (comp))
Dickey Bird, (Woodruff, Elizabeth)
Dickie-Burdie Book, (Anderson, Anne)
Dickon Bend-The-Bow, (McNeil, Everett)
Dickydidos, (Kidd, Will)
Dictionary of Chivalry, (Uden, Grant)
Did You Carry the Flag Today, Charlie?, (Caudill, R.)
Did You Say Dogs?, (Palazzo, Tony)
Did a Bear Just Walk There?, (Rand, Ann)
Diddie, Dumps & Tot, (Pyrnelle, Louise C.)
Diesel-Electric 4030, (Billings, Henry)
Different Dog, (Everson, Dale)
Dig for a Treasure, (Marshall, Dean)
Digby, the Only Dog, (Carroll, Ruth)
Digger Wasp, (Mendoza, George)
Diggers, (Brown, Margaret W.)
Diggers and Builders, (Lent, Henry B.)
Digging for China: A Poem, (Wilbur, Richard)
Digging in Yucatan, (Morris, Ann A.)
Dilly-Dally Sally, (Henry, Marguerite)
Ding Dong Bell, (Hader, B.& E.)
Ding Dong Bell, (Young, Percy)
Dinky Ducklings, (Campbell, Lang)
Dinny & Danny, (Slobodkin, Louis)
Dinosaur Alphabet, (Palazzo, Tony)
Dinosaur Twins, (Hogan, Inez)

Diogenes: Story of Greek Philosopher, (Aliki)
Dionysos & the Pirates, (Proddow, Penelope)
Dipper of Copper Creek, (George, Jean C.)
Directions to Servants, (Swift, Jonathan)
Dirk's Dog Bello, (DeJong, Meindert)
Dirt Book, (Evans, Eva K.)
Dirty Eddie, (Bemelmans, Ludwig)
Disappearing Dog Trick, (Corbett, Scott)
Disappointed Squirrel, (Hudson, Wm. Henry)
Discontented Stuffed Cat, (Thurston, Clara B.)
Discouraging Model, (Riley, James W.)
Disentanglers, (Lang, Andrew)
Dish of Apples, (Phillpotts, Eden)
Dismal Jimmy of the Fourth, (Mowbray, John)
Dissertation Upon a Roast Pig, (Lamb, Charles)
Distant Prize..., (Finger, Charles J.)
Diva's Ruby, (Crawford, F. Marion)
Diverting History of John Gilpin, (Cowper, William)
Divine & Moral Songs for Children, (Watts, Isaac)
Dixie, (Ralph, Julian)
Do Baby Bears Sit in Chairs?, (Kessler, Ethel)
Do Tigers Ever Bite Kings?, (Wersba, Barbara)
Do You Know What I'll Do?, (Zolotow, Charlotte)
Do You Know about Fishes?, (Smalley, Janet)
Do You Know?, (Smalley, Janet)
Do You Remember What Happened?, (Chapman, Jean)
Do You Want to Hear a Secret?, (Redman, Sylvia)
Do-Nothing Days, (Skinner, Charles M.)
Do-Well & Do-Little, (Sigerson, Dora)
Dobry, (Shannon, Monica)
Doctor Danny, (Sawyer, Ruth)
Doctor George Owl, (Joslin, Sesyle)
Doctor Paracelsus, (Rosen, Sidney)
Doctor Rabbit, (Wahl, Jan)
Doctor Sevier, (Cable, George W.)
Doctor of the Old School, (MacLaren, Ian)
Doctor, his Wife and the Clock, (Green, Anna K.)
Doctor, the Puppy Who Learned, (Hoke, Helen)
Dodge's Red Picture Book, (N/A)
Does Poppy Live Here?, (Gregor, Arthur)
Dog Book, (Bicknell, Ethel)
Dog Book, (Thorne, Diana)
Dog Came to School, (Lenski, Lois)
Dog Cantbark, (Fischer, Marjorie)
Dog Day, (Emanuel, Walter)
Dog Doctor, (Black, Irma S.)
Dog Next Door, (Robertson, Keith)
Dog Show, (Harper, Wilhelmina)
Dog So Small, (Pearce, Philippa)
Dog Stories, (Coatsworth, Eliz.)
Dog Stories, (Held, John)
Dog Who Lives at the Waldorf, (Brough, James)
Dog Who Thought He was a Boy, (Annett, Cora)
Dog Who Wouldn't Be, (Mowat, Farley)
Dog and the Boat Boy, (Martin, Patricia)
Dog at His Heel, (Finger, Charles J.)
Dog for David, (Bischoff, Julia B.)
Dog from Nowhere, (Coatsworth, Eliz.)
Dog in the Tapestry Garden, (Lathrop, Dorothy)
Dog of his Own, (Hobson, Laura Z.)
Dog on Barkham Street, (Stolz, Mary S.)
Dog that Could Swim Underwater, (Selden, George)
Dog that Lost his Family, (Latham, Jean L.)
Dog's Book of Bugs, (Griffen, Elizabeth)
Dog's Boy, (Hall, Rosalys)
Dog's Tale, (Twain, Mark)
Dog, the Fox and the Fleas, (Wiese, Kurt)
Dogcatcher's Dog, (Dugo, Andre)

Dogie Boy, (Heal, Edith)
Dogs, (Terhune, Albert P.)
Dogs as I See Them, (Dawson, Lucy)
Dogs of Character, (Aldin, Cecil)
Dogs of Destiny, (Downey, Fairfax)
Dogs of War, (Emanuel, Walter)
Doings of Dicky Daw, (Wagstaff, Hester)
Doings of the Dollivers, (Cooke, Grace M.)
Doings of the Dollymites, (Howard, Henry)
Doki the Lonely Papoose, (Mariana)
Doll Dreams, (Morrison, Lucile P.)
Doll Rosy's Days, (Bates, Clara D.)
Doll Who Came Alive, (Tregarthen, Enys)
Doll and the Kitten, (Wright, Dare)
Doll for Marie, (Fatio, Louise)
Doll in the Bakeshop, (York, Carol B.)
Doll in the Window, (Bianco, Pamela)
Doll's Christmas, (Tudor, Tasha)
Doll's House, (Fyleman, Rose)
Doll's House, (Godden, Rumer)
Doll, Two Children & Three Storks, (Teresah)
Dollar Horse, (Young, Miriam)
Dollar for Luck, (Coatsworth, Eliz.)
Dollies, (Hunter, Richard)
Dollies in Happy-Land, (Pease, Leonora)
Dolls, (Bettina)
Dolls from Cheyenne, (Martin, Patricia)
Dolly & Molly... [All titles], (Gordon, Elizabeth)
Dolly Book, (Herbertson, Agnes)
Dolly Dialogues, (Hope, Anthony)
Dolly Dimples and Bobby Bounce, (Drayton, Grace)
Dolly Drake, (Wiederseim, Grace)
Dolly Moses: Cat & the Clam Chowder, (Chase, Mary E.)
Don Coyote, (Peck, Leigh)
Don Gypsy, (Starkie, Walter)
Don Juan, (Lord Byron)
Don MacGrath, (Parrish, Randall)
Don Quixote, (Cervantes)
Don't Be Scared Book, (Vogel, Ilse-Margret)
Don't Blame Me!, (Hughes, Richard A.)
Don't Count Your Chicks, (D'Aulaire, I.& E.)
Don't Ever Cross a Crocodile, (Starbird, Kaye)
Don't Frighten the Lion, (Brown, Margaret W.)
Don't Open Until Christmas, (Morley, Christopher)
Don't Run, Apple!, (Hawkins, Quail)
Don't Tell, (Farrow, George E.)
Don't You Turn Back, (Hughes, Langston)
Don: Story of Lion Dog, (Grey, Zane)
Donald Duck & his Friends, (Ayer, Jean)
Donald Duck & his Nephews, (Brumbaugh, Florence)
Donald Duck('s)...[Most titles], (Disney, Walt)
Donald McKay: Designer of Clipper Ships, (Judson, C.I.)
Donald in Numberland, (Peedie, Jean M.)
Donald's Lucky Day, (Disney, Walt)
Donald's Penguin, (Disney, Walt)
Done in the Open, (Remington, Frederic)
Donegal Fairy Stories, (MacManus, Seumas)
Donegal Wonder Book, (MacManus, Seamus)
Dong with a Luminous Nose, (Lear, Edward)
Donkey Beads, (Ratzesberger, Anna)
Donkey Cart, (Bulla, Clyde R.)
Donkey Goes Visiting, (Lynch, Patricia)
Donkey Inside, (Bemelmans, Ludwig)
Donkey Prince, (Carter, Angela)
Donkey Ride, (Showalter, Jean B.)
Donkey Rustlers, (Durrell, Gerald M.)
Donkey Work, (Tovey, Doreen)
Donkey for the King, (Price, Olive M.)

Donkey-Donkey, (Duvoisin, Roger)
Doodles, (Dowd, Emma C.)
Doom of King Acrisius, (Morris, William)
Door Opens, (Lothar, Ernest)
Door in the Wall, (DeAngeli, Marguerite)
Door to the North, (Coatsworth, Eliz.)
Doors..., (Richardson, Emmeline)
Doorway in Fairyland, (Housman, Laurence)
Dopey: He Don't Talk None, (Disney, Walt)
Dora, (Spyri, Johanna)
Dora: High School Girl, (Baldwin, May)
Dorcas Porkus, (Tudor, Tasha)
Dorinda, (Howard, Elizabeth)
Doris & David All Alone, (Marc, Elizabeth)
Doris and the Trolls, (Atwater, Richard)
Dorothy Dimity, (Bingham, Clifton)
Dorothy Q., (Holmes, Oliver W.)
Dorothy Vernon of Haddon Hall, (Major, Charles)
Dorothy and the Wizard of Oz, (Baum, L. Frank)
Dorothy's Dolls..., (Goldsmith, Milton)
Dorothy's Rabbit Stories, (Calhoun, Mary Eliz.)
Dorothy, the Motor Girl, (Carleton, Katherine)
Dorp Dead, (Cunningham, Julia)
Dot and Tot of Merryland, (Baum, L. Frank)
Dot in Dreamland, (Clayton, John)
Dotzie the Dancey Duck, (Norris, June)
Double Birthday Present, (Hunt, Mabel L.)
Double Discovery, (Ness, Evaline M.)
Double Knights, (McNeill, James)
Double Quest, (Sobol, Donald J.)
Double or Nothing, (Erickson, Phoebe)
Double-Barrelled Detective Story, (Twain, Mark)
Doubledarling & Dreamspinner, (Wheeler, Candace)
Doubtful Guest, (Gorey, Edward)
Dougal's Wish, (Alger, Leclaire)
Doughnuts for Lin, (Unwin, Nora S.)
Douglas of Porcupine, (Kent, Louise A.)
Dove in the Eagle's Nest, (Yonge, Charlotte)
Down Along Apple Market Street, (Hill, Mabel B.)
Down Come the Leaves, (Bancroft, Henreitta)
Down Comes the Wilderness, (Price, Margaret E.)
Down Durley Lane, (Cloud, Virginia W.)
Down Half the World, (Coatsworth, Eliz.)
Down Historic Waterways, (Thwaites, Reuben G.)
Down Huckleberry Hill, (Weisgard, Leonard)
Down Ryton Water, (Gaggin, Eva R.)
Down South, (Eickemeyer, Rudolf)
Down Spider Web Lane, (Donahey, Mary D.)
Down Town: Betsy-Tacy Story, (Lovelace, Maud H.)
Down from the Lonely Mountain, (Curry, Jane L.)
Down in the Cellar, (Gray, Nicholas S.)
Down in the Grass, (Kellock, Harold)
Down the Big River, (Meader, Stephen W.)
Down the River, (Bates, Herbert E.)
Down the River, (Colmont, Marie)
Down the Road with Johnny, (Smith, Irene)
Down the Snow Stairs, (Corkran, Alice)
Down with Dinosaurs!, (Graham, Al)
Down, Down the Mountain, (Credle, Ellis)
Down-Adown-Derry, (De La Mare, Walter)
Downright Dencey, (Snedeker, Caroline D.)
Downstreet with Edith, (Wriston, Hildreth T.)
Downy Woodpecker, (Sears, Paul M.)
Doyle Fairy Book, (Montalba, Anthony R.)
Dozen Dinosaurs, (Armour, Richard)
Dozen Dogs or So, (Chalmers, Patrick)
Dozens of Cousins, (Watts, Mabel)
Dr. Dolittle('s)... [All titles], (Lofting, Hugh)

Dr. Jekyll & Mr. Hyde, (Stevenson, Rbt. L.)
Dr. Lavendar's People, (Deland, Margaret)
Dr. Ox's Experiment, (Verne, Jules)
Dr. Rabbit & Ki-Yi Coyote, (Hinkle, Thomas C.)
Dr. Seuss's ABC, (Seuss, Dr.)
Dr. Seuss's Sleep Book, (Seuss, Dr.)
Dragon Fish, (Buck, Pearl S.)
Dragon Fly of Zuni, (Malkus, Alida S.)
Dragon John, (Lawson, Marie A.)
Dragon Liked Smoked Fish, (Laskowski, Jerzy)
Dragon Run, (Dawson, Carley)
Dragon Ship, (Resnick, William S.)
Dragon Stew, (McGowen, Tom)
Dragon Treasure, (Paschang, Adolph)
Dragon and the Book, (Price, Christine)
Dragon of Wantley, (Wister, Owen)
Dragon of an Ordinary Family, (Mahy, Margaret)
Dragon that Lived Under Manhattan, (Hildick, E.W.)
Dragon's Thunder, (Kempton, Kenneth P.)
Dragons of Blueland, (Gannett, Ruth S.)
Dragons of the Queen, (Stolz, Mary S.)
Drake and his Yeomen, (Barnes, James)
Drake's Drum..., (Newbolt, Henry J.)
Drake's Quest, (Rogers, Cameron)
Drake: The Man they Called a Pirate, (Latham, Jean L.)
Dramatis Personae..., (Browning, Robert)
Draw Horses: It's Fun & Easy, (Brown, Paul)
Drawings, (Christy, Howard C.)
Drawings, (Gibson, Charles D.)
Drawings, (Remington, Frederic)
Drawn from the Wood, (Shay, Frank)
Dreadful Dragon of Hay Hill, (Beerbohm, Max)
Dream & the Business, (Hobbes, John O.)
Dream Bag, (Haldane, Winifred A.)
Dream Blocks, (Higgins, Aileen C.)
Dream Boats, (Walker, Dugald S.)
Dream Book, (Brown, Margaret W.)
Dream Children, (Brownell, Elizabeth)
Dream Coach, (Parrish, A.& D.)
Dream Days, (Grahame, Kenneth)
Dream Imp & Others, (Sefton, Harriet L.)
Dream Keeper, (Hughes, Langston)
Dream Pedlar, (Sackville, Margaret)
Dream Time, (Treece, Henry)
Dream World of Dion McGregor, (McGregor, Dion)
Dream of Fair Women, (Tennyson, Alfred)
Dream of Little Hazy Cream, (Arthur, Lady Kate)
Dream of the Blue Heron, (Barnouw, Victor)
Dreamer of Dreams, (Queen Marie)
Dreamer's Tales, (Lord Dunsany)
Dreamers, A Club, (Bangs, John K.)
Dreaming Zoo, (Unterecker, John)
Dreamland, (Lippmann, Julie M.)
Dreamland Express, (Millar, H.R.)
Dreamland Shores, (Ault, Norman)
Dreams & Fables, (Woodward, Clifford)
Dreams of Glory, (Steig, William)
Dress Up & Let's Have a Party, (Charlip, Remy)
Drifting Cowboy, (James, Will)
Drinking Gourd, (Monjo, Ferdinand N.)
Driving Lessons, (Howlett, Edwin)
Droll Doings, (N/A)
Droopsi, (Kahl, Virginia)
Droopy, (Beatty, Hetty B.)
Dross, (Merriman, Henry S.)
Drowsy, (Mitchell, John A.)
Drugstore Cat, (Petry, Ann)
Druid Path, (Ryan, Marah E.)

Drummer Boy, (Garfield, Leon)
Drummer Hoff, (Emberley, Barbara)
Drummer's Coat, (Fortesque, J.W.)
Drums, (Boyd, James)
Drums at Dusk, (Bontemps, Arna)
Drums of Monmouth, (Sterne, Emma G.)
Dual Alliance, (Cooke, Marjorie B.)
Duchess Bakes a Cake, (Kahl, Virginia)
Duck & the Kangaroo, (Lear, Edward)
Duck in the Gun, (Cowley, Joy)
Duck's Adventure, (Muter, Gladys N.)
Duck-Footed Hound, (Kjelgaard, Jim)
Ducks Don't Get Wet, (Goldin, Augusta)
Ducky Daddles, (Wiederseim, Grace)
Ducky Daddles and the Three Bears, (Hall, Bertha P.)
Ducky Dee, (Toon, Gladys E.)
Dudley Pippin, (Ressner, Phil)
Duff, Story of a Bear, (Rush, William M.)
Dugan and the Hobo, (Arundel, Jocelyn)
Duke of Plaza Toro, (Gilbert & Sullivan)
Dulcibel, (Peterson, Henry)
Dulcibella & the Fairies, (Raiker, Alice M.)
Dull Miss Archinard, (Sedgwick, Anne D.)
Dumas Fairy Tale Book, (Dumas, Alexandre)
Dumb Juan & the Bandits, (Brenner, Anita)
Dumblebum, (Glenn, Elsie)
Dumbo of the Circus, (Disney, Walt)
Dunderpate, (Baker, Margaret)
Dunkard, (Selden, George)
Dusky Day: A College Story, (Means, Florence C.)
Dusty & his Friends, (Black, Irma S.)
Dusty Star, (Baker, Olaf)
Dusty and the Fiddlers, (Miles, Miska)
Dutch Cheese, (De La Mare, Walter)
Dutch Colt, (Meigs, Cornelia L.)
Dutch Ditties for Children, (Terhune, Anice)
Dutch Doll Ditties, (Robbins, Louis)
Dutch Twins, (Perkins, Lucy F.)
Dutch West Indies & Philippines, (DeLeeuw, Cateau)
Dwarf Long-Nose, (Hauff, Wilhelm)
Dwarf Pine Tree, (Lifton, Betty)
Dwarf's Tailor..., (Underhill, Zoe (ed))
Dwellings of an Old World Town, (King, Jessie M.)
Dwindleberry Zoo, (Farrow, George E.)
Each in his Way, (Gall, Alice C.)
Eager Beaver, (Hogan, Inez)
Eagle Jake and Indian Pete, (Williams, Jay)
Eagle in Fact & Fiction, (Johnston, Johanna)
Eagle of the Ninth, (Sutcliff, Rosemary)
Eagle's Shadow, (Cabell, James B.)
Ear for Uncle Emil, (Gaggin, Eva R.)
Early Italian Love Stories, (Taylor, Una)
Early Life of Mr. Man before Noah, (Smith, E. Boyd)
Early Moon, (Sandburg, Carl)
Early Poems of..., (Morris, William)
Early Thunder, (Fritz, Jean)
Early Work of Aubrey Beardsley, (N/A)
Earth Breath, (A.E.)
Earth and Sky, (Dayton, Mona)
Earth is on a Fish's Back, (Belting, Natalia)
Earth is the Lord's, (Plotz, Helen (comp))
Earth's Enigmas, (Roberts, Chas. G.D.)
East of Suez, (Kipling, Rudyard)
East of the Sun, West of the Moon, (Asbjornsen, P.C.)
Easter, (Fisher, Aileen)
Easter Book of Legends and Stories, (Hazeltine, Alice)
Easter Bunny that Overslept, (Friedrich, Priscilla)
Easter Rabbit's Parade, (Lenski, Lois)

Easter Story, (Yates, Elizabeth)
Easter Treat, (Duvoisin, Roger)
Eastward Sweeps the Current, (Malkus, Alida S.)
Easy Does It, (Wier, Ester A.)
Easy Money, (Atkey, Bertram)
Ebb-Tide, (Stevenson, Rbt. L.)
Ecclesiasticus..., (Bible)
Echoing Green, (Estes, Eleanor)
Edda & the Oak, (Peattie, Elia W.)
Eddie Elephant, (Gruelle, Johnny)
Eddie Makes Music, (Haywood, Carolyn)
Eddie's Bear, (Miles, Miska)
Edgar Allan Crow, (Tudor, Tasha)
Edgar, Runaway Elephant, (Wahn, J.& G.)
Edgar: The 7:58, (Stong, Philip D.)
Edge of April... (Swift, Hildegarde H.)
Edge of Hazard, (Horton, George)
Edge of Two Worlds, (Jones, Weyman)
Edge of the Cloud, (Peyton, Kathleen M.)
Edge of the Forest, (Smith, Agnes)
Edie Changes her Mind, (Johnston, Johanna)
Edinburgh, (Fullylove, John)
Edith and Mr. Bear, (Wright, Dare)
Editha's Burglar, (Burnett, Frances H.)
Edmund Dulac's Fairy Book, (Dulac, Edmund)
Ednah and her Brothers, (White, Eliza O.)
Education of Mr. Pipp, (Gibson, Charles D.)
Edward Buttoneye and his Adventures, (Austin, Cyril F.)
Edward and the Horse, (Rand, Ann)
Edward, Hoppy & Joe, (Lawson, Robert)
Edwin A. Abbey, (Lucas, E.V.)
Eerie Book, (Armour, Margaret (ed))
Effelli, (Austin, Margot)
Egbert & his Marvelous Adventures, (Gilbert, Paul T.)
Egg Tree, (Milhous, Katherine)
Egypt, (Kelly, R. Talbot)
Egypt Game, (Snyder, Zilpha K.)
Egyptian Adventures, (Coolidge, Olivia)
Egyptian Tales of Magic, (Jewett, Eleanore)
Egyptians Knew, (Pine, Tillie S.)
Eight Cousins, (Alcott, Louisa M.)
Eight Lights: Story of Chanukah, (Rosenblum, Robert)
Eight Rings on his Tail, (Oldrin, John)
Eighteen Cousins, (Hogan, Carol)
Eighty Drawings including Weaker Sex, (Gibson, C.D.)
Eileen's Adventures in Wonderland, (MacDonald, Zillah)
Ekorn, (Lie, Haakon)
El Coyote the Rebel, (Perez, Luis)
El Estranjero, (Waters, Russell J.)
Elbert the Mind Reader, (Rinkoff, Barbara)
Elderberry Bush, (Gates, Doris)
Eleanor Roosevelt: Courageous Girl, (Weil, Ann Y.)
Elegy in a Country Church Yard, (Gray, Thomas)
Elegy on the Glory of Her Sex..., (Goldsmith, Oliver)
Elephant & Wishing Fairy, (Ingraham, Corinne)
Elephant Alphabet, (Palazzo, Tony)
Elephant Blue, (Nakano, Hirotaka)
Elephant Boy, (Kotzwinkle, William)
Elephant Boy of the Teak Forest, (Sowers, Phyllis A.)
Elephant Herd, (Schlein, Miriam)
Elephant Twins, (Hogan, Inez)
Elephant Up a Tree, (Van Loon, Hendrik)
Elephant Who Liked to Smash Small Cars, (Merrill, J.)
Elephant and the Bad Baby, (Vipont, Elfrida)
Elephant in the Barn, (Wood, James P.)
Elephant's Apology, (Morris, Alice T.)
Elephant's Bathtub, (Carpenter, Frances)
Elephant's Child, (Kipling, Rudyard)

Elephant, Mouse & the Flea, (Aichinger, Helga)
Elephants, (Robinson, William W.)
Elephants of Sargabal, (Guillot, Rene)
Elephi, (Stafford, Jean)
Eleven Comedies, (Aristophanes)
Elf Children of the Woods, (Beskow, Elsa)
Elf King's Flowers, (Halkett, Sarah P.)
Elf Owl, (Buff, M.& C.)
Elf Who Didn't Believe in Himself, (Ross, Geraldine)
Elf-Errant, (O'Neill, Moira)
Elfin Rhymes, (Norman)
Elfin Song, (Harrison, Florence)
Elfin-Land, (Pollard, Josephine)
Elfrida and the Pig, (Symonds, John)
Eli Whitney, (Latham, Jean L.)
Elijah the Slave, (Singer, Isaac B.)
Elin's Amerika, (DeAngeli, Marguerite)
Elisabeth the Cow Ghost, (DuBois, W.P.)
Elixir of Life, (Warren, Geoffrey)
Eliza & the Elves, (Field, Rachel)
Elizabeth in Toyland, (Collett, Marjorie)
Elizabeth of the Mayflower, (Trachsel, Myrtle)
Elizabite, (Rey, Hans A.)
Ella, (Peet, Bill)
Ella the Elephant, (Wiese, Kurt)
Ellen Grae, (Cleaver, Vera)
Ellen Jane, (Fox, Frances M.)
Ellen Tebbits, (Cleary, Beverly)
Ellen's Lion, (Johnson, Crockett)
Elmer & the Dragon, (Gannett, Ruth S.)
Elmer Buys a Circus, (Gilbert, Paul T.)
Elmer Elephant, (Disney, Walt)
Elmer, Story of a Patchwork Elephant, (McKee, David)
Elmo Doolan & Search for Golden Mouse, (Murphy, S.R.)
Eloise... [All titles], (Thompson, Kay)
Elsa's Gift Home, (Sawyer, Edith A.)
Elsa's Secret, (Grey, Eve)
Elsa: Story of a Lioness, (Adamson, Joy)
Elves & Fairies, (Werner, Jane)
Elves & Princes, (Darwin, Bernard)
Elves and Ellefolk, (Belting, Natalia)
Elvira Everything, (Asch, Frank)
Emblemland, (Bangs, John K.)
Emerald City of Oz, (Baum, L. Frank)
Emerald Story Book, (Skinner, Ada M.)
Emerson, Poet and Thinker, (Cary, Elisabeth L.)
Emil & the Detectives, (Kastner, Erich)
Emil & the Three Twins, (Kastner, Erich)
Emil in the Soup Tureen, (Lindgren, Astrid)
Emile, (Ungerer, Tomi)
Emily Climbs, (Montgomery, Lucy M.)
Emily Emerson's Moon, (Merrill, Jean)
Emily Emmins Papers, (Wells, Carolyn)
Emily of Deep Valley, (Lovelace, Maud H.)
Emily of New Moon, (Montgomery, Lucy M.)
Emily's Quest, (Montgomery, Lucy M.)
Emily's Runaway Imagination, (Cleary, Beverly)
Emily, the Traveling Guinea Pig, (Smith, Emma)
Emir's Son, (Ballard, Martin)
Emma, (Austen, Jane)
Emma in Winter, (Farmer, Penelope)
Emmett's Pig, (Stolz, Mary S.)
Emmy & the Blue Door, (Means, Florence C.)
Emperor & the Drummer Boy, (Robbins, Ruth)
Emperor Penguins, (Mizumura, Kazue)
Emperor and the Kite, (Yolen, Jane)
Emperor and the Nightingale, (Andersen, Hans C.)
Emperor of the Air, (Glendon, George)

Emperor's Englishman, (Whishaw, Frederick)
Emperor's Gifts, (Johnson, Crockett)
Emperor's New Clothes, (Andersen, Hans C.)
Empty Barn, (DeAngeli, Marguerite)
Empty Elephant, (Willson, Dixie)
Empty Schoolhouse, (Carlson, Natalie S.)
Enchanted Book, (Dalgliesh, Alice)
Enchanted Burro, (Lummis, Charles F.)
Enchanted Caravan, (Butters, Dorothy)
Enchanted Castle, (James, Hartwell)
Enchanted Castle, (Moore, Colleen)
Enchanted Castle, (Nesbit, Edith)
Enchanted Castle, (Nesbit, Edith)
Enchanted Doll, (Lemon, Mark)
Enchanted Eve, (Ley, Madeleine)
Enchanted Flivver, (Braley, Berton)
Enchanted Forest, (Bowen, William)
Enchanted Forest, (Outhwaite, Grenbry)
Enchanted Garden: Fairy Stories, (Molesworth, Mrs.)
Enchanted House, (Harrison, Edith O.)
Enchanted Island of Yew, (Baum, L. Frank)
Enchanted Land, (Chisholm, Louey)
Enchanted Peacock, (Brown, Julia)
Enchanted Road, (Howes, Edith)
Enchanted Schoolhouse, (Sawyer, Ruth)
Enchanted Sword, (Pasma, Henry K.)
Enchanted Typewriter, (Bangs, John K.)
Enchanted Wood, (Hamer, Sam H.)
Enchantment Tales for Children, (Price, Margaret E.)
Enchantress from the Stars, (Engdahl, Sylvia)
End of Black Dog, (Moore, David)
End of Elfintown, (Barlow, Jane)
Endless Party, (Delessert, Etienne)
Endless Story, (Higgins, Violet M.)
Enemy Brothers, (Savery, Constance)
Enemy at Green Knowe, (Boston, Lucy M.)
Engine, Engine No. 9, (Hurd, Edith T.)
English Fairy & Folk Tales, (Hartland, Edwin)
English Fairy Book, (Rhys, Ernest (ed.))
English Fairy Tales, (Jacobs, Joseph (ed))
English Fairy Tales, (Rhys, Ernest (ed.))
English Fairy Tales, (Steel, Flora A.)
English Hours, (James, Henry)
English Nursery Rhymes, (Broadwood, Lucy)
English Spelling Book, (Mavor, William)
Enormous Egg, (Butterworth, Oliver)
Eothen, (Kinglake, A.W.)
Epaminondas, (Merriam, Eve)
Epaminondas & his Auntie, (Bryant, Sara Cone)
Epaminondas & the Lettuces, (Egan, Constance)
Epaminondas & the Puppy, (Egan, Constance)
Epaminondas Helps in the Garden, (Egan, Constance)
Epaminondas Helps in the House, (Egan, Constance)
Epic of Ebenezer, (Cox, Florence T.)
Epiplectic Bicycle, (Gorey, Edward)
Episcopo & Co., (D'Annunzio, Gabrielle)
Erec and Enid, (Schiller, Barbara)
Eric Prince of Lorlonia, (Countess of Jersey)
Eric and Matilda, (Richter, Mischa)
Eric..., (Bond, Susan)
Erick and Sally, (Spyri, Johanna)
Erie Canal, (Spier, Peter E.)
Erik & the Christmas Horse, (Peterson, Hans)
Ernestine Takes Over, (Brooks, Walter)
Escape of the Mullingong, (Farrow, George E.)
Eskimo Hunter, (Hayes, Florence)
Eskimo Island & Penguin Land, (Snell, Roy J.)
Eskimo of Little Diomede, (Mayberry, Genevieve)

Eskimos Knew, (Pine, Tillie S.)
Eskimos: People of Alaska, (Martin, Patricia)
Esmeralda Ahoy!, (Fairholme, Elizabeth)
Essays, (DeMontaigne, Michel)
Essays of Elia, (Lamb, Charles)
Esther, a Story for Children, (Butt, Geraldine)
Eternal Masculine, (Andrews, Mary S.)
Ethan, the Shepherd Boy, (Ceder, Georgiana)
Ethelbert, (Hoyland, Rosemary)
Etienne-Henri and Gri-Gri, (Surany, Anico)
Etuk: The Eskimo Hunter, (MacMillan, Miriam)
Euphrosyne & her Golden Book, (Lawson, Ellsworth)
Europe After 8:15, (Mencken, H.L.)
Evan's Corner, (Hill, Elizabeth S.)
Evangelina Cisneros, (Decker, Karl)
Evangeline, (Longfellow, H.W.)
Evangeline, Pigeon of Paris, (Carlson, Natalie S.)
Eve's Diary, (Twain, Mark)
Eveli, (Spyri, Johanna)
Evelina..., (Burney, Fanny)
Evelyn and the Fish, (Chrestien, F.H.)
Even Steven, (Lipkind, Will)
Even Tiny Ants Must Sleep, (Saleh, Harold)
Ever Living Fairy Tales, (Lee, Ella D.)
Ever Ride a Dinosaur?, (Corbett, Scott)
Everglades Adventure, (Meader, Stephen W.)
Every Day Essays, (Washburne, Marion)
Every Day a Dragon, (Lexau, Joan M.)
Every Day in the Year, (Rowand, Phyllis)
Every Day is a World, (Bechtle, Raymond)
Every Dog has his Say, (Anthony, Edward)
Every Time I Climb a Tree, (McCord, David)
Every-Day Characters, (Praed, Winthrop M.)
Everybody Eats, (Green, Mary M.)
Everybody has Two Eyes, (Jaszi, Jean)
Everybody has a House, (Green, Mary M.)
Everybody's Pepys, (Morshead, O.F.)
Everybody's Saint Francis, (Egan, Maurice F.)
Everybody's Washington, (Knipe, A.A.)
Everychild, (Dodge, Louis)
Everyday & Nowaday Fairy Book, (Chapin, Anna A.)
Everyday Children, (Woodward, Hildegard)
Everyday Fairy Book, (Chapin, Anna A.)
Everyday Fun, (Hahn, Julia L.)
Everyday Honor, (Newberry, Fanny E.)
Everyday People, (Gibson, Charles D.)
Everyhow Remarkable, (Lincoln, Victoria)
Everyman & other Plays, (N/A)
Everyone but Thee and Me, (Nash, Ogden)
Evie & Cookie, (Eberle, Irmengarde)
Evie & the Wonderful Kangaroo, (Eberle, Irmengarde)
Evil Motherhood, (Ruding, Walter)
Evolution of Dodd's Sister, (Eastman, Charlotte)
Evolution of Woman, (McVickar, H.W.)
Exactly Alike, (Ness, Evaline M.)
Exciting Adventures of Waldo, (Burton, Earl & L.)
Excursions in Color, (Maxwell, Donald)
Excuse Me! Certainly!, (Slobodkin, Louis)
Excuse it Please, (Herford, Oliver)
Exploits of Don Quixote, (Reeves, James)
Exploits of Moominpappa, (Jansson, Tove)
Explorer's Digest, (Clark, Leonard)
Exploring the Jungle, (Waldeck, JoBesse)
Extracts from Adam's Diary, (Twain, Mark)
Extraordinary Tug-of-War, (Schatz, Letta)
Eye Book, (LeSieg, Theo)
Eye for Elephants, (Steig, William)
Eyes So-O Big, (Weil, Lisl)

Eyes for the Dark, (Shannon, Monica)
Eyes in the Fishbowl, (Snyder, Zilpha K.)
Ezekiel, (Garner, Elvira)
Ezekiel, (Pratt, Lucy)
Ezekiel Expands, (Pratt, Lucy)
Ezekiel Travels, (Garner, Elvira)
Ezra the Elephant, (Barrows, Marjorie)
Fables, (Stevenson, Rbt. L.)
Fables for the Frivolous, (Carryl, Guy W.)
Fables in Feathers, (Bourke, S.T.E.)
Fables in Rhyme for Little Folks, (La Fontaine, J.)
Fables of Aesop, (Jacobs, Joseph (ed))
Fables of Jean De La Fontaine, (La Fontaine, J.)
Fables of La Fontaine, (Brown, Margaret W.)
Fables of the Elite, (Dix, Dorothy)
Fabre's Book of Insects, (Fabre)
Fabre's Book of Insects, (Stawell, R. (ed.))
Fabulous Firework Family, (Flora, James)
Fabulous Flight, (Lawson, Robert)
Face in the Frost, (Bellairs, John)
Face in the Pool, (St. John, J. Allen)
Faery Tales of Weir, (Sholl, Anna M.)
Fafan in China, (Lederer, Joe)
Faint George Who Wanted to be a Knight, (Barry, R.E.)
Fair Adventure, (Gray, Eliz. J.)
Fair American, (Coatsworth, Eliz.)
Fair Americans, (Fisher, Harrison)
Fair Dominion, (Vernede, R.E.)
Fair Hills of Ireland, (Gwynn, Stephen L.)
Fair Lavinia, (Freeman, Mary E.W.)
Fair Play, (Leaf, Munro)
Fair Wind to Virginia, (Meigs, Cornelia L.)
Fair Women from Vogue, (N/A)
Fair of St. James, (Farjeon, Eleanor)
Fair, Fantastic Paris, (Ettinger, Harold)
Fairchild Family, (Sherwood, Mary M.)
Fairies & Chimneys, (Fyleman, Rose)
Fairies & Christmas Child, (Gask, Lilian)
Fairies & Suchlike, (Eastwick, Ivy O.)
Fairies Afield, (Molesworth, Mrs.)
Fairies I Have Met, (Stawell, Mrs. R.)
Fairies Up-to-Date, (Anthony, E. & J.)
Fairies and Fancies, (Bedford, Ruth)
Fairies of Sorts, (Molesworth, Mrs.)
Fairies of the Trees, (Barker, Cicely M.)
Fairies' Circus, (Cain, Neville)
Fairies' Fountain, (Martinengo-Cesaresco)
Fairy Alphabet, (MacKinstry, Eliz.)
Fairy Book, (Craik, Dinah)
Fairy Book, (Rackham, Arthur)
Fairy Caravan, (Potter, Beatrix)
Fairy Changeling, (Spofford, Harriet)
Fairy Circus, (Lathrop, Dorothy)
Fairy Detective, (Hughes, Rupert)
Fairy Doll, (Godden, Rumer)
Fairy Fleet, (MacDonald, George)
Fairy Flights in Cloudland, (Campbell, A.M.)
Fairy Flowers, (Newman, Isidora)
Fairy Frolics, (Comstock, Enos B.)
Fairy Garland, (Perrault, Charles)
Fairy Gifts, (Knox, Kathleen)
Fairy Gifts, (Rhys, Grace (ed.))
Fairy Godmother-in-Law, (Herford, Oliver)
Fairy Minstrel of Glenmalure, (Leamy, Edmund)
Fairy Nurse & other Stories, (Lang, Andrew (ed))
Fairy Operettas, (Richards, Laura E.)
Fairy Quackenbose, (Stern, Arthur K.)
Fairy Queen, (Fyleman, Rose)

Fairy Ring, (Wiggin, Kate D.)
Fairy Rings, (Howes, Edith)
Fairy Scales, (Smythe, Gladys)
Fairy Ship, (N/A)
Fairy Shoemaker, (Artzybasheff, Boris)
Fairy Spinning Wheel, (Mendes, Catulle)
Fairy Starlight, (Blakely, Elizabeth)
Fairy Stories, (Andersen, Hans C.)
Fairy Stories from France, (Ashley, Doris)
Fairy Tale Book, (Ponsot, Marie)
Fairy Tale Omnibus, (N/A)
Fairy Tale Picture Book, (Watson, Nancy D.)
Fairy Tale Tree, (Stanovsky, Vladislav)
Fairy Tales, (Blodgett, Mabel F.)
Fairy Tales, (Cummings, E.E.)
Fairy Tales, (D'Aulnoy)
Fairy Tales, (Hauff, Wilhelm)
Fairy Tales, (MacDonald, George)
Fairy Tales [Many titles], (Andersen, Hans C.)
Fairy Tales [Many titles], (Grimm Bros.)
Fairy Tales [Many titles], (Perrault, Charles)
Fairy Tales & Fables, (Morel, Eve (comp))
Fairy Tales Every Child Should Know, (Mabie, H.W.)
Fairy Tales From France, (Larned, William T.)
Fairy Tales for Little People, (Catrevas, Christine)
Fairy Tales from Arabian Nights, (Dixon, E. (ed))
Fairy Tales from Baltic Shores, (Mutt, Eugenie)
Fairy Tales from Czechoslovakia, (Haviland, Virginia)
Fairy Tales from England, (Christie, Ella R.)
Fairy Tales from Erin's Isle, (Bayne, Marie)
Fairy Tales from Far & Near, (Pyle, Katharine)
Fairy Tales from Far & Near, (Quiller-Couch, A.)
Fairy Tales from Finland, (Christie, Ella R.)
Fairy Tales from Folk Lore, (Williams, Wilbur H.)
Fairy Tales from India, (Pyle, Katharine)
Fairy Tales from Many Lands, (Pyle, Katharine)
Fairy Tales from Orient, (Martens, Frederick H.)
Fairy Tales from Sweedish, (Djurklou, Baron G.)
Fairy Tales from Viet Nam, (Robertson, Dorothy)
Fairy Tales from the Far North, (Asbjornsen, P.C.)
Fairy Tales from the Harz Mountains, (Fryer, Alfred C.)
Fairy Tales from the North, (Nerman, Einar)
Fairy Tales in Other Lands, (N/A)
Fairy Tales of Eastern Europe, (Curtin, Jeremiah)
Fairy Tales of Modern Greece, (Gianakoulis, T.P.)
Fairy Tales of Slav Peasants & Herdsmen, (Chodsko, A.)
Fairy Tales of a Parrot, (Stephan, A. Condie)
Fairy Tales of the Orient, (Buck, Pearl S.)
Fairy Tales, Stories and Legends, (Andersen, Hans C.)
Fairy Tales/Arabian Nights, (N/A)
Fairy Tales/Wonderland, (Westerman, J.M.E.)
Fairy Who Believed in Human Beings, (Kay, Gertrude A.)
Fairy of Old Spain..., (Stawell, Mrs. R.)
Fairy of the Rhone, (Carr, Alice V.)
Fairy-Folk of Blue Hill, (Wesselhoeft, Lily)
Fairy-Gold, (Rhys, Ernest (ed.))
Fairy-Land, (Attwell, Mabel L.)
Fairy-Lure, (Horwitz, Carolyn N.)
Fairyland, (Outhwaite, Annie R.)
Fairyland, (Outhwaite, Ida R.)
Fairyland of Opera, (Pleasonton, Louise)
Faithful Friends, (N/A)
Falcon Under the Hat, (Daniels, Guy (tran))
Falcon of Eric the Red, (Coblentz, Catherine)
Falcon, Fly Back, (Blaisdell, Elinore)
Fall of Ulysses, (Willard, Charles D.)
Fall of a Nation, (Dixon, Thomas)
Fall of the Nibelungs, (Armour, Margaret (tr))

Fallen Race, (Granville, Austyn)
False Flamingoes, (Damjan, Mischa)
False Gods, (Lorimer, George H.)
Family Conspiracy, (Phipson, Joan)
Family Grandstand, (Brink, Carol R.)
Family Sabbatical, (Brink, Carol R.)
Family Under the Bridge, (Carlson, Natalie S.)
Family at Caldicott Place, (Streatfeild, Noel)
Family at Dowbiggins, (Vipont, Elfrida)
Family from One End Street, (Garnett, Eve)
Family on Wheels, (Oxley, James M.)
Family that Grew and Grew, (Baker, Margaret)
Family to Raise, (Eberle, Irmengarde)
Famous Animal Tales, (Aris, Ernest A.)
Famous Baby-Sitter, (Bannon, Laura)
Famous Cats of Fairyland, (Wimberley, Lowry (comp))
Famous Dog Stories, (Cooper, Page (ed))
Famous Fables, (Aesopus)
Famous Jimmy, (Blyton, Enid)
Famous Love Songs, (N/A)
Famous Rhymes/Mother Goose, (Piper, Watty (ed))
Famous Sally, (Jackson, Shirley)
Fanchette & Jeannot, (Francoise)
Fanciful Tales, (Stockton, Frank)
Fancy Be Good, (Chalmers, Audrey)
Fancy Dresses Described, (Holt, Ardern)
Fang in the Forest, (Alexander, Charles)
Fantasia, (Taylor, Deems)
Fantasma Land, (Macauley, Charles R.)
Fantastic Mr. Fox, (Dahl, Roald)
Fantastic Toy Shop, (Weil, Lisl)
Fantasy Sketches, (Sendak, Maurice)
Far Distant Bugle, (MacKaye, David L.)
Far From Marlborough Street, (Philbrook, Elizabeth)
Far Frontier, (Steele, William O.)
Far Out the Long Canal, (DeJong, Meindert)
Far Voyager: Story of James Cook, (Latham, Jean L.)
Far and Few, (McCord, David)
Far from Maddening Girls, (Carryl, Guy W.)
Far-Away Desert, (Moon, Grace P.)
Far-Off Land, (Caudill, Rebecca)
Faraway Christmas, (Hurd, Edith T.)
Faraway Lurs, (Behn, Harry)
Faraway Meadow, (Handforth, Thomas)
Farewell to Shady Glade, (Peet, Bill)
Farm Babies, (Aldin, Cecil)
Farm Beyond the Town, (White, Eliza O.)
Farm Book, (Copeland, Walter)
Farm Boy, (Stong, Philip D.)
Farm Stories, (Jackson, Kathryn)
Farm Story, (Nast, Elsa R.)
Farm Wanted, (Hilles, Helen)
Farm in Fairyland, (Housman, Laurence)
Farm on the Hill, (Horn, Madeline D.)
Farmer Boy, (Wilder, Laura I.)
Farmer Brown's Boy Becomes Curious, (Burgess, T.)
Farmer Fox, (Bridgman, L.J.)
Farmer Giles of Ham, (Tolkien, J.R.R.)
Farmer in the Dell, (Hader, B.& E.)
Farmer in the Sky, (Heinlein, Robert)
Farmer's Year..., (Leighton, Clare)
Farming, (Munkittrick, R.K.)
Farming It, (Shute, Henry A.)
Farmyard Puppies, (Aldin, Cecil)
Farthest West, (Armer, Laura A.)
Fast Sooner Hound, (Bontemps, Arna)
Fast is Not a Ladybug, (Schlein, Miriam)
Fatapoufs & Thinifers, (Maurois, Andre)

Fate of a Crown, (Staunton, Schuyler)
Father Bear Comes Home, (Minarik, Else H.)
Father Goose's Yearbook, (Baum, L. Frank)
Father Goose: His Book, (Baum, L. Frank)
Father Junipero..., (Jackson, Helen H.)
Father Kino: Priest to the Primas, (Clark, Ann N.)
Father Time Stories, (Stevenson, John G.)
Father Tuck's Bird ABC, (N/A)
Father Tuck's Dog Show, (N/A)
Father's Gone A-Whaling, (Gardiner, Alice C.)
Father, Dear Father, (Bemelmans, Ludwig)
Fattypuffs & Thinifers, (Maurois, Andre)
Faun & the Woodcutter's Daughter, (Picard, Barbara)
Faust, (Goethe)
Favorite Animal Stories, (Salten, Felix)
Favorite Christmas Carols, (Boni, Margaret B.)
Favorite Fairy Tales, (Andersen, Hans C.)
Favorite Fairy Tales, (N/A)
Favorite Fairy Tales, (Osbourne, M. (ed.))
Favorite Fairy Tales Told... [All titles], (Haviland, Virginia)
Favorite Fairy Tales with New Pictures, (Perrault, Charles)
Favorite French Fairy Tales, (Douglas, Barbara)
Favorite Hymns for Children, (Bible)
Favorite Nursery Rhymes, (Mother Goose)
Favorite Nursery Songs, (Bertail, Inez)
Favorite Pets, (Tucker, Elizabeth S.)
Favorite Poems Old and New, (Ferris, Helen)
Favorite Psalms for Children, (Bible)
Favorites from Fairyland, (Harris, Ada V.)
Fearless Treasure, (Streatfeild, Noel)
Fearsome Inn, (Singer, Isaac B.)
Feast of Lamps, (Root, Charlet)
Feather Mountain, (Olds, Elizabeth)
Feathered and Four-Footed Friends, (Barker, Mrs. S.)
Feats on the Fiord, (Martineau, Harriet)
February Boys, (Molesworth, Mrs.)
Federico the Flying Squirrel, (Palazzo, Tony)
Fee-Fi-Fo-Fum, (Briggs, Raymond)
Feeling Blue, (Wolff, Robert)
Felice, (Brown, Marcia)
Felice, (Long, John L.)
Felicity, (Laughlin, Clara E.)
Felix the Bald-Headed Lion, (Townsend, Kenneth)
Fennel & Rue, (Howells, William D.)
Fenny the Desert Fox, (Baumann, Hans)
Ferdinand the Bull, (Leaf, Munro)
Fermentations of Eliza, (Hankins, Maude M.)
Ferryman, (Bishop, Claire H.)
Fibble, D.D., (Cobb, Irving)
Fiddle Away, (Justus, May)
Fiddle Dee-Dee, (Field, Eugene)
Fiddle Diddle Dee, (Lefevre, Felicite)
Fiddler Crab, (Adrian, Mary)
Fiddler in Barly, (Nathan, Robert)
Fiddler of High Lonesome, (Turkle, Brinton)
Fiddler's Fancy, (Street, Julia M.)
Fiddlesticks, (Cowham, Hilda)
Fidelia, (Adams, Ruth)
Fido, (Wiederseim, Grace)
Field & Forest Friends, (Hawkes, Clarence)
Field Babies, (Aldin, Cecil)
Field of Clover, (Housman, Laurence)
Fieldbook of Western Wilderness, (Armstrong, Margaret)
Fierce Face, (Mukerji, Dhan G.)
Fierce John, (Fenton, Edward)
Fife & Drum at Louisburg, (Oxley, James M.)
Fifi, (Bemelmans, Ludwig)
Fifteen, (Cleary, Beverly)

Fifteen Hundred Miles an Hour, (Dixon, Charles)
Fifteen Norse Tales, (Asbjornsen, P.C.)
Fifteen Tales for Lively Children, (Baker, Margaret)
Fifteenth Century Cook'ry Boke, (Anderson, John (ed))
Fifth String, (Sousa, John P.)
Fifth for the King, (Malkus, Alida S.)
Fifty Famous Fairy Tales, (McGovern, Mary H.)
Fifty Songs for Boys & Girls, (Graham, Mary N.)
Fifty-First Dragon, (Broun, Heywood)
Figaro and Cleo, (Disney, Walt)
Fight the Night, (DePaola, Tomie)
Fighting Six, (Gower, Margaret L.)
Fighting for the Empire, (Otis, James)
Figures of Speech, (Peake, Mervyn)
Filipino Twins, (Perkins, Lucy F.)
Filippo's Dome, (Rockwell, Anne)
Filly for Joan, (Anderson, C.W.)
Final War, (Tracy, Louis)
Finders Keepers, (Lipkind, Will)
Finders Keepers, Losers Weepers, (Lexau, Joan M.)
Finding a Fortune, (Alger, Horatio)
Finding a Poem, (Merriam, Eve)
Fine Lady Upon a White Horse, (Hunt, Enid)
Finger Plays for Nursery & Kindergarten, (Poulsson, Emilie)
Fingerfins, (Bronson, Wilfrid S.)
Fingers are Always Bringing Me News, (O'Neill, Mary)
Finkler's Field, (Barbour, Ralph H.)
Finn Family Moomintroll, (Jansson, Tove)
Finnegan II - His Nine Lives, (Bailey, Carolyn S.)
Fir Tree, (Andersen, Hans C.)
Fir-Tree Fairy Book, (Johnson, Clifton (ed))
Fire Bird, (Stratton-Porter, Gene)
Fire Cat, (Averill, Esther)
Fire Eye, (Lindman, Maj)
Fire on the Mountain, (Courlander, Harold)
Fire! The Mascot, (Brown, Paul)
Fire-Brigade Willie, (Clewes, Dorothy)
Fire-Hunter, (Kjelgaard, Jim)
Fireflies in the Night, (Hawes, Judy)
Firefly, (Sears, Paul M.)
Firefly Named Torchy, (Waber, Bernard)
Firelight Fairy Book, (Beston, Henry)
Firelight Stories, (Bailey, Carolyn S.)
Fireman: Save My Cat!, (Palazzo, Tony)
Fireside Battles, (Brown, Annie G.)
Fireside Book of Yuletide Tales, (Wagenknecht, Ed)
Fireside Poems, (Hutchinson, Veronica)
Fireside Saints, (Jerrold, Douglas W.)
Fireside Sphinx, (Repplier, Agnes)
Fireside Stories, (Hutchinson, Veronica)
First 3000 Years, (Falls, Charles B.)
First Adventure, (Coatsworth, Eliz.)
First Bible, (Sewell, Helen)
First Book of California Gold Rush, (Havighurst, Marion)
First Book of Dogs, (Taber, Gladys)
First Book of Drawing, (Slobodkin, Louis)
First Book of Krab, (Parry, Edward A.)
First Book of Negroes, (Hughes, Langston)
First Book of Oregon Trail, (Havighurst, Marion)
First Book of Pioneers, (Havighurst, Marion)
First Book of Rhythms, (Hughes, Langston)
First Book of Short Verse, (Howard, Coralie (comp))
First Book of Time, (Bendick, Jeanne)
First Book of the Ballet, (Streatfeild, Noel)
First Child, (Wells, Rosemary)
First Christmas, (Trent, Robbie)
First Christmas, (Wallace, Lew)
First Christmas Crib, (Milhous, Katherine)

First Christmas Tree, (Van Dyke, Henry)
First Days of the World, (Ames, Gerald)
First Delights, (Tudor, Tasha)
First Doll in the World, (Pape, Lee)
First Farmers in the New Stone Age, (Weisgard, L.)
First Graces, (Bible)
First Grade Book, (Pitts, Lilla B.)
First Living Things, (May, Julian)
First Men, (May, Julian)
First Men in the Moon, (Wells, H.G.)
First Nantucket Tea-Party, (Tittle, Walter)
First Night Away from Home, (Brown, Myra B.)
First Peko-Neko Bird, (Krahn, Fernando)
First People in the World, (Ames, Gerald)
First Poems of Childhood, (Tudor, Tasha)
First Prayers, (Bible)
First Prize for Danny, (Austin, Margot)
First Robin, (Kraus, Robert)
First Story, (Brown, Margaret W.)
First Thanksgiving, (Barksdale, Lena)
First Trousers, (Veale, E.)
First Year, (Meadowcroft, Enid)
First and Last Annual Pet Parade, (Neville, Mary)
First to Be Called Christians, (Smither, Ethel)
Fish Hawk's Nest, (Meader, Stephen W.)
Fish Head, (Fritz, Jean)
Fish Story, (Gay, Zhenya)
Fish from Japan, (Cooper, Elizabeth)
Fish in the Air, (Wiese, Kurt)
Fish is Fish, (Lionni, Leo)
Fish is Not a Pet, (Tabak, Mary N.)
Fish with a Deep Sea Smile, (Brown, Margaret W.)
Fisherman & his Soul, (Wilde, Oscar)
Fisherman Tommy, (Tousey, Sanford)
Fisherman Under the Sea, (Matsutani, Miyoko)
Fisherman and his Boat, (Floethe, Louise)
Fisherman and his Wife, (Grimm Bros.)
Fisherman of Galilee, (Fisher, Aileen)
Fisherman's Day, (Schlein, Miriam)
Fisherman's Luck, (Van Dyke, Henry)
Fisherman's Weather, (Aflalo, F.G.)
Fishing Cat, (Myers, Grace)
Five & Ten, (Whitehead, Roberta)
Five Bears & Miranda, (Beston, Henry)
Five Black Cousins..., (Allison, James M.)
Five Brothers, (Seeger, Elizabeth)
Five Bushel Farm, (Coatsworth, Eliz.)
Five Cent, Five Cent, (Chandler, Edna W.)
Five Children, (Nesbit, Edith)
Five Children and It, (Nesbit, Edith)
Five Chinese Brothers, (Bishop, Claire H.)
Five Dolls and the Duke, (Clare, Helen)
Five Fables from France, (Cooper, Lee)
Five Little Bears, (North, Sterling)
Five Little Friends, (Adams, Sherred W.)
Five Little Monkeys, (Kepes, Juliet A.)
Five Little Peppers Midway, (Sidney, Margaret)
Five Little Peppers in Little Brown House, (Sidney, M.)
Five Little Playmates, (Gay, Romney)
Five Mice in a Mousetrap, (Richards, Laura E.)
Five O'Clock Charlie, (Henry, Marguerite)
Five Pennies, (Brenner, Barbara)
Five Rollatinis, (Balet, Jan B.)
Five Senses, (Keyes, Angela M.)
Five Sons of King Pandu, (Seeger, Elizabeth)
Five Trials of the Pansy Bed, (Townsend, J. David)
Five of Us & Madeline, (Nesbit, Edith)
Fix Bayonets!, (Thomason, John W.)

Flag Day, (LesTina, Dorothy)
Flag of the Desert, (Best, Herbert)
Flags of Dawn, (Knox, Esther M.)
Flagship Hope and Aaron Lopez, (Alexander, Lloyd C.)
Flambards, (Peyton, Kathleen M.)
Flame Flower, (Saunders, Phyllis)
Flame, the Breeze & the Shadow, (Slobodkina, Esphyr)
Flames, (Hichens, Robert)
Flaming Arrows, (Steele, William O.)
Flaming Bear, (McCracken, Harold)
Flaming Sword, (Harrison, Edith O.)
Flamingo Feather, (Munroe, Kirk)
Flash of Washington Square, (Pratt, Margaret)
Flash, Crash, Rumble and Roll, (Branley, Franklyn)
Flash, Life of a Firefly, (Harris, Louise D.)
Flash: Story of a Horse, (Averill, Esther)
Flashlights from Mountain & Plain, (Davis, Duke)
Flat Iron for a Farthing, (Ewing, Juliana H.)
Flat Stanley, (Brown, Jeff)
Flat Tail, (Gall, Alice C.)
Flattered Flying Fish, (Rieu, E.V.)
Fleet of the Furtive, (Roberts, Chas. G.D.)
Fletcher & Zenobia, (Chess, Victoria)
Fleur & Blanchefleur, (Leighton (ed.))
Flibbity Jibbit & the Key Keeper, (Grant, Vernon)
Flicka, Ricka, Dicka & Little Dog, (Lindman, Maj)
Flicka, Ricka, Dicka & Three Kittens, (Lindman, Maj)
Flight Brothers, (Henderson, L.R.S.)
Flight of Fancy, (Honness, Elizabeth)
Flight of Pony Baker, (Howells, William D.)
Flight of Rosy Dawn, (Mackie, Pauline B.)
Flight of a Moth, (Post, Emily)
Flight of the Snow Goose, (Freschet, Berniece)
Flight to Arras, (Saint-Exupery, A.)
Flint Heart, (Phillpotts, Eden)
Flint Spears, (James, Will)
Flip, (Dennis, Wesley)
Flip Flop Show, (White, Constance)
Flip and the Cows, (Dennis, Wesley)
Flipper: Sea Lion, (Black, Irma S.)
Flippy and Skippy, (Crane, Donn)
Flivver, the Heroic Horse, (Kingman, Lee)
Floating Island, (Parrish, A.& D.)
Floating Prince..., (Stockton, Frank)
Flock of Girls & Boys, (Perry, Nora)
Flock of Watchbirds, (Leaf, Munro)
Flocks of Birds, (Zolotow, Charlotte)
Flood Friday, (Lenski, Lois)
Flood at Reedsmere, (Burton, Hester)
Flop-Eared Hound, (Credle, Ellis)
Flora's Feast, (Crane, Walter)
Flora: A Book of Drawings, (De La Mare, Walter)
Floral Fantasy, (Crane, Walter)
Florina & the Wild Bird, (Chonz, Selina)
Flossie & Bossie, (LeGallienne, Eva)
Flossy & Fluffy, (Wain, Louis)
Flower Babies, (May, Elizabeth)
Flower Babies' Book, (Scott, Anna M.)
Flower Book, (Armfield, Constance)
Flower Book, (Coybee, Eden)
Flower Children, (Gordon, Elizabeth)
Flower Fairies, (Judson, Clara I.)
Flower Fairies, (Whittemore, Maria)
Flower Fairies of... [Most titles], (Barker, Cicely M.)
Flower Fairy Alphabet, (Barker, Cicely M.)
Flower Folk, (Bicknell, Anne G.)
Flower Heaven, (Reinheimer, Sophie)
Flower Legends for Children, (Murray, Hilda)

Flower Maiden, (Andersen, Hans C.)
Flower Name Fancies, (Gordon, Hampden C.)
Flower Show, (Uttley, Alison)
Flower Songs of the Seasons, (Barker, Cicely M.)
Flower Wedding, (Crane, Walter)
Flower of the Mind, (Meynell, Alice)
Flowered Donkey, (MacKay, Margaret)
Flowers & Fancies, (Ranking, Boyd M.)
Flowers & Grasses & Weeds, (Mendoza, George)
Flowers I Love, (Thomas, Philip)
Flowers from Dell and Bower, (Skelding, Susie B.)
Flowers from Glade and Garden, (Skelding, Susie B.)
Flowers from Shakespeare's Garden, (Crane, Walter)
Flowers of Chivalry, (Clement, Marguerite)
Flowers, Facts & Fables, (Newman, Isidora)
Fluff, (Duplaix, Georges)
Flute Player of Beppu, (Gallant, Kathryn)
Flute of the Gods, (Ryan, Marah E.)
Flutter of an Eyelid, (Brinig, Myron)
Fly High, Fly Low, (Freeman, Don)
Fly Homer, Fly, (Peet, Bill)
Fly Went By, (McClintock, Marshall)
Fly-Away Fairies, (Clarkson, L.)
Flyaway Flippety, (Wilson, Eleanore H.)
Flying Carpet, (Asquith, C. (ed.))
Flying Carpet, (Prince Ahmed)
Flying Classroom, (Kastner, Erich)
Flying Cow, (Collins, Ruth P.)
Flying Death, (Adams, Samuel H.)
Flying Ebony, (Vinton, Iris)
Flying Girl, (Van Dyne, Edith)
Flying Girl & her Chum, (Van Dyne, Edith)
Flying Hoofs, (Harper, Wilhelmina)
Flying House, (Carroll, Ruth)
Flying House, (Hodges, C. Walter)
Flying Islands of the Night, (Riley, James W.)
Flying King of Kurio, (Benet, William R.)
Flying Legion, (England, George A.)
Flying Lesson of Gerald Pelican, (Benchley, Nathaniel)
Flying Locomotive, (DuBois, W.P.)
Flying Plover, (Roberts, Theodore G.)
Flying Postman, (Drummond, Violet H.)
Flying Saucer Full of Spaghetti, (Krahn, Fernando)
Fofana, (Guillot, Rene)
Fog Magic, (Sauer, Julia L.)
Foghorns, (Pease, Howard)
Folding Father, (Hauser, Heinrich)
Folk Songs of England/Ireland/Scotland, (Cole, William)
Folk Songs of Many Lands, (Van Loon, Hendrik)
Folk Tales from Many Lands, (Gask, Lilian)
Folk Tales of Bengal, (Day, Lal Behari)
Folk Tales of Flanders, (DeBosschere, Jean)
Folk of the Woods, (Pardee, Lucius C.)
Folks from Dixie, (Dunbar, Paul L.)
Follow Tomas, (Hurd, Edith T.)
Follow Your Nose, (Showers, Paul)
Follow the Brook, (Lathrop, Dorothy)
Follow the Fall, (Kumin, Maxine)
Follow the Road, (Tresselt, Alvin)
Follow the Sunset, (Schneider, Herman)
Follow the Wind, (Tresselt, Alvin)
Following The Guidon, (Custer, Elizabeth B.)
Following of the Star, (Barclay, Florence)
Folly for the Wise, (Wells, Carolyn)
Folly in Fairyland, (Wells, Carolyn)
Folly in the Forest, (Wells, Carolyn)
Foma the Terrible, (Daniels, Guy)
Fool of the World & Flying Ship, (Ransome, Arthur)

Fooling of King Alexander, (Skipper, Mervyn)
Foolish Fox, (N/A)
Foolish Virgin, (Dixon, Thomas)
Fools and Funny Fellows, (Fenner, Phyllis R.)
Fools over Horses, (Watson, Helen O.)
Foot Book, (Seuss, Dr.)
Football Grandma, (Cabot, Carolyn S.)
For Love of Mary Ellen, (Brainerd, Eleanor H.)
For Me to Say, (McCord, David)
For Pepita, An Orange Tree, (Oleson, Claire)
For a Little Child Like Me, (Stirling, John)
For the Children's Hour, (Bailey, Carolyn S.)
For the Leg of a Chicken, (Bettina)
For the White Christ, (Bennet, Robert A.)
Forbidden Frontier, (Harris, Christie)
Forest Beyond the Woodlands, (Kennedy, Mildred)
Forest Fairies, (Webb, M. St. John)
Forest Folk, (Buff, M.& C.)
Forest Foundling, (Hamer, Sam H.)
Forest Friends, (Dauzet, Marceline)
Forest Hearth, (Major, Charles)
Forest Lovers, (Hewlett, Maurice)
Forest Patrol, (Kjelgaard, Jim)
Forest Pool, (Armer, Laura A.)
Forest Ring, (DeMille, W.M.C.)
Forest Story, (Kozisek, Josef)
Forest of Arden, (Edwards, George W.)
Forest-Land, (Chambers, Robert)
Forever Christmas Tree, (Uchida, Yoshiko)
Forever Free, (Sterling, Dorothy)
Forever Laughter, (Freeman, Don)
Forge in the Forest, (Colum, Padraic)
Forgetful Elephant, (Greene, Jean)
Forgotten Daughter, (Snedeker, Caroline D.)
Forgotten Island, (Coatsworth, Eliz.)
Forgotten Tales of Long Ago, (Lucas, E.V.)
Fortunate Days, (Gate, Ethel M.)
Fortunate Princeling, (Bright, A.D.)
Fortunate Youth, (Locke, William J.)
Fortunately, (Charlip, Remy)
Fortunes of Fifi, (Seawell, Molly E.)
Fortunes of Oliver Horn, (Smith, Francis H.)
Forty Famous Ships, (Culver, Henry B.)
Forty Pounds of Gold, (Stong, Philip D.)
Forty Singing Seamen, (Noyes, Alfred)
Forty-Four Turkish Fairy Tales, (Kunos, Ignacz)
Forty-Ninth Magician, (Babbitt, Samuel F.)
Forward March, (Munroe, Kirk)
Forward, Commandos!, (Bianco, Margery W.)
Fossil Fountain, (Mason, Arthur)
Fountain of Youth, (Colum, Padraic)
Fountain of the Friendly Lion, (Floethe, Louise)
Four & Twenty Blackbirds, (Fish, Helen D.)
Four & Twenty Dollies, (Pease, Leonora)
Four & Twenty Toilers, (Lucas, E.V.)
Four Champions of Great Britain & Ireland, (Mord, W.)
Four Clever Brothers, (Grimm Bros.)
Four Corners, (Blanchard, Amy E.)
Four Corners of the World, (Duvoisin, Roger)
Four Cousins, (Zwilgmeyer, Dikken)
Four Farthings and a Thimble, (Baker, Margaret)
Four Feet by Two, (N/A)
Four Friends, (Hoffmann, Eleanor)
Four Friends, (Paull, Grace)
Four Funny Men, (Hogan, Erlin)
Four Fur Feet, (Brown, Margaret W.)
Four Gardens, (Handasyde, Emily)
Four Glass Balls, (Hamer, Sam H.)

Four Hedges..., (Leighton, Clare)
Four Legs and a Tail, (Gag, Flavia)
Four Little Children/Went around World, (Lear, Edward)
Four Little Foxes, (Schlein, Miriam)
Four Musicians, (Grimm Bros.)
Four Paws into Adventure, (Cenac, Claude)
Four Plays for Dancers, (Yeats, Wm. Butler)
Four Winds, (Price, Edith B.)
Four Winds Farm, (Molesworth, Mrs.)
Four and Lena, (Barringer, Marie)
Four-Footed Americans..., (Wright, Mabel O.)
Four-Footed Wilderness People, (Deming, Therese O.)
Four-Leaf Clover, (Lipkind, Will)
Four-Story Mistake, (Enright, Elizabeth)
Four-and-Forty Fairies, (Banta, Nathaniel M.)
Fourth of July Story, (Dalgliesh, Alice)
Fox Eyes, (Brown, Margaret W.)
Fox Friend, (Coatsworth, Eliz.)
Fox Jumps Over the Parson's Gate, (Caldecott, R.)
Fox Twins, (Hogan, Inez)
Fox Went Out on Chilly Night, (N/A)
Fox and the Fire, (Miles, Miska)
Fox at the Manger, (Travers, Pamela L.)
Fox in Socks, (Seuss, Dr.)
Fox in a Box, (Hurd, Edith T.)
Fox that Wanted 9 Golden Tales, (Knight, Mary)
Fox's Frolic, (Burnand, Francis)
Fox's Story, (Veale, E.)
Foxie, (D'Aulaire, I.& E.)
Fraidy Cat, (Barrows, Marjorie)
Fraidy Cat, (Hogan, Inez)
Frances Face-Maker, (Cole, William)
Francezka, (Seawell, Molly E.)
Francie on the Run, (Van Stockum, Hilda)
Francis Marion, Young Swamp Fox, (Steele, William O.)
Francis Scott Key, (Bates, Helen D.)
Francisco..., (Brooks, Eva C.)
Franconia Stories, (Abbott, Jacob)
Frank & Bessie's Forester, (Lounsberry, Alice)
Frank Brangwyn: His Work, (Sparrow, Walter S.)
Frankenstein, (Shelley, Mary W.)
Franklin D. Roosevelt... (Johnson, G.W.)
Franklin's Autobiography, (Pine, F.W. (ed.))
Franz Tovey & the Rare Animals, (Kesselman, Wendy)
Franzi and Gizi, (Bianco, Margery W.)
Frawg, (Weaver, Annie V.)
Freckle Face, (Anderson, Neil)
Freckles, (Stratton-Porter, Gene)
Freckles & Tan, (Bowman, Rowland)
Freddie Found a Frog, (Napjus, Alice)
Freddy Frizzylocks, (Clarke, Olive)
Freddy the Curious Cat, (Paull, Grace)
Freddy('s)... [Most titles], (Brooks, Walter)
Frederic Chopin, (Maurois, Andre)
Frederick, (Lionni, Leo)
Frederick Douglass..., (Bontemps, Arna)
Fredou, (Stolz, Mary S.)
Free Joe..., (Harris, Joel C.)
Free Rangers, (Altsheler, J.A.)
Free as a Frog, (Hodges, Elizabeth)
Free to Serve, (Rayner, Emma)
Freedom and Plenty, (Bronson, Wilfrid S.)
Freedom of the Fields, (Abbott, Charles C.)
French Are Coming, (Hays, Wilma P.)
French Canada, (Boswell, Hazel)
French Cathedrals, (Pennell, Joseph)
French School for Paul, (Marokvia, Mireille)
French Twins, (Perkins, Lucy F.)

Frenzied Prince, (Colum, Padraic)
Fresh Look at Night, (Bendick, Jeanne)
Fresh Posies, (Brown, Abbie F.)
Friday & Saturday..., (Byron, May)
Friday Night is Papa Night, (Sonneborn, Ruth)
Friend O'Mine, (Nesbit, Wilbur D.)
Friend and Foe, (Montefiore)
Friend in the Dark, (Knight, Ruth A.)
Friend is Someone Who Likes You, (Anglund, Joan W.)
Friend of Animals, (Pace, Mildred M.)
Friend of Miguel, (Martin, Patricia)
Friendly Animals, (Slobodkin, Louis)
Friendly Beasts, (Baker, Laura N.)
Friendly Fairies, (Gruelle, Johnny)
Friendly Gables, (Van Stockum, Hilda)
Friendly Little Jonathan, (Bryan, Dorothy)
Friendly Phoebe, (Hader, B.& E.)
Friendly Stories, (Gates, Arthur)
Friends & Foes from Fairy Land, (Lord Brabourne)
Friends In Feathers, (Stratton-Porter, Gene)
Friends from My Garden, (Pratt, Anna)
Friends in Strange Garments, (Upjohn, Anna M.)
Friends of Diggeldy Dan, (Norwood, Edwin P.)
Friends of Jimmy, (Kay, Gertrude A.)
Friends of the Forest, (Shankland, Frank)
Friends with God, (Marshall, Catherine)
Frigate's Namesake, (Abbot, Alice B.)
Frightened Baby, (Burgess, Thornton)
Frightened Hero, (Latham, Jean L.)
Frilly Lily and the Princess, (Gekiere, Madeleine)
Fringes of Paradise, (Drummond, Florence)
Fringilla, (Blackmore, R.D.)
Frisky, (Perera, Lydia)
Frog He Would a Wooing Go, (N/A)
Frog Went A-Courtin', (Langstaff, John)
Frog and Toad are Friends, (Lobel, Arnold)
Frog in the Well, (Tresselt, Alvin)
Frog, Where are You?, (Mayer, Mercer)
Frogmorton, (Colling, Susan)
Frogs Merry, (Kepes, Juliet A.)
From King Boggen's Hall to Nothing-At-All, (Lent, Blair)
From Mixed-Up Files... Frankweiler, (Konigsburg, E.L.)
From Pillar to Post, (Bangs, John K.)
From School to Battlefield, (King, Charles)
From Sioux to Susan, (Dalton, Agnes M.)
From Slavery to Freedom, (Macy, S.B.)
From Star to Star: Story of Krakow, (Kelly, Eric P.)
From the Cliffs of Croaghaun, (Cromie, Robert)
From the Eagle's Wing, (Swift, Hildegarde H.)
From the Horn of the Moon, (Mason, Arthur)
Frontier Ballads, (Finger, Charles J.)
Frontier Ballads, (Hanson, Joseph M.)
Frontier Days, (Swan, Oliver G.)
Frontier Humor, (Cox, Palmer)
Frontier Living, (Tunis, Edwin B.)
Frontier Sketches, (Remington, Frederic)
Frost King, (Alcott, Louisa M.)
Frosty, (Newberry, Clare T.)
Frosty Snow, (Harris, Isobel)
Frowning Prince, (Johnson, Crockett)
Frozen Fire, (Sperry, Armstrong)
Fruit of the Tree, (Wharton, Edith)
Fujio, (Creekmore, Raymond)
Full Circle, (Uchida, Yoshiko)
Full of Wonder, (Kirn, Ann)
Fumio and the Dolphins, (Nakatani, Chiyoko)
Fun & Fantasy, (Milne, A.A. (intro))
Fun & Nonsense, (Bonte, George W.)

Fun and Frolic, (Bingham, Clifton)
Fun for Freddy, (Quigg, Jane)
Fun for the Little Ones, (N/A)
Fun in the Radio World, (Smith, E. Boyd)
Fun with Music, (Nelson, Mary J.)
Fun with the Calendar, (Ford, Henry W.)
Funny Bunnies, (Parker, B.)
Funny Bunny, (Leanard, Rachel)
Funny Bunny ABC, (N/A)
Funny Bunny Factory, (Green, Adam)
Funny Doings in Animal Land, (Bingham, Clifton)
Funny Favorites, (Bingham, Clifton)
Funny Foxes, (Veale, E.)
Funny Friends, (Wood, Helen J.)
Funny Little Book, (Gruelle, Johnny)
Funny Little Boy, (Baruch, Dorothy W.)
Funny Little Darkies, (N/A)
Funny Noise, (Gay, Romney)
Funny Thing, (Gag, Wanda)
Funny Town, (Merriam, Eve)
Funnybone Alley, (Kreymborg, Alfred)
Funnyfeathers, (Campbell, Lang)
Funnyland Boys, (Brine, Mary D.)
Fur Magic, (Norton, Andre)
Fur Trail Adventurers, (Wallace, Dillon)
Fur or Feather, (Smith, Lawrence B.)
Fur-Seal's Tooth, (Munroe, Kirk)
Furious Flycycle, (Wahl, Jan)
Furnace of Gold, (Mighels, Philip V.)
Furry Bear, (Hoke, Helen)
Further Adventures of Lad, (Terhune, Albert P.)
Further Adventures of Nils, (Lagerlof, Selma)
Further Chronicles of Avonlea, (Montgomery, Lucy M.)
Further Doings of Milly-Molly-Mandy, (Brisley, Joyce L.)
Further Fables of Our Time, (Thurber, James)
Further Fortunes of Pinkey Perkins, (Hammond, Harold)
Further Nonsense Verse & Prose, (Carroll, Lewis)
Fusing Force, (Chapman, Katharine H.)
Fuzzypeg Goes to School, (Uttley, Alison)
Gabby Gaffer, (Justus, May)
Gabriel Churchkitten, (Austin, Margot)
Gabriel Churchkitten & Moths, (Austin, Margot)
Gabriel Wrinkles, (Doughtie, Charles)
Gaelic Ghosts, (Leodhas, Sorche)
Gaggle of Geese, (Merriam, Eve)
Gaily We Parade, (Brewton, John)
Gallant Little Patriots, (Humphrey, Maud)
Gallantry, (Cabell, James B.)
Gallery of Children, (Milne, A.A.)
Gallery of Girls, (Phillips, Coles)
Galloping Goat & other Stories, (Naylor, Phyllis)
Galumph, (Lansdown, Brenda)
Gamble Gold, (Parry, Edward A.)
Games for Playtime & Parties, (Wilman, Stanley)
Gammage Cup, (Kendall, Carol S.)
Gammon and Spinach, (Brymer, John)
Gandhi: Fighter Without a Sword, (Eaton, Jeanette)
Gao of the Ivory Coast, (Seabrook, Katie)
Garda, (O'Neill, Rose)
Garden Advens. of Tommy Tittlemouse, (Judson, C.I.)
Garden Behind the Moon, (Pyle, Howard)
Garden Fairies, (Paquin, Samuel S.)
Garden Spider, (Adrian, Mary)
Garden Under the Sea, (Selden, George)
Garden at 19, (Jepson, Edgar)
Garden in Pink, (Wade, Blanche E.)
Garden of Delight, (Syrett, Netta)
Garden of Girls, (Fisher, Harrison)

Garden of Hearts' Delight, (Huntington, Ida M.)
Garden of Years, (Carryl, Guy W.)
Garden of the Lost Key, (Hooker, Forrestine)
Garden of the Plynck, (Baker, Karle W.)
Garden-Land, (Chambers, Robert)
Gardens of Rome, (Faure, Gabriel)
Gargantua, (Sautriax [Rabelais])
Garibaldi, (Baker, Nina B.)
Garland for Girls, (Alcott, Louisa M.)
Garland of Roses, (Fyleman, Rose)
Garram the Chief, (Best, Herbert)
Garram the Hunter, (Best, Herbert)
Gas Station Gus, (Kunhardt, Dorothy)
Gaston & Josephine, (Duplaix, Georges)
Gate Swings In, (Burglon, Nora)
Gateway to Chaucer, (Chaucer, Geoffrey)
Gateway to Romance, (Underdown, E.)
Gateway to Spenser, (Underdown, E.)
Gathering of Brother Hilarius, (Fairless, Michael)
Gaucho Boy, (Obligado, George)
Gaudenzia, (Henry, Marguerite)
Gay ABC, (Francoise)
Gay Book, (Sowerby, Githa)
Gay Dog, (Aldin, Cecil)
Gay Madelon, (Phillips, Ethel C.)
Gay Neck, (Mukerji, Dhan G.)
Gay Pippo, (Pease, Eleanor F.)
Gay Rebellion, (Chambers, Robert)
General Felice, (Ipcar, Dahlov)
Genie and Joe Maloney, (Feagles, Anita M.)
Gennarino, (Simbari, Nicola)
Gentle Ben, (Morey, Walter)
Gentle Giraffe, (McCracken, Russell)
Gentle Knight, (Schickel, Richard)
Gentle Reader, (Crothers, Samuel M.)
Gentlemen All and Merry Companions, (Bergengren, Ralph)
Gentlest Giant, (Stewart, Anna B.)
Gentling of Jonathan, (Rankin, Louise S.)
George, (Turnbull, Agnes S.)
George Appleton, (Chalmers, Mary)
George Moorland..., (Gilby/Cuming)
George Washington, (D'Aulaire, I.& E.)
George Washington, (Foster, Genevieve)
George Washington, (Judson, Clara I.)
George Washington, (Wilson, Woodrow)
George Washington Jones, (Stuart, Ruth M.)
George Washington Lincoln Goes... (Thomas, M.L.)
George Washington's Breakfast, (Fritz, Jean)
George Washington's World, (Foster, Genevieve)
George Washington, Leader of the People, (Judson, C.I.)
George and Red, (Coatsworth, Eliz.)
George and his Horse Bill, (Alsop, Reese F.)
George and the Cherry Tree, (Aliki)
George's Store, (Asch, Frank)
Georgie Finds Grandpa, (Young, Miriam)
Georgie and the Magician, (Bright, Robert)
Georgie to the Rescue, (Bright, Robert)
Georgie's Halloween, (Bright, Robert)
Georgie-Porgie Book, (Clayton, Jacqueline)
Georgina of the Rainbows, (Johnston, Annie F.)
Geraint & Enid, (Tennyson, Alfred)
Geraldine Belinda, (Henry, Marguerite)
Gerbils, (Dobrin, Arnold)
German Folk and Fairy Tales, (Michael, Maurice)
Gerrit & the Organ, (Van Stockum, Hilda)
Gertie the Horse/Thought & Thought, (Glendinning, M.)
Gertrude's Child, (Hughes, Richard A.)
Gertrude's Pocket, (Miles, Miska)

Gervase, (Moray, Ann)
Gessar-Khan, (Zeitlin, Ida)
Get-A-Way & Harry Janos, (Petersham, Maud)
Ghond the Hunter, (Mukerji, Dhan G.)
Ghost Ship, (Burglon, Nora)
Ghost Town Adventure, (Montgomery, R.)
Ghost Town Cowboy, (Eames, Genevieve T.)
Ghost Town Treasure, (Bulla, Clyde R.)
Ghost in a Four-Room Apartment, (Raskin, Ellen)
Ghost in the Noonday Sun, (Fleischman, Sid)
Ghost of Five Owl Farm, (Gage, Wilson)
Ghost of Opalina, (Bacon, Peggy)
Ghosts Go Haunting, (Leodhas, Sorche)
Ghosts I Have Met, (Bangs, John K.)
Giant Alexander, (Herrmann, Frank)
Giant Alexander & the Circus, (Herrmann, Frank)
Giant Book, (DeRegniers, Beatrice)
Giant Crab, (Rouse, W.H.D.)
Giant Horse of Oz, (Thompson, Ruth P.)
Giant John, (Lobel, Arnold)
Giant Nursery Book, (Palazzo, Tony)
Giant Otto, (DuBois, W.P.)
Giant Scissors, (Johnston, Annie F.)
Giant Story, (DeRegniers, Beatrice)
Giant of Central Park, (Shaw, Charles G.)
Giant of Grabbist, (Lawrence, John)
Giant's Ruby, (Blodgett, Mabel F.)
Giants & Witches, (Fenner, Phyllis R.)
Giants are Very Brave People, (Heide, Florence P.)
Gibby of Clamshell Alley, (Van Dresser, Jasmine)
Gibson Book, (Gibson, Charles D.)
Gid Granger, (Davis, Robert)
Gift for Sula Sula, (Ness, Evaline M.)
Gift from the Lonely Doll, (Wright, Dare)
Gift of the Earth, (Crespi, Pachita)
Gift of the Magi, (Henry, O.)
Gift of the Magic Staff, (Ostrander, Fannie)
Gift of the Mountains, (Wier, Ester A.)
Giggle Box, (Fenner, Phyllis R.)
Gigi, (Foster, Elizabeth)
Gigi in America, (Foster, Elizabeth)
Gigin and Till, (Scharen, Beatrix)
Gilbert the Gay Poodle, (Billings, Augusta)
Gilberto and the Wind, (Ets, Marie H.)
Gilded Bat, (Gorey, Edward)
Giles of the Star, (Rice, Rebecca)
Gilgamesh: Dream of Eternal Quest, (Boyajian, Zabelle C.)
Gilgamesh: Man's First Story, (Bryson, Bernarda)
Gillespie & the Guards, (Elkin, Benjamin)
Gillyflower Garden Book, (N/A)
Gin & Ginger, (Vincent, Kitty)
Ginger & Pickles, (Potter, Beatrix)
Ginger Bread Boy, (Piper, Watty)
Ginger Horse, (Daly, Maureen)
Ginger Pye, (Estes, Eleanor)
Gingerbread, (Sandburg, Helga)
Gingerbread Boy, (N/A)
Gingerbread Boy, (Tietjens, Eunice H.)
Gingerbread Man, (Baum, L. Frank)
Gingerbread Man, (Fable, Leonard)
Gingerbread Rabbit, (Jarrell, Randall)
Gingerbread Stories, (Mabie, Peter)
Ginnie and Geneva, (Woolley, Catherine)
Ginnie and the New Girl, (Woolley, Catherine)
Ginny and Custard, (Sayers, Frances C.)
Giotto Tended the Sheep, (Wheeler, Opal)
Giovanni & the Other, (Burnett, Frances H.)
Giraffe Twins, (Hogan, Inez)

Giraffe of King Charles X, (Wyants, Miche)
Girl & The Faun, (Phillpotts, Eden)
Girl Called Al, (Greene, Constance)
Girl I Left Behind Me, (Mills, Weymer J.)
Girl Ranchers of San Coulee, (Marshall, Caroline)
Girl Scout, (Girvin, Brenda)
Girl Who Sat by the Ashes, (Colum, Padraic)
Girl Who Would Be Queen, (Kelly, Eric P.)
Girl Who was a Cowboy, (Krasilovsky, Phyllis)
Girl and her Room, (McGinley, Phyllis)
Girl and the Goatherd, (Ness, Evaline M.)
Girl at Cobhurst, (Stockton, Frank)
Girl in the White Hat, (Cummings, Walter)
Girl of the Forest, (Hardy, Mary E.)
Girl of the Governor, (Warren, Carro F.)
Girl of the Limberlost, (Stratton-Porter, Gene)
Girl's Life, (Fisher, Harrison)
Girls, (Haines, Alice C.)
Girls, (Hutt, Henry)
Girls & Boys, (France, Anatole)
Girls & I, (Molesworth, Mrs.)
Girls are Silly, (Nash, Ogden)
Girls in Africa, (Berry, Erick)
Girls of Glen Hazard, (Chapman, Maristan)
Giselle, or the Willis, (Verdy, Violette)
Give Me Freedom, (McNeer, May)
Give Me a River, (Palmer, Elizabeth)
Give a Guess, (Miller, Mary B.)
Give a Man a Horse, (Finger, Charles J.)
Giving Away Suzanne, (Duncan, Lois)
Giving Tree, (Silverstein, Shel)
Glad Book, (Joan, Natalie)
Glad Book, (Sowerby, Githa)
Gladys told Me to Meet her Here, (Sharmat, Marjorie)
Glasgow: City of the West, (King, Jessie M.)
Glass Ball, (Mayne, William)
Glass House, (Kingsley, Florence M.)
Glass Mender, (Baring, Maurice)
Glass Slipper, (Farjeon, Eleanor)
Glass Valentine, (Hopkins, Marjorie)
Gleam O'Dawn, (Goodrich, Arthur F.)
Gleanings from the Graphic, (Caldecott, R.)
Glenda, (Udry, Janice M.)
Glimpses from Wonderland, (Ingold, John)
Glimpses of Heavenly Life, (Miller, James R.)
Glinda of Oz, (Baum, L. Frank)
Glittering Festival, (Harrison, Edith O.)
Gloomy the Camel, (Paull, Grace)
Glory Be!, (Lambert, Janet)
Glory of the Seas, (Hewes, Agnes D.)
Gloucester Boy, (Holberg, Ruth)
Gnome King of Oz, (Thompson, Ruth P.)
Go Find Hanka!, (Crosby, Alexander)
Go West, Young Bear, (Hamilton, Elizabeth)
Go With the Sun, (Schlein, Miriam)
Go and Find Wind, (Berry, Erick)
Go! Champions of Light, (Olcott, F.J.)
Go-to-Sleep Book, (Gilbert, Helen E.)
Goat Boy, (Bettina)
Goat Boy of Brooklyn, (Fall, Thomas)
Goat that Went to School, (Credle, Ellis)
Goats Who Killed the Leopard, (Hawes, Judy)
Gobbo Bobo, (Inman, H.E.)
Goblin Gobblers, (Sherratt, J.H.L.)
Goblin Island, (Oxenham, Elsie J.)
Goblin Market, (Rossetti, Christina)
Goblin Under the Stairs, (Calhoun, Mary)
Goblin Woman, (O'Neill, Rose)

Goblin's Glen, (Gaze, Harold)
Goblins of Haubeck, (Bancroft, Alberta)
Gobolinks, (Stuart, Ruth M.)
God Beneath the Sea, (Garfield, Leon)
God Returns to Vuelta Abajo, (Keiser, Melanie E.)
God is in the Mountain, (Keats, Ezra J.)
God's Man, (Ward, Lynd)
God's Trombones, (Johnson, James W.)
Godmother's Garden, (Syrett, Netta)
Gods & Mortals in Love, (Williamson, Hugh R.)
Gods are Athirst, (France, Anatole)
Gods of Mount Olympus, (Warren, Robert P.)
Gods of Pegana, (Lord Dunsany)
Gods were Promiscuous, (Held, John)
Godstone and the Blackymor, (White, Terence H.)
Goggles, (Keats, Ezra J.)
Gogo: French Seagull, (Slobodkin, Louis)
Going Barefoot, (Fisher, Aileen)
Going to the Fair, (Uttley, Alison)
Going-on-Nine, (Stone, Amy W.)
Goings on at Little Wishful, (Miller, Warren)
Gold, (White, Stewart E.)
Gold Bat, (Wodehouse, P.G.)
Gold Dust, (Schultz, James W.)
Gold Fish of Gran Chimu, (Lummis, Charles F.)
Gold Rush, (McNeer, May)
Gold Seekers of '49, (Sabin, Edwin L.)
Gold Steps, Stone Steps, (Marguilies, John)
Gold Worshipers, (Harris-Burland, J.)
Gold of Fairnilee, (Lang, Andrew)
Gold!, (Sabin, Edwin L.)
Gold, Frankincense & Myrrh, (Robertson, W.G.)
Golden Age, (Grahame, Kenneth)
Golden Apple, (Bolliger, Max)
Golden Apple, (Gregory, Lady Isabella)
Golden Basket, (Bemelmans, Ludwig)
Golden Bible, (Werner, Elsa)
Golden Bird, (Grimm Bros.)
Golden Bird, (Jarrell, Randall)
Golden Blight, (England, George A.)
Golden Book of Christmas Tales, (Lewicki, Lillian)
Golden Book of Famous Women, (Brickdale, E.F.)
Golden Book of Poetry, (Warner, J. (ed.))
Golden Book of Songs & Ballads, (Brickdale, E.F.)
Golden Bunny, (Brown, Margaret W.)
Golden Child, (Engle, Paul)
Golden Cockerel, (Pushkin, Alexander)
Golden Crane, (Yamaguchi, Tohr)
Golden Days of '49, (Munroe, Kirk)
Golden Days of Greece, (Coolidge, Olivia)
Golden Door, (Pauli, Hertha)
Golden Doors, (Fenton, Edward)
Golden Egg Book, (Brown, Margaret W.)
Golden Fairy Book, (N/A)
Golden Fairy Book, (Various)
Golden Flash, (McNeer, May)
Golden Fleece, (Colum, Padraic)
Golden Fleece, (Phillips, David G.)
Golden Footprints, (Kubota, Hikoho)
Golden Frog, (Surany, Anico)
Golden Galleon, (Malet, Lucas)
Golden Gate, (Angelo, Valenti)
Golden Girl, (Palazzo, Tony)
Golden Goblet, (McGraw, Eloise J.)
Golden Goblin, (Dunham, Curtis)
Golden Goose, (Grimm Bros.)
Golden Goose, (N/A)
Golden Goose Book, (N/A)

Golden Heart, (Barbour, Ralph H.)
Golden Heart, (Jacobs, Violet)
Golden Hive, (Behn, Harry)
Golden Hollow, (Sheffield, Rena C.)
Golden Horseshoe, (Coatsworth, Eliz.)
Golden Journey, (Bogan, Louise)
Golden Journey of Mr. Paradyne, (Locke, William J.)
Golden Kate, (Bohanon, Paul)
Golden Key, (Gordon, Hampden C.)
Golden Key, (MacDonald, George)
Golden Legend, (Longfellow, H.W.)
Golden Locks & Pretty Frocks, (Vredenburg, Edric)
Golden Lynx, (Baker, Augusta)
Golden Name Day, (Lindquist, Jennie)
Golden Palace of Neverland, (Robinson, William H.)
Golden Porch, (Hutchinson, W.M.L.)
Golden Prince, (Joos, Dorothy H.)
Golden Road, (Allen, Frank W.)
Golden Road, (Montgomery, Lucy M.)
Golden Rod Fairy Book, (Singleton, Esther)
Golden Root, (Steele, William O.)
Golden Seed, (Konopnicka, Maria)
Golden Ship..., (N/A)
Golden Slippers, (Bontemps, Arna (comp))
Golden Sovereign, (Housman, Laurence)
Golden Sovereign, (Lyons, Dorothy)
Golden Spinning Wheel, (Weil, Lisl)
Golden Staircase, (Chisholm, Louey)
Golden Stallion... [All titles], (Montgomery, R.)
Golden Star of Halich, (Kelly, Eric P.)
Golden Summer, (Leodhas, Sorche)
Golden Swan, (Wood, James P.)
Golden Swans, (Krueger, Kermit)
Golden Tales from Far Away, (Finger, Charles J.)
Golden Tales of... [All titles], (Becker, May L.)
Golden Thorn, (Daringer, Helen F.)
Golden Touch, (Disney, Walt)
Golden Touch, (Hawthorne, Nathaniel)
Golden Treasure, (Reesink, Maryke)
Golden Treasury of Poetry, (Untermeyer, Louis (ed))
Golden Treasury of Songs & Lyrics, (Palgrave, Francis T.)
Golden Trumpets, (Thompson, Blanche J.)
Golden Vanity & Green Bed, (Smith, Pamela C.)
Golden Wedding, (Stuart, Ruth M.)
Golden Wedge, (Lovelace, Maud H.)
Golden Windows, (Richards, Laura E.)
Golden-Feather, (Capuana, Luigi)
Goldfish Bowl, (Austin, Phyllis)
Goldfish Under the Ice, (Morley, Christopher)
Goldie the Dollmaker, (Goffstein, M.B.)
Goldilocks, (N/A)
Goldilocks & Three Bears, (N/A)
Goldilocks & the Three Bears, (Palazzo, Tony)
Golf Courses of the British Isles, (Darwin, Bernard)
Golf Girl, (Humphrey, Maud)
Golfer's Alphabet, (Van Sutphen, Wm. G.)
Golfer's Rubaiyat, (Boynton, Henry W.)
Golliwogg's Dream... Little Folks, (Fisher, Murray)
Golliwogg... [Most titles], (Upton, B. (or) F.)
Gondola Days, (Smith, Francis H.)
Gone Away with O'Malley, (Knott, M.O.)
Gone Haywire, (Rollins Philip A.)
Gone is Gone, (Gag, Wanda)
Gone is My Goose, (Koch, Dorothy)
Gone-Away Lake, (Enright, Elizabeth)
Goober Village, (Bigham, Madge A.)
Goochy Goggles & Pollywog... (Underhill, A.F.)
Good Children & Bad, (DeMonvel, M.B.)

Good Dog Book, (Various)
Good Fairy, (Stewart, Grace B.)
Good Fairy & the Bunnies, (Green, Allen A.)
Good Friends, (Bianco, Margery W.)
Good Giant, (Sampson, Martin)
Good Hunting, Little Indian, (Parish, Peggy)
Good King Wenceslas, (Neale, Dr.)
Good Little Dog, (Stoddard, Anne)
Good Luck Colt, (Eames, Genevieve T.)
Good Luck Duck, (DeJong, Meindert)
Good Luck Spider, (Mendoza, George)
Good Man & his Good Wife, (Krauss, Ruth)
Good Master, (Seredy, Kate)
Good Medicine, (Russell, Charles M.)
Good Morning, Sun's Up, (Beach, Stewart)
Good Morrow, (Norris, Gunilla)
Good Night, (Gates, Eleanor)
Good Night Veronica, (Trez, Denise)
Good Old Clipsy, (Palmer, Elizabeth)
Good Old Nursery Rhymes, (Cowham, Hilda)
Good Old Story of Cinderella, (Seccombe, Lieut.)
Good Place to Hide, (Slobodkin, Louis)
Good Queen Bees, (Girvin, Brenda)
Good Samaritan, (Andrews, Mary S.)
Good Shabbos, Everybody, (Garvey, Robert)
Good Ship Red Lily, (Savery, Constance)
Good Wind & Good Water, (Osborne, Nancy C.)
Good Wives, (Alcott, Louisa M.)
Good Wolf, (Burnett, Frances H.)
Good Work! What Will You be... (McCullough, John)
Good for Scuffles, (Beattie, Janet)
Good-Bye Jim, (Riley, James W.)
Good-Bye Thunderstorm, (Marino, Dorothy)
Good-Byes of Magnus Marmalade, (Orgel, Doris)
Good-Luck Horse, (Chan, Chih-Yi)
Good-Natured Bear, (Horne, Richard H.)
Good-Night Stories, (Judson, Clara I.)
Good-Night Stories, (Smith, Laura R.)
Good-Time Book, (La Rue, Mabel G.)
Good-for-Nothing Burro, (Silverman, Mel)
Good-for-Nothing Prince, (Williams, Jay)
Good-for-Nothings, (Grimm Bros.)
Goodnight, (Hoban, Russell)
Goodnight Andrew, Goodnight Craig, (Sharmat, M.)
Goodnight Moon, (Brown, Margaret W.)
Goody Two Shoes, (N/A)
Goody Two Shoes..., (Crane, Walter)
Goody-Naughty Book, (Rippey, Sarah C.)
Goofy Mrs. Goose, (Potter, Miriam C.)
Google Book, (Vickers, Vincent C.)
Goomer, (Waldman, Dorothy)
Gooney, (Borack, Barbara)
Goop Directory of Juvenile Offenders, (Burgess, Gelett)
Goop Tales Alphabetically Told, (Burgess, Gelett)
Goops & How to be Them, (Burgess, Gelett)
Goose Family Tales, (Ostrander, Fannie)
Goose Girl, (Grimm Bros.)
Goose Girl of Nurnberg, (Hawley, Harriet S.)
Goose Grass Rhymes, (Shannon, Monica)
Goose that was a Watchdog, (Hays, Wilma P.)
Gooseberry Garden, (Lenski, Lois)
Gooseberry Jones, (Gerber, Will)
Gopher in the Garden, (Prelutsky, Jack)
Gordon & the Glockenspiel, (Ryland, Lee)
Gordon Keith, (Page, Thomas N.)
Gordon the Goat, (Leaf, Munro)
Gorgeous Isle, (Atherton, Gertrude)
Gourd Fiddle, (Cooke, Grace M.)

Grab Bag, (Davis, Lavinia R.)
Grabbit, the Rascal, (Wiesner, William)
Grabianski's Cats, (Grabianski, Janus)
Gracious Majesty, (Housman, Laurence)
Grains of Pepper, (Haskett, Edytha)
Grammar Town, (Addington, Sarah)
Gramp's Desert Chick, (Kissin, Rita)
Grampa in Oz, (Thompson, Ruth P.)
Grandfather Frog Gets a Ride, (Burgess, Thornton)
Grandfather Whiskers, M.D., (Leonard, Nellie)
Grandfather and I, (Buckley, Helen E.)
Grandfather's Broadaxe, (Stephens, Charles A.)
Grandfather's Follies, (Geller, James J.)
Grandma in the Apple Tree, (Lobe, Mira)
Grandma's Gun, (Martin, Patricia)
Grandmother Cat & the Hermit, (Coatsworth, Eliz.)
Grandmother Tippytoe, (Lenski, Lois)
Grandmother and I, (Buckley, Helen E.)
Grandmother's Doll, (Bouton, Elizabeth)
Grandmother's Fairy Tales, (Hewlett, Pia)
Grandmother's Story/Bunker Hill Battle, (Holmes, Oliver W.)
Grandpa, (Borack, Barbara)
Grandpa & the Tiger, (Heward, Constance)
Grandpa's Little Girls & Friends, (Curtis, Alice T.)
Grandpa's Little Girls at School, (Curtis, Alice T.)
Grange at High Force, (Turner, Philip)
Granny & the Desperadoes, (Parish, Peggy)
Granny Goose, (Rae, John)
Granny and the Indians, (Parish, Peggy)
Granny's Little Rhyme Book, (LeMair, H.W.)
Granny's Wonderful Chair, (Browne, Frances)
Graphic Pictures, (Caldecott, R.)
Grass Rope, (Mayne, William)
Grasses, (Eberle, Irmengarde)
Grasshopper Green and the Meadow Mice, (Rae, John)
Grateful Elephant, (Burlingame, Eugene W.)
Gray Dawn, (White, Stewart E.)
Gray Rabbit Finds a Shoe, (Uttley, Alison)
Gray Squirrel, (Adrian, Mary)
Gray Squirrel, (Lippincott, J.W.)
Gray Wolf, (Montgomery, R.)
Graymouse Family, (Leonard, Nellie)
Graywings, (Goudey, Alice)
Greased Lightning, (North, Sterling)
Greasy Luck, (Grant, Gordon)
Great Adventure, (Aldin, Cecil)
Great Adventure of Hare, (Uttley, Alison)
Great Adventure of Mrs. Santa Claus, (Addington, Sarah)
Great Aunt Victoria's House, (Otto, Margaret G.)
Great Battles of the World, (Crane, Stephen)
Great Bear Island, (McFarlane, Arthur E.)
Great Big Animal Book, (N/A)
Great Big Enormous Turnip, (Tolstoy, Alexei)
Great Big Schoolhouse, (Scarry, Richard)
Great Blueness & other Predicaments, (Lobel, Arnold)
Great Cheese Conspiracy, (Van Leeuwen, Jean)
Great Claus and Little Claus, (Andersen, Hans C.)
Great Day in the Morning, (Means, Florence C.)
Great Duffy, (Krauss, Ruth)
Great Emergency, (Ewing, Juliana H.)
Great Expectations, (Dickens, Charles)
Great Geppy, (DuBois, W.P.)
Great God Pan & Inmost Light, (Machen, Arthur)
Great Gravity the Cat, (Johnston, Johanna)
Great Hamster Hunt, (Blegvad, Lenore)
Great Heritage, (Shippen, Kath. B.)
Great Horse Stories, (Cooper, Page)
Great House, (Harnett, Cynthia)

Great Joke on Jimmy Skunk, (Burgess, Thornton)
Great Jug, (Raphael, Arthur)
Great Ker-Plunk, (King, Alexander)
Great Men, (Begbie, Harold)
Great Othello, (Palazzo, Tony)
Great Picture Robbery, (Harris, Leon)
Great Plains, (Parrish, Randall)
Great Plan, (Mason, Edith H.)
Great Quest, (Hawes, Charles B.)
Great Quillow, (Thurber, James)
Great Rebellion, (Stolz, Mary S.)
Great Refusal, (Gray, Maxwell)
Great Sea Horse, (Anderson, Isabel)
Great Sleigh Robbery, (Foreman, Michael)
Great Stone of Sardis, (Stockton, Frank)
Great Sweeping Day, (Wood, Esther)
Great Tradition, (Allee, Marjorie H.)
Great Venture, (Carse, Robert)
Great Wheel, (Lawson, Robert)
Great White Way, (Paine, Albert B.)
Great Wolf & the Good Woodsman, (Hoover, Helen)
Great Year, (Dudley, Albertus T.)
Greater Abbeys of England, (Gasquet, Abbot)
Greedy Goat, (Brock, Emma)
Greedy One, (Martin, Patricia)
Greek Gods and their Heroes, (Graves, Robert)
Greek Heroes, (Niebuhr)
Green & Gold, (Hader, B.& E.)
Green Arras, (Housman, Laurence)
Green Bough, (Faulkner, William)
Green Door, (White, Eliza O.)
Green Door to the Sea, (Berry, Erick)
Green Eggs & Ham, (Seuss, Dr.)
Green Eyes, (Birnbaum, Abe)
Green Fairy Book, (Lang, Andrew)
Green Forest Fairy Book, (Brady, Loretta E.)
Green Ginger Jar, (Judson, Clara I.)
Green Gravel, (Aydelotte, Dora)
Green Grows the Garden, (Bianco, Margery W.)
Green Hornet Lunchbox, (Gordon, Shirley)
Green Lacquer Pavillion, (Beauclerk, Helen)
Green Magic, (Wilson, Romer)
Green Mansions, (Hudson, Wm. Henry)
Green Mouse, (Chambers, Robert)
Green Noses, (Wiesner, William)
Green Poodles, (Baker, Charlotte)
Green Says Go, (Emberley, Edward)
Green Song, (Plenn, Doris T.)
Green Thumb Story, (Fiedler, Jean)
Green Timber Trails, (Chapman, William G.)
Green Wagons, (Seidlin, Oskar)
Green Willow..., (James, Grace)
Green-Faced Toad, (Birch, Vera B.)
Green-Pipes, (Paget-Fredericks, J.)
Greenaway's Babies, (Greenaway, Kate)
Greg's Microscope, (Selsam, Millicent)
Gregori's Lamb, (Beim, Lorraine)
Gregorio & the White Llama, (Bannon, Laura)
Gremlins, (Dahl, Roald)
Gresha and his Clay Pig, (Grishina-Givago, N.)
Greta and Peter in the Flower Garden, (Hartley, Dick)
Greta the Strong, (Sobol, Donald J.)
Grettir and Outlaw, (Baring-Gould, Sabine)
Grey City of the North, (King, Jessie M.)
Grey Fairy Book, (Lang, Andrew)
Grey Goose of Kilnevin, (Lynch, Patricia)
Grey House on the Hill, (Greene, Mrs.)
Grey Lady, (Merriman, Henry S.)

Grey Rabbit & the Circus, (Uttley, Alison)
Grey Rabbit's May Day, (Uttley, Alison)
Greyfriars Bobby, (Atkinson, Eleanor)
Greyfur's Neighbors, (Nyce, Vera)
Greyhounds of the Sea, (Cutler, Carl)
Greylock & the Robins, (Robinson, Tom P.)
Greypaws..., (Creswick, Paul)
Griffin and the Minor Canon, (Stockton, Frank)
Grim House, (Molesworth, Mrs.)
Grim: Story of a Pike, (Fleuron, Svend)
Grimbold's other World, (Gray, Nicholas S.)
Grimm Tales Made Gay, (Carryl, Guy W.)
Grindstone Farm, (Lent, Henry B.)
Grindstone of God, (Withers, Carl)
Gritli's Children, (Spyri, Johanna)
Groaning Board, (Addams, Charles)
Grocery Mouse, (Clymer, Eleanor)
Grodge-Cat & the Window Cleaner, (Symonds, John)
Groundhog and his Shadow, (Wiese, Kurt)
Groundsel and Necklaces, (Barker, Cecily M.)
Group of Noble Dames, (Hardy, Thomas)
Grover, (Cleaver, Vera)
Growing Pains, (Gag, Wanda)
Growing Story, (Krauss, Ruth)
Growing Summer, (Streatfeild, Noel)
Growl Bear, (Austin, Margot)
Grubby Gets Clean, (Vorse, Mary E.)
Gruesome Green Witch, (Coffin, Patricia)
Grumpus and the Venetian Cat, (Seidler, Rosalie)
Gryll Grange, (Peacock, Thomas L.)
Guard Mouse, (Freeman, Don)
Gub Gub's Book, (Lofting, Hugh)
Guernsey Lily, (Coolidge, Susan)
Guess, (Bridgman, L.J.)
Guess Again, (Bridgman, L.J.)
Guess Book, (Shaw, Charles G.)
Guess What's in the Grass, (Mitchell, Lucy S.)
Guest at the Ludlow, (Nye, Edgar W.)
Guinevere..., (Tennyson, Alfred)
Gull Number 737, (George, Jean C.)
Gullible's Travels, (Lardner, Ring)
Gulliver Joins the Army, (Dalgliesh, Alice)
Gulliver's Bird Book, (Gulliver, Lemeul)
Gulliver's Travels, (Swift, Jonathan)
Gulliver's Travels into Lilliput, (DeBosschere, Jean)
Gunpowder Tower, (Schaad, Hans)
Guns for the Saratoga, (Meader, Stephen W.)
Gunsmith's Boy, (Best, Herbert)
Gus Was a Friendly Ghost, (Thayer, Jane)
Gustavus and Stop, (Krahn, Fernando)
Gutta-Percha Willie, (MacDonald, George)
Gwendolyn, (Helm, Ruth)
Gwendolyn & Weathercock, (Sherman, Nancy)
Gwendolyn, the Miracle Hen, (Sherman, Nancy)
Gwinellen, Princess Who Could Not Sleep, (Yolen, Jane)
Gwot! Horribly Funny Hairticklers, (Mendoza, George)
Gyp's Hour of Bliss, (Aldin, Cecil)
Gypsy, (Seredy, Kate)
Gypsy Bridle, (Weber, Lenora M.)
Gypsy Caravan, (Pease, Howard)
Gypsy Fiddle, (Hampden, John)
Gypsy Story-Teller, (Morris, Cora)
Gypsy and the Bear, (Borski, Lucia M.)
H.M.S. Pinafore, (Wheeler, Opal)
Habit of Empire, (Horgan, Paul)
Habits of Rabbits, (Kahl, Virginia)
Hah-Nee of the Cliff Dwellers, (Buff, M.& C.)
Hail Columbia, (Lawson, Marie A.)

Hailstones & Halibut Bones, (O'Neill, Mary)
Hairy Horror Trick, (Corbett, Scott)
Hajji Baba of Ispahan, (Morier, James)
Hakon of Rogen's Saga, (Haugaard, Erik)
Half Magic, (Eager, Edward)
Half a Dozen Boys, (Ray, Anna C.)
Half a Rogue, (MacGrath, Harold)
Half the World is Isfahan, (Singer, Caroline)
Half-Back, (Barbour, Ralph H.)
Half-Hours with Jimmie-Boy, (Bangs, John K.)
Half-Past Seven Stories, (Anderson, Rbt. G.)
Half-Sisters, (Carlson, Natalie S.)
Half-Time Gypsy, (Varney, Joyce)
Half-as-Big and the Tiger, (Frankel, Bernice)
Halfway to Heaven, (Knight, Ruth A.)
Halloween, (Borten, Helen)
Hallowell Partnership, (Brown, Katharine H.)
Hamlet, (Shakespeare, Wm.)
Hamlet and Brownswiggle, (Reynolds, Barbara)
Hamlet: A Cocker Spaniel, (Black, Irma S.)
Hammet and the Highlanders, (McGowen, Tom)
Hampton Court, (Hutton, William H.)
Hand Clasp, (Seegmiller, Wilhelmia)
Hand in Hand We'll Go, (Burns, Robert)
Hand in the Picture, (Kelly, Eric P.)
Hand of Apollo, (Coatsworth, Eliz.)
Hand-Book of Golf for Bears, (VerBeck, Frank)
Handful of Surprises, (Heathers, Anne)
Handley Cross, (Surtees, Robert S.)
Handsome Donkey, (Davis, Mary G.)
Handy Andy, (Lover, Samuel)
Handy Guide to Grownups, (Owsley, Jennifer)
Handy Mandy in Oz, (Thompson, Ruth P.)
Hanging Garden..., (Armfield, Maxwell)
Hanging of the Crane, (Longfellow, H.W.)
Hannah Marie, (Bennett, Richard)
Hannibal and the Bears, (Baker, Margaret)
Hans Brinker, (Dodge, Mary Mapes)
Hans Christian of Elsinore, (Kristoffersen, Eva)
Hans the Eskimo, (Rich, Edwin G.)
Hansel and Gretel, (Grimm Bros.)
Hansel the Gander, (Kuebler, Katharine)
Hansi, (Bemelmans, Ludwig)
Hansi the Stork, (Ludmann, Oscar)
Happily Ever After, (Dalgliesh, Alice)
Happiness Flower, (Wuorio, Eva-Lis)
Happiness for Kimi, (Lattimore, Eleanor)
Happy Annual, (Aldin, Cecil)
Happy Average, (Whitlock, Brand)
Happy Birthday, (Crespi, Pachita)
Happy Birthday Present, (Heilbroner, Joan)
Happy Birthday in Barcelona, (Weil, Lisl)
Happy Birthday to You!, (Seuss, Dr.)
Happy Childhood, (Weatherly, Fred E.)
Happy Children, (Pratt, Ella)
Happy Christmas, (Bishop, Claire H.)
Happy Day, (Krauss, Ruth)
Happy Day Begins, (N/A)
Happy Day Fair, (Matthews, Harry B.)
Happy Days, (Herford, Oliver)
Happy Days, (Nash, Ogden)
Happy Dollies, (Keys, Leonora)
Happy Easter, (Wiese, Kurt)
Happy Flute, (Mandal, Sant Ram)
Happy Hanukah Everybody, (Chanover, Hyman)
Happy Harbor, (Hauman, George)
Happy Heart Family, (Gerson, Virginia)
Happy Home Children, (Gordon, Elizabeth)

Happy Hunter, (Duvoisin, Roger)
Happy Hypocrite, (Beerbohm, Max)
Happy Island, (Lee, Jennette)
Happy Jack, (Burgess, Thornton)
Happy Lion... [All titles], (Fatio, Louise)
Happy Little Family, (Caudill, Rebecca)
Happy Orpheline, (Carlson, Natalie S.)
Happy Owls, (Piatti, Celestino)
Happy Piper and the Goat, (Martin, Patricia)
Happy Place, (Bemelmans, Ludwig)
Happy Pollyooly, (Jepson, Edgar)
Happy Prince, (Wilde, Oscar)
Happy Rain, (Sendak, Jack)
Happy School Year, (Dalgliesh, Alice)
Happy Ski ABC, (Weil, Lisl)
Happy Sound, (Graham, Ruth M.)
Happy Surprises, (Olcott, Julia)
Happy Time, (Fontaine, Robert)
Happy Times, (N/A)
Happy Times in Czechoslovakia, (Bartusek, Libushka)
Happy Times in Noisy Village, (Lindgren, Astrid)
Happy all Day Through, (Bowman, John G.)
Happy's Christmas, (Gramatky, Hardie)
Happy-Go-Lucky, (Wiesner, William)
Happy-Go-Lucky, (Wister, Annis L.)
Happychaps, (Wells, Carolyn)
Hard Lines, (Nash, Ogden)
Harding's Luck, (Nesbit, Edith)
Hare & the Easter Egg, (Uttley, Alison)
Hare & the Tortoise, (La Fontaine, J.)
Hare Goes Shopping, (Uttley, Alison)
Hare and the Easter Eggs, (Uttley, Alison)
Hare and the Tortoise, (Aesopus)
Hari: The Jungle Lad, (Mukerji, Dhan G.)
Harlequin, (Mincieli, Rose)
Harlequin Hullabaloo, (Lyons, Dorothy)
Harlequin and Mother Goose, (Robbins, Ruth)
Harlot's House, (Wilde, Oscar)
Harold... [Most titles], (Johnson, Crockett)
Harper Book of Princes, (Johnson, Sally (ed))
Harquin, (Burningham, John)
Harriet & the Promised Land, (Lawrence, Jacob)
Harriet Hare, (Layard, Arthur)
Harriet the Spy, (Fitzhugh, Louise)
Harriett, (McKinley, Charles)
Harrison Loved his Umbrella, (Levine, Rhoda)
Harry and the Lady Next Door, (Zion, Gene)
Harry by the Sea, (Zion, Gene)
Harry the Dirty Dog, (Zion, Gene)
Harvest Feast, (Harper, Wilhelmina)
Harvest of World Folk Tales, (Rugoff, Milton (ed))
Harvey's Hideout, (Hoban, Russell)
Hassan, (Flecker, James E.)
Hastings the Pirate, (Creswick, Paul)
Hat House, (Beskow, Elsa)
Hat Tub Tale..., (Emerson, Caroline)
Hat for Amy Jean, (Chalmers, Mary)
Hat with a Rose, (Zemach, Harve)
Hat-Shaking Dance, (Courlander, Harold)
Hathoo of the Elephants, (Wheeler, Post)
Hating Book, (Zolotow, Charlotte)
Hattie the Backstage Bat, (Freeman, Don)
Haunt Fox, (Kjelgaard, Jim)
Haunted House, (Belloc, Hilaire)
Haunted House, (Hood, Thomas)
Haunted Man, (Dickens, Charles)
Haunted Omnibus, (Laing, Alexander (ed))
Haunted Photograph, (Stuart, Ruth M.)

Haunters of the Silences, (Roberts, Chas. G.D.)
Have Space Suit-Will Travel, (Heinlein, Robert)
Have You Seen Tom Thumb?, (Hunt, Mabel L.)
Have You Seen my Puppy?, (Holl, Adelaide)
Haven's End, (Marquand, John)
Having Fun, (Wright, Isa L.)
Hawaii: Book to Begin On, (Swenson, Juliet)
Hawaiian Coffee Picker, (Bannon, Laura)
Hawaiian Legends of Tricksters... (Thompson, V.L.)
Hawaiian Myths of Earth, Sea & Sky, (Thompson, V.L.)
Hay-Foot, Straw-Foot, (Berry, Erick)
Hazel, (Ovington, Mary W.)
He Drew as He Pleased, (Hurter, Albert)
He Leadeth Me, (Barker, Dorothy O.)
He Was There from Day We Moved In, (Levine, Rhoda)
Head for Happy, (Sewell, Helen)
Head of a Hundred, (Goodwin, Maud W.)
Headed for Trouble, (Rinkoff, Barbara)
Headlong Hall & Nightmare Abbey, (Peacock, T.L.)
Heads Up and Heels Down, (Anderson, C.W.)
Hear Ye of Boston, (Curren, Polly)
Heart Line, (Burgess, Gelett)
Heart of Boyhood, (DeAmicis, Edmondo)
Heart of Happy Hollow, (Dunbar, Paul L.)
Heart of Lady Ann, (Castle, Agnes)
Heart of Stone, (Hauff, Wilhelm)
Heart of Toil, (Thanet, Octave)
Heart of a Dog, (Terhune, Albert P.)
Heart of a Soldier, (Pickett, George E.)
Heart of the Hills, (Fox, John Jr.)
Heart of the World, (Haggard, H. Rider)
Heart's Highway, (Wilkins, Mary E.)
Heartbreak Hill, (Viele, Herman K.)
Hearts & Creeds, (Ray, Anna C.)
Hearts Content, (Barbour, Ralph H.)
Heartsease, (Dickinson, Peter)
Heartsease & Happy Days, (Clarkson, L.)
Heather and Broom, (Leodhas, Sorche)
Heavenly Tenants, (Maxwell, William)
Heavy is a Hippopotamus, (Schlein, Miriam)
Hebrew Alphabet Book, (Margalit, Avi)
Hector the Protector, (Sendak, Maurice)
Hector the Stowaway Dog, (Dodson, Kenneth)
Hedgehog and the Hare, (Grimm Bros.)
Heedless Susan, (Brock, Emma)
Heidi, (Spyri, Johanna)
Heidi Grows Up, (Tritten, Charles)
Heinrich Schliemann, (Selden, George)
Heir of Redclyffe, (Yonge, Charlotte)
Heirlooms in Miniatures, (Wharton, Anne H.)
Held Fast for England, (Henty, G.A.)
Held's Angels, (Gilbreth, Frank)
Helen, (Edgeworth, Maria)
Helen and the Fifth Cousins, (Gilchrist, Beth B.)
Helga and the White Peacock, (Meigs, Cornelia L.)
Hell-Fire Harrison, (Wattles, Wallace D.)
Helldorado, (Breakenridge, Wm.)
Hello Hippopotamus, (Kraus, Robert)
Hello Peter, (Gipson, Morrell)
Hello, Alaska!, (Litchfield, Sarah)
Hello, Elephant, (Wahl, Jan)
Hello, Mrs. Goose, (Potter, Miriam C.)
Hello, Mrs. Piggle-Wiggle, (MacDonald, Betty)
Hello, the Boat!, (Crawford, Phyllis)
Help, Help, the Golobolinks, (Menotti, Gian-Carlo)
Helpers Without Hands, (Davidson, Gladys)
Helping the Weatherman, (Kay, Gertrude A.)
Helter Skelters, (Daulton, George)

Hen that Kept House, (Brock, Emma)
Henner's Lydia, (DeAngeli, Marguerite)
Henny Penny, (N/A)
Henny-Penny and Chicken Little, (Palazzo, Tony)
Henri's Walk to Paris, (Klein, Leonore)
Henrietta & the Hat, (Watts, Mabel)
Henrietta's House, (Goudge, Elizabeth)
Henry 3, (Krumgold, Joseph)
Henry David Thoreau, (Daugherty, James)
Henry Fisherman, (Brown, Marcia)
Henry Huggins, (Cleary, Beverly)
Henry Hutt Picture Book, (Hutt, Henry)
Henry Reed... [All titles], (Robertson, Keith)
Henry and Beezus, (Cleary, Beverly)
Henry and Ribsy, (Cleary, Beverly)
Henry and the Monstrous Din, (Hoban, Russell)
Henry of Agincourt, (Strong, L.A.G.)
Henry the Navigator, (Lynch, Maude B.)
Henry the Uncatchable Mouse, (Simon, Sidney)
Henry's Dog Henry, (Brooks, Walter)
Henry's Lincoln, (Neyhart, Louise A.)
Henry's Ride, (Schlein, Miriam)
Henry, the Hand-Painted Mouse, (Merrill, Jean)
Hepatica Hawks, (Field, Rachel)
Her Father's Daughter, (Stratton-Porter, Gene)
Her Fiance, (Daskam, Josephine)
Her Ladyship's Elephant, (Wells, David D.)
Her Letter, (Harte, Bret)
Her Majesty the King, (Roche, James J.)
Herbert Situation, (Levine, Rhoda)
Herbert the Lion, (Newberry, Clare T.)
Hercules, (Gramatky, Hardie)
Hercules: Gentle Giant, (Schneider, Nina)
Herdboy of Hungary, (Finta, Alexander)
Here Bingo!, (Stoddard, Anne)
Here Come the Bears!, (Goudey, Alice)
Here Comes Daddy, (Milius, Winifred)
Here Comes Daddy, (Parks, Gale T.)
Here Comes Kristie, (Brock, Emma)
Here Comes Mary Ellen, (Justus, May)
Here Comes Night, (Schlein, Miriam)
Here Comes Pete, (Clymer, Eleanor)
Here Comes Thursday, (Bond, Michael)
Here Comes the Circus, (Moses, Horace S.)
Here Comes the Peddler!, (Moody, Marion M.)
Here Comes the Showboat, (Credle, Ellis)
Here Comes the Trolley Car, (Chalmers, Mary)
Here I Stay, (Coatsworth, Eliz.)
Here and There and Everywhere, (Gall, Alice C.)
Here and There..., (Parker, Elinor)
Here is Henri!, (Vacheron, Edith)
Here they Are, (Wavle, Ardra)
Here's Howie, (Malone, Mary)
Here's Juggins, (Stone, Amy W.)
Here's a Penny, (Haywood, Carolyn)
Here, There, Everywhere, (Lecky, E.)
Hereward the Wake, (Kingsley, Charles)
Herford Aesop, (Herford, Oliver)
Herman the Loser, (Hoban, Russell)
Herman's Hat, (Mendoza, George)
Hermit Crab Lives in a Shell, (Stephens, William)
Hermy, Story of a Little Girl, (Molesworth, Mrs.)
Hernani the Jew, (Homer, A.N.)
Hero Tales & Legends of Serbians, (Petrovitch, W.)
Hero by Mistake, (Brenner, Anita)
Hero in Homespun, (Barton, William E.)
Hero of Vincennes, (Thomas, Lowell)
Herodia the Lovely Puppet, (Milhous, Katherine)

Herodotus, (King, Gordon (ed))
Heroes & Heroines, (Farjeon, Eleanor)
Heroes & Wizards, (Coburn, Grace)
Heroes from Hakluyt, (Finger, Charles (ed))
Heroes of Chivalry and Romance, (Church, Alfred J.)
Heroes of the Kalevala, (Deutsch, Babette)
Heroes of the Norselands, (Boult, Katharine F.)
Heroes/Greek Fairy Tales, (Kingsley, Charles)
Heroic Legends, (Herbertson, Agnes)
Heroines of the Early West, (Ross, Nancy W.)
Heron Ride, (Treadgold, Mary)
Herrick's Poems, (Herrick, Robert)
Hester & the Gnomes, (Hunt, Marigold)
Hester Mouse who Became a Writer, (Hoban, Russell)
Hester and Timothy, Pioneers, (Holberg, Ruth)
Hetty of the Grande Deluxe, (Means, Florence C.)
Hey, Horses!, (Graves, Elizabeth)
Hey, What's Wrong with This One?, (Wojciechowska, M.)
Heyo, Brer Rabbit, (Blyton, Enid)
Hezekiah Horton, (Tarry, Ellen)
Hi Guy the Cinderella Horse, (Brown, Paul)
Hi! Ho! Pinocchio, (Marino, Josef)
Hi, Cat!, (Keats, Ezra J.)
Hi, Mister Robin!, (Tresselt, Alvin)
Hi, Tom, (Ward, Nanda)
Hi-Po the Hippo, (Thomas, Dorothy)
Hiawatha, (Disney, Walt)
Hiawatha, (Longfellow, H.W.)
Hiawatha Alphabet, (Holbrook, Florence)
Hiawatha Primer, (Holbrook, Florence)
Hickory Lane, (Quigg, Jane)
Hickory Limb, (Fillmore, Parker H.)
Hidden Faces, (Dali, Salvador)
Hidden House, (Brown, Margaret W.)
Hidden People, (Miller, Leo E.)
Hidden Trapezes, (Fenton, Edward)
Hidden Treasure of Glaston, (Jewett, Eleanore)
Hidden Valley, (Benet, Laura)
Hidden Valley of Oz, (Cosgrove, Rachel R.)
Hidden Water, (Coolidge, Dane)
Hidden Year of Devlin Bates, (Muehl, Lois B.)
Hide and Go Seek, (Lathrop, Dorothy)
Hide and Seek, (Coatsworth, Eliz.)
Hide and Seek Day, (Zion, Gene)
Hide and Seek Fog, (Tresselt, Alvin)
Hide-Rack Kidnapped, (Balch, Glenn)
Higgins and the Great Big Scare, (Caudill, Rebecca)
Higglety Pigglety Pop!, (Sendak, Maurice)
High Courage, (Anderson, C.W.)
High Deeds of Finn MacCool, (Sutcliff, Rosemary)
High Flying Hat, (Ward, Nanda)
High History of the Holy Grail, (Evans, Sebastian (tr))
High King, (Alexander, Lloyd C.)
High Society, (Parker, Dorothy)
High Sounds, Low Sounds, (Branley, Franklyn)
High Timber, (Nelson, Rhoda)
High Trail, (Breckenfeld, Vivian)
High Water, (Stong, Philip D.)
High Water in Arkansas, (Finger, Charles J.)
High Wind for Kansas, (Calhoun, Mary)
High World, (Bemelmans, Ludwig)
High in the Mountains, (Brock, Emma)
High-Noon Rocket, (May, Charles P.)
High-Rise Secret, (Lenski, Lois)
Highland Halloween, (Hays, Wilma P.)
Highly Trained Dogs of Professor Pettit, (Brink, Carol R.)
Highwaymen..., (Finger, Charles J.)
Highways & Byways of North Wales, (Bradley, Arthur G.)

Hike & the Aeroplane, (Graham, Tom)
Hiker Joy, (Connolly, James B.)
Hilary Knight's Mother Goose, (Knight, Hilary)
Hilda and the Wishes, (Peck, Harry T.)
Hildegarde & Maximilian, (Krahn, Fernando)
Hilding's Summer, (Lindgren, Barbo)
Hilili and Dilili, (Walker, Barbara)
Hill Ranch, (Montgomery, R.)
Hill of Little Miracles, (Angelo, Valenti)
Hill that Fell Down, (Sharp, Evelyn)
Hills of Ruel, (MacLeod, Fiona)
Himself and Burlap on TV, (Dennis, Morgan)
Hindu Fairy Tales, (Griswold, Florence)
Hindu Stories, (Williston, Teresa P.)
Hippolyte: Crab King, (Anderson, Joy)
Hira Singh, (Mundy, Talbot)
Hired Man's Elephant, (Stong, Philip D.)
Hirum, the Hillbilly, (Stong, Philip D.)
His Apologies, (Kipling, Rudyard)
His Courtship, (Martin, H.R.)
His Excellency & Peter, (Harper, Theodore A.)
His Grace of Osmonde, (Burnett, Frances H.)
His Indian Brother, (Wilson, Hazel)
His Lordship's Puppy, (Elmslie, Theodora C.)
His Version of It, (Ford, Paul L.)
His Volpone, (Johnson, Ben)
History of Ali Baba, (N/A)
History of Cinderella, (N/A)
History of Don Quixote..., (Cervantes)
History of Henry Esmond, (Thackeray, Wm. M.)
History of New York, (Irving, Washington)
History of Over Sea, (Morris, William)
History of Reynard the Fox, (Ellis, Frederick S.)
History of Simple Simon, (N/A)
History of Whittington, (Lang, Andrew (ed))
History of the Hoppers, (Parker, B.)
History with a Match, (Van Loon, Hendrik)
Hitting the Line, (Barbour, Ralph H.)
Hitty, Her First Hundred Years, (Field, Rachel)
Ho for a Hat!, (Smith, William J.)
Ho-Ming, Girl of New China, (Lewis, Eliz. F.)
Hoagie's Rifle Gun, (Miles, Miska)
Hobby Horse Hill, (Davis, Lavinia R.)
Hobo Hill, (Philbrook, Elizabeth)
Hobo Hound, (Edwards, May)
Hole & Corner Book, (Parker, B.)
Hole Book, (Newell, Peter)
Hole in the Tree, (George, Jean C.)
Hole in the Wall, (Alcott, Louisa M.)
Hole in the Wall, (Byron, May)
Hole is to Dig, (Krauss, Ruth)
Holiday, (Dennis, Wesley)
Holiday Book, (Warde, Margaret)
Holiday Hill, (Patch, Edith M.)
Holiday Rat & Utmost Mouse, (Holman, Felice)
Holiday Time on Butternut Hill, (Cady, Harrison)
Holiday Trench, (Ballantyne, Joan)
Holiday for Edith & the Bears, (Wright, Dare)
Holiday for Mister Muster, (Lobel, Arnold)
Holiday in France, (Bemelmans, Ludwig)
Holidays & Happy Days, (Hendry, Hamish)
Holland, (Jungman, B.)
Holland Sketches, (Penfield, Edward)
Hollow Tree... [All titles], (Paine, Albert B.)
Holly & Pizen, (Stuart, Ruth M.)
Holly Berries, (Waugh, Ida)
Holly House and Ridges Row, (Baldwin, May)
Holly Tree Inn, (Dickens, Charles)

Holly in the Snow, (Lattimore, Eleanor)
Holy Cross, (Field, Eugene)
Holy Land, (Hichens, Robert)
Holy Night, (Von Juchen, Aurel)
Home Life in Colonial Days, (Earle, Alice M.)
Home Life of Wild Birds, (Herrick, Francis H.)
Home Ranch, (James, Will)
Home for a Bunny, (Brown, Margaret W.)
Home is If You Find It, (Nye, Harry)
Home is the North, (Morey, Walter)
Home is the Sailor, (Godden, Rumer)
Home on the Range..., (Hader, B.& E.)
Home: the Tale of a Mouse, (Schlein, Miriam)
Homebodies, (Addams, Charles)
Homer & the Circus Train, (Gramatky, Hardie)
Homer Price, (McCloskey, Robert)
Homes in the Wilderness, (N/A)
Homing With Birds, (Stratton-Porter, Gene)
Hominy and his Blunt-Nosed Arrow, (Mason, Miriam E.)
Honest John & Giddy, (Disney, Walt)
Honey Bear, (Willson, Dixie)
Honey Boat, (Angelo, Valenti)
Honey Chile, (Braune, Anna)
Honey Jane, (Justus, May)
Honey Land, (Lupprian, Hildegard)
Honey of the Nile, (Berry, Erick)
Honey on a Raft, (Paltenghi, Madalena)
Honey the City Bear, (Paltenghi, Madalena)
Honey-Bee, (France, Anatole)
Honeybee, (Adrian, Mary)
Honk! the Moose, (Stong, Philip D.)
Honorable Mr. Tawnish, (Farnol, Jeffery)
Hoo! Hoo! DeWitt!, (Duncombe, Frances)
Hooded Crow, (Monsell, J.R.)
Hoof and Claw, (Roberts, Chas. G.D.)
Hooligan Nights, (Rook, Clarence)
Hooray for Jasper, (Horvath, Betty)
Hooray for Us, (Warburg, Sandol)
Hoosier Chronicle, (Nicholson, Meredith)
Hoosier Holiday, (Dreiser, Theodore)
Hoosier Schoolboy, (Eggleston, Edward)
Hoot-Owl, (La Rue, Mabel G.)
Hop O' My Thumb, (N/A)
Hop on Pop, (Seuss, Dr.)
Hop, Skip & Fly, (Eberle, Irmengarde)
Hop, Skip & Jump, (Leet, Frank R.)
Hop, Skippy & Jump, (Vivienne)
Hop-High, the Goat, (Bannon, Laura)
Hopalong Cassidy, (Mulford, Clarence)
Hopalong Cassidy Returns, (Mulford, Clarence)
Hope Hathaway, (Parker, Frances)
Hopi Way, (Elting, Mary)
Hopping Knapsack, (Weil, Lisl)
Hoppity, (Mason, Miriam E.)
Horace, (Urquhart, Elizabeth)
Horatio, (Clymer, Eleanor)
Horizon is Calling, (Yashima, Taro)
Horn that Stopped the Band, (Parsons, Arthur)
Horned Helmet, (Treece, Henry)
Horns Everywhere, (Schmid, Eleonore)
Horrible, (Ungerer, Tomi)
Horse & his Boy, (Lewis, C.S.)
Horse Called Mystery, (Reynolds, Marjorie)
Horse Came Running, (DeJong, Meindert)
Horse Haven, (Caffrey, Nancy)
Horse Named Joe, (Gard, Robert)
Horse Show, (Anderson, C.W.)
Horse Who Lived Upstairs, (McGinley, Phyllis)

Horse Who had Picture in Paper, (McGinley, Phyllis)
Horse for the Island, (Bettina)
Horse in Danger, (Balch, Glenn)
Horse in the Camel Suit, (DuBois, W.P.)
Horse of Another Color, (Kravetz, Nathan)
Horse of Hurricane Hill, (Anderson, C.W.)
Horse on a Houseboat, (Bannon, Laura)
Horse that Liked Sandwiches, (Thompson, Vivian L.)
Horse that Swam Away, (Farley, Walter)
Horse that Takes Milk Around, (Sterling, Helen)
Horse to Remember, (Eames, Genevieve T.)
Horse to Ride, (Paull, Grace)
Horse with the Easter Bonnet, (Thayer, Jane)
Horse with the High-Heeled Shoes, (Slobodkin, Louis)
Horse's Tale, (Twain, Mark)
Horse, Foot & Dragoons, (Zogbaum, Rufus F.)
Horse-Tamer, (Farley, Walter)
Horses, (Hay, Timothy)
Horses & Colts, (Montgomery, F.T.)
Horses I've Known, (James, Will)
Horses Nine, (Ford, Sewell)
Horses and Americans, (Stong, Philip D.)
Horses are Folks, (Anderson, C.W.)
Horses of Destiny, (Downey, Fairfax)
Horses of Long Ago, (Ipcar, Dahlov)
Horses, Horses, Horses, (Fenner, Phyllis R.)
Horses, how They Came to Be, (May, Julian)
Hortense, the Cow for a Queen, (Carlson, Natalie S.)
Horton Hatches the Egg, (Seuss, Dr.)
Horton Hears a Who!, (Seuss, Dr.)
Host of Children, (Riley, James W.)
Hot Countries, (Waugh, Alec)
Hot Dog Man, (Lynch, Lorenzo)
Hotel Bemelmans, (Bemelmans, Ludwig)
Hotspur, (Mariana)
Houn' Dog, (Calhoun, Mary)
Hound Dog Moses & the Promised Land, (Edmonds, W.D.)
Hound Dog Zip to the Rescue, (Steele, William O.)
Hound of Florence, (Salten, Felix)
Hound of Ulster, (Sutcliff, Rosemary)
Hour of Magic, (Davies, William H.)
Hours of Gladness, (Maeterlinck, Maurice)
House Above the Trees, (Eliot, Ethel C.)
House Afire!, (Follett, Helen T.)
House Beyond the Meadow, (Behn, Harry)
House Boat on the Styx, (Bangs, John K.)
House Next Door: Utah, 1896, (Sorensen, Virginia)
House Under the Hill, (Means, Florence C.)
House Under the Sea, (Pemberton, Max)
House Without Windows, (Sandoz, Maurice)
House at 12 Rose Street, (Brodsky, Mimi)
House at Cherry Hill, (Weik, Mary H.)
House at Pooh Corner, (Milne, A.A.)
House by the Sea, (Swift, Hildegarde H.)
House for Elizabeth, (Marshall, Dean)
House in No-End Hollow, (Justus, May)
House in Robin Lane, (Voight, Virginia F.)
House in Turner Square, (Thwaite, Ann)
House in the Hedge, (Barbour, Ralph H.)
House in the Hoo, (Wood, Esther)
House in the Mountains, (Demuth, Averil)
House in the Tree, (Cone, Molly)
House in the Wood, (Grimm Bros.)
House of Arden, (Nesbit, Edith)
House of Cards, (Wolf, Alice S.)
House of Dies Drear, (Hamilton, Virginia)
House of Egremont, (Seawell, Molly E.)
House of Fancy, (Cradock, H.C.)

House of Flowers, House of Stars, (Montresor, Beni)
House of Four Seasons, (Duvoisin, Roger)
House of Hawley, (Peake, Elmore E.)
House of Her Own, (Allee, Marjorie H.)
House of Joy, (Housman, Laurence)
House of Mirth, (Wharton, Edith)
House of Pomegranates, (Wilde, Oscar)
House of Prayer, (Converse, Florence)
House of Sixty Fathers, (DeJong, Meindert)
House of Thirty Cats, (Calhoun, Mary)
House of Vanities, (Preston, Hayter)
House of a Hundred Windows, (Brown, Margaret W.)
House of a Thousand Candles, (Nicholson, Meredith)
House of the Black Ring, (Pattee, Fred L.)
House of the Dawn, (Ryan, Marah E.)
House of the Fifers, (Caudill, Rebecca)
House of the Red Fox, (Byrne, Miriam)
House of the Swan, (Coatsworth, Eliz.)
House on E. 88th Street, (Waber, Bernard)
House on Stilts, (Hazard, R.H.)
House that Grew, (Boston, Lucy M.)
House that Grew, (Molesworth, Mrs.)
House that Grew Smaller, (Bianco, Margery W.)
House that Jack Built, (Denslow, W.W.)
House that Jack Built, (N/A)
House with Red Sails, (Adelson, Leone)
House with the Silver Door, (Tappan, Eva M.)
House-Boat Summer, (Coatsworth, Eliz.)
Houseboat Girl, (Lenski, Lois)
Household Stories, (Grimm Bros.)
Household Tales, (Grimm Bros.)
Household of Sir Thomas More, (Manning, Anne)
Houses from the Sea, (Goudey, Alice)
How Animals Talk, (Long, William J.)
How Big am I?, (Heide, Florence P.)
How Big is Big?, (Schneider, Herman)
How Cinderella Was Able to Go..., (King, J.M.)
How Come Christmas, (Bradford, Roark)
How Come Elephants?, (Simont, Marc)
How Could You, Jean?, (Brainerd, Eleanor H.)
How Dear to My Heart, (McBride, Mary M.)
How Do You Travel?, (Schlein, Miriam)
How Fletcher was Hatched, (Devlin, Wende)
How God Fix Jonah, (Graham, Lorenz)
How I Tamed the Wild Squirrels, (Tyrell, Eleanor)
How Insects Grow, (Conklin, Gladys)
How It All Began, (Smalley, Janet)
How It Came About Stories, (Linderman, Frank B.)
How Joe the Bear & Sam..., (DeRegniers, B.)
How Little Lori Visited Times Square, (Vogel, Amos)
How Many Bears?, (Zirbes, Laura)
How Many Blocks is the World?, (Blue, Rose)
How Many Kisses Good Night?, (Monrad, Jean)
How Many Miles to Babylon?, (Fox, Paula)
How Medicine Man Cured Paleface...., (McGaw, J.B.)
How Percival Caught the Python, (Stutters, Percival)
How Percival Caught the Tiger, (Stutters, Percival)
How Punky Dunk Helped Old Prince, (Herr, Charlotte)
How Santa Found the Cobbler's Shop, (Harmon, M.)
How Sing Found the World is Round, (Reid, Sydney)
How Six Found Christmas, (Hyman, Trina S.)
How Summer Came to Canada, (Toye, William)
How it Happened, (Power, Rhoda)
How the Brothers Joined Cat Club, (Averill, Esther)
How the Buffalo Lost his Crown, (Beacom, John)
How the Camel Got his Hump, (Kipling, Rudyard)
How the Derrick Works, (Jones, Wilfred)
How the Grinch Stole Christmas, (Seuss, Dr.)

How the Leopard Got his Spots, (Kipling, Rudyard)
How the Mouse Deer Became King, (Bro, Marguerite)
How the People Sang the Mountains Up, (Leach, Maria)
How the Rhinoceros Got his Skin, (Kipling, Rudyard)
How the Two Ends Met, (Leonard, Mary F.)
How the Whale Became, (Hughes, Ted)
How they Carried the Goods, (Muller, Charles G.)
How they Carried the Mail, (Walker, Joseph)
How to Be a Nature Detective, (Selsam, Millicent)
How to Be a Puppeteer, (Boylan, Eleanor)
How to Become Extinct, (Cuppy, Will)
How to Catch a Crocodile, (Pack, Robert)
How to Find Happyland, (Van Dresser, Jasmine)
How to Get to First Base, (Simont, Marc)
How to Go about Laying an Egg, (Waber, Bernard)
How to Hide a Hippopotamus, (Croswell, Volney)
How to Know the Ferns, (Parsons, Frances T.)
How to Listen to Music, (Krehbiel, Henry E.)
How to Make a Garden Grow, (Browne, K.R.G.)
How to Make an Earthquake, (Krauss, Ruth)
How to Read a Rabbit, (Fritz, Jean)
How to Scare a Lion, (Stephenson, Dorothy)
How, Hippo, (Brown, Marcia)
Howard Pyle: A Chronicle, (Abbott, Charles D.)
Howards Go Sledding, (Wahl, Jan)
Hubert, (Stang, Wendy)
Hubert's Hair-Raising Adventure, (Peet, Bill)
Huckleberry Finn, (Twain, Mark)
Hudson Bay Express, (Davis, Robert)
Huff Puff Hickory Hill, (Budney, Blossom)
Huge Harold, (Peet, Bill)
Hugh Gwyeth: Roundhead Cavalier, (Dix, Beulah M.)
Hugh Thomson: His Art, (Spielmann, M.H.)
Hugo, (Gripe, Maria)
Huldah, (Cooke, Grace M.)
Hull-Down for Action, (Sperry, Armstrong)
Hullabaloo ABC, (Cleary, Beverly)
Human Side of Birds, (Dixon, Royal)
Humanities, (Vassos, Ruth)
Humbo the Hippo, (Berry, Erick)
Humerous Poems, (Hood, Thomas)
Humours of Golf, (Robinson, W. Heath)
Humphrey, (Flack, Marjorie)
Humpty & Dumpty Give a Fancy Dress Ball, (Byron, May)
Humpty Dumpty, (Mother Goose)
Humpty Dumpty & other Songs, (Mourat, Joseph)
Humpty Dumpty..., (Rey, Hans A.)
Humpty-Dumpty, (N/A)
Humpy, (Yershov, P.)
Humpy, Son of the Sands, (Williamson, Hamilton)
Hums of Pooh, (Fraser-Simson, H.)
Hunch, Munch and Crunch, (Norman, Charles)
Hunchback of Notre-Dame, (Hugo, Victor)
Hundred Dresses, (Estes, Eleanor)
Hundred Fables of La Fontaine, (La Fontaine, J.)
Hundred Trips to Storyland, (Bonner, Mary G.)
Hundred Tuftys, (Lilly, Jean)
Hundred and One Dalmations, (Smith, Dodie)
Hundreds and Hundreds of Pancakes, (Chalmers, Audrey)
Hungarian Fairy Book, (Pogany, Nebby)
Hungry Fred, (Fox, Paula)
Hungry Leprechaun, (Calhoun, Mary)
Hungry Moon, (Ross, Patricia)
Hungry Peter, (Byron, May)
Hungry Tiger of Oz, (Thompson, Ruth P.)
Hunlikely!, (Robinson, W. Heath)
Hunt for the Yule Log, (Morgan, Carol)
Hunt the Mountain Lion, (Tavo, Gus)

Hunted Piccaninnies, (Fleming, W.M.M.)
Hunting, (Paget, John O.)
Hunting of the Snark, (Carroll, Lewis)
Hunting with Mr. Jorrocks, (Surtees, Robert S.)
Huon of the Horn, (Norton, Andre)
Hurdy Gurdy Holiday, (Gale, Leah)
Hurdy-Gurdy Man, (Bianco, Margery W.)
Hurly Burly & the Knights, (Rugoff, Milton)
Hurrah for Freddie!, (Bright, Robert)
Hurrah, We're Outward Bound!, (Mother Goose)
Hurricane Yank, (Montgomery, R.)
Hurry Home, Candy, (DeJong, Meindert)
Hurry Hurry, (Hurd, Edith T.)
Hurry, Skurry & Flurry, (Buff, M.& C.)
Hurry, Spring!, (North, Sterling)
Husbands of Edith, (McCutcheon, George B.)
Hush Little Baby, (Aliki)
Hush, Jon!, (Gill, Joan)
Husky: Co-Pilot of the Pilgrim, (Montgomery, R.)
Hustle & Bustle, (Slobodkin, Louis)
Hymie's Fiddle, (Silverman, Mel)
I Am Better than You, (Lopshire, Robert M.)
I Am! Says the Lamb, (Roethke, Theodore)
I Can Count, (Memling, Carl)
I Can Lick 30 Tigers Today..., (Seuss, Dr.)
I Can't, Said the Ant, (Cameron, Polly)
I Caught a Lizard, (Conklin, Gladys)
I Discover Columbus, (Lawson, Robert)
I Feel the Same Way, (Moore, Lilian)
I Give You my Colt, (Kelsey, Alice)
I Go Out, (Rukeyser, Muriel)
I Go by Sea, I Go by Land, (Travers, Pamela L.)
I Had Trouble Getting to Solla Sollew, (Seuss, Dr.)
I Hate to Cook Book, (Bracken, Peg)
I Have Twenty Teeth - Do You?, (Kessler, Ethel)
I Have a Horse of My Own, (Zolotow, Charlotte)
I Heah de Voices Callin', (Gaines, Mary L.)
I Hear America Singing, (Barnes, Ruth A.)
I Know a City... Shippen, Kath. B.)
I Know a Lot of Things, (Rand, Ann)
I Know a Magic House, (Schwartz, Julius)
I Like Animals, (Baruch, Dorothy W.)
I Like Animals, (Ipcar, Dahlov)
I Like Automobiles, (Baruch, Dorothy W.)
I Like Caterpillars, (Conklin, Gladys)
I Like Red, (Bright, Robert)
I Like Trains, (Woolley, Catherine)
I Like Weather, (Fisher, Aileen)
I Like Winter, (Lenski, Lois)
I Love my Anteater with an A, (Ipcar, Dahlov)
I Married a Redhead, (Musselman, M.M.)
I Met a Man, (Ciardi, John)
I Never Knew that Before, (Bender, Eric)
I Often Wish, (Deutsch, Babette)
I Once Knew a Man, (Brandenberg, Franz)
I Play at the Beach, (Koch, Dorothy)
I Saw Three Ships, (Goudge, Elizabeth)
I Saw a Ship A-Sailing, (Montresor, Beni)
I Saw the Sea Come In, (Tresselt, Alvin)
I See What I See!, (Selden, George)
I See a Kitty, (Flack, Marjorie)
I See the Winds, (Mizumura, Kazue)
I Should Say So, (Flagg, James M.)
I Should have Stayed in Bed, (Lexau, Joan M.)
I Spy, (Beistle, Aldarilla)
I Spy, (Kirn, Ann)
I Think I Saw a Snail, (Hopkins, Lee B. (comp))
I Think I will Go to the Hospital, (Tamburine, Jean)

I Want to Fly, (Brenner, Anita)
I Want to Paint My Bathroom Blue, (Krauss, Ruth)
I Was Kissed by a Seal at the Zoo, (Palmer, Helen)
I Went for a Walk, (Bulla, Clyde R.)
I Went to the Animal Fair, (Cole, William)
I Will Adventure, (Gray, Eliz. J.)
I Will Tell You of a Town, (Reid, Alastair)
I Wish that I Had Duck Feet, (LeSieg, Theo)
I Wish, I Wish, (Weil, Lisl)
I Won't, said the King, (Jordan, Mildred)
I Wonder Why?, (Gordon, Elizabeth)
I Wonder Why?, (Scott-Gatty, Alfred)
I Would Like to be a Pony, (Baruch, Dorothy W.)
I Write It, (Krauss, Ruth)
I am Your Misfortune, (Rudolph, Marguerita)
I am the Darker Brother, (Adoff, Arnold (ed))
I'll Be You & You Be Me, (Krauss, Ruth)
I'll Fix Anthony, (Viorst, Judith)
I'll Show You Cats, (Bonsall, Crosby)
I'm Going to the Ocean, (Schick, Eleanor)
I'm Not a Cat, Said Emerald, (Thayer, Jane)
I'm Tired of Lions, (Gay, Zhenya)
I'm for You and You're for Me, (Watts, Mabel)
I, Adam, (Fritz, Jean)
I, Autobiography of a Cat, (White, Eliza O.)
I, Juan de Pareja, (DeTrevino, Elizabeth)
I, Momolu, (Graham, Lorenz)
I, Mouse, (Kraus, Robert)
I-A-Goo & his Forest Friends, (Ewing, Frank)
Ice Cream for Two, (Newberry, Clare T.)
Ice Dragon, (Postgate, Oliver)
Iceblink, (Montgomery, R.)
Iceland in Story and Pictures, (Bailey, Bernadine)
Icelandic Fairy Tales, (Hall, A.W. (ed.))
Ida Waugh's Alphabet Book, (Blanchard, Amy)
Ideal Fairy Tales, (Perrault, Charles)
Ideal Heads, (N/A)
Ideal Heads, (Waugh, Ida)
Ideals in Art, (Crane, Walter)
Idiot at Home, (Bangs, John K.)
Idle Idyls, (Wells, Carolyn)
Idy, the Fox-Chasing Cow, (Margolis, Ellen)
Idyll of All Fool's Day, (Bacon, Josephine D.)
Idylls of the King, (Tennyson, Alfred)
Idyls and Pastorals, (Thaxter, Celia)
Idyls of the Months, (Lathbury, M.A.)
If I Could Fly, (Hubbell, Rose S.)
If I Drove a Truck, (Young, Miriam)
If I Flew a Plane, (Young, Miriam)
If I Had a Boat, (Smith, William J.)
If I Had a Lion, (Skorpen, Liesel)
If I Ran the Circus, (Seuss, Dr.)
If I Ran the Zoo, (Seuss, Dr.)
If I Were Captain, (Floethe, Richard)
If I Were a Mother, (Mizumura, Kazue)
If I were a Bird, (Conklin, Gladys)
If Wishes Were Horses, (Robertson, Keith)
If You Grew Up with Abraham Lincoln, (McGovern, A.)
If You Lived in Colonial Times, (McGovern, Ann)
If You're a Bear, (Udry, Janice M.)
Igloo, (Walden, Jane B.)
Ilenka, (Kingman, Lee)
Ill-Made Knight, (White, Terence H.)
Illegitimate Sonnets, (Moore, Merrill)
Illustrated Bible Story Book, (Loveland, Mrs. S.)
Illustrations of Cynthia, (Berry, Erick)
Imagina, (Ford, Julia E.)
Imagination's Other Place, (Plotz, Helen)

Imitation of Christ, (Kempis, Thomas)
Immensee, (Storm, Theodor)
Immortal Moment, (Sinclair, May)
Imogen, (Molesworth, Mrs.)
Imp & The Angel, (Daskam, Josephine)
Impassioned Clay, (Powys, Llewelyn)
Impeachment of President Israels, (Copley, Frank B.)
Impertinent Poems, (Cooke, Edmund V.)
Important Book, (Brown, Margaret W.)
Improving Songs for Anxious Children, (Carpenter, John)
Impudent Comedian, (Moore, Frank F.)
Impunity Jane, (Godden, Rumer)
In & Out, (Robinson, Tom P.)
In & Out of the Nursery, (Rowland, Eva E.)
In ALL France, (France, Anatole)
In Alfred's Days, (Creswick, Paul)
In Arcady, (Mabie, Hamilton W.)
In Beaver World, (Mills, Enos A.)
In Blue Bird Time, (Donaldson, Ellen M.)
In Came Horace, (Beattie, Janet)
In Camp with a Tin Soldier, (Bangs, John K.)
In Cat & Dog Land, (Wain, Louis)
In Childhood Land, (Page, Margaret)
In Childhood's Country, (Moulton, Louise C.)
In Clean Hay, (Kelly, Eric P.)
In Colonial Days, (Hawthorne, Nathaniel)
In Cupid's Court, (Warren, Ina R.)
In Dickens' London, (Smith, Francis H.)
In Enemy Hands, (Belting, Natalia)
In Fairyland, (Chisholm, Louey)
In France, (Clement, Marguerite)
In Happy Hollow, (Montgomery, R.)
In Happy Valley, (Fox, John Jr.)
In Laughland, (Mayer, Henry)
In My Garden, (Zolotow, Charlotte)
In My Mother's House, (Clark, Ann N.)
In Nature's Image, (Adams, W.I.L.)
In Navajo Land, (Armer, Laura A.)
In Nurseryland, (Braine/Floyd)
In Old New York, (Janvier, Thomas A.)
In One Door and Out the Other, (Fisher, Aileen)
In One Ear, (Sullivan, Frank)
In Our Town, (Runyon, Damon)
In Pastures New, (Ade, George)
In Place of Katia, (Kay, Mara)
In Place of Profit, (Ward, Harry F.)
In Powder & Crinoline, (Quiller-Couch, A.)
In Russet & Silver, (Gosse, Edmund)
In Savage Africa, (Glave, E.J.)
In School, (Hautzig, Esther)
In Search of a Whale, (Eckert, Allan W.)
In Shadow Town, (Day, Leigh G.)
In Sight of Eden, (Vercel, Roger)
In Simpkinsville, (Stuart, Ruth M.)
In Sunshine Land, (Thomas, Edith M.)
In The Bishop's Carriage, (Michelson, Miriam)
In Tumbledown Town, (Nesbit, Wilbur D.)
In Tune with the Infinite, (Trine, Ralph W.)
In a Car of Gold, (Gray, P.L.)
In a City Garden, (Aitken, James R.)
In a Forgotten Place, (Orgel, Doris)
In a Glass Darkly, (LeFanu, J. Sheridan)
In a Pumpkin Shell, (Anglund, Joan W.)
In a Spring Garden, (Lewis, Richard)
In the Arms of the Mountain, (Seeman, Elizabeth)
In the Beginning, (Evers, Alf)
In the Beginning, (Van Eyssen, Shirley)
In the Beginning..., (Bible)

In the Border Country, (Bacon, Josephine D.)
In the Child's World, (Poulsson, Emilie)
In the Closed Room, (Burnett, Frances H.)
In the Court of King Arthur, (Lowe, Samuel E.)
In the Days of Giants, (Brown, Abbie F.)
In the Days of the Han, (Jagendorf, Moritz)
In the Deep Woods, (Paine, Albert B.)
In the Fairy Ring, (Harrison, Florence)
In the Fairyland of America, (Quick, Herbert)
In the Flaky Frosty Morning, (Kuskin, Karla)
In the Fog, (Davis, Richard H.)
In the Forest, (Ets, Marie H.)
In the Great Apache Forest, (Schultz, James W.)
In the Green Forest, (Pyle, Katharine)
In the Heart of the Rockies, (Henty, G.A.)
In the Key of Blue, (Symonds, John)
In the Land of Diggeldy Dan, (Norwood, Edwin P.)
In the Land of Make-Believe, (Smith, E. Boyd)
In the Land of Nod, (Marzetti, Ada C.)
In the Middle of the Night, (Fisher, Aileen)
In the Middle of the Trees, (Kuskin, Karla)
In the Miz, (Ward, Grace)
In the Morning, (N/A)
In the Morning Glow, (Gilson, Roy R.)
In the Night, (Showers, Paul)
In the Night Kitchen, (Sendak, Maurice)
In the Park, (Hautzig, Esther)
In the Reign of Queen Dick, (Wells, Carolyn)
In the Rockies with Kit Carson, (McIntyre, John T.)
In the Saddle with Uncle Bill, (James, Will)
In the Story World, (Harrison, Elizabeth)
In the Tiger's Lair, (Miller, Leo E.)
In the Woods, (Hart, Ruby)
In the Woods and on the Shore, (Ware, Richard D.)
In the Woods, In the Meadow, In the Sky, (Fisher, Aileen)
In-Between Miya, (Uchida, Yoshiko)
Inatuck's Friend, (Morrow, Suzanne)
Inch by Inch, (Lionni, Leo)
Incompleat Angler, (Burnand, Francis (ed))
Incomplete Amorist, (Nesbit, Edith)
Increase Rabbit, (McCready, Thomas L.)
Incredible Adventures/Professor Brawnestawm, (Hunter, N.)
Incredible Journey, (Burnford, Sheila)
Incubator Baby, (Butler, Ellis P.)
Incurable Filibuster, (Lamb, Dean I.)
India Impressions, (Crane, Walter)
India Rubber Jack, (Richardson, W.C.F.)
India's Gods & Heroes, (Monro, W.D.)
Indian & Scout, (Brereton, Frederick)
Indian Boyhood, (Eastman, Charles A.)
Indian Boys & Girls, (Haines, Alice C.)
Indian Brother, (Coryell, Hubert)
Indian Captive, (Lenski, Lois)
Indian Child Life, (Deming, Therese O.)
Indian Children of America, (Farquhar, Margaret)
Indian Encounters, (Coatsworth, Eliz.)
Indian Fairy Book, (N/A)
Indian Fairy Stories, (Mackenzie, Donald A.)
Indian Fairy Tales, (Jacobs, Joseph (ed))
Indian Hill, (Bulla, Clyde R.)
Indian Hunting Grounds, (Emerson, Caroline)
Indian Legends in Rhyme, (Moon, Grace P.)
Indian Mound Farm, (Coatsworth, Eliz.)
Indian Myth & Legend, (Mackenzie, Donald A.)
Indian Old-Man Stories, (Linderman, Frank B.)
Indian Paint, (Balch, Glenn)
Indian Saddle-Up, (Balch, Glenn)
Indian Story Book, (Wilson, Richard)

Indian Summer, (Clarkson, L.)
Indian Summer, (Monjo, Ferdinand N.)
Indian Tales, (Kipling, Rudyard)
Indian Twins, (Perkins, Lucy F.)
Indian Why Stories, (Linderman, Frank B.)
Indian, Indian, (Zolotow, Charlotte)
Indians, (Tunis, Edwin B.)
Indians & Cowboys, (Tousey, Sanford)
Indians Knew, (Pine, Tillie S.)
Indians of Yesterday, (Gridley, Marion)
Indians of the Plains, (Tousey, Sanford)
Indians of the Wigwams, (Deming, Therese O.)
Indians: The First Americans, (Martin, Patricia)
Indigo Hill, (Lattimore, Eleanor)
Indigo Treasure, (Rogers, Frances)
Indoor Noisy Book, (Brown, Margaret W.)
Indy and Mr. Lincoln, (Belting, Natalia)
Inemak: Little Greenlander, (Lide, Alice A.)
Inga of Porcupine Mine, (Stone, Caroline R.)
Inger Johanne's Lively Doings, (Zwilgmeyer, Dikken)
Ingoldsby Legends, (Ingoldsby, Thomas)
Initials Only, (Green, Anna K.)
Injun Babies, (Dixon, Maynard)
Innocence of Father Brown, (Chesterton, G.K.)
Innocent Industries, (Von Gottschalck, O.)
Insect Fairies, (Webb, M. St. John)
Intimations of Immortality..., (Wordsworth, William)
Intrusion of Jimmy, (Wodehouse, P.G.)
Invincible Louisa, (Meigs, Cornelia L.)
Invisible Island, (Marshall, Dean)
Inway Investigators, (Yolen, Jane)
Iolanthe..., (Gilbert, W.S.)
Iole, (Chambers, Robert)
Iona, (Erskine, Payne)
Ionia..., (Craig, Alexander)
Iorana!, (Gibbings, Robert)
Irene of Tundra Towers, (Burrows, Elizabeth)
Irish Fairy Book, (Graves, Alfred P.)
Irish Fairy Tales, (N/A)
Irish Fairy Tales, (Stephens, James)
Irish Fairy and Folk Tales, (Yeats, Wm. Butler)
Irish Twins, (Perkins, Lucy F.)
Irish Ways, (Barlow, Jane)
Iron Charm, (Williamson, Joanne)
Iron Duke, (Tunis, John R.)
Iron Giant, (Hughes, Ted)
Iron Trail, (Beach, Rex)
Is That a Happy Hippopotamus?, (Morrison, Sean)
Is There a Doctor in the Barn?, (Yates, Elizabeth)
Is There a Mouse in the House?, (Gibson, Josephine)
Is This You?, (Krauss, Ruth)
Is it Blue as a Butterfly?, (Kalusky, Rebecca)
Is it Hard? Is it Easy?, (Green, Mary M.)
Isabel's Noel, (Yolen, Jane)
Isabella..., (Keats, John)
Isabelle and the Library Cat, (Bason, Lillian)
Ishi, Last of his Tribe, (Kroeber, Theodora)
Ishybushy & Topknot, (Darwin, Bernard)
Isidro, (Austin, Mary)
Isla Heron, (Richards, Laura E.)
Island Boy, (Harry, Robert)
Island Boy, (Holdridge, Betty)
Island City, (Davis, Lavinia R.)
Island Garden, (Thaxter, Celia)
Island Impossible, (Morgan, Harriet)
Island Mackenzie, (Williams, Ursula)
Island Stallion's Fury, (Farley, Walter)
Island of Enchantment, (Forman, Justus M.)

Island of Enchantment, (Perry, Catherine)
Island of Fish in the Trees, (Wuorio, Eva-Lis)
Island of the Blue Dolphins, (O'Dell, Scott)
Island of the Mighty, (Colum, Padraic)
Islanders, (Pertwee, Rowland)
Islands in the Sky, (Clarke, Arthur)
Isle of Que, (Singmaster, Elsie)
Isn't It So?, (Murphy, Nettie S.)
Isn't it Funny, (N/A)
Issun Boshi, the Inchling, (Ishii, Momoko)
It All Began with Drip, Drip, Drip, (Lexau, Joan M.)
It Doesn't Always Have to Rhyme, (Merriam, Eve)
It Looks Like This, (Webber, Irma E.)
It Never is Dark, (Heide, Florence P.)
It Shouldn't Happen, (Freeman, Don)
It Was the Road to Jericho, (Johnston, Annie F.)
It is Night, (Rowand, Phyllis)
It's About Time, (Schlein, Miriam)
It's Like this, Cat, (Neville, Emily C.)
It's Me O Lord..., (Kent, Rockwell)
It's Mine!, (Bonsall, Crosby)
It's Nesting Time, (Gans, Roma)
It's Perfectly True..., (Andersen, Hans C.)
It's Snowing, (Hurd, Edith T.)
It's Time Now!, (Tresselt, Alvin)
It's a Secret!, (Deutsch, Babette)
Italian Backgrounds, (Wharton, Edith)
Italian Fairy Book, (MacDonell, Anne)
Italian Fairy Tales, (Faulkner, Georgene)
Italian Holiday, (Bemelmans, Ludwig)
Italian Hours, (James, Henry)
Italian Peepshow, (Farjeon, Eleanor)
Italian Twins, (Perkins, Lucy F.)
Italian Villas and their Gardens, (Wharton, Edith)
Ivan the Iron Horse, (Rohmer, Albert)
Ivanhoe, (Scott, Walter)
Ivanko and the Dragon, (Bloch, Marie (tran))
Ivanov Seven, (Janeway, Elizabeth)
Ivory Child, (Haggard, H. Rider)
Ivory Trail, (Mundy, Talbot)
J. Cole, (Gellibrand, Emma)
Jacanapes, (Ewing, Juliana H.)
Jack & the Bean Stalk, (Denslow, W.W.)
Jack & the Bean Stalk, (Tennyson, H.)
Jack & the Beanstalk, (De La Mare, Walter)
Jack & the Beanstalk, (N/A)
Jack Among the Indians, (Grinnell, George B.)
Jack Ballister's Fortunes, (Pyle, Howard)
Jack Finds Gold, (Tousey, Sanford)
Jack Frost Arrives on Butternut Hill, (N/A)
Jack Hall, (Grant, Robert)
Jack Holburn, (Garfield, Leon)
Jack Horner's Pie, (Lenski, Lois)
Jack Jingling in Jungleland, (Sherwood, E. Hugh)
Jack Mack, (Smith, Robert P.)
Jack O'Health, Peg O'Joy, (Herben, Beatrice S.)
Jack Pumpkinhead of Oz, (Thompson, Ruth P.)
Jack Tar, (Larson, Jean R.)
Jack and Jill, (Alcott, Louisa M.)
Jack and Jill, (Aldin, Cecil)
Jack and Jim, (Slobodkina, Esphyr)
Jack and the Check Book, (Bangs, John K.)
Jack and the Three Sillies, (Chase, Richard)
Jack in the Pulpit, (Whittier, John G.)
Jack in the Rockies, (Grinnell, George B.)
Jack of All Trades, (Bell, John J.)
Jack of Hearts, (French, Fiona)
Jack the Giant Killer, (N/A)

Jack the Giant Killer, (Thomson, Hugh)
Jack the Giant-Killer, (Latham, Jean L.)
Jack, the Young Ranchman, (Grinnell, George B.)
Jackdaw of Rheims, (Ingoldsby, Thomas)
Jackie Boy in Rainbowland, (Hill, William)
Jacks of All Trades, (Birdsall, Katharine N.)
Jacob Faithful, (Marryat, Frederick)
Jacoble Tells the Truth, (Weil, Lisl)
Jacqueline Kennedy Onassis, (Martin, Patricia)
Jake, (Kitt, Tamara)
Jamaica, (Henderson, John)
Jamaica Johnny, (Hader, B.& E.)
Jamba the Elephant, (Waldeck, Theodore)
Jamboree of Laughter, (Robinson, W. Heath)
James & the Giant Peach, (Dahl, Roald)
James & the Rain, (Kuskin, Karla)
James Madison, (Martin, Patricia)
Jamesville Jets, (Jackson, C. Paul)
Jamie Looks, (Holl, Adelaide)
Jan & Wonderful Mouth-Organ, (Alger, Leclaire)
Jan and the Reindeer, (Palazzo, Tony)
Jan of the Windmill, (Ewing, Juliana H.)
Jane Cable, (McCutcheon, George B.)
Jane Eyre, (Bronte, Charlotte)
Jane Jones and Some Others, (King, Ben)
Jane of Lantern Hill, (Montgomery, Lucy M.)
Jane's Blanket, (Miller, Arthur)
Jane's Island, (Allee, Marjorie H.)
Jane's Silver Chair, (La Farge, Phyllis)
Jane, Joseph and John, (Bergengren, Ralph)
Janet & the Fairies, (Danks, Bertha M.)
Janet's College Career, (Blanchard, Amy E.)
Janet: Her Winter in Quebec, (Ray, Anna C.)
Janey, (Fox, Frances M.)
Janie Belle, (Tarry, Ellen)
Janko's Wish, (Varga, Judy)
Jannot, a French Rabbit, (Marokvia, Mireille)
Japan, (Menpes, Mortimer)
Japanese Blossom, (Watanna, Onoto)
Japanese Child Life, (Haines, Alice C.)
Japanese Fairy Tales, (Hearn, Lafcadio)
Japanese Fairy Tales, (Williston, Teresa P.)
Japanese Twins, (Perkins, Lucy F.)
Japhet in Search of a Father, (Marryat, Frederick)
Japonette, (Chambers, Robert)
Japonica, (Arnold, Edwin)
Jareb, (Powell, Miriam)
Jared's Island, (DeAngeli, Marguerite)
Jasmine: Story of Present Day Persia, (Ratzesberger, A.)
Jason & the Princess, (Colvile, Kathleen)
Jasper, (Lattimore, Eleanor)
Jasper Makes Music, (Horvath, Betty)
Jasper the Drummin' Boy, (Burroughs, Margaret)
Jasper the Gypsy Dog, (Kahmann, Chesley)
Jasper, a Story for Children, (Molesworth, Mrs.)
Jaufry the Knight & Fair Brunissende, (Jaufre)
Java Jungle Tales, (DeLeeuw, Hendrik)
Jaw Breaker's Alphabet, (Tietjens, Eunice H.)
Jazz Man, (Weik, Mary H.)
Jean & Johnny, (Cleary, Beverly)
Jean & Jon are Six, (Quigg, Jane)
Jean-Claude's Island, (Carlson, Natalie S.)
Jeanne d' Arc, (DeMonvel, M.B.)
Jeanne d'Arc, (Fisher, Aileen)
Jeanne d'Arc: Warrior Saint, (Eaton, Jeanette)
Jeanne-Marie Counts her Sheep, (Francoise)
Jeanne-Marie In Gay Paris, (Francoise)
Jeanne-Marie and her Golden Bird, (Phillips, Ethel C.)

Jed, (Burchard, Peter)
Jeems the Door Keeper, (Brown, Dr. John)
Jeff and Mr. James' Pond, (Meeks, Esther)
Jefferson Davis, (Martin, Patricia)
Jeffie's Party, (Zion, Gene)
Jellybeans for Breakfast, (Young, Miriam)
Jemmie, Kitten from Maine, (Wheeler, Eleanor)
Jennie's Hat, (Keats, Ezra J.)
Jennifer & Josephine, (Peet, Bill)
Jennifer, Hecate, Macbeth...., (Konigsburg, E.L.)
Jenny, (Kennedy, Mary)
Jenny & the Wonderful Jeep, (Scott, Sally)
Jenny Jones and Skid, (Quigg, Jane)
Jenny Wren's Boarding House, (Otis, James)
Jenny's... [All titles], (Averill, Esther)
Jenny: Bus that Nobody Loved, (Dolbier, Maurice)
Jeptha, (Buchanan, George)
Jeptha and the New People, (Vance, Marguerite)
Jeremy, (Walpole, Hugh)
Jeremy Mouse Book, (Scarry, Patricia)
Jeremy's Isle, (Lattimore, Eleanor)
Jerome Anthony, (Evans, Eva K.)
Jerome, A Poor Man, (Wilkins, Mary E.)
Jerry & Pony Express, (Tousey, Sanford)
Jerry Juddikins, (Addington, Sarah)
Jerry Junior, (Webster, Jean)
Jerry Muskrat Wins Respect, (Burgess, Thornton)
Jerry Muskrat at Home, (Burgess, Thornton)
Jerry and the Pusa, (Lattimore, Eleanor)
Jerry the Jeep, (Hurd, Edith T.)
Jersey Boy in the Revolution, (Tomlinson, Everett)
Jersey Street and Jersey Lane, (Bunner, H.C.)
Jessica's Journal, (Reynolds, Jessica)
Jesus of the Emerald, (Stratton-Porter, Gene)
Jesus' Story, (Bible)
Jew at Home, (Pennell, Joseph)
Jewel Story Book, (Evans, Florence A.)
Jewel Weed, (Winter, Alice A.)
Jewel's Story Book, (Burnham, Clara L.)
Jeweled Sea, (Hartwell, James (ed))
Jeweled Toad, (Johnston, Isabel M.)
Jewish Fairy Book, (Friedlander, Gerald)
Jewish Sabbath, (Cone, Molly)
Jewish Tales, (Sacher-Masoch, L.)
Jexium Island, (Grattan, Madeleine)
Jezebel the Jeep, (Downey, Fairfax)
Jiggy Likes Nantucket, (Quigg, Jane)
Jiji Lou, (Mayol, Lurline B.)
Jill & the Applebird House, (Holberg, Ruth)
Jim & the Beanstalk, (Briggs, Raymond)
Jim Davis, (Masefield, John)
Jim Tiger, (Hough, Charlotte)
Jim at the Corner, (Farjeon, Eleanor)
Jim the Cat, (Colby, Jean P.)
Jiminy Cricket, (Disney, Walt)
Jimmy & Jemima, (Sewell, Helen)
Jimmy Takes Vanishing Lessons, (Brooks, Walter)
Jimmy has Lost his Cap..., (Munari, Bruno)
Jimmy the Groceryman, (Miller, Jane)
Jimmy's Shoes, (Treffinger, Carolyn)
Jimsey, (Van Dresser, Jasmine)
Jingle Book, (Dana, Mary P.)
Jingle Book, (N/A)
Jingle Book, (Wells, Carolyn)
Jingle Jangle Jumbly Lays..., (Wightman, Francis P.)
Jingle Jangle Rhyme Book, (Simmons, Henry B.)
Jingle of a Jap, (Thurston, Clara B.)

Jinglebob, (Rollins, Philip A.)
Jingles, Jokes & Funny Folks, (Bingham, Clifton)
Jinks of Jayson Valley, (Rechnitzer, F.E.)
Jinx Ship, (Pease, Howard)
Jo and Uncle George Kritters, (Aunt Jo)
Jo's Boys..., (Alcott, Louisa M.)
Jo-Yo's Idea, (Elliot, Kathleen)
Joan & the Three Deer, (Medary, Marjorie)
Joan Wanted a Kitty, (Gemmill, Jane B.)
Joan in Flowerland, (Tarrant, Margaret)
Joan of Arc, (DeMonvel, M.B.)
Joan of Arc, (Holmes, Mabel D.)
Joan of Arc, (Johnston, Johanna)
Joan of Arc, (Madison, Lucy F.)
Joan's Door, (Farjeon, Eleanor)
Joanjo, (Balet, Jan B.)
Jock Barefoot, (Lindsay, Maud)
Jock O'Dreams, (Lippmann, Julie M.)
Jock and Some Others, (Waylett, Richard)
Jock of the Bushveld, (Fitzpatrick, Percy)
Jock the King's Pony, (Johns, Rowland)
Jock the Scot, (Rosman, Alice G.)
Jock's Castle, (Gibson, Katharine)
Jock's Island, (Coatsworth, Eliz.)
Jockeys, Crooks and Kings, (O'Connor, Winfield)
Joe Bean, (Agle, Nan H.)
Joe Buys Nails, (Wiese, Kurt)
Joe and the Snow, (DePaola, Tomie)
Joel & the Wild Goose, (Sandburg, Helga)
Joey's Cat, (Burch, Robert)
Johann Sebastian Bach, (Bunn, Harriet)
John Barleycorn, (London, Jack)
John Billington, Friend of Squanto, (Bulla, Clyde R.)
John Brown's Body, (Benet, Stephen)
John Burningham's ABC, (Burningham, John)
John Dough and the Cherub, (Baum, L. Frank)
John Ermine of the Yellowstone, (Remington, Frederic)
John Fitzgerald Kennedy, (Martin, Patricia)
John Gayther's Garden..., (Stockton, Frank)
John Hassall, R.I., (Johnson, A.E.)
John Henry, (Bradford, Roark)
John Henry & Double-Jointed Steam Drill, (Shapiro, Irwin)
John Henry Davis, (Leaf, Munro)
John Henry Smith, (Adams, Frederick)
John Henry and his Hammer, (Felton, Harold)
John Henry, Rambling Black Ulysses, (Bowman, James C.)
John Henry: American Legend, (Keats, Ezra J.)
John J. Plenty & Fiddler Dan, (Ciardi, John)
John John Twilliger, (Wondriska, William)
John March, Southerner, (Cable, George W.)
John Marshall, (Martin, Patricia)
John Marvel, Assistant, (Page, Thomas N.)
John Paul Jones: Fighting Sailor, (Sperry, Armstrong)
John Phillip Sousa: Marching Boy, (Weil, Ann Y.)
John Quincy Adams: Boy Patriot, (Weil, Ann Y.)
John Rattling-Gourd of Big Cove, (Bell, Corydon)
John Rawn, Prominent Citizen, (Hough, Emerson)
John Sevier, Pioneer Boy, (Steele, William O.)
John Tabor's Ride, (Lent, Blair)
John Wesley, (McNeer, May)
John and the Rarey, (Wells, Rosemary)
John of Pudding Lane, (Hunt, Mabel L.)
John of the Woods, (Brown, Abbie F.)
Johnnie, (Laughlin, Elmer O.)
Johnny Apple-Seed, (Atkinson, Eleanor)
Johnny Appleseed, (Lindsay, Vachel)
Johnny Blossom, (Zwilgmeyer, Dikken)
Johnny Crow('s)... [All titles], (Brooke, L. Leslie)

Johnny Goes to the Fair, (Lenski, Lois)
Johnny Hong of Chinatown, (Bulla, Clyde R.)
Johnny Jack & his Beginnings, (Buck, Pearl S.)
Johnny Lion's Bad Day, (Hurd, Edith T.)
Johnny Lion's Book, (Hurd, Edith T.)
Johnny Littlejohn, (Hurd, Edith T.)
Johnny Maple-Leaf, (Tresselt, Alvin)
Johnny Mouse & Wishing Stick, (Gruelle, Johnny)
Johnny Nut & Golden Goose, (Lang, Andrew)
Johnny Tremain, (Forbes, Esther)
Johnny and his Mule, (Credle, Ellis)
Johnny the Clockmaker, (Ardizzone, Edward)
Johnny-Up and Johnny-Down, (Hunt, Mabel L.)
Joie, Tommie & Kittie Kat, (Garis, Howard)
Joji and the Amanojaku, (Lifton, Betty)
Joji and the Dragon, (Lifton, Betty)
Joking Man, (Flora, James)
Jolly Animals, (Gaggin, Eva R.)
Jolly Chinee, (Veale, E.)
Jolly Jack Horner, (Lightfoot, Beryl H.)
Jolly Jingle Picture Book, (Jackson, Leroy F.)
Jolly Jungle Jingles, (Amend, Ottillie)
Jolly Kid Alphabet, (Lamb, Tom)
Jolly Kid Book, (Nesbit, Wilbur D.)
Jolly Little Clown, (Pease, Eleanor F.)
Jolly Old Shadow Man, (Kay, Gertrude A.)
Jolly Old Sports, (N/A)
Jolly Old Whistle, (Williams, Herschel)
Jolly Polly Stories, (Smith, Gertrude)
Jolly Rhymes of Mother Goose, (Piper, Watty (ed))
Jolly Tailor, (Borski, Lucia M.)
Jon the Unlucky, (Coatsworth, Eliz.)
Jonah, (Nathan, Robert)
Jonah, the Fisherman, (Zimnik, Reiner)
Jonathan & the Rainbow, (Blanck, Jacob)
Jonathan Bing, (Brown, Beatrice C.)
Jonathan Goes West, (Meader, Stephen W.)
Jonathan Visits the White House, (Benchley, Peter)
Jonnikin and the Flying Basket, (Manning-Sanders, Ruth)
Jorinda and Joringel, (Grimm Bros.)
Jorrock's on 'Unting, (Surtees, Robert S.)
Jory's Cove, (Bice, Clare)
Jose's Christmas Secret, (Lexau, Joan M.)
Josefina February, (Ness, Evaline M.)
Joseph and Koza, (Singer, Isaac B.)
Joseph and his Brothers, (Petersham, Maud)
Joseph's Yard, (Keeping, Charles)
Josephine, (Coyle, Kathleen)
Josephine, (Gripe, Maria)
Josephine('s)... [Many titles], (Cradock, H.C.)
Josey & the Chipmunk, (Reid, Sydney)
Josie and the Snow, (Buckley, Helen E.)
Josie's Buttercup, (Buckley, Helen E.)
Jothy: Story of South Indian Jungle, (Wyckoff, C.C.)
Journey Between Worlds, (Engdahl, Sylvia)
Journey Cake, (McMeekin, Isabel)
Journey Cake, Ho!, (Sawyer, Ruth)
Journey Outside, (Steele, Mary Q.)
Journey from Peppermint Street, (DeJong, Meindert)
Journey in Other Worlds, (Astor, John J.)
Journey in Search of Christmas, (Wister, Owen)
Journey into America, (Peattie, Donald C.)
Journey of Bangwell Put, (Mariana)
Journey of Joy, (Blanchard, Amy E.)
Journey of the Kiss, (DePaola, Tomie)
Journey of the Toys, (Rahr, Ruth)
Journey to Jericho, (O'Dell, Scott)
Journey to the Garden Gate, (Townsend, Ralph M.)

Journey to the Sea, (Holl, Adelaide)
Journey with Jonah: One Act Play, (L'Engle, Madeleine)
Journeys in Storyland, (Seegmiller, Wilhelmia)
Journeys of Sebastian, (Krahn, Fernando)
Journeys to Baghdad, (Brooks, Charles S.)
Joy & the Christmas Angel, (Bianco, Pamela)
Joy to the World, (Sawyer, Ruth)
Joyous Aztecs, (Francis, J.G.)
Joyous Guests, (Lindsay, Maud)
Joyous Story of Toto, (Richards, Laura E.)
Joyous Travelers, (Lindsay, Maud)
Ju-Ju and his Friends, (Van Vrooman, Maria)
Juan, (Stolz, Mary S.)
Juan and Juanita, (Baylor, Frances C.)
Juan and the Asuangs, (Aruego, Jose)
Juanita, (Politi, Leo)
Jubilant for Sure, (Lansing, Elisabeth H.)
Jude the Obscure, (Hardy, Thomas)
Judgment of Eve, (Sinclair, May)
Judith Lankester, (Allee, Marjorie H.)
Judith and Jane, (Jewett, Eleanore)
Judith of Bethulia, (Aldrich, Thomas B.)
Judy and Chris, (Govan, Christine)
Judy and her Turtle Osmond, (Quigg, Jane)
Judy of the Whale Gates, (Burrows, Elizabeth)
Judy's Baby, (Scott, Sally)
Judy's Journey, (Lenski, Lois)
Judy's Summer Adventure, (Scott, Sally)
Juggernaut of the Rangers, (Strickland, Harold)
Julia Bride, (James, Henry)
Julie's Heritage, (Marshall, Catherine)
Juliette Low, (Pace, Mildred M.)
Julio, (Tyman, Loretta)
Juma of the Hills, (Berry, Erick)
Jumble Book, (Cory, David)
Jump Frog Jump, (Martin, Patricia)
Jump Lively, Jeff!, (Darby, Ada C.)
Jump to Glory Jane, (Meredith, George)
Jump-Shy, (Houston, Joan)
Jumper, (Kalashnikoff, N.)
Jumper Goes to School, (Parish, Peggy)
Jumping Frog, (Twain, Mark)
Jumping Kangaroo & Apple-Butter Cat, (Harrington, J.)
Jumping Lions of Borneo, (Dunne, John W.)
Jumping Mouse, (Freschet, Berniece)
Jumping-Off Place, (McNeely, Marion H.)
Jumpy the Kangaroo, (Howard, Janet)
June Romance, (Gale, Norman)
Juneau: Sleigh Dog, (Lathrop, West)
Jungle Babies, (Kaigh-Eustace, E.)
Jungle Beasts and Men, (Mukerji, Dhan G.)
Jungle Book, (Kipling, Rudyard)
Jungle Journey, (Waldeck, JoBesse)
Jungle Jumble, (Surany, Anico)
Jungle Man & his Animals, (Wells, Carveth)
Jungle Picnic, (Webb, Clifford)
Jungle River, (Pease, Howard)
Jungle School, (Hamer, Sam H.)
Jungle Twins, (Roberts, Irma)
Junior Officer of the Watch, (Zogbaum, Rufus F.)
Junior Starke, Poundman, (Righter, Linwood)
Junior, Colored Boy of Charleston, (Lattimore, Eleanor)
Junior, the Spoiled Cat, (Kraus, Robert)
Juniper Farm, (Bazin, Rene)
Junk Day on Juniper Street, (Moore, Lilian)
Junket, (White, Anne H.)
Junket is Nice, (Kunhardt, Dorothy)
Jupie the Wise Old Owl, (McCoy, Neely)

Just Across the Street, (Field, Rachel)
Just Among Friends, (Aldin, Cecil)
Just Because of You, (Nesbit, Wilbur D.)
Just Beyond London, (Maxwell, G.S.)
Just Jenifer, (Lambert, Janet)
Just Like Abraham Lincoln, (Waber, Bernard)
Just Like David, (DeAngeli, Marguerite)
Just Like Everyone Else, (Kuskin, Karla)
Just Like Me, (Weisgard, Leonard)
Just Me, (Ets, Marie H.)
Just Peggy, (Beistle, Aldarilla)
Just Plain Maggie, (Beim, Lorraine)
Just Rhymes, (Loomis, Charles B.)
Just So Stories..., (Kipling, Rudyard)
Just You, (Gordon, Elizabeth)
Just for Fun..., (N/A)
Just for Fun: Humerous Stories & Poems, (Hazeltine, Alice)
Just for You, (Croll, Pauline)
Justin Morgan had a Horse, (Henry, Marguerite)
Kabumpo in Oz, (Thompson, Ruth P.)
Kalak of the Ice, (Kjelgaard, Jim)
Kaleidoscope, (Farjeon, Eleanor)
Kaleidoscope in Woodcuts, (Frasconi, Antonio)
Kali and the Golden Mirror, (Wuorio, Eva-Lis)
Kangaroo Red, (Freschet, Berniece)
Kangaroo Twins, (Hogan, Inez)
Kangaroo and Kangaroo, (Braun, Kathy)
Kangaroo for Christmas, (Flora, James)
Kantchil's Lime Pit, (Courlander, Harold)
Kap the Kappa, (Lifton, Betty)
Kaptin Kiddo & Puppo, (Hays, M.G.)
Kari, (Scott, Gabriel)
Kari: The Elephant, (Mukerji, Dhan G.)
Karl's Journey to the Moon, (Lindberg, Maja)
Karl's Wooden Horse, (Donaldson, Lois)
Karoo the Kangaroo, (Wiese, Kurt)
Kashtanka, (Chekhov, Anton)
Kasidah of Haji Abdu El-Yezdi, (Burton, Richard F.)
Kasimir's Journey, (Stearns, Monroe)
Kaspar & Seven Wonderful Pigeons/Wurzburg, (Goddard, J.)
Kasperle's Adventures, (Siebe, Josephine)
Katawampus: Its Treatment & Cure, (Parry, Edward A.)
Kate Bonnet, (Stockton, Frank)
Kate Greenaway, (Spielmann, M.H.)
Katherine the Komical Kow, (Norris, June)
Kati and Kormos, (Surany, Anico)
Kati in Italy, (Lindgren, Astrid)
Kati in Paris, (Lindgren, Astrid)
Katie Goes to Camp, (Schick, Eleanor)
Katie John, (Calhoun, Mary)
Katie Meets Buffalo Bill, (Koch, Katharine)
Katie and the Sad Noise, (Gannett, Ruth S.)
Katie's Magic Glasses, (Goodsell, Jane)
Katooticut, (Carter, Charles F.)
Katrina, (Gilson, Roy R.)
Katrina Van Ost & Silver Rose, (Gale, Elizabeth)
Katrina and Jan, (Bailey, Alice C.)
Katrinka Grows Up, (Haskell, Helen E.)
Katy & the Big Snow, (Burton, Virginia L.)
Katy Comes Next, (Bannon, Laura)
Katy Kruse Dolly Book, (Fyleman, Rose)
Katy Kruse Play Book, (Fyleman, Rose)
Katy Kruse at the Seaside, (Farjeon, Eleanor)
Katy No-Pocket, (Payne, Emmy)
Katy's Quilt, (Holbrook, Ruth)
Kavik the Wolf Dog, (Morey, Walter)
Kay-Kay Comes Home, (Samstag, Nicholas)
Kee-Kee and Company, (Hollister, Mary)

Keep 'Em Rolling, (Meader, Stephen W.)
Keep Singing, Keep Humming, (Bradford, Margaret)
Keep Your Mouth Closed, Dear, (Aliki)
Keep it Like a Secret, (Warburg, Sandol)
Keeper of the Bees, (Stratton-Porter, Gene)
Keeping of Christmas..., (Irving, Washington)
Keepsake Ring, (Daringer, Helen F.)
Kees, (King, Marian)
Kees & Kleintje, (King, Marian)
Keiko's Bubble, (Lewis, Janet)
Keith of the Border, (Parrish, Randall)
Kellyburn Braes, (Leodhas, Sorche)
Kelpie's Pearls, (Hunter, Mollie)
Kemi: Indian Boy Before White Man Came, (Buff, M.& C.)
Ken of Kipling, (Clemens, Will)
Kenilworth, (Scott, Walter)
Kenny's Window, (Sendak, Maurice)
Kensington Rhymes, (Mackenzie, Compton)
Kent Hampden, (Davis, Rebecca H.)
Kentucky Cardinal Aftermath, (Allen, James L.)
Kermit the Hermit, (Peet, Bill)
Kernel Cob & Little Miss Sweetclover, (Mitchell, G.W.)
Kersti and St. Nicholas, (Van Stockum, Hilda)
Kevin, (Chalmers, Mary)
Kevin, (Moery, Robert)
Kewpie... [All titles], (O'Neill, Rose)
Key Corner, (Evans, Eva K.)
Key of Gold, (Cheney, Cora)
Key to Betsy's Heart, (Noble-Ives, Sarah)
Key to New York, (Slocum, Rosalie)
Key to the Kitchen, (Stewart, John)
Khasa Goes to the Fiesta, (Sotomayor, Antonio)
Ki-Ki: Circus Trouper, (Craine, Edith)
Ki-Yu: Story of Panthers, (Haig-Brown, R.L.)
Kibby's Big Feet, (Corddry, Thomas)
Kibun Daizin, (Murai, Gensai)
Kick, Pass & Run, (Kessler, Leonard)
Kickapoo, (Miles, Miska)
Kid Sister, (Embry, Margaret)
Kid from Tomkinsville, (Tunis, John R.)
Kiddie Land, (Hays, M.G.)
Kiddie Rhymes, (Hays, M.G.)
Kiddie-Kar Book, (Welsh, Richard)
Kidnapped, (Stevenson, Rbt. L.)
Kidnappers at Coombe, (Ballantyne, Joan)
Kids of Many Colors, (Boylan, Grace D.)
Kikeri, (Ehrhardt, Reinhold)
Kiki... [All titles], (Steiner, Charlotte)
Kildee House, (Montgomery, R.)
Killer-of-Death, (Baker, Betty)
Kilmeny, (Hogg, James)
Kilmeny of the Orchard, (Montgomery, Lucy M.)
Kim, (Kipling, Rudyard)
Kim and Me, (Kessler, Ethel)
Kim of Korea, (Norris, Faith)
Kimo, (Bailey, Alice C.)
Kincaid's Battery, (Cable, George W.)
Kind Adventure, (Perry, Stella G.)
Kindergarten Limericks, (Scott, Florence E.)
Kindred of the Dust, (Kyne, Peter B.)
Kindred of the Wild, (Roberts, Chas. G.D.)
King & Noble Blacksmith, (Blanck, Jacob)
King Albert's Book, (N/A)
King Arthur, (Gilbert, Henry)
King Arthur & Knights of Roundtable, (Holland, R. (ed.))
King Arthur & Knights/Roundtable, (Schneider, E.B.)
King Arthur & Noble Knights, (Macleod, Mary)
King Arthur & his Knights, (Frith, Henry)

King Arthur & his Knights, (Knowles, J. (arr.))
King Arthur & his Knights, (Malory, Thomas)
King Arthur & his Knights, (Winder, Blanche)
King Arthur and His Knights, (Robinson, Mabel L.)
King Arthur and his Knights, (Allen, Phil S.)
King Arthur's Knights, (Gilbert, Henry)
King Arthur's Wood, (Forbes, Elizabeth S.)
King Arthur..., (Malory, Thomas)
King Carlo of Capri, (Miller, Warren)
King Cotton, (Barske, Charlotte)
King Gumdrop, (Gordon, Elizabeth)
King Henry the Mouse, (Massie, Diane R.)
King Kojo, (Thompson, Ruth P.)
King Lavra & the Barber, (Auerbach, Marjorie)
King Longbeard, (MacGregor, Barrington)
King Midas and the Golden Touch, (Perkins, Al)
King Oberon's Forest, (Van Stockum, Hilda)
King Penguin, (Horne, Richard H.)
King Philip: Indian Chief, (Averill, Esther)
King Richard's Land, (Strong, L.A.G.)
King Snake, (Eckert, Allan W.)
King Thrushbeard, (Grimm Bros.)
King Thrushbeard, (Werth, Kurt)
King Time, (Fitzhugh, Percy K.)
King Who Saved Himself..., (Ciardi, John)
King and his Friends, (Aruego, Jose)
King and the Broom Maker, (Balet, Jan B.)
King and the Princess, (O'Brien, Jack)
King of Gee Whiz, (Hough, Emerson)
King of Ireland's Son, (Colum, Padraic)
King of Kinkiddie..., (Ayers, Ray F.)
King of Men, (Coolidge, Olivia)
King of Wreck Island, (Cooney, Barbara)
King of the Broncos, (Lummis, Charles F.)
King of the Castle, (Montgomery, R.)
King of the Golden River, (Ruskin, John)
King of the Grizzlies, (Richardson, Alfred)
King of the Hermits, (Sendak, Jack)
King of the Hills, (Meader, Stephen W.)
King of the Kerry Fair, (Meredith, Nicolete)
King of the Khyber Rifles, (Mundy, Talbot)
King of the Mountains, (About, Edmond)
King of the Nogs, (Postgate, Oliver)
King of the Stallions, (Tracy, Edward B.)
King of the Tinkers, (Lynch, Patricia)
King of the Wind, (Henry, Marguerite)
King with Six Friends, (Williams, Jay)
King's Beard, (Wibberley, Leonard)
King's Breakfast, (Milne, A.A.)
King's Butterfly, (Everett-Green, Evelyn)
King's Contest, (Holding, James)
King's Day, (Bishop, Claire H.)
King's Drum and other African Stories, (Courlander, H.)
King's Falcon, (Fox, Paula)
King's Fifth, (O'Dell, Scott)
King's Gardens, (Farrow, George E.)
King's Jewel, (Berry, Erick)
King's Liege, (Hinkson, Henry A.)
King's Mule, (Akers, Dwight)
King's Own, (Marryat, Frederick)
King's Pleasure, (Zeitlin, Ida)
King's Procession, (McCrea, James & Ruth)
King's Sons, (Fenn, Geo. Manville)
King's Stilts, (Seuss, Dr.)
King's Wish, (Elkin, Benjamin)
King, the Mice and the Cheese, (Gurney, Nancy)
Kingdom & Power & Glory, (Bible)
Kingdom and the Cave, (Aiken, Joan)

Kingdom of Carbonel, (Sleigh, Barbara)
Kingdom of Why, (Stone, Stuart B.)
Kingdom of the Pearl, (Rosenthal, Leonard)
Kingdom of the Winding Road, (Meigs, Cornelia L.)
Kingdoms Curious, (Hamilton, Myra)
Kings & Queens, (Farjeon, Eleanor)
Kings & Queens, (Wilkinson, Florence)
Kings and the Cats, (Hannon, John)
Kinkajou on the Town, (Montgomery, R.)
Kintu, (Enright, Elizabeth)
Kip: Young Rooster, (Black, Irma S.)
Kirdy, (Lamb, Harold)
Kisington Town, (Brown, Abbie F.)
Kiss for Little Bear, (Minarik, Else H.)
Kiss for a Warthog, (Devlin, Wende)
Kiss is Round: Verses, (Budney, Blossom)
Kiss of Glory, (Boylan, Grace D.)
Kit Koala, (Ninon)
Kitchen Fun, (Bell, Louise P.)
Kitchen Knight, (Schiller, Barbara)
Kitchen Madonna, (Godden, Rumer)
Kite Book, (Kilvert, Cory)
Kite Over 10th Avenue, (Lexau, Joan M.)
Kits and Cats, (Wain, Louis)
Kitten Pilgrims, (Ballantyne, R.M.)
Kitten Stand, (Coatsworth, Eliz.)
Kitten Who Barked, (Untermeyer, Louis)
Kitten Who Listened, (Nura)
Kitten on the Keys, (Dennis, Morgan)
Kitten that Grew Too Fat, (Winlow, Clara V.)
Kitten's ABC, (Newberry, Clare T.)
Kitten's Garden of Verses, (Herford, Oliver)
Kitten's Tale, (Chalmers, Audrey)
Kittenland, (Bingham, Clifton)
Kittens, (N/A)
Kittens and Cats, (Grover, Eulalie O.)
Kittens and Puppies, (Newton, Ruth E.)
Kittens, Cubs & Babies, (Schlein, Miriam)
Kitty Come Down, (Bacon, Frances A.)
Klepty, (Montgomery, R.)
Klondike Gold, (Coryell, Hubert)
Klondike Nuggets, (Ellis, Edward S.)
Knave of Hearts, (Saunders, Louise)
Knee Deep in Thunder, (Moon, Sheila)
Knee-High to a Grasshopper, (Parrish, A.& D.)
Knee-Knock Rise, (Babbitt, Natalie)
Knight Crusader, (Welch, Ronald)
Knight of the Cross, (Saint, Lawrence B.)
Knight of the Lion, (Hieatt, Constance)
Knight of the Nets, (Barr, Amelia E.)
Knight of the White Cross, (Henty, G.A.)
Knight's Fee, (Sutcliff, Rosemary)
Knighting of the Twins, (Fitch, William C.)
Knightly Legends of Wales, (Lanier, Sidney)
Knights of King Midas, (Berna, Paul)
Knights of the Silver Shield, (Alden, Raymond M.)
Knights, Beasts & Wonder, (Miller, Margaret)
Knights, Goats & Battleships, (Colt, Terry S.)
Knock at the Door, (Coatsworth, Eliz.)
Knock at the Door, Emmy, (Means, Florence C.)
Knocking the Neighbors, (Ade, George)
Knot Squirrel Tied, (Uttley, Alison)
Koala Bear Twins, (Hogan, Inez)
Kobi, a Boy of Switzerland, (Buff, M.& C.)
Koko and the Ghosts, (Kusan, Ivan)
Kokwa: Little Koala Bear, (Kalab, Theresa)
Komantica, (Keith, Harold V.)
Kongo the Elephant, (Smith, Eugene C.)

Koos the Hottentot, (Marais, Josef)
Kootenai Why Stories, (Linderman, Frank B.)
Krag & Johnny Bear, (Seton, Ernest T.)
Kris & Kristina, (Bruce, Marie)
Krishna & the White Elephants, (Collins, Ruth P.)
Kriss Kringle, (N/A)
Kristie and the Colt, (Brock, Emma)
Kristy's Rainy Day Picnic, (Miller, Olive Thorne)
Kritters of Kitchen Kingdom, (Aunt Jo)
Kubla Kahn, (Coleridge, Samuel T.)
Kumi and the Pearl, (Martin, Patricia)
Kurly Kew & Tree-Princess, (Shipman, Nell)
Kwaidan, (Hearn, Lafcadio)
Kwik and Kwak, (Fabres, Oscar)
Kylle Kluk, (Moe, Louis M.)
LO!, (Fort, Charles)
Lad with a Whistle, (Brink, Carol R.)
Ladder of Ricketty Rungs, (O'Donnell, T.C.)
Ladder to the Sky, (Chandler, Ruth F.)
Laddie, (Stratton-Porter, Gene)
Lady Anne's Fairy Tales, (Gaskell, C.M.)
Lady Arabella's Birthday Party, (Baker, Margaret)
Lady Bird, Quickly, (Kepes, Juliet A.)
Lady Doc, (Lockhart, Caroline)
Lady Hollyhock & her Friends, (Walker, Margaret C.)
Lady Jane, (Jamison, C.V.)
Lady Laughter, (Barbour, Ralph H.)
Lady Maud, (Russell, William C.)
Lady Mechante, (Burgess, Gelett)
Lady Tabitha and Us, (Ainslie, Kathleen)
Lady and the Tramp, (Greene, Ward)
Lady in the White Veil, (O'Neill, Rose)
Lady of King Arthur's Court, (Sterling, Sara H.)
Lady of Quality, (Burnett, Frances H.)
Lady of Shalott, (Tennyson, Alfred)
Lady of the Flag-Flowers, (Wilkinson, Florence)
Lady of the Lake, (Scott, Walter)
Lady of the Linden Tree, (Picard, Barbara)
Ladybug! Ladybug!, (Fry, Rosalie K.)
Ladybug, Ladybug, (Kraus, Robert)
Ladybug, Ladybug, Fly Away Home, (Hawes, Judy)
Ladycake Farm, (Hunt, Mabel L.)
Lafayette, (Madison, Lucy F.)
Lafayette: French-American Hero, (Bishop, Claire H.)
Laird of Cockpen, (Leodhas, Sorche)
Lake of Gold, (Buchan, John)
Lakerim Athletic Club, (Hughes, Rupert)
Lalla Rookh, (Moore, Thomas)
Lamb and the Child, (Frye, Dean)
Lambert's Bargain, (Newberry, Clare T.)
Lament of Billy Villy, (Watson, Emily R.)
Lance and his First Horse, (Holt, Jack)
Lance of Kanana, (French, Harry)
Lances of Lynwood, (Yonge, Charlotte)
Land of Delight, (Gates, Josephine S.)
Land of Don't-Want-To, (Bell, Lilian)
Land of Dreams, (Blake, William)
Land of Enchantment, (N/A)
Land of Forgotten Beasts, (Wersba, Barbara)
Land of Goodness Knows Where, (Pedley, Muriel)
Land of Hearts Desire, (Yeats, Wm. Butler)
Land of Little Rain, (Austin, Mary)
Land of Little Rain, (Fellows, Muriel)
Land of Lost Handkerchiefs, (Knight, Marjorie)
Land of Make-Believe, (Nesbit, Wilbur D.)
Land of Never Was, (Olmsted, Millicent)
Land of Nod, (Byron, May)
Land of Nod, (Price, Margaret E.)

Land of Nursery Rhyme, (Daglish, Alice (ed.))
Land of Play, (Noseworthy, F.)
Land of Pluck, (Dodge, Mary Mapes)
Land of Poco Tiempo, (Lummis, Charles F.)
Land of Really True, (Olmsted, Millicent)
Land of Right Up and Down, (Wuorio, Eva-Lis)
Land of the Blue Flower, (Burnett, Frances H.)
Land of the Lost, (Hewson, Isabel)
Landing of the Pilgrims, (Daugherty, James)
Lane that Had No Turning, (Parker, Gilbert)
Langford of the Three Bars, (Boyles, Kate)
Language of Flowers, (Greenaway, Kate)
Lantern Bearers, (Sutcliff, Rosemary)
Lantern in the Window, (Fisher, Aileen)
Larder Lodge, (Parker, B.& N.)
Lark in the Morn, (Vipont, Elfrida)
Lark on the Wing, (Foulds, Elfrida V.)
Lark on the Wing, (Vipont, Elfrida)
Larky Legends, (Hunter, Norman)
Larry, (Agnew, Edith)
Larry and the Undersea Raider, (Farley, Walter)
Last Battle, (Lewis, C.S.)
Last Cruise of the Electra, (Chipman, Charles P.)
Last Days of Pompeii, (Lytton, Edward B.)
Last Days of Shylock, (Lewisohn, Ludwig)
Last Dodo, (Boyde, Richard)
Last Dragon, (Blitch, Fleming)
Last Dragon, (Totheroh, Dan)
Last Egyptian, (Baum, L. Frank)
Last Essays of Elia, (Lamb, Charles)
Last Fairy Tales, (Laboulaye, E.R.)
Last Fort, (Coatsworth, Eliz.)
Last Free Bird, (Stone, A. Harris)
Last Galley, (Doyle, Arthur Conan)
Last Graphic Pictures, (Caldecott, R.)
Last Horse, (Steiner, Stan)
Last Hunt, (Genevoix, Maurice)
Last Hurdle, (Brown, Frieda)
Last Little Cat, (DeJong, Meindert)
Last Muster, (Chalmers, Patrick)
Last One Home is a Green Pig, (Hurd, Edith T.)
Last Ride Together, (Browning, Robert)
Last Savage, (Menotti, Gian-Carlo)
Last Two Elves in Denmark, (Calhoun, Mary)
Last Voyage of the Donna Isabel, (Parrish, Randall)
Last of the Flatboats, (Eggleston, George C.)
Last of the Mohicans, (Cooper, James F.)
Last of the Plainsmen, (Grey, Zane)
Last of the Sea Otters, (McCracken, Harold)
Late Cuckoo, (Slobodkin, Louis)
Late Spring, (Fritz, Jean)
Lattitude 19, (Crowninshield, Mrs.)
Laughing Dragon of Oz, (Baum, Frank J.)
Laughing Matter, (Smith, Helen)
Laughing Prince, (Fillmore, Parker H.)
Laughing Time, (Smith, William J.)
Laughing Willow, (Herford, Oliver)
Laura Ingalls Wilder Songbook, (Garson, Eugenia)
Laura's Luck, (Sachs, Marilyn)
Laurie, (Clapp, Estelle)
Laurie's New Brother, (Schlein, Miriam)
Lavender Cat, (Lowrey, Janette S.)
Lavender Garden, (Edmondson, Norah M.)
Lavender's Blue, (Lines, Kathleen)
Lavengro, (Borrow, George H.)
Law of the Land, (Hough, Emerson)
Lays of Ancient Rome, (Macaulay, Thomas B.)
Lays of the Grays, (Parker, B.)

Lazarre, (Catherwood, Mary)
Lazy Bear Lane, (Smith, Thorne)
Lazy Beaver, (Bowen, Vernon)
Lazy Blackbird, (Prelutsky, Jack)
Lazy Day, (Schlein, Miriam)
Lazy Jack, (Werth, Kurt)
Lazy Little Zulu, (Holding, James)
Lazy Liza Lizard, (Rains, Marie C.)
Lazy Matilda..., (Pyle, Katharine)
Lazy Tinka, (Seredy, Kate)
Lazy Tommy Pumpkinhead, (DuBois, W.P.)
Lazy Young Duke of Dundee, (Wise, William)
Le Morte D'Arthur, (Malory, Thomas)
Leader by Destiny, (Eaton, Jeanette)
Leaders in Other Lands, (Eaton, Jeanette)
Least One, (Sawyer, Ruth)
Leather Bottel, (Unknown)
Leaves from The Golden Bough, (Frazer, Lilly)
Lee: Gallant General, (Eaton, Jeanette)
Leerie, (Sawyer, Ruth)
Leftover Elf, (Stolz, Mary S.)
Legend Laymone, (Toland, M.B.M.)
Legend of Camelot, (DuMaurier, George)
Legend of Sleepy Hollow, (Irving, Washington)
Legend of St. Columbia, (Colum, Padraic)
Legend of Willow Plate, (Tresselt, Alvin)
Legend of the Lilac, (Newman, Isidora)
Legend of the Palm Tree, (Duarte, Margarida)
Legend of the Tulip..., (Newman, Isidora)
Legendary Ballads, (Sidgwick, Frank (ed))
Legends & Stories of Italy..., (Steedman, Amy)
Legends for Lionel, (Crane, Walter)
Legends from Fairyland, (Lee, Holme)
Legends from River & Mountain, (Sylva, Carmen)
Legends from the Outback, (Power, Phyllis)
Legends of Charlemagne, (Bulfinch, Thomas)
Legends of Flowers, (King, Jessie M.)
Legends of King Arthur & his Knights, (Clark, Janet M.)
Legends of our Little Brothers, (Gask, Lilian)
Legends of the Alhambra, (Irving, Washington)
Legends of the City of Mexico, (Janvier, Thomas A.)
Legends of the North, (Coolidge, Olivia)
Legends of the Saints, (Petry, Ann)
Legends of the Seven Seas, (Price, Margaret E.)
Leif Erikson the Lucky, (Kummer, Frederic)
Leif the Lucky, (D'Aulaire, I.& E.)
Leif the Lucky: Discoverer of America, (Berry, Erick)
Lemonade Trick, (Corbett, Scott)
Lending Mary, (White, Eliza O.)
Lenin, (Baker, Nina B.)
Lentala of the South Seas, (Morrow, W.C.)
Lentil, (McCloskey, Robert)
Leo of Alaska, (Agnew, Edith)
Leo, the Little St. Bernard, (L'Hommedieu, Dorothy)
Leopard on a String, (Kirn, Ann)
Leopard's Spots, (Dixon, Thomas)
Leopold, See-through Crumbpicker, (Flora, James)
Les Miserables, (Hugo, Victor)
Lesser Destinies, (Gordon, Samuel)
Let 'er Buck, (Furlong, Charles W.)
Let Them Live, (Lathrop, Dorothy)
Let it Rain, (Koch, Dorothy)
Let's Be Early Settlers with Daniel Boone, (Parish, Peggy)
Let's Be Enemies, (Udry, Janice M.)
Let's Be Indians, (Parish, Peggy)
Let's Build a Railroad, (Seeger, Ruth C.)
Let's Catch a Monster, (Scott, Ann H.)
Let's Fight, (Mikhalkov, Sergei)

Let's Find Out, (Schneider, Nina)
Let's Find Out about Summer, (Shapp, Martha)
Let's Get Turtles, (Selsam, Millicent)
Let's Go to the Circus, (Palazzo, Tony)
Let's Go to the Jungle, (Palazzo, Tony)
Let's Go to the Zoo, (Drayton, Grace)
Let's Go!, (Crawford, Phyllis)
Let's Keep Christmas, (Marshall, Peter)
Let's Look Inside your House, (Schneider, Nina)
Let's Look Under the City, (Schneider, Herman)
Let's Look at Tracks, (Kirn, Ann)
Let's Play House, (Lenski, Lois)
Let's Pretend, (Agnew, Georgette)
Let's Pretend..., (MacHarg, Wm. B.)
Let's Read Aloud, (Gagliardo, Ruth)
Let's Steal the Moon, (Serwer, Blanche L.)
Let's Walk up the Wall, (Johnson, Ryerson)
Letter on the Tree, (Carlson, Natalie S.)
Letter to Amy, (Keats, Ezra J.)
Letter to Popsey, (La Rue, Mabel G.)
Letters from my Mill, (Daudet, Alphonse)
Letters of a Woman Homesteader, (Stewart, Elinore)
Letty, (Fyleman, Rose)
Level Land, (DeJong, Dola)
Lewis Carroll Birthday Book, (Herrick, Christina)
Li Lun: Lad of Courage, (Treffinger, Carolyn)
Li'L' Gal, (Dunbar, Paul L.)
Li'l Hannibal, (Bailey, Carolyn S.)
Li'l Verses for Li'l Fellers, (Hobart, George V.)
Liang & Lo, (Wiese, Kurt)
Libby's Uninvited Guest, (Woolley, Catherine)
Liberty Belles, (N/A)
Licorice, (Briggs, Barbara)
Lie-Down Stories, (Joan, Natalie)
Life & Adventures of Peter Wilkins, (Paltock, Robert)
Life & Death of Mr. Badman, (Bunyan, John)
Life & Times of Madame Du Barry, (Douglas, Robert B.)
Life Class, (Bemelmans, Ludwig)
Life Everlasting, (Fiske, John)
Life I Live: Collected Poems, (Lenski, Lois)
Life Story: Play in Five Acts, (Burton, Virginia L.)
Life Worth Living, (Dixon, Thomas)
Life and Adventures of Santa Claus, (Baum, L. Frank)
Life and Death of Jason, (Morris, William)
Life in Arcadia, (Fletcher, Joseph S.)
Life of Jesus Retold for Children, (Banks, Helen W.)
Life of Nicholas Nickleby, (Dickens, Charles)
Life of Numbers, (Krahn, Fernando)
Life of Our Lord, (Dickens, Charles)
Life of St. Mary Magdalen, (Hawtrey, Valentina)
Life of the Bee, (Maeterlinck, Maurice)
Life's Book of Animals, (Kemble, Edward W.)
Light Across Piney Valley, (Watts, Mabel)
Light Princess, (MacDonald, George)
Light Side of Egypt, (Thackeray, Lance)
Light and Sight, (Alexenberg, Melvin)
Light at Tern Rock, (Sauer, Julia L.)
Light in the Forest, (Richter, Conrad)
Light in the Tower, (Howard, Joan)
Light of Asia, (Arnold, Edwin)
Light of Western Stars, (Grey, Zane)
Light-House Children Abroad, (Crowninshield, Mrs.)
Lighted Heart, (Yates, Elizabeth)
Lighter Side of School Life, (Hay, Ian)
Lightfoot the Deer, (Burgess, Thornton)
Lightfoot: Story of an Indian Boy, (Shippen, Kath. B.)
Lighthouse Island, (Coatsworth, Eliz.)
Lighthouse Keeper's Son, (Chauncy, Nan)

Like Nothing at All, (Fisher, Aileen)
Likely Place, (Fox, Paula)
Lilac Fairy Book, (Lang, Andrew)
Lilliput Lyrics, (Rands, William B.)
Lily of Life, (Sylva, Carmen)
Limericks by Lear, (Lear, Edward)
Limpy: Tale of a Monkey Hero, (Matzdorff, Hyde)
Lincoln, (Madison, Lucy F.)
Lincoln's Gettysburg Address, (Daugherty, James)
Linda, (Asch, Frank)
Linda & her Little Sisters, (Wilkin, Esther B.)
Linda and the Indians, (Anderson, C.W.)
Line & Form, (Crane, Walter)
Line of Love, (Cabell, James B.)
Lines and Shapes, (Russell, Solveig)
Lines, Spines & Porcupines, (Samson, Anne S.)
Ling Tang & the Lucky Cricket, (Stafford, Kay)
Ling, Grandson of Yen-Foh, (Eldridge, Ethel)
Linnets and Valderians, (Goudge, Elizabeth)
Linsey Woolsey, (Tudor, Tasha)
Lion, (DuBois, W.P.)
Lion & the Ox, (Lebedev, Vladimer)
Lion & the Unicorn, (Davis, Richard H.)
Lion Cub: Jungle Tale, (Williamson, Hamilton)
Lion Hound, (Kjelgaard, Jim)
Lion I Can Do Without, (Spilka, Arnold)
Lion and the Rat, (La Fontaine, J.)
Lion for Patsy, (Mason, Miriam E.)
Lion in Fact and Fiction, (Cherr, Pat)
Lion in the Woods, (Dolbier, Maurice)
Lion of Barbary, (Hoffmann, Eleanor)
Lion of Poland, (Hume, Ruth & Paul)
Lion of St. Mark, (Henty, G.A.)
Lion on Scott Street, (Siepmann, Jane)
Lion's Own Story, (Johnson, Crockett)
Lion, the Witch & the Wardrobe, (Lewis, C.S.)
Lion-Hearted Kitten, (Bacon, Peggy)
Lioness Who Made Deals, (Gardner, Fred)
Lionhearted One, (Weil, Lisl)
Lions & Tigers & Elephants Too, (Hader, B.& E.)
Lions 'n' Elephants & Everything, (Smith, E. Boyd)
Lions Fed the Tigers, (Angus, Douglas)
Lions in the Barn, (Voight, Virginia F.)
Lions of the Lord, (Wilson, Harry L.)
Lions on the Hunt, (Waldeck, Theodore)
Lisa and Lottie, (Kastner, Erich)
Liselott and the Goloff, (Peterson, Hans)
Lisette, (Holl, Adelaide)
Listen -- the Birds, (Miller, Mary B.)
Listen Hitler! Gremlins are Coming, (Hogan, Inez)
Listen Little Girl, (Leaf, Munro)
Listen Rabbit, (Fisher, Aileen)
Listen to my Seashell, (Steiner, Charlotte)
Listen! And Help Tell the Story, (Carlson, Bernice)
Listen! Listen!, (Rand, Ann)
Listening, (Seredy, Kate)
Listening Child, (Thacher, Lucy W.)
Listening Walk, (Showers, Paul)
Listing Attic, (Gorey, Edward)
Literary Life & the Hell with It, (Burnett, Whit)
Lito and the Clown, (Politi, Leo)
Little 1, (Rand, Ann)
Little Airplane, (Lenski, Lois)
Little American Girl, (Allee, Marjorie H.)
Little Amish Schoolhouse, (Seyfert, Ella)
Little Angel, (Dalgliesh, Alice)
Little Angel of Canyon Creek, (Brady, Cyrus T.)
Little Angela and her Puppy, (Marino, Dorothy)

Little Ann..., (Taylor, Jane)
Little Antelope..., (Hader, B.& E.)
Little Ape, (Keen, Ralph H.)
Little Apes, (Conklin, Gladys)
Little Appaloosa, (Hader, B.& E.)
Little Arthur, (Gilkison, Grace)
Little Auto, (Lenski, Lois)
Little Babs, (Mitchell, George W.)
Little Baby Ann, (Lenski, Lois)
Little Ballet Dancer, (Stirling, Monica)
Little Baptiste, (McNeer, May)
Little Bear, (Minarik, Else H.)
Little Bear Island, (Clymer, Eleanor)
Little Bear Who Wanted Friends, (Lowe, Edith)
Little Bear's Adventures, (Fox, Frances M.)
Little Bear's Friend, (Minarik, Else H.)
Little Bear's Mother, (Memling, Carl)
Little Bear's Pinto Pony, (Tousey, Sanford)
Little Bear's Sunday Breakfast, (Janice)
Little Bear's Visit, (Minarik, Else H.)
Little Belles & Beaux, (Tucker, Elizabeth S.)
Little Bermuda, (Pool, Maria L.)
Little Betty Marigold..., (Warren, Carro F.)
Little Big Feather, (Longstreth, Joseph)
Little Big-Bye-and-Bye, (Holling, Holling C.)
Little Bim the Circus Boy, (Muter, Gladys N.)
Little Black & White Lamb, (Hogan, Inez)
Little Black Ant, (Gall, Alice C.)
Little Black Bobtail, (Bannerman, Helen)
Little Black Hen, (Deihl, Edna G.)
Little Black Mingo, (Bannerman, Helen)
Little Black Quasha, (Bannerman, Helen)
Little Black Quibba, (Bannerman, Helen)
Little Black Sambo & Monkey People, (VerBeck, Frank)
Little Black Sambo & the Tiger Kitten, (VerBeck, Frank)
Little Black Sambo... [Most titles], (Bannerman, Helen)
Little Black Stories for Little White Children, (Cendrars, B.)
Little Black: A Pony, (Farley, Walter)
Little Blacknose, (Swift, Hildegarde H.)
Little Blossoms, (Andre, R.)
Little Blue & Little Yellow, (Lionni, Leo)
Little Blue Rabbit, (Austin, Cyril F.)
Little Bo Peep, (N/A)
Little Book, (DeRegniers, Beatrice)
Little Book about God, (Bible)
Little Book of Bores, (Herford, Oliver)
Little Book of Children, (Brown, Dr. John)
Little Book of Christmas, (Bangs, John K.)
Little Book of Colors, (Fish, Helen D.)
Little Book of Courtesies, (Tynan, Katharine)
Little Book of Days, (Field, Rachel)
Little Book of Dogs, (Brown, John)
Little Book of Necessary Nonsense, (Johnson, Burges)
Little Book of Prayers, (Johnson, Emilie F.)
Little Book of Prayers and Graces, (Hawkins, Quail)
Little Book of Singing Rhymes, (Stitch, Wilhelmina)
Little Bookroom, (Farjeon, Eleanor)
Little Boy & the Birthdays, (Buckley, Helen E.)
Little Boy Bear, (Maniates, Belle)
Little Boy Brown, (Harris, Isobel)
Little Boy Lost, (Hudson, Wm. Henry)
Little Boy Lost in Brazil, (Wiese, Kurt)
Little Boy Who was Drawing, (Duvoisin, Roger)
Little Boy and his House, (Bone, Stephen)
Little Boy with Big Apples, (Moeschlin, Elsa)
Little Brass Band, (Brown, Margaret W.)
Little Braves, (Deming, Therese O.)
Little Bright Eyes, (Mack, Robert E.)

Little Brother Francis of Assisi, (Williams, Michael)
Little Brother Goose, (Stewart, Anna B.)
Little Brother O'Dream, (Eastman, Elaine G.)
Little Brother and Little Sister, (Grimm Bros.)
Little Brother of the Wilderness, (LeSueur, Meridel)
Little Brothers of the West, (Deming, Therese O.)
Little Brothers to the Scouts, (Hyde, Elizabeth)
Little Brown Bear, (Gruelle, Johnny)
Little Brown Bear... [Most titles], (Upham, Elizabeth)
Little Brown Hen, (Farrow, Dorothy P.)
Little Brown Hen, (Martin, Patricia)
Little Brown Horse, (Otto, Margaret G.)
Little Brown Jug at Kildare, (Nicholson, Meredith)
Little Brown Koko has Fun, (Hunt, Blanche S.)
Little Brown Monkey, (Upham, Elizabeth)
Little Brown Rooster, (Byron, May)
Little Browns, (Wotton, Mabel E.)
Little Bruin and Per, (Christensen, Haaken)
Little Brute Family, (Hoban, Russell)
Little Buffalo Boy, (Holling, Holling C.)
Little Calf, (Scheffer, Victor)
Little Canadian Cousin, (MacDonald, Eliz. R.)
Little Captive Lad, (Dix, Beulah M.)
Little Carousel, (Brown, Marcia)
Little Cat Lost, (Garner, Elvira)
Little Cat that Could Not Sleep, (Fox, Frances M.)
Little Chicken, (Brown, Margaret W.)
Little Chicks and Baby Tricks, (Waugh, Ida)
Little Chief, (Pollard, Eliza F.)
Little Child, (Jones, Jessie O.)
Little Child's Book of Stories, (Skinner, Ada M.)
Little Child's Wreath, (Chapman, E.R.)
Little Chip of Willow Hill, (Hader, B.& E.)
Little Christmas, (Jewett, John H.)
Little Christmas Book, (Fyleman, Rose)
Little Church on the Big Rock, (Allen, Hazel)
Little Circus Dog, (Barr, Jene)
Little City of Hope, (Crawford, F. Marion)
Little Cock, (Hardendorff, Jeanne)
Little Cockerel, (Ambrus, Victor G.)
Little Colonel, (Johnston, Annie F.)
Little Colonel's Knight Comes Riding, (Johnston, Annie F.)
Little Colonial Dame, (Sage, Agnes C.)
Little Continentals, (Humphrey, Mabel)
Little Cow & the Turtle, (DeJong, Meindert)
Little Cowboy, (Brown, Margaret W.)
Little Cumsee in Dixie, (Kyser, Halsa A.)
Little Days, (Gill, Frances)
Little Degchie Head, (Bannerman, Helen)
Little Dignity, (Gerson, Virginia)
Little Dinghy, (Slobodkina, Esphyr)
Little Dog Lost, (Guillot, Rene)
Little Dog Toby, (Field, Rachel)
Little Dog, Dreaming, (Hurd, Edith T.)
Little Drummer Boy, (Davis, Katherine)
Little Duchess Anne of Britany, (Brock, Emma)
Little Duke, (Yonge, Charlotte)
Little Dusty Foot, (Magoon, Marian)
Little Dutch Book, (N/A)
Little Dutch Cousin, (McManus, Blanche)
Little Dutchy..., (Ransom, Will)
Little Eagle: A Navaho Boy, (Sperry, Armstrong)
Little Elephant, (Koffler, Camilla)
Little Elephant, (Williamson, Hamilton)
Little Elephant's Christmas, (Washburne, Heluiz)
Little Elephant's Picnic, (Washburne, Heluiz)
Little Engine that Could, (Piper, Watty (ed))
Little Era in Old Russia, (Skariatina, Irina)

Little Eskimo, (Jackson, Charlotte)
Little Fairy Sister, (Outhwaite, Ida R.)
Little Family, (Lenski, Lois)
Little Farm, (Lenski, Lois)
Little Farm in the Big City, (Berry, Erick)
Little Farmer, (Brown, Margaret W.)
Little Fat Gretchen, (Brock, Emma)
Little Fellow, (Henry, Marguerite)
Little Fir Tree, (Brown, Margaret W.)
Little Fire Engine, (Lenski, Lois)
Little Fireman, (Brown, Margaret W.)
Little Fish that Got Away, (Cook, Bernadine)
Little Fisherman, (Brown, Margaret W.)
Little Fishes, (Haugaard, Erik)
Little Flower Girl, (Tate, Elizabeth)
Little Flute Player, (Bothwell, Jean)
Little Folk Lyrics, (Sherman, Frank D.)
Little Folk of '76, (Humphrey, Mabel)
Little Folks of Animal Land, (Frees, Harry W.)
Little Folks of Other Lands, (Piper, Watty)
Little Fox, (Frost, Frances)
Little Fox in the Middle, (Buck, Pearl S.)
Little Freckled Person, (Davies, Mary C.)
Little French Cousin, (McManus, Blanche)
Little French Farm, (Lida)
Little Frightened Tiger, (Brown, Margaret W.)
Little Fu, (Creekmore, Raymond)
Little Fur Family, (Brown, Margaret W.)
Little Gardeners, (Morgenstern, Eliz.)
Little Ghost, (Preussler, Otfried)
Little Giant, (Kraus, Robert)
Little Giant Girl & Elf Boy, (Minarik, Else H.)
Little Giant of the North, (Malkus, Alida S.)
Little Giant's Neighbours, (Fox, Frances M.)
Little Giant, Big Dwarf, (English, Thomas D.)
Little Gift Book, (Fisher, Harrison)
Little Gingerbread Man, (Putnam, George H.)
Little Girl & Phillip, (Smith, Gertrude)
Little Girl & the Tiny Doll, (Ardizzone, Edward)
Little Girl Blue Lives in the Woods..., (Gates, J.S.)
Little Girl Blue Plays I-Spy, (Gates, Josephine S.)
Little Girl and her Mother, (DeRegniers, Beatrice)
Little Girl from Next Door, (Mockler, Geraldine)
Little Girl of 1900, (Lenski, Lois)
Little Girl with Seven Names, (Hunt, Mabel L.)
Little Glad Heart, (Almond, Linda S.)
Little Golden Hair & the Three Bears, (N/A)
Little Good People, (Foyle, Kathleen)
Little Goody Two-Shoes, (Goldsmith, Oliver)
Little Governor in Fableland, (Jewett, John H.)
Little Gray Colo, (Hawkins, Sheila)
Little Green Car, (Emerson, Caroline)
Little Green Cart, (McNeil, Marion)
Little Green Road to Fairyland, (Outhwaite, I. & A.)
Little Grey Gown, (Hunt, Mabel L.)
Little Grey Men, (B.B.)
Little Grey Rabbit... [All titles], (Uttley, Alison)
Little Grown-Ups, (Tucker, Elizabeth S.)
Little Handful, (Scripps, Harriet J.)
Little Hans, (Wilde, Oscar)
Little Hatchy Hen, (Flora, James)
Little Hawaiian Horse, (Hays, Wilma P.)
Little Hawk and the Free Horses, (Balch, Glenn)
Little Haymakers, (Coatsworth, Eliz.)
Little Hearts, (Upton, Bertha)
Little Hedgehog, (Ruck-Pauquet, Gina)
Little Helicopter, (Kinert, Reed)
Little Henry and the Tiger, (Lefevre, Felicite)

Little Heroes & Heroines, (Humphrey, Maud)
Little Hill, (Behn, Harry)
Little Hindu Cousin, (McManus, Blanche)
Little Homespun, (Ogden, Ruth)
Little Homespun Songs, (Hubbell-Plummer, B.)
Little Hop Skipper, (Malloch, Douglas)
Little Horse Bus, (Greene, Graham)
Little Horse that Raced a Train, (Hays, Wilma P.)
Little House, (Burton, Virginia L.)
Little House, (Dawson, Coningsby)
Little House in Big Woods, (Wilder, Laura I.)
Little House in Green Valley, (Hunt, Clara W.)
Little House in Pimlico, (Bouvet, Marguerite)
Little House in the Big Woods, (Wilder, Laura I.)
Little House of Your Own, (DeRegniers, Beatrice)
Little House on the Desert, (Hooker, Forrestine)
Little House on the Prairie, (Wilder, Laura I.)
Little Housekeepers, (N/A)
Little Houses far Away, (Bianco, Pamela)
Little Hunchback Zia, (Burnett, Frances H.)
Little Igloo, (Beim, Lorraine)
Little Indian, (Parish, Peggy)
Little Indian Basket Maker, (Clark, Ann N.)
Little Indian Folk, (Deming, Therese O.)
Little Indian Pottery Maker, (Clark, Ann N.)
Little Indians, (La Rue, Mabel G.)
Little Island, (MacDonald, Golden)
Little Italian Cookbook, (Lindsay, Christina)
Little Jack Rabbit, (Dussauze, Alice)
Little Japs at Home, (Haines, Alice C.)
Little Jeemes Henry, (Credle, Ellis)
Little Joe, (Clark, Dorothy)
Little Joe Otter, (Burgess, Thornton)
Little Jonathan, (Mason, Miriam E.)
Little Juggler, (Cooney, Barbara)
Little Juggler, (Higgins, Violet M.)
Little Karl, (Uncle Milton)
Little Kettle-Head, (Bannerman, Helen)
Little King, (Soglow, Otto)
Little King and the Princess True, (Hardy, Mary E.)
Little Lamb, (Martin, Dahris)
Little Lame Prince, (Craik, Dinah)
Little Land, (Housman, Laurence)
Little Laundress & the Fearful Knights, (Bloch, Bertram)
Little Lead Soldier, (Franchi, Anna)
Little Leather Breeches, (Wightman, Francis P.)
Little Legacy, (Walford, Lucy B.)
Little Leo, (Politi, Leo)
Little Lives of the Saints, (Dearmer, Percy)
Little Lone Coyote, (Hays, Wilma P.)
Little Long Ago, (Porter, Laura S.)
Little Lord Fauntleroy, (Burnett, Frances H.)
Little Lost Bear, (Hogan, Inez)
Little Lost Lamb, (MacDonald, Golden)
Little Lost Pigs, (Orton, Helen F.)
Little Lost Sioux, (Raabe, Martha)
Little Lost Squirrel, (Tresselt, Alvin)
Little Lucia's School, (Robinson, Mabel L.)
Little Lucy's Wonderful Globe, (Yonge, Charlotte)
Little Machinery, (Liddell, Mary)
Little Magic Horse, (Ershov, Peter P.)
Little Magic Painter, (Fellows, Muriel)
Little Maid of Old New York, (Curtis, Alice T.)
Little Man, (Kastner, Erich)
Little Marjorie's Love Story, (Bouvet, Marguerite)
Little Match Girl, (Andersen, Hans C.)
Little Match Man, (Barzini, Luigi)
Little Maude & her Mama, (Loomis, Charles B.)

Little Me, (Cory, Fanny)
Little Men, (Alcott, Louisa M.)
Little Men & Maids, (Tucker, Elizabeth S.)
Little Men in Scarlet, (Low, Frances H.)
Little Mermaid, (Andersen, Hans C.)
Little Mermaid Who Could Not Sing, (Slobodkin, Louis)
Little Miss Mouse, (Blanchard, Amy E.)
Little Miss Peggy, (Molesworth, Mrs.)
Little Missy, (Lindsay, Maud)
Little Mistress Goodhope, (Taylor, Mary I.)
Little Money Ahead, (Singmaster, Elsie)
Little Monkey with the Sad Face, (Jacobs-Bond, Carrie)
Little Mother and Georgie, (Smith, Gertrude)
Little Mothers, (Joan, Natalie)
Little Mr. Greenthumb, (Thayer, Jane)
Little Mr. Thimblefinger, (Harris, Joel C.)
Little Mr. Van Vere of China, (Cheever, Harriet A.)
Little Naturalist, (Frost, Frances)
Little Navajo Bluebird, (Clark, Ann N.)
Little Nemo in Slumberland, (Levine, Edna S.)
Little Night-Music, (Johnson, Gerald W.)
Little Nugget, (Wodehouse, P.G.)
Little O, (Unnerstad, Edith)
Little Old Automobile, (Ets, Marie H.)
Little Old Bear, (Van Stockum, Hilda)
Little Old Truck, (Barnum, Jay H.)
Little One, (Wright, Dare)
Little One in Between, (Webb, M. St. John)
Little One's Peter Pan and Wendy, (Barrie, James M.)
Little Ones, (Hogan, Inez)
Little Ones, (Kunhardt, Dorothy)
Little Oven, (Estes, Eleanor)
Little Owl, (Zimnik, Reiner)
Little Owl Indian, (Beatty, Hetty B.)
Little Pancho, (Politi, Leo)
Little Panjandrum's Dodo, (Farrow, George E.)
Little Peachling, (Faulkner, Georgene)
Little Pear... [All titles], (Lattimore, Eleanor)
Little People, (Elkin, R.H.)
Little People of the Hills, (Choate, Florence)
Little People of the Night, (Bannon, Laura)
Little People's Book of Airships, (N/A)
Little Pete's Adventure, (Burgess, Thornton)
Little Peter, (Malet, Lucas)
Little Pets Book, (Hays, M.G.)
Little Pickaninnies, (Chubb, Ida M.)
Little Pickle, (Weatherly, Fred E.)
Little Pickles, (Hunter, Richard)
Little Pictures of Japan, (Miller, Olive B.)
Little Pierre & Big Peter, (Ogden, Ruth)
Little Pig in the Cupboard, (Buckley, Helen E.)
Little Pig's Picnic..., (Brown, Margaret W.)
Little Pioneers, (Warren, Maude R.)
Little Plays for Little People, (N/A)
Little Plum, (Godden, Rumer)
Little Polish Cousin, (Mendel, Florence)
Little Polly Prentiss, (Gould, Elizabeth L.)
Little Prairie Dog, (Barr, Jene)
Little Prayer, (Cooney, Barbara)
Little Precious, (Smith, Gertrude)
Little Prince, (Saint-Exupery, A.)
Little Prince Toofat, (Chester, Geo. R.)
Little Prince and the Tiger Cat, (Damjan, Mischa)
Little Princess, (Burnett, Frances H.)
Little Princess Nina, (Charskaya, L.A.)
Little Princess and the Great Plot, (Eckenstein, Lina)
Little Puritan Rebel, (Robinson, Edith)
Little Queen of Hearts, (Ogden, Ruth)

Little Question of Ladies' Rights, (Fillmore, Parker H.)
Little Rabbit, (N/A)
Little Rabbit the High Jumper, (Schlein, Miriam)
Little Rag Doll, (Phillips, Ethel C.)
Little Rascal, (North, Sterling)
Little Red Balloon, (Hofman, Caroline)
Little Red Computer, (Steadman, Ralph)
Little Red Ferry Boat, (Potter, Russell)
Little Red Flower, (Tripp, Paul)
Little Red Hen, (Hader, B.& E.)
Little Red Horse, (Sawyer, Ruth)
Little Red House, (Skaar, Grace M.)
Little Red Lighthouse/Great Gray Bridge, (Swift, H.H.)
Little Red People, (Deming, Therese O.)
Little Red Riding Hood, (Denslow, W.W.)
Little Red Riding Hood, (Grimm Bros.)
Little Red Riding Hood, (Jones, Eliz. O.)
Little Red Riding Hood, (N/A)
Little Red Riding Hood & Big Bad Wolf, (Disney, Walt)
Little Red Train, (Weelen, Guy)
Little Red's Adventure, (Burgess, Thornton)
Little Red, White, Blue, (Gates, Josephine S.)
Little Red-Nose, (Schlein, Miriam)
Little Redskins, (Jamieson, M.M.)
Little Rhymes for Little Readers, (Seegmiller, Wilhelmia)
Little Riders, (Shemin, Margarteha)
Little River, (Rand, Ann)
Little Rivers, (Van Dyke, Henry)
Little Roaring Tiger, (Zimnik, Reiner)
Little Runner of the Longhouse, (Baker, Betty)
Little Sail Boat, (Lenski, Lois)
Little Sailor's Big Pet, (Ziner, Feenie)
Little Sally Waters, (Phillips, Ethel C.)
Little Sam in Volendam, (Kerr, Estelle)
Little School at Cottonwood Corners, (Schick, Eleanor)
Little Scotish Cousin, (McManus, Blanche)
Little Sea-Dogs, (France, Anatole)
Little Shepherd of Kingdom Come, (Fox, John Jr.)
Little Silk, (Ayer, Jacqueline)
Little Silver House, (Lindquist, Jennie)
Little Silver Tail, (Hart, Helen)
Little Singer, (Spyri, Johanna)
Little Sioux Girl, (Lenski, Lois)
Little Sister Doll, (Bannon, Laura)
Little Sister Snow, (Little, Frances)
Little Sister Su, (Chiang, May-Ling)
Little Sister to the Wilderness, (Bell, Lilian)
Little Skipper, (Creekmore, Raymond)
Little Slam Bang, (Van Derveer, Helen)
Little Smoke, (Kendall, Lace)
Little Smoke, (Stoddard, William O.)
Little Snow Drop, (N/A)
Little Soldiers, (Crommelin, May)
Little Soldiers & Sailors, (Humphrey, Maud)
Little Songs of Long Ago, (Moffat, Alfred)
Little Spanish Cousin, (Nixon-Roulet)
Little St. Elizabeth, (Burnett, Frances H.)
Little St. Sunshine, (Goss, Charles F.)
Little Steamroller, (Greene, Graham)
Little Steps, (Nast, Elsa R.)
Little Stone House, (Hader, B.& E.)
Little Stories for Little People, (Sowerby, Githa)
Little Story Book, (Brown, Elinor)
Little Stray Dog, (DeJong, Meindert)
Little Sunny Stories, (Gruelle, Johnny)
Little Ta-Wish, (Hardy, Mary E.)
Little Tailor, (Gropper, William)
Little Tailor of Windy Way, (Crownfield, Gertrude)

Little Teddy & the Big Sea, (Tate, Elizabeth)
Little Tigress, (Smith, Wallace)
Little Tim & the Brave Sea Captain, (Ardizzone, Edward)
Little Tiny Rooster, (Lipkind, Will)
Little Tiny Woman, (Zemach, Margot)
Little Tom Tucker, (N/A)
Little Tooktoo, (Peary, Marie A.)
Little Toot... [All titles], (Gramatky, Hardie)
Little Tour in France, (James, Henry)
Little Town, (Hader, B.& E.)
Little Town of Bethlehem, (Pauli, Hertha)
Little Town on the Prairie, (Wilder, Laura I.)
Little Toy Airplane, (Hogan, Inez)
Little Toy Bearkins, (Jewett, John H.)
Little Train, (Greene, Graham)
Little Train, (Greene, Grahame)
Little Train, (Lenski, Lois)
Little Travelers in Wales, (Lyle, G.M.)
Little Tuck, (Baldwin, Clara)
Little Twin, (Paull, Grace)
Little Twin Dragons, (Praeger, Sophia R.)
Little Two and the Peach Tree, (Martin, Patricia)
Little Ugly Face, (Coolidge, Florence C.)
Little Una, (Olds, Elizabeth)
Little Union Scout, (Harris, Joel C.)
Little Vic, (Gates, Doris)
Little Wars, (Wells, H.G.)
Little Ways & Great Plays, (Tucker, Elizabeth S.)
Little Wee Bear, (Byron, May)
Little Whistler, (Frost, Frances)
Little White Barbara, (March, Eleanor S.)
Little White Bird, (Barrie, James M.)
Little White Foot, (Hader, B.& E.)
Little White Goat, (Lathrop, Dorothy)
Little White Hen, (Hewett, Anita)
Little White Horse, (Goudge, Elizabeth)
Little White Teddy Bear..., (Sherrill, Dorothy)
Little White Town of Never Weary, (King, Jessie M.)
Little Wiener, (Scott, Sally)
Little Wild Horse, (Beatty, Hetty B.)
Little Wildrose, (Lang, Andrew)
Little Wise Hen, (Disney, Walt)
Little Witch, (Bennett, Anna E.)
Little Wizard Stories of Oz, (Baum, L. Frank)
Little Woman Wanted Noise, (Teal, Valentine)
Little Women, (Alcott, Louisa M.)
Little Woodcock, (Freschet, Berniece)
Little Wooden Doll, (Bianco, Margery W.)
Little Wooden Farmer, (Dalgliesh, Alice)
Little Wrangler, (Wood, Nancy)
Little Yellow Duckling, (Byron, May)
Little Yellow Duckling, (Prendergast, Mabel)
Little-or-Nothing from Nottingham, (Henry, Marguerite)
Littlebits, (Craine, Edith)
Littledom Castle, (Spielmann, M.H.)
Littlest Angel, (Tazewell, Charles)
Littlest Bear, (Hogan, Inez)
Littlest Fairy, (Webb, E. & D.)
Littlest House, (Coatsworth, Eliz.)
Littlest Mouse, (Lathrop, Dorothy)
Littlest One, (Adcock, Marion)
Littlest One Again, (Webb, M. St. John)
Littlest Ones, (Doane, Pelagie (ed))
Littlest Ones, (Tucker, Elizabeth S.)
Littlest Rabbit, (Kraus, Robert)
Littlest Reindeer, (De Witt, Johanna)
Littlest Satellite, (Hogan, Inez)
Littlest Witch, (Massey, Jeanne)

Littling of Gaywood, (Turpin, Edna)
Live Dolls... [All titles], (Gates, Josephine S.)
Lively City O'Ligg, (Burgess, Gelett)
Lives of Famous Romans, (Coolidge, Olivia)
Lives of the Hunted, (Seton, Ernest T.)
Livestock in Barracks, (Armstrong, Anthony)
Living in Navajoland, (Hood, Flora)
Liz'beth Ann's Goat, (Provines, Mary V.)
Liza Jane & the Kinkies, (Phipps, Mary)
Lob Lie-by-the-Fire, (Ewing, Juliana H.)
Lobo, (Kantor, MacKinley)
Lobsterman, (Ipcar, Dahlov)
Lochinvar Luck, (Terhune, Albert P.)
Lock her Through, (Berry, Erick)
Lodestone and Toadstone, (Elmer, Irene)
Log Cabin Family, (Horn, Madeline D.)
Log Cabin in the Forest, (Peterson, Phyllis)
Log of a Cowboy, (Adams, Andy)
Lokoshi Learns to Hunt Seals, (Creekmore, Raymond)
Lola the Bear, (Rideout, Henry M.)
Lollipop Party, (Sonneborn, Ruth)
Lollipop Princess, (Estes, Eleanor)
Lona, a Fairy Tale, (Wright, Dare)
London Bridge is Falling Down, (Emberley, Edward)
London Bridge is Falling Down, (Mother Goose)
London Men and English Men, (Hoban, Russell)
London Street Arabs, (Stanley, H.M.)
London Types, (Henley, William E.)
Londoners, (Gorham, Maurice)
Lone Bull's Mistake, (Schultz, James W.)
Lone Cowboy, My Life Story, (James, Will)
Lone Hunt, (Steele, William O.)
Lone Hunter's Gray Pony, (Worcester, Donald)
Lone Journey, (Eaton, Jeanette)
Lone Star, (Lyle, Eugene P.)
Lone Wolf, (Hogan, Inez)
Lone Woodsman, (Miller, Warren H.)
Lonely Doll Learns a Lesson, (Wright, Dare)
Lonely Dwarf, (Lamkey, Rosemary)
Lonely Maria, (Coatsworth, Eliz.)
Lonely Ones, (Steig, William)
Lonely Veronica, (Duvoisin, Roger)
Lonesome Boy, (Bontemps, Arna)
Lonesome End, (Meader, Stephen W.)
Lonesome Little Colt, (Anderson, C.W.)
Lonesomest Doll, (Brown, Abbie F.)
Long Ago Christmas, (Martin, Patricia)
Long Ago People, (Lamprey, Louise)
Long Ago When I was Young, (Nesbit, Edith)
Long Bright Land, (Howes, Edith)
Long Chance, (Kyne, Peter B.)
Long Christmas, (Sawyer, Ruth)
Long Christmas Eve, (Duryea, Elizabeth)
Long Grass Whispers, (Elliot, Geraldine)
Long Lane, (Stong, Philip D.)
Long Live the King!, (Dalgliesh, Alice)
Long Piece of String, (Wondriska, William)
Long Roll, (Johnston, Mary)
Long Ships Passing, (Havighurst, Walter)
Long Trains Roll, (Meader, Stephen W.)
Long Way to Frisco, (Powers, Alfred)
Long Winter, (Wilder, Laura I.)
Long Year, (Wier, Ester A.)
Long, Broad and Quickeye, (Ness, Evaline M.)
Long, Long Time, (Rice, Inez)
Long-Tailed Bear, (Belting, Natalia)
Longlegs the Heron, (Burgess, Thornton)
Longshanks, (Meader, Stephen W.)

Look Out Yonder, (Angelo, Valenti)
Look Out for Pirates!, (Vinton, Iris)
Look Out for the Ostriches!, (Juta, Jan)
Look Out the Window, (Anglund, Joan W.)
Look Through My Window, (Little, Jean)
Look at Me, (Rudolph, Marguerita)
Look at Your Eyes, (Showers, Paul)
Look at the Moon, (Garelick, May)
Look for the Letters, (Rey, Hans A.)
Look!, (Gay, Zhenya)
Look-Inside Easter Egg, (Bianco, Pamela)
Look-See with Uncle Bill, (James, Will)
Look: There is a Turtle Flying, (Domanska, Janina)
Looking Down Game, (Dean, Leigh)
Looking Out of Jimmie, (Flanders, Helen H.)
Looking for Lucas, (Beckman, Per)
Looking for Lucky, (Quigg, Jane)
Looking for Something, (Clark, Ann N.)
Looking for Susie, (Cook, Bernadine)
Loom of Destiny, (Stringer, Arthur J.)
Loopy, (Gramatky, Hardie)
Loot of the Flying Dragon, (Kempton, Kenneth P.)
Lord Fish, (De La Mare, Walter)
Lord Will Love Thee, (Clarke, Sara K.)
Lord is My Shepherd, (Bible)
Lord is My Shepherd: 23rd Psalm, (Bible)
Lord of the Sea, (Shiel, Matthew P.)
Lord's Prayer, (D'Aulaire, I.& E.)
Lords of High Decision, (Nicholson, Meredith)
Lords of the Wild, (Scoville, Samuel)
Lorenzo, (Waber, Bernard)
Loretta Mason Potts, (Chase, Mary)
Lorimer of the Northwest, (Bindloss, Harold)
Lorna Doone, (Blackmore, R.D.)
Lorraine & the Little People [All titles], (Gordon, E.)
Lost Boy, (Van Dyke, Henry)
Lost City, (Badger, Joseph E.)
Lost Dispatch, (Sobol, Donald J.)
Lost Dog Jerry, (Robinson, Tom P.)
Lost Fairy Tales, (Malone, Henry)
Lost Gospel, (Train, Arthur)
Lost Horizon, (Hilton, James)
Lost Indian Magic, (Moon, Grace P.)
Lost Island, (Burglon, Nora)
Lost Karin, (Kyle, Elisabeth)
Lost King of Oz, (Thompson, Ruth P.)
Lost Legends of the Nursery Songs, (Clark, Mary S.)
Lost Leopard, (Lattimore, Eleanor)
Lost Locket, (Parton, Ethel)
Lost Merry-Go-Round, (Lathrop, Dorothy)
Lost Prince, (Burnett, Frances H.)
Lost Princess, (Gordon, Hampden C.)
Lost Princess, (MacDonald, George)
Lost Princess, (Queen Marie)
Lost Princess of Oz, (Baum, L. Frank)
Lost Provinces, (Tracy, Louis)
Lost Race of Mars, (Silverberg, Robert)
Lost Treasure Cave, (McNeil, Everett)
Lost Village, (Bancroft, Alberta)
Lost Violin..., (Judson, Clara I.)
Lost World, (Doyle, Arthur Conan)
Lost Zoo, (Cullen, Countee)
Lost at the Fair, (Sharp, Margery)
Lost in the Barrens, (Mowat, Farley)
Lost in the Jungle, (DuChaillu, Paul)
Lost in the Zoo, (Hader, B.& E.)
Lost, Stolen and Strayed, (Ashmore, Marion)
Lotta on Troublemaker Street, (Lindgren, **Astrid**)

Lotte's Locket, (Sorensen, Virginia)
Loudest Noise in the World, (Elkin, Benjamin)
Loudmouse, (Wilbur, Richard)
Louis of New Orleans, (Cavanah, Frances)
Louisa Alcott's People, (Becker, May L.)
Louise's Adventure, (Blumenthal, Gertrude)
Lovable Lyle, (Waber, Bernard)
Love, (De La Mare, Walter)
Love Books of Ovid, (DeBosschere, Jean)
Love Family, (Spielmann, M.H.)
Love Finds the Way, (Ford, Paul L.)
Love Insurance, (Biggers, Earl D.)
Love Lyrics, (Untermeyer, Louis)
Love Song, (Wither, George)
Love Songs & Verses, (Leigh, Mabel C.)
Love Songs Old & New, (N/A)
Love Sonnets of an Office Boy, (Kiser, Samuel E.)
Love Story of Ursula Wolcott, (Bolton, Charles K.)
Love Under Fire, (Parrish, Randall)
Love and Dishes, (DeQuattrociocchi, N.)
Love and Knishes, (Kasdan, Sara)
Love in Art, (Potter, Mary K.)
Love in Old Cloathes, (Bunner, H.C.)
Love is a Special Way of Feeling, (Anglund, Joan W.)
Love of the Foolish Angel, (Beauclerk, Helen)
Love's Dilemmas, (Herrick, Robert)
Loveable Tales of Janey, Josey & Joe, (Smith, Gertrude)
Lovely Garden, (Snyder, Fairmont)
Lovely Summer, (Simont, Marc)
Lovely Woman, (N/A)
Lovely is The Lee, (Gibbings, Robert)
Lover's Baedeker & Guide to Arcady, (Wells, Carolyn)
Lovers' Mother Goose, (Clay, John Cecil)
Loves of Edwy, (O'Neill, Rose)
Loves of Lady Arabella, (Seawell, Molly E.)
Loves of Miss Ann, (Crockett, Samuel R.)
Lovey Mary, (Rice, Alice H.)
Lovina, (Milhous, Katherine)
Loving Heart, (Singmaster, Elsie)
Low Bridge & Punk Pungs, (Hellman, Sam)
Low Tide on Grand Pre, (Carman, Bliss)
Loyal Little Maid, (Robinson, Edith)
Loyal Little Redcoat, (Ogden, Ruth)
Loyal Traitor, (Barnes, James)
Lucian's Wonderland..., (Willson, John B.)
Lucid Intervals, (Martin, Edward S.)
Lucille, (Lobel, Arnold)
Lucille, (Meredith, Owen)
Lucille, (Meredith, Owen)
Lucinda: Little Girl of 1860, (Hunt, Mabel L.)
Lucio and his Nuong, (Crockett, Lucy H.)
Luck Book, (Leach, Maria)
Luck Child, (Chapman, Gaynor)
Luck O'Lady Joan, (Bacon, Josephine D.)
Luck of Denewood, (Knipe, A.A.)
Luck of Lowry, (Bacon, Josephine D.)
Luck of the Bean Rows, (Nodier, Charles)
Luck of the Roll and Go, (Carroll, Ruth)
Luck of the Trail, (Darling, Esther B.)
Lucky Blacky, (Lackey, Eunice)
Lucky Bucky in Oz, (Neill, John R.)
Lucky Days for Johnny, (Smith, Irene)
Lucky Ducks, (Molesworth, Mrs.)
Lucky Ladybugs, (Conklin, Gladys)
Lucky Llama, (Desmond, Alice C.)
Lucky Mischief, (Burgwyn, Mebane)
Lucky Mrs. Ticklefeather, (Kunhardt, Dorothy)
Lucky Ones, (Coatsworth, Eliz.)

Lucky Orphan, (Moore, Ida C.)
Lucky Pete, (Learnard, Rachel)
Lucky Pierre, (Beim, Lorraine)
Lucky Seventh, (Barbour, Ralph H.)
Lucky Sixpence, (Knipe, E.& A.)
Lucky You, (Leaf, Munro)
Lucy, (De La Mare, Walter)
Lucy & Little Red Horse, (Unwin, Nora S.)
Lucy & Tom's Day, (Hughes, Shirley)
Lucy & their Majesties, (Farjeon, B.L.)
Lucy Brown and Mr. Grimes, (Ardizzone, Edward)
Lucy Locket..., (Rae, John)
Lucy McLockett, (McGinley, Phyllis)
Lucy and Loki, (Buckmaster, Henrietta)
Lucy's Christmas, (Molloy, Anne)
Lucy's Village, (Harrison, Ada)
Lucy-Mary, (Herbertson, Agnes)
Luigi and the Long-Nosed Soldier, (Slobodkin, Louis)
Luigi on the Streets, (Carlson, Natalie S.)
Luke's Quest, (Snedeker, Caroline D.)
Lullabies and Jingles, (Sidney, Margaret (comp))
Lullabies and Night Songs, (Engvick, Wm. (ed))
Lullabies of Many Lands, (Strettell, Alma)
Lullabies of Many Lands, (Withington, Eliz.)
Lullabies of the World, (Commins, Dorothy)
Lullaby Book, (Shelby, Annie B.)
Lullaby Land, (Field, Eugene)
Lullaby for Eggs, (Bridgman, Betty)
Lulu, (Steiner, Charlotte)
Lulu's Play School, (Steiner, Charlotte)
Lulu's Window, (Lansing, Elisabeth H.)
Lumbercamp, (Rounds, Glen)
Lumberjack, (Meader, Stephen W.)
Lumberjack Bill, (Tousey, Sanford)
Lunch Box Story, (Goldberg, Martha)
Lunch for Lennie, (Woolley, Catherine)
Lure of the Dim Trails, (Bower, B.M.)
Lure of the Garden, (Hawthorne, Hildegarde)
Lute of Love, (Fraser, Claud L.)
Lutie, (Austin, Margot)
Luxury of Children, (Martin, Edward S.)
Lyle & the Birthday Party, (Waber, Bernard)
Lyle, Lyle, Crocodile, (Waber, Bernard)
Lyrics Pathetic & Humorous from A to Z, (Dulac, Edmund)
Lysbeth: Tale of the Dutch, (Haggard, H. Rider)
Lysis Goes to the Play, (Snedeker, Caroline D.)
Mac, (Aldin, Cecil)
Macaroni Tree, (Amsden, Dora)
Macaroon, (Cunningham, Julia)
Macbeth, (Shakespeare, Wm.)
Mad Motor, (Copeland, Walter)
Mad Scientist, (MacDonald, Ray)
Mad-Hatter's Tea Party, (Carroll, Lewis)
Mad-Man's Drum, (Ward, Lynd)
Madam Mary of the Zoo, (Wesselhoeft, Lily)
Madam Red Apple, (Bonner, Mary G.)
Madame Bovary, (Flaubert, Gustave)
Madame Butterfly, (Long, John L.)
Madame Roland, (Tarbell, Ida M.)
Made in China, (Spencer, Cornelia)
Made-to-Order Stories, (Canfield, Dorothy)
Madeline... [All titles], (Bemelmans, Ludwig)
Mademoiselle Misfortune, (Brink, Carol R.)
Madicken, (Lindgren, Astrid)
Madonna of the Goldfinch, (Steedman, Amy)
Madrigali, (Daly, Thomas A.)
Magda, (Sudermann, Hermann)
Maggie Rose: Her Birthday Christmas, (Sawyer, Ruth)

Maggie, Mischievous Magpie, (Black, Irma S.)
Magic Aeroplane, (Henderson, L.R.S.)
Magic Animals of Japan, (Pratt, Davis)
Magic Bed, (Hartwell, James (ed))
Magic Bed-Knob, (Norton, Mary)
Magic Book, (Williams, C.A.)
Magic Bus, (Dolbier, Maurice)
Magic Butterfly, (Obligado, George)
Magic Carousel, (Levenson, Dorothy)
Magic Casement, (Noyes, Alfred (ed))
Magic Christmas Tree, (Kingman, Lee)
Magic Circle, (Corkey, Ethel)
Magic Circle, (Untermeyer, Louis)
Magic Circus, (Higgins, Violet M.)
Magic City, (Nesbit, Edith)
Magic Cloak..., (Baum, L. Frank)
Magic Clock, (Bonner, Mary G.)
Magic Crook, (MacDonald, George)
Magic Currant Bun, (Symonds, John)
Magic Doll of Roumania, (Queen Marie)
Magic Dragon, (Harvey, Baldwin)
Magic Egg, (Black, Dorothy)
Magic Feather Duster, (Lipkind, Will)
Magic Finger, (Dahl, Roald)
Magic Firecrackers, (Dawson, Micthell)
Magic Fishbone, (Dickens, Charles)
Magic Flute, (Spender, Stephen)
Magic Flutes, (Kozisek, Josef)
Magic Forest, (Ross, Patricia)
Magic Forest, (White, Stewart E.)
Magic Garden, (Stratton-Porter, Gene)
Magic Gold, (Lansing, Marion)
Magic Hill, (Milne, A.A.)
Magic Horse, (Housman, Laurence)
Magic Image from India, (Baker, Cornelia)
Magic Ink Spot, (Marchioness/London)
Magic Jacket, (De La Mare, Walter)
Magic Jaw Bone, (James, Hartwell)
Magic Journeys, (Bonner, Mary G.)
Magic Key, (Van Sickle, James H.)
Magic Knocker, (Lea, John)
Magic Lake, (Deihl, Edna G.)
Magic Lamplighter, (Webb, M. St. John)
Magic Lassoo, (McClelland, Hugh)
Magic Listening Cap, (Uchida, Yoshiko)
Magic Maize, (Buff, Mary)
Magic Maker, (Varney, Joyce)
Magic Makers and Bramble Bush Man, (Sutton, M.)
Magic Map, (Bonner, Mary G.)
Magic Mashie, (Sabin, Edwin L.)
Magic Meadow, (D'Aulaire, I.& E.)
Magic Michael, (Slobodkin, Louis)
Magic Mirror, (Gilbert, William)
Magic Mitt, (Kay, Helen)
Magic Money, (Clark, Ann N.)
Magic Music Shop, (Bonner, Mary G.)
Magic Nuts, (Molesworth, Mrs.)
Magic Pawnshop, (Field, Rachel)
Magic People Around the World, (Softly, Barbara)
Magic Pictures, (Ayme, Marcel)
Magic Pin, (Forbus, Ina B.)
Magic Portholes, (Follett, Helen T.)
Magic Pudding, (Lindsay, Norman)
Magic Rug, (D'Aulaire, I.& E.)
Magic Shop, (Byron, May)
Magic Shop, (Dolbier, Maurice)
Magic Slippers, (Blodgett, Mabel F.)
Magic Spectacles, (Moore, Lilian)

Magic Squirrel, (Grishina-Givago, N.)
Magic Stone, (Farmer, Penelope)
Magic Stone, (Wade, Blanche E.)
Magic Story Tree, (Holling, H.C. (ed))
Magic Strings..., (Bufano, Remo)
Magic Summer, (Streatfeild, Noel)
Magic Switch, (Hess, Fjeril)
Magic Tooth, (Eells, Elsie S.)
Magic Touch, (Bacon, Peggy)
Magic Tower, (Finger, Charles J.)
Magic Trail, (Moon, Grace P.)
Magic Tree, (McCrea, James & Ruth)
Magic Tunnel, (Emerson, Caroline)
Magic Walking Stick, (Buchan, John)
Magic Wallpaper, (Francis, Frank)
Magic Wand, (Hamer, Sam H.)
Magic Whistle, (Browne, Edgar G.)
Magic Wood Beyond the World, (Rhys, Grace (ed.))
Magic World, (Beresford, Elisabeth)
Magic World, (Nesbit, Edith)
Magic at Midnight, (Arkle, Phyllis)
Magic at Wychwood, (Watson, Sally)
Magic by the Lake, (Eager, Edward)
Magic for Marigold, (Montgomery, Lucy M.)
Magic in My Shoes, (Savery, Constance)
Magic in the Alley, (Calhoun, Mary)
Magic of Millicent Musgrave, (Turkle, Brinton)
Magic of Oz, (Baum, L. Frank)
Magic to Burn, (Fritz, Jean)
Magical Egg, (Read, Elfreida)
Magical House of Zur, (Donahey, Mary D.)
Magical Land of Noom, (Gruelle, Johnny)
Magical Man of Mirth, (Sabin, Elbridge H.)
Magical Melons, (Brink, Carol R.)
Magical Mimics in Oz, (Snow, Jack)
Magical Monarch of Mo, (Baum, L. Frank)
Magician for One Day, (Jenks, Tudor)
Magician's Nephew, (Lewis, C.S.)
Magna Charta, (Daugherty, James)
Magnificent Milo, (Payne, Joan B.)
Magnificent Mr. Toad, (Disney, Walt)
Magnificent Squeak, (Peat, Fern B.)
Magnus & the Wagon Horse, (Peterson, Hans)
Magpie Lane, (Turner, Nancy B.)
Magyar Fairy Tales, (Pogany, Nebby)
Mahatma & the Hare, (Haggard, H. Rider)
Maid He Married, (Spofford, Harriet)
Maid Marian & Crotchet Castle, (Peacock, Thomas L.)
Maid of Artemis, (Coolidge, Olivia)
Maid of Middies' Haven, (Jackson, Gabrielle)
Maid of the Forest, (Parrish, Randall)
Maid-at-Arms, (Chambers, Robert)
Maidens Fair, (Fisher, Harrison)
Maila and the Flying Carpet, (Trez, Denise)
Mailbox Trick, (Corbett, Scott)
Main Chance, (Nicholson, Meredith)
Maine Ways, (Coatsworth, Eliz.)
Maine Woods, (Thoreau, Henry D.)
Maisie & her Dog Snip in Fairyland, (Musson, Bennet)
Maisie-Daisie Book, (Anderson, Anne)
Maje: A Love Story, (Gordon, Armistead)
Majesty of Grace, (Langton, Jane)
Major and his Camels, (Mason, Miriam E.)
Major and the Kitten, (Hoke, Helen)
Make Way for Ducklings, (McCloskey, Robert)
Make-Believe, (Lowry, H.D.)
Make-Believe Men & Women, (Tucker, Elizabeth S.)
Make-Believe Parade, (Margo, Jan)

Maker of Moons, (Chambers, Robert)
Maker of Rainbows, (LeGallienne, R.)
Making Friends, (Schick, Eleanor)
Making Good, (Nichols, William T.)
Making of Man, (Cornwall, Ian W.)
Making of Matthais, (Fletcher, Joseph S.)
Making of William Penn, (Brailsford, Mabel)
Making the Mississippi Shout, (Calhoun, Mary)
Makon and the Dauphin, (Agle, Nan H.)
Makoto, the Smallest Boy, (Uchida, Yoshiko)
Malachi Mudge, (Cecil, Edward)
Malachy's Gold, (Surany, Anico)
Malice in Kulturland, (Wyatt, Horace)
Malory's King Arthur, (Malory, Thomas)
Malou, (Criss, Mildred)
Mam' Linda, (Harben, William N.)
Mama Hattie's Girl, (Lenski, Lois)
Mama Nelly & I, (Gregory, L.F.)
Mama's Black Nurse Stories, (Milne-Home, M.P.)
Mama, I Wish I Was Snow, (Krauss, Ruth)
Maminka's Children, (Jones, Eliz. O.)
Mamma's Angel Child, (Sadler, Marie C.)
Mammy 'mongst the Wild Nations, (Bibbins, Ruthella)
Mammy's Baby, (Blanchard, Amy E.)
Mammy's Lil'l Chillums, (Williams, C.A.)
Man About Town, (Steig, William)
Man O'War, (Farley, Walter)
Man Who Could Grow Hair, (Attwood, William)
Man Who Didn't Wash his Dishes, (Krasilovsky, Phyllis)
Man Who Drew Cats, (Lambert, Emily)
Man Who Ended War, (Godfrey, Hollis)
Man Who Lost his Head, (Bishop, Claire H.)
Man Who Never Snoozed, (Latham, Jean L.)
Man Who Sang the Sillies, (Ciardi, John)
Man Who Talked to a Tree, (Schweitzer, Byrd B.)
Man With the Hoe..., (Markham, Edwin)
Man from Brodneys, (McCutcheon, George B.)
Man from Glengarry, (Gordon, Charles W.)
Man from Home, (Tarkington, Booth)
Man from the Bitter Roots, (Lockhart, Caroline)
Man from the Moon, (Carmichael, Philip)
Man in the Camlet Cloak, (Bateson, Carlen)
Man in the Lower Ten, (Rinehart, Mary R.)
Man in the Manhole & Fix-It-Men, (Sage, Juniper)
Man in the Moon, (N/A)
Man in the Moon, (Otto, Margaret G.)
Man in the Moon Stories..., (Lawrence, Josephine)
Man in the Moonlight, (Cross, John K.)
Man of the Hour, (Thanet, Octave)
Man of the Monitor..., (Latham, J.L.)
Man on the Box, (MacGrath, Harold)
Man with Four Lives, (Cowen, William J.)
Man with the Bushy Beard, (Suba, Susanne)
Man with the Purple Eyes, (Zolotow, Charlotte)
Man's Long Climb, (Lansing, Marion)
Manabozho the Great White Rabbit, (Warren, Maude R.)
Mandarin's Kite, (Farrow, George E.)
Manger Babe, (Price, Margaret E.)
Manhattan is Missing, (Hildick, E.W.)
Manners Can be Fun, (Leaf, Munro)
Manny & Co., (Sylvester, Charles)
Manoel & the Morning Star, (Peck, Anne M.)
Mantel-Piece Minstrels, (Bangs, John K.)
Manuel's Kite String, (Austin, Margot)
Manuel, Little Boy of Mexico, (Brown, Jeanette)
Manuela's Birthday in Old Mexico, (Bannon, Laura)
Manuelito of Costa Rica, (Crespi, Pachita)
Manxmouse, (Gallico, Paul)

Many Mansions, (Jones, Jessie O. (ed))
Many Moons, (Thurber, James)
Many Snows Ago, (Deming, Therese O.)
Many Ways of Seeing, (Moore, Janet G.)
Maori and Settler, (Henty, G.A.)
Maple Street, (Agle, Nan H.)
Maple Sugar for Windy Foot, (Frost, Frances)
Mara, (McGraw, Eloise J.)
Marathon Looks on the Sea, (Coolidge, Olivia)
Marbeau Cousins, (Edwards, Harry S.)
Marble Fountain, (Angelo, Valenti)
Marcel Marceau Alphabet Book, (Mendoza, George)
Marcella Stories, (Gruelle, Johnny)
March Has Horse's Ears, (Nye, Robert)
March Wind, (Rice, Inez)
March of the White Guard, (Parker, Gilbert)
Marchers for the Dream, (Carlson, Natalie S.)
Marco's Chance, (Young, Miriam)
Marcos, Mountain Boy of Mexico, (Lee, Melicent)
Marcus and Narcissa Whitman, (Daugherty, James)
Mardo's Animal Rhymes, (DeWolf, Wallace L.)
Margaret Tudor, (Colcock, Annie T.)
Margaret's Book, (Fielding-Hall, H.)
Margot and the Golden Fish, (Steedman, Amy)
Maria, (Lexau, Joan M.)
Maria Rosa, (Kelsey, Vera)
Marian, (Armstrong, Annie)
Marigold Garden, (Greenaway, Kate)
Marika, (Szekely, Sari)
Marilka, (Domanska, Janina)
Marina, (Bemelmans, Ludwig)
Mario's Castle, (Forbes, Helen)
Marionette in Motion, (Dwiggins, Wm. A.)
Marionettes, (Flack, Edith)
Marionettes, Masks & Shadows, (Mills, Winifred H.)
Marjorie Daw, (Aldrich, Thomas B.)
Marjorie's Literary Dolls, (Beard, Patten)
Marjorie's Little Doll School, (Beard, Patten)
Mark Twain and the River, (North, Sterling)
Mark, Mark, Shut the Door!, (Hawkins, Quail)
Market Day for 'Ti Andre, (Rodman, Maia)
Market Place, (Frederic, Harold)
Marlows Wins a Prize, (Boden, Hilda)
Marmaduke of Tennessee, (Cummings, Edward)
Marriage of Guenevere, (Hovey, Richard)
Marsh King, (Hodges, C. Walter)
Marshfield the Observer, (Castle, Egerton)
Marshmallow, (Newberry, Clare T.)
Marshmallow Ghosts, (Friedrich, Otto)
Marta, (Vance, Marguerite)
Martha Matilda O'Toole, (Copp, Jim)
Martha the Movie Mouse, (Lobel, Arnold)
Martha's Birthday, (Wells, Rosemary)
Martha, Daughter of Virginia, (Vance, Marguerite)
Martha-Jane: Nursery Nonsense, (Krag, Martha A.)
Martial Adventures of Henry and Me, (White, Wm. A.)
Martin DePorres, Hero, (Bishop, Claire H.)
Martin Hyde, (Masefield, John)
Martin Luther, (McNeer, May)
Martin Pippin in the Apple Orchard, (Farjeon, Eleanor)
Martin Pippin in the Daisy-Field, (Farjeon, Eleanor)
Martin and Abraham Lincoln, (Coblentz, Catherine)
Martin in Fairyland, (Darwall, Blanche)
Martin the Goose Boy, (Barringer, Marie)
Martin's Dinosaur, (Davis, Reda)
Martze, (Sendak, Jack)
Marv, (Sachs, Marilyn)
Marvelous Land of Oz, (Baum, L. Frank)

Marvelous Merry-Go-Round, (Ipcar, Dahlov)
Marvin's Manhole, (Rosen, Winifred)
Mary, (Molesworth, Mrs.)
Mary & her Kitchen Garden, (Crew, Alice C.)
Mary Ann's First Picture, (Bromhall, Winifred)
Mary Ann's Mud Day, (Udry, Janice M.)
Mary Christmas, (Chase, Mary Ellen)
Mary Frances... [All titles], (Fryer, Jane E.)
Mary Had a Little Lamb, (Denslow, W.W.)
Mary Jane, (Sterling, Dorothy)
Mary Jane's Friends in Holland, (Judson, Clara I.)
Mary Montgomery, Rebel, (Daringer, Helen F.)
Mary North, (Meyer, Lucy)
Mary Paxon, her Book, (Paxon, Mary)
Mary Poppins... [All titles], (Travers, Pamela L.)
Mary Redding Takes Charge, (Almond, Linda S.)
Mary Ware of Texas, (Johnston, Annie F.)
Mary the Mouse Champion, (Simmons, Ellie)
Mary's Marvelous Mouse, (Shura, Mary F.)
Mashinka's Secret, (Daugherty, Sonia)
Masked Prowler..., (George, Jean C.)
Masque of Days, (Crane, Walter)
Masque of Dead Florentines, (Hewlett, Maurice)
Masque of May Morning, (Robertson, W.G.)
Master Fritz, (Ewing, Juliana H.)
Master Key, (Baum, L. Frank)
Master Monkey, (Mukerji, Dhan G.)
Master Simon's Garden, (Meigs, Cornelia L.)
Master Skylark, (Bennett, John)
Master of Ballantrae, (Stevenson, Rbt. L.)
Master of Strong Hearts, (Brooks, Elbridge S.)
Master of the Royal Cats, (Laskowski, Jerzy)
Master-Mistress, (O'Neill, Rose)
Masterman Ready, (Marryat, Frederick)
Masters of the Wheat-Lands, (Bindloss, Harold)
Matchlock Gun, (Edmonds, Walter D.)
Matelot, Little Sailor of Brittany, (Fry, Rosalie K.)
Mathematics for Success, (Potter, Mary A.)
Matilda Who Told Lies..., (Belloc, Hilaire)
Matilda's Buttons, (Hunt, Mabel L.)
Matthew Looney in the Outback, (Beatty, Jerome)
Matthew Looney's Voyage to the Earth, (Beatty, Jerome)
Mau: King of the Cats, (Damjan, Mischa)
Maud, (Tennyson, Alfred)
Maude: Prose & Verse, (Rossetti, Christina)
Maui's Summer, (Bare, Arnold E.)
Maurice's Room, (Fox, Paula)
Max & the Truffle Pig, (Brown, Judith)
Maxie, (Kahl, Virginia)
Maxie, (Kantrowitz, Mildred)
Maximilian, (Heide, Florence P.)
Maximilian's World, (Stolz, Mary S.)
Maxims for Mice, (Macgregor, Angusine)
Maxims of Methuselah, (Burgess, Gelett)
Maxims of Noah, (Burgess, Gelett)
Maxims to Music, (Spaeth, Sigmund)
May & November Correspondence, (N/A)
May Flowers, (Alcott, Louisa M.)
May Horses, (Wahl, Jan)
May I Bring a Friend?, (DeRegniers, Beatrice)
May Iverson: Her Book, (Jordan, Eliz. G.)
May Margaret, (Crockett, Samuel R.)
May Ware, Little Colonel's Chum, (Johnston, Annie F.)
Maybelle the Cable Car, (Burton, Virginia L.)
Mayflower Maid, (Knipe, E.B.)
Mayor of New York, (Gratacap, L.P.)
Mayor's Wife, (Green, Anna K.)
Mazel Tov Y'All, (Kasdan, Sara)

Mazel and Shlimazel, (Singer, Isaac B.)
Mazli, (Spyri, Johanna)
McBroom Tells the Truth, (Fleischman, Sid)
McBroom and the Big Wind, (Fleischman, Sid)
McBroom's Ear, (Fleischman, Sid)
McCall's Read-Me-a-Story Book, (Bevans, Margaret)
McElligot's Pool, (Seuss, Dr.)
McGonnigle's Lake, (Montgomery, R.)
McNulty's Holiday, (Montgomery, R.)
McWhinney's Jaunt, (Lawson, Robert)
Me, (Hogan, Inez)
Me, (Saroyan, William)
Me & Caleb, (Meyer, Franklyn)
Me & Lawson, (Webb, Richard)
Me & the Bears, (Bright, Robert)
Me an' Pete, (McKown, Wendell)
Me and My Bike, (Thomas, Dylan)
Me! A Book of Poems, (Hopkins, Lee B. (comp))
Me'ow Jones, (Lyman, Edward B.)
Meadow Grass, (Brown, Alice)
Meadows in the Sea, (Malkus, Alida S.)
Mean Mouse & other Mean Stories, (Udry, Janice M.)
Meanest Squirrel I Ever Met, (Zion, Gene)
Medal of Honor, (King, Charles)
Medals for Morse: Artist & Inventor, (Latham, Jean L.)
Meddlesome Matty, (Taylor, Anne & Jane)
Medieval Stories, (Shuck, Professor H.)
Meet Mary Kate, (Morgan, Helen)
Meet the Malones, (Weber, Lenora M.)
Meeting with a Stranger, (Bradley, Duane)
Meggy McIntosh, (Gray, Eliz. J.)
Mei Li, (Handforth, Thomas)
Mein Rant, (Patterson, R.F.)
Melincourt, (Peacock, Thomas L.)
Melindy's Medal, (Faulkner, Georgene)
Melisande, (Sharp, Margery)
Melissa, (Forbus, Ina B.)
Melissa, (Weil, Lisl)
Melissa Ann, (Parton, Ethel)
Melissa's Friend Fabrizzio, (Weil, Lisl)
Mellop(s)... [All titles], (Ungerer, Tomi)
Melody, Mutton, Bone & Sam, (Davis, Lavinia R.)
Melvin the Moose Child, (Slobodkin, Louis)
Members of the Family, (Wister, Owen)
Memoirs of Sherlock Holmes, (Doyle, Arthur Conan)
Memoirs of Simple Simon, (Keeler, David B.)
Memoirs of a Baby, (Daskam, Josephine)
Memoirs of a Certain Mouse, (King, Alexander)
Memoirs of a Donkey, (DeSegur, Sophie)
Memoirs of a Fox Hunting Man, (Sassoon, Siegfried)
Memoirs of a London Doll, (Horne, Richard H.)
Memories, (Galsworthy, John)
Memories and other Rhymes, (Johnson, Abner M.)
Memories..., (Muller, F. Max)
Men Can Take It, (Hawes, Elizabeth)
Men and Women, (Browning, Robert)
Men at Work, (Hine, Lewis W.)
Men of Athens, (Coolidge, Olivia)
Men of Concord, (Thoreau, Henry D.)
Men of Iron, (Pyle, Howard)
Men of Medicine, (Shippen, Kath. B.)
Men of Power, (Carr, Albert)
Men with The Bark On, (Remington, Frederic)
Men, Microscopes & Living Things, (Shippen, Kath. B.)
Men, Moss and Reindeer..., (Berry, Erick)
Menagerie, (Miller, Mary B.)
Meph: Pet Skunk, (George, Jean C.)
Mephistopheles, (Keiro)

Merchant of Venice, (Shakespeare, Wm.)
Mercury the Story Teller, (Campbell, A.M.)
Mercy and the Mouse, (Bacon, Peggy)
Meredith's Ann, (Gray, Eliz. J.)
Merlin's Mistake, (Newman, Robert)
Mermaid & the Simpleton, (Picard, Barbara)
Mermaid Reader, (O'Clery, Helen (comp))
Mermaid and other Tales, (Andersen, Hans C.)
Mermaid's Gift, (Brown, Julia)
Merrimeg, (Bowen, William)
Merriweathers, (Torrey, Marjorie)
Merry Adventures of Robin Hood, (Pyle, Howard)
Merry Book, (Sowerby, Githa)
Merry Chase, (Hurd, Clement)
Merry Children's Nursery Rhymes, (N/A)
Merry Christmas to You, (Harper, Wilhelmina)
Merry Christmas, Happy New Year, (McGinley, Phyllis)
Merry Go Round in Oz, (McGraw, Eloise J.)
Merry Marcos, (Angelo, Valenti)
Merry Matchmakers, (Kristoffersen, Eva)
Merry Men, (Stevenson, Rbt. L.)
Merry Mice, (Veale, E.)
Merry Multifleet & Mounting Multicorps, (O'Cluny, T.)
Merry Murphy, (Campbell, Lang)
Merry Piper, (Gaze, Harold)
Merry Pranks, (Jagendorf, Mortiz)
Merry Puppy Book, (Aldin, Cecil)
Merry Shipwreck, (Duplaix, Georges)
Merry Times, (N/A)
Merry Times, (Various)
Merry Wives of Windsor, (Shakespeare, Wm.)
Merry and Bright, (Aldin, Cecil)
Merry, Rose & Christmas-Tree June, (Orgel, Doris)
Merry-Go-Round, (Johnson, Crockett)
Merry-Go-Round, (Richards, Laura E.)
Merry-Go-Round, (Wells, Carolyn)
Merry-Go-Round of Modern Tales, (Emerson, Caroline)
Merrylegs, (Brown, Paul)
Merrylinks, (Brown, Alice)
Merrylips, (Dix, Beulah M.)
Message of the Bells, (Van Loon, Hendrik)
Message of the Lilies, (Cawein, Madison J.)
Messer Marco Polo, (Byrne, Donn)
Messiah of the Cylinder, (Rousseau, Victor)
Metten of Tyre, (Carus, Helena)
Mexicali Soup, (Hitte, Kathryn)
Mexican Journey, (Blichfeldt, E.H.)
Mexican Story, (McNeer, May)
Mexican Twins, (Perkins, Lucy F.)
Mexicana, (D'Harnoncourt, R.)
Mexico City: Idler's Note-Book, (Percival, Olive)
Mice, the Monks & the Christmas Tree, (Selden, G.)
Michael Angelo Mouse, (Evans, Katherine)
Michael O'Halloran, (Stratton-Porter, Gene)
Michael Strogoff, (Verne, Jules)
Michael Thwaites's Wife, (Michelson, Miriam)
Michael and the Mitten Test, (Wells, Rosemary)
Michael's Victory, (Judson, Clara I.)
Michael, the Upstairs Dog, (Ormondroyd, Edward)
Michel's Island, (Hunt, Mabel L.)
Mick & Mac, (Brown, Paul)
Mickey & the Beanstalk, (Disney, Walt)
Mickey & the Monkeys, (Kirk, Victorine)
Mickey Mouse('s)... [All titles], (Disney, Walt)
Mickey Never Fails, (Palmer, Robin)
Mickey Sees the U.S.A., (Emerson, Caroline)
Mickey's Clock, (Disney, Walt)
Mickey's Magnet, (Branley, Franklyn)

Micky Magee's Menagerie, (Hamer, Sam H.)
Micky..., (Sharp, Evelyn)
MidSummer Night's Dream, (Shakespeare, Wm.)
Middle Button, (Worth, Kathryn)
Middle Matilda, (Bromhall, Winifred)
Middle Moffat, (Estes, Eleanor)
Middle Sister, (Mason, Miriam E.)
Midget & Bridget, (Hader, B.& E.)
Midnight, (Montgomery, R.)
Midnight & Jeremiah, (North, Sterling)
Midnight Alarm... (Phelan, M.K.)
Midnight Colt, (Balch, Glenn)
Midnight Folk, (Masefield, John)
Midnight Fox, (Byars, Betsy C.)
Midnight Moon, (Lyons, Dorothy)
Midshipman Paulding, (Seawell, Molly E.)
Midsummer Night, (Wilhelmson, Carl)
Mieko, (Politi, Leo)
Mighty Hunter, (Hader, B.& E.)
Mighty Mo, (Arundel, Jocelyn)
Mighty Ones, (DeJong, Meindert)
Mighty Soo..., (Judson, Clara I.)
Mik and the Prowler, (Uchida, Yoshiko)
Mike, (Wodehouse, P.G.)
Mike Mulligan & his Steam Shovel, (Burton, Virginia L.)
Mike and his Neighbors, (Klem, Grace)
Mike of Company D., (Aspden, Don)
Mike's House, (Sauer, Julia L.)
Mike's Toads, (Gage, Wilson)
Mike: Story of a Young Circus Acrobat, (Stong, Philip D.)
Miki, (Petersham, Maud)
Miki & Mary..., (Petersham, Maud)
Mikko's Fortune, (Kingman, Lee)
Mildred's Inheritance, (Johnston, Annie F.)
Mile of Freedom, (Hilles, Helen)
Miller, His Son & their Donkey, (Aesopus)
Millet Tilled the Soil, (Wheeler, Opal)
Millicent in Dreamland, (Brainerd, Edna S.)
Millicent the Monster, (Lystad, Mary)
Millicent's Ghost, (Lexau, Joan M.)
Millions & Millions & Millions!, (Slobodkin, Louis)
Millions of Cats, (Gag, Wanda)
Milly & Olly, (Ward, Mrs. H.)
Milly and Olly, (Ward, Mrs. H.)
Milly and her Dogs, (Barksdale, Lena)
Milly-Molly-Mandy Stories, (Brisley, Joyce L.)
Mimff-Robinson, (Kaeser, Hildegarde)
Mimi, (Simont, Marc)
Mimi, (Weil, Lisl)
Mimi, Momo and Miss Tabby Tibbs, (Sturges, Katharine)
Mince Pie Dream, (Elton, Emily D.)
Mince Pie and Mistletoe, (McGinley, Phyllis)
Mine for Keeps, (Little, Jean)
Ming & Mehitable, (Sewell, Helen)
Minn of the Mississippi, (Holling, Holling C.)
Minnie the Mermaid, (Jones, Thomas O.)
Minnow on the Say, (Pearce, Philippa)
Minou, (Francoise)
Minstrel & the Mountain, (Yolen, Jane)
Minstrel Dick, (Coleridge, Christabel)
Mio, my Son, (Lindgren, Astrid)
Mirabeau & the French Revolution, (Warwick, Charles)
Miracle of Sage Valley, (Randall, Janet)
Miracle of the Talking Jungle, (Bartlett, Ruth)
Miracles on Maple Hill, (Sorensen, Virginia)
Miranda & the Cat, (Smith, Linell)
Miranda is a Princess, (Sterne, Emma G.)
Miranda the Great, (Estes, Eleanor)

Miranda's Beautiful Dream, (Kraus, Robert)
Miranda's Dragon, (Hall, Rosalys)
Miranda's Pilgrims, (Wells, Rosemary)
Mirandy, (Dix, Dorothy)
Mirror of Music, (Makower, Stanley)
Mirth by Maybank, (Maybank, Thomas)
Mis' Beauty, (Woodruff, Helen S.)
Misadventures at Margate, (Ingoldsby, Thomas)
Mischief in Fez, (Hoffmann, Eleanor)
Mischief in Mayfield, (Bacon, Peggy)
Mischievous Meg, (Lindgren, Astrid)
Misfortunes of Elphin & Rhododaphne, (Peacock, Thos. L.)
Misrepresentative Women, (Graham, Harry)
Miss Agatha's Lark, (Sherman, Nancy)
Miss Angelina Adorable, (Bonner, Mary G.)
Miss Ayr of Virginia, (Magruder, Julia)
Miss Bianca... [All titles], (Sharp, Margery)
Miss Billy: Neighborhood Story, (Hurd, Marian K.)
Miss Bounce, (Woodhouse, S.C.)
Miss Carlotta, (Reid, Lionel)
Miss Cayley's Adventures, (Allen, Grant)
Miss Emily, (Gould, Jean)
Miss Flora McFlimsey [All titles], (Mariana)
Miss Happiness and Miss Flower, (Godden, Rumer)
Miss Hickory, (Bailey, Carolyn S.)
Miss Jellytot's Visit, (Hunt, Mabel L.)
Miss Jemima, (De La Mare, Walter)
Miss Lollipop's Lion, (Varga, Judy)
Miss Lovemouse's Letters, (N/A)
Miss Manners, (Orr, Aileen)
Miss Minerva's Scallywags, (Sampson, Emma S.)
Miss Mouse & her Boys, (Molesworth, Mrs.)
Miss Muffet's Christmas Party, (Crothers, Samuel M.)
Miss Osborne-the-Mop, (Gage, Wilson)
Miss Pattie, (Bright, Robert)
Miss Pennyfeather & the Pooka, (O'Faolain, Eileen)
Miss Pert's Christmas Tree, (Paget-Fredericks, J.)
Miss Petticoats, (Tilton, Dwight)
Miss Pickerell... [All titles], (MacGregor, Ellen)
Miss Pooky Peckinpaugh, (Thompson, Kay)
Miss Posy Longlegs, (Mason, Miriam E.)
Miss Santa Claus of the Pullman, (Johnston, Annie F.)
Miss Suzy, (Young, Miriam)
Miss Twiggley's Tree, (Fox, Dorothea)
Miss Z: Dark Young Lady, (Carter, Angela)
Missee Lee, (Ransome, Arthur)
Missing Brother, (Robertson, Keith)
Missing Katchina, (Moon, Grace P.)
Missing Masterpiece, (Belloc, Hilaire)
Missing Milkman, (Duvoisin, Roger)
Missing Prince, (Farrow, George E.)
Mission Bell, (Politi, Leo)
Missionary Sheriff, (Thanet, Octave)
Mississippi Bubble, (Hough, Emerson)
Mississippi Possum, (Miles, Miska)
Missouri Canary, (Stong, Philip D.)
Mist Men, (Mendoza, George)
Mister Dog, (Brown, Margaret W.)
Mister Jim, (Montgomery, R.)
Mister Ole, (Bennett, Richard)
Mistress Masham's Repose, (White, Terence H.)
Mistress Pat, (Montgomery, Lucy M.)
Mistress of Shenstone, (Barclay, Florence)
Misty of Chincoteague, (Henry, Marguerite)
Misty, Wonder Pony..., (Henry, Marguerite)
Mitch and Amy, (Cleary, Beverly)
Mittens, (Newberry, Clare T.)
Mitty Children Fix Things, (Nura)

Mitty and Mr. Syrup, (Holberg, Ruth)
Mitty on Mr. Syrup's Farm, (Holberg, Ruth)
Mixed Pickles, (Bingham, Clifton)
Mixed Pickles, (Waylett, Richard)
Moby Dick, (Melville, Herman)
Moccasin Trail, (McGraw, Eloise J.)
Moccasins on the Trail, (Thompson, Wolfe)
Modern ABC Book, (Falls, Charles B.)
Modern Aladdin, (Pyle, Howard)
Modern Arms and a Feudal Throne, (Harrison, T.M.)
Modern Fairy Stories, (Green, Roger L.)
Modern Obstacle, (Miller, Alice D.)
Modern Story Book, (Wadsworth, Wallace)
Modern Struwwelpeter, (Struther, Jan)
Modern Traveller, (Belloc, Hilaire)
Modern Utopia, (Wells, H.G.)
Mogo's Flute, (Van Stockum, Hilda)
Moldy Warp the Mole, (Uttley, Alison)
Mole Family's Christmas, (Hoban, Russell)
Moll Flanders, (Defoe, Daniel)
Molly & the Tool Shed, (Scott, Sally)
Molly Cottontail, (Caldwell, Erskine)
Molly Make-Believe, (Abbott, Eleanor H.)
Molly Whuppie, (Jacobs, Joseph)
Molly and The Unwiseman, (Bangs, John K.)
Molly and Unwiseman Abroad, (Bangs, John K.)
Molly and the Golden Wedding, (Sheehy, Emma)
Molly in the Middle, (Lattimore, Eleanor)
Mom Du Jos..., (Berry, Erick)
Mommies are for Loving, (Penn, Ruth B.)
Mommies at Work, (Merriam, Eve)
Mommy, Buy Me a China Doll, (Zemach, Harve)
Momo's Kitten, (Yashima, Taro)
Mona Minim & the Smell of the Sun, (Frame, Janet)
Monarch Butterfly, (Marcher, Marion W.)
Monarch the Big Bear of Tallac, (Seton, Ernest T.)
Monarchs of Merry England, (Carse, Roland)
Money Magic, (Garland, Hamlin)
Money Master, (Parker, Gilbert)
Money Moon, (Farnol, Jeffery)
Money Spinner, (Merriman, Henry S.)
Mongo Homecoming, (Elting, Mary)
Mongrel Puppy Book, (Aldin, Cecil)
Moni the Goat Boy, (Spyri, Johanna)
Monica, (Bourget, Paul)
Monkey & the Wild, Wild Wind, (Johnson, Ryerson)
Monkey Alphabet, (Palazzo, Tony)
Monkey Day, (Krauss, Ruth)
Monkey Island, (Rietveld, Jane)
Monkey See, Monkey Do, (Credle, Ellis)
Monkey See, Monkey Do, (Hogan, Inez)
Monkey Shines, (Hall, Bolton)
Monkey Shines, (Miers, Earl S.)
Monkey Tale, (Williamson, Hamilton)
Monkey Twins, (Christopher, Anne)
Monkey Twins, They Saw it All, (Hogan, Inez)
Monkey and the Crocodile, (Galdone, Paul)
Monkey in the Jungle, (Preston, Edna M.)
Monkey that Would not Kill, (Drummond, Henry)
Monkey's Fist, (Molloy, Anne)
Monkey's Tale, (Kravetz, Nathan)
Monkey, the Lion & the Snake, (Werth, Kurt)
Monkey-Do, (Price, Margaret E.)
Monkeys and the Pedlar, (Suba, Susanne)
Monkeys are Funny that Way, (Koch, Dorothy)
Monochromes, (D'Arcy, Ella)
Monologues, (Herford, Beatrice)
Monsieur Jolicoeur's Umbrella, (Surany, Anico)

Monster Den, (Ciardi, John)
Monsters' Ball, (DePaola, Tomie)
Monstrous Glisson Glop, (Massie, Diane R.)
Montezuma's Daughter, (Haggard, H. Rider)
Month Brothers, (Nathan, Dorothy)
Monty Marine, (MacNeil, Marion)
Moo-Wee: The Musk-Ox, (Tompkins, Jane)
Mooky & Tooky, (Heath, Janet F.)
Moominpappa at Sea, (Jansson, Tove)
Moon Ahead, (Greener, Leslie)
Moon Babies, (Clark, G.O.)
Moon Baby, (Nash, Dorothy)
Moon Blossom and the Golden Penny, (Slobodkin, Louis)
Moon Eyes, (Poole, Josephine)
Moon Jelly Swims through the Sea, (Jenkins, Marie M.)
Moon Jumpers, (Udry, Janice M.)
Moon Man, (Ungerer, Tomi)
Moon Mouse, (Holl, Adelaide)
Moon Party, (Bragdon, Ollie)
Moon Pony, (Pomerantz, Charlotte)
Moon Pool, (Merritt, Abraham)
Moon Prince & Other Nabobs, (Munkittrick, R.K.)
Moon Princess, (Harrison, Edith O.)
Moon Seems to Change, (Branley, Franklyn)
Moon Singer, (Bulla, Clyde R.)
Moon and a Star, (Livingston, Myra C.)
Moon in My Room, (Shulevitz, Uri)
Moon in the Cloud, (Harris, Rosemary)
Moon is a Crystal Ball, (Belting, Natalia)
Moon of the... [All titles], (George, Jean C.)
Moon or a Button, (Krauss, Ruth)
Moon, for What Do You Wait?, (Tagore, Rabindranath)
Moon-Boat, (Hopkins, Henry C.)
Moonbeams & Brownies, (White, Roma)
Moonblight, (Beard, Dan C.)
Mooncoin Castle, (Turkle, Brinton)
Mooneyed Hound, (Clark, Billy C.)
Moons of Balbanca, (Davis, M.E.M.)
Moonshine & Clover, (Housman, Laurence)
Moonshine & Magic, (Uttley, Alison)
Moonshine in Candle Light, (Savery, Constance)
Moorland Mousie, (Gorse, Golden)
Moorland Pony, (Beatty, Hetty B.)
Mop Top, (Freeman, Don)
Mops Versus Tails, (Ainslie, Kathleen)
Mopsa the Fairy, (Ingelow, Jean)
Moral Alphabet, (Belloc, Hilaire)
More About Animals, (Bianco, Margery W.)
More About Henri!, (Vacheron, Edith)
More About Me, (Drinkwater, John)
More About Paddington, (Bond, Michael)
More About the Squirrels, (Tyrell, Eleanor)
More Adventures of the Happy Heart Family, (Gerson, V.)
More Animals, (Herford, Oliver)
More Beasts for Worse Children, (Belloc, Hilaire)
More Beautiful than Flowers, (Lexau, Joan M.)
More Boners, (Abingdon, Alex)
More Celtic Fairy Tales, (Jacobs, Joseph (ed))
More Cheerful Americans, (Loomis, Charles B.)
More English Fairy Tales, (Jacobs, Joseph (ed))
More Fables, (Ade, George)
More Graphic Pictures, (Caldecott, R.)
More Jingles, Jokes & Funny Folks, (Bingham, Clifton)
More Monarchs of Merry England, (Carse, Roland)
More Mother Goose Village Stories, (Bigham, Madge A.)
More Nursery Rhymes of London Town, (Farjeon, Eleanor)
More Pious Friends, (Shay, Frank)
More Prayers, (Bible)

More Really So Stories, (Gordon, Elizabeth)
More Tales of Faraway Folk, (Deutsch, Babette)
More Tales of the Arabian Nights, (Olcott, F.J. (ed))
More To and Again, (Brooks, Walter)
More Tongue Tanglers & a Rigamarole, (Potter, Charles F.)
More Very Young Songs, (Fraser-Simpson, H.)
More about Teddy B. & Teddy G., (Eaton, Seymour)
More of Brer Rabbit's Tricks, (Rees, Ennis)
More than You Bargained For, (Aiken, Joan)
Morgan's Fourth Son, (Ross, Margaret I.)
Moriah's Mourning, (Stuart, Ruth M.)
Morning Face, (Stratton-Porter, Gene)
Morning is a Little Child, (Anglund, Joan W.)
Morocco, (Forrest, A.S.)
Morte d'Arthur, (Tennyson, Alfred)
Mortgage on the Brain, (Harper, Vincent)
Moses, (Petersham, Maud)
Moses, (Shippen, Kath. B.)
Mossy Trotter, (Taylor, Elizabeth)
Most Beautiful House..., (Pauli, Hertha)
Most Popular Mother Goose Songs, (Mother Goose)
Most Terrible Turk, (Krumgold, Joseph)
Most Women, (Waugh, Alec)
Most Wonderful Animals that Never Were, (Krutch, J.W.)
Most Wonderful Doll in the World, (McGinley, Phyllis)
Mota & the Monkey Tree, (Price, Margaret E.)
Mother, (Wister, Owen)
Mother & Baby, (Brine, Mary D.)
Mother & Father, (Gilson, Roy R.)
Mother Brown Earth's Children, (Deihl, Edna G.)
Mother Carey's Chickens, (Wiggin, Kate D.)
Mother Duck's Children, (Gugu)
Mother Earth's Children, (Gordon, Elizabeth)
Mother Goose & her Friends, (Warren, Maude R.)
Mother Goose Etiquette Rhymes, (Bartrug, Carey M.)
Mother Goose Fun, (Byington, Eloise)
Mother Goose Handicraft, (Jordan, Nina)
Mother Goose Nursery Rhymes, (Hosie, Margaret)
Mother Goose Parade, (Gruelle, Justin)
Mother Goose Treasury, (Briggs, Raymond)
Mother Goose for Grown Folks, (Whitney, A.D.T.)
Mother Goose for Grownups, (Carryl, Guy W.)
Mother Goose in Prose, (Baum, L. Frank)
Mother Goose's Menagerie, (Wells, Carolyn)
Mother Goose's Teddy Bears, (Cavally, Fred. L.)
Mother Goose('s)... [Most titles], (Mother Goose)
Mother Hubbard's Book of Rhymes, (N/A)
Mother Let Me Do It, (Muter, Gladys N.)
Mother Love, (Warren, Ina R.)
Mother Makes Christmas, (Meigs, Cornelia L.)
Mother Nature, (Long, William J.)
Mother Nature's Little Ones, (Fox, Frances M.)
Mother West Wind('s)... [All titles], (Burgess, Thornton)
Mother Wild Goose & Wild Beast Show, (Bridgman, L.J.)
Mother Wore Tights, (Young, Miriam)
Mother and Child, (Dorr, Nell)
Mother of Pearl, (France, Anatole)
Mother's Book of Song, (Burn, John H.)
Mother's Day, (Phelan, Mary K.)
Mother's Little Rhyme Book, (LeMair, H.W.)
Mother's Nursery Tales, (Pyle, Katharine)
Mother, Mother, I Feel Sick..., (Charlip, Remy)
Moths of the Limberlost, (Stratton-Porter, Gene)
Motor-Flight through France, (Wharton, Edith)
Motorcycle Dog, (Barnum, Jay H.)
Mountain Born, (Yates, Elizabeth)
Mountain Door, (Fry, Rosalie K.)
Mountain Goats of Temlaham, (Toye, William)

Mountain Lovers, (MacLeod, Fiona)
Mountain Pony, (Larom, Henry)
Mountain Woman, (Peattie, Elia W.)
Mountain and the Summer Stars, (Baker, Michael)
Mountain of Jade, (Irwin, Violet)
Mountain of Magic, (Nichols, Beverly)
Mountain-Land, (Chambers, Robert)
Mountain-Sprite's Kingdom, (Knatchbull-Hugessen)
Mountains are Free, (Adams, Julia D.)
Mourka: Mighty Cat, (Wyndham, Lee)
Mouse & the Motorcycle, (Cleary, Beverly)
Mouse Chorus, (Coatsworth, Eliz.)
Mouse House, (Godden, Rumer)
Mouse Manor, (Eager, Edward)
Mouse Palace, (Carpenter, Frances)
Mouse Telegrams, (Uttley, Alison)
Mouse and his Child, (Hoban, Russell)
Mouse and the Elephant, (Walker, Barbara)
Mouse and the Lion, (Titus, Eve)
Mouse with a Small Guitar, (Graham, Al)
Mousechildren & the Famous Collector, (Fine, Warren)
Mousekin's Family, (Miller, Edna)
Mouseknees, (White, William C.)
Mouseskin's Woodland Sleepers, (Miller, Edna)
Mousewife, (Godden, Rumer)
Moustachio, (Rigby, Douglas)
Moved-Outers, (Means, Florence C.)
Moxie and Hanty and Bunty, (Austin, Margot)
Moy, Moy, (Politi, Leo)
Moya and the Flamingoes, (Hallin, Emily)
Mozart: Music Magician, (Bishop, Claire H.)
Mr. & Mrs. So and So, (Francoise)
Mr. Angelo, (Schwalje, Marjory)
Mr. Apple's Family, (McDevitt, Jean)
Mr. Arctic..., (Berry, Erick)
Mr. Bass's Planetoid, (Cameron, Eleanor)
Mr. Baxter's Dandelion Garden, (Shirk, Jeannette C.)
Mr. Bear Goes to Boston, (French, Marion)
Mr. Bell Invents the Telephone, (Shippen, Kath. B.)
Mr. Benedict's Lion, (Edmonds, Walter D.)
Mr. Biddle & the Dragon, (Farmiloe, Edith)
Mr. Billy's Gun, (Hader, B.& E.)
Mr. Blanding Builds his Dream House, (Hodgins, Eric)
Mr. Blue, (Embry, Margaret)
Mr. Bonaparte of Corsica, (Bangs, John K.)
Mr. Brown Can Moo: Can You?, (Seuss, Dr.)
Mr. Brown and Mr. Grey, (Wondriska, William)
Mr. Bumps & His Monkey, (De La Mare, Walter)
Mr. Bunny · His Book, (Sutton, Adah L.)
Mr. Bunny Paints the Eggs, (Maril, Lee)
Mr. Cat's Wonderful Surprise, (Chalmers, Mary)
Mr. Chick: his Travels & Adventures, (Perkins, Lucy F.)
Mr. Chu, (Keating, Norma)
Mr. Cinnamon Bear, (Lefferts, Sara T.)
Mr. Corbett's Ghost, (Garfield, Leon)
Mr. Crow & the Whitewash, (Paine, Albert B.)
Mr. Doodle, (Scott, Sally)
Mr. Dooley's Philosophy, (Dunne, Finley P.)
Mr. Ferguson of the Fire Department, (MacGregor, E.)
Mr. Flip Flop, (Garrett, Helen)
Mr. Gallagher's Donkey, (Windsor, Mary)
Mr. Gumpy's Outing, (Burningham, John)
Mr. Heff & Mr. Ho, (Lowrey, Janette S.)
Mr. Heinie, (Beistle, Aldarilla)
Mr. Heinie & Scroot, (Beistle, Aldarilla)
Mr. Hermit Crab, (Rhys, Mimpsy)
Mr. Hermit Miser & Neighborly Pumpkin, (Govan, C.)
Mr. Jensen and Cat, (Blegvad, Lenore)

Mr. Jones & Mr. Finnigan, (Evans, Eva K.)
Mr. Justice Holmes, (Judson, Clara I.)
Mr. Kelso's Lion, (Bontemps, Arna)
Mr. Kris Kringle, (Mitchell, S. Weir)
Mr. Miacca, an English Folktale, (N/A)
Mr. Milo Bush, (Carruth, Hayden)
Mr. Mogo Mouse, (Ort, Jane)
Mr. Moonlight and Omar, (Holding, James)
Mr. Munchausen, (Bangs, John K.)
Mr. Mushroom, (Slobodkin, Louis)
Mr. Mysterious and Company, (Fleischman, Sid)
Mr. Nip & Mr. Tuck, (Emerson, Caroline)
Mr. Papadilly and Willy, (Slobodkin, Florence)
Mr. Peaceable Paints, (Weisgard, Leonard)
Mr. Pearly of Pepper Pot Lane, (Thomas, Eleanor)
Mr. Peck's Pets, (Seaman, Louise)
Mr. Penny('s)... [All titles], (Ets, Marie H.)
Mr. Petersand's Cats & Kittens, (Slobodkin, Louis)
Mr. Piccolo, (Girvin, Brenda)
Mr. Pickles and the Party, (Heward, Constance)
Mr. Pickwick's Christmas, (Dickens, Charles)
Mr. Piper's Bus, (Clymer, Eleanor)
Mr. Popper's Penguins, (Atwater, Richard)
Mr. Pringle and Mister Buttonhouse, (MacGregor, Ellen)
Mr. Punch's Country Songs, (Lucas, E.V.)
Mr. Putterbee's Jungle, (Helm, Ruth)
Mr. Pye, (Peake, Mervyn)
Mr. Rabbit & the Lovely Present, (Zolotow, Charlotte)
Mr. Rabbit at Home, (Harris, Joel C.)
Mr. Rabbit's Wedding, (Paine, Albert B.)
Mr. Red Squirrel, (Robinson, Tom P.)
Mr. Revere & I, (Lawson, Robert)
Mr. Robbins Rides Again, (Streeter, Edward)
Mr. Sheridan's Umbrella, (Strong, L.A.G.)
Mr. Songcatcher & Co., (Justus, May)
Mr. Spindles and the Spiders, (Packard, Andrew)
Mr. Stubbs, (McCready, Thomas L.)
Mr. Sun & Mrs. Moon, (LeGallienne, R.)
Mr. Sweeny, (Hoke, Helen)
Mr. T.W. Anthony Woo, (Ets, Marie H.)
Mr. Tall & Mr. Small, (Brenner, Barbara)
Mr. Tidy Paws, (Sayers, Frances C.)
Mr. Tittlewit's Holiday, (Knight, M. Forster)
Mr. Tootleoo & Co., (Darwin, Bernard)
Mr. Tootwhistle's Invention, (Wells, Peter)
Mr. Topple's Wish, (Chalmers, Audrey)
Mr. Twigg's Mistake, (Lawson, Robert)
Mr. Upstairs and Mr. Downstairs, (Norman, Charles)
Mr. Whistle's Secret, (Palazzo, Tony)
Mr. Wicker's Window, (Dawson, Carley)
Mr. Willowby's Christmas Tree, (Barry, Robert E.)
Mr. Wilmer, (Lawson, Robert)
Mr. Wind & Madam Rain, (DeMusset, Paul)
Mr. Woodchuck, (Bancroft, Laura)
Mr. Wubbles Bubbles, (Merryman, Mildred P.)
Mr. and Mrs. Noah, (Lenski, Lois)
Mrs. 'Arris... [All titles], (Gallico, Paul)
Mrs. Cliff's Yacht, (Stockton, Frank)
Mrs. Cockle's Cat, (Pearce, Philippa)
Mrs. Cucumber Green, (Bonner, Mary G.)
Mrs. Doodlepunk Trades Work, (Dodworth, Dorothy)
Mrs. Easter and the Storks, (Drummond, Violet H.)
Mrs. Fox, (Erwin, John)
Mrs. Gerald, (Pool, Maria L.)
Mrs. Goose and Three Ducks, (Potter, Miriam C.)
Mrs. Grumble and Fire Engine Number 7, (Martin, Patricia)
Mrs. Herring, (Shemin, Margaretha)
Mrs. John Vernon, (Addison, Julia)

Mrs. Kindbush, (Howes, Edith)
Mrs. Knollys, (Stimson, Frederic J.)
Mrs. Leicester's School, (Lamb, Charles)
Mrs. Mallard's Ducklings, (Delafield, Celia)
Mrs. Malone, (Farjeon, Eleanor)
Mrs. McGarrity's Peppermint Sweater, (Holl, Adelaide)
Mrs. McThing: A Play, (Chase, Mary)
Mrs. Mouse Spring-Cleans, (Uttley, Alison)
Mrs. Neverbody's Recipes, (Yeo, Wilma)
Mrs. Overtheway's Rememberances, (Ewing, Juliana H.)
Mrs. Peregrine & the Yak, (Burns, Esther)
Mrs. Peregrine at the Fair, (Burns, Esther)
Mrs. Perrywinkle's Pets, (Thayer, Jane)
Mrs. Peter Rabbit, (Burgess, Thornton)
Mrs. Piggle-Wiggle... [All titles], (MacDonald, Betty)
Mrs. Polly's Party, (Bromhall, Winifred)
Mrs. Purdy's Children, (Loomis, Ruth)
Mrs. Roo and the Bunnies, (Learnard, Rachel)
Mrs. Silk, (Hoke, Helen)
Mrs. Tickler's Caravan, (Aldin, Cecil)
Mrs. Tree, (Richards, Laura E.)
Mrs. Updaisy, (Lampman, Evelyn)
Mrs. Wappinger's Secret, (Hightower, Florence)
Mud Pies & other Recipes, (Winslow, Marjorie)
Muddy Road to Glory, (Meader, Stephen W.)
Muffin Shop, (Garnett, Louise A.)
Muffy: Tale of a Muskrat, (Bird, Zenobia)
Muggins Mouse, (Barrows, Marjorie)
Muggsy, (Holland, Marion)
Mulberry Village, (Hollister, Mary)
Mule Twins, (Hogan, Inez)
Mule of the Parthenon, (Parton, Ethel)
Muley-Ears, Nobody's Dog, (Henry, Marguerite)
Mullingar Heifer, (Walsh, Mary R.)
Mumfie's Magic Box, (Tozer, Katharine)
Mummy's Bedtime Story Book, (Marion)
Musa the Shoemaker, (Stinetorf, Louise)
Mushroom Boy, (Harper, Theodore A.)
Mushroom Fairies, (Sutton, Adah L.)
Music Master, (Klein, Charles)
Music in Pussytown, (Wain, Louis)
Music of the Wild, (Stratton-Porter, Gene)
Musical Box, (Leighton, Clare)
Musical Tree, (Stilwell, Sarah)
Musical Zoo, (Nash, Ogden)
Musings by Campfire & Wayside, (Gray, William C.)
Musket and the Cross, (Edmonds, Walter D.)
Muskox: Little Tootoo's Friend, (Stafford, Marie A.)
Mustang: Wild Spirit of the West, (Henry, Marguerite)
Mustard, Pepper and Salt, (Uttley, Alison)
My Antonia, (Cather, Willa)
My Apingi Kingdom, (DuChaillu, Paul)
My Appalachia: A Reminiscence, (Caudill, Rebecca)
My Blue Book, (Read, Helen S.)
My Book of Best Fairy Tales, (Bayne, C. (ed.))
My Book of Favorite Fairy Tales, (Vredenburg, Edric)
My Book of Parties, (Snyder, Madeline)
My Brother, (Brown, Vincent)
My Brother Bird, (Ames, Evelyn)
My Brother Mike, (Gates, Doris)
My Brothers & I, (Finta, Alexander)
My Bunny Feels Soft, (Steiner, Charlotte)
My Busy Days, (Sturgis, Edith B.)
My Country, (Tittle, Walter)
My Cousin Abe, (Fisher, Aileen)
My Days with the Fairies, (Stawell, Mrs. R.)
My Dear Patsy, (Weil, Ann Y.)
My Dog, (Maeterlinck, Maurice)

My Dog Rinty, (Tarry, Ellen)
My Dog and I, (Lord, Nancy)
My Dog is Lost!, (Keats, Ezra J.)
My Dolly and Me, (Scarry, Patricia)
My Fairyland: Child's Own Visions, (Malcolm, Fiona)
My Father's Dragon, (Gannett, Ruth S.)
My Favorite Age, (Morrow, Elizabeth)
My First Horse, (James, Will)
My First Picture Book, (Weisgard, Leonard)
My Five Senses, (Aliki)
My Five Tigers, (Alexander, Lloyd C.)
My Friend Charlie, (Flora, James)
My Friend Flicka, (O'Hara, Mary)
My Friend John, (Zolotow, Charlotte)
My Friend Mac, (McNeer, May)
My Friend Mr. Leakey, (Haldane, J.B.S.)
My Friend Phil, (Peacocke, Isabel M.)
My Friend Yakub, (Kalashnikoff, N.)
My Friend the Dog, (Terhune, Albert P.)
My Golden Book of Manners, (Parish, Peggy)
My Grandpa's Farm, (Thompson, Mary W.)
My High School Days, (N/A)
My Kingdom for a Dragon, (Haley, Gail E.)
My Lady, (Bouvet, Marguerite)
My Lady Caprice, (Farnol, Jeffery)
My Lady Nicotine, (Barrie, James M.)
My Lady Peggy Goes to Town, (Mathews, Frances A.)
My Lady of the South, (Parrish, Randall)
My Lady's Slipper, (Brady, Cyrus T.)
My Life in Art, (Bemelmans, Ludwig)
My Lives & How I Lost Them, (Cullen, Countee)
My Love Affair with Music, (Alexander, Lloyd C.)
My Mother and I, (Fisher, Aileen)
My Mother/Most Beautiful Woman... (Reyher, R.)
My Name Is..., (Muehl, Lois B.)
My Name is Aram, (Saroyan, William)
My Name is Lion, (Embry, Margaret)
My New Home, (Molesworth, Mrs.)
My Own Dolly, (Blanchard, Amy E.)
My Own Fairy Book, (Lang, Andrew)
My Pet Peepelo, (Credle, Ellis)
My Poetry Book, (Huffard, Grace T.)
My Red Umbrella, (Bright, Robert)
My Rhyme & Picture Book, (Barrows, Marjorie)
My Robin, (Burnett, Frances H.)
My Side of the Mountain, (George, Jean C.)
My Sister and I, (Buckley, Helen E.)
My Sixty Years on the Plains, (Hamilton, William T.)
My Slippers are Red, (Steiner, Charlotte)
My Snuggly Bunny, (Scarry, Patricia)
My Son & I, (Spielmann, M.H.)
My Son the Mouse, (Kraus, Robert)
My Time of Year, (Dow, Katherine)
My Twin Kitties, (Deihl, Edna G.)
My Uncle Silas, (Bates, Herbert E.)
My Very Own Fairy Stories, (Gruelle, Johnny)
My Very Own Special Particular...Cat (Warburg, Sandol)
My Village, (Smith, E. Boyd)
My Visit to the Dinosaurs, (Aliki)
My World, (Brown, Margaret W.)
Myrtle Albertine's Song, (Pohlmann, Lilton)
Myself & I, (Van Valkenburgh, H.)
Myself when Young, (Mirza, Youel B.)
Mysterious Christmas Shell, (Cameron, Eleanor)
Mysterious Island, (Verne, Jules)
Mysterious Leaf, (Banks, Richard)
Mysterious Machine, (Dines, Glen)
Mysterious Stranger, (Twain, Mark)

Mysterious Voyage, (Farrow, George E.)
Mystery Club, (Whitney, Elinor)
Mystery Island, (Hurst, Edward H.)
Mystery Mountain, (Bowman, James C.)
Mystery at Boulder Point, (Jewett, Eleanore)
Mystery at Deserted Mill, (Govan, Christine)
Mystery at East Hatchett, (Bacon, Peggy)
Mystery at Moccasin Bend, (Govan, Christine)
Mystery at the Red House, (Meigs, Cornelia L.)
Mystery for Mr. Bass, (Cameron, Eleanor)
Mystery of Carmen the Cow, (McCracken, Russell)
Mystery of Crystal Canyon, (Montgomery, R.)
Mystery of Dog Flip, (Lenotre, Therese)
Mystery of Musical Umbrella, (Feld, Freidrich)
Mystery of Obadiah, (Armstrong, Richard)
Mystery of Willet, (Watkins, Richard)
Mystery of the Fat Cat, (Bonham, Frank)
Mystery of the Flaming Hut, (Best, Herbert)
Mystery of the Gulls, (Whitney, Phyllis)
Mystery of the Pacific, (Smeaton, William H.)
Mystery of the Red Tide, (Bonham, Frank)
Mystery of the Turquoise Frog, (Montgomery, R.)
Mystery of the Woods, (Stolz, Mary S.)
Mystery on the Isle of Skye, (Whitney, Phyllis)
Mythological Zoo, (Herford, Oliver)
Myths & Enchantment Tales, (Price, Margaret E.)
Myths & Legends of Japan, (Davis, Frederick H.)
Myths Every Child Should Know, (Mabie, Hamilton W.)
Myths of Babylonia & Assyria, (Spence, Lewis)
N by E, (Kent, Rockwell)
N is for Nursery School, (Budney, Blossom)
Nacar, the White Deer, (DeTrevino, Elizabeth)
Nadita, (Moon, Grace P.)
Nadya Makes her Bow, (Haskell, Helen E.)
Nail Soup: Swedish Folktale, (Zemach, Harve)
Nails to Nickels, (Campbell, Elizabeth)
Naja the Snake & Mangus the Mongoose, (Kirkpatrick, O.)
Name for Kitty, (McGinley, Phyllis)
Name for Obed, (Phillips, Ethel C.)
Nameless Cat, (Lockridge, Frances)
Nan in the City, (Hamlin, Myra)
Nan of Music Mountain, (Spearman, Frank)
Nan's Chicopee Children, (Hamlin, Myra)
Nancy Alden, (White, Eliza O.)
Nancy Davenport, (Fox, Frances M.)
Nancy Hanks of Wilderness Road, (LeSueur, Meridel)
Nancy Keeps House, (Laird, Helene)
Nancy Owlett, (Phillpotts, Eden)
Nancy Rutledge, (Pyle, Katharine)
Nancy Sails, (Wasson, Mildred)
Nancy and Plum, (MacDonald, Betty)
Nancy in the Wood, (Bryce, Marion)
Nancy the Joyous, (Stow, Edith)
Nancy's Country Christmas, (Hoyt, Eleanor)
Nanette Goes to Visit Grandmother, (Gates, Josephine S.)
Nannabah's Friend, (Perrine, Mary)
Nannette, (Fox, Frances M.)
Nansen, (Hall, Anna G.)
Napoleon Jackson, (Stuart, Ruth M.)
Napoleon of Notting Hill, (Chesterton, G.K.)
Nappy... [All titles], (Hogan, Inez)
Narcissa Whitman, (Eaton, Jeanette)
Narcissus an' De Chillun, (Govan, Christine)
Nathalie's Chum, (Ray, Anna C.)
Nathalie's Sister, (Ray, Anna C.)
National Cook Book, (Harland, Marion)
National Velvet, (Bagnold, Enid)
Nature Detective, (Selsam, Millicent)

Naughty Boy, a Poem, (Keats, John)
Naughty Children, (Brand, Christianna)
Nautical Lays of a Landsman, (Irwin, Wallace)
Navaho Sister, (Lampman, Evelyn)
Navaho Tales, (Whitman, William)
Navarre of the North, (Darling, Esther B.)
Navy Alphabet, (Baum, L. Frank)
Ne'er-Do-Well, (Beach, Rex)
Near East, (Hichens, Robert)
Near Side and Far, (Justus, May)
Nearsighted Knight, (Shura, Mary F.)
Neatness of Bobby Coon, (Burgess, Thornton)
Necklace of Jewels, (Murphy, Marguerite)
Necklace of Princess Fiorimonde, (DeMorgan, Mary)
Necklace of Raindrops, (Aiken, Joan)
Ned & the Rustlers, (Tousey, Sanford)
Ned and Ed and the Lion, (Balet, Jan B.)
Nedra, (McCutcheon, George B.)
Needle in the Haystack, (Matheson, John)
Nehru's Story, (Masani, Shakuntala)
Nellie & her Flying Crocodile, (Walsh, Chad)
Nellie and the Mayor's Hat, (Baker, Charlotte)
Nelson's Yankee Boy, (Costello, F.H.)
Nemo Meets the Emperor, (Bannon, Laura)
Never-Grow-Old Stories, (Aesopus)
New & True, (Staver, Mary W.)
New Adventures of Alice, (Rae, John)
New Alice in the Old Wonderland, (Richards, Anna M.)
New Baby, (Shane, Ruth & Harold)
New Book of the Fairies, (Harraden, Beatrice)
New Boy, (Tovey, Doreen)
New Boy, (Urmston, Mary)
New Boy in School, (Justus, May)
New Cautionary Tales, (Belloc, Hilaire)
New Chronicles of Rebecca, (Wiggin, Kate D.)
New England Butt'ry Shelf Almanac, (Campbell, Mary M.)
New Feathers for the Old Goose, (Becker, John L.)
New Fire Engine, (Barnum, Jay H.)
New Found World, (Shippen, Kath. B.)
New Friend, (Zolotow, Charlotte)
New Friends for Susan, (Uchida, Yoshiko)
New Home for Billy, (Justus, May)
New House that Jack Built, (King, Elizabeth)
New Illustrated Book of Favorite Hymns, (Bertail, Inez)
New Land, (Schmidt, Sarah L.)
New Life, (Dante)
New Lights O'London, (Maxwell, Donald)
New Mexican Boy, (Marshall, Helen L.)
New Moon, (Meigs, Cornelia L.)
New Negro, (Locke, Alain L. (ed))
New Noah's Ark, (Bell, John J.)
New Northland, (Gratacap, L.P.)
New Nutcracker Suite, (Nash, Ogden)
New Order, (Szyk, Arthur)
New Pacific, (Bancroft, Hubert H.)
New Panjandrum, (Farrow, George E.)
New Pet, (Flack, Marjorie)
New Shoes, (Streatfeild, Noel)
New Singing Time, (Coleman, Satis)
New Songs for New Voices, (Untermeyer, Louis)
New Story of Little Black Sambo, (Vetsch, Earnest)
New Story of Peter Rabbit, (Lowe, Samuel E.)
New Sun, (Yashima, Taro)
New Swiss Family Robinson, (Wister, Owen)
New Tall Tales of Pecos Bill, (Felton, Harold)
New Treasure Seekers, (Nesbit, Edith)
New Vestments, (Lear, Edward)
New Wizard of Oz, (Baum, L. Frank)

New Wonderland, (Baum, L. Frank)
New World Fairy Book, (Kennedy, Howard A.)
New World for Nellie, (Emett, Rowland)
New Year's Carol, (Spyri, Johanna)
New York Nights, (Graham, Stephen)
New Zealand, (Reeves, William P.)
New at the Zoo, (Lippman, Peter J.)
News from Notown, (Perkins, Eleanor E.)
News of Spring, (Maeterlinck, Maurice)
Newton Foster, (Marryat, Frederick)
Next Door to Xanadu, (Orgel, Doris)
Next Fine Day: A Novel, (Yates, Elizabeth)
Next-Door House, (Molesworth, Mrs.)
Next-Door Morelands, (Lewis, Emily W.)
Next-Night Stories, (Messer, Clarence J.)
Nibble Nibble, (Brown, Margaret W.)
Nibble Nibble Mousekin, (Anglund, Joan W.)
Nibby, (Meyer, Ann)
Nibs: Orphan Deer of the Adirondacks, (Lang, Don)
Nic of the Woods, (Ward, Lynd)
Nicanor, Teller of Tales, (Taylor, C. Bryson)
Nicholas, (Kempner, Carol)
Nicholas, (Moore, Ann C.)
Nicholas & Golden Goose, (Moore, Ann C.)
Nicholas Arnold, Toolmaker, (Lansing, Marion)
Nicholas Needlefoot, (Nesbitt, Philip)
Nicholas and Fast Moving Diesel, (Ardizzone, Edward)
Nicholas and the Wool-Pack, (Harnett, Cynthia)
Nicky's Bugle, (Rietveld, Jane)
Nicodemus... [All titles], (Hogan, Inez)
Nicolau's Prize, (Foltz, Mary Jane)
Night & the Cat, (Coatsworth, Eliz.)
Night Adventures of Alexis, (Graham, Eleanor)
Night Before Christmas, (Moore, Clement C.)
Night Before Christmas & Jingles, (N/A)
Night Cat, (Black, Irma S.)
Night Side of London, (Machray, Robert)
Night They Stole the Alphabet, (Joslin, Sesyle)
Night and Day, (Brown, Margaret W.)
Night in Acadie, (Chopin, Kate R.)
Night it Rained Toys, (Stephenson, Dorothy)
Night of Wonders, (Bedford, Francis D.)
Night the Lights Went Out, (Freeman, Don)
Night's Nice, (Emberley, Barbara)
Night-Caps for the Babies, (Young, Charles)
Nightbirds on Nantucket, (Aiken, Joan)
Nightcrawlers, (Addams, Charles)
Nightingale House, (Palmer, Elizabeth)
Nightmare Land, (Clark, G.O)
Nihal, (Murphey, Eleanor A.)
Nikkos of the Pink Pelican, (Tooze, Ruth)
Nikolenka's Childhood, (Tolstoy, Leo)
Nikos and the Sea God, (Gramatky, Hardie)
Nils, (D'Aulaire, I.& E.)
Nils All Alone, (Sigsgaard, Jens)
Nimbo, (Pease, Josephine)
Nimrod's Wife, (Seton, Grace G.)
Nine Days to Christmas, (Ets, Marie H.)
Nine Lives, (Fenton, Edward)
Nine Lives of Homer C. Cat, (Calhoun, Mary)
Nine Questions, (Fenton, Edward)
Nine Tales of Coyote, (Martin, Fran)
Nine Unlikely Tales for Children, (Nesbit, Edith)
Ning's Pony, (Hawkes, Hester)
Nino, (Angelo, Valenti)
Nino & his Fish, (Hurd, Edith T.)
Ninth Man, (Vorse, Mary Heaton)
Nip & Tuck, (Freeman, Leila C.)

Nip & Tuck in Toyland, (Freeman, Leila C.)
Nipper Shiffer's Donkey, (Rosenquist, Fingal)
Nipper the Little Bull Pup, (L'Hommedieu, Dorothy)
Nita, (Saunders, Marshall)
Nitty Gritty, (Bonham, Frank)
Nkwala, (Sharp, Edith L.)
No Beat of Drum, (Burton, Hester)
No Children, No Pets, (Holland, Marion)
No Ducks for Dinner, (Hall, Rosalys)
No Fighting! No Biting!, (Minarik, Else H.)
No Flying in the House, (Brock, Betty)
No Funny Business, (Hurd, Edith T.)
No One Must Know, (Sleigh, Barbara)
No Place Like Home, (N/A)
No Ponies, (Treadgold, Mary)
No Road Too Long, (Hawthorne, Hildegarde)
No Room, (Dobbs, Rose)
No Room for Nicky, (Kaufmann, Alicia)
No Room for a Dog, (Holland, Marion)
No Roses for Harry!, (Zion, Gene)
No Rubbish Here, (Evans, Myfanwy)
No Surrender!, (Henty, G.A.)
No Time for Funnies, (Todd, Ann)
No Trouble at All, (Brown, Paul)
No, No Rosina, (Martin, Patricia)
No, No, Taffy, (McDevitt, Jean)
No-Name Man of the Mountain, (Steele, William O.)
No-Sitch: the Hound, (Stong, Philip D.)
Noah an' Jonah an' Cap'n John Smith, (Marquis, Don)
Noah's Ark, (Palazzo, Tony)
Noah's Ark Book, (Fish, Anne H.)
Noah's Nightmare, (McNagny, Bob)
Noble Doll, (Coatsworth, Eliz.)
Nobody Listens to Andrew, (Guilfoile, Elizabeth)
Nobody Plays with a Cabbage, (DeJong, Meindert)
Nobody's Birthday, (Colver, Anne)
Nobody's Boy, (Malot, Hector)
Nobody's Cat, (Miles, Miska)
Nobody's Doll, (DeLeeuw, Adele)
Nobody's Mouse, (Brock, Emma)
Nock Family Circus, (Huber, Ursula)
Noel for Jeanne-Marie, (Francoise)
Nogbad and the Elephants, (Postgate, Oliver)
Noggin and the Moon Mouse, (Postgate, Oliver)
Noise in the Night, (Alexander, Anne)
Noises & Mr. Flibberty-Jib, (Crampton, Gertrude)
Noisy Bird Book, (Brown, Margaret W.)
Noisy Book, (Brown, Margaret W.)
Noisy Nancy Norris, (Gaeddert, Lou Ann)
Noisy Nora, (Lofting, Hugh)
Nomi and the Lovely Animals, (Slobodkin, Louis)
Nonsense Nonsense!, (Jerrold, Walter)
Nonsense Novels, (Leacock, Stephen B.)
Nonsense Songs, (Lear, Edward)
Noodle, (Leaf, Munro)
Noodles, Nitwits and Numskulls, (Leach, Maria)
Noon Balloon, (Brown, Margaret W.)
Noonday Friends, (Stolz, Mary S.)
Nordy Bank, (Porter, Sheena)
Norman the Doorman, (Freeman, Don)
Norse Fairy Tales, (Asbjornsen, P.C.)
Norse Gods and Giants, (D'Aulaire, I.& E.)
Norse Stories, (Mabie, Hamilton W.)
North Cornwall Fairies and Legends, (Tregarthen, Enys)
North Star Shining, (Swift, Hildegarde H.)
North Wind and the Sun, (La Fontaine, J.)
North of Fifty-Three, (Sinclair, Bertrand)
North of Nowhere, (Sleigh, Barbara)

Northanger Abbey, (Austen, Jane)
Northern Christmas, (Kent, Rockwell)
Northern Lights, (Parker, Gilbert)
Northern Trails, (Long, William J.)
Norwegian Fairy Book, (Stroebe, C. (ed.))
Not Over Ten Inches High, (Levy, Harry)
Not So Long Ago, (Holberg, Ruth)
Not Without Danger, (Best, Herbert)
Not a Little Monkey, (Zolotow, Charlotte)
Nothing But Cats, Cats, Cats, (Skaar, Grace M.)
Nothing Ever Happens on my Block, (Raskin, Ellen)
Nothing at All, (Gag, Wanda)
Nothing to Do, (Hoban, Russell)
Now I Know, (Schwartz, Julius)
Now I Lay Me Down to Sleep, (Bemelmans, Ludwig)
Now It's Fall, (Lenski, Lois)
Now Open the Box, (Kunhardt, Dorothy)
Now This, Now That, (Baer, Howard)
Now Try This, (Schneider, Herman)
Now We Are Six, (Milne, A.A.)
Now and Then..., (Smalley, Janet)
Nowadays Fairy Book, (Chapin, Anna A.)
Nu Dang and his Kite, (Ayer, Jacqueline)
Nubber Bear, (Lipkind, Will)
Number 5 Hackberry Street, (Govan, Christine)
Numerous Names Nimbly Narrated, (Sandys, Ruth)
Nuova or the New Bee, (Kellogg, Vernon L.)
Nura's Garden of Betty & Booth, (Nura)
Nurnberg Stove, (De La Rame, M.)
Nurse Heatherdale's Story, (Molesworth, Mrs.)
Nurse Matilda, (Brand, Christianna)
Nurse Matilda Goes to Town, (Brand, Christianna)
Nurse Nora's Up-to-Date Fairy Tales, (Flower, Esther)
Nursery & Mother Goose Rhymes, (DeAngeli, Marguerite)
Nursery Alice, (Carroll, Lewis)
Nursery Cats, (Wain, Louis)
Nursery Friends from France, (Miller, Olive B.)
Nursery Garland, (Cheatham, Kitty)
Nursery Geography, (Dickson, George S.)
Nursery Nights, (Haviland-Taylor, K.)
Nursery Peter Pan, (Barrie, James M.)
Nursery Rhyme Book, (Lang, Andrew)
Nursery Rhyme Picture Book, (N/A)
Nursery Rhymes, (Fraser, Claud L.)
Nursery Rhymes, (N/A)
Nursery Rhymes & Fables, (N/A)
Nursery Rhymes and Songs, (Dallam, Helen)
Nursery Rhymes from Bohemia, (Sedlacek, Hanus)
Nursery Rhymes of London Town, (Farjeon, Eleanor)
Nursery Stories from Silly Symphony, (Disney, Walt)
Nursery Zoo, (Anderson, Anne)
Nursie's Little Rhyme Book., (LeMair, H.W.)
Nutcracker, (Latham, Jean L.)
Nutcracker & Mouse King, (Hoffmann, Ernst T.)
Nutcracker Suite, (Disney, Walt)
Nutcracker and Mouse King, (Browne, Edgar G.)
Nutcracker of Nuremberg, (Cooke, Donald E.)
Nutcracker of Nuremberg, (Dumas, Alexandre)
Nuts & May, (Farjeon, Eleanor)
Nuvat the Brave, (Doone, Radko)
Nymphidia, (Drayton, Michael)
O-Heart-San, (Haskell, Helen E.)
Oak that Would not Pay, (De La Iglesia, Maria)
Oakleigh, (Deland, Ellen D.)
Oaktree Fairy Book, (Johnson, Clifton (ed))
Oars, Sails & Steam, (Tunis, Edwin B.)
Oasis of the Stars, (Economakis, Olga)
Obadiah the Bold, (Turkle, Brinton)

Object Lesson, (Gorey, Edward)
Oboli Boboli & Little Joboli, (Darwin, Bernard)
Observations, (Beerbohm, Max)
Ocean Outposts, (Follett, Helen T.)
Ocean-Born Mary, (Lenski, Lois)
Octagon Magic, (Norton, Andre)
October Vagabonds, (LeGallienne, R.)
Octopus Lives in the Ocean, (Stephens, William)
Odd Old Mammals, (Armour, Richard)
Odd One, (LeFevre, A.)
Oddity Land, (Anthony, Edward)
Oddland and other Fairy Tales, (James, Harry A.)
Odie Seeks a Friend, (King, Julius)
Odysseus, Hero of Ithaca, (Burt, Mary E.)
Odysseus, Sage of Greece, (Chidsey, Alan)
Odyssey of Courage, (Wojciechowska, Maia)
Odyssey of Homer, (N/A)
Odyssey of Homer, (Palmer, G. (tr))
Of Courage Undaunted, (Daugherty, James)
Of Dikes and Windmills, (Spier, Peter E.)
Of Houses and Cats, (DeChazeau, Eunice)
Of Uncles and Aunts, (Bettina)
Off With Their Heads!, (Bacon, Peggy)
Off to Bed, (Petersham, Maud)
Off to Philadelphia, (Allee, Marjorie H.)
Off to the Gold Fields, (Fisher, Aileen)
Og - Son of Fire, (Crump, Irving)
Oh Lord, I Wish I was a Buzzard, (Greenberg, Polly)
Oh Skin-nay!, (Nesbit, Wilbur D.)
Oh Susannah, (Holberg, Ruth)
Oh What Nonsense!, (Cole, William)
Oh! Poor Amelia Jane!, (Ainslie, Kathleen)
Oh, How Silly!, (Cole, William)
Oil Comes to Us, (Wyler, Rose)
Ojo in Oz, (Thompson, Ruth P.)
Ol' Dan Tucker, (Langstaff, John)
Ol' Paul, Mighty Logger, (Rounds, Glen)
Ola, (D'Aulaire, I.& E.)
Ola & Blakken & Line Sine & Trine, (D'Aulaire, I.& E.)
Ola and the Runaway Bread, (Himes, Vera C.)
Olaf Reads, (Lexau, Joan M.)
Olaf is Late, (Lexau, Joan M.)
Olaf the Glorious, (Leighton, Robert)
Old Abe, American Eagle, (Sherwood, Lorraine)
Old Ballads in Prose, (Tappan, Eva M.)
Old Ben, (Otis, James)
Old Ben, (Stuart, Jesse)
Old Bet, (Colver, Anne)
Old Blue, (Tousey, Sanford)
Old Bones, the Wonder Horse, (Pace, Mildred M.)
Old Bullfrog, (Freschet, Berniece)
Old Charlie, (Bulla, Clyde R.)
Old Chester Tales, (Deland, Margaret)
Old Christmas... [All titles], (Irving, Washington)
Old Con and Patrick, (Sawyer, Ruth)
Old Country House, (LeGallienne, R.)
Old Crackfoot, (Allred, Gordon)
Old Creole Days, (Cable, George W.)
Old Crow Stories, (Judson, Katherine)
Old Curiosity Shop, (Dickens, Charles)
Old Dutch Nursery Rhymes, (Elkin, R.H.)
Old English Christmas, (Irving, Washington)
Old English Fairy Tales, (Baring-Gould, Sabine)
Old English Nursery Songs, (Mansion, Horace)
Old English Nursery Tales, (Faulkner, Georgene)
Old English Singing Games, (Gomme, Alice B.)
Old English Songs... [All titles], (N/A)
Old Fairy Tales, (N/A)

Old Fairy Tales, (Vredenburg, Edric)
Old Farm Fairies, (McCook, Henry C.)
Old Fashioned Christmas Day, (Irving, Washington)
Old Fashioned Fairy Tales, (Ewing, Juliana H.)
Old Fashioned Fairy Tales, (Washburne, Marion)
Old Fashioned Flowers, (Maeterlinck, Maurice)
Old Fashioned Girls, (Fyleman, Rose)
Old Fashioned Tales, (Lucas, E.V.)
Old Father Christmas, (Mack, Robert E.)
Old Father Santa Claus, (Mack, Robert E.)
Old Father Time & his 12 Children, (Mack, Robert E.)
Old French Fairy Tales, (DeSegur, Sophie)
Old French Nursery Songs, (Anderson, Anne)
Old Friends and New Fables, (Morris, Alice T.)
Old Garden, (Deland, Margaret)
Old Gentleman of the Black Stock, (Page, Thomas N.)
Old Gold, (Fenn, Geo. Manville)
Old Granny Fox, (Burgess, Thornton)
Old House, (Boylan, Grace D.)
Old Indian Days, (Eastman, Charles A.)
Old Inns, (Aldin, Cecil)
Old Jim Badger on the Moccasin Trail, (Sabin, Edwin L.)
Old Joe, (De La Mare, Walter)
Old John, (Cregan, Mairin)
Old King Cole's Book of Nursery Rhymes, (N/A)
Old Lines & New in Black & White, (Smith, Francis H.)
Old Lion, (De La Mare, Walter)
Old Man is Always Right, (Andersen, Hans C.)
Old Man of the Mountain, (Strang, Herbert)
Old Manor Houses, (Aldin, Cecil)
Old Mother Hubbard, (Costello, Charles J.)
Old Mother Hubbard, (Denslow, W.W.)
Old Mother Hubbard, (N/A)
Old Mother Hubbard and Her Dog, (Martin, Sarah C.)
Old Mother West Wind, (Burgess, Thornton)
Old Mrs. Billups and the Black Cats, (Carroll, Ruth)
Old Mrs. Twindlytart, (Livingston, Myra C.)
Old Neapolitan Fairy Tales, (Mincieli, Rose)
Old Nurse's Stocking Basket, (Farjeon, Eleanor)
Old Nursery Rhymes, (N/A)
Old Nursery Stories & Rhymes, (N/A)
Old Old Tales Retold, (Various)
Old Peabody Pew, (Wiggin, Kate D.)
Old Perisher, (Ross, Diana)
Old Peter's Russian Tales, (Ransome, Arthur)
Old Pincushion, (Molesworth, Mrs.)
Old Plantation Days, (Gielow, Martha S.)
Old Possum's Book of Practical Cats, (Eliot, T.S.)
Old Rabbit the Voodoo, (Owen, Mary A.)
Old Ramon, (Schaefer, Jack W.)
Old Raven's World, (Maury, Jean W.)
Old Rhymes with New Tunes, (Terry, Richard R.)
Old Rose and Silver, (Reed, Myrtle)
Old Rosie, the Horse Nobody Understood, (Moore, Lilian)
Old Sailor, (Milne, A.A.)
Old Sam & the Horse Thieves, (Taylor, Don A.)
Old Santa Fe Trail, (Inman, Henry)
Old Silversides, (Hurd, Edith T.)
Old Songs for Young Americans, (Forsythe, Clarence)
Old Songs in French & English, (N/A)
Old Swedish Fairy Tales, (Wahlenberg, Anna)
Old Sweetheart of Mine, (Riley, James W.)
Old Testament, (Bible)
Old Time Rhymes, (N/A)
Old Time Stories, (Perrault, Charles)
Old Tobacco Shop, (Bowen, William)
Old Whirlwind, (Coatsworth, Eliz.)
Old Willow-Tree & other Stories, (Ewald, Carl)

Old Winkle and the Seagulls, (Rose, Elizabeth)
Old Woman & Crooked Sixpence, (Hader, B.& E.)
Old Woman & her Pig, (N/A)
Old World Japan, (Rinder, Frank)
Old Yeller, (Gipson, Fred B.)
Old Youngsters, (Tucker, Elizabeth S.)
Old Zion, (Mayne, William)
Old-Fashioned Girl, (Alcott, Louisa M.)
Old-Time Stories, (Perrault, Charles)
Old-World Love Stories, (Mason, Eugene (tr))
Oldest Story..., (Thompson, Blanche J.)
Ole Mammy's Torment, (Johnston, Annie F.)
Oley, the Sea Monster, (Ets, Marie H.)
Olive Fairy Book, (Lang, Andrew)
Oliver & the Crying Chip, (Durant, Nancy M.)
Olivia, (Molesworth, Mrs.)
Olle's Ski Trip, (Beskow, Elsa)
Olly's Polliwogs, (Rockwell, Anne)
Olode the Hunter, (Courlander, Harold)
Olympian Nights, (Bangs, John K.)
Omar the Discontented Cat, (Chamberlin, Ethel C.)
Omen of the Birds, (Behn, Harry)
Omjee, The Wizard, (Hulbert, Homer B.)
Omnibus Boners, (Abingdon, Alex)
Omoo, (Melville, Herman)
On Beyond Zebra!, (Seuss, Dr.)
On Board Noah's Ark, (Bemelmans, Ludwig)
On Canada's Frontier, (Ralph, Julian)
On Christmas Day in the Evening, (Richmond, Grace S.)
On Christmas Eve, (Brown, Margaret W.)
On Earth Peace..., (Kent, Rockwell)
On My Beach there are Many Pebbles, (Lionni, Leo)
On Newfound River, (Page, Thomas N.)
On Safari, (Waldeck, Theodore)
On Snow-Shoes to the Barren Grounds, (Whitney, Caspar)
On Stage, Mr. Jefferson!, (Latham, Jean L.)
On That Night, (Yates, Elizabeth)
On Your Mark, (Barbour, Ralph H.)
On a Lark to the Planets, (Montgomery, F.T.)
On a Summer Day, (Lenski, Lois)
On the Banks of Plum Creek, (Wilder, Laura I.)
On the Broads, (Dodd, Anna B.)
On the Contrary, (McGinley, Phyllis)
On the Field of Waterloo, (Brereton, Frederick)
On the Golden Trail, (Hawthorne, Hildegarde)
On the Green Meadows, (Burgess, Thornton)
On the Irrawaddy, (Henty, G.A.)
On the Plains with Custer, (Sabin, Edwin L.)
On the Plantation, (Harris, Joel C.)
On the Road to Make-Believe, (Forster, Frederick J.)
On the Sand Dune, (Orgel, Doris)
On the Staked Plain, (Kelly, Eric P.)
On the Tree Top, (Bates, Clara D.)
On the Verge, (Sandoz, Maurice)
On the Way to Wonderland, (Bates, Clara D.)
Once Around the Sun, (Atkinson, Brooks)
Once On a Time, (Dalgliesh, Alice)
Once On a Time, (Milne, A.A.)
Once There Was and was Not, (Dane, George E.)
Once There was a Prince, (Dunbar, Aldis)
Once Upon a Monday, (Willson, Dixie)
Once Upon a Mountain, (Bolognese, Don)
Once Upon a Season, (Moore, Lilian)
Once Upon a Springtime, (Austin, Margot)
Once Upon a Time, (Bates, Katharine L.)
Once Upon a Time, (Dobbs, Rose)
Once Upon a Time, (Perrault, Charles)
Once Upon a Time Tales, (Stewart, Mary)

Once Upon a Time in Egypt, (Gere, Frances K.)
Once Upon a Totem, (Harris, Christie)
Once When I was Five, (Zimelman, Nathan)
Once a Mouse, (Brown, Marcia)
Once in the Year, (Yates, Elizabeth)
Once on Christmas, (Thompson, Dorothy)
Once the Hodja, (Kelsey, Alice)
Once there Was a King, (Alden, Raymond M.)
Once there Was and Was Not, (Tashjian, Virginia)
Once there was a Little Boy, (Kunhardt, Dorothy)
Once to Every Man, (Evans, Lawton)
Once-Upon-a-Time Story Book, (Dobbs, Rose)
Ondine, (Osborne, Maurice M.)
One Bad Thing About Father, (Monjo, Ferdinand N.)
One Dark Night, (Preston, Edna M.)
One Day at Teton Marsh, (Carrighar, Sally)
One Day in Betty's Life, (Gates, Josephine S.)
One Day it Rained Cats and Dogs, (Kohn, Bernice)
One Day on Beetle Rock, (Carrighar, Sally)
One Day with Jambi in Sumatra, (Sperry, Armstrong)
One Day with Manu, (Sperry, Armstrong)
One Day with Tuktu, (Sperry, Armstrong)
One Fish Two Fish Red Fish Blue Fish, (Seuss, Dr.)
One Foot in Fairyland, (Farjeon, Eleanor)
One Happy Day, (Dauzet, Marceline)
One Horse Farm, (Ipcar, Dahlov)
One Hundred Great Guns, (Lindsay, Merrill)
One I Knew Best of All, (Burnett, Frances H.)
One Kitten for Kim, (Holl, Adelaide)
One Kitten too Many, (Bradbury, Bianca)
One Little Drum, (Hodges, Margaret)
One Little Indian, (Moon, Grace P.)
One Little Indian Boy, (Brock, Emma)
One Long Picnic, (Frazier, Neta L.)
One Mitten Lewis, (Kay, Helen)
One Monday Morning, (Shulevitz, Uri)
One Morning in Maine, (McCloskey, Robert)
One Rainy Night, (Doane, Pelagie)
One Small Blue Bead, (Schweitzer, Byrd B.)
One Snail and Me, (McLeod, Emilie)
One Special Dog, (Martin, Patricia)
One Step, Two, (Zolotow, Charlotte)
One Thousand Christmas Beards, (Duvoisin, Roger)
One Too Many, (Byrne, Mary Agnes)
One Two, Buckle My Shoe, (Haley, Gail E.)
One Way Out, (Von Hutten, Bettina)
One Wide River to Cross, (Emberley, Barbara)
One and One and One, (Untermeyer, Louis)
One in the Middle is Green Kangaroo, (Blume, Judy)
One is God: Two Old Counting Songs, (Price, C.)
One is Good, but Two are Better, (Slobodkin, Louis)
One is for the Sun, (Blegvad, Lenore)
One of Us, (Hicks, Granville)
One, Two, Three, Four, (Cone, Helen G.)
One-Eyed Griffin..., (Inman, H.E.)
One-Footed Fairy, (Brown, Alice)
One-Hoss Shay, (Holmes, Oliver W.)
One-String Fiddle, (Berry, Erick)
Ong, the Wild Gander, (Henry, Vera)
Onion John, (Krumgold, Joseph)
Onion Journey, (Cunningham, Julia)
Only Child, (White, Eliza O.)
Ood-Le-Uk: Wanderer, (Lide, Alice A.)
Oomi, the New Hunter, (Schlein, Miriam)
Ootah and his Puppy, (Stafford, Marie A.)
Ootah's Lucky Day, (Parish, Peggy)
Opal Sea, (Van Dyke, John C.)
Open Boat, (Crane, Stephen)

Open Daily, (Beistle, Aldarilla)
Open Gate, (Seredy, Kate)
Open House for Butterflies, (Krauss, Ruth)
Open Road, (Lucas, E.V.)
Open Window, (Thurston, Ernest T.)
Opera Guyed, (Levy, Newman)
Opera Souffle: 60 Pictures in Bravura, (Simont, Marc)
Operas of Richard Wagner, (Hadden, James C.)
Operation Sippacik, (Godden, Rumer)
Orange Fairy Book, (Lang, Andrew)
Orange Tree, (N/A)
Oranges & Lemons, (N/A)
Orchard Princess, (Barbour, Ralph H.)
Orchard-Land, (Chambers, Robert)
Orcutt Girls, (Vaile, Charlotte)
Oregon Trail, (Parkman, Francis)
Oriel Window, (Molesworth, Mrs.)
Oriental Fairy Tales, (N/A)
Original Melodies from..., (Mother Goose)
Original Poems, (Taylor, Anne & Jane)
Orlando Buys a Farm, (Hale, Kathleen)
Orlando the Brave Vulture, (Ungerer, Tomi)
Orlando, Marmalade Cat-Camping Holiday, (Hale, Kathleen)
Orphans of the Range, (Martin, Charles M.)
Orphant Annie Book, (Riley, James W.)
Orphant Annie Story Book, (Gruelle, Johnny)
Orphelines in the Enchanted Castle, (Carlson, Natalie S.)
Orpheus with his Lute, (Hutchinson, W.M.L.)
Orpheus: Myths of the World, (Colum, Padraic)
Osbert, (Streatfeild, Noel)
Oscar Lobster's Fair Exchange, (Selden, George)
Oscar Otter, (Benchley, Nathaniel)
Oscar the Trained Seal, (Neikirk, Mabel O.)
Oswald Bastable & Others, (Nesbit, Edith)
Oswald's Pet Dragon, (Glick, Carl)
Ote, a Puerto Rican Folktale, (Belpre, Pura)
Other Fellow, (Smith, Francis H.)
Other People's Houses, (Bianco, Margery W.)
Other Side of the Fence, (Cone, Molly)
Other Side of the Mountain, (Leydenfrost, Robert)
Other Side of the Sun, (Sharp, Evelyn)
Other Side of the Tunnel, (Kendall, Carol S.)
Otherside Book, (Mitchell, Edith)
Otis Spofford, (Cleary, Beverly)
Otter Twins, (Tompkins, Jane)
Otter's Story, (Liers, Emil)
Otterbury Incident, (Day-Lewis, Cecil)
Otto of the Silver Hand, (Pyle, Howard)
Otto... [Most titles], (DuBois, W.P.)
Ottoman Wonder Tales, (Garnett, Louise A.)
Ounce, Dice, Trice, (Reid, Alastair)
Our Amateur Circus, (N/A)
Our Animal Friends, (Golding, Harry)
Our Baby Book, (Cory, Fanny)
Our Children, (France, Anatole)
Our Country's Story, (Cavanah, Frances)
Our Darlings, (N/A)
Our Davie Pepper, (Sidney, Margaret)
Our Eddie, (Ish-Kishor, Salamith)
Our Empire Story, (Marshall, Henrietta)
Our Forests & Woodlands, (Nisbet, John)
Our Friend the Atom, (Disney, Walt)
Our Friend the Dog, (Maeterlinck, Maurice)
Our Friendly Friends, (Slobodkin, Louis)
Our Garden, (Ewing, Juliana H.)
Our Girls, (Christy, Howard C.)
Our House, (Pennell, Eliz. R.)
Our Island Saints, (Steedman, Amy)

Our Lady of Darkness, (Dorrington, Albert)
Our Lady of Guadalupe, (Parish, Helen R.)
Our Lady's Book, (Ford, Lauren)
Our Little African Cousin, (Hazelton, Mary)
Our Little Aztec Cousin of Long Ago, (Borton, Elizabeth)
Our Little Ethiopian Cousin, (Borton, Elizabeth)
Our Little Mexican Cousin, (Butler, Edward C.)
Our Little Neighbors, (Kaberry, Charles J.)
Our Miss Boo, (Runbeck, Margaret)
Our Neighbors, (Gibson, Charles D.)
Our Neighbors, (MacLaren, Ian)
Our Next-Door Neighbors, (Maniates, Belle)
Our Old Fairy Stories, (Strang, Mrs. H.)
Our Old Nursery Rhymes, (Moffat, Alfred)
Our Oldest Friends, (Eberle, Irmengarde)
Our Philadelphia, (Pennell, Joseph)
Our Presidents, (Armour, Richard)
Our Puppy, (Nast, Elsa R.)
Our Rice Village in Cambodia, (Tooze, Ruth)
Our Sentimental Garden, (Castle, A.& E.)
Our Veronica Goes to Petunia's Farm, (Duvoisin, Roger)
Our Village, (Mitford, Mary R.)
Our Western Archipelago, (Field, Henry M.)
Out of Provincetown, (Hall, Rosalys)
Out of Town, (Weatherly, Fred E.)
Out of the Crucible, (Chilvers, Hedley A.)
Out of the Flame, (Lownsbery, Eloise)
Out of the Silent North, (Sinclair, Harry D.)
Out of the Sun, (Montgomery, R.)
Out on the Pampas, (Henty, G.A.)
Out with Garibaldi, (Henty, G.A.)
Outdoor Sketching, (Smith, Francis H.)
Outdoorland, (Chambers, Robert)
Outlaw, (Anderson, C.W.)
Outside Cat, (Thayer, Jane)
Outside My Window, (Skorpen, Liesel)
Over Indian and Animal Trails, (Thompson, Jeannette)
Over Sea, Under Stone, (Cooper, Susan)
Over and Over, (Zolotow, Charlotte)
Over in the Meadow, (Langstaff, John)
Over the Alps on a Bicycle, (Pennell, Eliz. R.)
Over the Big Hill, (Lovelace, Maud H.)
Over the Blue Mountain, (Richter, Conrad)
Over the Hills, (Waugh, Ida)
Over the Hills and Far Away, (Cook, Hartley K.)
Over the Hills to Nugget, (Fisher, Aileen)
Over the Nonsense Road, (Gulliver, Lemeul)
Over the Rainbow Bridge, (Haynes, Louise M.)
Over the Reefs, (Gibbings, Robert)
Over-Mountain Boy, (Steele, William O.)
Overall Boys, (Grover, Eulalie O.)
Overall Boys in Switzerland, (Grover, Eulalie O.)
Overhead the Sun, (Whitman, Walt)
Overheard in Fairyland, (Bigham, Madge A.)
Overheard in a Garden, (Herford, Oliver)
Owl & the Prairie Dog, (Freschet, Berniece)
Owl & the Pussycat, (Lear, Edward)
Owl King..., (Inman, H.E.)
Owl Service, (Garner, Alan)
Owl Who Hated the Dark, (Goodenow, Earle)
Owl and the Woodchuck, (Neidlinger, Wm. H.)
Owl in the Attic, (Thurber, James)
Owls in the Family, (Mowat, Farley)
Oxford Book of Poetry for Children, (Blishen, Ed (comp))
Oxford From Within, (DeSelincourt, Hugh)
Ozma of Oz, (Baum, L. Frank)
Ozmar the Mystic, (Beaman, Emeric H.)
Ozoplaning with the Wizard of Oz, (Thompson, Ruth P.)

P-Penny & his Little Red Cart, (Stone, Amy W.)
P-Zoo, (Hamilton, Elizabeth)
P.S. Happy Anniversary, (Wyse, Lois)
Pa Cats, Ma Cats & their Kittens, (Father Tuck)
Pa Flickinger's Folks, (Hoover, Bessie R.)
Pablo Paints a Picture, (Miller, Warren)
Pablo and Petra, (Lee, Melicent)
Pacific Islands Speaking, (Sperry, Armstrong)
Paco Goes to the Fair, (Gill, Richard)
Paddington Goes to Town, (Bond, Michael)
Paddington at Work, (Bond, Michael)
Paddle to the Sea, (Holling, Holling C.)
Paddlewings, (Bronson, Wilfrid S.)
Paddy and Sam, (Bothwell, Jean)
Paddy the Penguin, (Galdone, Paul)
Paddy's Christmas, (Monsell, Helen)
Padre Ignacio, (Wister, Owen)
Padre Porko, (Davis, Robert)
Pads, Paws & Claws, (Pycraft, W.P.)
Pagan Papers, (Grahame, Kenneth)
Pageant & other Poems, (Rossetti, Christina)
Pageant of Chinese History, (Seeger, Elizabeth)
Pages from the Book of Paris, (Washburn, Claude C.)
Pagoo, (Holling, Holling C.)
Painted Cave, (Behn, Harry)
Painted Moccasin, (Moon, Carl)
Painted Pig, (Morrow, Elizabeth)
Painting Book, (Greenaway, Kate)
Painting the Moon, (Withers, Carl)
Pair of Captains, (Keith, Harold V.)
Pair of Madcaps, (Trowbridge, John T.)
Pair of Red Clogs, (Matsuno, Masako)
Pair of Red Polls, (Quiller-Couch, Mabel)
Pajaro-Cu-Cu, (Wolf, Ingrid)
Paji, (Kiviat, Esther)
Pal: Story of an Airedale, (Jenkins, Alexandra)
Palace in Bagdad, (Larson, Jean R.)
Palace in the Garden, (Molesworth, Mrs.)
Paladins in Spain, (Farjeon, Eleanor)
Pale Mountains, (Wolff, Carl F.)
Palmiero and the Ogre, (Domanska, Janina)
Palomino Boy, (Emblen, Don L.)
Pam & Billy, (Girvin, Brenda)
Pam's Paradise Ranch, (Tempski, Armine)
Pan Pipes, (Marzials, Theo)
Pan's Garden, (Robertson, W.G.)
Pancake Brownies, (Byington, Eloise)
Pancakes and the Merry-Go-Round, (Brock, Emma)
Pancakes for Breakfast, (Paull, Grace)
Pancakes, Pancakes, (Carle, Eric)
Pancakes-Paris, (Bishop, Claire H.)
Panchito, (Good, Loren D.)
Pancho & His Burro, (Gay, Zhenya)
Pandora, (Newberry, Clare T.)
Pandora's Box, (Hawthorne, Nathaniel)
Pandy, (Broughton, Philip)
Panjandrum Picture Book, (Caldecott, R.)
Pansy Wedding, (Lefferts, Sara T.)
Pantalette Doll, (Beard, Patten)
Pantaloni, (Bettina)
Pantaloon, (Stokely, Edith K.)
Pantaloons, (Johnson, Osa)
Panther Magic, (Baker, Olaf)
Panther's Moon, (Bond, Ruskin)
Paolo and Panetto, (Bettina)
Papa Albert, (Moore, Lilian)
Papa Bouchard, (Seawell, Molly E.)
Papa Dolphin's Table, (Butters, Dorothy)

Papa Small, (Lenski, Lois)
Paper Dragon, (Gruelle, Johnny)
Paper Zoo, (Weiss, Renee K.)
Paper-Flower Tree, (Ayer, Jacqueline)
Papillot, Clignot et Dodo, (Field, Eugene)
Parables from Nature, (Gatty, Mrs. Alfred)
Parables of Jesus, (Cadman, S. Parkes)
Parade Book, (Emberley, Edward)
Paradise Square, (Bianco, Pamela)
Paradise Valley, (Angelo, Valenti)
Paradoc to the Rescue, (Gordon, Hampden C.)
Pardoner's Wallet, (Crothers, Samuel M.)
Parents Keep Out, (Nash, Ogden)
Paris Pair, (Brown, Beatrice B.)
Paris of Today, (Whiteing, Richard)
Park Book, (Zolotow, Charlotte)
Parker Pig, Esquire, (DePaola, Tomie)
Parrot Dealer, (Wiese, Kurt)
Parsifal, (Wagner, Richard)
Parsifal the Poddley, (Chenault, Nell)
Parsley, (Bemelmans, Ludwig)
Parsley the Horse, (Filosa, Dorothea)
Parson's Devil, (Johnson, Clifton)
Partners of Powder Hole, (Davis, Robert)
Partouche Plants a Seed, (Shecter, Ben)
Party Shoes, (Streatfeild, Noel)
Party at the Zoo, (Roethke, Theodore)
Party for Poodles, (Hogan, Inez)
Pasha the Pom, (Frazer, Sir James)
Passing of the Old West, (Evarts, Hal G.)
Passionate Journey, (Masereel, Franz)
Password to Fairyland, (Southwart, Elizabeth)
Pastime Stories, (Page, Thomas N.)
Pastor Sang, (Bjornstjerne, Bjorn)
Pastoral, (Disney, Walt)
Pat & Pips, (Freckles)
Pat and the Spider, (Bannerman, Helen)
Pat of Silver Bush, (Montgomery, Lucy M.)
Patch, (Elting, Mary)
Patches, (Stolper, Joel)
Patchwork Girl of Oz, (Baum, L. Frank)
Patchwork Madonna, (Weston, Harold)
Patchwork Plays, (Field, Rachel)
Patricia Crosses Town, (Baum, Betty)
Patrick & the Golden Slippers, (Milhous, Katherine)
Patriotic Jubilee, (Lefferts, Sara T.)
Patsy & the Pup, (Van Stockum, Hilda)
Patsy Book, (Anderson, Anne)
Patsy and the Leprechaun, (Baker, Margaret)
Patsy for Keeps, (Ames, Esther M.)
Patsy's Pet, (Steiner, Charlotte)
Pattern for Liberty, (Johnson, Gerald W.)
Patterns on the Wall, (Yates, Elizabeth)
Patty Paints a Picture, (Bannon, Laura)
Patty on Horseback, (Brock, Emma)
Paul & Virginia of a Northern Zone, (Drachmann, Holger)
Paul Bunyan, (Shephard, Esther)
Paul Bunyan, (Stevens, James)
Paul, Hero of the Fire, (Ardizzone, Edward)
Paula, (Vance, Marguerite)
Pavilion on the Links, (Stevenson, Rbt. L.)
Pavo and the Princess, (Ness, Evaline M.)
Pawnee, (Bell, Thelma H.)
Pawpaw's Run, (Boegehold, Betty)
Pax and Carlino, (Beckman, Ernst)
Pay Dirt, (Rounds, Glen)
Peace at any Price, (Browne, Porter E.)
Peaceable Kingdom, (Coatsworth, Eliz.)

Peachblossom, (Lattimore, Eleanor)
Peachtree Island, (Lawrence, Mildred)
Peacock & Wishing-Fairy, (Ingraham, Corinne)
Peacock Country, (Waring, P. Alston)
Peacock Pie, (De La Mare, Walter)
Peacock Who Lost his Tail, (Hamberger, John)
Peacock and the Crow, (Kirn, Ann)
Peanut, (Carroll, Ruth)
Peanut Butter's Slide, (Paull, Grace)
Peanuts for Billy Ben, (Lenski, Lois)
Pear Tree, Birch Tree & Barberry Bush, (Carigiet, Alois)
Pearce Amerson's Will, (Johnston, Richard M.)
Pearl & Pumpkin, (West, Paul)
Pearls of Fortune, (Lide, Alice A.)
Peasblossom, (Blodgett, Mabel F.)
Pebble in a Pool, (Yates, Elizabeth)
Peck's Bad Boy & his Chums, (Peck, George W.)
Pecos Bill, (Bowman, James C.)
Pecos Bill & Lightning, (Peck, Leigh)
Pecos Bill & the Mustang, (Felton, Harold)
Pecos Bill, Texas Cowpuncher, (Felton, Harold)
Peculiar Magic, (Johnson, Annabel)
Peculiar Penguins, (Disney, Walt)
Pedaling Man and other Poems, (Hoban, Russell)
Pedant and the Shuffly, (Bellairs, John)
Peddler's Cart, (Coatsworth, Eliz.)
Peddler's Clock, (Hunt, Mabel L.)
Pedie and the Twins, (Bryant, Bernice M.)
Pedlar & His Dog, (Rowsell, Mary)
Pedlar's Progress, (Shepard, Odell)
Pedro, (Flack, Marjorie)
Pedro of Santa Fe, (Cavanah, Frances)
Pedro's Choice, (Blanton, Catherine)
Pedro's Coconut Skates, (Wood, Esther)
Pedro, Angel of Olvera Street, (Politi, Leo)
Pedro, Nina & Perrito, (Duplaix, Lily)
Pee-Gloo, (Duplaix, Georges)
Peek the Piper, (Bianki, Vitali)
Peek-a-Boo, (Kessler, Ethel)
Peek-a-Boo Twins, (Preston, Tom)
Peek-a-Boo's Desert Island, (Hoyle, Zoe)
Peek-a-Boo's Holiday, (Preston, Tom)
Peek-a-Boo(s)... [Most titles], (Byron, May)
Peep into Cat-Land, (Various)
Peep-Lo, (Castle, Jane)
Peep-Show Man, (Colum, Padraic)
Peep-in-World, (Crichton, Frances E.)
Peeping Pansy, (Sylva, Carmen)
Peeps at People, (Bangs, John K.)
Peeps into Fairyland, (Knowles, Horace J.)
Peeps: Really Truly Sunshine Fairy, (Cox-McCormack, N.)
Peer Gynt, (Ibsen, Henrik)
Peetie: Story of a Real Cat, (Jones, Inis)
Peewee the Mousedeer, (DeLeeuw, Hendrik)
Peg Woffington, (Reade, Charles)
Peg-Leg Willy, (Embry, Margaret)
Peg-Legged Pirate of Sulu, (Cheney, Cora)
Pegasus, the Winged Horse, (Hawthorne, Nathaniel)
Pegeen, (Van Stockum, Hilda)
Peggy, (Richards, Laura E.)
Peggy & Paul & Laddy, (Carr, Mary J.)
Peggy & the Pony, (Sewell, Helen)
Peggy & the Pup, (Sewell, Helen)
Peggy O'Neal, (Lewis, Alfred H.)
Peggy and Joan, (Cradock, H.C.)
Peggy in Toyland, (Marshall, Archibald)
Peggy's New Brother, (Schick, Eleanor)
Peggy's Playhouses, (Hunt, Clara W.)

Peggy's Travels, (Cook, Walter)
Peggy's Trial, (Potter, Mary K.)
Pegs of History, (Fish, Helen D.)
Peik, (Ring, Barbara)
Pekin White, (McCready, Thomas L.)
Pelican Chorus, (Lear, Edward)
Pelican Here, Pelican There, (Weisgard, Leonard)
Pen & Inklings, (Herford, Oliver)
Penelope Ellen, (Parton, Ethel)
Penelope's Irish Experiences, (Wiggin, Kate D.)
Penguin Island, (France, Anatole)
Penguin Twins, (Tompkins, Jane)
Penguin's Pal, (Kraus, Robert)
Penguins' Way, (Johnston, Johanna)
Penn, (Gray, Eliz. J.)
Penny, (DeRegniers, Beatrice)
Penny, (Torrey, Marjorie)
Penny & Peter of the Island, (Lloyd, Marion)
Penny Candy, (Fenton, Edward)
Penny Fiddle, (Graves, Robert)
Penny a Day, (De La Mare, Walter)
Penny and Peter, (Haywood, Carolyn)
Penny and a Periwinkle, (Aldridge, Josephine)
Penny and the White Horse, (Bianco, Margery W.)
Penny for Luck: Story of the Rockies, (Means, F.C.)
Penny that Rolled Away, (MacNeice, Louis)
Penny's Worth of Character, (Stuart, Jesse)
Penny-Whistle, (Berry, Erick)
Penrod, (Tarkington, Booth)
Penrod & Sam, (Tarkington, Booth)
Penrod Jashber, (Tarkington, Booth)
People I'd Like to Keep, (O'Neill, Mary)
People Who Come to Our House, (Judson, Clara I.)
People Who Work Near our House, (Judson, Clara I.)
People Who Work in Country & City, (Judson, Clara I.)
People You Know, (Ade, George)
People are Important, (Evans, Eva K.)
People from Dickens, (Field, Rachel)
People of Concord, (Wood, James P.)
People of Our Neighborhood, (Freeman, Mary E.W.)
People of the Abyss, (London, Jack)
People of the Frozen North, (Rasmussen, K.)
People of the Mist, (Haggard, H. Rider)
People of the Short Blue Corn, (Courlander, Harold)
Pepe was the Saddest Bird, (Stone, William S.)
Pepito at Capistrano, (Costantino, Joan)
Pepito the Colt, (Orton, Ruth)
Pepito's Story, (Fern, Eugene)
Pepper, (Reynolds, Barbara)
Pepper Moon, (Wood, Esther)
Pepper and Salt, (Pyle, Howard)
Pepperfoot of Thursday Market, (Davis, Robert)
Peppermint Family, (Brown, Margaret W.)
Peppernuts, (Petersham, Maud)
Pepperpot in the Magic Wood, (Proysen, Alf)
Peppi the Duck, (Wells, Rhea)
Peppino, (Spyri, Johanna)
Pepys' Boy, (Varble, Rachel)
Peradventures of Private Pagett, (Drury, William P.)
Percy, Polly and Pete, (Newberry, Clare T.)
Perez and Martina, (Belpre, Pura)
Perfect Pancake, (Kahl, Virginia)
Perfect Present, (Foreman, Michael)
Perfect Zoo, (Farjeon, Eleanor)
Perhappsy Chaps, (Thompson, Ruth P.)
Perilous Road, (Steele, William O.)
Perilous Seat, (Snedeker, Caroline D.)
Perkin the Pedlar, (Farjeon, Eleanor)

Perri, (Salten, Felix)
Perrito's Pup, (Latham, Barbara)
Perry the Imp, (Lipkind, Will)
Perseus & Andromeda, (LeGallienne, R.)
Persian Tales, (Lorimer, D.& E.)
Persistent Faces, (Steig, William)
Perverse Widow, (Steele, Richard)
Pet Parade, (Sickels, Evelyn)
Pet Tale, (Carroll, Ruth)
Pet for Barbi, (Brock, Emma)
Pet for the Orphelines, (Carlson, Natalie S.)
Pet of the Met, (Freeman, Lydia)
Pete, (Robinson, Tom P.)
Pete & Polly Stories, (Wells, Carolyn)
Pete and Peter, (Steiner, Charlotte)
Pete the Pelican, (Kissin, Rita)
Pete's Puddle, (Foster, Joanna)
Pete's Puppets, (Steiner, Charlotte)
Peter & Gretchen of Old Nuremberg, (Jones, Viola M.)
Peter & Penny Plant a Garden, (Dubois, Gertrude)
Peter & Prue..., (Donahey, Mary D.)
Peter & the Piskies, (Manning-Sanders, Ruth)
Peter & the Princess, (Grabo, Carl H.)
Peter & the Wolf, (Prokofieff, Serge)
Peter Churchmouse, (Austin, Margot)
Peter Duck, (Ransome, Arthur)
Peter Graves, (DuBois, W.P.)
Peter Kroak, (Moe, Louis M.)
Peter Makebelieve, (Van Sinderen, Adrian)
Peter Opens the Door, (Whitehead, Roberta)
Peter Painter & the Holidays, (Webber, Frank M.)
Peter Painter's Merry-Go-Round, (Webber, Frank M.)
Peter Paints the U.S.A., (Colby, Jean P.)
Peter Pan, (Barrie, James M.)
Peter Pan Alphabet, (Herford, Oliver)
Peter Pan Picture Book, (Barrie, James M.)
Peter Pan and Wendy, (Barrie, James M.)
Peter Pan's ABC, (N/A)
Peter Panda, (Walker, Paul E.)
Peter Patter Book, (Jackson, Leroy F.)
Peter Peppercorn, (Phillips, Ethel C.)
Peter Pickle and his Dog Fido, (N/A)
Peter Pink-Eye, (Rountree, Harry)
Peter Piper's Alphabet, (Brown, Marcia)
Peter Piper's Pickled Peppers, (Hunt, Mabel L.)
Peter Pixie at Play, (Lambert, H.G.C.)
Peter Poodle..., (Bradley, Will)
Peter Pumpkin, (Ott, John)
Peter Pumpkin in Wonderland, (Huntington, Ida M.)
Peter Rabbit, (Potter, Beatrix)
Peter Rabbit & the Fairies, (Hudson, Alma)
Peter Rabbit Goes to School, (Field, Louis A.)
Peter Rabbit Goes-a-Visiting, (Almond, Linda S.)
Peter Rabbit Story Book, (Potter, Beatrix)
Peter Rabbit and his Ma, (Field, Louis A.)
Peter Rabbit and his Pa, (Field, Louis A.)
Peter Rabbit and the Little Girl, (Almond, Linda S.)
Peter Rabbit and the Tinybits, (Almond, Linda S.)
Peter Rabbit in Mother Goose Land, (Hudson, Alma)
Peter Schlemihl, (Chamisso, A.)
Peter Teeter Stories, (Schwetzky, Otto)
Peter and Veronica, (Sachs, Marilyn)
Peter and Wendy, (Barrie, James M.)
Peter and the Wolf, (Deakin, Irving)
Peter by the Sea, (Meade, Julian R.)
Peter in Grand Central Station, (Shortall, Leonard)
Peter is Sweeter, (Cannon, Wilma)
Peter of the Mesa, (Means, Florence C.)

Peter on the Min, (Clark, Dorothy)
Peter the Goat, (Thorne, Diana)
Peter the Great, (Baker, Nina B.)
Peter the Stork, (Vaygouny, Margarite)
Peter the Wanderer, (Ardizzone, Edward)
Peter's Adventure, (Gay, Romney)
Peter's Brownstone House, (Colman, Hila)
Peter's Chair, (Keats, Ezra J.)
Peter's Long Walk, (Kingman, Lee)
Peter's Pinto, (Buff, M.& C.)
Peter's Tent, (Smaridge, Norah)
Peter's Voyage, (Beskow, Elsa)
Peter, Patter & Pixie, (Kay, Gertrude A.)
Peter, a Cat O' One Tail, (Morley, Charles)
Peter-Pan Twins are Glad to Help, (Lyman, Betty K.)
Peter-Pea, (Grishina-Givago, N.)
Peterkin, (Jackson, Gabrielle)
Peterkin, (Molesworth, Mrs.)
Peterkin, (Pogany, Elaine)
Peterkin Papers, (Hale, Lucretia)
Peterli and the Mountain, (Engelhard, Georgia)
Petersham's Hill, (Hallock, Grace T.)
Petey, (Jackson, Linda)
Petite Suzanne, (DeAngeli, Marguerite)
Petunia Be Keerful, (Christopher, Anne)
Petunia... [Most titles], (Duvoisin, Roger)
Phantastes, (MacDonald, George)
Phantom Deer, (Lippincott, J.W.)
Phantom Tollbooth, (Juster, Norton)
Phantom of Walkaway Hill, (Fenton, Edward)
Phantom of the Blockade, (Meader, Stephen W.)
Phantoms of the Foot-Bridge, (Craddock, Charles E.)
Pheasant on a Route Seven, (Starbird, Kaye)
Phebe Fairchild, (Lenski, Lois)
Phenomenal Fauna, (Wells, Carolyn)
Phil Stong's Big Book, (Stong, Philip D.)
Philbert the Fearful, (Williams, Jay)
Philippe's Hill, (Kingman, Lee)
Philomena, (Seredy, Kate)
Phinny's Fine Summer, (Govan, Christine)
Phoebe Daring..., (Baum, L. Frank)
Phoebe and the Prince, (Orgel, Doris)
Phoebe's Revolt, (Babbitt, Natalie)
Phoebe-Belle, (Eberle, Irmengarde)
Phoenix & the Carpet, (Nesbit, Edith)
Phronsie Pepper, (Sidney, Margaret)
Phyllis in Bohemia, (Powell, R.S.)
Pi Gal, (Page, Valerie K.)
Piccadilly Jim, (Wodehouse, P.G.)
Piccino, (Burnett, Frances H.)
Piccolina and the Easter Bells, (Priolo, Pauline)
Piccolino, (King, Marian)
Piccolo, (Bettina)
Piccolo's Prank, (Politi, Leo)
Pick the Vegetables, (Reno, Esther W.)
Pickaback Songs, (Reed, Myrtle)
Pickaninny Twins, (Perkins, Lucy F.)
Picken's Exciting Summer, (Davis, Norman)
Picken's Treasure Hunt, (Davis, Norman)
Pickles, (Aldin, Cecil)
Picnic Adventures, (Gilman, Eliz. L.)
Picnic Book, (Ayer, Jean)
Picnic on a Pyramid, (Loud, Marian V.)
Picnic: Frolic in 2 Colors & 3 Parts, (Daugherty, James)
Picture & Rhyme Book, (N/A)
Picture Birthday Book for Boys & Girls, (Cole, Frank (ed.))
Picture Book for the French Red Cross, (Dulac, Edmund)
Picture Book of Flying, (Dobias, Frank)

Picture Book of Musical Instruments, (Lacey, Marion)
Picture Book of Poems, (Gay, Romney)
Picture Book of Robinson Crusoe, (Defoe, Daniel)
Picture Book of Ships, (Gimmage, Peter)
Picture Book of Travel, (Hader, B.& E.)
Picture Book of the States, (Hader, B.& E.)
Picture Posters, (Hiatt, Charles)
Picture Rhymes from Foreign Lands, (Fyleman, Rose)
Picture Story Book, (N/A)
Picture Story of China, (Hahn, Emily)
Picture Story of Holland, (DeJong, Dola)
Picture Story of the Philippines, (O'Neill, Hester)
Picture Tales from Spain, (Sawyer, Ruth)
Picture for Harold's Room, (Johnson, Crockett)
Picture-Skin Story, (Bealer, Alex W.)
Pictures & Poems, (Rossetti, Dante G.)
Pictures from Birdland, (Shuldham, Edward B.)
Pictures in Color, (Fisher, Harrison)
Pictures of Panama Canal, (Pennell, Joseph)
Pictures of People, (Gibson, Charles D.)
Pictures on the Pavement, (Stonier, George W.)
Pie & Patty Pan, (Potter, Beatrix)
Piece of Fire, (Courlander, Harold)
Piece of String, (Mendoza, George)
Pieces of Home, (Miles, Miska)
Pied Piper of Hamelin, (Browning, Robert)
Pied Piper of Pudding Lane, (Addington, Sarah)
Pierino and the Bell, (Cassedy, Sylvia)
Pierre Pidgeon, (Kingman, Lee)
Pierre of Kaskaskia, (Belting, Natalia)
Pierre of the Big Top, (Meeker, Col. S.P.)
Pierrette, (Stacpoole, H.D.)
Pierrot!, (Stacpoole, H.D.)
Pig Tales, (Gask, Lilian)
Pig for Tom, (Palazzo, Tony)
Pig in the Parlor, (Varga, Judy)
Pig that Ate Truffles, (MacIntyre, Carlyle F.)
Pig with a Front Porch..., (Brock, Emma)
Pig-O-Wee, (Credle, Ellis)
Pigeon Flight, (Stolz, Mary S.)
Pigeon Post, (Ransome, Arthur)
Pigeon, Fly Home!, (Liggett, Thomas)
Pigeons and Princesses, (Reeves, James)
Pigs and Pirates, (Walker, Barbara)
Pigs is Pigs, (Butler, Charles)
Pigtail of Ah Lee Ben Loo, (Bennett, John)
Pigtails, (Hekking, Johanna)
Pike County Ballads, (Hay, John)
Pilgrim Goose, (Robertson, Keith)
Pilgrim Kate, (Daringer, Helen F.)
Pilgrim's Progress, (Bunyan, John)
Pilgrim's Progress told to Children, (MacGregor, Mary)
Pilgrims Knew, (Pine, Tillie S.)
Pilgrims' Progress, (Godolphin, Mary)
Pillow Stories, (Heward, Constance)
Pillow-Time Tales, (Beard, Patten)
Pilot & Other Stories, (Greene, Harry P.)
Pinafore Picture Book, (Gilbert, W.S.)
Pinafores & Pantalets, (Choate, Florence)
Ping Pong, (Bingham, Clifton)
Pinion & Paw, (St. Mars, F.)
Pink Fairy Book, (Lang, Andrew)
Pink Hat, (Ilsley, Velma)
Pink Knight, (Monsell, J.R.)
Pink Maple House, (Govan, Christine)
Pink Marsh, (Ade, George)
Pink Motel, (Brink, Carol R.)
Pink Suit, (Hirsh, Marilyn J.)

Pink-Tails, (Merwin, Decie)
Pinkey & the Plumed Knight, (Chapin, Frederic)
Pinkey Perkins, Just a Boy, (Hammond, Harold)
Pinkie & the Fairies, (Robertson, W.G.)
Pinkish, Purplish, Bluish Egg, (Peet, Bill)
Pinky Finds a Home, (Nelson, Margaret W.)
Pinky Marie, (Graham, Lynda)
Pinky Pye, (Estes, Eleanor)
Pinky and the Petunias, (Slobodkina, Esphyr)
Pinky-Pup & Empty Elephant, (Willson, Dixie)
Pinocchio Picture Book, (Disney, Walt)
Pinocchio in America, (Patri, Angelo)
Pinocchio... [Most titles], (Collodi, Carlo)
Pint of Judgment, (Morrow, Elizabeth)
Pinto's Journey, (Bronson, Wilfrid S.)
Pioneer Girl, (Judson, Clara I.)
Pioneer's Hoard, (Van Gorden, Scott)
Pioneers in Canada, (Johnston, Harry)
Piper's Pony, (Brown, Paul)
Piper's Son, (Mother Goose)
Pipes of Clovis, (Boylan, Grace D.)
Pipetown Sandy, (Sousa, John P.)
Piping Down the Valleys Wild, (Larrick, Nancy)
Pipkin, (Forst, S.)
Pipkin Sees the World, (Fry, Rosalie K.)
Pippa Passes, (Browning, Robert)
Pippi... [All titles], (Lindgren, Astrid)
Pippin's House, (Savery, Constance)
Pippins and Cheese, (Peattie, Elia W.)
Pirate Frog, (Frisbie, William A.)
Pirate Twins, (Nicholson, William)
Pirate Waters, (Sabin, Edwin L.)
Pirate of Chatham Square, (Sterne, Emma G.)
Pirate's Apprentice, (Wells, Peter)
Pirate's Bridge, (Stuart, Mary)
Pirate's Island, (Townsend, John R.)
Pirate's Loot, (Rodgers, Carolyn)
Pirate's Treasure, (Wilson, Edward A.)
Pirates, (Fraser, Claud L.)
Pirates in Oz, (Thompson, Ruth P.)
Pirates in Panama, (Monjo, Ferdinand N.)
Pirates in Petticoats, (Yolen, Jane)
Pirates in the Deep Green Sea, (Linklater, Eric)
Pirates of Samarkand, (Ritchie, Rita)
Pirates!, (Banning, Kendall)
Pirates' Port: Tale of Old New York, (Malkus, Alida S.)
Piruwayu and the Rainbow, (Saint-Cecere, Gilles)
Pistachio, (Lent, Blair)
Pitschi, (Fischer, Hans)
Pixie Pickles, (Farrow, George E.)
Pixie in the House, (Smith, Laura R.)
Pixy & the Lazy Housewife, (Calhoun, Mary)
Pixy Book, (Harrison, Florence)
Place Mill, (Softly, Barbara)
Place for Ann, (Whitney, Phyllis)
Place for Peter, (Yates, Elizabeth)
Plaid Cow, (Brock, Emma)
Plaid Peacock, (Alan, Sandy)
Plain Girl, (Sorensen, Virginia)
Plain Jane, (N/A)
Plain Jane, (Softly, Barbara)
Plain Princess, (Maunder, Irene)
Plain Princess, (McGinley, Phyllis)
Plan for Birdsmarsh, (Peyton, Kathleen M.)
Plant Sitter, (Zion, Gene)
Plantation Bird Legends, (Young, Martha)
Plantation Christmas, (Peterkin, Julia)
Plantation Doll, (Cheney, Cora)

Plantation Pageants, (Harris, Joel C.)
Plantation Sketches, (Phillips, Jay C.)
Plantation Songs for My Lady's Banjo, (Shepperd, Eli)
Plated City, (Perry, Bliss)
Play Away, (Allen, Willis B.)
Play Days, (Judson, Clara I.)
Play Dollies, (Keys, Leonora)
Play in Provence, (Pennell, Joseph)
Play the Game, (Avery, Harold)
Play with Me, (Ets, Marie H.)
Play with Me, (Wilkin, Esther B.)
Play-Book of Words, (Lecky, Prescott)
Playground Toni, (Ray, Anna C.)
Playing Airplane, (McNamara, John F.)
Playing Possum, (Eager, Edward)
Playmate, A Christmas Mystery, (Dearmer, Mabel)
Playmates, (Mallett, Beatrice)
Plays by..., (Davidson, John)
Plays for an Irish Theatre, (Yeats, Wm. Butler)
Playtime & Company, (Lucas, E.V.)
Playtime for the Peter-Pan Twins, (Lyman, Betty K.)
Playtime in Cherry Street, (Bianco, Pamela)
Pleasant Fieldmouse, (Wahl, Jan)
Pleasant Pirate, (Goodwin, John B.)
Pleasant Tragedies of Childhood, (Johnson, Burges)
Please Pass the Grass!, (Adelson, Leone)
Please Share that Peanut, (Joslin, Sesyle)
Plenty to Watch, (Yashima, M. & T.)
Plink, Plink!, (Kessler, Ethel)
Plop Plop Ploppie, (Olds, Elizabeth)
Plot Night, (Mayne, William)
Plouf the Little Wild Duck, (Lida)
Plow Penny Mystery, (Davis, Lavinia R.)
Plucky Allens, (Pierson, Clara D.)
Plucky Sailor and Postage Stamp, (Corrin, Stephen)
Plum Daffy Adventure, (Coatsworth, Eliz.)
Plum Pudding for Christmas, (Kahl, Virginia)
Plum to Plum Jam, (Smalley, Janet)
Plumber Out of the Sea, (Simont, Marc)
Plumed Snake Medicine, (Schultz, James W.)
Plunkety Plunk, (Lippman, Peter J.)
Pluto & the Puppy, (Disney, Walt)
Plymouth Thanksgiving, (Weisgard, Leonard)
Pocahantas, (D'Aulaire, I.& E.)
Pocahontas, (Martin, Patricia)
Pocahontas & Captain Smith, (Smith, E. Boyd)
Pocahontas in London, (Wahl, Jan)
Pocket Full of Posies, (Brown, Abbie F.)
Pocket-Handkerchief Park, (Field, Rachel)
Pocketful of Cricket, (Caudill, Rebecca)
Pocketful of Proverbs, (Anglund, Joan W.)
Pocketful of Rhymes, (Allen, Marie L.)
Podgy Book of Tales, (Ault, L.& N.)
Poe's Run...., (Sykes, M'Cready)
Poems, (Arnold, Matthew)
Poems, (Field, Rachel)
Poems, (Yeats, Wm. Butler)
Poems Here at Home, (Riley, James W.)
Poems by Christina Rossetti, (Rossetti, Christina)
Poems by Dobson, Locker & Praed, (Dobson, L.)
Poems by Robert Browning, (Garnett (ed.))
Poems for Counting, (Quackenbush, Robert)
Poems for Galloping, (N/A)
Poems from France, (Smith, William J.)
Poems of American Patriotism, (Matthews, Brander)
Poems of Cabin and Field, (Dunbar, Paul L.)
Poems of Childhood, (Field, Eugene)
Poems of Childhood, (Field, Eugene)

Poems of Childhood, (Riley, James W.)
Poems of Childhood, (Sowerby, Githa)
Poems of E. Dowson, (Dowson, Ernest)
Poems of Edgar Allan Poe, (Poe, Edgar A.)
Poems of Leaves & Grass, (Whitman, Walt)
Poems of Passion & Pleasure, (Wilcox, Ella W.)
Poems of Shelley, (Shelley, Percy B.)
Poems of Spenser, (Yeats, Wm. Butler)
Poems of a South African, (Hall, Arthur V.)
Poet's Corner, (Beerbohm, Max)
Poetic Parrot, (MacKay, Margaret)
Poetical Works of Edgar A. Poe, (Poe, Edgar A.)
Poetry for Chuckles and Grins, (Jacobs, Leland (ed))
Poetry for Young Scientists, (Jacobs, Leland (ed))
Poetry of..., (Herrick, Robert)
Poilu, Dog of Roubaix, (Atkinson, Eleanor)
Point Lace and Diamonds, (Baker, George A.)
Pointed Brush, (Martin, Patricia)
Pointed People, (Field, Rachel)
Poison Belt, (Doyle, Arthur Conan)
Poketown People, (Tybout, Ella M.)
Poky Little Puppy, (Lowrey, Janette S.)
Polar Bear Twins, (Tompkins, Jane)
Police!, (Chambers, Robert)
Policeman Blue Jay, (Bancroft, Laura)
Policeman Small, (Lenski, Lois)
Polish Fairy Book, (Byrde, Elsie)
Polish Fairy Tales, (Glinski, Antoni J.)
Polite Penguin, (Brown, Margaret W.)
Political Struwwelpeter, (Begbie, Harold)
Polka Dot, (Steiner, Charlotte)
Polka-Dot Goat, (Slobodkin, Louis)
Pollwiggle's Progress, (Bronson, Wilfrid S.)
Polly & the Wishing Ring, (Johnson, Margaret)
Polly Patchwork, (Field, Rachel)
Polly Peters, (Quigg, Jane)
Polly's Garden, (Banks, Helen M.)
Polly's Oats, (Simont, Marc)
Polly: An Opera, (Gay, John)
Pollyanna, (Porter, Eleanor)
Pollyanna & the Secret Mission, (Borton, Elizabeth)
Pollyanna Grows Up, (Porter, Eleanor)
Pollyanna in Hollywood, (Borton, Elizabeth)
Pollyanna of the Orange Blossoms, (Smith, Harriet L.)
Pollyanna's Castle in Mexico, (Borton, Elizabeth)
Pollyanna's Door to Happiness, (Borton, Elizabeth)
Pollyanna's Golden Horseshoe, (Borton, Elizabeth)
Pollyanna's Jewels, (Smith, Harriet L.)
Polo, (Brown, Paul)
Pomander Walk, (Parker, Louis N.)
Pomander of Verse, (Nesbit, Edith)
Pomona's Travels, (Stockton, Frank)
Pompom, (Lida)
Pond Fairies, (Webb, M. St. John)
Pond Mermaid, (Talbot, Alfred J.)
Ponder Heart, (Welty, Eudora)
Ponies of Mykillengi, (Anderson, Lonzo)
Pony Called Lightning, (Mason, Miriam E.)
Pony Farm, (Brown, Paul)
Pony School, (Brown, Paul)
Pony Tracks, (Remington, Frederic)
Pony Worth his Salt, (Lansing, Elisabeth H.)
Pony in the Schoolhouse, (Miles, Miska)
Pony that Kept a Secret, (Lansing, Elisabeth H.)
Pony that Ran Away, (Lansing, Elisabeth H.)
Poo Poo & the Dragons, (Forester, C.S.)
Poo-Tsee the Water Tortoise, (Bettina)
Poodle & the Sheep, (Brown, Margaret W.)

Poodle Who Barked at the Wind, (Zolotow, Charlotte)
Poodle-Oodle on Doodle Farm, (Mackall, Lawton)
Poogie & Sibella, (Van Housen, Nita)
Pooh Cook Book, (Ellison, Virginia)
Pool in the Meadow, (Frost, Frances)
Pool of Stars, (Meigs, Cornelia L.)
Poor Boy Who Followed his Star, (Graves, Robert)
Poor Cecco, (Bianco, Margery W.)
Poor Folk, (Dostoievsky, Fedor)
Poor Merlo, (O'Neill, Mary)
Poor Richard, (Daugherty, James)
Poor Sally/her Christmas, (Brine, Mary D.)
Poor Shaydullah, (Artzybasheff, Boris)
Poor Uncle Harry, (Jacberns, Raymond)
Pop Corn and Ma Goodness, (Preston, Edna M.)
Pop-Corn Lamb & Peppermint Sticks, (Cross, Genevieve)
Popcorn Dragon, (Thayer, Jane)
Pope Leo's Elephant, (Lawrence, John)
Popo & Fifina, (Bontemps, Arna)
Popo the Hippopotamus, (Duplaix, Georges)
Poppadilly, (Chalmers, Audrey)
Poppet, (Austin, Margot)
Poppy Seed Cakes, (Clark, Margery)
Poppy Seeds, (Bulla, Clyde R.)
Poppy and other Deadly Plants, (Baskin, Esther)
Poppy, Adventures of a Fairy, (Perez-Guerra, A.)
Poppyland, (Stacpoole, H.D.)
Poquito, Little Mexican Duck, (Unwin, Nora S.)
Porcupine and the Tiger, (Powell, Fern)
Porko Von Popbutton, (DuBois, W.P.)
Porpoise of Pirate Bay, (Howard, F. Martin)
Porridge Poetry, (Lofting, Hugh)
Portals to the Past, (Shippen, Kath. B.)
Porterhouse Major, (Baker, Margaret)
Portrait of Ivan, (Fox, Paula)
Portrait of an Era, (Downey, Fairfax)
Portraits from a Chinese Scroll, (Lewis, Eliz. F.)
Posey & the Pedlar, (Lindsay, Maud)
Positive Pete, (Stong, Philip D.)
Posson Jane & Pere Raphael, (Cable, George W.)
Posters in Miniature, (Pollard, Percival)
Posthumous Papers/Pickwick Club, (Dickens, Charles)
Postmaster-General, (Belloc, Hilaire)
Pot of Gold, (Atkins, Elizabeth H.)
Pot of Gold, (Judah, Aaron)
Potatoes, Potatoes, (Lobel, Anita)
Pothooks & Perseverance, (Crane, Walter)
Potiphar's Wife, (Arnold, Edwin)
Potter Pinner Meadow, (Kaye, Mollie)
Potter and the Clay, (Peterson, Maud H.)
Powder, (Averill, Esther)
Power Lot, (Greene, Sarah P.M.)
Practical Man, (Mendoza, George)
Practical Pig, (Disney, Walt)
Practical Princess, (Williams, Jay)
Prairie School, (Lenski, Lois)
Prairie Schooner, (Barton, William E.)
Prairie Schooners, (Rounds, Glen)
Prairie Songs, (Garland, Hamlin)
Prairie Star, (Morgan, Nina)
Prairie-Dog Town, (Bancroft, Laura)
Prairie-Town Boy, (Sandburg, Carl)
Pran of Albania, (Miller, Elizabeth C.)
Prance, a Carousel Horse, (Young, Miriam)
Prayer for Little Things, (Farjeon, Eleanor)
Prayer for a Child, (Field, Rachel)
Prayers & Graces, (Laing, Allan M.)
Prayers & Graces for Small Children, (Hawkins, Quail)

Prayers for Little Men & Women, (Martin, John)
Prayers from the Ark, (Gasztold, Carmen)
Preacher of Cedar Mountain, (Seton, Ernest T.)
Prefabulous Animiles, (Reeves, James)
Prehistoric Man & Beast, (Hutchinson, Henry N.)
Prehistoric Proverbs, (Wood, Lawson)
Present for Auntie, (Brock, Emma)
Present from Petros, (Bishop, Claire H.)
Presents for Lupe, (Lathrop, Dorothy)
Pretty Little Doll, (Berry, Erick)
Pretty Peggy..., (Emmet, Rosina)
Pretty Pets, (Bingham, Clifton)
Pretty Polly Flinders, (Blaisdell, Mary F.)
Pretty Pretty Peggy Moffitt, (DuBois, W.P.)
Pretty Sister of Jose, (Burnett, Frances H.)
Pretzel, (Rey, Margret E.)
Pretzel & the Puppies, (Rey, Margret E.)
Pretzel Hero, (Rinkoff, Barbara)
Price of Blood, (Pyle, Howard)
Price of Peace, (Ackerman, A.W.)
Priceless Cats, (Jagendorf, Moritz)
Pride and Prejudice, (Austen, Jane)
Primer of Economics, (Chase, Stuart)
Primrose Day, (Haywood, Carolyn)
Primrose Path, (Nash, Ogden)
Primrose Ring, (Sawyer, Ruth)
Prince & Betty, (Wodehouse, P.G.)
Prince & the Page, (Yonge, Charlotte)
Prince & the Pauper, (Twain, Mark)
Prince Ahmed & the Fairy Perie Banou, (N/A)
Prince Babillon, (Nella)
Prince Bantam, (McNeer, May)
Prince Bertram the Bad, (Lobel, Arnold)
Prince Boo Hoo & Little Smuts, (Jones, Harry)
Prince Caspian, (Lewis, C.S.)
Prince Commands, (Norton, Andre)
Prince Domino & Muffles, (Eaton, Seymour)
Prince Ivan, Firebird & Gray Wolf, (Whitney, Thomas)
Prince Izon, (Kelly, James P.)
Prince Mud-Turtle, (Bancroft, Laura)
Prince Pimpernel, (Rix, Herbert)
Prince Por Quoi, (Sherwood, Mary M.)
Prince Prigio, (Lang, Andrew)
Prince Rabbit & Princess/Could not Laugh, (Milne, A.A.)
Prince Ricardo of Pantouflia, (Lang, Andrew)
Prince Silverwings..., (Harrison, Edith O.)
Prince Tip-Top, (Bouvet, Marguerite)
Prince Trixie, (Sabin, Elbridge H.)
Prince Who Gave up a Throne, (Serage, Nancy)
Prince Who was a Fish, (Wahl, Jan)
Prince Without a Country, (Donahey, Mary D.)
Prince and the Porker, (Stong, Philip D.)
Prince from Nowhere..., (Tappan, Eva M.)
Prince of Gravas, (Fleckenstein, Alfred)
Prince of the Pale Mountains, (Kyle, Anne D.)
Prince of the Pin Elves, (Sleight, Charles L.)
Prince's Progress, (Rossetti, Christina)
Princess & Curdie, (MacDonald, George)
Princess & Joe Potter, (Otis, James)
Princess & Woodcutter's Daughter, (Bromhall, Winifred)
Princess & the Apple Tree, (Milne, A.A.)
Princess & the Dragon, (Hamer, Sam H.)
Princess & the Goblin, (MacDonald, George)
Princess Badoura, (Housman, Laurence)
Princess Comes to Our Town, (Fyleman, Rose)
Princess Elizabeth Gift Book, (Disney, Walt)
Princess Finds a Playmate, (Hofman, Caroline)
Princess Goldenhair & Wonderful Flower, (Spiegelberg, F.)

Princess Ida, (Gilbert, W.S.)
Princess Kallisto, (Orcutt, William D.)
Princess Liliwinkins, (Wright, Henrietta)
Princess Maritza, (Brebner, Percy)
Princess Marries the Page, (Millay, Edna St. V.)
Princess Mary of Maryland, (Agle, Nan H.)
Princess Nobody, (Lang, Andrew)
Princess Passes, (Williamson, C.& N.)
Princess Pocahontas, (Watson, Virginia)
Princess Rags & Tatters, (Comstock, Harriet T.)
Princess September & Nightingale, (Maugham, W. S.)
Princess Sonia, (Magruder, Julia)
Princess Thora, (Harris-Burland, J.)
Princess White Flame, (Crownfield, Gertrude)
Princess Who Grew, (DeVries, P.J.C.)
Princess and Curdie, (MacDonald, George)
Princess and the Lion, (Coatsworth, Eliz.)
Princess of Cozytown, (Thompson, Ruth P.)
Princess of Hearts, (Braine, Sheila E.)
Princess of Mars, (Burroughs, Edgar R.)
Princess of Yucatan, (Lide, Alice A.)
Princess of the Full Moon, (Guirma, Frederic)
Princess with Pea-Green Nose, (Knatchbull-Hugessen)
Princess's Story Book, (Gomme, George L.)
Princess's Token, (Everett-Green, Evelyn)
Princesses & Peasant Boys, (Fenner, Phyllis R.)
Princesses: 16 Stories...   (Johnson, Sally (ed))
Prints & Drawings of Frank Brangwyn, (Sparrow, W.S.)
Prisoners of Chance, (Parrish, Randall)
Prisoners of Hope, (Johnston, Mary)
Private Memoirs of Madame Roland, (Johnson, E. (ed))
Prize Song, (Weber, Henriette)
Pro Patria, (Pemberton, Max)
Probability: Science of Chance, (Razzell, Arthur)
Professor Bull's Umbrella, (Lipkind, Will)
Professor Philanderpan, (Farrow, George E.)
Project Boy, (Lenski, Lois)
Project Cat, (Burchardt, Nellie)
Prose Fancies, (LeGallienne, R.)
Proserpina: Duck that Came to School, (Georgiou, C.)
Proud Cat, (Lockridge, Frances)
Proud Circus Horse, (Zimnik, Reiner)
Proud Little Kitten, (Lasky, Muriel)
Proud Roxana, (Dow, Ethel C.)
Proverbs in Porcelain, (Dobson, Austin)
Prudence & Peter..., (Robins, Elizabeth)
Prudence Crandall, Woman of Courage, (Yates, Eliz.)
Prue & I, (Curtis, George W.)
Prunella, (Housman, Laurence)
Psalms of David, (Bible)
Psmith in the City, (Wodehouse, P.G.)
Puck in Pasture, (MacKinstry, Eliz.)
Puck of Pook's Hill, (Kipling, Rudyard)
Puck's Broom, (Browne, Edgar G.)
Pudding Lane People, (Addington, Sarah)
Pudding's Wonderful Bone, (Weil, Lisl)
Pudgy: The Little Bear, (Barrows, Marjorie)
Pueblo Indian Folk Stories, (Lummis, Charles F.)
Pueblo Playmates, (Brown, Marjorie)
Puff, (Wondriska, William)
Puff Ball, (Brown, Paul)
Puffin, Puma & Co., (Evans, F. Gwynne)
Puffy & Seven Leaf Clover, (Lathrop, Dorothy)
Pug Peter, (Nesbit, Edith)
Pulcinella, (Mincieli, Rose)
Pulling Strings, (Myers, Madeleine)
Puma & the Pearl, (Sanford, Wendy)
Pumpkin Giant, (Greene, Ellin)

Pumpkin Moonshine, (Tudor, Tasha)
Pumpkin Patch, (Martin, Patricia)
Pumpkin, Ginger & Spice, (Otto, Margaret G.)
Pumpkinseeds, (Yezback, Steven)
Punch & Robinetta, (Gate, Ethel M.)
Punch and Judy, (Brown, Margaret W.)
Punch and Judy, (Emberley, Edward)
Punch and Judy Book, (Whitney, Helen H.)
Punia and the King of the Sharks, (Mohan, Beverly)
Pup Called Cinderella, (Reno, Esther W.)
Pup Himself, (Dennis, Morgan)
Pup Who Became a Police Dog, (Hays, Wilma P.)
Puppies for Keeps, (Lathrop, Dorothy)
Puppy & the Cat, (Lewis, Lorna)
Puppy Called Spinach, (Baker, Margaret)
Puppy Named Gih, (Machetanz, Sara)
Puppy Pie, (Williams, Jay)
Puppy Summer, (DeJong, Meindert)
Puppy Tales, (Waylett, Richard)
Puppy for Keeps, (Hawkins, Quail)
Puptents & Pebbles, (Smith, William J.)
Puritan Adventure, (Lenski, Lois)
Puritan Twins, (Perkins, Lucy F.)
Purple Book, (Anderson, Anne)
Purple Land, (Hudson, Wm. Henry)
Purple Parasol, (McCutcheon, George B.)
Purple Pennant, (Barbour, Ralph H.)
Purple Prince of Oz, (Thompson, Ruth P.)
Purr & Miew, (Leet, Frank R.)
Pursuit of the House Boat, (Bangs, John K.)
Push Kitty, (Wahl, Jan)
Pushcart War, (Merrill, Jean)
Puss in Boots, (Fischer, Hans)
Puss in Boots, (Kastner, Erich)
Puss in Boots, (Latham, Jean L.)
Puss in Boots, (N/A)
Puss in Boots, (Perrault, Charles)
Puss in Boots, Sleeping Beauty & Cinderella, (Moore, M.)
Pussies & Puppies, (Wain, Louis)
Pussy & Doggy Tales, (Nesbit, Edith)
Pussy Purr-Mew, (Winfrey, Guy)
Pussy Willow, (Brown, Margaret W.)
Pussy Willow's Naughty Kittens, (Young, Lillian E.)
Pussy-Cat Town, (Taggart, Marion A.)
Pussycat Princess, (Anthony, Edward)
Pussycat's Breakfast, (Weil, Ann Y.)
Pussycat's Christmas, (Brown, Margaret W.)
Putter Perkins, (Brown, Kenneth)
Puzzling Pair, (LeFevre, A.)
Pygmalion & the Image, (Morris, William)
Pygmy's Arrow, (Fleming, Waldo)
Pysen, (Unnerstad, Edith)
Pyxie, Little Boy of the Pines, (Phillips, Ethel C.)
Quack! Said Jerusha, (Merryman, Mildred P.)
Quack-Quack..., (Hader, B.& E.)
Quackles Junior, (Hamer, Sam H.)
Quacky Doodles..., (Hubbell, Rose S.)
Quake, Quake, Quake, (Dehn, Paul)
Quality Street, (Barrie, James M.)
Quangle Wangle's Hat, (Lear, Edward)
Quarreling Book, (Zolotow, Charlotte)
Quarry Adventure, (Kingman, Lee)
Quart of Moonlight, (Sherman, James W.)
Queen Bee, (Smith, C.M. (tran))
Queen Elizabeth Story, (Sutcliff, Rosemary)
Queen Mab's Fairy Realm, (N/A)
Queen Silver-Bell, (Burnett, Frances H.)
Queen Summer, (Crane, Walter)

Queen Tiny's Little People, (Wetmore, Claude H.)
Queen Victoria's Dolls, (Low, Frances H.)
Queen Victoria's Jubilee Garland, (Greenaway, Kate)
Queen Who Flew, (Ford, Ford Madox)
Queen Zixi of Ix, (Baum, L. Frank)
Queen of Atlantis, (Aubrey, Frank)
Queen of Hearts, (Caldecott, R.)
Queen of the City of Mirth, (Sabin, Elbridge H.)
Queen of the Meadow, (Mack, Robert E.)
Queen of the Pirate Isle, (Harte, Bret)
Queen's Museum, (Stockton, Frank)
Queen's Page, (Baker, Cornelia)
Queen's Story Book, (Gomme, George (ed))
Queenie Peavy, (Burch, Robert)
Queer Cousin Claude, (Girvin, Brenda)
Queer People with Paws & Claws, (Cox, Palmer)
Queer Person, (Hubbard, Ralph)
Queerie Queers with Hands, Wings & Claws, (Cox, P.)
Queerie at the Pole, (Lea, John)
Quentin Durward, (Scott, Walter)
Quest Flower, (Burnham, Clara L.)
Quest for Sita, (Collis, Maurice)
Quest in the Desert, (Andrews, Roy)
Quest of the Dream, (Wallace, Edna K.)
Quest of the Fish-Dog Skin, (Schultz, James W.)
Quest of the Golden Girl, (LeGallienne, R.)
Quest of the Holy Grail, (Greenslet, Ferris)
Quest of the Silver Fleece, (DuBois, W.E.B.)
Quest of the Snow Leopard, (Andrews, Roy)
Quest of the White Merle, (Gask, Lilian)
Question Box, (Williams, Jay)
Question of Our Speech, (James, Henry)
Questions of Lifu, (Lattimore, Eleanor)
Quicksilver Sue, (Richards, Laura E.)
Quiet Noisy Book, (Brown, Margaret W.)
Quiet Place, (Blue, Rose)
Quiet Story, (Levine, Rhoda)
Quito Express, (Bemelmans, Ludwig)
R. Holmes and Co., (Bangs, John K.)
Rabbi Ben Ezra, (Browning, Robert)
Rabbit Bros. Circus: One Night Only, (Wiese, Kurt)
Rabbit Catcher, (Bechstein, Ludwig)
Rabbit Fires, (Johnson, Siddie)
Rabbit Garden, (Miles, Miska)
Rabbit Hill, (Lawson, Robert)
Rabbit Lantern, (Rowe, Dorothy)
Rabbit Story, (Tresselt, Alvin)
Rabbit Witch, (Pyle, Katharine)
Rabbit and Skunk & the Scary Rock, (Stevens, Carla)
Rabbit's Day in Town, (Procter, E.H.)
Rabbit's Nest, (Morrow, Elizabeth)
Rabbit's Revenge, (Wiese, Kurt)
Rabbit's Umbrella, (Plimpton, George)
Rabbit's Wedding, (Williams, Garth)
Raccoon Lake Mystery, (Hopkins, Nevil M.)
Raccoon Twins, (Hogan, Inez)
Raccoon Twins, (Tompkins, Jane)
Raccoon and Mrs. McGinnis, (Martin, Patricia)
Raccoons are for Loving, (Bourne, Miriam)
Race Between the Monkey & the Duck, (Hurd, Clement)
Race of the Swift, (Litsey, E. Carl)
Rachel & the Seven Wonders, (Syrett, Netta)
Rachel Field Story Book, (Field, Rachel)
Rachel Jackson, Tennessee Girl, (Govan, Christine)
Racing Rhymes, (Gordon, Adam L.)
Racketty-Packetty House, (Burnett, Frances H.)
Rackham's Book of Pictures, (Rackham, Arthur)
Radium Terrors, (Dorrington, Albert)

Radium Woman, (Doorly, Eleanor)
Raffie, (Barr, Catherine)
Raffy & the 9 Monkeys, (Rey, Hans A.)
Rag Animals ABC, (Hays, M.G.)
Rag Doll Jane, (Treffinger, Carolyn)
Rag Doll Susie, (Wurth, Anne)
Ragged Robin, (Reeves, James)
Raggedies in Fairy Land, (Ripley, Sherman)
Raggedy Andy Goes Sailing, (Gruelle, Johnny)
Raggedy Andy Stories, (Gruelle, Johnny)
Raggedy Animal Book, (Ripley, Sherman)
Raggedy Ann('s)... [Most titles], (Gruelle, Johnny)
Raggedy Man, (Riley, James W.)
Ragman of Paris & his Ragamuffins, (Jones, Eliz. O.)
Rags, (Peat, Fern B.)
Rags the Firehouse Dog, (Morton, Elizabeth)
Railroad ABC, (Townend, Jack)
Railroad Book, (Smith, E. Boyd)
Railroad West, (Meigs, Cornelia L.)
Railroad to Freedom, (Swift, Hildegarde H.)
Railway Children, (Nesbit, Edith)
Railway Engineer, (Judson, Clara I.)
Railway Ribaldry, (Robinson, W. Heath)
Rain Drop Splash, (Tresselt, Alvin)
Rain Forest, (Sperry, Armstrong)
Rain Makes Applesauce, (Scheer, Julian)
Rain Mouse, (Aichinger, Helga)
Rain Puddle, (Holl, Adelaide)
Rain Rain Rivers, (Shulevitz, Uri)
Rain and Hail, (Branley, Franklyn)
Rain in the Woods, (Rounds, Glen)
Rain on the Roof, (Meigs, Cornelia L.)
Rainbow 'Round the World, (Yates, Elizabeth)
Rainbow Book, (Spielmann, M.H.)
Rainbow Book of American Folk Tales, (Leach, Maria)
Rainbow Book of American History, (Miers, Earl S.)
Rainbow Book of Bible Stories, (Becker, May (ed))
Rainbow Cat, (Fyleman, Rose)
Rainbow Children, (Howes, Edith)
Rainbow Gold, (Teasdale, Sara)
Rainbow Hill, (Lawrence, Josephine)
Rainbow Houses for Boys & Girls, (Hall, Arthur V.)
Rainbow Twins, (Anderson, Florence)
Rainbow Valley, (Montgomery, Lucy M.)
Rainbow for Me, (Kiser, Martha G.)
Rainbow of My Own, (Freeman, Don)
Rainbow's End, (Hader, B.& E.)
Rainbows, (Spicer, Marion D.)
Raining Cats and Donkeys, (Tovey, Doreen)
Rains Will Come, (Means, Florence C.)
Rakoto & the Drongo Bird, (McKown, Robin)
Ralestone Luck, (Norton, Andre)
Ralph Somerby at Panama, (Raleigh, Francis)
Rama, Hero of India, (Mukerji, Dhan G.)
Rama, the Gypsy Cat, (Byars, Betsy C.)
Rambillicus Book, (McDougall, Walter)
Rambles on the Riviera, (Miltoun, Francis)
Raminagrobis and the Mice, (Berson, Harold)
Ramona, (Jackson, Helen H.)
Ramona Knew What She Wanted, (Palazzo, Tony)
Ramona the Pest, (Cleary, Beverly)
Ranch Life & the Hunting Trail, (Roosevelt, Theodore)
Ranch Verses, (Chittenden, Wm. L.)
Ranch and Ring, (Means, Florence C.)
Ranching Sport and Travel, (Carson, Thomas)
Ranching on Eagle Eye, (Schmidt, Sarah L.)
Randy's Dandy Lions, (Peet, Bill)
Range & Trail, (Sabin, Edwin L.)

Range Boss, (Seltzer, Charles A.)
Range Dwellers, (Bower, B.M.)
Range Riders, (Seltzer, Charles A.)
Ranger's Arctic Patrol, (Strong, Charles)
Ranger's Ransom, (Best, Herbert)
Ransom for a Knight, (Picard, Barbara)
Ranson's Folly, (Davis, Richard H.)
Rape of the Lock, (Pope, Alexander)
Rapunzel, (Grimm Bros.)
Raquel of the Ranch Country, (Malkus, Alida S.)
Rascal..., (North, Sterling)
Rasmus & the Vagabond, (Lindgren, Astrid)
Raspberry Patch, (Paull, Grace)
Rataplan, a Rogue Elephant, (Velvin, Ellen)
Ratcatcher to Scarlet, (Aldin, Cecil)
Raven's Cry, (Harris, Christie)
Ravensgill, (Mayne, William)
Raw Gold, (Sinclair, Bertrand)
Ray Coon to the Rescue, (Turner, Nancy B.)
Read About the... [All titles], (Slobodkin, Louis)
Read Aloud Stories, (Bailey, Carolyn S.)
Read to Me Storybook, (N/A)
Read to Me about... [All titles], (Hogan, Inez)
Readings, (De La Mare, Walter)
Ready Rangers, (Munroe, Kirk)
Ready the Reliable, (Wesselhoeft, Lily)
Real Diary of a Real Boy, (Shute, Henry A.)
Real Hole, (Cleary, Beverly)
Real Latin Quarter, (Smith, F. Berkeley)
Real Princess, (Andersen, Hans C.)
Real Queen's Fairy Book, (Sylva, Carmen)
Real Santa Claus, (Walters, Marguerite)
Real Story of a Real Doll, (Higgins, Violet M.)
Real Tales of Real Dogs, (Terhune, Albert P.)
Real Thing..., (Bangs, John K.)
Real Tin Flower, (Barnstone, Aliki)
Really Babies, (Brownell, Elizabeth)
Really Not Really, (Frost, Lesley)
Really So Stories, (Gordon, Elizabeth)
Really Spring, (Zion, Gene)
Really and Truly, (Ames, Mrs. E.)
Reaper Man, (Judson, Clara I.)
Reason for the Pelican, (Ciardi, John)
Reb and the Redcoats, (Savery, Constance)
Rebecca Mary, (Donnell, Annie H.)
Rebel Mail Runner, (Wellman, Manly W.)
Rebel Siege, (Kjelgaard, Jim)
Rebellious Heroine, (Bangs, John K.)
Rebels of the New South, (Raymond, Walter)
Recollection Creek, (Gipson, Fred B.)
Rectory Children, (Molesworth, Mrs.)
Red Apple & Silver Bells, (Hendry, Hamish)
Red Axe, (Crockett, Samuel R.)
Red Bantam, (Fatio, Louise)
Red Blooded, (Bronson, E.B.)
Red Book of Animal Stories, (Lang, Andrew)
Red Book of Heroes, (Lang, Leonora B.)
Red Cap Tales, (Crockett, Samuel R.)
Red Caps and Lilies, (Adams, Katharine)
Red City, (Mitchell, S. Weir)
Red Cross Knight & Sir Guyan, (Macleod, Mary)
Red Eagle, (Key, Alexander)
Red Fairy Book, (Lang, Andrew)
Red Falcons of Tremoine, (Peart, Hendry)
Red Feathers, (Roberts, Theodore G.)
Red Folk & Wild Folk, (Deming, Therese O.)
Red Fox, (Roberts, Chas. G.D.)
Red Fox and His Canoe, (Benchley, Nathaniel)

Red Fox and the Hungry Tiger, (Anderson, Paul S.)
Red Head, (Eager, Edward)
Red Horse, (Moeschlin, Elsa)
Red Horse Hill, (Meader, Stephen W.)
Red House, (Nesbit, Edith)
Red Indian Fairy Book, (Olcott, F.J.)
Red Jungle Boy, (Steen, Elizabeth)
Red Light Green Light, (MacDonald, Golden)
Red Magic..., (Wilson, Romer)
Red Men & White, (Wister, Owen)
Red Men of the Dusk, (Finnemore, John)
Red Mother, (Linderman, Frank B.)
Red Mule, (Stuart, Jesse)
Red People of the Wooded Country, (Deming, T.O.)
Red Planet, (Heinlein, Robert)
Red Pottage, (Cholmondeley, M.)
Red Puppy Book, (Aldin, Cecil)
Red Rajah, (Kent, Louise A.)
Red Riding Hood Goes Sledding, (Steiner, Charlotte)
Red Roan Pony, (Lippincott, J.W.)
Red Romance Book, (Lang, Andrew)
Red Rooster, (Boutwell, Edna)
Red Sails to Capri, (Weil, Ann Y.)
Red Sky over Rome, (Kyle, Anne D.)
Red Squirrel Twins, (Tompkins, Jane)
Red Tag Comes Back, (Phleger, Fred)
Red True Story Book, (Lang, Andrew)
Red is Never a Mouse, (Clifford, Eth)
Red, White & Blue Auto, (Mitchell, Lucy S.)
Red-Bridge Neighborhood, (Pool, Maria L.)
Red-Head, (Lloyd, John U.)
Redcoat Captain, (Ollivant, Alfred)
Reggie & I, (Shirley, Edward)
Reggie's No-Good Bird, (Burchardt, Nellie)
Reign of King Herla, (Canton, William)
Reign of King Oberon, (Jerrold, Walter)
Reign of Old King Cole, (Gibbon, James M.)
Reign of William and Mary, (Morris, M.)
Reindeer Trail, (Hader, B.& E.)
Reindeer Twins, (Tompkins, Jane)
Rejected Lovers, (Steig, William)
Rejuvenation of Mama & Papa Goose, (Pancoast, M.H.)
Relief's Rocker, (Dalgliesh, Alice)
Reluctant Dragon, (Grahame, Kenneth)
Remarkable Advens. of Little Boy Pip, (Francis, Philip W.)
Remarkable Egg, (Holl, Adelaide)
Remarkable Tale of a Whale, (Wright, Isa L.)
Rembrandt, (Menpes, Mortimer)
Remember Rhymes, (Knipe, A.A.)
Remembered Visit, (Gorey, Edward)
Reminiscences of a Ranchman, (Bronson, E.B.)
Reminiscences/Chest of Drawers, (Sill, S.C.)
Remus Goes to Town, (Paltenghi, Madalena)
Renaud of Montauban, (Steele, Robert (tr))
Renni the Rescuer, (Salten, Felix)
Renowned History/Little Red Riding Hood, (Hogrogian, N.)
Requiem for a Princess, (Arthur, Ruth)
Rescue Syndicate, (Jenks, Tudor)
Rescuers: a Fantasy, (Sharp, Margery)
Resolute, (Henderson, Lima L.)
Restless Johnny, (Holberg, Ruth)
Restless Robin, (Flack, Marjorie)
Return of Peter Grimm, (Belasco, David)
Return of Silver Chief, (O'Brien, Jack)
Return of the Twelves, (Clarke, Pauline)
Return of the Weed, (Horgan, Paul)
Return to Gone-Away, (Enright, Elizabeth)
Return to Hackberry Street, (Govan, Christine)

Return to Taos, (Sloane, Eric)
Reuben & his Red Wheelbarrow, (Dalgliesh, Alice)
Reuben James, (Brady, Cyrus T.)
Reverence for Wood, (Sloane, Eric)
Reveries of a Bachelor, (Marvel, Ik.)
Reversible Santa Claus, (Nicholson, Meredith)
Revolt Against Beauty, (Fry, John H.)
Revolt of the Angels, (France, Anatole)
Revolt of the Darumas, (Wise, Winifred)
Reward of Faith, (Goudge, Elizabeth)
Rewards & Fairies, (Kipling, Rudyard)
Rex, (Sharmat, Marjorie)
Reynard the Fox, (Evans, C.S.)
Reynard the Fox, (Masefield, John)
Rhamon: Boy of Kashmir, (Washburne, Heluiz)
Rhinegold & the Valkyrie, (Wagner, Richard)
Rhyme Garden, (Allan, Marguerite B.)
Rhyme of a Run..., (Harrison, Florence)
Rhyme of the Duchess May, (Browning, Eliz. B.)
Rhyme? And Reason?, (Carroll, Lewis)
Rhymes & Jingles, (Dodge, Mary Mapes)
Rhymes & Stories of Olden Times, (Tucker, Eliz.S.)
Rhymes & Verses, (De La Mare, Walter)
Rhymes About the City, (Chute, Marchette)
Rhymes About the Country, (Chute, Marchette)
Rhymes and Reasons, (Harrison, Florence)
Rhymes and Roses, (Weatherly, Fred E.)
Rhymes for Kindly Children, (Fairmont, Ethel)
Rhymes for Kindly Children, (Snyder, Fairmont)
Rhymes for Wee Sweethearts, (Hamill, Katharine F.)
Rhymes for the Young Folks, (Allingham, William)
Rhymes from a Roundup Camp, (Coburn, Wallace D.)
Rhymes of Early Jungle Folk, (Marcy, Mary E.)
Rhymes of Happy Childhood, (Fillebrown, R.H.)
Rhymes of If & Why, (Sage, Betty)
Rhymes of Old Times, (N/A)
Rhymes of Real Children, (Sage, Betty)
Rhymes of Squire O'Squirrel, (Graham, Al)
Rhymes of a Red Cross Man, (Service, Robert W.)
Rhymes of the Golden Age, (Brill, George R.)
Rhymes of the Red Triangle, (Gordon, Hampden C.)
Rhymes without Reason, (Peake, Mervyn)
Rhyming Ring, (Garnett, Louise A.)
Rhyming Will, (Reeves, James)
Rib of the Green Umbrella, (Mitchison, Naomi)
Ribsy, (Cleary, Beverly)
Rice Bowl Pet, (Martin, Patricia)
Rice to Rice Pudding, (Smalley, Janet)
Rice-Cake Rabbit, (Lifton, Betty)
Rich Cargoes, (Rowland, Sydney)
Rich Cat, Poor Cat, (Waber, Bernard)
Rich Man and the Shoemaker, (La Fontaine, J.)
Richard Brown & Dragon, (Bright, Robert)
Richest Boy in the World, (Kalnay, Francis)
Rick & Ruddy, (Garis, Howard)
Rick & Ruddy in Camp, (Garis, Howard)
Rick Dale, (Munroe, Kirk)
Rickety Rackety Rooster, (Wahl, Jan)
Riddle Me, Riddle Me, Ree, (Leach, Maria)
Riddle of Time, (Bell, Thelma H.)
Riddles Around the World, (Zoff, Otto (ed))
Riddles, Riddles from A to Z, (Memling, Carl)
Ride 'Em Peggy!, (Bialk, Elisa)
Ride a Cock-Horse, (N/A)
Ride a Wild Dream, (Hall, Lynn)
Ride a Wild Horse, (Carlsen, Ruth C.)
Ride on the Wind, (Dalgliesh, Alice)
Ride the Cold Wind, (Surany, Anico)

Ride with Me through ABC, (Bond, Susan)
Ride with the Sun, (Courlander, Harold)
Riders of Many Lands, (Dodge, Theodore A.)
Riders of the Gabilans, (Dean, Graham M.)
Riders of the Purple Sage, (Grey, Zane)
Riders of the Winds, (Shenton, Edward)
Riding Rhymes for Young Readers, (Disston, Harry)
Riding the Pony Express, (Bulla, Clyde R.)
Riding the Rails, (Olds, Elizabeth)
Ridolfo, (Williams, Egerton)
Riema..., (Elliot, Kathleen)
Rifles for Washington, (Singmaster, Elsie)
Rifles for Watie, (Keith, Harold V.)
Right Royal, (Masefield, John)
Right Side of the Car, (Lloyd, John U.)
Riley Goes to Obedience School, (Robinson, Mabel L.)
Rilla of Ingleside, (Montgomery, Lucy M.)
Rime of the Ancient Mariner, (Coleridge, Samuel T.)
Rimskittle's Book, (Jackson, Leroy F.)
Rin Tin Tin, (Kearns, Frank)
Ring O' Roses, (Brooke, L. Leslie)
Ring and a Riddle, (Segal, E.A.)
Ring in the Prairie, (Bierhorst, John)
Ring of Bells, (Slade, Irene (comp))
Ring of the Nibelung, (Henderson, Gertrude)
Ring-a-Ring O'Roses, (Briggs, Raymond)
Ring-a-Round-a-Rosy, (Lathbury, M.A.)
Rings and Things, (Posey, Anita)
Ringtail, (Gall, Alice C.)
Rinkitink in Oz, (Baum, L. Frank)
Riot of Quiet, (Sicotte, Virginia)
Rip & Royal, (Scott, Sally)
Rip Van Winkle, (Irving, Washington)
Rise & Fall of Prohibition, (Towne, Charles H.)
Ritz Carltons, (Hyde, Fillmore)
River Boy of Kashmir, (Bothwell, Jean)
River Horse, (Frey, Nina A.)
River Queen, (Burchard, Peter)
River Ranch, (Gates, Doris)
River Treasure, (Burgwyn, Mebane)
River Winding, (Zolotow, Charlotte)
River at Green Knowe, (Boston, Lucy M.)
River of Life, (Platt, Rutherford)
River of the West, (Sperry, Armstrong)
River of the Wolves, (Meader, Stephen W.)
River's Children, (Stuart, Ruth M.)
River-Land, (Chambers, Robert)
Road Builders, (Merwin, Samuel)
Road in Storyland, (Piper, Watty (ed))
Road of the Loving Heart, (Johnston, Annie F.)
Road to Agra, (Sommerfelt, Aimee)
Road to Carolina, (Allee, Marjorie H.)
Road to Cathay, (Sherwood, Merriam)
Road to Enchantment, (Faulkner, Georgene)
Road to Fairyland, (Fay, Erica)
Road to Miklagard, (Treece, Henry)
Road to Nowhere, (Morse, Livingston B.)
Road to Oz, (Baum, L. Frank)
Road, Rail & Sea, (Jerrold, Clare)
Roads and Vagabonds, (Hare, Kenneth)
Roar & More, (Kuskin, Karla)
Robber Bridegroom, (Grimm Bros.)
Robber Hotzenplotz, (Preussler, Otfried)
Robber Kitten, (Disney, Walt)
Robber Kitten, (N/A)
Robbers of Squeak, (Lockyer, A.M.)
Robbie, Brave Little Collie, (L'Hommedieu, Dorothy)
Robbut: Tale of Tails, (Lawson, Robert)

Robert Francis Weatherbee, (Leaf, Munro)
Robert Fulton: Boy Craftsman, (Henry, Marguerite)
Robert Goddard: Trail Blazer to Stars, (Daugherty, Charles)
Robert Kimberly, (Spearman, Frank)
Robert Orange, (Hobbes, John O.)
Roberta Goes Adventuring, (Raymond, Margaret T.)
Roberta and her Brothers, (Bailey, Alice W.)
Robertson, Ugly & Nohow, (Ibbotson, M.C.)
Robin & Angus, (Robinson, Mabel L.)
Robin & Tito, (Robinson, Mabel L.)
Robin Hood, (Gilbert, Henry)
Robin Hood, (Heal, Edith)
Robin Hood, (N/A)
Robin Hood, (Rhead, Louis)
Robin Hood & his Adventures, (Creswick, Paul)
Robin Hood & his Merry Men, (Finnemore, John)
Robin Hood & his Merry Men, (Finnemore, John)
Robin Hood & his Merry Men, (Sterling, Sara H.)
Robin Hood & his Merry Men, (Warren, Maude R.)
Robin Hood & his Merry Outlaws, (McSpadden, J.W.)
Robin Hood & his Merry Outlaws, (Tilney, Frederick C.)
Robin Hood's Arrow, (Stone, Eugenia)
Robin Hood: His Book, (Tappan, Eva M.)
Robin and Heather, (Robinson, Mabel L.)
Robin and his Merry Men, (Serraillier, Ian)
Robinson Crusoe, (Defoe, Daniel)
Rocco Came In, (Beecroft, John)
Rocket Away!, (Frost, Frances)
Rocket Book, (Newell, Peter)
Rocket Ship Galileo, (Heinlein, Robert)
Rocket in My Pocket, (Withers, Carl (comp))
Rocking Chair Buck, (Cheney, Cora)
Rocking Chair Ranch, (Weber, Lenora M.)
Rocking Island, (Love, Edwin M.)
Rocking-Chair Ghost, (Jane, Mary C.)
Rockwellkentiana, (Kent, Rockwell)
Rocky Billy, (Holling, Holling C.)
Rocky Mountain Tipi Tales, (Borland, Hal)
Rocky Summer, (Kingman, Lee)
Rodeo: Bulls, Broncs & Buckaroos, (Rounds, Glen)
Roderick, (Behn, Harry)
Roger & the Fox, (Davis, Lavinia R.)
Roger and Rose, (Beebe, Katharine)
Roger and the Fishes, (Jackson, Charlotte)
Roggie & Reggie Stories, (Smith, Gertrude)
Rogue Reynard, (Norton, Alice)
Rogue's Gallery, (Parker, Edgar)
Rogues in Porcelain, (Austen, Jane)
Roland, (Stephane, Nelly)
Roland the Minstrel Pig, (Steig, William)
Roland the Warrior, (Collier, Virginia M.)
Rolf in the Woods, (Seton, Ernest T.)
Roll Call of Honor, (Quiller-Couch, A.)
Roll of Drums, (Wallower, Lucille)
Roller Skates, (Sawyer, Ruth)
Rollicking Rhymes for Youngsters, (Wells, Amos R.)
Rolling Rice Ball, (Yoda, Junichi)
Rolling Round, (Myller, Rolf)
Rolling Season, (Mayne, William)
Rolling Show, (Voight, Virginia F.)
Rolling the Cheese, (Martin, Patricia)
Rollo in Society, (Chappell, George S.)
Roly Poly Pudding, (Potter, Beatrix)
Roly-Poly Snowman, (Otto, Margaret G.)
Roma Rabbit's Picnic, (Richards, Dorothy)
Roman People, (Coolidge, Olivia)
Romance, (Conrad, Joseph)
Romance of Antar, (Tietjens, Eunice H.)

Romance of Billy-Goat Hill, (Rice, Alice H.)
Romance of Cinderella, (Boult, Ella M.)
Romance of King Arthur, (Pollard, Alfred (ed))
Romance of Lohengrin, (Capes, Bernard E.)
Romance of Old Japan, (Champney, Elizabeth)
Romance of Perfume, (LeGallienne, R.)
Romance of Tristam & Isoude, (N/A)
Romance of Tristan and Iseult, (Bedier, Joseph)
Romance of Zion Chapel, (LeGallienne, R.)
Romance of a Boo-Bird Chick, (Gotch, Phyllis M.)
Romance of a Child, (Loti, Pierre)
Romance of a Christmas Card, (Wiggin, Kate D.)
Romance of a Rogue, (Sharts, Joseph W.)
Romance of an Old Fashioned Gentleman, (Smith, F.H.)
Romance of the Milky Way, (Hearn, Lafcadio)
Romance of the Moon, (Mitchell, John A.)
Romance of the Netherlands, (MacGregor, Mary)
Romance of the Nursery, (Harker, L. Allen)
Romance of the River, (Ponsot, Georges)
Romance of the Road, (Aldin, Cecil)
Romance of the Three R's, (Crane, Walter)
Romantic America, (Schauffler, Rbt. H.)
Romantic Rascals, (Finger, Charles J.)
Romantic Rebel, (Hawthorne, Hildegarde)
Romaunt of the Rose, (Chaucer, Geoffrey)
Romeo & Juliet, (Shakespeare, Wm.)
Romney Gay ABC, (Gay, Romney)
Ronald Bannerman's Boyhood, (MacDonald, George)
Ronald's Burglar, (Chaundler, Christine)
Ronnie, (Rowntree, Lester)
Ronnie and the Chief's Son, (Coatsworth, Eliz.)
Ronnie's Wish, (Brown, Jeanette)
Roof & Meadow, (Sharp, Dallas L.)
Rooftop Mystery, (Lexau, Joan M.)
Rookie, (Flagg, Elisha)
Room for Randy, (Jackson, Jesse)
Roosevelt Bears, (Eaton, Seymour)
Roosevelt Bears Abroad, (Eaton, Seymour)
Roosevelt Grady, (Shotwell, Louisa)
Rooster Club, (Angelo, Valenti)
Rooster Crows, (Petersham, Maud)
Rootabaga... [All titles], (Sandburg, Carl)
Rosa, (Politi, Leo)
Rosa-Too-Little, (Felt, Sue)
Rosalina, (Archer, Jean C.)
Rosalynde's Lovers, (Thompson, Maurice)
Rose & the Ring, (Thackeray, Wm. M.)
Rose Book of the Fairies, (Strang, Herbert)
Rose Fairies, (McCabe, Olivia)
Rose Fairy Book, (Lang, Andrew)
Rose Fairy Book, (Strang, Herbert)
Rose Fyleman Fairy Book, (Fyleman, Rose)
Rose Island, (Russell, William C.)
Rose Island, (Vildrac, Charles)
Rose for Mr. Bloom, (Waber, Bernard)
Rose in Bloom, (Alcott, Louisa M.)
Rose of Old Harpeth, (Davies, Maria T.)
Rose of Paradise, (Pyle, Howard)
Rose of the World, (Castle, A.& E.)
Rose on My Cake, (Kuskin, Karla)
Rose, a Bridge & Wild Black Horse, (Zolotow, C.)
Rosebud, (Bemelmans, Ludwig)
Rosebud, (Emberley, Edward)
Rosebud Stories, (Humphrey, Maud)
Rosebud and Other Tales, (Kelly, Arthur)
Rosebuds, (Hutt, Henry)
Roseen, (Casserley, Anne)
Rosemary and Rue, (Amber)

Roses of the Winds, (Lustig, Sonia)
Rosie the Rhino, (Conger, Marion)
Rosie's Walk, (Hutchins, Pat)
Rosie-Posie Book, (Anderson, Anne)
Rossetti and his Circle, (Beerbohm, Max)
Rosy, (Molesworth, Mrs.)
Rosy Childhood, (Hays, M.G.)
Rotten Book, (Rodgers, Mary)
Rough Riders Ho!, (Montgomery, R.)
Rough Shaking, (MacDonald, George)
Rough and Tumble, (Aldin, Cecil)
Roughing It in the Bush, (Moodie, Susanna)
Round De Ole Plantation, (Christie, G.F.)
Round Dozen Stories by Louisa M. Alcott, (Alcott, L.M.)
Round Fairyland with Alice, (Girvin, Brenda)
Round Meadow, (Oldrin, John)
Round Rabbit, (Lee, Agnes)
Round Robin, (Davis, Lavinia R.)
Round Sultan & the Straight Answer, (Walker, Barbara)
Round Things Everywhere, (Reit, Seymour)
Round and Round Horse, (Gury, Jeremy)
Round of Carols, (Noble, Thomas T.)
Round the Afternoon, (Jackson, Charlotte)
Round the Hearth, (Bennet, H.)
Round the Mulberry Bush, (Fyleman, Rose)
Round the Mulberry Bush, (McNeil, Marion)
Round the World ABC, (Farrow, George E.)
Round the World We Sail, (Scott, Janet L.)
Round the World to Wympland, (Sharp, Evelyn)
Round the Year on Pudding Lane, (Addington, Sarah)
Round the Yule Log, (Asbjornsen, P.C.)
Round-Trip Space Ship, (Slobodkin, Louis)
Roundabout, (Dalgliesh, Alice)
Roundabout Turn, (Charles, Robert H.)
Roundhouse Cat and other Railroad Animals, (Hubbard, F.)
Rountree's Ridiculous Rabbits, (Rountree, Harry)
Roving Lobster, (Mason, Arthur)
Rowena Carey, (Holberg, Ruth)
Rowena Teena Tot & Blackberries, (Blumberg, Fannie B.)
Rowena the Sailor, (Holberg, Ruth)
Rowena the Skating Cow, (Schackne, Stewart)
Royal Book of Oz, (Thompson, Ruth P.)
Royal Children of English History, (Nesbit, Edith)
Royal Little People, (Tucker, Elizabeth S.)
Royal Mimkin, (Gall, Alice C.)
Royal Progress of King Pepito, (Cresswell, Beatrice)
Royal Reflections, (Goulden, Shirley)
Rrou, (Genevoix, Maurice)
Rrra-ah, (Keith, Eros)
Rubaiyat of Bridge, (Wells, Carolyn)
Rubaiyat of Doc Sifers, (Riley, James W.)
Rubaiyat of Omar Khayyam [All titles], (Omar Khayyam)
Rubaiyat of a Motor Car, (Wells, Carolyn)
Rubaiyat of a Persian Kitten, (Herford, Oliver)
Ruby Fairy Book, (Various)
Ruby Ring, (Molesworth, Mrs.)
Ruby of Kishmoor, (Pyle, Howard)
Rudi and the Mayor of Naples, (Osborne, Maurice M.)
Ruff and Reddy, (Byron, May)
Ruffs & Pompons, (King, Beulah)
Rufie Had a Monkey!, (Sechrist, Eliz. H.)
Rufus, (Ungerer, Tomi)
Rufus M., (Estes, Eleanor)
Rufus the Fox, (Bianco, Margery W.)
Rug that Went to Mecca, (Mirza, Youel B.)
Rule Britannia, (Unknown)
Rules of the Game, (White, Stewart E.)
Rum-Tum-Tummy..., (Holling, Holling C.)

Rumanian Legends & Fairy Tales, (Gaster, Moses)
Rumbo Rhymes, (Calmour, Alfred C.)
Rumpelstilskin, (Grimm Bros.)
Rumpty-Dudget's Tower, (Hawthorne, Julian)
Rumpus Rabbit, (Paltenghi, Madalena)
Runaway Balboa, (Johnson, Enid)
Runaway Boy, (Riley, James W.)
Runaway Bunny, (Brown, Margaret W.)
Runaway Bunny, (Smith, Laura R.)
Runaway Deer, (Fleury, Barbara)
Runaway Elephant, (Tarry, Ellen)
Runaway Equator, (Bell, Lilian)
Runaway Flea Circus, (Lauber, Patricia)
Runaway Giant, (Holl, Adelaide)
Runaway Hat, (Holl, Adelaide)
Runaway Home, (Lyon, Elinor)
Runaway House, (Thomajan, Puzant K.)
Runaway Jonah..., (Wahl, Jan)
Runaway Lamb at County Fair, (Disney, Walt)
Runaway Linda, (Allee, Marjorie H.)
Runaway Papoose, (Moon, Grace P.)
Runaway Pony, Runaway Dog, (Carroll, Ruth)
Runaway Ralph, (Cleary, Beverly)
Runaway Rhymes, (Higgins, Alice)
Runaway Rocking Horse, (Robertson, Lilian)
Runaway Sardine, (Brock, Emma)
Runaway Settlers, (Locke, Elsie)
Runaway Smalls, (Campbell, Ruth)
Runaway Summer of Davie Shaw, (Puzo, Mario)
Runaway Toys, (Hogan, Inez)
Runaway Toys, (Sturges, Lilian B.)
Runner of the Mountain Tops, (Robinson, Mabel L.)
Running Away with Nebby, (Garrard, Phillis)
Runny Days, Sunny Days, (Fisher, Aileen)
Runzel-Punzel, (Donaldson, Lois)
Russet and the Two Reds, (Lipkind, Will)
Russian Ballet, (Johnson, A.E.)
Russian Fairy Book, (Dole, Nathan H.)
Russian Fairy Tales, (Bain, Robert N.)
Russian Folk Tales, (Duddington, Natalie)
Russian Garland, (Steele, Robert (ed))
Russian Story Book, (Wilson, Richard)
Russian Wonder Tales, (Bilibin, Ivan)
Rustam Lion of Persia, (Chidsey, Alan)
Rusted Knight and other Stories, (Von Volkmann, Richard)
Rusty Rings a Bell, (Branley, Franklyn)
Rusty Ruston, (McNeely, Marion H.)
Rusty at Ram's Horn Ranch, (Garst, Shannon)
Rusty's Space Ship, (Lampman, Evelyn)
Rusty, Little Red Dachshund, (L'Hommedieu, Dorothy)
Ruth, (Petersham, Maud)
Rutherford T. Finds 21B, (Rinkoff, Barbara)
Ruthless Rhymes for Heartless Homes, (Streamer, Col. D.)
Ryecroft Rivals, (Bird, Richard)
S.O.S. Geneva, (Plant, Richard)
SHHhhh... Bang!, (Brown, Margaret W.)
Sabre Pilot, (Meader, Stephen W.)
Sabrina Warham, (Housman, Laurence)
Sad Day, Glad Day, (Thompson, Vivian L.)
Sad End of Erica's Blackamoor, (Kempson, Frederick C.)
Sad-Faced Boy, (Bontemps, Arna)
Saga of Frankie & Johnny, (Held, John)
Saga of Gisli, (Allen, Ralph B.)
Saga of the Sea-Swallow, (Dickson, Maidie)
Sail Ho!, (Grant, Gordon)
Sailboat Time, (Lindman, Maj)
Sailor Rumbelow, (Reeves, James)
Sailor Sam, (Dalgliesh, Alice)

Sailor's Choice, (Carlson, Natalie S.)
Sailor's Life, (DeHartog, Jan)
Sails of Gold, (Asquith, C. (ed.))
Saint George & the Dragon, (Johnson, Richard)
Saint's Garden, (Radcliffe, Winifred)
Saints & their Stories, (Webling, Peggy)
Sakimura, (Gay, Zhenya)
Salamina, (Kent, Rockwell)
Salem Kittredge, (Perry, Bliss)
Sally Castleton, Southerner, (Marriott, Crittenden)
Sally Gabble & the Fairies, (Potter, Miriam C.)
Sally Saucer, (Weiss, Edna S.)
Sally Tait, (Sayers, Frances C.)
Sally's ABC, (Walker, Dugald S.)
Salome..., (Wilde, Oscar)
Salomy Jane, (Harte, Bret)
Salt & Pepper, (Carroll, Ruth)
Salt Boy, (Mauzey, Merritt)
Salt Boy, (Perrine, Mary)
Salt, a Russian Tale, (Zemach, Harve)
Salute, (Anderson, C.W.)
Salve Venetia, (Crawford, F. Marion)
Sam, (Scott, Ann H.)
Sam Bottleby, (Carlsen, Ruth C.)
Sam Patch..., (Bontemps, Arna)
Sam Steele's Adventures in Panama, (Fitzgerald, Hugh)
Sam Steele's Advens. on Land & Sea, (Fitzgerald, H.)
Sam and the Impossible Thing, (Kitt, Tamara)
Sam and the Superdroop, (Leaf, Munro)
Sam's Secret Journal, (Yates, Elizabeth)
Sam, Bangs & Moonshine, (Ness, Evaline M.)
Sam, the Minuteman, (Benchley, Nathaniel)
Sambo & Susanna, (Byron, May)
Sambo and the Twins, (Bannerman, Helen)
Sammy, (Justus, May)
Sammy & Silverband, (Miller, Janet)
Sammy Goes a Hunting, (Ainslie, Kathleen)
Sammy and the Snarlywink, (Ault, L.& N.)
Sammy the Seal, (Hoff, Syd)
Sammy, the Crow Who Remembered, (Hazelton, Eliz.)
San Francisco Boy, (Lenski, Lois)
San Isidro, (Crowninshield, Mrs.)
Sancho & Stubborn Mule, (Keats, Mark)
Sanctuary, (Wharton, Edith)
Sand, (James, Will)
Sand and Snow, (Kuskin, Karla)
Sand for the Sandmen, (DeJong, Dola)
Sandals of Pearl, (Howes, Edith)
Sandburrs, (Lewis, Alfred H.)
Sandman's Forest, (Dodge, Louis)
Sandman's Mountain, (Dodge, Louis)
Sandman: His Animal Stories, (Frees, Harry W.)
Sandpipers, (Hurd, Edith T.)
Sandra and the Right Prince, (Anderson, Mildred)
Sandy, (Gray, Eliz. J.)
Sandy Sandman, (Summers, Clara)
Sandy's Kingdom, (Davis, Mary G.)
Sandy's Spurs, (Davis, Lavinia R.)
Sandy, Skip & Man in the Moon, (Hogan, Inez)
Sandy, Tin Soldier of the A.E.F., (Connor, J. Hall)
Santa Claus & All About Him, (Smith, E. Boyd)
Santa Claus & his Works, (Webster, George)
Santa Claus Brownies, (Phillips, Ethel C.)
Santa Claus Club, (Bridgman, L.J.)
Santa Claus Comes to America, (Singer, Caroline)
Santa Claus Picture Book, (N/A)
Santa Claus Up-to-Date, (N/A)
Santa Claus in Summer, (Mackenzie, Compton)

Santa Claus in Toyland, (Lawrence, C.H.)
Santa Claus's Partner, (Page, Thomas N.)
Santa Fe's Partner, (Janvier, Thomas A.)
Santa Go Home, (Nash, Ogden)
Santa's Footprints, (N/A)
Santa's Workshop, (Disney, Walt)
Santiago, (Belpre, Pura)
Santiago, (Clark, Ann N.)
Sara Crew, (Burnett, Frances H.)
Sara and the Winter Gift, (Mason, Miriam E.)
Sara's Granny & the Groodle, (Gill, Joan)
Sarah & Simon and No Red Paint, (Ardizzone, Edward)
Sarah Deborah's Day, (Jackson, Charlotte)
Sarah Faith Anderson, (Garner, Elvira)
Sarah Somebody, (Slobodkin, Florence)
Sarah's Daikin, (Robinson, Mabel L.)
Sarah's Idea, (Gates, Doris)
Sarah's Room, (Orgel, Doris)
Saranga the Pygmy, (Gatti, Attilio)
Sardines and the Angel, (Bettina)
Sartor Resartus, (Carlyle, Thomas)
Sasha and the Samovar, (Beim, Lorraine)
Sashes Red & Blue, (Carlson, Natalie S.)
Satchkin Patchkin, (Morgan, Helen)
Saturday Cousins, (Caudill, Rebecca)
Saturday Flight, (Wright, Ethel B.)
Saturday Walk, (Wright, Ethel B.)
Saturday to Monday, (Levy, Newman)
Sauce for the Gander, (Corbett, Scott)
Saucepan Journey, (Unnerstad, Edith)
Sausages & Sundials, (Reed, Langford)
Savage Sam, (Gipson, Fred B.)
Save my Place, (Hoban, Russell)
Savoy Cocktail Book, (Craddock, Harry (comp))
Savoy Operas, (Gilbert, W.S.)
Sawdust Doll, (DeKoven, Mrs. R.)
Sawdust in his Shoes, (McGraw, Eloise J.)
Say Something, (Stolz, Mary S.)
Sazada Tales, (Fraser, William A.)
Scalawagons of Oz, (Neill, John R.)
Scamper's Christmas, (Dall, Anna R.)
Scamper: Bunny Who Went to White House, (Dall, A.R.)
Scampers and Scrapes, (N/A)
Scampy the Little Black Cocker, (L'Hommedieu, Dorothy)
Scandalous Advens. of Reynard the Fox, (Owens, Harry J.)
Scarab for Luck..., (Meadowcroft, Enid)
Scareboy, (Hart, Jeanne M.)
Scarecrow & other Stories, (De La Mare, Walter)
Scarecrow & the Tin Man, (Denslow, W.W.)
Scarecrow of Oz, (Baum, L. Frank)
Scaredy Cat, (Krasilovsky, Phyllis)
Scarface, (Norton, Andre)
Scarlet Blue and Green, (Fife, Duncan)
Scarlet Car, (Davis, Richard H.)
Scarlet Cockerel, (Sublette, Clifford)
Scarlet Empire, (Parry, David M.)
Scarlet Herring, (Parry, Edward A.)
Scarlet Letter, (Hawthorne, Nathaniel)
Scarlet Oak, (Meigs, Cornelia L.)
Scarlet Plague, (London, Jack)
Scarlet Thread, (Weik, Mary H.)
Scarlet to M.F.H., (Aldin, Cecil)
Scars & Stripes, (Browne, Porter E.)
Scary Thing, (Bannon, Laura)
Scary-Ann/Cookie Man, (Howland, Ethel)
Scat, Scat, (Francis, Sally R.)
Scatter the Chipmunk, (Coblentz, Catherine)
Scenery of London, (Mitton, G.E.)

Scenes from Clerical Life, (Eliot, George)
Scenes in Fairyland, (Atkinson, John C.)
Scholar-Gypsy, (Arnold, Matthew)
Scholar-Gypsy and Thyrsis, (Arnold, Matthew)
School Bell in the Valley, (Carlson, Natalie S.)
School Days, (Bruce, Josephine)
School Days in Disneyville, (Emerson, Caroline)
School Train, (Acker, Helen)
School for Cats, (Averill, Esther)
School for Saints, (Hobbes, John O.)
School for Scandal, (Sheridan, Richard B.)
School in Fairyland, (Strain, E.H.)
School in Our Village, (Goldman, Joan M.)
School in the Sky, (Carroll, Ruth)
Schoolhouse in the Woods, (Caudill, Rebecca)
Schoolmaster Whackwell's Wonderful Sons, (Brentano, C.)
Schoolroom in the Parlor, (Caudill, Rebecca)
Scorpion: Good Bad Horse, (James, Will)
Scotch Circus, (Powers, Tom)
Scottish Chiefs, (Wiggin, Kate D.)
Scottish Fairy Book, (Grierson, Eliz. W.)
Scottish Songbook, (Leodhas, Sorche)
Scout of Today, (Hornibrook, Isabel)
Scouting with Daniel Boone, (Tomlinson, Everett)
Scrambled Eggs Super, (Seuss, Dr.)
Scrap Basket Sam, (Boyle, E.)
Scrap Irony, (Lamport, Felicia)
Scrappy the Pup, (Ciardi, John)
Scroggins, (Lloyd, John U.)
Scroobius Pip, (Lear, Edward)
Scuff the Seal, (Lida)
Scuttle, the Stowaway Mouse, (Soule, Jean)
Sea & Sussex, (Kipling, Rudyard)
Sea & the Jungle, (Tomlinson, H.M.)
Sea Beach Adventure, (Saxon, Gladys)
Sea Beach Express, (Panetta, George)
Sea Broke Through, (Flakkeberg, Ardo)
Sea Change, (Armstrong, Richard)
Sea Egg, (Boston, Lucy M.)
Sea Fairies, (Baum, L. Frank)
Sea Fever, (Peyton, Kathleen M.)
Sea Horse, (Van Anrooy, Frans)
Sea Horse: Fish in Armor, (Stephens, William)
Sea Legs, (Herford, Oliver)
Sea Magic..., (Beaumont, Cyril W.)
Sea Raiders Ho!, (Montgomery, R.)
Sea Snake, (Meader, Stephen W.)
Sea Star: Orphan of Chincoteague, (Henry, Marguerite)
Sea Sums, (Morse, Samuel)
Sea Turn, (Aldrich, Thomas B.)
Sea Wolf, (London, Jack)
Sea is All Around, (Enright, Elizabeth)
Sea is Blue, (Lawson, Marie A.)
Sea of Gold, (Uchida, Yoshiko)
Sea-Horse Adventure, (Eberle, Irmengarde)
Sea-Prince, (Larken, Edmund P.)
Sea-Shore Fairies, (Webb, M. St. John)
Sea-Spell and Moor-Magic, (Leodhas, Sorche)
Seabird, (Holling, Holling C.)
Seacrow Island, (Lindgren, Astrid)
Seal of Frog Island, (Rumsey, Mirian)
Seal of the White Buddha, (Daniel, Hawthorne)
Seal that Couldn't Swim, (Ladas, Alexis)
Seamstress of Salzburg, (Lobel, Anita)
Sean & Sheela, (King, Marian)
Search for Delicious, (Babbitt, Natalie)
Seashore Book, (Smith, E. Boyd)
Seashore Noisy Book, (Brown, Margaret W.)

Seashore Story, (Yashima, Taro)
Season of Ponies, (Snyder, Zilpha K.)
Seatmates, (Reely, Mary K.)
Seaweed Hat, (Slobodkin, Louis)
Sebastian Bach, (Wheeler, Opal)
Second Barrel, (Sloane, Eric)
Second Book of 50 Drawings, (Beardsley, Aubrey)
Second Deluge, (Serviss, Garrett P.)
Second Froggy Fairy Book, (Biddle, Anthony)
Second Jungle Book, (Kipling, Rudyard)
Second Shift, (Crawford, Phyllis)
Second Witch, (Sendak, Jack)
Second Wooing of Salina Sue, (Stuart, Ruth M.)
Secret Agents Four, (Sobol, Donald J.)
Secret Brother, (Crawford, Phyllis)
Secret Circle, (Forbus, Ina B.)
Secret Fiord, (Trease, Geoffrey)
Secret Garden, (Burnett, Frances H.)
Secret Hiding Place, (Bennett, Rainey)
Secret Journey of Hugo the Brat, (Ruy-Vidal, Francois)
Secret Journey of the Silver Reindeer, (Kingman, Lee)
Secret Language, (Nordstrom, Ursula)
Secret Life of Salvador Dali, (Dali, Salvador)
Secret Passage, (Cavanna, Betty)
Secret Play, (Barbour, Ralph H.)
Secret River, (Rawlings, Marjorie K.)
Secret Sea, (White, Robb)
Secret Seller, (Lifton, Betty)
Secret Shoemakers, (Reeves, James)
Secret Three, (Myrick, Mildred)
Secret Trails, (Roberts, Chas. G.D.)
Secret Valley, (Bulla, Clyde R.)
Secret Voyage, (Grant, Gordon)
Secret Water, (Ransome, Arthur)
Secret of Alexander's Horse, (Palazzo, Tony)
Secret of Crossbone Hill, (Steele, Mary Q.)
Secret of Dark Entry, (Lansing, Elisabeth H.)
Secret of Fiery Gorge, (Gage, Wilson)
Secret of Indian Mound, (Gage, Wilson)
Secret of Lonesome Cove, (Adams, Samuel H.)
Secret of Silver Peak, (Schmidt, Sarah L.)
Secret of Stonehouse, (Hall, Lynn)
Secret of the Ancient Oak, (Wolo)
Secret of the Andes, (Clark, Ann N.)
Secret of the Bog, (Stone, Eugenia)
Secret of the Clan, (Brown, Alice)
Secret of the Hawk, (Wibberley, Leonard)
Secret of the Lodge, (Streatfeild, Noel)
Secret of the Porcelain Fish, (Evernden, Margery)
Secret of the Ron Mor Skerry, (Fry, Rosalie K.)
Secrets, (Jones, Jessie O.)
Secrets of the Elves, (McElhone, Helen K.)
See & Say, (Frasconi, Antonio)
See Again, Say Again, (Frasconi, Antonio)
See Along the Shore, (Selsam, Millicent)
See What I Found, (Livingston, Myra C.)
See a White Horse, (Miles, Miska)
Seed Fairies, (Webb, M. St. John)
Seed that Peacock Planted, (Kepes, Juliet A.)
Seeds & More Seeds, (Selsam, Millicent)
Seem-So's, (Bridgman, L.J.)
Seesaw, (Kahn, Joan)
Seffy, (Long, John L.)
Seizer of Eagles, (Schultz, James W.)
Seldom & the Golden Cheese, (Schrank, Joseph)
Selected Poems..., (Swinburne, A.C.)
Selected Tales of Mystery, (Poe, Edgar A.)
Selections from LeMorte D'arthur, (Thomson, Clara L.)

Selfish Giant, (Wilde, Oscar)
Selfish Giant..., (Harper, Wilhelmina)
Senor Baby Elephant the Pirate, (Joslin, Sesyle)
Senor Castillo, (Caire, Helen)
Sensational Trance, (Dawson, Forbes)
Sense and Sensibility, (Austen, Jane)
Sensible Kate, (Gates, Doris)
Sensitive Plant, (Shelley, Percy B.)
Sentimental Journey/France & Italy, (Sterne, Laurence)
Sentimental Tommy, (Barrie, James M.)
Sequoya, (Coblentz, Catherine)
Serafina the Giraffe, (DeBrunhoff, Laurent)
Serafina's Lucky Find, (DeBrunhoff, Laurent)
Serbian Fairy Tales, (Mijatovich, Elodie)
Serendipity Tales, (Hodges, Elizabeth)
Sergeant O'Keefe and his Mule Balaam, (Felton, Harold)
Sermon on the Mount, (Bible)
Sermons in Song, (Nesbit, Wilbur D.)
Seth Way, (Owen, Caroline D.)
Seven Ages of Childhood, (Wells, Carolyn)
Seven Beads of Wampum, (Gale, Elizabeth)
Seven Beaver Skins, (Berry, Erick)
Seven Champions of Christendom, (Darton, F.J.H.)
Seven Christmas Candles, (Fox, Frances M.)
Seven Cities of Cibola, (Nusbaum, Aileen)
Seven Crowns, (Lattimore, Eleanor)
Seven Days from Sunday, (Galt, Tom)
Seven Diving Ducks, (Friskey, Margaret)
Seven Glass Gooseberries, (Cumberland, Charles)
Seven Keys to Baldpate, (Biggers, Earl D.)
Seven Lady Godivas, (Seuss, Dr.)
Seven Little Elephants, (Hall, William N.)
Seven Little Postmen, (Brown, Margaret W.)
Seven Little Spillikins, (Gilmour, Margaret)
Seven O'Clock Stories, (Anderson, Rbt. G.)
Seven Peas in the Pod, (Bailey, Margery)
Seven Ravens, (Grimm Bros.)
Seven Remarkable Bears, (McLeod, Emilie)
Seven Seas, (Kipling, Rudyard)
Seven Silly Wise Men, (Bowman, James C.)
Seven Simeons, (Artzybasheff, Boris)
Seven Skinny Goats, (Ambrus, Victor G.)
Seven Special Cats, (Koenig, Richard)
Seven Stories about Cat Named Sneakers, (Brown, M.W.)
Seven Tales, (Andersen, Hans C.)
Seven Voyages of Sinbad, (N/A)
Seven Voyages of Sinbad the Sailor, (N/A)
Seven and Sam, (Urmston, Mary)
Seven for St. Nicholas, (Hall, Rosalys)
Seven in a Bed, (Sonneborn, Ruth)
Seventeen, (Tarkington, Booth)
Seventeen to Sing, (Adshead, Gladys)
Seventeenth Street Gang, (Neville, Emily C.)
Seventh Mandarin, (Yolen, Jane)
Seventh Son of a Seventh Son, (Littlefield, Wm. J.)
Seventh's Staghound, (Downey, Fairfax)
Several Tricks of Edgar Dolphin, (Benchley, Nathaniel)
Severed Mantle, (Lindsey, William)
Shades of Blue, (Newman, Isidora)
Shadow Between his Shoulder Blades, (Harris, Joel C.)
Shadow Book, (DeRegniers, Beatrice)
Shadow Over Wide Ruin, (Means, Florence C.)
Shadow Show, (Newell, Peter)
Shadow and the Stocking, (Tippett, James S.)
Shadow in the Pines, (Meader, Stephen W.)
Shadow of Love, (Armour, Margaret)
Shadow of a Bull, (Wojciechowska, Maia)
Shadow of the Rope, (Hornung, E.W.)

Shadow over Winding Ranch, (Schmidt, Sarah L.)
Shadow's Holiday, (June, Larry)
Shadowed!, (Belloc, Hilaire)
Shadows into Mist, (Turngren, Ellen)
Shadrach, (DeJong, Meindert)
Shaggy Man of Oz, (Snow, Jack)
Shakespeare's Heroines, (Jameson, Anna)
Shakespeare's Sweetheart, (Sterling, Sara H.)
Shakespearian Fairy Tales, (Britton, Fay A.)
Shakespearian Tales in Verse for Children, (Mrs. Valentine)
Shamrock and Spear, (Pilkington, Francis)
Shan's Lucky Knife, (Merrill, Jean)
Shane, (Schaefer, Jack W.)
Shannon, (Morrow, Elizabeth)
Shanty Ann, (Moon, Grace P.)
Shape of the Earth, (Bendick, Jeanne)
Shapes, (Schlein, Miriam)
Shapes & Sounds, (Peake, Mervyn)
Shapes in the Fire, (Shiel, Matthew P.)
Shark Hole, (Burglon, Nora)
Shasta of the Wolves, (Baker, Olaf)
Shaun & the Cart Horse, (Keeping, Charles)
Shaun and the Boat, (Molloy, Anne)
Shaw's Fortune, (Tunis, Edwin B.)
She, (Haggard, H. Rider)
She Loves Me, (Hutt, Henry)
She Loves Me, She Loves Me Not, (Keeshan, Robert)
She Shall Have Music, (Barne, Kitty)
She Stoops to Conquer, (Goldsmith, Oliver)
Sheaf of Roses, (Gordon, Elizabeth)
Sheep, (Gilfillan, Archer B.)
Sheep Ahoy!, (Kingman, Lee)
Sheep Wagon Family, (Richardson, Myra)
Sheila's Mystery, (Molesworth, Mrs.)
Sheker's Lucky Piece, (McDonald, Lucile S.)
Shen of the Sea, (Chrisman, Arthur B.)
Shep and the Baby, (Hoke, Helen)
Shepheard's Calendar, (Spenser, Edmund)
Shepherd Psalm, (Petersham, Maud)
Shepherd of the Sun, (Appel, Benjamin)
Sherlock on the Trail, (Holding, James)
Sherwood, (Noyes, Alfred)
Sherwood Ring, (Pope, Elizabeth M.)
Sherwood Walks Home, (Flora, James)
Shield Ring, (Sutcliff, Rosemary)
Shine, (Van Vrooman, Maria)
Shining Bird, (Tolboom, Wanda)
Ship of Flame, (Stone, William S.)
Ship that Came Down the Gutter, (Kotzwinkle, William)
Ship that Flew, (Lewis, Hilda)
Ship that Sailed to Mars, (Timlin, William M.)
Ship's Monkey, (Morrow, Honore)
Shipmates Down Under, (Collins, Dale)
Shipment for Susannah, (Nolen, Eleanor W.)
Ships Under Sail, (Grant, Gordon)
Ships and Sailors, (Barnes, James)
Shire Colt, (Gay, Zhenya)
Shirley, (Bronte, Charlotte)
Shirley Temple in Heidi, (Spyri, Johanna)
Shivers..., (Weil, Lisl)
Shoe Bird, (Welty, Eudora)
Shoe Full of Shamrock, (Shura, Mary F.)
Shoelace Robin, (Hall, William N.)
Shoemaker and the Elves, (Grimm Bros.)
Shoemaker's Apron, (Fillmore, Parker H.)
Shoes Fit for a King, (Bill, Helen)
Shoes, Ships & Sealing Wax, (Chamberlin, Ethel C.)
Shoo-Fly Girl, (Lenski, Lois)

Shoo-Fly Pie, (Jordan, Mildred)
Shoot for a Mule, (Lansing, Elisabeth H.)
Shooting Star Farm, (Molloy, Anne)
Shopping Day, (Bridgman, Clare)
Short Poems for Short people, (Aspinall, Alicia)
Short Stories of Musical Melodies, (Waterstone, Satella)
Short Walk from the Station, (McGinley, Phyllis)
Shorter Poems of Christina Rossetti, (Rossetti, C.)
Shorty: Nursery Tale/Far Away, (Grishina-Givago, N.)
Shotgun Shaw: A Baseball Story, (Keith, Harold V.)
Show and Tell, (Martin, Patricia)
Showmen and Suckers, (Gorham, Maurice)
Shrieks at Midnight, (Brewton, Sara W.)
Shrimps, (Hawes, Judy)
Shuttered Windows, (Means, Florence C.)
Shy Little Girl, (Krasilovsky, Phyllis)
Shy Ones, (Hall, Lynn)
Shy Stegosaurus of Cricket Creek, (Lampman, Evelyn)
Shy Stegosaurus of Indian Springs, (Lampman, Evelyn)
Siamese Cat, (Morse, Elizabeth)
Sibby Botherbox, (Hunt, Mabel L.)
Siberian Gold, (Harper, Theodore A.)
Sick-a-Bed-Lady, (Abbott, Eleanor H.)
Side Saddle for Dandy, (Faulkner, Nancy)
Side Show Studies, (Metcalfe, Francis)
Sidi: Boy of the Desert, (Malkus, Alida S.)
Sidney's Ghost, (Iden, Carol)
Sidney: Summer on St. Lawrence, (Ray, Anna C.)
Sidsel Longskirt & Solve Suntrap, (Aanrud, Hans.)
Siege of the Seven Suitors, (Nicholson, Meredith)
Siegfried, (Baring-Gould, Sabine)
Siegfried, (Heal, Edith)
Siegfried & Kriemhild, (N/A)
Siegfried..., (Wagner, Richard)
Sign at Six, (White, Stewart E.)
Sign of the Buffalo Skull, (Lamb, Peter O.)
Sign of the Seven Seas, (Dawson, Carley)
Sign on Rosie's Door, (Sendak, Maurice)
Sigurd Eckdal's Bride, (Voss, Richard)
Silas Marner, (Eliot, George)
Silent Concert, (Leister, Mary)
Silent Storm, (Brown, Marion)
Silently, the Cat & Miss Theodosia, (Holman, Felice)
Silhouette Stories, (Stranathan, May)
Silk, (Merwin, Samuel)
Silk and Satin Lane, (Wood, Esther)
Silkspinners, (Larson, Jean R.)
Silky: An Incredible Tale, (Coatsworth, Eliz.)
Silly Billy, (Scott, Sally)
Silly Book, (Hample, Stoo)
Silly Hare, (N/A)
Silly Songs and Sad, (Raskin, Ellen)
Silly Submarine, (Robinson, Charles)
Silly Willy Nilly, (Weisgard, Leonard)
Silvanus Goes to Sea, (Lovell, Dorothy A.)
Silver & Gold, (Blyton, Enid)
Silver Bear, (Brown, Edna)
Silver Birch, (Lyons, Dorothy)
Silver Boy, (Hoyt, Vance J.)
Silver Branch, (Sutcliff, Rosemary)
Silver Bubbles..., (Hunter, Richard)
Silver Chair, (Lewis, C.S.)
Silver Chief, (O'Brien, Jack)
Silver Chief to the Rescue, (O'Brien, Jack)
Silver Crown, (O'Brien, Robert)
Silver Crown, (Richards, Laura E.)
Silver Curlew, (Farjeon, Eleanor)
Silver Dollar, (Lowrey, Janette S.)

Silver Fawn, (Weil, Ann Y.)
Silver Fleece, (Means, Florence C.)
Silver Heels, (Brown, Paul)
Silver Hills, (Montgomery, R.)
Silver Horde, (Beach, Rex)
Silver Llama, (Malkus, Alida S.)
Silver Mace, (Petershams)
Silver Magic, (Wilson, Romer)
Silver Nutmeg, (Brown, Palmer)
Silver Pencil, (Dalgliesh, Alice)
Silver Pitchers, (Alcott, Louisa M.)
Silver Princess in Oz, (Thompson, Ruth P.)
Silver Purse, (Bialk, Elisa)
Silver Robin, (Marshall, Dean)
Silver Ship, (Higgins, Violet M.)
Silver Sixpence, (Sawyer, Ruth)
Silver Sword, (Serraillier, Ian)
Silver Trumpet, (Barfield, Arthur O.)
Silver Wings, (Whitfield, Raoul)
Silver from the Sea, (Tooze, Ruth)
Silverfoot, (Lindsay, Maud)
Silverhorn, (Conkling, Hilda)
Silversheene: King of Sled Dogs, (Hawkes, Clarence)
Simba of the White Mane, (Arundel, Jocelyn)
Simon and the Game of Chance, (Burch, Robert)
Simon's Song, (Emberley, Barbara)
Simple Addition, (N/A)
Simple Jography, (Herford, Oliver)
Simple Simon, (Denslow, W.W.)
Simple Simon, (Palazzo, Tony)
Simple Simon..., (Lyons, A. Neil)
Simple Susan and other Tales, (Edgeworth, Maria)
Sinbad the Cygnet, (Unwin, Nora S.)
Sinbad the Sailor, (N/A)
Sinfi and Little Gypsy Goat, (Kahmann, Chesley)
Sing & Sing Again, (Boesel, Ann S.)
Sing Down the Moon, (O'Dell, Scott)
Sing Mother Goose, (Wheeler, Opal)
Sing Sang Sung & Willie, (Gulick, Peggy)
Sing Song, (Rossetti, Christina)
Sing Song Stories, (Herbertson, Agnes)
Sing a Song of Safety, (Marks, Gerald)
Sing a Song of Seasons, (Brewton, Sara W.)
Sing a Song of Seasons, (Gag, Flavia)
Sing a Song of Sixpence, (N/A)
Sing for America, (Wheeler, Opal)
Sing for Christmas, (Wheeler, Opal)
Sing in Praise, (Wheeler, Opal)
Sing, Little Mouse, (Fisher, Aileen)
Sing, Sailor, Sing, (Martin, Patricia)
Sing-A-Song, (Broadbent, Helen)
Sing-Song, (Rossetti, Christina)
Singing Cupboard, (Faralla, Dana)
Singing Family of the Cumberlands, (Ritchie, Jean)
Singing Games for Children, (Farjeon, Eleanor)
Singing Hill, (DeJong, Meindert)
Singing Mouse Stories, (Hough, Emerson)
Singing Rhinoceros, (Standon, Anna)
Singing Sands, (Moon, Grace P.)
Singing Time, (Somervell, Arthur)
Singing Town, (Ramsden, Evelyn (ed))
Singing Tree, (Seredy, Kate)
Singing Verses for Children, (Coonley, Lydia A.)
Singing Wood, (Lady Frazer)
Singing Wood: College Story, (Means, Florence C.)
Singing and the Gold, (Parker, Elinor)
Singing with Peter and Patsy, (Boesel, Ann S.)
Singular Hen & her Peculiar Children, (Stolz, Mary S.)

Sinopah, the Indian Boy, (Schultz, James W.)
Sintram & his Companions, (Foque, De La Motte)
Sintram and his Companions, (Fouque, La Motte)
Sir Arthur Evans..., (Selden, George)
Sir Bob, (Madariaga, Salvador)
Sir Christopher, (Goodwin, Maud W.)
Sir Gawain & the Green Knight, (Hieatt, Constance)
Sir Gawain & the Green Knight, (Weston, Jessie L.)
Sir Gleges/Sir Libeaus Desconus, (Weston, Jessie L.)
Sir Kevin of Devon, (Holl, Adelaide)
Sir Machinery, (McGowen, Tom)
Sir Nigel, (Doyle, Arthur Conan)
Sir Ribbeck of Ribbeck..., (Fontane, Theodore)
Sir Toady Crusoe, (Crockett, Samuel R.)
Sirens Three, (Crane, Walter)
Siri the Conquistador, (Stolz, Mary S.)
Sister Anne, (Potter, Beatrix)
Sister Sally, (Fox, Frances M.)
Sister Susie and the Twins, (N/A)
Sister of the Angels, (Goudge, Elizabeth)
Sister of the Bride, (Cleary, Beverly)
Sitter Who Didn't Sit, (Puner, Helen)
Six Giants & a Griffin, (Edey, Birdsall O.)
Six Little Ducklings, (Pyle, Katharine)
Six Trees, (Wilkins, Mary E.)
Six Who were Left in a Shoe, (Colum, Padraic)
Six to Sixteen, (Ewing, Juliana H.)
Sixpence to Spend, (Outhwaite, Ida R.)
Sixteen and other Stories, (Daly, Maureen)
Skating Gander, (Bailey, Alice C.)
Skating Party, (Daley, C.F.)
Skazki, (Zeitlin, Ida)
Skeeter: Story of an Arabian Gazelle, (Shaffer, Robert)
Skeleton in Armor, (Longfellow, H.W.)
Sketch Book, (Caldecott, R.)
Sketches in Egypt, (Gibson, Charles D.)
Sketches in Stable and Kennel, (Edwards, Lionel)
Ski Pup, (Freeman, Don)
Skid, (Hayes, Florence)
Skiddycock Pond, (Tudor, Bethany)
Skin Horse, (Bianco, Margery W.)
Skinny Gets Fat, (Vorse, Mary E.)
Skip Rope Book, (Butler, Francelia)
Skip-Come-a-Lou, (Darby, Ada C.)
Skippack School, (DeAngeli, Marguerite)
Skipper John's Cook, (Brown, Marcia)
Skipper Riley: Terrier Dog, (Robinson, Mabel L.)
Skipping Along, (Welles, Winifred)
Skipping Island, (Brock, Emma)
Skipping Village, (Lenski, Lois)
Skippy's Family, (Meader, Stephen W.)
Skit and Skat, (Dennis, Morgan)
Skittle-Skattle Monkey, (Lathrop, Dorothy)
Skookum and Sandy, (Bennett, Richard)
Skrallan and the Pirates, (Lindgren, Astrid)
Skull Head the Terrible, (Schultz, James W.)
Skunny Wundy, (Parker, Arthur C.)
Skwee-Gee, (Teilhet, Darwin)
Sky Dog, (Turkle, Brinton)
Sky High, (Hurd, Edith T.)
Sky High: Flight of Fancy for Children, (Furniss, Dorothy)
Sky Highways: Geography from the Air, (Lloyd, Trevor)
Sky Island, (Baum, L. Frank)
Sky Was Blue, (Zolotow, Charlotte)
Sky-Eater, (Holding, James)
Slams of Life..., (McEvoy, Joseph P.)
Slant Book, (Newell, Peter)
Slappy Hooper..., (Bontemps, Arna)

Slateandpencilvania, (Crane, Walter)
Slave to Duty, (Thanet, Octave)
Slave's Tale, (Haugaard, Erik)
Sled Trails and White Waters, (Marsh, George)
Sleeping Beauty, (Evans, C.S.)
Sleeping Beauty, (Grimm Bros.)
Sleeping Beauty, (N/A)
Sleeping Beauty, (Perrault, Charles)
Sleeping Beauty Picture Book, (N/A)
Sleeping Beauty and Blue Beard, (Crane, Walter)
Sleeping Beauty..., (Quiller-Couch, A.)
Sleeping Giant, (Estes, Eleanor)
Sleeping Partners, (Aldin, Cecil)
Sleepy ABC, (Brown, Margaret W.)
Sleepy Book, (Zolotow, Charlotte)
Sleepy Nicholas, (Brande, Marlie)
Sleepy People, (Goffstein, M.B.)
Sleepy Quilt, (Steiner, Charlotte)
Sleepy Steve, (Berger, Josef)
Sleepy Watchdog, (Bolognese, Elaine)
Sleepy-Song Book, (Various)
Sleepy-Time Stories, (Booth, Maud B.)
Sleepy-Time Story Book, (Dyer, Ruth O.)
Sleepyhead, (Lipkind, Will)
Slice of Snow, (Anglund, Joan W.)
Slim, (Haines, William)
Slip! Slop! Gobble!, (Hardendorff, Jeanne)
Slippers of Cinderella, (Robertson, W.G.)
Slovenly Peter, (Hoffmann, Heinrich)
Sly Mongoose, (Pollock, Katherine)
Small Bear, (Bemelmans, Ludwig)
Small Boy is Listening, (Zemach, Harve)
Small Child's Bible, (Doane, Pelagie)
Small Child's Book of Verse, (Doane, Pelagie)
Small Circus, (Lansing, Elisabeth H.)
Small Clown, (Faulkner, Nancy)
Small Fry, (Steig, William)
Small Fry and the Winged Horse, (Campbell, Ruth)
Small One, (Gay, Zhenya)
Small Pig, (Lobel, Arnold)
Small Rain, (Jones, Jessie O.)
Small Songs for Small Singers, (Neidlinger, Wm. H.)
Small War of Sargeant Donkey, (Daly, Maureen)
Small-Trot, (Francoise)
Smallest Boy in Class, (Beim, Jerrold)
Smallest Elephant in the World, (Tresselt, Alvin)
Smart Little Boy & Smart Little Kitty, (Woodcock, L.)
Smeller Martin, (Lawson, Robert)
Smile Within a Tear, (Ramsden, Helen G.)
Smiles Yoked with Sighs, (Burdette, Robert J.)
Smiling Duke, (Low, Joseph)
Smiling Hill Farm, (Mason, Miriam E.)
Smiling Princess, (Aikins, Ruth)
Smiling Road, (Rion, H.)
Smith, (Garfield, Leon)
Smith of Wootton Major, (Tolkien, J.R.R.)
Smiths & Rusty, (Dalgliesh, Alice)
Smiths of Surbiton, (Howard, Keble)
Smoke Above the Lane, (DeJong, Meindert)
Smoke Bellew, (London, Jack)
Smoke Jumper, (Allee, Marjorie H.)
Smoke Rings, (Lyons, Dorothy)
Smoker's Yearbook, (Herford, Oliver)
Smokey, (Peet, Bill)
Smokey, the Well-Loved Kitten, (Goudey, Alice)
Smoky Bay, (Arason, Steingrimus)
Smoky God, (Emerson, Willis G.)
Smoky House, (Goudge, Elizabeth)

Smoky and Pinocchio, (Carter, Helene)
Smoky the Cow Horse, (James, Will)
Smudge, (Newberry, Clare T.)
Smuggler's Gap, (Atkinson, Mary E.)
Smuggler's Island, (Kneeland, Clarissa A.)
Smuggler's Sloop, (White, Robb)
Smugglers of Sandy Bay, (Holberg, Ruth)
Smugglers' Gallows, (Hope, Stanton)
Snail Who Ran, (Lathrop, Dorothy)
Snail, Where are You?, (Ungerer, Tomi)
Snake Gold, (White, Hervey)
Snake Tree, (Rounds, Glen)
Snapping Turtle's All Wrong Day, (Parish, Peggy)
Snarleyyow, (Marryat, Frederick)
Sneetches and other Stories, (Seuss, Dr.)
Sneezles, (Milne, A.A.)
Snickerty Nick, (Ford, Julia E.)
Snip and Snap and the Lost Baby, (Mason, George)
Snipp, Snapp, Snurr... [All titles], (Lindman, Maj)
Snippy & Snappy, (Gag, Wanda)
Snoopy and the Red Baron, (Schulz, Charles)
Snow, (Bell, Thelma H.)
Snow & the Sun, (Frasconi, Antonio)
Snow Baby, (Peary, Josephine)
Snow Before Christmas, (Tudor, Tasha)
Snow Bird & Water Tiger..., (Compton, Margaret)
Snow Birthday, (Kay, Helen)
Snow Dog, (Kjelgaard, Jim)
Snow Fox, (Dobrin, Arnold)
Snow Image, (Hawthorne, Nathaniel)
Snow Man's Christmas, (Bird, Mary H.)
Snow Over Bethlehem, (Milhous, Katherine)
Snow Party, (DeRegniers, Beatrice)
Snow Queen, (Andersen, Hans C.)
Snow Queen, (Ponsot, Marie (tran))
Snow Storm Before Christmas, (Palmer, Candida)
Snow Tracks, (George, Jean C.)
Snow White & Rose Red, (Grimm Bros.)
Snow White & Rose Red, (N/A)
Snow White & Seven Dwarfs, (Disney, Walt)
Snow White & Seven Dwarfs, (Grimm Bros.)
Snow for Christmas, (Bowen, Vernon)
Snow in the City: Winter's Tale, (Hader, B.& E.)
Snow is Falling, (Branley, Franklyn)
Snow on Blueberry Mountain, (Meader, Stephen W.)
Snowboot, Son of Fire Eye, (Lindman, Maj)
Snowbound, (Whittier, John G.)
Snowdrop..., (Grimm Bros.)
Snowdrop...., (Grimm Bros.)
Snowed Up, (Fry, Rosalie K.)
Snowflake, (Gallico, Paul)
Snowflake, (Hogner, Dorothy)
Snowflake & the Starfish, (Nathan, Robert)
Snowman, (Montgomery, R.)
Snowplow that Tried to Go South, (Retan, Walter)
Snowshoe Twins, (Tompkins, Jane)
Snowy Day, (Keats, Ezra J.)
Snowy Tail: Champion Jack Rabbit, (Hinkle, Thomas C.)
Snowy for Luck, (Russell, Arthur)
Snug & the Chimney-Sweeper, (Uttley, Alison)
Snug and Serena Pick Cowslips, (Uttley, Alison)
Snug in the Snow, (Low, Elizabeth)
Snuggy Bedtime Stories, (Jewett, John H.)
Snythergen, (Garrott, Hal)
So Big, (Wilkin, Esther B.)
So Long Ago, (Smith, E. Boyd)
So Many Ways, (Cawein, Madison J.)
So Red the Nose, (North, Sterling)

So Small, (Rand, Ann)
So-So Cat, (Hurd, Edith T.)
Sociable Toby, (Clymer, Eleanor)
Social Ladder, (Gibson, Charles D.)
Social Life in Old Virginia, (Page, Thomas N.)
Sod House, (Coatsworth, Eliz.)
Sojo: Story of Little Lazy Bones, (Berry, Erick)
Solario the Tailor, (Bowen, William)
Soldier Boy, (Lefevre, Felicite)
Soldier Doctor: Story of William Gorgas, (Judson, Clara I.)
Soldier Sammy, (MacNeil, Marion)
Soldier Tales, (Kipling, Rudyard)
Soldier of the Valley, (Lloyd, Nelson M.)
Soldier's Children, (Ewing, Juliana H.)
Soldiers of Fortune, (Davis, Richard H.)
Soldiers of the King, (Unknown)
Solita, (Moon, Grace P.)
Solomon Crow's Christmas Pockets, (Stuart, Ruth M.)
Solomon's Search, (Holman, Felice)
Some British Ballads, (N/A)
Some Cheese for Charles, (Buckley, Helen E.)
Some Dogs, (Parker, Elinor)
Some Frightful War Pictures, (Robinson, W. Heath)
Some Old Nursery Tales, (N/A)
Some One Like You, (Foley, James W.)
Some Smiles, (Gordon, Elizabeth)
Some Snow said Hello, (Hoban, Russell)
Some of the Days of Everett Anderson, (Clifton, Lucille)
Somebody Came, (Van Doren, Mark)
Somebody Else's Nut Tree, (Krauss, Ruth)
Somebody's Baby, (Cowham, Hilda)
Somebody's House, (Hurd, Edith T.)
Somebody's Pussies, (Wain, Louis)
Someday, (Zolotow, Charlotte)
Someone Could Win a Polar Bear, (Ciardi, John)
Someone Small, (Borack, Barbara)
Someone to Care, (Malloch, Douglas)
Somersaulting Rabbit, (Bullard, Marion)
Something Old, Something New, (Rhinehart, Susan)
Something Perfectly Silly, (Wood, Marni & Harrie)
Something Special, (DeRegniers, Beatrice)
Something for Christmas, (Brown, Palmer)
Sometime Never, (Leighton, Clare)
Somi Builds a Church, (Busoni, Rafaello)
Son of Columbus, (Baumann, Hans)
Son of God..., (Bible)
Son of Light Horse, (Barnes, James)
Son of Satsuma, (Munroe, Kirk)
Son of the Iroquois, (Bunce, William)
Son of the Lamp Maker, (North, Sterling)
Son of the Middle Border, (Garland, Hamlin)
Son of the Sun, (London, Jack)
Son of the Sword, (Mirza, Youel B.)
Son of the Walrus King, (McCracken, Harold)
Son of the White Man, (Best, Herbert)
Sonbonnet Babies in Holland, (Grover, Eulalie O.)
Sondo: A Liberian Boy, (Joseph, Alfred W.)
Song Celestial, (Arnold, Edwin)
Song Devices & Jingles, (Smith, Eleanor)
Song for Clowns, (Wersba, Barbara)
Song in my Drum, (Hoban, Russell)
Song of Robin Hood, (Malcolmson, Anne)
Song of Saint Francis, (Bulla, Clyde R.)
Song of Songs..., (Bible)
Song of a Single Note, (Barr, Amelia E.)
Song of the Cardinal, (Stratton-Porter, Gene)
Song of the Day Birds & Night Birds, (Ipcar, Dahlov)
Song of the Empty Bottles, (Molarsky, Osmond)

Song of the English, (Kipling, Rudyard)
Song of the Lop-Eared Mule, (Carlson, Natalie S.)
Song of the Pines, (Havighurst, Walter)
Song of the River, (Clark, Billy C.)
Song of the Sun, (St. Francis/Assisi)
Song of the Swallows, (Politi, Leo)
Songs, (Shakespeare, Wm.)
Songs & Sonnets, (Lovelace, Richard)
Songs & Sonnets, (Shakespeare, Wm.)
Songs Along the Way, (Allstrom, Elizabeth)
Songs about Life, Love and Death, (Aldrich, Anne R.)
Songs for Little People, (Gale, Norman)
Songs for Music...., (Farjeon, Eleanor)
Songs for Somebody, (Radford, Dollie)
Songs for a Small Guitar, (Graham, Al)
Songs from Alice in Wonderland, (Broadwood, Lucy)
Songs from Alice... & Through..., (Carroll, Lewis)
Songs from Around a Toadstool Table, (Bennett, R.B.)
Songs from Bad Child's Book of Beasts, (Belloc, H.)
Songs from Now We are Six, (Fraser-Simpson, H.)
Songs of Bryn Mawr College, (N/A)
Songs of Childhood, (De La Mare, Walter)
Songs of Childhood, (Ramal, Walter)
Songs of Ettrick Shepherd, (Hogg, James)
Songs of Experience, (Blake, William)
Songs of Father Goose, (Baum, L. Frank)
Songs of Happy Children, (Maunder, Irene)
Songs of Innocence, (Blake, William)
Songs of Love & Praise, (Matheson, Annie)
Songs of Mr. Small, (Bulla, Clyde R.)
Songs of Near & Far Away, (Richardson, Emmeline)
Songs of Sentiment, (Christy, Howard C.)
Songs of the Pogo, (Monath, Norman)
Songs of the Sea, (Kipling, Rudyard)
Songs of the Shining Way, (Noble-Ives, Sarah)
Songs of the Trees, (Robinson, Mary Y.)
Songs with Music..., (Stevenson, Robert L.)
Sonnets from the Portuguese, (Browning, Eliz. B.)
Sonny Elephant, (Bigham, Madge A.)
Sonny Sayings, (Cory, Fanny)
Sonny's Father, (Stuart, Ruth M.)
Sonny, A Christmas Guest, (Stuart, Ruth M.)
Sonny-Boy Sim, (Baker, Elizabeth W.)
Sons of the Dragon, (Sowers, Phyllis A.)
Sons of the Volsungs, (Hosford, Dorothy)
Soo Ling Finds a Way, (Behrens, June)
Soomoon, Boy of Bali, (Elliot, Kathleen)
Sophia Scrooby Preserved, (Bacon, Martha)
Sophie, Story of a Bad Little Girl, (DeSegur, Sophie)
Sophocles the Hyena, (Moran, Jim)
Sorcerer's Apprentice, (Disney, Walt)
Sorely Trying Day, (Hoban, Russell)
Sorrows of Sap'ed, (Roche, James J.)
Sorry to Be So Cheerful, (Dolson, Hildegarde)
Soul of Melicent, (Cabell, James B.)
Souls of Passage, (Barr, Amelia E.)
Sound, (Miller, Lisa)
Sound Science, (Alexenberg, Melvin)
Sound of Bells, (Sloane, Eric)
Sound of Sunshine, Sound of Rain, (Heide, Florence P.)
Sounder, (Armstrong, William)
Sounds of a Summer Night, (Garelick, May)
South Wind, (Douglas, Norman)
South of Cape Horn..., (Sperry, Armstrong)
Southern Harvest, (Leighton, Clare)
Southern Mail, (Saint-Exupery, A.)
Space Cadet, (Heinlein, Robert)
Space Cat... [All titles], (Todd, Ruthven)

Space Child's Mother Goose, (Winsor, Frederick)
Space Hut, (Wier, Ester A.)
Space Ship Returns to Apple Tree, (Slobodkin, Louis)
Space Ship Under Apple Tree, (Slobodkin, Louis)
Space Witch, (Freeman, Don)
Spanish Dollars, (Kauffman, Reginald)
Spanish Fairy Book, (Segovia, Gertrudis)
Spanish Peggy, (Catherwood, Mary)
Spanish Raggle-Taggle, (Starkie, Walter)
Spanish Sketches, (Penfield, Edward)
Sparkie & Puff Ball, (Brown, Paul)
Sparkle & Spin, (Rand, Ann)
Sparkplug of the Hornets, (Meader, Stephen W.)
Sparky: Story of a Little Trolley Car, (Gramatky, Hardie)
Sparrow Bush, (Coatsworth, Eliz.)
Sparrow House, (Grishina-Givago, N.)
Spartan Primer, (Cammack, Key)
Spartan Twins, (Perkins, Lucy F.)
Speaking of Cows, (Starbird, Kaye)
Speaking of Mrs. McCluskie, (Maiden, Cecil)
Spear of Ulysses, (Alessios, Alison B.)
Special Birthday/Someone Very Special, (Kitt, Tamara)
Special Branch Willie, (Clewes, Dorothy)
Special Bravery, (Johnston, Johanna)
Special Trick, (Mayer, Mercer)
Speckled Hen, (Zemach, Harve)
Spectacles, (Raskin, Ellen)
Speed of the Reindeer, (Wilhelmson, Carl)
Speedy Digs Downside Up, (Kumin, Maxine)
Speedy in Oz, (Thompson, Ruth P.)
Speedy, Hook & Ladder Truck, (Hurd, Edith T.)
Spell is Cast, (Cameron, Eleanor)
Spice & Devil's Cave, (Hewes, Agnes D.)
Spice Ho! Story of Discovery, (Hewes, Agnes D.)
Spice on the Wind, (Eberle, Irmengarde)
Spider Silk, (Goldin, Augusta)
Spider's Palace, (Hughes, Richard A.)
Spiderweb for Two: Melendy Maze, (Enright, Elizabeth)
Spikenard, (Housman, Laurence)
Spiky the Hedgehog, (Lida)
Spin Top Spin, (Eisgruber, Elsa)
Spinach-Boy, (Lenski, Lois)
Spindle Imp, (Malkus, Alida S.)
Spirit Trail, (Boyles, Kate)
Spirit of Bambatse, (Haggard, H. Rider)
Spirit of Christmas, (Van Dyke, Henry)
Spirit of Spring, (Proddow, Penelope)
Spirit of the Border, (Grey, Zane)
Splasher, (Gall, Alice C.)
Splendid Idle Forties, (Atherton, Gertrude)
Splendid Knight, (Hinkson, Henry A.)
Splendid Spur, (Quiller-Couch, A.)
Spliced Yarn, (Cupples, George)
Split-Ear, (Hinkle, Thomas C.)
Spoodles, Puppy Who Learned, (Black, Irma S.)
Spook Ballads, (Parkes, William T.)
Spooky Thing, (Steele, William O.)
Sporting Pilgrimage, (Whitney, Caspar)
Spotty, (Rey, Margret E.)
Spreading Stain, (Finger, Charles J.)
Spring Begins in March, (Little, Jean)
Spring Cleaning, (Burnett, Frances H.)
Spring Comes to the Ocean, (George, Jean C.)
Spring Fairies & Sea Fairies, (Mockler, Geraldine)
Spring Snow, (Duvoisin, Roger)
Spring Song, (Nash, Thomas)
Spring Songs with Music, (Barker, Cicely M.)
Spring Songs with Music, (Linnell, Olive)

Spring is Here, (Lenski, Lois)
Spring is Like the Morning, (Craig, M. Jean)
Spring is a New Beginning, (Anglund, Joan W.)
Springing of the Rice, (Berry, Erick)
Springtide of Life, (Swinburne, A.C.)
Springtime in Noisy Village, (Lindgren, Astrid)
Spunky, (Hader, B.& E.)
Squaps the Moonling, (Ziegler, Ursina)
Square Book of Animals, (Waugh, Alec)
Square Sails & Spice Islands, (Long, Laura)
Square as a House, (Kuskin, Karla)
Squash for the Fair, (Paull, Grace)
Squawky, Advens. of a Clasperchoice, (Potter, Stephen)
Squeaky & the Scare Box, (Faulkner, Georgene)
Squiffer, (Garrott, Hal)
Squire for King Arthur, (Stone, Eugenia)
Squirrel Goes Skating, (Uttley, Alison)
Squirrel Hotel, (DuBois, W.P.)
Squirrel Inn, (Stockton, Frank)
Squirrel Redcoat, (Werner, Jadwiga)
Squirrel and the Harp, (DeJong, David C.)
Squirrely of Willow Hill, (Hader, B.& E.)
St. Bartholomew's Eve, (Henty, G.A.)
St. Francis & the Animals, (Politi, Leo)
St. Francis of Assissi, (Chesterton, G.K.)
St. George and the Dragon, (Warburg, Sandol (adap))
St. George's Day in Williamsburg, (Hurd, Edith T.)
St. Ives, (Stevenson, Rbt. L.)
St. Jerome and the Lion, (Godden, Rumer)
St. Joan, (Shaw, George B.)
St. Joan of Arc, (Twain, Mark)
St. Lawrence Seaway, (Judson, Clara I.)
St. Nicholas and the Tub, (Burland, Brian)
St. Valentine's Day, (Bulla, Clyde R.)
Staffan, (Shideler, Ross (tran))
Stage Coach and Tavern Days, (Earle, Alice M.)
Stagecoach Sam, (Tousey, Sanford)
Staircase of Stories, (Chisholm, Louey)
Stallion, (Steen, Margarite)
Stallion King, (Balch, Glenn)
Stallion from the North, (Rourke, Thomas)
Stan Ball of the Rangers, (Montgomery, R.)
Stanley, (Hoff, Syd)
Star Fairies, (Harrison, Edith O.)
Star Girl, (Winterfeld, Henry)
Star Jewels..., (Brown, Abbie F.)
Star Man's Son, 2250 A.D., (Norton, Andre)
Star People, (Dewey, Katharine F.)
Star Spangled Banner, (D'Aulaire, I.& E.)
Star Thief, (DiNoto, Andrea)
Star for Hansi, (Vance, Marguerite)
Star in the Well, (Bailey, Temple)
Star of Wonder, (Coles, Robert)
Star-Spangled Summer, (Lambert, Janet)
Starfish, (Hurd, Edith T.)
Starfish Trilogy, (Mendoza, George)
Stargazer to the Sultan, (Walker, Barbara)
Starlight Barking, (Smith, Dodie)
Starlight Wonder Book, (Beston, Henry)
Starlings, (Bronson, Wilfrid S.)
Starlit Journey, (Bianco, Pamela)
Starman Jones, (Heinlein, Robert)
Stars Tonight, (Teasdale, Sara)
Stars are Silver Reindeer, (Belting, Natalia)
Stars for Cristy, (Hunt, Mabel L.)
Stars to Steer By, (Follett, Helen T.)
Starting from Scratch, (Bacon, Peggy)
Steadfast Tin Soldier, (Andersen, Hans C.)

Stealers of Light, (Queen Marie)
Steam Shovel for Me!, (Edelstat, Vera)
Steam Shovel that Wouldn't Eat Dirt, (Walters, George)
Steamboat Billy, (Tousey, Sanford)
Steel, (Schwarzman, Marguerite)
Steel Flea, (Leskov, Nicholas)
Steel Magic, (Norton, Andre)
Steffie and Me, (Hoffman, Phyllis)
Stella's Adventures in Starland, (Sabin, Elbridge H.)
Stephen's Train, (Otto, Margaret G.)
Steppin & Family, (Newell, Hope)
Steps to Nowhere, (Boylan, Grace D.)
Stepsister Sally, (Daringer, Helen F.)
Stevenson Song Book, (Stevenson, Rbt. L.)
Stevie, (Steptoe, John)
Stick-in-the-Mud, (Ketchum, Jean)
Stickeen..., (Muir, John)
Sticks Across the Chimney, (Burglon, Nora)
Stillmeadow Road, (Taber, Gladys)
Stirabout Stories, (Barnes, Madeline)
Stolen Necklace, (Rockwell, Anne)
Stolen Oracle, (Williams, Jay)
Stolen Pony, (Rounds, Glen)
Stolen Treasure, (Pyle, Howard)
Stone Daggers, (Lauring, Paul)
Stone Doll of Sister Brute, (Hoban, Russell)
Stone Knife Boy, (Malkus, Alida S.)
Stone Soup, (Brown, Marcia)
Stone of Victory, (Colum, Padraic)
Stone-Faced Boy, (Fox, Paula)
Stop Tim!, (McNeer, May)
Stop, Look & Listen, (Hader, B.& E.)
Stops of Various Quills, (Howells, William D.)
Storied Holidays, (Brooks, Elbridge S.)
Stories Barry Told Me, (Pain, Eva)
Stories California Indians Told, (Fisher, Anne B.)
Stories Children Like, (Peat, Fern B.)
Stories Children Love, (Piper, Watty (ed))
Stories Children Love, (Welsh, Charles)
Stories From Wagner, (McSpadden, J.W.)
Stories Merry and Wise, (N/A)
Stories Polly Pepper Told, (Sidney, Margaret)
Stories True & Fancies New, (Morrison, Mary J.)
Stories and Rhymes for a Child, (Bailey, Carolyn S.)
Stories by J.H. Ewing, (Ewing, Juliana H.)
Stories by Katherine Mansfield, (Mansfield, Katherine)
Stories by Mrs. Molesworth, (Molesworth, Mrs.)
Stories for Little Children, (Buck, Pearl S.)
Stories for Pictures, (MacKay, Helen)
Stories from Andersen, (Andersen, Hans C.)
Stories from Arabian Nights, (Housman, Laurence (ed))
Stories from Arabian Nights, (N/A)
Stories from Aunt Judy, (N/A)
Stories from Chaucer, (Kelman, Janet H.)
Stories from Chaucer, (Underdown, E.)
Stories from Dante, (Cunnington, Susan)
Stories from Faerie Queen, (Dawson, L.H. (ed.))
Stories from Fantasia, (Disney, Walt)
Stories from Great Metropolitan Operas, (Dike, Helen)
Stories from Grimm..., (Steedman, Amy)
Stories from Lowly Life, (Duppa, C.M.)
Stories from the Americas, (Henius, Frank)
Stories from the Bible, (De La Mare, Walter)
Stories from the Bible, (Farrar, Evelyn)
Stories from the Illiad, (Lang, Jeanie)
Stories from the Magic World, (Woodruff, Elizabeth)
Stories from the Odyssey, (N/A)
Stories from the Old Testament, (Petersham, Maud)

Stories from the Pentamerone, (Basile, Giovanni B.)
Stories of Enchantment, (Myers, Jane P.)
Stories of Jesus, (Smither, Ethel)
Stories of King Arthur, (Clay, Beatrice)
Stories of King Arthur, (Cutler, U. Waldo)
Stories of King Arthur, (Haydon, Arthur L.)
Stories of King Arthur's Knights, (MacGregor, Mary)
Stories of Little Brown Koko, (Hunt, Blanche S.)
Stories of Love, (Hazeltine, Alice)
Stories of Mother Goose Village, (Bigham, Madge A.)
Stories of Peace & War, (Remington, Frederic)
Stories of Peter & Ellen, (Smith, Gertrude)
Stories of the Days of King Arthur, (Hanson, Charles H.)
Stories of the First American Animals, (Langford, George)
Stories of the Little Fishes, (Mulets, Lenore E.)
Stories of the Norsemen, (Johnston, Johanna)
Stories of the Sea, (Fenner, Phyllis R.)
Stories that Glue Told, (Williams, C.A.)
Stories to Live By, (McKelvey, Gertrude)
Stories to Tell the Littlest Ones, (Bryant, Sara Cone)
Stories..., (Andersen, Hans C.)
Storks Fly Home, (Tompkins, Jane)
Storm Book, (Zolotow, Charlotte)
Storm Canvas, (Sperry, Armstrong)
Stormy, (Kjelgaard, Jim)
Stormy: Misty's Foal, (Henry, Marguerite)
Story Book, (N/A)
Story Book of Clothes, (Petersham, Maud)
Story Book of Cotton, (Petersham, Maud)
Story Book of Iron and Steel, (Petershams)
Story Book of Silhouettes, (Williams, C.A.)
Story Club, (Cooke, Edmund V.)
Story Girl, (Montgomery, Lucy M.)
Story Grandmother Told, (Alexander, Martha G.)
Story Lady('s)... [All titles], (Faulkner, Georgene)
Story Number 1, (Ionesco, Eugene)
Story Number 2, (Ionesco, Eugene)
Story Song Book, (Warner, Harriette)
Story Teller's Holiday, (Bonner, Mary G.)
Story Without an End, (Grove, F.)
Story about Ping, (Flack, Marjorie)
Story my Doggie Told to Me, (Barbour, Ralph H.)
Story of AB, (Waterloo, Stanley)
Story of Aaron, (Harris, Joel C.)
Story of Aladdin, (N/A)
Story of Alaska, (Lambert, Clara)
Story of Alexander, (Steele, Robert)
Story of America, (Peattie, Donald C.)
Story of Ancient Civilization, (Peattie, Donald C.)
Story of Appleby Capple, (Parrish, Anne)
Story of Babette, (Stuart, Ruth M.)
Story of Bayard, (Hare, Christopher)
Story of Ben Franklin, (Merriam, Eve)
Story of Betty, (Wells, Carolyn)
Story of Blue-Beard, (Perrault, Charles)
Story of Bread, (Watson, Elizabeth)
Story of Buffalo Bill, (Garst, Shannon)
Story of California, (McNeer, May)
Story of Casey Jr., (Disney, Walt)
Story of Chan Yuc, (Rhoads, Dorothy)
Story of Chanticleer, (Rostand, Edmond)
Story of Colette, (Francoise)
Story of Dago, (Johnston, Annie F.)
Story of Damon and Pythias, (Terhune, Albert P.)
Story of Daniel Boone, (Steele, William O.)
Story of Delicia, (Newman, Gertrude)
Story of Eli Whitney, (Latham, Jean L.)
Story of Ferdinand, (Leaf, Munro)

Story of Five Rebellious Dolls, (Nesbit, Edith)
Story of Flip & Fuzzy, (Pope, Jessie)
Story of France, (MacGregor, Mary)
Story of Freginald, (Brooks, Walter)
Story of Fuzzypeg the Hedgehog, (Uttley, Alison)
Story of George Washington Carver, (Bontemps, Arna)
Story of Good Queen Bess, (Malkus, Alida S.)
Story of Hannibal, (Johnston, Johanna)
Story of Health, (Holway, Hope K.)
Story of Holly and Ivy, (Godden, Rumer)
Story of Jack Ballister's Fortunes, (Pyle, Howard)
Story of Jackie Thimble, (Reeves, James)
Story of Jesus for Young People, (Bowie, Walter R.)
Story of Johnny Appleseed, (Aliki)
Story of King Arthur, (Brooks, Edward)
Story of King Arthur..., (Pyle, Howard)
Story of Leif Ericson, (Steele, William O.)
Story of Light, (Eaton, Jeanette)
Story of Little Red Hen, (N/A)
Story of Louis Pasteur, (Malkus, Alida S.)
Story of Louise, (Welch, D.)
Story of Man's Work, (Johnson, Gerald W.)
Story of Mankind, (Van Loon, Hendrik)
Story of Milk & How it Came About, (Watson, Elizabeth)
Story of Miss Jemima, (De La Mare, Walter)
Story of Miss Moppet, (Potter, Beatrix)
Story of Moses, (De La Mare, Walter)
Story of Mr. Korah, (Aberconway, Christabel)
Story of Mr. Punch, (Feuillet, Octave)
Story of Mrs. Tubbs, (Lofting, Hugh)
Story of My Dolls, (Trimpey, Alice)
Story of New England, (McClintock, Marshall)
Story of Noah's Ark, (Smith, E. Boyd)
Story of Noah's Ark, (Weigle, Oscar)
Story of Old Dame Trot and her Pig, (N/A)
Story of Ophelia, (Gibbons, Mary)
Story of Pancho, (Hader, B.& E.)
Story of Paul Bunyan, (Emberley, Barbara)
Story of Pennsylvania Dutch, (Hark, Ann)
Story of Peter Pan, (Barrie, James M.)
Story of Peter Rabbit, (Potter, Beatrix)
Story of Phillis Wheatley, (Graham, Shirley)
Story of Pink Jade, (Lederer, William J.)
Story of Rico, (Spyri, Johanna)
Story of Roland, (Baldwin, James)
Story of Roly & Poly, (Sherrill, Dorothy)
Story of Rosina, (Dobson, Austin)
Story of Serapina, (White, Anne H.)
Story of Siegfried, (Baldwin, James)
Story of Siegfried, (Baldwin, James)
Story of Siegfried, (Diller, Angela)
Story of Simple Simon, (N/A)
Story of Simpson & Sampson, (Leaf, Munro)
Story of Sir Galahad, (Malory, Thomas)
Story of Sir Lancelot, (Pyle, Howard)
Story of Snips, (Macgregor, Angusine)
Story of Snowmand, (Palazzo, Tony)
Story of Teddy the Bear, (Noble-Ives, Sarah)
Story of Thyrza, (Brown, Alice)
Story of Timothy's House, (Disney, Walt)
Story of Tonty, (Catherwood, Mary)
Story of Transportation, (Eaton, Jeanette)
Story of Valentine, (Hays, Wilma P.)
Story of Vania, (Pons, Helene)
Story of Walt Disney, (Miller, Diane D.)
Story of William Tell, (Aliki)
Story of Winston Churchill, (Malkus, Alida S.)
Story of Zachary Zween, (Watts, Mabel)

Story of a Baby, (Ets, Marie H.)
Story of a Happy Doll, (Mayol, Lurline B.)
Story of a Little Colored Coon, (Hall, Conrad)
Story of a Little Duck, (Sherrill, Dorothy)
Story of a Little Poet, (Taylor, Sophie C.)
Story of a Little Tin Soldier, (Hawley, Harriet E.)
Story of a Puppet, (Collodi, Carlo)
Story of a Toy Car, (Brett, Molly)
Story of a Wonder Man, (Lardner, Ring)
Story of a Yankee Boy, (Hamblen, Herbert E.)
Story of an Old Fashioned Doll, (Connolly, John)
Story of our Country, (Smith, E. Boyd)
Story of the American Firemen, (N/A)
Story of the Amulet, (Nesbit, Edith)
Story of the Barber of Seville, (Johnston, Johanna)
Story of the Bold Pecopin, (Hugo, Victor)
Story of the Coal-Black Horse, (Heimeran, Ernst)
Story of the Cowboy, (Hough, Emerson)
Story of the Early Sea People, (Dopp, Katharine E.)
Story of the First Men, (Peattie, Donald C.)
Story of the Four Little Children..., (Lear, Edward)
Story of the Golden Age, (Baldwin, James)
Story of the Golden Fleece, (Lang, Andrew)
Story of the Grail, (Pyle, Howard)
Story of the Great Lakes, (Gilchrist, Marie)
Story of the Great Plains, (McNeer, May)
Story of the Little Merman, (Reader, Ethel)
Story of the Live Dolls, (Gates, Josephine S.)
Story of the Lost Doll, (Gates, Josephine S.)
Story of the Markets, (Camp, Ruth O.)
Story of the Mikado, (Gilbert, W.S.)
Story of the Mince Pie, (Gates, Josephine S.)
Story of the Mississippi, (McClintock, Marshall)
Story of the Negro, (Bontemps, Arna)
Story of the Other Wise Man, (Van Dyke, Henry)
Story of the Philippines, (Halstead, Murat)
Story of the Ring, (Hamer, Sam H.)
Story of the Seven Young Goslings, (Housman, L.)
Story of the Ship, (Grant, Gordon)
Story of the South-West, (McNeer, May)
Story of the Teasing Monkey, (Bannerman, Helen)
Story of the Three Bears, (Hader, B.& E.)
Story of the Three Bears, (Stobbs, William)
Story of the Three Dolls, (Gates, Josephine S.)
Story of the Three Wise Men, (Locke, William J.)
Story of the Treasure Seekers, (Nesbit, Edith)
Story of the Weathercock, (Sharp, Evelyn)
Story, a Story, (Haley, Gail E.)
Story-Land, (Grey, Sydney)
Story-Teller, (Lindsay, Maud)
Storybook, (Kramer, Nora)
Storyteller's Pack, (Stockton, Frank)
Stowaway to the Mushroom Planet, (Cameron, Eleanor)
Straggler: Adventures of a Sea Bird, (Wier, Ester A.)
Straight Hair, Curly Hair, (Goldin, Augusta)
Straight Shooting, (Burtis, Thomson)
Strange Disappearance of Arthur Cluck, (Benchley, N.)
Strange Disappearance of Mr. Toast, (Brent, Stuart)
Strange Story Book, (Lang, Andrew)
Stranger at Green Knowe, (Boston, Lucy M.)
Stranger in Primrose Lane, (Streatfeild, Noel)
Stranger on Big Hickory, (Meader, Stephen W.)
Straps the Cat, (Lewis, Claudia)
Strawberry Girl, (Lenski, Lois)
Strawberry Roan, (Lang, Don)
Strawberry Roan, (Rounds, Glen)
Strawman Who Smiled by Mistake, (Tripp, Paul)
Stray Birds, (Tagore, Rabindranath)

Stray Child, (Joyce, Robert)
Stream of History, (Parsons, Geoffrey)
Stream that Stood Still, (Nichols, Beverly)
Streamlined Pig, (Brown, Margaret W.)
Street Dog, (Drdek, Richard E.)
Street Fair, (Fischer, Marjorie)
Street Kids, (Danska, Herbert)
Street Where the Heart Lies, (Bemelmans, Ludwig)
Street of Little Shops, (Bianco, Margery W.)
Street of the Islands, (Young, Stark)
Streets of Ascalon, (Chambers, Robert)
Strella's Children, (Newman, Carol)
Strength of Gideon, (Dunbar, Paul L.)
String & the No-Tail Cat, (Govan, Christine)
String of Blue Beads, (Oursler, Fulton)
Strings to Adventure, (Berry, Erick)
Stringtown on the Pike, (Lloyd, John U.)
Striped Ice Cream, (Lexau, Joan M.)
Stripes & Spots, (Ipcar, Dahlov)
Stripey, (Williamson, Hamilton)
Strong Arm, (Barr, Robert)
Strong Hearts, (Cable, George W.)
Strong Wings, (Robinson, Mabel L.)
Stronger than Hate, (Baker, Elizabeth)
Struwwelpeter Alphabet, (Begbie, Harold)
Stuart Little, (White, Elwyn B.)
Stubby Pringle's Christmas, (Schaefer, Jack W.)
Stuck with Luck, (Johnson, Elizabeth)
Studies & Stories, (Molesworth, Mrs.)
Studies in Art Anatomy of Animals, (Seton, Ernest T.)
Studies in Pictures, (Van Dyke, John C.)
Stuff & Nonsense, (De La Mare, Walter)
Stuff & Nonsense, (Frost, A.B.)
Stuffed Owl, (Lewis, D.B.W.)
Stuffy, (Laird, Rowena)
Su An, (Johnson, Doris)
Su-Mei's Golden Year, (Bro, Marguerite)
Suburban Child, (Kenward, James)
Suburban Whirl, (Cutting, Mary S.)
Successful Houses, (Coleman, Oliver)
Successful Secretary, (Pratt, Margaret)
Such a Kind World, (Hunt, Mabel L.)
Such is the Way of the World, (Elkin, Benjamin)
Sue & Sew-and-Sew, (Gag, Asta)
Sue Ann's Busy Day, (Scott, Sally)
Sue Barton: Rural Nurse, (Boylston, Helen D.)
Sugar & Spice & all that's Nice, (Tileston, Mary W.)
Sugar Mouse Cake, (Zion, Gene)
Sugar Pear Tree, (Bulla, Clyde R.)
Sugar for the Horse, (Bates, Herbert E.)
Sugar on Snow, (Watson, Nancy D.)
Sugar-Loaf Mountain, (Bancroft, Laura)
Sugar-Plum Tree, (Field, Eugene)
Sugarbush Family, (Mason, Miriam E.)
Sugarplum, (Johnston, Johanna)
Sugarplum House, (Lenski, Lois)
Suho and the White Horse, (Otsuka, Yuzo)
Suitable Child, (Duncan, Norman)
Suitors of Aprille, (Garstin, Norman)
Suki the Siamese Pussy, (Weisgard, Leonard)
Suki: A Little Tiger, (Huxley, Elspeth)
Sultan of Sulu, (Ade, George)
Sultan's Fool, (Gilstrap, Robert)
Sumi... [All titles], (Uchida, Yoshiko)
Summer Adventure, (Lewis, Richard W.)
Summer Birds, (Farmer, Penelope)
Summer Day with Ted & Nina, (DeAngeli, Marguerite)
Summer Green, (Coatsworth, Eliz.)

Summer Noisy Book, (Brown, Margaret W.)
Summer Snowman, (Zion, Gene)
Summer Songs with Music, (Barker, Cicely M.)
Summer Time, (Judson, Clara I.)
Summer is Fun, (Davis, Lavinia R.)
Summer is Magic, (Howard, Joan)
Summer is for Growing, (Clark, Ann N.)
Summer of the Falcon, (George, Jean C.)
Summer of the Swans, (Byars, Betsy C.)
Summer's Coming In, (Belting, Natalia)
Summerfield Farm, (Black, Mary M.)
Sun Looks Down, (Schlein, Miriam)
Sun Slower, Sun Faster, (Trevor, Meriol)
Sun Up, (Tresselt, Alvin)
Sun Up, Tales of the Cow Camps, (James, Will)
Sun is a Golden Earring, (Belting, Natalia)
Sun's Babies, (Howes, Edith)
Sun's Diary, (Coatsworth, Eliz.)
Sun, Moon & Stars..., (Richardson, Emmeline)
Sun, Moon & a Rabbit, (Del Rio, A.M.)
Sun, Wind & Mr. Todd, (Estes, Eleanor)
Sun-Bonnet Babies, (Corbett, Bertha)
Sun-Egg, (Beskow, Elsa)
Sunbonnet Babies... [All titles], (Grover, Eulalie O.)
Sunbonnets & Overalls..., (Hogate, Etta C.)
Sunday Morning, (Viorst, Judith)
Sunday in Autumn, (Rowley, Anthony)
Sunday in Monterey, (Frasconi, Antonio)
Sundials, (Daley, C.F.)
Sundiata: Epic of the Lion King, (Bertol, Roland)
Sundown Leflare, (Remington, Frederic)
Sunflower Garden, (Udry, Janice M.)
Sunflowers for Tina, (Baldwin, Anne)
Sung Under the Silver Umbrella, (Various)
Sunhelmet Sue, (Berry, Erick)
Sunken Forest, (Prud'Hommeaux, Rene)
Sunlight and Shadow, (Adams, W.I.L.)
Sunlit Sea, (Goldin, Augusta)
Sunny Bunny, (Putnam, Nina W.)
Sunny Jim the Uppity Kitten, (Scott, Sally)
Sunny Land Stories, (Molesworth, Olive)
Sunny Rhymes/Happy Children, (Miller, Olive B.)
Sunny Southerner, (Magruder, Julia)
Sunny-Sulky Book, (Rippey, Sarah C.)
Sunnyfield, (Sill, Louise M.)
Sunnyvale Fair, (Goudey, Alice)
Sunrise-Land, (Berlyn, Annie)
Sunset of the Heroes, (Hutchinson, W.M.L.)
Sunshine, (Bemelmans, Ludwig)
Sunshine Annie, (Gates, Josephine S.)
Sunshine for Merrily, (Kiser, Martha G.)
Super Duper Car, (Govan, Christine)
Superlative Horse, (Merrill, Jean)
Supply at St. Agatha's, (Phelps, Eliz. S.)
Supposin', (Baxter, Betty)
Supposing, (Reid, Alastair)
Supposings, (Johnston, Johanna)
Suppressed Plates..., (Layard, George S.)
Supreme Court, (Johnson, Gerald W.)
Sure Thing for Shep, (Lansing, Elisabeth H.)
Surprise Book, (McElhone, Helen K.)
Surprise Party, (Hutchins, Pat)
Surprise Place, (Bonner, Mary G.)
Surprise for Araminta, (Evans, Eva K.)
Surprise for Davy, (Lenski, Lois)
Surprise for Mother, (Lenski, Lois)
Surprise for Three Little Steps, (Becker, Charlotte)
Surprise for Timmy, (Hauman, George)

Surprise in the Forest, (Schick, Eleanor)
Surprise to the Children, (Kennedy, Mary)
Surprising Advens. of Man in Moon, (Steward, R.M.)
Surprising Advens. of Sir Toady Lion, (Crockett, S.R.)
Surprising Advens. of Tuppy & Tue, (Brown, Maggie)
Surprising Summer, (Govan, Christine)
Surrey, (Moncrieff, Ascott)
Susan, (Hacker, Lilian P.)
Susan Beware!, (Hunt, Mabel L.)
Susan Clegg & the Man in the House, (Warner, Anne)
Susan Cornish, (Caudill, Rebecca)
Susan Grows Up, (Leonard, Mary F.)
Susan Sometimes, (Krasilovsky, Phyllis)
Susan and the Butterbees, (Bergengren, Ralph)
Susan's Secret, (Wriston, Hildreth T.)
Susan's Surprise, (Mills, Freya)
Susan's Year, (Johnson, Siddie)
Susanna & Sue, (Wiggin, Kate D.)
Susanna B. & William C., (Field, Rachel)
Susanna and Tristram, (Allee, Marjorie H.)
Susannah: Pioneer Cow, (Mason, Miriam E.)
Susi, (Filosa, Dorothea)
Susie, (Justus, May)
Susie Mariar, (Lenski, Lois)
Susie Sneakers, (Corbett, Scott)
Susie the Cat, (Palazzo, Tony)
Suzu and the Bride Doll, (Martin, Patricia)
Suzuki Beane, (Scoppettone, Sandra)
Suzy and the Dog School, (MacLellan, Esther)
Sven the Wise & Svea the Kind, (Overbeck, Alice)
Sven's Bridge, (Lobel, Anita)
Swallow, Tale of the Great Trek, (Haggard, H. Rider)
Swallowdale, (Ransome, Arthur)
Swallows & Amazons, (Ransome, Arthur)
Swamp Cat, (Kjelgaard, Jim)
Swamp Spring, (Carrick, Carol)
Swanhilda-of-the-Swans, (Faralla, Dana)
Swans of Ballycastle, (Hackett, Walter)
Swapping Boy, (Langstaff, John)
Swarm in May, (Mayne, William)
Swedish Fairy Tales, (Wahlenberg, Anna)
Sweeny's Adventure, (Krumgold, Joseph)
Sweepers of the Sea, (Wetmore, Claude H.)
Sweet P's, (Lippmann, Julie M.)
Sweet Patootie Doll, (Calhoun, Mary)
Sweet Pea, (Krementz, Jill)
Sweet Possom Valley, (Govan, Christine)
Sweet William, (Bouvet, Marguerite)
Sweetheart Travellers, (Crockett, Samuel R.)
Sweethearts Always, (Madison, Janet (comp))
Swift Flies the Falcon, (Knox, Esther M.)
Swift Rivers, (Meigs, Cornelia L.)
Swimming Hole, (Beim, Jerrold)
Swimmy, (Lionni, Leo)
Swing in the Summerhouse, (Langton, Jane)
Swiss Family Robinson, (Wyss, Johann D.)
Swiss Twins, (Perkins, Lucy F.)
Switch on the Night, (Bradbury, Ray)
Switzerland, (Kuhns, Oscar)
Sword in Sheath, (Norton, Andre)
Sword in the Stone, (White, Terence H.)
Sword in the Tree, (Bulla, Clyde R.)
Sword is Drawn, (Norton, Andre)
Sword of Dundee, (Peck, Theodora A.)
Sword of King Arthur, (Williams, Jay)
Sword of Roland Arnot, (Hewes, Agnes D.)
Sword of Welleran, (Lord Dunsany)
Sword of the Old Frontier, (Parrish, Randall)

Sword of the Wilderness, (Coatsworth, Eliz.)
Swords & Statues, (Stratton, Clarence)
Swords and Iris, (Strack, Lilian H.)
Swords of Steel, (Singmaster, Elsie)
Swords on the Sea, (Hewes, Agnes D.)
Sybil Lidington's Ride, (Berry, Erick)
Sycamore Square, (Struther, Jan)
Sylvester & the Magic Pebble, (Steig, William)
Sylvester Jones & Voice in the Forest, (Martin, Patricia)
Sylvia in Flowerland, (Gardiner, Linda)
Sylvia the Sloth, (Knight, Hilary)
Sylvia's Lovers, (Gaskell, Mrs.)
Sylvia's Travels, (Armfield, Constance)
Sylvie & Bruno, (Carroll, Lewis)
Symmetry, (Razzell, Arthur)
Syrup, (Otto, Margaret G.)
T-Bone the Baby-Sitter, (Newberry, Clare T.)
T-Model Tommy, (Meader, Stephen W.)
Tabbykin Town in School & at Play, (Kitty Cat)
Tabitha Mary, (Parton, Ethel)
Tabitha Smallways, Schoolgirl, (Jacberns, Raymond)
Tabitha's Hill, (Holberg, Ruth)
Tackroom Tattles, (McKenney, John)
Tad Sheldon, Boy Scout, (Wilson, John F.)
Taffy & Joe, (Burton, Earl & L.)
Taffy & Melissa Molasses, (Haywood, Carolyn)
Taffy's Foal, (Bialk, Elisa)
Tag-Along Tooloo, (Sayers, Frances C.)
Tahiti Landfall, (Stone, William S.)
Tail of Hunky Dory, (Helps, Racey)
Tail of a Guinea-Pig, (Englefield, Cicely)
Tailbone Patrol, (English, James W.)
Tailor & the Crow, (Brooke, L. Leslie)
Tailor of Gloucester, (Potter, Beatrix)
Taiwo and her Twin, (Schatz, Letta)
Takao and Grandfather's Sword, (Uchida, Yoshiko)
Take Joy! Tasha Tudor Christmas Bk, (Tudor, Tasha (ed))
Take Sky, (McCord, David)
Take Ten, (Silverstein, Shel)
Take a Giant Step, (Hahn, Hannelore)
Take a Nap, Harry, (Chalmers, Mary)
Take a Number, (O'Neill, Mary)
Take this Hammer, (Epstein, Samuel)
Taken From the Enemy, (Newbolt, Henry J.)
Taktuk, Arctic Boy, (Flack, Marjorie)
Tal & the Magic Barruget, (Wuorio, Eva-Lis)
Tal of the Four Tribes, (Best, Herbert)
Tale for Easter, (Tudor, Tasha)
Tale of Alain, (Ormondroyd, Edward)
Tale of Balen, (Swinburne, A.C.)
Tale of Beatrix Potter, (Lane, Margaret)
Tale of Benjamin Bunny, (Potter, Beatrix)
Tale of Bingo, (Lamb, Tom)
Tale of Flopsy Bunnies, (Potter, Beatrix)
Tale of Gockel, Hinkel & Gackeliah, (Brentano, Clemens)
Tale of Jemima Puddle Duck, (Potter, Beatrix)
Tale of Johnny Mouse, (Gordon, Elizabeth)
Tale of Johnny Town Mouse, (Potter, Beatrix)
Tale of Little Pig Robinson, (Potter, Beatrix)
Tale of Little Priscilla Purr, (N/A)
Tale of Lohengrin, (Wagner, Richard)
Tale of Middle Length, (Shura, Mary F.)
Tale of Mr. Jeremy Fisher, (Potter, Beatrix)
Tale of Mr. Tod, (Potter, Beatrix)
Tale of Mrs. Tiggy-Winkle, (Potter, Beatrix)
Tale of Mrs. Tittlemouse, (Potter, Beatrix)
Tale of Peter Rabbit, (Potter, Beatrix)
Tale of Pigling Bland, (Potter, Beatrix)

Tale of Squirrel Nutkin, (Potter, Beatrix)
Tale of Stolen Time, (Schwartz, Evgeny)
Tale of Timmy Tiptoes, (Potter, Beatrix)
Tale of Tiny Tutak, (Wiig, Hanna)
Tale of Tom Kitten, (Potter, Beatrix)
Tale of Tom Tiddler, (Farjeon, Eleanor)
Tale of Tubby the Tuba, (Tripp, Paul)
Tale of Two Bad Mice, (Potter, Beatrix)
Tale of Two Cities, (Dickens, Charles)
Tale of Two Glimps, (Bemelmans, Ludwig)
Tale of Two Horses, (Tschiffely, Aime)
Tale of Wee Little Old Woman, (Beskow, Elsa)
Tale of a Black Cat, (Withers, Carl)
Tale of a Crocodile, (Kirn, Ann)
Tale of a Donkey, (Angelo, Valenti)
Tale of a Lucky Dog, (Proctor, Beth)
Tale of a Pig, (Tripp, Wallace)
Tale of a Wood, (Kane, Henry B.)
Tale of the Cauldron, (McKay (ed.))
Tale of the Enchanted Bunnies, (Sawyer, Ruth)
Tale of the Faithful Dove, (Potter, Beatrix)
Tale of the Land of Green Ginger, (Langley, Noel)
Tale of the Little Bunnies, (N/A)
Tale of the Long-Eared Bat, (Barnaby, Horace T.)
Tale of the Tabby Twins, (Ruthley, Cecily)
Tale of the Whitefoot Mouse, (Kane, Henry B.)
Tales & Talks About Animals, (N/A)
Tales Come True & Tales Made New, (Walker, M.C.)
Tales For Toby, (Hope, Ascott R.)
Tales Told Near a Crocodile, (Harman, Humphrey)
Tales Told by Gander, (Warren, Maude R.)
Tales Told in Holland, (Miller, Olive B.)
Tales Told in the Twilight, (Molesworth, Mrs.)
Tales Told in the Zoo, (Gould, F.C.)
Tales Worth Telling, (Finger, Charles J.)
Tales You Won't Believe, (Stratton-Porter, Gene)
Tales for Teeny Wee, (Joan, Natalie)
Tales from Boccaccio, (Jacobs (ed.))
Tales from Andersen, (Andersen, Hans C.)
Tales from Arabian Nights, (N/A)
Tales from Chaucer, (Farjeon, Eleanor)
Tales from Ebony, (Williams, Harcourt)
Tales from Enchanted Isles, (Gate, Ethel M.)
Tales from Greek Mythology, (Pyle, Katharine)
Tales from Norse Mythology, (Pyle, Katharine)
Tales from Shakespeare, (Lamb, Charles)
Tales from Silver Lands, (Finger, Charles J.)
Tales from Storyland, (Piper, Watty (ed))
Tales from Storyteller's House, (Burgess, Thornton)
Tales from Tennyson, (Chesson, Nora)
Tales from Timbuktu, (Armfield, Constance)
Tales from a Finnish Tupa, (Bowman, James C.)
Tales from the Ballet, (Untermeyer, Louis)
Tales from the Crescent Moon, (McNeer, May)
Tales from the Edda, (Zimmern, Helen)
Tales from the Field, (Asbjornsen, P.C.)
Tales from the Secret Kingdom, (Gate, Ethel M.)
Tales from the Story Hat, (Aardema, Verna)
Tales from...., (Edgeworth, Maria)
Tales of Don Quixote, (Palazzo, Tony)
Tales of Enchantment from Spain, (Eells, Elsie S.)
Tales of Faraway Folk, (Deutsch, Babette)
Tales of Folk & Fairies, (Pyle, Katharine)
Tales of Hoffmann, (Hoffmann, Ernst T.)
Tales of Home Folks in Peace & War, (Harris, Joel C.)
Tales of India, (Kipling, Rudyard)
Tales of Laughter, (Wiggin, Kate D.)
Tales of Little Cats, (Jacobs-Bond, Carrie)

Tales of Little Dogs, (Jacobs-Bond, Carrie)
Tales of Mystery..., (Poe, Edgar A.)
Tales of Our Coasts, (Crockett, Samuel R.)
Tales of Past Times..., (Perrault, Charles)
Tales of Poindi, (Mariotti, Jean)
Tales of Raindrop, Cloud Fairy, (Scott, Barbara)
Tales of Temba, (Arnott, Kathleen)
Tales of Toytown, (Beaman, S.G.H.)
Tales of Troy & Greece, (Lang, Andrew)
Tales of Two Bunnies, (Pyle, Katharine)
Tales of Wonder & Magic, (Pyle, Katharine)
Tales of a Chinese Grandmother, (Carpenter, Frances)
Tales of a Fairy Court, (Lang, Andrew)
Tales of a Poultry Farm, (Pierson, Clara D.)
Tales of a Russian Grandmother, (Carpenter, Frances)
Tales of a Traveller, (Irving, Washington)
Tales of an Old Chateau, (Bouvet, Marguerite)
Tales of the Cheyennes, (Penney, Grace)
Tales of the Fairies, (Marsh, Lewis)
Tales of the Fish Patrol, (London, Jack)
Tales of the Homeland, (Marsh, Lewis)
Tales of the Pampas, (Hudson, Wm. Henry)
Tales of the Persian Genii, (Olcott, F.J. (ed))
Tales of the Punjab, (Kipling, Rudyard)
Tales of the Red Children, (Brown, Abbie F.)
Tales of the Rue Broca, (Gripari, Pierre)
Tales of the Spinner, (Doucet, Jerome)
Talking Beasts, (Wiggin & Smith)
Talking Bird, (Purnell, Idella)
Talking Bird & Wonderful Wishes, (Donahey, Mary D.)
Talking Cat, (Carlson, Natalie S.)
Talking Crocodile, (Campbell, M. Rudolph)
Talking Dolls, (Mills, G.R.)
Talking Drums, (Fleming, Waldo)
Talking Skyscraper, (Brown, Slater)
Talking Stone, (Cunningham, Caroline)
Talking Thrush, (Rouse, W.H.D.)
Talking Tree, (Baker, Augusta)
Talking Typewriter, (Pratt, Margaret)
Talking Without Words, (Ets, Marie H.)
Tall Book of Fairy Tales, (Vance, Eleanor G.)
Tall Book of Make-Believe, (Werner, Jane)
Tall Book of Nursery Tales, (N/A)
Tall Tale America, (Blair, Walter)
Tall Tales of Kentucky Mountains, (MacKaye, Percy)
Tall Tales of the Catskills, (DuMond, Frank)
Tall Timber, (Holbrook, Stewart)
Tally-Ho, (Johnson, Margaret)
Tam Morgan, (Holberg, Ruth)
Tama, (Watanna, Onoto)
Tamarindo!, (Brown, Marcia)
Taming of Amorette, (Warner, Anne)
Taming of Red Butte Western, (Lynde, Francis)
Tan & Teckle, (Bryson, Charles L.)
Tan's Fish, (Todd, Ruthven)
Tan-Ta-Ka, (Coryell, Hubert)
Tang of Life, (Knibbs, Henry H.)
Tangara, (Chauncy, Nan)
Tangle Garden, (Gray, Eliz. J.)
Tangle-Coated Horse, (Young, Ella)
Tangled Tale, (Carroll, Lewis)
Tangled Waters, (Means, Florence C.)
Tangles & Curls, (Blanchard, Amy E.)
Tanglewood Tales, (Hawthorne, Nathaniel)
Tannhauser, (Wagner, Richard)
Tap, Tap, Lion - 1 2 3, (Fritz, Jean)
Tapiola's Brave Regiment, (Nathan, Robert)
Tappan's Burro, (Grey, Zane)

Tar-Baby, (Harris, Joel C.)
Tara, Daughter of the Gypsies, (Kahmann, Chesley)
Taran Wanderer, (Alexander, Lloyd C.)
Tarnish: True Story of a Lion Cub, (Johnson, Osa)
Taro and the Tofu, (Matsuno, Masako)
Tartan Tales, (Lang, Andrew)
Tarzan & the Jewels of Opar, (Burroughs, Edgar R.)
Tarzan Twins, (Burroughs, Edgar R.)
Taste of Spruce Gum, (Jackson, Jacqueline)
Tatoosh, (Hardy, Martha)
Tatsinda, (Enright, Elizabeth)
Tattlings of a Retired Politician, (Crissey, Forrest)
Tattooed Man, (Pease, Howard)
Tawny Goes Hunting, (Chaffee, Allen)
Tawny's Trick, (Forbus, Ina B.)
Tawnymore, (Shannon, Monica)
Taxis & Toadstools, (Field, Rachel)
Tea Party in Plumpudding Street, (Maloy, Lois)
Tea-Table Talk, (Jerome, Jerome K.)
Teacher's Pet, (Miles, Miska)
Teacup Whale, (Gibson, Lydia)
Ted & Nina Go to Grocery Store, (DeAngeli, Marguerite)
Ted & Nina Have a Happy Rainy Day, (DeAngeli, M.)
Teddy, (Janus, Grete)
Teddy & Carrots, (Otis, James)
Teddy & Trots in Wonderland, (Herbertson, Agnes)
Teddy Bear & other Songs, (Milne, A.A.)
Teddy Bear Book, (Byron, May)
Teddy Bear that Prowled the Night, (Deihl, Edna G.)
Teddy Bearoplane, (Byron, May)
Teddy Bears, (Sutton, Adah L.)
Teddy Bears Come to Life, (Towne, Robert D.)
Teddy Bears at the Circus, (Towne, Robert D.)
Teddy Bears in Hot Water, (Towne, Robert D.)
Teddy Bears in a Smashup, (Towne, Robert D.)
Teddy Bears on a Lark, (Towne, Robert D.)
Teddy Bears on a Tobaggon, (Towne, Robert D.)
Teddy Tail of the Daily Mail, (Folkard, Charles)
Teddy Tail's Fairy Tale, (Folkard, Charles)
Teddy's Camp Out, (Holland, Marion)
Teddy's Year with the Fairies, (Gullick, M.E.)
Teddy-B & Teddy-G/Bear Detectives, (Eaton, Seymour)
Teddy-Bear ABC, (Johnson, Laura R.)
Teddybears 1 to 10, (Gretz, Susanna)
Teem: A Treasure-Hunter, (Kipling, Rudyard)
Teenie Weenies... [All titles], (Donahey, William)
Teeny & the Tall Man, (Meade, Julian R.)
Teletrips of Alala, (Monreal, Guy)
Tell 'Em Again Tales, (Day, Marguerite)
Tell Me About Heaven, (Jones, Mary A.)
Tell Me About Prayer, (Jones, Mary A.)
Tell Me Why Stories, (Claudy, C.H.)
Tell Me a Mitzi, (Segal, Lore)
Tell Me a Story, (Blanchard, Amy E.)
Tell Me, Little Boy, (Foster, Doris)
Tell Me, Mister Owl, (Foster, Doris)
Temple of Fire, (Ashley, Fred)
Temple on a Hill, (Rockwell, Anne)
Templelogue Lever, (Lever, Charles)
Temptation of St. Anthony, (Flaubert, Gustave)
Ten Apples Up on Top!, (LeSieg, Theo)
Ten Big Farms, (Ipcar, Dahlov)
Ten Black Dots, (Crews, Donald)
Ten Boys from Dickens, (Sweetser, Kate D.)
Ten Boys from History, (Sweetser, Kate D.)
Ten Brave Women, (Daugherty, Sonia)
Ten Girls from Dickens, (Sweetser, Kate D.)
Ten Little Babies, (Robinson, Charles)

Ten Little Boer Boys, (Norman)
Ten Little Puppy Dogs, (Robinson, Charles)
Ten Saints, (Farjeon, Eleanor)
Ten and a Kid, (Weilerstein, Sadie)
Ten to Seventeen, (Bacon, Josephine D.)
Tenant of Wildfell Hall..., (Bronte, Anne)
Tenement Tree, (Seredy, Kate)
Tenggren Tell-It-Again Book, (Gibson, Katharine)
Tenggren's Cowboys & Indians, (Jackson, Kathryn)
Tennessee Shad, (Johnson, Owen)
Tennis Shoes, (Streatfeild, Noel)
Tennyson, (Cary, Elisabeth L.)
Tent Dwellers, (Paine, Albert B.)
Tent on the Beach, (Whittier, John G.)
Tenting on the Plains, (Custer, Elizabeth B.)
Tents in the Wilderness, (Lips, Julius)
Teri Taro from Bora Bora, (Stone, William S.)
Termite Works for his Colony, (DeSeyn, Donna E.)
Terrapin's Pot of Sense, (Courlander, Harold)
Terrible Churnadryne, (Cameron, Eleanor)
Terrible Mr. Twitmeyer, (Moore, Lilian)
Terrible Nuisance, (Bacon, Peggy)
Terrible Terrifying Toby, (Johnson, Crockett)
Terrible Tiger, (Prelutsky, Jack)
Terrible Trick or Treat, (Battles, Edith)
Terry and the Caterpillars, (Selsam, Millicent)
Tessie, (Jackson, Jesse)
Tewa Firelight Tales, (James, Ahlee)
Texas Matchmaker, (Adams, Andy)
Texas Tomboy, (Lenski, Lois)
Thai, Kao and Tone: Elephant Story, (Palazzo, Tony)
Thais, (France, Anatole)
Thank You, Amelia Bedelia, (Parish, Peggy)
Thank You, You're Welcome, (Slobodkin, Louis)
Thank-You Book, (Francoise)
Thanks to Trees, (Webber, Irma E.)
Thanksgiving Story, (Dalgliesh, Alice)
That Boy Johnny!, (Sickels, Evelyn)
That Cat! 1-2-3, (Martin, Patricia)
That Colt, Fireplug, (Coates, Belle)
That Girl of Pierre's, (Davis, Robert)
That Jud!, (Bragdon, Elspeth)
That Little Limb, (Baldwin, May)
That Lively Man: Ben Franklin, (Eaton, Jeanette)
That Mario, (Crockett, Lucy H.)
That Mean Man, (Skorpen, Liesel)
That Pest Jonathan, (Cole, William)
That Ruby, (Brown, Margery)
That's Good, That's Bad, (Lexau, Joan M.)
That's Right, Edie, (Johnston, Johanna)
That's What Friends are For, (Heide, Florence P.)
Thatched Roof, (Nichols, Beverly)
The Adventurers, (Watson, H.B.M.)
The Alhambra, (Irving, Washington)
The Alley, (Estes, Eleanor)
The Alphabet, (Orr, Monro S.)
The Alternative, (McCutcheon, George B.)
The B Book, (McGinley, Phyllis)
The Barkingtons, (Palmer, Robin)
The Barn, (Schoenherr, John)
The Bastille, (Bingham, D.)
The Bells..., (Poe, Edgar A.)
The Bicyclers, (Bangs, John K.)
The Bird, (Lowrey, Janette S.)
The Birthday, (Fischer, Hans)
The Blackberries..., (Kemble, Edward W.)
The Borrowers, (Norton, Mary)
The Boy Jesus, (Doane, Pelagie)

The Brethren, (Haggard, H. Rider)
The Bridge, (Barman, Christian)
The Bridge, (Ogburn, Charlton)
The Brook, (Carrick, Carol)
The Brownies, (Ewing, Juliana H.)
The Buccaneers, (Seitz, Don C.)
The Bumbletoes, (Sowerby, Githa)
The Cabinet, (Johnson, Gerald W.)
The Candlestick, (Bianco, Margery W.)
The Captain, (Lent, Henry B.)
The Caravan, (Hauff, Wilhelm)
The Carlyles, (Harrison, Mrs. Burton)
The Cavalier, (Cable, George W.)
The Cave, (Coatsworth, Eliz.)
The Challenge, (Cheney, Warren)
The Changeling, (Mayne, William)
The Changeling, (Snyder, Zilpha K.)
The Chase, (Somerville, William)
The Chatterlings, (Lipman, Michael)
The Children, (Meynell, Alice)
The Chimes, (Dickens, Charles)
The Clansman, (Dixon, Thomas)
The Congress, (Johnson, Gerald W.)
The Cossacks, (Bartos-Hoppner, B.)
The Cost, (Phillips, David G.)
The Courtin', (Lowell, James R.)
The Crane, (Zimnik, Reiner)
The Creators, (Sinclair, May)
The Crossing..., (Churchill, Winston)
The Daybreakers, (Curry, Jane L.)
The Decameron..., (Aldington (tr.))
The Deerslayer, (Cooper, James F.)
The Defender, (Kalashnikoff, N.)
The Deliverance, (Glasgow, Ellen)
The Deliveryman, (Kuh, Charlotte)
The Dolomites, (Hamer, Sam H.)
The Dragon, (Marshall, Archibald)
The Duck, (Brown, Margaret W.)
The Duenna, (Sheridan, Richard B.)
The Dumpies, (VerBeck, Frank)
The Eggs, (Aliki)
The Enchanted, an Incredible Tale, (Coatsworth, Eliz.)
The Engineer, (Kuh, Charlotte)
The Farmer, (Lent, Henry B.)
The Fence, (Balet, Jan B.)
The Firebird, (Cooke, Donald E.)
The Firebird, (Stanovsky, Vladislav)
The Fireflies, (Bolliger, Max)
The Fireman, (Kuh, Charlotte)
The Fishermen, (Wahl, Jan)
The Flock, (Austin, Mary)
The Flower, (Downer, Mary L.)
The Flowers, (Gerry, Margarita S.)
The Ford, (Austin, Mary)
The Forest, (White, Stewart E.)
The Game, (London, Jack)
The Gats!, (Goffstein, M.B.)
The General, (Charters, Janet)
The Giant, (DuBois, W.P.)
The Gigglequicks, (Potter, Miriam C.)
The Gillygoofang, (Mendoza, George)
The Glob, (O'Reilly, John)
The Gnomobile, (Sinclair, Upton)
The Grandissimes, (Cable, George W.)
The Grenadier, (Farmer, James E.)
The Greyhound, (Griffiths, Helen)
The Grizzly, (Johnson, Annabel)
The Groober, (Byars, Betsy C.)

The Gunniwolf, (Harper, Wilhelmina)
The Harvester, (Stratton-Porter, Gene)
The Hat, (Ungerer, Tomi)
The Headswoman, (Grahame, Kenneth)
The Heroes, (Kingsley, Charles)
The Hobbit, (Tolkien, J.R.R.)
The Hollyberrys, (Dalgliesh, Alice)
The Honeybees, (Russell, Franklin)
The Hostages, (Mitchison, Naomi)
The House, (Allee, Marjorie H.)
The Hunkendunkens, (Livingston, Richard)
The Idiot, (Bangs, John K.)
The Incas, (Groesbeck, Telford)
The Inspector, (Mendoza, George)
The Intruder, (Townsend, John R.)
The Invaders, (Tracy, Louis)
The Jingo, (Chester, Geo. R.)
The Judge: An Untrue Tale, (Zemach, Harve)
The Jumblies, (Lear, Edward)
The Jungle, (Borten, Helen)
The Kellyhorns, (Cooney, Barbara)
The Kingfisher, (Lida)
The Leader, (Dillon, Mary)
The Liar, (Goldoni, Carlo)
The Limbersnigs, (Speed, Flora)
The Lion, (Kessel, Joseph)
The Littlebits, (Potter, Miriam C.)
The Local, (Gorham, Maurice)
The Lollipops, (Long, Olive M.)
The Loner, (Wier, Ester A.)
The Mansion, (Van Dyke, Henry)
The Martian, (DuMaurier, George)
The Mavericks, (Schaefer, Jack W.)
The Mayfly, (Hutchins, Ross)
The Maze, (Sandoz, Maurice)
The Mediterranean, (Bloomfield, Paul)
The Mediterranean, (Bonney, Thomas G.)
The Mermaid, (Andersen, Hans C.)
The Merrymakers, (Garnett, Louise A.)
The Message, (Dawson, Alec J.)
The Mikado, (Gilbert, W.S.)
The Militants, (Andrews, Mary S.)
The Missourian, (Lyle, Eugene P.)
The Mitchells, (Van Stockum, Hilda)
The Mitten, (Tresselt, Alvin)
The Moffats, (Estes, Eleanor)
The Monster..., (Crane, Stephen)
The Moon, (Asimov, Isaac)
The Moonball, (Williams, Ursula)
The Motorman, (Kuh, Charlotte)
The Mountains, (White, Stewart E.)
The Muffletumps, (Wahl, Jan)
The Mushmen, (Russell, Solveig)
The Mystics, (Thurston, Katherine)
The Namesake, (Hodges, C. Walter)
The Neighbors, (Brown, Marcia)
The Net, (Beach, Rex)
The Nightingale, (Andersen, Hans C.)
The Oddity, (Bacon, Peggy)
The One Woman, (Dixon, Thomas)
The Orphan, (Mulford, Clarence)
The Other Side, (Desmond, G.G.)
The Outcasts, (Fraser, William A.)
The Outlet, (Adams, Andy)
The Panther, (Warner, Anne)
The Parasite, (Doyle, Arthur Conan)
The Pass, (White, Stewart E.)
The Pathfinder, (Cooper, James F.)

The Pets, (Phillips, Henry W.)
The Piccolo, (Richards, Laura E.)
The Pigeoneers, (Molloy, Anne)
The Pioneer, (Bonner, Geraldine)
The Pioneers, (Cooper, James F.)
The Piper, (Stevens, Eden V.)
The Place, (Coatsworth, Eliz.)
The Plainsmen, (Schaefer, Jack W.)
The Poet, (Nicholson, Meredith)
The Policeman, (Kuh, Charlotte)
The Pond, (Carrick, Carol)
The Presidency, (Johnson, Gerald W.)
The Princess, (Tennyson, Alfred)
The Pursuer, (Golding, Louis)
The Quoks, (Price, Luxor)
The Race, (Hurd, Clement)
The Rainbow, (Thaler, Mike)
The Ramayana, (Seeger, Elizabeth)
The Raven, (Poe, Edgar A.)
The Raven & other Fairy Tales, (Payne, Joan B.)
The Rivals, (Sheridan, Richard B.)
The Riverman, (White, Stewart E.)
The Road, (London, Jack)
The Rosary, (Barclay, Florence)
The Rose, (Riley, James W.)
The Rossettis, (Cary, Elisabeth L.)
The Rumptydoolers, (Wier, Ester A.)
The Runaways, (Hader, B.& E.)
The Runner, (Annixter, Jane)
The Rustler, (McElrath, Frances)
The Sampo, (Baldwin, James)
The Sangamon, (Masters, Edgar L.)
The Saturdays, (Enright, Elizabeth)
The Seasons, (Burningham, John)
The Secret, (Coatsworth, Eliz.)
The Seeker, (Wilson, Harry L.)
The Seekers, (Waterloo, Stanley)
The Shepherd, (Aichinger, Helga)
The Sherrods, (McCutcheon, George B.)
The Shortstop, (Grey, Zane)
The Simpletons, (Kastner, Erich)
The Skyrocket, (Hader, B.& E.)
The Skyscraper, (Liang, Yen)
The Sleepers, (Curry, Jane L.)
The Slowcoach, (Lucas, E.V.)
The Smashers, (Anderson, C.W.)
The Snob, (Emanuel, Walter)
The Snowstorm, (Chonz, Selina)
The Something, (Babbitt, Natalie)
The Sphinx, (Wilde, Oscar)
The Spy, (Cooper, James F.)
The Stars: New Way to See Them, (Rey, Hans A.)
The Storekeeper, (Lent, Henry B.)
The Strollers, (Isham, Frederic S.)
The Swarm, (Maeterlinck, Maurice)
The Swineherd, (Andersen, Hans C.)
The Tempest, (Shakespeare, Wm.)
The Texican, (Coolidge, Dane)
The Throwback, (Lewis, Alfred H.)
The Timbertoes, (Aldredge, Edna)
The Tomten, (Lindgren, Astrid)
The Traitor, (Dixon, Thomas)
The Tree, (Delessert, Etienne)
The Truants, (Walsh, John)
The Turnip, (Domanska, Janina)
The Turret, (Sharp, Margery)
The Twins, (Aldin, Cecil)
The Twins, (Shane, Ruth & Harold)

The Twins, (Shirley, Edward)
The Undercurrent, (Grant, Robert)
The Undergrounders, (Bradbury, Bianca)
The Uproar, (Orgel, Doris)
The Vagabond, (Palmer, Frederick)
The Varmint, (Johnson, Owen)
The Vegetabull, (LeWitt, Jan)
The Violet, (Magruder, Julia)
The Virginian, (Wister, Owen)
The Voyagers, (Colum, Padraic)
The Wave, (Hodges, Margaret)
The Wayfarers, (Cutting, Mary S.)
The Wayfarers, (Peabody, Josephine)
The Weathercock, (Ratel, Simonne)
The Weavers, (Parker, Gilbert)
The Welcome, (Deutsch, Babette)
The Whirligig, (Raymond, Evelyn)
The Whirlpool, (Gissing, George)
The Widow, (Aldin, Cecil)
The Winners, (Wier, Ester A.)
The Wolfling, (North, Sterling)
The Woman, (Terhune, Albert P.)
The Wombles, (Beresford, Elisabeth)
The Woover, (Merrill, Jean)
The Wouldbegoods, (Nesbit, Edith)
The Yearling, (Rawlings, Marjorie K.)
The Yoke, (Miller, Elizabeth)
Theater Shoes, (Streatfeild, Noel)
Theatre Cat, (Streatfeild, Noel)
Thee, Hannah!, (DeAngeli, Marguerite)
Their First Formal Call, (Cooke, Grace M.)
Their First Igloo on Baffin Island, (True, Barbara)
Their Hearts' Desire, (Perry, Francis F.)
Then & Now, (Vaughn, Robert)
Then Came Timothy, (Frost, Frances)
Then There were Five, (Enright, Elizabeth)
Theodora, (Pyle/Porter)
Theodore, (Ormondroyd, Edward)
Theodore Turtle, (MacGregor, Ellen)
Theodore's Parents, (Udry, Janice M.)
Theras & his Town, (Snedeker, Caroline D.)
There & Then, (Weston, Christine)
There Goes the Tiger!, (Martin, Patricia)
There Really Was a Hiawatha, (Malkus, Alida S.)
There Were Giants, (Adams, Kathleen)
There is No Rhyme for Silver, (Merriam, Eve)
There is a Dragon in my Bed, (Joslin, Sesyle)
There is the Land, (Berry, Erick)
There was Timmy!, (Scott, Sally)
There was a Child Went Forth, (Whitman, Walt)
There was a Wise Crow, (Low, Joseph)
There's a Nightmare in My Closet, (Mayer, Mercer)
These Happy Golden Years, (Wilder, Laura I.)
These Little Ones, (Nesbit, Edith)
Theseus, (Kingsley, Charles)
They, (Kipling, Rudyard)
They Came from... [All titles], (Judson, Clara I.)
They Had a Horse, (Edmonds, Walter D.)
They Loved to Laugh, (Worth, Kathryn)
They Put Out to Sea, (Duvoisin, Roger)
They Say Stories, (Chappell, Warren)
They Walk in the Night, (Coatsworth, Eliz.)
They Were Strong & Good, (Lawson, Robert)
They and Brushwood Boy, (Kipling, Rudyard)
Thidwick the Big-Hearted Moose, (Seuss, Dr.)
Thief Island, (Coatsworth, Eliz.)
Thief and the Blue Rose, (Schaeffler, Ursula)
Thief in the Attic, (Wiese, Kurt)

Thieves & the Raven, (Janosch)
Thimble Summer, (Enright, Elizabeth)
Thin Ice, (Beim, Jerrold)
Things, (Wyllarde, Dolf)
Things I Like, (Francoise)
Things New and Old, (Beerbohm, Max)
Things that Go Bang, (Weil, Lisl)
Third Monkey, (Clark, Ann N.)
Thirsty Lion, (Forbes, Katherine)
Thirsty Pony, (Laune, Paul)
Thirteen Clocks, (Thurber, James)
Thirteen Days of Yule, (Hogrogian, Nonny)
Thirteen Such Years, (Waugh, Alec)
Thirteenth Orphan, (Chaundler, Christine)
Thirty Old-Time Nursery Songs, (Moorat, Joseph)
Thirty-Nine Steps, (Buchan, John)
This & That, (Molesworth, Mrs.)
This Cat Came to Stay, (Kinsey, Elizabeth)
This Dear-Bought Land, (Latham, Jean L.)
This Earth We Live On, (Duval, Elizabeth)
This Giddy Globe, (Herford, Oliver)
This He Believed, (Ballou, Robert)
This Little Pig, (Evers, Helen)
This Old Man, (Bone, Gertrude)
This Street's for Me!, (Hopkins, Lee B. (comp))
This Thumbprint, (Krauss, Ruth)
This Way Delight, (Read, Herbert)
This Way to Christmas, (Sawyer, Ruth)
This Year: Next Year, (De La Mare, Walter)
This for That, (Clark, Ann N.)
This is 4: Idea of a Number, (Razzell, Arthur)
This is Ann, She's Dying to Meet You, (Leaf, Munro)
This is My Family, (Fehr, Howard F.)
This is New York, (Sasek, Miroslav)
This is Paris, (Sasek, Miroslav)
This is my Own, (Kent, Rockwell)
This is the Bread that Betsy Ate, (Black, Irma S.)
This is the House Where Jack Lives, (Heilbroner, Joan)
This is the Milk that Jack Drank, (Scott, William R.)
This is the Moon, (Cothren, Marion)
This is the Way, (Jones, Jessie O. (ed))
This is the Way the Animals Walk, (Woodcock, Louise)
Thistle and Thyme..., (Leodhas, Sorche)
Thistly B., (Tudor, Tasha)
Thomas Jones & his Nine Lives, (Watkin, Lawrence)
Thomasina, (Gallico, Paul)
Thompson Street Poker Club, (Carleton, Henry G.)
Thord Firetooth, (Lide, Alice A.)
Thoreau of Walden Pond, (North, Sterling)
Thornbush Jungle, (Montgomery, R.)
Thornton Burgess Bedtime Stories, (Burgess, Thornton)
Thoroughbreds, (Anderson, C.W.)
Those Brewster Children, (Kingsley, Florence M.)
Those Dale Girls, (Carruth, Frances W.)
Those Plummer Children, (Govan, Christine)
Thread Soldier, (Heathers, Anne)
Three & Domingo, (Bro, Marguerite)
Three & the Moon, (Dorey, Jacques)
Three Apples Fell from Heaven, (Belting, Natalia)
Three Bad Ducklings, (Aris, Ernest A.)
Three Bears, (N/A)
Three Bears, (VerBeck, Frank)
Three Billy Goats Gruff, (Asbjornsen, P.C.)
Three Billy Goats Gruff, (N/A)
Three Birthday Wishes, (Holberg, Ruth)
Three Boys and... [All titles], (Agle, Nan H.)
Three Brothers, (Clarke, Mollie)
Three Brothers and a Lady, (Black, Margaret)

Three Caballeros, (Palmer, H. Marion)
Three Christmas Trees, (Ewing, Juliana H.)
Three Chums, (Leighton, Mary)
Three Famous Ugly Sisters, (Dyer, Caroline)
Three Funny Friends, (Zolotow, Charlotte)
Three Gay Tales from Grimm, (Gag, Wanda)
Three Goats, (Hillert, Margaret)
Three Godfathers, (Kyne, Peter B.)
Three Gold Pieces, (Aliki)
Three Golden Nobles, (Price, Christine)
Three Golden Oranges, (Boggs, Ralph S.)
Three Good Friends, (Wiesner, William)
Three Hanses, (David, Julian)
Three Happy Lions, (Fatio, Louise)
Three J's, (Johnson, Enid)
Three Jolly Huntsmen, (Pope, Jessie)
Three Jovial Huntsmen, (Caldecott, R.)
Three Jovial Puppies, (Cuming, E.W.D.)
Three Kings, (Chambers, Maria C.)
Three Kings of Saba, (Evers, Alf)
Three Ladies Beside the Sea, (Levine, Rhoda)
Three Little Animals, (Brown, Margaret W.)
Three Little Chipmunks, (Torrey, Marjorie)
Three Little Dachshunds, (Otto, Margaret G.)
Three Little Frogs, (Mee, John)
Three Little Indians, (Leavitt, Ann H.)
Three Little Kittens, (Kauffman, Ruth)
Three Little Kittens, (N/A)
Three Little Kittens, (Palazzo, Tony)
Three Little Pigs, (Benstead, V. (adap))
Three Little Pigs, (Disney, Walt)
Three Little Pigs, (N/A)
Three Little Warrens, (Wheelock, Sarah)
Three Men on Wheels, (Jerome, Jerome K.)
Three Miracles, (Blanton, Catherine)
Three Mulla Mulgars, (De La Mare, Walter)
Three Musketeers, (Dumas, Alexandre)
Three Mustangeers, (James, Will)
Three Naughty Children, (Williams, Orlando)
Three Naughty Elves, (March, Eleanor S.)
Three Operettas, (Bunner, H.C.)
Three Orphan Kittens, (Disney, Walt)
Three People, (Wolff, Carolyn)
Three Policemen, (DuBois, W.P.)
Three Poor Tailors, (Ambrus, Victor G.)
Three Prayers for Children, (Bible)
Three Pretty Maids, (Blanchard, Amy E.)
Three Princes of Serendip, (Hodges, Elizabeth)
Three Ring Circus, (Brock, Emma)
Three Rings: A Circus Book, (Brown, Paul)
Three Robbers, (Ungerer, Tomi)
Three Rolls & One Doughnut, (Ginsburg, Mirra)
Three Royal Monkeys, (De La Mare, Walter)
Three Saxon Nobles, (Prelutsky, Jack)
Three Seeds, (Hawkes, Hester)
Three Ships Came Sailing In, (Mason, Miriam E.)
Three Sides of Agiochook, (Kelly, Eric P.)
Three Sillies: A Folk Tale, (Zemach, Margot)
Three Silly Kittens, (Austin, Margot)
Three Sisters, (Spencer, Cornelia)
Three Sneezes..., (Duvoisin, Roger)
Three Strong Women, (Stamm, Claus)
Three Sunsets..., (Carroll, Lewis)
Three Tall Tales, (Sewell, Helen)
Three Trees of the Samurai, (Cocagnac, A.M.)
Three Visitors, (Hopkins, Marjorie)
Three White Cats of Avignon, (Stewart, Anna B.)
Three Wishes, (Jacobs, Joseph (ed))

Three Wishes of Hu, (Holding, James)
Three Witches, (Molesworth, Mrs.)
Three Young Kings, (Albee, George)
Three Young Rats, (Sweeney, James J.)
Three and the Shape of Three, (Razzell, Arthur)
Three by Candlelight, (Southwold, Stephen)
Three for an Acorn, (Baker, Margaret)
Three from Greenways, (Dalgliesh, Alice)
Three on the Run, (Bawden, Nina)
Three to Get Ready, (Boegehold, Betty)
Three-Four Kittens, (Dell, Stanley)
Three-Seated Space Ship, (Slobodkin, Louis)
Three-in-One Prince, (Johnson, Elizabeth)
Thrilling Days in Army Life, (Forsyth, George A.)
Through All the Years, (Foley, James W.)
Through Merrie England, (Stevens, Frank L.)
Through South America, (Van Dyke, Henry)
Through Space to Mars, (Rockwood, Roy)
Through These Arches, (Milhous, Katherine)
Through Welsh Doorways, (Marks, Jeannette)
Through the Cloud Mountain, (Bernard, Florence S.)
Through the Earth, (Fezandie, Clement)
Through the Enchanted Wood, (Gordon, Hampden C.)
Through the Fray, (Henty, G.A.)
Through the Gates of Old Romance, (Mills, Weymer J.)
Through the Harbor from Everywhere, (Eberle, I.)
Through the Little Green Door, (Donahey, Mary D.)
Through the Looking Glass, (Carroll, Lewis)
Through the Picture Frame, (Disney, Walt)
Through the Rainbow, (Peltier, Florence)
Through the Window, (Keeping, Charles)
Through the Woods, (Bates, Herbert E.)
Throw a Kiss, Harry, (Chalmers, Mary)
Thumbelina, (Andersen, Hans C.)
Thumbelisa..., (Andersen, Hans C.)
Thumper, (Disney, Walt)
Thumps, (Beatty, Hetty B.)
Thunder Boy, (Baker, Olaf)
Thunder Country, (Sperry, Armstrong)
Thunder Hill, (Nicholds, Elizabeth)
Thunder Island, (Stone, William S.)
Thunder in the Sky, (Peyton, Kathleen M.)
Thunder's Tail, (Greer, Blanche)
Thunderboats Ho!, (Montgomery, R.)
Thunderbolt House, (Pease, Howard)
Thunderbolt Men, (MacArthur, David)
Thursday Ahoy!, (Bond, Michael)
Thus Think and Smoke Tobacco, (Edwards, George W.)
Thy Friend Obadiah, (Turkle, Brinton)
Thyra Varrick, (Barr, Amelia E.)
Thyra: Romance of the Polar Pit, (Bennet, Robert A.)
Tia Maria's Garden, (Clark, Ann N.)
Tibby's Venture, (Holberg, Ruth)
Tic, Tac, and Toc, (Munari, Bruno)
Tick-Tock Tales, (Piper, Watty)
Ticktock and Jim, (Robertson, Keith)
Tico and the Golden Wings, (Lionni, Leo)
Tiddledywink Tales, (Bangs, John K.)
Tiddledywink's Poetry Book, (Bangs, John K.)
Tiger & the Insect, (Habberton, John)
Tiger Called Thomas, (Zolotow, Charlotte)
Tiger Flower, (Vavra, Robert)
Tiger and the Rabbit, (Belpre, Pura)
Tiger in the Cherry Tree, (Dines, Glen)
Tiger in the Teapot, (Yurdin, Betty)
Tiger of Mysore, (Henty, G.A.)
Tiger's Chance, (Henry, Jan)
Tiger's Whisker, (Courlander, Harold)

Tigers Don't Bite, (Tworkov, Jack)
Tigers in the Cellar, (Fenner, Carol E.)
Tik-Tok of Oz, (Baum, L. Frank)
Tikki-Tikki Tembo, (Mosel, Arlene)
Tilio, Boy of Papua, (Voorhoeve, Rudolf)
Till Death Do Us Part, (Steig, William)
Tilly Witch, (Freeman, Don)
Tilly's Strange Secret, (Govan, Christine)
Tilly-Tod, (Gray, Eliz. J.)
Tilted Sombrero, (Lampman, Evelyn)
Tim & Tip, (Otis, James)
Tim All Alone, (Ardizzone, Edward)
Tim Chick, (Meyer, Edith P.)
Tim Tadpole..., (Flack, Marjorie)
Tim Tubby-Toes, (Golding, Harry)
Tim and Charlotte, (Ardizzone, Edward)
Tim and Ginger, (Ardizzone, Edward)
Tim and Lucy Go to Sea, (Ardizzone, Edward)
Tim and the Dusty Man, (Ames, Mrs. E.)
Tim in Danger, (Ardizzone, Edward)
Tim to the Lighthouse, (Ardizzone, Edward)
Tim to the Rescue, (Ardizzone, Edward)
Tim's Friend Towser, (Ardizzone, Edward)
Tim's Mountain, (Montgomery, R.)
Timber Line, (Malkus, Alida S.)
Timber Line Treasure, (Stoutenburg, Adrien)
Timber! Logging in Michigan, (Fisher, Aileen)
Timberline Tales, (Montgomery, R.)
Time & the Gods, (Lord Dunsany)
Time Cat..., (Alexander, Lloyd C.)
Time Garden, (Eager, Edward)
Time I Was Dead, (Aldin, Cecil)
Time Was, (Woodward, Hildegard)
Time and Mr. Bass, (Cameron, Eleanor)
Time at the Top, (Ormondroyd, Edward)
Time for Bed, (Bertail, Inez)
Time for Lissa, (Caudill, Rebecca)
Time for Spring, (Johnson, Crockett)
Time of Man, (Roberts, Elizabeth M.)
Time of Trial, (Burton, Hester)
Time of Wonder, (McCloskey, Robert)
Time of the Lamb, (Wibberley, Leonard)
Time of the Wolves, (Davis, Verne)
Time to Get Up, (Cady, Harrison)
Time to Go House, (Edmonds, Walter D.)
Time-Ago Tales of Jahdu, (Hamilton, Virginia)
Timi: Tale of a Griffin, (Freeman, Barbara)
Timid Elmer, (Disney, Walt)
Timid Ghost, (Brenner, Anita)
Timid Timothy, (Williams, Gwen M.)
Timimoto's Great Adventure, (Francis, Frank)
Timmy Mouse, (Potter, Miriam C.)
Timmy Rides the China Clipper, (Nay, Carol)
Timmy and the Tiger, (Paradis, Marjorie)
Timmy and the Tin-Can Telephone, (Branley, Franklyn)
Timmy's Search, (Behn, Harry)
Timothy & the Blue Cart, (Whitney, Elinor)
Timothy Robbins Climbs the Mountain, (Tresselt, Alvin)
Timothy Toddlekin, (Hawley, Harriet E.)
Timothy Turtle, (Davis, Alice V.)
Timothy Turtle, (Graham, Al)
Timothy has Ideas, (Mason, Miriam E.)
Timothy's Angels, (Benet, William R.)
Timothy's Flower, (Van Leeuwen, Jean)
Timothy's Horse, (Mayakovsky, Vladimir)
Timothy's Magical Afternoon, (Jenks, Tudor)
Timothy's Song, (Lederer, William J.)
Timur and his Gang, (Gaidar, Arkady)

Tin Fiddle, (Tripp, Edward)
Tin Woodman of Oz, (Baum, L. Frank)
Tina and the Too-Big Doll, (Anderson, Neil)
Ting-Ling and Mee-Too, (Keto, Emma)
Tiniest Sound, (Evans, Melvin)
Tinka Minka & Linka, (McNeer, May)
Tinkelly Winkle, (Syrett, Netta)
Tinker Tailor, (Vredenburg, Edric)
Tinker Tailor Folk Song Tales, (Keeping, Charles)
Tinker Takes a Walk, (Scott, Sally)
Tinker Tim, (Tousey, Sanford)
Tinker Tim the Toy Maker, (Grant, Vernon)
Tinker's Castle, (Mantle, Winifred)
Tinker, Tailor, (Vredenburg, Edric)
Tinkers of Turntable, (Herzog, Elizabeth)
Tinkie, (Kirn, Ann)
Tinkler Johnny, (Herbertson, Agnes)
Tiny Book of Nursery Rhymes, (Mother Goose)
Tiny Folk of Sunny Days, (Thomas, Edith M.)
Tiny Folk of Wintery Days, (Thomas, Edith M.)
Tiny Pin, (Massie, Diane R.)
Tiny Seed, (Carle, Eric)
Tiny Toddlers, (Humphrey, Maud)
Tiny Tots: their Adventures, (Wiederseim, Grace)
Tip and Dip, (Gleaves, Suzanne)
Tip for Tap, (Kirn, Ann)
Tippletappleteven Town, (Taylor, Paul B.)
Tippy, (Scott, Sally)
Tippytoes Comes to Town, (Forster, Frederick J.)
Tired Trolley Car, (Retner, Beth)
Tirra Lirra, (Richards, Laura E.)
Tish, (Rinehart, Mary R.)
Tiss - A Little Alpine Waif, (Spyri, Johanna)
Tistou of the Green Thumbs, (Druon, Maurice)
Tisza Tales, (Schwimmer, Rosika)
Tit for Tat, (Durham, Mae)
Tit for Tat, (Rey, Hans A.)
Tita of Mexico, (Moon, Grace P.)
Tito's Hats, (Ferrer, Melchor)
Tito: Pig of Guatemala, (Jackson, Charlotte)
Titus Groan, (Peake, Mervyn)
Titus in Trouble, (Reeves, James)
Tiverton Tales, (Brown, Alice)
To Be a Logger, (Lenski, Lois)
To Be a Slave, (Lester, Julius B.)
To Beat a Tiger One Needs..., (Lewis, Eliz. F.)
To Catch a Mongoose, (Ritchie, Barbara)
To Church We Go, (Trent, Robbie)
To Gypsyland, (Pennell, Eliz. R.)
To Have & to Hold, (Johnston, Mary)
To Make a Duck Happy, (Lester, Carol E.)
To Make a Wee Moon, (Naylor, Phyllis)
To Market! To Market!, (Brock, Emma)
To Market! To Market!, (Mother Goose)
To Nursery Land, (Bingham, Clifton)
To Sing a Song as Big as Ireland, (Zimelman, Nathan)
To Tell My People, (Polland, Madeleine)
To Tell the King the Sky is Falling, (Braine, Sheila E.)
To Unknown Lands, (Wellman, Manly W.)
To and Again, (Brooks, Walter)
To the Circus the Children Go, (Leet, Frank R.)
To the Front, (King, Charles)
To the One I Love Best, (Bemelmans, Ludwig)
To the Rescue, (Van Der Veer, Judy)
Toad's Castle, (Uttley, Alison)
Toast to the King, (Coatsworth, Eliz.)
Tobias & his Big Red Satchel, (Warner, Sunny B.)
Toby & Sue, (Gay, Romney)

Toby & the Odd Beasts, (Syrett, Netta)
Toby Tyler, (Otis, James)
Toby and Doll, (Watson, Nancy D.)
Toby's Goblin, (Atkins, Elizabeth H.)
Toby: A Curious Cat, (Black, Irma S.)
Toco Toucan, (Bridges, William)
Tod of the Fens, (Whitney, Elinor)
Today is Saturday, (Snyder, Zilpha K.)
Toilers of the Trails, (Marsh, George)
Told After Supper, (Jerome, Jerome K.)
Told Again, (De La Mare, Walter)
Told Beneath the Northern Lights, (Snell, Roy J.)
Told Under the Blue Umbrella, (Various)
Told Under the Christmas Tree, (Various)
Told Under the Magic Umbrella, (Various)
Told in Our Neighborhood, (Muter, Gladys N.)
Told in the Twilight, (Harrington, Isis)
Told in the Twilight, (N/A)
Told in the Twilight, (Weatherly, Fred E.)
Told on the King's Highway, (Jewett, Eleanore)
Told to the Little Tot, (Cooke, Edmund V.)
Tom Brown's School Days, (Hughes, Thomas)
Tom Cringle's Log, (Scott, Michael)
Tom Grogan, (Smith, Francis H.)
Tom Paine, Freedom's Apostle, (Gurko, Leo)
Tom Sawyer Abroad, (Twain, Mark)
Tom Stapleton the Boy Scout, (Brereton, Frederick)
Tom Sylvester, (Sullivan, Thomas R.)
Tom Thumb, (Denslow, W.W.)
Tom Thumb, (Perrault, Charles)
Tom Tiddler's Ground, (De La Mare, Walter)
Tom Tit Tales, (Gilly Bear)
Tom Tit Tot: English Folk Tale, (Jacobs, Joseph (ed))
Tom Tucker and Little Bo Peep, (Hood, Thomas)
Tom Whipple, (Edmonds, Walter D.)
Tom and Sam, (Hutchins, Pat)
Tom and Tabby, (Symonds, John)
Tom and the Two Handles, (Hoban, Russell)
Tom of the Raiders, (Bishop, Austin)
Tom the Piper's Son, (N/A)
Tom's Midnight Garden, (Pearce, Philippa)
Tom, Dick and Harriet, (Lyons, A. Neil)
Tom, Sue and the Clock, (Aiken, Conrad)
Tom, Tom the Piper's Son, (Mother Goose)
Tomahawk Family, (Carlson, Natalie S.)
Tomahawk Trail, (Lamprey, Louise)
Tomahawks and Trouble, (Steele, William O.)
Tomas & the Red-Headed Angel, (Garthwaite, Marion)
Tomato Patch, (Wondriska, William)
Tommy & Jane & the Birds, (Semple, Daisy)
Tommy & the Telephone, (MacGregor, Ellen)
Tommy & the Wishing-Stone, (Burgess, Thornton)
Tommy Grows Wise, (Gay, Romney)
Tommy Sweet Tooth, (Gates, Josephine S.)
Tommy Thatcher Goes to Sea, (Hader, B.& E.)
Tommy Tingle-Tangle, (Addington, Sarah)
Tommy Toodles, (Lee, Al)
Tommy Tregennis, (Phillips, Mary E.)
Tommy Trot's Visit to Santa Claus, (Page, Thomas N.)
Tommy on Time, (Novinger, Virginia)
Tommy's Wonderful Airplane, (Clymer, Eleanor)
Tommy, Tilly & Mrs. Tubbs, (Lofting, Hugh)
Tomorrow's Champion, (Anderson, C.W.)
Tomorrow's House, (O'Neill, George)
Tomten and the Fox, (Lindgren, Astrid)
Tonio & the Stranger, (Coatsworth, Eliz.)
Tonio, Son of Sierras, (King, Charles)
Tonk and Tonka, (Ackerman, Francis)

Tono Antonio, (Sawyer, Ruth)
Tonto and Pronto, (Keto, Emma)
Tony Drum, (Pugh, Edwin W.)
Tony and the Wonderful Door, (Fast, Howard (ed))
Tony for Keeps, (Clark, Electa)
Tony's Birds, (Selsam, Millicent)
Tony-O'-Dreams, (Nightingale, Madeleine)
Too Big, (D'Aulaire, I.& E.)
Too Many Cherries, (Carmer, Carl)
Too Many Crackers, (Buckley, Helen E.)
Too Many Dogs, (Hawkins, Quail)
Too Many Kittens, (Hoke, Helen)
Too Many Mittens, (Slobodkin, Florence)
Too Many Pets, (Aldrich, Mary M.)
Too Much Noise, (McGovern, Ann)
Too Much Nose..., (Zemach, Harve)
Tooky..., (Hader, B.& E.)
Toolittle, (Preston, Edna M.)
Toontoony Pie, (Siddiqui, Ashraf)
Tooseys, (La Rue, Mabel G.)
Tootleoo Two, (Darwin, Bernard)
Top of the Morning, (Carr, Mary J.)
Topaz Story Book, (Skinner, Ada M.)
Topgallant: A Herring Gull, (Medary, Marjorie)
Tops and Bottoms, (Conger, Lesley)
Tops and Whistles, (Bailey, Carolyn S.)
Topsail Island Treasure, (Meader, Stephen W.)
Topsy, (Flack, Marjorie)
Topsy Turvey, (Minnion, W.J.)
Topsy Turvies, (Anno, Mitsumasa)
Topsy Turvy Circus, (Duplaix, Georges)
Topsy Turvy's Pigtails, (Anderson, Bernice)
Topsy-Turvey Tales, (Munro, E.S.)
Topsy-Turvy Family, (Brock, Emma)
Topsys & Turvys, (Newell, Peter)
Torch: Book of Poems for Boys, (Willcox, Louise C.)
Torten's Christmas Secret, (Dolbier, Maurice)
Tortilla Girl, (McElravy, May F.)
Tortoise & Turtle Abroad, (Gendel, Evelyn)
Tortoise & the Hare, (Disney, Walt)
Tortoise & the Turtle, (Gendel, Evelyn)
Tortoise and the Geese, (Dutton, Maude B. (tr))
Tosie of the Far North, (Tolboom, Wanda)
Tot & Tim, (N/A)
Tot Botot and his Little Flute, (Cathon, Laura)
Toto's Triumph, (Bishop, Claire H.)
Toucans Two, (Prelutsky, Jack)
Touch of Greatness, (Anderson, C.W.)
Touchdown Trouble, (Miers, Earl S.)
Tough Enough... [All titles], (Carroll, Ruth)
Tough Winter, (Lawson, Robert)
Toughy & his Trailer Truck, (Hurd, Edith T.)
Tournament of the Lions, (Williams, Jay)
Toutou in Bondage, (Coatsworth, Eliz.)
Toward Daybreak, (Hutchison, Collister)
Tower by the Sea, (DeJong, Meindert)
Tower of Babel, (Wiesner, William)
Town Cats, (Gay, Zhenya)
Town of the Fearless, (Snedeker, Caroline D.)
Toy Bearkins Christmas, (Robinson, Geraldine)
Toy Maker, (Enckling, Louise)
Toy Shop, (Lindsay, Maud)
Toy Trumpet, (Grifalconi, Ann)
Toy Workshop in Land of Silvery Blue, (Ramsay, Tamara)
Toyon: Dog of the North, (Kalashnikoff, N.)
Toys and Toy Makers, (Tippett, James S.)
Toys at Play, (Reid, Carol M.)
Toys of Nuremberg, (Sturges, Lilian B.)

Trace through the Forest, (Robinson, Barbara)
Track's End, (Carruth, Hayden)
Trade Wind, (Meigs, Cornelia L.)
Trader's Children, (Armer, Laura A.)
Tragedy of Ida Noble, (Russell, William C.)
Tragedy of Pelee, (Kennan, George)
Tragic Idyl, (Bourget, Paul)
Tragic Mary, (Field, Michael)
Trail & Camp Fire, (Grinnell, George B.)
Trail Blazer of the Seas, (Latham, Jean L.)
Trail Book, (Austin, Mary)
Trail Drive, (Adams, Andy)
Trail Dust of a Maverick, (Brininstool, E.A.)
Trail of Apple Blossoms, (Hunt, Irene)
Trail of Courage, (Watson, Virginia)
Trail of Ninety-Eight, (Service, Robert W.)
Trail of the Lonesome Pine, (Fox, John Jr.)
Trail of the Sandhill Stag, (Seton, Ernest T.)
Trail through Danger, (Steele, William O.)
Trail to Boyland, (Nesbit, Wilbur D.)
Trail-Driving Rooster, (Gipson, Fred B.)
Trailer Dog Trix & Nancy, (Bourgeois, Florence)
Trailer Tracks, (Bunn, Harriet)
Trails Plowed Under, (Russell, Charles M.)
Train for Tiger Lily, (Riley, Louise)
Train that Never Came Back, (Hubbard, Freeman)
Train to Spain, (Ray, Wade)
Train to Timbuctoo, (Brown, Margaret W.)
Train, a Boat & an Island, (Kuh, Charlotte)
Trainful of Strangers, (Hull, Eleanor)
Tramp: The Sheep Dog, (Lang, Don)
Tranquilina's Paradise, (Smith, Susan C.)
Transfiguration of Miss Philura, (Kingsley, Florence M.)
Transformations of the Truefitts, (Hamer, Sam H.)
Transparent Tree, (Van Doren, Mark)
Trapped by the Mountain Storm, (Fisher, Aileen)
Trappers and Traders of the Far West, (Daugherty, James)
Trash Pile Treasure, (Govan, Christine)
Traveler from a Small Kingdom, (Neville, Emily C.)
Travelers All, (Webber, Irma E.)
Travelers Three, (Symonds, John)
Traveling Bird, (Burch, Robert)
Traveling Musicians, (Grimm Bros.)
Traveling Shops, (Rowe, Dorothy)
Traveller in Time, (Uttley, Alison)
Travelling Bears... [All titles], (Eaton, Seymour)
Travelling Companions..., (Sackville, Margaret)
Travelling Toys, (DuBois, Theodora)
Travels in Hope, (Milne, James)
Travels in a Treetop, (Abbott, Charles C.)
Travels of Ching, (Bright, Robert)
Travels of Horatio, (Foreman, Michael)
Travels of a Snail, (Hoffmann, Eleanor)
Travels with a Donkey in Cevennes, (Stevenson, Rbt. L.)
Treasure Book of Best Stories, (Clinton, Althea L.)
Treasure Book of Children's Verse, (Quiller-Couch, A.)
Treasure Cave, (Asquith, C. (ed))
Treasure Cave, (Tousey, Sanford)
Treasure Divers, (Holder, Charles F.)
Treasure Hunter, (Proudfit, Isabel)
Treasure Island, (Stevenson, Rbt. L.)
Treasure Mountain, (Kelly, Eric P.)
Treasure Mountain, (Lampman, Evelyn)
Treasure Ship, (Asquith, C. (ed))
Treasure Trove of the Sun, (Prishvin, Mikhail)
Treasure Valley, (Lamprey, Louise)
Treasure of Carcassone, (Robida, Albert)
Treasure of Green Knowe, (Boston, Lucy M.)

Treasure of Isle of Mist, (Tarn, William W.)
Treasure of the Incas, (Henty, G.A.)
Treasure of the Turkish Pasha, (Biber, Yehoash)
Treasure on the Hill, (Killilea, Marie)
Treasures Long Hidden, (Chrisman, Arthur B.)
Treasures to See, (Weisgard, Leonard)
Treasury of Cat Stories, (Zistel, Era (comp))
Treasury of English Verse, (Gowans, Adam I.)
Treasury of French Tales, (Pourrat, Henri)
Treasury of Plays for Children, (Moses, Montrose (ed))
Treasury of Stories Jingles & Rhymes, (Thomas, E.M.)
Treasury of Verse for School and Home, (Edgar, M.G.)
Treasury of Verse..., (Edgar, M.G.)
Treatment of Drapery in Art, (Rhead, George W.)
Tree Angel, (Martin, Judith)
Tree For Me, (Simon, Norma)
Tree Frog, (Sears, Paul M.)
Tree Grew & Birds Flew, (Spina, Paul)
Tree House Island, (Corbett, Scott)
Tree House of Jimmy Domino, (Merrill, Jean)
Tree Toad, (Davis, Robert)
Tree Wagon, (Lampman, Evelyn)
Tree and Me, (Sage, Michael)
Tree for Peter, (Seredy, Kate)
Tree for Teddy, (Holland, Marion)
Tree in the Trail, (Holling, Holling C.)
Tree is Nice, (Udry, Janice M.)
Tree of Freedom, (Caudill, Rebecca)
Tree of Life, (Smith, Ruth (ed))
Tree that Ran Away, (Beston, Henry)
Tree this Tall, (Rice, Inez)
Treeless Plains, (Rounds, Glen)
Trees, (Kilmer, Joyce)
Trees Kneel at Christmas, (Lovelace, Maud H.)
Tremendous Twins, (Ames, Mrs. E.)
Trending into Maine, (Roberts, Kenneth L.)
Tribune Primer, (Field, Eugene)
Trick or Treat, (Slobodkin, Louis)
Tricks of Master Dabble, (Zemach, Harve)
Tricky Peik & other Picture Tales, (Hardendorff, J.)
Trigger John's Son, (Robinson, Tom P.)
Trilby, (DuMaurier, George)
Trillium Hill, (Marsh, Edith)
Trimmed Lamp, (Henry, O.)
Trina's Boxcar, (Martin, Patricia)
Trip Around the World, (Moerleim, G.)
Trip to Fairyland, (Phillips, J.)
Trip to Mars, (Ash, Fenton)
Trip to Toyland, (Mayer, Henry)
Triplets, (Crane, Walter)
Triumph for Flavius, (Snedeker, Caroline D.)
Trix and Vix, (Buff, M.& C.)
Trixie and the Tiger, (Cabassa, Victoria)
Trojan Horse, (Reeves, James)
Trojan War, (Coolidge, Olivia)
Troll Music, (Lobel, Anita)
Troll Weather, (Coatsworth, Eliz.)
Trolling with Susie Bennett, (Quigg, Jane)
Troopers Three, (Montgomery, R.)
Trot's Journey, (Greenaway, Kate)
Troubadour Tales, (Stein, Evaleen)
Trouble River, (Byars, Betsy C.)
Trouble Woman, (Morris, Clara)
Trouble at Beaver Dam, (Tchaika, Florence)
Trouble for Jerry, (Gates, Doris)
Trouble in the Gulch, (Tousey, Sanford)
Trouble with Jenny's Ear, (Butterworth, Oliver)
Trouble with Spider, (Kraus, Robert)

Troubles of Tatters, (Morris, Alice T.)
Troubles of a Gnome, (Kossak-Szczucka, Z.)
Troublesome Dog, (Jacberns, Raymond)
Troublesome Tuba, (Rinkoff, Barbara)
Troublesome Ursula, (Quiller-Couch, Mabel)
Trovato, (Bettina)
Truant Tricycle, (Marion, Francis)
Trubloff, (Burningham, John)
Truce of God, (Rinehart, Mary R.)
Truce of the Wolf, (Davis, Mary G.)
Trudi and Hansel, (Demuth, Averil)
Trudy and the Tree House, (Coatsworth, Eliz.)
Trudy's First Day at Camp, (Hendrich, Paula)
True Bills, (Ade, George)
True Dog Stories, (Terhune, Albert P.)
True Monkey Stories, (Fox, Frances M.)
True Philosopher, (Bacon, Peggy)
True Stories of Big Game & Jungles, (Gask, Lilian)
True Story Book, (Lang, Andrew)
True Story of Humpty Dumpty, (Chapin, Anna A.)
True Story of Smokey the Bear, (Watson, Jane W.)
True Travellers, (Davies, William H.)
Truly Elizabeth, (Weiss, Edna S.)
Trum Peter's Tea-Party, (Nesbitt, Philip)
Trumpet, (Austin, Margot)
Trumpet in the Dust, (Holme, Constance)
Trumpet of the Swan, (White, Elwyn B.)
Trumpeter of Krakow, (Kelly, Eric P.)
Trumpeter's Tale...., (Eaton, Jeanette)
Trumpets from Montparnasse, (Gibbings, Robert)
Trumpets in the West, (Trease, Geoffrey)
Trust a City Kid, (Huston, Anne)
Trusty John..., (Lang, Andrew)
Truth Dexter, (McCall, Sidney)
Truthful Harp, (Alexander, Lloyd C.)
Try It Again, Sam, (Viorst, Judith)
Tryphena In Love..., (Raymond, Walter)
Tsar's Riddles, (Daniels, Guy)
Tub-Time Tales, (Barnes, Madeline)
Tuck-Me-In Stories, (Comstock, Enos B.)
Tucker's Countryside, (Selden, George)
Tuesday Elephant, (Garfield, Nancy)
Tuffy Good Luck, (Willson, Dixie)
Tuffy and the Merboo, (Gotch, Phyllis M.)
Tuftoo the Clown, (Garis, Howard)
Tumble Bear, (Austin, Margot)
Tumble Down Pictures, (Carlton, Maud)
Tumble, Story of a Mustang, (Dennis, Wesley)
Tumble-Bug, (Andersen, Hans C.)
Tune is in the Tree, (Lovelace, Maud H.)
Tunes for Tiny Troubadours, (Willoughby, Rachel)
Tupak of the Incas, (Means, Philip A.)
Turf-Cutter's Donkey, (Lynch, Patricia)
Turi's Poppa, (DeTrevino, Elizabeth)
Turkey Tale, (Bacon, Frances A.)
Turkey Trott & the Black Santa, (Dyer, Kate G.)
Turkey for Christmas, (DeAngeli, Marguerite)
Turkish Fairy Tales..., (Kunos, Ignacz)
Turkistan Reunion, (Lattimore, Eleanor)
Turn Again Tales, (Housman, Laurence)
Turn of the Tide, (Porter, Eleanor)
Turn to the East, (Singer, Caroline)
Turn-Around Book, (Beardsley, Alice)
Turnabout, (Leaf, Munro)
Turnabout Trick, (Corbett, Scott)
Turnaside Cottage, (Clark, Mary S.)
Turned-Intos, (Gordon, Elizabeth)
Turquoise Cup, (Smith, Arthur C.)

Turquoise Story Book, (Skinner, Ada M.)
Turtle Whose Snap Unfastened, (Campbell, Ruth)
Turtle and the Dove, (Freeman, Don)
Tweedles, Be Brave!, (Wolo)
Tweeter of Prairie Dog Town, (Gag, Flavia)
Twelve Dancing Princesses, (Grimm Bros.)
Twelve Dancing Princesses, (N/A)
Twelve Dancing Princesses, (Quiller-Couch, A.)
Twelve Dancing Princesses, (Quiller-Couch, A.)
Twelve Days of Christmas, (Karasz, Ilonka)
Twelve Labors of Wimpole Stout, (Webb, Wheaton P.)
Twelve Months, (Powys, Llewelyn)
Twelve Months Make a Year, (Coatsworth, Eliz.)
Twelve Sisters, (Ewald, Carl)
Twelve and the Genii, (Clarke, Pauline)
Twenty & Ten, (Bishop, Claire H.)
Twenty Centuries of Paris, (Smith, Mabell S.)
Twenty Jataka Tales, (Inayat, Noor)
Twenty Little Maidens, (Blanchard, Amy E.)
Twenty Miracles of St. Nicolas, (Bryson, Bernarda)
Twenty-Dollar Horse, (Raftery, Gerald)
Twenty-Four Days before Christmas, (L'Engle, Madeleine)
Twenty-Four Unusual Stories, (Tyler, Anna C.)
Twenty-One Balloons, (DuBois, W.P.)
Twenty-Third Psalm, (Bible)
Twenty-Two Bears, (Bishop, Claire H.)
Twenty-Two Goblins, (Ryder, Arthur)
Twig, (Jones, Eliz. O.)
Twilight Fairy Tales, (Booth, Maud B.)
Twilight Land, (Pyle, Howard)
Twilight Stories, (Peto, Gladys)
Twilight Tales, (Beard, Patten)
Twilight of Magic, (Lofting, Hugh)
Twin Colts, (Hogan, Inez)
Twin Kids, (Hogan, Inez)
Twin Kittens, (Hogan, Inez)
Twin Lambs, (Orton, Helen F.)
Twin Otters and the Indians, (Hogan, Inez)
Twin Puppies, (Hogan, Inez)
Twin Seals, (Hogan, Inez)
Twin Spell, (Lunn, Janet)
Twinkle and Chubbins, (Bancroft, Laura)
Twinkle's Enchantment, (Bancroft, Laura)
Twins & Tabiffa, (Heward, Constance)
Twins Who Flew Around the World, (Holling, Holling C.)
Twirly Skirt, (Goldberg, Martha)
Twirly-Whirly Book, (Clayton, Jacqueline)
Twistum Tales, (Ames, Esther M.)
Twixt You & Me, (LeBaron, Grace)
Two Boys and a Dog, (Chipman, Charles P.)
Two Bridgets, (Hathaway, Cynthia)
Two Brothers & their Animal Friends, (Lenski, Lois)
Two Brothers & their Baby Sister, (Lenski, Lois)
Two Captains, (Russell, William C.)
Two Cars, (D'Aulaire, I.& E.)
Two Cats at Large, (Woodhouse, S.C.)
Two Children of Brazil, (Brown, Rose)
Two Children of Tyre, (Kent, Louise A.)
Two Crabs and the Moonlight, (Yamaguchi, Tohr)
Two Dog Biscuits, (Cleary, Beverly)
Two Funny Clowns, (Hader, B.& E.)
Two Giants, (Foreman, Michael)
Two Girls of Old New Jersey, (Sage, Agnes C.)
Two Grey Girls & their Opposite Neighbors, (Haile, Ellen)
Two Hundred Pennies, (Woolley, Catherine)
Two Hundred Rabbits, (Anderson, Lonzo)
Two Jolly Mariners, (N/A)
Two Little Birds & Three, (Kepes, Juliet A.)

Two Little Confederates, (Page, Thomas N.)
Two Little Knights of Kentucky, (Johnston, Annie F.)
Two Little Mice, (Pyle, Katharine)
Two Little Miners, (Brown, Margaret W.)
Two Little Pilgrims' Progress, (Burnett, Frances H.)
Two Little Runaways, (Buckland, James)
Two Little Savages, (Seton, Ernest T.)
Two Little Trains, (Brown, Margaret W.)
Two Little Waifs, (Molesworth, Mrs.)
Two Logs Crossing, (Edmonds, Walter D.)
Two Lonely Ducks, (Duvoisin, Roger)
Two Oceans to Canton, (Hewes, Agnes D.)
Two Old Bachelors, (Lear, Edward)
Two Piano Tuners, (Goffstein, M.B.)
Two Prisoners, (Page, Thomas N.)
Two Reds, (Lipkind, Will)
Two Runaways, (Edwards, Harry S.)
Two Stonecutters, (Titus, Eve)
Two Uncles of Pablo, (Behn, Harry)
Two Vanrevels, (Tarkington, Booth)
Two Well-Worn Shoe Stories, (N/A)
Two Wise Children, (Graves, Robert)
Two Worlds of Damyan, (Bloch, Marie H.)
Two Wyoming Girls, (Marshall, Caroline)
Two Years Before the Mast, (Dana, Richard H.)
Two Young Corsicans, (Stewart, Anna B.)
Two and Me Makes Three, (Greene, Roberta)
Two and Two are Four, (Haywood, Carolyn)
Two are Better than One, (Brink, Carol R.)
Two from a Teapot, (Helps, Racey)
Two is a Team, (Beim, Lorraine)
Two on an Island, (Bradbury, Bianca)
Two-Bow Bill, (Brown, Gladys)
Tyke, the Little Mutt, (L'Hommedieu, Dorothy)
Tyke-Y: His Book & his Mark, (Whitney, Elinor)
Tyltyl, (Maeterlinck, Maurice)
Typee, (Melville, Herman)
Typewriter Town, (Smith, William J.)
Tyranny of the Dark, (Garland, Hamlin)
US: An Old Fashioned Story, (Molesworth, Mrs.)
Ugly Bird, (Hoban, Russell)
Ugly Dachshund, (Stern, Gladys B.)
Ugly Duckling, (Andersen, Hans C.)
Ultimo, (Vassos, Ruth)
Umbrella, (Yashima, Taro)
Umbrella Bird & other Verses, (Johnson, Emilie F.)
Umbrella that Got Wet, (Todd, Ann)
Umbrellas, Hats & Wheels, (Rand, Ann)
Una & Red Cross Knight, (Spenser, Edmund)
Uncanny Stories, (Sinclair, May)
Uncharted Ways, (Snedeker, Caroline D.)
Uncle Ali's Secret, (Blatter, Dorothy)
Uncle Amos Puppet Show, (Brown, Neva K.)
Uncle Andy's Island, (Molloy, Anne)
Uncle Ben's Whale, (Edmonds, Walter D.)
Uncle Bennie Goes Visiting, (Brock, Emma)
Uncle Bill, (James, Will)
Uncle Bouqui of Haiti, (Courlander, Harold)
Uncle Fonzo's Ford, (Miles, Miska)
Uncle Frank's Visit to Fairy-Land, (Uncle Frank)
Uncle Noah's Christmas Inspiration, (Dalrymple, Leona)
Uncle Peter-Heathen, (Stapp, Emilie B.)
Uncle Remus... [All titles], (Harris, Joel C.)
Uncle Sam's Story Book, (Harper, Wilhelmina)
Uncle Shelby('s)... [All titles], (Silverstein, Shel)
Uncle Swithin's Inventions, (Webb, Wheaton P.)
Uncle Timothy's Traviata, (Krahn, Fernando)
Uncle Tom's Cabin, (Stowe, Harriet B.)

Uncle Walt, (Mason, Walt)
Uncle Wiggily('s)... [All titles], (Garis, Howard)
Uncrowned King, (Wright, Harold Bell)
Under Blue Skies, (Brigham, S.J.)
Under Glass, (Clemens, Nancy)
Under The Hill, (Beardsley, Aubrey)
Under The Trees, (Mabie, Hamilton W.)
Under Wellington's Command, (Henty, G.A.)
Under a Mushroom, (Lobel, Anita)
Under the Black Raven, (Creswick, Paul)
Under the Crust, (Page, Thomas N.)
Under the Flag of the Cross, (Sedbery, J. Hamilton)
Under the Great Bear, (Munroe, Kirk)
Under the Greenwood Tree, (Hardy, Thomas)
Under the Greenwood Tree, (Shakespeare, Wm.)
Under the Lilacs, (Alcott, Louisa M.)
Under the Little Fir, (Yates, Elizabeth)
Under the Mistletoe, (Mack, Robert E.)
Under the Pig-Nut Tree, (Hader, B.& E.)
Under the Roof of the Jungle, (Bull, Charles L.)
Under the Rose, (Isham, Frederic S.)
Under the Rowan Tree, (Brown, Abbie F.)
Under the Southern Cross, (Robins, Elizabeth)
Under the Story Tree, (La Rue, Mabel G.)
Under the Tent of the Sky, (Brewton, John (ed))
Under the Tree, (Roberts, Elizabeth M.)
Under the Trees and Through the Grass, (Tresselt, Alvin)
Under the Window, (Greenaway, Kate)
Underground Alley, (Mayne, William)
Underground Hideaway, (Goodwin, Murray)
Underground Sketchbook, (Ungerer, Tomi)
Understood Betsy, (Canfield, Dorothy)
Undertaker's Garland, (Wilson, Edmund)
Underwater Warriors, (Berry, Erick)
Underwater Zoos, (Selsam, Millicent)
Undine, (Fouque, La Motte)
Unhappy Hippopotamus, (Moore, Nancy)
Unicorn Who Wanted to be Seen, (Hahn, Lotte K.)
Unicorn with Silver Shoes, (Young, Ella)
Unidentified Flying Elephant, (Kraus, Robert)
Uninvited Donkey, (White, Anne H.)
Unknown Quantity, (Van Dyke, Henry)
Unknown to History, (Yonge, Charlotte)
Unleavened Bread, (Grant, Robert)
Unselfish Pig, (Herr, Charlotte)
Unstill Life, (Benedetti, Mario)
Unstrung Harp, (Gorey, Edward)
Unsuccessful Elf, (Wing, Paul)
Untold Adventures of Santa Claus, (Nash, Ogden)
Untold Tales of the Past, (Harraden, Beatrice)
Untune the Sky, (Plotz, Helen)
Up & Down and All Around, (Walters, Marguerite)
Up Above & Down Below, (Webber, Irma E.)
Up Grade, (Goodwin, Wilder)
Up High and Down Low, (Slobodkin, Louis)
Up Hill and Down, (Coatsworth, Eliz.)
Up a Crooked River, (McNeer, May)
Up a Road Slowly, (Hunt, Irene)
Up and Away, (Young, Miriam)
Up and Down the River, (Caudill, Rebecca)
Up in The Air, (Flack, Marjorie)
Up the Hill, (DeAngeli, Marguerite)
Up the River to Danger, (Palmer, Elizabeth)
Up the Trail and Down the Street, (Jupo, Frank)
Up, Up the Mountain, (Fisher, Aileen)
Uphill Climb, (Bower, B.M.)
Upside Down Book, (Hogan, Inez)
Upside Down Day, (Scheer, Julian)

Upstairs & Downstairs, (Johnson, Ryerson)
Upstairs Donkey, (Morris, James)
Uptown, (Steptoe, John)
Upward Path, (Pritchard, Myron T.)
Ursula's Freshman, (Ray, Anna C.)
Us, (Aldin, Cecil)
Us Fellers, (Forrester, Izola)
Us Kids at the Circus, (Kay, Gertrude A.)
Us and the Duchess, (Fenton, Edward)
Useful Dragon of Sam Ling Toy, (Dines, Glen)
Utter Zoo, (Gorey, Edward)
Vain Pussy Cat, (Moe, Louis M.)
Vaino: Boy of New Finland, (Adams, Julia D.)
Vale of Cedars, (Aguilar, Grace)
Valentine Box, (Lovelace, Maud H.)
Valentine Cat, (Bulla, Clyde R.)
Valentine and Orson, (Littlewood, Samuel R.)
Valentine for Candy, (Cumming, Marian)
Valiant Chattee-Maker, (Price, Christine)
Valiant Runaways, (Atherton, Gertrude)
Valiant, Dog of the Timberline, (O'Brien, Jack)
Valiants of Virginia, (Rives, Hallie E.)
Valley Grows Up, (Osmond, Edward)
Valley of Color Days, (Sandwell, Helen B.)
Valley of Song, (Goudge, Elizabeth)
Valley of the Giants, (Kyne, Peter B.)
Valley of the Moon, (London, Jack)
Van Bibber & Others, (Davis, Richard H.)
Van Rensselaers of Old Manhattan, (Mills, Weymer J.)
Vandemark's Folly, (Quick, Herbert)
Vanilla Village, (Carden, Priscilla)
Vanished Island, (Meigs, Cornelia L.)
Vanishing Princess, (Syrett, Netta)
Vanity Fair, (Thackeray, Wm. M.)
Vanka's Donkey, (Daugherty, Sonia)
Vanya of the Streets, (Kennell, Ruth E.)
Varsity Double Play, (Hirshberg, Al)
Vasilisa the Beautiful, (Whitney, Thomas)
Vavache: Cow who Painted Pictures, (Attwood, Frederic)
Vege-Men's Revenge, (Upton, Bertha)
Vegetable Verselets, (Hays, M.G.)
Velvet Room, (Snyder, Zilpha K.)
Velveteen Rabbit, (Williams, Margery)
Vendor of Dreams, (Coffin, Julia H.)
Venus & Adonis, (Shakespeare, Wm.)
Verity Mullens and the Indian, (Belting, Natalia)
Veronica, (Duvoisin, Roger)
Veronica Ganz, (Sachs, Marilyn)
Veronica's Smile, (Duvoisin, Roger)
Verotchka's Tales, (Mamin-Siberiak, D.N.)
Verses for Jock & Joan, (Hay, Helen)
Verses from Alice, (Carroll, Lewis)
Vertigo, (Ward, Lynd)
Very Far Away, (Sendak, Maurice)
Very Fine Clock, (Spark, Muriel)
Very First Day, (Weil, Ann Y.)
Very Little Boy, (Krasilovsky, Phyllis)
Very Little Child's Book of Stories, (Skinner, Ada M.)
Very Little Dog, (Skaar, Grace M.)
Very Little Girl, (Krasilovsky, Phyllis)
Very Little Person, (Vorse, Mary Heaton)
Very Obliging Flowers, (Roy, Claude)
Very Small Person, (Donnell, Annie H.)
Very Special Badgers, (Stamm, Claus)
Very Special House, (Krauss, Ruth)
Very Special Pet, (Davis, Lavinia R.)
Very Stupid Folk, (Rosvall, Toivo D.)
Very Young Verses, (Milne, A.A.)

Vi-Daylin Book of Minnie the Mump, (Tripp, Paul)
Vicar of Wakefield, (Goldsmith, Oliver)
Victoria and the Golden Bird, (Baynes, Pauline)
Victoria's Castle, (Holman, Felice)
Viking's Dawn, (Treece, Henry)
Viking's Sunset, (Treece, Henry)
Village School, (Read, Miss)
Village Tree, (Yashima, Taro)
Village in Normandy, (Cruse, Laurence)
Vinzi, (Spyri, Johanna)
Violet Among the Lilies, (Clarkson, L.)
Violet Fairy Book, (Lang, Andrew)
Violets are Blue, (Kennedy, Mary)
Viollet, (Cunningham, Julia)
Virgin with Butterflies, (Powers, Tom)
Virginia Lee, (Judson, Clara I.)
Virginia of Elk Creek Valley, (Chase, Mary)
Virginia of the Air Lanes, (Quick, Herbert)
Vision of Francois the Fox, (Cunningham, Julia)
Visions in Fairyland, (Sewell, Daisy)
Visions of Spring..., (Maeterlinck, Maurice)
Visit from Santa Claus, (Moore, Clement C.)
Visit from St. Nicholas, (Moore, Clement C.)
Visit to London, (Lucas, E.V.)
Visit to Santa Claus, (Price, Margaret E.)
Visiting Jimpsons, (Eberle, Irmengarde)
Visitors from London, (Barne, Kitty)
Vison: The Mink, (George, Jean C.)
Vivian's Lesson, (Grierson, Eliz. W.)
Voice in the Rice, (Morris, Gouverneur)
Voices in the Night, (Bacmeister, Rhoda)
Voodoo Tales, (Owen, Mary A.)
Voyage of Ithobal, (Arnold, Edwin)
Voyage of the Dawn Treader, (Lewis, C.S.)
Voyage of the Flying Bird, (Titcomb, Margaret)
Voyage of the Hoppergrass, (Pearson, Edmund L.)
Voyage of the Javelin, (Meader, Stephen W.)
Voyage of the Rattletrap, (Carruth, Hayden)
Voyage of the Wishbone Boat, (Riley, Alice C.)
Voyages of Christopher Columbus, (Sperry, Armstrong)
Voyages of Doctor Dolittle, (Lofting, Hugh)
Voyages of Jacques Cartier, (Averill, Esther)
Voyaging: Southward..., (Kent, Rockwell)
Vulpes: The Red Fox, (George, Jean C.)
Wabeno the Magician, (Wright, Mabel O.)
Wag by Wall, (Potter, Beatrix)
Wagging Tails, (Henry, Marguerite)
Wagner's Heroes, (Maud, Constance E.)
Wagner's Parsifal, (Huckel, Oliver)
Wagner's Tristan & Isolde, (LeGallienne, R.)
Wagon Train West, (Nelson, Rhoda)
Wagons Westward, (Sperry, Armstrong)
Wagtail, (Gall, Alice C.)
Wahoo Bobcat, (Lippincott, J.W.)
Waif Maid, (McNeer, May)
Wait Till the Moon is Full, (Brown, Margaret W.)
Wait for William, (Flack, Marjorie)
Wait for the Rain, (Goldberg, Martha)
Wait till Sunday, (Dorritt, Susan)
Wakaima & the Clay Man, (Davis, Mary G.)
Wake Up! Wake Up!, (Steiner, Charlotte)
Wake Up, City!, (Tresselt, Alvin)
Wake Up, Farm!, (Tresselt, Alvin)
Wakey Goes to Bed, (Vorse, Mary E.)
Walcott Twins, (Lovell, Lucille)
Waldo the Wood Chuck, (Palazzo, Tony)
Walk the Mouse Girls Took, (Kuskin, Karla)
Walker in the City, (Kazin, Alfred)

Walking Hat, (Hall, William N.)
Walking Stones, (Hunter, Mollie)
Walking on Gold, (Crawford, Phyllis)
Wallie the Walrus, (Wiese, Kurt)
Wally Wanderoon..., (Harris, Joel C.)
Wally the Wordworm, (Fadiman, Clifton)
Wallypug... [All titles], (Farrow, George E.)
Walt Disney's Alice in Wonderland, (Carroll, Lewis)
Walt Whitman's America, (Daugherty, James)
Walter the Lazy Mouse, (Flack, Marjorie)
Wanda and Greta at Broby Farm, (Palm, Amy)
Wanderer of the Wasteland, (Grey, Zane)
Wanderer's Necklace, (Haggard, H. Rider)
Wandering Moon, (Reeves, James)
Wanted - A King, (Browne, Maggie)
Wanted a Chaperone, (Ford, Paul L.)
Wanted a Matchmaker, (Ford, Paul L.)
Wapiti the Elk, (Montgomery, R.)
War, (Long, John L.)
War Cry of the West, (Burt, Nathaniel)
War Paint: An Indian Pony, (Brown, Paul)
War Wings, (Montgomery, R.)
War in the Air, (Wells, H.G.)
War is Kind, (Crane, Stephen)
War of the Ghosts, (Burtis, Thomson)
War of the Wooden Soldiers, (F.M.H.)
War of the Worlds, (Wells, H.G.)
War-Whirl in Washington, (O'Malley, Frank W.)
Warm-Hearted Polar Bear, (Murphy, Robert)
Warrior & the Princess, (Obligado, George)
Wart Snake in a Fig Tree, (Mendoza, George)
Warwick's 3 Bottles, (Hodeir, Andre)
Was It a Good Trade?, (DeRegniers, Beatrice)
Washington, (Madison, Lucy F.)
Washington Picture Book, (Lenski, Lois)
Washington: Man of Action, (Hill, Frederick T.)
Washington: Nation's First Hero, (Eaton, Jeanette)
Watch Cat, (Northrup, Mili)
Watch Honeybees with Me, (Hawes, Judy)
Watch Me, said the Jeep, (Ferris, Helen)
Watch the Birdie!, (Rowand, Phyllis)
Watch the Kitten Grow, (Hall, William N.)
Watch the Pony Grow, (Hall, William N.)
Watchdog, (Bannon, Laura)
Watched by Wild Animals, (Mills, Enos A.)
Watchers of the Trails, (Roberts, Chas. G.D.)
Watchwords of Liberty, (Lawson, Robert)
Water Babies, (Kingsley, Charles)
Water Babies' Circus, (Disney, Walt)
Water People, (Bronson, Wilfrid S.)
Water that Jack Drank, (Scott, William R.)
Water-Buffalo Children, (Buck, Pearl S.)
Water-Carrier's Secrets, (Chambers, Maria C.)
Watercolors of William Russell Flint, (Flint, William R.)
Waterless Mountain, (Armer, Laura A.)
Waters of Caney Fork, (Read, Opie)
Watson, Smartest Dog in the USA, (Kuskin, Karla)
Way Down Cellar, (Stong, Philip D.)
Way Down in Tennessee, (Garner, Elvira)
Way of an Ant, (Mizumura, Kazue)
Way of an Eagle, (Daugherty, Sonia)
Way of an Indian, (Remington, Frederic)
Way of the Shepherd, (Unwin, Nora S.)
Way the Tiger Walked, (Chaconas, Doris)
Way to Glory, (McNeely, Marion H.)
Way to Peace, (Deland, Margaret)
Way to Wonderland, (Stewart, Mary)
Way to the House of Santa Claus, (Burnett, Frances H.)

Way to the West, (Hough, Emerson)
Wayfarer's Love, (Various)
Wayland's Keep, (Bull, Angela)
We & the World, (Ewing, Juliana H.)
We Alcotts, (Fisher, Aileen)
We Are thy Children, (Bulla, Clyde R.)
We Couldn't Leave Dinah, (Treadgold, Mary)
We Dickinsons, (Fisher, Aileen)
We Have Tomorrow, (Bontemps, Arna)
We Help Mommy, (Cushman, Jean)
We Live in the City, (Lenski, Lois)
We Read: A and Z, (Crews, Donald)
We Three Kings, (Waldstein, Henry F.)
We Went Looking, (Fisher, Aileen)
We Were There at Battle of Gettysburg, (Malkus, Alida S.)
We Were There on the Oregon Trail, (Steele, William O.)
We are a Family, (Hogan, Inez)
Weather Signs & Rhymes, (Barney, Maginel W.)
Weatherby's Inning, (Barbour, Ralph H.)
Weaver of Dreams, (Reed, Myrtle)
Wedding Bells, (N/A)
Wedding Journey, (Edmonds, Walter D.)
Wedding Procession/Rag Doll/Broomhandle, (Sandburg, C.)
Wee Ann, (Phillips, Ethel C.)
Wee Babies, (Blanchard, Amy E.)
Wee Brigit O'Toole, (Holberg, Ruth)
Wee Gillis, (Leaf, Munro)
Wee Joseph, (MacKellar, William)
Wee Men, (Girvin/Cosens)
Wee Men of Ballywooden, (Mason, Arthur)
Wee Miss Violet..., (Newman, Isidora)
Wee Moose, (Bell-Zano, Gina)
Wee Wee Woman, (N/A)
Wee Willie Winkie, (Kipling, Rudyard)
Wee Willow Whistle, (Avery, Kay)
Wee Winkles... [All titles], (Jackson, Gabrielle)
Week Along Concord & Merrimack Rivers, (Thoreau, H.D.)
Week Spent in a Glass Pond, (Ewing, Juliana H.)
Weighing and Balancing, (Srivastava, Jane)
Weir of Hermiston, (Stevenson, Rbt. L.)
Weird Islands, (DeBosschere, Jean)
Weird Tales from Northern Seas, (Bain, Robert N.)
Welcome Christmas, (Eaton, Anne T.)
Welcome Home!, (Bemelmans, Ludwig)
Welcome Santza, (Savery, Constance)
Well O'the World's End, (MacManus, Seumas)
Well in the Wood, (Taylor, Bert L.)
Well of St. Clare, (France, Anatole)
Well-Wishers, (Eager, Edward)
Welsh Fairy Book, (Jenkyn-Thomas, W.)
Wembley in Colour, (Maxwell, Donald)
Were-Wolf, (Housman, Clemence)
West From a Car Window, (Davis, Richard H.)
West Indian Play Days, (Dalgliesh, Alice)
West Wind, (Brady, Cyrus T.)
West is West, (Rhodes, Eugene M.)
West of Boston, (Daugherty, James)
West with the White Chiefs, (Harris, Christie)
Westminster Abbey, (Troutbeck, G.E.)
Westward Ho!, (Kingsley, Charles)
Westwoods, (Farjeon, Eleanor)
Wet Magic, (Nesbit, Edith)
Wet World, (Simon, Norma)
Whale People, (Haig-Brown, R.L.)
Whale's Way, (Johnston, Johanna)
Whaler 'Round the Horn, (Meader, Stephen W.)
Whales Go By, (Phleger, Fred)
What Baby Reads, (Strang, Herbert)

What Can I Buy?, (Marks, Mickey)
What Can You Do with a Shoe?, (DeRegniers, Beatrice)
What Color is Love?, (Anglund, Joan W.)
What Did I See?, (Smith, William J.)
What Did You Dream?, (Craig, M. Jean)
What Do I Do?, (Simon, Norma)
What Do People Do All Day?, (Scarry, Richard)
What Do You Do, Dear?, (Joslin, Sesyle)
What Do You Say, Dear?, (Joslin, Sesyle)
What Do You Want to Be?, (Francoise)
What Do they Say!, (Skaar, Grace M.)
What Does it Do and How Does it Work?, (Hoban, R.)
What Every Young Rabbit Should Know, (Denison, C.)
What Gladys Saw, (Fox, Frances M.)
What Good Man Does/Always Right, (Andersen, H.C.)
What Good is a Tail?, (Russell, Solveig)
What Happened After Stories, (Beard, Patten)
What Happened at Christmas, (Sharp, Evelyn)
What Happened to Hannah, (Garth, Mary)
What Happened to Inger Johanne, (Zwilgmeyer, Dikken)
What Happened to a Hamburger?, (Showers, Paul)
What Have I Got?, (McClintock, Marshall)
What I Have Done with Birds, (Stratton-Porter, Gene)
What I Like about Toads, (Hawes, Judy)
What Katy Did, (Coolidge, Susan)
What Maisie Knew, (James, Henry)
What Makes a Bird a Bird?, (Garelick, May)
What Makes a Shadow, (Bulla, Clyde R.)
What Makes the Wheels Go 'Round, (Bock, George E.)
What Mary Jo Shared, (Udry, Janice M.)
What Miranda Knew, (Adshead, Gladys)
What O'Clock Jingles, (Johnson, Margaret)
What Sami Sings with the Birds, (Spyri, Johanna)
What Shall We Do & Allee Galloo!, (Winn, Marie)
What Shall We Play?, (Geister, Edna)
What Spot?, (Bonsall, Crosby)
What Susan Wanted, (Scott, Sally)
What Whale? Where?, (Hurd, Edith T.)
What Whiskers Did, (Carroll, Ruth)
What Will I Wear?, (Olds, Helen D.)
What a Fine Day for...., (Krauss, Ruth)
What a Silly Thing to Do, (Smaridge, Norah)
What is Red?, (Gottlieb, Suzanne)
What is Right for Tulip, (Duvoisin, Roger)
What is Symmetry?, (Sitomer, Mindel)
What is a Child?, (Richelson, Geraldine)
What is a Color?, (Provensen, A.& M.)
What is it For?, (Humphrey, Henry)
What is that Sound!, (O'Neill, Mary)
What is the World?, (Miles, Betty)
What the Blackbird Said, (Locker, Mrs. F.)
What the Moon is Like, (Branley, Franklyn)
What then, Raman?, (Arora, Shirley L.)
What'll You Do When You Grow Up?, (Hader, B.& E.)
What's His Name?, (McCutcheon, George B.)
What's Inside?, (Garelick, May)
What's Your Name?, (Gay, Zhenya)
What's for Lunch, Charlie?, (Hodges, Margaret)
What-O'Clock Tales, (Housman, Laurence)
What? Another Cat!, (Beecroft, John)
Wheel Within a Wheel, (Willard, Frances E.)
Wheel on the Chimney, (Brown, Margaret W.)
Wheel on the School, (DeJong, Meindert)
Wheels, (Jackson, Kathryn)
Wheels Over the Bridge, (DeJong, Meindert)
Wheels Toward the West, (Hawthorne, Hildegarde)
When All is Young, (Mack, Robert E.)
When Christmas Came Too Early, (Blodgett, Mabel F.)

When Christmas Comes Around, (Underwood, P.)
When Coyote Walked the Earth, (Running, Corinne)
When Cupid Calls, (Hall, Tom)
When Grandma Was a Little Girl, (Shetter, Stella C.)
When Grandmamma Was 14, (Harland, Marion)
When Guns Thundered at Tripoli, (Finger, Charles J.)
When Hearts are Trumps, (Hall, Tom)
When Homer Honked, (Latham, Jean L.)
When I Go to the Moon, (Lewis, Claudia)
When I Grow Up, (Denslow, W.W.)
When I Grow Up, (Haywood, Carolyn)
When I Have a Little Girl, (Zolotow, Charlotte)
When I Have a Son, (Zolotow, Charlotte)
When I am Big, (Smith, Robert P.)
When I was Little, (Kelly, Ethel M.)
When Insects are Babies, (Conklin, Gladys)
When Jays Fly to Barbmo, (Balderson, Margaret)
When Jenny Lost her Scarf, (Averill, Esther)
When Jesus was Born, (Bowie, Walter R.)
When Jesus was Here Among Men, (Helm, Nellie L.)
When Life is Young, (Dodge, Mary Mapes)
When Little Boys Sing, (Carpenter, John)
When Little Thoughts Go Rhyming, (Knobel, E.)
When London Burned, (Henty, G.A.)
When Malindy Sings, (Dunbar, Paul L.)
When Molly was Six, (White, Eliza O.)
When Mother was Little, (Yorke, S.P.)
When Noodlehead Went to the Fair, (Hitte, Kathryn)
When Our Ship Comes In, (Foley, Dorothy C.)
When Peter Rabbit Went a-Fishing, (Almond, Linda S.)
When Peter Rabbit Went to School, (Almond, Linda S.)
When Peter Was Lost in the Forest, (Peterson, Hans)
When Roggie and Reggie were Five, (Smith, Gertrude)
When Sarah Saved the Day, (Singmaster, Elsie)
When She Came Home from College, (Hurd, Marian K.)
When Shlemiel Went to Warsaw, (Singer, Isaac B.)
When Toys Could Talk, (Randall, Jane)
When Valmond Came to Pontiac, (Parker, Gilbert)
When Wagon Trains Rolled to Sante Fe, (Berry, Erick)
When Water Animals are Babies, (Schwartz, Elizabeth R.)
When We Were Very Young, (Milne, A.A.)
When Wilderness was King, (Parrish, Randall)
When Will my Birthday Be?, (Schatz, Letta)
When Will the World be Mine?, (Schlein, Miriam)
When Woman Proposes, (Warner, Anne)
When You Were a Boy, (Sabin, Edwin L.)
When a Boy Goes to Bed at Night, (McNulty, Faith)
When a Boy Wakes Up in the Morning, (McNulty, Faith)
When a Feller Needs a Friend, (Nesbit, Wilbur D.)
When a Maid Marries, (Hart, Lavinia)
When a Man Marries, (Rinehart, Mary R.)
When is Tomorrow?, (Watson, Nancy D.)
When it Rained Cats & Dogs, (Turner, Nancy B.)
When the Cows Got Out, (Koch, Dorothy)
When the Monkeys wore Sombreros, (Prieto, Mariana)
When the Moon is New, (Bannon, Laura)
When the Root Children Wake Up, (Fish, Helen D.)
When the Sandman Comes, (Kay, Gertrude A.)
When the Sleeper Wakes, (Wells, H.G.)
When the Snow is Blue, (Dorian, Edith)
When the Stones Were Soft, (Heady, Eleanor)
When the Typhoon Blows, (Lewis, Eliz. F.)
When the Wind Blew, (Brown, Margaret W.)
When the Wind Stops, (Zolotow, Charlotte)
Where Any Young Cat Might Be, (Denison, Carol)
Where Did Josie Go?, (Buckley, Helen E.)
Where Did Tuffy Hide?, (Eberstadt, Isabel)
Where Does Everyone Go?, (Fisher, Aileen)

Where Does the Day Go?, (Myers, Walter)
Where Flies the Flag, (Harbour, Henry)
Where Ghosts Walk, (Harland, Marion)
Where Have You Been?, (Brown, Margaret W.)
Where Laborers are Few, (Deland, Margaret)
Where Land Meets Sea, (Leighton, Clare)
Where Souls of Men are Calling, (Harris, Credo)
Where There's a Will, (Rinehart, Mary R.)
Where Was Bobby?, (Clement, Marguerite)
Where is Adelaide?, (White, Eliza O.)
Where is Everybody?, (Charlip, Remy)
Where is Tommy?, (Sarg, Tony)
Where is Yonkela?, (Hirsh, Marilyn J.)
Where the Bee Sucks, (Williams, Iolo A.)
Where the Blue Begins, (Morley, Christopher)
Where the Good Luck Was, (Molarsky, Osmond)
Where the Lilies Bloom, (Cleaver, Vera)
Where the Trail Divides, (Callahan, Lorna)
Where the Wild Things Are, (Sendak, Maurice)
Where the Wind Blows, (Pyle, Katharine)
Where the Winds Never Blew..., (Colum, Padraic)
Where's Jeremy?, (Brown, Myra B.)
Where's Wallace?, (Knight, Hilary)
Where's the Bunny?, (Carroll, Ruth)
Where's the Kitty?, (Carroll, Ruth)
Where, O Where?, (Bevans, Tom)
Which Horse is William?, (Kuskin, Karla)
Which is Which, (Russell, Solveig)
Which was Witch?, (Jewett, Eleanore)
Whiffy McMann, (Hader, Berta)
While Susie Sleeps, (Schneider, Nina)
While the Heart Beats Young, (Riley, James W.)
While the Story Log Burns, (Burgess, Thornton)
Whilomville Stories, (Crane, Stephen)
Whingdingdilly, (Peet, Bill)
Whins of Knockattan, (Casserley, Anne)
Whirly Bird, (Varley, Dimitry)
Whisk Away on a Sunbeam, (Miller, Olive B.)
Whiskers of Ho Ho, (Littlefield, Wm. J.)
Whiskers, My Cat, (Schatz, Letta)
Whisper of Glocken, (Kendall, Carol S.)
Whispering Girl, (Means, Florence C.)
Whispering Mountain, (Aiken, Joan)
Whispering Smith, (Spearman, Frank)
Whispering Winds & Tales they Told, (Debenham, Mary H.)
Whisperings & other Things, (Ipcar, Dahlov)
Whispers, (Livingston, Myra C.)
Whistle Round the Bend, (Berry, Erick)
Whistle for Willie, (Keats, Ezra J.)
Whistle for a Pilot, (Bannon, Laura)
Whistle for the Train, (MacDonald, Golden)
Whistler in the Mist, (Fry, Rosalie K.)
Whistler's Van, (Jones, Idwal)
Whistling Rufus, (Mayne, William)
Whistling-Two-Teeth, (Averill, Naomi)
White Archer, an Eskimo Legend, (Houston, James A.)
White Bird, (Bulla, Clyde R.)
White Boy, (Manzi, Alberto)
White Bungalow, (Sommerfelt, Aimee)
White Bunny & his Magic Nose, (Duplaix, Lily)
White Cat..., (D'Aulnoy)
White Company, (Doyle, Arthur Conan)
White Conquerors, (Munroe, Kirk)
White Crystals, (Garis, Howard)
White Czar..., (Hawkes, Clarence)
White Darkness, (Mott, Lawrence)
White Deer, (Thurber, James)
White Elephant, (Faulkner, Georgene)

White Falcon, (Ogburn, Charlton)
White Fang, (London, Jack)
White Flag, (Stratton-Porter, Gene)
White Gate, (Chase, Mary Ellen)
White Giant & Black Giant, (Franchot, Annie W.)
White Goose, (Tudor, Tasha)
White Heron, (Jewett, Sarah O.)
White Heron Feather, (Robinson, Gertrude)
White Horse, (Coatsworth, Eliz.)
White Horse, (Hurd, Edith T.)
White House, (Phelan, Mary K.)
White Indian, (Moon, Grace P.)
White Isle, (Snedeker, Caroline D.)
White Kitten Book, (Aldin, Cecil)
White Kitten and Blue Plate, (Hogan, Inez)
White Land, (Briggs, Raymond)
White Leopard: Tale of the African Bush, (Fletcher, I.)
White Man's Africa, (Bigelow, Poultney)
White Marble, (Zolotow, Charlotte)
White Mountaineer, (Montgomery, R.)
White Palace, (O'Neill, Mary)
White Panther, (Waldeck, Theodore)
White People, (Burnett, Frances H.)
White Plume of Navarre, (Carter, Russell)
White Prince, the Arabian Horse, (Tousey, Sanford)
White Puppy Book, (Aldin, Cecil)
White Rat's Tale, (Schiller, Barbara)
White Reindeer, (James, Neill)
White Ring, (Tregarthen, Enys)
White Room, (Coatsworth, Eliz.)
White Roses, (Brown, Katharine H.)
White Shield, (Reed, Myrtle)
White Snow, Bright Snow, (Tresselt, Alvin)
White Sparrow, (Colum, Padraic)
White Stag, (Seredy, Kate)
White Stallion of Lipizza, (Henry, Marguerite)
White Stars of Freedom, (Isasi, Miriam)
White Stone, (Linde, Gunnell)
White-Ear and Peter, (Heiberg, Neils)
Whitefoot Mouse, (Peterson, Barbara)
Whitefoot the Wood Mouse, (Burgess, Thornton)
Whitetail: Story of a Prairie Dog, (Montgomery, R.)
Whitey... [All titles], (Rounds, Glen)
Who Blew that Whistle?, (Adelson, Leone)
Who Blowed Up the Church House?, (Randolph, Vance)
Who Built the Bridge?, (Bate, Norman)
Who Dreams of Cheese?, (Weisgard, Leonard)
Who Ever Heard of Kangaroo Eggs?, (Vaughan, Samuel)
Who Gave Us Peacocks...., (Gekiere, Madeleine)
Who Goes There?, (Lathrop, Dorothy)
Who Goes to the Wood, (Inchfawn, Fay)
Who Is at the Door?, (Eberstadt, Isabel)
Who Knows: A Little Primer, (Hahn, Julia L.)
Who Likes the Dark?, (Howell, Virginia)
Who Likes the Sun?, (DeRegniers, Beatrice)
Who Needs Holes?, (DePaola, Tomie)
Who Rides in the Dark?, (Meader, Stephen W.)
Who Wants a Cheap Rhinoceros?, (Silverstein, Shel)
Who Wants an Apple, (Hawkins, Quail)
Who Was Tricked?, (Bowman, James C.)
Who Will Comfort Toffle?, (Jansson, Tove)
Who Woke the Sun?, (Seidman, Mitzi)
Who is Johnny?, (Gedo, Leopold)
Who is Paddy?, (Cooper, Elizabeth)
Who's Afraid of the Big Bad Wolf, (Disney, Walt)
Who's Afraid?, (Engle, Paul)
Who's There? Open the Door!, (Munari, Bruno)
Who's Upside Down?, (Johnson, Crockett)

Who's Who in Mother Goose Land, (Murphy, Ruby B.)
Who's Who in Oz, (Snow, Jack)
Who's Who in Tony Sarg's Zoo, (Munson, Nelson)
Who's Who in the Zoo, (Barrows, Marjorie)
Who's Who in the Zoo, (Morton, John B.)
Who's in the Egg?, (Provensen, A.& M.)
Whole Family, (Various)
Wholly Cats, (McNulty, Faith)
Whom Shall I Marry?, (Spilka, Arnold)
Whom the Gods Destroyed, (Daskam, Josephine)
Whose Little Bird Am I?, (Weisgard, Leonard)
Whose Little Kitty are You?, (N/A)
Whose Mouse are You?, (Kraus, Robert)
Whose Turtle?, (Orgel, Doris)
Why Be a Goop?, (Burgess, Gelett)
Why Birds Migrate, (May, Julian)
Why Don't You Draw a Dog, (Melcher, Marguerite)
Why Frogs are Wet, (Hawes, Judy)
Why Heimdall Blew His Horn, (Laing, Frederick)
Why So Much Noise?, (Domanska, Janina)
Why Sun and Moon Live in the Sky, (Dayrell, Elphinstone)
Why Was He Late?, (Ainslie, Kathleen)
Why We have Day and Night, (Neumeyer, Peter)
Why You Look Like You..., (Pomerantz, Charlotte)
Why the Chimes Rang, (Alden, Raymond M.)
Why the Sun was Late, (Elkin, Benjamin)
Why they Married, (Flagg, James M.)
Why-So Stories, (Rich, Edwin G.)
Why: Reflections for Children, (Rae, John)
Wicked Enchantment, (Benary-Isbert, Margot)
Wicked Kings of Bloon, (Kellogg, Steven)
Wicked Pigeon Ladies in the Garden, (Chase, Mary)
Widdy-Widdy-Wurkey, (Fyleman, Rose)
Wide Awake, (Livingston, Myra C.)
Wide Fields, (Eberle, Irmengarde)
Wide, Wide World, (Warner, Susan)
Wide-Awake Owl, (Slobodkin, Louis)
Widget, (Newberry, Clare T.)
Widow & Her Friends, (Gibson, Charles D.)
Widow Guthrie, (Johnston, Richard M.)
Widow Woman and her Goat, (Walsh, Mary R.)
Wife of His Youth, (Chesnutt, Charles)
Wiggins for President, (Brooks, Walter)
Wiggle & Waggle, (Rice, Ethel)
Wiggles, (Woodcock, Louise)
Wigwam Children, (Deming, Therese O.)
Wigwam Evenings, (Eastman, Charles A.)
Wigwam Wonder Tales, (Thompson, William)
Wigwam in the City, (Smucker, Barbara)
Wilbur the Hat, (Van Loon, Hendrik)
Wilby's Dan, (Cook, William W.)
Wild Animal Babies, (Daly, Kathleen N.)
Wild Animal Homesteads, (Mills, Enos A.)
Wild Animal Play for Children, (Seton, Ernest T.)
Wild Animals & their Little Ones, (Celli, Rose)
Wild Animals I Have Known, (Seton, Ernest T.)
Wild Animals as I Know Them, (Knecht, Klara)
Wild Animals at Home, (Reynier, Marguerite)
Wild Animals at Home, (Seton, Ernest T.)
Wild Bill Hickok - Frontier Marshall, (Tousey, Sanford)
Wild Birthday Cake, (Davis, Lavinia R.)
Wild Dog, (Rietveld, Jane)
Wild Ducks and Daffodils, (Garelick, May)
Wild Fire, (Valens, Evan G.)
Wild Flower Children, (Gordon, Elizabeth)
Wild Flower Fairy Book, (Singleton, Esther)
Wild Folk, (Chaffee, Allen)
Wild Fruit Fairies, (Webb, M. St. John)

Wild Geese Flying, (Meigs, Cornelia L.)
Wild Goose Tale, (Gage, Wilson)
Wild Heart, (Squier, Emma-Lindsay)
Wild Horse Island, (Bialk, Elisa)
Wild Horses of Iceland, (Fleuron, Svend)
Wild Horses of the Red Desert, (Rounds, Glen)
Wild Life in Hampshire Highlands, (Dewar, G.A.B.)
Wild Orphan, (Rounds, Glen)
Wild Pasture, (Stratton, Elenore)
Wild Pilgrimage, (Ward, Lynd)
Wild Pony Island, (Meader, Stephen W.)
Wild Season, (Eckert, Allan W.)
Wild Stranger, (Burke, Trude)
Wild Swans, (Andersen, Hans C.)
Wild West Bill Rides Home, (Millen, Muriel)
Wild Whirlwind, (Ipcar, Dahlov)
Wild Wild West, (Daugherty, James)
Wild and Tame Animals, (Ipcar, Dahlov)
Wildcat Furs to China, (Carmer, Carl)
Wilderness, (Kent, Rockwell)
Wilderness Champion, (Lippincott, J.W.)
Wilderness Clearing, (Edmonds, Walter D.)
Wilderness Journey, (Steele, William O.)
Wilderness Ways, (Annixter, Paul)
Wildling Princess, (Fox, Frances M.)
Will I Have a Friend?, (Cohen, Miriam)
Will James Cowboy Book, (James, Will)
Will You Carry Me?, (Chandler, Edna W.)
Will to Win and other Stories, (Meader, Stephen W.)
Willa, (Franchere, Ruth)
Willamette Way, (Austin, Margot)
William, (Guy, Anne W.)
William & Woggs, (Byron, May)
William & his Kitten, (Flack, Marjorie)
William Morris, (Cary, Elisabeth L.)
William Morris to Whistler, (Crane, Walter)
William Tell Told Again, (Wodehouse, P.G.)
William Tell and his Son, (Hurlimann, Bettina)
William's Shadow, (Austin, Margot)
Willie Goes to the Seashore, (Vinson, Pauline)
Willie Was Different, (Rockwell, Norman)
Willie Wimple's Adventures, (Lea, John)
Willie Winkie..., (Golding, Harry)
Willie's Adventures, (Brown, Margaret W.)
Willie's Walk to Grandmama, (Brown, Margaret W.)
Willow Landing, (Govan, Christine)
Willow Whistle, (Meigs, Cornelia L.)
Willow Witches Brook, (Kaye, Mollie)
Willowdale Handcar, (Gorey, Edward)
Willy Nilly, (Flack, Marjorie)
Willy O'Dwyer Jumped in the Fire, (DeRegniers, Beatrice)
Willy Wong, American, (Oakes, Vanya)
Willy is my Brother, (Parish, Peggy)
Willy's Farm, (Hurd, Edith T.)
Willy, Willy, Don't Be Silly, (Vogel, Ilse-Margret)
Wily Woodchucks, (Travers, Georgia)
Wimp & the Woodle, (Various)
Winabojo, (Bowman, James C.)
Wind Boy, (Eliot, Ethel C.)
Wind Call, (Fry, Rosalie K.)
Wind Chasers, (Wier, Ester A.)
Wind Has Wings, (Downie, Mary (ed))
Wind Song, (Sandburg, Carl)
Wind and Arabella, (Bohanon, Paul)
Wind in the Chimney, (Allen, Marian)
Wind in the Chimney, (Meigs, Cornelia L.)
Wind in the Rose Bush, (Wilkins, Mary E.)
Wind in the Willows, (Grahame, Kenneth)

Wind of the Vikings, (Cormack, Maribelle)
Wind on the Moon, (Linklater, Eric)
Wind on the Prairie, (Weber, Lenora M.)
Wind that Wouldn't Blow, (Chrisman, Arthur B.)
Wind, Sand & Stars, (Saint-Exupery, A.)
Windfairies and other Tales, (DeMorgan, Mary)
Windmill Family, (Brown, Pamela)
Windmills, (Preston, Hayter)
Window at the White Cat, (Rinehart, Mary R.)
Windows on Henry Street, (Wald, Lilian D.)
Winds, (O'Neill, Mary)
Winds that Come from Far Away, (Minarik, Else H.)
Windy Hill, (Meigs, Cornelia L.)
Windy Morning, (Behn, Harry)
Windy Shore, (Price, Margaret E.)
Wine of Astonishment, (Bradley, Mary H.)
Wine-Press, (Brown, Anna R.)
Wing on a Flea, (Emberley, Edward)
Winged Girl of Knossos, (Berry, Erick)
Winged Watchman, (Van Stockum, Hilda)
Wingfin & Topple, (Valens, Evan G.)
Wings Against the Wind, (Carlson, Natalie S.)
Wings Around South America, (Dalgliesh, Alice)
Wings for Per, (D'Aulaire, I.& E.)
Wings for the Smiths, (Dalgliesh, Alice)
Wings from the Wind, (Tudor, Tasha (comp))
Wings of Adventure, (Rowland, Sydney)
Wings of Glory, (Daugherty, Sonia)
Wings of the Morning, (Palmer, Robin)
Wings of the Morning, (Tracy, Louis)
Winkie's World, (Hall, William N.)
Winkle, Twinkle & Lollypop, (Putnam, Nina W.)
Winnie Wimple & Ragged Robin, (Cowham, Hilda)
Winnie-the-Pooh, (Milne, A.A.)
Winning Out, (McNeely, Marion H.)
Winning Your Spurs, (Moore, Elaine T.)
Winning of the West, (McCracken, Harold)
Winona's Pony Cart, (Lovelace, Maud H.)
Winston of the Prairie, (Bindloss, Harold)
Winter Cottage, (Brink, Carol R.)
Winter Danger, (Steele, William O.)
Winter Flight, (Gall, Alice C.)
Winter Holiday, (Carman, Bliss)
Winter Noisy Book, (Brown, Margaret W.)
Winter Pilgrimage, (Haggard, H. Rider)
Winter Princess, (Treadgold, Mary)
Winter Swallow..., (Thomas, Edith M.)
Winter on the Prairie, (Curtis, Alice B.)
Winter's Eve, (Belting, Natalia)
Winter's Mischief, (Allee, Marjorie H.)
Winter's Tale, (Shakespeare, Wm.)
Winterbound, (Bianco, Margery W.)
Wise Book, (Sowerby, Githa)
Wise Fool, (Rabelais)
Wise Gray Cat, (Hofman, Caroline)
Wise Little Donkey, (DeSegur, Sophie)
Wise Little Hen, (Disney, Walt)
Wise Mamma Goose, (Herr, Charlotte)
Wise Old Aard-Vark, (Kunhardt, Dorothy)
Wise Owl's Story, (Uttley, Alison)
Wisest Man in the World, (Elkin, Benjamin)
Wish Fairy of Sunshine/Shadow Forest, (Colver, A.M.)
Wish Workers, (Aliki)
Wish for Little Sister, (Ayer, Jacqueline)
Wish on the Moon, (Hader, B.& E.)
Wish on the Moon, (Marshall, Dean)
Wish-Tree, (Ciardi, John)
Wishbone Children, (Byington, Eloise)

Wisher, (Daugherty, Charles)
Wishes Come True, (Brown, Jeanette)
Wishing Fairies, (Bigham, Madge A.)
Wishing Fairy's Animal Friends, (Ingraham, Corinne)
Wishing Horse of Oz, (Thompson, Ruth P.)
Wishing Pear, (Coatsworth, Eliz.)
Wishing Penny, (N/A)
Wishing Shoe, (Jupo, Frank)
Wishing Tree, (Faulkner, William)
Wishing Well in the Woods, (Friedrich, Otto)
Witch Crow & Barney Bylow, (Naylor, James B.)
Witch Family, (Estes, Eleanor)
Witch Who Wasn't, (Yolen, Jane)
Witch Wolf..., (Harris, Joel C.)
Witch in the Wood, (White, Terence H.)
Witch of Scrapfaggot Green, (Gordon, Patricia)
Witch on the Corner, (Holman, Felice)
Witch's Hollow, (Brook, Arthur W.)
Witch's Kitchen, (Young, Gerald)
Witchcraft in England, (Hole, Christina)
Witchery Ways, (Wells, Amos R.)
Witches of Venice, (Montresor, Beni)
With Bells On: A Christmas Story, (Milhous, Katherine)
With Bertram in Africa, (Gilbert, Paul T.)
With Books on her Head, (Chandler, Edna W.)
With Buller in Natal, (Henty, G.A.)
With Cap & Bells, (Davis, Mary G.)
With Cortes the Conqueror, (Watson, Virginia)
With Daniel Boone on Carolina Trail, (Key, Alexander)
With Feet to the Earth, (Skinner, Charles M.)
With Fife and Drum, (Taylor, Florance)
With Frederick the Great, (Henty, G.A.)
With Harp and Lute, (Thompson, Blanche J.)
With Kit Carson in the Rockies, (McNeil, Everett)
With LaSalle the Explorer, (Watson, Virginia)
With Love and Irony, (Lin, Yutang)
With Might and Main, (Fenner, Phyllis R.)
With Pipe, Paddle and Song, (Yates, Elizabeth)
With Trumpet and Drum, (Field, Eugene)
With the Dream Maker, (Habberton, John)
With the Indians in the Rockies, (Schultz, James W.)
With the Night Mail, (Kipling, Rudyard)
With the Will to Go, (Hewes, Agnes D.)
Within an Inch of His Life, (Gaboriau, Emile)
Wives and Daughters, (Gaskell, Mrs.)
Wizard in the Well, (Behn, Harry)
Wizard of Earthsea, (Le Guin, Ursula K.)
Wizard of Oz, (Baum, L. Frank)
Wizards of Ryetown, (Smedley, A. Constance)
Wobble the Witch Cat, (Calhoun, Mary)
Woggle-Bug Book, (Baum, L. Frank)
Wolf & the Seven Little Kids, (Grimm Bros.)
Wolf Hunt, (Edmonds, Walter D.)
Wolf King, (Lippincott, J.W.)
Wolf Song, (Hubbard, Ralph)
Wolf Story, (McCleery, William)
Wolf and the Kid, (Damjan, Mischa)
Wolf of Lambs Lane, (McNeer, May)
Wolf of My Own, (Wahl, Jan)
Wolf's Head & the Queen, (Morris, William)
Wolf's Long Howl, (Waterloo, Stanley)
Wolf-Tracker, (Grey, Zane)
Wolfie, (Chenery, Janet)
Wolfville... [All titles], (Lewis, Alfred H.)
Wolves of Willoughby Chase, (Aiken, Joan)
Woman Reigns, (New, Catherine M.)
Woman Tenderfoot, (Seton, Grace G.)
Woman Who Did, (Allen, Grant)

Woman in the Alcove, (Green, Anna K.)
Woman of My Life, (Bemelmans, Ludwig)
Woman of No Importance, (Wilde, Oscar)
Women of Morte Darthur, (Malory, Thomas)
Wonder Book, (Thompson, Ruth P.)
Wonder Book of Beasts, (Darton, F.J.H.)
Wonder Book of Myths & Legends, (Forbush, Wm. B.)
Wonder Book of Old Romance, (Darton, F.J.H.)
Wonder Book... [Most titles], (Hawthorne, Nathaniel)
Wonder Cat, (Martin, Dahris)
Wonder City of Oz, (Neill, John R.)
Wonder City: Picture Book of New York, (Lenski, Lois)
Wonder Clock, (Pyle, Howard)
Wonder Flights of Long Ago, (Barry, Mary E.)
Wonder Hill, (Hall, Albert N.)
Wonder Rock, (Ludins, Ryah)
Wonder Smith & His Son, (Young, Ella)
Wonder Stories, (Bailey, Carolyn S.)
Wonder Stories from Herodotus, (N/A)
Wonder Tales, (Hawthorne, Nathaniel)
Wonder Tales Retold, (Pyle, Katharine)
Wonder Tales from Baltic Wizards, (Olcott, F.J.)
Wonder Tales from China Seas, (Olcott, F.J.)
Wonder Tales from Goblin Hills, (Olcott, F.J. (ed))
Wonder Tales from Pirate Isles, (Olcott, F.J. (ed))
Wonder Tales from Tibet, (Jewett, Eleanore)
Wonder Tales from Windmill Lands, (Olcott, F.J. (ed))
Wonder Tales of Ancient Wales, (Henderson, Bernard)
Wonder Tales of Dogs & Cats, (Carpenter, Frances)
Wonder Tales of Old Japan, (Whitehorn, Alan L.)
Wonder Tales of Seas and Ships, (Carpenter, Frances)
Wonder Tales of the World, (Armfield, Constance)
Wonder World Fairy Tale Book, (Bourne, Gwen)
Wonder World of Ants, (Bronson, Wilfrid S.)
Wonder of Work, (Pennell, Joseph)
Wonderbox Stories, (Bradley, Will)
Wonderful Adventure, (Dearden, Harold)
Wonderful Adventures of Nils, (Lagerlof, Selma)
Wonderful Adventures of Ting Ling, (Bowen, Vernon)
Wonderful Baker, (Hunt, Mabel L.)
Wonderful Bed, (Knevels, Gertrude)
Wonderful Cornet, (Wilson, Barbara K.)
Wonderful Day, (Coatsworth, Eliz.)
Wonderful Days, (Bailey, Carolyn S.)
Wonderful Dragon of Timlin, (DePaola, Tomie)
Wonderful Egg, (Ipcar, Dahlov)
Wonderful Egg, (Schloat, G. Warren)
Wonderful Eggs of Furicchia, (Rockwell, Anne)
Wonderful Electric Elephant, (Montgomery, F.T.)
Wonderful Farm, (Ayme, Marcel)
Wonderful Fashion Doll, (Bannon, Laura)
Wonderful Feast, (Slobodkina, Esphyr)
Wonderful Flight to Mushroom Planet, (Cameron, Eleanor)
Wonderful Flying-Go-Round, (Faralla, Dana)
Wonderful Garden, (Nesbit, Edith)
Wonderful Garden, (Olcott, F.J.)
Wonderful House, (Brown, Margaret W.)
Wonderful House-Boat-Train, (Gannett, Ruth S.)
Wonderful Isles, (Hamer, Sam H.)
Wonderful Kite, (Wahl, Jan)
Wonderful Kittens, (N/A)
Wonderful Little Boy, (Buckley, Helen E.)
Wonderful Locomotive, (Meigs, Cornelia L.)
Wonderful Merry Go Gound, (Tague, Lola)
Wonderful Mission of Earl Lavender, (Davidson, John)
Wonderful Night, (Snowden, James H.)
Wonderful O., (Thurber, James)
Wonderful Poodle, (Bischoff, Ilse)

Wonderful Stories of Jane & John, (Smith, Gertrude)
Wonderful Story, (Brown, Margaret W.)
Wonderful Tar Baby, (Disney, Walt)
Wonderful Terrible Time, (Stolz, Mary S.)
Wonderful Things!, (Gay, Zhenya)
Wonderful Time, (McGinley, Phyllis)
Wonderful Tumble of Timothy Smith, (Faber, Doris)
Wonderful Voyage, (Holberg, Ruth)
Wonderful Winter, (Chute, Marchette)
Wonderful Wishes/Jacky & Jean, (Dickerson, Mary A.)
Wonderful Wizard of Oz, (Baum, L. Frank)
Wonderful World of Aunt Tuddy, (Gury, Jeremy)
Wonderful Year, (Barnes, Nancy)
Wonders in Monsterland, (Cuming, E.W.D.)
Wonders of Herodotus, (Farjeon, Eleanor)
Wonders of Wilmington, (Unknown)
Wongo & the Wise Old Crow, (Moon, Grace P.)
Wood Fire in No.3, (Smith, Francis H.)
Wood that Came Back, (Leighton, Clare)
Wood-Folk Comedies, (Long, William J.)
Woodcuts & Some Words, (Craig, Edward G.)
Woodcutter's Dog, (Nodier, Charles)
Woodcutter's Son, (Higgins, Violet M.)
Wooden Shoes in America, (Maloy, Lois)
Wooden Willie, (Gruelle, Johnny)
Woodland Party, (Hawley, Harriet E.)
Woodmyth & Fable, (Seton, Ernest T.)
Woody and Me, (Neville, Mary)
Woody's Big Trouble, (Martin, Patricia)
Wooing of Malkatoon, (Wallace, Lew)
Wooing of the Water-Witch, (Daldorne, Evan)
Wooster-Poosters, (Mallison, Clare)
Words to the Wise, (Sewell, Helen)
Works of James McNeill Whistler, (Cary, Elisabeth L.)
World Full of Horses, (Ipcar, Dahlov)
World Pictures, (Menpes, Dorothy)
World Round, (Hogan, Inez)
World Series, (Tunis, John R.)
World Song, (Clark, Ann N.)
World Wonderful, (Squire, Robert)
World from My Window, (Mendoza, George)
World in 2030, (Earl of Birkenhead)
World in the Candy Egg, (Tresselt, Alvin)
World is Round, (Stein, Gertrude)
World of Bemelmans, (Bemelmans, Ludwig)
World of Captain John Smith, 1580-1631, (Foster, G.)
World of Manabozho, (Leekley, Thomas)
World of Nonsense, (Withers, Carl)
World on a Farm, (Warner, Gertrude)
World's Children, (Menpes, Mortimer)
World's Christmas Tree, (Jefferson, Charles E.)
World's Fairy Book, (N/A)
Worm Ouroboros, (Eddison, Eric R.)
Would You Like to be a Monkey?, (Weisgard, Leonard)
Would-Be Witch, (Byrne, Miriam)
Wrath of Moto, (Gatti, Attilio)
Wreath of Carols, (Owen, Betty M.)
Wreath of Christmas Legends, (McGinley, Phyllis)
Wreck of the Golden Fleece, (Leighton, Robert)
Wreck of the Wild Wave, (Hurd, Edith T.)
Wren, (Killilea, Marie)
Wrinkle in Time, (L'Engle, Madeleine)
Wrong Side of the Bed, (Ardizzone, Edward)
Wu & Lu & Li, (Young, Evelyn)
Wulf the Saxon, (Henty, G.A.)
Wulnoth the Wanderer, (Escott-Inman, H.)
Wump World, (Peet, Bill)
Wurra-Wurra, (Dunham, Curtis)

Wuthering Heights, (Bronte, Emily J.)
Wymps & other Fairy Tales, (Sharp, Evelyn)
Wynken, Blyken and Nod, (Field, Eugene)
Wyoming, (Raine, William M.)
Xingu, (Viertel, Violette)
Yale Yarns, (Wood, John S.)
Yaller-Eye, (Bell, Thelma H.)
Yama Yama Land, (Boylan, Grace D.)
Yammy Buys a Bicycle, (Bryant, Bernice M.)
Yankee Captain in Patagonia, (Finger, Charles J.)
Yankee Clippers: Story of Donald McKay, (Judson, C.I.)
Yankee Doodle, (Fenner, Phyllis R.)
Yankee Doodle, (N/A)
Yankee Doodle, (Pyle, Howard)
Yankee Doodle, (Schackburg, Richard)
Yankee Doodle's Cousins, (Malcolmson, Anne)
Yankee Enchantments, (Loomis, Charles B.)
Yankee Privateer, (Norton, Andre)
Yankee Ships and Yankee Sailors, (Barnes, James)
Yankee Ships in Pirate Waters, (Holland, Rupert S.)
Yankee Thunder, (Shapiro, Irwin)
Yard for John, (Clymer, Eleanor)
Yasu and the Strangers, (Slobodkin, Louis)
Ye Booke of Nursery Rhymes, (Moorat, Joseph)
Ye Second Book of Nursery Rhymes, (Moorat, Joseph)
Year Round, (Clark, Leonard)
Year Santa Went Modern, (Armour, Richard)
Year Without a Santa Claus, (McGinley, Phyllis)
Year is Round, (Anglund, Joan W.)
Year is a Window, (Jackson, Richard)
Year of Columbus, 1492, (Foster, Genevieve)
Year of Independence, 1776, (Foster, Genevieve)
Year of Jubilo, (Sawyer, Ruth)
Year of Songs for a Baby in a Garden, (Robertson, W.G.)
Year of the Bloody Sevens, (Steele, William O.)
Year of the Christmas Dragon, (Sawyer, Ruth)
Year of the Wood Dragon, (Abdullah, Achmed)
Year to Grow, (Holman, Felice)
Year with the Fairies, (Scott, Anna M.)
Year's at the Spring, (Walters, L.)
Yellow & White, (Dawe, William C.)
Yellow Boat, (Hillert, Margaret)
Yellow Cat, (Griggs, Mary)
Yellow Cat & Friends, (Dwight, Grace)
Yellow Eyes, (Montgomery, R.)
Yellow Fairy Book, (Lang, Andrew)
Yellow Knight of Oz, (Thompson, Ruth P.)
Yellow Shop, (Field, Rachel)
Yellow Violin, (Denison, Mary)
Yelly, (Jahn, Mary L.)
Yen-Foh, a Chinese Boy, (Eldridge, Ethel)
Yeoman of the Guard, (Gilbert, W.S.)
Yertle the Turtle, (Seuss, Dr.)
Yeshu, Called Jesus, (Bishop, Claire H.)
Yesterday's Children, (Sowerby, Githa)
Yesterday's Daughter, (Daringer, Helen F.)
Yinka-Tu the Yak, (Lide, Alice A.)
Yipe, (Malcolmson, David)
Yonie Wondernose, (DeAngeli, Marguerite)
Yossele's Holiday & Brave Maccabees, (Mazer, Sonia)
You Are Ri-di-cu-lous, (Francois, Andre)
You Can Write Chinese, (Wiese, Kurt)
You Can't Get There from Here, (Nash, Ogden)
You Can't Pet a Possum, (Bontemps, Arna)
You Come Too, (Frost, Robert)
You Have to Draw the Line Somewhere, (Harris, Christie)
You Know Who, (Ciardi, John)
You Look Ridiculous, (Waber, Bernard)

You Make Your Own Luck, (Singmaster, Elsie)
You Never Can Tell, (Ritter, Elizabeth)
You Read to Me, I'll Read to You, (Ciardi, John)
You Say You Saw a Camel?, (Coatsworth, Eliz.)
You Shall Have a Carriage, (Coatsworth, Eliz.)
You Will Go to the Moon, (Freeman, Mae & Ira)
Young Acadian, (Roberts, Chas. G.D.)
Young Alaskans, (Hough, Emerson)
Young Aunts, (Dalgliesh, Alice)
Young Blackbird, (Palmer, Ernest C.)
Young Brontes, (Jarden, Mary L.)
Young Cowboy, (James, Will)
Young Eagle, (Freschet, Berniece)
Young Folks Birthday Book, (N/A)
Young Folks Uncle Tom's Cabin, (Boylan, Grace D.)
Young Fu of the Upper Yangtze, (Lewis, Eliz. F.)
Young Hopeful, (Dunbar, Jennie)
Young Inca Prince, (Malkus, Alida S.)
Young Kangaroo, (Brown, Margaret W.)
Young Lafayette, (Eaton, Jeanette)
Young Lives, (LeGallienne, R.)
Young Mac of Fort Vancouver, (Carr, Mary J.)
Young Man in a Hurry, (Latham, Jean L.)
Young Man of the House, (Hunt, Mabel L.)
Young Man's Fancy, (Phillips, Coles)
Young Mark, (Almedingen, Edith M.)
Young Miss Burney, (Stewart, Anna B.)
Young Mountaineers, (Craddock, Charles E.)
Young Musician, (Alger, Horatio)
Young Peggy McQueen, (Stables, Gordon)
Young People in Old Places, (Baker, Cornelia)
Young Puritans in Captivity, (Smith, Mary P.W.)
Young Puritans of Old Hadley, (Smith, Mary P.W.)
Young Ravenals, (Singmaster, Elsie)
Young Russian Corporal, (Iogolevitch, Paul)
Young Settler, (Stong, Philip D.)
Young Tentmaker, (Mirza, Youel B.)
Young Trajan, (Miller, Elizabeth C.)
Young Visitors, (Ashford, Daisy)
Young Walter Scott, (Gray, Eliz. J.)
Young and Happy Rooster, (Gleason, Jane)
Youngest Camel, (Boyle, Kay)
Youngest Girl in the School, (Sharp, Evelyn)
Youngest One, (Yashima, Taro)
Your Hand in Mine, (Cornish, Sam)
Your Prayers and Mine, (Yates, Elizabeth)
Your Skin and Mine, (Showers, Paul)
Yours Truly, (N/A)
Yours with Love, Kate, (Mason, Miriam E.)
Youth Youth!, (Coke, Desmond)
Yoyo's Animal Friends, (Strong, Rowland)
Yu Lan, Flying Boy of China, (Buck, Pearl S.)
Yuletide Yarns, (Henty, G.A.)
Yvette, (Harris, Leon)
Zachary Taylor, (Martin, Patricia)
Zachary, the Governor's Pig, (Grant, Bruce)
Zamani Goes to Market, (Feelings, Muriel)
Zankiwank & Bletherwitch, (Fitzgerald, S.)
Zauberlinda: Wise Witch, (Gibson, Eva K.)
Zebra & the Wishing Fairy, (Ingraham, Corinne)
Zebrology, (Rey, Hans A.)
Zeee, (Enright, Elizabeth)
Zeely, (Hamilton, Virginia)
Zeke, (Ovington, Mary W.)
Zeke & the Fisher-Cat, (Voight, Virginia F.)
Zeke the Raccoon, (Wells, Rhea)
Zeki and the Talking Cat, (Kubinyi, Laszlo)
Zelda Dameron, (Nicholson, Meredith)

Zephir's Holidays, (DeBrunhoff, Jean)
Zeralda's Ogre, (Ungerer, Tomi)
Zest, (Norris, Charles G.)
Zig Zag Fables, (Shepherd, J.A.)
Zip the Toy Mule, (La Rue, Mabel G.)
Zip: Advens./Frisky Fox Terrier, (Montgomery, F.T.)
Zipper ABC Book, (North, Sterling)
Zlateh the Goat, (Singer, Isaac B.)
Zodiac Stories, (Channing, Blanche)
Zodiac Town, (Turner, Nancy B.)
Zomo the Rabbit, (Sturton, Hugh)
Zoo Babies, (Farrow, George E.)
Zoo Book, (Garthwaite, Jimmy)
Zoo Days, (Golding, Harry)
Zoo for Mister Muster, (Lobel, Arnold)
Zoo of Zeus, (Bryson, Bernarda)
Zoo's Who, (Tobias, Doris G.)
Zoo, Where Are You?, (McGovern, Ann)
Zoo: A Scamper, (Emanuel, Walter)
Zoological Soliloquies, (Harshberger, Kay)
Zooparade, (Perkins, Marlin)
Zozo, (Rey, Hans A.)
Zuleika Dobson, (Beerbohm, Max)
Zuni Indian Tales, (Nusbaum, Aileen)